THE MICROBIOLOGY OF FOODS

THE MICROBIOLOGY OF FOODS

BY

FRED WILBUR TANNER, Ph.D., D.Sc.

Professor of Bacteriology and Head of the Department
University of Illinois

SECOND EDITION

This book was reproduced in 1946 by the
Offset Method from the original printing.

PUBLISHED IN CHAMPAIGN, ILLINOIS, BY

GARRARD PRESS

IN THE YEAR 1944

589.95

TT66m

MANUFACTURED IN THE UNITED STATES OF AMERICA

PREFACE

Food is probably man's primary interest in times of peace and his main worry in times of stress such as wars and economic depressions. During these times, every effort is made to maintain and increase food supplies by relief and victory gardens. New methods of food preservation are introduced, in addition to those used during times of peace. Some well-known methods have had their origin in times of wars. The canning industry, for instance, originated in the desires of Emperor Napoleon to have new sources and supplies of food when he was moving vast armies across the face of Europe. Appert was stimulated to study the problem and won a a prize for his suggestions which started interest in sealing foods in containers and subjecting them to heat. Great progress has been made since then because it has been possible to use such sciences as physics, chemistry, and bacteriology on problems of the food industry. As these words are being written the Allied Armies are receiving better foods in the field than armies have ever before received. Many of the foods are preserved and packed in new ways.

Since publication of the first edition of this book, many advances have been made in the science of bacteriology and especially in its application to foods. These have made it necessary to completely rewrite the book. The subjects of mycology and microbiology have been greatly expanded. Since it is intended that this book be a source book to the literature as well as to methods of analysis, much of the recent literature has been reviewed. References are at the bottom of the pages containing the context which they support.

The present edition includes all major methods of analysis which have been issued up to the time of publication. Especially to be mentioned are "The Bacteriological Examination of Water Supplies" and "Bacteriological Tests for Graded Milk" prepared by the Ministry of Health of Great Britain, arrangements for reproduction of which in this book were made with His Britannic Majesty's Stationery Office, London, from which original copies may be purchased; also to "British Standard Methods for the Microbiological Examination of Butter," prepared and published by the British Standards Institution of London. The author is, also, grateful to the Association of Official Agricultural Chemists for permission to include procedures of analyses of various foods which have been published in the Association's Journal. References to these methods are given in the text.

The literature of food microbiology and technology has expanded during recent years. Such publications as *Food Research*, the *Journal of Dairy Science*, the *Journal of Dairy Research*, *Journal of the American Dietetic Association*, *Cereal Chemistry*, the *Analyst*, not to mention many others, and the regular publications of various scientific associations, such as the American Chemical Society, Society of American Bacteriologists and the Institute of Brewing, publish results of original investigations on which the science is based. In addition are good trade association publications.

v

The Annual Reports of the Food Investigation Board of Great Britain and the *Special Reports* of the same institution should not be overlooked by the food microbiologist who is up-to-date. Numerous reference publications. such as *Chemical Abstracts, Biological Abstracts, Experiment Station Record, Index to the Literature of Food Investigation,* are also available to help those who "search the literature."

Little emphasis has been given in this volume to food infections and intoxications because these subjects are covered in a companion volume "Food-Borne Infections and Intoxications" published in 1933. A new edition of this book is being prepared for publication sometime in the future. This problem is of far less importance than some are prone to believe. Billions of pounds of food are processed and distributed in the United States without causing illness.

Food technology has profited greatly by activities of many laboratories supported by trade associations and private industrial concerns, in addition to laboratories in academic institutions. Many could be mentioned from which come reports of results of experimental work carried on under the best of conditions. Typical of them are the research laboratories of the National Canners Association and the Institute of Paper Chemistry. The former does much work which benefits not only the industry from which it receives its main support, but others as well. The latter has done much to improve paper wrappings for foods and is thus contributing to better and safer living. In addition are the many research laboratories supported by private industrial concerns in whose laboratories are the best trained men available. In such laboratories talent from various sciences is available on all problems.

Owing to the time required for manufacturing this book, it has been possible to include more recent literature citations in the later chapters than was possible in the early ones.

The author also gratefully recognizes the assistance of his wife, Dr. Louise Pickens Tanner, who has assisted with the manuscript and proof, and who has been a constant source of inspiration and helpful frank critic during the preparation of this book. Special acknowledgment is given to Mrs. Blanche Young and to Mr. James Garrard of my publishers, without whose constant interest and helpful suggestions the work would have been more difficult; also to Mr. Van Easterday, Jr., Mr. Leo Althaus, and Mr. Neil Covington, results of whose technical skills are apparent in every page.

FRED W. TANNER.

Urbana, Illinois
March, 1944

TABLE OF CONTENTS

THE MICROBIOLOGY OF FOODS

CHAPTER 1

FOOD PRESERVATION

Food is one of the few necessary requisites in life. Much of primitive man's time was spent searching for it. Later, complexities of life made it desirable for him to use some of his time for other things and compelled him to save the abundance of "the hunt" for times of need. The first methods employed to preserve foods were probably drying and smoking. Early man shared with his family or clan the duty of providing for the family food needs. As time passed and specialization became the order, only relatively few men gave their entire attention to various vocations involved in supplying foods. Early man was concerned mainly with quantity. Today man is concerned also with quality and recognizes among food problems those relating to purity and cleanliness of foods supplied the public.

When specialization was introduced, unscrupulous individuals tried to profit by cheating their fellows. Today sophistication involves problems usually discussed under two names — misbranding and adulteration. These terms are fully defined in food and drug control acts. While neither of them is as common as it once was, they do occur. Some treatments which are applied to foods should probably not be considered as adulteration; for example, some oranges are dyed and waxed to improve their appearance. Such a practice is objectionable only if it conceals inferiority or misleads the consumer into believing that he is getting better fruit. The issue may be properly raised when dyeing is used to make green fruit look like ripe fruit. Dyeing is permitted in some places in order that oranges raised in one section of the country may compete on a more even basis with those raised in another section.

Offenses against esthetic taste and decency are also encountered by food control officials. These involve such things as worm infestation, preservation of decomposed foods, and insanitary methods of preparation and handling. Some of these more general problems have been discussed by Howell.[1] Insanitary methods of handling and preparation are not limited to those who work with foods on a large scale; for instance, foods prepared for church suppers or sold at food sales of charitable organizations may be prepared and handled under insanitary conditions. Outbreaks of disease have been traced to foods obtained on such occasions and health officers in a few cases have tried to supervise them. Lesem[2] issued permits to organizations conducting sales of bakery goods. He insisted that they be prepared and handled under clean conditions.

1. Howell. 1936. J. Roy. San. Inst. 58, 292-297.
2. Lesem. 1938. Calif. State Dept. Health, Weekly Bull., Dec. 31, 1938.

The object of preservation is to keep foods for relatively long times as near their natural state as possible. Practically all methods, however, leave their stamp on the product through altered flavor, appearance, or texture. In some cases, quality of the product may be improved. Preservation may involve holding the food for years or only for some immediate emergency. On the basis of time Barcroft[3] arranged foods in three groups: (1) those which can be kept for 10 years or longer; (2) those which can be kept for 10 months; and (3) those which can be kept only for the duration of a voyage, about two months. Grains are in the first group. Wheat may be stored for many years; some wheats will keep better than others. A major problem is weevil infestation. The moisture content of wheat is near 15 per cent while that of flour is about 11 per cent. Flour may be stored for quite long times in tin cans where it is inaccessible to weevils. Canned foods, also, fall into the group of foods which may be stored for long periods. In the middle group of foods with only moderate keeping qualities are dried milk and the root vegetables. Eggs may be kept for long periods in cold storage in an atmosphere of carbon dioxide of two to two and a half per cent. Foods which have only short-term storage possibilities are fresh meats and fish. When they are frozen solid, however, their storage life is greatly prolonged. The need of giving more attention to the effects of preservation procedures on the vitamin content of foods is now recognized. Rahn,[4] grouped foods according to their chemical constitution which largely determines the types of microbial deterioration and the methods of preservation.

The many methods of food preservation may be classified in various ways; some of the more common methods are given below.

I. Asepsis
II. Addition of chemical substances
    A. Sodium benzoate
    B. Salt or sugar, or both
    C. Spices
    D. Acids (vinegar, sour milk, etc.)
    E. Smoking
III. Low temperatures
    A. Refrigeration
    B. Slow-freezing
    C. Quick-freezing

IV. High temperatures
    A. Pasteurization
    B. Boiling
    C. Canning
V. Fermentation
    A. Sauerkraut
    B. Pickles
    C. Milk (fermented milks)
VI. Abstraction of moisture
    A. Meats
    B. Vegetables
    C. Fruits

FRESH FOODS AND ASEPSIS

Fresh foods are those which are in their natural state and which have not been subjected to some special treatment to preserve them. Refrigeration may, perhaps, be an exception. Ordinarily, as applied to foods the term "fresh" means newly produced, harvested, or gathered. Examples are the leaf vegetables, fruits, and eggs. "Fresh" is also used to indicate foods which have not been preserved with salt, or foods from

3. Barcroft. 1939. Brit. Med. J., Aug. 12, 1939, 324-327.
    4. Rahn. 1913. Centbl. Bakt., Pt. 2, 37, 492-497; Kuhl's Hilfsbuch der Bakteriologie. Leipzig. 1920.

which the salt has been removed by soaking in water. It is probably best to retain the word "fresh" for natural foods which have been recently harvested. Problems immediately arise, however, as to how this condition can be carefully measured so far as eggs and meats, for instance, are concerned. In the United States fresh foods probably present few hazards to health. Vegetables are not usually raised, as they are in certain foreign countries, on land which has been fertilized with human excreta or domestic sewage. Use of sewage sludge from treatment plants may introduce certain hazards, the magnitude of which, is probably not known today. Tanner [5] reviewed results of investigations on survival of *Eberthella typhosa* in sewage sludge and soil and concluded that, while there is probably little actual danger in using sewage sludge as a fertilizer, it should be used with caution.

Foods which are rid of microorganisms, and kept so, will not undergo microbial spoilage, but some of them may be susceptible to chemical spoilage. Some fruits which are freed from living microorganisms by processing in tin containers do not spoil from action of bacteria. However, chemical reactions may cause losses of color, flavor, and texture. Efforts are now made to keep foods as free as possible from undue numbers of microorganisms. In some cases this effort is carried to an extreme. Foods with a low number of bacteria will have less opportunity of harboring undesirable species than those with a larger number. Furthermore few microorganisms mean lighter loads on preserving processes to be used later. Ample proof of this are the advances which have been made in the canning industry. This does not mean, however, that low numbers always mean high quality. Nature has used asepsis for preservation of various products. Starches are packed in sealed packages which are not broken by microorganisms under ordinary conditions. Fruits and vegetables are also covered with an impervious skin which resists microbial invasion.

Freshness is a quality of food which resists absolute definition. With fruits and vegetables freshness implies crispness and firmness and is related to water content. With meat and dairy products it may be more often associated with chemical and microbial phenomena. As chemical and microbial changes occur, these products lose their freshness.

Satisfactory procedures for determining freshness of foods have been difficult to find. Proctor and Greenlie [6] suggested a modified resazurin technic for detecting large numbers of bacteria, the assumption being that large numbers of them could be used as an index of age. They compared bacterial plate counts and resazurin reduction rates of fresh and frozen foods, including ground meat, fish, crab meat, eggs, and vegetables, for the purpose of determining whether the use of redox-potential indicators offers a relatively accurate and prompt evaluation of quality. Their procedures need not be given here. Foods which had high bacterial plate counts, i.e., over one million per gram, had reduction rates such that the

5. Tanner. 1935. Sewage Works J., 7, 611-617.
6. Proctor and Greenlie. 1939 Food Research 4, 441-446.

color changes of the dye could usually be noted within three to five hours of incubation. In the case of foods with very high plate counts reduction was complete, or almost so, in 30 minutes. Proctor and Greenlie believed that a modified resazurin procedure might be used by food control officials and others for detection of foods having abnormally high bacterial contents or foods which have been improperly handled or stored.

It is difficult to distinguish between essential and unessential procedures for restricting microorganism content of foods. In the dairy industry, for instance, barn and stable conditions were once supposed to greatly influence the bacterial content of milk. However, it was found that milk from dirty barns had no more bacteria than milk from clean barns. This did not mean that stables may be neglected but that the real origin of bacteria in milk had not been discovered. Further experiments in the dairy industry showed that utensils contributed most of the bacteria to milk. Every effort should be made to have foods prepared and handled by clean people, and one of the best methods of gaining this end is to have clean physical plants. In some food industries, it is necessary even to filter the air which comes into the plant to remove mold spores that may infect the food.

CHEMICAL PRESERVATIVES

As soon as it was established that certain chemical substances were lethal to microorganisms or would suppress their development, suggestions were made to add them to foods to prevent spoilage generally considered to be caused by microorganisms. Of the various chemicals proposed, only sodium benzoate is now permitted and its use is being curtailed. Sulfur dioxide is permitted in dried fruits under certain conditions. The fact that foods can be made to keep by better methods of processing and that most of the so-called chemical preservatives were supposed to have been harmful to health, caused them to be banned. Whether they were actually deleterious to health is a matter over which there has been much debate. However, the fact that they are not needed and that the consumer's welfare is paramount, justifies their prohibition.

Control of such substances which have become known as "chemical preservatives" rests on "An Act to Prohibit the movement in interstate commerce of adulterated and misbranded food, drugs, devices, and cosmetics, and for other purposes," otherwise known as the Food, Drug, and Cosmetic Act of 1938. The sections of this act which would affect so-called chemical preservatives are as follows:

"Sec. 402—A food shall be deemed to be adulterated—(a) (2) if it bears or contains any added poisonous or added deleterious substance which is unsafe within the meaning of section 406;

"Sec. 406 (a)—Any poisonous or deleterious substance added to any food, except where such substance is required in the production thereof or cannot be avoided by good manufacturing practice shall be deemed to be unsafe for purposes of the application of clause (2) of section 402."

Chemical preservatives would also be affected by part of the definition of misbranding:

"Sec. 403—A food shall be deemed to be misbranded (k) if it bears or contains any artificial flavoring, artificial coloring, or chemical preservative, unless it bears labeling stating that fact:"

Owing to the fact that strict adherence to these edicts is practically impossible with certain foods the administrator of the Food and Drug Administration of the Federal Security Agency under whose jurisdiction enforcement of the act now rests, may at times permit deviations. For instance under Sec. 406, quóted above, it is stated:

"But when such substance is so required or cannot be so avoided the Secretary shall promulgate regulations limiting the quantity therein or thereon to such extent as he finds necessary for the protection of public health, and any quantity exceeding the limits so fixed shall also be deemed to be unsafe for purposes of the application of clause (2) of section 402 (a)." (See Sec. 402a on page 52.)

This clause provides for so-called *tolerances* for undesirable ingredients in foods. Thus tolerances have been established for lead and arsenic contents of sprayed fruits and vegetables and for mold content of certain tomato products.

The administrator is also empowered to make exceptions in enforcement of Sec. 403 (k) quoted above:

"That to the extent that compliance with the requirements of this paragraph is impracticable, exemptions shall be established by regulations promulgated by the Secretary."

These last-mentioned provisions make it possible to debate whether the administrator should make these exceptions.

Interest by both the general public and food-control officials has been focused on "so-called chemical preservatives" for some 40 years.

By Act of Congress, in 1903, the United States Department of Agriculture was directed to investigate preservatives in food and their effect upon digestion and health. The Act was stated as follows: "To investigate the character of proposed food preservatives and coloring matters, to determine their relation to digestion and to health, and to establish principles which should guide their use."

The Food and Drug Act of 1906 was in part, the result of this effort. In this Act it is stated that food shall be considered to be adulterated if it contains any added poisonous or other added deleterious ingredient, which may render such article injurious to health. It became necessary, then, to determine the possible poisonous properties of chemical preservatives. This was not an easy matter, as indicated by contradictory reports which were published.

The conclusions reached in some of the investigations are interesting. In some cases the decisions have been contested and the field has been left in a controversial state. Barnard [7] stated that a suitable food preservative should have the following characteristics:

1. It must not make possible the employment of careless and imperfect methods of manufacture.

2. It must not, under any reasonable conditions, injure the health of the consumer.

3. It must not allow the use of unfit raw material.

7. Barnard. 1911. Chem. Eng. 12, 104.

4. It must be nonirritant.

5. It must not retard the action of the digestive enzymes.

6. It must be efficient in its preservative action.

7. It must have no tendency to decompose in the body into poisonous substances, the dose of which is smaller than its own.

8. Easily detected for control work.

It is obvious that such requirements would be found with difficulty in one chemical substance.

What is a "Chemical Preservative?" Few food-control officials or technologists have tried to define the term although it is used especially by the former. It is our purpose to analyze in this paragraph what Congress meant by the statement, in Sec. 403 (k) of the Food, Drug, and Cosmetic Act of 1938, that a food shall be deemed to be misbranded if it contains a "chemical preservative" unless its label states that fact.

The term "chemical preservative" grew out of the controversies incident to the so-called "pure-food movement" so ardently sponsored by Dr. Harvey Wiley. It was applied to several chemical substances which are discussed in the next few pages, i.e., sodium benzoate, formaldehyde, salicylic acid, sulfites, and boric acid. These are the substances to which the term "chemical preservatives" should be applied for they brought it into being. The term should not be applied to all chemical substances which are added for one purpose or another to food substances to prevent various types of deterioration unless these newer substances have about the same characteristics. When the term was first introduced it was applied to substances which had such marked characteristics that they were sharply set apart as follows:

1. They were foreign to the human body—were not found in it and were probably not formed in it during digestion.

2. The body had to have some definite method of detoxifying and eliminating them.

3. They were used to conceal inferiority in raw materials and avoidable difficulties in processing.

4. They were not normal constituents of foods.

5. Where used in food they stigmatized the food on account of the evil connotation which the term had.

This problem simmers down to the meaning of words when they were first coined and used. Laws and rulings must be construed in light of new and changing conditions and advances in science. The courts, for instance, have said that the language of legislative enactments should be construed in accordance with its meaning at the time used rather than by a meaning attributed to it many years later.

In People v. Barnett, 319. Ill. 403, the court said:

"... The true rule is that statutes are to be construed as they were intended to be understood when they were passed. Statutes are to be read in light of attendant conditions and that state of law existent at the time of their enactment. The words of the statute must be taken in the sense in which they were understood at the time the statute was enacted. . . .

"... The legislative intent that controls in the construction of the statute has reference to the legislature which passed the given act. . . . In interpreting a statute the question is what the words meant to those using them. . . ."

The term preservative is so general and indefinite that much trouble is experienced in using it. The British Food and Drug Act of 1928 defined it as follows:

"'Preservative' means any substance which is capable of inhibiting, retarding, or arresting the process of fermentation, acidification, or other decomposition of food or of masking any of the evidences of any such process or of neutralizing the acid generated by any such process; but does not include common salt (sodium chloride), saltpeter, (sodium or potassium nitrate), sugars, acetic acid, or vinegar, alcohol or potable spirits, spices, essential oils or any substance added to food by the process of curing known as smoking."

The committee appointed by the Minister of Health of Great Britain to study the use of preservatives and coloring matters in 1923, found that it was undesirable to add to foods any material not of the nature, substance, and quality of food and recommended that preservatives should be prohibited in all articles of food and drink offered or exposed for sale, with a few exceptions. The term preservative, it was stipulated, was not to include salt, saltpeter, sugar, vinegar, acetic acid, alcohol, spices, or the agents introduced into food by the process of curing known as smoking. It was further stated that preservatives were used in a haphazard way. Three groups were recognized:

1. Formaldehyde and its derivatives; fluorides.
2. (Not so desirable.) Boric acid and salicylic acid and their salts.
3. (Least harmful.) Benzoic acid and sulfurous acid and their salts.

The committee stated that if preservatives were necessary only those in Group 3 should be permitted. This conclusion was of great importance because those in Group 2 were being used at the time of the investigation. This investigation resulted in the permitted use of two preservatives— benzoic and sulfurous acids and their salts. They were to be allowed in sausages, wines, dried fruit, fruit pulp, beer, cider, cordials, and fruit juices. It was suggested that sulfur dioxide be used in all of these foods in certain quantities. The committee further stated that presence of a preservative should be stated on the label. Thus the recommendations placed the use of preservatives in foods in Great Britain on the same bases as in the United States. British manufacturers were given two years to arrange their affairs under the new order. The conditions under the old order were reported in part by McFadden.[8] As would be expected, this order aroused considerable discussion, most of which centered about boric acid.

Another attempt at defining the term "chemical preservative" appears in an "advisory definition" attached to Sec. 403 (k) (a) (3) of the U. S. Food, Drug, and Cosmetic Act of 1938.

"The term 'chemical preservative' means any chemical which, when added to food, tends to prevent or retard deterioration thereof; but does not include common salt, sugars, vinegars, spices, or oils extracted from spices, or substances added to food by direct exposure thereof to wood smoke."

This definition does not appear in the Food, Drug, and Cosmetic Act approved June 25, 1938, and was not, therefore, passed by Congress. It

8. McFadden. 1908. Local Govt. Bd., Gt. Brit.. Rev. in Exp. Sta. Rec. 21 (1909), 164.

is a suggestion issued by the Food and Drug Administration as an aid in enforcing the act. It was apparently based on the definition which appears in the British Food and Drug Act of 1928. If this is true, some modifications were made, for the American version makes no exception of "alcohol or potable spirits" and saltpeter.

Mere definition of the term "chemical preservative" does not prove whether a substance is one or not. Actually this can be determined only by long experiments if it can ever be satisfactorily proved. These must involve use of various microorganisms, or various strains of the same organism, in varying numbers under varying conditions, and finally actual use under practical conditions with thorough laboratory examination.

Must the term "chemical preservative" be limited only to those substances which interfere with microbial deterioration? Such a distinction should probably not be made. If a definition for the term "chemical preservative" must be established it should be so worded that any chemical substance, irrespective of its nature or the reasons for which it is added to food, is included. No exceptions should be made for any substance. Such exceptions are arbitrary and become subject to discussion and controversy.

Reckless addition of all sorts of chemical substances to food is to be deplored. They should be permitted only if they are harmless and improve the food.

On the other hand, refusal on the part of food-control officials to permit addition of a harmless chemical substance to food "where such substance is required in the production thereof or cannot be avoided in good manufacturing practice" and to accord it the dignity of an "optional ingredient" is equally to be deplored. Research in the food industries has given us in the United States the finest foods of any nation in the world and technology has played a great role, especially chemistry and bacteriology. Any such chemical substance accepted as an "optional ingredient" should have the following general properties:

1. It should have some definite role in the food.
2. It should be harmless to health—not deleterious.
3. It should not conceal inferiority or faulty processing.
4. It should preferably be a substance normally in food or formed in foods by accepted processes, such as fermentation.

Several such substances have already been accepted as "optional ingredients" and are not required to be listed on labels. Some of these are the following:

Disodium phosphate or sodium citrate, or both, or calcium chloride in evaporated milk as a stabilizer.

Sodium carbonate or hydroxide as a neutralizer in cream.

Brine acidified with citric acid as a medium into which crab meat may be dipped to prevent discoloration before canning.

Calcium chloride in canned tomatoes to prevent physical deterioration.

Vinegar and various inorganic salts in bread.

Citric acid in canned artichokes and mushrooms.

Closely related to "chemical preservatives" are so-called "inhibitors." These are agents which act temporarily for a few days or so, whose action is soon gone, and deterioration continues. Are they preservatives? Probably not, for two reasons: (1) they do not preserve over a sufficiently long time; and (2) they are not in the same category with those substances from which the term originated and which Congress had in mind when it passed the Food and Drug Act of 1906.

BORIC ACID (BORACIC ACID)

This compound has been one of the last to be placed on the prohibited list of preservatives for foods by most nations. It has had a few proponents for use in certain foods, out in later years the opponents have prevailed. There is probably no valid reason why it should be used. Boron compounds have been prohibited for a number of years in France, Germany, Holland, Italy, Spain, the United States, and since 1927 in Great Britain. In the United States use of boron compounds in meats is prohibited by the Bureau of Animal Industry Order 211, Regulation 18, Section 6, Paragraph I.

Before being placed on the prohibited list in England, boric acid was largely used in butter, cream, margarine, imported liquid eggs, sausages, potted meats, potted fish, and some beverages. It was also permitted for packing hams and bacon for import into England.[9] When so used it was ordinarily dusted over these products. According to this practice large amounts were frequently present. Thus 175, 140, and 110 grains per pound have been found in margarine, butter, and bacon, respectively. Usually, however, the quantity did not exceed and rarely amounted to 35 grains. One trade representative told the committee that 52 grains of boric acid per pound were necessary for his product. When boric acid was permitted, the government had little control over the amounts. In 1917, an order [10] was issued that no more than .4 per cent should be used in cream and that cream so treated should be sold as preserved cream. Robertson [11] cited experiments and authorities to show that small amounts (.2 per cent) added to milk were not deleterious to human health. Therefore, he believed that its addition to milk as a preservative should be allowed, because it would help avoid the use of milk undergoing decomposition. The enforcements of the Food and Drugs (Adulteration) Act of 1928 in England developed considerable opinion against the prohibition of the use of boron compounds. Many protests were made against the Act. The arguments, in general, were that boric acid was needed as a preservative in order to prevent decomposition and that refrigeration had not been developed to such an extent that it could take the place of boric acid. Many eminent medical men and men of science in England declared themselves against the prohibition.[12] On the other hand, those who favored it argued that the food preservatives then in use were drugs and that pharmacopoeias laid down limits for use in prescriptions. There was justification, therefore, in the prohibition.

9. J. Amer. Med. Assoc. 1924. 83, 1699.
10. Idem. 1917. 68, 860.
11. Robertson. 1915. J. State Med. 23, 176-182.
12. J. Amer. Med. Assoc. 1925. 85, 1148.

It is generally accepted that boric acid is poisonous when taken in sufficiently large amounts. Furthermore, some of those who participated in the boric acid controversy in Great Britain after 1927, believed that small amounts of foods consumed over a long period of time might cause diseases of the kidney. Wiley [13] stated that boric acid or borax, when administered in small doses for a long period or in large quantities for a short period, created disturbances of appetite, digestion, and health. He, therefore, believed that it should be absolutely prohibited in foods. Harrington [14] and Kister [15] also reported that boric acid was harmful.

Several instances have been recorded of the presence of boric acid in foods. A medical officer in London found sponge cake on the market which contained 35 grains of boric acid per pound. The source was found to be liquid eggs which had been imported from China. Dudding [16] attributed illness among soldiers to boric acid in sausage (800 grams per pound). Levine [17] and Edmondson, Thom, and Giltner [18] discovered a canning powder which contained 95 per cent of boric acid and five per cent of salt. Sea foods have also been reported to contain boric acid. Smelts imported into Great Britain [19] contained it and it was found in imported herrings in sauce and mackerel in oil, in amounts as great as 3,000 p.p.m.

Boric acid at best exerts only a feeble action on bacteria. According to Rost [20] large amounts must be used to be effective.

Owing to the emergencies incident to the second World War the Ministry of Food of Great Britain rescinded its former prohibition of the use of boron compounds in the preservation of bacon. According to the order "bacon" included hams and any other part of the carcass of the pig which had been cured in any way but did not include pickled pork. Borax included boric acid and borates. The permission was also extended to the presence of boron compounds in those articles of foods in which bacon and ham are constituents. No mention was made in the order of the maximum amount of boron compounds which would be permitted.[21]

FORMALDEHYDE

Formaldehyde was rather widely used at one time as a preservative in milk. It was placed on the prohibited list after the passage of the Food and Drug Act of 1906. Wiley [22] concluded that it deranged metabolism, disturbed the normal functions, and produced irritation and undue stimulation of the secretory activities and, therefore, was never justifiable. While formaldehyde is banned when added as such, it is not prohibited when added in some other ways. Recent work on smoking of

13. Wiley. 1904. U. S. Dept. Agr., Bur. Chem. Bull. 84. Wash., D. C.
14. Harrington. 1904. Brit. Food J. 6, 203.
15. Kister. 1901. Ztschr. Hyg. 37, 225.
16. Dudding. 1922. J. Roy. Army Med. Corps 38, 138-140.
17. Levine. 1923. J. Home Econ. 15, 64-70.
18. Edmondson, Thom, and Giltner. 1922. U. S. Dept. Agr. Circ. 237.
19. Report of Chief Medical Officer of Ministry of Health for 1934, p. 119.
20. Rost. 1903. Borsäure als Konservierungsmittel. J. Springer, Berlin.
21. Food. 1940. 9, 193.
22. Wiley. 1908. U. S. Dept. Agr., Bur. Chem. Bull. 84, Pt. 4, Wash., D. C.

meats and fish has revealed the presence of considerable amounts in smoke and smoked products. In the definition of a preservative in the Food and Drug Act of 1928 in Great Britain, it is specifically stated that products added to foods by the process of curing known as smoking, shall not be considered preservatives. Even though formaldehyde has been on the prohibited list of food preservatives for many years, it is occasionally used by unscrupulous and ignorant individuals. The Food and Drug Administration, as late as 1931, seized 143 gallons of cream which had been preserved with formaldehyde.[23]

SALICYLIC ACID AND SALICYLATES

Salicylic acid and its salts are prohibited as food preservatives in the United States. Wiley[24] stated that while the compounds were harmful and should be prohibited in foods, they were not as harmful as generally believed. Examination of Wiley's report indicates that the results were not as clear-cut as could be desired. While the statements were general, addition of salicylic acid and salicylates to foods was considered to be reprehensible in every respect leading to injury to the consumer, which, though in many cases not easily measured, must finally be productive of great harm.

SULFUROUS ACID AND SULFITES

The primary purpose of sulfur dioxide in dried fruits is to preserve as far as possible the natural color of the fruit. The amount which has to be used, therefore, depends on several different factors. They must not be used in excess of the amounts really needed, conceal inferiority, or endanger the health of the consumer. When used in dried foods, it must be clearly stated on the label. Sulfur compounds may not be added to meat products according to Bureau of Animal Industry Order 211, Regulation 18, Section 6, Paragraph I.

According to Bitting,[25] sulfurous acid was used in 1813 by Hildebrand for preserving meats. It did not, however, have wide application. In 1939, Jordan suggested the use of this agent for preserving meat and fish. Wiley[26] stated that administration of sulfurous acid in food was objectionable and produced disturbances of metabolic functions and injury to health and digestion.

Sulfur dioxide does not completely sterilize but probably acts as an antiseptic; nor does it affect fermentation to an injurious extent when nitrogenous food is too low.[27] Cruess and Berg[28] found that 1,500 p.p.m. of sulfites kept grape juice from fermenting for two years and Nichols[29] found it impossible to isolate bacteria from sulfured dried fruits which had been present before sulfuring. Molds, however, were isolated from dried apricots containing 315 p.p.m. of sulfur dioxide. Molds were ob-

23. Report of Chief of the Food and Drug Administration for year ended June 30, 1932, p. 6.
24. Wiley. 1908. U. S. Dept. Agr., Bur. Chem. Bull. 84, Pt. 2, Wash., D. C.
25. Bitting. 1924. The Canning Age. October.
26. Wiley. 1907. U. S. Dept. Agr., Bur. Chem. Bull. 84, Pt. 3, Wash., D. C.
27. Barker and Grove. 1926. Ann. Rept. Agr. and Hort. Sta., Univ. of Bristol, 98-109.
28. Cruess and Berg. 1925. Ind. Eng. Chem. 17, 849.
29. Nichols. 1934. Amer. J. Pub. Health 24, 1129-1134.

served growing on dried pears containing 700 p.p.m. of sulfur dioxide. Nichols attributed this to inadequate sulfuring.

Whether a certain amount is excessive or not depends largely on the reasons for using it as well as the actual conditions which obtain when it is used. Since it is used to retain the natural color of dried fruits the amount needed is determined by the degree of natural color desired. Nichols,[29] Chace, Church, and Sarber,[30] and Nichols and Christie [31] stated that satisfactory color retention was not consistently attained if the sulfur dioxide content was below 1,000 p.p.m.; 2,000 p.p.m. are usually necessary and in some cases even 3,000 p.p.m. Nichols and Christie observed a distinct loss of sulfur dioxide during storage for six months. Cooking also destroys much of it.

Despite statements of a few investigators to the contrary, sodium sulfite in amounts used in dried fruits, is probably harmless. Flury [32] reported it to be so. Nichols referred to unpublished work of the United States Bureau of Chemistry between 1909 and 1914 which indicated the harmlessness of sulfites and to a declaration of the American Medical Association to the same effect.[33] The British tolerance for sulfur dioxide is 2,000 p.p.m. for strawberries and raspberries and 1,500 p.p.m. for other fruits (Atkinson [34]).

Sulfur dioxide is also used as a preservative for fruits during shipment because they may be sent without refrigeration. The preservative was found by Atkinson [34] to be effective up to two years and to be easily removed.

SODIUM BENZOATE

This is the only chemical preservative which is allowed in the United States. One of the most interesting controversies, in which eminent chemists and physiologists of the day participated, was waged over its use.

Sodium benzoate is not an active preservation agent. Lucas [35] reported that it preserved strong acid fruits, but that cider with .1 per cent of sodium benzoate developed mold. Barnard,[36] Herter,[37] Held,[38] and Tanner and Strauch [39] all showed the weak action of this compound on bacteria. Held observed a greater effect than the others. Lagoni [40] recognized a bacteriostatic action of benzoic acid.

Passage of the Food and Drug Act in 1906, in which it was stated that food was adulterated if "it contained any added poisonous or other added deleterious ingredient which may render such article injurious to health," compelled investigations to determine whether sodium benzoate came within these limits. Wiley, then Chief of the U. S. Bureau of Chem-

30. Chace, Church, and Sarber. 1930. Ind. Eng. Chem. 22, 1317.
31. Nichols and Christie. 1930. Calif. Agr. Exp. Sta. Bull. 485.
32. Flury. 1929. Deut. Nährungs-Rundschau, No. 9.
33. Hygeia 12, 464.
34. Atkinson. 1941. The Canner, Dec. 13, 1941, 14-15.
35. Lucas. 1909. Proc. Soc. Expt. Biol. & Med. 6, 122-126.
36. Barnard. 1911. Chem. Eng. 12, 104.
37. Herter. 1910. J. Biol. Chem. 7, 59-67.
38. Held. 1915. Arch. Hyg. 84, 287-336.
39. Tanner and Strauch. 1926. Proc. Soc. Exper. Biol. & Med. 23, 449-450.
40. Lagoni. 1941. Zentbl. Bakt., Abt. 2, 103, 225-231.

istry, became an unalterable foe of the compound and remained so until his death.

As a result of the Act of Congress, 1903, Wiley [22] and his collaborators conducted an extensive investigation, all of the results of which need not be reported here. They consisted, however, in the administration of benzoic acid and benzoates to a squad of normal, healthy human beings. They concluded that administration of benzoic acid,* either as such or as sodium benzoate, was highly objectionable and produced a serious disturbance of the metabolic functions, attended with injury to digestion and health. This statement covers the conclusion with sufficient completeness.

The group of men to whom Wiley fed sodium benzoate was called a "poison squad," a name certain to attract the attention of the public, and by implication to suggest the harmfulness of the preservative under study. The question was not settled by Wiley's conclusions, for demands were made that unbiased investigations be made. Consequently, former President Theodore Roosevelt appointed a Referee Board of Consulting Scientific Experts, to study the question. This board, which consisted of eminent physiological chemists of the day, concluded that sodium benzoate in small doses (under .5 mg. per day), mixed with food was without deleterious or poisonous effect, and was not injurious to health. In large doses (up to four grams per day), mixed with food, it did not exert a deleterious effect. Further review of conclusions would only amplify what has just been stated, and would add nothing new. These conclusions of the Referee Board were the reverse of those reached by Wiley. Consequently, the Department of Agriculture permitted the use of sodium benzoate as a preservative in foods.

Food Inspection Decision No. 76 issued July 13, 1907, forbade the use of certain preservatives in foods under Section 7 of the Food and Drugs Act of June 30, 1906. Sodium benzoate was reluctantly permitted until more information could be secured. Food Inspection Decision No. 89, issued March 5, 1908, pending determination by the Referee Board, read as follows:

"Benzoate of soda, in quantities not exceeding one-tenth of one per cent may be added to those foods in which generally heretofore it has been used. The addition of benzoate of soda shall be plainly stated upon the label of each package of such food."

After the Referee Board, composed of Dr. Ira Remsen, Dr. R. H. Chittenden, Dr. J. H. Long, Dr. A. Taylor, Dr. C. A. Herter, and Otto Folin, reported on their extensive investigations, Food Inspection Decision No. 104, issued March 3, 1909, read as follows:

"The Board reports, as a result of three extensive and exhaustive investigations, that benzoate of soda mixed with food is not deleterious or poisonous, and is not injurious to health. The summary of the report of the Referee Board is published herewith.

"It having been determined that benzoate of soda mixed with food is not deleterious or poisonous, and is not injurious to health, no objection will be raised under the

---

* Other chemical compounds which have at times been used in food preservation, but which have since been placed on the prohibited list, will not be discussed in this book. They will be considered in the companion volume ou "Food Poisoning and Food Infection," the second edition of which is in preparation.

Food and Drug Act to the use in food of benzoate of soda, provided that each container is plainly labeled to show the presence and amount of benzoate of soda.

"Food Inspection Decisions 76 and 89 are amended accordingly."

While Wiley may have been too arbitrary with respect to the harmfulness of sodium benzoate, his great contribution to the pure-food movement must not be overlooked. This came at a time when it was sorely needed. Few can deny the validity of his argument that if sound raw materials were preserved by adequate procedures, a preservative would not be needed. This position has been vindicated by experience. Sodium benzoate is not now used to any extent if at all.

Acidity of food apparently has considerable effect on the activity of sodium benzoate according to results of experiments by Cruess and his colleagues, Richert and Irish,[41] who used various microorganisms and several different preservatives. Concentrations of all of the latter except sodium chloride and formaldehyde required to prevent growth of the organisms were much greater at a pH from 5 to 5.9 than at a pH from 2 to 4.5. At pH 7, as much as 300 times the concentration of certain preservatives was required to prevent growth as at pH 3 to 3.5.

At neutrality, approximately four per cent of sodium benzoate was required to prevent growth of most of the fermentation organisms studied; whereas at pH 2.3 to 2.4, only .02 to .03 per cent was required, and at pH 3.5 to 4 (the range for most fruit juices) only .06 to 1.10 per cent. The nonacid-tolerant organisms (Escherichia coli, Bacillus subtilis, Clostridium sporogenes, Clostridium botulinum) did not grow at pH values below 4; nevertheless, the inhibiting action of sodium benzoate depended on hydrogen-ion concentration. A Penicillium was found growing profusely, although not sporulating, in a 10-per cent sodium benzoate solution near neutrality. Their results showed that salts of these weak acids exert relatively slight toxic action on microorganisms, near neutrality, but exert their maximum effect in the moderately strong acid range. Toxicity was believed to depend on concentration of undissociated acid, rather than on that of their anions. In asparagus juice, Clostridium botulinum grew and formed toxin at pH 7.4 with .8 gram of sodium benzoate per 100 ml., but failed to grow or form toxin at pH 4.7 with .1 gram. Observations at other pH values confirmed the theory that hydrogen-ion concentration is of primary importance in preventing growth of this organism; it was therefore believed to be dangerous to attempt to preserve nonacid foods with sodium benzoate. Near neutrality, two per cent of benzoate failed to prevent spoilage of ripe olives, avocado pulp, melon preserves, maraschino-type grapes. prune pulp, carbonated beverages, asparagus, string beans, green peas, and artichokes packed in dilute brines or sirups; whereas at pH 4 (or lower) spoilage was prevented by .1 per cent or less of the preservative. At pH values of 4 to 7 the concentrations to prevent spoilage were intermediate between these extremes. Schmidt-Lange [42] also

41. Crues et al. 1929. J. Bact. 17, 363-371; Hilgardia 6 (1931), 295-314; Ind. Eng. Chem. 24 (1932), 648-649; J. Bact. 23 (1932), 163-166; Fruit Prod. J. 10 (1931), 242-244.

42. Schmidt-Lange. 1937. Arch. Hyg. 118, 354-361.

found sodium benzoate to inhibit *Clostridium botulinum*. The influence of hydrogen-ion concentration was also observed by Goshorn, Degering, and Tetrault.[43]

Besides chemically known substances just discussed, there are others such as those found in wood smoke used in meats and other foods. Pettet[44] found several constituents in wood smoke which might have significance in food preservation. Among these were formaldehyde, higher aldehydes, formic acid, acetic acid, and higher acids. Tar amounted to 12 per cent of dry wood. Such a mixture should be quite bactericidal.

ACIDS AND HYDROGEN-ION CONCENTRATION

The hydrogen-ion concentration of food influences its deterioration by microorganisms. This is discussed at various places in this book. Some study has been given to the effect on microorganisms of the acids themselves. Kruger[45] added organic acids to nutrient broth to produce final concentrations of 1 to 10 to 1 to 1,000,000, after which they were inoculated with pure cultures. Subcultures were made during incubation. *Escherichia coli* was most resistant to lactic acid, withstanding a concentration of 1 to 100 for four hours. *Salmonella enteritidis* was least resistant withstanding a concentration of 1 to 100 for only two hours. *Pseudomonas aeruginosa*, *Proteus vulgaris*, and *Staphylococcus aureus* were approximately equal in resistance to lactic acid but were less so than *Escherichia coli*. Differences were observed among all strains of a species. The bactericidal effect of the organic acids tested was not attributable to the hydrogen-ion concentration but to the chemical character of the acid. Lactic acid showed the greatest activity, its inhibiting ability being influenced largely by the time of exposure. Levine and Fellers[46] found that acetic acid in nutrient broth inhibited various organisms related to food spoilage. The organisms which they used did not grow in broth adjusted to a pH of 4.9 with acetic acid. *Saccharomyces ellipsoideus* did not grow at pH of 3.9 and *Aspergillus niger* was inhibited at pH 4.1. An increase in the hydrogen-ion concentration resulted in a decrease in thermal death time. Reduction in the lethal temperature was more marked in the case of *Bacillus mesentericus* and *Bacillus cereus* than with the non-spore forming organisms. Thermal death times of the yeast and mold were not altered by addition of small amounts of acetic acid. Acetic acid was more toxic than either lactic or hydrochloric acids for *Salmonella aertrycke*, *Saccharomyces cerevisiae*, and *Aspergillus niger*. Levine and Fellers did not attribute the action of these acids to hydrogen ions alone but in part to undissociated acetic acid molecules. Tetsumoto[47] also reported a strong sterilizing power of vinegar toward *Eberthella typhosa* and *Vibrio comma*.

Reaction of foods has been found to be of primary importance with respect to development of *Clostridium botulinum*. This organism does not

43. Goshorn. Degering, and Tetrault. 1938. Ind. Eng. Chem. 30, 646-648.
44. Pettet. 1938. Ann. Rept. for 1937. Food Invest. Bd., Great Britain, 90-91.
45. Kruger. 1937. Rev. in Biol. Absts. 14, 486.
46. Levine and Fellers. 1940. J. Bact. 39, 499-514.
47. Tetsumoto. 1934. J. Agr. Chem. Soc., Japan, 10, 123-127.

develop in foods more acid than pH 4.5. When foods originally more acid than this have caused botulism, presence of other bacteria have been shown which have destroyed some of the acid. Therefore, this critical hydrogen-ion concentration (pH 4.5) probably cannot apply to unprocessed foods with a heterogeneous flora of microorganisms, or processed foods in which all of the microorganisms have not been destroyed.

CONCENTRATED SOLUTIONS

Concentrated solutions of salts, sugars, or mixtures of them are used in preservation of certain foods to repress development of microorganisms. Salt, for instance, is used in curing meats, in cucumber pickles, and in sauerkraut fermentations. In these cases the microbial flora is greatly simplified and reduced to types which can endure large concentrations of salt.

Concentrated Sugar Solutions. Sirups, or solutions of sugar in water, are used in preservation of fruits. They are used more for their effect on flavor than for their ability to harm bacteria. Other methods, such as heating to high temperatures, must be used for ridding fruits in sirup of microorganisms. Sirups alone cannot be used because some microorganisms are able to remain viable in heavy sirups. Honey may contain microorganisms which are quite tolerant to high sugar concentration and even grow. According to Grove [48] yeasts and molds cannot ordinarily develop in sugar solutions of over 50 per cent. Penicillium was checked at 65 per cent, but after a month, feeble growth was noticed at even 70 per cent. Heidemann, in the author's laboratory, secured results with yeasts which agreed with those of Grove.

Fruits preserved with sugar are usually heated for final destruction of microorganisms. Rahn [49] showed that heavy sirups may protect microorganisms from heat since pure cultures of yeasts showed longer death times when heated in sirups. This subject is dealt with a little later in this chapter and in several others.

Molds cause considerable deterioration of fruit products containing large amounts of sugar. Macara [50] found that at relative humidities below 82 per cent, fruit jams containing from 70 to 72 per cent solids will prevent germination of mold spores. He said the osmotic pressure of the jam must equal or exceed that of the spores if mold growth is to be prevented. Jams stored in relative humidities in excess of 82 per cent will absorb moisture. Such moisture may enable spoilage to start at least on the surface.

Occasionally high sugar concentrations alone are suggested for fruit preservation. Nepomniashcha and Liberman,[51] for instance, reported preservation of mixed prunes with 50 to 65 per cent of sugar without heat treatment. After sealing in tins they were reported to have kept for 19 months without swelling. Periodic microbiological examinations did not

48. Grove. 1918. Univ. of Bristol, Ann. Rept. Agr. and Hort. Res. Station, 34-38.
49. Rahn. 1928. Canning Age, Aug., 705-706.
50. Macara. 1937. Proc. Roy. Inst., Gt. Brit., Chem. Absts. 31, 5883.
51. Nepomniashcha and Liberman. 1938. Rev. in Biol. Absts 14, 6.

reveal any coliform bacteria, anaerobes, or yeasts. The flora consisted exclusively of sporeformers. They suggested that this method might be used for large-scale preservation of fruits. Whether such a method could be used with good results would depend on the bacterial load present, the amount of acid, and other factors. It should not be attempted in the United States for too many microorganisms would develop, as shown by Andreicha,[52] among others. Neither the highest sugar concentrations used in commercial jams and jellies nor an atmosphere of carbon dioxide approaching 100 per cent alone, suppressed development of common molds; combined action, however, of these two preserving agents was successful. An atmosphere containing 10 per cent of carbon dioxide prevented development of *Aspergillus repens*, *Penicillium areuarum*, and *Penicillium glaucum* on 60 per cent glucose broth. Lower sugar concentrations required higher concentrations of carbon dioxide. Further work on this question is discussed in Chapter 14.

Microorganisms in Sugar. The microbial content of sugar has been studied for several reasons. It was necessary to have information on this subject to know the effect of various processes used in its manufacture on microorganisms, to learn the origin of various species which deteriorate sugar during storage, and to determine whether microorganisms may be present which may cause undue spoilage when the sugar is added to other foods. Since these subjects are discussed in a later chapter, they will not be considered here.

Effect of Concentrated Salt Solutions on Microorganisms. Concentrated solutions are widely used for preservation of meats and some vegetables. The bacteria responsible for desirable fermentations in meat curing and sauerkraut fermentation are relatively salt tolerant. The action of salt in food preservation is generally attributed to plasmolysis. Although the results of Lindet's [53] experiments seem to confirm this opinion, it is doubtful whether the explanation is so simple. Fischer stated that plasmolysis lasted only for a certain length of time, usually a few hours, and that not all bacterial cells would be affected. Rockwell and Ebertz [54] believed that at least five factors were involved in the detrimental action of salt on bacteria: dehydration, direct effect of the chloride ion, removal of oxygen, sensitization against carbon dioxide, and interference with rapid action of proteolytic enzymes. Pettersson [55] observed a marked simplification of the flora with increasing salt concentration. In low concentration the flora was heterogeneous; the rods were eliminated between 12 and 15 per cent; wild yeasts dominated the flora at 25 per cent. LeFevre and Round [56] reported bacteria which were said to require 25 per cent of salt to grow. Others who made significant contributions are Stadler,[57] de Freytag,[58]

52. Andreicha. 1936. Microbiologia 5, 709-715.
53. Lindet. 1912. Comp. Rend. Acad. Sci. 155, 790-792.
54. Rockwell and Ebertz. 1924. J. Infect. Diseases 35, 573-575.
55. Pettersson. 1900. Arch. Hyg. 37, 170-238.
56. LeFevre and Round. 1919. J. Bact. 4, 177-182.
57. Stadler. 1899. Arch. Hyg. 35, 40-82.
58. de Freytag. 1890. Idem 11, 60.

Lewandowsky,[59] Weichel,[60] and Serkowski and Tomczak.[61] The effect of salt seems to be influenced greatly by the substrate to which it is added and the microorganisms which are present. While it is generally stated that 10 per cent of salt will inhibit *Clostridium botulinum*, some strains are apparently able to endure greater amounts.

Less information is available on the effect of salt solutions on yeasts and molds. The latter are inhibited by 20 to 30 per cent solutions although slight growth may occur after long times. Wehmer [62] isolated a yeast from herring brine which was inhibited by 15 per cent of salt. Speakman, Gee, and Luck [63] reported that solutions with 10 per cent of salt were fermented by *Saccharomyces cerevisiae*. Above this concentration fermentation became slower and slower. Other yeasts are salt resistant as indicated by Karaffa-Korbutt.[64] According to Thom,[65] Penicillia are inhibited by 15 per cent of salt.

Various microorganisms in addition to bacteria may persist in strong brines. Baas-Becking [66] reported several species of protozoa as well as several species of higher bacteria. Both halophilic and non-halophilic species were isolated from brines by Hof.[67] Microorganisms from saltless sources were less tolerant to salt as a rule. However, some halophilic species isolated from soil were believed to have originated from normal soil bacteria.

Halophilic bacteria are not restricted in habitat to salt or concentrated brines but may be cultivated from other sources. Stuart [68] found them widely distributed.

Microorganisms in Salt. A diverse flora would not be expected in salt produced and handled under good conditions. Large numbers, however, have been obtained in some cases. Pierce [69] who examined the flora of brines of salt works in the San Francisco Bay region for three years, found that the concentration of the brine was the most important factor relating to numbers of microorganisms found. All of the species which he isolated were saprophytic. Wolff [70] urged that salt used in the dairy industry be examined bacteriologically. He found bacteria, yeasts, and molds to be common. In one case the brine contained 315,000 bacteria per ml., some of which would have been troublesome in butter. Rappin and Weigmann [71] published similar conclusions. In a later publication, Rappin [72] reported a salt with 1,300 to 38,000 bacteria and 100 to 400 fungi per

59. Lewandowsky. 1904. Arch. Hyg. 49, 47.
60. Weichel. 1910. Arb. a. d. k. Gsndhtsamte 34, 247-265.
61. Serkowski and Tomczak. 1911. Ztschr. f. Untersuch. d. Nahrungs- u. Genussmittel. 21, 211-216.
62. Wehmer. 1897. Centbl. Bakt. 3, 209.
63. Speakman, Gee, and Luck. 1928. J. Bact. 15, 319-340.
64. Karaffa-Korbutt. 1912. Ztschr. Hyg. 71, 162-170.
65. Thom. 1914. Conn. Agr. Exp. Sta. Bull. 79, 387-394.
66. Baas-Becking. 1928. Tijdschr. Nederlands Dierkunde Ver. 1, 6-9.
67. Hof. 1935. Rec. d. Trav. Bot. Neerland. 32, 92-173.
68. Stuart. 1938. Food Research 3, 417-420.
69. Pierce. 1914. The Salton Sea, Washington, 1914.
70. Wolff 1914. Milchwirtschaft. Zentbl. 43, 545-551.
71. Rappin and Weigmann. 1913. Jahresb. Vers. Stat. Mölk. u. Landw. Schleswig-Holstein, 9-10.
72. Rappin. 1920. Rev. in J. Amer. Med. Assoc. 75, 618-619.

gram. In America, Yesair [73] recommended that the bacteriological condition of salt be considered and understood by food preservers. He found putrefactive anaerobic bacteria in some salts and advised against the use of such salt in the meat industry. Rahn [74] has also pointed out the need for handling salt properly in food-preservation establishments. He called attention to the ease with which it may be contaminated and the evil consequences which may result. In this connection Baas-Becking [75] discussed early methods of salt manufacture and a few microbiological problems related thereto.

LOW TEMPERATURES

The inhibitive effects of low temperatures on bacterial development in foods are pointed out at various places in this book. Cold storage and refrigeration are important for preservation of such foods as meats, milk, and eggs. Variations of only a few degrees are of great significance. Refrigeration above freezing cannot be relied upon to hold foods indefinitely. As long as moisture is available for bacterial development, foods will undergo slow deterioration. Most bacteria and parasites survive freezing although their numbers may be markedly reduced. *Trichinella spiralis* in pork is killed by freezing at —15°C.(5°F.) for 24 to 36 hours. Freedom from these parasites is insured by holding them for not less than 20 days at this temperature. This allows an ample margin of safety.

The Committee on Foods of the American Public Health Association has on several occasions discussed the health aspects of refrigeration.[76] The factors involved in successful refrigeration, according to Ferguson,[77] are, in general, low temperatures, correct humidity, proper atmosphere, controlled odors, and sound foodstuffs in the beginning. Prescott and Tanner [78] also discussed the health aspects of foods preserved by low temperatures.

Introduction of the electric refrigerator into the home was probably one of the most significant events which has happened in food preservation in several decades. It is now possible to maintain constant temperatures which are known to keep food in a satisfactory manner. These instruments have not only made it possible to preserve food better but have added much to the convenience and pleasure of living, especially in warm climates. Cold is the most satisfactory agent for preservation of foods for short periods of time. Refrigeration preserves large amounts of food during shipment. The committee appointed by the Ministry of Health of Great Britain to investigate the use of chemical preservatives in food advised that refrigeration be employed as much as possible.

Introduction of "dry ice," solid carbon dioxide, into food preservation has also been a significant event. It is now being used for shipment of meat, yeast, fish, and other foods. Very low temperatures are obtained.

73. Yesair. 1930. Canning Trade 52, 112-115.
74. Rahn. 1934. The National Provisioner, p. 13.
75. Baas-Becking. 1931. Scientific Monthly 32, 434-446.
76. Amer. Pub. Health Assoc. Year Book, 1935-36, 47-51.
77. Ferguson. 1931. Canad. Pub. Health J. 22, 467-473.
78. Prescott and Tanner. 1938. Food Research 3, 189-197.

Killeffer [79] stated that the actual temperature of a block of "dry ice" is not higher than —74°C.(—101.2°F.) and may be as low as —109°C. (—165°F.). Its cooling value is twice that of ice. According to Killeffer. carbon dioxide itself exercises a preservative action on certain food products. He stated that meat and fish can be kept fresh longer when refrigerated in carbon dioxide atmosphere than in air. Furthermore, it was also shown that carbon dioxide in culture media repressed, if it did not kill, common bacteria. It is a controversial question whether carbon dioxide has any pronounced effect on keeping quality.

In some cases, it has been necessary to determine what temperatures of storage constitute effective refrigeration. Such is the case for *Clostridium botulinum*. Tanner and Oglesby [80] and Tanner, Beamer, and Rickher [81] found that 10°C.(50°F.) prevented development of and toxin formation by this organism for a considerable period of time. Growth occurred and toxin was produced within a few days at 20°C:(68°F.) when either vegetative cells or spores were inoculated, and at 15°C.(59°F.) when vegetative cells were inoculated. At 15°C.(59°F.) toxin production by detoxified spores rarely occurred. At 10°C.(50°F.) growth of vegetative cells, if their appearance in eight cultures is taken as being normal for that temperature and not as the result of the short exposure to higher temperature, occurred only after 27 days. Growth of detoxified spores did not occur in 47 days, and no growth occurred at 5°C.(41°F.) in any medium, though incubation was continued to 108 days in some cases. This would seem to indicate that foods stored at room temperature or under only slight refrigeration may become dangerous fairly rapidly, but when kept at less than 10°C.(50°F.) will remain safe for a considerable length of time.

The relation of time of appearance of growth to development of toxin was shown with two strains at 20°C.(68°F.) and one strain at 15°C. (59°F.). In two cases the filtrate injected as soon as a heavy turbidity of growth appeared required two days to cause the death of a mouse. When the same cultures were injected after one more day of incubation, death of the mouse occurred in one day. In the case of one culture results were similar except that two days intervened between two injections. Tanner and Oglesby found appreciable difference among strains of *Clostridium botulinum* in temperature relations. Results of the investigation by Tanner, Beamer, and Rickher [81] with food products confirmed the work just reported. The same problem was studied by Prescott and Geer [82] for other bacteria. With *Clostridium botulinum*, refrigeration of properly prepared foods at temperatures below 10°C.(50°F.) prevented formation of toxins for extended but undetermined periods. Spoilage of food by other types of bacteria can, however, take place at 50°F. In food-poisoning, such as that caused by the Salmonella group, limitation of numbers

79. Killeffer. 1930. Ind. Eng. Chem. 22, 140-143.
80. Tanner and Oglesby. 1936. Food Research 1, 481-494.
81. Tanner, Beamer, and Rickher. 1940. Food Research 5, 323-334.
82. Prescott and Geer. 1936. Refrig. Engin. 32, 211-212.

of the organisms to a minimum is the essential result to be attained. For these organisms refrigeration at 10°C.(50°F.) is not sufficiently effective, and if security against growth is to be attained, it is necessary to maintain the foods at temperatures not above 3.9°C.(39°F.).

When large numbers of bacterial cells belonging to different types of milk streptococci were added to milk by Foter and Rahn[83] and incubated at 0 to 2° C. (32 to 35.6° F.), lactic acid was produced. Fermentation occurred slowly and ceased at low acidity. It did not appear to depend entirely upon growth, though it was more marked with such organisms as *Streptococcus fecalis*, *Streptococcus cremoris*, and *Streptococcus lique-faciens* which were able to grow at 0°C.(32°F.) than with organisms like *Streptococcus lactis* and *Lactobacillus acidophilus* which failed to do so. Growth curves showed that *Streptococcus lactis* and *Lactobacillus acidophilus* both multiplied slowly at 5°C.(41°F.). The shortest generation times occurred with *Streptococcus fecalis* at about 37°C.(98.6°F.), with *Streptococcus lactis* at about 30°C.(86°F.) and with *Lactobacillus acidophilus* at about 40°C.(104°F.). The greatest bacterial crops were yielded between the optimum and 10° below optimum.

The practical effects of low temperatures are also indicated in other ways. Barker and Grove[84] stored cider in bottles for four or five months. Part was held in cold storage at 1°C.(33.8°F.) and part in cellar storage at about 13 to 16°C.(55.4 to 60.8°F.). That held at 1°C. retained better flavor and color, lost less in acidity and specific gravity, and contained much less deposit of yeast and bacteria than that held at high temperature. The influence of temperature upon autolytic and bacterial decomposition of haddock muscle within the range of 2.2 to —1.1°C.(36 to 30°F.) was followed by Hess[85] by determining the increase in the amount of volatile basic nitrogen parallel with the increase in the number of bacteria. A mixed flora of bacteria normally occurring on haddock was used for inoculation. The experimental results showed that practically no autolysis took place at these temperatures, and that bacterial decomposition and bacterial growth rate at —1.1°C.(30°F.) is about half that at 2.2°C. (36°F.). The practical application of these findings has been demontrated to be of economical importance in the holding of fresh fish at —1.1°C.(30°F.) instead of the customary holding in crushed ice at about 2.2°C.(36°F.).

Laboratory tests by Danner[86] indicated a range of 4.4 to —7.2° C. (40 to 45° F.) as the most efficient food-storage temperature for the home. Foods lost less weight in ice than in electric refrigerators, when stored at the same temperature. Foods in the gas refrigerator lost, in most instances, more weight at corresponding temperatures than in the electric refrigerator. Temperature in ice refrigerators increased with increase in room temperature. Foods spoil more readily with a heavy frost on the cooling

83. Foter and Rahn. 1936. J. Bact. 32, 485-497.
84. Barker and Grove. 1930. Ann. Rept., Agr. and Hort. Res. Station, Univ. of Bristol, 1929, 196-199.
85. Hess. 1932. Canad. Biol. and Fisheries 7 No. 13.
86. Danner. 1933. Agr. Engin. 14, 99-100.

unit. Moran and Pique,[87] and several others later, advised incorporation of antiseptics in ice to be used for preserving foods.

PRESERVATION OF FOODS BY FREEZING

This method of food preservation has enjoyed wide and rapid expansion in recent years. Development of varieties of fruits and vegetables which, upon thawing, retain their shape and flavor, has placed the industry on a firmer basis, as has availability of freezing-storage display cases for merchandising frozen foods. The nutritional aspects, not to be ignored for any preserved food, are not within the scope of this book. Those who are interested in this subject may consult a review by Rose [88] and numerous other discussions of a similar nature.

The history of preservation by cold, prior to and since the advent of quick-freezing, has been reviewed by Birdseye and Fitzgerald [89] The quick-freezing industry developed slowly and was concerned almost wholly with fish until about 1929, when it was applied to other food products. Laboratory research and commercial applications have made it possible to preserve meats, fish, fruits, and vegetables with little or no loss of natural flavor and color. This industry appears to merit consideration as one of the most important developments of the 20th century. Freezing brings to the consumers foods nearer to their fresh state than any other method of preservation. Frozen foods are probably nearer fresh foods than canned foods and may be better from the nutritional standpoint. So far as bacteriological examination is concerned, frozen foods are in a class by themselves. Enumeration of viable bacteria, according to Sanderson.[90] as a means of sanitary control, does not solve the problem of pathogenic bacteria. Count of *Escherichia coli* along with the total count, would be better than the total count alone. Whether sufficient work has been done to show the true value of the count is doubtful. If counts are to be used, standards must be set up and standard methods developed to accompany them. Tressler [103] found a low bacterial count in frozen foods which were prepared from good raw materials.

Fundamental Principles Involved. Thorough freezing of foods involves changes in the state of moisture in the tissue. Slow-freezing yields a product with undesirable characteristics, such as loss of shape after thawing, loss of color, and finally loss of considerable amounts of moisture, spoken of as "drip" in the meat-preservation industry. The problems involved were early studied by Richardson and Scherubel [91] who described separation of water from tissues and its freezing between the muscle fibers. When the meat thawed some of this water was reabsorbed. That which was not was released from the meat as "drip." Since then many investigators have found the freezing process to be much more complicated. Publica-

87. Moran and Pique. 1924. Ann. Rept. Food Invest. Bd. for 1923, 12.
88. Rose. 1940. J. Amer. Med. Assoc. 114, 1356-1361.
89. Birdseye and Fitzgerald. 1932. Ind. Eng. Chem. 24, 676-678.
90. Sanderson. 1941. Refrig. Engin. 42, 228.
91. Richardson and Scherubel. 1908. J. Amer. Chem. Soc. 30, 1515

tions by Stiles,[92] Diehl,[93] and various notes in the annual reports of the Food Investigation Board are concerned with the latest ideas on the subject.

Development of Methods for Freezing Foods. Freezing is a natural phenomenon but apparatus which has been developed for using it under controlled conditions for preservation of foods has greatly influenced the effects it may have on the food. Grayson [94] stated that there were six fundamental systems for quick-freezing foods:

1. Direct still air—numerous systems
2. Brine immersion—Cook, Kolbe, and Peterson
3. Atomized brine—"Z" system and Bloom system
4. Pressure-plate, direct-expansion, portable freezers (General Food Corp.)
5. Direct, carbon dioxide, instantaneous system—Grayson
6. Direct, high-velocity air with multistage intense refrigeration—Grayson

Direct still air was said to be the oldest method although it did not permit quick-freezing.

Air-frozen, slow-frozen, and sharp-frozen are synonyms for products frozen in modern "sharp-freezers" with a minimum temperature of —23.3 to —26.1°C. (—10 to —15°F.). "Quick-frozen," according to Birdseye,[95] is used to designate products which have been frozen by direct immersion in a liquid refrigerant, such as sodium chloride brine, or by indirect contact with a cold liquid refrigerant, such as calcium chloride brine. Birdseye attributed the merits of quick-freezing to the size of ice crystals in the cells. During that period in which most of the moisture is being frozen, individual ice crystals are constantly increasing in size. After the temperature has reached —3.9°C. (25°F.) most of the water has frozen and the growth of individual crystals largely ceases. Birdseye characterized the temperature zone from —.6°C. (31°F.) to about —3.9°C. (25°F.) as the zone of "maximum crystal formation." Since the size of crystals depends on the time allowed for them to form, it is obvious that the more quickly flesh, for instance, is passed through this zone the smaller the crystals will be in the product. Birdseye stated that in the usual sharp-freezing of fish, much time is allowed for formation of large crystals, some of which are as much as one inch in length. These large crystals rupture the cells and bring about changes which make the flesh more susceptible to attacks of bacteria and to autolysis. Birdseye reported data secured with haddock which showed that the quick-frozen product was superior to the slow-frozen. Apparent difficulties are involved in freezing large particles of food, such as whole quarters of beef. Heat cannot be removed rapidly enough for the meat to freeze quickly.

Not all have accepted this explanation for superiority of "quick-frozen" over "slow-frozen" foods. Taylor,[96] for instance, does not accept it. He stated that the amount of "drip" from thawed frozen meats bears

92. Stiles. 1922. Special Rept. No. 7, Food Invest. Bd
93. Diehl. 1932. Ind. Eng. Chem. 24, 661-665.
94. Grayson. 1938. The Canner, April 2, 1933.
95. Birdseye. 1929. Ind. Eng. Chem. 21, 414-417; 573-576; 854-857.
96. Taylor. 1931. Food Indus. 3, 205-206.

no relation to the rapidity of freezing. He furthermore stated that the true explanation of what happens will be found in the province of colloid chemistry rather than mechanics. Those especially interested in the subject should consult the publications of Birdseye, Taylor, and the annual reports of the Food Investigation Board of the Department of Scientific and Industrial Research of Great Britain. This bureau observed that such foods as eggs and meat frozen at —5°C.(23°F.) and stored at the same temperature, reverted when thawed to their original state; but if after being frozen at —5°C.(23°F.) they are stored at a lower temperature, e.g., —10°C.(14°F.), they quickly change.[97]

Preparation of Foods for Freezing. While some foods are ready for freezing as soon as harvested, others must receive special treatment. Certain vegetables are scalded and blanched in order to reduce volume and to remove extraneous matter such as soil. Wiegand[98] stated that the blanch removes gases, saturates the tissues with water, inactivates enzymes, and minimizes discoloration and deterioration during storage. Packing products in brine or sirup protects them from air and causes them to have a better quality.

One of the most important reasons for treating vegetables and fruits before freezing is to destroy or inactivate their enzymes. Fitzgerald,[99] Dingle and Berry,[100] Balls and Lineweaver,[101] and Joslyn and Marsh[102] have stressed this. Enzymes may not be completely destroyed by blanching. Fitzgerald stated that only those which would spoil the food during storage at —17.8°C.(0°F.) for a year or so were inactivated. To destroy all of them the food would have to be virtually cooked and thus harmed for freezing. Enzymatic activity was observed by Dingle and Berry in thawed foods which had been frozen for some time. Thawed tissues which have been frozen disintegrate more rapidly than those which have never been frozen, according to Balls and Lineweaver. Tressler[103] believed that a low bacterial content in a frozen vegetable indicated good methods of packing and storage and that it had probably not been defrosted since freezing. Absence of enzymes indicates sufficient blanching which will prevent development of off-flavor and loss of color during storage at —17.8°C.(0°F.) for a year. Smart and Brunstetter[104] removed samples of lima beans for bacteriological examination at each step in preparation. The first were taken after the beans were shelled and washed. Considerable variation occurred in the microbial content of different lots. Some of this variation was attributed to the weather, for one lot, picked just after a heavy rain, was contaminated with soil which increased the number of bacteria present. Scalding and blanching of the beans at 100°C.(212°F.)

97. Ann. Rept. Food Invest. Bd. for 1922, 11; also Rept. for 1923, 9.
98. Wiegand. 1936. Oregon Agr. Exp. Sta. Circ. 116.
99. Fitzgerald. 1938. The Canner, Nov. 19, 13 *et seq.*
100. Dingle and Berry. 1933. Food Indus. 5, 300-301.
101. Balls and Lineweaver. 1938. Food Research 3, 57-67; Ice and Cold Storage 41 (1938), 101.
102. Joslyn and Marsh. 1938. Food Indus. 10, 379-381 *et seq.*
103. Tressler. 1939. Refrig. Engin. 36, 319-321.
104. Smart and Brunstetter. 1936. The Canner, Aug. 15, 14-16; 1937. Food Research 2, 151-163.

and 87.8°C.(190°F.) reduced the number of bacteria in proportion to the length of time they were treated. The reduction in count was over 99 per cent. The organisms remaining on the beans were further reduced by freezing and continued storage at —9.4°C.(15°F.). While considerable variation occurred in counts from different cans, the counts were so low that they would be negligible were it not for the fact that partly cooked lima beans form an excellent growth medium. For this reason Smart and Brunstetter advised placing the frozen beans directly in boiling water instead of allowing them to defrost slowly in the refrigerator This is sound advice from the health viewpoint. Smart and Brunstetter [104] also studied the blanching of spinach and kale. A large variety of bacteria were isolated from fresh, scalded, and frozen spinach and kale. The general bacteria content in both was reduced by over 99 per cent by steam scalding for three to five minutes, and also in most cases further reduced by freezing and storage. There were wide variations in the bacterial counts of the fresh material, but in general the bacterial count of the frozen-packs was low, so with proper care in the handling of spinach and kale and with effective scalding and freezing, high counts should not be encountered. The bacteria present were those ordinarily found in fresh vegetables and do not affect the wholesomeness of the product provided that in cooking the vegetables are placed in boiling water prior to, or immediately after, defrosting.

Effect of Freezing on Bacteria and Related Microorganisms. Introduction of quick-freezing as a method of food preservation revived interest in the general effect of freezing on microorganisms. Many investigations were carried out to determine whether new factors were involved under the conditions which obtain in frozen foods.

Some of the conclusions reached in early investigations of this subject, the literature of which was reviewed by Wallace and Tanner,[105] were based on poor logic. Since a few cells survived in suspensions which were subjected to liquid air temperatures when subcultures were made, it was believed that freezing did not kill microorganisms. These conclusions were based on qualitative work. When quantitative data were collected, however, which involved the actual number of living cells present before and after freezing, a marked death rate was noted. Most of the cells were killed, however, only a small percentage remaining alive. The actual number surviving would be influenced by the number in the initial product. Freezing could not be relied upon to sterilize, for a few bacteria would survive for a long time. Magoon [106] reported that molds, yeast, and bacteria are responsible for spoilage of frozen foods; and that the old belief that freezing destroys them must be revised, for, while the majority of a microbial population is usually killed by freezing temperatures in food products, a small proportion whose vitality is unaffected by subzero temperature survive. Some have been found to resist —252°C.(—421.6°F.) for as long as 10 hours, with no apparent harmful effect. Some are not

105. Wallace and Tanner. 1933. Fruit Prod. J. 13, 52-54; 14, 109-113.
106. Magoon. 1932. Ind. Eng. Chem. 24, 668-671.

only unharmed by cold but are even able to increase in numbers at temperatures well below 0°C.(32°F.). The changes brought about in frozen-pack foods differ with the nature of substances and with microorganisms concerned; they are both physical and chemical in nature. Alterations in texture, color, flavor, and healthfulness of the foods result from these microbial activities. When Hess [107] exposed marine bacteria to a moderate freezing temperature, —16°C.(3.2°F.), for short periods, sea water offered greater protection than broth media or distilled water. Reduction in number of bacteria was least severe in broth media of optimum salt concentration. During freezing in distilled water, transfer of bacteria from the crystallizing portion of the liquid part occurred. Old strains were more resistant to freezing, and previous cultivation at —3°C.(26.6°F.) produced more resistant strains. A higher percentage of cells was killed by freezing at lower freezing temperatures, by prolonged freezing, rapid freezing, and repeated freezing. In truly supercooled sea water higher percentage reduction occurred than in frozen sea water at —6.5°C.(20.3°F.) and —10°C. (14°F.).

Haines [108] froze suspensions of bacteria in a few seconds at —70°C. (—94°F.) in small tubes. The tubes were stored at different temperatures and examined for viable cells at regular intervals. Death was not most rapid at —20°C.(—4°F.), the lowest temperature of storage, but in the range of —1°C.(30.2°F.) to —5°C.(23°F.). Microorganisms were found to vary in their susceptibility to freezing. Spores and *Staphylococcus aureus* were resistant, while *Pseudomonas pyocyaneus* was quite sensitive. Haines did not find the death rate by freezing to be logarithmic over its entire course. Death was logarithmic for about 75 per cent of the population after which a slower rate was evident for the remaining 25 per cent. He believed death to be due to denaturation of cellular proteins. Examination of suspensions of bacteria before and after freezing in different ways, did not reveal rupture of bacterial cells to any extent.

Just what happens in the bacterial cell when it is frozen, is a question that has not been answered. Results of experiments by Haines [109] are pertinent. Aqueous suspensions of cells from young cultures, usually 20 hours old, were prepared and small quantities were frozen rapidly with solid carbon dioxide at —70°C.(—94°F.). Variable counts of viable microorganisms were secured with the several cultures used before and after freezing. With the most susceptible organism, *Pseudomonas pyocyaneus,* about 80 per cent of the cells were killed, with *Escherichia coli* about 40 per cent, and with the spores of *Bacillus mesentericus* about 27 per cent. The rate of freezing seemed to have little effect on the proportion of cells killed. Since freezing is presumably slower at —5°C.(23°F.) than at —70°C.(—94°F.) and since larger ice crystals ought to be formed at the former temperature than at the latter, freezing at a slow rate ought to

107. Hess. 1934. Atlantic Fisheries Exp. Sta., J. Biol. Bd. Canada 1, 95-108.

108. Haines. 1933. Ann. Rept. Food Invest. Bd. for 1932, p. 48; also Repts. for 1935 and 1936.

109. Haines. 1938. Proc. Roy. Soc., Ser. B. 124, 451-463; Bull. Hyg. 13, 476.

cause more destruction than at a high rate. Because Haines did not find this to be the case (there was no difference) he believed that the theory was untenable. Careful measurements of cells of large organisms, such as *Saccharomyces cerevisiae*, failed to show any significant change in size on freezing or on thawing. No evidence was obtained that alternate freezing and thawing had any disruptive effect on the cells. Very interesting results were obtained when bacterial suspensions, which had been frozen rapidly at —70°C.(—94°F.), were stored at different temperatures below zero and examined from time to time. At —20°C.(—4°F.) the rate of death was slow; for instance, with *Escherichia coli* 25 per cent of the organisms were still alive after storage for 163 days. At —1°C.(30.2°F.) and —2°C.(28.4°F.), on the other hand, death occurred rapidly, the viable population of *Escherichia coli* at —2°C.(28.4°F.) being reduced to four per cent in 11 days. The effect was even more striking with *Pseudomonas pyocyaneus*, while with the spores of *Bacillus mesentericus* there was practically no difference between the rate of death at —20°C. (—4°F.) and —2°C.(28.4°F.). These findings suggest that there is a critical temperature of storage in the frozen state for bacteria analogous to that of muscle and approximating —1°C.(30.2°F.) to —2°C.(28.4°F.).

In view of these results and others not discussed here, Haines considered it probable that death of bacteria in the frozen state is due to some change in one moiety of the cellular proteins leading to denaturation and subsequent flocculation. The success of methods of rapid freezing, with desiccation, for the storage of bacteria and sera is probably due to the fact that under such conditions no denaturation of the proteins occurs. It is interesting to note that, though no protein flocculation was demonstrable as the result of a single freezing and thawing, nevertheless some vegetative organisms experienced a high mortality during this process. A similar phenomenon has been observed in the death of muscle, and is interpreted as being due to a time lag. Presumably some change is brought about in the organization of the cellular proteins which is sufficient to destroy the vitality of the cell without producing actual coagulation. Experiments of a similar nature were also made by McFarlane,[110] results of which showed the complexity of the question. Presence of hydrogen ions hastened destruction of yeast cells by freezing. The significance of McFarlane's results justifies more extended review.

Cells of a cold-tolerant Saccharomyces species and of *Escherichia coli* were suspended in distilled water and in 1, 5, 10, 15, 20, 30, and 50 per cent sucrose solutions. In three series of experiments these media were adjusted to pH 6.5, 5, and 3.6 to 3.7. The suspensions were dispensed in 10-ml. quantities in sterile pyrex test tubes. The tubes were stoppered with sterile corks; half were stored at —10°C.(14°F.) in still air and half at —20°C.(—4°F.). The number of viable microbial cells surviving different storage intervals in each frozen suspension was determined by plate count.

After several weeks' storage at —10°C.(14°F.) or at —20°C.(—4°F.) the number of viable microorganisms in the different sucrose media of a given pH series did not always vary as the concentrations of sucrose except when the hydrogen-ion concentration of the series was high (pH 3.6 to 3.7). When the series of sucrose media possessed a reaction, pH 6.5 or 5, there were fewer viable yeast cells after several weeks' storage in some of the intermediate concentrations of sucrose. The same observation was made with regard to the survival of *Escherichia coli* in sucrose media of pH 5. Higher concentrations of sucrose, 30 to 50 per cent, tended to retard destruction of the two microorganisms. There was less destruction of yeast cells in distilled water after long storage periods than in some of the lower concentrations of sucrose, especially at —20°C. (—4°F.). On the other hand, greater destruction of *Escherichia coli* tended to take place in distilled water than in any of the sucrose concentrations tested.

When the hydrogen-ion concentration was the only variable, a reaction of pH 6.5 was found to be more favorable than a reaction of pH 5 for hastening the destruction of yeast cells in some of the sucrose media; but in the case of *Escherichia coli* the experimental evidence indicated greater destruction occurred in those samples which possessed the greater hydrogen-ion concentration. Of the conditions investigated the most destructive for both microorganisms was pH 3.6 to 3.7.

When temperature was the only variable, greater kills, after several weeks' storage, tended to occur at —10°C.(14°F.) than at —20°C.(—4°F.).

From these results and those of Berry [111] and Haines, it is evident that microorganisms are apparently destroyed more quickly at lower temperatures. Haines froze suspensions rapidly at —70°C.(—94°F.) and stored them at temperatures between —20°C.(—4°F.) and —1°C.(30.2°F.). Death was most rapid between —1°C.(30.2°F.) and —5°C.(23°F.). Berry [111] found that death more rapid in frozen fruits at —9.4°C.(15°F.) than at —20.6°C.(—5°F.) Presence of carbon dioxide had no influence.

The constitution of the menstruum in which organisms are frozen seems to have some influence. McFarlane [110] observed that higher concentrations of sucrose than 30 and 35 per cent tended to retard destruction of a cold-resistant Saccharomyces and *Escherichia coli*. Freezing also had a more destructive effect on these species at pH 3.6 to 3.7.

Growth of Microorganisms Below Freezing. It has been generally believed that microorganisms cannot grow below freezing. The explanation has usually been that absence of sufficient water would prevent metabolism and growth. Apparently this is untenable, for considerable evidence exists to show that some microorganisms are able to develop. Proof of this is found in the literature. Frozen foods prompted further investigations. Berry and Magoon [112] demonstrated it with various species isolated from frozen fruits and vegetables. They found growth to be slow although a strain of *Pseudomonas fluorescens* in three per cent sodium chloride broth

111. Berry. 1936. Proc. Amer. Soc. Hort. Sci. 33, 224-226.
112. Berry and Magoon. 1934. Phytopathology 24, 780-796.

increased at —4°C.(24.8°F.) from 200,000 to 6,000,000 per ml. in 36 days. Smart [113] observed growth with eight species held at —8.89°C.(16°F.). A few others grew after they had been held at room temperature. Haines [114] also made similar observations. The Frozen Pack Laboratory of the United States Department of Agriculture, as reported by Berry,[115] observed the deadline for microbial growth to be somewhere between —9.4°C.(15°F.) and —6.67°C.(20°F.). Certain members of the genera Cladosporium and Sporotrichum were not inhibited at —6.67°C.(20°F.). False yeasts were found to grow at this temperature. Several frozen fruits and vegetables stored for three and one-half years in non-airtight containers showed no bacterial growth. Under aerobic conditions, Cladosporium sp. and Torula sp. grew at —18.9°C.(—2°F.) and Pseudomonas at —20°C.(—4°F.). Many factors in the environment of the cells influence the death rate.

Effect of Freezing on Pathogenic Microorganisms in Foods. Preservation of foods by freezing introduced new problems. Since some of the raw materials may harbor pathogenic bacteria or other species which elaborate products that are toxic by mouth, it is desirable to ascertain the effects of freezing on such microorganisms. Because freezing does not destroy all microorganisms the behavior of those which survive is of considerable consequence. In order to determine whether common pathogens could survive in frozen fruits, Wallace and Tanner [116] inoculated cherries and cherry juice with cultures of *Eberthella typhosa, Salmonella schottmülleri, Salmonella aertrycke, Escherichia coli*, and *Proteus vulgaris*. The inoculated fruits were sealed in suitable containers and stored at —17.8°C. (0°F.) and —40°C.(—40°F.) for 20 weeks in the case of the cherries and four weeks in the case of the cherry juice. In the latter the organisms survived for less than four weeks and in the cherries for two to three months. Such results indicate that efforts should be made to safeguard the picking and handling of such products for they receive no treatment which will destroy objectionable microorganisms. Experiments of a similar nature were made with sliced, sweetened strawberries by McCleskey and Christopher.[117] After storage at —18°C.(—4°F.) the following survival periods were reported: *Eberthella typhosa,* six months; *Staphylococcus aureus,* five months; *Salmonella aertrycke,* and *Salmonella schottmülleri,* one month; *Salmonella paratyphi,* not recovered at any time from the frozen berries. *Eberthella typhosa* inoculated into unsliced, sweetened berries was present in small numbers after 14 months' storage at —18°C. (—.4°F.). At room temperatures, the death rate of *Eberthella typhosa* was very rapid; heavily inoculated berries were free of living organisms in six hours. At 5°C.(41°F.) 98 per cent of the cells were killed in one day and sterility was reached in eight days.

Effect of Freezing on Toxicogenic Microorganisms in Foods. Microorganisms which elaborate products that are toxic by mouths have caused

113. Smart. 1934. Phytopathology 24, 1319-1331.
114. Haines. 1934. Ann. Rept. Food Invest. Bd. for 1933, 31.
115. Berry. 1934. The Canner, Feb. 24, 1934; Bact. 26 (1933), 459.
116. Wallace and Tanner. 1933. J. Infect. Diseases 52, 146-149.
117. McCleskey and Christopher. 1941. Food Research 6, 327-333.

much trouble in the food-preservation industry. Canned vegetables and meats have been especially involved. They are foods in which the general flora has been greatly simplified by heat so that the field has been left for those which survived. In frozen foods this is not the case. Those organisms which form toxins must compete with all of the others present. Some may favor their growth while others may inhibit it. Up to the present time frozen foods have been quite free from health hazards. Only one outbreak has been traced to frozen fish. That *Clostridium botulinum* is present on vegetables to be frozen is admitted. Wallace and Tanner [116] observed that frozen foods inoculated with *Clostridium botulinum* were not hazardous as long as they were kept frozen. They stated that data from these studies would indicate that if foods were prepared properly and used immediately after defrosting there is little danger of botulism from frozen foods. Toxin is not readily destroyed by freezing, but there is little chance of toxin being present in properly prepared frozen foods. Toxin was not produced before freezing or, with few exceptions, during freezing. It must be remembered that the inoculations used were massive compared with the natural inoculation encountered in food. The spores of *Clostridium botulinum* are resistant to freezing, and once in frozen food they probably remain there for long periods of time. This is not of great importance if foods are frozen properly and if they are consumed soon after thawing. If foods containing spores are allowed to thaw and stand at room temperature for several days before using, they may become dangerous. The possibility of botulism from mishandled frozen vegetables was looked into by Straka and James.[118] Samples prepared and inoculated in the Northwest were packed in sealed tin cans, in glass, and in paper cartons. These containers were used to give varying conditions of anaerobiosis. Some of the containers were closed under vacuum. Heavy and light inoculations with toxin-free spores of a mixture of *Clostridium botulinum*, types A and B, were used. Two of 24 tin containers of uninoculated peas, most of which were held for three days after defrosting, were toxic; eight others were shown to harbor *Clostridium botulinum*. The contents of some of the packages which had received both light and heavy inoculation were toxic several days after defrosting, showing that freezing did not kill the spores and that frozen foods which are not properly handled may become poisonous. In general, peas which became toxic were badly spoiled.

Dried spores of *Clostridium botulinum*, according to James,[119] are not killed or materially reduced in numbers by either slow- or quick-freezing. Botulinum toxin frozen and defrosted 15 times was not reduced in strength. In another paper more data on the same subject were reported by Straka and James.[120] Seventy-two glass containers, 24 uninoculated, 24 with light inoculation, and 24 with heavy inoculation, were examined. No toxin was present in peas which had just been defrosted or which had been

118. Straka and James. 1932. Amer. J. Pub. Health 22, 473-492.
119. James. 1933. J. Infect. Diseases 52, 236-241.
120. Straka and James. 1933. Amer. J. Pub. Health 23, 700-703; J. Bact. 29, 313-322.

held in the icebox for three days. It is interesting that one of 24 uninoculated jars was toxic while positive cultures for *Clostridium botulinum* were secured from eight other containers. A few toxic jars were found in the inoculated jars, more occurring in those which had received heavy inoculation.

All the experiments were with frozen peas and all were concerned with the toxins of *Clostridium botulinum*. Sixty experimental containers of frozen peas were examined for this organism. Of these 30 were uninoculated controls and *Clostridium botulinum* was isolated from 15 of them. The other 30 were inoculated with this organism (one million spores per container) which was recovered in each case. Of 83 uninoculated controls defrosted and held at various temperatures 26.6, 15.5, and 10°C. (80, 60, and 50°F.) for two to seven days, one gave positive evidence of a weak toxin. Of 15 containers receiving a dilute inoculum of these spores, defrosted and held at 80°F. for two days, none gave any evidence of toxin. Of 100 containers receiving a concentrated inoculum 30 were defrosted and held at 26.6°C.(80°F.) for two days; 15 were defrosted and held at 15.5°C.(60°F.) for six days; 15 were defrosted and held at 15.5°C.(60°F.) for three days; 30 were defrosted and held at 10°C.(50°F.) for seven days; and 10 were defrosted and held at 5.5°C.(42°F.) for seven days. Of these samples nine gave definite evidence of toxin; six had been held at 26.6°C.(80°F.) for two days and three at 10°C.(50°F.) for seven days. The authors conclude that when peas preserved by freezing are properly handled there is no danger of botulism.

Some frozen-food specialists do not view the botulism situation with respect to frozen foods with much alarm. They base their assurance on the fact that there is little danger from properly handled frozen foods. Diehl [121] has stated that apprehension as to the public-health aspect of canned foods, need not be entertained. Such statements fail to recognize that many food-poisoning outbreaks are caused by foods which are not properly handled. If foodstuffs were properly handled there would probably be no food-poisoning outbreaks. Berry [122] placed much reliance on the fact that lactic acid bacteria exist in frozen foods and that they might form enough acid to inhibit toxicogenic organisms which could not tolerate such acid. He states: ''Considering the unfavorable influence of organisms of these types on *Clostridium botulinum* and the fact that, in actual test, upwards of 100 containers of frozen-pack vegetables, chiefly peas, artificially inoculated one to one and one-half years previously with from four to 10 million spores of *Clostridium botulinum*, types A and B, uniformly underwent souring on standing and failed to become toxic, the possibility of botulism from frozen products seems remote. While with appropriate technic *Clostridium botulinum* has been recovered in pure culture from vegetables inoculated 19 months previously and stored at —9.4°C.(15°F.) and the toxicity of the A type at least has been well maintained, it certainly appears that, as frozen-pack vegetables are han-

121. Diehl. 1938. The Canner, Feb. 19, 15-17.
122. Berry. 1933. Canning Age, Oct., 1933, 446-447.

dled in practice, botulism organisms if present at all, do not have a chance to develop. Thus the uncertainty and even anxiety which formerly surrounded the freezing preservation of vegetables, though commendable at the time, appeared in the light of the more complete knowledge to have been unnecessary.''

This is a strong position for anyone to take. It is doubtful whether lactic acid bacteria would always be present in all frozen vegetables unless they were placed there by inoculation. Furthermore, Meyer and Gunnison,[123] in a Bartlett pear outbreak of botulism, attributed the ability of *Clostridium botulinum* to develop in a food which was so acid (pH 3.86) to the presence of yeasts and members of lactobacilli group which used the acid. The experience with forage poisoning in cattle, which may be botulism, again showed that *Clostridium botulinum* could develop in an acid environment. In this case, molds were believed to make alkaline areas or pockets in the silage in which *Clostridium botulinum* could grow. Such situations could easily occur in frozen foods.

Enterotoxin-producing bacteria, such as Staphylococci, would also be of interest in frozen foods. Jones and Lochhead [124] found that they survived freezing in vegetables. Fifty different types of Staphylococci were isolated. Using corn, Jones and Lochhead showed that enterotoxin-producing Staphylococci could rapidly develop at room temperature, 20°C. (68°F.), but at 4.4°C.(40°F.) no multiplication was observed. Using 18 strains which produced enterotoxin, eight strains still produced toxin in frozen corn defrosted at room temperature but none in corn defrosted at from 4.4 to 10°C.(40 to 50°F.).

Such work as just reviewed does not indicate that frozen foods need be dangerous but that they must be carefully handled and kept frozen. Installation of many freezing lockers in America makes it imperative that sound practices be followed by those who operate them.

HIGH TEMPERATURES

The marked susceptibility of bacteria to high temperatures has made possible the best known and most reliable methods of food preservation. Mere heating of bacteria in various menstrua does not always destroy them; for instance, Rahn,[49] Fay,[125] and Baumgartner and Wallace [126] have shown that heavy sirups and foods containing large amounts of sugar are not as easily rid of microorganisms by heat as are lighter sirups. Rahn [49] first reported the observation after heating yeasts in sugar solutions. Baumgartner and Wallace carried out experiments using spores of an anaerobic and an aerobic organism; in concentrations up to 50 per cent sucrose no effect on the thermal resistance of spores in acid or alkaline solution was observed. This was believed to be due to the resistant spore envelope. In the case of the vegetative cell, tests using *Escherichia coli* show that a minimum concentration of about 10 per cent sucrose affords

123. Meyer and Gunnison. 1929. J. Infect. Dis. 45, 118.
124. Jones and Lochhead. 1939. Food Research 4, 203-216.
125. Fay. 1934. J. Agr. Res. 48, 453-468.
126. Baumgartner and Wallace. 1934. J. Soc. Chem. Ind. 53, 297.

appreciable protection at pasteurizing temperatures in neutral solutions. This protective action varied directly with the sugar concentration. In very acid solutions, such as fruit sirup, however, this effect is masked by the toxicity of the hydrogen ion.

Strains of Torula, heated in varying sugar concentrations in neutral solution, showed no increase in thermal resistance. As would be expected, a sugar-tolerant strain also proved insensitive in this respect. A concentration of up to 50 to 55 per cent sucrose has no inhibitive action on either the vegetative growth or spore germination of the organisms encountered in underprocessed fruit. The inhibiting factor in such cases appeared to be one of acidity. An increase of pH up to the maximum for growth of the organisms concerned had no lowering effect on the sugar tolerance.

Fay [125] observed a protective action of sugars on *Escherichia coli*. The protective action increased with the osmotic pressure but equimolar solutions of different sugars did not show the same protective action. Fay pointed out that this may occur in heat sterilization of various foods containing sugar. Beamer and Tanner [127] also noticed the effect of increasing sugar concentrations on thermal resistance of microorganisms.

Pasteurization. This is a process in which the food materials are heated below the boiling point for various lengths of time. Pasteur preserved beer and vinegar by pasteurization. Today, fruit juices are preserved by pasteurization because this treatment causes little change in flavor and aroma. Since the temperatures used are considerably below the boiling point, foods preserved in part by pasteurization may have to be held in a cool place to absolutely keep them.

Boiling. Boiling probably has greater effect on bacteria in food than pasteurization. It may not be a reliable heat treatment, however. Whether or not it is a safe step depends on several factors, such as altitude, size of the food mass, and reaction. Bitter's [128] work on heat penetration into large sausages indicated that even after prolonged boiling the rise in temperature at the center of the mass was very slow. In the first procedures for the so-called cold-pack process for canning foods, the United States Department of Agriculture advised processing in boiling water. The outbreaks of botulism traced to foods processed in this manner caused the Department of Agriculture to finally recommend the pressure cooker for nonacid foods.

Processing (Canning): Preservation of foods by canning and packing in glass jars has become a great industry. The subject will be discussed in a later chapter. The method involves preservation of the food in hermetically sealed tin or glass containers. The canner attempts to destroy bacteria in food by high temperatures and to hold it under conditions which prevent the ingress of other bacteria.

FERMENTATION

Certain foods are also preserved by the products of fermentation. Milk, vegetables, and meats may be preserved in this manner. Carbo-

127. Beamer and Tanner. 1939. Zentbl. Bakt., Pt. 2, 100, 81-98, 202-211.
128. Bitter. 1911. Hyg. Rundschau, 181-189.

hydrates in the foods, or extracted from them, are fermented to organic acids, among which lactic acid predominates. These acids make it impossible for putrefactive bacteria to function. Fermented foods have a characteristic flavor.

DEHYDRATION

Foods have been preserved for centuries by drying. It was probably one of the first methods to be used by primitive man for preserving meat and vegetables. He soon learned the value of smoke as an adjunct to drying. Cruess [129] stated that the Boer War and the first World War greatly stimulated interest in drying as a means of food preservation. Prescott stated that dried vegetables were used during the Civil War to prevent scurvy. Cruess and Mrak [130] questioned their ability to function in this manner in view of the methods used for drying at that time.

Microorganisms cannot endure absence of water indefinitely. While they seem to get along without it for long periods, they eventually die. Man has used drying for preservation of cereals, meats, fruits, and vegetables. Much attention was given to dehydration of foods during the first World War, and while many different dehydrated foods were placed on the market, they have gradually disappeared. The main reasons for this are probably the marked alteration in flavors, and the fact that methods of preservation are available with which the consumer is more familiar. Nichols,[131] after a comprehensive review of literature and public-health aspects of dried fruits, vegetables, eggs, milk, fish, and meats, concluded that these foods presented no great health hazard. Only four outbreaks of illness have been attributed to dried foods; most of the evidence suggests contamination after preparation. Dehydration of fruit was considered preferable to sun drying.

Considerable discussion is given to the possible disadvantages of the use of sulfur dioxide or sulfites in the drying of certain fruits. Sulfur dioxide is largely used to preserve the natural color. The evidence presented by Nichols is in favor of its harmlessness. The average amounts absorbed are given as between 2,000 and 3,000 parts per million for apricots, peaches, and pears for good color retention; with apples less is required. Results of investigations suggest that the sulfur dioxide has a destructive effect upon thiamin but not on vitamin A or ascorbic acid, retention of which is indeed improved. Restrictive limitations against sulfur dioxide retention are not required or should be liberal.

According to Clague [132] numbers of microorganisms on dried foods vary from a few thousand per gram as a maximum on dried fruits up to several millions per gram on dried vegetables. Tests conducted with a small tunnel drier showed that artificial drying, or dehydration, effectively eliminated yeasts and materially reduced the numbers of bacteria and molds on dried fruits. *Escherichia coli* inoculated on the surface of grapes

129. Cruess. 1938. Commercial Fruit and Vegetable Products.
130. Cruess and Mrak. 1942. Fruit Prod. J. 21, 201-204 *et seq.*
131. Nichols. 1934. Amer. J. Pub. Health 24, 1129-1134.
132. Clague. 1936. Food Research 1, 45-59.

was destroyed by the drying process. Reduction of the number of micro-organisms on vegetables during the drying process was not so marked as on the fruits. In fact, dehydration did not completely kill *Escherichia coli* although the blanching process which ordinarily precedes dehydration was effective in eliminating this organism. Types of microorganisms found on dried foods were for the most part Gram-positive, sporulating bacteria and molds, although Gram-negative bacteria and yeasts were occasionally observed. Lactose fermenters, not of the *Escherichia coli* type, were found in dried vegetables.

Modern methods of dehydration have been reviewed by Nichols, Powers, Gross, and Noel.[133] Whether the second World War will accomplish for dehydrated foods what the first did not remains to be seen. With the exception of certain meat products, fruits, eggs, and milk, dried foods have never been widely accepted in the United States. As this is written in the summer of 1942 much more consideration is being given them in order to conserve as much space as possible in shipment of foods to other countries.

CARBON DIOXIDE

Atmospheres of carbon dioxide have been used for many years for preserving foods from attack by microorganisms. Owing to the fact that microorganisms respond in different manners to this gas, some being inhibited and development of others enhanced, the results have been variable. Carbon dioxide today is used mainly along with low temperatures and with freezing. Killeffer[134] reviewed in a general way the results along these lines up to 1930. Much has been done, however, since then with more success. Franks[135] was issued a patent for keeping fruits and vegetables fresh under a carbon dioxide pressure of 60 pounds per square inch applied in such a manner that "air and obnoxious germs" were eliminated. Air was removed by discharging the gas several times and recharging. The use of this gas for fruit preservation since this time has involved much lower concentrations of carbon dioxide. "Gas storage" of apples in an atmosphere of 12 to 15 per cent of carbon dioxide has been found to be advantageous by Kidd, West,[136] and others in England.

Moran[137] pointed out that storage in carbon dioxide is not a new method of preservation. It is a more elaborate method of cold storage involving in addition to control of temperature and humidity, control of the composition of the gaseous atmosphere. Addition of this factor makes it possible to do for some foods what temperature and humidity alone cannot do. Carbon dioxide was found to show variable effects on molds according to the medium. Growth of *Rhizopus nigricans* on two per cent malt agar and on acidified malt agar was reduced as concentration of carbon dioxide increased. On an alkaline medium more carbon dioxide was necessary to restrict growth than on an acid medium. Concentrations

133. Nichols *et al.* 1925. U. S. Dept. Agr. Bull. 1335.
134. Killeffer. 1930. Ind. Eng. Chem. 22, 140-143.
135. Franks. 1917. U. S. Patent No. 1, 232, 271, July 3, 1917.
136. See Annual Repts., Food Invest. Bd., for 1921 and later.
137. Moran. 1938. Food Research 3, 149-154; Ann. Rept. Food Invest. Bd. for 1937, p. 34.

up to 20 per cent under some conditions were found to favor growth. Two and one-half per cent concentration of carbon dioxide in meat storage boxes was found to prolong the keeping quality of meat by Mallmann and Zaikowski.[138] These observations were made on 74 cultures of bacteria representing various genera isolated from beef.

According to Moran,[139] Moran and Smith,[140] Smith[141] and Tomkins[142] germination of Thamnidium, Mucor, and Cladosporium was delayed and growth markedly inhibited in air containing as little as four per cent of carbon dioxide. In 20 per cent carbon dioxide the rate of growth was one-half to one-fifth that in air, the inhibition being more marked the lower the temperature. Their experiments showed that development of the naturally accumulated microflora in stale meat was retarded by action of carbon dioxide to less than 10 per cent of the normal rate. Out of 37 different species of bacteria studied only five proved to be stable to the action of carbon dioxide. At lower temperatures the depressing qualities of carbon dioxide were manifested to a lesser degree. Later work by Tomkins[143] indicated that presence of carbon dioxide might even favor development of molds on foods. Carbon dioxide dissolves in them to alter their pH in a direction which favors growth of microorganisms. Concentrations up to 20 per cent may encourage mold growth.

That general statements cannot be made about effects of carbon dioxide on microorganisms is indicated by Hes,[144] who established three groups according to their reactions to it: (1) autotrophic organisms, such as nitrifying and sulfur bacteria, which utilize carbon dioxide as a source of carbon; (2) parasitic bacteria which grow better in an atmosphere enriched with carbon dioxide than in air; and (3) bacteria which require only traces of carbon dioxide. Stewart[145] observed extreme sensitivity of Achromobacter to carbon dioxide with little effect on *Aerobacter cloacae*. Harmful effects of carbon dioxide were not attributed to acidity. Haines[146] applied carbon dioxide at 20°C.(68°F.) in 60 to 80 per cent concentrations to nine strains of Pseudomonas species and noticed considerable variation. Two strains were scarcely affected. *Bacterium pyocyaneus* and *Escherichia coli* were not affected at all. At lower temperatures, however, between 15°C.(59°F.) and 10°C.(50°F.), the effect of 60 per cent carbon dioxide was decided. While growth occurred at the higher temperature in eight days, none occurred in six months at 10°C.(50°F.). The organisms were not destroyed as shown by other experiments.

In Coyne's[147] experiments growth of a number of bacteria in the presence of different amounts of carbon dioxide from 5 to 100 per cent at 0, 10,

138. Mallmann and Zaikowski. 1940. National Provisioner 103, 16-17.
139. Moran. 1937. J. Soc. Chem. Ind. 57, 56T.
140. Moran and Smith. 1933. Ann. Rept. Food Invest. Bd., 1932, 23.
141. Smith. 1929. Ann. Rept. Food Invest. Bd., 1929, 74.
142. Tomkins. 1932. J. Soc. Chem. Ind. 51, 261T.
143. Tomkins. 1938. Ann. Rept. Food Invest. Bd., 1937, 30
144. Hes. 1938. Ann. des Ferm. 4, 547-556.
145. Stewart. 1935. Ann. Rept. Food Invest. Bd., 1934, 95.
146. Haines. 1937. Ann. Rept. Food Invest. Bd. for 1936, p. 64: also Special Report No. 45, p. 67.
147. Coyne. 1933. Proc. Roy. Soc. London B-113, 196-216.

25, and 37°C.(32, 50, 77, and 98.6°F.) showed that, in general, carbon dioxide exercised an inhibitory action on growth varying from complete inhibition in some cases to an almost negligible effect in others. At temperatures below optimum for growth the influence was invariably more marked. In 20 per cent of carbon dioxide at 0°C., growth of bacteria responsible for spoilage of fresh fish is almost completely inhibited. Haines made counts of viable bacterial species to determine their rate of growth in nutrient broth saturated with air and air containing 10 per cent and 20 per cent of carbon dioxide, respectively, at 20, 4, and 0°C. (68, 39.2, and 32°F.). In these concentrations carbon dioxide had but little effect on Proteus; it increased the lag period and lengthened the generation time by about one-half for Pseudomonas and Achromobacter at 20°C. On the last two organisms the effect was more marked at a lower temperature, the generation time being more than doubled by 10 per cent of carbon dioxide at 0°C. Change in pH did not explain the retarding effect of carbon dioxide. Results of similar investigations with actual foods, such as ice cream and milk, by Salmon and LeGall [148] showed that in highly buffered menstrua the bactericidal effects of carbon dioxide were negligible. Pure-culture studies with various microorganisms showed that the inhibition obtained in poorly buffered media were analogous to those with the same organisms on an agar medium adjusted to a corresponding pH.

When 30 to 100 per cent carbon dioxide was supplied, considerable increase in acidity was observed. By buffering the agar medium deleterious effects were greatly lessened or entirely prevented, depending on degree of buffering. More than 100 species representing various bacterial groups were studied as to carbon dioxide requirements. Growth inhibition was obtained by removal of carbon dioxide from the cultural environment. Many organisms were actually killed in 24 hours under carbon dioxide-free conditions. The carbon dioxide requirements of various strains and species varied within wide limits. Growth of many organisms was greatly facilitated by small increments of added carbon dioxide (above ordinary atmospheric carbon dioxide). *Lactobacillus acidophilus, Bacterium pullorum,* and *Bacterium pneumoniae* are good examples (Valley and Rettger [149]).

Carbon dioxide has been used to control development of mold on bread. Skovholt and Bailey [150] found that while 17-per cent concentrations would suppress mold spores, they were not killed and would develop unless this concentration was maintained.

Carbon dioxide has also been used for preserving strawberries during shipment; 25 per cent in the atmosphere held berries in good condition over a 14-hour period at 10 to 12.78°C.(50 to 55°F.), according to van Doren.[151] According to Tomkins [152] 20 per cent of carbon dioxide might enhance rather than restrict development of certain molds. Haines be-

148. Salmon and LeGall. 1936. Ann. Hyg. Pub. Ind. Sociale 84-93.
149. Valley and Rettger. 1927. J. Bact. 14, 101-137.
150. Skovholt and Bailey. 1933. Cereal Chem. 10, 446-451.
151. van Doren. 1940. Ice and Refrig. 99, 136.
152. Tomkins. 1938. Ann. Rept. Food Invest. Bd., 1937, 33-34.

lieved that carbon dioxide was not a bactericide but a marked inhibitor of growth. Successful application of it to storage of meat depends on the chance that the flora present is susceptible to it.

Sides of bacon were kept successfully by Callow [153] for eight months at —10°C.(14°F.) in carbon dioxide provided they were first frozen at —20°C.(—4°F.). He found that carbon dioxide delayed development of rancidity for seven months. Air-stored bacon was rancid after four months, and after 12 months it was too rancid to be edible, while the gas-stored bacon was just beginning to show signs of rancidity.

Another situation which cannot be overlooked in gas storage of foods is due to deteriorative changes which may result from carbon dioxide. Brooks [154] found no discoloration of beef in 10 per cent carbon dioxide. In 35 per cent, the color was only fair to poor.

OZONE

Ozone is a powerful germicide when it can reach naked microorganisms. When the latter are imbedded in organic matter, ozone may not exert appreciable effect. It has been recommended as a deodorizer and it was hoped that it would also function as a bactericide. While many statements have been made about this property, few are based on results of experiments and are somewhat contradictory. Haines [156] observed variation in resistance of bacteria to ozone. Staphylococci and Proteus were sensitive to ozone while Achromobacter was less so. Much more was needed to control large numbers than few, and actively growing cultures decomposed it. The germicidal concentration of ozone toward Achromobacter, introduced when the inoculum was made, appeared to be 300 p.p.m. by volume at 20°C.(68°F.) and 10 to 100 p.p.m. by volume at 0°C.(32°F.). In the next report, Haines [157] published results of experiments with other microorganisms under other conditions. Variations in results were observed when the bacteria were grown on agar or in broth. Pseudomonas and Achromobacter spores were more resistant than Staphylococci, Proteus, *Bacillus subtilis*, or *Bacillus mesentericus*. In general, the order of susceptibility toward ozone was just opposite to that toward carbon dioxide. When the bacteria were allowed to multiply much more ozone was necessary to destroy them. Bacteria suspended in water were readily destroyed by ozone. Suspensions containing one million organisms per milliliter were sterilized in two hours by 100 p.p.m. by volume. The curve was not logarithmic over its entire range.

When molds were growing on malt agar, concentrations of ozone required to inhibit them were the same as those required for bacteria. Haines believed that concentrations between 10 and 1,000 p.p.m. by volume would be necessary for inhibition of microorganisms depending on temperature, humidity, medium, and age of the culture.

153. Callow. 1935. Ann. Rept. Food Invest. Bd., 1934; also Rept. for 1935, 61.
154. Brooks. 1935. Ann. Rept. Food Invest. Bd., 1934, 34.
155. Belousskaya. 1940. Voprosy Pitaniya 9, 61-64.
156. Haines. 1934. Ann. Rept. Food Invest. Bd., 1933, 40-42.
157. Haines. 1935. Idem for 1934, 44-47.

Haines also applied ozone to meat and eggs in storage. With meat, no difference in the time of onset of "slime" could be detected between meat stored in ozonized and in ordinary air. Eggs stored in ozonized air containing 10 p.p.m. by volume for five months had "off-flavors"; three p.p.m. of ozone in the air, however, did not produce this flavor and inhibited molds markedly. Haines [158] believed that much of the ozone in the presence of organic matter is dissipated by reacting with it because smaller amounts were required where the bacteria were in saline media. Haines [159] claimed that the value of ozone would be greatest when applied during the lag phase and in presence of the minimum of nutriments. A marked advantage of ozone in meat storage was diminution of the "bad-meat" smell. Haines was led to conclude that ozone was of little value in inhibiting growth of bacteria on stored tissues; the concentrations required to be effective are higher than those which can be tolerated by human beings, have a deleterious effect on the fat of the carcass, and even in the case of eggs cause "strong" flavors to be developed in the yolk. Haines stated that the practical value of the gas was greatest when it could be applied during the lag-phase of growth and in presence of minimum nutrients.

Ozone, as is the case with carbon dioxide, also causes deteriorative changes to occur in fatty constituents of foods. Lea [160] found beef fat, egg oil, and lard to oxidize rapidly in presence of ozone. In ozonized air the fats assumed the characteristic cucumber as well as tallowy odor in 12 days.

Ewell [161] has reported that except in special cases ozone is the best available agent for improving and prolonging the storage of foodstuffs. The growth of mold on eggs stored in an atmosphere of high humidity can be prevented by maintaining an ozone concentration 1.5-2 p.p.m. in air of the aisles between the egg cases. This gives a concentration of about .6 p.p.m. of ozone within the egg cases. The growth of mold on meat can also be prevented by maintaining an ozone concentration of about 1.5 p.p.m. in the storage-room atmosphere. The safe storage period for many fruits and vegetables can be prolonged by the use of ozone. High concentrations of ozone (50 p.p.m.) may injure such products as bacon, lard, butter, cream, dried eggs, meat, and bananas. The effect of ozone on oxidizable material is roughly proportional to the amount of ozone in contact with the surface. Heiling and Scupin [162] found ozone to be more lethal for fungus spores than for bacteria.

Molds are especially troublesome in storage of certain foods under refrigeration for relatively long periods. Haines found that they were susceptible to ozone while Lea [163] stated that high concentrations must

158. Haines. 1936. Ann. Rept. Food Invest. Bd. for 1935, 30-31.
159. Haines. 1937. Food Invest. Bd., Special Rept. No. 45, 68.
160. Lea. 1936. Ann. Rept. Food Invest. Bd., 1936, 25; also Rept. for 1936, 33.
161. Ewell. 1936. Ice and Refrig. 91, 295-296; Refrig. Engin. 37 (1939), 27-28; Food Indus., Nov., 1937; Food Research 3 (1938), 101-108.
162. Heiling and Scupin. 1935. Rev. in Chem. Absts. 31, 5401.
163. Lea. 1938. Special Rept. No. 46, Food Invest. Bd., p. 72.

be used for long periods to destroy them. Spores of four species were found to be capable of germination after exposure to 400 p.p.m. of ozone for 10 to 15 hours but were killed within 20 hours. Smaller concentrations inhibited germination and growth. Spores sown on bacon, sausage, etc, failed to germinate at 9°C.(48.2°F.) in atmospheres containing as little as .5 p.p.m., and similar concentration prevented development of hyphae already present. Ewell [164] observed that destruction of microorganisms was related to both ozone concentration and time of application. A given concentration produced about the same lethal effect at 4°C.(39.2°F.) as at 20°C.(68°F.).

Opinions with respect to ozone or ionized oxygen as a practical agent for microorganism control are not always in agreement. One authority [165] stated that with a continuous concentration of one of two parts of ozone, at the end of eight months, eggs may be as fresh as when stored. With special attention to temperature and humidity, they may be kept for 15 months.

Ewell [166] has stated that .6 p.p.m. of ozone is necessary in the atmosphere to prevent development of bacterial and fungus growth in egg rooms. A concentration of 2 p.p.m. in meat rooms was said to be sufficient for this purpose.

FOOD PRESERVATION WITH ULTRAVIOLET LIGHT

Although the lethal effects of ultraviolet light have been known for many years when applied to unprotected cells under certain conditions in the laboratory, and its limitations appreciated, it is being heralded again for new uses in practically all industries where it is desirable to destroy certain microorganisms or where the general flora of microorganisms must be reduced to a minimum. That this form of energy is lethal to living matter, when it reaches it directly and when living matter such as bacterial cells are directly exposed to it, cannot be denied. Skeptics may raise the question, however, whether results secured in the laboratory under the most ideal conditions, where the rays may penetrate or be absorbed to the maximum, have any relation to those secured under practical conditions in the food-preservation industry. Does the fact that microorganisms are destroyed in the laboratory under most ideal conditions of exposure prove that they are destroyed also in foods where they may be protected by being imbedded and not even exposed to the rays? In other words, how much weight in the food-preservation industry should be given to pure-culture laboratory experiments in which microorganisms are exposed under conditions which do not obtain in practice? If one believes all of the enthusiastic statements in advertising literature prepared by those who make ultraviolet-producing lamps or the statements of salesmen who base their remarks mainly on a few dried-up, petri-dish cultures of bacteria, or even the observations of some in the meat industry who do not know the necessity of controlled experimental methods, the millenium has come

164. Ewell. 1941. Refrig. Engin. 41, 331-334.
165. Food Indus. 8 (1936), 307.
166. Ewell. 1936. Food Indus. 8, 621.

in food preservation. Owing to many factors, some of which have just been mentioned, this subject has become quite confused.

Several types of lamps under different trade names are now available for use in the food-preservation industry. The so-called "Sterilamp" has been widely advertised as an important adjunct in meat preservation and storage. Its use has been discussed by James [167] and Broadbent [168]; both are from the laboratories of the concern which makes it. The "Sterilamp" is especially recommended for use in coolers in which meat is stored for aging and ripening. Such coolers are operated at higher temperatures and humidities which, of course, make microorganisms develop much faster. In order to keep them under some control, the meat is exposed to ultraviolet rays and the air is circulated at the same time. As applied to the meat industry Broadbent reported that four simple steps were involved:

1. Installation of Sterilamps in coolers, using a 30-inch lamp for every 30 to 40 square feet of floor area.
2. Raise the temperature to not exceeding 7.2°C.(45°F.).
3. Circulate the air in the cooler by means of a fan.
4. Raise the relative humidity to 90 per cent.

Over 80 per cent of the radiant energy from the "Sterilamp" is said to be in the region of 2537 Å. This is considered to be the most powerful permissible as a practical bactericide, by Ewell,[169] and superior to an atmosphere of ozone. If ozone were used to accomplish what ultraviolet light is claimed to do, its concentration would have to be so high that discoloration and rancidity would appear in meats. The germicidal properties of this lamp probably cannot be questioned under laboratory conditions where microorganisms are exposed directly to the rays. This has been definitely shown by Rentschler, Nagy, and Mouromseff.[170] They confirm what has been known for many years, i.e., that this form of energy is destructive to microorganisms when it can reach them.

Another type of lamp is known as the "Spertifier" and is also recommended by its manufacturers as most desirable in storage of foods, especially meats. This lamp is claimed to be specific in its action according to the wave length which it emits. The one recommended for meat coolers is claimed to reduce molds and bacteria causing slime on the surface of the carcass, to tenderize (ripen) the meat more quickly, to assist in retaining moisture and flavor, to destroy odors and to minimize trim losses. Some of these· advantages are attained, not from exposure to ultraviolet rays, but to the fact that higher temperatures and humidities during storage are possible and that the air is circulated in the cooler by a fan. When the lamp known as the "Spertifier" is used, temperatures of 3.3°C. (38°F.) to 5.6°C.(42°F.) with relative humidities of 85 to 95 are recommended. These conditions are claimed to permit enzymes to act, render

167. James. 1936. Food Indus. 8, 295-297.
168. Broadbent. 1938. Idem 10, 263-265.
169. Ewell. 1941. 37th Annual Meeting Amer. Soc. Refrig. Engineers; Refrig. Engin., May, 1941.
170. Rentschler, Nagy, and Mouromseff. 1941. J. Bact. 41, 745-774.

tough meat more tender and to even raise its grade. Surface sterilization on the dark side of the meat could hardly be explained by action of ultraviolet light. Some agent formed by the light must be carried by air currents throughout the cooler or else movement of air in it by means of electric fans brings all bacteria-laden air in contact with the lamps.

The sum and substance of this method of holding meat is that by destroying surface bacteria on the meat in the cooler, it may be held at a higher temperature and humidity which allows the endotryptases to function more rapidly and completely. Once bacteria have been destroyed it is not necessary to keep the meat at low temperatures. This would suggest that some agent is emitted by the lamps which is carried in the air to the meat where it destroys surface microorganisms. With the older quartz lamps this may have been ozone. The fact that ozone is not germicidal to any extent in low concentrations would suggest that in the newer glass lamps emitting a wave-length of 2537 Å it is not the agent. Elwell stated that the latter lamps yield at the most only a few tenths of a part of ozone per million of air.

Ultraviolet light has recently come into considerable prominence in the United States through its recommendation for destruction and control of microorganisms in and on various foods (James,[167]). Lea stated that those who wish to use it must determine for themselves whether microorganisms may be usefully reduced without introducing another form of spoilage. Much work has been done with bacterial cells under conditions which make it difficult to evaluate some of it. Various factors, such as type and species of microorganism, numbers of cells, distance, actual wave-length, and dosage, must be considered. Coblentz and Fulton[171] found that less energy was necessary to kill *Escherichia coli* at wave-lengths shorter than 3050 Å than at longer wave lengths; as far as 3660 Å lethal action was apparent when heavy dosages were used.

While ultraviolet light is a powerful bactericide under some conditions when it can act directly on unprotected cells, its low penetrating power seriously interferes with its activity. Lea stated that effectiveness of ultraviolet light in destroying bacteria is comparatively low at wave lengths above 3100 Å but much greater between 2900 and 2250 Å. Radiation below 2250 Å is said to be even more efficient.

Studies of the effect of ultraviolet light on foods must consider the action of products of the quartz lamp other than rays. Chief among the latter is ozone. Most of the ozone is formed quite close to the lamp and is carried throughout the cooler in the moving air. Lea[172] found that the presence of a few parts per million of ozone in the atmosphere greatly increased the rate of oxidation of fats and production of rancidity and consequent off-flavors. Lea believed that use of glass which would absorb ultra-short wave lengths while still transmitting fairly freely at 2536 Å would restrict formation of ozone. Moran[173] also observed that ozone

171. Coblentz and Fulton. 1924. Sci. Papers U. S. Bureau of Standards 19, 641.
172. Lea. 1936. Ann. Rept. Food Invest. Bd., 1935, 25; also Rept. for 1936, 37.
173. Moran. 1937. Ann. Rept. Food Invest. Bd., 1936, 29.

produced by some lamps is a real disadvantage. Light rays do not penetrate. Surface organisms, as observed by Haines and Lea,[174] are readily
destroyed but not just below the surface. A film of beef juice .2 mm.
thick reduced the intensity of ultraviolet light a thousandfold. To be
of reasonable value, foods must be exposed before much penetration of
microorganisms has occurred. Possibility of undesirable changes from
irradiation were also stressed by Dumeste.[175] He said that irregularities
on the surface of the meat would prevent full success from use of the
method. Only surface effects would be obtained since the ultraviolet
light cannot penetrate to any extent. While bacteria are destroyed fat
may be made rancid from its reaction with the ozone formed by the
quartz tube. The lean meat may also be blackened.

Haines,[176] of the Low Temperature Research Station, University of
Cambridge, stated that while ultraviolet light can, under certain conditions, kill or inhibit growth of bacteria and molds on foodstuffs, it also
accelerates other and undesirable changes, e.g., oxidation of fats and
formation of methemoglobin. Its use, therefore, in prolonging the storage
life of foodstuffs is not straightforward. Experiments were carried out
to determine how far the separate effects of the light can be controlled.
In his early experiments Haines used a cold-type mercury-in-quartz lamp
in which approximately 90 per cent of the light was that of wave-length
2536 A. Appreciable amounts of ozone were formed. The older type
quartz lamps have now been replaced by those made of glass which have
greatly reduced ozone formation.

Beef fat exposed to ultraviolet light at a distance of 25 cm. for various
periods of time by Lea caused appearance of a foreign odor in uncooked
samples after five minutes' irradiation. Samples exposed for 10 minutes
and cooked were unpalatable. Chemical changes induced in the fat were
limited to a thin superficial layer. These data were from small pieces
cooked in glass after irradiation. Lea thought it probable that greater
deterioration could be tolerated in meat exposed and cooked in the normal
manner. The tallowy odor, however, might be objectionable.

Quality is a property of meat which depends on more than one factor.
Only one of them is tenderness, and this may not be the most important
to some individuals. To some discriminating individuals flavor is just as
important if not more so. Various investigations, results of which are
discussed in these pages, indicate that irradiation of fresh beef with ultraviolet light affects flavor unfavorably. Most of the benefits which have
been claimed for this process are based on greater tenderness resulting
mainly from higher temperatures in the coolers during ripening. On these
grounds, it has been stated that quality of meat has been raised one grade.
Such a statement is only partly true, for many factors must be considered
in grading beef. The question to be settled is whether good meat properly
handled in clean coolers by competent, responsible men needs this special

174. Haines and Lea. 1937. Idem p. 30.
175. Dumeste. 1939. Rev. generale du Froide 20, 56.
176. Haines. 1937. Ann. Rept. Food Invest. Bd., 1938, 29.

treatment. Apparently many believe that it does not and among them are the largest meat-packing concerns in the United States. After reviewing the evidence Jones [177] believed the results of experimental work indicate that so far as meat is concerned, the advantages of irradiation with ultraviolet light are outweighed by the disadvantages, notably, loss of appearance and production of unpleasant flavors.

Moldy bread during hot, humid seasons is a real problem. This difficulty has been increased since loaves of bread have been sliced and wrapped. One method of coping with this difficulty is to irradiate the bread before and during slicing and thus attempt to eliminate distribution of the spores over freshly cut surfaces. Owen's [178] investigations indicated that some success might be attained. Irradiation sterilizes slicer saws as well as inactivates the spores. These results seeem to agree with those of Welch and Perkins.[179] Although resistant molds exist, Welch found that 90 per cent were killed in one minute. Broadbent [180] also observed that molds required longer exposure than bacteria. Under ordinary conditions more lamps must be installed where a more difficult job is to be done. Tanner and Appling [181] also observed differences in resistance to ultraviolet light among molds. Further work on the use of ultraviolet light in bakeries is discussed in a later chapter.

The Council of Physical Therapy of the American Medical Association [182] recently discussed acceptance of ultraviolet lamps for disinfecting purposes. While their report concerned other situations than those which exist in the food industry, it is indirectly pertinent to it. It was stated that the spectral band at 2652 Å appeared to produce the maximum bactericidal action and that the emission band at 2537 Å is only 70 per cent as effective. This difference was said to be negligible, however, in their investigations because the ultraviolet radiant power of wave-lengths 2652 A is less than .2 per cent of that of wave-length 2537 Å. The Council on Therapy stated that satisfactory evidence was not available to warrant acceptance of ultraviolet lamps for disinfecting solids. It was stated that the whole subject is too new, too complex, and apparently too uncertain where virulent microorganisms may be concerned. This statement would include application of ultraviolet radiation in meat-storage coolers, a much-exploited application today.

SPICES

Spices are interesting microbiologically for various reasons. They may harbor types which cause spoilage of foods to which they are added; efforts have been made to rid them of such microorganisms. Certain spices also show appreciable germicidal properties which give them a double function in foods.

177. Jones. 1942. Food 11, 75.
178. Owen. 1932. Food Indus. 4, 208-210.
179. Welch and Perkins. 1929. J. Prev. Med. 3, 363.
180. Broadbent. 1938. Food Indus. 10, 263-265; 327 et seq.
181. Tanner and Appling. 1941. Proc. Soc. Exper. Biol. & Med. 47, 47-51.
182. J. Amer. Med. Assoc. 118 (1942), 298-299.

Germicidal Action of Spices. This is probably not a property of great significance in itself but perhaps important when superimposed on other methods of preservation. Bitting [183] found cinnamon and cloves to possess stronger bactericidal activity than other spices. Hoffman and Evans [184] and Bachmann,[185] in general, confirmed Bitting's work. Cinnamic aldehyde found in cinnamon and eugenol found in cloves were especially active. In a later paper Bachmann [185] and Grove [186] reported more confirmatory conclusions on these two spices.

Extracts of various substances which are used for improving flavor of foods have also been investigated. Morel and Rochaix [187] observed only feeble action of such products as extracts of thyme, bergamot, and lavender. They believed that they could not replace other established agents of preservation. Similar investigations were carried out by Corran and Edgar [188] with various spices, condiments, and herbs and their oils on the fermentation of beer wort by yeast at room temperature; ground mustard was the most effective preservative followed by cloves and cinnamon. The other spices tested showed little or no preserving action. Some of the substances used—thyme, bay leaves, marjoram, savory, and rosemary—appeared to stimulate yeast action; this was also true for black pepper. The volatile oil of mustard was the strongest preservative of the oils, followed by cinnamon oil and the oils of cloves, thyme, and bay leaves.

Fabian, Krehl, and Little's [189] work showed that cinnamon and cloves were the only spices that exhibited any inhibiting action on bacterial growth in low concentrations. Ground peppercorn and allspice showed inhibiting action in one-per cent concentrations; mustard, mace, nutmeg, and ginger, in five-per cent concentrations; and celery used in 10- and 20-per cent concentrations in nutrient agar, against a majority of bacteria. Some species grow on all concentrations of spices. Fabian and his colleagues observed a great difference in the resistance of different bacteria to the same spice and the same organism to different spices. *Staphylococcus aureus* was more susceptible to the action of spices than many of the bacteria examined. The oils of spices were more inhibitory than ground spices.

Germicidal Action of Condiments. These are seasonings which are widely used in foods. Their germicidal properties have been found to be appreciable. Crushed horse-radish vapors were found to be inhibitory by Foter and Golick.[190] Such test organisms as *Serratia marcescens*, *Bacillus subtilis*, *Escherichia coli*, *Mycobacterium phlei*, and *Mycobacterium tuberculosis* (hominis) were used. One-gram amounts of the material were placed in the tops of inverted Petri dishes, the bottoms of which contained 15 ml. of a suitable agar medium. The plates were sealed and incubated

183. Bitting. 1909. Bureau of Chemistry, U. S. Dept. Agr. Bull. 119.
184. Hoffmann and Evans. 1911. J. Ind. and Eng. Chem. 3, 835-838.
185. Bachmann. 1916. J. Ind. Eng. Chem. 8, 620-623; 10 (1918), 121-123.
186. Grove. 1918. Ann. Rept. Agr. and Hort. Res. Sta., Univ. Bristol, 34-38.
187. Morel and Rochaix. 1922. Comp. Rend. Soc. Biol. 96, 1311-1312.
188. Corran and Edgar. 1933. J. Soc. Chem. Ind., Trans. 149T-152T.
189. Fabian, Krehl, and Little. 1939. Food Research 4, 269-286.
190. Foter and Golick. 1938. Food Research 3, 609-613.

at the different temperatures for varying lengths of time, after which the covers were replaced, the plates streaked with the test organisms, sealed, and incubated at 37.5°C.(99.5°F.). The inhibitory effects were most pronounced at 37.5°C. and decreased with the lowering of the temperature of exposure. *Bacillus subtilis* was the least resistant, *Escherichia coli* the most resistant of the test organisms. Growth of the test organisms was inhibited to some degree by an exposure as short as 16 minutes in all cases and at all temperatures used. The inhibitory substance emitted by one gram of horse-radish was almost exhausted after six hours of exposure at 37.5°C. Minchin [191] attributed germicidal properties to garlic. This was also observed by Vollrath, Walton, and Lindegren [192] who made the same observation for onions. The bactericidal substance in garlic has been shown to be allyl aldehyde. When an agar plate was exposed to freshly crushed garlic enough bactericidal substance was absorbed in 30 minutes to destroy *Escherichia coli*. The well-known sulfides responsible for the peculiar odor of garlic were found not responsible for its bactericidal activity. Vollrath *et al.* believed that acrolein might be the bactericide of garlic. It was found to have active bactericidal properties. On the other hand, Kitagawa and Amano [193] related the germicidal properties of garlic to unstable sulfur in the polysulfides produced from glucosides by enzyme action. About all that Böker [194] could do was to attribute this action to a volatile substance.

Oligodynamic Action of Metals in Food Preservation. Much work has been done in late years on the effect of metals on microorganisms. Nägeli,[195] who did some of the pioneer work used the term "oligodynamic" to express the action of heavy metals on bacteria. The term "oligodynamic" today signifies the sterilizing effect of very small amounts of certain metals. Silver has been most generally used, being brought into solution by electrolysis from silver electrodes. This method has been much studied for sterilizing water, with which it seems to have given some success. It has also been suggested for other fluids as well as for foodstuffs. Many investigators have reported that when an electric current is passed through thin silver plates in water the water becomes highly bactericidal. According to Metalnikoff,[196] a current as low as .3 to 4 milliamperes and 1.5 to 4.5 volts passed through water containing representative bacteria, such as *Escherichia coli, Vibrio cholerae, Salmonella paratyphi, Eberthella typhosus,* and *Staphylococcus aureus*, killed all of them in a few minutes and often in a few seconds when the silver plate is the anode. Boiling does not destroy the germicidal efficiency of the water so treated. This bactericidal power remains for more than three months. The concentration of germicide in the water can be increased by prolonged exposure to the current or increasing the plate surface. Silver in a concentration of 1/5,000,000

191. Minchin. 1917. Med. Press and Circ. 103, 493-495.
192. Vollrath, Walton, and Lindegren. 1937. Proc. Soc. Expt. Biol. & Med. 36, 55.
193. Kitagawa and Amano. 1935. Rev. in Chem. Absts. 30, 3019.
194. Böcker. 1938. Ztschr. Hyg. 121, 166-180.
195. Nägeli. 1893. Schweizer Gesellsch. f. d. gesamte Naturwissench. 33, 1.
196. Metalnikoff. 1935. Comp. Rend. Acad. Sci. 201, 411-412.

will kill *Escherichia coli* and staphylococci in three hours. Water does not become germicidal if the silver is the cathode.

In early work or the problem the silver ions were secured from sand grains which had been coated with silver. Heiss [197] reported that a piece of silver wire showed no bactericidal action unless a minute quantity of silver chloride or silver nitrate was placed on it. Then the whole length of wire became active. Fromherz and Heiss [197] stated that experimental evidence showed the oligodynamic action of silver to be due to silver ions in a concentration greater than 2×10^{-11} moles per liter. The silver ions either come directly from silver compounds, or are sent out by means of localized currents in concentration cells on superficially oxidized or impure silver parts.

A well-known method of getting silver into the water is the Katadyn process of Krause. In the first process, silver existed in the water as ionic silver. It was derived from sand grains coated with silver. The Electro-Katadyn process is so designed that silver is derived by passing on electric current between silver electrodes immersed in water. Perini [199] reported that silver ions in water exerted a bactericidal effect; he inoculated various foodstuffs with several members of the coliform group and then washed them with water containing silver. A contact time of from 20 to 30 minutes was sufficient to destroy pathogenic bacteria. Slavin [200] could find no reason for using silver-treated water in the food industry. Herrmann [201] concurred in this opinion. Perini,[199] however, reported satisfactory results with fresh vegetables, oysters, and other foods. The process has been reviewed by Callister.[202]

Kufferath [203] described briefly the development and uses of the Katadyn process in which silver ions are discharged into the water from silver electrodes by a weak current. It has the advantages that the amount of silver going into solution can be regulated by the strength of the current; large quantities of water can be treated; water with strong bactericidal power can be prepared so that the process can be used in ice making, in mineral-water factories, and in breweries; water containing suspended matter can be treated by increasing the amount of silver dissolved. The apparatus is simple in construction and wholly or partially automatic in action, and costs for current and silver are low. Oligodynamic power of silver was tested by Ruge [204] on organisms of the coliform group and on staphylococcus by subjecting them to the action in various concentrations for varying lengths of time at room temperature. Efficient results in domestic or commercial sterilization of water with a simple Katadyn apparatus were reported.

197. Heiss. 1937. Biochem. Ztschr. 290, 99-103.
198. Fromherz and Heiss. 1937. Angew. Chem. 50, 679-681.
199. Perini. 1936. Ann. d'ig. 46, 505-510.
200. Slavin. 1935. Voprosui Pitaniya 4, 147-152.
201. Herrmann. 1935. Schweis. Ver. Gas. Wasserforsch. Monats. Bull. 15, 262.
202. Callister. 1935. Soc. Chem. Ind., Victoria, Proc. 35, 1068-1091.
203. Kufferath. 1936-1937. Rev. in Bull. Hyg. 12, 442-443.
204. Ruge. 1932. Scritti biol. 7, 359-366.

Results of extensive studies on this problem were reported by Grimmer and Grenz [205] on the effect of "Katadynized" water on lactobacilli, lactic-acid streptococci, tetracocci, micrococci, sarcinae, on the colon-aerogenes, proteus and fluorescens groups, aerobic sporeformers, chromogenic cocci and bacilli, yeasts, and *Oospora* spores and molds, especially in connection with disinfection of churns. With a colloidal silver concentration of .65 microgram per liter of water, after four hours exposure, the total number of microorganisms in a churn rinse was reduced 20 per cent. Aerogenes, proteus, and fluorescens types were rapidly destroyed. Lactobacilli, lactic acid streptococci, and coliform types were sensitive to silver, while aerobic sporeformers, Sarcinae, and yeasts were scarcely affected and molds increased. Decreases were greater with higher concentrations of silver. In the churns the Katadyn water had no marked residual effect; it was necessary to use it regularly to obtain satisfactory results. Other studies were made to determine the effect of the activated water on the keeping quality and microflora of butter. The silver exerted a detrimental effect on keeping quality, with tallowy and oily flavors developing. The total number of microorganisms in butter was not appreciably lower at the end of the storage period than for butter washed with ordinary water. The lactic acid bacteria were most affected, while nonacid formers, yeasts, and molds increased.

The Katadyn process was not approved by Shapiro and Hale [206] for swimming pools because bacteria growing at 37° C. (98.6° F.) are not affected: too much time is required; the treatment must be adjusted to individual waters; the presence of ammonia interferes with good results; there is no adequate method for determining the presence of silver; there is a question as to economy as compared with chloride, and there is the danger of the development of argyrosis.

Attempts have also been made to introduce this method into the food industry. Perini [199] inoculated various foodstuffs with bacterial cultures (*Escherichia coli, Eberthella typhosa, Salmonella paratyphi, Salmonella schottmülleri,* as well as *Vibrio comma*) and then subjected the foodstuffs to washing with the water containing silver ions. He showed that the washing of these substances in water which has been subjected to the Electro-Katadyn process suffices to kill pathogenic intestinal organisms with which the foodstuffs may have been affected. A contact time of 20 to 30 minutes is sufficient.

According to Mehlitz [207] turbid must from pressed fruit or apple and grape juices previously clarified to a certain extent by decantation can be rendered stable by the Electro-Katadyn process with the use of a minimum of about 20,000 μg. per liter of silver. The process can be used with complete certainty in practice only with clear, filtered, and therefore slime-free juices low in bacteria. To make certain the products will keep for many months in this case at least about 5,000 μg. per liter of silver are required.

205. Grimmer and Grenz. 1933. Milchw. Forsch. 15, 367-380.
206. Shapiro and Hale. 1937. J. New England Water Works Assoc. 51, 113-124.
207. Mehlitz. 1936. Obst-., u. Gemüse-Verwertungsind 23, 49-53.

When well-cleaned glass containers are used, the walls of the container itself are found to be sterile after filling with the activated juices. Even after the germicidal action has disappeared, no bacterial life develops. With the use of 7,500 or more μg. per liter of silver for activation, a definite metallic taste appears which, however, (even with 20,000 μg.) completely disappears after storage for several months. Activation with from 5,000 to 20,000 μg. silver leaves the juice practically unchanged analytically. During storage the activating silver separates out continuously to a greater or less degree; with turbid juices, it separates completely. This precipitation process appears to be largely dependent upon the composition of the fruit juices. A modification of the method by Jendrassik [208] is described for the determination of very small amounts of silver as the original method is unsuitable for use with musts. Two hundred milliliters of the must is fermented with yeast, evaporated to 20 to 25 ml., and oxidized with $HNO_3 + H_2SO_4$ according to more specific directions given in the original. The solution is then diluted with water, made ammoniacal, and the silver determined with p-dimethylaminobenzilidene thiocyanate.

As certain commercial organizations are recommending silver for use as a bactericidal and preserving agent, not only for water but also for a number of foodstuffs and beverages, Gibbard [209] believed it desirable for public-health authorities to know whether the process is harmful to health and whether it is efficient. Experiments here recorded confirm the view of other workers that it is the silver ions, probably derived from silver oxide, which possess bactericidal action. This action is markedly reduced by the presence of proteins or of glucose. Grape juice purported to have been treated by a silver process did not contain silver in significant amount.

Enzymes in Foods. Practically all foods contain enzymes and it is important to learn what becomes of them after the food is harvested and stored or during processing. Balls [209a] stated that preservation of food is a matter of stopping enzyme action, whether the enzymes come from microorganisms or are inherent in the food itself. Cold storage and drying slow down enzyme action but application of heat is the main method for destroying them. In view of this fact, foods which are processed by heat must be carefully and adequately heated. Unless most of the enzymes are destroyed, the foods must be stored either very dry or cold. The problem is not great with heat processed foods but is with frozen foods. In the latter enzymes may lead to untoward changes.

FOOD STANDARDS AND FOOD-CONTROL ACTS

These have been necessary since certain members of society took it upon themselves to prepare and sell foods to others. Some of them proved to be unscrupulous and sold food which was unfit for consumption. Food-control acts had to be established to control such practices. Probably the first effort along these lines was the code given to the Israelites by Moses.[210]

208. Jendrassik. 1935. Rev. in Chem. Absts. 29, 7519.
209. Gibbard. 1937. Amer. J. Pub. Health 27, 112-119.
209a. Balls. 1941. U. S. Dept. Agr., Circular 631; Fruit Prod. J., 22 (1942) 36-39.
210. The Bible. An American Translation, Book of Leviticus, Chapter 11; Book of Deuteronomy, Chapter 14.

In this respect Moses may be considered to be the first food inspector. He classed foods as either clean or unclean with a different meaning for those terms than they have today. Those which were to be eaten were said to be clean. The others were unclean. Such a separation was made on the basis of a natural abhorrence of certain species, a demonstrated unsuitableness, or on habits of prey. Probably bitter experience with certain foods caused Moses to place them on the prohibited list. Animals which ate carrion and blood were not accepted. A religious repugnance probably existed for serpents.

The following quotation from Deuteronomy, Chapter 14,[210] summarizes the statements of Moses with respect to foods:

"You must not eat anything abominable. The following are animals that you may eat: the ox, the sheep, the goat, the deer, the gazelle, the roebuck, the wild-goat, the ibex, the antelope, and the mountain-sheep. Also, you may eat any animal with a cloven hoof, that has the hoof divided completely in two, and that chews the cud. However, of those that chew the cud or have the hoof completely cloven, you must not eat the following: the camel, the hare, and the rockbadger, because, although chewing the cud, they do not have the hoof cloven—they are unclean for you; also the pig, because, although having the hoof cloven, it does not chew the cud—it is unclean for you. Of their flesh you must not eat, and their carcasses you must not touch.

"Of all things that live in the water you may eat the following: whatever has fins and scales you may eat; but whatever has not fins and scales you must not eat; it is unclean for you.

"You may eat any clean bird; but the following are the ones of which you must not eat: the griffon, the vulture, the eagle, the buzzard, the kite in its several species, the raven in all its species, the screech-owl, the eagle-owl, the horned owl, the jackdaw, the carrion-vulture, the cormorant, the stork, the heron in its several species, the bittern, and the bat. Also, all winged insects are unclean for you; they must not be eaten. Any winged thing that is clean you may eat.

"You must not eat anything that has died a natural death; for you are a people consecrated to the LORD your God; you may give it to any alien residing in your community to eat, or sell it to a foreigner."

Foods require inspection and control for many reasons, some of which are obscure. Not all of them are prepared and handled under conditions which keep them clean and safe until delivered to the consumer. In some cases health hazards are not involved while fraud and adulteration are. Manley[211] pointed out, in this respect, the substitution of a cheaper for a more expensive food, such as incorporation of undue amounts of starch in certain meat products. He believed that high food standards were desirable, especially for compound foods. This subject was discussed by the Ministry of Health of Great Britain in its annual report for 1934.

Food control in Great Britain was said to rest upon two broad principles: first, fair trading, in the sense that the public buying food should have some guarantee that they are getting what they ask and pay for; and second, that the food shall not contain ingredients which will render it injurious to health. These are expressed in our own food and drug act as honesty and fair dealing.

With respect to the first principle, it was believed that little gross adulteration or deliberate substitution of one article of food for another

211. Manley. 1933. J. Roy. San. Inst. 54, 214-318.

occurred. The Minister did mention a sophistication of substitution of Ailanthus leaves for mint. He also reported a substitution which might not be construed to be an adulteration. Cakes, however, were colored brown as if they contained chocolate when no chocolate was used in their preparation. In some cases it was said to be very difficult for a purchaser to judge the quality of food which had been skillfully prepared, packed, and advertised for sale. In an earlier annual report the Ministry of Health called attention to the fact that employment of chemists and other scientists by food purveyors has greatly complicated the situation for control officials. Every effort should be made to compel those who speak about their products to give nothing but the absolute truth; for instance, the Minister mentioned the advertising of a margarine as being blended with butter, whereas in reality it contained only one-half per cent butter.

As a general rule standards of quality were deemed necessary although in some cases it might be difficult to determine them. It was suggested that careful descriptive labeling be required to protect the consumer.[212] This has been attempted in the United States in the Food, Drug, and Cosmetic Act of 1938.

The second principle that foods shall not contain any ingredients which will render them injurious to health could be defined more strictly. The Food and Drug Act forbids addition of such ingredients to foods but it is difficult to determine whether added substances are deleterious to health. It was pointed out that it is almost impossible for anyone to decide with respect to the amount of copper, for instance, which may be considered negligible in foods. This is due to the fact that the factors which contribute to daily health and well-being of individuals are numerous and very complex. Furthermore, it would require a well-balanced, thorough laboratory investigation to prove the situation. Consequently the Ministry of Health believed that the safest course was to limit the amount of some substances in question to the smallest that can be achieved in practice. This was said to have been the course adopted by the Commission on Arsenical Poisoning in 1903. They found that it was possible for manufacturers to keep the amount of arsenic in food below 1/100 grain per pound. Therefore, the Commission recommended this limit, not because it had any definite relation to the dose required to produce arsenical neuritis but because it was a limit which could be achieved without hardship to the manufacturer and appeared to provide a satisfactory margin of safety to the consumer. It was stated that the same considerations were taken into account in the regulations of 1925 dealing with the addition of chemical preservatives to food. It aids in fixing the amounts of unavoidable impurities at low amounts which could be achieved by competent manufacturers. The Ministry of Health said that a number of other varied problems awaited the food manufacturer. He mentioned, for instance, the increasing use of ethylene glycol as a solvent for essences.

212. Report of the Chief Medical Officer of the Ministry of Health for Year the 1934. (1935) 122-125.

The United States Food and Drug Act of 1906. This was the first effort in the United States to control quality of food. It resulted from much agitation on the part of food-control officials and those who realized the need for control. The Dominion of Canada passed a similar act respecting food and drugs in 1920. The United States Food and Drug Act aims to prevent the misbranding and adulteration of foods and drugs. As used in the Act, the term "food" includes all articles used for food, drink, confectionery, or condiment by man or other animals, whether simple, mixed, or compound. In the case of food it is considered as "adulterated" under the Act if:

1. Any substance has been mixed and packed with it so as to reduce or lower or injuriously affect its quality or strength.

2. Any substance had been substituted wholly or in part for the article.

3. Any valuable constituent of the article has been wholly or in part abstracted.

4. It be mixed, colored, powdered, coated, or stained in a manner whereby damage or inferiority is concealed.

5. It contain any added poisonous or other added deleterious ingredient which may render such article injurious to health; Provided, That when in the preparation of food products for shipment they are preserved by an external application applied in such manner that the preservative is necessarily removed mechanically, or by maceration in water, or otherwise, and directions for the removal of said preservative shall be printed on the covering or the package, the provisions of this act shall be construed as applying only when said products are ready for consumption.

6. It consist in whole or in part of a filthy, decomposed, or putrid animal or vegetable substance, or any portion of an animal unfit for food, whether manufactured or not, or if it is the product of a diseased animal, or one that has died otherwise than by slaughter.

Control of food products in the United States is centered in the various bureaus and administrations of the United States Department of Agriculture. The Food, Drug, and Insecticide Administration has jurisdiction over foods distributed in interstate commerce and the enforcement of the Food and Drug Act. Thom [65] called attention to the fact that the Food and Drug Act of 1906 is a corrective rather than punitive measure.

The United States Food, Drug, and Cosmetic Act of 1938. After some five years of consideration in Congress, President F. D. Roosevelt signed the Food, Drug, and Cosmetic Act on June 25, 1938. Several bills were proposed and debated at length before a satisfactory bill was proposed. The old Food and Drug Act of 1906 was automatically repealed with minor exceptions. The new act greatly extended the definitions of adulteration and misbranding of foodstuffs. That part of the act which concerns foods is quoted below:

ADULTERATED FOOD

"Sec. 402. A food shall be deemed to be adulterated

"(a) (1) If it bears or contains any poisonous or deleterious substance which may render it injurious to health; but in case the substance is not an added substance such food shall not be considered adulterated under this clause if the quantity of such substance in such food does not ordinarily render it injurious to health; or (2) if it bears or contains any added poisonous or added deleterious substance which is unsafe within the meaning of section 406; or (3) if it consists in whole or in part of any filthy, putrid, or decomposed substance, or if it is otherwise unfit for food; or (4) if it has been prepared, packed, or held under insanitary conditions whereby it may have become contaminated with filth, or whereby it may have been rendered injurious to health; or (5) if it is, in whole or in part, the product of a diseased animal or of an animal which has died otherwise than by slaughter; or (6) if its container is composed, in whole or in part, of any poisonous or deleterious substance which may render the contents injurious to health.

"(b) (1) If any valuable constituent has been in whole or in part omitted or abstracted therefrom; or (2) if any substance has been substituted wholly or in part therefor; or (3) if damage or inferiority has been concealed in any manner; or (4) if any substance has been added thereto or mixed or packed therewith so as to increase its bulk or weight, or reduce its quality or strength, or make it appear better or of greater value than it is.

"(c) If it bears or contains a coal-tar color other than one from a batch that has been certified in accordance with regulations as provided by section 406; *Provided*, That this paragraph shall not apply to citrus fruit bearing or containing a coal-tar color if application for listing of such color has been made under this Act and such application has not been acted on by the Secretary, if such color was commonly used prior to the enactment of this Act for the purpose of coloring citrus fruit.

"(d) If it is a confectionery, and it bears or contains any alcohol or nonnutritive article or substance except harmless coloring, harmless flavoring, harmless resinous glaze not in excess of four-tenths of 1 per centum, natural gum, and pectin: *Provided*, That this paragraph shall not apply to any confectionery by reason of its containing less than one-half of 1 per centum by volume of alcohol derived solely from the use of flavoring extracts, or to any chewing gum by reason of its containing harmless nonnutritive masticatory substances."

MISBRANDED FOOD

This provision of the Food, Drug, and Cosmetic Act of 1938 concerns mainly the element of fair dealing in transactions involving foods. Violation of it may not necessarily be injurious to health. Section 403 states that a food shall be deemed to be misbranded:

"(a) If its labeling is false or misleading in any particular.

"(b) If it is offered for sale under the name of another food.

"(c) If it is an imitation of another food, unless its label bears, in type of uniform size and prominence, the word 'imitation' and, immediately thereafter, the name of the food imitated.

"(d) If its container is so made, formed, or filled as to be misleading.

"(e) If in package form unless it bears a label containing (1) the name and place of business of the manufacturer, packer, or distributor; and (2) an accurate statement of the quantity of the contents in terms of weight, measure, or numerical count: *Provided*, That under clause (2) of this paragraph reasonable variations shall be permitted, and exemptions as to small packages shall be established, by regulations prescribed by the Secretary.

"(f) If any word, statement, or other information required by or under authority of this Act to appear on the label or labeling is not prominently placed thereon with such conspicuousness (as compared with other words, statements, designs, or devices, in the labeling) and in such terms as to render it likely to be read and understood by the ordinary individual under customary conditions of purchase and use.

"(g) If it purports to be or is represented as a food for which a definition and standard of identity has been prescribed by regulations as provided by section 401, unless (1) it conforms to such definition and standard, and (2) its label bears the name of the food specified in the definition and standard, and, insofar as may be required by such regulations, the common names of optional ingredients (other than spices, flavoring, and coloring) present in such food.

"(h) If it purports to be or is represented as—

"(1) a food for which a standard of quality has been prescribed by regulations as provided by section 401, and its quality falls below such standard, unless its label bears, in such manner and form as such regulations specify, a statement that it falls below such standard; or

"(2) a food for which a standard or standards of fill of container have been prescribed by regulations as provided by section 401, and it falls below the standard of fill of container applicable thereto, unless its label bears, in such manner and form as such regulations specify, a statement that it falls below such standard.

"(i) If it is not subject to the provisions of paragraph (g) of this section unless its label bears (1) the common or usual name of the food, if any there be, and (2) in case it is fabricated from two or more ingredients, the common or usual name of each such ingredient; except that spices, flavorings, and colorings, other than those sold as such, may be designated as spices, flavorings, and colorings without naming each: *Provided*, That, to the extent that compliance with the requirements of clause (2) of this paragraph is impracticable, or results in deception or unfair competition, exemptions shall be established by regulations promulgated by the Secretary.

"(j) If it purports to be or is represented for special dietary uses, unless its label bears such information concerning its vitamin, mineral, and other dietary properties as the Secretary determines to be, and by regulations prescribes as necessary in order fully to inform purchasers as to its value for such uses.

"(k) If it bears or contains any artificial flavoring, artificial coloring, or chemical preservative, unless it bears labeling stating that fact: *Provided*, That to the extent that compliance with the requirements of this paragraph is impracticable, exemptions shall be established by regulations promulgated by the Secretary. The provisions of this paragraph and paragraphs (g) and (i) with respect to artificial coloring shall not apply in the case of butter, cheese, or ice cream."

The food and drug law which became effective June 25, 1939, contains the better features of the old act and many new ones which changes in modern life made necessary.[213] Greater power is given the government to control foods and drugs. The Secretary of Agriculture is authorized to promulgate definitions and standards. The new act according to Dunbar [214] preserves all of the valuable features of the older one of 1906 and includes valuable new ones.

One difficulty which food processors face is contamination of the food after it leaves their warehouse. Through ignorance and carelessness, all the good results of technical service in the factory may be negated by improper handling by the retailer or in the consumer's kitchen. Examples of this are food-poisoning cases which have resulted from eating smoked sausage packed in oil. In most of these cases, contamination of the food after opening in the retailer's store was indicated.

Definitions and Standards for Food. These are necessary for use of food-control officials. They must have an acceptable definition of a food in order to know whether foods which they investigate on the market are satisfactory. Definitions and standards for food are provided for in the Food, Drug, and Cosmetic Act of 1938. Sec. 401 reads as follows:

"Whenever in the judgment of the Secretary such action will promote honesty and fair dealing in the interest of consumers, he shall promulgate regulations fixing and establishing for any food, under its common or usual name so far as practicable, a reasonable definition and standard of identity, a reasonable standard of quality, and/or reasonable standards of fill of container: ... In prescribing a definition and standard of identity for any food or class of food in which optional ingredients are permitted,

213. Hubbard. 1938. Modern Brewer 20, 38-40.
214. Dunbar. 1939. News Edition, Ind. Eng. Chem. 17, 225-227.

the Secretary shall, for the purpose of promoting honesty and fair dealing in the interest of consumers, designate the optional ingredients which shall be named on the label . . ."

Public hearings are held at which any interested person may present his views. The evidence thus recorded is used as a basis for whatever rulings are made by the Administrator.

WRAPPING AND PACKAGING OF FOODS

Proper wrapping and packaging is an integral part of making high-grade foods available to the public. Unless they are distributed from the processing plant to the consumer under proper conditions quality and safety may not be maintained. Food products distributed by American vendors are, in general, wrapped or packaged in the place where they are processed. The food itself is not handled by anyone until it is prepared for the table. Tin and glass containers and paper and paper board in various forms have been used largely to attain this ideal situation. The former are discussed later in the chapter on canning.

Many questions have to be considered and the wrapper must always be considered in relation to the foodstuff to be wrapped. Points to be considered are strength, permeability to moisture, actual waterproof qualities, liability of odors, addition of harmful substances from the wrappers, such as poisonous metals or preservatives, effect on rancidity production (for fatty foods), and price. Moisture-vapor-proof wrappings are liable to cause odors to be developed. Foods may be contaminated with formaldehyde if packed in transparent wrappings of gelatin hardened with it. Tin, lead, and even arsenic may be added to foods from wrappers in poisonous amounts. Chese packed in tinfoil has been found to contain up to 23,000 p.p.m. of tin, the usual permitted limit being 287 parts per million. Permeability to light affects rancidity, and wrappers only permeable to certain light wave lengths which are inoperative in these matters have been placed on the market.[215]

Besides these possibilities are those involving microorganisms which have been carefully considered in the chapter on milk under the discussion of the milk bottle.

Paper Containers and Wrappings for Foods. Paper has played an important role for decades in storage and shipment of foods. Despite the fact that other materials have been used for this purpose, treated paper seems to have made a distinct place of its own. Paper containers and wrappings have one distinct advantage over those made of other materials in that they are used but once. They do not present, therefore, the sanitary hazards which are inherent in containers used over and over again. That sanitary hazards exist for the latter is evidenced by regulations of many health departments prohibiting removal of milk bottles from homes in which there is a case of communicable disease.

Cleaning and sterilization of multi-use containers present problems which have not been easily solved. Many committees of various organiza-

215. Forstner. 1936. J. Roy. San. Inst. 57, 283-287.

tions have discussed the problems involved in cleaning and sterilizing the glass milk bottle. Carbonated beverage bottles are also in this same category. Such problems as these would be solved if containers could be developed which could be discarded after use.

Little worry need be caused by the fact that some paperboard containers are made from paper which has been used once. This material is subjected in the paper mill to several processes which greatly reduce its content of microorganisms and destroy pathogenic bacteria. These processes include cooking at high temperatures, bleaching with chlorine, and drying on rolls at high temperatures on the papermaking machines.

Much paper and paperboard is paraffined for various reasons given by Tanner and Lewis.[216] More recently the germicidal properties of this treatment of paper have become important for the single-service paper milk container.

Methods for Bacteriological Examination of Paper. These are only of relatively recent origin. Such procedures involve disintegration of the paper or paperboard to a thin homogeneous suspension of fiber which is then plated and cultured in various culture media. A procedure was published in 1940 by the Technical Association of the Pulp and Paper Industry.[217]

Another procedure for determining the bacterial content of paper, outlined by Cartwright and Epstein[218] will not be presented here. The great problem is to determine what results of a technic just presented mean. The high temperatures attained in cooking the pulp, the heavy chlorination to bleach it, and finally, the temperature on the drying rolls are lethal agents of known efficiency. Experiments have shown that pathogenic bacteria cannot survive on drying rolls.

The Food Investigation Board of Great Britain[219] has found that wrapping individual units of fruits is beneficial. The wrappers are impregnated with various substances which either inhibit microorganisms or destroy them. The first work was done by soaking the wrappers in odorless mineral oil. Tomkins[220] found iodized wrappers to reduce rotting of fruits, which prompted him to experiment with other possible chemical substances. Among the many which were studied, diphenyl, in addition to iodine, was found to be usable. Use of wrappers treated with such substances function in reducing rot by mechanically restricting the spores of rot-producing fungi as well as by destroying them. Ortho-phenylphenol to the extent of 8.7 to 23.3 mg. per square foot in wrappers was found by Van der Plank and Rattray[221] to reduce decay of stored lemons. Glyceride oil, such as olive oil, retarded fruit injury caused by ortho-phenylphenol.

216. Tanner and Lewis. 1940. Oil and Soap 17, 26-30.
217. Paper Trade J. 1940. 111, 27-30.
218. Cartwright and Epstein. 1940. Paper Trade J. 11, 27-29
219. Rept. Food Invest. Bd. for 1922, p. 26; also succeeding reports.
220. Tomkins. 1934. J. Pomology 12, 311.
221. Van der Plank and Rattray. 1940. Union So. Africa, Dept. of Agr., Ann. Rept. Low Temp. Res. Sta., Cape Town, 1938-1939, 88-93.

REFERENCE BOOKS

BAILEY, E. H. S., 1917. A Text Book of Sanitary and Applied Chemistry. The Macmillan Co., New York, N. Y.

BITTING, A. W., 1937. Appertizing or the Art of Canning. Trade Pressroom, San Francisco, Calif.

CARLTON, H., 1941. The Frozen Food Industry. University of Tennessee Press, Knoxville.

Cereal Laboratory Methods. American Association of Cereal Chemists, 110 Experiment Station Hall, Lincoln, Neb.

COX, H. E., 1938. The Chemical Analysis of Food. P. Blakiston's Son and Co., Philadelphia, Pa.

CRUESS, W. V., 1938. Commercial Fruit and Vegetable Products. McGraw-Hill Book Co., New York, N. Y.

CRUESS, W. V., 1922. Laboratory Manual of Fruit and Vegetable Products. McGraw-Hill Book Co., New York, N. Y.

Diagnostic Procedures and Reagents. Technics for the Laboratory Diagnosis and Control of the Communicable Diseases. First edition, 1941. Am. Pub. Health Assoc., New York, N. Y.

DUKES, A. C., 1918. The Bacteriology of Food. H. K. Lewis and Co., London.

EDELMANN, R., MOHLER, J. R., AND EICHORN, A., 1925. Meat Hygiene. Lea and Febiger, Philadelphia, Pa.

ELLIS, C., AND WELLS, A. A., 1941. The Chemical Action of Ultraviolet Light. Reinhold Publishing Corp., New York, N. Y.

FOLIN, O. K., 1914. Preservatives and Other Chemicals in Foods; Their Use and Abuse. Harvard University Press, Cambridge, Mass.

JENNINGS, W. I., AND COLE, G. J., 1938. The Law of Food and Drugs. Chas. Knight and Co., London.

JONES, O., AND JONES, T. W., 1937. Canning Practice and Control. Chapman Hall, Ltd., London.

KLING, A., 1921. Methodes Actuelles d'Expertises Employees au Laboratoire Municipal de Paris et Documents sur les Materies Relatives a l'Alimentation, Pub. sous la Direction de M. Andre Kling. Dimod. Paris.

KOSSOWICZ, A., 1911. Einführung in die Mykologie Nährungsmittelgewerbe. Börntraeger, Berlin.

KOSSOWICZ, A., 1911. Einführung in die Mykologie der Genussmittel und in die Gärungsphysiologie. Börntraeger, Berlin.

Laboratory Manual. Methods of Analysis. American Butter Institute. 47 pp. (undated).

LEACH, A. E., 1920. Food Inspection and Analysis. John Wiley and Sons, Inc., New York, N. Y.

VON LOESECKE, H. W., 1942. Outlines of Food Technology. Reinhold Pub. Corp., New York, N. Y.

MACEWEN, H. A., 1922. Food Inspection, a Practical Handbook. Blackie and Son, Ltd., London.

MARSHALL, M. S., 1937. Bacteriology of. Specific Communicable Diseases. Dept. Pub. Health, San Francisco, Calif.

NEWMAN, G. W., 1904. Bacteriology and the Public Health. P. Blakiston's Son and Co., Philadelphia, Pa.

PARK, W. H., 1920. Public Health and Hygiene. Lea and Febiger, Philadelphia, Pa.

PRESCOTT, S. C., AND DUNN, C. D., 1940. Industrial Microbiology. McGraw-Hill Book Co., New York, N. Y.

PRESCOTT, S. C., AND PROCTOR, B. E., 1937. Food Technology. McGraw-Hill Book Co., New York, N. Y.

PURVIS, J. E., 1922. The Chemical Examination of Water, Sewage, Foods, and Other Substances. Cambridge University Press.

RIDEAL, S., 1903. Disinfection and Preservation of Foods. John Wiley and Sons, Inc., New York, N. Y.

ROSENAU, M. J., 1927. Preventive Medicine and Hygiene. D. Appleton and Co., New York, N. Y.

SAVAGE, W. G., 1914. The Bacteriological Examination of Food and Water. Cambridge University Press.

SAVAGE, W. G., 1919. Food and Public Health. Cassell and Co., Ltd., New York, N. Y.

SCHNEIDER, A., 1915. Bacteriological Methods in Food and Drug Laboratories With an Introduction to Microanalytical Methods. P. Blakiston's Son and Co., Philadelphia, Pa.

SCHNEIDER, A., 1920. The Microbiology and Microanalysis of Foods. P. Blakiston's Son and Co., Philadelphia, Pa.

SHERMAN, H. C., 1933. Food Products. The Macmillan Co., New York, N. Y.

SHRADER, J. H., 1939. Food Control and Its Public Health Aspects. John Wiley and Sons, Inc., New York, N. Y.

TANNER, F. W., 1933. Food-Borne Infections and Intoxications. The Twin City Printing Co., Champaign, Illinois.

Technical Manual, Methods for Laboratory Technicians, War Department, Washington, D. C., October 17, 1941.

THOM, C., AND HUNTER, A. C., 1924. Hygienic Fundamentals of Food Handling. Williams and Wilkins, Baltimore, Md.

TRESSLER, D. K., et al., 1923. Marine Products of Commerce. Reinhold Pub. Co., New York, N. Y.

TRESSLER, D. K., AND EVERS, C. F., 1942. The Freezing Preservation of Fruits, Fruit Juices, and Vegetables, 2nd ed. Avi Publishing Co., New York, N. Y.

WILEY, H. W., 1929. The History of a Crime Against the Food Law. Published by Harvey W. Wiley, Washington, D. C.

WILSON, S., 1942. Food and Drug Regulations. American Council on Public Affairs, 2153 Florida Ave., N. W., Washington, D. C.

WOODCOCK, F. H., AND LEWIS, W. R., 1938. Canned Foods and the Canning Industry. Sir I. Pitman & Sons, Ltd., London.

WOODMAN, A. G., 1941. Food Analysis, Typical Methods and Interpretation of Results. McGraw-Hill Book Co., Inc., New York, N. Y.

CHAPTER 2

THE BACTERIA

Food microbiologists frequently find it necessary to determine certain characteristics of an organism if not characterize it completely. This is especially true for those which cause spoilage or which may have some special role such as those in butter cultures. Some confusion has always existed in classification and nomenclature of microorganisms. This has led to duplication of names and diversity of characteristics for the same organism.[1] Winslow,[2] recognizing the difficulties of such a situation, appealed for careful preservation of original types so that future investigators could have the type species for study. This is of great importance in microbiology of foods.

The Descriptive Chart of the Society of American Bacteriologists. The Descriptive Chart [3] of the Society of American Bacteriologists is the result of years of effort to secure a concise means of recording characteristics of microorganisms. Harding [4] reviewed the earlier contributions. Johnston,[5] Harding and Prucha,[6] Conn,[7] and others have used the chart in the study of several of the more common groups of bacteria. The value of the chart is especially apparent in the study of many closely related strains or in the study of the flora of a particular material, such as canned corn, pasteurized milk, and similar foods.

Procedure for Studying Characteristics of Bacteria. Failure to use comparable methods for determining the characteristics of bacteria has often resulted in confusion and conflicting opinions about the characteristics of bacteria. In order to remedy this situation and to insure availability of suitable methods, the Society of American Bacteriologists appointed a committee to study bacteriological technic. Under the direction of Dr. H. J. Conn, of the Agricultural Experiment Station, Geneva, New York, *A Manual of Methods for Pure Culture Study of Bacteria* was published.[8] This manual contains recommended procedures for characterizing bacteria and has helped to bring some order into a confused situation.

Media. The importance of using carefully prepared media needs emphasis. All media should be prepared according to recognized authority such as the Standard Methods of the American Public Health Association. This organization has two reports of such a nature: *Standard Methods for the Examination of Dairy Products* was prepared in collaboration with the Association of Official Agricultural Chemists; a new edition of *Stan-*

1. The details of elementary technic may be found in the author's "Practical Bacteriology," published by John Wiley & Sons, Inc., New York City, 1928.
2. Winslow. 1921. J. Bact., 6, 133-134.
3. These charts may be purchased from Dr. H. J. Conn, Agr. Exp. Sta., Geneva, N. Y.
4. Harding. 1910. Tech. Bull. 13, N. Y. Agr. Exp. Sta., Geneva.
5. Johnston. 1884. Amer. Pub. Health Assoc. Proc. 20, 445-449.
6. Harding and Prucha. 1908. Tech. Bull., N. Y. Agr. Exp. Sta., Geneva.
7. Conn. 1915. Science, N. S., 41, 618.
8. Copies of this pamphlet, as well as the Descriptive Chart mentioned above, may be secured from Dr. H. J. Conn, Agricultural Experiment Station, Geneva, N. Y.

dard Methods for the Examination of Water is published about every five years. Both of these reports should be in every laboratory concerned with food microbiology. *Manual of Methods for Pure Culture Study of Bacteria*[8] also contains information about media. A large number of formulas for media useful in food bacteriology are given in Chapter 26 of this book.

Media should always be incubated before use to make certain that they are sterile. Especially is this true when studying thermophilic bacteria or other heat-resistant species. Such media should be tested at 55°C.(131°F.) for the colonies of many thermophiles will not appear at 37°C.(98.6°F.). Their spores are resistant to heat and many survive sterilization methods which are adequate for mesophilic species. Spores of *Clostridium botulinum* are also especially heat resistant.

Motility. Some care is necessary in interpreting results of motility determinations. Positive results are probably satisfactory, but negative results are convincing only after a number of attempts. The safest method is to make flagella stains, for if the organism possesses flagella, it is reasonable to assume that it is motile. Various procedures for flagella staining are given under "Staining Reactions" in a paragraph to follow. Sturges[9] stated that flattened capillary tubes made excellent cells for examination of bacteria. Filled with drops of broth cultures and sealed off, these cells may be used for observations on motility.

Carnot and Halle's[10] Method for Determining Motility. These investigators devised a unique method for determining the rate of motion exhibited by an organism. The method has been adapted to isolating the motile *Eberthella typhosa* from water. A U-shaped tube into which are placed sterile bouillon, sand, and the material under examination, or in pure culture work a broth culture of the bacterium whose motility is under study, is used. Bacteria which are motile will propel themselves through the sand layer in a given time. By establishing standard arbitrary conditions, the relative motility of an organism may be found.

Procedure. Draw out a seven-mm. piece of glass tubing in a flame and then bend to make the Carnot and Garnier U-tube. Each limb of this tube should have a length of about 25 cm. A small amount of glass wool should be forced down into the larger arm. Sterile broth is then poured into the larger tube until about 10 cm. of the limbs of the tube are filled. Into the large tube should then be poured sufficient purified sand thoroughly washed in acid and sterilized to come up to between 10 or 15 cm. The pure culture of the organism whose motility is under study is inoculated into the broth of the smaller arm. If the tube is incubated at the optimum temperature, the time for passage through the sand may thus be determined. According to Carnot and Garnier *Microspira cholerae* passed through one inch of sand in one hour and 38 minutes. Cloudiness in the uninoculated arm is the index of the organism's presence. Gautier[11] and Levy[12] used the sand tube with success for isolating motile organisms.

STAINING REACTIONS

To make a complete study of the staining properties of an organism all of the stains mentioned on the Descriptive Chart should be used. Common special stains, such as the acid-fast should also be tried. Pro-

9. Sturges. 1927. J. Bact., 15, 7.
10. Carnot and Halle. 1915. J. Amer. Med. Assoc. 66, 667.
11. Gautier. 1915. Rev. med. de la Suisse Rom. 34, 361-445.
12. Levy. 1916. J. Amer. Med. Assoc. 66, 1022-1023.

cedures for staining microorganisms have been given in several places in this book. Supplement A (entitled Staining Procedures) to the *Manual of Methods for Pure Culture Study of Bacteria* contains a compilation of useful methods. This should be available to all food bacteriologists.

Staining of Flagella. This has been a difficult procedure for many bacteriologists. It may be due to lack of care in some of the preparatory procedures. Smith[13] has mentioned some of the common errors:

1. Oily or otherwise dirty cover glasses.
2. Unsuitable cultures.
3. Breaking off the flagella.
4. Uneven or too copious distribution of the bacteria.
5. Imperfect mordanting.
6. Understaining or overstaining.
7. Precipitates on the cover glass during some stage of the process.

The greatest error probably lies in dirty slides and cover glasses. These should be cleaned in strong alkali, in order to saponify any animal grease which may be on them, and thoroughly rinsed. Otherwise, the film will "roll" and not spread evenly. The culture which is stained must be young and vigorous. A small amount of this growth should be transferred to a test tube of sterile water and incubated at 37°C.(98.6°F.). After several hours, some of this suspension should be put on slides and allowed to dry by placing the slides in the 37°C. incubator. The film should then be fixed and stained.

The author has secured the best results with Loeffler's and Plimmer and Paine's methods. A double boiler is prepared from two beakers. The inner is supported by pieces of cork. The staining solution should be put into the inner one and the temperature raised to about 65°C.(149°F.) or until the stain steams. The slides are immersed in this solution and stained as long as required.

Loeffler's Flagella Stain.

LOEFFLER'S MORDANT.

Tannic acid, 20 per cent aqueous	10 ml.
Ferrous sulfate, saturated aqueous	5 ml.
Basic fuchsin, saturated alcoholic	1 ml.

Mix and filter after a short time.

LOEFFLER'S STAIN.

Carbolic acid	20.0 ml.
Basic fuchsin, saturated alcoholic	2.5 ml.

After the film has been prepared it should be covered with the mordant and heated for two minutes. Wash in tap water and cover with the stain. Heat for two minutes as before. Wash, dry, and mount.

Plimmer and Paine's[14] Modification of the Cesares-Gil Method for Staining Bacterial Flagella. Plimmer and Paine have proposed the following method:

The following ingredients are employed in making up the stain:

Tannic acid	10.0 grams
Aluminum chloride (hydrated)	18.0 grams
Zinc chloride	10.0 grams
Rosaniline hydrochloride	1.5 grams
Alcohol, 60 per cent	40.0 ml.

13. Smith. 1905. Smithsonian Inst., Washington, D. C.
14. Plimmer and Paine. 1921. J. Path. & Bact. 24, 286-288.

Place the solids in a mortar, add 10 ml. of the alcohol and mix thoroughly, taking care to smash up all the zinc chloride. Stir in the rest of the alcohol slowly. At this point the mass goes gradually into a viscous solution of a deep red color, and in this state appears to remain stable for several years. For use, dilute with water, one part stain to four of water; when nearly complete precipitation occurs, a small amount remaining in solution as a balanced colloid.

Method of application:

1. The culture must be 18-24 hours old and must be removed carefully. Slides should be cleaned with chromic acid, and all grease removed by roasting them over a Bunsen burner. When they have cooled to blood heat, a small drop of the bacterial suspension is placed at one end, the slide tilted, and the drop allowed to run down, or it may be smeared gently with a strip of gutta-percha tissue. Quick drying of the film seems to be important, hence the warm slide. No fixing is required.

2. Apply the diluted mordant, allowing it to stand one minute after mixing with water. Filter into the slide and allow to stand for one minute, when a slight surface bronzing should be visible. Wash rapidly under the tap.

3. Flood the film with cold carbol fuchsin for five minutes, wash, dry, and examine in oil. If satisfactory, mount in balsam or euparal.

The advantages claimed for this method are the following:

1. The ease with which successful preparations are obtained makes it a useful stain in the hands of inexperienced students.

2. It is possible to have the background absolutely free from stain .

3. The flagella are uniformly stained without the appearance of granular deposits, and do not appear to be unduly magnified.

4. The mordant is a one-solution stain, seems to keep indefinitely in a well-stoppered bottle, and is always ready for use.

5. The materials are relatively cheap, as compared with other methods using osmic acid as a fixative.

Thatcher [15] reported better preparations when the mordant was diluted with an equal amount of water. In the author's laboratory this has not been the case.

Conn and Wolfe [16] raised the question whether the flagella stain could be made simple enough to be used as a routine test in studying pure cultures of bacteria. Motility as determined under the microscope in hanging drops, yields the first information on the presence or absence of flagella. They found the Gray [17] procedure to give consistent results even in the hands of inexperienced technicians.

Gray's [17] Flagella Stain as Modified by Conn and Wolfe.[16] Conn and Wolfe hoped to develop a procedure which could be used in place of the test for motility. Despite the fact that flagella staining methods have been quite complicated and have often yielded erratic results, a modified Gray procedure was recommended for even inexperienced workers. The procedure is as follows:

Preparation of Glass Slides. Use new slides if possible. (This is because under the drastic method of cleaning to remove grease, old slides have a greater tendency to break, owing to crystallization of the glass.) Clean first in a dichromate cleaning fluid, wash in water, and rinse in 95 per cent alcohol; then wipe with a clean piece of cheesecloth. (Wiping is not always necessary but is advisable unless fresh alcohol is used after every few slides.) Pass each slide back and forth through a flame for some time, ordinarily until the appearance of an orange color in the flame; some experience is necessary before the proper amount of heating can be accurately judged.

Cool slides gradually in order to reanneal, and thus to minimize breakage. A crude but ordinarily satisfactory method of annealing is to place the flamed slides on a metal plate (flamed side up) standing on a vessel of boiling water; and then to remove the

15. Thatcher. 1927. J. Stain Tech. 1, 143.
16. Conn and Wolfe. 1938. J. Bact. 36, 517-520.
17. Gray. 1929. Idem 12, 273-274.

flame under the water so as to allow gradual cooling. (Failure to anneal may result in breakage, sometimes as long as two weeks after the heating.)

Preparation of Suspensions. Use young and actively growing cultures (e.g., 18 to 22 hours old), on agar slants. With a flamed *but well-cooled* loop, transfer a small amount of growth to five or 10 ml. of sterile distilled water, which has been held for several hours at room temperature. (Poor slides result from suspensions made in water that is too hot or too cold.)

Mix thoroughly in the distilled water and allow to stand five to 30 minutes, according to the type of growth produced. Gum-forming bacteria require 30 minutes, as recommended by Hofer and Wilson; those that produce no gum must stand in the water only five to 10 minutes. Standing in the water should be just long enough to allow the flagella to become untangled; too long a time results in their breaking off.

With a loop that has been flamed *and cooled*, remove a drop from the top of the suspension and place it on a glass slide prepared as above described. (The reason for taking material from near the surface of the suspension is because the nonmotile cells tend to settle, while the motile cells—at least in the case of aerobes—collect at the top.) Smear the drop over the slide with the use of a second slide, as in preparing blood films; the film should be thin enough to dry rapidly and thus to minimize distortion.

Staining. Use the mordant recommended by Gray: 5 ml. saturated aqueous solution potassium alum; 2 ml. saturated aqueous solution mercuric chloride; 2 ml. 20 per cent aqueous solution tannic acid; .4 ml. saturated alcoholic solution basic fuchsin (presumably about six per cent, which was the strength employed by Conn and Wolfe). For best results, filter just before using. The technic is essentially that of Gray. Apply cold for eight to 10 minutes; 10 minutes is ordinarily best, but this varies with the organism studied. (More than 10 minutes of mordanting is apt to cause too much precipitate.)

After mordanting, wash slides about 10 seconds in running water. Dry in the air, without heating. Stain five minutes, without heating, with Ziehl's carbol fuchsin; wash in running water; dry and examine.

Tittsler and Sandholzer[18] suggested use of semisolid agar medium, results from use of which are macroscopic, thus obviating use of hanging drops. Motility was manifested by a diffuse zone of growth spreading from the line of inoculation. Conn and Wolfe said that this test picked out many organisms as motile which would not appear to be motile under the microscope.

Capsules. Several methods are available for demonstrating capsules. One method may supplement another and make results more convincing.

Consistency of Growth in Common Media. Capsulated bacteria usually grow with a slimy, sticky growth on common media. When touched with a sterile needle, it will pull out into threads.

Ordinary Aqueous-Alcoholic Stains. Films of capsulated bacteria when stained with ordinary aqueous-alcoholic stains, will show the bacteria with halos about the cells. These halos are capsules which have resisted penetration of the dye.

Special Staining Procedures. Special staining procedures for staining capsules are given below. These should be employed in research work to confirm evidence secured by other methods.

The Gins Method of Demonstrating Capsules. Hagan[19] has called attention to the value of the Gins method for demonstration of capsules. The procedure, which involves staining of India-ink films of bacteria, is as follows (after Hagan):

18. Tittsler and Sandholzer. 1936. J. Bact. 31, 575-580.
19. Hagan. 1927. Science 66, 173.

1. Dilute the ink with an equal amount of sterile water, or dilute and sterilize.

2. Place a drop of the ink near one end of a very clean slide and carefully mix in a loopful of the bacterial suspension.

3. Then spread the mixture across the slide with the edge of a second slide. A properly prepared specimen should be uniformly spread and of a grayish color rather than black. (Films that are too thick may loosen after fixation.)

4. After drying in the air, fix the film with heat or by dipping in methyl alcohol.

5. Stain with an ordinary bacteriological stain. Microscopic examination will reveal well-stained bacteria lying in lacunae in the film of ink. The margin of the capsule is sharply delineated by the ink and the margin of the cells by the stain.

This is a very satisfactory method.

Endospores. Two methods are available. One involves the use of stains while the other is a heat test.

Ordinary Aqueous-Alcoholic Stains. Films may be stained with ordinary aqueous-alcoholic stains. The vegetative protoplasm (vegetative cells) will take the stain while the spores will resist and appear as colorless or very faintly colored units. Several different methods have been suggested at various times for staining bacteria.

Neisser's Method. Flood the smear with hot aniline fuchsin for about an hour. Wash in water and decolorize with acid alcohol (one part HCl and three parts alcohol). Too long decolorization may remove the stain from the spores also. Counterstain with methylene blue if desired.

May's[20] Method. 1. Make a film and fix in the usual manner.

2. Cover with a small amount of five per cent chromic acid.

3. After 30 seconds add about twice as much concentrated ammonia as there is chromic acid on the slide. Allow to act about two minutes.

4. Rinse with tap water.

5. Steam with carbol fuchsin for two or three minutes.

6. Rinse.

7. Restain with one per cent sulfuric acid for 15 to 30 seconds.

8. Rinse again and flood the slide with tap water.

9. Add to this a few drops of Loeffler's methylene blue and allow to stain for 10 to 30 seconds.

10. Rinse, blot, dry, and examine.

Dorner's[21] Method for Demonstrating Spores. This method which combines vital staining and a dark background is quite satisfactory. A heavy suspension of cells should be made in a small amount of water. To this suspension an equal amount of Ziehl-Nielsen carbol fuchsin solution is added and the mixture heated at 100°C.(212°F.) 10 to 15 minutes. A mixture of this stained suspension with an equal amount of nigrosin solution (five to 10 per cent) is made on a cover glass. This is then spread as thinly as possible and dried. Dorner later suggested addition of formalin as a preservative.

Schaeffer and Fulton's[22] Method for Staining Endospores. This proposed procedure was said by the authors to be superior to other methods, such as those of Wirtz,[20] Hansen,[24] and Möeller.[25] The technic is as follows:

Make films in the usual manner and fix by flaming three times. Flood with malachite green solution (five per cent aqueous solution) and heat to steaming three or four times within one-half minute. Wash off the excess stain under the tap for about one-half minute. Apply a .5 per cent aqueous safranin solution one-half minute. Wash, blot, dry, and examine. This procedure is evidently more simple than the original method. The whole staining time involved is less than two minutes, and a minimum of steaming is required. Within wide limits it is impossible to overstain or wash too long.

20. May. 1926. Stain Tech. 1, 105-106.
21. Dorner. 1922. Landw. Jahrb. d. Schweisz. 36, 595-597.
22. Schaeffer and Fulton. 1933. Science 77, 194.
23. Wirtz. 1908. Zentbl. Bakt., Pt. 1, Orig., 46, 727.
24. Hansen. Cited from Schaeffer and Fulton.
25. Moeller. Idem.

Gray's[20] **Method for Differential Staining of Spores and Vegetative Cells of Microorganisms.** A solution for staining differentially spores and vegetative cytoplasm of bacteria, yeasts, and certain fungi was developed by Gray. Two forms of the solution have been developed—an aqueous concentrated solution and a saline dilution prepared from that.

Solution A. The Aqueous Concentrated Solution.

The solution is composed of the following amounts of the dyes in distilled water:

Malachite green .... 0.05 per cent
Fuchsin, basic .... 0.05 per cent

It has been found convenient to prepare separate solutions of the two dyes, in double strength; solution may be hastened by placing the containers in a water bath at 56°C. (132.8°F.); equal volumes of these solutions are mixed to obtain the staining solution with the dyes in the proportions stated. The staining solution appears to be stable. It should be noted that as there may be differences in dye content in dyes of different manufacture, or in different batches from a factory, a slight modification in quantities may be necessary. The malachite green used in this laboratory was supplied by the British Drug Houses, Limited, Toronto; the basic fuchsin by Coleman and Bell.

Solution B. The Saline, Diluted Solution.

This is prepared by diluting two parts of solution A with eight parts of an .8 per cent sodium chloride solution. This mode of dilution was adopted since it was found that dilution of the aqueous, concentrated solution with water, or 10 per cent glycerine solution, rapidly altered the cellular contents of the fungi used.

METHOD OF STAINING

The solution is allowed to act on fixed films for three or four minutes at room temperature; excess of stain is then washed off in running water, the film dried, and examined under the oil immersion objective. Spores in the early stage of development stain blue, in older stages, greenish-blue; ripe spores within the cell are tinged greenish-blue; free spores are unstained; the cytoplasm of vegetative cells stains violet in young cells, light violet in older cells, in some species pink rather than light violet.

Another simple method is to mix the cells in a loopful of the solution, on a slide, and allow it to dry. Fixing does not appear to be necessary. The excess of dry stain is washed off. The differentiation by this method is not as clear-cut as it is by the method described above.

By staining over steam, or by heating in a flame until steam rises, a sharper differentiation is obtained. The method adopted for heating has been to place the slide, with the stain on the film, on a 100-ml. beaker containing a little water; as soon as the water boils the flame is removed and the heating continued for one minute, though less may be all that is required; the slide is then cooled, washed, and dried. By this method (with solution A) the young spores may be masked by excess of violet; this may be removed by washing for a few seconds with 95-per cent ethyl alcohol, or by covering the film with a thin layer of a sterile two per cent solution of nigrosin. A loopful of the nigrosin is placed near the film after it has been stained, washed, and dried; by means of a strip of unsized (letterhead) paper, measuring one-half inch wide by one and one-half inches long, it is drawn with firm pressure and rapid movement over the film on which it thus dries quickly. The nigrosin (which is not recommended for films that have been stained with the saline solution) is useful to demonstrate "capsules" in young cultures in which spores have begun to develop; these have been found in *Bacillus megatherium.* It has been found that broth is a better medium than water for preparing suspensions of this organism, which tends to "clump" in water. Most of the violet color is removed by the nigrosin but the spores are left stained.

Heat-Resistance Test for Demonstrating Bacterial Spores. Bacterial spores are heat resistant, a characteristic which may be used for demon-

26. Gray. 1941. Canad. J. Res. 19, C, 95-98.

strating them in unknown cultures. If viable cells survive exposure to heat at 80°C.(176°F.) for 30 minutes it may be assumed that the organism is a sporeformer. A longer period of heating must be used for thermophilic bacteria. They should be heated for five or 10 minutes at 100°C.(212°F.).

The Gram Stain. The Gram stain must be carried out according to standard technic, if comparable results are to be secured. That the procedure is not entirely satisfactory is indicated, perhaps, by the many methods which have been proposed. Results of a comparative study of a number of these methods by Hucker and Conn [27] indicated that the methods of Jordan,[28] Buchanan,[29] Atkins,[30] and Hucker [31] gave most satisfactory results. Hucker and Conn found the Gram stain to give variable results, even under the most carefully controlled conditions. In another publication Hucker and Conn [32] reported results of a comparative study of the Gram stain in different laboratories. Slides were prepared bearing films of six different bacteria known to differ widely in their behavior to the Gram reaction. They were distributed to 10 different collaborators with identical directions. With four of the six organisms consistent results were secured. The other two organisms gave such variable results that it was impossible to consider them either Gram negative or Gram positive. Conn suggested that these organisms be called Gram variable.

Hucker's Modification of the Gram Stain. The following solutions are needed:

Solution A

Crystal violet (85 per cent dye content)	4	grams
Ethyl alcohol (95 per cent)	20	ml.

Solution B

Ammonium oxalate	0.8	gram
Water	80.0	ml.

Mix solutions *A* and *B*.

Lugol's Iodine Solution

Iodine	1	gram
Potassium iodide	2	grams
Water	200	ml.

Counterstain

Safranin (saturated solution in 95 per cent alcohol)	10	ml.
Water	100	ml.

Procedure. Stain for one minute with the crystal violet mixture; wash in water and then stain for one minute with the iodine solution; wash in water and dry with bibulous paper. Decolorize in 95 per cent alcohol for 30 seconds; counterstain for 10 seconds. Wash, dry, and examine.

The Ziehl-Nielsen Acid-Fast Staining Procedure. The original procedure of acid-fast staining is known as the Ziehl-Nielsen stain. There are many modifications of this procedure, the following being typical:

27. Hucker and Conn. 1923. N. Y. Agr. Exp. Sta. Tech. Bull. 93, 37.
28. Jordan. 1908. General Bacteriology, Saunders, Phila.
29. Buchanan. 1911. Veterinary Bacteriology. W. B. Saunders Co., Phila.
30. Atkins. 1920. J. Bact. 5, 321-324.
31. Hucker. 1921. J. Bact. 6, 395-397.
32. Hucker and Conn. 1927. N. Y. Agr. Exp. Sta. Tech. Bull. 128, 1-34.

1. Prepare film in the usual manner.

2. Flood with steaming carbol fuchsin for five minutes. The slide or cover glass may be immersed in the staining fluid and the fluid heated.

Basic fuchsin	1 part
Absolute alcohol	10 parts
Carbolic acid (1 to 20)	100 parts

3. Wash in water.

4. Decolorize with 25 per cent hydrochloric acid. This will remove the red color.

5. Counterstain with methylene blue for about one minute.

6. Wash, dry, mount, if desired, and examine.

7. The film may be counterstained with picric acid if desired.

Negative Staining of Microorganisms. This technic which has become known as "negative staining" because the cells are unstained on an opaque black background was probably first described by Burri.[33] He diluted India or Chinese ink 1 to 10 with water and sterilized it in small portions of 5 to 10 ml. When used a drop of the diluted ink is inoculated with enough growth to give about one cell per droplet of .1 to 2 mm. in diameter. Then with the aid of a sterile pen or other instrument, groups of droplets of three are made on the surface of a solid medium. These droplets may be examined to determine the number of cells. Dorner [34] called attention to this method and outlined the technic as follows: Boil 10 gm. of nigrosin in 100 ml. of water for about 30 minutes. Filter several times through the same filter paper, adding 10 drops of formalin before the last filtration as a preservative. Place a small loopful of this solution on a clean slide and add the bacteria with a needle in loop. After mixing spread the mixture a little irregularly on the slide and dry either at room temperature or slowly over the flame. The preparation may be examined without use of a cover glass with the oil immersion lens.

Oxygen Relations. Relation of microorganisms to oxygen may be determined from the closed arm of fermentation tubes. Before using, however, it is advisable to reduce the dissolved oxygen to a minimum either by a vacuum pump or boiling.

Incubation of streak plates by means of Torrey's method will give good results. Also agar streaks of the organism may be incubated in a Novy jar.

Two methods are generally used by bacteriologists:

Agar Shake Method. The medium to be used, usually plain agar, is melted and cooled to about 45°C.(113°F.). The organism, the oxygen relations of which are to be studied, is inoculated into the melted agar, the agar thoroughly shaken and cooled. Strictly anaerobic bacteria will grow in the deeper layers of the culture but not at or near the surface.

Fermentation Tube Method. The appearance of growth in the closed arm of the fermentation tube is evidence of anaerobic growth.

Nutrient Broth or Bouillon. After this medium has been inoculated from a young culture of the organism, it should be incubated at its optimum temperature. The characteristics may be marked on the Descriptive Chart. These observations include pellicle formation, turbidity, etc. Be-

33. Burri. 1908. Cent. Bakt., Pt. 2, 20, 95-96.
34. Dorner. 1930. Stain Tech. 5, 25-27.

sides these uses of the nutrient broth culture, it may also be used for observations for formation of hydrogen sulfide, indol, etc.

Pellicle formation is influenced by several different factors. Larson stated that surface tension was important. Bacteria which usually grow with pellicle formation were made to grow down in a medium whose surface tension had been depressed.

Welch's [35] Method of Cultivating and Examining Microorganisms. This method enables colonies of bacteria, yeasts, etc., to be cultivated on flat slips of glass covered with a very thin layer of solid culture medium, thus allowing subsequent examination of the colonies under a high magnification if necessary. Three slips of glass, about five inches in length, are place in a test tube (seven by one inch) in the form of a triangle and after the addition of a small amount of an agar culture medium the tube is plugged with cotton wool and sterilized. The medium is melted by immersing the tube in boiling water and after cooling to about 50°C.(122°F.) the medium is inoculated and mixed by rotating the tube, after which this is tilted several times to allow the medium to run up and down the outer surfaces of the glass slips. It is then placed in cold water in a vertical position over the mouth of the tube to prevent evaporation during incubation. If necessary, the addition of five per cent of glycerol may be made to the medium as a further precaution against dessication. After growth is complete one or more of the slips may be removed with sterile forceps and a cover glass placed over the colonies of which microscopic examination is desired, the remainder of the slip being cleaned with damp cotton wool. The colonies of bacteria thus obtained are practically in one plane and may be stained or examined by dark-background illumination with facility.

Frost's [36] little plate method may also be used for studying the colonies of bacteria. The application of this technic to milk is given in Chapter 5. The technic is also outlined in the author's *Practical Bacteriology*.[1]

Gelatin Liquefaction. Liquefying action on gelatin yields information on the proteolytic activities of an organism. Other proteins should also be used, since Diehl [37] has shown that bacterial proteases may be specific for certain proteins. The older method consisted of inoculating a tube of gelatin medium with a straight needle. The tubes were then held for six weeks to determine whether the medium was liquefied. Rothberg [38] proposed giving the organism a preliminary cultivation in one per cent gelatin solution at 25°C.(77°F.) or 37°C.(98.6°F.) and then inoculating the surface of gelatin medium in a culture tube incubated at 20°C.(68°F.) for 15 days. Rush and Palmer [39] reported that the results were influenced by the methods which were used. Levine and Carpenter [40] proposed the use of viscosity determinations. Liquefying bacteria caused a marked reduction in viscosity and a distinct increase in formol titration. The method was discussed further by Levine and Shaw.[41] Allen [42] also proposed a method based on changes in viscosity. The suggestions were founded on the procedure for measuring fluidity of starch. These methods have not had wide application. Before they are generally adopted, much more work would have to be done with them.

35. Welch. 1926. J. Roy. Micro. Soc. 46, 262-264.
36. Frost. 1919. J. Amer. Med. Assoc. 72, 343-344.
37. Diehl. 1919. J. Infect. Diseases 24, 347-361.
38. Rothberg. 1917. Paper read before the Soc. Am. Bact., Dec., 1917.
39. Rush and Palmer. 1921. J. Bact. 6, 571-574.
40. Levine and Carpenter. 1923. Abst. Bact. 7. 9.
41. Levine and Shaw. 1924. J. Bact. 9, 225-234.
42. Allen. 1923. Abst. Bact. 7, 4.

Frazier's[43] **Method of Determining Gelatin Liquefaction.** Plates are poured with gelatin-agar which contains .4 per cent of gelatin together with salts and small amounts of peptone and beef infusion. Duplicate plates are inoculated at the center to form a giant colony and incubated at 30°C.(86°F.) for 48 hours. Then one plate is flooded with an acid solution of bichloride of mercury while the other plate is flooded with a one per cent solution of tannic acid. In the first a clear zone around the giant colony indicates decomposition of the gelatin as far, at least, as peptones. Similarly a heavy precipitate about the giant colony in the plate flooded with tannic acid solution shows decomposition of the gelatin. There is also about the colony of an organism which breaks down gelatin to a considerable extent, a clear zone surrounded by a strikingly white halo. The tannic acid precipitates the gelatin and decomposition products down through some of the amino acids. By use of the two plates, then, a fair idea can be obtained of the amount of decomposition of the gelatin. Results were said to be available in two days.

Starch Hydrolysis. Methods for the determination of the action of bacteria on starch are about as unsatisfactory as those for studying gelatin decomposition. The starch agar plate described by Went,[44] Eijkmann[45] and Allen[46] seems to be as satisfactory as any method. Agar with .2 per cent of soluble starch may be used. After incubation, the medium is flooded with iodine solution. Eckford[47] used a soluble-starch broth. Other procedures were suggested by Gottheil,[48] Edson and Carpenter,[49] Crabill and Reed,[50] Smith,[51] and Müller[52] and others.

FERMENTATION REACTIONS

These are used by practically all microbiologists for identifying microorganisms and characterization of new species. The sugars to be used depend largely on the purpose of the investigation. Great care should be used in sterilizing carbohydrate media, since Mudge[53] and Hasseltine[54] have shown that polysaccharides are easily hydrolyzed to monosaccharides. The latter of these investigators found that serious errors were introduced in the study of *Bacillus proteus*, for instance, on common carbohydrates. For investigations requiring accurate data other methods of sterilization than moist heat should be used. The broth may be sterilized by filtration after the carbohydrates have been added, or the carbohydrate solutions may be sterilized by filtration and added to the broth with a sterile pipette just before the tubes are inoculated. For determining the reaction of media in fermentation tubes, it was once the custom to titrate five milliliters of the medium with N/20 NaOH (or HCl) with phenolphthalein as the indicator. Today the actual hydrogen-ion concentration is determined by any of several methods and with various apparatus. Reference may be

43. Frazier. 1926. J. Bact. 11, 80.
44. Went. 1901. Centbl. Bakt., Pt. 2, 7, 544.
45. Eijkmann. 1906. Centbl. Bakt., Orig., 37, 1.
46. Allen. 1918. J. Bact. 3, 15-17.
47. Eckford. 1927. Amer. J. Hyg. 7, 201-221.
48. Gottheil. 1901. Centbl. Bakt., Pt. 2, 7, 463.
49. Edson and Carpenter. 1912. Vermont Agr. Exp. Sta. Bull. 167.
50. Crabill and Reed. 1915. Biochem. Bull. 4, 30-44.
51. Smith. 1905. Bacteria in Relation to Plant Diseases. Carnegie Inst., Washington, D. C.
52. Müller. 1908. Med. Klin.. Breslau.
53. Mudge. 1917. J. Bact. 2, 403-415.
54. Hasseltine. 1917. Pub. Health Repts. 32, 1879-1887.

made to *Manual of Methods for Pure Culture Study of Bacteria*, Leaflet IX, eighth edition, February, 1941.

Determination of Acid Formation From Sugars. Acids without gas may be formed and consequently it is necessary to test the medium. Joffe and Conn [55] believed that many unwarranted statements have been made about acid formation from sugars. The presence of acid in cultures has been generally attributed to decomposition of sugars and the presence of alkaline compounds to peptone splitting. Working with certain soil bacteria, Joffe and Conn found that they imparted definite changes in media irrespective of glucose fermentation. The appearance of acid is influenced by several factors and should not be attributed entirely to sugar fermentation.

Carbohydrate Solid Media. Liquefiable solid media containing the carbohydrate may be used. The organism should be stabbed into the medium or incorporated in it, just before the medium hardens.

Conn and Hucker [56] have found agar slants to be more useful for determining fermentability of sugars than the old media. One per cent of the sugar is added to the agar the reaction of which is adjusted to pH between 6.8 and 7.2 by brom thymol blue. An indicator whose range lies just to the acid side of pH 7.0, such as china blue or brom cresol purple, is added. The following concentration of indicators was recommended:

Brom cresol purple	0.001 %
Brom cresol purple and cresol red, each	0.0005%
China blue	0.0025%
plus Na salt of rosolic acid	0.005 %

The data in some cases may be secured in a very short time. The method has much in common with Bronfenbrenner and Schlesinger's.

Paraffin Plugged Tubes. The carbohydrate medium may be overlaid with sterile paraffin. When gas is formed, the plug will be forced up away from the surface of the medium. This method was suggested by Beattie [57] when tests were to be made with rare sugars.

Ordinary Culture Tubes. The organisms may be inoculated into an ordinary culture tube without any special device. Gas formation may be determined by watching the tube for rising gas bubbles. They may be more readily observed by tapping the tube.

A method for analyzing the gases formed by bacteria in culture media, was described by Brown. [58]

Bronfenbrenner and Schlesinger's [59] Method for Determining Fermentation of Carbohydrates by Microorganisms. Bronfenbrenner and Schlesinger, realizing the value of early fermentation results, suggested a method for securing results earlier than is possible by the ordinary procedure. They planted each of the suspected colonies (if doing confirmation work with *Escherichia coli*, or sample under study) in an agar drop. They outlined their technique as follows:

"One prepares a medium containing 1.5 per cent of agar, 0.5 per cent of sodium chloride, 1 per cent of peptone; this mixture is brought to boiling and the reaction not adjusted. At this point a suitable quantity of indicator [60] is added, the medium distributed into small tubes containing 1 or 2 cc. of medium in each, autoclaved for 20 minutes at 13 pounds pressure and stored on ice. When needed for use, this medium is melted and 0.1 or 0.2 cc. of 20 per cent lactose solution is added to each tube, thus

55. Joffe and Conn. 1924. Absts. Bact. 4, Abst. No. 44.
56. Conn and Hucker. 1920. J. Bact. 5, 433-435.
57. Beattie. 1916. Brit. Med. J. 1, 756-757.
58. Brown. 1922. J. Exper. Med. 35, 667-684.
59. Bronfenbrenner and Schlesinger. 1918. Amer. J. Pub. Health 8. 922-923.
60. While litmus or any other indicator may be used, we find it especially convenient to use CR indicator, described in the September, 1918, issue of the Journal of Medical Research.

obtaining 2 per cent concentration of the carbohydrate. While hot this lactose agar is deposited in drops by means of a sterile capillary pipette on the inner surface of the bottom of a Petri plate. The drops can be placed very symmetrically and regularly if the outside of the Petri dish is previously marked to show the points at which the drops are to be deposited. Each drop is inoculated with the material from individual suspected colonies, leaving two drops on each plate inoculated to serve as controls of the original color of the medium. When all of the drops are inoculated, one places fresh drops of the same lactose agar over each one of the primary drops, thus securing conditions of slightly lowered oxygen tension, favorable for carbohydrate metabolism of bacteria. . . . . Since CO_2 and some of the other acids produced by bacteria are volatile, the atmosphere of the Petri plate soon becomes saturated with these acids which may partly diffuse into the other drops and affect the color of the agar and so confuse the results. We found it possible to obviate this difficulty by inverting the plate and placing within its cover a circular piece of filter paper soaked in 2 per cent NaOH solution."

These authors regarded this method with favor. They also used a method wherein a sterile concave slide was used to hold the carbohydrate agar. After inoculation, a sterile cover glass was dropped over this.

Lindner's [61] Method for Determining Fermentability of Sugars by Microorganisms. This method is especially applicable to rare expensive sugars which can only be used in small amounts. The fermentation vessel consists of a hollow microscope slide provided with a cover glass. The yeast, or organism, under examination is suspended in sterile yeast-water and a few drops are placed in the hollow of the slide; a small quantity of the sugar to be tested, previously powdered, is then added by means of a flattened platinum rod. The quantity of liquid used must be accurately gauged so as not to leave an air bubble and not to overflow the sides of the hollow when the cover glass is applied. Any slight excess of liquid may be removed by means of sterilized filter paper. The cover is made airtight by means of sterilized vaseline. The slide is kept in the incubator at $25°C.(77°F.)$ overnight and the relative fermentability of the sugar can be judged by the size of the bubble of carbon dioxide which has formed beneath the cover glass by morning. It is simplest and most convenient to perform the experiments in series; testing one organism against a series of different sugars, the slides of each series then afford a certain amount of control over each other. On account of the large excess of yeast, and the short duration of the test, it is not absolutely necessary to sterilize the sugars before use each time. A bubble of carbon dioxide may be distinguished from a bubble of air by placing a drop of caustic alkali on the edge of the cover glass.

Schmidt-Jensen's [62] Method for Determining Fermentation of Carbohydrates by Microorganisms. Schmidt-Jensen worked out a micro method for use with the rarer substances and showed that with inverted tubes it was satisfactory with quantities of half a milligram of the carbohydrate, thus giving 2,000 possible estimations per gram —a quantity 40 times less than that required in the ordinary way. Glass tubing 1.5 mm. in diameter was used, and one end was slightly constricted in the flame. The other end was provided with a cotton plug armed with an insect needle for convenience of handling, or plugged in the ordinary way. The tubes were about 100 mm. long. After dry sterilization, a quantity of broth was sucked in. This was easily controlled by measuring the length of the column of the fluid, 56.5 mm. corresponding to .1 ml. in a 1.5 mm. tube. After the end of the tube was removed from the broth it was sealed, care being taken not to burn the contents, which can be dislodged to the closed end by tapping gently on a table. It was stated that all air bubbles should be made to burst before the tubes are sterilized, during which process they should be protected from moisture by cotton-wool or filter paper. Inoculations were made with a fine wire or with capillary tubes, the tubes being closed by the plugs above mentioned or by means of an outside cotton-wool closure. This is applied by taking a series of tubes (four cm. long and five mm. dia.) containing very loosely-packed cotton wool into which the microculture is *inverted*.

61. Lindner. 1900. Woch. f. Brau. 336.
62. Schmidt-Jensen. 1920. Meddelser f. d. Kgl. Vet. oz. Land.

Schmidt-Jensen also discussed the value of bacterial fermentation tests as a control of chemical purity of carbohydrate preparations. They were able to detect the presence of foreign sugars in those which were thought to be pure.

Stiles and Peterson's[63] Method for Rapid Determination of Sugar in Bacterial Cultures. Stiles and Peterson stated that it was preferable to analyze the culture for its unfermented sugar instead of determining titratable acid, hydrogen ion concentration, or using other indirect means of measuring sugar fermentation. This can be done quickly and accurately by means of the Shaffer-Hartmann micro-method as adapted to bacterial cultures. They described the following technic:

Ten ml. of culture should be placed in a 50-ml. volumetric flask, neutralized with NaOH, clarified with one ml. of lead subacetate (30%) and without removing the precipitate deleaded with three ml. of disodium phosphate (10%) and the volume made to 50 ml. The contents are shaken by inverting; in about three minutes the precipitate has settled and two ml. may be removed without filtration for determination of sugar by the micro-method of Shaffer and Hartmann. The procedure is accurate to within 10-20 mg. per gm. of sugar. If a somewhat less degree of accuracy is sufficient, as is usually the case in determining the question of the fermentability of the sugar, one ml. of culture should be removed with a sterile pipette, neutralized, made to five ml. and the sugar determined without clarification. This modification gives results that are one to two per cent higher than when the culture is clarified.

Hasting's[64] Method for Determining Casein Hydrolysis. Melt and cool some plain agar at 50°C.(122°F.), add 10 per cent of sterile skimmed milk, and pour into sterile Petri dishes. Allow the medium to harden. Streak the culture across the surface of the medium and incubate. Proteolytic action will be indicated by a clear zone immediately about the growth. To make certain that this clear zone is due to proteolysis, flood the plate with dilute acetic acid; if the clear zone remains, it will indicate that it is due to proteolysis.

Conn's[65] Method for Determining Production of Rennin by Bacteria. Conn proposed the following method for determining the production of rennin. Inoculate the pure culture into milk in the usual manner. Incubate for a time sufficient to allow the organism to produce distinct change in the milk with the formation of at least .5 ml. of whey on the surface. At the end of this incubation period secure some fresh, unsterilized milk. Place 10 ml. in a test tube and add .5 ml. of the whey from the milk culture and place in the 37°C.(98.6°F.) incubator. Examine every five minutes for the first half hour and if not curdled then, at less frequent intervals for a few hours longer. With active rennin-producing organisms, the milk will be curdled in a half hour.

Formation of Hydrogen Sufide.

Variable results may be secured in this test, depending on the peptone which is used. Some commercial peptones contain sufficient cystine, as discussed in the chapter on "Media" to give a test for hydrogen sulfide. Others may not, even though the organism is able to produce it. Various procedures have been devised for detecting its formation.

Bibulous Paper Method for Determining Hydrogen Sulfide Formation. A strip of bibulous paper impregnated with lead acetate may be suspended above the plain broth culture. This will be blackened by hydrogen sulfide which rises from the medium. Precautions must be used to maintain sterility and control tubes should be used.

Lead Acetate Agar Method for Determining Hydrogen Sulfide Formation. This method was used by Kligler.[66] The composition of his medium is given in Chapter 26. The lead acetate agar may be slanted or not in the culture tube. The medium will be darkened or blackened along the line of inoculation. Wilson[67] used a ferric chloride

63. Stiles and Peterson. 1926. J. Bact. 11, 79.
64. Hastings. 1904. Centbl. Bakt. II, 12, 590-592.
65. Conn. 1922. J. Bact. 7, 447-448.
66. Kligler. 1917. Amer. J. Pub. Health 7, 1042.
67. Wilson. 1923. J. Hyg. 21, 392-398.

medium in which the iron acted as the indicator of sulfide formation. If desired, any of the media described here may be used in Petri dishes. They may be melted and poured into the dishes and allowed to harden, after which the organisms may be streaked on the surface or the agar may be inoculated and poured into the dish. If the lead acetate agar slant is used, it should be inoculated both on the surface as well as in the butt.

Experiments by Hunter and Crecelius [68] to determine the sensitivity of ferric ammonium citrate and bismuth liquor for detecting hydrogen sulfide definitely showed the superiority of bismuth over iron irrespective of the pH. The most sensitive range of iron was in alkaline menstruum while with bismuth the pH had no effect. The variable factor was the tryptone, not all lots being uniform composition. The bismuth sulfite medium was reported to be superior to any containing lead or iron. Hunter and Crecelius stated that in reporting results of tests on hydrogen sulfide formation, the method used be stated.

FAT DECOMPOSITION

This is an important subject in the food industry. Microorganisms which decompose fats are of interest mainly because of the products which they form. These impart bad odors and flavors to the fats. Two fine reports have been published on this subject by Lea [69] and Jensen and Grettie.[70] The latter covers the microbiology of fat decomposition very satisfactorily.

Early work by Schreiber[71] showed that pure fat is not decomposed by bacteria. Nutrient materials and oxygen were said to be necessary. Cleavage was most rapid when the fat was finely divided as in an emulsion. Experiment by Söhngen [72] and Kraay and Wolff [73] showed the lipolytic abilities of microorganisms to be more common than had been believed. The latter workers showed that lipolytic action of bacteria was somewhat specific. Some split both lecithin and fat while other species split only one. More information of this nature resulted from Seliber's [74] experiments. Such oils as cod-liver and olive oils are utilizable by bacteria. Heukelekian [75] observed that the carbon in these fats could serve bacteria. These oils are typical oils serving as foods and are therefore subject to microbial decomposition. Large amounts were said by Tuason and Shapiro [76] to be oxidized by bacteria in spite of the relative slowness of the process; they observed that 45 per cent of the raw oil introduced into a culture may be oxidized.

Forty pure cultures of bacteria were allowed to act on triolein in experiments by Castell and Garrard.[77] Most of the Gram-negative lipolytic bacteria also oxidized the fat; there appeared to be a definite relation

68. Hunter and Crecelius. 1938. J. Bact. 35, 185.
69. Lea. 1939. Food Invest. Bd., Spec. Rept. No. 46.
70. Jensen and Grettie. 1937. Food Research 2, 97-120.
71. Schreiber. 1902. Arch. Hyg. 41, 328-347.
72. Söhngen. 1910-1911. Rev. in Exp. Sta. Rec. 26, 370-371.
73. Kraay and Wolff. 1923. Proc. Soc. Acad., Amsterdam 26, 436-437.
74. Seliber. 1926. Rev. in Exp. Sta. Rec. 58 (1928), 502; Biol. Absts. 3, 212.
75. Heukelekian. 1929. N. J. Agr. Exp. Sta. Bull. 486, 51-54.
76. Tuason and Shapiro. 1934. Microbiol. 3, 79-87.
77. Castell and Garrard. 1941. Canad. J. Res. 19, 106-110; 111-120.

between the "oxidase reaction" of a bacterial colony and the ability of the organism to produce oxidative rancidity. Lipolytic activity, as indicated by the color reactions of Nile-blue sulfate and methylene blue and blue soap formation with copper sulfate, was shown to coincide with that of the same organism as measured by titratable acidity they produced in larger samples of the oil. Castell and Bryant had shown earlier that color changes in Nile blue sulfate and similar media must be interpreted carefully.

While it is known that fats are susceptible to decomposition by many microorganisms, the above discussion holds mainly when they are added to culture media. They apparently function in about the same manner in natural foods and may be responsible for some of the undesirable changes which are observed. Vickery [78] observed lipolysis of beef fat by one strain of Achromobacter and several of Pseudomonas and asporogenous yeasts. Vickery did not believe, however, that the level of free acidity of beef fat could be used as an index of spoilage occurring in beef fatty tissues. These organisms were capable of growth at low temperatures. Lipolytic activity was said to be distributed in a random fashion among strains of each genus. Hammer and Collins [79] reported lipolytic bacteria to be common in dairy products. They were present in butter which had become rancid and which had been churned from raw cream. Lipolytic bacteria were relatively scarce in fresh butter made from pasteurized cream. This work seemed to show that one type of rancidity in dairy products was caused by lipolytic bacteria.

Several methods have been devised for detecting and estimating the number of lipolytic bacteria in foods. Among the first media for this purpose was Nile-blue sulfate agar in which the fat was dispersed. Butter fat was commonly used in this medium by Hammer and Collins. This medium employs the contrasting pink of unchanged fat and blue of hydrolyzed fat. The differentiation was said to be easy by Long and Hammer,[80] but the toxicity of the dye and the necessary flooding disturbs colonies. They substituted acid-base indicators and copper sulfate for Nile-blue. Demeter [81] reviewed the merits and difficulties encountered in using the more important methods, such as Eijkmann's natural fat, Barry's copper salts, Anderson's tributyrin, and Turner's Nile-blue with Stark and Scheib's modification. Since Nile-blue is markedly toxic to many microorganisms and often indicates spurious lipolysis, owing to production of acid from sources other than fat, Demeter suggested extracts previously fermented by coliform bacteria to remove all traces of carbohydrates, and which might be rich in nitrogenous substances and vitamins. To overcome toxicity of Nile-blue, China blue was suggested as a substitute; the latter allowed some of the fungi to develop which did not develop on Nile-blue but gave less sharp differentiation.

78. Vickery. 1936. J. Council Sci. Ind. Res. 9, 107-112; 196-198.
79. Hammer and Collins. 1934. Iowa Agr. Exp. Sta., Res. Bull. 169.
80. Long and Hammer. 1937. Iowa State Coll. J. Sci. 11, 343-352.
81. Demeter. 1938. Deutsche. Mölkereiztg. 51, 10.

Turner's[82] **Method for Fat Decomposition by Bacteria.** Turner devised a medium which could be used for following bacterial lipolysis in the intestines. Its formula is given in the chapter on "Media." The lipase-producing colony is characterized by a dark blue zone surrounding it in striking contrast to the dull bluish-gray color of the remainder of the plate. The colony, itself, is usually colorless. The zones are usually greater in diameter than the colonies except in those with a marked tendency to spread. When examined under the low power of the microscope, the zone is seen to be made up of tiny blue globules or shapeless masses of the same color. None of the colorless globules of oil seen elsewhere through the plate is observed in the zone. If the colony under study is well separated from others, a faded circular zone two to three mm. wide is observed surrounding the blue zone.

In some cases colonies themselves may take the color. In such cases, it is necessary to distinguish between a blue colony and a blue zone which is usually not difficult. Jensen and Grettie[70] modified Turner's medium. Their modification is given in the chapter on "Media."

Opaqueness in the fat globules surrounding lipolytic colonies in fat-emulsion agar plates is owing, at least in part, according to Castell and Garrard,[83] to rapid formation of fat crystals as well as to formation of fatty acids. The rapidity with which crystals form and their general conformation and texture are capable of considerable variation. This depends on the previous history of the fat, temperature, and the characteristics of the agar medium in which the fat is suspended.

Ammonia Production. Demonstration of formation of ammonia in cultures of bacteria is an unsatisfactory procedure. Formerly it was customary to use Nessler's reagent. The culture was diluted with ammonia-free water and a little Nessler's reagent was added. Presence of a yellowish-green color indicated the presence of ammonia. This method was given up because many uninoculated media gave strong tests for ammonia. The advantages of being able to use a solid medium for determining ammonia caused Hucker and Wall[84] to develop such a method. They prepared a solid medium, the formula for which is given in the chapter on "Media." As a test of ammonia production from organic compounds, one ml. of a 10-per cent phenol and one per cent (available chlorine) sodium hypochlorite solutions are added to the surface of an agar slant after incubation at the optimum temperature. A blue color appears in one-half hour if ammonia is formed.

Hansen's[85] **Method for Detecting Ammonia Production by Bacteria in Agar Slants.** The difficulties encountered in maintaining hypochlorite solutions for the Thomas test for ammonia prompted Hansen* to seek a new reagent. He found that hypobromite solution gave just as good results. The reagent was prepared by adding 25 ml. of 2N sodium hydroxide to 100 ml. of saturated bromine water. The bromine water may be made by adding a sufficient amount of bromine to cold, distilled water in a glass-stoppered bottle. Hansen stated that such solutions are quite uniform—at least suffi-

82. Turner. 1928. Proc. Soc. Exper. Biol. & Med. 25, 318-320; J. Infect. Dis. 44, 126-133.
83. Castell and Garrard. 1940. Canad. J. Res. 18, 158-168.
84. Hucker and Wall. 1922. J. Bact. 7, 515-518.
85. Hansen. 1930. J. Bact. 19, 223-229.

* Hansen's reagents have the following composition:

I.		II.	
Thymol	2 gm.	Bromine water	100 ml.
Sodium hydroxide	10 ml.	Sodium hydroxide	35 ml.
Water	90 ml.		

ciently so for the test. Thymol was used by Hansen in place of phenol as required in the Thomas test.

The test is carried out by adding one mL. of the thymol solution and hypobromite successively to the culture and allowing it to act for 20 minutes. If ammonia is present, the mixture becomes blue or greenish blue.

Nitrate Reduction in Nitrate Broth. The amount of nitrate decomposed readily by an organism may be determined quantitatively by the aluminum-reduction method which is commonly used in water analysis. For qualitative results the presence of nitrites or ammonia in a medium free from these substances before inoculation may be taken as sufficient evidence of nitrate reduction.

The presence of a reductase for nitrates was regarded as an important characteristic by the early workers. The method for conducting the test was considered quite simple. Conn and Breed,[86] however, carried out a thorough investigation which would indicate that the test is not as simple as commonly thought. They pointed out certain sources of error which might be mentioned here: (1) Poor growth; (2) presence of more readily available nitrogen; (3) reduction without accumulation of nitrite. These authors claim that an organism must not be called a non-reducer until exhaustive studies have been made.

The Griess method has been generally used for detecting the presence of nitrite in water, cultures, meat-curing solutions, etc. It is based on the formation of azobenzolnaphthylamin whenever naphthylamin and sulphanilic acid are present in an acid solution of nitrites. It is a delicate test and is considered by some to be too much so for bacteriological work. A control tube should always be made to check the dilution water, etc.

Wallace and Neave[87] stated that fading in the standard nitrite test was caused by an excess of nitrite. The substitution of dimethyl-alpha-naphthylamine for the alpha-compound was reported to give a reagent of high sensitivity and to produce a permanent nitrite color.

As stated above, we are indebted to the investigations of Conn and Breed for better methods for determining nitrate reduction. The test may be run in both liquid and solid media.

Nitrate-Peptone-Agar. Prepare this medium according to the formula in Chapter 26 and slant in culture tubes. Inoculate by streaking the surface in the usual manner and incubate. Test for the presence of nitrite by placing a few drops of the reagent-dimethyl-alpha-naphthylamine on the surface of the slant. The appearance of a red or pink color indicates the presence of nitrite. Always run a sterile control tube.

Nitrate-Peptone-Broth-Method. The nitrate-peptone broth should be sterilized in culture tubes, inoculated with the organism and incubated. At the end of the incubation period, add a few drops of the indicator. Always run a sterile control tube.

Synthetic-Nitrate-Medium Method. The formula for this medium is given in Chapter 26.

Randall and Reedy[88] suggested a simple method for determining bacterial reduction of nitrate. A solution of potassium nitrate is added to a suspension of bacteria cells and, after 15 minutes to one hour, the mixture

86. Conn and Breed. 1919. J. Bact. 4, 267-290.
87. Wallace and Neave. 1927. J. Bact. 14, 377-384.
88. Randall and Reedy. 1939. J. Lab. & Clin. Med. 25, 315-316.

is tested for nitrite. This procedure was used on 24 different species of bacteria and gave complete agreement with the routine method which consisted in inoculating broth containing potassium nitrate with the test culture and testing for the presence of nitrite after incubation.

Pathogenicity to Animals. It is frequently necessary to determine whether bacteria which have been isolated from foods are detrimental to human beings. Bacteriologists, in this case, have to resort to the use of experimental animals. However, data secured with animals must be carefully interpreted. There is possibility for error in applying results secured with animals to human beings. An organism, or its toxin, which is detrimental to animals, might have no such action on human beings. Furthermore, selection of animals which shall be used, is frequently determined by cost as well as by convenience. Guinea pigs, rabbits, mice, chickens, and kittens have been used in many investigations in the field of food bacteriology. Those who wish to study the methods of handling animals should consult the discussion of the subject by Kolmer and Boerner [89] as well as Leaflet VII, The Study of Pathogenic Aerobes, May, 1940, Manual of Methods.

Oral Administration. This method of using animals is perhaps the most useful to the food bacteriologist. Oral administration is the most direct method of studying the toxins of *Clostridium botulinum.* Before conclusions are reached on the poisonous properties of any substance which may be present in foods, it should be fed by mouth. Many data supposed to support the poisonous properties of "ptomaines" were secured by injection experiments and not by feeding. In fact, very few of the compounds which would be classed with ptomaines have been studied by feeding. Conclusions as to their poisonous properties are based almost entirely upon injection experiments.

In a study of the possible toxic effects of putrified foods, Savage used kittens stating that they were more sensitive than other animals to such foods. Guinea pigs have been used in the laboratory for feeding experiments with *Clostridium botulinum.*

Müller [90] claimed that animal feeding should supplement chemical and bacteriological examination of meat. He claimed that the presence or absence of certain poisons in food cannot be determined otherwise than by feeding. Schellhorn [91] reported that not much reliance can be placed on the mouse-feeding method for determining the fitness of meat for consumption. Mice were fed normal meat and many of them died.

Intraperitoneal Injections. These must be made with great care in order not to puncture the intestines. Intraperitoneal injections into such small animals as mice are not easily made. Peritonitis may result if the intestines are entered or the organism which is injected may not produce its effects.

89. Kolmer and Boerner. 1941. Approved Laboratory Technic. D. Appleton-Century Co., New York, N. Y.

90. Müller. 1914. Ztschr. f. Hyg. 16, 115-128.

91. Schellhorn. 1910. Centbl. Bakt. 54, 428-450.

Intravenous Injection. There are injections directly into the circulatory system. They require usually the larger animals. Rabbits are usually injected in the posterior auricular vein in the ear. Roth [92] suggested a convenient method for injecting guinea pigs intravenously.

Subcutaneous Injection. Such injections are made by introducing the substance under study under the skin.

THERMAL DEATH TIME

Data from such determinations must, obviously, be collected under very carefully controlled conditions, else they may not be compared with those secured by others. The Society of American Bacteriologists once recommended that the organism be exposed in nutrient broth for 10 minutes when this medium is adapted to the growing of the organism. Sternberg in the early days proposed sealing the organisms in a tube before exposure to the heat. The Sternberg bulb consisted of a glass bulb with the neck tapering down to a fine bore, the neck being at right angles to the bulb. To fill it, the bulb was gently heated, after which the tip was immersed into the culture of which the thermal death time was to be determined. As the bulb cooled, some of the culture was drawn into it. The neck was then sealed in the flame. The bulbs were suspended by a wire in a water or oil bath, the temperature of which was raised periodically. Eijkmann [93] pointed out that such treatment might so devitalize the cells that they would be slow to reproduce. Brown and Peiser [94] and others have used other methods.

Results of thermal death-time determinations are influenced by many factors some of which have been discussed in the chapter on "Canning." Magoon [95] and many others have pointed out that heat resistance of spores is not a fixed property but subject to many variables. Dickson *et al.*[96] observed marked variations in heat resistance of spores of *Clostridium botulinum.* Consideration of results on this subject found in many publications tempts one to wonder just how far thermal death-time results should be accepted. They probably hold only for the exact conditions under which they were determined. The most difficult controlled element and one impossible of exact duplication is the spore itself. Variations in thermal death-time which have been attributed to certain factors, such as salt, may have been due to variable resistance of the spores in the suspension.

The following are said to affect the heat resistance of bacterial spore suspensions:

1. *Nutritional Status of the Organism.* Spores produced in various media have been shown to possess quite different resistances to heat. Williams [97] produced spores of *Bacillus subtilis* under a wide variety of nutritive and environmental conditions and exposed them to high temperatures. The strain which he used gave a basic resistance

92. Roth. 1921. J. Bact. 6, 249-252.
93. Eijkmann. 1909. Centbl. Bakt., Pt. 2, 22, 508-509.
94. Brown and Peiser. 1916. Mich. Agr. Exp. Sta. Tech. Bull. 30.
95. Magoon. 1926. J. Bact. 11, 253-283.
96. Dickson *et al.* 1922. J. Amer. Med. Assoc. 79, 1239.
97. Williams. 1929. J. Infect. Diseases 44, 421-465.

of six minutes at 105°C.(221°F.), 14 minutes at 100°C.(212°F.), and 35 minutes at 95°C.(203°F.). By changing the nutritive substrate, the heat resistance of the spores was changed. The type but not the concentration of peptone used in the medium was important. Spores of greater heat resistance were secured from casein digest medium. The higher the incubation temperature, the greater was the resistance to heat. Other factors were also mentioned as causes of changes in heat resistance. Another investigation which brought out the effect of the medium was that by Sommer [98] with spores of *Clostridium botulinum.* The details of this work need not be presented here but they show that the nutritive condition of the organism is very important. Spores of *Clostridium botulinum* grown in four per cent peptone showed resistance of one and one-half to two and one-half hours. Addition of phosphate raised the heat resistance to four hours.

Curran and Evans [99] observed that spores which had been exposed to ultraviolet light were sensitive to heat. Ultraviolet rays of wave lengths longer than 2000 Å under suitable conditions sensitize spores to heat. Angerer [100] also reported evidence that various treatment of spores altered their heat resistance. Defatting bacterial spores, for instance, decreased their resistance. Other agents either decreased or increased heat resistance. One cannot help but wonder whether they were due to the agents and conditions imposed on the spores or to unavoidable variations in the experiments.

2. *The Particular Strain Studied.* No two strains of bacteria are just alike. Results collected with just one strain do not necessarily represent others. This was noticed by Dickson *et al.*[96] who studied the resistance of 40 strains at 100°C.(212°F.). These varied in resistance from 30 minutes to six hours. A very heat resistance strain was studied by Esty and Meyer.[104] They reported the following heat resistances for its spores under artificial but favorable conditions when heated in phosphate solution at pH 7.0.

4 minutes at 120°C.(248°F.)
10 minutes at 115°C.(239°F.)
32 minutes at 110°C.(230°F.)
100 minutes at 105°C.(221°F.)
330 minutes at 100°C.(212°F.)

While these resistances of *Clostridium botulinum* to heat are widely quoted and used in calculations for canned food processes the author is not aware that they have been secured by other investigators since. Especially is this true for the resistance of 330 minutes at 100°C.(212°F.). The strain and spore suspension used by Esty and Meyer was undoubtedly much more resistant to heat than strains now used in experimental work.

3. *Reaction of the Menstruum in Which Spores Are Heated.* This is an important factor in the food-preservation industry. Microorganisms are much more easily killed by heat in an acid than in an alkaline solution. Weiss [101] observed lowered heat resistance with spores of *Clostridium botulinum* in the presence of acid ions. The greatest resistance to killing by heat occurred close to the neutral point; as the hydrogen-ion concentration increased a rapid reduction in that resistance resulted. This was emphasized in a practical manner in Weiss' [101] second paper in which the effect of pH of foods on heat resistance of spores of the above organism, was shown. In acid foods, such as egg plums, the spores survived only about 10 minutes, whereas in foods pH of which was on the alkaline side of the neutral point, about 170 minutes were required (lima beans, pH 5.7).

Murray [102] found that the greatest heat resistance of spores of *Bacillus anthracis* was shown in all cases at pH 8. While much of the work on this subject has been done with microorganisms in food products, results with other materials are confirmatory. Increase in acidity made it easier for Sabalitschka and Maas [103] to sterilize soil. The

98. Sommer. 1930. J. Infect. Diseases 46, 85-114.
99. Curran and Evans. 1938. J. Bact. 36, 455-465.
100. Angerer. 1938. Arch. Hyg. 121, 12-55.
101. Weiss. 1921. J. Infect. Diseases 28, 70-92; 29, 362-368.
102. Murray. 1931. Idem 48, 436-467.
103. Sabalitschka and Maas. 1939. Suddtsch. Apothekarztg. 79, 244.

subject was studied by Weiss [101] from the standpoint of various canned foods. The hydrogen-ion concentration of the food was observed to be very important. *Clostridium botulinum* in more acid foods was destroyed much more easily than in alkaline. According to Dickson *et al.*[96] spores propagated in a neutral medium showed greater heat resistance than those from acid or alkaline media.

4. *Concentration of Organisms or Spores.* This is another important factor. It is reasonable that it would require more drastic treatment, either more heat, a longer time, or both, to destroy many cells than a few. This is important in food preservation, for it is the basis for efforts to keep bacterial loads of foods to be processed by heat, low.

About everyone who has worked on heat resistance has found this to be the case. Weiss [101] observed it with *Clostridium botulinum.* Convincing evidence on this point was published by Esty and Meyer [104] from experiments with *Clostridium botulinum.*

5. *Age of Spores.* This has been found by many to influence heat resistance of suspensions. Weiss [101] found that young moist spores of *Clostridium botulinum* had a greater heat resistance than old moist spores. Spores one month old were found to be three times as resistant as spores five months old. A general decrease in resistance was believed to occur as the spores age. The more resistant individuals changed more rapidly than the less resistant. Esty and Meyer [104] stated that young moist spores, probably those of the first generation, were most heat resistant. They worked with spores of *Clostridium botulinum.* Magoon [105] used an aerobic spore forming organism *Bacillus mycoides.* The heat resistance became greater for about 30 days, was constant for a second 30-day period and then gradually fell off. There was some fluctuation in resistance which might have been due to technic.

Dickson and his colleagues [96] also noticed considerable variation in heat resistance among spores of the same culture of the same strain. About 95 per cent of the spores were destroyed in relatively short time but among the remaining five per cent were some highly resistant spores. Spores from old cultures were observed to be more resistant than from young cultures.

Heat resistance of non-spore-forming bacteria is also influenced by age of the cells. Robertson [106] observed that young, rapidly growing, or adolescent, cells are more susceptible than older, mature cells to destruction by high temperatures. He used three heat-resistant species, *Microbacterium lacticum, Sarcina lutea,* and *Streptococcus thermophilus.* Stark and Stark [107] also found that young cells of *Streptococcus fecalis* and two species of encapsulated bacteria were markedly less resistant to heat.

6. *Presence of Salt.* This would be expected to affect heat resistance. The subject is of interest because several foods are salted before they are heated to preserve them. The results of observations on it, however, are not always in agreement. This may be due to the fact that different species were used as well as to conditions which obtained in the experiments. Weiss,[101] working with *Clostridium botulinum,* stated that presence of salt materially lowered the heat resistance, the rate of lowering being proportional to the amount of salt. Viljoen,[108] on the other hand, observed that salt up to four per cent concentration protected spores of canned food spoilage bacteria in pea liquor.

7. *Influence of Sugar.* Microorganisms are more difficultly destroyed by heat in sirups or in the presence of sugar. This seems to be the case with practically all of the bacteria which have been used. Weiss [101] observed it with spores of *Clostridium botulinum.* The heavier the sirup, the longer was the time required to kill the spores. About the same conclusions were reached by Fay [109] in studies on pasteurization of ice cream mix. Addition of sugar made it more difficult to destroy microorganisms.

These observations are based on alterations in the environment of the cells which make it harder to destroy the cells rather than to make any change in the cell itself. Slower heating of heavy sirups may be the best explanation.

104. Esty and Meyer. 1922. J. Infect. Diseases 31, 650-663.
105. Magoon. 1926. J. Bact. 11, 253-283.
106. Robertson. 1928. J. Bact. 15, 27.
107. Stark and Stark. 1929. Idem 18, 333-337.
108. Viljoen. 1926. J. Infect. Diseases 39, 286-290.
109. Fay. 1934. J. Agr. Res. 48, 453-468.

Baumgartner and Wallace [110] also observed a protective effect of sugars when microorganisms are heated. Concentrations of sucrose up to 50 per cent had no effect on heat resistance of spores in either acid or alkaline solutions. These investigators attributed this to a resistant spore envelope. With nonsporulating organisms, such as *Escherichia coli*, a minimum concentration of 10 per cent of sucrose protected the cells. This phenomenon is apparently not restricted to bacteira, for Rahn [111] and Peterson and Levine [112] observed it with yeasts. Baumgartner and Wallace, however, did not observe it with strains of Torula heated in varying sugar concentrations in neutral media.

The practical significance of this matter was shown by Braun [113] in studies on "dry sweetening" of nonacid canned foods. In contrast with the conventional method of adding sugar in the form of a syrup, some canners have attempted to add dry sugar to the empty container before the food product was added. The assumption was that the sugar would dissolve and distribute itself throughout the can. When spoilage occurred, it was found that the sugar had layered in the can and caused an average decrease of 32 per cent in the thermal effect of the sterilizing process of 70 minutes at 116°C.(240°F.). This decrease in sterilizing efficiency was caused by the fact that at one place in the can there was a heavy syrup where the sugar had not completely dissolved.

8. *Influence of Fat on Heat Resistance.* While too little information is available to permit general conclusions, it is generally believed that microorganisms in fat are protected from the action of heat. This, if it is true, may be due to actual inhibition of penetration of heat through the fat, or to the absence of moisture. This position was defended by Rogacheva [114] who worked with common aerobic sporeforming bacteria of the subtilis-mesentericus type. He believed that the anhydrous condition of fats and oils explained survival of microorganisms in them when subjected to heat. Spores survived only when the fats were free from moisture.

Dried Spores. Water has generally been considered necessary for destruction of bacteria. This has been borne out in the food industry in the few investigations which have been completed on the subject. Cameron, Yesair, and Williams [115] observed destruction of streptococci in 305 minutes at 55°C.(131°F.) in the moist condition, but an exposure of 230 minutes at 110°C.(230°F.) was required when they were heated in the dry state. Similar results were secured with putrefactive anaerobes and thermophilic bacteria. Spores were also found to be more resistant in oil free from moisture than in the same oil with moisture. Similar results were observed in general by Murray [102] with *Bacillus anthracis, Clostridium tetani,* and *Clostridium welchii.* Absence of moisture made it necessary to heat the spores at higher temperatures for destruction. These data may be important in those food-preservation industries in which fats or oils are heated for preservation. In experiments of Sommer [98] with spores of *Clostridium botulinum,* drying on sand had little effect on their resistance to heat. Esty and Meyer [104] also observed no change in heat resistance of the same spores during storage in the dry state.

Oag [116] found that spores of various virulent strains of *Bacillus anthracis, Bacillus welchii, Vibrion septique,* and *Bacterium anthracoides*

110. Baumgartner and Wallace. 1934. J. Soc. Chem. Ind. 53, 297.
111. Rahn. 1928. The Canning Age 9, 705-706.
112. Peterson and Levine. 1927. Iowa State Coll. J. Sci. 2, 31-41.
113. Braun. 1941. The Canner. Conv. number, Feb. 22, 1941.
114. Rogacheva. 1939. Rev. in Chem. Absts. 34, 21.
115. Cameron, Yesair, and Williams. 1934. Canning Trade 56, 30-32.
116. Oag. 1940. J. Path. & Bact. 51, 137-141.

require an exposure to 400°C.(752°F.) (dry heat) for 20 to 30 seconds before they are killed. At lower temperatures, longer exposures are necessary. By constructing a graph it seems probable that these spores may withstand even higher temperatures for a few seconds.

Two and one-half hours' heating were required in a hot-air oven for destruction of *Bacillus subtilis* (Barkworth[117]). Within 30 minutes a temperature of 160°C.(320°F.) was reached in the interior of vessels being sterilized, while 200°C.(392°F.) was recorded on a thermometer in the oven.

Heat Resistance of Nonsporeforming Bacteria. Nonsporeforming bacteria are generally considered to possess little resistance to heat. Much of the work on these bacteria is open to criticism because of the fact that quantitative data were not collected and the heating times were not properly spaced. More recently it has been found that more knowledge of the heat resistance of nonsporeforming microorganisms is necessary in preservation industries which involve acid foods. Baker and McClung[118] pointed out some of the points of technic which should be observed. Their work was done with *Escherichia coli*. Its thermal death-time at 57.3°C. (135°F.) was between 20 and 30 minutes. Working with an initial concentration of five to 10 million cells in broth at pH 7.05 Beamer and Tanner[119] found the following times in minutes necessary to sterilize the suspension:

	55°C.(131°F.)	65°C.(149°F.)	60°C.(140°F.)
Eberthella typhosa	23.8 min.	8.9 min.	4.3 min.
Salmonella paratyphi		8.9 min.	4.3 min.
Salmonella schottmülleri		18.8 min.	13.8 min.
Salmonella typhi-murium	23.8 min.	13.8 min.	
Salmonella enterilidis		23.8 min.	13.8 min.
Staphylococcus aureus			18.8 min.

In the brewing industry nonsporeforming microorganisms must be killed by heat. Epstein and Snell[120] who worked with both yeasts and bacteria reported that the heat resistance of *Lactobacillus pedicoccus (sarcinae)* and *Acetobacter* decreases, all being killed in 10 minutes at 60°C.(140°F.). Of the yeasts examined, the same order of heat resistance was observed for *Saccharomyces pastorianus*, *S. ellipsiodeus*, and brewers' culture yeasts, *Mycoderma* and *Torula*. Excepting the first two all were killed within five minutes at 54°C.(129.2°F.) and within 10 minutes at 52°C.(125.6°F.). The two first named yeasts required five minutes at 66°C. (150.8°F.) for destruction. Yeast spores were killed within 20 minutes at 58°C.(136.4°F.) and within 15 minutes at 60°C.(140°F.).

METHODS FOR THERMAL DEATH-TIME DETERMINATION

Most of these methods have been developed in the canned food field because it is so necessary to know heat resistance of various microorgan-

117. Barkworth 1939. J. Southeastern Agr. Coll. Wye, 100-102.
118. Baker and McClung. 1939. Food Research 4, 21-29.
119. Beamer and Tanner. 1939. Zentbl. Bakt., Pt. 2, 100, 81-98; 200-211.
120. Epstein and Snell. 1940. J. Inst. Brewing 37, 175-178.

isms. Recently, greater efforts have been made to heat the organisms in the food itself or in an extract. Even the latter along with phosphate solutions, presents conditions quite different from those which exist in the food itself. Ball [121] classified heat-resistance test methods as follows:

"(1) Heating microorganisms in a highly buffered, nonnutrient, aqueous solution and then *subculturing* in a nutrient medium to determine whether or not any microorganisms remained viable through the heating treatment;

"(2) Heating microorganisms in a highly buffered, nonnutrient, aqueous solution and then *plating* in a mixture of agar and broth to permit counting of the viable organisms remaining after the heating treatment;

"(3) Heating microorganisms in the food under investigation, and then incubating *without transferring* the microorganisms from this material, so that growth of the organisms that remained viable through the heating treatment will occur.

"(4) Heating microorganisms in the food under investigation, and then *plating* in a mixture of agar and broth to permit counting the viable organisms remaining after the heating treatment."

Bigelow and Esty's [122] Method for Determining Thermal Death Time. Thermal death point in relation to time was defined as the time necessary to destroy a known number of spores at each of several temperatures. The organisms studied are isolated from the foods (usually canned foods spoiled on account of understerilization). The temperatures used are from $100°C.(212°F.)$ to $125°C.(257°F.)$ at intervals of five degrees. The medium used is the juice expressed from canned peas, corn, spinach, pumpkin, string beans, lima beans, baked beans, beets, or milk. A De Khotinsky electric bath with a thermo-regulator attachment is used, containing Crisco instead of water; the temperature is kept uniform throughout the bath by means of a turbine stirrer. A steam-heated bank of cells [123] may also be used in laboratories where such apparatus is available.

Cultures of the organism to be tested are grown on nutrient agar slants until a luxuriant growth occurs along the inoculated area (about 48 hours). This growth is then inoculated into nutrient broth of pH 7.0 and incubated at the optimum temperature of that specific organism for one week. One ml. of this suspension is inoculated into 10 ml. of the medium to be used and heated to $85°C.(185°F.)$ for 15 minutes to kill all vegetative forms. Special culture tubes, 7 mm. (inside diam.) x 250 mm. long (or 125 mm. if desired) and 1 mm. thickness of wall, are sterilized and inoculated with a suspension of spores of the organism under study.

The tubes are sealed off to within two inches of the surface of the liquid, placed in a Wasserman rack, and held temporarily in an ice bath until heated. The rack of sealed tubes is transferred to the oil bath, adjusted to the desired temperature, and subjected to this temperature for different lengths of time. Upon removal from the bath the tubes are cooled in ice water and held in an ice box until determinations can be made on the sterility of these cultures after heating. The initial count should be made according to Standard Methods, and the hydrogen-ion concentration of the medium should be determined.

This method usually shows the presence of "skips" when a single series of tubes is run. Esty suggests that large number of tubes, at least 25, be heated at four different times.

Hastings, Fred, and Carroll [124] believed that the "skips and stops" recorded by different investigators in thermal death-time work were due to imperfections in technic, such as uneven suspensions of cells, contamination, or the selection of an unsuitable

121. Ball. 1942. Ind. and Eng. Chem. 35, 71-84.

122. Bigelow and Esty. 1920. J. Infect. Diseases 27, 602-617.

123. This is a series of six or eight steam-heated brass cylinders about 10 inches high and eight inches in diameter. They may be tightly closed. The sealed thermal death-time tubes are placed in them and heated under pressure. This permits heating a considerable number of tubes in a shorter time.

124. Hastings, Fred, and Carroll. 1926. Centbl. Bakt. II, 67, 162-166.

medium into which the heated cells are placed. They believed that these inconsistencies could be overcome by a general improvement in technic. Williams [125] also used a modification of this technic when studying the resistance of the spores of *Bacillus subtilis* to heat.

Esty and Williams [126] Method for Determining Heat Resistance of Bacterial Spores. Esty and Williams encountered "skips" in thermal death-time work and reported a modification of the Bigelow and Esty technic designed to avoid them. They introduced what is called the "multiple tube method." In this method different numbers of tubes containing the same suspension are heated for different times within the range of "skips." They advised the use of great care to avoid the presence of clumps of spores. On account of the important place which this technic has had in applied bacteriology, their description is quoted below verbatim. While their description involves the use of a thermophilic spoilage organism, it may be applied to any organism.

"Several Kolle flasks containing nutrient agar were each inoculated with two ml. of a stock spore suspension of a pure culture of the organism to be tested (in this case, organism 1518). If no stock spore suspension was available, growth from two or more agar slants was suspended in a small amount of sterile distilled water and the resulting suspension used as the inoculum. This suspension was distributed uniformly over the surface of the agar in the Kolle flasks and incubated under optimum conditions (55°C.) for 48 hours. At the end of this incubation period, the bacterial growth in each flask was washed off by the addition of a little sterile water, and the suspension was removed to a sterile flask. Care was taken not to cut the agar and mix any fragments with the bacterial suspension. This resulting suspension was thoroughly shaken and placed again at 55°C. for another 24 hours. Smears from 48-hour cultures showed numerous vegetative organisms and some spores, while stained preparations after the second incubation showed an abundance of spores and fewer vegetative cells. This final suspension was again thoroughly shaken, filtered through a heavy layer of sterile cotton, heated to 90°C. for 10 minutes, to kill the vegetative forms, and again shaken. The suspension was then counted and placed in sterile ampules, which were sealed, and held at ice-box temperature as the stock on which the heat-resistance tests were made. If the suspension was not sufficiently concentrated, it was centrifuged, the supernatant liquid decanted and the spore sediment resuspended and made up to the desired concentration. In some cases, a sand filter was also used and the suspension shaken with sterile sand or glass beads. Plate counts made in triplicate according to standard methods on different suspensions that had received both the above treatment and that filtered through cotton alone showed uniform results without any evidence of clumps. Furthermore, heat-resistance tests on these suspensions prepared by the different methods of filtering showed no indication of variation in this respect.

"After vigorous shaking of the spore suspension in the sealed ampule, the tube was opened aseptically, and definite amounts were inoculated into solutions of different chemical composition, such as M/15 phosphate solution of different pH values (Sorension mixture of Na_2HPO_4), nutrient broth, pH about 7, and certain food juices, notably canned corn and peas. The concentration of the spores in these solutions was so adjusted that only one or two ml. of the stock spore suspension was added to each 100 ml. of the solution to be heated. In this way the inoculum did not affect the composition of these solutions appreciably nor was the pH value altered. The results thus obtained apply to the conditions under which the spores were heated. After thoroughly shaking, one ml. of these suspensions was inoculated into sterile tubes similar to those used formerly, immediately sealed and heated as usual. The inoculation of these tubes was made from a sterile 10 ml. pipet graduated to .1 ml., and the sealed tubes were held in ice water until heated. The heating of the cultures was carried out as described in the other method. The temperature readings were taken from a Beckmann thermometer and the heat controlled by means of a Sligh thermoregulator. The temperature was kept uniform by means of a turbine stirrer and constant movement of the

125. Williams. 1929. J. Infect. Diseases 44, 421-465.
126. Esty and Williams. 1924. J. Infect. Diseases 34, 516-528.

tubes by hand. Cultures in phosphate solutions were always subcultivated. In the other cases the heated solutions served as culture medium for growth; accordingly, whenever possible the sealed tubes were incubated and growth observed by turbidity and confirmed by production of acid.

"Growth is confirmed by acid production which is determined either by adding two ml. of the stock brom-cresol purple indicator (.4 per cent) to each 100 ml. of the solution containing the spores in which they can grow at the time the solution is inoculated or by emptying the heated contents of the tube after sufficient incubation into .4 per cent of the indicator solution. Subcultures from the phosphate solutions were made in dextrose broth pH 7, to which had been added .4 per cent of brom-cresol purple indicator.

"The addition of this indicator to the solution to be heated does not appear to inhibit the development of viable organisms but it does affect slightly the hydrogen-ion concentration of the solution and the heat resistance. This phase will be discussed further in a subsequent paper. In view of the fact that material in which spores of this organism have grown and produced acid may show no viable organisms after the third day of incubation, and after the fourth day consistently no growth, making recovery of this organism impossible, it is essential that some criterion be found to determine whether or not growth did occur. On this basis, heated cultures of acid-producing organisms should be tested for acid production by using brom-cresol purple indicator either in the medium used for subculturing or by emptying the contents into this indicator solution after sufficient incubation. These methods give clear-cut results and afford an easy means for determining the growth of this organism."

Dickson and Burke's [127] Method for Determining the Thermal Death Time of Spores of Clostridium botulinum. As a result of the difficulty in preventing spoilage of a small percentage of tubes in the method for determining thermal death time recommended by Bigelow and Esty, a method was devised which was said to eliminate all possibility of contamination of the contents of the tubes after they have been subjected to the required amount of heat. The technic is as follows:

"Three ml. of a one per cent glucose peptic digest liver broth adjusted to a final pH of 7.3 to 7.5 is placed in a soft glass tube 10 by 150 mm., and covered with a thin layer of oil [128] to prevent evaporation. The medium is sterilized at 15 lb. pressure for 30 minutes. Immediately before inoculation the tubes of broth are exposed to live steam for 20 minutes to expel the air, and a known number of spores is then added to each tube in .5 ml. of the medium in which they have grown. The tubes are then sealed in an oxygen flame and are ready for heating by immersion in racks into oil which is maintained at the required temperature and vigorously agitated. At the end of the heating period the tubes are removed from the oil, placed in deep pans of cold water to cool, immediately labelled, and then incubated at 37°C. (98.6°F.).

"Incubation is continued for at least 10 days after growth is recognized, in order to allow time for the formation of toxin. The tubes are then opened under sterile conditions, deep agar, broth, and meat mediums are inoculated, and guinea pigs are immediately injected. No test is considered positive unless the broth culture within the sealed tube contains a virulent botulinus toxin at the time the tube is broken."

Magoon's [129] Method for Determining the Thermal Death Time of Bacterial Spores. Magoon's method involved the use of capillary tubing. On account of the work by Esty and Cathcart,[130] showing that soft glass tubes might yield sufficient alkali to affect the results, "Pyrex" tubing was used. Tubing with an internal diameter of four mm. was drawn out to capillaries of one to 1.5 mm. internal diameter; these were cut into lengths of nine to 10 cm. and the ends sealed immediately in the flame in order to

127. Dickson and Burke. 1921. Proc. Soc. Exper. Biol. & Med. 19, 99-100.

128. Recent work in the field of food bacteriology indicates that oil may have a protective action on bacterial spores when they are exposed to heat. This fact should be borne in mind when this technic is followed. Until more is known about the survival of microorganisms heated in oil, perhaps the oil should not be added.

129. Magoon. 1926. J. Infect. Diseases 38, 429-439.

130. Esty and Cathcart. 1921. J. Infect. Diseases 29, 29-39.

keep the interior sterile. The tubes were kept in a glass stender dish in alcohol. As each was needed, it was picked out with freshly flamed forceps, the alcohol burned off to sterilize the outside, and the sealed tips clipped off by means of a special instrument freshly sterilized in the flame. One end of the tube is then dipped into the spore suspension which rises in the tube by capillary attraction. When sufficient liquid has been taken into the tube, it may be centered so as to leave a free space at each end. The ends of the tube may then be sealed. As soon as the ends are tipped, drop the sealed tubes into cold potassium dichromate-sulfuric acid cleaning solution and let them stand for a few minutes in order to destroy any spores which may adhere to the outside of the tubes. The tubes should be kept cold to prevent the germination of the spores.

To make the test, Magoon heated five of the suspension charged tubes in an electrically controlled oil bath. At the end of the exposure, the tubes should be placed in fresh acetone to dissolve the oil. They may then be stored in alcohol until inoculations are made into nutrient media.

The sterility tests are made by breaking the sterilized capillary tube in the medium. Magoon described his technic for this as follows: The capillary tubes were withdrawn from the alcohol with sterile forceps; without flaming, one sealed tip was removed with a freshly flamed clipper. The open end is then inverted over the mouth of the culture tube from which the cotton plug has been removed and the upper tip of the capillary snipped off. At the same instant the capillary tube is dropped into the culture tube. These simple operations must be rapidly performed.

Williams, Merrill, and Cameron's [131] Apparatus for Determination of Spore-Destruction Rates.

This apparatus was developed to yield information on destruction rates rather than absolute death times. It permits heating under pressure of a mass suspension of spores in almost any menstruum and withdrawal of test samples without disturbing the heating test. Anyone familiar with the older methods will recognize the advantages of the new apparatus. The early predictions of those who developed the method have been fully justified by results over recent years. They have been able to obtain reproducible destruction-rate curves and satisfactory thermal death-time curves.

THE THERMAL DEATH-TIME CURVE

For some time canning technologists and others who have had to study heat resistance of bacterial cells and spore suspensions, have plotted the data secured on semilogarithmic paper to secure what is called a thermal death-time curve. No attempt will be made here to show the development of this procedure for it may be found in the literature, especially in papers of Bigelow and Esty,[132] Ball,[133] and Townsend, Esty, and Baselt.[134]

The thermal death-time curve approximates a straight line on semilogarithmic paper. From Ball's [133] work and much other work since then which has been based on it, two factors have resulted which mathematically describe the thermal death-time curve. They were described by Townsend et al.[134] as follows:

F—The number of minutes required to destroy the organism (in any specific medium) at 121.1°C.(250°F.).

131. Williams, Merrill, and Cameron. 1937. Food Research 2, 369-375.

132. Bigelow and Esty. 1920. J. Infect. Diseases 27, 602.

133. Ball. 1927. The Canner, Jan. 22, 1927; Univ. Cal. Pub. in Pub. Health 1 (1928), No. 2; 1923. Nat. Res. Council Bull. 37.

134. Townsend, Esty, and Baselt. 1938. Food Research 3, 323-346.

It is obvious that the value of F will depend on the food.

z—The slope of the thermal death-time curve expressed as degrees F. (This is the interval in temperature required for the line to pass through one log cycle on semilogarithmic paper.)

This is an important value and for process calculations of nonacid foods, excepting milk, has generally been given a value of 18. They should be identical for each food but will vary with the food under study. Town-

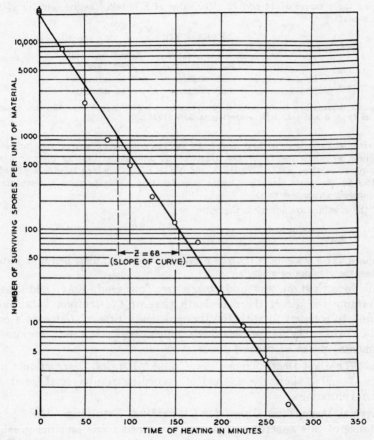

FIG. 1. Ideal Thermal Death Time Curve for *Clostridium botulinum*. (After Ball.[121])

send, Esty, and Baselt [134] corrected the z value for the ideal thermal death-time curve to 17.6. This value for z has generally been used for calculating processes for all nonacid foods, with the exception of milk. Competent bacteriologists, however, familiar with the various factors which influence thermal death times, know that it would vary for each food and even for some of the conditions under which it was heated. It is, therefore, recognized that this value should be determined for each food.

Townsend, Esty, and Baselt [134] discussed this as follows:

"These two factors, being a point and a slope, determine the thermal death-time curve precisely. The value of F is the thermal death time at 250°F. and, when the z values are identical, is used to compare the resistance of organisms. If the z values are not identical, however, this comparison is invalid, since the ratio of the resistance will vary throughout the temperature range. The z value measures the change in thermal death time with changing temperature. As the z value diminishes, the effect of temperature change becomes more marked.

"This can be seen in the following processes calculated for the same can of food, comparing the z values of 14 and 22. The value of F is taken as five minutes (250°F.) in both cases:

PROCESS TIME

z	Retort temperature 121.1°C.(250°F.)	Retort temperature 110°C.(230°F.)
14	5.11 minutes	138 minutes
22	5.47 minutes	44 minutes

The can temperature at the start of the process was 65.6°C.(150°F.). The heat-penetration factors are fh = 3 and j = 1.20, according to Ball (1928).[133]

"Owing to variations in heat resistance of suspensions of spores and influence of the medium upon this resistance, the practice was adopted of heating them in a standard phosphate solution (M/15 Na_2HPO_4 and M/15 KH_2PO_4 mixed to give a pH of 7.0) as well as in the particular food under consideration. This permits a comparison of suspensions on a common basis.

"If the z values are identical the ratio

$$\frac{\text{Resistance in food}}{\text{Resistance in standard phosphate}}$$

may be used. This is known as the food phosphate factor and, while useful, is justifiable only when the z values coincide."

This investigation was undertaken by Townsend, Esty, and Baselt[134] to determine the direct thermal death time of Clostridium botulinum in foods and to compare it with the thermal death time of Cameron's organism No. 3679. The latter has been much used as a test organism in experimental packs of canned foods.

The "Thermal Death Time Curve" and "Rate of Destruction Curve" in Figs. 1 and 2 show the method of recording results of thermal death time determinations.

Thermal Death-Time Curve for Clostridium Botulinum. Owing to the importance of this anaerobic organism to canned foods and the great heat resistance of its spores much attention has been given to the effect of processing on it. Townsend, Esty, and Baselt [134] conducted an investigation to determine direct thermal death-time data on Clostridium botulinum in various foods and to compare Cameron's organism No. 3679 with it as far as heat resistance is concerned. The latter organism is almost identical with Clostridium botulinum, type C. with exception of formation of toxin. Consequently, it is often used in experimental work where the former cannot be used.

Esty and Meyer [104] were among the first to report extensive data on the heat resistance of spores of Clostridium botulinum. One important observation was that the heat resistance of spores of this organism varied considerably—even spores from the same strain. While some of the factors are known, Esty and Meyer suggested that others were unknown. Heat resistance of spores of *Clostridium botulinum* in 17 varieties of canned food juices showed a variation from less than 10 minutes to 230 minutes at 100°C.(212°F.). The importance of using the right medium for spore production was brought out in this investigation. Esty and Meyer reported that spores generated in different flasks of the same medium but prepared

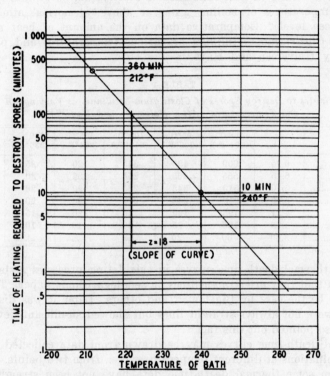

FIG. 2. Rate of Destruction Curve for Organism 1518 (Flat Sour Producing Organism in Non-Acid Canned Foods). Temperature of Heating 104.4°C.(220°F.). (After Ball.[121])

and handled in exactly the same manner may produce spores with striking differences in heat resistance.

Townsend, Esty, and Baselt[134] made their observation on suspensions of spores of two strains of *Clostridium botulinum*. They found the heat resistance of this organism in canned foods to be different from that in neutral phosphate. The z values in food media were said to lie in the range 13.4 to 15.6 as contrasted with the range 16.5 to 18.0 in neutral phosphate. The heat resistance of Cameron's organism No. 3679* were

* These numbers refer to certain spoilage microorganisms which have been used in the field of canned food technology. They are described in Chapter 23.

found to be unlike those of *Clostridium botulinum* in food media but are nearly similar in neutral phosphate. The *z* values of No. 3679 are higher in food media than the *z* values of *Clostridium botulinum*. Townsend, Esty, and Baselt [134] confirmed the work of Esty and Meyer [104] on heat resistance of *Clostridium botulinum* referred to above. They corrected the factors for the ideal thermal death-time curve of *Clostridium botulinum* in neutral phosphate, as determined by Esty and Meyer,[104] to $F = 2.45$ and $z = 17.6$.

Most of the work on heat resistance of *Clostridium botulinum* has been done at temperatures of boiling water or above, at normal atmospheric pressure (sea level). Comparative data on the amount of heat required to destroy *Clostridium botulinum* at various temperatures and pH were reported by Halversen and Hays.[135]

TABLE 1

Time in Minutes to Destroy Spores of Clostridium botulinum at Varying pH Values and Temperatures (After Halversen and Hays [135])

Foods	pH	90°C. (194°F.)	95°C. (203°F.)	100°C. (212°F.)	105°C. (221°F.)	110°C. (230°F.)	115°C. (239°F.)
Hominy	6.95	600	495	345	120	35	10
Corn	6.45	555	465	255	105	30	15
Spinach	5.10	510	345	225	90	20	10
String beans	5.10	510	345	225	90	20	10
Pumpkin	4.21	195	120	45	20	15	10
Pears	3.75	135	75	30	10	10	5
Prunes	3.60	60	20	....	....	....	....

Use of thermal death-time curves in calculating processes rests on the assumption that they are straight lines on semilogarithmic paper. This was believed to be the case by Bigelow [136] and others. Later it was discovered that they were not always straight lines but showed significant deviations. Rahn [137] also pointed out this fact.

Thermal death-time curves may be drawn from data collected in only two determinations at different temperatures, i.e., from two points. Curves drawn from some thermal death-time data have not been straight lines, and those who wish to use them in computing processes have had to approximate a straight line using some part of the actual curve. An error may be introduced because one may not know what part of the curve should be chosen for determining the curve finally adopted. Whether the practice to "straighten a curve" is sound is quite doubtful. Perhaps it is wrong to always expect and demand a straight-line curve.

Dormancy or Delayed Germination of Spores. Numerous observations have shown in recent years that spores may not germinate even under what would ordinarily be called ideal conditions. This was first observed

135. Halversen and Hays. 1936. J. Bact. 32, 466; Idaho Agr. Exp. Sta. Bull. 221 (1937) 26, 27.

136. Bigelow. 1921. J. Infect. Diseases 29, 528-536.

137. Rahn. 1930. J. Gen. Physiol. 13, 395.

with spores which had been heated and it was suggested that their delayed germination was due to heat injury. When it was observed that unheated spores might also show dormancy, this explanation was abandoned.

Dickson *et al.*[138] noticed dormancy with the spores of *Clostridium botulinum.* Burke, Sprague, and Barnes[139] stated that the spores of common aerobic bacteria could lie dormant for months under favorable growth conditions. Spores of *Bacillus subtilis* and *Bacillus megatherium* remained dormant for 39 and 90 days, respectively. Burke[140] had previously reported dormancy of a small percentage of the spores of *Clostridium botulinum.* Williams,[141] who could not observe the phenomenon with *Bacillus subtilis*, has reviewed most of the literature. The possibility of dormancy makes it necessary to hold subcultures for a sufficiently long time before negative growth is reported. The phenomenon may also be important in foods which are heated for preservation but which are not sterilized. Such is the case with canned foods which are "commercially sterilized." The microorganisms may be dormant and develop later if the cans are stored under suitable conditions.

Preservation of Microorganisms. In several applications of bacteria to food investigations, it is necessary to preserve cultures of microorganisms. This is the case with species which are to be used in dairy starters, pure-culture inoculum for making vinegar, etc. A number of methods have been proposed. Hansen[142] suggested the use of 10 per cent sucrose solution for preserving yeasts. A small amount of the culture was added to the sterilized solution. Tanner and Burrows[143] found that this method was unsatisfactory for some species, even though Klöcker[144] had reported that yeasts could be preserved in this manner for 25 years. Swift[145] suggested a method based on freezing to dry the cells, which were to be preserved. Thaysen[146] kept bacteria for long periods without frequent transferring, by adding a little calcium carbonate or calcium diphosphate to a culture which had been allowed to grow vigorously. A second method was suggested for sporeformers, involving the use of dry sterile sand. In both cases, the tubes were sealed in the flame for storage. Barthel[147] suggested sterilized soil in Freudenreich flasks as a good medium for keeping yeasts and fermentation organisms. This method has been used for storage of certain organisms concerned in spoilage of canned foods. Other methods have been proposed by Sartory and Mahen,[148] Kiefer,[149] and Truche.[150]

138. Dickson, *et al.* 1925. J. Infect. Diseases 36, 472-483.
139. Burke, Sprague, and Barnes. 1925. J. Infect. Diseases 36, 555-560.
140. Burke. 1919. J. Bact. 4, 555-565.
141. Williams. 1929. J. Infect. Dis. 44, 421-465.
142. Hansen. 1888. Compt. Rend. d. trav. du lab. Carlsberg, serie physiol. 2, Book 5.
143. Tanner and Burrows. 1931. J. Bact. 21, 32.
144. Klöcker. 1917. Compt. Rend. d. trav. du lab. Carlsberg, serie physiol. II, 297-311.
145. Swift. 1921. J. Exper. Med. 33, 69-75.
146. Thaysen 1924. J. Inst. Brew 30, 349-355.
147. Barthel. 1918, 1919. Centbl. Bakt. II, 48, 340-349; Meddel. K. Vet. Akad. Nobelinstitut, Stockholm 5, 1-13.
148. Sartory and Mahen. 1909. Compt. rend. Soc. de biol. 66, 968.
149. Kiefer. 1923. Centbl. Bakt. 2, 90, 1-5.
150. Truche. 1924. Ann. Inst. Pasteur 38, 516-519.

Sartory and Mahen found some broth cultures sealed in tubes to be viable after 16 years.

von Daranyi [151] sealed his cultures with sterilized liquid paraffin. His cultures are grown on 45°C.(113°F.) agar-slants and paraffin is poured over them sufficient to cover the upper end of the slant to a depth of several millimeters with tube held upright. When it is necessary to use the sealed culture, the tube is slanted in the opposite direction, so as to expose part of the surface of the culture without drawing off the paraffin. The author claims a considerably longer period of viability for cultures so treated than for those under ordinary conditions.

Swift [152] again discussed his method, the principle of which consists of the removal of water while the cells are frozen, either by a chemical desiccant or by low-temperature evaporation and condensation. The former method is simpler for cultures. Young cultures grown in broth were centrifuged and resuspended in a small amount of the same medium. This suspension was distributed in tubes and frozen under vacuum. All investigators are not agreed that this is the best method. Morton and Pulaski [153] studied three methods — storage of broth cultures in sealed ampoules, agar-slant cultures overlaid with paraffin oil, and the freezing-drying method. The second method, in which growth on agar slants is covered with sterile paraffin oil, gave best results. A heavy mineral oil is most suitable, and it must fill the tube to a point one centimeter above the top of the slope. The oil should be sterilized in the oven at 150 to 170°C.(302 to 338°F.) for one hour, as it becomes mixed with water if autoclaved.

GROUPS OF BACTERIA OF SPECIAL INTEREST TO FOOD BACTERIOLOGY

The arrangement of bacteria into groups has been done mostly for convenience. In some instances, probably, these groups are made up of very closely related organisms; in other cases too insignificant characteristics have been taken. As mentioned above, many of the groups are arbitrary and often depend upon characteristics which are not fixed. Many of the groups need to be subjected to careful study. This will tell whether they approach natural units and, if they do, the relation and characters of the members. The groups of pathogenic bacteria and those which have sanitary significance have already received careful study.

The groups which are treated in the following pages are those frequently encountered by the food microbiologist. A discussion of all of the larger groups would be unnecessary.

Aerobic Sporeforming Group. These bacteria cause the food preserver little trouble. Their spores are not especially heat resistant and do not ordinarily survive processes given canned foods. They do appear, however, in some of the foods preserved by other methods.

151. von Daranyi. 1928. Centbl. Bakt. Pt. 1, Orig. 108, 160-162.
152. Swift. 1937. J. Bact. 33, 411-421.
153. Morton and Pulaski. 1938. J. Bact. 35, 163-566.

Many different aerobic sporeforming bacteria have been described in the literature. To Ford [154] and his colleagues, we are indebted for an analysis of the nonpathogenic, aerobic, sporeforming bacilli. Ford mentioned the chaotic condition in which these bacteria were grouped. Almost any large aerobic sporeformer would be called *Bacillus subtilis* although the organisms isolated by different investigators might have little in common. From a study of more than 1,700 cultures from different sources, Ford made the following groups for his sporeformers:

GROUP I. SUBTILIS GROUP.

Small, homogeneous, sluggishly motile organisms, measuring .375 by 1.5 to 2.5 microns. No threads on glucose agar. Central or excentric spores, oval, measuring .5 by .75 to .875 micron, often retaining tags of protoplasm. Growth on solid media hard and penetrating with tenacious scums on fluid media.

Represented by:
Bacillus subtilis Cohn.
Bacillus subtilis-viscosus Chester.

GROUP II. MESENTERICUS GROUP.

Small, homogeneous, actively motile organisms, measuring .5 by 2 to 4 microns. Often produce long threads on glucose agar. Spores measure .5 by 1 to 1.125 microns, oval, retaining terminal tags of protoplasm. Growth on hard media as soft pultaceous mass with tendency to wrinkle, on fluid media as friable, easily broken scums.

Represented by:
Bacillus vulgatus (Flügge) Trevisan.
   (Bacillus mesentericus vulgatus Flügge.)
Bacillus mesentericus (Flügge) Migula.
   (Bacillus mesentericus fuscus Flügge.)
Bacillus aterrimus Lehmann and Neumann.
   (Bacillus mesentericus niger Lunt.)
Bacillus globigii Migula.
   (Bacillus mesentericus ruber Globig.)
Bacillus niger Migula.
   (Bacillus lactis niger Gorini.)
Bacillus mesentericus var. *flavus*
Bacillus panis Migula.
   (Bacillus mesentericus panis viscosi I Vogel.)
   (Motility lost by capsule formation.)

GROUP III. COHAERENS-SIMPLEX GROUP.

Motile organisms, somewhat larger than either *Bacillus subtilis* or *Bacillus mesentericus*, measuring .375 to .75 by .75 to 3 microns. Thicker and longer forms on glucose agar. Involution forms and shadow forms common and appear early. Spores cylindrical, measuring .5625 to .75 by 1 to 1.5 microns. Growth as a soft mass on hard media, as turbidity with little or no scum on fluids.

Represented by:
Bacillus cohaerens Gottheil.
Bacillus simplex Gottheil.
Bacillus agri Ford.

GROUP IV. MYCOIDES GROUP.

Large organisms with square ends growing in long chains. Single cells measure .5 to 3 to 6 microns. On glucose agar organisms are thicker and longer and made up of

154. A series of papers was published by Ford and his colleagues in the Journal of Bacteriology 1 (1916), 273-319. These descriptions are taken from these papers.

globular bodies. Tendency for organisms to grow in curves or spirals. Spores central or excentric, round or oval to cylindrical measuring .75 to 1 to 2 microns. Spores vary greatly in size and often appear in chains. Growth on hard media dry and penetrating, on fluid media as firm, tenacious scum.

Represented by:

> *Bacillus mycoides* Flügge.
> *Bacillus prausnitzii* Trevisan.
>   (*Bacillus ramosus liquefaciens* Prausnitz.)
> *Bacillus adhaerens* Ford.
>   (No motility.)

GROUP V. CEREUS GROUP.

Large, motile organisms with round ends, measuring .75 by 2.25 to 4 microns. Tend to grow in short chains. Thicker and longer on glucose agar where protoplasm is converted into globular bodies. Central or excentric spores, cylindrical, measuring .5 to .75 by 1.125 to 1.5 microns. Spores retaining protoplasm at one or both ends often resembling enlarged subtilis or mesentericus spores. Growth on hard media as soft, pultaceous mass with tendency to fold or wrinkle, on fluid media as thick, friable scum.

Represented by:

> *Bacillus cereus* Franjkland.
> *Bacillus albolactus* Migula.
> *Bacillus cereus* var. *fluorescens* Ford.

GROUP VI. MEGATHERIUM GROUP.

Very large, actively motile organisms, measuring .75 to 1.25 by 3 to 9 microns. Often in long forms which spread out, lose their cytoplasm, and show peculiar aggregations of protoplasm at their periphery. Protoplasm rapidly converted into peculiar globular, highly refractive bodies, particularly on glucose agar. Shadow and transparent forms appear early. Spores central, excentric or subterminal, oval to cylindrical, measuring usually .75 to 1.125 by 1.5 to 2 microns. Spores vary greatly in shape, sometimes round, sometimes rectangular, often reniform. Growth on solid media as thick, pultaceous mass, on fluid media as turbidity with little or no scum formation.

Represented by:

> *Bacillus megatherium* DeBary.
> *Bacillus petasites* Gottheil.
> *Bacillus ruminatus* Gottheil.

GROUP VII. ROUND TERMINAL SPORE GROUP.

Small, actively motile organisms, measuring .5 to .75 by 1.5 to 3 microns, often forming long threads in old cultures. Protoplasm homogeneous. Spores subterminal or terminal, round, thicker than the organisms from which they spring, measuring 1 to 1.5 microns in diameter.

Represented by:

> *Bacillus pseudotetanicus* (Kruse) Migula.
> *Bacillus fusiformis* Gottheil.

GROUP VIII. CYLINDRICAL TERMINAL SPORES GROUP.

Small, thin, actively motile organisms, measuring .375 to .5 by 2.5 to 4 microns. Slightly larger on glucose agar but no changes in character of protoplasm. Spores terminal, cylindrical, measuring usually .75 by 1.125 to 1.5 microns.

Represented by:

> *Bacillus circulans* Jordan.
> *Bacillus brevis* Migula.
> *Bacillus terminalis* Migula.

GROUP IX. CENTRAL SPORED GROUP.

Long, actively motile organisms with pointed ends, measuring .375 to .5 by 1.125 to 4 microns. Slightly larger on glucose agar, but no change in character of protoplasm. Spores develop in the middle of the rods which become spindle-shaped. Spores large, cylindrical, measuring .625 to .875 by 1.125 to 1.5 microns.

Represented by:

Bacillus centrosporus Ford.

Bacillus laterosporus Ford.

The species characterization of these bacteria appears in the author's "Bacteriology."

Bergey's "Manual of Determinative Bacteriology," fifth edition, 1939, lists descriptions of many species of aerobic, sporeforming bacteria.

One species, *Bacillus betanigrificans*, first described by Cameron, Esty, and Williams [155] as the cause of blackening of canned beets, probably belongs in this group. This organism is facultative with respect to oxygen and produces spores which probably explain its resistance to heat.

Heat-resistance observations were made using the method of Esty and Williams.[126] At 110°C.(230°F.), using a concentration of spores of 150,000 per ml. in phosphate buffer solution (pH 7.0) and in beet juice (pH 5.5), survival in the former was 20 minutes and destruction 25 minutes; in beet juice no survival was observed in the shortest heating time of five minutes.

THE COCCACEAE

The Coccaceae have been studied by Hucker.[156] Into the group were placed most of the bacteria with round cells, irrespective of the space arrangement of the cell masses. Hucker believed that Micrococci Rhodococci, and Staphylococci could be placed in one genus for which the name Micrococci was retained. The group was characterized as follows:

Micrococcus (Cohn, 1872): Cell division in two or three planes. Generally does not produce regular tetrads or packets. Typically saprophytic or a facultative parasite. May or may not produce red, yellow, or orange pigment. Produce moderate to abundant growth on ordinary nutrient media. Gram-positive, variable, or negative. Aerobic or a facultative anaerobe. Does not produce indol. Gelatin often liquified. Rarely attacks starch. True endospores have not been found. Nitrates often reduced. Motile species have been described. Produces acid but rarely gas from the fermentation of sugars.

After studying a great number of coccus forms, Hucker prepared the following key: The term Micrococcus has been employed to designate the genus of irregular mass-forming cocci and, after a study of a long series of cultures, 16 species have been found which appear to be more or less constant. Gelatin liquefaction, nitrate reduction, and ability to utilize certain ammonium salts as the only source of nitrogen have served as the most important basis for the differentiation of these species. The species of this genus may be outlined as follows:

KEY TO THE SPECIES OF THE GENUS MICROCOCCUS.

A. Pigment produced.

    I. Yellow pigment produced.

        1. Gelatin liquefied.

            a. Nitrates reduced.

                * Utilizes $NH_4H_2PO_4$ as a source of nitrogen.

                        M. conglomeratus

                ** Does not utilize $NH_4H_2PO_4$ as a source of nitrogen.

                        M. citreus

155. Cameron, Esty, and Williams. 1936. Food Research 1, 73-85.
156. Hucker. 1924. N. Y. Agr. Exp. Sta. Bulletins 135, 136, 141, 142, 143, 144.

    b. Nitrates not reduced.
          M. flavus

  II. Red pigment produced.
    1. Gelatin liquefied.
          M. roseus

    2. Gelatin not liquefied.
          M. cinnebareus

  III. Orange pigment produced.
    1. Gelatin liquefied.
          M. aureus

    2. Gelatin not liquefied.
          M. aurantiacus

B. No pigment produced.
  I. Cells in irregular masses.
    1. Gelatin liquefied.
      a. Nitrates reduced.
        * Utilizes $NH_4H_2PO_4$ as a source of nitrogen. Acid proteolytic action upon milk.
            M. casei
        ** Does not utilize $NH_4H_2PO_4$ as a source of nitrogen.
            M. albus

      b. Nitrates not reduced.
        * Utilizes urea as a source of nitrogen.
            M. ureae
        ** Does not utilize urea as a source of nitrogen.
            M. freudenreichii

    2. Gelatin not liquefied.
      a. Nitrates reduced.
          M. epidermis
      b. Nitrates not reduced.
          M. candidus

  II. Cells in definite tetrads.
          M. tetragenus

The Genus Leuconostoc. Members of this genus have been encountered by bacteriologists in various fields. They were encountered by early investigators as the causes of gum formation in sugar factories; they have also been isolated from numerous food products. Food bacteriologists are indebted to Hucker and Pederson [157] for a report on this genus. They observed sufficiently fundamental physiological characteristics to justify a genus for which the name *Leuconostoc* was said to have priority. Morphologically the genus is intermediate between the streptococci and lactobacilli. Hucker and Pederson classified the genus as follows:

CLASSIFICATION OF THE GENUS LEUCONOSTOC
LEUCONOSTOC VAN TIEGHEM, 1878 EMEND

"Cells normally occurring as spheres. Under certain conditions, such as in acid fruits and vegetables, the cells may lengthen and become pointed or even elongated into a rod. Grows on ordinary media, but growth is enhanced by the addition of yeast cells, extract of yeast or other vegetable tissues. Generally produces a limited amount of acid. Rarely curdles milk. Produces mannitol from fructose. By-products of the

157. Hucker and Pederson. 1930. N. Y. Agr. Exp. Sta. Tech. Bull. 167.

fermentation of glucose include carbon dioxide, lactic acid, acetic acid, and ethyl alcohol. Approximately one-fourth of the glucose fermented is converted to carbon dioxide. Levo-lactic acid is always produced and sometimes dextro-lactic acid. Gram positive. Nonmotile. Certain types grow with characteristic slime formation in sucrose media. Ordinarily does not increase the amount of soluble nitrogen in medium even after long periods of incubation.

"Synonyms:

Lactococcus Beijerinck 1912 (pro parte).

Betacoccus Orla-Jensen 1919.

"Type Species:

"1. *Leuconostoc mesenterioides* (Cienkowski 1878) Van Tieghem 1878.

"Produces slime from sucrose. Ferments xylose or arabinose, fructose, ·glucose, mannose, galactose, sucrose, and generally raffinose, salicin, lactose, and mannitol. Rarely ferments dextrin, starch, inulin, sorbitol, rhamnose, or glycerol. Grows quickly in sucrose gelatin and produces characteristic growth. Most active of the genus. Generally encountered in vegetable and other plant materials. Frequently isolated from slimy sugar solutions. Optimum growth temperature 21°C.

"Synonyms:

Leuconostoc aller Zettnow 1907.

Leuconostoc opalanitza Zettnow 1907.

Betacoccus arabinosaceus Orla-Jensen 1919.

Leuconostoc pleofructi (Savage and Hunwicke) Pederson 1929 A.

Ninety-seven strains of this species were investigated, fifty-eight of which were studied in detail. Among the well-authenticated cultures coming within the confines of this description are *Leuconostoc pleofructi, Betacoccus arabinosaceus, Betacoccus No. 12* (Orla-Jensen) and *Betacoccus No. 11* (Orla-Jensen).

"*Leuconostoc mesenterioides* is the most active species of the genus and is generally associated with vegetable and other plant materials.

"2. *Leuconostoc dextranicus* (Beijerinck, 1912) Comb. nov.

"Produces slime only in rapidly growing cultures. Ferments sucrose, glucose, galactose, maltose, levulose, and generally lactose and mannose. Does not ferment xylose or arabinose, glycerol, rhamnose, sorbitol, mannitol, starch, rarely raffinose, inulin, dextrin. Found both in plant materials and in milk products. Optimum temperature of growth 21 to 25°C.

"Synonyms:

Lactococcus dextranicus Beijerinck 1912.

Betacoccus bovis Orla-Jensen 1919.

Streptococcus kefir Migula 1900 emend. Evans 1918.

Streptococcus paracitrovorus Hammer 1920 A.

"Thirty-four strains of *Leuconostoc dextranicus* were available for study, 14 of which were studied in detail. A culture of *Streptococcus citrovorus* was found to be included in this group as well as a strain of *S. paracitrovorus*.

"*Leuconostoc dextranicus* is much less active in almost every respect than *L. mesenterioides*, and is not as commonly encountered. The two types, however, are quite distinct and may be differentiated with certainty by the fermentation of pentoses.

3. *Leuconostoc citrovorus* (Hammer 1920 A) Comb. nov.

"Grows poorly on ordinary media without the addition of yeast extract or other growth accessory substance. Produce acid from fructose, glucose, galactose, lactose. Generally does not produce acid from glycerol, xylose, arabinose, rhamnose, sorbitol, mannitol, sucrose, mannose, maltose, raffinose, inulin, dextrin, starch, or salicin. Found in milk and dairy products. Optimum temperature from 20 to 25°C.

"Synonyms:

Streptococcus citrovorus Hammer 1920 A.

Betacoccus cremoris Soncke Knudsen and Sorensen 1929."

Bergey's "Manual of Determinative Bacteriology," fifth edition, described 46 species of Micrococcus and nine of Staphylococcus. Aerobic, sporeforming bacteria are not especially heat resistant and consequently are of little significance as spoilage organisms. Three species of Leuconostoc were recognized: *Leuconostoc mesenterioides, Leuconostoc dextranicum,* and *Leuconostoc citrovorum.* Spiegelberg[158] found *Leuconostoc mesenterioides* to be one of the causes of bursting swells in canned pineapple.

THERMOPHILIC BACTERIA

Thermophilic bacteria are important organisms in spoilage of canned foods. The literature has become quite large and was reviewed by Morrison and Tanner [159] and by Robertson.[160] The term "thermophilic" comes from the Greek words meaning "heat loving." The optimum temperature for growth is around 55 to 60°C.(130 to 140°F.). The first work on thermophilic bacteria was done on strains from soil, water, etc. In 1879, Miquel described a strain to which he gave the name *Bacillus thermophilus.* Since then the thermophilic bacteria have been shown to be of great significance in the canned food, sugar, and dairy industries. The reader is referred to Chapters 5 and 23 of this book and to the publications mentioned above for the literature. This brief discussion of thermophilic bacteria does not indicate that they are relatively unimportant in food bacteriology. With the possible exception of the anaerobic sporeformers, one would find it quite difficult to find a more important group. Since they are discussed fully in other chapters, they will not be considered at great length here.

Some fungi which may cause spoilage in canned foods are also thermophilic. Sartory and Meyer [161] isolated such an organism from swelled cans. Its properties were much like *Actinomyces thermophilus.* However, on the basis of its staining properties it was placed with Mycobacteriaceae and apparently identified as *Corynebacterium necrophorum.*

THE COLIFORM GROUP

This group of organisms has played a great role in sanitary bacteriology where its most important member, *Escherichia coli,* is the main biological indicator of pollution. Its role in this case has been reviewed in the chapter on "Water Bacteriology" and need not, therefore, be discussed again here. A few other species in the group have roles in the field of food microbiology which makes it desirable to mention their characteristics here. The group has been known under various names. Breed and Norton [162] suggested the term "coliform" to designate the lactose-fermenting, aerobic bacteria used as a measure of pollution of water. It was hoped that, when the same term is applied in milk and oyster examination, it will be used with a similar meaning. Reconsider-

158. Spiegelberg. 1940. Food Research 5, 115-130; 439-455.
159. Morrison and Tanner. 1922. J. Bact. 7, 343-366.
160. Robertson. 1927. N. Y. Agr. Exp. Sta. Bull. 130.
161. Sartory and Meyer. 1940. Bull. Acad. Med. 123, 98-101.
162. Breed and Norton. 1937. Amer. J. Pub. Health 27, 560-563.

ation of the use of the coliform group as the sole index of dangerous contamination of water supplies was requested.

Bergey's "Manual of Determinative Bacteriology," fifth edition, recognizes but two species in the genus Escherichia; these are *Escherichia coli* and *Escherichia freundii*. The definition of *Escherichia coli* for sanitary analysis is *all aerobic and facultative anaerobic Gram-negative, nonspore-forming bacilli which ferment lactose with gas formation* (Standard Methods of Water Analysis).

A critical review of the group was prepared by Parr,[163] which every one who has any interest whatever in it, should read. This author explained the origin of many of the names which have been used, and stressed the confusion which has resulted from excluding some species. Confusion has been caused in the past by failure to recognize variations which have led to many names and false species. The coliform group was said to be a large one of closely related, highly intergrading, and somewhat unstable bacteria which form a fairly wide gamut or continuum extending from the lactose-negative paracolon forms at one extreme to the highly reactive *Aerobacter aerogenes* at the other. Standing with the paracolon forms next to *Salmonella* one finds the Morgan bacillus. In about the same positions, and leading to *Eberthella* and *Shigella*, are located the anaerogenous *Escherichia coli*. Next to these varieties come the slow lactose-fermenting *Escherichia coli* so likely to be manifested as "unstable variants." Completing one side of the picture, one finds the typical *Escherichia coli* which bridge over to the *Aerobacter aerogenes* side by way of the "intermediates." Below *Aerobacter aerogenes* we find *Aerobacter cloacae* which appears to point toward the genus *Proteus*, and, above all forms but particularly above *Aerobacter aerogenes*, are located the Friedlander organisms.

In an ecological study of the coliform group, Griffin and Stuart[164] isolated 6,500 strains from various sources. Escherichia strains were said to be normal inhabitants of feces while Aerobacter strains are typical of non-fecal materials. Griffin and Stuart admitted that the latter might, at times, be found in fecal materials but considered this occurrence to be adventitious.

Not many investigators have attempted to determine the possible relationship of the important members of the coliform group. It is reasonable to assume that they have developed from one another because their characteristics are so much alike. Horwood and Webster[165] believed that they had observed a transformation of *Aerobacter aerogenes* into *Escherichia coli* in the human intestine and that the former organism might have more sanitary significance than is generally accorded to it.

Weldin[166] prepared a classification and key to genera of coliform bacteria and some of the pathogens related to them.

163. Parr. 1939. Bact. Rev. 3, 1.
164. Griffin and Stuart. 1940. J. Bact. 39, 40.
165. Horwood and Webster. 1937. J. Bact. 33, 21.
166. Weldin. 1928. Iowa State Coll. J. Sci. 1, 121-197.

THE LACTIC ACID-PRODUCING BACTERIA

While much has been written on the lactic acid-producing bacteria, few complete characterizations of species have been published. Henneberg[167] and Orla-Jensen[168] described a few of the many species which are included in this group. Several of the more common species are described in the chapter on "Milk and Milk Products." They play important roles in many places in food bacteriology.

Several lactobacilli have been isolated from spoiled fruit juices and tomato products. These are discussed in the several chapters on these products in this book. They are also important in butter cultures.

They have been studied from the taxonomic viewpoint by several investigators. Kitahara[169] claimed to have isolated about all of the known species and presented a classification based on his work. His conclusions in some places conflict with those of Shimwell[170] who studied the lactic acid bacteria of beer. Both of these investigators reported new strains which should be of interest to food bacteriologists.

ANAEROBIC BACTERIA

Anaerobic bacteria have not received the attention which is due them in food bacteriology. Special methods are required for cultivating them, many of which are not adapted to routine work.

Anaerobes are significant only as spoilage organisms. *Clostridium botulinum*, in addition to its ability to spoil foods, also produces a powerful toxin and is, therefore, the best example of an organism which causes food poisoning. *Clostridium putrificum* causes trouble in the meat-preservation industry. Other anaerobic sporeformers are mentioned at various places in this book, especially in Chapter 23. Canned foods are subject to considerable spoilage by these forms.

Several reviews of the anaerobes have been published, from which the bibliography of the forms may be secured. Kahn[171] studied those from the human alimentary tract. Another excellent report was published by the Special Committee upon Anaerobic Bacteria and Infections, of the Medical Research Committee (Special Report Series No. 39, 1919, of Great Britain). Hall[172] and Spray[173] have published differential keys to anaerobes. Spray's which is more recent, is given here.

TENTATIVE KEY TO THE SPORULATING ANAEROBES

I. Iron-Milk, active gaseous fermentation; early coagulation (24-48 hours); no digestion of clot; no blackening:

A. Lead Acetate, strongly blackened;
  1. Sucrose fermented; Salicin not fermented.
     Nitrite +; Indol —; Violet —; Gelatin +; Motility —;
     Dextrose +; Lactose +; Sucrose +; Salicin—;
     Spores ovoid, central-excentric, not swelling rod; (spores infrequently observed); not in fermentable sugars;

167. Henneberg. 1903. Ztschr. Spiritusind., Nos. 22 and 31.
168. Orla-Jensen. 1919. Mem. Acad. Roy. des Sci. et des Lettres de Danemark 5, No. 2.
169. Kitahara. 1940. J. Agr. Chem. Soc., Japan 16, 137.
170. Shimwell. 1941. Wallerstein Lab. Communications 4, 41-48.
171. Kahn. 1924. J. Infect. Diseases 35, 423-478.
172. Hall. 1922. Idem 30, 445-504.
173. Spray. 1936. J. Bact. 32, 135-155.

1. Clostridium welchii

2. Sucrose, not fermented; Salicin, Fermented;
   Nitrite +; Indol —; Violet —; Gelatin +; Motility +;
   Dextrose +; Lactose +;
   Spores ovoid, excentric-subterminal; distinctly swelling rod; (spores infrequently observed, apparently not in fermentable sugars);

2. Clostridium aerofoetidum

B. Lead Acetate, not blackened; no browning;
   Nitrite +; Indol —; Violet —; Gelatin—; Motility +;
   Dextrose +; Lactose +; Sucrose +; Salicin +;
   Spores ovoid, central-excentric, not swelling rod; (spores abundant, even in fermentable sugars);

3. Clostridium multifermentans
a. Glycerol, fermented;
b. Glycerol, not fermented *
4. Clostridium butyricum Group

II. Iron-Milk, inactive gaseous fermentation; late coagulation at 4-6 days; no digestion of clot; no blackening:
   A. Lead Acetate, strongly blackened;
      1. Indol, positive;
         Nitrite +; Violet —; Gelatin —; Motility +;
         Dextrose +; Lactose +; Sucrose +; * Salicin +;
         *(pH in sucrose reduced from 7.2 to 6.4 only);
         Spores almost spherical, abundant, subterminal, becoming terminal; swelling rod;
         Vegetative cells distinctly navicular, pointed;

5. Clostridium sphenoides

      2. Indol, Negative;
         Nitrite +; Violet —; Gelatin —; Motility +;
         Dextrose +; Lactose +; Sucrose +; Salicin +;
         Spores ovoid, excentric-subterminal; swelling rod; (spores infrequently observed, not abundant);
         Vegetative cells slender, round to pointed ends;

6. Clostridium fallax

   B. Lead Acetate, slight smoky browning; not blackened;
      Nitrite +; Indol —; Violet —; Gelatin —; Motility +;
      Dextrose +; Lactose +; Sucrose +; Salicin +;
      Spores ovoid, terminal, swelling rod; grows aerobically (Micro-aerophile);
      Spores abundant even in fermentable sugars.

7. Clostridium tertium

   C. Lead Acetate, no blackening; no browning;
      Nitrite +; Indol —; Violet —; Gelatin +; Motility +;
      Dextrose +; Lactose +; Sucrose —; Salicin +;
      Spores ovoid, abundant, excentric-subterminal; swelling rod;

8. Clostridium septicum
(Vibrion septique)
(Clostridium oedematis-maligni)

III. Iron-Milk, inactive gaseous fermentation; (Long continued)
   Late, if any, coagulation (10-20-30 days, or not even at 60 days); no digestion, no blackening;
   A. Lead Acetate, strongly blackened;
      1. Lactose, not fermented;
         Nitrite —; Indol —; Violet —; Gelatin +; Motility +;
         Dextrose +; Sucrose —; Salicin —;
         Spores ovoid, not abundant, excentric-subterminal, swelling rod;

---

* In the original publication, Spray quoted McCoy that this was not entirely and uniformly true.

[Some few strains coagulate Iron-Milk (5-12 days), others not 30 days, although gas bubbles are constantly evolved];

                                        9. *Clostridium novyi*
                                        (Clostridium oedematiens)

2. Lactose, fermented;
    Nitrite +; Indol —; Violet —; Gelatin +; Motility +;
    Dextrose +; Sucrose +; Salicin —;
    Spores ovoid, abundant, excentric-subterminal, swelling rod;
    [Some strains coagulate Iron-Milk (12 days); others not at 56 days];

                                        10. *Clostridium chauvoei*

B. Lead Acetate, no blackening; no browning;
    Nitrite —; Indol —; Violet —; Gelatin +; Motility +;
    Dextrose +; Lactose —; Sucrose —; Salicin —;
    Spores ovoid, not abundant, terminal, slightly swelling rod;
    [No coagulation of Iron-Milk (30 days), although gas bubbles are constantly evolved (15-20 days)];

                                        11. *Clostridium luciliae*
                                        (Clostridium botulinum C)

IV. Iron-Milk, inactive gaseous fermentation; more or less rapid digestion, with or without previous clotting); strongly blackened, early (48 hours) or late (8-9 days);
A. Lead Acetate, strongly and rapidly blackened (24-48 hours);
    1. Salicin, fermented;
        Nitrite —; Indol —; Violet +; Gelatin +; Motility +;
        Dextrose +; Lactose —; Sucrose —;
        Spores ovoid, not usually abundant, excentric-subterminal; swelling rod;
        [Iron-milk softly coagulated (2-5 days); first blackened (5-7 days); clot slowly digested at 10-20 days];
        (Differentiated by toxin-antitoxin);

                                        12. *Clostridium botulinum (A&B)*

    2. Salicin, not fermented (see *Clostridium centrosporogenes*);
        a. Vanillin Violet +; Indol —;
            Nitrite —; Gelatin +; Motility +;
            Dextrose +; Lactose —; Sucrose —;
            Spores ovoid, abundant, excentric-subterminal, swelling rod;
            [Iron-milk not coagulated, translucent, then flocculent precipitate, rapidly blackened (24-48 hours); rapidly digested (8-10 days)];
            1) Tyrosine crystals not observed;

                                        13. *Clostridium sporogenes*

            2) Tyrosine crystals in old cultures;

                                        14. *Clostridium tyrosinogenes*

        b. Vanillin Violet —; Indol +;
            Nitrite —; Gelatin +; Motility +;
            Dextrose +; Lactose —; Sucrose —; Salicin —†;
            Spores ovoid, abundant, central-excentric; not markedly swelling rod;
            1. Pathogenic;

                                        15. *Clostridium sordelli*

            2. Nonpathogenic;

                                        16. *Clostridium bifermentans*
                                        (Clostridium centrosporogenes)

B. Lead Acetate, not blackened; no browning;
    Nitrite —; Indol —; Violet —; Gelatin +; Motility +;
    Wine-red color in Iron-Gelatin at 24-48 hours;
    Dextrose —; Lactose —; Sucrose —; Salicin —;
    (No sugars fermented)

† Five of thirteen cultures studied by Spray and labeled *Cl. centrosporogenes* fermented salicin.

Grows aerobically (Microaerophile);
Spores ovoid, abundant, excentric-subterminal, swelling rod;

17. Clostridium histolyticum

V. Iron-Milk, no gaseous fermentation; no blackening; no digestion; coagulation late, if any (15-20 days or more):

A. Lead Acetate, not blackened, but showing smoky brown at 24-48 hours; not increased with incubation;
   Nitrite —; Indol +‡; Violet —; Gelatin +; Motility +;
   Dextrose —; Lactose —; Sucrose —; Salicin —;
   (No sugars fermented)
   Spores spherical, terminal, swelling rod;
   a. Toxic;

18. Clostridium tetani

   b. Nontoxic;

19. Clostridium lentoputrescens
(Clostridium putrificum)

B. Lead Acetate, not blackened; no trace of browning;
   Nitrite —; Indol +; Violet —; Gelatin —; Motility +;
   Dextrose +; Lactose —; Sucrose —; Salicin — §;
   Spores spherical to slightly ovoid, terminal, swelling rod;

20. Clostridium tetanomorphum.

Brewer [174] reported a clear medium for cultivation of anaerobic bacteria "aerobically." To provide proper oxidation-reduction potential, .1 per cent of sodium thioglycollate was added. Brewer found it unnecessary to use Smith fermentation tubes or other special equipment or to heat the medium just before use. McClung [175] also found this medium to be satisfactory. A special Petri dish cover to be used with the medium has also been devised by Brewer.[174]

One objection to Spray's [173] scheme for the identification of anaerobes, mentioned by Reed and Orr,[176] is the fact that many of the differential reactions require up to two weeks for completion. Introduction of reducing agents into fluid media, such as Brewer's medium has made it possible to secure results more rapidly. Reed and Orr confirmed the utility of such media and arranged a group of diagnostic reactions with these new media which yielded precise results for pathogenic anaerobes in 24 hours. Their system will not be reviewed here because it applies mainly to pathogenic anaerobes.

Other species than those mentioned in Spray's key have become important in the food-preservation industry. *Clostridium nigrificans* (Werkman and Weaver [177]) was reported as the cause of sulfide spoilage of canned peas. It brings about a malodorous spoilage accompanied by a blackening and later some disintegration.

Anaerobic, sporeforming, butyric acid-producing bacteria have been troublesome bacteria in canned fruits. *Clostridium pasteurianum* has been

‡ Occasional strains are indol weak or apparently indol negative.
§ Some strains lower pH slightly (from 7.2-6.8).
174. Brewer. 1939. J. Bact. 39, 10; J. Amer. Med. Assoc. 115 (1940), 598-600; Science 95, 567.
175. McClung. 1940. Science 92, 340.
176. Reed and Orr. 1941. War. Med. 1, 493-510.
177. Werkman and Weaver. 1927. Iowa State Coll. J. Sci. 2, 77.

found in this role by Townsend,[178] Spiegelberg,[158] and others. Spiegelberg reported at great length on the characteristics of strains isolated from canned pineapple. They were essentially like the strain of *Clostridium pasteurianum* first described by Winogradsky.

CULTIVATION OF ANAEROBIC BACTERIA

Anaerobic bacteria are quite important in many foods because of the fact that they are hard to kill and are able to grow in closed containers. Knowledge concerning these important organisms has been greatly amplified during the past few years by Hall,[179] Heller,[180] Kahn,[181] Weinberg and Ginsbourg,[182] and many others. It is not a simple matter to secure pure cultures of these organisms. Barber,[183] Hall,[179] Kahn,[181] and Kendall *et al.*[184] advised the isolation of the single cells for pure cultures.

Several indicators have been used by those who have worked with anaerobes, to determine the oxygen tension of various anaerobic methods. Hall[179] used methylene blue. It is colorless in the absence of oxygen and blue in its presence. Van Riemsdijk[185] prepared a special indicator which he claimed could be used in the same manner as methylene blue.

A few of the methods especially useful in food bacteriology will now be presented:

A number of methods, many of which rest on the same principle, have been devised by growing an anaerobic organism in symbiosis with an aerobe; it is assumed that the aerobe uses up the free oxygen, thereby creating the desirable conditions necessary for the anaerobe. Hall[179] showed that methylene blue could not be used as a criterion of anaerobiosis in this case, because some organisms reduce the dye themselvse and might give the technician false information. The presence of another organism, which removes the oxygen and gives off carbon dioxide, is an advantage as Rockwell[186] has shown. While other explanations have been offered to explain how the association functions in creating favorable conditions for the anaerobe, Novy[197] was satisfied that the removal of oxygen by the aerobe was the best explanation.

Torrey's Method. Torrey,[188] Zinsser,[189] and Beijerinck[190] suggested methods which were based on the cultivation of the anaerobe in the presence of an aerobe which absorbed the oxygen. A Petri dish about 10 cm. in diameter and two cm. high is poured with the medium which has been inoculated with the organism under study, or with the sterile medium if the plate is to be streaked. The plate is then placed in an incubator to dry, after which it is inverted into another dish at least 12 cm. in diameter, containing agar heavily inoculated with *Bacillus cereus*. The strictly aerobic *Bacillus cereus* will use the oxygen allowing the anaerobe to grow. Beijerinck used *Oidium lactis* instead of *Bacillus cereus*, because of its greater oxygen-consuming capacity.

178. Townsend. 1929. Centbl. Bakt., Pt. 2, 78, 161-172; Food Research 4 (1939), 231-237.
179. Hall. 1922. J. Infect. Diseases 30, 445-504.
180. Heller. 1922. Idem, 1-49.
181. Kahn. 1922. J. Med. Res. 43, 155-206.
182. Weinberg and Ginsbourg. 1927. Donnees Recentes sur les Microbes Anaerobes et leur Role n Pathologie, Masson et Cie, Paris.
183. Barber. 1920. J. Exper. Med. 32, 295-311.
184. Kendall *et al.* 1921. Infect. Dis. 29, 227-234.
185. Van Riemsdyk. 1922. Centbl. Bakt., Pt. 1, Orig. 88, 229-252.
186. Rockwell. 1924 J. Infect. Diseases 35, 581-586.
187. Novy. 1925. J. Infect. Diseases 36, 343-382.
188. Torrey. 1917. J. Bact. 2, 435-439.
189. Zinsser. 1906. J. Exper. Med. 8, 542.
190. Beijerinck. 1920. Rev. in Absts. Bact. 4 (1920), 34.

Giltner's [191] H Tube Method. This tube consists of two culture tubes fastened together to make an H. Pyrogallol may be placed in one arm and the culture in another. In place of alkaline pyrogallol an oxygen-consuming bacterium may be grown. Novy [187] reported that cultivation of *Bacillus subtilis* in one arm allowed an anaerobe to grow in the other. When H tubes are not available the culture tubes may be connected by means of glass tubing through one-hole rubber stoppers.

For the absorption of oxygen with chemicals alkaline pyrogallol, which has marked affinity for oxygen, is used. Many different contrivances have been devised for getting rid of oxygen in this manner.

Buchner's Method. In this method the culture tube is placed in a larger one, which contains the alkaline pyrogallol. It has the disadvantage that if some special support is not used to keep the culture tube above the surface of the pyrogallol, it is difficult to follow growth during incubation. These tubes may be prepared as follows:

Introduce two grams of pyrogallol into the bottom of a large test tube and place therein a support for the culture tube. This may be made from wood, cotton, glass, etc. After the culture tube has been placed on its support, introduce the sodium hydroxide by means of a pipette into the bottom of the tube, and seal the tube immediately with a rubber stopper.

Dimond [192] modified the Buchner method in two ways. Bitting and Bitting [193] also suggested a modified Buchner method. The material was "plated out" in the bottom of an Erlenmeyer flask. The flask was then inverted in the absorbent.

Morse and Kopeloff's [194] Method. The main advantage of this method is that no special apparatus is required. Ordinary Petri dishes are used, and they may be sterilized in the usual manner. The procedure consists in taking two tops and two bottoms of ordinary Petri dishes and placing them edge to edge. They may be paired just before the medium is poured. The inoculated medium is poured into the bottom part, or sterile agar may be used and streaked with the inoculum later. After the medium has hardened and been inoculated, the dishes are turned over and five to 10 grams of dry pyrogallic acid are placed in the bottom dish to which are added 30 ml. of a five-per cent sodium hydroxide solution. A strip of surgeon's adhesive tape is then placed around the equator uniting the two halves. Morse and Kopeloff proved the integrity of their anaerobic culture dish with methylene blue.

Wright's Method. This is another absorption method and differs from the others only in method of procedure. It is especially adaptable to the isolation of anaerobic sporeforming bacteria. Decimal dilutions of the sample are introduced into sterile litmus milk. About one inch above the meniscus of the milk a tight cotton cylinder is forced, upon which are put about two grams of pyrogallol. This is treated with strong sodium hydroxide and the original plug replaced in the tube. This tube should then be heated for 15 minutes at 80°C.(176°F.) to kill all vegetative bacteria. Later incubation will give the characteristic changes. This method has several objections. It is difficult to remove the microorganisms which have grown without having some of the pyrogallol solution run down into the culture. Rockwell [186] reported that the use of pyrogallic acid was not entirely satisfactory since the carbon dioxide was entirely removed. Rockwell accordingly proposed charging the alkaline water with carbon dioxide before addition to the pyrogallic acid.

Other methods depending on about the same principles have been proposed by Zinsser, [189] Lentz, [195] Kuster, [196] and McLeod. [197]

Varney's [198] Method for Cultivating Anaerobes. Varney proposed a method in which phosphorus was used for removing the oxygen in a tightly closed container. The apparatus consists of a standard museum jar into which is fitted a heavy wire frame to

191. Giltner. 1915. Science 41, 663.
192. Dimond. 1915. Brit. Med. J. 2, 778.
193. Bitting and Bitting. 1917. Nat. Canners Assoc. Bull. 14.
194. Morse and Kopeloff. 1922. Amer. J. Pub. Health 12, 119-121.
195. Lentz. 1910. Centbl. Bakt., Pt. 1, Orig. 53, 358-365.
196. Kuster. 1913. Centbl. Bakt., Ref., 57, 269-271.
197. McLeod. 1913. J. Path. & Bact. 4, 454-457.
198. Varney. 1926. J. Lab. & Clin. Med. 11, 1183-1186.

hold the Petri dishes or tubes. Various sizes of museum jars may be used. When the jar is filled and the apparatus assembled ready for use, about one-half inch of water is placed in the bottom of the jar. The water absorbs the phosphorus pentoxide vapor formed by combustion of the phosphorus. To secure anaerobic conditions a piece of yellow stick phosphorus about one-eighth to one-quarter inch long is placed in the evaporating dish. This is a sufficient charge for the 5 x 12 inch jar. The asbestos disc is quickly placed over the dish and fitted snugly into it. The cover is then fastened on the jar and the phosphorus begins to burn promptly.

The air and oxygen may also be removed physically by a vacuum pump. In food-preservation factories where vacuum closing machines are available, the cultures may be hermetically sealed in a vacuum.

Boiling. Air is very soluble in water at room temperature. Winkler has found that one liter of water at 20°C.(68°F.) will dissolve about nine mg. of oxygen. By boiling water for some time, dissolved oxygen may be driven off. Special methods are then necessary to prevent reabsorption of air. In liquid media where heating will cause no change, this may be done by a layer of sterile vaseline or ligroin.

Novy's Method. The apparatus used in the application of this method consists of a large glass jar with a removable top, which has become known as the Novy jar. The culture may be grown away from oxygen by using an inert gas, vacuum, or alkaline pyrogallol. The jar is constructed with a glass stopcock, which will allow the removal of air with a vacuum pump. This may be combined with alkaline pyrogallol and give an atmosphere which is entirely free from oxygen.

The exclusion of oxygen mechanically is accomplished by a number of ingenious devices. Some of them are simple, while others are objectionable on account of the cost of apparatus or increased burden in the preparation room.

Dick's Method for Anaerobic Plates. Dick[199] suggested the use of paraffin for covering the inoculated agar in Petri dishes to make anaerobic conditions. The paraffin was sterilized and spread quickly over the surface while hot. One of the advantages of this method is that enumeration of the anaerobic bacteria is possible. The only disadvantage is the difficulty of seeing the colonies of the bacteria. Northrup[200] proposed the addition of the dye Sudan III to the paraffin. This produces a color deep enough for distinguishing the white bacterial colonies. She finds it just as convenient to lift the paraffin cover from the surface of the agar when it is desirable to inoculate media, instead of cutting out a portion of it, as was suggested by Dick. This method is especially valuable for the isolation of anaerobic bacteria in pure culture where subsequent cultural and morphological examinations are desired.

Marino's[201] Method for Cultivating Anaerobic Bacteria as Modified by Krumwiede and Pratt. This method was used by Krumwiede and Pratt[202] for isolating fusiform bacilli. Two halves of a Petri dish are sterilized so that the bottom is placed in the inverted cover. The inoculated agar is then poured into the cover of the dish and the bottom of the dish laid on top of the agar, while it is still fluid. After the agar has solidified, the edges of the dish may be painted with paraffin to prevent the entrance of oxygen. According to Hall,[206] unless this is done, there will be a progressive ingress of oxygen from the periphery inward, as indicated by the recoloration of methylene blue when that substance is used as a criterion of anaerobiosis. To prevent this, a seal of vaseline or paraffin had to be employed.

Liquid oils, such as paraffin oils, may be used in covering media to prevent the entrance of oxygen. It is generally supposed that these function mainly in a mechanical manner, but the statements of Larson[203] and his colleagues seem to indicate that the oil functions by reducing the surface tension. Thompson[204] has stated that solid paraffin gave better results than these liquid mineral oils. A greater percentage of

199. Dick. 1918. J. Infect. Diseases 23, 578-579.
200. Northrup. 1919. J. Bact. 4, 299-300.
201. Marino. 1907. Ann. Inst. Pasteur 21, 1005.
202. Krumwiede and Pratt. 1913. J. Infect. Diseases 12, 199-201.
203. Larson. 1919. J. Infect. Diseases 25, 41-46.
204. Thompson. 1920. J. Infect. Diseases 27, 240-244.

positive cultures were secured with solid paraffin than with liquid paraffin. This action was explained by the fact that solid paraffin prevents the downward diffusion of oxygen by convection currents. Gates and Olitsky [205] also found that solid vaseline or paraffin gave more satisfactory anaerobiosis than the liquid mineral oils. These latter oils did not prevent the ingress of oxygen. The length of the column of liquid seemed to be of minor importance under a vaseline seal. Hall [206] also reached the conclusion that solid paraffin or vaseline was a much better seal for anaerobic cultures. His statements were based on data secured with methylene blue as a criterion.

Beattie's [207] Method. Ordinary test tubes containing plain or carbohydrate broths are used. Melted, sterilized vaseline is poured into the tube until a plug about one-half inch long is formed. The broth and vaseline are then boiled for 20 to 30 minutes, in order to expel any dissolved air, and allowed to cool. These tubes may be kept for an indefinite time and are airtight. When they are to be inoculated they may be melted in a water bath at 55°C.(131°F.). The sample may be introduced by means of a sterile pipette. The vaseline may then be heated over a flame to reform the solid plug, and the tube placed in the incubator. In order to remove any portion of the culture, a sterile sealed pipette (capillary) is thrust through the plug. This may be broken by forcing the end against the bottom of the tube, after which any portion of the culture may be removed. By melting the vaseline plug again the culture tube is sealed for further incubation. Kahn [171] stated that the vaseline-boiling method was the most reliable for obtaining anaerobiosis especially in liquid media. He did not find the other methods involving the use of pyrogallic acid, vacuum exhaustion, platinized carbon, etc., reliable.

Brewer's Petri Dish Cover and Technic for Cultivation of Anaerobic Bacteria. Brewer devised a special cover to work in combination with a solid medium containing a reducing agent. It obviates use of anaerobic jars, petroleum seals, and chemicals other than those in the medium itself and makes possible surface cultivation. The medium which Brewer recommended is his sodium thioglycollate medium. Either a pour or streak plate may be made. After the agar medium has solidified, the Petri dish cover is replaced by the special "anaerobic lid" which is so designed that it touches the agar at the periphery and results in trapping a small amount of air over the surface of the agar. The reducing agent in the medium uses up this small amount of air, and an anaerobic condition is thus made. A glass rim on the lid forms a seal with the moist solidified agar; no other seal is required. One ml. of a 1-500 methylene blue solution may be added to each liter of agar to act as an indicator, the reduced center of the medium in the dish becoming colorless with an oxygenated periphery.

The Deep Agar Shake Culture. This is one of the older methods which has enjoyed wide usage down to the present day. It consists in distributing the material, from which it is hoped to isolate anaerobic bacteria, throughout melted cooled agar medium in a culture tube. The organisms develop colonies which may be seen by holding the culture tube against the light. Veillon [208] adapted this method by preparing dilutions of the material to be analyzed. Three to six tubes of glucose agar were liquefied and cooled to 45°C.(113°F.) in a water bath. A small amount of the sample was placed in the first tube and carefully mixed. From this a series of dilutions was made in the other tubes. The medium was solidified and the tubes were incubated.

Miller, Garrett, and Prickett's [209] Modified Deep Agar Shake Culture for Anaerobic Bacteria. This procedure is a modification of the older deep-tube methods of Roux [210] and Hall.[211] Advent of the oval tube, the two broader sides of which are parallel, enabled Miller and his colleagues to develop a modified and more accurate deep agar shake culture for quantitative results. The ordinary oval tube was improved by providing it with a round neck and lip. The tubes are filled to the neck with medium, plugged, and

205. Gates and Olitsky. 1920. Proc. Soc. Exper. Biol. & Med. 18, 93.
206. Hall. 1921. J. Bact. 6, 1-42.
207. Beattie. 1916. Brit. Med. J. 1916—1, 756-757.
208. Veillon. Rev. in Mac Neal's (1920) Pathogenic Microorganisms.
209. Miller, Garrett, and Prickett. 1939. Food Research 4, 447-451.
210. Roux. 1887. Ann. Inst. Pasteur 1, 49-62.
211. Hall. 1929. J. Bact. 17, 255-301.

sterilized. Before use they are heated in a flowing steam sterilizer for 10 minutes. After cooling they are given decimal dilutions of the sample, and the medium is allowed to solidify. The necks are then filled with reduced methylene-blue agar containing 1/20,000 parts of dye and two per cent of dextrose at pH 8.2. This permits following the rate and depth of oxygen absorption.

Burri's [212] **Method for Isolating Obligate Anaerobic Bacteria.** This was a deep-tube method, much like the agar-shake. The bottom of the tube was closed with a rubber stopper, which could be removed. The agar could then be forced out of the tube. The tubes, which were about the size of culture tubes, were plugged at both ends with cotton and sterilized in the hot-air oven. The rubber stoppers are sterilized under water in an autoclave. When the tubes are to be used, one of the cotton plugs is replaced with a rubber stopper. Three dilutions of the material under study in two per cent nutrient agar are layered into the tube and finally covered with a layer of sterile agar. After incubation, the agar plug may be pressed out into a sterile Petri dish. Hall,[213] who has given the anaerobic bacteria much study, stated that the Burri method is better than the so-called surface methods. He modified Burri's method as follows: The most suitable size of tube is 9 x 180 mm. The cork or rubber stoppers are placed in position before sterilization when they are used. Owing to the fact that they loosen during sterilization, Hall later found that Capes-Viscose caps could be placed over the stopper to hold it in place.

Greenberg's [214] **Method for Single-Colony Isolation of Anaerobic Bacteria.** This method was proposed as a reliable one for isolating anaerobic bacteria. It is based on a procedure for separation of single colonies of streptococci of Ward and Rudd.[215]

Procedure: Using a one-mm. platinum loop, one loopful of an 18 to 24 hour broth culture is touched gently on the inside of the culture tube, so that only the barest film of culture remains on the loop. This inoculum is then transferred to a tube containing five ml. of sterile broth (type of broth is immaterial)and thoroughly mixed. The loop is flamed and a loopful of the inoculated broth is transferred to a tube of the semisolid medium, which has been heated in boiling water to displace oxygen and cooled to 45°C. (113°F.) immediately before use. The tube should then be rotated to distribute the organisms evenly. It is then placed in the incubator under ordinary aerobic conditions. The formula for the semisolid medium is given in the chapter on "Media."

The incubation period will vary with the organism under study. For *Clostridium welchii* the best incubation period was found to be overnight (16 to 18 hours) at 37°C. (98.6°F.). For all other anaerobes studied it was found best to leave the cultures at room temperature—approximately 22°C.(71.6°F.)—and place them in the 37°C. incubator the following morning. The development of colonies is then watched closely (up to 10 hours), the cultures being removed from the incubator when the colonies have reached a suitable size. Prolonged incubation at 37°C. may result in confluent growth, making it impossible to obtain single colonies.

In the case of mixtures of anaerobes and aerobes it has been found possible to eliminate the latter by (a) preliminary anaerobic cultivation of the mixture in fluid medium, and (b) by dilution of the resultant growth to the point where aerobic organisms are eliminated in the majority of tubes planted. The following procedure for dealing with contaminated material has been tried and has proved successful:

1. The product on test, or representative portion, is inoculated into 250 ml. of Brewer's thioglycollate medium (without dextrose) which has been previously heated in boiling water, and cooled to 45°C.

2. The inoculated flask is incubated anaerobically in a McIntosh and Fildes' jar for 24 hours at 37°C.

3. From this, at least 20 tubes, containing semisolid medium, are inoculated using the previously described method. These are incubated aerobically. Using the above technic and medium, separate colonies were successfully obtained from each of the

212. Burri. 1902. Centbl. Bakt., Pt. 2, 8, 533-537.
213. Hall. 1930. J. Infect. Diseases 27, 576-590.
214. Greenberg. 1941. Canad. Pub. Health J., 32, 84-85.
215. Ward and Rudd. 1939. Australian J. Exper. Biol. & Med. Sci., 17, 77-79.

following cultures of anaerobes: *Cl. botulinum, Cl. chauvei, Cl. fallax, Cl. histolyticum, Cl. novyi, Cl. putrificum, Cl. sordelli, Cl. sporogenes, Cl. tertium, Cl. tetani, Cl. tetanoides, Vibrion septique,* and *Cl. welchii.*

REFERENCE BOOKS

EYRE, J. W. H., 1934. The Elements of Bacteriological Technique. Wm. Wood & Co., New York.

GATENBY, J. B., 1928. Bolles Lee's Microtomists Vade-Mecum. P. Blakiston's Son & Co., Philadelphia, Pa.

JOHNSTON, J. H., AND SIMPSON, R. H. The Principles of Practical Bacteriology for Scientific Workers. Churchill, London.

MANUAL OF METHODS. For Pure Culture Study of Bacteria. Prepared by The Committee on Bacteriological Technic of the Society of American Bacteriologists, Geneva, N. Y.

McCLUNG, C. E., 1929. Handbook of Microscopical Technic. Paul B. Hoeber, Inc., New York.

McCOY, E. F., AND McCLUNG, L. S., 1939. The Anaerobic Bacteria and Their Activities in Nature and Disease: A Subject Bibliography. Univ. of California Press, Berkeley, Calif.

Medical Research Council. Reports of the Committee Upon Pathological Methods VI. The Laboratory Diagnosis of Acute Intestinal Infections, Including the Principles and Practice of the Agglutination Test. His Majesty's Stationery Office, 1920.

PREVOT, A. R., 1940. Manuel de Classification et de Détermination des Bactéries Anaérobies. Masson et Cie, Paris.

WEBSTER, R. W., 1923. Diagnostic Methods—Chemical, Bacteriological and Microscopical. P. Blakiston's Son & Co., Philadelphia, Pa.

WEINBERG, M., NATIVELLE, R., AND PREVOT, A., 1937. Les Microbes Anaérobies. Masson et Cie, Paris.

CHAPTER 3

YEASTS AND MOLDS

These fungi interest microbiologists in food preservation industries. They bring about both desirable changes and undesirable changes which cause spoilage in foods. Only those topics about organisms which have to do directly with food microbiology, are discussed below. Various fungi have made important places for themselves. The molds produce large amounts of useful enzymes which are used in food industries and medicine. Ramsbottom [1] has reviewed many of these applications. *Mucor rouxii* functions in the "amylo" process for changing starch to sugar. It does quite as well what malt has done. Certain Penicillium species have been used for a long time for ripening cheese. In some cases, as for certain fermented milks, mixtures of yeasts and molds are used. Yeasts are important not only in making alcoholic beverages but glycerol and fats.

RESISTANCE OF MOLDS AND OTHER FUNGI TO UNFAVORABLE CONDITIONS

Mold spores seem to be more resistant to certain unfavorable conditions than either yeasts or bacteria. Generally speaking, however, the bacteria are most resistant.

Concentrated Sugar Solutions. Grove [2] reported that a species of Penicillium, with which he worked, was inhibited by 65 per cent of sugar but showed scant growth even in 70 per cent solutions. Such concentrations cannot be tolerated by bacteria. Bezssonof [3] also reported development of *Penicillium glaucum* in saturated sugar solutions while Kopeloff and Byall [4] observed development of *Aspergillus sydowi, Aspergillus niger,* and *Penicillium expansum* in 60° Brix blackstrap molasses.

Heat. Mold spores are far less resistant to heat than bacterial spores. On account of their wide distribution in nature and the fact that heat is used to rid foodstuffs of objectionable microorganisms, heat resistance of mold spores had to be determined. According to Lode,[5] dry heat at 125°C.(257°F.) killed mold spores in 15 minutes, but a temperature of 80°C.(176°F.) did not destroy them in seven hours. Thom and Ayers,[6] however, found *Rhizopus nigricans* and *Oidium lactis* to be destroyed by pasteurization of milk at 54.5°C.(130.1°F.) in 30 minutes but that most strains of Aspergillus and Penicillium resisted this temperature to be killed only at 60°C.(140°F.) for 30 minutes. Streider and McClellan [7] submerged flasks containing mold spores in a water bath at 20°C.(68°F.) and slowly raised the temperature to 100°C.(212°F.) to simulate as nearly

1. Ramsbottom. 1936. J. Soc. Chem. Ind. 55, 717-724.
2. Grove. 1918. Univ. of Bristol., Ann. Rept. Agr. and Hort. Res. Sta.
3. Bezssonof. 1918. Ber. Deut. Bot. Gesell. 36, 646-648.
4. Kopeloff and Byall. 1920. J. Ind. Eng. Chem. 12, 256-257.
5. Lode. 1902. Arch. Hyg. 42, 107.
6. Thom and Ayers. 1916. J. Agr. Res. 6, 153-166.
7. Streider and McClellan. 1922. Baking Tech. 1, 230 and 282.

as possible conditions in bread baking. During this time of 35 minutes all mold spores were killed. Loaves of bread which had been exposed to molds were heated to 110°C.(230°F.) at 15-lb. pressure for 30 seconds and live steam for four minutes. The molds were not completely destroyed, but were markedly reduced in numbers. In the meat-packing industry Roderick[8] found that molds in sausages were killed when they were heated in water at 60°C.(140°F.) for 10 minutes. Lewis and Yesair,[9] using temperatures of 50°C.(122°F.), 55°C.(131°F.), and 60°C.(140°F.) exposed pure cultures of molds for periods of five minutes to one hour. None survived 60°C.(140°F.) for five minutes. Wallace and Tanner[10] used a wider variety of species, reaching conclusions which, in general, agreed with those presented above.

An undescribed species of Penicillium was isolated by Williams, Cameron, and Williams[11] from blueberries and from soil of blueberry fields. Growth from ascospores occurred in a vacuum of 28.5 inches and from sclerotia in a vacuum of 26 inches. The destruction time at 82.2°C. (180°F.) was 9.7 minutes for ascospores and 1,000 minutes for sclerotia.

Ultraviolet Light. Use of this form of energy has been tried for controlling many different kinds of fungi. Whether it is successful depends on the fungus as well as the conditions under which it is used. It must penetrate to the fungus to destroy it. Mere irradiation of the food product will not necessarily destroy fungi in it. Meier and Crampoloff[12] were able to destroy cultures of *Cladosporium lycopersici, Botrytis cinera*, and *Penicillium glaucum* from tomatoes by 12, 10, and 40 minutes' exposure, respectively, to ultraviolet rays at a distance of 21 centimeters. In certain instances, however, even longer exposures did not destroy the cultures, probably because some spores were buried and accordingly not touched by the rays. Continuous irradiation was better than discontinuous. Meier and Crampoloff found that exposure of fresh fruit to ultraviolet light reduced rotting. Whether the process would be practical is difficult to infer from their results. Smith[13] has reviewed much literature on this question. Mold spores on cardboard strips were not entirely killed in experiments by Tanner and Appling.[14] On the underside of the strips which were not exposed many mold colonies developed, as would be expected. The conditions on the strips were not unlike those which would obtain on the surface of foods which were exposed to ultraviolet light. Sutton[15] reported similar results. Molds were destroyed under some of the conditions which might exist in cheese factories. Sutton observed that dark-colored molds were much more resistant to exposure to ultraviolet light. Presence of pigment in the cells prevents penetration or absorption

8. Roderick. 1926. Quoted from Lewis and Yesair.
9. Lewis and Yesair. 1928. Bull. Inst. Amer. Meat Packers, Chicago.
10. Wallace and Tanner. 1931. Proc. Soc. Expt. Biol. and Med. 28, 970-972.
11. Williams, Cameron, and Williams. 1941. Food Research 6, 69-73.
12. Meier and Crampoloff. 1936. Ann. Agr. Suisse 37, 951-977.
13. Smith. 1936. Rev. in Rev. Appl. Mycol. 16, 200.
14. Tanner and Appling. 1941. Proc. Soc. Exptl. Biol. and Med. 47, 47-51.
15. Sutton. 1941. J. Australian Inst. Agr. Sci. 7, 67-73.

of the energy. Spores of *Thamnidium elegans* and *Trichoderma lignorum* were spread on the surfaces of agar in Petri dishes and irradiated. Short exposures were found to appreciably reduce the load of spores and to check the growth of active mycelia present on the surface of foods. Exposure to the lamp for 40 minutes did not inhibit growth for more than two days. Thus it seems possible that short exposures to the lamp might appreciably reduce the load of spores and check growth of active mycelia on the surfaces of foods. Further work by Tomkins [16] with such foods as oranges, eggs, and beef fat showed that while some destruction of these fungi resulted, the effect was not pronounced. Three types of lamps used by Schroeder [17] on a mixture of several species of molds secured from a loaf of moldy bread, including *Aspergillus niger* and *Rhizopus nigricans*, were shown to differ considerably in killing molds. The lamps used were quartz 75-watt medium-pressure mercolite, QZ 15-watt low-pressure mercolite, and QZ 75-watt medium-pressure mercolite. The quartz lamp showed great killing power but was said to be too expensive and to give off too much ozone and short radiations to be used on foods. This lamp had the most energy in the 2537 Å region and shorter. The 15-watt QZ lamp, which was next in killing power, was second also in intensity of the 2537 Å line; and the QZ 75-watt arc was lowest in killing power on molds and had the weakest emission at 2537 Å.

Low Temperatures. Fungi are materially inhibited by low temperatures as are the bacteria. They cause some trouble, however, in foods in cold storage, such as meats and eggs. So-called "whiskers" and "black-spot" on such meats are caused by development of fungi which are discussed in several places in this book. Semeniuk and Ball [18] identified many different fungi from meat from cold-storage lockers in Iowa. More information on this subject was published in 1940.[19] Minimum temperature at which molds could develop was said to be clearly below 0°C.(32°F.). Even a temperature of —5°C.(23°F.) was said not to be a guarantee against development of molds; only a few developed at —8.3°C.(17.6°F.), while at —12.2°C.(10°F.) there was no development. Between this temperature and —17.8°C.(0°F.) no mold developed over a period of 27 months. Results of similar investigations have been reported by Panasenko and Tatarenko.[20]

Carbon Dioxide. This is not a very active inhibitory agent. Tomkins [21] observed that storage of foods in concentrations up to 20 per cent encouraged rather than restricted growth of certain molds.

Direct Sunlight. Weinzirl [22] reported that rather long exposure was necessary to harm mold spores, but they were killed. Viability of spores

16. Tomkins. 1937. Ann. Rept., Food Invest. Bd. for Year 1936, 32.

17. Schroeder. 1941. Studies of the Institutum Divi Thomae 3, 159-166.

18. Semeniuk and Ball. 1937. Proc. Iowa Acad. Sci. 44, 37-43.

19. Brewing Trade Review 54 (1940), 12.

20. Panasenko and Tatarenko. 1940. Microbiology 9, 579-584.

21. Tomkins. 1938. Ann. Rept., Food Invest. Bd. for Year 1937, 30-40.

22. Weinzirl. 1921. Univ. Wisconsin, Studies in Science, No. 2, 55-59.

in conidial material for 20 years was observed by McCrae.[23] This was in general confirmed by Becquerel.[24]

Chemical Disinfectants. According to Lode [25] mold spores are killed by .2 per cent solutions of mercuric chloride, 5 per cent solutions of phenol, and 3 per cent of chloride of lime. More work could well be done in this field. It is known that boric acid is quite toxic to molds. Calcium and sodium salts of propionic acid have been found to inhibit molds in lower concentrations.

Tomkins [26] has shown that volatile substances, such as formaldehyde, ethyl alcohol, ether, and esters, exert a repressive action on the rate of growth of molds. When normally growing cultures were introduced into an atmosphere containing acetaldehyde, the growth was immediately changed. It was completely inhibited, inhibited for a short period after it was resumed, or was not materially affected, although it may have been slightly reduced. Such factors as temperature, concentration of acetaldehyde, and size of the colony determined into which of these three categories the behavior fell. It would take too much space to review all of Tomkin's conclusions. Volatile substances which retard and inhibit the growth of molds seem to fall into two broad groups, i.e., those which when present in definite concentrations retard growth irrespective of the age of the culture and time of exposure and those in whose presence there is a certain measure of adaptation with a consequent increase in the rate of growth ratio. This situation is somewhat complicated by numerous factors but in general the above statements reflect the conclusions which Tomkins reached.

In addition to the chemical substances just discussed, are the "mold inhibitors" or mycostatic salts much used in certain industries to control mold growth. Some of these are calcium or sodium proprionate ("Mycoban") and sodium pentachlorphenate.

Tomkins' [27] Method for Determining the Action of Volatile Substances on Fungi. The fungus is cultured in a liquid culture medium contained in a Petri dish. Ten ml. of the medium are placed in a dish about 9 cm. in diameter to form a shallow layer about 1.5 mm. in depth. To start growth a small sterile piece of porous material (flower pot) on which has been placed a drop of water suspension of spores is placed in the middle of the dish. Extreme care should be used not to move the dish. The fungus grows out from the porous material evenly in all directions in exactly the same way as when it grows on a nutrient medium solidified with agar. The diameter of the colony can be measured by arranging the dish on a piece of glass covering a sheet of squared paper. This method has advantages over a solid medium. The nutrient medium and the solution of the inhibitor may be sterilized slightly and mixed in the Petri dish in any desired proportion. Also, growth may be allowed to start in the absence of the inhibitor which can be added later, or the nutrient liquid may be removed by using pipettes and replaced by a fresh solution.

Production of Bactericidal Substances by Molds. Fleming [28] reported that a certain type of Penicillium produced a powerful bactericidal sub-

23. McCrae. 1923. Science 58, 426.
24. Becquerel. 1910. Compt. Rend. Acad. Sci. 150, 1437-1439.
25. Lode. 1902. Arch. Hyg. 42, 107.
26. Tomkins. 1931. Ann. Rept., Food Invest. Bd. for Year 1930, 48.
27. Tomkins. 1936. Idem for Year 1935, 131.
28. Fleming. 1929. Brit. J. Expt. Path. 10, 226-236; J. Path. and Bact. 35, 831.

stance. The active agent was readily filterable and the name Penicillin was given to filtrates of broth cultures of the mold. It lost its power after 10 to 14 days at room temperature but could be preserved longer by neutralization. It was not destroyed by boiling for a few minutes; in alkaline solution, boiling for an hour markedly reduced its power. Autoclaving for 20 minutes at 115°C.(239°F.) practically destroyed it. While many bacteria are quite insensitive to it, pyogenic cocci are especially sensitive to it. White [29] found a strain of *Aspergillus flavus* which also produced bactericidal substances. Other strains had no such action. Since the application of this substance seems to be in other fields than microbiology of foods, it will not be discussed further.

Activity of Fungus Spores. Since spores are generally considered as resting stages in the life cycle of the fungus, some believe that they are entirely inactive. Such is not the case. They are living protoplasm and are, consequently, carrying on the functions of all living cells, although much more slowly. Effront [30] was able to demonstrate active enzymes in fungus spores. He reported that bacterial spores may be brought into such a state that while losing the essential properties of living cells they retain their ability to produce enzymes. Spores of *Bacillus subtilis* produced a large quantity of amylase and peptase. These conclusions were confirmed by Ruehle [31] and Kopeloff and Kopeloff.[32] Spores are, therefore, not to be considered as inactive agents. They are able to bring about changes in foodstuffs and other materials.

Effect of Moisture Concentration on Growth of Molds. Many foods, such as flour and cereals, keep as long as the moisture content is kept below a certain concentration. In an investigation of the flora of corn meal, Thom and Le Fevre [33] found that the moisture content greatly influenced development of both molds and bacteria. *Aspergillus repens* became an active agent in spoilage when the water content reached 13 per cent and above. At a moisture content of 16 per cent several other species of molds began to develop, while at 18 to 20 per cent, bacteria appeared. Quite similar conclusions were reached by Bailey and Thom.[34] The subject has also been studied by Tomkins [35] in connection with investigation conducted by the Food Investigation Board of Great Britain. The first work apparently considered only temperature and humidity. In this work, germination of *Alternaria citri* was observed in a relative humidity of 91 per cent, but not in 87 per cent.

The next report included the results of studies of the relation between temperature, humidity, and germination in the presence of nutrients. A drop of nutrient agar was placed on a slide and evaporated to dryness. Dry spores were then added and the slides placed in atmospheres with different relative humidities. Growth was found to be best at a temperature called

29. White. 1940. Science 92, 127.
30. Effront. 1907. Monit. Sci. 21, 81-87.
31. Ruehle. 1923. J. Bact. 8, 487-491.
32. Kopeloff and Kopeloff. 1919. Science 49, 573.
33. Thom and LeFevre. 1921. J. Agr. Res. 22, 179-183.
34. Bailey and Thom. 1920. Oper. Miller 25, 368-371.
35. Tomkins. 1928. Ann. Rept., Food Invest. Bd. for Years 1927 and 1928.

the optimum, which varied with the species. At this optimum temperature growth was possible over a wider range of humidities.

Tomkins observed that the surface on which the mold was placed had considerable to do with its ability to germinate.

RHIZOPUS

Rhizopus molds belong to the family of Mucoraceae. Great numbers of spores are borne in a sporangium. Hanzawa [36] grouped a number of Rhizopus species of industrial significance according to their morphological and physiological properties. Many different species have been described and it is probable that some of them are identical. Many descriptions are too incomplete and do not permit satisfactory comparison with an unknown species.

Rhizopus nigricans (Mucor stolonifer). This is a very common mold in certain types of foods. It seems to be widely disseminated in nature, having been isolated from soils in Europe and America by many investigators. *Rhizopus nigricans* was reported by Lloyd and Newell [37] and Stevens [38] to be important in rot of strawberries during shipment. Harter and Weimer [39] and Schneider-Orelli [40] gave the fungus wider significance in fruit spoilage. Storage of fruits at low temperature (below 1°C.[33.8°F.]) protects against spoilage by this mold.

Other species have been reported to play important roles in industrial processes and food spoilage. *Rhizopus delemar* was described by Hanzawa [36] and, on account of its very vigorous amylase, was said to be important in the manufacture of ethyl alcohol by the "amylo-process." *Rhizopus oligosporus, Rhizopus chinensis, Rhizopus tritici,* and *Rhizopus japonicus* are other species which are employed in fermentation where starch must be changed to fermentable sugars.

"Chinese Yeast." This is a "starter" used in China and other countries for preparation of an alcoholic drink from rice starch. It appears as little balls in which is a mixed flora of microorganisms, among which a few active ones have been singled out for intensive study. Calmette [41] and Eijkmann [42] described its manufacture. A mixture of husked rice mashed in cold water is treated with a number of drug preparations, among which garlic is usually found. A stiff paste is secured which is made into little balls. These are covered with straw in thin layers on mats placed in rooms heated to about 30°C.(86°F.). During this treatment the balls become covered with a velvety growth and assume the odor of yeast. Calmette stated that *Mucor rouxii* gained entrance to "Chinese yeast" from the rice husks and straw in which the small balls of rice are placed. Saito [43] isolated a species to which he gave the name *Rhizopus oligosporus* from rice flour used by the Chinese for making rice wine. Chrzaszca [44] reported another mold in Chinese yeast. He gave it the name

36. Hanzawa. 1912. Mycol. Centbl. 1, 76-91.
37. Lloyd and Newell. 1929. Ill. Agr. Expt. Sta. Bull. 333.
38. Stevens. 1917. U. S. Dept. Agr. Bull. 531.
39. Harter and Weimer. 1922. Phytopathology 12, 205-212.
40. Schneider-Orelli. 1911. Centbl. Bakt., Pt. 2, 32, 161.
41. Calmette. 1892. Ann. Inst. Pasteur 6, 604-620.
42. Eijkmann. 1894. Centbl. Bakt., Pt. 1, 16, 97-103.
43. Saito. 1904. Centbl. Bakt., Pt. 2, 13, 153-161.
44. Chrzaszca. 1901. Centbl. Bakt., Pt. 2, 7, 326-338.

Mucor cambodja. A large number of different microorganisms were found in Korean koji, a kind of Chinese yeast, by Naganishi.[45] Korean koji was said to be more active than the Chinese product. Thirty-seven molds, nine yeasts, and four bacteria were isolated from 18 different koji preparations. Among the species studied were the following: *Absidia* sp., *Rhizopus* sp., *Willia anomala, Mycoderma* sp., *Bacillus subtilis,* and various members of the lactic acid-producing group of bacteria.

Yamazaki[6] observed that "Chinese Yeast Cakes," obtained in China and adjacent countries and used in the preparation of both fermented and distilled beverages, varied greatly in weight (.2-2,500 gm.), and also in size, color, and shape. The chief gross constituents were rice meal, other grains, vegetable drugs, and mineral matter in variable proportions. *Rhizopus,* yeasts, and *Mucor* were the organisms most commonly found; *Monascus, Penicillium, Monilia,* and *Aspergillus* were less frequent.

The Amylo-Process. This process has been used for many years in the Orient for fermenting grain mashes to alcohol. Molds are used in place of malt for hydrolyzing starch to fermentable sugars. In many cases the actual fungi which were involved were not known. *Aspergillus oryzae* was found to be one of the important species in use in Japan. *Amylomyces rouxii* is the name given to the fungus accomplishing the same ends in China. Owen[47] stated that the former fungus has never been successfully used in alcohol fermentation because it uses the alcohol toward the end of the fermentation; the latter fungus, however, is satisfactory both for saccharification of starch and fermentation of the sugar into alcohol. Owen stated that the amylo-process was developed by Calmette and Voidin in France and Belgium; since that time it has been used in many countries for fermenting starch to alcohol. While their first work was done with *Amylomyces rouxii,* Calmette later isolated and used *Rhizopus delemar* and several species of Mucor. Owen described the use of these fungi in the fermentation.

Among the various molds which have been found to be directly applicable in the amylo-process is *Rhizopus japonicus,* cells of which are especially rich in amylase. Ploberger[48] and Leopold and Buka[49] mentioned some of the factors which influence its activities. The former investigator mentioned other molds which are active destroyers of starch, *Aspergillus oryzae, Amylomyces delemar, Amylomyces rouxii,* and several Aspergilli.

MUCORS

In the same family with *Rhizopus* species are *Mucors.* The latter differ mainly in the fact that but one sporangiophore rises from the same place on the stolons. Some of the Mucors are important in industrial fermentations. A key to common Mucors was published by Jensen.[50] *Mucor*

45. Naganishi. 1929. Rept. Central Lab. So. Manchurian Ry. Co., 41-42.
46. Yamazaki. 1932. Bull. Utunomyia Agr. Coll. 2, 1-24.
47. Owen. 1933. Ind. and Eng. Chem. 25, 87-89.
48. Ploberger. 1940. Wchnschr. Brau. 57, 99-102.
49. Leopold and Buka. 1938. Zentbl. Bakt., Pt. 2, 97, 353-386.
50. Jensen. 1912. Cornell Univ. Agr. Expt. Sta. Bull. 315.

mucedo, one of the first species studied by Brefeld,[51] is widely distributed in nature and is probably the species usually encountered. It has been found in various foods. *Mucor cambodja*, described *by Chrzaszca*,[44] from rice cakes ("ragi") was reported to have much in common with Rhizopus species which are actively amylolytic. Wehmer [52] described a species from the same source under the name of *Mucor javanicus*. According to Wai,[53] *Mucor sufu* functions in ripening of soybean cheese. *Mucor mucedo*, with a few other molds, is responsible for the white cotton-like growth, often called "whiskers," on foods which have been held in cold storage.

THAMNIDIUM

The members of this group resemble Mucor in many respects. They possess two kinds of sporangia. One is borne at the tip of a sporangiophore and contains many spores while the other is borne on the hyphae and usually contains two spores. This fungus causes some trouble in meat coolers.

Low concentrations of carbon dioxide were found to be markedly inhibitory, by Moran *et al.*,[54] to development of *Thamnidium chaetocladioides* when growing on lean meat, and in artificial media at low temperatures.

Smith and Tomkins [55] described a case in which lean meat became brown and sticky, with an unpleasant taint, after hanging in a cold room. The cause was attributed to unusually heavy growth of *Thamnidium chaetocladioides*.

BOTRYTIS

This fungus is occasionally found by microbiologists on various organic materials. The characteristics of the group may be secured from the description of such a species as *Botrytis cinerea* as reported by Jensen.[50] Stevens and Hawkins,[56] when studying *Botrytis cinerea* spoilage of strawberries, reported that spread of the infection was favored by moisture and low temperatures which restricted the growth of other fungi. They found that the fungus grew on strawberries under very good refrigeration. The gray mold of hops was found to be *Botrytis cinerea* by Wormald and Cheal.[57] Bidault [58] found Botrytis species on frozen meats.

According to Smith,[59] phenol in a concentration of .4 per cent is fatal to spores of Botrytis.

DEMATIUM

This genus and its best known species, *Dematium pullulans*, has received much attention of mycologists and fermentologists. It is easily isolated from fruits such as grapes and may grow with appearances of typical yeast cells. *Dematium pullulans* forms a mycelium on which numerous conidia appear. It seems quite probable that conditions of

51. Brefeld. 1874. Landw. Jahrb., Vols. 3, 4, and 5, 1874, 1875, and 1876.
52. Wehmer. 1900. Centbl. Bakt., Pt. 2, 6, 610-619.
53. Wai. 1929. Science 70, 307-308.
54. Moran, Smith, and Hopkins. 1932. J. Soc. Chem. Ind. 51, 114T.
55. Smith and Tomkins. 1932. Cold Storage Prod. Rev. 35, 36.
56. Stevens and Hawkins. 1925. Ice and Refrig. 59, 375-376.
57. Wormald and Cheal. 1926. J. Min. Agr. London 33, 456-458.
58. Bidault. 1921. Compt. Rend. Soc. Biol. 85, 1017-1018.
59. Smith. 1921. Ann. Appl. Biol. 8, 27 50.

growth have much to do with appearance of these conidia. Klöcker and Schiönning [60] studied the fusion of cells for which this fungus is so well known. Two cells situated close to one another fuse, one cell seeming to penetrate the other. In the cell which is invaded by the other, elliptical cells appear, which may also bud. Such units are to be distinguished from ascospores. Weleminsky [61] studied two cultures which were secured by exposing plates of wort gelatin in an orchard. One of these had quite a normal appearance, but the other varied considerably. The ability to form endogenous cells was retained in the later generations; these cells often separated and behaved perfectly similarly to the other free cells. The number of spore-bearing mycelial threads and the number of spores varied. One and the same thread often showed spores separated by normal forms at different places; the number of spores varied between two and eight. In order to find a cause for the variations, the author studied the effects of diff·rent conditions. Simple grape juice gave the best results. Varying the temperature and the nature of the light had no influence on the spore formation. Previous culture of the colonies on fruits and leaves and on gypsum blocks was also without effect on the spore-bearing capacities. The best method of inducing sporulation appeared to be to let the colonies dry and remain for one to three weeks, and then moisten them again with water. Weleminsky concluded that *Dematium pullulans*, de Bary, must be placed amongst Ascomycetes, and belongs to the simplest group, which comprises the Saccharomycetes and Exoascus organisms.

According to von Skerst,[62] *Dematium pullulans*, under certain conditions, may cause ropiness in beer. Between .5°C. and 30°C. a yellow-white sediment forms on the bottom of the culture flask; later a characteristic film covers the surface of the liquid. Ropiness appears more readily in media poor in nutriments.

PENICILLIUM

This genus was established in 1809 by Link for all molds having a brush-like type of conidial fructification. The conidiophores branch at the apex and at the tip of each branch conidia are formed in chains. Several investigators have studied this important group of fungi. Results of one such study was reported by Thom,[63] whose report is illustrated with drawings which could be of great assistance to the food mycologist in determining unknown Penicillia. The Penicillia seem to be able to bring about desirable and undesirable changes in foods. Dox [64] studied the endoenzymes of *Penicillium camemberti* and reported the presence of erepsin, nuclease, lipase, emulsin, amylase, inulase, raffinase, sucrase, maltase, and lactase. Such an array of enzymes would seem to indicate a marked ability to decompose organic matter. While the green Penicillia cause spoilage in certain foods it should also be remembered that they bring about quite desirable changes as well. They act in certain cheeses

60. Klöcker and Schiönning. 1900. Compt. Rend. Lab. Carlsberg 5. 47.
61. Weleminsky. 1899. Centbl. Bakt., Pt. 2, 5, 297-303.
62. von Skerst. 1898. Wchnschr. Brau. 15, 354.
63. Thom. 1930. The Penicillia. Williams and Wilkins. Baltimore, Md.
64. Dox. 1910. U. S. Dept. Agr., Bureau of Animal Industry Bull. 120.

to bring out a characteristic flavor (Thom,[63] Stewart[65]). *Penicillium camemberti* and *Penicillium roqueforti* have been used for ripening the cheeses which bear their names. Thom stated that *Penicillium roqueforti* has been described in dairy literature as *P. glaucum.* Dvorak[66] found that the mold formed a typical aroma without symbiotic development of another species as was suggested by Jensen.[50]

In preparing mold powder to be used as a starter for blue-veined cheeses Hussong and Hammer[67] grew the mold on bread under aseptic conditions, dried it, and ground it to a fine powder. The advantages of this procedure are a powder rich in mold spores, short time for preparation of the starter, and freedom of the powder from contamination.

Penicillium brevicaule is another cosmopolitan species which has been put to practical use. It has been utilized in a technic for detecting the presence of arsenical compounds in various materials. *Penicillium crustaceum* is found on decaying wood, bread, etc. It grows on bread at temperatures between 10°C.(50°F.) and 25°C.(77°F.). It gives an abundant even growth, white in the beginning, turning to a dark brown. Bidault[58] found the fungus on frozen meat. Other species have been found in cheese and other dairy products.

Biological Test for Arsenic (Schneider[68]). Tests for arsenic are usually carried out by the different chemical methods. In foreign countries, however, a biological test with *Penicillium brevicaule* is used. This mold, when grown on a medium containing arsenic, gives off garlic-like odors. Gosio[69] first observed this and found seven different molds which formed this garlic-like odor from foods containing small amounts of arsenic. Crumbs of bread (wheat) form the best culture medium for this mold and the incubation is done at a temperature of from 28 to 32°C.(82.4 to 98.6°F.). In the presence of not more than .00001 gram of arsenic in such culture, there will be noticeable a distinct and very characteristic garlic odor which may persist for months if the culture is not killed. These molds do not produce garlic odors with sulfur, phosphorus, antimony, boron, and bismuth compounds, but they do have the power of converting selenium and tellurium compounds into volatile substances having the garlic-like odor. The following is the procedure for making the test:

Procedure: If the material to be examined is liquid, let the dry bread crumbs (either white or graham) absorb it to saturation, then scatter a small quantity of fine crumbs over the surface. If the material to be tested is solid, grind or cut and mix with an equal amount of bread crumbs and then moisten with a little sterile distilled water. Place the prepared material in a sterile flask of suitable size and plug with sterile cotton. Sterilize the flask and contents by the usual fractional method at 100°C.(212°F.) or for 30 minutes in the autoclave. Absolute sterilization must be secured. There is no danger of volatilizing the arsenic at these temperatures. As soon as the flask and contents are cold, inoculate with the mold, as follows: The mold cultures may be grown on bread or pieces of potato. Remove a small quantity of the

65. Stewart. 1919. Dairy Sci. 2, 407-414.
66. Dvorak. 1920. Milchw. Zentbl. 3, 200-207.
67. Hussong and Hammer. 1935. J. Dairy Sci. 18, 599-602.
68. Schneider. 1915. J. Amer. Pharm. Assoc. 4, 1307.
69. Gosio. 1892. Riv. Ig. e Sanit. Pub. 9, 201-230; 261-273.

mold in the spore forming stage and mix with peptone salt solution or sterilized water. Add enough of the mold suspension to moisten the bread in the flask. Do not add more of the spore-bearing material than the mass (bread and arsenical substance) in the flask will absorb, as too much moisture will retard the growth of the fungus. Cover the inoculated flask with a rubber cap and incubate at a temperature of 37°C.(98.6°F.), although the ordinary room temperature will answer the purpose. As soon as the growth is clearly visible to the naked eye, which may be within 24 hours, the characteristic garlic odor will be noticeable on opening the flask. If no odor is apparent, again seal and incubate for 24 hours or longer. In case the substances to be tested are strongly acid, they may be first neutralized by means of calcium carbonate. It must be kept in mind that *Penicillium brevicaule* as well as other molds, will convert tellurium and selenium salts into volatile substances having a garlic-like odor. The arsenic and selenium odors are closely similar, but that from selenium is somewhat different in quality, more like that of mercaptan. The test is extremely delicate, .00001 gram of arsenic can be recognized with a certainty. A solution of .00001 gram of potassium tellurite in 10 ml. of mold-infested gelatin medium, in a cotton-plugged test tube, gave a strong odor of garlic for several weeks.

Another statement of procedure was prepared by Smith and Cameron.[70] Bisbini[71] reported that the most sensitive fungus for detecting arsenic is *Penicillium brevicaule*. He was able to find two other fungi in the air which had the same ability. Husz[72] tested potato cultures of 90 different molds respecting their action on various compounds and preparations containing arsenic. The following organisms were found to produce free arsine: Two forms of *Penicillium brevicaule* and an organism probably closely related, and possessing a chocolate brown color; *Aspergillus candidus, A. clavatus,* and three other *Aspergillus* forms (A. D. and T) not identified, two of which were found on oil paint on the walls of a damp room; finally, an *Actinomyces* form found on the same paint and apparently very widely distributed. The last-mentioned organism, when grown in lactose, or maltose-agar cultures, forms colonies, which after a time appear as if covered with a white chalky powder; this is due to the formation of spores.

According to Tiego,[73] fungi, such as *Penicillium brevicaule, Aspergillus glaucus, A. virescens,* and *A. niger, Mucor mucedo,* and *M. ramosus,* have the ability to decompose arsenic compounds, with formation of diethylarsine, which has a very characteristic odor. This makes possible the detection of .001 mg. of arsenic. Similar reactions are obtained with selenium and tellurium compounds.

CITROMYCES

The members of this group are especially well known on account of their marked ability to form acids. Citromyces are quite closely related to Penicillium. They differ, however, by possessing a simpler structure with less branching. Wehmer described two species, *Citromyces Pfefferianus* and *Citromyces glaber* as important in transforming sugar into citric acid. Wehmer[74] and Schreyer[75] stated that a species of *Aspergillus niger*

70. Smith and Cameron. 1933. Ind. and Eng. Chem., Anal. Ed. 5, 400-401.
71. Bisbini. 1922. Ann. Ig. 32, 757.
72. Husz. 1913. J. Inst. Brewing 19, 472.
73. Tiego. 1925. Rev. in Chem. Absts. 22, 4561
74. Wehmer. 1925. Berichte 58B, 2616-2619.
75. Schreyer. 1925. Idem 58B, 2647.

converted calcium gluconate into citric acid and smaller quantities of oxalic acid; oxalic acid was said to be produced almost exclusively by *Aspergillus niger cinnamomeus*. The mechanism of citric acid fermentation was unexplained. Fernbach *et al.*[76] received a British patent for making citric acid with Aspergillus species. This fungus is inoculated into a solution of salts and dextrose with sufficient hydrochloric acid to give an acid medium. Other organisms are kept out in this manner. A yield of citric acid amounting to 65 per cent of the sugar is secured. The residual sugar is fermented with yeast and the alcohol and carbon dioxide boiled off. Martin[77] secured a yield of citric acid amounting to 50 per cent of the sugar. Currie[78] secured the formation of large amounts of citric acid from sugars by the action of Aspergillus species. Currie used a mineral-salt-sugar medium. The average yield was about 11 per cent of citric acid. Other species of molds which produce citric acid from sugars have been described by Butkewitsch.

ASPERGILLUS

The members of this group are widely disseminated in nature. The conidia are borne on a fruiting organ called a basidium. The immediate structures which support them are sterigmata. The most recent reliable discussion of the group is by Thom and Church.[79] This book contains keys, discussions of nomenclature, and descriptions of species. The *Aspergillus glaucus* group has been studied by Thom and Raper.[80]

SACHSIA

Sachsia albicans, discovered by Bay,[81] was one of the first species in the genus to be reported. Later, Lindner added the species, *Sachsia suaveolens*, said to produce a desirable odor in certain fermentation products.

FUSARIUM

Fusarium species have been connected with the spoilage of various foodstuffs. While vegetables have been attacked especially, members of this genus have also been isolated as the cause of spoilage of cheese. Loubiere[82] isolated *Fusarium sarcochroum* on a brick cheese; Laxa[83] isolated a Fusarium species from a cheese which was covered with a reddish, slimy layer. The same difficulties and confusion so often encountered in the study of other groups of fungi are encountered in the study of Fusaria.

So much uncertainty existed, however, over identification and taxonomic relationships that a conference of specialists was held in August, 1924, at Madison, Wisconsin. At this conference cultures were compared and information collected which has given a firmer basis for future progress. The first problem which the conference had to settle were the criteria

76. Fernbach. 1927. Engin. Patent No. 266, 414.
77. Martin. 1916. Amer. J. Pharm. 88, 337-338.
78. Currie. 1917. J. Biol. Chem. 31, 15.
79. Thom and Church. 1926. The Aspergilli. Williams and Wilkins, Baltimore, Md.
80. Thom and Raper. 1941. U. S. Dept. Agr. Misc. Pub. 426.
81. Bay. 1894. Ber. Deut. Bot. Gesell. 12, 90-93.
82. Loubiere. 1920. Compt. Rend. Acad. Sci. 170, 336-339.
83. Laxa. 1929. Centbl. Bakt., Pt. 2, 78, 93-95.

of the norm. A complete discussion has been published by Sherbakoff [84] and Wollenweber.[85] The criteria of the norm were tabulated under the headings: normal reproductive states, color characteristics, minor characters, and abnormal characters. This characterization cannot be reproduced here. They should be consulted by food bacteriologists since Fusaria may be encountered in many foods.

CLADOSPORIUM (HORMODENDRON)

Members of this genus have been isolated from various foods. *Cladosporium herbarum* is probably identical with *Hormodendron cladosporoides*. Such is the opinion of Brooks and Hansford,[86] who published an investigation of the fungi on cold-storage meat. They also discussed at considerable length the relation of Cladosporium to Hormodendron. Brooks and Hansford could not confirm the observations of Bancroft [87] that conidia of the Hormodendron type were formed by Cladosporium at a temperature of 15.5°C.(60°F.) or above, while below 13.5°C.(56°F.) conidia of the same type were secured. The Hormodendron type of conidia was secured in every culture grown at low as well as at high temperatures, both on solid and liquid media. In nature the Hormodendron type was less common than the Cladosporium type. Brooks and Hansford believed that *Cladosporium epiphyllum* and *Cladosporium aphidis* must be considered as synonyms of *Cladosporium herbarum*.

Hormodendron cladosporoides. This fungus, which resembles some of the common molds, is commonly present in certain foodstuffs. It has been recently characterized by Jensen [50] and by Brooks and Hansford.[86] The latter investigators carried out a complete investigation on strains which were isolated from frozen meat and on strains from pure culture collections. On account of its length, the excellent characterization of this species by Brooks and Hansford cannot be reproduced here. The species is of special interest on account of its ability to grow below the freezing point. This ability gives the species its significance in "black spot" on frozen meat. Temporary freezing at —6°C.(21.2°F.), according to Brooks and Hansford, did not injure the organism, but prolonged freezing up to a month at —6°C. eventually killed the spores of most strains, except those which could grow and germinate at this temperature.

SPOROTRICHUM

The best known species of this genus is *Sporotrichum carnis*. It has been completely characterized by Brooks and Hansford. This species is capable of growing just below zero and gives rise to the white woolly patches on frozen beef. It grows very slightly, if at all, at —6°C. Brooks and Hansford believed that the strains isolated from meat belonged to one species.

84. Sherbakoff. 1915. Cornell Univ. Agr. Expt. Sta., Mem. No. 6.
85. Wollenweber. 1914. J. Agr. Res., 2, 251-285.
86. Brooks and Hansford. 1923. Food Invest. Bd., Spec. Rept. 17.
87. Bancroft. 1910. Ann. Bot. 24, 359.

Haines [88] found that the optimum temperature for growth of *Sporotrichum carnis* on Czapek's agar medium was 25°C.(77°F.). Growth can occur at 30°C.(86°F.) but is restricted. Fairly good growth occurred at —5°C.(23°F.) on supercooled agar; growth also occurred at —7°C. (19.4°F.). In no case was growth observed on frozen agar up to two months.

WARDOMYCES

This genus of the Dematiaceae was made by Brooks and Hansford [86] for a fungus isolated from a consignment of skinned Australian rabbits. The genus was named in honor of Professor Marshall Ward, the British botanist. Brooks and Hansford stated the characteristics of the genus as follows:

Wardomyces anomala on the rabbit flesh was almost indistinguishable from *Sporotrichum carnis*. When isolated, however, it showed quite different characteristics. The spores germinate to form a branched mycelium of hyaline hyphae 2-4μ wide. The conidiophores rise as short lateral branches, 15 to 25μ long from the vegetative hyphae; they remain hyaline and become septate with age. Some conidiophores are unbranched and form rarely short chains of two or three conidia, the distal conidium being the oldest; others branch repeatedly and form heads of spores which usually arise separately, although under certain cultural conditions two spores are formed occasionally in a chain. Two or three spores are often produced on each of the terminal cells of the branches conidiophore, one spore being formed terminally and the others in succession laterally.

ALTERNARIA

These fungi are characterized by muriform conidia which are in chains. Conidiophores are erect.

CLAVICEPS

One of the best known members of this group is *Claviceps purpurea*. This species attacks rye and the sclerotium constitutes ergot. Ergot is a vasomotor stimulant and causes contraction of the involuntary muscles. Ergotized grain has caused a number of very serious outbreaks of poisoning when such grain is made into flour.

OIDIUM

These fungi lack well-defined fruiting bodies. Each mycelial thread seems to be able to break up into reproductive units called oidia. The shape of the oidia is quite characteristic and, once it has been learned, serves to aid in identification of the species.

Odium lactis. This mold oftens referred to as the sour milk mold will develop on sour milk as a dull white, velvety layer. The greater part of the mycelium is submerged beneath the surface of the medium. It is especially characterized by dichotomous branching as shown in the illustrations in many publications. It has been encountered in a number of industries and plays an important role in the making of certain kinds of cheese. Jensen reported it in the soil. *Oidium lactis* has caused some large losses in the dairy industry. In Tasmania, this fungus is regarded as one of the main causes in the spoilage of butter. It seems that the fungus will grow in butter when the water content is sufficient and when the temperature is not too low. The presence of this mold in butter was also observed by Thom and Shaw.[89] In margarine it seems that

88. Haines. 1931. J. Expt. Biol. 8, 379-388.
89. Thom and Shaw. 1915. J. Agr. Res. 3, 301-310.

Odium lactis does not cause rancidity (Jacobson[90]). *Odium lactis* is widely disseminated in nature and has appeared in many foods.

Other oidia, such as *Oidium caseovarans* of Burri and Straub[91] and *Oidium rubrum* of Proks,[92] have been isolated from cheese. Smith[93] reported that the sour rot of lemons in California was due to *Oidium citri*. Artificial inoculation of the fungus into sound fruit reproduced the spoilage in 48 hours.

Not many investigations have been carried out on *Oospora lactis*. Gibson[94] studied 61 cultures isolated from butter. The temperature optimum for growth was between 20°C.(68°F.) and 28°C.(82.4°F.) with abnormal or restricted growth at 10°C.(50°F.) and 30°C.(86°F.) except in two cultures where the optimum was 30°C.(86°F.). Three cultures resisted 57.2°C.(135°F.) for 30 minutes, one survived 60°C.(140°F.) for 30 minutes. However, none of them resisted 62.8°C.(145°F.) for 30 minutes. A salt concentration of 7.5 per cent interfered with growth while only five showed any sign of growth at 10 per cent of salt. Tanner and Hofer[95] also sought information on heat resistance of *Oospora lactis*. Two hundred and twenty-four cultures were isolated from samples of cream from a wide geographical area; none was able to resist pasteurization in cream at 62.8°C. for 30 minutes; 144 cultures were exposed in cream to 57.2°C. for 30 minutes; eight resisted this temperature. Pasteurization at 51.7°C. (125° F.) did not kill any of the cultures used in this investigation. Temperatures ranging from 125 to 145°F. at 5°F. intervals were used to determine thermal resistance of nine cultures in phosphate solution; one fairly heat-resistant strain withstood pasteurization for 30 minutes at all temperatures used up to 20 minutes at 145°F.

MARGINOMYCES

This is a relatively new genus, proposed by Laxa[96] for a mold which caused black spots in margarine. The fungus was believed to be a new species to which the name *Marginomyces bubaki* was given. The mold grew in margarine as a thread-like net-work, green at first, but later becoming black. Long threads and conidia were produced. As is the case with most molds, the species is not very heat resistant. It was killed in five minutes at temperatures between 60°C.(140°F.) and 70°C.(158°F.). One minute at 100°C.(212°F.) killed it. The fungus was sensitive to boric acid, a preservative prohibited in foods in many countries. It was somewhat resistant to sodium benzoate. On account of this fact, Laxa stated that control of the fungus is dependent on the use of sterilization and control of such factors as water supply, etc.

ACTINOMYCES

Actinomycetes are filamentous, mold-like organisms quite widely distributed in soil and may, consequently, be expected in certain foodstuffs.

90. Jacobson. 1918. Folia Microbiol. 5, 94-102.
91. Burri and Staub. 1921. Landw. Schweiz., 35, 655-666.
92. Proks. 1922. Le Lait 2, 716-719.
93. Smith. 1917. Phytopathology 7, 37-41.
94. Gibson. 1937. Thesis, Univ. of Minnesota, June, 1937.
95. Tanner and Hofer. 1937. Food Research 2, 505-513.
96. Laxa. 1930. Centbl. Bakt., Pt. 2, 81, 392-396.

Buchanan [97] and Breed and Conn [98] have discussed the nomenclature and classification of Actinomycetes. The soil species have been studied especially by Waksman [99] in America. Conn stated that nearly 40 per cent of the soil microorganisms that develop on laboratory media are Actinomycetes. There is little doubt but what some bacteriologists unfamiliar with the characteristics of organisms in this group are confusing them with bacteria.

Mycelial Formation. The members of this family form a complex mycelium, much as do the molds. It is branched and may be submerged in the medium or develop on the surface with aerial hyphae. The hyphae from the aerial mycelium may "break up" into shorter or longer particles. According to Orskov [100] this disintegration has nothing to do with the reproduction of the fungus. The aerial hyphae may be straight or they may be bent and curled. During growth the aerial mycelium may be seen to develop peculiar globules at the tips or on the sides of the hyphae. These are liquid in nature and appear more abundantly when the fungus is growing best.

Spore Formation by Actinomycetes. Orskov [100] described the formation and appearance of spores somewhat as follows: After a lapse of time, the hyphae in certain places become irregular in outline so that the threads beginning from the tips display a series of baggings and constrictions; one might be tempted to compare the picture to a string of sausages, the constriction between the sausages being but slightly pronounced. Tracing this irregular thick portion of the hypha downwards from the tip, it will be seen that it passes into a regular, somewhat thinner, filament. The irregular portions of the filaments begin almost simultaneously from the tips downward to divide into a series of equal-size parts of oval or spherical shapes, lying quite closely to one another. The spores are not separated from one another by septa; sporulation occurs by division of the protoplasm into almost equal-size parts, without the walls of the hyphae having any part in the process. Thus the individual spores are separated from one another by "empty" spaces.

Actinomyces were found by Haines [101] in all stores examined where meat was being held. They were found in scrapings from the walls and in straw and other debris on the floor. Haines believed that these organisms which contribute so greatly to abnormal flavor of meats may be brought into meat-preservation establishments on such material. Haines thought that these organisms were probably responsible for off-flavors and odors of cold-stored meats. Actinomyces in culture gave rise to peculiarly characteristic musty odors. Stored foodstuffs, particularly fats and eggs, were said to be extraordinarily sensitive to the presence of such odors. Results of experiments were reported during which fats were stored in a

97. Buchanan. 1918. J. Bact. 3, 403-406.
98. Breed and Conn. 1919. Idem 4, 585-602.
99. Waksman. 1927. Principles of Soil Microbiology. Williams and Wilkins, Baltimore, Md.
100. Orskov. 1923. Investigations Into the Morphology of the Ray Fungi. Levin and Muksgaard. Copenhagen, Denmark.
101. Haines. 1931. Ann. Rept., Food Invest. Bd. for the Year 1930, 39.

glass jar above, but distant from, cultures of actinomyces. After two weeks' storage at —5°C.(23°F.) observers stated that the exposed fat had an odor which was generally characterized as "musty." After cooking, however, this taste could not be detected. After three months' storage, however, cooking for one hour did not dissipate the odor. Haines [102] observed that measurements of the rate of growth of actinomyces from cold-stored food show that the majority of the strains studied have their optimum temperature at 37°C.(98.6°F.). They are capable of growth from 40 to 5°C. (104 to 41°F.), growth becoming infinitely slow at just above 0°C.(32°F.). One strain, however, had its optimum temperature for growth less sharply defined at 20 to 30°C.(68 to 86°F.) and grew well, though slowly, at 0°C. The curve obtained by plotting the "velocity constant of growth" against temperature suggests that growth becomes infinitely slow at about —5°C. (23°F.).

An actinomyces-like fungus was isolated by Sartory and Meyer [103] from swollen cans of preserved foods. It was much like *Actinomyces thermophilus*, Gilbert, but certain characteristics seemed to place it among the Mycobacteriaceae in the genus Corynebacterium. The fungus was apparently quite thermophilic in nature. Unfortunately the authors gave no information on its heat resistance.

Certain species of Actinomyces have been found recently to produce bactericidal substances. Whether they might be significant in the food-preservation industry is not known.

ENDOMYCES

The organisms in this family, like those in Monilia, are between the true yeasts and molds. Zender [104] has characterized the family Endomycetaceae and included three genera, *Williopsis*, *Schwanniomyces*, and *Endomyces*. Several species are commonly encountered. Lindner described *Endomyces fibuliger* from bread on which it formed white chalky spots. *Endomyces mali* was isolated for the first time by Lewis.[105] Rose,[106] however, believed that it was identical with *Endomyces fibuliger*.

Nadson and Konokotina [107] were members of a commission appointed in Russia in 1917 to investigate the utilization of yeasts for the supply of foodstuffs, of which the war had brought about an acute shortage. Attention was first drawn by Lindner to the possibility of cultivating certain yeasts for the production of fat. Various fat-producing molds occur in the sap which exudes from birch trees in the spring, and from this source *Endomyces vernalis* was isolated, previously described by Ludwig and by Lindner.

The fat produced by *Endomyces vernalis* is liquid, yellowish in color, and resembling olive oil in appearance and flavor. The chief constituent is triolein, but there are also present free fatty acids. On heating for sev-

102. Haines. 1932. J. Expt. Biol. 9, 55-60.
103. Sartory and Meyer. 1940. Bull. Acad. Med. 123, 98-101.
104. Zender. 1925. Univ. of Geneva, Inst. Bot. 10.
105. Lewis. 1909. Maine Agr. Expt. Sta. Bul. 178.
106. Rose. 1910. Wchnschr. Brau. 27, 440.
107. Nadson and Konokotina. 1924. Wchnschr. Brau. 41, 249-251.

eral hours at 100°C.(212°F.), a loss of weight occurs which may amount to as much as 30 to 40 per cent owing to decomposition and escape of volatile acids.

Fat yeasts, after drying or boiling, are palatable and perfectly wholesome. Potato cultures, mixed with flour and some sugar, have been eaten with relish.

BYSSOCHLAMYS

This genus has become of interest to food technologists on account of the fact that one member, *Byssochlamys fulva*, disintegrates the tissues of processed fruit. The genus was proposed by Westling [108] and Olliver and Smith [110] described *Byssochlamys fulva*. This fungus is readily cultivated on laboratory culture media. It is present on ripening fruits in the fields and orchards and is probably associated with the soil. The ascospores were reported by Olliver and Rendle [109] to be able to resist a temperature of 86 to 88°C.(186.8 to 190.4°F.) for 30 minutes in many fruit sirups. Ability to develop under reduced oxygen pressures makes it possible for the organism to develop in canned fruits after it has survived the process. Olliver and Rendle [109] reported the fungus could be cultivated on a potato-extract agar made from a base solution of inorganic salts containing 10 per cent of sucrose. Details of morphology and physiology will not be presented here. Reference may be made to the paper by Olliver and Smith.[110] Results of heat-resistance studies on its spores have been reported in the chapter on "Canning."

SPORENDONEMA

A member of this genus, *Sporendonema epizoum*, has been found to be the cause of discoloration of salt fish by Frank and Hess [111] who stated that Ciferri and Redaelli [112] grouped all of the brown molds, heretofore placed in several genera, into one genus, Sporendonema. Reasons for doing this were morphological and cultural. Frank and Hess studied 26 cultures. They believed that *Torula minuta* of Hoye should also be placed in this genus.

MONILIA

Monilia are fungi which possess characteristics of both yeasts and molds. *Monilia candida* is, perhaps, the best known saprophytic species. Discovered by Bonarden, it was completely characterized by Hansen, who found it in fresh dung and fruits. A very active fermenting species is *Monilia vini* of Osterwalder.[113] It is of special interest because it ferments cane sugar without secretion of invertase. *Monilia variabilis*, isolated by Lindner [114] from white bread, is quite pleomorphic. The mycelium and conidia of *Monilia sitophila* impart to "Outjorm," an edible cake made

108. Westling. 1909. Svensk Bot. Tidskr. 3, 134.
109. Olliver and Rendle. 1934. J. Soc. Chem. Ind. 53, 177T-176T.
110. Olliver and Smith. 1933. J. Bot. 72. 196.
111. Frank and Hess. 1941. J. Fish. Res. Bd. Canad. 5, 276-286; 287-292.
112. Ciferri and Redaelli. 1933. J. Trop. Med. and Hyg. 36, 167-171.
113. Osterwalder. 1912. Centbl. Bakt., Pt. 2, 33, 257-272.
114. Lindner. 1898. Wchnschr. Brau. No. 16.

in Java from ground nuts, an orange color. Went [115] found that ordinary simple substances supported growth of the fungus.

Black spots on cheese rinds have been found by Burri and Staub [116] to be *Monilia niger*. Further data were published by Maurizio and Staub.[117] Two species, *Monilia nigra* and *Monilia fusca*, described by Browne,[118] were said to be destructive organisms in raw cane sugar.

Henneberg and Kniefall [119] reported a case where *Monilia sitophila* infected and grew in a dairy plant.

Pathogenicity of Molds in Foodstuffs. There is very little evidence that moldy food causes illness. Church and Buckley [120] fed common saprophytic species to laboratory animals without ill effects. Dinwiddie [121] reported similar observations after feeding a colt pure cultures of *Penicillium glaucum*. Gortner and Blakeslee [122] and Bodin and Gautier [123] reported the formation of toxin by *Rhizopus nigricans* and *Aspergillus fumigatus*. Too little is known about such toxins to know whether they would be of significance.

Himmel's [124] Method for Studying Mold Mycelium. In order to avoid the unsatisfactory method of studying mold hyphae which is now commonly used, Himmel proposed the following:

Between two glass slides (5 cm. by 11½ cm.) are placed layers of filter paper of the same size as the glass slides, the interior portions of which have been cut so as to form a border of filter paper about 1 cm. wide. A small piece (2 or 3 cu. mm.) of the moist bread on which the culture is growing is placed between the glass slides in the center of the band of filter paper. The slides are then tied together with thread, the filter paper moistened by dipping the edges of the slides in water, and the whole mount placed under a bell jar. In about two or three days the stolonifers will extend outward in various directions from the moist bread, and wherever they come in contact with the glass surface rhizoid-like hyphae and sporangiophores are produced. This may now be studied either with the compound microscope or with the binocular microscope.

This enables the student to trace the stolonifers with ease from their origin to their attachments to the glass and to study the sporangiophores and rhizoid-like hyphae in their natural positions without any disturbance of the hyphae or any danger of their drying during the study.

Coupin's [125] Method of Preparing Permanent Preparation of Molds. Hanging drop preparations of molds may be made by suspending them in a drop of alcohol (50 to 95 per cent) and then adding after the alcohol has about one-half evaporated, a drop of a solution prepared as follows: .8 per cent of mercuric chloride (aqueous); gum arabic, 30 grams; glucose, 10 grams. Coupin was able to prepare permanent preparation of some of the common molds.

Detection of Molds in Foods. That this group of fungi has been closely related to food spoilage is quite apparent, but it remained for Viehoever [126]

115. Went. 1910. Centbl. Bakt., Pt. 2, 7, 544-550; 591-598.
116. Burri and Staub. 1909. Landw. Schweiz. 23, 487-522.
117. Maurizio and Staub. 1928. Centbl. Bakt., Pt. 2, 75, 375-403.
118. Browne. 1918. J. Ind. Eng. Chem. 10, 178.
119. Henneberg and Kniefall. 1932. Milchw. Forsch. 13, 1.
120. Church and Buckley. 1923. North Amer. Vet. 4, 7-12.
121. Dinwiddie. 1896. Ark. Agr. Expt. Sta. Bull.
122. Gortner and Blakeslee. 1914. Amer. J. Physiol. 34, 353-367.
123. Bodin and Gautier. 1906. Ann. Inst. Pasteur 20, 209-224.
124. Himmel. 1927. Science 66, 136.
125. Coupin. 1919. Compt. Rend. Soc. Biol. 82, 209-210.
126. Viehoever. 1917. J. Amer. Pharm. Assoc. 6, 518-524.

to suggest a laboratory method which could be used for detecting their presence.

Cultural Method. Specimens of the suspected food may be inoculated onto solid media and incubated to allow germination of the mold spores or vegetation of the hyphae. This method is applicable to only those foods which contain living molds or spores. It could not be applied to foods which have been prepared for a long period. It might take several days for the molds to grow.

Microscope Examination Without Special Treatment. This involves what is ordinarily called direct examination. A portion of the material is examined in a hanging drop or between a cover glass and slide. With this method the detection of molds rests on the absence of extreme decomposition processes. Howard's method for the control of tomato products is an example of the use of this method in practice.

Microscope Examination After Special Treatment. Viehoever [126] has proposed a test which is based on the fact that certain fungi posseess a substance chemically different from cellulose in their cell walls. A large number of investigations has shown this substance to be chitin, a compound of complex structure. Viehoever (1912) also demonstrated the presence of chitin in the walls of certain fungi. Using this information Viehoever proposed the use of this substance as an index of the presence of mold or ergot in foods and flour. According to Viehoever, the material should be heated to almost boiling with 40 or 50 per cent KOH or NaOH for 40 to 60 minutes. After centrifuging if necessary, the excess alkali should be decanted and possibly pressed out with a glass rod. The material should then be washed with alcohol or glycerol and perhaps even neutralized with acid. The mixture is then treated with iodine-potassium iodide solution (two parts of iodine and one part of potassium iodide in 200 parts water). The excess iodine is then replaced by dilute sulfuric acid (1%). Chitin is indicated by a red or violet color.

Mol's [127] Method for Estimating Molds in Foods.

Emmerling first proposed this method which Mol modified. Emmerling's method consisted of mixing five grams of the substance to be examined with a definite amount of sterile water, preferably in a sterile Petri dish. This mixture was then allowed to incubate at 37°C.(98.6°F.) for several days. The interpretation of results depends on the amount of surface covered. In view of various objections to this method, Mol modified it by studying growth on a solid medium. For this purpose a plum infusion-agar medium was prepared. Two hundred grams of plums were soaked in 500 ml. of water, heated, and filtered several times. Later, sterile agar solution was added.

One gram of the material to be tested is ground in a sterile mortar with 10 ml. of sterile water until a homogeneous suspension is secured. One ml. of this suspension is placed in a sterile Petri dish to which are added 10 ml. of the sterile plum agar. The plates are incubated for three days at 25°C.(77°F.) and the colonies counted. At the end of this time they are usually small enough to count.

Determination of Smut Spores in Flour and Cereals (Bredemann [128]). Grind from three to five grams of flour to pass through a .3-mm. square mesh and dry. Clear with 10 parts of chloral hydrate in five parts of water to which are added five parts of glycerol and three parts of 25 per cent hydrochloric acid. A preliminary test is made by adding a few drops of the clearing solution to a small amount of the sample on a slide; this is covered and boiled and examined. If there are fewer than five spores per field with a magnification of 150, the main samples may be used. If there are more than this number dilute one part of the sample with nine parts of rice starch and thoroughly

127. Mol. 1937. Ztschr. Untersuch. Lebensm. 74, 189-191.

128. Bredemann. 1912. Landw. Vers. Stat. 75, 134-157.

grind in a mortar. Five to eight milligrams of the flour are weighed onto a slide and rubbed up with a suitable amount of the clearing solution after which it is heated over a small burner but not boiled. The preparation is then covered with a 20-mm. cover glass and heated slowly to boiling to remove air bubbles and clear the preparation. Then count the smut spores with a magnification of 165. The number is calculated for 10 grams and this divided by 450,000 for the milligram *Telletia* spores in 10 milligrams. Ten times this is the per cent smut present.

Determination of Rust Spores in Cereals (Groh[129]). Groh proposed two methods for determining rust spores in bran.

First Method. Ten grams of the sample are shaken in water in a 100-ml. flask which is diluted to the mark. The contents is then poured into a beaker. A drop of this is then taken by means of a stirring rod and placed on a counting cell of such size that the number of counts made by the microscope corresponds to the number of millions of spores in 10 grams. Groh found on an average 1,002 million rust spores in a gram.

Second Method. The bran is shaken up in water and then thrown onto a sieve and the liquor collected. Several washings are made until the liquor reaches 175 ml. in quantity. Then 20 ml. of zinc chloride solution are added and the liquor made up to the mark. Fifty ml. are centrifuged and the precipitate of spores and other material is treated with H_2SO_4 so that the volume is about five ml. The spore count is then made on this liquid by by means of the hemocytometer as shown in the first method above.

Control of Molds. Development of molds in factories causes considerable loss. Some factories have had to resort to expensive air-conditioning systems in attempts to control these fungi. These have done much but have not entirely eliminated mold spores in all cases. Some food preparation plants are kept under air pressure to prevent ingress of mold spores in air. Germicidal paints are also used. A new departure in this effort is use of ultraviolet light which probably works under some conditions and not under others. Any microorganism which it is hoped will be killed by this form of energy must be directly exposed and not imbedded under the surface. Ultraviolet light has low penetrating power.

Mold inhibitors in the form of chemical salts are also used in some foods. Chief among these are the calcium and sodium salts of propionic acid which have shown considerable effect in bread and cheese. They are also incorporated in paper in which butter is wrapped.

Preservation of Molds. Microbiologists are always searching for improved methods of preserving cultures. Stock cultures must be maintained in vigorous condition from which cultures may be made when needed. The usual procedure is to use ordinary culture media, such as plain or carbohydrate agar. Other methods have been proposed. One such by Greene and Fred[130] for molds is an adaptation of one by Barthel[131] for yeasts and bacteria. It involves use of sterilized soil in which the molds can grow and survive. Greene and Fred used air-dried orchard loam soil with sufficient added water to bring it to a moisture content of about 20 per cent. The soil is then added to half-inch culture tubes in five-gram quantities. These tubes are plugged and given four three-hour sterilizations at 15 pounds per square inch pressure on alternate days. A few may be tested by addition of yeast-water-glucose-broth. The tubes may be inoculated

129. Groh. 1912. Arch. Chem. u. Mikros. 5, 177-187.
130. Greene and Fred. 1934. Ind. and Eng. Chem. 26, 1297-1299.
131. Barthel. 1918. Centbl. Bakt., Pt. 2, 48, 340-349.

with one ml. of a heavy spore or mycelium suspension and held at room temperature. Greene and Fred were able to maintain three species of molds for over two years, without loss of characteristics.

YEAST AND YEAST-LIKE FUNGI

Yeasts are microorganisms which are able to decompose carbohydrates into alcohol and carbon dioxide; they are unicellular and reproduce in two different ways. They are of special interest to food microbiologists. Certain species are used as leavening agents in bread; others are used in the vinegar fermentation and the manufacture of beverages. They are also of interest in the spoilage of certain foods, such as honey, tomato products, etc.

The methods used for cultivating the yeasts in the laboratory differ but slightly from those used for the bacteria. The fact that the yeasts desire acid in their metabolism is made use of in many media for favoring their growth and repressing the development of bacteria. Much difficulty is encountered by those who try to identify pure cultures of the budding fungi. They soon find that many of the descriptions in the literature are only approximately correct. Such work is also made confusing by the fact that more refined methods of working are available today. This is especially true for the determination of reactions of media.

Ascospore Formation by Yeasts. Ascopores are formed in some yeast cells. They are formed in a case or sac called an ascus. The presence or absence of asci and ascospores are used as differential characteristics of classification. Ascospores are formed in yeast cells probably for the same reason that spores are formed in bacterial cells. They may function to carry the cell over unfavorable periods or as reproductive units. It is quite well established, however, that ascospores are not as resistant as spores of bacteria. By means of ascospores fermenting species of yeasts are believed to survive the winter in the soil of vineyards and orchards. That ascospores are resistant stages in the life-cycle of the yeast is evidenced by the fact that the laboratory methods for demonstrating them are, in general, unfavorable to rapid development. They are cultured on media which are not entirely adequate.

While the knowledge that the composition of the medium may greatly influence the appearance of ascospores in yeasts has been known for a long time, much may still be learned from investigations. Kufferath[132] studied the subject with many varieties of yeasts. In most cases a slightly alkaline medium was more favorable to sporulation than was a slightly acid one. The difference was less marked as the concentration of the medium rose. An increase in sporulation with alkaline media was reported for the following species: *Saccharomyces cerevisiae, Saccharomyces logos, Saccharomyces occidentalis, Willia anomala, Pichia farinosa* and *Pichia vini. Endomyces capsularis* was not affected by the reaction. *Schizosaccharomyces pombe* and *Pseudosaccharomyces apiculatus* sporulated as well on acid media. Kufferath also stated that temperature was very important.

132. Kufferath. 1930. Ann. Soc. Zymol., Pure and Appliquee 2, 33.

He believed that sporulation was a sexual phenomenon, and, consequently, any factor that affected chromosomial formation, would influence it.

The presence or absence of asci and ascospores and the method of formation when they are present are used by the taxonomist as characteristics for classification. In the Hansen-Guilliermond classification, it will be seen that ascospore formation is the important characteristic for making two large families *Saccharomycetes*, or true yeasts, and non-*Saccharomycetes*, or false yeasts. The former form asci and ascospores while the latter do not. *Saccharomycetes* are then subdivided according to the method of spore formation. Marchand [133] reported that in the majority of yeasts all traces of sexuality have been lost, but three cases were known (the yeast *Johannisberg* II, *Saccharomycodes ludwigi*, and *Willia saturus*) in which, although the formation of the ascus takes place parthenogenetically, the germination of the spores was preceded by conjugation. Marchand found that *Saccharomyces intermedius* (*Pastorianus* II), *Saccharomyces turbidans* (*Pastorianus* III), *Saccharomyces ellipsoideus*, and *Saccharomyces validus* behaved similarly. Conjugation occurred within the ascus, but only with about 50 per cent of the spores. In many cases the membrane of the ascus broke before this stage was reached, and then the spores developed without conjugation. These results show that, with yeasts, conjugation of spores is not exceptional, and it may possibly serve as a means of distinguishing certain yeasts; for example, *Saccharomyces pastorianus* from *Saccharomyces intermedius* and *Saccharomyces turbidans*, for the first-mentioned one forms parthenogenetic spores only.

Sexual union of the cells in certain species is now known to precede the formation of the ascus. This was seen probably for the first time by Schiönning who reported that asci in *Schizosaccharomyces octosporus* resulted from the fusion of two cells. Guilliermond [134] stated that this fusion was a true copulation. By using cells in hanging drops in moist chambers, he was able, after a few days, to observe the union of cells by a copulation canal formed by the union and fusion of two little projections from the cells. There is an intermingling of cell contents which results in the formation of a zygospore by isogamic copulation. These cells eventually germinate and grow in size. The nucleus divides into four or eight nuclei which surround themselves with protoplasm to form ascospores.

Guilliermond also reported heterogamic copulation in *Zygosaccharomyces chavalieri*. The asci resulted from copulation between cells of different size. A very small one functions as the male gamete while a larger one as the female. This latter is much older and has approached maturity. The two cells unite by a copulation canal and the contents of the male gamete is poured into the female gamete. Nuclear fusion takes place, resulting in the formation of one to four nuclei from which the ascospores are formed.

Hybridization of Yeasts. Fertilization and sexual processes were demonstrated in yeasts many years ago by Hansen and confirmed by Guilliermond and others. The full significance of these observations to industries

133. Marchand. 1912. Compt. Rend. Soc. Biol. 72, 410-412.
134. Guilliermond. 1901. Compt. Rend. Acad. Sci. 133, 242-244.

involving yeasts was not appreciated because modern genetics had not been developed at that time and there was no technic with which single cells of microorganisms could be isolated under the microscope. The latter was made possible by Barber [135] and others since, who developed apparatus for single-cell isolation under the microscope. This technic has more recently been used for breeding new yeast types through hybridization by Winge and Lausten.[136] They showed that sporulation of a yeast is associated with a genetic segregation which makes the spores in any ascus differ genetically. Sporulation in yeasts is considered to be quite comparable to formation of gametes in higher plants and when two ascospores fuse during germination, as has been known for some 50 years, this is a regular process of fertilization. On account of this, Winge pointed out the uncertainty that a pure culture of yeast, even if it originates from a single yeast cell, will keep uniform. If the yeast forms spores, entirely new types may segregate when the spore germinates. Winge proved this in the case of many species of Saccharomyces by isolating all four ascospores in one ascus, under the microscope, and making them germinate. Pure cultures developed from these ascospores differ distinctly. While segregation in sporulation involves morphological characters, physiological characters may also be involved. It is this possibility that gives Winge's work such import in the industries. It may be possible by segregation to breed a yeast with properties of special importance to a single industry. Winge made this significant statement:

"When we keep in mind that all high-breeding in higher plants and domestic animals has taken place through crossing and subsequent selection of the more superior individuals, it seems obvious that from now on there may be a chance also for a rational high-breeding of yeasts. Previously one had to be content to select the superior types among the ones that Nature has produced herself, but now it seems possible by crossing rationally to try to combine the desirable characteristics of several yeast types into a single new type."

Copulation of ascospores in yeasts has been observed for many years. Marchand [137] discussed it for various common species.

Demonstration of Ascospores in Yeasts. This is more difficult than the detection of endospores in bacteria. Several different methods have been proposed. Some of them are given below.

Hansen's Gypsum Block Method. This is the method usually advised for demonstrating ascospores in yeast cells. However, it leaves much to be desired since there are probably methods which yield more certain results. The plaster of Paris block may be made by pouring wet plaster of Paris into a cone of paper. After it has begun to set, the paper may be removed and the top of the cone cut off to give a flat surface on which to place the yeast cells. After the cone has been cut off, the block should be placed in a Petri dish or Esmarch dish, a little water added, and the dish sterilized in the autoclave. The yeast cells should be placed on the block with a loop and allowed to remain there for 30 to 48 hours, when ascospores are supposed to appear in the cells if the species forms them.

135. Barber. 1914. Philippine J. Sci. 9, 307-360.

136. Winge and Lausten. 1935. Compt. Rend. Lab. Carlsberg, série physiol. 21, 77; 22 (1937), 99; 22 (1938), 235; The Bakers Tech. Digest, Jan., 1939, 123-125.

137. Marchand. 1912. Compt. Rend. Soc. Biol. 72, 410-412.

Gorodkowa's [138] **Method.** This method consists essentially in growing the yeasts on a special agar. The formula for preparation of this agar is given in Chapter 26. It is a medium somewhat deficient in nutrients. Cultures of ascospore-forming yeasts on this medium were rich in ascospores while the same organisms on five per cent dextrose media were devoid of spores.

Maneval's [139] **Method.** Maneval noticed that cakes of compressed yeast that were kept in the ice box for six or eight days showed abundant spore formation in cells from the outer layers of the cake. The spores were easily demonstrable by mounting them in a drop of Gram's iodine solution and examining under a microscope with a magnification of 600 diameters.

Stained preparations were made as follows:

1. Spread a film in a small drop of water on a slide and dry in the air.
2. Fix by passing through the flame 12 to 15 times.
3. Stain with hot carbol fuchsin one to three minutes.
4. Wash with water.
5. Decolorize with five per cent sulfuric acid for two to three seconds.
6. Wash with water.
7. Stain with methylene blue about three seconds.
8. Wash and examine.

The spores should be stained a bright red, and the vegetative protoplasm blue. Much greater abundance of spores followed the propagation of pure cultures of yeasts on Maneval's modification of Gorodkowa's agar. Very good spore formation took place in four to five days; in eight to 12 days 50 per cent of all cells developed spores.

Carrot slants have also been found to stimulate ascospore formation in yeast cells. The slants should be prepared in the same manner as potato slants. The slant should be inoculated with the yeast and kept at room temperature.

McKelvey's [140] **Medium for Demonstrating Ascospores in Yeasts.** Details for the preparation of this medium were not given. It was stated, however, that carrot agar, saturated with calcium sulfate, was suitable for the development of ascospores.

Lindegren's Method [141] **for Producing and Demonstrating Ascospores in Yeasts.** This is one of the most successful methods for the purpose which the author has seen. The medium on which the yeast is grown consists of equal portions of bottled grape-juice and canned apricot juice (nectar) to which 3 per cent agar is added along with an excess of calcium carbonate. This medium is tubed, sterilized and slanted. A slant is inoculated with the yeast and allowed to grow for 48 hours or more. Full growth on this medium, according to Lindegren, occurs within 24 hours but he advises leaving the culture for another 24 hours or longer since some of the by-products of fermentation accumulate and are removed with the yeast cells to the gypsum slant. An increased number of spores are obtained. Lindegren believes that in addition to proper nutrition, it is necessary that certain by-products be present in the water saturating the gypsum blocks. Then 1 ml. of sterile water is added to the slant and the growth washed from the slant to the bottom of the tube. This suspension is then transferred to the top of a plaster of Paris (gypsum) slant in a test tube and the yeasts allowed to develop for about 24 hours.

The gypsum slants are prepared by mixing 100 gms. of plaster of Paris with 110 ml. of water. About 10 ml. of this mixture are placed in a large culture tube about 8 x 1 inch and slanted. These slants should then be dried at about 60°C.(140°F.) for 24 hours, plugged and sterilized. After inoculation with yeast suspension about 5 ml. of sterile water are placed at the bottom of the slant to moisten the gypsum slant.

Ascospores were stained by Lindegren by preparing a film on a glass slide with some of the growth on the gypsum slant. The film is fixed with heat and then placed in carbol-fuchsin in a Coplin jar for 30 minutes or longer. Destaining is accomplished

138. Gorodkowa. 1908. Centbl. Bakt., Pt. 2, 24, 318-319.
139. Maneval. 1924. Bot. Gaz. 78, 122-123.
140. McKelvey. 1926. J. Bact. 11, 98.
141. Lindegren. 1942. Private communication.

by holding the slide with forceps in 30 per cent acetic acid. One or two quick swishes are sufficient. The slide should not be rinsed before destaining. This prevents formation of a precipitate on the slide if it is put into water from the staining fluid. If the slide is left too long in the acetic acid solution or not rinsed quickly enough in water, it will be completely destained. Success of this method depends largely on careful control of destaining. After the rinse in water, methylene blue staining fluid may be used as a counter stain. Ascospores will then appear as deep red bodies among cells which are stained blue.

Resistance of Yeasts to Unfavorable Agents. Yeasts, like other organisms, are endowed with characteristics which make them capable of resisting unfavorable conditions. To temperature, however, they do not seem to be so resistant, although those species which possess spores are able to withstand boiling for a few minutes. They are able to survive much cold since they live through the winter in the soil, even in fairly cold climates. The spores of yeasts are responsible for their resistance, although the spores are probably not so resistant as the spores of the bacteria and molds.

Resistance of Yeasts to Freezing. The effect of freezing on yeasts has not received much study, at least under conditions which give information concerning their longevity, rate of death, etc. Doemens [142] exposed beer yeast to a temperature of about —190°C.(—310°F.) for six minutes. It still retained its vitality. When he suspended the yeast in water and exposed it to liquid air for five minutes and 20 minutes, and then thawed in cold water, its power of development was totally destroyed. Macfadyen and Rowland [143] subjected microorganisms, among which were yeasts, to a temperature of —252°C.(—421.6°F.) for six months, after which the yeasts were reported to have suffered no reduction in vitality. They gave good growth and possessed unaltered powers of fermentation. One would infer from this report that yeasts are resistant to freezing and that there was no reduction in numbers. Bokorny [144] kept a sample of brewers' pressed yeast at a temperature of —15°C.(5°F.) for 24 hours, and then allowed it to warm up slowly to a temperature of 7°C.(44.6°F.); fermentation and reproduction went on for a short time but soon stopped. In another experiment the yeast was very quickly warmed to 10°C.(50°F.); after four weeks in a suitable medium it exhibited slight fermentation. Microscope examination at this stage showed that most of the cells were dead and only a few were budding. Bokorny thus showed that beer yeast was resistant to cold, but not as resistant as other microorganisms.

Tanner and Williamson,[145] working with eight species of yeasts, found that there was a rather rapid death rate during the early periods of freezing. In 160 weeks, at from —13 to —15°C.(8.6 to 5°F.), there was a rapid decrease in number of viable cells. Some of the suspensions had been entirely sterilized during that time. Irish and Joslyn [146] reported that yeasts survived freezing in grape juice for 18 weeks and that their vitality was not lowered. Lange-Pozdeeva [147] reported that a temperature of —1 to

142. Doemens. 1899. Sixth Jahresber. Lehranst. Versuchsstat. Münch. Brauerakad 28.
143. Macfadyen and Rowland. 1902. Ann. Bot. 16, 589-590; Proc. Roy. Soc. 66, 180-182.
144. Bokorny. 1927. Brau. u. Hopfen-Zeit; Rev. in J. Inst. Brewing 33, 520.
145. Tanner and Williamson. 1928. Proc. Soc. Expt. Biol. and Med. 25, 377-381.
146. Irish and Joslyn. 1929. Fruit Prod. J., August, 11.
147. Lange-Pozdeeva. 1933. Rev. in Biol. Absts. 10, 960.

—170°C.(30.2 to 1.4°F.) killed most of the cells of Race XII, distillers yeast and pressed yeast, during the first eight to 12 hours after which the decrease in viable cells was slow. Freezing in water had greater destructive effect than freezing in must. Intermittent freezing and thawing had a more marked effect than continuous freezing. The method of storage at low temperatures influenced the vitality of the yeast.

Resistance of Yeasts to Ultraviolet Light. Yeasts are not very resistant to ultraviolet light, although there is some variation in response to it by various strains. Buchta,[148] Feuer and Tanner,[149] Nadson and Phillipov,[150] Tanner and Ryder,[151] and Lindner [152] published results of investigations which confirm this statement. The rapidity of destruction was found to vary with conditions under which the experiments were carried out. Feuer and Tanner noticed that pigmented yeasts were more resistant than unpigmented species. Lindner and others reported that in order to secure rapid destruction of yeasts, they must be exposed in thin layers. Substrates containing colloidal substances are not as easily penetrated as are clear substrates. This fact has been overlooked in some investigations.

Resistance of Yeasts to Heat. The budding fungi are not as resistant to heat as are some of the bacteria, especially those which form spores. However, yeasts are occasionally found in food products which have been heated, and it becomes important to know how the species involved react to high temperatures. Kayser [153] found that yeasts are more resistant in the dry state than in the moist state. Cochran and Perkins [154] tested the resistance of yeasts in sugar solutions of varying densities reporting that the cells were killed more quickly in the more dense solutions. This has not been the observation of Dougherty [155] and Rahn [156] whose reports are discussed below. Wells [157] investigated bread for living yeasts and was able to demonstrate viable cells in three of 20 specimens. Living cells were found in bread baked at 66°C.(150.8°F.), but not in bread baked at 68°C.(154.4°F.). It has been generally assumed that yeasts could not survive heating for more than 10 minutes at temperatures between 50 and 60°C.(122 and 140°F.). Hansen reported that strong young cells of *Saccharomyces ellipsoideus II* were killed by heating for five minutes between 54 and 56°C.; old cells under the same conditions were said to survive for longer times. Matured spores of the same species, partially dried on gypsum blocks, withstood 62°C., but not 68°C. Similar experiments with *Saccharomyces cerevisiae I* showed that strong young cells resisted 52° but not 54°C. Each species has its own temperature relations, as would be expected. Kayser [158] found that *Saccharomyces mali Duclaux* was

148. Buchta. 1915. Centbl. Bakt., Pt. 2, 40, 176.
149. Feuer and Tanner. 1920. J. Ind. Eng. Chem. 12, 740.
150. Nadson and Phillopov. 1928. Compt. Rend. Acad. Sci. 98, 366-368.
151. Tanner and Ryder. 1923. Bot. Gaz. 75, 309-317.
152. Lindner. 1923. Wchnschr. Brau. 39, 366.
153. Kayser. 1889. Ann. Inst. Pasteur 3, 513-525.
154. Cochran and Perkins. 1914. J. Ind. Eng. Chem. 6, 480.
155. Dougherty. 1920. Thesis, University of Illinois.
156. Rahn. 1928. Canning Age, August, 1928, 705-706.
157. Wells. 1917. Vermont Agr. Expt. Sta. Bull. 203.
158. Kayser. 1890. Ann. Inst. Pasteur 4, 484-499.

killed at 55°C.; Johnson [159] found *Saccharomyces thermantitonum* to be especially resistant to heat. Other data may be found in the publications of Will, Owen,[160] and Bay (1893). The data are frequently a little unsatisfactory because the time is frequently omitted. Dougherty [155] carried out a number of experiments in the author's laboratory. Twenty-four species of budding fungi were heated in various menstrua such as varying concentrations of salt and sugar, plain broth, distilled water, vinegar, etc. None of the species were destroyed at 40, 43, or 46°C.(104, 109.4, or 114.8°F.). Heating at 58°C.(136.4°F.) for 10 minutes caused the death of most of the species. *Willia belgica, Torula monosa,* and *Parasaccharomyces thomasi* were especially resistant to heat when heated in broth and milk. *Torula monosa* was killed only by heating the milk suspension at 98°C.(208.4°F.) for 10 minutes. Five species (*Mycoderma vini, Parasaccharomyces thomasi,* brewers' yeast, *Saccharomyces anomalous,* and *Cryptococcus ludwigi*) were heated in vinegar. Only *Parasaccharomyces thomasi* survived and then for only 10 minutes. The five species just mentioned were heated also in 5, 10, 15, 20, 30, 40, 50, and 60 per cent solutions of cane sugar and in 5, 10, 15, 20, 30, and saturated solutions of sodium chloride. The data secured with these solutions were quite similar. In no case was death of the cells more easily accomplished in the solutions with more sugar and salt. If anything, there was a tendency for the yeasts to possess greater longevity when heated in the more concentrated solutions. Rahn [156] published a note showing the sparing effect of concentrated solutions of sugar on yeasts when they are subjected to heat. He stated that it would take more heat to kill a yeast cell in a sweetened fruit juice than in an unsweetened juice. In this respect, he confirmed more definitely the observation that yeasts did not die as quickly when heated in concentrated sugar solutions as when heated in unsweetened solutions. Another bit of information on the subject was published by Ayers, Barnby and Voight [161] for Mycoderma causing clouding of the brine in which olives are packed. This species was destroyed in five minutes at 54.4°C.(130°F.). Townsend and Powers [162] found a yeast in spoiled canned orange juice which resisted 76.7°C.(170°F.) for one minute. More information on this subject will be found in Chapter 19.

Longevity of Yeasts. This is a subject of much practical importance. Information on it appeared in the early days of microbiology. Kayser [163] called attention to the fact that longevity of microorganisms depends on many factors, such as supply of oxygen, presence of moisture, hydrogen-ion concentration, exposure to light, and temperature. The necessity of pure cultures in fermentology caused Pasteur to report that brewery yeast, when dried and mixed with plaster of Paris, retained its vitality for 10 months. Duclaux, however, reported that such yeast remained viable for 15 years

159. Johnson 1905. J. Inst. Brewing 11, 466.
160. Owen. 1914. La. Agr. Expt. Sta. Bull. 146.
161. Ayers, Barnby, and Voight. 1930. Food Indus. 2, 161-164.
162. Townsend and Powers. 1938. Ann. Rept. to Research Committee, Nat. Canners Assoc. 1938, 29.
163. Kayser. 1889. Ann. Inst. Pasteur 3, 513; Les Levures, Paris, 1896.

when kept in beer, in which it had been cultivated. The same investigator showed that yeast in the dry state, kept in the dark, was not alive after 23 years; spores of *Aspergillus niger* lost their vitality even in three years.

In November, 1889, Kayser placed yeasts and mixtures of spores and yeasts upon bands of sterilized paper in test tubes. The yeasts were top fermentation brewery yeasts, a wine yeast, and *Saccharomyces pastorianus*. One-half of the tubes were placed in the laboratory exposed to diffused light, and the other half in an incubator at 28°C.(82.4°F.). Every three months a suitable medium was added to a certain number of tubes and the development of yeasts noted. *Saccharomyces pastorianus* was not alive three years later, but its spores were capable of germinating up to four years; the other three yeasts continued to germinate for four years. Their spores were killed in five years. Kayser also found the fermenting ability to be unimpaired by such treatment. Will [164] reported that yeasts remained viable many years in 1ᶜ per cent sucrose solutions in Freudenreich flasks. Meissner [165] suspended 25 species in 10 per cent sucrose solutions, and seven years later found that nine had died. Other cultures were quite devitalized, for they showed signs of growth only after a long time. Results of an investigation by Tanner and Burrows [166] were in accord with those of Meissner. Klöcker [167] found that most cultures were capable of remaining viable for at least 30 years, but that some died in much shorter time. Klöcker stated that sucrose solution was not a suitable medium for preservation of some yeasts.

Another method, the utility of which is not fully appreciated by microbiologists, was suggested by Barthel.[168] It has been shown by many that yeasts are able to survive for long periods in soil in nature. Without reviewing the results which Barthel presented, it may be stated that microorganisms so preserved seemed to remain as active as those preserved by other methods.

The most recent method to be used is lyophilization—freezing in a vacuum. Various types of apparatus have been devised for applying this method to yeasts and bacteria.

Distribution of Yeasts in Nature. That yeasts are quite widely distributed in nature seems to be borne out by the fact that fermentable materials usually contain many different species without inoculation with pure cultures. Pasteur [169] was one of the first to show this. Hansen [170] subjected this statement to critical investigation and reported yeasts in soil throughout the year. Furthermore, inoculation of soils with yeasts indicated that they could endure low temperatures. Hansen's results were nicely confirmed by Müller-Thurgau,[171] Berlese,[172] and Ludwig.[173] The

164. Will. 1909. Centbl. Bakt., Pt. 2, 24, 405-415.
165. Meissner. 1911. J. Inst. Brewing 17, 621.
166. Tanner and Burrows. 1930. J. Bact. 21, 32.
167. Klöcker. 1917. Compt. Rend. Lab. Carlsberg 11, 297-311.
168. Barthel. 1918. Centbl. Bakt., Pt. 2, 48, 340-349.
169. Pasteur. 1876. Étude sur le Biere 150, 155.
170. Hansen. 1890. Ann. Sci. Nat., Bot., Series 7.
171. Müller-Thurgau. 1889. Weinblau. Nos. 40-41.
172. Berlese. 1897. Riv. Patol. Veg. 5, 211, 295, 394.
173. Ludwig. 1918. Thesis, Univ. of Geneva, Switzerland.

last-mentioned investigator reported yeasts to be commonly present in vineyards, as did Hansen. They were believed to be carried to the fruit by dust, insects, rain, etc.

Budding fungi have also been found in the air by Biacosa (1883), Nakazawa,[174] and others. Nakazawa stated that a strong wind seemed to increase the number in the air.

This subject has also been of significance in spoilage of honey by yeasts. Many of the investigators who have studied this question have tried to determine whether the flowers visited by bees during the honey season harbor osmophilic yeasts. Reukauf,[175] Stoltz,[176] Schuster and Ulehla,[177] and Jimbo,[178] among others, have been able to show the presence of yeasts in flowers. Lochhead and Heron [179] reported yeasts in practically all of 34 different kinds of flowers. The above data show the wide distribution of yeasts in flowers, and the probability that they are disseminated by insects. Budding fungi are just as widely distributed as are other fungi.

CLASSIFICATION OF YEASTS AND RELATED ORGANISMS

Two general methods have been used for classifying yeasts. One is used by industrial fermentologists who are not especially interested in taxonomic problems. According to this method, pseudoscientific names are used, such as beer yeast, yeast XII, etc. The other method is used by botanists who try to give every organism a name which connects it with a larger group and also serves to identify it. It is unfortunate that so little attention is given to taxonomy by fermentologists.

Grouping of Yeasts in the Industries. The yeasts are grouped according to some salient characteristics, such as pigment-formation, or according to the special use to which they are put. Below are given a few of these names.

Distillers' Yeast. Distillers' yeasts usually differ from types used in other industries. These yeasts form greater amounts of alcohol and are grown in different kinds of substrates. Distillers' yeasts are not grown in hopped wort like the brewery yeasts. On the other hand, the distillers' yeast shows greater activity in flour and water than brewers' yeast. This has been explained by some fermentologists as due to the toxic action of flour, or some of its constituents, on brewers' yeast.

Top Yeasts. These are species which ferment at the top of the substrate. Such yeasts are distillers' yeasts, and those usually used in breadmaking. The separation of yeasts into the two varieties, top and bottom yeasts, is not a sharp one, and consequently confusion exists on this subject.

Top yeasts have been said to contain less trypsin than bottom yeasts and consequently do not reduce the carbon dioxide retaining ability of the dough. They also contain more amylase. Many experiments have been carried out on the change of top yeasts into bottom yeasts. Changes in the opposite direction are more rare. Rathke and Windisch[180] stated that even in a pure culture of one or the other kind, cells of the opposite kind may be produced, and the two types may continue to develop side by

174. Nakazawa. 1922. Quoted by Saito. Jap. J. Bot. 1, 1-53.
175. Reukauf. 1911. Die Kleinwelt, p. 25.
176. Stoltz. 1911. Mikrokosmos 5, 202-206.
177. Schuster and Ulehla 1913. Ber. Deut. Bot. Gesell. 31, 129-139.
178. Jimbo. 1926. Sci. Repts., Tohoku. Imperial Univ., Ser. 4, 161-187.
179. Lochhead and Heron. 1929. Bull. 116, Dept. of Agriculture, Canada.
180. Rathke and Windisch. 1926. Wchnschr. Brau. 43, 537-540.

side in the same nutrient liquid. The cause of the change and the conditions which bring it about are not understood.

Bottom Yeasts. These types ferment at the bottom of the culture tubes. This type is often called sedimentary yeast, on account of its accumulation at the bottom of the culture tubes. When these yeasts are used in brewing, a lower temperature is also used. Consequently, fermentation proceeds more rapidly while growth and reproduction proceed more slowly. Bottom yeasts are poor in amylase and excrete more trypsin than do top yeasts.

Distinction of top from bottom yeasts is not clear-cut. Rommel[181] was unable to detect any distinctive features between top and bottom fermentation yeasts. Top yeasts were found to possess somewhat higher ash content than bottom yeasts; they also possessed higher specific gravity than bottom yeasts. The differences, however, were not sharp. Hansen at an earlier date, showed that under some conditions some bottom yeasts could be converted into top yeasts. Changes in the other direction were said to be more rare. The evidence on which the latter change was based consisted only in the non-formation of head by supposedly bottom yeasts. Schönfeld and Rossman[182] reported that permanence of this property may be questioned. The rate of respiration was reported by Trautwein and Wassermann[183] to distinguish top and bottom yeasts. The rate for top yeasts was on the average 77 per cent higher than bottom yeasts. Top yeasts were said to rise to the surface during fermentation, where they can find oxygen and thus become acclimated to an aerobic existence. These authors stated that 40 per cent of the total metabolism of top yeasts was respiratory and 60 per cent fermentative, while with the bottom yeasts the ratio was 32 and 68 per cent respectively. Hansen was able to develop top yeasts from bottom yeasts by growth at low temperatures. Winge and Lausten's[136] spore-segregation method discussed above has made it possible to produce the reverse change.

Brewers' Yeast. Brewers' yeast, since it is used for a different purpose, has special properties. It is used for leavening bread to some extent, but imparts certain undesirable characteristics to the bread. It is darkened considerably. Brewers' yeast is also less active than the bakers' yeast, and if used for leavening must be used in larger amounts.

Classification of Yeasts. Yeasts are Ascomycetes which have many affinities in other groups of fungi. This has made classification quite difficult. Hensen[184] suggested a classification which has been used by many workers since then; it was later modified by Guilliermond.[185] Another modification was made later by Zender[186] because of the discovery of a new species of Endomyces. The latest contribution to classification of yeasts is by Stelling-Dekker[187] and Lodder,[188] the former dealing with sporeformers, and the latter with nonsporeformers. These last-mentioned classifications present entirely new arrangements with new family, genera, and species names, as does one by Langeron and Talice.[189] Asporogenous yeasts have been classified by Lodder.[188] Some of her suggestions are given later in this chapter under Torulopsis.

Identification of Yeasts. This is a very unsatisfactory if not difficult procedure. For some of the characters which must be determined, there

181. Rommel. 1907. J. Inst. Brewing 14, 409-410.
182. Schönfeld and Rossmann. 1908. Wchnschr. Brau. 25, 525-530.
183. Trautwein and Wassermann. 1930. Biochem. Ztschr. 229, 128-133.
184. Hansen. 1904. Centbl. Bakt., Pt. 2, 12, 529.
185. Guilliermond. 1928. Clef Dichotomique pour la Determination des Levures. Le Francois, Paris. Also, The Yeasts. Trans. by F. W. Tanner. John Wiley & Sons, N. Y.
186. Zender. 1925. Univ. of Geneva, Inst. of Botany, 10th Ser., Pt. 12.
187. Stelling-Dekker. 1931. Verhandel. K. Akad. Wetensch. 28, 1-546.
188. Lodder. 1934. Idem 32, 1-256.
189. Langeron and Talice. 1932. Ann. de parisitol. 10, 1-80.

is no satisfactory technic. Furthermore, the student may have to make many observations before satisfactory convincing evidence is available. Negative results are always unsatisfactory. If one desires to identify the strain under study, it is best to study the characteristics of similar yeasts which have been reported in the literature or to secure a transplant from the type culture. The latter is always preferable if its authenticity can be established. In many cases, the original strain has been lost and only the description in the literature is available. This is frequently of little value on account of ambiguous, indefinite statements. Reactions of media may be given without stating the indicator; resistance to heat may bear only the temperature without any statement of time, etc. In order to facilitate the study of yeasts, Guilliermond [185] prepared an outline of technic which may be used.

METHODS FOR STUDYING YEASTS

Yeasts are microorganisms which are grown much as the bacteria are grown. They differ by the fact that they are able to tolerate acid; consequently, if a little organic acid is added to the medium, the yeasts will grow while the bacteria will not. In Chapter 26 are given numerous formulas of media and solutions for cultivating yeasts.

Microscope Study of Yeast. Such examinations are constantly made by fermentologists to control the activity, purity, etc., of their yeast. The cells should be single or in pairs and not in large masses. If this condition exists, it indicates an immature yeast since the cells have not grown large enough to break away from the mother cell. The cells should be of about the same size and not vary from giant cells to small ones. Very young yeast is also evidenced by very thin cell walls and old yeast by very thick walls. The cells should also be intact and not show signs of breaking up. Such a yeast will, of course, be weakened in bread making. Young yeast cells should show one or two vacuoles when placed on a slide in wort. Poorly nourished yeast cells, also, have very thin walls and thin watery fluid contents instead of the thick walls and a gelatinous granulated protoplasm (Jago).

The microscope study of yeast cells may be made by mounting a little of the yeast in a warm chamber in a little wort. They should be watched over a period of time to ascertain the changes which take place in the cell as fermentation begins. For this purpose, the microscope should be kept in a warm place. The same observations should be made over a period of a week with some of the yeast in a culture flask. The constitution of the new cells should be compared with that of the cells which were first used.

Hansen's Single-Cell Method for Cultivating Yeasts. Hansen devised a method for securing single cells of yeasts. It was based on the method used by Lister for counting bacteria in milk. A special cover glass ruled in squares was used. One drop of the liquid dilution of the yeast cells was placed on the cover glass within the limits of the large square. The small squares only assisted in counting. This cover glass with the hanging drop was then fixed to a glass ring on a slide and the number of cells counted. If the drop was found to contain 20 cells it was then introduced into 40 ml. of sterile water. This would give approximately one cell in each two ml. of the water. The diluted yeast could then be introduced into flasks and each flask would probably contain a single cell although this was not always attained.

Lindner's Drop Culture for Testing Yeast. This method when applied to compressed yeasts, will give information on purity in a short time. The yeast is diluted with sterile wort until each drop contains one cell. Then a number of these droplets are placed on a sterile cover glass and inverted over a ring to make a Böttcher moist chamber. Development may be followed and inoculations made into other suitable media. Vuckovic [190] modified this procedure as follows: The original culture is suspended in either water or physiological sodium chloride solution. One small drop of this suspension is then transferred to a microscope slide and examined with the microscope. If the drop is found to contain only a few cells, about three, it may be transferred with a sterile loop to the surface of one or more agar slants. If the number of colonies which subsequently develop corresponds to the number of cells previously seen in the droplet, each can safely be considered as a single-cell colony.

Lindner's Adhesion Culture. According to this method, which was first stated by Lindner,[191] a thin layer of the yeast culture adhering to a cover glass is placed in a moist chamber. The yeast cells thus develop in their natural medium. It has various possibilities. It may be employed to determine the types of microorganisms on the outside of a piece of fruit. A little water would be put on the cover glass and the fruit pressed into it.

Microscope Examination of Pressed Yeasts.
Prepare a thin mixture of the yeast in distilled water. To this mixture or a small portion of it, add a little of a .1-per cent solution of methylene blue. Mount a drop of this under a cover glass on a slide and enumerate the dead and living bacteria. The dead cells will stain but the living cells will not. Henrici [192] found that yeast cells retained Gram's stain more firmly than the common Gram-positive bacteria. It has been further shown that, unlike the bacteria, the cytoplasm of the yeast cell is not homogenous with regard to its ability to retain the stain, certain granules appearing in the decolorizing cell which hold the dye longer than others. It is suggested that the ability of these granules to resist decolorization is in direct proportion to their ability to resist autolysis.

Boas [193] believed that bakers' and brewers' yeast differed sufficiently to make it possible to tell whether bakers' yeast has been falsified with brewers' yeast. Colingsworth and Baldwin [194] observed numerous small areas of discoloration owing to growth of various yeasts, molds, bacteria, and actinomycetes when various brands of pressed yeast were held at room temperature for four to six days. Frequently, numerous black areas of about one millimeter in diameter appeared. The organism associated with the black areas was found to resemble the organisms which are commonly referred to as "black-yeasts." On culture media, yeast-like cells of the organism contain a black pigment in the cell wall. A white mycelium is formed under certain conditions. Destruction of sugar does not result in formation of appreciable amounts of acid or gas. On most media the organism grows very slowly. A medium was developed for the detection of small numbers of this organism in the presence of numerous cells of *Sac-*

190. Vuckovic. 1938. Zentbl. Bakt., Pt. 2, 99, 32.
191. Lindner. 1901. Wchnschr. Brau., p. 354.
192. Henrici. J. Med. Res. 30, 409-415.
193. Boas. 1934. Mitt. Geb. Lebensmittelunt. u. Hyg. 25, 22-39.
194. Colingsworth and Baldwin. 1938. J. Bact. 35, 69.

charomyces cerevisiae. A mannitol yeast-infusion agar, to which copper sulfate was added to give a two-per cent concentration, permitted good growth of the "black yeast" but inhibited the growth of various other organisms, especially *Saccharomyces cerevisiae.* With this medium, three of four "black yeast" organisms per milliliter could be detected, although millions of other organisms were present in the sample. Commercial yeast cakes were found to contain from four to 100 "black yeast" cells per gram.

Strength of Physiological State of Yeast. In the fermentation industries it is necessary to have active, healthy yeast. This is especially desirable if pure-culture inoculation is used for introducing the yeast. Henneberg [195] stated that physiological state of yeast is chiefly characterized by its enzyme content, its enzyme-forming ability, and its chemical composition. He proposed a method for determining the "growing power" of individual cells. The yeast was treated with a solution of sucrose in distilled water. A droplet of the yeast suspension was examined after a lapse of 24 hours, under the microscope, in order to determine how often the individual cells have budded, numerous countings being made in order to obtain average values. The yeast is stimulated in this method to activity by the sugar; since there is no material for the formation of new protein, the yeast must employ its reserve protein. In this manner, its activity measured by its growing power is an indication of its physiological state. With the yeasts studied, Henneberg found that the growing power was dependent on the degree to which the yeast was washed. Higher "growth numbers" (*i.e.,* ratios of numbers of cells observed after 24 hours to the numbers initially present) were obtained with a large inoculum since (1) foreign matter adheres to the cells despite washing and (2) extractives from dead cells can probably be used. With a still larger inoculum growing power showed a great decrease or disappeared altogether on account of too-rapid fermentation of sugar. The alcohol formed exerts a toxic action. Henneberg reported "growth numbers" from 1.16 for a top "Weissbier" brewery yeast, to 4.57 for nonaerated, Race XII species. The highest number produced from one cell was 11, while the average of the maximum numbers in different experiments was 5.1. It is very interesting from a biological aspect, that one cell can store so much reserve material that it is sometimes able to bud from five to 11 times. Well-nourished, ordinary yeast, as well as well-nourished aeration yeasts, present growing numbers of 3 to 4.5. Insufficiently nourished, pressed yeast, prepared by the aeration process, and also old yeasts present low growing numbers. Further investigations will show what are the conditions that influence budding. For practical purposes, and especially in the manufacture of yeast, the growing test appears to be of considerable value. The more a yeast cell can grow without addition of nitrogenous matter, the better is its quality; and the greater the proportion of vigorous cells in the yeast mass, the greater must be the value of the latter. A yeast containing a large proportion of immature, badly-nourished, or old, half-starved cells

195. Henneberg. 1910. Wchnschr. Brau. 27, 350-352.

is unsuitable for practical purposes. Such cells, when introduced into worts or mashes, must first assimilate much nutriment before they can bud, and the result is that both the quantity and the quality of the yeast crop suffer. The enzyme content and the enzyme forming power of such yeasts is small, so that these yeasts are useless for baking purposes. An active yeast is one which contains a good energy reserve (reserve protein) and can, therefore, begin budding or fermenting at once. Dietrich [196] placed some of the burden on the medium. Sugars, proteins, and mineral substances, should be present in the wort in the right amounts. Oxygen absorption and the right temperature were other factors of vital importance. If these factors are not right, the yeast will be poorly nourished and will degenerate. The microscopic appearance of such yeast is characterized by alteration in shape with a tendency for the cells to elongate. The protoplasm is more or less granular and contains droplets of oil.

Characteristics of Good Compressed Yeast. 1. It should be moist, but not too much so.

2. Should not be too dry—so much so that it is powdery.

3. Should be well mixed and not show striated areas of different colors.

4. Should dissolve readily in the mouth and not remain as a lump.

5. Should have a pleasant, aromatic odor and pleasant taste.

The compressed yeast cake contains, besides the yeast cells, numerous bacteria. Since the yeast cells are present in such large numbers they overgrow the bacteria. However, if the yeast is kept at a warm temperature, the bacteria may spoil the yeast. Henneberg [197] found lactic acid and acetic acid bacteria. Russell [198] also found that the bacteria which cause ropy bread may also be present.

Conditions under which pressed yeast is stored seem to influence its fermenting ability. Storage at low temperatures preserves its activity to a marked extent as shown by results of experiments by Larmour and Brookington [199] and Bailey, Bartram, and Rowe.[200] The former found that storage of pressed yeast on ice resulted in improvement of its activities. Bailey, Bartram, and Rowe (1932) in quite extensive experiments concluded the pressed yeast should be stored around —1.1°C.(30°F.). Frozen yeast made good bread at first by deteriorated rapidly and yielded progressively poorer bread as it was stored.

Detection of Yeasts in Foods. In some foods yeasts are known to be present and special effort must be made to repress the growth of other microorganisms and favor their development. This may usually be done by using a medium made acid with such acids as acetic, lactic, and tartaric. In the chapter on "Media" are given some formulas for media made acid with lactic acid. In the case of agar media, the lactic acid solution must be added after sterilization, else the solidifying properties of the agar will be destroyed. The acid solutions should be sterilized

196. Dietrich. 1916. J. Inst. Brewing 23, 276-278.

197. Henneberg. 1906. Wchnschr. Brau. p. 188.

198. Russell. 1898. Fifteenth Ann. Rept. Wis. Agr. Expt. Sta., 110-113.

199. Larmour and Brookington. 1932. Canad. J. Res. 6, 614-621.

200. Bailey, Bartram, and Rowe. 1940. Cereal Chem. 17, 55-66.

separately and added to the melted agar aseptically. The acid in the media will favor growth of yeasts but repress growth of bacteria.

Examination of Yeast. It is often necessary in the fermentation industries to examine yeast in order to determine its fermenting ability, purity, contamination, etc. Two general types of yeast are recognized—cultivated yeast and wild yeast. Cultivated yeasts are those which have been propagated under controlled conditions and the characteristics of which are well known. They usually have a beneficial effect on the fermentation. Wild yeasts are made up of contaminating varieties and they usually cause the many undesirable fermentations (diseases) often encountered.

Pressed yeast is often made from top fermentation species; the water is removed and the cells mixed with some inert substance, such as starch and lactose. Effort is made not to use yeast of the bottom fermentation type on account of the absence of amylase and the presence of active trypsin. When trypsin-forming yeasts are used, the proteins are attacked, which interferes with retention of carbon dioxide. The use of a species which does not produce trypsin causes a tough glutenin which easily retains the carbon dioxide. Schweizer stated that pressed brewery yeast (bottom fermentation yeast?) was more active in dough in the early stages but the fermentation stops when bakers' yeast is still active. Pressed brewery yeast was said to be more sensitive to salt than is bakers' yeast, the fermentation of the two kinds being arrested by 2.8 and 4.0 parts of salt per 100 parts of flour respectively. Schweizer suggested that 2.8 per cent of salt be used for testing the value of the yeast in breadmaking. Harrison [201] made an investigation of yeast, finding that distillery yeast was superior for breadmaking to some of the so-called bread yeasts. Lindet [202] reported that one gram of bakers' yeast contained between five and six million cells. Such data are influenced, of course, by many factors. He also found that one gram of dough from the same bakery contained about the same number of cells.

Differential Staining of Living and Dead Yeast Cells. When the microscope was used for counting microorganisms, results secured with it were criticized because living and dead cells could not be differentiated. Investigations were soon started to discover a method by which living and dead cells could be differentiated. These, in general, have been staining methods.

Some investigators use a .1-per cent aqueous solution of methylene blue for this purpose. Schlichting and Winther [203] studied the common methods used for this purpose and reported that they were not accurate enough. They found that different concentrations of stain gave different results. They preferred a solution of sulfo-indigotate in a dilution of 1-30. The most appropriate dilution of yeast was one with about 40,000 cells per ml. Haehn and Glaubnitz [204] pointed out the difficulties of interpreting the results of staining suspensions of yeast with methylene blue. If all of the cells are absolutely dead or absolutely sound, staining will indicate it, but if cells are present which are neither completely dead or sound, but merely weakened, the difficulties are apparent. Some of the cells which stain blue are able to ferment and even regenerate themselves. These facts were demonstrated with a healthy yeast which had been weakened with acid. Even though the cells stained blue, they were not dead, but fermented as

201. Harrison. 1902-03. Ontario Agr. Coll. and Expt. Sta. Bul. 118.
202. Lindet. 1910. Ann. Brass. et Dist. 13, 155-164.
203. Schlichting and Winther. 1910. Seventh Internatl. Cong. Appl. Chem. 6B.

soon as they were put into wort. Haehn and Glaubnitz [204] stated that the concentration of the stain influenced the number of cells stained. The greater the concentration of dye, the greater was the number of stained cells. These investigators reported that the best concentration of dye was 1 to 10,000. Counting was advised immediately after addition of the staining solution to the yeasts. If the counts were delayed for 15 minutes after the dye was added, the number of stained cells was three times as great. Furthermore, Haehn and Glaubnitz recommended thorough mixing, because the condition of yeast varies with its position in the cake. Fuchs [205] recommended that the concentration of methylene blue should not exceed one part in 10,000 when testing yeast for dead cells. He also stated that the test was best carried out on washed yeast, after the wort or culture fluid had been removed. If the yeast is suspended in wort a larger amount of staining solution has to be added to produce a distinct blue color, e.g., three volumes of staining solution to one volume of suspension, because the colloids of the wort take up part of the dyestuff. As a rule, while some of the cells take a deep stain, others are only faintly colored. Fuchs' experiments indicated that the former are really dead, but the latter may still be capable of reproduction, and it is probable that the faint staining is due to a layer of mucilaginous matter on the cell walls. If a yeast suspension remains a long time in contact with an excess of the staining solution a number of cells which are at first uncolored become stained in the course of hours or days. In some cases the staining is gradual and in others very sudden, as if a rent had formed in the cell wall. The number of cells which thus die in the course of one or two days depends naturally on the age of the original culture. Dead cells stained with methylene blue may, if suspended in water, become bleached again after a time. This is due to the action of the reductases which may remain active after the cells are dead. The bleaching is much more rapid in wort, owing, doubtless, to the acidity of the wort; for equally rapid decoloration is produced by a .2-per cent solution of lactic acid or a 2-per cent solution of monopotassium phosphate.

Studies on the Bios question, in which it was very desirable to know whether cells were dead or alive, stimulated considerable study of the effect of various stains on yeasts. Fraser [206] employed a large group of stains, including many which are commonly used in the bacteriology laboratory. The action of these stains was determined on ''boiled'' and ''live'' bakers' yeast, and on yeast mixed with .25 per cent of phenol. Erythrosin gave a sharp separation between living (stained red) and dead (colorless) cells in three minutes, and methylene blue in one minute, after the addition of the dye. Devereux and Tanner [207] also reported erythrosin in .25 per cent aqueous solution when mixed with a yeast suspension to be the most efficient and desirable of 10 stains examined. It has been recently stated [208] that results obtained with the use of stains for differentiating living and dead cells are greatly influenced by the conditions which obtain during the experiment. The pH value of the liquid in which the yeast cells are suspended was said to influence their staining properties. The fact was mentioned that methylene blue was a base, the hydrochloride of which is soluble in neutral or acid solution, while in alkaline solution the less soluble free base is set free and is available for adsorption. The electrolytic content of the liquid was also mentioned as an influencing factor. It is not clear to what extent this is due to a corresponding change in pH value, since the presence of certain substances, such as dextrose and

204. Haehn and Glaubnitz. 1929. Wchnschr. Brau. 46, 315-320.
205. Fuchs. 1929. Wchnschr. Brau. 46, 437-439.
206. Fraser. 1920. J. Phys. Chem. 24, 741-748.
207. Devereux and Tanner. 1927. J. Bact. 14, 317-333.
208. Staining Yeasts With Methylene Blue. 1930. Nature 126, 491-492.

levulose, predispose the yeast to staining. A number of electrolytes inhibit staining in various degrees, and it may be that their absence renders the yeast cell walls more permeable to the stain. Standard conditions of staining cannot therefore be formulated for all strains of yeast, and it seems desirable to study further possible substitutes for methylene blue. Erythrosin, methyl green, and methylene blue sharply differentiated living and dead yeast cells in Mill's [209] experiments. A solution containing 1 to 10,000 methylene blue is best for differential staining.

Nadson and Burgwitz's [210] Method for Determining Fermenting Power of Yeasts. The complicated and expensive apparatus required for the determination of fermentative power, according to the methods of Hayduck, Meissl, or Kleinschmidt, induced Nadson and Burgwitz to put forward a cheap and simple contrivance, the construction of which was described in detail.

An Erlenmeyer flask with cork stopper is closed by a head-piece consisting of a U-formed bent glass tube of 3.4 to 4 mm. internal diameter, the limbs being of different length. The longer juts into the flask and the shorter is led into a small glass cylinder through a cork stopper, and so placed that the shorter limb reaches to within a millimeter of the bottom of the cylinder, which is from one-quarter to one-third full of dilute sulphuric acid (5 H_2SO_4.7.5 H_2O). In making the estimation, the apparatus is first sterilized, liquid and yeast then introduced, corks vaselined, sulphuric acid poured into the small cylinder, and the complete apparatus weighed. The carbon dioxide passes out through the sulphuric acid, leaving behind the alcohol and water, and escapes by the slit in the side of the cork cylinder. Before weighing,[211] on conclusion of the fermentation period, the carbon dioxide must be removed by careful shaking. The loss of weight of the apparatus is taken as equal to the carbon dioxide evolved, and this is adopted as a measure of the fermentative power of the yeast. The apparatus is unsuitable for work of great accuracy or for experiments of long duration, and it should not be used where widely-changing temperatures or humidities occur. Nevertheless, it is easy to handle and for ordinary technical purposes does not yield to more complicated and more expensive apparatus such as that of Meissl.

Efficiency of Bread Yeasts. This may be determined in different ways. A representative sample of the yeast should be obtained and divided into three parts. Store separately at 20, 30, and 40°C. (68, 86, and 104°F.). At regular intervals test each part for dead cells, gas formation, and dough-rising power. Test once or twice for adulteration with beer yeast and with mycoderma.

Dough-Rising Power of Bread Yeast. Mix 100 grams of flour, two grams of yeast and 60 ml. of distilled water by first making a thin batter of the yeast, water, and a little of the flour. Then add the rest of the flour and knead for five minutes. About three grams of flour should be kept with which to clean the glass rod. The dough should be molded into a cylinder and dropped into a warmed graduate cylinder which has been greased or powdered with flour. Press the dough down into the cylinder and place at 30°C. The volume is read every 30 minutes until the maximum is reached. Compute the maximum volume in terms of the original. Plot a curve which will show the activity of the yeast.

Determination of Fermenting Power of Yeasts, Meissl [212] Method. A saccharose phosphate mixture is prepared as follows: 400 grams of saccharose, 25 grams ammonium phosphate, and 50 grams of calcium sulfate. To 4.5 grams in 50 ml. of tap water of this substrate in an Erlenmeyer flask, fitted with a Meissl ventilation valve, add one gram of the yeast. Concentrated sulfuric acid may be used to absorb the H_2O, thus

209. Mills. 1941. Food Research 6, 361-371.
210. Nadson and Burgwitz. 1925. Wchnschr. Brau. 42, 41.
211. The apparatus is shown in the author's *Practical Bacteriology*, John Wiley and Sons, Inc., New York, N. Y.
212. Meissl. 1884. Ztschr. Gesam. Brauw. 7.

allowing the CO_2 to escape. The flask with inoculated contents should be kept at 30°C. for six hours. Meissl reported that a normal yeast would form 1.75 grams of carbon dioxide. The fermenting ability of such a yeast would be taken as 100 and the activity of the yeast under investigation as a percentage of this. The fermenting ability of an average bread yeast is about 80 per cent. Different types of valves are available. Alwood [213] used a convenient type for studying the fermenting capacity of pure strains of yeasts. The valves are so constructed that the activities of the yeast may be observed and the gases from the fermentation may escape. The moisture is retained by some absorbent such as calcium chloride or sulphuric acid. The apparatus should be weighed before and after the test.

Holm's [214] Method for Detecting Mycoderma and Mycoderma-Like Organisms in Yeast. Most of the Mycodermae and film-forming budding fungi which occur in distilleries and yeast factories are not alcohol-producing organisms, but generally decompose the alcohol formed by the yeast. Their presence in the pressed yeast weakens the latter and diminishes its commercial value. Yeast that has been prepared by the aeration process is especially liable to be infected with such Mycodermae. Holm described a simple and rapid method for the detection of Mycodermae in yeast, the essential feature of which consists in making a surface culture in which all the colonies will at once manifest their peculiarities. Ten or 20 small portions of yeast are taken, some from the surface and some from the interior of the yeast sample, with a sterilized needle or glass spatula, and transferred to a Freudenreich flask containing 10 ml. of sterile water. The liquid is shaken, and one or a few drops are transferred to a second flask also containing 10 ml. of sterile water so that the latter becomes very slightly but distinctly turbid. A second and a third dilution are made in the same way, the third being used for seeding. The most suitable medium consists of unhopped wort to which has been added five per cent of gelatin and 1½ per cent of agar. The medium is liquefied, poured into a Petri dish (15 cm. diameter), and allowed to solidify. The contents of the flask containing the third dilution are then poured so as to cover the surface of the medium; to prevent aerial contamination, Hansen's infection box may be used. The water is left to stand for a moment on the medium and then poured off quickly, the dish is covered and placed horizontally (with the cover turned upwards) in a thermostat at 25 to 27°C.(77 to 80.6°F.). After one or two days the culture is examined, and it may be easily seen with the naked eye which colonies are formed by the yeast and which by Mycodermae; the latter are large and flat, and also differ from the yeast colonies in color. The percentage of each kind of organisms may be easily found by counting.

Hayduck's [215] Method for Testing Fermenting Activities of Yeasts. Hayduck measured the amount of carbon dioxide liberated by yeasts, volumetrically. To a mixture of 40 grams of sucrose in 400 ml. of water in a flask are added 10 grams of the yeast to be studied. This flask is connected to a gas burette; the culture flask is maintained at 30°C. for one hour. By the usual technic the number of ml. of carbon dioxide formed may be read off. The weight of sugar decomposed by 100 grams of yeast may be determined by multiplying the number of ml. of CO_2 formed by the factor .03841. According to Nägeli,[216] comparison of Hayduck's method for determining the fermenting power of pressed yeast with baking tests, showed that while on the whole the former method distinguishes correctly between good and bad yeasts, it often gives untrustworthy results respecting samples intermediate in quality. Better results are obtained if the following salts are dissolved in the 400 ml. of 10-per cent sucrose solution employed: two grams of acid potassium phosphate, one gram of acid ammonium phosphate, .25 gram of magnesium sulfate, and .20 gram of calcium sulfate. By means of the modified method, pressed yeasts may be divided into good baking yeasts, producing more than 1,000 ml. of carbon dioxide in two hours; medium yeast, producing 800-1,000 ml.; and

213. Alwood. 1908. U. S. Dept. Agr., Bur. Chem. Bull. 111.
214. Holm. 1911. Brewers J. 47, 248.
215. Hayduck. 1881-1882. Quoted from Nägeli (1911).
216. Nägeli. 1911. Rev. in J. Inst. Brewing 18, 132.

bad yeasts, producing less than 800 ml. Cook and Malloch [217] pointed out some of the conditions which must be maintained if accurate results were to be obtained.

Determination of Fermenting Power of Yeasts (Kusserow's Method [218]**).** Put 400 ml. of 10-per cent saccharose solution and 10 grams of the yeast under examination into the fermentation flask of the Kusserow apparatus. Warm the flask and solution to 30°C. before starting. After the apparatus has stood for an hour at 30°C., it is connected and the amount of gas formed in the next half hour is measured; it should be 250 ml. The amount of gas for the first and second half hours is usually about 50 and 150 ml., respectively. Five grams of yeast in 400 ml. of 10 per cent saccharose solution in a flask fitted with a fermentation valve will cause a loss of about 6.5 grams of carbon dioxide in 24 hours if distilled water is used; with tap water the loss should approximate eight to 12 grams.

Another method for testing the fermentation ability of yeast involves the collection of the CO_2 evolved in a graduated container. The use of such a method is probably more accurate than the methods described above but has the disadvantage of requiring the maintenance of a constant temperature. Some liquid having a low absorption power for CO_2 should also be used. For this purpose a solution of calcium chloride of a specific gravity 1.4 may be used.

Determination of Mycoderma in Bread Yeast. Press the yeast with a sterile spatula into the bottom of a small Petri dish and incubate at 37°C.(98.6°F.) for two days. If the yeast contains a Mycoderma, pure white, characteristic colonies will appear on the yellowish background of the bread yeast. Numerous biological analyses of press yeast by Henneberg and Neumann [219] showed that 50 to 80 per cent of the yeast consisted of *Mycoderma cerevisiae* species. From the experiments made it was concluded that such a mixture of wild and cultivated species cannot be employed for making bread.

Test for Adulteration With Beer Yeast. Practically all of the beer yeasts ferment raffinose while the bread yeasts generally do not. One gram of the yeast is mixed with about 10 ml. of a one-per cent solution of raffinose broth and placed into a fermentation tube. Incubate this tube for about 24 hours at 30°C. A blank tube without raffinose should be prepared in order to test for gas produced from stored glycogen. If the difference between the two tubes is decided (about 50 per cent) adulteration with beer yeast is probable. A greater difference renders the test more conclusive.

Bau's Method for Testing the Purity of Yeasts. This determination depends on the fact that most bottom yeasts ferment raffinose while the top yeasts (compressed bread yeasts) do not. According to Bau [220] the following technic is followed: Test tubes are filled with 10 ml. of a one-per cent solution of raffinose in plain broth, plugged, and sterilized. Then .4 gram of the yeast under study is inoculated into the tube, which is then incubated at 30°C. for 24 hours. At the end of this time the substrate in the tube should be filtered and three ml. of the filtrate tested with Fehling's solution. If the solution is not reduced and remains blue it is fair evidence of not more than 10 per cent of bottom yeast in the compressed yeast. This same test should be made after 48 and 72 hours with tubes which have been held for that purpose. If, however, Fehling's solution is reduced and a yellow or yellow-brown color appears, it indicates that the bread yeast (top yeast) is free from bottom yeasts. Keuttner and Ulrich [221] reported results which confirmed the reliability of Bau's method. On the other hand, Langfurth [222] stated that contrary to the observations of Keuttner and Ulrich, Bau's raffinose method only gives perfectly reliable results when a really pure culture, top-fermentation yeast is being dealt with; but, on the other hand, it gives erroneous indications with commercial

217. Cook and Malloch. 1930. Cereal Chem. 7, 133-142.
218. Kusserow. See Lindner's "Betriebskontrolle" p. 289.
219. Henneberg and Neumann. 1910. Ztschr. Spiritusindus. 33, 13-14.
220. Bau. 1898. Wchnschr. Brau. p. 397.
221. Keuttner and Ulrich. 1901.
222. Langfurth. 1901. Ztschr. Offentl. Chem. 7, 198-199.

yeasts. Consequently, the method is incapable of determining whether beer yeast is present in pressed yeast. Saare and Bode [223] reported Bau's method to be reliable.

Lindner's [224] Method for Detection of Bottom Fermentation Beer Yeast in Pressed Yeast. The failure of Bau's method to satisfactorily separate top from bottom yeasts by melibiose fermentation caused Lindner to propose another method. According to Lindner, the most characteristic difference between top and bottom fermentation yeasts lies in the structure of the branches of their budding chains. To examine this, the yeast must be allowed to bud freely and unconfined. The yeast should be suspended in wort at such a dilution that, when droplets are prepared on a cover glass with a pen, each hemispherical pearl-shaped droplet contains not more than two or three cells. About 30 droplets containing about 100 cells are allowed to hang freely and are examined under the microscope after a period of not more than 24 hours. At that period the plant produced by the budding of each cell can be detected with ease and its characteristic form can be traced. The branches of the top-fermentation yeasts, so far as Lindner's experience goes, always grow in a sparlike formation. The top-fermentation yeasts bud with a monopodial ramification in which the original axis is continued as such. The bottom fermentation yeasts, on the other hand, bud with a sympodial ramification, in which the original axis suddenly disappears, while a side axis assumes the function of the main axis. If the yeast plants could grow upwards perfectly freely, the top-fermentation yeasts might be likened to fir trees and the bottom yeasts to birch trees. This method of diagnosis is the most reliable and occupies less time than other biological tests, the same series of observations can also be made to serve for the determination of the purity of yeast. In doubtful cases, where a confirmation is required, recourse may be had to the slower and less definite method of making a dilute streak culture of the sample of yeast with a point brush on a gelatin plate.

After the colonies have developed they should be picked off with a needle and stirred in a drop of water. As a general rule the colonies of top yeast will form a homogeneous turbid suspension in water, while those of bottom yeast tend to form a flocculent, clotted suspension in water.

Detection of Wild Yeasts in Pressed Yeast. This is not so necessary with the compressed yeast of the present day. It probably contains few bacteria and other objectionable fungi and a sufficient number of healthy cells. Hansen (1904), however, used a method for accomplishing this. A little of the yeast under investigation was inoculated into a tube of sterile wort and shaken in order to break up the cells. This culture tube was then incubated at 25°C.(77°F.) for 24 hours or for 48 hours at room temperature. After this time a growth appears at the bottom of the tube. This may be transferred several times to fresh tubes. Finally, some of this deposit is transferred to a sterile gypsum block contained in a Hansen flask or dish with a liberal supply of water. After from 40 to 72 hours an attempt should be made to determine the presence of spore formation. The presence of wild yeast is indicated by the presence of spores within this time.

Lindner's [225] Method for Testing Homogeneity of Pressed Yeast. A sample of yeast may be said to be homogeneous when all the cells in the sample are approximately of the same size and appearance, belong to the same species, and are in the same physiological condition. When a growth of pure yeast is first started in the propagating apparatus, it is very rarely homogeneous, although it consists of a single species; it is therefore readily understood that such a yeast will give very different results in the fermentation tuns, as compared with a stock yeast which has been in use for a considerable time, and which is generally homogeneous. The process of washing the pitching yeast with water, as practiced in Germany, tends to eliminate the young budding cells of low specific gravity, leaving the heavy, agglomerated, and mature cells behind, thus favoring the homogeneity, which suffers if the washing be not properly performed.

223. Saare and Bode. 1903. Wchnschr. Brau. 20, 101-105.
224. Lindner. 1904. Ztschr. Spiritusindus., 26, 229; Through J. Fed. Inst. Brew.
225. Lindner. 1904. Wchnschr. Brau. 21, 621-622; Through J. Fed. Inst. Brew.

In order to test whether yeast is homogeneous or not, a small quantity of the sample should be suspended in fresh wort and examined in droplet cultures ("Federstrich" cultures), note being taken of the form and tendency to budding, how many of the cells are still capable of budding, how many descendants are produced from each cell in a given time, and whether the descendants are alike or different. In some cases, the cultivation of the yeast in a thin layer of beer gelatin (Will's test) will afford valuable information, and it may thus be concluded, according to whether the colonies are mulberry-shaped or extend in streamers, whether the mother cells belong to the fermentative form or are film cells of the first or second generation; a preponderance of the latter forms indicates that the yeast has been exposed to the air to an excessive extent during its growth. The droplet test, if a standard number of cells be taken in each droplet, also gives a quantitative expression for the degree of infection with wild yeasts, and, according to the form of the budding chains, the presence of bottom-fermentation yeast in a sample of top-fermentation yeast can also be detected and estimated. When a sporulating yeast is examined in droplets, some cells may contain spores, while others in the same droplet may be devoid of spores, showing a lack of homogeneity in the condition of the yeast.

Detection of Starch in Pressed Yeast. Starch in pressed yeast may be detected with the microscope. The type of starch may be determined from the characteristics of the granules.

Many of the various species of yeasts are found in food and beverage products. In some cases, they are responsible for costly spoilage.

Schizosaccharomyces. The species in this group divide by transverse division. The first species to be reported was isolated from fruits by Beijerinck [226] and described under the name *Schizosaccharomyces octosporus*. *Schizosaccharomyces mellacei* was discovered in molasses by Greg. The species in this group have in general been isolated from products from the warmer climates.

Zygosaccharomyces. Ascospores in the species of this group result from conjugations. While the species which have been described come from different sources, only those which are related to food products will be mentioned here. The more recently described species have been reported by Fabian and Quinet [227] and Lochhead and Heron [228] from honey. Richter [229] described *Zygosaccharomyces mellis acidi* from fermenting honey. It was believed that the organism was contributed to the honey by the bees—a reasonable assumption. Fabian and Quinet described *Zygosaccharomyce mellis* and Lochhead and Heron *Zygosaccharomyces richteri* and *Zygosaccharomyces nussbaumeri* from the same source. Many of the species in this genus are able to live in concentrated sugar solutions.

Zygosaccharomycodes. This genus is of recent origin, having been made by Nishiwaki [230] for a species *(Zygosaccharomycodes japonicus)* isolated from saké. As the generic name indicates, it combines characteristics found in the older genera Saccharomycodes and Zygosaccharomyces. Nishiwaki believed that the species studied copulated as do the Zygosaccharomyces and multiplied by a process intermediate between budding and partition. The genus is still too young for general acceptance.

Debaromyces. Members of this genus have been isolated from cheese, sausage, and soil. Some pathogenic species have also been described.

Nadsonia. This genus was made to take care of an unusual method of conjugation which takes place between a mother cell and a bud from it. It includes one species, *Nadsonia fulvescens*. All of the contents of one gamete, the male, are poured into the other, the female; later on the ascus is formed. Nadson and Konokotin (1912) proposed the generic name Guilliermondia, for these species.

226. Beijerinck. 1894. Centbl. Bakt. 16, 49-58.
227. Fabian and Qinet. 1928. Mich. Agr. Expt. Sta. Tech. Bull. 92.
228. Lochhead and Heron. 1929. Bull. 116, Dept. Agr. Canada.
229. Richter. Mycol. Centbl. 1, 67-76.
230. Nishiwaki. 1929. Centbl. Bakt., Pt. 2, 79, 194-204.

Schwanniomyces. Each cell possesses a single spore about which is a projecting collar. Many of the cells in a suspension of this species show the presence of a short tube or beak, giving the cell the appearance of a retort.

Torulaspora. This genus is not sharply distinguishable from Schwanniomyces.

Saccharomycodes. This genus was made for a very few species which divide by a process which is intermediate between budding and partition. Only a very few species are known. It is interesting to note that Nishiwaki [230] found a species, *Zygosaccharomycodes japonicus*, which he thought sufficiently different to justify the new genus just mentioned.

Saccharomycopsis. Only one species has been described. Ascospores are formed. The cells are large. It has not been found in food products .

Saccharomyces. The members of this genus are important in the industries and are usually active fermenters. *Saccharomyces crevisiae* is the best-known species and was studied at great length by Hansen. *Saccharomyces pastorianus* and *Saccharomyces ellipsoideus* are other species from fermented products.

These species are generally considered to be the best representatives of so-called "industrial yeasts." *Saccharomyces cerevisiae* is generally considered to be a round or oval-celled species with little ability to form alcohol, while *Saccharomyces ellipsoideus* possesses long cells and forms much alcohol. The latter has generally been known as the wine yeast. This distinction, based on work of Hansen, has been losing its significance as recently pointed out by Henrici.[231] Stelling-Dekker even went so far as to reduce *Saccharomyces ellipsoideus* to *Saccharomyces cerevisiae* var. *ellipsoideus*. Henrici was of the opinion that this idea might be applied to other industrial yeasts, although difficulties are encountered because industrial yeasts are often known for some special property, little attention being paid to species relationships.

Pichia. The members of this genus form mycelia and grow well on the surface of liquid culture media. Ascospores are formed. The genus is characterized by absence of fermentative activity. The shape of the cells of Pichia species is sausage-like.

Hansenula (Willia). The derby hat shape of the ascospores is the most characteristic thing about this genus. A thick film is formed on liquid culture media.

Monospora. Not much is known about this genus, but one species having been described. The ascospores are characteristic in that they are long and slender with sharp ends.

Nematospora. The ascospores of this genus are long and slender with a long polar flagellum at the end. Those species which have been described have come from food products. Those species which are known have come from hazelnuts, tomatoes, and string beans.

Torulopsis (Torula). Members of the genus Torula do not form ascospores and are, consequently, not considered to be true yeasts. Interest in the species of this genus started with the investigations of Hansen and several other early fermentologists. Like Mycodermae, Torulae are found widely distributed in saccharine material, even though they are generally nonfermenters. The group consists of two sections; one, the members of which are pathogenic and the other, the members of which are nonpathogenic.

Classification of Torula is in an unsatisfactory state. The term Torula was used by Turpin in 1838 for fungi which are now considered as Sac-

231. Henrici. 1942. Brewers' Digest 17, 34-36.

charomycetes. He called beer yeasts *Torula cerevisiae*. Hansen, however, with whose investigations started real progress on systematization of yeasts, included among the Torulaceae only those budding fungi which produced neither endospores nor typical mycelial vegetation. According to Hansen, only globular forms are found with perhaps occasionally elongated cells in films. He also stated that some Torulae can cause alcoholic fermentation. More recently, the Torulae have been studied by Ciferri and Redaelli[232] and Harrison.[233]

Ciferri and Redaelli's[232] **Classification of Torulae.** Budding fungi which do not form ascospores have been studied at some length by these investigators. They stated that they based their system on earlier ones, especially that of Will which has not been generally accepted by microbiologists. Only that part of Ciferri and Redaelli's classification which deals with Torulae will be reproduced here.

SUBFAMILY A.—TORULOPSIDEAE

1. Cells showing a vestige of copulation of the
   germinative tubules   Genus 3. *Asporomyces* Chaborski.
   Cells without traces of sexuality 2
2. Apiculate cells (lemon shaped)   Genus 4. *Kloeckeria* Janke
   Rounded, oval, elliptical cells, rarely apiculate
   and then mixed with the foregoing 3
3. Cells normally very small and without a clearly visible
   double contour   Genus *Pityrosporum* Sabouraud
   Young cells with one or more oleose corpuscles, growing according to Will's fundamental form I   Genus 6. *Eutorulopsis* Ciferri
   Young cells without oleose corpuscles and growing according to Will's form III   Genus 7. *Torulopsis* Berlese

Harrison's[233] **Classification of Torulae.** A great many species of budding fungi which did not form ascospores were studied by Harrison. He paid most attention to functional characteristics, especially fermentation reactions. Harrison could not accept Ciferri and Redaelli's classification because they paid no attention to priority in the use of names. Harrison preferred to follow Will's suggestion, which may be tabulated as follows:

Mycotorula = forming rudimentary mycelium.
Rhodotorula = red pigment.
Chromotorula = Yellow, brown, or black pigment.
Torula = no pigment formed.

Torulae have been reported from a number of foods. Browne[234] isolated *Torula communis* from raw Cuban sugar. Wehmer[235] described several from sauerkraut. *Torula mellis* was described by Fabian and Quinet[227] from honey. Two interesting lactose-fermenting Torulae were isolated from "yeasty" cream by Hammer and Cordes.[236] They were named *Torula cremoris* and *Torula sphaerica*. Hammer[237] also described *Torula lactis-condensi* from swelled cans of condensed milk.

A more recent attempt to classify the asporogenous yeasts was by Lodder[188] who arranged them into the following groups:

232. Ciferri and Redaelli. 1929. Ann. Mycol. 27, 243-295.
233. Harrison. 1928. Trans. Roy. Soc. Canada, Sect. V, 22, 187-225.
234. Browne. 1918. J. Ind. Eng. Chem. 10, 178.
235. Wehmer. 1905. Centbl. Bakt., Pt. 2, 14, 682-713.
236. Hammer and Cordes. 1920. Iowa Agr. Expt. Sta. Res. Bul. 61.
237. Hammer. 1919. Iowa Agr. Expt. Sta. Res. Bul. 52.

ASPOROGENOUS YEASTS

Family 1(?)	Family 2	Family 3
Nectaromycetaceae	Torulopsidaceae	Rhodotorulaceae
Producing conidia	No conidia produced. Carotinoid pigments not produced.	No conidia produced. Cells contain carotinoid pigments. Genus: Rhodotorula.

Subfamily A	Subfamily B
Torulopsoideae	Mycotoruloideae
With or without a primitive pseudomycelium. No sporeforming organs.	With pseudomycelium and possessing sporeforming organs.

Genera: Torulopsis
        Pityrosporium
        Mycoderma
        Kloeckera
        Asporomyces
        Trigonopsis
        Schizoblastosporion

This arrangement will probably be generally accepted by microbiologists.

Mycoderma. Into this genus are placed species in which ascospore formation has not been demonstrated. This does not always mean that they do not form them but that they have not been observed. It is quite probable that some non-ascospore-forming strains of other species have been placed here. Mycoderma species usually grow with a heavy film or pellicle on the surface of fluid media, such as beer wart, pickle brine, and fruit juices. They often cause trouble by using the acids formed by bacteria, which are necessary in food preservation.

Pseudosaccharomyces. The cells of the species in this genus are lemon-shaped.

Sporobolomyces. This is one of the more recent genera of yeasts made by Kluyver and van Niel [238] for several species which, while growing like true yeasts, later show a tendency to put out organs much like sterigmata at the tip of which conidia are formed. While Kluyver and van Niel described three species, others are known to exist. Since sterigmata are formed it was proposed to consider these fungi as Basidiomycetes in which Lohwag [239] and Guilliermond [240] did not agree.

Anthomyces. This genus was made by Nadson and Krassilnikow [241] for a species, *Anthomyces Reukaufii*, isolated from the nectar of flowers. In nectar pairs of cells were first formed and later groups of four; since the cells are club-shaped with their narrow ends in contact the groups have been said to resemble airplanes or crosses. When the cells separate they assume oval or round shapes, becoming filled with fat to form resting cells (Dauernzellen). Under some conditions of culture a mycelium is formed with conidia.

238. Kluyver and van Neil. 1924. Centbl. Bakt., Pt. 2, 63, 1-20.
239. Lohwag. 1926. Ann. Mycol. 24, 194-201.
240. Guilliermond. 1927. Compt. Rend. Acad. Sci. 184, 217.
241. Nadson and Krassilnikow. 1928. Bul. Soc. Mycol. France 43, 232-214.

REFERENCE BOOKS

DELBRÜCK, M., Hefe, Gärung and Faulniss. Parey, Berlin.

GALLOWAY, L. D., AND BURGESS, R., 1937. Applied Mycology and Bacteriology. Leonard Hill, Ltd., London.

GLAUBITZ, M., 1932. Atlas der Gärungsorganismem. Parey, Berlin.

GUILLIERMOND, A., 1920. Les Levures (Translated by F. W. Tanner). John Wiley and Sons, Inc., New York, N. Y.

GUILLIERMOND, A., 1928. Clef Dichotomique pour la Determination des Levures. Le Francois, Paris.

GWYNNE-VAUGHAN, H. C., AND BARNES, B. The Structure and Development of the Fungi. The Macmillan Co., New York, N. Y.

HANSEN, E. C., 1896. Practical Studies on Fermentation. Spon and Chamberlain, New York, N. Y.

HANSEN, E. C., 1911. Gesammelte theoretische Abhandlungen über Gärungsorganismem. Gustav Fischer, Jena.

HENRICI, A. T., 1930. Molds, Yeasts and Actinomycetes. John Wiley and Sons, Inc., New York, N. Y.

HENNEBERG, W., 1926. Handbuch der Gärungsbakteriologie. Two volumes. Berlin.

HENNEBERG, W., 1923. Die Gärungsgewerbe und ihre Naturwissenschaftlichen Grundlagen. Quelle and Meyer, Leipsiz.

HENNEBERG, W., 1934. Bakteriologische Mölkereikontrolle: Mikroskopische Bestimmung der fur die Milchwirtschaft nützlichen und schädlichen Backteien-, Hefen- und Schimmelpilzarten. Parey, Berlin.

JORGENSEN, A., HANSEN, A., AND LUND, A., 1939. Microorganisms and Fermentation. Griffin, London.

KLOCKER, A., 1903. Fermentation Organisms; A Laboratory Handbook. Longmans Green and Co., New York, N. Y.

LAFAR, F., 1904. Handbuch der technischen Mykologie. Fischer, Jena. In five volumes.

LINDER, P., 1930. Mikroskopische und Biologische Betrienskontrolle in den Gärungsgewerben mit besonderer Berucksichtung der Brauerei. Berlin.

LODDER, J., 1934. Die anaskosporogenen Hefen. Erste Halfte. Verhandelingen der Koninklijke Akademie van Weterschnappen te Amsterdam. Afd. Natuurkunde (Tweed Sectie) Deel 32, 1-256.

Oeuvres de Pasteur. In seven volumes. Masson et cie, Paris.

SMITH, G., 1938. An Introduction to Industrial Mycology. Edward Arnold and Co., Ltd., London.

STELLING-DEKKER, N. M., 1931. Die Sporogenen Hefen. (Same as Lodder above.)

THOM, C., AND CHURCH, M. B., 1926. The Aspergilli. Williams and Wilkins, Baltimore, Md.

THOM, C., 1930. The Penicillia. Williams and Wilkins, Baltimore, Md.

CHAPTER 4

BACTERIOLOGY OF WATER AND SEWAGE

By collecting data from the large registration cities of the United States Johnson [1] in 1916 gave ample proof that polluted water caused illness. During recent years, however, relation of water to disease dissemination has been diminishing progressively. Milk probably causes more epidemics now than water. Bacteria in water may also be significant in industry. They cause undesirable deterioration in certain foods. Harrison and Sadler,[2] for example, stated that *Pseudomonas fluorescens* caused discoloration of halibut. Shutt [3] found the same organism the cause of flavor deterioration in pasteurized creamery butter. Shutt [3] stated that a water supply might be satisfactory for human consumption but be unsuitable for butter making. A serious defect caused by several types of bacteria, among which *Pseudomonas fluorescens* is most important, results in the development of disagreeable odors and flavors over the whole surface of butter. It gains access to water from surface drainage especially from swamp lands. The only permanent solution is to pasteurize or chlorinate the water or obtain it from a pure source. Shutt mentioned a creamery so affected where the water supply seeped through vegetation to collect in ditches filled with large stones. The surface flavor bacteria disappeared when the water was collected directly from springs. Surface taint of butter was traced by Linneboe [4] to *Achromobacter putrescens* in water supplies of creameries. This has been confirmed also by Wolochow, Thornton, and Wood [5] who found in creamery waters many bacteria which could grow at 10 to 15°C.(50 to 59°F.). Many were actively proteolytic. These investigators thought that waters used in creameries might have to be given bactericidal treatment. The same opinions were also expressed by Castell and Garrard.[6] Salting butter to the extent of 2.5 per cent, did not prevent these waters organisms from growing (Turgason [7]). Heavy chlorination was required to destroy them.

Possible infection of food by contaminated water is indicated by Meyer, Phillips, Lind, and Board [8] who traced a milk-borne outbreak of typhoid fever to this source. Water from a cistern used for washing utensils contained *Eberthella typhosa*. Many such instances might be mentioned. Even water from deep wells may be polluted.

Heater [9] reported an interesting case where polluted water from a well 155 feet deep was responsible for typhoid fever. A small stream of water

1. Johnson. 1916. J. Amer. Water Wks. Assoc. 3, 239-326.
2. Harrison and Sadler. 1929. Food Indus. 1, 308-312.
3. Shutt. 1936. Canad. Pub. Health J. 27, 226-227.
4. Linneboe. 1940. Sci Agr. 21, 133-138.
5. Wolochow, Thornton, and Wood. 1941. J. Dairy Sci. 24, A 270.
6. Castell and Garrard. 1941. Canad. Dairy and Ice Cream J. 20, 18.
7. Turgason. 1940. Nat. Butter and Cheese J. 31, 39-40.
8. Meyer *et al*. 1941. J. Milk Tech. 4, 123-127.
9. Heater. 1926. Water Wks. Engin. 79, 272.

was encountered during drilling, which was not cased off. Ten years afterward, owing to a typhoid outbreak, a connection between the well and an abandoned quarry was discovered. Lewis[10] reported coliform bacteria in fissure springs of the Balcones fault zone in Texas. He ascribed this contamination to animals pastured on the plateau on which the water was collected. Other industries may also suffer from objectionable bacteria in their water supplies. According to Feys[11] various methods may be used for treating such water.

Besides the troubles just mentioned there are some of lesser importance; for instance, Green, Judd, and Marx[12] attributed ''ropiness'' in tea to a capsulated bacterium present in the water from which it was made.

Sanitary Inspection of Water Supplies. Sanitary inspection is an important part of water-supply investigation. Laboratory results alone are not sufficient to judge quality of a water supply. Sawyer[13] quoted an instance of a water-borne epidemic which could have been prevented had a sanitary inspection been made. Indications of pollution appeared two months before the epidemic broke out. A sanitary inspection would probably have prevented seven deaths and many cases of typhoid fever. Laboratory examinations should be used to check the results of remedial measures, when such measures are adopted. Cobb[14] suggested the use of the engineering point of view and more attention to sanitary inspection than to bacterial analysis. This might reveal sources of coliform bacteria not revealed in any other way. Water mains, for instance, if new or recently repaired, may be contaminated. Harris[15] recommended chlorination of such mains before use. Contamination was said to be possible from fecal matter of careless workmen or from jute or hemp packing as well as from other sources.

Types of Water. Chemically speaking, water is hydrogen monoxide and regarded as a universal solvent. Only with the greatest difficulty and with the most carefully constructed apparatus can the chemist prepare water which approaches pure hydrogen monoxide and be free from all traces of metals, salts, gases, dust, or bacteria.

Different adjectives are used to indicate quality of potable water—pure, safe, polluted, infected, bad, etc. To the sanitarian, a pure water is one which is free from pathogenic bacteria and which has had a good clinical experience. It should also be free from chemical substances, such as lead and fluorine, which cause disturbances in the body. This subject is complicated somewhat by the fact that individuals vary in their response to different waters. A water which is wholesome to one person may cause severe disturbances in another. Rosenau, in his *Preventive Medicine and Hygiene*, classified waters as good, polluted, and infected. A *good* water was defined as above for pure water. A *polluted* water was one which had

10. Lewis. 1926. J. Amer. Water Wks. Assoc. 15, 158-168.
11. Feys. 1937. Bull. Assoc. Anciens Etudiants de l'Ecole de Brass., de Louvain 37, 136-151.
12. Green *et al.* 1940. Amer. J. Pub. Health 30, 680-682.
13. Sawyer. 1915. Cal. State J. Med., May, 1915.
14. Cobb. 1919. Indiana San. and Water Supply Assoc. 2, 12-22.
15. Harris. 1937. J. Amer. Water Wks. Assoc. 29, 1868-1875.

received organic wastes of either man or animal. Such a water is not necessarily harmful. An *infected* water is one which contains disease-producing microorganisms.

Relation of Chemical to Bacterial Examination. In the past, discussion has centered about superiority of the chemical or bacterial analysis of water. Much of this has probably been quite useless since both are important and necessary for an accurate opinion on potability. The more information at hand, the more accurate will be the opinion. The chemical analysis may give information about the history and possibly the age of the water. It gives information about the content of organic matter and the stage of its decomposition, as indicated by the nitrogen compounds present. It enables the sanitary engineer, for instance, to maintain sufficient alkalinity in the water to prevent alum used in its purification from passing into the filtered water. Chemical analysis also detects objectionable trade wastes, the presence of heavy metals, and indicates to some extent how water may be expected to behave in the human body.

The bacteriological examination is made to determine the kind and number of microorganisms present. It is easy to conceive that a water of good quality by chemical analysis might contain pathogenic bacteria. While isolation of specific pathogenic bacteria from water is not attended with much success, the bacterial examination yields more definite knowledge of their possible presence than can be obtained by chemical means. Bacteriological examination is especially important also for determining the efficiency of filters and the value of other methods of treatment. Negative results in the bacteriological examination might have little significance.

For our purposes, sanitary water analysis may be regarded as made up as follows:

I. Sanitary chemical examination
   A. Physical (organoleptic) tests
      a. Turbidity
      b. Color
      c. Odor

   B. True chemical determinations
      a. Residue
      b. Chloride
      c. Nitrogen as
         1. Nitrates
         2. Nitrites
         3. Free ammonia
         4. Albuminoid organic ammonia
      d. Alkalinity
      e. Oxygen consumed

Collection of Samples. Collection of the sample of water is an important part of the analysis. It must be done carefully. For chemical analysis, samples should be collected in glass-stoppered bottles which are scrupulously clean. The stoppers should fit tightly and be protected during transportation. For bacteriological analysis, four-, six-, or eight-ounce, glass-stoppered bottles, cleaned and sterilized, should be used. They should have been rinsed in water and sterilized thoroughly either at 160°C. (320°F.) for one hour, or for 30 minutes at 15 pounds pressure. Before shipment, the top of each bottle should be protected by a piece of cloth or tin foil. Specimens for bacteriological analysis should probably be packed in ice during transportation (Hasseltine [16]). Instructions for sampling usually accompany the bottle. Schmidt [17] also gave procedures for collecting water samples.

Interval Between Collection and Analysis. Analysis of samples of water should be started as soon as possible after collection. Since changes may occur in the sample, certain examinations may be made in the field. The committee which prepared the 1917 *Standard Methods for the Examination of Water and Sewage* suggested the following as being within reasonable limits.

Physical and Chemical Analysis
Ground waters	72 hours
Fairly pure surface waters	48 hours
Polluted surface water	12 hours
Sewage effluents	6 hours
Raw sewage	6 hours

Microscopical Examination
Ground waters	72 hours
Fairly pure surface waters	24 hours
Waters containing fragile organisms	Immediate examination

Bacteriological Examination
Samples kept at less than 10°C.	24 hours

The committee which prepared the 1925 edition of *Standard Methods* placed a time limit, between collection and analysis, of six hours for impure waters and not more than 12 hours for relatively pure waters. During the storage period the temperature should be kept between 6 and 10°C. (42.8 and 50°F.). It is stipulated that any deviation from this shall be stated in the reports.

Identical recommendations appear in the eighth edition of *Standard Methods of Water Analysis*. Water bacteriologists have frequently stated that samples should not be held very long before analysis. Eijken [18] reported that changes occurred even at 0°C.(32°F.). Despite this opinion most of the samples analyzed in large central laboratories are shipped, and some time interval exists between collection and analysis. It is probable that a general rule should not be applied to all samples for their bacterial flora differs. Berry [19] found no change in the number of coliform bacteria in samples of ground water in the first 48 hours after collection regardless of whether the samples were iced or not. Uniced samples were said to yield dependable results. Ellison, Hackler, and Buice [20]; McCrady [21];

16. Hasseltine. 1919. Pub. Health Repts., 32, 2016-2032.
17. Schmidt. 1939. Gas. u. Wasser. 82, 135; J. Amer. Water Wks. Assoc. 31, 1421.
18. Eijken. 1919. Geneesk. Tijdschr. Nederland. Indië 58, 163-167.
19. Berry. 1926. Amer. J. Pub. Health 16, 700-703.
20. Ellison *et al.* 1929. J. Amer. Water Wks. Assoc. 21, 528-530.
21. McCrady. 1920. Idem 7, 845-851.

Tanner and Schneider,[22] and perhaps some of the results secured by Boruff and Buswell [23] confirmed this opinion. McCrady described a mailing case for sending water samples for analysis. Castell and McDermott [24] condemned this procedure. Their results with it were too erratic.

Other investigators have reached different conclusions. Kelso [25] exchanged a series of samples with three laboratories to determine the effect of mailing uniced samples. Plate counts increased materially after 24 hours; after 48 hours the counts were lower than after 24 hours. It was stated that examination of uniced samples gave results of doubtful value. Effect of shipping was not pronounced in the finished water but was noticeable in the raw water.

Keiper and Flinn [26] observed that higher counts and greater coliform-bacteria content were secured with samples sent through the mail. Such samples were not considered to be satisfactory.

Analysis by Caldwell and Parr [27] of 50 replies from state and insular laboratories indicated that in most cases the procedure prescribed in *Standard Methods of Water Analysis* for storage and time of examination of water samples is not observed; a large number of samples were examined after 24 hours and a considerable number after 48 hours. Comparison of recovery of coliform bacteria from iced and uniced samples examined at varying periods indicated a very rapid death rate of *Escherichia coli* in bottled samples of contaminated waters, which was progressively greater as the period of holding increased. Icing, though of secondary importance, was definitely advantageous.

Chemical constitution of the water apparently has much effect on results of storage of water samples. Few who have worked on the problem have considered this factor. Castell and McDermott [24] observed that growth in water of low organic content was restricted to certain groups of Gram-negative bacteria. They showed the danger of delaying analysis of samples too long, especially if results are to be considered in terms of food spoilage rather than potability.

Boruff and Buswell [23] were among the few to point out that the type of water and other factors may influence the results. They observed that icing of warm waters caused a marked decrease in the total count. On the other hand, warm waters with a low total count frequently were said to increase slightly in total count when iced for short periods. Boruff and Buswell found little change in total counts of cold water—1 to 4°C. (33.8 to 39.2°F.)—when such samples were collected from rivers and brought to the laboratory and incubated at 2°C. (35.6°F.) for one to five days. These data indicate that icing may have profound effect on the bacterial content of samples of water, depending on the source of the sample and the time of year when it is taken. Other factors also help to explain the

22. Tanner and Schneider. 1935. Proc. Soc. Expt. Biol. and Med. 32, 960.
23. Boruff and Buswell. 1929. Ill. State Water Survey Bull. 28.
24. Castell and McDermott. 1942. Food Research 7, 244-253.
25. Kelso. 1933. J. Penn. Water Wks. Operators Assoc. 5, 27-29.
26. Keiper and Flinn. 1940. Amer. J. Med. Tech. 6, 11-14.
27. Caldwell and Parr. 1933. Amer. J. Pub. Health 23, 467-472.

discordant results which have been secured by so many different investigators. The best practice is probably to continue icing samples until more evidence is available that it is unnecessary.

Effect on Bacterial Count of Shaking the Sample. *Standard Methods for the Examination of Water and Sewage* have, for many years, prescribed shaking vigorously for 25 times. Green's [28] work would indicate that vibrating (frequency of 60 per second) instead of shaking is more desirable on account of higher counts secured. The increase in bacterial numbers was 67 per cent. It is questionable whether such matters really affect the plate count more than the inherent errors in the method itself.

Data Required With Specimens Submitted for Analysis. Laboratories engaged in water analysis require complete information about the source of the sample. This information is usually supplied on a certificate which accompanies the sample bottles and is necessary for accurate interpretation of results of examination. Failure to supply it usually means delay and in no manner increases the value of the opinions of the laboratory. Most laboratories will not report results and opinions without full information. This is a sound practice.

BACTERIOLOGICAL EXAMINATION OF WATER

The main purpose of bacteriological examination of water is to determine the presence of microorganisms which may cause deterioration in foods or which may produce diseases in man and animals. Owing to difficulties in isolation of pathogenic bacteria with certainty within a reasonable time to be of any value, bacteriologists have developed another procedure of testing for presence of bacteria which live in the human intestines along with pathogenic bacteria, should they be present. This is the test for coliform bacteria. It is not an ideal procedure but an expedient. Hoskins and Butterfield [29] have stated that a satisfactory procedure to determine promptly and satisfactorily when a water is free from pathogenic bacteria does not exist. In some cases too much emphasis may be given to bacteriological methods of analysis. Howard [30] pointed out, for instance, that a negative bacteriological result may not be a guarantee of safety. Further positive findings may not indicate human pollution because it is quite impossible to distinguish accurately between human and animal pollution. Despite these shortcomings, considerable progress has been made with bacteriological methods.

Bacteriological methods are, in general, used for determining quality of potable water. These do not involve attempts to isolate specific pathogenic bacteria but to demonstrate the presence of bacteria which originate in fecal matter, sewage, and other types of contamination. Methods for isolating pathogenic bacteria from water are not entirely satisfactory and pathogenic bacteria may not live as long in water as the indicators of pollution. Present practice seems to be more concerned with showing that

28. Green. 1941. Ohio Conf. Water Purification, 20th Ann. Rept., 1940, 59-62.
29. Hoskins and Butterfield. 1935. J. Amer. Water Wks. Assoc. 27, 1101-1109.
30. Howard. 1939. New Hamp. St. Bd. Health, Health News 17.

possibilities of pollution exist than in showing that disease-producing bacteria are present. In pages to follow various indicators of pollution and procedures for demonstrating their presence are discussed.

Significance of Bacterial Count of Water. In the early days of laboratory examination of water, the bacterial count was thought to be a reliable index of pollution. Many standards, based on counts, were formulated for determining quality. An elaborate but quite useless one was suggested by Miquel.[31] Probably Koch's old standard of not over 100 bacteria per ml. on gelatin is as reliable as any. High counts in themselves are probably meaningless. However, water with a consistently high count stands a greater chance of containing objectionable forms. In natural waters, a high content of organic matter is usually accompanied by a higher number of bacteria.

Two methods were used in the past for enumerating water bacteria. A 37°C.(98.6°F.) colony count was secured with agar plates incubated for 48 hours and a 20°C.(68°F.) colony count on gelatin after 24 hours' incubation. It was believed that at 37°C. those forms which originated in the alimentary tract of man and animals would develop, while at 20°C. the soil forms would develop. Later, it was found that the colony counts secured at both temperatures overlapped greatly. The relative merits of the two procedures have been discussed by Whipple,[32] Caird,[33] Baton,[34] Gaub,[35] Harrison,[36] Cumming,[37] Tanner,[38] and Race.[39] Most of these papers, published about the same time, were stimulated by suggested changes in "standard methods." Hoskins,[40] and Frost and Streeter[41] observed season variations in counts as well as in the relation of the gelatin count to the *Escherichia coli* count.

Little agreement exists on the number of bacteria which may be allowed in a safe potable water. The bacteria themselves are not important but the conditions which they reflect are important. In the fourth edition of the *Swiss Alimentary Codex*[42] for bacteriological and chemical analysis of water, the counts are below 100 bacteria per ml. for spring water and 10 per ml. for ground water. *Escherichia coli* must be absent in 20 ml. of spring water and in 100 ml. of ground water.

The plate counts secured in water analysis are markedly influenced by the media used. Not as much study has been given to media to be used in water analysis as in milk analysis. Gurfein,[43] after a comparative investigation of various proposed methods, concluded that not over 50 per

31. Miquel. 1891. Manuel pratique d'analyse bacteriologique des eaux Paris, 1891.

32. Whipple. 1913. Amer. J. Pub. Health 3, 36-43.

33. Caird. 1913. Proc. Amer. Water Wks. Assoc. 1913, 325-351.

34. Baton. 1914. J. Amer. Water Wks. Assoc. 1, 11-23.

35. Gaub. 1913. Proc. Ill. Water Supply Assoc. 1913, 155-159.

36. Harrison. 1912. In Marshall's *Microbiology.*

37. Cumming. 1916. Hyg. Lab., U. S. Pub. Health Ser. Bull. 104.

38. Tanner. 1916. Ill. State Water Survey Bull. 12, Urbana, Ill.

39. Race. 1916. Amer. J. Pub. Health 6, 488-496.

40. Hoskins. 1922. Engin. News-Rec. 89, 1078-1079.

41. Frost and Streeter. 1942. Pub. Health Bull. 143, U. S. Pub. Health Ser.

42. Mohler. Schweiz. Verein von Gas und Wasserfachmännern Monatsbulletin 16, 209.

43. Gurfein. 1930. Arch. Biol. Nauk. 30, 529-547.

cent of the organisms developed into colonies in beef infusion-peptone agar media.

Introduction of a new plating medium for counting bacteria in milk, which gave more colonies than the old medium, prompted Mallmann and Breed [44] to study its use in water analysis. Counts with the new medium were relatively high when parallel old standard agar plates were sterile. The difference in counts was not considered to be sufficient to require changes in standards. Such a position would seem to indicate that the bacterial count has little significance if it can vary from zero to "relatively high." This is probably the case, for a few pathogenic bacteria would be absolutely significant when a great number of harmless saprophytes would not.

The intervals between analyses should be as short as possible for supplies serving many people. Results of a single analysis are of doubtful value whether they are satisfactory or not. Frequent and regular examination of large city water supplies, or supplies in important food-preservation industries, is the best practice. Results of any examination merely indicate the sanitary condition at the time when the sample is taken.

Dilution Water in Bacteriological Water Examination. Many samples of water must be diluted before plating. Usually distilled water or tap water is sterilized in known amounts for this purpose. Several publications have suggested that the type of dilution water used is important. Distilled water buffered with sodium and potassium phosphates at pH 7.2 was suggested by Butterfield [45] as a suitable and easily prepared synthetic dilution water. Distilled water and waters with a pH of 9 or over were found to be harmful to bacteria. Besides hydrogen-ion concentration, mineral salt content is important. Butterfield believed that such tests should be made only after sterilization because dilution waters are changed by heat. It is apparent from this work that more attention should be paid dilution waters, for bacteria may die rapidly in some.

American Public Health Association Procedure for Colony Count. These recommendations include details of careful bacteriological technic which have been found necessary for accurate results. All sample and dilution bottles shall be shaken 25 times before samples are removed for plating. Plating shall be done immediately after dilutions are made. One ml. of sample is placed in a sterile Petri dish and 10 ml. of standard nutrient agar are added. Incubation follows immediately after the medium has hardened at 20°C.(68°F.) for 48 hours or 37°C.(98.6°F.) for 24 hours. When nutrient gelatin is the plating medium, the plates are incubated at 20°C. for 48 hours. When results are reported the medium used shall be stated.

Irrespective of the procedures used to obtain the colony or cell count of water, as well as foods in general, the results are quite likely to vary widely. Good practice suggests that amounts of water be used which will give between 30 and 300 colonies on a plate. This cannot always be done and the analyst must then use his best judgment in securing the colony count. *Standard Methods of Water Analysis*, Eighth Edition, 1936, p. 209, suggested a method for reporting the number of colonies of bacteria per ml. of water to avoid fictitious accuracy and yet express the results with reasonable

44. Mallmann and Breed. 1941. Amer. J. Pub. Health 31, 341-343.
45. Butterfield. 1933. Pub. Health Repts. 48, 681-691; J. Bact. 23, 355.

precision. This suggestion concerns only a method for reporting counts. They are probably of no more significance than if they were reported in a different manner.

Ministry of Health,[45a] Great Britain, Procedures for Plate Count of Water. The following is an abstract of the official procedure:

Diluent. Tap water may be used provided it is free from any marked germicidal activity. Distilled water, prepared in glass (not metal) stills, is permissible. One-quarter strength Ringer's solution is preferred.

Preparation of Dilutions. Shake the bottle 25 times by a rapid rotatory movement of the wrist and, after flaming the mouth of the bottle, pour off one-quarter of its contents, reinsert the stopper, and shake 25 times with an up-and-down movement. One, two, or rarely three dilutions, according to the nature of the sample, each 10 times the previous one, should be made in dilution bottles or in test tubes by carrying over a suitable quantity of water to nine times its volume of diluent, mixing thoroughly, and repeating if necessary. Either bottles or test tubes may be used as diluent receptacles. Only nine ml. of diluent are used in the latter. Specific instructions are given for handling the pipettes and transferring portions.

Inoculation of Plates. Two Petri dishes are to be inoculated, each with one-ml. portions from the second dilution, if one has been made, and four plates from the original water. Again explicit instructions are given for handling the pipettes and making dilutions.

Each Petri dish then receives 10 ml. of melted, cooled nutrient agar. The plate is rotated five times and then given five to-and-fro movements. The plates are then cooled and placed in the incubator.

Incubation of Plates. Two of each set of four plates made with original water and with 1-10 dilution should be incubated at 37°C.(98.6°F.) for two days, and two at 20 to 22°C.(68 to 71.6°F.) for three days, in each case bottom upwards. The two plates made with the 1-100 dilution should be incubated at 20 to 22°C. for three days. Temperature should be checked in air incubators and the air should be kept moist. Care should be used to prevent plates near the source of heat from becoming too hot. If plates are stacked, they should be staggered to permit good air circulation.

Counting of Plates. Plates incubated at 42 to 48°C.(107.6 to 118.4°F.) should be counted in from 42 to 48 hours. Those with from 30 to 300 colonies should be selected for counting. They should be counted within four hours after removal from the incubator, or placed in a refrigerator. The plate should be examined with a magnifying glass of four inches focal length, giving a magnification of two and one-half diameters. A specially constructed box which allows examination by combined reflected and transmitted artificial light against a dark background is recommended.

The plates incubated at 20 to 22°C. are to be counted after 66 to 72 hours.

Reporting Results. Plate-count results are reported not as the number of organisms per ml. but as the number of colonies developing per ml. of original water. For estimating this number, all plates containing between 30 and 300 colonies should be taken, the number of colonies multiplied by the reciprocal of the dilution, and the arithmetic mean determined.

In the plates made with the undiluted water it may be found that one of a pair incubated at the same temperature develops less than 30 colonies and the other more than 30, or that in the 1 to 10 dilution one of the plates develops more than 300 colonies and the other less. In either of these cases the mean of the two plates should be taken in estimating the number of colonies per ml. The same applies to plates of 1 in 100 dilution incubated at 20 to 22°C.

If in both plates made from the original water the number of colonies is less than 30, the mean of the two plates should be taken and the results expressed as "approximate only." If in both 37°C. plates (made from the 1 in 10 dilution), or in both 20 to 22°C. plates (made from the 1 in 100 dilution), there are more than 300 colonies, the

45a. The Bacteriological Examination of Water Supplies. Repts. on Public Health and Medical Subjects, No. 71 (Revised Edition), 1939, 20-23.

results should be expressed as "more than 3,000 colonies per ml." or "more than 30,000 colonies per ml." respectively.

Direct Methods for Counting Bacteria in Water. The utility of such methods for examination of other foods prompted attempts to develop similar methods for water examination. Nelson [46] suggested that the results with direct methods would be higher than those secured with the standard agar plate. He found it necessary to concentrate the bacteria in water before counting them by his method. Zinc hydroxide was used for this purpose; it was dissolved later by ammonium chloride. The bacteria were counted with a Thoma-Zeiss haemocytometer.

Amann [47] used a Turk haemocytometer, and made the observation with a dry objective. (D. Zeiss or Seibert IV) and a strong compensation ocular (12 or 18). An electric arc light, a Nernst lamp, or direct sunlight must be used as source of light. Against a black background, the strongly illuminated bacteria may be fairly easily recognized and distinguished from other particles by their form and arrangement, or their motility and translatory motion, which differ from the characteristic Brownian motion of ultra-microscopic particles. A larger number of organisms is found by counting in this way than by the method of gelatin plate culture; thus, a well-water was found to yield only 584 bacterial colonies per ml., whereas the number of organisms found by direct counting was 86,000. One cause of such a difference is the fact that bacteria often occur in aggregations, and an aggregation often gives only one colony, whereas under the ultra-microscope the aggregations are easily perceived and the number of organisms that they contain can be determined approximately. The ultra-microscope method has the advantage of being very expeditious, but on the other hand the bacterial forms cannot be distinguished as in the plate method, and dead cells and sometimes particles are included; moreover, the quantities of water employed in the analysis are too small. Hence the method can only be regarded as a valuable supplement to the usual cultivation method. The Frost "little plate" method was adapted to water analysis and found to yield results which agreed with those secured with the gelatin plate (Eijkmann [48]).

Indicators of Pollution. As soon as sanitary science had shown that diseases were spread by polluted water and foods, it became necessary to find some method of determining whether a water supply was potentially dangerous. Since chemical methods are not delicate enough, sanitarians have found it necessary to turn to bacteriological methods and indicators. Probably an ideal biological indicator of pollution does not exist and bacteriologists have had to accept those which come the nearest to fulfilling the following requirements as stated by Furphy [49] and others before him.

1. It should occur universally and plentifully in human excreta.
2. It should have no other source than the human intestines (owing to the fact that water-borne diseases are entirely those of human origin, the organisms being of intestinal nature and discharged in human feces).

46. Nelson. 1917. J. Amer. Chem. Soc. 39, 515-523.
47. Amann. 1910. Wchnschr. Chem. u. Pharm. 48, 647-665.
48. Eijkmann. 1927. Tijdschr. Hyg. Microbiol. en Serol. 2, 123-131.
49. Furphy. 1925. Australian Commonwealth Dept. Health 3, 168-171.

3. It should live longer in water than the chief water-borne pathogens, but shall die off fairly rapidly.

4. Its occurrence in water should bear a quantitative relation to the pollution received by the water.

5. It should be readily discoverable by simple bacteriological methods.

6. It should have somewhat constant characteristics and not be subject to great change owing to conditions in the environment.

THE STREPTOCOCCI AS INDICATORS OF POLLUTION OF WATER

Presence of many streptococci in the intestinal tracts of animals and man has prompted some bacteriologists to suggest them as indicators of pollution. Since they disappear more rapidly than coliform bacteria during water purification, their presence in filtered water indicates recent pollution. While they have been studied most by British bacteriologists, it is possible that they should receive more attention from Americans. Among the first to seriously study the streptococci as indicators of pollution were Savage and Read[50] who stated that absence of these bacteria in a water supply is to be considered of less significance than their presence, and even their absence from a considerable bulk of water is not accepted to the same extent as the absence of coliform bacteria, as reliable evidence of freedom from serious contamination. Absence of streptococci is, however, a point in favor of purity. In general, these investigators believed that streptococci in large numbers in a water indicated unsatisfactory source. To test the other matter of longevity which must always be considered, Savage and Wood[51] used strains of streptococci and *Escherichia coli*. At the end of two weeks when *Escherichia coli* was multiplying, streptococci were all dead. Presence of streptococci seemed to indicate to them that the water had been either recently polluted or had received heavy contamination. For this purpose, streptococci may be more valuable than *Escherichia coli*. Hemolytic streptococci in Livingston's[52] experiments remained alive for varying lengths of time, depending on environmental conditions. Recently isolated strains succumbed quite quickly in water. Houston,[53] of the Metropolitan Water Board, was one of the first to attach practical significance to fecal streptococci in water. He studied the streptococcus test for many years and considered it to have merits because streptococci are abundant in human feces, they are absent in fairly large quantities of *pure* water, they do not multiply in *pure* water, and since some are not long-lived in water, their presence might indicate recent pollution. In America, Greer[54] also looked with favor on the streptococcus test. In a later report[57] Houston said this test could not compete with the coliform test but could corroborate it as a means of determining excretal pollution. Attempts have been made now and then to differentiate fecal from non-fecal streptococci. Winslow and Hunnewell,[55] and Fuller

50. Savage and Read. 1916. J. Hyg. 15, 334-351.
51. Savage and Wood. 1917. Idem 16, 227-229.
52. Livingston. 1921. Amer. J. Hyg. 1, 239-251.
53. Houston. 1910. Fifth Rept. on Res., to the Metropolitan Water Bd., London.
54. Greer. 1928. J. Infect. Dis. 42, 501-513.
55. Winslow and Hunnewell. 1902. Science 15, 827.
57. Houston. 1930. Twenty-fifth Ann. Rept., Metropolitan Water Bd.

and Armstrong [56] tried to use the amounts of acid formed in carbohydrate media as a means of such differentiation. Streptococci from human sources formed high acid content in glucose, lactose, and mannite broths and low acidity in raffinose broth. Equine and bovine strains had the opposite abilities.

British practice in water analysis does not recommend search for fecal streptococci as a routine procedure. It is suggested as a supplementary procedure when the results of the coliform test are anomalous. The technic which is recommended is quite like that given below in the Metropolitan Water Board procedures. *Streptococcus fecalis*, considered to be the most characteristic streptococcus in feces, is defined as a ''Gram-positive coccus, generally occurring in pairs or short chains, growing in the presence of .5 per cent bile salt, usually capable of development at 45°C., producing acid but not gas in mannitol and lactose, failing to attack raffinose, failing to reduce nitrate to nitrite, producing acid in litmus milk, and precipitating the casein in the form of a loose but solid curd, and exhibiting a greater resistance to heat than most vegetative bacteria.''

Houston's Method for Demonstrating Presence of Streptococci in Feces. Drigalski and Conradi plates are inoculated from an emulsion of the feces, made in sterile water. After incubation at 37°C.(98.6°F.), the minute colonies are subcultured in "litmus lemco, lactose peptone" medium. After 24 hours the tubes showing no acidity are discarded; those showing acidity are examined microscopically and if results are satisfactory further subcultures are made into a series of lemco-peptone-sugar media untinted with litmus. After three days incubation at 37°C. the acidity produced is estimated with N/20. NaOH, using phenolphthalein as the indicator. Control tubes are also inoculated. (Mtr. Water Bd. 10th Ann. Report, p. 25, 1914.)

The streptococcus colonies on Drigalski and Conradi plates are small colonies with a tinge of violet. They are to be distinguished from colonies of *Eberthella typhosa* which possess larger colonies.

Detection of Sewage Streptococci. "For this purpose many methods have been devised, but the simplest and best appears to be the examination of the bile-salt glucose broth used for the 'presumptive test' for coliform bacteria. The incubation should, however, be prolonged to 48 hours, and, at the end of that period a loopful from the surface of each tube should be examined in a hanging drop under the microscope. The broth should then be carefully poured off so as to leave at the bottom any precipitate which has been produced. Add a few drops of dilute sodium carbonate solution to dissolve the bile salts and examine again in the hanging drop. If distinct chains are not found, streptococci may be regarded as absent." This method has been found by Thresh to yield the best results.

Savage's Method for Isolation of Streptococcus From Water, Etc. Add .1 and 1 ml. of the sample (water) to tubes of glucose neutral red broth and 10 ml. of the sample to a tube of double strength neutral red broth. Incubate the tubes at 37°C.(98.6°F.) for 48 hours and then examine microscopically in hanging drop for chains of cocci. The broth tube containing the quantity of water next below the one giving a positive result is examined several times in fresh preparations. Where it is doubtful whether chains are present, a little of the fluid is centrifugalized and stained with methylene blue. The streptococci are best isolated from glucose broth tubes by adding a platinum loopful to a litmus lactose plate and distributing over its surface. All suspicious strains must be subcultured and worked out.

Method for Separation of Escherichia coli and Streptococci in Water. "Inoculate the desired quantity of water, preferably 1 ml., into dextrose broth fermentation tube. In-

56. Fuller and Armstrong. 1913. J. Infect. Dis. 13, 142.

cubate at 37°C.(98.6°F.) Examine after six to 12 hours. Within two to three hours after gas formation has appeared, plate the broth into litmus-lactose agar, incubating for 12 to 18 hours at 37°C.(98.6°F.) If, at the end of this time, no acid-producing colonies are present, it is probably safe to assume that there were no colon bacilli present."

After the first plating from dextrose broth, replace the fermentation tube for 36 hours and plate in litmus-lactose agar. This culture should give a nearly pure culture of streptococci, if these organisms were originally present in the water.

Houston's[67] **Method for Determining the Presence of Fecal Streptococci in Water.** The procedure starts in the usual manner for determining presence of *Escherichia coli*. One hundred ml. of water are added to 50 ml. of triple-strength lactose peptone bile-salt broth; 10 ml. of water are added to 10 ml. double-strength medium and one ml. to 10 ml. of single-strength medium. The tubes are then placed in water at 37°C. (98.6°F.) for one-half hour and then in the 37°C. incubator. These are *primary* cultures. All tubes showing no visible change after 24 hours are discarded on the presumption that *Escherichia coli* and Streptococci are absent. Those in which gas formation occurs are subcultured in the following manner: After shaking, from two to four drops are spread over the bottom of a sterile Petri dish. The dish, with lid raised, is then placed in a dry 37°C. incubator for about 15 minutes to dry the liquid onto the glass; it is then placed in a moist 37°C. incubator with 85 per cent humidity for 45 minutes. After such treatment from 30 to 40 ml. of melted agar are poured over the culture and the dish gently rotated. The plates are then incubated for 24 hours at 37°C. After incubation the agar is removed with a sterile spatula and the colonies on the underside are cultured in lactose-lemco-peptone-litmus broth and on a fresh agar slant containing .1 per cent sodium nitrate. These should be incubated at 37°C. for 24 hours. Acid without gas in lactose broth, presence of chains on the agar slant, and absence of reduction of nitrates to nitrites indicate presence of fecal streptococci.

This technic was slightly modified in the report for 1931. The purpose in drying the culture as outlined above was to eliminate most of the *Escherichia coli*. In the new modification, one ml. of the culture was added to 10 ml. sterile water and the mixture heated to 60°C.(140°F.). After some 10 to 20 minutes a few drops of the mixture were spread over Drigalski and Conradi medium in plates. It was stated that ordinary agar could be used if less of the liquid were used for inoculation. After the plates had been incubated for 24 hours the colonies were subcultured as described above.

The Metropolitan Water Board Method for Determining Presence of Fecal Streptococci in Water. This method would, of course, be quite similar to the one just quoted from Houston.

The Metropolitan Water Board of London in its 31st annual report (1936) proposed two methods for the isolation of streptococci in water, as follows:

The first, or "drying method," essentially that credited to Houston above, entails somewhat lengthy manipulation, provides many opportunities for contamination, and is not often employed.

The second method, commonly used, depends upon the bile insoluble and heat-resistant properties of the fecal streptococcus, which permits utilization of the positive lactose MacConkey broths of the test for coliform bacteria as a dual enrichment medium. Briefly, the procedure is to heat a small quantity of fluid from a presumptive tube in the coliform test to 60°C.(140°F.) for 15 to 20 minutes and plate a loopful of the suspension on Conradi-Drigalski medium. Positive results were generally obtainable with samples of raw Thames water in the 10-ml. and one-ml. amounts, but the recovery of the streptococcus is less successful from the 100-ml. amounts, where a larger variety of other organisms are present in competition. On such occasions, plates are crowded with Gram-negative bacilli, which have heat-resisting powers similar to the fecal streptococcus.

The following year results of a comparison of the coliform test with the streptococcus test by examining MacConkey tubes giving acid or acid and gas were reported. Three methods were used: the heating method and the direct tellurite and enrichment tellurite methods which are described below. The resulting colonies were confirmed. It was pointed out that *Streptococcus fecalis* was resistant to a temperature of 60°C. (140°F.) for 30 minutes.

(a) *Direct plating method.* This consisted of the subculture of fluid from unheated presumptive tubes on the surface of an agar medium containing potassium tellurite of the composition:

> Agar, 2 per cent
> Lactose, .5 per cent
> Peptone, 1 per cent
> Di-potassium hydrogen phosphate (anhydrous), .2 per cent
> Sodium chloride, .5 per cent
> Potassium tellurite, 1 in 15,000 added as sterile solution.

Plates were poured, dried for one to two hours, spread with one drop of fluid from the MacConkey broths and incubated at 37°C.(98.6°F.) for 24 hours. *Streptococcus fecalis* appeared as small bluish-black colonies about one mm. in diameter, with opalescence of the periphery.

The organisms were characterized by the production of acid, without gas, a deposit in lactose "lemco" medium, the non-reduction of nitrates under aerobic conditions and morphologically.

The results obtained were closely comparable to the heating method with the added advantage of ease of manipulation. However, occasionally other tellurite resistant organisms were found, which persisted in concentrations of one in 5,000. Some provided coliform reactions.

(b) *Enrichment method.* Two drops of the contents of a positive McConkey tube were used as an inoculum into a fluid medium, having the following composition:

> Peptone, .5 per cent
> Lactose, .5 per cent
> Di-potassium hydrogen phosphate (anhydrous), .5 per cent.
> Potassium tellurite, 1 in 15,000.

After incubation for 24 hours at 37°C., single colonies were obtained by placing on lactose tellurite agar as described above.

This method gave better results than the direct plating method, the preliminary enrichment leading to the elimination of resistant coliform and other organisms which, at times, overcrowded the plates during heating and direct tellurite technics.

As already stated, the isolation of *Streptococcus fecalis* supports the *Escherichia coli* test and, generally speaking, the organisms are 10 times less prevalent than coliforms; but with excessive pollutions failures of recovery are frequent, owing to competition with the other organisms and to the presence of particularly resistant types, the characters of which are being investigated.

Since the tellurite methods outlined do not include a heating process, the possibility arises that certain of the streptococcal types isolated may not prove to be heat-resistant and therefore should not be termed *Streptococcus fecalis.* Yet, presumably these organisms are of human or animal origin and therefore their presence must have some significance. Furthermore, long experience with heating methods up to 60°C. proves that this is associated with considerable mortality of *Streptococcus fecalis.*

Nevertheless, after extensive trials, the tellurite enrichment method of streptococcal isolation has proved itself far superior to the original drying or heating technics, and its use is to be strongly recommended.

Eberthella typhosa and Salmonella strains were found by Fleming and Young [58] to be very sensitive to the inhibitory action of potassium tellurite in agar medium or in broth. Growth was suppressed in concentrations as low as one to one million. Dysentery bacilli are almost as sensitive. *Pseudomonas aeruginosa (Bacillus pyocyaneus)* is inhibited by one in 100,000 tellurite. Many strains of *Proteus vulgaris* and some *Escherichia coli* will grow in concentrations of one in 100,000. Resistant and sensitive strains of *Escherichia coli* or *Proteus vulgaris* do not differ in their fermentative or antigenic characters. Insensitive bacteria absorb tellurite from the culture medium and so allow growth of sensitive bacteria in the neighborhood. Bacteria can be readily acclimatized to tellurite. Use of tellurite to facilitate the isolation of Gram-positive cocci from feces, septic wounds, or other material is indicated.

A new medium for fecal streptococci was reported by Hajna and Perry (1942) at the St. Louis convention of the American Public Health Association. Sodium azide was the inhibiting agent for Gram-negative bacteria with temperature selection at 45.5°C. Mere presence of acid and growth is confirmatory evidence of presence of fecal streptococci. The medium may be inoculated directly with water, milk, or sewage.

ANAEROBIC BACTERIA AS INDICATORS OF POLLUTION IN WATER AND FOODS

Anaerobic bacteria in water have received much less attention than aerobic species. Believing that a large number of anaerobes indicated active organic decomposition and fecal pollution, Vincent [59] suggested their enumeration as an index of pollution. Satisfactory waters were said to contain one to two anaerobes, or less, per ml. Waters containing more were regarded as progressively unsatisfactory. Meader and Bliss [60] found anaerobic bacteria in water responsible for gas formation in the presumptive test in water analysis. In pure culture the anaerobes formed no gas from lactose, which led Meader and Bliss to believe that a symbiotic condition existed, as was later shown to be the case by Holman and Meekison.[61] Horovitz [62] identified a number of anaerobic bacteria from water which had been treated with ozone. Such forms would be among those which would survive any effort to reduce the general flora. This would affect their use as indicators of pollution.

Clostridium sporogenes was discovered by Klein in 1895 in diarrhea stools. Its use as an indicator of pollution rests on the fact that it is present in feces and, therefore, in sewage. This organism should be regarded as one of a group of bacteria the members of which are very closely related. *Clostridium welchii* is probably identical with Klein's *Bacillus enteritidis sporogenes*. Welch described his bacillus as nonmotile but otherwise the descriptions and the changes produced in milk are identical. The nomenclature of this group is confused. Examination of water for this organism may require concentration either by filtration or evaporation under reduced pressure at low temperatures. Decimal dilutions of this concentrated sample should be made and one-ml. quantities added to sterile litmus milk. It is a good plan to boil the tubes of milk for five

57a. Hajna and Perry. 1942. Mimeographed paper distributed at Amer. Pub. Health Assoc. Conv., St. Louis.

58. Fleming and Young. 1940. J. Path. and Bact. 51, 29-35.

59. Vincent. 1907. Ann. Inst. Pasteur 21, 62-75.

60. Meader and Bliss. 1923. Amer. J. Hyg. 3, 394-400.

61. Holman and Meekison. 1926. J. Infect. Dis. 39, 145-172; see also Sears and Putnam. Idem 32 (1923), 270.

62. Horovitz. 1916. J. Microbiol 3, 306-314.

or 10 minutes before inoculating in order to expel as much air as possible. After the tubes have been inoculated they should be heated on a water bath at 80°C.(176°F.) for 20 minutes to kill vegetative forms. They are then incubated under anaerobic conditions, made anaerobic by the Wright method. If anaerobes are present a "stormy fermentation" results. It is characterized by separation of curd from the whey and violent gas formation. A quite similar test has also been proposed for demonstrating anaerobic bacteria in milk.

Clostridium welchii has at times assumed some importance in water analysis; it has been suggested as the cause of severe outbreaks of enteritis. Larner [63] suggested a probable relation of *Clostridium welchii* to intestinal disturbances among those who drank polluted water. In some cases, the symptoms disappeared when the patients drank boiled water. Meader and Bliss [60] did not find *Clostridium welchii* in water. The question of its sanitary significance is further complicated by the fact that *Clostridium welchii* is said to serve useful ends in the preparation of certain foods. Koser, for instance, found it as the leavening agent in a starter for self-rising bread, while Albus [64] reported it as the cause of gassy fermentation in Niszler cheese. Such reports complicate its use as an indicator of pollution. Wilson and Blair [65] prepared a special sulfite-glucose-iron agar medium for determining *Clostridium welchii* in water and observed a close correlation between the results of the *Escherichia coli* and *Clostridium welchii* tests. The latter was believed to be a good supplement to the former. In an investigation of the significance of lactose-fermenting bacteria in water by Greer, Noble, and Tonney [66] *Clostridium welchii* was suggested as of less value as an indicator of pollution than *Escherichia coli*. Sudden increase in the number of *Clostridium welchii* and other lactose fermenters in Lake Michigan water when the ice breaks up, was attributed by Gorman, Greer, and Hlavacek [67] to filling material along the lake front. Such a situation would lead to a greater incidence of false presumptive tests for *Escherichia coli*. Anaerobic sporeforming bacteria would also be resistant to water-treatment methods. That *Clostridium welchii* is present in large numbers in soil was shown by Skinner and Baskin.[68] Contrary to the experience just discussed, Lewis, Green, and Hamilton [69] found no merits in the *Clostridium welchii* test for water. The results of this test did not correlate with those of the *Escherichia coli* test. A similar opinion was reached by Matheson [70] in a sanitary survey of Burlington Bay and Lake Ontario. Definite correlation of results with the *Escherichia coli* test with those from use of sulfite-glucose-iron agar were not satisfactory. This latter medium had been suggested by Adams [71]

63. Larner. 1922. J. Amer. Med. Assoc. 78, 276-279.
64. Albus. 1924. Abst. Bact. 1813.
65. Wilson and Blair. 1924. J. Path. and Bact. 27, 119-121.
66. Greer, Noble, and Tonney. 1928. J. Infect. Dis. 42, 525-588.
67. Gorman, Greer, and Hlavacek. 1926. Trans. Ill. Acad. Sci. 19, 345.
68. Skinner and Baskin. 1932. Proc. Soc. Expt. Biol. and Med. 29, 551-554.
69. Lewis, Green, and Hamilton. 1930. J. Amer. Water Wks. Assoc. 22, 667-672.
70. Matheson. 1937. Canad. Pub. Health J. 28, 241-242.
71. Adams. 1928. Water and Water Engin. 31, 412-415.

as especially suitable for enumerating anaerobic bacteria in water. He favored the use of anaerobes as indices of pollution.

Larner's [72] Method for Showing the Presence of Clostridium welchii (Bacillus welchi) in Water. In making the *Clostridium welchii* test at the Montclair Board of Health laboratory 10-ml. samples of water are inoculated into each of five fermentation tubes containing lactose peptone broth. The tubes are incubated at 37.5°C.(99°F.) for 72 hours. From tubes showing the production of gas in amounts varying from 40 to 100 per cent, and having a typical butyric acid odor, a loopful of medium is placed in a Petri dish and an Endo plate poured (not smeared) about one-fourth inch thick. The plates are incubated at 37.5°C.(99°F.) for 24 hours. A typical red colony showing a bubble of gas at the bottom of the dish is then fished and inoculated into a tube containing five ml. of sterile whole milk which has been recently boiled to drive off absorbed oxygen. Hot sterile paraffin is next poured on top of the milk so that when cool it forms a solid air-tight seal about one-half inch thick with the production of anaerobic conditions. The tube is then incubated 24 hours at 37.5°C.(99°F.). Coagulation of milk with typical stormy fermentation and gas production, which forces the paraffin seal to the top of the tube, is taken as confirmatory evidence of the presence of *Clostridium welchii.*

Jackson and Muer's [73] Method for Showing Presence of Clostridium welchii in Water. 1. Inoculate various dilutions (usually .1, 1, and 10 ml.) of the water or milk to be tested into fermentation tubes containing liver broth, and incubate for 24 hours at 37°C.(98.6°F.). If *Clostridium sporogenes* is present either in the spore or vegetative state in the dilutions used, there will be gas formation, accompanied by an offensive cheesy odor, and microscopic examination will show numerous and vigorous spores. *Clostridium welchii* in liver broth gives no odor and no spores, but an abnormal amount of gas. By observing in which dilutions they are present, the relative degree of contamination of these bacteria will be apparent. Numerous bacteria, both vegetative and sporeforming, have been examined but none have been found that give this strong peculiar odor in liver broth except *Clostridium sporogenes*. This is the presumptive test for the presence of *Clostridium sporogenes*. Large rounded bacilli with heavy gas formation, no spores, and no odor is the presumptive test for *Clostridium welchii.*

2. To complete the test for *Clostridium sporogenes* and isolate a pure culture of the organism, transfer the entire contents of each tube showing gas plus characteristic odor into separate sterile Erlenmeyer flasks or large test tubes and heat to 80°C.(176°F.) for 10 minutes. Any attenuated spores or vegetative bacteria present in the original samples will have formed vigorous spores, and the heating destroys all species of vegetative bacteria that might interfere with its further separation.

3. One ml. or less of broth containing sediment may be withdrawn from the bottom of the flasks or tubes after heating and planted separately into a second set of sterile liver broth fermentation tubes and incubated for 24 hours at 37°C., after which time gas formation and characteristic odor will again be observed. Microscopic examination will reveal the presence of numerous large sluggishly motile bacilli containing spores. Often *Clostridium sporogenes* is now present in pure culture.

A stab culture made from this 24-hour liver broth culture into dextrose liver gelatin, will demonstrate the presence of *Clostridium sporogenes* by its characteristic growth. Within 48 hours after incubation at 20°C.(68°F.) a distinct anaerobic growth will be observed, beginning about two ml. below the surface. Liquefaction will be well advanced and gas bubbles will accumulate at the top of the liquefied area.

4. To obtain colonies of *Clostridium sporogenes* on agar plates it is necessary to transplant a few drops of broth and sediment from the second set of fermentation tubes, in step 3, into a third set of tubes and incubate for three to five hours at 37°C. After that period a distinct anaerobic growth will be observed in the closed arm, and a few bubbles of gas will be found at the top. The *Clostridium sporogenes* is now in the vegetative state and this is the only condition in which it will grow on the plates.

72. Larner. 1922. J. Amer. Med. Assoc. 78, 276-279.
73. Jackson and Muer. 1911. J. Infect. Dis. 8, 289-294.

The contents of the closed arm are transferred to the bulb by tilting forward and plating in dilutions of 1 to .00001 ml. on dextrose liver agar, and incubating for 12 to 18 hours in hydrogen at 37°C.(98.6°F.). Typical colonies will then be visible, consisting of one or more gas bubbles surrounded by a delicate white fringe. The plate cultures also will have a disagreeable cheesy odor.

5. From one of these colonies a deep stab culture is made into dextrose liver agar and incubated for 24 hours at 37°C.(98.6°F.). A distinct anaerobic growth will be observed along the line of puncture, and sometimes the agar is split into two or three layers by the gas evolved. A liver gelatin tube inoculated and incubated at 20°C. (68°F.) will also give a very distinctive anaerobic growth.

6. A subculture may also be made into litmus milk and incubated for 48 hours, anaerobically, after which time there will be a complete separation of curd and whey and a strong odor of butyric acid. Sometimes the curd adheres to the sides of the tubes and has a peculiar shredded appearance.

Many other types of sporeforming bacteria may be isolated by this method. By this procedure Jackson and Muer several times isolated large numbers of *Bacillus vulgaris* and other similar species from condensed milk which caused diarrheal disturbances. As *Clostridium welchii* does not form spores in liver broth it must be isolated direct from the liver broth without heating.

Metropolitan Water Board Procedure [74] **for Estimating Clostridium Welchii in Waters.** A test was described in the Thirty-third Annual Report as follows:

Reagents Required:

    a) 20 per cent solution of anhydrous sodium sulphite

    b) 8 per cent solution of ferrous sulphate

    c) glucose agar (1 per cent glucose and 3 per cent agar)

Two milliliters of solution (a) are introduced into a large sterile Petri dish (4½ in. diam.) and a suitable volume (10 ml., 1 ml., etc. according to the expected degree of pollution) of the sample, which has previously been heated to 80°C.(176°F.) for 10 minutes, and .2 ml. of solution (b) in 10 ml. of sterile distilled water are then added, and the plate poured with the agar mixture (c) and thoroughly mixed. Finally, when the plates are cool and the agar has solidified, a thin layer of the same agar mixture is poured over the surface to produce somewhat anaerobic conditions.

Plates are then incubated at 44°C.(111.2°F.) for 24 hours following the method of Wilson *et al.* (1935). This temperature obviates the necessity for a special incubator and it has been found as efficient as the higher temperature for inhibition of *Bacterium effluviei* and other saprophytic organisms.

The appearance of black colonies three millimeters or more in diameter is highly significant of the presence of *Clostridium welchii* and justifies the presumption that fecal pollution of recent or remote origin has taken place. The test, however, was said to be insufficiently delicate for use with natural water when the standard of purity is *Escherichia coli* absent in 100 ml. It was believed that the test might be of use with supplies such as surface wells which were intermediary polluted.

The bacteriological laboratory of the Metropolitan Water Board of London has also studied the significance of *Clostridium welchii* in water. According to their results the *Clostridium welchii* test does not follow the coliform index quite as closely as does the fecal streptococcus test. Improved results, however, were secured by heating samples for Wilson's test at 80°C.(176°F.) for 10 minutes with subsequent incubation at 45°C.(113°F.). This eliminates *Bacillus effluviei* in the summer. Testing of large or medium colonies from Wilson's plates in milk gave only 78.6 per cent positive stormy fermentation. Heating of the samples to 80°C.(176°F.) and incubation in litmus milk at 37°C.(98.6°F.) gave the best results on the whole. Under these conditions both methods correlated better with the coliform and streptococcus tests.

In the thirty-third annual report for the year 1938 the Metropolitan Water Board reported more data on the *Clostridium welchii* test. Incuba-

74. Thirtieth Ann. Rept., Metropolitan Water Bd., London, 1935, p. 10; also 33rd Ann. Rept. 1938.

tion at 45°C.(113°F.) did not completely inhibit them. Since 1935 it has been the practice of these laboratories to heat the sample to 80°C.(176°F.) for 10 minutes previous to inoculation in order to destroy nonsporeforming bacteria so that the test became an estimation of organisms of the anaerobic-sporeforming group. Other media for cultivation of streptococci from water have been proposed by Folpmers.[75]

British standard practice [45a] of water examination apparently does not provide for demonstrating presence of *Clostridium welchii* in potable water. Two methods are given, however, for this purpose, a litmus-milk method and a sulfite-reduction method.

THE COLIFORM GROUP AS INDICATORS OF POLLUTION

Presence and estimation of the number of coliform bacteria in water has become an integral part of the bacteriological procedure for judging quality. The most direct and satisfactory procedure would be to plate the water on a medium which would permit direct enumeration for coliform bacteria. Despite development of several media for this purpose, they have not generally been viewed with approval by those who prepare standard methods. Some of the difficulties with such media are quite apparent and have, in general, been reviewed a few pages further on in this chapter. They involve the necessity of proving that each colony which appears to be *Escherichia coli* is really such a colony.

Standard Methods of Water Analysis, eighth edition, 1936, recommended that the *coliform group be considered as including all aerobic and facultative, anaerobic, Gram-negative, nonsporeforming bacilli which ferment lactose with gas formation.* This group has been referred to in sanitary literature as the coli-aerogenes group. Breed and Norton,[76] however, suggested introduction of the term *coliform* to designate lactose-fermenting, aerobic bacteria used as a measure of pollution in water. They hoped that the term would be used in milk and oyster contamination with similar meaning, which seems to have been done.

The generally accepted procedure today involves use of liquid media and dilutions of the water sample to show not only presence of coliform bacteria but to yield information about their probable numbers and types. Procedures for determining probable numbers from dilutions in liquid media are discussed later in this chapter.

The procedures used in sanitary work are not fixed. The marked changes which are made in standard procedures by every committee indicate the difficulties involved.

Escherich isolated *Escherichia coli* soon after discovery of solid media by Koch. He was attempting to find the causal organism of cholera. At first he thought that he had found it because *Escherichia coli* was found in the intestinal tract of each patient. Later investigations indicated that it was always present in the feces, and from these facts bacteriologists attempted to use it as an indicator of the presence of fecal matter in

75. Folpmers. 1939. Leeuwenhoek J. Microbiol. et. Serol. 6, 22-29.
76. Breed and Norton. 1937. Amer. J. Pub. Health 27, 560-563.

foods and beverages. For some time it was accepted as a reliable indicator, but as knowledge increased it became apparent that some limitations had to be placed on the test. Much of our work since this time has been concerned with finding out what these limitations are.

The value of the *Escherichia coli* test was attacked by some practical waterworks operators. They argued from the several researches which had shown that the organism may not at all times be restricted to sources which have received sewage pollution. Rogers, Clark, and Evans.[77] Prescott,[78] Metcalf,[79] Smith,[80] and others reported the isolation of the organism, or *Escherichia coli*-like organisms, from grain fields and grains which had not received sewage pollution. Their work was of such import that it was believed necessary to differentiate fecal from non-fecal *Escherichia coli*. The English and American bacteriologists have regarded the *Escherichia coli* test with favor while some German bacteriologists have objected to it. Kruse,[81] for instance, believed that *Escherichia coli* could be found in any water, no matter from what source, provided a large enough sample is examined. Chick,[82] on the other hand, believed that *Escherichia coli* is not present in water unless it has received sewage pollution. Race[83] believed that *Escherichia coli* was a reliable indicator of pollution and stated that those cities which have many *Escherichia coli* in their water usually have a high typhoid fever death rate. He warned that *Escherichia coli* should not be considered merely an inferential indicator. The fact that its presence in a sample of water may not be sufficient evidence of serious pollution does not mean that the organism may be safely overlooked. Houston[84] considered *Escherichia coli* to be the best index for control of water purification process. Winslow,[85] in tracing the history of this organism as an indicator, advised accumulation of as much data as possible to determine more definitely whether *Escherichia coli* is purely a fecal form and *Aerobacter aerogenes* a saprophytic form. Thus supposition has involved differentiation of *Escherichia coli* from *Aerobacter aerogenes*. The methods for doing this are given below. Before this differentiation was done, bacteriologists had probably used the term *Escherichia coli* as a collective one, including many lactose-fermenting bacteria with characteristics in common but differentiable when certain other tests were applied. Bacteriologists were soon convinced that the mere presence of bacteria which formed acid and gas from lactose could not be accepted as evidence of fecal pollution. Acid and gas may result from the activities of other bacteria which are devoid of sanitary significance. This made it imperative to study the lactose fermenters from sources, pollution of which was beyond question, and from sources which were satisfactory as far as could be determined by careful examination.

77. Rogers, Clark, and Evans. 1915. J. Infect. Dis. 17. 137-159.
78. Prescott. 1906. Biol. Studies by the Pupils of W. T. Sedgwick. Boston,, 1906.
79. Metcalf. 1905. Science 22, 434-441.
80. Smith. 1905. Idem 21, 710-711.
81. Kruse. 1894. Ztschr. Hyg. u. Infektionskrank. 17. 1894.
82. Chick. 1901. Thompson Yates Lab., Rept., Pt. 1, 1; Pt. 2, 317.
83. Race. 1914. Amer. J. Pub. Health 26, 758-759.
84. Houston. 1915. Rept. Metropolitan Water Board. London.
85. Winslow. 1916. J. Amer. Water Wks. Assoc. 3, 927-946.

Rogers and his colleagues instituted investigations to determine whether coliform bacteria from polluted sources differed in any way from those from unpolluted sources. The results of these investigations were published by Rogers, Clark, and Davis [86]; Rogers, Clark, and Evans [87]; and Rogers, Clark, and Lubs.[88] Their investigations showed that coliform bacteria could be divided into two groups on the basis of the amount of carbon dioxide and hydrogen formed—spoken of as the gas ratio. The subgroup peculiar to the bovine intestinal tract was characterized by a relatively low gas ratio of one part of carbon dioxide to 1.06 parts of hydrogen. These strains from the bovine intestinal tract also differed a little in other characteristics. A series of strains from grains gave a high gas ratio between 1.9 and 2.2. The former are known as *Escherichia coli* and the latter as *Aerobacter aerogenes*. The gas ratio, under very carefully controlled conditions, functions as a means for distinguishing between lactose-fermenting bacteria from polluted sources and those from unpolluted sources. It is not suitable for routine analysis.

The next important step was to show that the electrometric determination of hydrogen-ion concentration could also be used for distinguishing between the two subgroups. The fecal type *(Escherichia coli)* had a higher hydrogen-ion concentration than did the grain type *(Aerobacter aerogenes)*. The electrometric determination of hydrogen-ion concentration is not suited to routine analytical work, and therefore cannot be used.

Clark and Lubs [89] found that under certain conditions methyl red could be used for distinguishing between the hydrogen-ion concentrations of the two subgroups. They reported that this test correlated perfectly with the gas ratio. Clark [90] found remarkable agreement in the final hydrogen-ion concentrations of different strains of *Escherichia coli*.

While such a distinction between these two closely related bacteria was a part of water analysis for several years, it seems to have lost its significance in recent years. The cleavage on the basis of source, that *Escherichia coli* meant fecal pollution, and *Aerobacter aerogenes* was of no sanitary significance, is now considered to be of little value. This change in opinion has been due, in part, to presence of *Aerobacter aerogenes* in materials which were known to be polluted.

Standard Methods of Water Analysis, eighth edition, 1936, states that the standard tests for the coli-aerogenes groups shall be either of the following:

A. *Presumptive Test.* Formation of gas in a standard lactose broth fermentation tube at any time within 24 hours with incubation at 37°C., or formation of gas during a second 24-hour period with confirmation as described below, is presumptive evidence of presence of members of the coliform group.

86. Rogers, Clark, and Davis. 1914. J. Infect. Dis. 14, 411-475.
87. Rogers, Clark, and Evans. 1914. Idem 15, 99-123.
88. Rogers, Clark, and Lubs. 1916. J. Bact. 1, 82; 3 (1918), 231-251.
89. Clark and Lubs. 1915. J. Infect. Diseases 17, 160.
90. Clark. 1915. J. Biol. Chem. 22, 87-98.

B. *Confirmed Test.* Formation of gas at any time within 48 hours with incubation at 37°C. in a fermentation tube containing a specified liquid confirmatory medium which has been seeded from a lactose broth fermentation tube in which gas has been formed (in the presumptive test), or appearance of lactose splitting colonies on a specified solid confirmatory medium, confirms the presumption that gas in the presumptive test resulted from presence of members of the coliform group.

C. *Completed Test.* To complete proof that gas resulted from an organism in the coli-aerogenes group, it is necessary to show that one or more aerobic plate colonies consist of Gram-negative, nonsporeforming bacilli which form gas in lactose broth.

THE PRESUMPTIVE TEST FOR PRESENCE OF COLIFORM BACTERIA

The ability of bacteria, other than *Escherichia coli*, to form acid and gas from media used in the presumptive test in water analysis, has made it necessary to consider this acid and gas as presumptive evidence only of the presence of coliform bacteria. It is necessary to continue observations to prove that coliform bacteria of sanitary significance are the source of the gas and acid observed in the presumptive test.

The Presumptive Test Medium. Various media have been used in the presumptive test. Dextrose broth was once recommended by *Standard Methods of Water Analysis* of the American Public Health Association. Lactose broth was finally substituted and has been in use since. British sanitary bacteriologists have used MacConkey's [91] broth because they believe it reduces false presumptive tests to a minimum, owing to the bile salt contained in it. They further believe that lactose broth recommended in American practice does not do this but yields positive presumptive tests which will not confirm.

Lactose broth, the standard medium, has been compared with various other media on different occasions, and has, in general, been found to be about as good. Darby and Mallmann [92] stated that tryptose was superior to peptone in the base medium for coliform bacteria. A concentration of two per cent yielded best results. The concentration of lactose seemed to be less important.

From time to time substances have been added to lactose broth to make it better by either suppressing development of other organisms which may give spurious positive tests or by favoring development of fecal *Escherichia coli*. Some of them are discussed below. Several comprehensive comparative studies with different media have revealed that standard lactose broth is about as satisfactory as many of its modifications. Horwood and Heifetz [93] recommended its retention although brilliant green lactose bile did show considerable promise.

91. MacConkey. 1901. Centbl. Bakt. 29, 740.
92. Darby and Mallmann. 1939. J. Amer. Water Wks. Assoc. 31, 689-706.
93. Horwood and Heifetz. 1936. J. Bact. 28, 199-211.

A. Presumptive Test

The presumptive test indicates the presence only of bacteria which form acid and gas from lactose. They may be coliform bacteria or other bacteria of no sanitary significance. The eighth edition (1936) of *Standard Methods of Water Analysis* defines *the presumptive test as formation of gas in standard lactose broth at any time within 24 hours at 37°C., or its formation during a second 24-hour period with confirmation.*

American Public Health Association Method of Testing for Presence of Members of Coli-Aerogenes Group. It is recommended that the Escherichia coli group be considered as including all nonsporeforming bacilli which ferment lactose with gas formation and grow aerobically on standard solid media.

1. Inoculate a series of lactose broth fermentation tubes with appropriate graduated quantities of the water to be tested. Each fermentation tube must contain at least twice as much medium as the portion of sample to be tested, or the concentration of peptone and lactose in the mixture of medium and added portion of sample must conform to the requirements given under Part VII, Sec. III, N, 2. The portions of the water sample used for inoculating the lactose broth fermentation tubes will necessarily vary in size with the character of the water under examination. (This refers to instructions concerning strength of media. Where large quantities of water are examined, stronger media should be used to compensate for dilution—Author.)

2. Incubate the fermentation tubes at 37°C. for 48 hours unless gas appears earlier. Examine each tube at the end of 24 hours, and if no gas then appears again at the end of 48 hours. Record presence or absence of gas formation at each examination of the tubes.

More detailed records of the amount of gas formed, though desirable for the purpose of study, are not necessary for carrying out the standard tests prescribed.

3. Formation within 24 hours of gas in the inverted vial in the fermentation tube constitutes a *positive presumptive test.*

4. If no gas or only a small bubble of gas is formed in 24 hours, the incubation shall be continued to 48 hours. If gas in any quantity is present after the second but not the first 24-hour incubation period, the test is considered as doubtful and the presence of organisms of the coli-aerogenes group should be confirmed. Confirmed tubes may then be given the same consideration in the presumptive test as those showing gas formation in the first 24-hour incubation period.

5. The absence of gas formation after 48 hours' incubation constitutes a negative test. (An arbitrary limit of 48 hours' observation doubtless excludes from consideration occasional members of the coli-aerogenes group which form gas very slowly. For the purpose of a standard test the exclusion of these occasional slow gas-forming organisms is considered immaterial. (From *Standard Methods of Water Analysis*, 8th Edition, pp. 211-212.)

According to Levine, the *positive presumptive test* is a reliable index to the probable presence of *Escherichia coli* when dealing with untreated waters but is not to be depended upon for chlorinated waters. The *doubtful presumptive test* is found to be only a fair index of the probable presence of *Escherichia coli* in untreated waters, while it is practically of no value for treated waters. The amount of gas has little significance. The rate of gas formation is said to be more significant.

Many reasons exist for spurious presumptive tests. A few are discussed below.

1. *Presence of other lactose-fermenting bacteria of doubtful or no sanitary significance.* Several such bacteria exist. Some of them are quite widely distributed and may cause trouble in water analysis. Certain

Streptococci, members of the proteus group, and *Bacterium capsulatum* are examples. The most significant bacterium in this category is probably *Bacillus asteroporous* (Meyer), an organism having all the characteristics of *Escherichia coli* with exception that it forms spores. It appears in soil, for Bredemann[95] found it in soils from various parts of the world. It has also been found by Gottheil,[96] Ankersmit,[97] Behrens,[98] Aderhold,[99] Meyer,[100] and Ewing.[101]

Bacillus asterosporous has been shown by different investigators to cause spurious presumptive tests in water analysis as well as in analysis of other foods. Hinman and Levine[102] reported this organism to be in Iowa surface water. More recently it has been isolated from other water supplies.

Sohn[103] reported the presence of sporeforming, lactose-fermenting bacteria in 21 of 99 samples of Ohio river water. Of these 18 were capable of growing aerobically and 16 anaerobically. Only six of the 21 cultures survived plating and purification. During this period 85 per cent of positive presumptive tests were confirmed. Berry[104] found a sporeforming, lactose-fermenting organism in the water supply of Akron, Ohio. Ginter,[105] at Tulsa, Oklahoma, reported that 27 per cent of samples of chlorinated water gave positive results which would not confirm. These were due to an organism similar to the one described by Norton and Weight.[106] He reported that neither 17 p.p.m. of chlorine nor 19 p.p.m. of copper (in terms of metallic copper) killed the organism. A sporeforming, lactose-fermenting bacterium was also found by Calvert[107] in the Indianapolis water supply in the winter months only. Greer[108] reported a lactose-fermenting, aerobic, sporeforming bacterium which was believed to be sufficiently different to justify a new name. The name *Bacillus aerosporous* was proposed by Norton, who had observed the organism before.

These species were studied by Porter, McCleskey, and Levine.[109] Included in their investigation were all of the available organisms of this group, e.g., the original strains of A. Meyer, Bredermann, Wagner, Schardinger, and Northrop. The cultures studied fell into two distinct species, *Asterosporous polymyxa* and *Asterosporous macerans*. Hupp[110] stated that these forms could be suppressed by adding sodium lauryl sulfate to the broth.

95. Bredemann. 1909. Centbl. Bakt., Pt. 2, 22, 44-89.
96. Gottheil. 1901. Centbl. Bakt., Pt. 2, 7, 449-465.
97. Ankersmit. 1906. Idem Pt. 1, Orig., 40, 107.
98. Behrens. 1903. Idem Pt. 2, 10, 524-530.
99. Aderhold. 1899. Idem Pt. 2, 5, 511.
100. Myer. 1918. J. Bact. 3, 9-14.
101. Ewing. 1919. Amer. J. Pub. Health 9, 257-258.
102. Hinman and Levine. 1922. J. Amer. Water Wks. Assoc. 9, 330-342.
103. Sohn. 1924. Fourth Ann. Rept., Ohio Conf. on Water Purification.
104. Berry, 1925. Fifth Ann. Rept., Ohio Conf. on Water Purification.
105. Ginter. 1927. J. Amer. Water Wks. Assoc. 17, 591-594.
106. Norton and Weight. 1924. Amer. J. Pub. Health 14, 1020.
107. Calvert. 1924. J. Amer. Water Wks. Assoc. 12, 307-310.
108. Greer. 1928. J. Infect. Dis. 42, 514-524.
109. Porter, McClesky, and Levine. 1937. J. Bact., 163-183.
110. Hupp. 1940. J. Bact. 39, 631.

2. *Anaerobic bacteria.* Besides the aerobic bacteria just discussed there are numerous anaerobic forms which may cause much confusion in the presumptive test. *Clostridium welchii* is a good example. Greer [108] and Spray and Laux [111] found anaerobic bacteria to be causes of lactose fermentation in presumptive tests which could not be confirmed. Kahn [112] stated that differentiation between *Escherichia coli* and anaerobic lactose fermenters was accomplished on Endo's medium when it is incubated aerobically. He used Endo's medium slants instead of plates. Anaerobes are able to develop in the lower reaches of the fermentation tube even though no attempt is made to create anaerobic conditions. Skinner and Baskin [113] found by one method from six to 5,699 anaerobes in a gram of soil and with another method, two to 10,000. They concluded that these organisms could not be of sanitary significance in water examination. Anaerobic bacteria have been found in well water by Bohdanowicz and Piotrowska [114] using Wilson and Blair's medium. No relation between the *Escherichia coli*-index or the number of aerobic bacteria and the number of anaerobic bacteria was observed. The presence of anaerobes usually indicated extreme pollution where *Bacillus perfrigens* showed that pollution was pathogenic and of long standing. Atkinson and Wood [115] observed that false presumptive tests might be due to presence of anaerobic bacteria of the *Clostridium welchii* group in association with a member of the Proteus group.

3. *Presence of lactose-fermenting yeasts.* Lactose-fermenting yeasts are by no means uncommon in nature and might occasionally cause trouble in the presumptive test. They are encountered frequently in the dairy industry, where they bring about very active fermentation.

4. *Production of a lethal hydrogen-ion concentration during preliminary enrichment.* This possibility was proposed by Thompson [116] who investigated true positive presumptive tests which failed to confirm. In order to avoid this difficulty he prepared standard lactose broth buffered with dipotassium phosphate. Janzig and Montank [117] reported that the use of lactose broth with a decreased hydrogen-ion concentration resulted in the elimination of 47 per cent of false presumptive tests. This reduction allowed a great saving in time and materials.

5. *Presence of bacteria with all of the characteristics of Escherichia coli (Bacterium coli) but originating probably from unpolluted sources.* Reinke [118] found that samples of water collected from well pumps in Chicago were frequently contaminated with bacteria which could not be differentiated from *Escherichia coli* by any of the ordinary methods. It was found that these bacteria were coming from pump leathers, replacement of which caused the bacteria to disappear from the water. Greer,[119]

111. Spray and Laux. 1930. J. Amer. Water Wks. Assoc. 22, 235-241.
112. Kahn. 1918. J. Bact. 3, 561-564.
113. Skinner and Baskin. 1932. Proc. Soc. Expt. Biol. and Med. 29, 551-554.
114. Bohdanowicz and Piotrowska. 1931. Off. Internatl. Hyg. Pub. 23, 189.
115. Atkinson and Wood. 1938. Aust. J. Expt. Biol. and Med. Sci. 16, 111.
116. Thompson. 1927. J. Bact. 13, 3.
117. Janzig and Montank. 1928. J. Amer. Water Wks. Assoc. 20, 684-695.
118. Reinke. 1928. Engin. News-Rec. 101, 407.
119. Greer. 1928. Engin. News-Rec. 101, 407.

and Greer and Kells [120] described this organism under the name of "The Leather Bacillus." This organism was confirmed as *Escherichia coli* (*Bacterium coli*). Washers from a pump were found to be impregnated with it. The first washer had been kept in the laboratory for nine months when the report was made and was still giving off great numbers of cells. Organisms from such a source could hardly be considered of sanitary significance. Frantsev [121] found that *Escherichia coli* could grow abundantly on lubricating grease in stuffing boxes of water pumps. Parr [122] believed that such bacteria might vary from the true type. However, if they enter the water they give evidence of pollution and must be considered.

Fish and amphibians may also seed water with *Escherichia coli*. Johnson [123] pointed out that the colon organisms could multiply in the intestinal tract of fish and that the fish migrating from polluted water might seed unpolluted water with *Escherichia coli*. While *Eberthella typhosa* might also be carried, it is still pertinent to wonder what effect such observations should have on interpretation of results of water analysis. Another animal which might play a similar role is the salamander. Kline and Fuller [124] showed that they continue to shed large numbers of *Escherichia coli* into water after they have fed on food containing these microorganisms. Similar observations were reported by Hassler.[125]

These creatures occur, often in large numbers, in springs and streams throughout the country. One hundred salamanders were collected from different springs by Hassler, placed in sterilized cans, and taken to the laboratory where they were autopsied and bacteriological examinations made of portions of their gastrointestinal tracts. A small percentage were found to contain typical coliform bacteria, when little or no food was found in the alimentary tracts. Additional tests, made on the large purple salamanders, indicated how they might infect a spring. Tests showed that over a period of 122 days one salamander excreted a sufficient number of coliform bacilli per day to contaminate 237 gallons of water heavily enough to be considered dangerous on every test. It is believed that they act as reservoirs or incubators and, having once been infected with coliform bacteria, continue to excrete them as long as there is food in the salamander's stomach or intestines to supply nourishment to the bacteria. Bacteriological examination of water in which salamanders were living might result in condemnation even though the supply was otherwise unpolluted. The question is whether pathogenic bacteria might be carried in this manner. Houser [126] mentioned pollution of reservoirs by sea gulls and other birds. Houston [127] found no *Eberthella typhosa* in droppings of sea gulls but did find *Escherichia coli*. Adams[128] also confirmed this.

120. Greer and Kells. 1929. Canad. Engin. 57, 229-230.
121. Frantsev. 1935. Microbiologia 4, 655-659.
122. Parr. 1937. J. Infect. Dis. 60, 291-301.
123. Johnson. 1904. Idem 7, 348-354.
124. Kline and Fuller. 1932. Amer. J. Pub. Health 22, 691-699.
125. Hassler. 1932. Natural History 32, 303.
126. Houser. 1931. J. New England Water Wks. Assoc. 45, 15.
127. Houston. 1929. Med. Officer 42 42, 153-154.
128. Adams. 1933. Penn. Water Wks. Operators Assoc. 5, 12-13.

6. *Overgrowing of Escherichia coli by other bacteria.* This was referred to as "masked positive" by Atkinson and Wood.[115] Coliform bacteria were present but were overgrown by Proteus species. *Streptococcus fecalis* is another aerobic lactose fermenter. Greer [108] did not find it commonly present in Chicago water, probably due, however, to the methods which were used for its detection.

7. *Formation of gas due to symbiosis ("synergism").* Gas formation has been shown to be possible by Sears and Putnam [129] when two species of bacteria grow together in the presence of a carbohydrate when neither organism growing alone can produce it. Holman and Meekison [130] proposed the name "synergism" for this phenomenon. They stated that one of the species must be able to ferment glucose. Leitch [125] believed that this phenomenon might explain many of the positive presumptive tests which would not confirm. He isolated a number of pure cultures and found that gas resulted from certain combinations, whereas no gas was formed when the pure cultures were grown alone. He stated that one member of the combination had to produce acid from glucose. Holman and Meekison's experiments involved the use of *Streptococcus fecalis* and *Escherichia coli.* The former organism splits sucrose with the formation of acid and the latter had no action. When the two organisms were grown together gas was produced. Such results may also be secured in the fermentation tube.

Atkinson and Wood [115] believed that synergism explained many false presumptive tests. Of 112 false positive tests, 84 were of this type. Similar observations were reported by Thompson [116] and Graham.[132] Graham called attention to the synergic reaction in production of gas from mannitol by *Eberthella typhosa* and *Salmonella morgani* when grown together, though neither bacillus gives this reaction when grown separately. *Eberthella typhosa* grown alone in the medium produced an intermediate substance which, when the *Eberthella typhosa* was killed, was decomposed with development of gas by the *Salmonella morgani* grown subsequently in the medium. Acid formation in the medium hindered growth of organisms and so hindered gas formation. The hydrogen-ion concentration should, therefore, be adjusted at intervals. A larger proportion of hydrogen was formed by the organisms acting alone on glucose or mannitol, and this corresponded with that produced by the glucose-fermenting organisms when acting alone on formates.

Synergism was also found to be one of the causes of spurious presumptive tests in analysis of Ohio River water by Evans.[133] Attempts to isolate an anaerobe were unsuccessful but an aerobic sporeformer which produced gas slowly and a non-gas-producing sporeformer were isolated which together gave violent gas formation and produced butyric acid.

8. *Dissolved Air in Presumptive Test Media.* When such media are stored in tubes at low temperatures, many of them may contain enough

129. Sears and Putnam. 1923. J. Infect. Dis. 32, 270-279.
130. Holman and Meekison. 1926. Idem 39, 145-172.
131. Leitch. 1925. J. Amer. Water Wks. Assoc. 13, 186-192.
132. Graham. 1932. J. Hyg. 32, 385-395.
133. Evans. 1937. Fourteenth Ann. Rept., Ohio Conf. Water Purification.

air to produce bubbles when incubated at 37°C. Archambault and Mc-Crady [113a] recommended storage at 25°C. for only a limited period.

9. *Loss of Escherichia coli during confirmation.* Another reason for failure to confirm gas formation in the presumptive test is loss of *Escherichia coli* during the confirmatory procedure.

Another possible explanation is toxic action of dyes on bacteria. Not all of them used in culture media have been studied as Ritter [134] has done with fuchsin.

B. CONFIRMED TEST

Standard Methods of Water Analysis permits use of Endo's or eosin-methylene blue plates or any of the liquid media: brilliant green lactose bile, crystal violet lactose broth, fuchsin lactose broth or formate ricimoleate broth. All of these media were said to be equivalent in value.

1. ENDO OR EOSIN METHYLENE BLUE PLATES

1. 1. Streak one or more plates from a tube which shows gas formation in lactose broth from the smallest amount of water tested. It is desirable to make transfers as soon as possible after gas formation occurs. In order to obtain typical results it is essential that the plates be streaked so as to insure the presence of some discreet colonies. Transfers should be made not later than at the end of the first 24-hour incubation period if gas has formed during this time. If at the end of 48 hours gas has formed in tubes containing less of the sample of water than at 24 hours, transfers should be made from these tubes. (For example, if the water has been tested in amounts of 10 ml., 1 ml., and .1 ml., and gas is formed in 10 ml. and 1 ml., not in .1 ml. the test need be confirmed only in the 1-ml. amount. But if the larger amounts are not transplanted for confirmation, they shall be recorded as confirmed, even though the smaller portion may fail subsequently to confirm.)

1. 2. Incubate the plates at 37°C. (98.6°F.) for 18 to 24 hours.

1. 3. Results, typical and atypical. If typical colonies have developed upon the plate within this period, the confirmed test may be considered positive. If, however, no typical colonies have developed within 24 hours, the test cannot yet be considered definitely negative, since it not infrequently happens that members of the coli-aerogenes group fail to form typical colonies on Endo or eosin methylene blue plates, or that the colonies develop slowly. In such case, it is always necessary to complete the test as directed under D.

2. LIQUID CONFIRMATORY MEDIA

2. 1. Transfer from a lactose broth tube showing gas to the fermentation tube containing the selected confirmatory medium. It is recommended that all lactose broth tubes showing gas be confirmed to comply with this test, but it is allowable to follow the recommendations in C, 1. Transfers should be made as soon as gas appears within the 48-hour incubation period. In routine testing it is convenient to make observations and transfers if required at the end of 24 and 48 hours. In making transfers from the lactose broth fermentation tubes showing gas, the tube should first be gently shaken or mixed by rotating and the transfer should be made by means of a wire loop, the loop to be not less than three mm. in diameter; or it is permissible to use a sterile capillary tube or sterile pipette when it is considered desirable to transfer larger amounts. (From *Standard Methods of Water Analysis*, 8th Edition, pp. 212-213.)

2. 2. Incubate the inoculated tubes containing the confirmatory medium for 48 hours at 37°C.

2. 3. The formation and presence of gas in any amount in the inverted vials in the fermentation tubes at any time within 48 hours constitutes a confirmed test.

133a. Archambault and McCrady. 1942. Amer. J. Pub. Health 32, 1164-1168.
134. Ritter. 1940. Amer. J. Pub. Health 30, 59-65; 28 (1938) 616-620.

To find the best medium for the confirmed test, many comparative investigations have been made. Hoak [135] presented a fine summary of this situation as well as results of a comparative study made by himself. Except for the direct pour-plate methods, none of the differential tests mentioned were believed to be reliable enough to give dependable results without the supporting evidence of other related tests. Indol production, methyl-red and Voges-Proskauer reactions, and the citrate test when used together afford the most reliable differential group of tests now in use. Direct pour-plate media, however, offer the most promise for the future of coli-aerogenes differentiation. It is interesting that several investigators found lactose broth to be just about as useful as some of the special media. Ruchhoft,[136] Ruchhoft and Norton,[137] Atkinson and Wood,[138] Horwood and Heifetz,[139] all spoke well of this medium. McCrady [140] and Howard, Lochhead, and McCrady [141] found brilliant green to be reliable for confirming lactose broth.

C. THE COMPLETED TEST

In the methods given below, attempt is made to determine whether gas secured in the presumptive test was formed by *Escherichia coli*.

1. 1. Streak one or more Endo or eosin methylene blue plates from the lactose broth tubes which show gas from the smallest amount of water tested or from the secondary selective medium tubes which show gas. If these plates are streaked from the original lactose broth tube they should be made at the same time that the secondary selective medium tubes are planted. If plates are used for the confirmed test, completion may be continued after incubation.

1. 2. Incubate the plates at 37°C.(98.6°F.) for 18 to 24 hours.

1. 3. Identification. From the plates fish one or more typical colonies, or if no typical colonies are present, fish two or more colonies considered most likely to be organisms of the coli-aerogenes group, transferring each to an agar slant and a lactose broth fermentation tube. The lactose broth fermentation tubes thus inoculated shall be incubated until gas formation is noted—the incubation not to exceed 48 hours. The agar slants shall be incubated at 37°C. for 24 hours, when a microscopic examination for the presence of spores and a Gram stain of at least one culture shall be made, selecting when possible the one which corresponds to one of the lactose broth fermentation tubes which has shown gas formation. If none of the lactose broth fermentation tubes contain gas at the end of 24 hours, all the agar slants shall be examined, and corresponding tubes examined on the following day.

1. 4. Results. The formation of gas in lactose broth and the demonstration of Gram-negative, nonsporeforming bacilli in the agar culture shall be considered a satisfactory completed test, demonstrating the presence of a member of the coli-aerogenes group.

Absence of gas formation in lactose broth or failure to demonstrate Gram-negative, nonsporeforming bacilli in a gas-forming culture constitutes a negative test.

When sporeforming, lactose-fermenting organisms are found, the culture should be further studied to ascertain the possible presence of bacteria of the coli-aerogenes group with the spore-bearing organisms. This may be done by transferring the culture to formate ricinoleate broth and incubating at 37°C. for 48 hours. If no gas is produced, only sporeforming lactose fermenters are present. If gas is produced in the formate

135. Hoak. 1935. J. Penn. Water Wks. Operators Assoc. 7, 75-93.
136. Ruchhoft. 1935. J. Amer. Water Wks. Assoc. 27, 1732-1745.
137. Ruchhoft and Norton. 1935. Idem 27.
138. Atkinson and Wood. 1938. Aust. J. Expt. Biol. and Med. Sci. 16, 103-109.
139. Horwood and Heifetz. 1936. J. Bact. 28, 199-211.
140. McCrady. 1937. Amer. J. Pub. Health 27, 1243.
141. Howard et al. 1940. Canad. Pub. Health J. 31, 16-17.

ricinoleate broth, members of the coli-aerogenes group may be present. If gas is produced, the presence of coli-aerogenes group organisms should be verified by inoculation of a tube of standard lactose broth and an agar slant. If, after 48 hours, gas is produced in the former and no spores are present in the latter, the test may be deemed "completed." If spores are present, for practical purposes the organisms of the coli-aerogenes group may be considered absent. (From *Standard Methods of Water Analysis*, 8th Edition, pp. 213-214.)

At one time this separation of coliform bacteria into fecal and non-fecal types was considered to be sharp and reliable. More experience, however, indicated that too much confidence had been placed in it. *Aerobacter aerogenes* was frequently found in excreta and *Escherichia coli* was occasionally isolated from materials which had a satisfactory sanitary history. Horwood and Webster [142] attributed considerable sanitary importance to *Aerobacter aerogenes*. They also believed that *Escherichia coli* might be a derivative of *Aerobacter aerogenes* in the human body. Raghavachari and Iyer [143] also believed that opinions about sanitary significance of *Aerobacter aerogenes* would have to be changed. This opinion seems to be well supported by Cruickshank, in an unpublished communication to the Pathological Society of Great Britain and Ireland, who isolated from 98 to 135 specimens of human feces. In 24 of the 37 specimens that gave negative results, he ascribed his failure to isolate that organism to an overgrowth of the cultures with *Pseudomonas pyocyanea*. Gray,[144] examining 40 specimens of feces from 10 human subjects, and employing in addition to other methods the lithium containing medium that he has previously described, which inhibits the growth of *Pseudomonas pyocyanea*, isolated *Aerobacter aerogenes* from 37 of the samples. The frequent reports, especially in tropical countries, of the presence of methyl-red positive, citrate positive strains in samples of water taken from apparently unpolluted sources have led to the view that these intermediate forms should be grouped, in respect to their sanitary significance, with *Aerobacter aerogenes* rather than with *Escherichia coli*. Gray concurred in the opinion that a clean dichotomy of habitat does not in truth exist. This seems to be borne out by a recent investigation by Krishnan and Chawla [145] in which they studied the incidence of coliform types in stools of persons suffering from specific intestinal infections. They concluded that *Aerobacter aerogenes* should be considered an indicator of pollution even though it may be present in other situations than in the intestines of man and animals. Until a satisfactory method is found with which to distinguish between strains from soil and from feces, no definite opinion as to the sanitary significance of *Aerobacter aerogenes* in water can be given.

Weiss and Hunter's [146] Method for Bacteriological Examination of Water. A simplified method for determining the potability of water was developed and compared with the standard method. The new or "bottle" method consisted of adding five ml. of a concentrated broth (24 gm. of nutrient broth (Difco) to 100 ml. of water) to the sample bottle containing approximately 150 ml. of water, thus making 155 ml. of

142. Horwood and Webster. 1937. J. Bact. 33, 21.
143. Raghavachari and Iyer. 1940. Indian J. Med. Res. 28, 55-60.
144. Gray. 1932. J. Hyg. 32, 132-142.
145. Krishnan and Chawla. 1941. Indian Med. Gaz. 76, 628-631.
146. Weiss and Hunter. 1938. J. Bact. 36, 312.

nutrient broth. After adding the concentrated broth to the water in the bottle, the mixture was incubated at 37°C. overnight. The next day a loopful of broth from the bottle was streaked on a plate of eosin-methylene blue agar. Confirmation was carried out in the usual manner.

The "bottle" method was compared with the standard method using 638 water samples. It was found that 29.4 per cent of the samples gave positive results by both methods, that 60.2 per cent were negative by both methods, and that there was disagreement in 10.2 per cent. Of the 65 water samples showing disagreement, the standard method was positive and the "bottle" method was negative in 1.9 per cent of the samples, and the standard method was negative and the "bottle" method was positive in 8.3 per cent of the samples. Thus, the difference in favor of the "bottle" method was 6.4 per cent.

Sterile bottles containing the required amount of concentrated broth were sent into the field for trial with a number of samples of water. The results were excellent. The "bottle" method proved to be much more rapid and yielded fewer false reactions. Thus, while being more efficient, it was simpler and more economical.

Ministry of Health of Great Britain Procedures for Examination of Water for Coliform Bacteria.

To provide uniformity in procedures, the Ministry of Health of Great Britain [147] prepared the following technic for determining coliform bacteria in water.

The procedures include the plate count, the presumptive coliform count, and the differential coliform test. They are not considered as a rigid set of rules from which any deviation is deprecated but rather a technic which is accompanied by the smallest error and which may be followed by bacteriologists in various laboratories. The British procedure for the plate count is given in full on page 164.

Technic of the Presumptive Coliform Count:

"(a) Inoculation of the MacConkey Broths—With good waters one 50 ml. quantity and five 10 ml. quantities of water should be inoculated into MacConkey broth; with medium waters one 50 ml., five 10 ml., and five 1 ml. quantities should be used; with poor waters five 1 ml. quantities of a 1 in 10 dilution should be included in addition, the single 50 ml. quantity being omitted if desired. The mixing of the water in the sample bottle and the preparation of the dilutions are carried out in the same way as in the plate count. Except with very bad waters, only a single dilution (1 in 10) is required.

"In the actual process of inoculation a sterile 1 ml. delivery pipette should be introduced into the bottle or test tube containing the 1 in 10 dilution of water with its tip reaching not more than 1 in. below the surface of the diluent. The fluid should be sucked up ten times to the 1 ml. mark in order to wet the interior of the pipette thoroughly and 1 ml. of fluid should then be measured out, the pipette being held in the vertical position. The pipette should be withdrawn and the tip touched against the neck of the bottle, or the side of the test tube, to remove excess fluid adhering to its exterior. It is then introduced into a tube containing 5 ml. of *single strength* MacConkey broth with the tip touching the side of the tube about 1 in. above the level of the broth. The contents should be blown out, 3 seconds allowed to elapse, and the last drop blown out. With the same pipette a fresh 1 ml. quantity is taken up from the 1 in 10 dilution and inoculated into a second tube of MacConkey broth. The process is repeated till all five tubes of broth have been inoculated from the 1 in 10 dilution. The same pipette is then transferred to the sample bottle containing the original water. The water is sucked up ten times to the 1 ml. mark, and five more tubes of single strength

147. Reprinted by permission of the Controller of His Britannic Majesty's Stationery Office from Reports on Public Health and Medical Subjects No. 71 (Revised Edition, 1939), entitled "The Bacteriological Examination of Water Supplies," official copies of which may be purchased from the British Information Service, 30 Rockefeller Plaza, New York, N. Y.

MacConkey broth are inoculated in the same way as before. The pipette is then discarded.

"A sterile 10 ml. pipette should then be taken and inserted into the sample bottle containing the original water with its tip reaching not more than 1 in. below the surface. The water should be sucked up ten times approximately to the 10 ml. mark. and 10 ml. of water should be measured out, the pipette being held in the vertical position. The pipette should be withdrawn and the tip touched against the neck of the bottle about ½ in. below the rim so as to remove any excess water adhering to the *double strength* MacConkey broth, the tip being held about 3 ins. above the surface. The pipette should be allowed to discharge by gravity in the vertical position, and before removal its tip should be touched against the side of the test tube about 1 in. above the level of the medium. The same pipette is used to inoculate a total of five *double strength* MacConkey broths. It is then discarded.

"Finally, using a bulb pipette, one 50 ml. quantity of the original water should be inoculated into a bottle or large tube containing 50 ml. of *double strength* MacConkey broth. The transfer should be made under the same conditions as those used for the 10 ml. quantities, but is advisable in the interests of sterility not to suck the water up in the pipette more than once or twice before carrying it over to the medium for inoculation. The pipette is then discarded.

"*Incubation and Examination of the MacConkey broths.*—The inoculated MacConkey broths should be incubated at 37°C. and examined after 18 to 24 hours. All tubes showing both acid and gas formation should be regarded as "presumptive positives."

"It may be noted that the amount of gas formed depends partly on the type of organism and partly on the nature of the peptone used. Typical coliform organisms, particularly *Bact. Coli* I, usually produce sufficient gas in 24 hours to displace at least a quarter of the medium in the Durham tube. Organisms of the I. A. C.* group, on the other hand, though often producing as much or more gas than *Bact. coli* I, may produce little or none during the first 24 hours, and perhaps only a small amount after 48 hours. Some of them grow much better at 30°C. than at 37°C. If, in a series of routine examinations, the amount of gas formed seems to be unusually small, it is well to try another brand of peptone.

"For practical purposes readings should be taken at the end of 18-24 hours, and all tubes showing acid and an amount of gas sufficient or more than sufficient to fill the concavity at the top of the Durham tube reported as positive. If it should be judged desirable to undertake confirmatory and differential tests, the presumptive positive tubes should be treated in the way described later. The remaining tubes should be re-incubated and examined after another 24 hours. Any further tubes in which acid and gas formation become apparent should similarly be regarded as "presumptive positives" and submitted, if necessary, to further examination. In routine control work, however, if a number of tubes show acid and gas in the first 24 hours, there is usually no need to re-incubate the negative tubes."

Reporting Results. Specific instructions are given for reporting results. Owing to the fact that so much space would be required, they will not be given here.

TECHNIC OF DIFFERENTIAL COLIFORM TEST

A. Plating Method. One or two of the fermented MacConkey broth tubes—usually those seeded with the smallest quantity of water—are plated out on to a suitable solid medium.

"In this country, MacConkey's neutral-red bile-salt lactose agar plates are ordinarily used. Other valuable media are, however, much employed abroad, as, for example, Endo agar and Eosin-methylene-blue agar (Levine). It is claimed for some of these media that they enable the observer to differentiate between *Bact. coli* and *Bact. aerogenes* by direct inspection of the colonies. With Eosin-methylene-blue agar, differences between the colonies of *Bact. coli* and *Bact. aerogenes* can, in fact, often be made out within 24 hours, though in 48 hours differentiation is much easier. The formulae for the

---

* Intermediate-aerogenes-cloacae group.

preparation of these media will be found in Appendix C * and it is hoped that workers in this country who have the opportunity of doing so will employ them and report their results.

"Petri dishes of standard size into which about 15 ml. of melted MacConkey agar have been poured *without bubbles* and allowed to set, are first well dried by several hours' incubation at 37°C. (or, preferably, by one hour in an incubator at 55°C.) in the inverted position and with the inner dish, which contains the medium, supported on the edge of the cover; such dried agar plates may be kept in stock, wrapped in paper, for several weeks in the refrigerator. A loopful (1 to 2 mm. diameter) of the primary culture, or preferably of a dilution of it prepared by mixing one loopful with one ml. of sterile broth, is then placed half way between the center and the edge of the plate and spread over the surface by a sterile right-angled glass rod. In spreading, the drop should first be well-distributed along the contact portion of the rod (about 1½ in. long) by a to-and-fro motion and the rod then drawn round the rest of the plate; it should be kept gently but firmly in contact with the medium and parallel with the radii, until it has almost completed a circuit. Interruptions in the circuit by lifting the rod and reapplying a short distance further on help to increase the number of isolated colonies which is the object of plating; the rod should not cover the same surface of agar more than once. Other devices for obtaining isolated colonies, e.g., previous dilution of the primary culture, parallel and cross striations with a loop or straight wire, may be used according to personal preference.

"The plate is then incubated, bottom up, at 37°C. for 24 hours.

"*Appearance of colonies; subculturing for differential tests.*—On MacConkey agar coliform colonies are usually circular in shape, convex or low convex in elevation, with a smooth surface and an entire edge. They are coloured red, but the depth of tint varies considerably. The normal colony of *Bact. coli* is deeply coloured and non-mucoid, whereas that of *Bact. aerogenes* is often a paler colour and mucoid in consistency. For further examination two or three coliform colonies, as far as possible of different appearance are selected and subcultured. Should no typical colonies appear on the plate within 48 hours, it is well to select at least one of the predominant variety for further investigation bearing in mind the possibility that such atypical colonies may owe their absence of redness to a mere temporary slowing of their action on lactose. Should there be any doubt in the observer's mind whether the colonies selected are those of coliform or coliform-like bacilli, a film preparation should be made and stained by Gram. Only colonies consisting of Gram-negative, non-sporing rods should be subcultured.

"In the process of subculture a speck of the bacterial mass forming the colony should be picked off with a straight wire, suspended thoroughly in a tube of peptone water, and incubated at 37°C. After 4-6 hours' incubation the culture should be used for the inoculation of two tubes of glucose phosphate medium for the methyl-red and Voges-Proskauer tests, one tube of citrate medium for the citrate-utilization test, one tube of gelatin for the liquefaction test, one tube of MacConkey's broth to test for gas production at 44°C., and one tube of lactose peptone water for confirmation of lactose fermentation. The original peptone water culture can be reincubated and used to test for indole formation.

"*Technique for Differential Tests*—In the performance of these various tests, the following procedures are recommended.

"(1) *Indole Test*—The peptone water culture already referred to is removed from the incubator after three days and 1 ml. of ether added to it with vigorous shaking. It is then allowed to stand for a minute or two to allow separation of the ether layer containing any dissolved indole, and a few drops (0.5 ml.) of Erlich's reagent are allowed to run down inside the test tube. If the test is positive, the pink colour of rosindole appears within a few minutes.

"An alternative method, that of Holman and Gonzales [148] (1923), which is said to be slightly more delicate, makes use of the volatility of indole at 37°C. It consists in

---

* The reader is referred to Chapter 26 for a discussion of Culture Media and the changes which occur in differential media.

148. Holman and Gonzales. 1923. J. Bact. 8, 577.

placing a strip of filter paper, soaked in a saturated water solution of oxalic acid and subsequently dried, between the cottonwool plug and the tube at the time of inoculation. The paper should be carefully folded so as to present the maximum surface to the volatilizing indole during the growth of the culture. If indole is formed, the paper is turned pink.

"(2) *Methyl-Red Test*—Glucose phosphate broth is inoculated with a loopful of the stock peptone water culture 4-6 hours old, and incubated for three days at 37°C. Five drops of 0.04% methyl red solution are then added to the culture. A magenta red colour is considered a positive result: a yellow colour is negative; pink or pale red are best considered as doubtful results.

"(3) *Voges-Proskauer Test*—Glucose phosphate broth, similarly inoculated and incubated for two days at 37°C. has added to it 5 ml. of a 10% solution of sodium hydroxide. The result is read after the tube has stood 24 hours at room temperature, or after heating the mixture to near boiling point for about half an hour. If positive, a pinkish-green fluorescent colour develops; if negative, no colour.

"A modified method has been put forward by O'Meara:[189] A knife point of creatine is introduced into the culture as above and 5 ml. of 40% potassium f.c. hydroxide are added. The tube is shaken for two to five minutes. If positive, a pink colour develops; if negative, no colour.

"(4) *Growth in Citrate*—Tubes of citrate medium should be inoculated from the stock peptone water culture of 4 to 6 hours' age by means of a straight wire, not a loop, so as to carry over as little as possible of the inoculating medium. The tube is then incubated for 24 hours at 37°C., or if no growth has occurred, for 48 hours. Opacity is considered evidence of growth. If difficulty is experienced in determining the presence of opacity, brom-thymol-blue may be added in 0.008% concentration as an indicator. Growth is accompanied by a change in colour from a pale green to a bluish-green or blue. Occasionally no growth may be evident for 3 or 4 days.

"(5) *Gelatin liquefaction*—Inoculation of the solid medium should be performed with a straight needle charged with the stock peptone water culture (stab culture) or with a loop on the surface (slope culture), and the tube incubated at 20°-22°C. for 7 days. This time may be prolonged, if desired, to 21 days.

"(6) *44°C. MacConkey test*—The success of this test depends on the most rigid conformity to the technique about to be described. If an accurately regulated 44°C. water bath is not available, the test should be omitted. A tube of single-strength Mac-Conkey broth should be heated in a water bath to 44°C., and then inoculated lightly from the peptone water culture. It should be immediately returned to the 44°C. water bath, and examined after 18-24 hours. The presence of gas in the enclosed Durham tube is regarded as a positive reaction; absence of gas formation, even though growth or acid production is present, is regarded as a negative reaction. If no gas is present after 18-24 hours, the tube should be reincubated for a further 24 hours. Very occasionally a strain of fecal coli may not form gas for 72 hours, but under ordinary routine conditions the tubes may be discarded as soon as gas is evident, or after 48 hours' incubation. Gas production under these conditions is practically characteristic of *Bact. coli*, type I, faecal. Except for quite occasional irregular strains, the only other organism in this country likely to be met with giving a positive reaction in this test is Irregular II.

"It is very important that the water bath used should be maintained at a temperature of 44°C. with only the minimum variation. The bath should be properly lagged; it should be placed in a part of the laboratory that is free from draughts and from direct sunshine; and the temperature should be regulated with a mercury-toluol or other reliable thermostat. The indicator thermometer should be checked against an N. P. L. standard, and should have its bulb placed at the level of the medium in the MacConkey tubes. It is advisable, in addition, to use a continuous recording thermometer in order to make certain that the temperature does not depart from the 44°C. level by more than .5°C. Two control tubes of MacConkey broth should be included, one inoculated with

189. O'Meara. 1931. J. Path. and Bact. 34, 401-406.

a known strain of *Bact. coli* the other with a known strain of intermediate or aerogenes type. If, for any special purpose, an even greater degree of temperature control should be required, a constant temperature bath of the type described by Temple & Mc-Clemont [149] may be used.

"(7) *Fermentation of lactose*—A tube of lactose peptone water is inoculated with a loopful of the peptone water culture, and incubated at 37°C. All the members of the coliform group produce acid and gas from lactose, the great majority within 24 hours. Some strains, however, particularly of the I. A. C.* types, ferment lactose very slowly, and may form only a minimal amount of gas. Some of these strains grow much better and produce more active fermentation at (22°-30°C.) than at 37°C.

"B. Selective liquid media method. The rationale and general description of this method have already been given on pp. 32-34. It was pointed out that the original method was not altogether suitable for water analysis, but that modifications of the method might prove useful. The three modifications suggested are as follows:

"(1) The presumptive positive MacConkey tubes at 37°C. are subcultured into MacConkey at 44°C. and incubated for 24-48 hours. The presumptive fecal coli count is calculated by means of the ordinary probability tables from the proportion of tubes at 44°C. showing gas formation. If no gas is produced in any of the 44°C. tubes or in only a very small proportion of them, the original fermented 37°C. MacConkey tubes that remain negative on subculture at 44°C. are inoculated into Koser's citrate at 37°C. Growth within 2-3 days is regarded as presumptive evidence of the presence of I. A. C. organisms. Since the citrate test is not strictly specific under these conditions for organisms of the I. A. C. group, but may be given by late lactose fermenters or glucose fermenters, it is wiser not to express the results in probable numbers, but to confine the report to saying that the coliform organisms present appeared to belong to the I. A. C. or to irregular types. The occurrence of a certain proportion of false positives due to atypical organisms is to some extent counterbalanced by the rapidity and ease of the test, and by the fact that, even though typical I. A. C. organisms may not be present, late lactose fermenters and glucose fermenters are regarded by some workers as indicative of a minor degree of pollution and should not therefore be completely ignored.

"(2) As in (1) the fermented 37°C. MacConkey tubes are subcultured into Mac-Conkey at 44°C. for the presumptive fecal coli count. If the 44°C. tubes are negative, the original fermented 37°C. tubes are plated on to MacConkey's agar, and colonies are picked off the following day and identified by the tests already described under the Plating Method. By this method, which takes at least four days, the coliform organisms present can be identified, and mentioned in the report.

"(3) If only the fecal coli count is required, or is required very rapidly, the original water can be inoculated into MacConkey broth and incubated at 44°C. The presumptive fecal coli count can be estimated after 1-2 days from the probability tables. It is possible that this method may slightly underestimate the fecal coli count, but for certain purposes this risk may be worth taking.

REPORTING THE RESULTS OF THE DIFFERENTIAL COLIFORM TEST

"(a) *When Method A is used*—It has been pointed out at some length that the proportions of coliform colonies of different types on the MacConkey plates correspond as a rule to the proportions in the fermented MacConkey tubes from which the plates were made rather than to the proportions present in the original water. For this reason it is advisable not to make any numerical estimate of the proportions of the different types of coliform bacilli present in the water itself, but to confine the report to stating that the presence of *Bact. coli*, *Bact. aerogenes*, or other coliform types was demonstrated by the usual differential tests in tubes seeded with a given amount of water. For example, supposing in Table II acid and gas were produced in one tube of 50 ml.

149. Temple and McClemont. 1937. Med. Officer 58, 241

* Intermediate-aerogenes-cloacae (I.A.C.) group.

and two tubes of 10 ml., and supposing the 50 ml. tube and one of the 10 ml. tubes were plated out, with the result that colonies of fecal coli were found on both plates, and colonies of *Bact. aerogenes* only on the plate made from the 50 ml. quantity, then the report might read as follows:

"Probable number of coliform bacilli present—6 per 100 ml. of water.

"Fecal coli were demonstrated in 50 ml. and 10 ml. of water.

"*Bact. aerogenes* was demonstrated in 50 ml. of water.

"(b) *When Method B₁ is used*—If gas is produced in the MacConkey broths at 44°C. that were seeded from the fermented 37°C. MacConkey tubes, and fecal coli are thus shown to be present, the report should simply state the probable numbers of coliform bacilli and of fecal coli present. For example, supposing . . . gas were produced in one 50 ml. and two 10 ml. quantities, and subcultures of each tube into MacConkey at 44°C. produced gas, then the report might read as follows:

"Probable number of coliform bacilli present—6 per 100 ml. of water.

"Probable number of fecal coli present—6 per 100 ml. of water.

"If no fecal coli were present and subculture of the fermented 37°C. MacConkey tubes into citrate was undertaken as in method B (1), and growth occurred in citrate, then attention should be drawn in the report to the presence of coliform organisms of non-fecal type. Since, however, the citrate test is not strictly specific for organisms of the I. A. C. group, but may be given by late lactose fermenters or by glucose fermenters, it is wiser not to express the results in terms of probable numbers, but to confine the report to saying that the coliform bacilli present appeared to belong to I. A. C. or irregular types. As an example, the report might read thus:

"Probable number of coliform bacilli present—6 per 100 ml. of water.

"Fecal coli absent from 100 ml. of water.

"Coliform organisms appear to belong to the intermediate-aerogenes-cloacae or to irregular types.

'If fecal coli were present, but in numbers constituting only a small proportion of the total coliform organisms, and subculture into citrate of the fermented 37°C. MacConkey tubes that remained negative on subculture at 44°C. was undertaken in order to confirm the presence of other types of coliform bacilli, and growth in citrate occurred, then this should be noted in the report. Thus supposing in the previous example, only one of the 10 ml. tubes at 37°C. when subcultured into MacConkey broth at 44°C. produced gas, the other 10 ml. tube and the 50 ml. tube remaining negative, and subculture of these last two tubes into citrate yielded growth, then the report might read as follows:

"Probable number of coliform bacilli present—6 per 100 ml. of water.

"Probable number of fecal coli present—1 per 100 ml. of water.

"Majority of coliform organisms present appear to belong to the intermediate-aerogenes-cloacae or to irregular types.

"*When Method B₂ is used*—If no fecal coli are present, or present in numbers constituting only a very small proportion of the total coliform organisms, and the fermented 37°C. MacConkey tubes are plated out as in method B (2) and the resulting colonies identified, the report might read as follows:

"Probable number of coliform bacilli present—6 per 100 ml. of water.

"Fecal coli absent from 100 ml. of water.

"*Bact. aerogenes*, or other identified type, was demonstrated in 50 and 10 ml. of water.

"*When Method B₃ is used*—If only the number of fecal coli present in the water is required, and method B (3) is used, the report can simply state whether fecal coli were present in 100 ml., and if so what their probable numbers were. If, for example, in Table II gas was produced in the tube of MacConkey broth at 44C. seeded with 50 ml. of water, but not in any of the five tubes seeded with 10 ml., then the report would read as follows:

"Probable number of fecal coli present—2 per 100 ml. of water."

American Public Health Association Method for Differentiation of Members of the Coliform Group. The eighth edition (1936) of *Standard Methods of Water Analysis* prescribes four tests for satisfactory differentiation of the coliform group into the *Escherichia coli, Aerobacter aerogenes,* and intermediate sections: *indol test, methyl-red test, Voges-Proskauer reaction,* and *sodium citrate fermentation test.* Additional tests may be added if desired. This work was not considered to be desirable in routine water work. If only two differential tests are desired, a combination of the indol and sodium citrate tests or methyl-red and sodium citrate tests may be employed. The following reaction classification for coli-aerogenes bacteria was published in *Standard Methods of Water Analysis,* eighth edition.

COLI-AEROGENES GROUP—REACTION CLASSIFICATION

Reaction combinations				Possible interpretation when isolated from water by the standard method		Common source
Indol	M.R.	V.R.	Citrate	Usually	Occasionally	Applies to pure strain members of C-a group only
+	+	—	—	*Esch. coli*	....	Predominant in feces about 50 per cent of total group in sewage
—	+	—	—	*Esch. coli*	Non-members of group	Minority form in feces
+	+	—	+	Mixture	Intermediate strain sometimes considered nontypical *Esch. coli*	Minority form in soil and sewage, rarely feces
—	+	—	+	Intermediate strain	Mixtures or slow secondary reacting *A. aerogenes*	Soil, minority forms in sewage and feces
+	+	+	+	Mixture	Atypical	Soil, sewage
+	—	—	+	Always mixture		
+	—	+	+	Mixture	*A. cloacae*	Soil, minority forms in sewage and feces
—	+	+	+	*A. aerogenes*	Mixture	Majority forms in soil and on vegetables
—	—	+	+	*A. aerogenes*		Up to 50 per cent of total group in sewage
—	—	—	+	Extraneous form	*A. aerogenes*	Minority forms in feces

These tests may be made as follows:

Methyl-Red Test. Inoculate the culture into 10 ml. of the standard peptone medium (dextrose potassium phosphate broth). Incubate at 37°C. (98.6°F.) for three or preferably four days. To five ml. of each culture add five drops of methyl red solution. Record distinct red color as methyl red +, distinct yellow color as methyl red —, and intermediate colors as ?.

Voges-Proskauer Test. To the remaining five ml. of medium add five **ml. of** a 10-per cent solution of potassium hydroxide. A positive test is indicated by an eosin pink color. To hasten the appearance of the red color the tubes treated with sodium hydroxide should be incubated at 37°C.(98.6°F.) or 45°C.(113°F.) for six hours. The Werkman technic for hastening appearance of the pink color may be used if desired.

Sodium Citrate Test. The citrate medium should be inoculated only with a needle or loop. A pipette is prohibited on account of the ease of introducing nutrient material which would invalidate the results. Incubate the culture at 37°C.(98.6°F.) for 72 to 96 hours and record growth as + or —.

Indol Test. Determine indol formation in tryptone broth by adding, drop by drop, to avoid mixing with the medium, about one ml. of a two-per cent alcoholic solution of p-dimethyl amido-benzaldehyde, then a few drops of concentrated hydrochloric acid. The presence of indol is indicated by a violet color.

	Fecal type *Escherichia coli*	Non-fecal type *Aerobacter aerogenes*
Gas ratio	1 p. CO_2 to 1 p. H.	2 p. CO_2 to 1 p. H.
Hydrogen-ion conc'n.	Acid to methyl red	Alkaline to methyl red
Voges-Proskauer	V-P negative	V-P plus
Uric acid test as sole source of N.	No growth	Growth
Citric acid test source of carbon..	No growth	Luxuriant growth

Methyl-Red Test. As sanitary knowledge increased and it became apparent that *Escherichia coli* or bacteria of the coli group could be present on substances which had not received fecal pollution, studies were made to detect those *Escherichia coli* which came from fecal sources. Rogers [150] and his co-workers found that the gas ratio could be used for this purpose. *Escherichia coli* from bovine feces fermented dextrose with the formation of equal volumes of carbon dioxide and hydrogen while those from grains formed two or three times as much carbon dioxide. The next step was to find a simple procedure for determining this ratio or finding some procedure which correlated with it, since the determination of the gas ratio is too exacting for routine analyses. Clark and Lubs,[151] working in the same laboratory, discovered a constant correlation between the gas ratio and the hydrogen-ion concentration. *Escherichia coli* strains from bovine feces were found to possess a higher hydrogen-ion concentration than those from grains or non-fecal origins. A study of indicators yielded the information that methyl red was yellow with the high-ratio group and red or acid with the low-ratio group.

Voges-Proskauer Reaction. Levine correlated the Voges-Proskauer [152] with the methyl red test. He found that bacteria which gave the Voges-Proskauer reaction were rarely found in feces and that the Voges-Proskauer reaction, like the high-gas ratio and the alkalinity to methyl red, is characteristic of non-fecal strains and, therefore, of much sanitary significance. Harden,[153] in his various publications, reported his studies

150. Rogers. 1915. J. Infect. Dis. 14, 411; 15 (1914) 99; 17 (1915) 137.
151. Clark and Lubs. 1915. J. Wash. Acad. Sci. 5, 609-617.
152. Voges and Proskauer. 1898. Ztschr. Hyg. u. Infektionskrank. 28, 33.
153. Harden. 1901. J. Chem. Soc. 79, 610-628.

on the chemistry of this reaction which are well reviewed by Levine.[154] The red color which results is due to a definite end product in the fermentation of glucose. Voges and Proskauer, in their original publication, describe the test as follows:

"On addition of caustic potash, we observed a new and interesting color reaction. If the tube be allowed to stand twenty-four hours and longer at room temperature, after the addition of the potash, a beautiful fluorescent color somewhat similar to that of a dilute alcoholic solution of eosin forms in the culture fluid particularly at the open end of the tube exposed to the air. We have investigated a few of the properties of this coloring substance which is not produced by the action of the alkali on the sugar and have found that it is fairly resistant to the action of the external air. After a time, however, it becomes paler, and finally gives place to a dirty greenish brown."

Harden and Walpole[155] could not account for all of the carbon in the dextrose by the ordinary products (organic acids, alcohol, etc.); along with these substances was secured a glycol which was made up of 2:3 butylene glycol. This was oxidized to acetyl-methyl-carbinol.

When this was mixed with potassium hydroxide, in the presence of peptone, an eosin-like color was obtained after a period. Walpole[156] found that under aerobic conditions *Aerobacter aerogenes* gave a greater amount of acetyl-methyl-carbinol. The coloration was not secured when butylene glycol or acetyl-methyl-carbinol were mixed with potassium hydroxide. Harden[157] later explained this by finding that the acetyl-methyl-carbinol was oxidized to diacetyl $CH_3CO—CO—CH_3$. This, in some way, acted with This, in some way, acted with the peptone to give a pink color. Harden and Norris[158] later secured the same pink color between diacetyl and arginine, dicyanamide, creatin, and guanidine acetic. They state that the reaction depending upon the group $NH=C(NH_2)—N=HR$, R has not been determined. The origin of acetyl-methyl-carbinol was reported by Barritt[159] to be 2:3 butylene glycol and pyruvic acid, and in small amounts from lactic acid, but not from preformed acetaldehyde or methyl-glyoxal. This substance is also readily formed by *Escherichia coli* from 2:3 butylene glycol and to a slight but variable extent from high concentrations of glucose, pyruvic acid. Pyruvic acid may be an intermediate product in forming of acetyl-methyl-carbinol from glucose and 2:3 butylene glycol may perhaps be the immediate precursor. Differences in the production of the carbinol by members of the coli-aerogenes group appear to be quantitative rather than qualitative. Many organisms can oxidize 2:3 butyl glycol to acetyl-methyl-carbinol.

Several investigators have found that incubation temperature greatly affects the Voges-Proskauer reaction. To reduce this error, Bunker[160] sug-

154. Levine. 1916. J. Infect. Dis. 18, 358-367.
155. Harden and Walpole. 1905-06. Proc. Roy. Soc., Ser. B, 77, 399.
156. Walpole. 1910. Proc. Roy. Soc., Ser. B, 83, 272-286.
157. Harden. 1905. J. Hyg. 5, 488.
158. Harden and Norris. 1911. J. Physiol. 47, 332.
159. Barritt. 1936. J. Path. and Bact. 42, 441; 44 (1937) 679-690
160. Bunker *et al.* 1918. J. Bact. 3, 493-498.

gested the following technic which allows the test to be made in an hour and a half. Place one ml. of a glucose potassium phosphate broth culture incubated for 48 hours at 30°C.(86°F.) in a Syracuse watch glass, and add .5 ml. of a 45-per cent solution of sodium hydroxide. The definite color reaction (a deep pink) is secured in one and one-half hours. Linton [161] also found that temperature of incubation was very important. Link isolated 37 strains of *Aerobacter aerogenes* which gave positive Voges-Proskauer reactions for 48 hours but which were negative on longer incubation. Levine, Weldin, and Johnson [162] reported that the Voges-Proskauer reaction could be reported in five hours after addition of the potassium hydroxide to the test culture. It has also been suggested that the sugar content of culture media could be lowered. For instance, Burling and Levine [163] stated that one per cent of glucose or lactose in the medium and an incubation period of 48 hours was not favorable to isolation of *Escherichia coli*. They suggested that the amount of carbohydrate could be reduced to .5 per cent and the confirmatory tests applied more quickly. Wagner [164] reported that even .1 per cent of lactose gave better results than one per cent. Wagner and Monfort [165] advised the pasteurization of the carbohydrate media, rather than sterilization. They also stated that if sufficient peptone is added, the meat extract may be left out. Their findings with regard to pasteurizing instead of high pressure-temperature sterilization are in keeping with the work of Hasseltine [166] and Mudge,[167] but not in accord with Wolf's [168] statements that the dangers from combined sterilization have been overemphasized. In this paper they also advised reduction of the amount of lactose as did Wagner.

The methyl-red test and Voges-Proskauer reactions were introduced to differentiate fecal lactose-fermenting bacteria *(Escherichia coli)* from those which possessed no sanitary significance *(Aerobacter aerogenes)*. Almost as soon as *Standard Methods* provided for this differentiation, results of investigators were published which suggested that such a differentiation could not exist. This was stated to be the situation by Monfort and Perry[169] who studied 391 cultures of coliform bacteria from natural waters and found that "intermediates" were common. They stated that averages and percentages do not always show the characteristics of these variants. They secured only imperfect correlation between the methyl-red test and the Koser uric acid reaction which seemed to be discriminative of *Aerobacter aerogenes*. A longer presentation of these data in 1921 by the same authors indicated again that the uric acid medium, discussed in another paragraph, was useful for separating the *Aerobacter aerogenes* type of organisms. Bardsley [170] examined 525 samples of water, 265 of which

161. Linton. 1924. Absts. Bact., Abst. No. 1684.
162. Levine, Weldin, and Johnson. 1917. J. Infect. Dis. 21, 39-46.
163. Burling and Levine. 1918. Amer. J. Pub. Health 8, 306-307.
164. Wagner. 1919. Thesis, Univ. of Illinois, Urbana, Ill.
165. Wagner and Monfort. 1921. Amer. J. Pub. Health 11, 203-208.
166. Hasseltine. 1917. Pub. Health Repts. 32, 1879-1887.
167. Mudge. 1917. J. Bact. 2, 403-415.
168. Wolf. 1921. Brit. J. Expt. Path. 2, 266-275.
169. Monfort and Perry. 1920. Absts. Bact. 4, 8.
170. Bardsley. 1926. J. Hyg. 25, 11-25.

contained lactose-fermenting bacteria; 1,441 strains were isolated and subjected to the various differential tests. Only 1.73 per cent were either double positive or double negative when tested with methyl-red and the Voges-Proskauer reactions. The small existence of these types was not regarded as indicating that they complicated the use of these tests under routine conditions. Bardsley stated that organisms should be regarded as significant which have typical morphology and staining reaction, produce acid and gas in lactose, fail to liquefy gelatin, clot milk, and give a positive methyl-red reaction and a negative Voges-Proskauer reaction.

Peragallo,[171] after examination of many samples of soil from various Alpine mountain tops, found the predominating fermenter to be *Aerobacter aerogenes*. Examination of excreta from man, animals, and birds revealed *Escherichia coli*. Peragallo, therefore, placed great weight on presence of *Escherichia coli* in water as indicating pollution. Ferramola and Monteverde [172] found birds to be the source of *Escherichia coli* in reservoirs. Sea gulls have also been found to pollute reservoirs.

There is, however, no question of the wide difference in frequency of these types in the different habitats examined. *Escherichia coli* is certainly the predominant coliform inhabitant of the intestine, *Aerobacter aerogenes* the predominant coliform inhabitant of the soil, and the intermediate type far more frequent in the soil than in the intestine. Bardsley [173] believed that, inasmuch as coliform bacteria were not widely distributed in nature except where fecal contamination had occurred, the differential tests might be discarded.

Irregular correlation of Voges-Proskauer reaction with the methyl-red test was also observed by Stovall and Nichols,[174] Berry,[175] Koser,[176] and Hicks.[177] These results soon led to the opinions that differentiation was necessary.

Stokes,[178] in studying this question, stated that a water could not be considered to be safe if but two or three colonies were studied from each specimen. He suggested that perhaps 20 or 25 colonies be examined from a water which has no evidences of pollution as determined by either laboratory examination or by sanitary inspection. Winslow and Cohen [179] reported results of a study of 255 strains of coliform organisms, 202 of which were methyl-red positive and 53 methyl-red negative. They could detect no marked differences between the organisms from different sources and stated that no necessity existed for differentiating between coliform organisms for determining sanitary quality of water. Many *Aerobacter aerogenes* organisms in water might indicate remote pollution.

Various investigators have at times desired to distinguish between coliform bacteria found in the feces of different animals and, in that way, to

171. Peragallo. 1938. Ann. Ig. 48, 49.
172. Ferramola and Monteverde. 1940. Rev. in Pub. Health Engin. Absts. 20, 7.
173. Bardsley. 1934. J. Hyg. 34. 38-68; 38 (1938), 309-334.
174. Stovall and Nichols. 1918. J. Infect. Dis. 23, 229.
175. Berry. 1926. Amer. J. Pub. Health 16, 590-594.
176. Koser. 1926. J. Amer. Water Wks. Assoc. 15, 641-646.
177. Hicks. 1927. J. Hyg. 26, 357-361.
178. Stokes. 1919. Amer. J. Pub. Health 9, 571-574.
179. Winslow and Cohen. 1918. J. Infect. Dis. 23, 90-101.

find out what type of pollution was present in water or foods. Darling [180] isolated 113 strains of colon bacilli from feces, including 20 from man, 23 from horses, 23 from sheep, 26 from rabbits, and 21 from chicks, and found that none of them were of the *Aerobacter aerogenes* type, as determined by the methyl-red and Voges-Proskauer tests; this author stated that water may contain *Escherichia coli* from other sources than man, but that there was no means of differentiating them.

Levine's [181] Method for Rapid Determination of the Colon Group. Levine suggested the following method for obtaining the standard presumptive and confirmed test simultaneously in 24 hours.

"From a consideration of the rates of growth of the coli-aerogenes group in broth it is contended that, if one organism capable of growing in the medium is introduced with 10 ml. of water into 30 ml. of broth, after an incubation period of 10 hours at 37°C. there should generally be over 2,000 bacteria in the tube, or 50 per milliliter. The number of these organisms is too small to show any visible evidence of growth, such as gas formation. If, however, .1 ml. were smeared over the surface of an eosin-methylene-blue agar plate, the organisms introduced onto the plate (theoretically at least 5) would grow very rapidly as they are in their logarithmic growth phase (i.e., the stage of most vigorous growth) so that colonies would develop very quickly, generally in 12 to 16 hours, on this solid medium. If these plates and the preliminary enrichment medium are both kept at 37°C. then those plates made from tubes which show gas the next morning (24 hours presumptive test) should have colonies of the coli-aerogenes group (partially confirmed test).

"A number of samples of the Missouri and Iowa river waters were tested in this way and it was found that in over 90 per cent of the trials, E. M. B. plates made after 10 hours' incubation from tubes which proved to be positive 24 hour presumptive tests were positive for the partially confirmed test."

The methyl-red test and Voges-Proskauer reaction are usually carried out at 37°C.(98.6°F.). Vaughn and Levine [182] recommended 30°C.(86°F.) because at the higher temperature cultures of the aerogenes-cloacae group may fail to revert to alkaline reaction or to produce acetyl methyl carbinol. Strains of the coli type were unaffected. In practice it was recommended that in classifying coliform strains, cultures for the methyl-red test should be incubated for five days at 30°C.(86°F.) as originally prescribed by Clark and Lubs. The Voges-Proskauer test should be carried out on cultures incubated for one to two days at 30°C.(86°F.), and the Barritt method should be used for bringing out the color (.6 ml. of five per cent alpha-naphthol in absolute ethyl alcohol and .2 ml. of 40 per cent KOH added to one ml. of culture). The results of the O'Meara and the Barritt methods are, however, almost identical.

Werkman's [183] Improved Technic for the Voges-Proskauer Test. This method involves the use of ferric chloride as a catalyst to avoid some of the disadvantages of the original Voges-Proskauer reaction. The eosin-like color secured by the older technic is quite transitory. That secured by the suggested new technic gives a copper color which appears at the surface of the tube and extends to the bottom of the tube in a few minutes. This color was said to remain for several days and to be clearly visible for a week or longer. The test may be positive for organisms of the Aerogenes group after three days incubation at 30°C.(86°F.), but four-day cultures were recommended. Two drops

180. Darling. 1919. Amer. J. Pub. Health 9, 844-848.
181. Levine. 1930. J. Amer. Water Wks. Assoc. 22, 234.
182. Vaughn and Levine. 1939. Idem 31, 993-1001.
183. Werkman. 1930. J. Bact. 20, 121-126.

of a two-per cent solution of ferric chloride are added to five ml. of the culture. Five ml. of a 10-per cent solution of sodium hydroxide are then added and the tube shaken. The ferric chloride solution should be added before the addition of the sodium hydroxide, since a flocculation results if this is not done. The reaction may be accelerated by heating in boiling water for one minute.

Lindsey and Meckler [184] were able to confirm Werkman's conclusions. They found that identical results could be obtained with Werkman's technic when it was applied to 24-hour cultures. They said that ordinary glucose broth could be used in place of special media and results were more easily read than in the older test. They also attempted to distinguish between *Escherichia coli* and *Aerobacter aerogenes* by dye reduction. They observed that *Aerobacter aerogenes* reduced methylene blue in a lactose broth fermentation tube in a few minutes while *Escherichia coli* gave no visible reduction in several hours. This agreed with results of the Voges-Proskauer test in 44 out of 45 cases. The advantage of their technic is that much time is saved in running the Voges-Proskauer reaction.

Barritt's [159] Method for Voges-Proskauer Reaction. According to Barritt, addition of alpha-naphthol to the Voges-Proskauer reaction intensifies the reaction. The test is applied by adding one ml. of a culture, .6 ml. five-per cent alcoholic solution of alpha-naphthol, and .2 ml. 40-per cent potassium hydroxide. Color appears in two to three minutes and lasts four to 24 hours. The reaction, which is very delicate and specific shows that many species of bacteria which are usually considered unable to do so, produce acetyl-methyl carbinol.

According to Vaughn, Mitchell, and Levine [185] the technics recommended in *Standard Methods of Water Analysis* for the Voges-Proskauer reaction [24 to 48 hours at 37°C. (98.6°F.) with 10 per cent KOH as the test reagent], and for the methyl red test [three to four days at 37°C. (98.6°F.)] are not suitable for detection of the maximal number of positive strains in either case. The Barritt alpha-naphthol reagent and a temperature of 30°C. (86°F.) should be used. Iyer and Raghavachari [186] also advised Barritt's modification.

As previous workers have done, Tittsler [187] showed that the Voges-Proskauer reaction should be carried out on cultures not more than two days old; otherwise positive cultures become negative on further incubation. Whether this is due to fermentation of the acetyl-methyl-carbinol by the *Aerobacter aerogenes* group or to its reducton to 2:3-butylene glycol has not so far been clear. Tittsler, however, brought evidence to show that true fermentation does occur. Out of 90 strains of the aerogenes type, i.e., M.R. —, V.P. +, citrate +, 37 gave a positive V.P. reaction during the first three days and a negative one after five days. All of these 37 strains were found capable of growing and producing acid in a synthetic medium containing acetyl-methyl-carbinol as the sole source of carbon. The remaining strains were unable to ferment this substance, and gave a

184. Lindsey and Meckler. 1932. J. Bact. 23, 115-121.
185. Vaughn, Mitchell, and Levine. 1938. J. Bact. 36, 313-314.
186. Iyer and Raghavachari. 1939. Indian J. Med. Res. 26, 885-888.
187. Tittsler. 1938. J. Bact. 35, 157.

persistently positive V.P. reaction in the ordinary glucose broth medium. The 37 strains that fermented acetyl-methyl-carbinol comprised about half of the strains labelled *Aerobacter aerogenes* and *Aerobacter oxytocum*, but none of the strains labelled *Aerobacter cloacae*.

Bacteriologists in the laboratory of the Metropolitan Water Board of London,[188] found some of the technics recommended for the Voges-Proskaur reaction to yield faint and inconclusive reactions. This is the reason why so many modifications have been proposed. They compared O'Meara's [189] and Barritt's [159] technics and found both to agree on *Escherichia coli* and *Aerobacter aerogenes*; marked discrepancies were observed, however, with the "intermediate" group of coliform organisms. Their work was discussed as follows:

Four-day cultures grown at 37°C. in buffered glucose phosphate peptone water were tested for the Voges-Proskauer reaction in three ways:

1. *Old method:* Five ml. of 10 per cent caustic soda solution were added to five ml. of the culture, thoroughly shaken, and allowed to stand in the dark overnight at room temperature. Many of the reactions were faint and difficult to read, but the slightest trace of pink coloration was considered a positive.

2. *O'Meara's modification:* A knife-point of creatine and five ml. of 40-per cent caustic potash solution were added to five ml. of the culture and thoroughly shaken. Vigorous shaking was required to produce a coloration within 10 minutes with positive strains, but when left overnight deeper tints were obtained than with the old test, and no fading occurred. Ten-per cent caustic soda solution was found to act as well as the caustic potash solution.

3. *Barritt's modification:* One ml. of the culture was transferred to a clean, dry test tube, six inches by three-fourths inch in size, and .5 ml. of a six-per cent alcoholic solution of alpha-naphthol and .5 ml. of a 16-per cent solution of caustic potash added. A bright cherry-red coloration appeared within five to 15 minutes after shaking, but faded after a few hours.

Both the creatine and alpha-naphthol tests revealed more positives than the old method. Of the two modifications, alpha-naphthol produced 62 positives and creatine 57; also the color obtained with the former test was very distinct and few faint reactions were obtained compared with the other two tests. Twenty-five strains that were negative with the old method yielded positive results with alpha-naphthol, 16 of these were indole positive and nine were indole negative.

Tests with typical *Escherichia coli* and *Aerobacter aerogenes* showed the three methods to be in complete agreement, all coli strains were Voges-Proskauer negative and all aerogenes strains Voges-Proskauer positive.

Cultures giving the reaction "methyl red +, citrate +, Voges-Proskauer +, indole + or —," have been previously classed as irregular coliform types and probably mixtures of two or more known types. A number of "Methyl Red +, citrate +," cultures showing this irregular reaction with the old method of testing for acetyl methyl carbinol were carefully re-tested by repeated platings on the lines advocated by Ruchhoft (1932), and, although some were converted into pure types, no mixtures were encountered, and the majority continued to give anomalous results. With the alpha naphthol test more of these Voges-Proskauer positive organisms would be detected owing to the sensitiveness of the modification. In the future, such strains may be considered as a pure coliform type.

The alpha naphthol modification of the Voges-Proskauer test is welcome for its sharply defined coloration, obtainable within a few minutes. The modification shortens the time required to type a coliform organism by at least 18 hours. A comparative in-

188. Thirty-first Ann. Rept., Metropolitan Water Bd., London, for 1936, p. 21.

189. O'Meara 1931. J. Path. and Bact. 34, 401-406.

vestigation of the Barritt and O'Meara methods by Batty-Smith[190] revealed the former to give the most positive results. There was four per cent difference between the two methods. This difference was said to represent non-coliform bacteria.

Methylene-Blue Reduction Test for Distinguishing Escherichia coli from Aerobacter aerogenes. Lindsey and Meckler[1,4] suggested a methylene-blue reduction test for distinguishing *Escherichia coli* from *Aerobacter aerogenes*. They reported that when one drop of saturated aqueous solution of methylene blue was added to a 24-hour culture of *Aerobacter aerogenes* in a lactose broth fermentation tube, the dye was reduced within a few minutes. With *Escherichia coli* no visible reduction took place within several hours. Lindsey and Meckler stated that the lactose broth fermentation tube used in the "complete test" could be used for the methylene-blue reduction test.

Tests on 359 strains show that methylene blue will not distinguish between the genera, that oxidation-reduction potentials do not always parallel reduction of the dye, and that eosin-methylene-blue agar is a good index for behavior of these strains in lactose with respect to oxidation-reduction potentials (Epstein[191]).

Many modifications of the presumptive test medium have been proposed. Most of them involve addition of some substance which is supposed to inhibit other bacteria and either favor development of *Escherichia coli* or leave the field less encumbered for its development. These modifications have made it necessary to carry out many comparative studies with older media to determine whether the new proposal had merits. In some cases it was shown that newly proposed ingredients were inhibitory to *Escherichia coli* as well as to the other forms.

Lactose Peptone Bile. MacConkey in 1900, as discussed below, suggested a medium containing bile salts (sodium taurocholate) for differentiating *Escherichia coli* from *Eberthella typhosa*. Jackson[192] probably was the first to use bile media in the United States. He departed, however, from MacConkey's medium by using ox-gall itself instead of bile salts. He proposed lactose broth with one per cent of bile as the standard medium. This medium was recognized in the second edition of *Standard Methods for the Examination of Water and Sewage* (1912) but not in the third edition published in 1917. It has never been an official medium in the United States. One reason for this may be that several investigators, Jordan[193] and Obst,[194] found that the bile inhibited *Escherichia coli* as well as other bacteria.

Much of the earlier work is contradictory. Cumming[195] in stream-pollution studies on the Potomac River, found lactose broth to be superior to lactose bile. On the other hand, Ritter[196] found lactose bile to be as satisfactory as lactose broth when comparisons were made on 1,899 sam-

190. Batty-Smith. 1941. J. Hyg. 41, 521-529.
191. Epstein. 1936. Iowa State Col. J. Sci. 10, 303.
192. Jackson. 1906. J. Infect. Dis., Supplement No. 3, 30.
193. Jordan. 1915. Trans. XV. Internatl. Cong. Hyg. & Demog. 2, 47-50.
194. Obst. 1916. U. S. Dept. Agr. Bull. 396.
195. Cumming. 1916. U. S. Pub. Health Serv. Hyg. Lab. Bull. 104.
196. Ritter. 1919. J. Bact. 3, 609-613.

ples of water. In an examination of 482 samples of water from farm wells, Lochhead and Hewer [197] found no advantage in lactose bile if the presence of coliform bacteria is regarded as the criterion of pollution; if, however, the fecal type of *Escherichia coli* is to be the criterion of pollution, lactose bile was better.

Seeking to determine the effect of bile on growth of *Aerobacter aerogenes* Levine [198] added varying amounts of sodium taurocholate and found that up to 1.5 per cent caused an acceleration of growth. Concentrations of about two per cent of evaporated bile stimulated the growth of *Escherichia coli*, but slightly inhibited *Aerobacter aerogenes*. Higher concentrations were inhibitory. According to Coles and Levine [199] evaporated bile may inhibit or stimulate the growth of *Escherichia coli* depending on the concentration of bile, reaction of the medium, and the strain of the organism used. With all samples of bile used, a concentration of two per cent accelerated growth, whereas five per cent inhibited in media having a pH of 6.0; in alkaline media (pH 7.3-7.8) the organism was stimulated.

According to Poe [200] a bile content of five to seven per cent gives best results. Aerobic sporeforming, lactose-fermenting organisms were said to be inhibited by more than five per cent bile. Poe reported that boric acid in amounts of .1 per cent and above in bile-lactose media distinctly inhibited growth of both Escherichia and Aerobacter groups. Values of pH between 6.75 and 7.25 made little difference in growth of strains used. Aerobic sporeformers grew well in media containing boric acid up to .3 per cent. Anaerobes grew well in the boric acid-bile media. Boric acid-bile agar offered no advantages as a differential medium. Fuller [201] grew thirty carefully purified strains in a suitable medium to which one per cent or five per cent of bile or bile salts was added; cultures were transferred each week for five months. The results argue in favor of the stability of the cultural reactions of pure established cultures in so far as the influence of bile or bile salts alone is concerned.

MacConkey's Bile Salt Broth. This is an ancient and honorable medium in sanitary work, much better known to English bacteriologists than American. It was introduced by MacConkey [202] for differentiating intestinal bacteria. The coliform-inhibitor is sodium taurocholate to the amount of five grams per liter. *Escherichia coli* and *Aerobacter aerogenes* produce both acid and gas. Since 1901 MacConkey's broth has undergone modification. Dessicated bile has been largely substituted for sodium taurocholate and seems to give as satisfactory, if not better, results. It is probably the precursor of the various bile media which came after it and has been compared with the many other media proposed for the same purpose. MacConkey's broth is the standard medium in procedures of water analysis of the Ministry of Health of Great Britain.

197. Lochhead and Hewer. 1931. Canad. Pub. Health J. 22, 10-15.
198. Levine. 1922. Absts. Bact. 6, 7.
199. Coles and Levine. 1927. Iowa Acad. Sci. Proc. 34, 92.
200. Poe. 1938. Univ. of Colorado Studies 25, 209-224; Poe, Edson, and Witt 23 (1936), 281.
201. Fuller. 1938. Soc. Expt. Biol. and Med. Proc. 38, 507-510.
202. MacConkey. 1901. Centbl. Bakt. 29, 740; J. Hyg. 5 (1905), 333; 8 (1908), 322.

Raghavachari and Iyer [203] found MacConkey's medium to be superior to Dominick-Lauter's medium when applied to water collected in India. In fact they believed the MacConkey medium to be the most satisfactory one available for *Escherichia coli* tests. They compared a number of media, including lactose broth containing one per cent Andrade's indicator, Mac-Conkey broth, crystal violet broth, the Dominick-Lauter medium, and a synthetic medium containing lactose, asparagin, and brom-cresol-purple, for use in the presumptive coliform test. The most sensitive medium was found to be lactose broth, and with this medium plating revealed coliform organisms in greater numbers than with any other medium. As has been found in Great Britain and Australia,[204] MacConkey's broth yielded fewer presumptive positives than lactose broth, but in contradiction to experience in these countries attempts to confirm the presence of coliform organisms in presumptive positive MacConkey tubes frequently failed. In other words, MacConkey broth, like lactose broth, was often subject to false positive reactions. MacConkey's medium was found to be inferior to eosin methylene blue agar. Eosin methylene blue agar had the advantage of inhibiting the growth of non-lactose-fermenters to a greater extent than MacConkey agar. In practice they recommended the use of lactose broth for primary inoculation of water. Confirmation of tubes giving acid and gas within 24 hours is regarded as unnecessary. Tubes in which acid and gas formation is delayed for 48 hours should be plated on eosin methylene blue agar. The experience with MacConkey's broth in India does not parallel that in England. The reasons are not apparent. McCrady [205] found that MacConkey's broth gave too many false positive tests which did not confirm. He preferred lactose broth with confirmation (gas only) in secondary brilliant green bile, two per cent.

The Metropolitan Water Board of London annual report for the year 1937 stated that MacConkey broth compared favorably in selective ability with brilliant green broth and Dominick-Lauter medium with various types of water which were analyzed. In fact, the results with these three media agreed so closely that each was considered about equally sensitive in demonstrating coliform bacteria. MacConkey broth proved superior in the case of stored water, which is an essential part of protective measures. With filtered waters there was a slight advantage in favor of brilliant green. On the other hand, Dominick-Lauter medium appeared to inhibit *Escherichia coli* slightly with consequent increase in frequency of atypical forms. The percentage of false presumptive tests was low in all media being less than eight per cent with the highest numbers in chloraminated river water undergoing storage and especially indicated that sporeforming, lactose-fermenting bacteria were almost completely suppressed by brilliant green bile and Dominick-Lauter media. MacConkey broth also exerted strong inhibitory powers which were attributed to its bile salt content. It was believed, therefore, that by using McConkey primary enrichment medium water bacteriologists in England were not encountering the same diffi-

203. Raghavachari and Iyer. 1934. Indian J. Med. Res., April, 1934.
204. Atkinson and Wood. 1938. Aust. J. Expt. Biol. and Med. Sci. 16, 103-109.
205. McCrady. 1939. Amer. J. Pub. Health 29, 1250-1257.

culties with respect to false presumptive tests that are encountered in America with plain lactose broth. Brilliant green was considered to be the best supporting medium for MacConkey. In March, 1938, the Metropolitan Water Board of London substituted brilliant green bile broth incubated at 37°C.(98.6°F.) for the indol test as confirmation of the 10-ml. MacConkey broth tube in the presumptive test. Results which were secured with this new combination of media suggest that the change was a fine one.

Formate-Ricinoleate Broth. This medium, devised by Stark and England,[206] was found to inhibit organisms which give false-positive tests in the presumptive test in water analysis. This was attributed to the sodium ricinoleate. The sodium formate stimulated both growth and amount of gas formed by bacteria of the Escherichia-Aerobacter growth because they are able to produce gas from formic acid. Noble and White [207] observed that formate ricinoleate broth, among many which were tested, was the only one which met requirements when compared with the standard medium.

Boric Acid Lactose Broth. Boric acid was added to lactose broth in the presumptive test by Vaughn and Levine [208] to inhibit *Aerobacter aerogenes* and allow *Escherichia coli* to develop. They did observe a little evidence of inhibition of gas formation with some strains which grew. Poe and his colleagues [200] observed inhibition of both Aerobacter and Escherichia species. Both aerobic and anaerobic sporeformers grew well in boric acid media containing .1 per cent of boric acid.

Dominick-Lauter Selective Medium. This medium was devised to shorten the time required for the presumptive test in water analysis. Dominick and Lauter [209] claimed for it a saving of many hours. The medium is a lactose broth base to which a dye mixture made of erythrosin, methyleneblue and brom-cresol-purple is added. It was believed that lactose fermenters other than coliform bacteria, are inhibited leaving the field for the latter. Results of several comparative studies of various presumptive test media, including the Dominick-Lauter medium, have not always agreed. Leahy, Freeman, and Katsampes [210] found it superior to lactose broth, while Howard [211] preferred brilliant green bile medium. Nolte and Kramer [212] found it superior to other media as did Stewart.[213] The last mentioned, however, desired more information before giving up the regular medium. MacConkey's medium was superior to this one in the hands of Raghavachari and Iyer [203]

Inhibition of coliform bacteria must always be considered when other agents are added to the presumptive test medium. Dominick-Lauter's medium was reported by Evans and Bahlman [214] and Butterfield [215] to inhibit

206. Stark and England. 1935. J. Bact. 29, 26.
207. Noble and White. 1935. J. Bact. 29, 23-24.
208. Vaughn and Levine. 1935. J. Bact. 29, 24-25.
209. Dominick and Lauter. 1929. J. Amer. Water Wks. Assoc. 21, 1067-1075.
210. Leahy, Freeman, and Katsampes. 1931. Amer. J. Pub. Health 21, 11.
211. Howard. 1932. J. Amer. Water Wks. Assoc. 24, 1305-1310.
212. Nolte and Kramer. 1933. J. Amer. Water Wks Assoc. 25, 383-389.
213. Stewart. 1933. Idem. 25, 855-858.
214. Evans and Bahlman. 1931. Eleventh Ann. Rept., Ohio Conf. on Water Purification, 15-16.
215. Butterfield. 1933. Amer. J. Pub. Health 23, 343-349.

coliform bacteria as well as the other water bacteria. In the hands of Butterfield it was more inhibitive than brilliant green bile.

DIRECT ENUMERATION OF COLIFORM BACTERIA IN WATER

Much time could be saved in sanitary work and more accurate results secured if coliform bacteria could be counted directly instead of using some of the indirect methods. It would obviate the necessity of using *Escherichia coli* index or "most probable numbers." Possibility of such procedure needs more study than has been given to it. Among others, the following have been used or proposed.

Eosin Methylene Blue Agar Medium. This plating medium was developed by Levine[216] for differentiating *Escherichia coli* from *Aerobacter aerogenes*. The differential characteristics are given in the chapter on "Media." This medium is accepted as a satisfactory medium in the "completed test" in water analysis where it is streaked with material from a lactose broth fermentation tube in which gas has been formed. The medium is best known for this use. Gehm and Heukelekian[217] reported much success when it was used in this manner. They ran one ml. of inoculum on the surface and spread it over the entire surface of the plate.

Poe[218] also found considerable merit in eosin-methylene blue agar medium for differentiating *Escherichia coli* from *Aerobacter aerogenes*.

Violet Red Bile Agar. This medium is the result of an attempt to find a solid selective medium for counting coliform bacteria in foods and beverages. Hostettler[219] found it satisfactory in water analysis. In addition to being more efficient, it gave the coliform bacteria density in actual counts instead of a number based on the theory of probability. The results, obtained in 24 hours, strongly suggest the possibility of using such a direct method. This medium, used by Bartram and Black[220] for isolation of coliform bacteria from milk, was found more satisfactory than several others. Miller and Prickett[221] also found it satisfactory as a plating medium. Other investigators have made the same observations on milk and its products. The medium ought to have possibilities with other foods and with water.

Brilliant Green Lactose Bile Agar. This is another medium proposed for estimation of coliform bacteria by direct plating. Noble and Tonney[223] stressed its advantages and believed that it could replace the liquid brilliant green broth. The results with it were said to be slightly superior to those secured with the liquid medium.

Sodium Citrate-Sodium Ricinoleate Agar. Following development of formate-ricinoleate broth by Stark and England,[224] Littman and Stark[225] attempted to prepare a new plating medium incorporating sodium ricino-

216. Levine. 1921. Iowa Engin. Expt. Sta. Bull. 62.
217. Gehm and Heukelekian. 1935. Amer. J. Pub. Health 25, 920-923.
218. Poe. 1931. J. Amer. Water Wks. Assoc. 23, 1218-1226.
219. Hostettler. 1940. Ohio Conf. Water Purification, 20th Ann. Rept., 56-58.
220. Bartram and Black. 1936. Food Research 1, 551-563.
221. Miller and Prickett. 1936. J. Dairy Sci. 21, 559.
223. Noble and Tonney. 1935. J. Amer. Water Wks. Assoc. 27, 108-119.
224. Stark and England. 1935. J. Bact. 29, 26-27.
225. Littman and Stark. 1938. J. Amer. Water Wks. Assoc. 30, 1808-1827.

leate. This compound lowers surface tension. Earlier investigators had observed that intestinal bacteria grew well in a medium having a low surface tension, while other bacteria were inhibited. Sodium ricinoleate was used to inhibit gas production of organisms which gave false positive tests. Citrate-ricinoleate agar was said to be a rapid routine test medium for coliform analysis of potable water. Furthermore the much-needed separation of Escherichia count from the Aerobacter count is now possible with this new agar medium and is available for such examinations as those of shellfish in which major importance is attached to the Escherichia count. The authors listed the following advantages of this medium over standard lactose broth: 1. An equal or slightly higher productivity of citrate ricinoleate agar over the standard lactose test. 2. Rapid observation and counting of coliforms possible with citrate ricinoleate agar with a completed count in 24 hours. The time required for the standard lactose test may vary from two to four days. 3. Elimination of false test and synergistic organisms by citrate ricinoleate agar and the elimination of the confirmation of false positive presumptive tests which characterize the standard lactose test. 4. Ability to make differential count between Escherichia and Aerobacter organisms. 5. Ability of Eberthella, Salmonella, and Shigella to grow on citrate ricinoleate agar with the inclusion of these pathogens among the coliforms in the classification. The standard lactose test fails to detect these organisms. 6. Higher counting accuracy is obtainable by a plating method against a dilution method per tube and plate of media. 7. Use of citrate ricinoleate agar enables a reduction in amount of media, time, and space necessary for routine analysis of water.

Ferrocyanide Citrate Agar Medium of Noble and Tonney. This medium was developed by Noble [226] and Tonney and Noble [227] for direct enumeration by plating of coliform bacteria in water. The advantages of this procedure are obvious. Noble stated that the coliform index of water could be determined in 42 to 48 hours, whereas from three to four days are required by the regular standard methods' technic. Coliform bacteria appear as small pink or brick-red colonies which are distinguishable with ease from other forms. When the medium was used on a large number of samples nearly 77 per cent gave coliform indices which equaled or exceeded those obtained by the standard fermentation method. Noble showed that the productivity or relative efficiency of this medium was superior to those of brilliant green lactose bile broth, and brilliant green lactose bile agar when raw lake water was examined. The various advantages of this medium were reviewed by Tonney and Noble. In addition to those mentioned above, they mentioned the greater accuracy of plating methods over liquid media and the ability to isolate pure cultures. Next Tonney and Noble [227] reported close correlation between the separate count of *Escherichia coli* and probable presence of fecal pollution as indicated by a sanitary survey. The separate *Aerobacter aerogenes* count was

226. Noble. 1928. J. Amer. Water Wks. Assoc. 19, 182-192; 733-746; 23 (1931), 1202-1208; 27 (1935), 1143-1160.

227. Tonney and Noble. 1931. J. Infect. Dis. 48, 413-417; J. Bact. 23 (1932), 473-477.

also uniformly positive in this class of surveys. Nolte and Kramer [212] found this medium to be unreliable for relatively pure waters. Hoak [228] recommended it although he recognized that it was a little complicated for routine work.

Other media could be used but these just mentioned have received attention from water bacteriologists.

Desoxycholate Agar. This agar-plating medium was devised by Leifson [229] and recommended for direct enumeration of lactose-fermenting bacteria in malk and water. Colonies of these bacteria appear very large and dark red. Colonies of other Gram-negative, non-lactose-fermenting bacteria are either colorless or slightly pink. Colonies of other bacteria are described in the chapter on "Media." Desoxycholate- citrate agar medium considerably inhibits development of *Escherichia coli*.

Brilliant Green in the Presumptive Test. Addition of this dye to the presumptive test medium has been done with the belief that it represses nonconfirming, lactose-fermenting bacteria but allows coliform bacteria to develop and that it, itself, does not inhibit the latter. Many investigations were carried out with it. Muer and Harris,[230] who used a brilliant green broth as a presumptive test medium for *Escherichia coli*, stated that 10 per cent of gas need no longer be regarded as a presumptive test for *Escherichia coli* but a positive test. A dilution of one to 10,000 prevented the development of *Clostridium welchii* and *Clostridium sporogenes*. *Clostridium welchii* was eliminated by a dilution of one to 30,000 while *Escherichia coli required* one to 100. In dilutions of one to 100,000 and one to 1,000,000 in broth, brilliant green in Winslow and Doloffs' [231] experiments, inhibited *Escherichia coli*, *Aerobacter aerogenes*, and *Bacterium pneumoniae*. Muer and Harris used brilliant green to accomplish the same results for which Hall used gentian violet. They added ox-gall to the medium and secured a medium which has been studied much since.

This lactose bile-brilliant green medium was found to prevent the development of the anaerobes which cause so much trouble in the presumptive test for *Escherichia coli*. Composition of this medium was studied by Dunham and Schoenlein,[232] who found that it did not show appreciable inhibition of *Escherichia coli*. They, accordingly, studied the concentration of the bile and brilliant green and the optimum hydrogen-ion concentration. A medium containing two per cent of bile, one per cent of peptone, one per cent of lactose, and one to 75,000 brilliant green permitted more rapid development of *Escherichia coli* at pH 6.9 than did the original brilliant green. It was also suggested that the medium should be so prepared that the concentration of ingredients would not be altered when the water sample was added. With large samples of water (10 ml.) double strength medium should be used. McCrady [233] reported that bile medium almost eliminated all sporeforming, lactose-fermenters. Lauter.[219] found

228. Hoak. 1935. J. Penn. Water Wks. Operators Assoc. 7, 75-93.
229. Leifson. 1935. J. Path. and Bact. 42, 345.
230. Muer and Harris. 1920. Amer. J. Pub. Health 10, 874-875.
231. Winslow and Doloffs. 1922. J. Infect. Dis. 31, 302-304.
232. Dunham and Schoenlein. 1926. Stain Technology 1, 129-134.
233. MacCrady. 1925. J. Amer. Water Wks. Assoc. 14, 538-542.

that brilliant green bile permitted results several days sooner than the present standard methods. It was also suggested (Dominick and Lauter[209]) that methylene blue and brom-cresol-purple could be used to advantage in the lactose broth medium for the presumptive test. Ginter,[220] as did Lauter, emphasized the saving of time which the addition of a low per cent of bile to the presumptive test medium permitted. He could find no evidence that as much bile as five per cent inhibited *Escherichia coli.* Jordan,[236] Ruchhoft,[237] Hale,[238] and Rakieten and Rettger [239] found the medium valuable.

One of the advantages of this medium was said to be elimination of anaerobic, sporeforming bacteria as causes of spurious presumptive tests. This was claimed by Muer and Harris [230] and McCrady.[233] This was also confirmed by Poe and Witt,[240] who reported anaerobes to be inhibited in lactose broth by a content of brilliant green and malachite green greater than one to 10,000; *Clostridium welchii* Type II, however, required a concentration of one to 20,000 before gas formation was prevented. Increasing amounts of bile interfered with the action of the dyes. This inhibition of anaerobes by brilliant green has not been confirmed by Parr and Caldwell.[241] In their hands, brilliant green bile was not entirely successful with all waters. Butterfield's [242] experience was quite similar. Other investigators have found brilliant green bile a good medium; such are Mallmann and Helper,[243] McCrady,[244] and Horwood and Heifetz.[139]

Several investigators have stated that brilliant green bile was a more reliable criterion of the presence of coliform bacteria than Standard Methods completed test. Kelly [245] made this observation with both water specimens and shellfish samples. If presence of gas in brilliant green bile medium were accepted as sufficient evidence of presence of coliform bacteria, much time would be saved. Taylor [246] was of the same opinion as were also Howard, Lochhead, and McCrady.[247] Development of Escherichia-Aerobacter species was greatly accelerated by addition of .5 per cent of sodium formate to brilliant green lactose bile in experiments by Stark and Curtis.[248] This was due to the fact that these organisms can form gas from formic acid. Thus, in this medium the brilliant green acts bacteriostatically against the general flora while sodium formate enhances development of the coliform bacteria.

Some attention must be given to the brand of dye and the amount used. That the brand of dye used may influence the results obtained with bril-

234. Lauter. 1926. Water Wks. 65, 451-453.
235. Ginter. 1927. J. Amer. Water Wks. Assoc. 17, 591-594.
236. Jordan. 1927. J. Amer. Water Wks. Assoc. 18, 337-346; 24 (1932), 1927.
237. Ruchhoft. 1926. J. Amer. Med. Assoc. 16, 778-785.
238. Hale. 1926. Amer. J. Pub. Health, 16, 428-431.
239. Rakieten and Rettger. 1927. J. Infect. Dis. 41, 93-110.
240. Poe and Witte. 1930. J. Amer. Water Wks. Assoc. 22, 1365-1373.
241. Parr and Caldwell. 1933. J. Infect. Dis. 53, 12-23.
242. Butterfield. 1933. Amer. J. Pub. Health 23, 343-349.
243. Mallmann and Helper. 1936. J. Amer. Water Wks. Assoc. 28, 411-420.
244. McCrady. 1937. Amer. J. Pub. Health 27, 1243-1258.
245. Kelly. 1940. Amer. J. Pub. Health 30, 1034-1039.
246. Taylor. 1940. J. Amer. Water Wks. Assoc. 32, 98-104.
247. Howard, Lochhead, and McCrady. 1940. Canad. Pub. Health J. 31, 16-17; 32 (1941), 29-36.
248. Stark and Curtis. 1936. J. Bact. 32, 385-391.

liant green-bile medium was reported by Rakieten and Rettger [239] and Berry and Daniels.[249] Different brands and lots of dye were found to vary greatly in efficiency. The amounts used must not be excessive because Coles and Levine [250] and Smith [251] found that growth of microorganisms might be retarded.

Alkyl Sulfates in Standard Lactose Broth. Cowles [252] suggested possible addition of alkyl sulfates, in the form of "Drene," to the standard lactose broth medium. Standard lactose broth was used for the basic medium, and to this was added a small amount of an alkyl sulfate. The alkyl sulfates seem to prevent, by and large, the growth of Gram-positive organisms, including the lactose-fermenting aerobes and anaerobes; while the Gram-negatives are, in general, able to develop in the presence of relatively high concentrations of these substances. Sodium lauryl sulfate is the most readily obtained pure compound. To each liter of standard lactose broth .2 gram of the sulfate is added and the pH adjusted to 7.2 before tubing and autoclaving. Ordinary "Drene" shampoo can be substituted in an amount of one ml. per liter, adjusted to pH 7.4. There is some evidence, in fact, that results with "Drene" are better. The finished medium looks like the standard broth, but can easily be distinguished from it by the fact that a lasting foam develops upon shaking, owing to the depressing action of the alkyl sulfate upon the surface tension. As yet insufficient data have been accumulated to permit a definite evaluation of the medium, but the available figures, for the most part, indicate that no inhibition takes place in the growth of the coliform bacteria and that the number of false positives, particularly in the case of finished waters, is decreased very materially. If these results are confirmed in other parts of the country the medium should find a useful place in water analysis. Results with media containing sodium lauryl sulfate were reported by Krasaukas.[253] When this substance was added to lactose broth to the amount of one ml. to the liter, fewer false positive results were secured. While somewhat satisfactory results were also reported by Mallmann and Darby,[254] they believed that further investigations were necessary. The selective action was not due alone to lowering of surface tension. Some toxicity to bacteria was shown with the one to 100 concentrations but none in higher dilutions. Hupp [255] used this substance to eliminate troublesome aerobic, sporeforming, lactose-fermenting bacteria by incorporating .01 per cent in the broth. Hajna and Perry [57a] also found lauryl sulfate tryptose broth to yield many more positives for coliform bacteria and to give comparatively few false presumptive reactions.

Gentian Violet Lactose Broth. After Churchman [256] had shown that gentian violet in low concentrations was toxic for Gram-positive bacteria,

249. Berry and Daniels. 1928. Amer. J. Pub. Health 18, 883-892.
250. Coles and Levine. 1927. Proc. Iowa Acad Sci. 34, 92.
251. Smith. 1940. J. New England Water Wks. Assoc. 54. 16.
252. Cowles. 1938. J. Amer. Water Wks. Assoc. 30, 979-980.
253. Krasaukas. 1939. Md.-Del. Water and Sewage Assoc. 13, 55.
254. Mallmann and Darby. 1941. Amer. J. Pub. Health 31, 127-134.
255. Hupp. 1940. J. Bact. 39, 631.
256. Churchman. 1912. J. Expt. Med. 16, 221.

it was suggested that it might be added to the presumptive test medium to inhibit development of these forms which cause trouble in this test. *Escherichia coli* is a Gram- negative bacterium and would, therefore, not be destroyed. Hall and Ellefson [257] found that both the coliform group and the anaerobic group were inhibited by gentian violet in proportion to the concentration and, whereas *Escherichia coli* is not inhibited by a much greater concentration of this dye, its use for the former organism was urged. Addition of one to 100,000 gentian violet to lactose broth inhibited 94.5 per cent of the spurious presumptives; one to 20,000 increased this inhibition to 95 per cent. This work was confirmed in the laboratories of the Illinois State Water Survey by Wagner.[164] She stated that a medium containing two per cent of peptone, .2 per cent of lactose, and .001 per cent of gentian violet, when used with an equal volume of water, gave superior results to those secured by using the standard .5 to .1 per cent carbohydrate broth. Wagner (Mrs. Stearn)[258] reported a later investigation to determine whether the modified lactose gentian violet broth showed any inhibitory action on *Escherichia coli* and other lactose-fermenting bacteria. She reported that culturing *Escherichia coli* in gentian violet broth, brought about an increase in fermentative activity, motility, and growth rather than a decrease. Winslow and Dolloffs [231] found an appreciable germicidal action of gentian violet in ordinary broth media. Its activity in this respect was greatly reduced in the presence of bile salts. Furthermore, they reported that the inhibitory properties of gentian violet depended on the medium in which it was placed. Salle [259] considered it unfortunate that gentian violet was ever used in bacteriological media to restrict the growth of certain organisms. Gentian violet is a term which does not refer to a definite chemical compound, but rather to a mixture of dyes of a certain group. Since crystal violet, one of the important constituents of gentian violet, has a definite chemical formula, he suggested that crystal violet be designated instead of gentian violet. Salle, therefore, proposed a crystal violet broth medium for the presumptive test in water analysis. Production of acid and gas in this medium in practically all of the samples examined was found to be due to members of the colonaerogenes group. An agar-dye differential medium was also reported with which *Escherichia coli* could be differentiated from *Aerobacter aerogenes* because of distinct differences in metabolism of carbohydrates. The amount of lactose used in this medium was so gauged that *Escherichia coli* produced its maximum acidity; this amount was inadequate for *Aerobacter aerogenes* to produce its limiting hydrogen-ion concentration. *Escherichia coli* produced brilliant metallic colonies, slightly raised, with the color of the surrounding medium changed from purple to an orange tinge. *Aerobacter aerogenes* forms colonies which tend to flow together; there is no change in the color of the surrounding medium. Stark and England [260] reported, however, that Salle's medium should not be used because it

257. Hall and Ellefson. 1918. J. Bact. 3, 329-360; J. Amer. Water Wks. Assoc. 6 (1919), 67.
258. Wagner (Mrs. Stearn). 1923. Amer. J. Pub. Health 13, 567-570.
259. Salle. 1930. J. Bact. 20, 380-406.
260. Stark and England. 1932. J. Bact. 23, 26.

inhibited fecal organisms. When it was inoculated with a pure culture of *Escherichia coli* from fresh feces and incubated at 37°(98.6°F.), 43 per cent of the tubes were negative after 48 hours' incubation while parallel inoculations in lactose broth gave positive results in all cases. If, however, the tubes were held for about five days, gas formation occurred. These results seem to indicate that *Escherichia coli* might be initially inhibited. Especially significant is the absence of gas formation in the first 48 hours. In a latter paper Stark and Curtis [248] confirmed these results. Salle's crystal violet broth, Dominick and Lauter's broth, gentian violet broth, and brilliant green bile (two per cent) broth were studied. Crystal violet, methylene blue, gentian violet, and brilliant green were found to be growth inhibiting. Shunk [261] also observed inhibition of small numbers of *Escherichia coli*.

Uric Acid Medium for the Presumptive Test. Among the many other media for use in the presumptive test for *Escherichia coli*, uric acid as the sole source of nitrogen in a medium was proposed by Koser.[262] Using 74 strains of *Escherichia coli* and 50 strains of *Aerobacter aerogenes*, he found a selective action since the *Aerobacter aerogenes* grew well. The uric acid medium, also used by Rettger and Chen [263] and Perry and Monfort [264] to make the same separation, produced the same results. Bardsley [265] reported that Koser's uric acid test gave imperfect correlations with other tests for *Escherichia coli*. Similar observations were reported by Lind [266] who tested 87 strains of *Escherichia coli* isolated from human feces. Satisfactory correlation was found between citrate, indol, methyl-red, and Voges-Proskauer tests, but none between these and the uric acid tests. Thus while most of the strains tested failed to grow upon citrate medium, 38 out of 88 grew well upon uric acid medium.

Cellobiose Fermentation as Presumptive Test. Jones and Wise [267] suggested use of cellobiose for sharply differentiating the genus Escherichia from Aerobacter. Cellobiose is a glucoside produced from cellobiose octaacetate, which is prepared from cotton cellulose or filter paper. The process of conversion must be carefully and accurately carried through to obtain a pure cellobiose. Cellobiose has not been used for practical bacteriological work; though it is rapidly utilized by *Aerobacter aerogenes* with gas and acid production, no changes are made by any strains of the *Escherichia coli* examined by the authors. A .5-per cent cellobiose was added to the nutrient broth, tubed, and sterilized by autoclaving 20 minutes at 120°C.(248°F.). Results were observed at 12, 24, and 120 hours, respectively. All known strains of *Aerobacter aerogenes* split cellobiose with gas and acid production, while *Escherichia coli* did not. These results are correlated with the Voges-Proskauer test. Koser [268] subjected

261. Shunk. 1935. J. Bact. 29, 163-172.
262. Koser. 1918. J. Infect. Dis. 23, 277-279.
263. Rettger and Chen. 1919. Absts. Bact. 3, 1.
264. Perry and Monfort. 1921. J. Bact. 6, 53-68.
265. Bardsley. 1926. J. Hyg. 25, 11-25.
266. Lind. 1932. Arch. Hyg. 107, 234-243.
267. Jones and Wise. 1926. J. Bact. 11, 359.
268. Koser. 1926. J. Amer. Water Wks. Assoc. 15, 641-646.

the cultures of his collection of coliform strains of bacteria to the cellobiose fermentation, and reported a striking correlation between the two well-defined sections of the group. However, the so-called intermediate strains did not exhibit this correlation.

According to Poe [269] and Poe and Klemme [269] the cellobiose test did not give a satisfactory correlation with the methyl-red and Voges-Proskauer reactions for coliform bacteria. The correlation for *Aerobacter aerogenes* was almost perfect.

Ratio of carbon dioxide to hydrogen was from .3 to .5 in gas produced from cellobiose by Escherichia strains. With Aerobacter and *Aerobacter cloacae*, ratio was close to .7. Cellobiose-negative strains of Escherichia which produced no gas did not ferment all cellobiose in .1 to one per cent solution in 72 hours at 37°C.(98.6°F.). Those which formed gas and the Aerobacter strains fermented it completely under the same conditions. With both groups of organisms in medium containing .1 per cent sugar, pH values reached minimum in about 12 hours and then increased to maximum of about 8.5. Minimum for cellobiose-negative organisms was not as low as for cellobiose-positive. Though difference in amounts of products formed by the two groups was slight, Aerobacter formed somewhat more succinic and lactic acids that did Escherichia.

After modification of the cellobiose broth of Jones and Wise, by reduction of the cellobiose to .25 per cent, Dowd [270] secured better results. Cost was reduced by tubing in small tubes requiring only one ml. of medium. Gas and acid formation were rapid and definite and sufficient study was made to indicate an excellent correlation with several other differentiating media in the two well-defined sections of the group. Correlation was especially good with known source of the culture and with results of Koser's citrate test. Tittsler [271] tested ability to ferment cellobiose of 755 cultures, representing approximately 50 species in various genera. Acid and gas were produced by Aerobacter cultures and most Escherichia-Aerobacter "intermediates" but not by typical Escherichia cultures. All strains of *Eberthella typhosa*, *Salmonella aertrycke*, and *Salmonella schottmülleri* and 17 of 19 strains of *Salmonella enteritidis* attacked cellobiose after four to 10 days, whereas all strains of *Salmonella suipestifer*, *Salmonella paratyphi*, *Salmonella gallinarum*, *Salmonella pullorum*, *Salmonella morgani*, and of dysentery bacilli failed to do so within 14 days. These results indicate that cellobiose fermentation might be of value in the Proteus and Salmonella group.

CITRATE (CITRIC ACID) FERMENTATION

This method has enjoyed the confidence of water bacteriologists. Koser [272] devised the test after observations made on utilization of the salts of organic acids by coliform bacteria. These organic acids were added to a synthetic medium in the form of their sodium salts. Striking

269. Poe. 1932. J. Amer Water Wks. Assoc. 24, 891-894; Poe and Klemme. 1935. J. Biol. Chem. 109, 43-46.
270. Dowd. 1932. Amer. J. Pub. Health 22, 537-539.
271. Tittsler. 1935. J. Bact. 29, 20-21; 31, 301-307.
272. Koser. 1924. J. Bact. 9, 59-77.

results were obtained with citric acid. Fecal *Escherichia coli* failed to develop while *Aerobacter aerogenes* produced luxuriant growth. While sodium citrate was used, Koser reported identical results with ammonium or potassium citrate. In his next report, Koser confirmed his former work. He collected cultures from various sources, keeping careful record of their history and source. One hundred and eighteen were obtained from fecal specimens and 72 from soils as far removed as possible from sources of pollution. Koser applied his uric acid and citric acid tests to these organisms and also the methyl-red and Voges-Proskauer tests of "standard methods." With these strains Koser also found that *Escherichia coli* of fecal origin was unable to utilize sodium or potassium citrate when supplied as the sole source of carbon, whereas the aerogenes-cloacae types, which represented the largest section of the soil cultures, all utilized citrate readily. As others have found, when differentiating members of the coliform group by different tests, Koser found "intermediates" which did not fall clearly into one or the other groups. These discrepancies occurred chiefly among the soil cultures. He had 23 soil strains which were consistently methyl-red positive and at the same time developed in the citrate medium. These organisms were proposed as constituting another section of the colon-aerogenes group which could be differentiated from fecal methyl-red positive type by utilization of citrate. Their presence in soil and apparent absence from fecal specimens constitutes evidence that not all of the methyl-red positive colon group organisms encountered in nature are of fecal origin. In a later paper, Koser reported that the citrate test correlated somewhat with the sanitary survey. Ability to utilize citrate also seemed to be a permanent characteristic and one not easily acquired or lost. Koser's work was nicely confirmed by Pawan,[273] working in Trinidad.

Murray and Skinner,[274] in isolating iron bacteria, used Harder's medium consisting of inorganic salts among which was ferric ammonium citrate. They were interested in trying *Escherichia coli* and comparing the results with Koser's citrate medium. They found a good correlation. In the Koser solid medium in which ferric ammonium citrate replaced the sodium citrate, good differentiation of organisms was possible.

Experiments were carried out by Koser to determine whether dicarboxylic and tricarboxylic acids could be used for separating *Escherichia coli* from *Aerobacter aerogenes*. Although several of these acids are structurally similar to citric none of them gave the same separation that citric acid gave. Koser[275] reviewed the literature which had been published on comparisons of the methyl-red, Voges-Proskauer, and citrate differentiation reactions. In general, it was shown that the citrate test gave good differentiation between *Escherichia coli* and *Aerobacter aerogenes*.

Observations by Taylor *et al.*[276] indicated that the results of the citrate fermentation test correlated well with sanitary inspection. Hicks[175] also

273. Pawan. 1925. Ann. Trop. Med. and Parasitol. 19, 319-326.
274. Murray and Skinner. 1925. Proc. Soc. Expt. Biol. and Med. 23, 104-106.
275. Koser. 1927. J. Bact. 11, 409-416.
276. Taylor *et al.* 1927. Indian J. Med. Res. 14, 801-836.

found Koser's medium to differentiate lactose-fermenting bacteria from polluted and unpolluted sources, as did Ruchhoft et al.[277] In the hands of Poe [218] correlation between the Voges-Proskauer and methyl-red tests, and the citrate test of Koser was almost perfect for the *Aerobacter aerogenes* section and 77 per cent perfect for the *Escherichia coli* section. That the results of the citrate test correlate well with those of the Voges-Proskauer and methyl-red tests was also reported by Hoak.[278]

Results of investigations by Kline [279] seem to indicate that *Escherichia coli* may acquire the ability to utilize citrate as the sole source of carbon. A carefully purified culture of this organism was introduced at one end of a 20-foot stovepipe filled with sterile soil. Sterile water was introduced at the head of the pipe and allowed to seep slowly through the soil. Samples of the soil were withdrawn from different parts of the pipe at intervals up to 400 days after inoculation. Altogether 726 strains were isolated and typed. During the first 100 days of the experiment the great majority of strains isolated were typical *Escherichia coli*, but after this time atypical strains began to appear frequently. No fewer than 75 cultures (10.3 per cent of the total) isolated after the 95th day proved to be citrate-positive. According to Parr and Simpson [280] some coliform bacteria may not readily utilize citrate. Coliform "mutants" were observed which persistently refused to grow on citrate agar.

A modification of Koser's citrate medium was made by Simmons [281] who added two per cent of agar and brom-thymol-blue to give a solid medium. Use of this solid medium obviates the use of turbidity as a criterion of growth. The medium may be used either as a slant or in Petri-dish cultures. *Aerobacter aerogenes* grows luxuriantly; *Escherichia coli* does not grow at all or so sparsely that no color change occurs in the medium. Another modification was reported by Perelli [282] as follows:

Two grams of agar are dissolved in 100 ml. distilled water in an autoclave; .25 per cent sodium citrate is added and the flask shaken until it is completely dissolved. Then .5 per cent picric acid solution (one per cent), two ml. of a .2-per cent solution of malachite green, and .5 ml. of a 1.5-per cent alcohol solution of brom-thymol blue are added. The mixture is shaken and distributed without sterilization into tubes and plates. The colon bacillus develops in this medium but leaves the color unaltered. *Aerobacter aerogenes* forms dew-drop colonies and turns the medium completely blue within 24 hours at 37°C.(98.6°F.). Harry [283] preferred the Simmons' modification of the citrate medium.

Considerable study has been given to the citrate test by the Metropolitan Water Board of London in its Thirty-Second Annual Report for the year 1937. Results of many investigations were reported. In general the citrate test has continued to yield satisfactory results. In the Thirty-Third

277. Ruchhoft, Kallas, Chinn, and Coulter. 1931. J. Bact. 22, 125-181.
278. Hoak. 1935. J. Penn. Water Wks. Operators Assoc. 7, 75-93.
279. Kline. 1935. Amer. J. Pub. Health 25, 833-838.
280. Parr and Simpson. 1939. J. Bact. 39, 12-13; 40 (1940), 467-482.
281. Simmons. 1926. J. Infect. Dis. 39, 209.
282. Perelli. 1936-37. Gior di batteriol. e immunol. 17, 841-845.
283. Harry. 1937. J. State Med. 44, 546-550.

Annual Report for 1938, the test was modified by addition of brom thymol blue to the medium so that growth was indicated by a color change from apple green to blue. Occasionally specimens were analyzed which did not appreciably alter the color of the medium while growth was shown by a heavy deposit. Fortunately such specimens were rare and were confined only to one or two sources. The test was introduced into the routine confirmation of coliform types from presumptive tubes and differentiated between *Escherichia coli* and intermediates. In spite of much previous work, some of which has just been reviewed. Stark and Straughn [284] stated that the utilization of citrate as the sole source of carbon is an unreliable and unjustifiable characteristic for differentiating the genera Escherichia and Aerobacter. They confirmed the validity of the methyl-red test, the Voges-Proskauer reaction, and the gas ratio for this purpose.

The Eijkmann [285] Test for Differentiating Coliform Bacteria. This method, proposed in 1904 by Eijkmann, was supposed to differentiate coliform bacteria from warm-blooded animals from strains of those from cold-blooded animals. It consists in the main of inoculating fermentation tubes containing dextrose broth with the samples and incubating at 46°C. (114.8°F.). The higher temperature of incubation was supposed to eliminate non-fecal strains and permit development of fecal strains. The method has been subjected to much study with conflicting and contradictory results. Among those who found the test satisfactory are Christian,[286] Neumann,[287] Thomann,[288] Hilgerman,[289] de Graaff,[290] and Van Hoytema.[91] Those who did not find it to be satisfactory were Nowack,[292] Konrich,[293] and Sachse.[294] Several of the latter based most of their objections on the fact that fecal coliform bacteria might be inhibited. Results of investigations by these earlier investigators will not be reviewed in order to consider more recent studies. Results of investigations are not always in agreement and consequently bacteriologists differ in their attitudes toward the test. More recently it has been found that the temperature must be carefully controlled. We may wonder whether this was always appreciated by the earlier investigators who have condemned the test.

Comparison of the Eijkmann test with the methods in *Standard Methods for the Examination of Water and Sewage*, by Leiter,[295] revealed some interesting facts. The investigation involved a number of questions, which were raised in connection with the test. Leiter concluded that the Eijkmann fermentation test, as applied to water, was selective for *Escherichia coli* through the inhibition of other organisms. He observed close relation

284. Stark and Straughn. 1941. J. Bact. 41, 88-89.
285. Eijkmann. 1904. Centbl. Bakt., Abt. I, Orig. 37-74.
286. Christian. 1905. Arch. Hyg. 54, 386-395.
287. Neumann. 1906. Arch. Hyg. 59, 174.
288. Thomann. 1907. Hyg. Rundschan. 17, 857.
289. Hilgermann. 1909. Klin. Jahresb., 22, 315.
290. de Graaff. 1928. Nederland. Tijdschr. Hyg. Microbiol. Serol. 3, 165-178.
291. Van Hoytema. 1928. Idem. 3, 165-178.
292. Nowack. 1907. Prufungsanstall Wasserversorg u. Beseitigung 9, 197.
293. Konrich. 1910. Klin. Jahresb. 23, 1.
294. Sachse. 1916. Ztschr. Hyg. u. Infektionskrank. 81, 296-310.
295. Leiter. 1929. Amer. J. Hyg. 9, 705-724.

between indol formation and fermentation of Eijkmann's medium. Other findings seemed to be favorable to the Eijkmann test. Leiter stated that it possessed some features which made it preferable to "standard methods" then in use. It is more rapid, requiring only 16 to 24 hours, and permits a higher percentage of positive tests. Positive Eijkmann tests infrequently yielded members of the Aerogenes-Cloacae group, whereas *Standard Methods* technique yielded them frequently. Brown and Skinner [296] found little merit in the Eijkmann test, as did Wagner.[297]

As would be expected, some strains of *Escherichia coli* have been found to be inhibited at 46°C.(114.8°F.). Barth [298] claimed that strains from cold-blooded animals would not grow much above 37°C.(98.6°F.). Magalhaes [299] secured results with the Eijkmann test quite like those of Leiter. He stated that in the majority of cases *Escherichia coli* from cold-blooded animals did not attack sugars at 46°C.(114.8°F.), while strains from warm-blooded animals cause fermentation with gas production. Only a small percentage of *Escherichia coli* from human feces produced gas, according to Brown and Skinner,[296] which contradicted the above statement of Magalhaes. Many strains produced gas in 24 hours in the Eijkmann test, but 48 hours were necessary to include all gas formers. Many "typical" *Escherichia coli* strains from water from a polluted stream failed to grow in the Eijkmann broth at 46°C.(114.8°C.). The Eijkmann test did not eliminate all positive results caused by *Aerobacter aerogenes* and citrate-positive *Escherichid coli*. Only *Escherichia coli* (never *Aerobacter aerogenes*) was found in human feces.

Skinner and Brown [300] reported that the Eijkmann and the Bulir [301] tests (glucose and mannitol broth, respectively, at 46°C.) detected significantly fewer *Escherichia coli* than did the usual method using lactose broth at 37.5°C. To a less degree, but still significantly, this was true when the 46°C. of the Eijkmann and Bulir methods was reduced in five hours by a gradual increase in temperature. Partial explanations for the conflicting results on the Eijkmann test, found in the literature, were proposed. Possibly the large amounts of media used by some investigators allowed some of the coliform bacteria to adapt themselves to a gradual increasing temperature. It was suggested that the Bulir test has a possible slight advantage over the modified Eijkmann test. A similar .but smaller advantage of the modified Bulir over the modified Eijkmann test is thought possible. This latter supposition, however, was not shown statistically by the data, based on over 4,500 inoculations. Necessity of rather heavy inoculations with the Eijkmann test was shown by Minkevich et al.[302] He concluded that 46°C. is the maximum temperature at which *Escherichia coli communis* will grow; it invariably grows at this temperature only when massive inoculations are employed; it frequently fails to grow if the

296. Brown and Skinner. 1930. J. Bact. 20, 139-150.
297. Wagner. 1931. Amer. J. Pub. Health 21, 1256-1257.
298. Barth. 1930. Zentbl. Bakt., Pt. 1, 115, 467.
299. Magalhaes. 1930. Arch. Hyg. (Rio de Janeiro) 4, 5-20.
300. Skinner and Brown. 1934. J. Bact. 27, 191-200.
301. Bulir. 1907. Arch. Hyg. 62, 1-14.
302. Minkevich *et al*. 1936. J. Hyg. 36, 50-63.

inoculation is not massive; if the incubation temperature is reduced to 43 to 43.5°C. (109.4°F.), even single-cell inoculations of *Escherichia coli communis* will demonstrate their presence.

They recommend the following procedure for obtaining the coli content of water: (1) test in Bulir's media at 43 to 43.5°C.; (2) transfer last two dilutions showing gas to Endo or E.M.B.; (3) transfer appropriate colonies from solid media to Bulir's media, massive inoculation, for incubation at 46°C. (114.8°F.). The authors state that this procedure obtains all *Escherichia coli communis* and "absolutely excludes *Bacterium aerogenes, Bacterium cloacae, Bacterium aquatilis,* communis and coliform varieties from the intestines of cold-blooded animals."

The original Eijkmann test required glucose as the carbohydrate; Perry and Hajna[303] and Hajna and Perry[304] studied other sugars. Hajna[305] reported an investigation in which the action of bacteria of the genus Escherichia on seven monosaccharides (arabinose, xylose, glucose, mannose, fructose, galactose, rhamnose), four disaccharides (lactose, sucrose, maltose, trehalose), and four alcohols (mannitol, dulcitol, sorbitol, and adonitol) at 37°C. (98.6°F.) and 46°C. (114.8°F.) were studied. Buffers enhanced gas production at both 37°C. and 46°C. In a well buffered basic medium all sugars and alcohols tested, except dulcitol and adonitol which were never fermented with gas at 46°C. (114.8°F.), were readily decomposed at both temperatures. In an adequately buffered medium, all the bacteria used remained viable after an incubation period of 72 hours. Gas production was likewise influenced greatly by the type of protein in the medium. Perry and Hajna[303] previously reported that more *Escherichia coli* were recovered from feces with "Standard Methods" lactose broth than with original Eijkmann medium at 46°C. (114.8°F.); but the reverse was true when the latter was modified by buffering with .4 per cent of di-potassium hydrogen phosphate and using .3 per cent of glucose instead of 1.4 per cent. *Escherichia coli* cultures in old medium were seldom viable after 24 hours incubation at 46°C. but in new medium all were viable 118 hours or longer. Tests showed that ability to ferment glucose at 46°C. is a fundamental characteristic of *Escherichia coli* as stated by Eijkmann. Hajna and Perry construe *Escherichia coli* to include only those members of the coliform group which invariably ferment glucose at 46°C. in suitable medium and are unable to utilize citrate carbon. The importance of Eijkmann test in water analysis is stressed. Further work by Hajna and Perry[306] led them to prefer for separation of fecal *Escherichia coli* from other coliform organisms the use of their modification of the Eijkmann medium in an air incubator at 45.5 to 46°C. (114.8°F.). Their medium contained 1.5 per cent of peptone, .3 per cent of lactose, and buffer salts. In tests made with Eijkmann media containing glucose, lactose, or mannite at temperatures of 42, 44, and 46°C. (107.6, 111.2, and 114.8°F.), all of 1,374 *Escherichia coli* strains produced gas at 46°C. from

303. Perry and Hajna. 1933. J. Bact. 26, 419-429.
304. Hajna and Perry. 1938. Sewage Wks. J. 10, 261.
305. Hajna. 1937. J. Bact. 33, 339.
306. Hajna and Perry. 1939. J. Bact. 38, 275-283.

mannite, while four and five strains, respectively, (all from raw sewage) failed in glucose and lactose. Few *Escherichia coli* strains produced gas at 46°C., but many did at the lower temperatures. Strains of *Aerobacter cloacae* and intermediate types frequently grew also at 44°C. but rarely at 46°C., and did not produce gas in glucose or lactose at the latter temperature. In parallel tests of their own medium and that of MacConkey in an air incubator and a water bath at 44°C., all of 66 *Escherichia coli* strains of human origin were positive in the modified Eijkmann medium, while two failed in air and 16 in the water bath in MacConkey's medium. Many *Aerobacter aerogenes* strains produced gas at 44°C., fewer, however, in MacConkey's medium. Both media were satisfactory for suppression of *Aerobacter cloacae* and intermediates under both conditions of incubation. It is claimed that isolation of coliform organisms is easy after growth for three days in Eijkmann's medium at 44°C., but difficult from MacConkey's even after 48 hours.

Results of more recent experiments have led investigators to opposite conclusions. Raven, Peden, and Wright,[307] Taylor and Goyle,[308] and Ferramolo and Monteverde [309] were favorable while Webster and Raghavachari [310] were not. These discrepancies may be due to lack of accurate control of temperature of incubation, as was stated by Clegg and Sherwood [311] who supported their contentions with many data. This is a difficult situation to comprehend.

The Metropolitan Water Board of London has carried out many investigations, results of which are reported in its annual reports for years before and after 1940. Their results were not especially favorable to this method as a routine procedure. The test as they carried it out seemed to give erratic results. Eijkmann's method has been used also for determining the quality of oysters and nut meats.

When applied to detection of the presence of *Escherichia coli* in nut meats, Ostrolenk and Hunter [312] found the Eijkmann test to be unreliable. Although it surpassed standard lactose broth in limiting development of Aerobacter and Citrobacter, it reduced development of Escherichia.

Neutral Red in the Presumptive Test. The use of neutral red lactose broth in water analysis was proposed by Rothberger.[313] After experimenting with various dyes, he noticed that *Escherichia coli* turned neutral red medium red, while *Eberthella typhosa* caused no change. This change in color was believed to be sufficiently specific for practical application. As might be expected, various investigators tried to confirm Rothberger's conclusions. Irons [314] and Gage and Phelps [315] were unable to do so. On the

307. Raven, Peden, and Wright. 1940. J. Path. and Bact. 50, 287-294.
308. Taylor and Goyle. 1931. Indian J. Med. Res. 18, 1177-1202.
309. Ferramolo and Monteverde. 1938. Bol. Abras. Samitarias Nacion 2, 265.
310. Webster and Raghavachari. 1934. Indian J. Med. Res. 21, 525-534.
311. Clegg and Sherwood. 1939. J. Hyg. 39, 361-374.
312. Ostrolenk and Hunter. 1940. Food Research 5, 141-145.
313. Rothberger. 1898. Centbl. Bakt., Pt. 1, 24, 513.
314. Irons. 1902. J. Hyg. 2, 314-319.
315. Gage and Phelps. 1903. Trans. Amer. Pub. Health Assoc. 28, 28, 402.

other hand, Makgill,[316] Savage,[317] and Stokes [318] considered the method to be a delicate one for determining the presence of pollution in water. Chamot and Sherwood [319] attempted to improve the medium and make it more reliable. They arrived at a formula which they believed gave a more suitable medium than lactose bile. Georgia and Morales,[320] after analyzing 185 samples of water, stated that neutral red medium was better than any medium yet proposed for a presumptive medium for *Escherichia coli*.

Concentration Methods for Coliform Bacteria. Coliform bacteria may not be abundant in some waters which have received pollution and may be lost during the tests designed to determine their presence. They may be concentrated in small amounts of water which may be subjected to routine examination. Edington [321] used the Seitz filter, Schulkoff and Heukelekian [322] the centrifuge. The latter investigators showed that results of examination of specimens prepared in this manner were satisfactory indices of quality. Their investigation is quite pertinent just now in view of the desire to use larger samples in the Treasury Department procedure. Zeetti [323] adapted a method previously reported by Rasumov.[324] Thin cellulose membrane was employed in infiltration of water and then placed on solid medium in a Petri dish, with surface, which was in contact with water, turned up. During the period in the thermostat, bacteria on cellulose membrane grew in colonies, as they would on underlying medium. After growth of bacteria, the membrane was examined microscopically.

LONGEVITY OF ESCHERICHIA COLI AND AEROBACTER AEROGENES

This is an important question in relation to the significance of these organisms in sanitary water analysis. Exact knowledge on the question, if it may ever be secured, would determine the significance of results of certain procedures in water analysis.

In Water: Longevity of *Escherichia coli* in water has much to do with its value as an indicator. Rogers [325] found that *Aerobacter aerogenes* was more resistant than *Escherichia coli*. During long periods of storage, its percentage gradually increased. In a later investigation Rogers artificially infected water with feces and held it at 20°C.(68°F.). At the end of nine months the relative numbers were reversed. There were 39 *Aerobacter aerogenes* to one of *Escherichia coli*. In sewage stored in running water there was more rapid decrease in *Escherichia coli* than *Aerobacter aerogenes*. At the beginning there were about three times as many *Escherichia coli*, but after seven days, there were a few more *Aerobacter aerogenes*. Greer and Nyhan[326] found that in mixtures of two

316. Makgill. 1901. J. Hyg. 1, 430.
317. Savage. 1902. Idem 2, 320.
318. Stokes. 1904. J. Infect. Dis. 1, 141.
319. Chamot and Sherwood. 1917. J. Amer. Chem. Soc. 39, 1755.
320. Georgia and Morales. 1926. J. Amer. Water Wks. Assoc. 16, 5.
321. Edington. 1934. Lancet 226, 132-133.
322. Schulkoff and Heukelekian. 1936. J. Amer. Water Wks. Assoc. 28, 1963-1974..
323. Zeetti. 1935. Soc. internaz. di microbiol., Boll. d. sez. ital. 7, 164-170.
324. Rasumov. 1932. Microbiologia.
325. Rogers. 1918. J. Bact. 3, 312-328.
326. Greer and Nyhan. 1928. J. Infect. Dis. 42. 525-536.

bacteria in a medium which each could use, there was a tendency for one to gain ascendency over the other. The experimental work of these investigators indicated that *Escherichia coli* may be overgrown by *Streptococcus fecalis*, *Clostridium welchii*, and *Pseudomonas pyocaneus* in 48 hours. Experiments along this same line were reported by Teissier and Couvier [327]; bacterial examination of water which had been collected for 20 years, taken in sterile bottles and kept in the dark, showed that ordinary saprophytic bacteria had died out while *Escherichia coli* remained viable and grew well when placed under favorable conditions.

The viability of organisms inoculated into water taken from the open sea and into sewage contaminated sea water was as follows in Trawinski's [328] experiments:

	Uncontaminated sea water	Contaminated sea water
Salmonella schottmülleri	12 days	12 days
Salmonella schottmülleri (Breslau)	12	7
Salmonella schottmülleri (Gaustedt)	16	16
Salmonella enteritidis	23	4
Salmonella paratyphi	18	6
Eberthella typhosa	16	3
Eberthella dysenteriae (Shiga)	12 hours	30 hours

According to Jones [329] *Escherichia coli* dies out during storage, more rapidly in the tropics and more slowly on voyages through cooler seas. Cleaning or "cement-washing" the storage tanks exerts no influence. The results of an investigation by Platt [330] of the influence of temperature, aeration, and light on survival of these two bacteria in water showed that (1) both organisms survived longer in sterilized than in raw river water; (2) they died out rapidly at 37°C.(98.6°F.) but survived for several weeks at 0°C.(32°F.); (3) if water kept at room temperature was shaken occasionally, actual multiplication of the organisms occurred owing to the beneficial effect of aeration; (4) the organisms survived longer at room temperature when kept in the dark than in daylight; (5) at 0°C. and 37°C. coli and aerogenes proved of much the same degree of resistance, but at room temperature 18 to 20°C.(64.4 to 68°F.) aerogenes survived considerably longer than coli. The general conclusion was that under ordinary environmental conditions *Aerobacter aerogenes* is likely to survive longer in raw water than *Escherichia coli*. Observations made with coliform bacilli of various types by Bigger [331] showed that in autoclaved waters multiplication occurred to a variable, and often considerable, extent in flasks incubated at 22°C.(71.6°F.) or 37°C.(98.6°F.). Growth frequently occurred in waves. In raw waters, on the other hand, multiplication was practically never observed and the organisms gradually died off. Numerous attempts were made to explain these facts. It was found that heating to 60°C.(140°F.) for one hour, filtration, or adsorption with kaolin

327. Tiessier and Couvrier. 1919. Compt. Rend. Soc. Biol. 82, 257-258.
328. Trawinski. 1929. Bull. Inst. Oceanog. 542, 1-5.
329. Jones. 1936. J. Path. and Bact. 42, 605-615.
330. Platt. 1935. J. Hyg. 35, 437-438.
331. Bigger. 1937. J. Path. and Bact. 44, 167-211.

or charcoal, rendered raw water quite suitable for growth of coliform bacilli, though not all waters behaved alike and several irregularities were met. Evidence was brought to show that the waters used contained enough nutritive material to support the growth of coliform bacilli, but that some inhibitory substance present in raw water, removed by autoclaving or one of the other treatments just mentioned, prevented their growth. It was therefore concluded that carbon dioxide destroyed its ability to support growth, and it is therefore concluded that carbon dioxide is probably responsible for the prevention of growth in raw water. These results are in accord with those reported by Platt, although the latter explained the wavy growth as being due to the beneficial action of oxygen which gained access to the flasks when they were intermittently shaken.

Much study has been given longevity of coliform bacteria in the laboratories of the Metropolitan Water Board of London.[332] In samples in which there was good development of saprophytes, the inoculated coliform bacteria disappeared after two to three weeks. Some coliform bacteria increased slightly in samples devoid of saprophytes. It would appear that the viability of coliform organisms is influenced by the presence and multiplication of saprophytic survivors, and the extent to which these prevail depends largely upon the efficacy of the initial process of disinfection employed. Further experiments are being devised in extension of this investigation, since undoubtedly a variety of other contributory factors exist.

Longevity studies of coliform bacteria in nature by Tonney and Noble [333] have thrown much light on this entire problem which is of considerable importance in interpreting results of laboratory examination in sanitary work. Under winter conditions *Escherichia coli* and *Aerobacter aerogenes*, both from fecal material and from cultures, underwent rapid decline without exhibiting significant change in relative numbers. At no time was there a material difference in surviving time of either type of organism in feces. The rather marked relative increase in growth of *Aerobacter aerogenes* over *Escherichia coli* occurring in certain culture plantings suggests the possibility that the commonly observed predominance of *Aerobacter aerogenes* in nature may be due in part to greater multiplication of certain hardy strains. Under such circumstances, the *Aerobacter aerogenes* count, if accepted as a quantitative index of fecal pollution, would tend to distort the sanitary picture, yielding no evidence of the recency of contamination, and giving an exaggerated idea of the amount of pollution after two months, at which time pollution is less dangerous from the standpoint of water-borne disease than at the outset. The coliform count, on the other hand, had a more consistent relation to initial amount of fecal pollution and to time elapsing after its occurrence, both of which factors are of essential importance in judging dangerous pollution. The high resistance of the colon-aerogenes group to action of the elements was evident, and gives further assurance that as test organisms,

332. Thirteenth Ann. Rept. Metropolitan Water Board, London.
333. Tonney and Noble. 1931. J. Bact. 22, 433-446.

their survival time affords a safe margin over that of the less resistant intestinal pathogens which constitute the real danger from fecal pollution. The plate-count method in ferrocyanide citrate agar was a sensitive measure of changes in numbers of coliform organisms under the test conditions. The fact that *Escherichia coli* and *Aerobacter aerogenes* live a long time in wood under natural conditions, has a practical bearing on the quality of water from any supply in which the water is in contact with wood. Wooden storage tanks are often used, especially in small supply systems. In older types of private wells, wooden casings are commonly used and sometimes wooden troughs or conduits as well. There also still remain a few "old oaken buckets." Under such conditions, presence of aerogenes alone would be of no sanitary significance.

In Sewage: The end desired in sanitary water analysis is knowledge with respect to safety of a water supply. Modern laboratory practice rests on determination of the presence of certain organisms indigenous to sewage, in the water. If the organisms which are used as indicators of pollution are short-lived in either sewage or water, the test has serious limitation. To determine the effect that natural purification processes might have on disappearance of *Escherichia coli* and *Aerobacter aerogenes*, Ruchhoft and Coulter [334] made a bacterial survey of samples ranging from raw sewage of Chicago plants to water from points in the Illinois river for about 125 miles below Lockport. In all cases inoculation ensued into standard lactose broth and on Noble medium within four hours after collection. Growth on eosin methylene-blue plates and subsequent gas formation in brilliant green tubes were used to confirm lactose presumptives. Direct plate counts gave lower, and probably more accurate, *Escherichia coli* densities. Conclusion is that self-purification in streams, including dilution, effects little change in ratio of *Escherichia coli* to *Aerobacter aerogenes* from that pre-existing in sewage; necessity for their differentiation is therefore slight.

The degree of contamination seems to have much to with the survival time of various bacteria. Rochaix [335] sterilized sewage which was free from industrial wastes and inoculated it with various pathogenic bacteria. The samples were held at room temperature for frequent examination. In one experiment *Eberthella typhosa*, *Salmonella paratyphi*, *Salmonella schottmülleri*, *Vibrio comma*, and *Pseudomonas aeruginosa* were alive after seven months and 14 days; *Salmonella schottmülleri* and *Pseudomonas eruginosa*, at the end of 20 months and eight days.

In other experiments *Vibrio comma* and *Eberthella typhosa* survived in sterilized sewage water only three months and seven days, while in sterilized distilled water they lived for six months and 23 days; in a fourth experiment *Salmonella schottmülleri* survived for 112 days in sterilized sewage, while in sterilized distilled water it lived for eight and one-half months. In the remaining four experiments *Salmonella schottmülleri*, *Vibrio comma*, and *Eberthella typhosa* were tested in sterilized sewage

334. Ruchhoft and Coulter. 1933. J. Bact. 25, 431.
335. Rochaix. 1930. Ann. Hyg. Pub. Indus. et Soc. 8, 669-675.

water, survival of each by itself being compared with its survival in a mixed culture of saprophytic organisms. In each case, the pathogenic organism lived longer in pure than in mixed culture, and in mixed culture the saprophyte survived the pathogen. These results indicate that, while sewage is in itself a good culture medium for pathogenic organisms, the "vital concurrence" of saprophytes must play a large part in the disappearance of the pathogens. Results of a similar investigation were reported by Heukelekian and Schulhoff.[336]

In Soil: Less is known about survival of coliform bacteria in soil than in water or sewage. Tonney and Noble [333] planted *Aerobacter aerogenes* cultures in decayed stumps without admixture with fecal material, after which plate counts were made until the organisms disappeared. After about 60 days, increase of *Aerobacter aerogenes* was considerable while *Escherichia coli* increase was only slight. From this Tonney and Noble stated that excessive concentrations of *Aerobacter aerogenes* might give a distorted sanitary picture with little evidence of fecal pollution. This was the case at the time when their paper was written; now however, when less importance is given to separation of *Aerobacter aerogenes* from *Escherichia coli* with the significance which was formerly given, these conclusions have less weight. Skinner and Murray [337] found little difference between *Escherichia coli* and *Aerobacter aerogenes* as regards longevity in soil. Both organisms disappeared from soil inoculated with manure after 150 to 200 days.

According to Minkevich and Rabinovich,[338] *Escherichia coli* is able to adapt itself to conditions in the soil. All soil strains are evolved from the fecal type. Isolation of strains capable of assimilating citrate in water and other materials before the lape of six months is without epidemiological significance so far as fecal contamination is concerned because pathogenic bacteria of the typhoid group perish in that period of time.

UNITED STATES PUBLIC HEALTH SERVICE STANDARDS OF PURITY FOR DRINKING WATER (TREASURY DEPARTMENT STANDARDS)

About 1914, the United States Public Health Service suggested that the quality of water served the traveling public on common carriers needed attention. The results of this suggestion was the formulation by a committee of sanitarians of a procedure for examination of such waters and a set of standards. The first standards will not be included in this book.[339]

They were applied to the examination of water from trains by Bartow,[340] Creel,[341] Hanford,[342] and to water from boats by Cobb, Williams, and Letton.[343] Bartow confirmed the presence of *Escherichia coli* in 83 per cent of the samples examined. Creel found that an anaerobic bacillus which formed gas was responsible for gas in the presumptive test in 91

336. Heukelekian and Schulhoff. 1936. N. J. Agr. Expt. Sta. Bull. 589.
337. Skinner and Murray. 1926. J. Infect. Dis. 38, 37-41.
338. Minkevich and Rabinovich. 1936. Arch. Sci. Biol. 43, 345-349.
339. Public Health Repts. 29 (1914), 2959-2966.
340. Bartow. 1916. J. Amer. Water Wks. Assoc. 2, 74-82.
341. Creel. 1914. Bull. 100, Hyg. Lab., Washington.
342. Hanford. 1916. Ill. Water Survey Bull. 13, 256-271.
343. Cobb, Williams, and Letton. 1916. Pub. Health Repts. 31, 2845-67.

out of 421 samples. Such data indicate the significance of the confirmatory test. More data are required before it may be determined whether this method is the best. Letton [344] later stated that the requirement of "not more than 100 colonies per milliliter on agar" of the Treasury Department standard was very lenient. He regarded the limit of permissible *Escherichia coli* (not more than two per 100 ml.) as not too low.

Considerable attention was given to this subject after the first proposed standard had been formulated and used. Gorman [345] gave advice on methods to be followed for taking the water. Connolly and Gorman [346] showed that a marked decrease had occurred in typhoid fever among seamen. Even as late as 1938, undesirable conditions existed on cars of some railroads. Miller and Garthe [347] found water to be handled in an unsanitary fashion without sufficient cleaning of water tanks.

In May, 1922, the Surgeon General of the United States Public Health Service appointed another committee to formulate definite specifications which could be used by the Public Health Service for controlling water supplied for drinking and culinary purposes on interstate carriers. The committee [Pub. Health Repts. Pt. 1, 40 (1925) 693-710] was loath to accept any one criterion. They recommended that the bacteriological standard outlined below be applied with same latitude. For instance, supplies which, on rigid inspection, are found to be satisfactory in other respects but fail to meet the bacteriological standard, may be accepted in the discretion of the certifying authority. This suggestion avoided some of the difficulties which arose in the application of the old standard.

STANDARDS

I. As to Source and Protection

1. The water supply shall be—
   (a) Obtained from a source free from pollution; or
   (b) Obtained from a source adequately protected by natural agencies from the effects of pollution; or
   (c) Adequately protected by artificial treatment.

2. The water supply system, including reservoirs, pipe lines, wells, pumping equipment, purification works, distributing reservoirs, mains, and service pipes, shall be free from sanitary defects.

NOTE. 1. *Natural agencies* affording more or less complete protection against the effects of pollution are, in surface water: dilution, storage, sedimentation, the effects of sunlight, and the associated biological process tending to natural purification; and, in the case of ground waters, percolation through the soil. Important items in the natural purification of ground water are the character and depth of the strata penetrated.

2. *Adequate protection* by artificial treatment implies that the method of treatment is appropriate to the source of supply; that the works are of sufficient capacity, well constructed, skillfully and carefully operated. The evidence that the protection thus afforded is adequate must be furnished by frequent bacteriological examinations and other appropriate analyses, showing that the purified water is of good and reasonably uniform quality, a recognized principle being that irregularity in quality is an indication of potential danger.

344. Letton. 1917. J. Amer. Water Wks. Assoc. 4, 478-481.
345. Gorman. 1922. Pub. Health Repts. 37, 1458-66; 1573-1580.
346. Connolly and Gorman. 1925. Pub. Health Repts. 40, 1042-1055.
347. Miller and Garthe. 1938. Pub. Health Repts. 53, 300.

3. *Sanitary defect* means faulty condition, whether of location, design, or construction of works, which may regularly or occasionally cause the water supply to be polluted from an extraneous source, or fail to be satisfactorily purified. (Examples were cited in Appendix I.)

An outline of the scope of sanitary survey ordinarily required in the investigation of a water supply to determine whether or not it conforms to these requirements was given in Appendix I.

II. As to Bacteriological Quality

1. Of all the standard (10 ml.) *portions* examined in accordance with the procedure specified below, not more than 10 per cent shall show the presence of organisms of the *Escherichia coli* group.

2. Occasionally three or more of the five equal (10 ml.) *portions* constituting a single standard *sample* may show the presence of *Escherichia coli*. This shall not be allowable if it occurs in more than—

(a) Five per cent of the standard samples when twenty (20) or more samples have been examined:

(b) One standard sample when less than twenty (20) samples have been examined.

NOTE. It is to be understood that in the examination of any water supply the series of samples must conform to *both the above requirements*, 1 and 2. For example, where the total number of samples is less than six, the occurrence of positive tests in three of the five portions of any single sample, although it would be permitted under requirement 2, would constitute a failure to meet requirement 1.

DEFINITION. The Escherichia coli group is defined, for the purpose of this test, as in Standard Methods of Water Analysis, American Public Health Association, New York, 1923, and the procedures for demonstration of organisms of this group shall conform to those of the "completed test" as therein specified.

The standard portion of water for this test shall be ten milliliters (10 ml.).

The standard sample for this test shall consist of five (5) standard *portions* of ten milliliters (10 ml.) each.

This was summarized in the *Journal of the American Water Works Association*, volume 10 (1923), p. 885, as follows:

1. *Index Organism.* *Escherichia coli* group, as determined in accordance with Standard Methods of the American Public Health Association, current edition, by inoculation in lactose broth fermentation tube, transplant to endo- or eosin-methylene blue agar plate and inoculate in secondary lactose broth fermentation tube.

2. *Standard Portion of Water.* Ten milliliters.

3. *Standard Sample of Water.* Five standard portions of ten milliliters each.

4. *Limits of Permissible Density of Escherichia coli Group.* Not more than 10 per cent of all the ten milliliter standard portions examined shall show the presence of organisms of the *Escherichia coli* group.

(a) When the number of standard samples collected is over twenty, not more than 5 per cent of all of the samples shall show three or more positive tests out of the five 10 ml. portions comprised in any single sample.

(b) When the number of standard samples collected is less than twenty, not more than *one sample* shall show three or more positive tests out of the five 10 ml. portions.

The suggested bacteriological standard was discussed at considerable length. The committee stated that the bacteriological examinations which have come generally to be recognized as of most value in the sanitary examination of water supplies are:

1. The count of total colonies developing from measured portions planted on gelatin plates and incubated for 48 hours at 20°C.

2. A similar count of total colonies developing on agar plates incubated for 24 hours at 37°C. (or in some laboratories incubated 48 hours at 20° C.).

3. The quantitative estimation of organisms of the *Escherichia coli* group by applying specific tests to multiple portions of measured volume.

They omitted the plate counts because the *Escherichia coli* is generally conceded to be the most significant. They stressed, however, the value of the count and advised its use where possible. The two limiting values to the density of *Escherichia coli* were admittedly arbitrary, and represented simply the judgment of the committee.

Some of the widespread benefits of the Federal supervision of water supplies of interstate traffic have been a marked increase in certified supplies and an increased interest in water hygiene (Allen [348]).

More recent standards have been adopted by the U. S. Public Health Service.[348a] (These supersede those adopted June 30, 1925.) The bacteriological part is as follows:

1. 7. The coliform group of bacteria is defined, for the purpose of this standard, as including all organisms considered in the coli aerogenes group as set forth in the *Standard Methods for Examination of Water and Sewage*, eighth edition (1936), prepared, approved, and published jointly by the American Public Health Association and American Water Works Association, New York City. The procedures* for the demonstration of bacteria of this group shall be specified herein, for:

(a) The completed test, or

(b) The confirmed test when the liquid confirmatory medium brilliant green bile lactose broth, two per cent is used, providing the formation of gas in any amount in this medium during 48 hours of incubation at 37°C. is considered to constitute a positive confirmed test, or

(c) The confirmed test when one of the following liquid confirmatory media are used: Crystal violet lactose broth, fuchsin lactose broth, or formate ricinoleate broth. For the purpose of this test, all are equivalent, but it is recommended that the laboratory worker base his selection of any one of these confirmatory media upon correlation of the confirmed results thus obtained with a series of completed tests, and that he select for use the liquid confirmatory medium yielding results most nearly agreeing with the results of the completed test. The incubation period for the selected liquid confirmatory medium shall be 48 hours at 37°C., and the formation of gas in any amount during this time shall be considered to constitute a positive confirmed test.

1. 8. *The standard portion* of water for the application of the bacteriological test may be either

(a) Ten milliliters (10 ml.), or

(b) One hundred milliliters (100 ml.).

1. 9. *The standard sample* for the bacteriological test shall consist of five (5) standard portions of either

(a) Ten milliliters (10 ml.), or

(b) One hundred milliliters (100 ml.) each.

In any disinfected supply the sample must be freed of any disinfecting agent within twenty (20) minutes of the time of its collection.†

348. Allen. 1926. Texas State J. Med. 22, 189-194.

348a. Public Health Reports, 58 (1943), 69-111

* This reference shall apply to all details of technique in the bacteriological examination, including selection and preparation of apparatus and media, collection and handling of samples, and the intervals and conditions of storage allowable between collection and examination of the water sample.

† In freeing samples of chlorine or chloramines, the procedure given on page 286 in Standard Methods for the Examination of Water and Sewage, 8th Edition (1936), paragraph A-1.—Option 1, or paragraph A-2 shall be followed.

1. 10. The certifying authority is the Surgeon General of the U. S. Public Health Service or his duly authorized and designated representatives and the *Reporting Agency* shall be understood to mean the respective state departments of health or their designated representatives.

2. AS TO SOURCE AND PROTECTION

2. 1. The water supply shall be.

(a) Obtained from a source free from pollution, or

(b) Obtained from a source adequately purified by natural agencies, or

(c) Adequately protected by artificial treatment.

2. 2. The water supply system in all its parts shall be free from sanitary defects and health hazards and shall be maintained at all times in a proper sanitary condition.

3. AS TO BACTERIOLOGICAL QUALITY

3. 1. *Sampling:* The bacteriological examination of water considered under this section shall be of samples collected at representative points throughout the distributive system.

The frequency of sampling and the location of sampling points on the distribution system should be such as to determine properly the bacteriological quality of the water supply. The frequency of sampling and the distribution of sampling points shall be regulated by the certifying authority after investigation of the source, method of treatment, and protection of the water concerned.

The minimum number of samples to be collected from the distribution system and examined by the reporting agency or its designated representative each month should be in accordance with the number as determined from the graph presented in Fig. 1‡ of these standards § which is based upon the following population served—minimum number of samples per month relationships:

2,500 and under	1
10,000	7
25,000	25
100,000	100
1,000,000	300
2,000,000	390
5,000,000	500

The laboratories in which these examinations are made and the methods used in making them shall be subject to inspection at any time by the designated representative of the certifying authority. Compliance with the specified procedures, or failure to comply therewith, and the results obtained shall be used as a basis for certification, or refusal of certification, by the certifying authority in accordance with the application given below:

3. 2. *Application:* Applications 3.21 and 3.22 given below shall govern when ten milliliter (10 ml.) portions are used and Applications 3.23 and 3.24 shall govern when one hundred milliliter (100 ml.) portions are used.

3. 21. Of all the standard ten milliliter (10 ml.) portions examined per month in accordance with the specified procedure, not more than ten (10) per cent shall show the presence of organisms of the coliform group.

‡ For the purpose of uniformity and simplicity in application, the numbers of samples to be examined each month for any given population served shall be determined from the graph (see footnote §) in accordance with the following:
For populations of 25,000 and under to the nearest 1.
For populations of 25,001 to 100,000 to the nearest 5.
For populations of 100,001 to 2,000,000 to the nearest 10.
For populations of over 2,000,000 to the nearest 25.

§ This figure is not reproduced in this book. From it may be secured the Minimum Number of Samples per Month to be examined in relation to the population served. It may be consulted in Public Health Reports, January 15, 1943.

3. 22. Occasionally three (3) or more of the five (5) equal ten milliliter (10 ml.) portions constituting a single standard sample may show the presence of organisms of the coliform group, provided that this shall not be allowable if it occurs in consecutive samples or in more than

(a) Five (5) per cent of the standard samples when twenty (20) or more samples have been examined per month.

(b) One (1) standard sample when less than twenty (20) have been examined per month.

Provided further than when three or more of the five equal ten milliliter (10 ml.) portions constituting a single standard sample show the presence of organisms of the the coliform group, daily samples from the same sampling point shall be collected promptly and examined until the results obtained from at least two consecutive samples show the water to be of satisfactory quality.

3. 23. Of all the standard one hundred milliliter (100 ml.) portions examined per month in accordance with the specified procedure, not more than sixty (60) per cent shall show the presence of organisms of the coliform group.

3. 24. Occasionally all of the five (5) equal one hundred milliliter (100 ml.) portions constituting a single standard sample may show the presence of organisms of the coliform group, provided that this shall not be allowable if it occurs in consecutive samples or in more than

(a) Twenty (20) per cent of the standard samples when five (5) or more samples have been examined per month.

(b) One (1) standard sample when less than five (5) samples have been examined per month.

Provided further that when all five of the standard one hundred milliliter (100 ml.) portions constituting a single standard sample show the presence of organisms of the coliform group, daily samples from the same sampling point shall be collected promptly and examined until the results obtained from at least two consecutive samples show the water to be of satisfactory quality.

3. 25. The procedure given, using a standard sample composed of five standard portions, provides for an estimation of the most probable number of coliform bacteria present in the sample as set forth in the following tabulation:

| Number of portions | | Most probable number of coliform bacteria per 100 ml. | |
Positive	Negative	When 5-10 ml. portions are examined	When 5-100 ml. portions are examined
0	5	Less than 2.2	Less than 0.22
1	4	2.2	0.22
2	3	5.1	0.51
3	2	9.2	0.92
4	1	16.0	1.60
5	0	More than 16.0	More than 1.60

These newer proposals have caused much discussion among bacteriologists. Suggestions that 100-ml. portions be examined are not new. Hoskins,[349] in his discussions of "most probable numbers" of coliform bacteria in water as indicated by results of fermentation tube results, directed attention to the fact that the older method of examining five 10-ml. portions of drinking water samples measures the coli-aerogenes Treasury Department Standard; such content is required to be not in excess of 1.05 per 100 ml. In other words, the measuring stick is too

349. Hoskins. 1934. Pub. Health Repts. 49, 393-405; J. Amer. Water Wks. Assoc. 25 (1933),

coarse for the purpose. The value of this test to the waterworks operator would be greatly enhanced if larger volumes, such as five 100-ml. portions of the sample, were examined which would measure the bacterial content in the range from .22 to 1.6 per 100 ml. By this change in procedure current analytical data would be always available that would indicate when the permissible upper bacterial limit was being approached or slightly exceeded. Such a radical change in technique would introduce modifications of laboratory routine which might be quite expensive. Not all water bacteriologists agree that examination of 100-ml. portions of water would be helpful. Noble [350] recommended use of such portions but Norcom [351] objected. Hoskins [352] again, some seven years after his first proposal, made a second statement concerning the proposed changes in standards. One of these concerned examination of larger portions of water than 10 ml. Where coliform density is approximately one per 100 ml. of sample, examination of 10-ml. portions does not permit detection of the coliform group.

Slow Lactose-Fermenting Coliform Bacteria. These organisms, members of the coliform group, ferment lactose with gas formation only after 48 hours. The significance of these organisms in sanitary work has been a problem. *Standard Methods of Water Analysis* stresses formation of gas in 24 hours but places lesser emphasis on its appearance after 48 hours. These bacteria are not of recent origin. They have been recognized to be problems for many years. Berry [353] studied these forms from ground waters including almost every type of dug, driven, or drilled well and a few springs. No seasonal prevalence was noticed. Whether these organisms are devoid of sanitary significance, as was believed in these earlier days, is probably not confirmed by present-day investigations. That they might be good indicators of pollution is indicated by results of investigations by Dulaney and Smith.[354] These strains were found in 20 per cent of 400 stools; usually they were present only in small numbers but sometimes made up to 10 to 50 per cent of all colonies. Thirteen per cent of 300 samples of water from various sources contained coliform bacteria which took longer than 48 hours to ferment lactose. These investigators could establish no relationship between slow lactose-fermenting bacteria and the source of the water. While it is known that these bacteria exist in human feces, it is impossible to say that they are of fecal origin, when they are found in water. McCrady [355] secured opinions of 30 laboratory workers as to whether they believed it to be desirable in routine work to include in coliform estimates these coliform organisms confirmed from lactose broth presumptive in which less than five per cent or more than 10 per cent gas had been produced after 48 hours' incubation at 37°C.(98.6°F.) from (1) finished or unfinished waters (treated) and (2) natural waters (un-

350. Noble. 1941. J. Amer. Water Wks. Assoc. 33, 1242-1248.
351. Norcom. 1941. Idem 33, 1819-1824.
352. Hoskins. 1941. J. Amer. Water Wks. Assoc. 33, 1804-1807.
353. Berry. 1926. Amer. J. Pub. Health 16, 590-594.
354. Dulaney and Smith. 1939. Amer. J. Pub. Health 29, 266-270.
355. McCrady. 1939. Amer. J. Pub. Health 29, 261-265; J. Amer. Water Wks. Assoc. 31 (1939), 911-912.

filtered and untreated). Of 25 replies 15 unqualifiedly favored inclusion in the coliform estimate of coliform organisms confirmed from every lactose broth tube containing gas regardless of amount. Six workers disregarded small gas formers because experience has shown failure to confirm. Only three frankly expressed doubt of sanitary significance of slow lactose fermenters. Following comments are quoted from McCrady[355]

The question of sanitary significance of the presence in water of coli-like organisms that produce small amounts (five or 10 ml.) of gas in lactose broth, upon incubation at 37°C.(98.6°F.) for 48 hours, has long been the subject of occasional informal discussion by laboratory workers; but in general these slow lactose fermenters have been accepted as genuine members of the coliform group of indicator organisms. *Standard Methods of Water Analysis*, for example, includes such organisms in the coliform group as therein defined. Since it is the usual practice to leave to the control authority the appraisal of the sanitary significance of the presence in a water of any organism of the coliform group, difficulties arising from contradictory evidence furnished, on the one hand, by the laboratory and, on the other hand, by the field survey of the supply are usually (although, unfortunately, not always) readily adjusted.

It is well known that coliform organisms frequently derive from sources unassociated with dangerous pollution, such as multiplication in sediments in mains, on wood, on other material of a vegetable nature, on tap washers, and from virgin soil, that such organisms are frequently atypical in character, and that many of them are slow lactose fermenters. When, therefore, the cause of any excessive coliform density is determined to be other than that of access of pollution to the supply, the coliform report is simply ignored. But is there reasonable justification for dismissing as of no sanitary significance all instances of slow lactose fermentation? One of the principal arguments favoring this course is that slow lactose fermentation is caused by "attenuated" organisms which have become so devitalized that they have lost their sanitary significance. This argument has been so frequently advanced that it deserved particular attention. In the first place, it perhaps will be admitted that the sanitary significance of the presence of coliform organisms in a treated, filtered, or filtered-treated water is ordinarily quite different from that of their presence in a natural water.

Coliform organisms in a natural water serve usually as an indicator of the presence of human, animal, or soil pollution; and, depending upon the further indications furnished by the field survey of the supply, greater or less significance is attached to their presence. When a treated, filtered, or filtered-treated water is examined, however, since it is usually known that the original raw water was polluted, the coliform estimate serves ordinarily, not as an index of pollution that may be more or less dangerous, but rather as a measure of the destruction or elimination by the treatment of associated disease organisms. Here there can be no question of tolerance—if the treatment is satisfactory, practically every disease organism of the raw water will have been eliminated and, by the same token, practically every coliform organism will have been eliminated. There exists no satisfactory evidence that slow lactose fermenters are more resistant to treatment than are typhoid or dysentery organisms; nor may it be contended that a treatment which reduces the gas production of a coliform organism 95 per cent necessarily deprives the typhoid bacillus of its pathogenicity. If, therefore, coliforms of any type persist in a treated water, and if their presence cannot satisfactorily be explained, the conclusion is inescapable that disease organisms may also persist in the water and that the treatment therefore, has not been satisfactory.

Turning now to the question of the significance of slow lactose fermenters in natural waters, it must be admitted that the experienced water bacteriologist is inclined to regard the presence of these organisms with some measure of tolerance, not because they are so attenuated that associated disease organisms may be considered to be deprived of their pathogenicity, but because they are encountered with some frequency in relatively unpolluted soil, in sediments in mains, and on plants. On the other hand, it is well known that the presence of other organisms may reduce or even prevent the production of gas by coliform organisms in the lactose broth tube.

Slow lactose fermenters have been shown by Parr to occur in fresh feces, sometimes in pure cultures. Since he finds that they occur occasionally during periods when the normal intestinal function is impaired, the presence in water of certain slow fermenters may be of more than ordinary sanitary significance. It is evident, therefore, that since the true slow lactose fermenters found in water may have derived from either fresh or stored feces, their presence, even in a natural water, cannot always be considered of no sanitary significance. Since the coliform density of a filtered, treated, or filtered-treated water is a measure of the effectiveness with which the treatment has eliminated disease organisms from the water, it is reasonable to attribute equal sanitary significance to the presence in such water of either typical or atypical coliform organisms, slow fermenters, or rapid fermenters. Slow lactose fermenters are found, although in small proportion, in fresh feces, in greater proportion in stored feces, and occasionally in discharges from cases of gastrointestinal disturbances; the presence of these organisms, even in natural water, therefore, cannot always be dismissed as of negligible sanitary significance. Furthermore, since other organisms contained in the sample may reduce the amount of gas produced in lactose broth by typical coliform organisms, the volume of gas produced cannot be accepted as a sure indication of the type of organism present.

Sanitary bacteriologists have also been troubled with so-called "intermediates" in attempts to differentiate members of the coliform group. These are strains which do not exactly conform to the characteristics of groups of bacteria which have been established. They became quite apparent when attempts were made to differentiate *Escherichia coli* from *Aerobacter aerogenes* by the methyl-red test, Voges-Proskauer reaction, and other reactions. Many strains were isolated which did not conform to the accepted definitions of the two above mentioned bacteria. Kline [356] stated that some "intermediates" are mixed cultures. Careful attempts to purify cultures even with single-cell isolations failed to reduce the number of kinds of intermediates. The characteristics of these intermediates were found to be constant. Kline found no evidence for a separate genus such as Citrobacter. Mundt and Hitchner [357] were able to isolate rapidly fermenting variants from slow lactose fermenters by training in lactose broth. Subculturing under certain conditions raised the percentage of rapid fermenters insufficiently to be of sanitary significance. Ziegler,[358] on the other hand, by proper subculturing, was able to transform slow lactose fermenters into rapidly fermenting forms. He believed that such bacteria were as definitely related to fecal contamination as *Escherichia coli*. Ziegler did a little theorizing on the origin of slow lactose fermenters which need not be reviewed here. Experiments by Mundt and Hitchner [357] along these lines may be presented briefly. They found that lactose-fermenting habits of some strains could be altered. The progeny of slow lactose-fermenting strains often exhibit marked variations in rate of lactose utilization. Rapidly fermenting variants are readily obtained by training in lactose broth. The purpose of their investigation was to develop strains which would exhibit rapid lactose utilization when in contact with it. Numerous daughter colonies from a slow lactose-fermenting culture, from a rapidly fermenting variant (48 hours) of this culture, and from a variant which failed to ferment lactose in 15 days were transferred to tubes of lactose broth and observed for lactose utilization (acid produc-

356. Kline. 1935. Amer. J. Pub. Health 25, 833-838.
357. Mundt and Hitchner. 1940. J. Bact. 39, 14.
358. Ziegler. 1939. Amer. J. Pub. Health 29, 257.

tion). Stock cultures of each of these daughter colonies were maintained on agar slants. From platings made from stock strain of a daughter culture in each series which fermented the sugar within two days or less, a number of subcultures were made and carried through the procedure mentioned above. This procedure was followed through 25 subcultures. The percentage of daughter strains which fermented lactose rapidly (within two days) varied from 12 to 60, with an average of approximately 30. A single exposure of the strain to lactose did not produce 100 per cent of rapidly fermenting daughter strains. Altering composition of the medium by decreasing the organic nitrogen, cultivating in lactose solution with a mineral salt base, using massive inocula, altering the ratio of surface area to volume of test medium, and inoculating with cultures obtained by single-cell isolation did not materially increase or retard the rate of lactose fermentation by these cults. Slow lactose fermenters were grouped by Stuart, Mickle, and Borman [359] into several subgroups. They believed that some bacteria now considered to be Shigella are really coliform bacteria.

These marginal coliform bacteria were believed by Parr and Friedlander [359a] to possess as much sanitary significance as the so-called normal forms. An important failing in present technic for coliform bacteria is its inability to determine the presence of these forms.

Density of Escherichia coli in Water. Attempts have been frequently made by bacteriologists to learn something about the density of *Escherichia coli* in water. An early result of these attempts was the *coli-index* proposed by Phelps.[360] The *Escherichia coli* index is the approximate number of *Escherichia coli* per ml. as determined from qualitative tests made on different quantities of water. For any individual sample, it may be taken as the reciprocal of the smallest volume of water used in the test which gave a positive result. Thus, if a sample gave a negative test with .1 ml. and a positive test with 1 ml. and 10 ml. the *Escherichia coli* index would be 1.0. The *Escherichia coli* index for a single sample is not very accurate. The index becomes more accurate as the square root of the number of tests increases. Phelps pointed out very specifically that the *Escherichia coli* index was of value only when determined for a large number of samples from the same source. It is not used today to any extent and need not be discussed further.

McCrady [361] proposed a method of calculating the concentration of cells of *Escherichia coli* from a series of dilutions of the water in fermentation tubes. This suggestion was further simplified by Wolman and Weaver.[362] Other discussions of such averages were prepared by Streeter [363] and Reed.[364] The former suggested expression of *Escherichia coli* densities in terms of "most probable numbers."

359. Stuart, Mickle, and Borman. 1940. Amer. J. Pub. Health 30, 499-508.
359a. Parr and Friedlander. 1942. Amer. J. Pub. Health 32, 381-384.
360. Phelps. 1908. Trans. Amer. Pub. Health Assoc., Pt. 2, 9-13.
361. McCrady. 1918. Amer. J. Pub. Health 9, 201-220.
362. Wolman and Weaver. 1917. J. Amer. Water Wks. Assoc. 4, 200-205.
363. Streeter. 1927. Pub. Health Repts. 42, 1841-1859.
364. Reed. 1925. Pub. Health Repts. 40, 693-721.

A method of arriving at "most probable numbers" proposed by Hoskins [365] is generally used today for indicating the concentration of coliform bacteria in water. It is derived from results of the dilution method for quantitative bacteriological analysis of samples. Based on a probability equation derived by Reed, Hoskins proposed his method for computing the "most probable number" per ml. to two significant figures of coliform bacteria in any sample, regardless of the number of portions examined, number of dilutions, amounts of dilutions, whether or not in geometric series. Hoskins and Butterfield [366] criticized the Phelps index but admitted that an absolutely satisfactory method is not yet available for determining promptly and definitely whether water is free from bacteria causing disease. The next best procedure is to determine the density of the indicator organisms. It leaves much to be desired, however. Another attempt to solve this problem was made by Buchanan and Wollaston. [367] It was recommended that the number of fertile tubes be employed rather than the most probable numbers of bacteria per 100 ml. Georgia [368] proposed a system of most-probable-range (M.P.R.) as preferable to the most-probable-number for coliform concentration. He stated that low concentrations are better detected by increase in the number of 10-ml. tubes than by adding 100-ml. tubes. Other proposals were made by Thomas [369] and Swaroop. [370]

One way to avoid using the indirect methods described above is to develop a solid plating medium for direct estimation of coliform bacteria. Several good ones have been proposed but have never been adequately investigated. They merit more study.

Bacteriological Standards for Potable Water. The ultimate purpose of analyzing water is to determine if it is safe to drink. To determine this the results of an analysis must be compared with "standards" which have been arrived at in previous study. The best known standard in the United States was that of the Treasury Department of not over one coliform cell per 100 ml. of water. Some sanitarians consider this to be lenient. Harting [371] has suggested that this standard might not be a sufficient safeguard against all water-borne disease. It has been suggested that mild and semi-mild intestinal disturbances, which become epidemic could be water-borne, even though the water in question satisfied Treasury Standards. While epidemiological data do not support such an opinion, they argue that drinking water should be above mild suspicion which they believe is possible only when water is bacteria-free.

The Metropolitan Water Board of London, England,[372] is operating under a classification of water which has been used for many years. These

365. Hoskins. 1933. J. Amer. Water Wks. Assoc. 25, 867-877; Pub. Health Repts. 49 (1934), 393-405.
366. Hoskins and Butterfield. 1935. J. Amer. Water Wks. Assoc. 27, 1101-1109.
367. Buchanan and Wollaston. 1941. J. Hyg. 41, 139-168.
368. Georgia. 1942. J. Amer. Water Wks. Assoc. 34, 577-584.
369. Thomas. 1942. Idem 572-576.
370. Swaroop. 1941. Indian J. Med. Res. 29, 499-510.
371. Harting. 1940. J. Bact. 40, 385.
372. Thirtieth Ann. Rept. Metropolitan Water Bd. for the year 1935, London, p. 6.

standards are based upon the coliform bacteria content of a water supply and seem to have been workable over many years. Taking the coliform content of sewage as about 100,000 per ml., they have grouped water into nine classes depending on the concentration of coliform bacteria. The first class permits none in 100 ml. The other classes contain more and more coliform bacteria until the ninth class is undiluted sewage.

The Metropolitan Water Board recognizes but one standard for water and that is the highest quality indicated by them as first-class. The Ministry of Health of Great Britain [373] also has standards but believes they should not be interpreted too rigidly but that serious discrepancies should be investigated promptly. Their standards are based on the presumptive coliform count in 100 ml. piped supplies: Class1, highly satisfactory, less than 1; Class 2, satisfactory, 1-2; Class 3, suspicious, 3-10; Class 4, unsatisfactory, greater than 10.

Some difficulties of an arbitrary standard applied indiscriminately to all samples, regardless of source and intervals between sampling, may give a false opinion concerning plant operation according to Borman et al.[374]

Microorganisms in Sterilized Water. These are microorganisms which are too chlorine-resistant to be destroyed by doses of chlorine usually used in water purification. Not much is known about resistance of ordinary species of bacteria to chlorine. The minimal "chlorine death points" required to kill in 15 to 30 seconds were determined for 503 strains of 48 bacterial species by Tonney et al.[375] Intestinal and respiratory vegetative pathogens were killed by .15 to .25 p.p.m. in 15 to 30 seconds; *Escherichia coli* was somewhat more resistant. Spore-bearers were 10 to 1,100 times more resistant than vegetative cells. Chlorine death points of spores ranged from 2.5 p.p.m. for *Clostridium welchii* to 280 p.p.m. for *Bacillus vulgatus*. *Bacillus subtilis* at 160 p.p.m. was considered best adapted and safest as an index organism of the spore-bearer group. The primary purpose of chlorination is to safeguard against a relatively few intestinal and respiratory vegetative pathogens. Regular and consistent destruction of *Escherichia coli* appears to be a more suitable practical criterion of effective chlorine disinfection than the total bacterial count or *Bacillus subtilis*. Other chlorine resistant nonsporeforming bacteria were studied by Charlton.[376] The chlorine species encountered in a public water supply were pigmented, Gram-negative rods. Most of them were assigned to Pseudomonas and Flavobacterium. They were more resistant to chlorine than intestinal rods as *Escherichia coli*. According to Plucker and Gautsch,[377] from .05 to .2 p.p.m. of free chlorine, acting for one hour, is more effective against *Escherichia coli* than either sodium hypochlorite or chloramines, at equivalent concentration. Results of similar experiments by Heathman and Pierce [378] indicate that the power of chlorine-treated water varies con-

373. Bulletin of Hygiene 14 (1939) 630.
374. Borman, Robinton, and Stuart. 1941. Amer. J. Pub. Health 31, 557-567.
375. Tonney, Greer, and Liebig, Jr. 1930. Idem. 20, 503-508.
376. Charlton. 1933. J. Amer. Water Wks. Assoc. 25, 851-854.
377. Plucker and Gautsch. 1933. Ztschr. Untersuch. Lebensmitt. 66, 62-81.
378. Heathman and Pierce. 1936. Pub. Health Repts. 51, 1367-1387.

siderably within certain limits, but that the killing time is, in a majority of instances, much greater at low than at room temperatures. While there is an appreciable variation in the resistance of freshly isolated strains of *Eberthella typhosa* to the disinfectant action of chlorine and chloramine, as a rule recently isolated strains of *Eberthella typhosa* were more resistant than old laboratory strains of this organism. In many instances freshly isolated strains of *Eberthella typhosa* were more resistant to the disinfectants than members of the coliform group. It appears there is a possibility of *Eberthella typhosa* living in chlorine or chloramine-treated waters as long as or longer at times than coliform. That chlorine sterilization of water is influenced by many factors was also shown by Rudolph and Levine.[379] This probably explains why troublesome bacteria survive treatment in some waters. Some lactose fermenters are in this group. They form gas in the presumptive test but do not confirm.

It is believed by some that some strains of *Escherichia coli may be* more resistant to chlorine than others and that such strains may thus appear in chlorinated water. Borman, Robinton, and Stuart [374] found no such forms nor evidence that coliform bacteria are more resistant.

Maintenance of chlorine residuals between .2 and .4 p.p.m. has generally been considered to be satisfactory for insuring coliform bacteria-free water. Levine, Carpenter, and Coblentz [380] however, stated that this was not a dependable criterion of water sterilization since nonsporeforming coliform bacteria may be isolated from waters having high chlorine residuals. Since the presence of coliform bacteria in water is the index of potability of a water supply, it is important that they be eliminated. Freiberg [381] observed coliform bacteria in water with as much residual chlorine as .5 to .8 p.p.m. Coblentz and Levine [382] described an organism meeting the definition of the coliform group as defined in *Standard Methods for the Examination of Water and Sewage* which resisted exposure to .6 p.p.m. chlorine plus .6 p.p.m. ammonium sulfate for one and one-half hours at 0°C.(32°F.) with residual chlorine of .45 p.p.m.

STERILIZATION OF WATER

Water is sterilized in the food industry to make it safe and to destroy microorganisms which may deteriorate foods. It may be treated in large quantities to make it safe for use, i.e., to destroy disease-producing bacteria. Examples of such troublesome microorganisms are mentioned early in this chapter. The method used depends on various factors such as cost, the amount of water to be treated, and the type of microorganisms to be destroyed.

Filtration. Various types of filters have been used varying from those made of sand to those made of special materials. The former are used largely for treatment of large quantities of water. It is not an infallible method, for some other method is required to destroy microorganisms

379. Rudolph and Levine. 1938. J. Bact. 35, 3.
380. Levine, Carpenter, and Coblentz. 1940. Water and Water Engin. 42. 281-283; J. Bact. 41 (1941), 89-90.
381. Freiberg. 1940. Water Wks. and Sewage 87. 65-69.
382. Coblentz and Levine. 1941. J. Bact. 41, 89-90.

which may pass through the filters. Filters of sand remove most of the microorganisms and much of the suspended matter. Other fillers have also been adopted in filters, such as activated carbon, diatomaceous earth, and asbestos. Activated carbon filters remove few bacteria but do remove flavors, odors, and colors. Asbestos and diatomaceous earth filters are bacteriologically satisfactory but require periodic washing or replacement.

The Seitz EK filter with surface of 350 square centimeters was tested by Boars and Lecluse-Asselbergs.[383] Results were found to depend on numerical density of organisms and on amount of suspended matter. The filter soon becomes permeable to bacteria and is clogged by suspended matter with reduction in filtration rate. They concluded that this filter was limited to sterilization of clear water containing only a few bacteria and even then it must be frequently changed or sterilized each time before use. It was of little value in sterilizing water with much suspended matter or contaminated muddy water.

Filtration has been used for purifying small quantities of water in homes. Many have been found to be unreliable. Bruns [384] observed that those which were filled with sand of a grain size of one mm. diameter retain only about 10 to 20 per cent of the bacteria. With a grain size of .5 mm. about 50 per cent of bacteria were retained, but "loss of head" was greatly increased.

Iodine. Iodine has been much recommended for emergency sterilization of drinking water, especially on a small scale. Pond and Willard [385] undertook a series of tests in which water, inoculated with one drop of a prepared *Escherichia coli* suspension, was subjected to the action of an iodine tincture of definite strength. The samples of water were then placed in a water bath at 17°C. (62.6°F.) for a contact period of 15 minutes. The bactericidal action was terminated by adding an excess of sodium thiosulphate and the water samples then examined. In 10 experiments a reduction in bacterial content of 99.999 per cent was obtained in six cases, 99.99 per cent in three cases, and 99.9 per cent in one case. The last case was that of a river water heavily polluted with organic matter. In a second series of 25 experiments all cases showed a reduction of 99.999 per cent.

A period of 15 minutes' contact was selected as being the maximum time to wait before drinking, although earlier investigators have suggested a 30 minutes' contact period. Conteras [386] believed iodine was a better purifying agent for water than any other known substance. It was said to equal chlorine and to be more easily applied.

Metals. That metals have a detrimental action on bacteria has been known for a long time. Harmful effects were noticed by Naegeli, who proposed the terms oligodynamy and oligodynamic action. Since these early days, many others have reported results of investigations and various patents have been issued. It will be impossible to review all of the literature here.

383. Boars and Lecluse-Asselbergs. 1932. Bull. Hyg. 7, 515.
384. Bruns. 1937. Gas. u. Wasser 80, 502.
385. Pond and Willard. 1937. J. Amer. Water Wks. Assoc. 29, 1995-1998
386. Conteras. 1930. Ann. Hyg. pub. Indus. et soc. 218-241.

In recent years ionic silver has been much studied, and a method known as the Katadyn Process has been used for getting the silver into the ionic state. The Electro-Katadyn-Sterilizer consists of two silver electrodes from which the silver is dissolved. The silver ions are discharged into the water from silver electrodes by a weak current. The amount of silver entering the solution can be regulated by the strength of current. It has been used for sterilization of water and food. The literature has become quite voluminous. Ruge [387] and Walton and Ayyar [388] observed good results when using the Katadyn method. Krause [389] observed that pure metals had oligodynamic action which differed from their germicidal activities. Colloidal silver was effective against bacteria, and water containing it remained germicidal. Degwitz,[390] found the method so effective that 100,000 coliform bacteria were killed in 10 minutes. Similar results were reported by Samaan.[391] However, he said that colloidal silver was less effective than ionic. As is the case with most disinfecting reactions, Gibbard [392] found temperature to be of considerable importance. Low temperatures retarded it as did presence of organic matter. While Gibbard observed germicidal properties in water so treated, he did not recommend the method for practical use at that time. Interfering factors were also noticed by Brandes,[393] who said that .05 p.p.m. would sterilize water and that the contact period depended on turbidity, composition, and hydrogen-ion concentration.

According to Metalnikoff [394] the silver must be the anode to exert germicidal action. Such bacteria as *Escherichia coli, Microspira cholerae, Salmonella paratyphi, Eberthella typhosa,* and *Staphylococcus aureus* were all killed in a few minutes and often in a few seconds. Boiling did not destroy the bactericidal property; it remained in the water for over three months. The concentration of silver in the water depended on the length of exposure to the electric current. A concentration of silver of one part in 5,000,000 killed *Escherichia coli* and staphlococci in three hours. Myers and Mauer [395] reported similar results; .10 to .15 p.p.m. of silver was sufficient to destroy 250,000 *Escherichia coli* cells per ml. of river water, or neutral distilled water, in 2.5 hours. *Staphylococcus aureus* was only a little more resistant.

Whether silver in water and foodstuffs would be harmful has never been adequately studied. Gibbard [396] pointed out that the silver ion was one of the most active ions. Since water containing colloidal silver has been recommended in many different kinds of foods Gibbard believed that the matter should be studied by health officials.

Ozone. The general bactericidal aspects of ozone have been reviewed in Chapter 1. It is not widely used even for sterilization of such a sub-

387. Ruge. 1932. Rev. in Biol. Absts. 9, 389.
388. Walton and Ayyar. 1932. Scritti biol. 7, 359-366.
389. Krause. 1929. Gesndh. Ing. 52, 500.
390. Degwitz. 1929. Klin. Wchnschr. 8, 342-348.
391. Samaan. 1930. Quart. J. Pharm. and Pharmacol. 3, 21-24.
392. Gibbard. 1933. Canad. Pub. Health J. 24, 96-97.
393. Brandes. 1934. Ind. Eng. Chem. 26, 962-964.
394. Metalnikoff. 1935. Compt. Rend. Acad. Sci. 201, 411-412.
395. Myers and Mauer. 1935. J. Bact. 29, 7-8.
396. Gibbard. 1937. Amer. J. Pub. Health 27, 112.

stance as water. In addition to its sterilizing ability, it reduces color, odor, and flavor and leaves nothing of a deleterious nature in the water. Historical information as well as its effect on various bacteria has been presented by Lipkowski [397] and Rich.[398] Its bactericidal action has been well established and it has wide application in France and Belgium.

Ultraviolet Light. Germicidal properties and practical use of this form of energy have been discussed in several places in this book. It now has a voluminous literature. There seems to be little doubt about the efficiency of the method if the rays can penetrate to the bacteria. It is a method which may be adapted to sterilization of water used in special industries, such as brewing, distilling, and dairying where it may be necessary.

One difficulty which should be considered is the low penetrating power through liquids containing various substances in suspension or solution. Courmont and Nogier,[399] who had previously shown that immersion of a mercury vapor quartz lamp in clear water destroyed ordinary bacteria and coliform bacteria within a distance of 30 centimeters in about a minute, showed here that colloidal substances, such as liquids with organic matter, were not easily penetrated. To treat some materials very thin layers must be used. This was found to be necessary by Maurain and Warcollier.[400] Sterilization of many substances is therefore limited to the surface. Turbidity and color were found by Oker-Blom[401] to retard germicidal properties of ultraviolet light. His observations were made with various pure cultures of bacteria. He added more data but they did not change the trend of opinion. Under practical conditions in large water plants turbidity would probably be a great problem. In Dallyn and Parkinson's [402] experiments, turbidities of five to 20 p.p.m. permitted bacterial removal of 97 per cent; 20 to 50 p.p.m. permitted a removal of 94 to 97 per cent. They believed that ultraviolet sterilization was a feasible method even though there were certain complicating factors.

Henri, Helbronner, and von Recklinghausen [403] devised an apparatus in which large quantities of water could be treated. Water inoculated with coliform bacteria, when pumped through it at the rate of 36 cubic meters per hour, was completely sterilized. Suspensions of pathogenic bacteria were sterilized in a short time. Similar results were secured by Grant [404] in the laboratory of the Sorbonne in Paris. He believed that he had shown the possibility of sterilizing water on a large scale. Fischer[405] found this treatment of water satisfactory for breweries. Favorable results were also reported by Spencer,[406] Smith,[407] Blocher,[408] and Springer.[409]

397. Lipkowski. 1937. La Tech. Sanit. et Munic. 32, 54.
398. Rich. 1935. Engineering 139, 9.
399. Courmont and Nogier. 1909. Compt. Rend. Acad Sci. 149, 364-365.
400. Maurain and Warcollier. 1909. Compt. Rend. Acad. Sci. 149, 155-156.
401. Oker-Blom. 1913. Ztschr. Hyg. 74, 197-247.
402. Dallyn and Parkinson. 1915. Canad. Engin. 29, 686-692.
403. Henri, Helbronner, and von Recklinghausen. 1910. Compt. Rend. Acad. Sci. 150, 932-934.
404. Grant. 1910. Engin. News-Rec. 64, 275.
405. Fischer. 1915. Rev. in J. Inst. Brewing 21, 474.
406. Spencer. 1917. J. Amer. Water Wks. Assoc. 4, 172-182.
407. Smith. 1917. Engin. News-Rec. 79, 1021-1022.
408. Blocher. 1929. J. Amer. Water Wks. Assoc. 21, 1361-1372.
409. Springer. 1931. Pub. Works 62, 39 and 51.

The last mentioned studied especially the cost of sterilization of water with ultraviolet light. That water to be sterilized in this manner had to be clarified should not be charged against this method. It should be done regardless.

Most of the work on germicidal action of ultraviolet light has been done with quartz lamps. Other sources of this form of energy are also possible. Davies [410] reported that sufficient ultraviolet rays are emitted from iron arcs to yield appreciable results. These rays, however, did not seem to have great penetrating powers.

This method of sterilization has certain benefits over other methods. It does not change the water. Especially important is the fact that no changes in taste are involved, which is not the case with some other practical methods.

Copper Salts. These were once considered to be active germicides. While they were mainly studied for disinfecting large bodies of water, such as reservoirs, they were also used for smaller amounts. Moore and Kellerman [411] and Kellerman and Beckwith [412] found copper sulfate satisfactory for destruction of bacteria in water. Considerable variation in susceptibility was observed among the bacteria which were used. The time factor was quite important. Stone and Monahan [413] found copper sulfate in a concentration of one part in 4,000,000 of water to possess appreciable effect on bacteria. Vincent [414] observed marked germicidal action of copper sulfate on *Bacillus perfrigens*. Stewart [415] concluded from results of experiments that water could be purified by standing in copper vessels for three hours. This same possibility was investigated by Kraemer [416] and Pilod and Codvelle [417]; the former suggested use of copper strips which were to be allowed to stand in the water overnight. This method of sterilizing water never had wide application because other more satisfactory methods were developed and because copper was looked upon with considerable suspicion.

BACTERIOPHAGE IN WATER

For a long time it has been known that the water in certain rivers in India has been germicidal. When d'Herelle announced the discovery of bacteriophage, he gave an explanation for these observations. Russell [418] observed the action of natural waters on bacteria, which might have been due to bacteriophage. When *Eberthella typhosa* and coliform bacteria were inoculated into boiled waters (surface, deep well, and spring) growth generally occurred. This was more marked with the latter than with the former, and was most pronounced where the seeding was light. When the same cultures were exposed to the action of water filtered through a Chamberland or Berkefeld filter or to etherized water from which the anaesthetic

410. Davies. 1913. Chem. Engin. 17, 177-179.
411. Moore and Kellerman. 1905. U. S. Dept. Agr., Bur. Plant Indus. Bull. 76.
412. Kellermann and Beckwith. 1906. U. S. Dept. Agr., Bur. Plant Indus. Bull. 100.
413. Stone and Monahan. 1906. Ann. Rept., Mass. Agr. Expt. Sta., 157-190.
414. Vincent. 1917. Compt. Rend. Acad. Sci. 164, 153-156.
415. Stewart. 1905. Amer. J. Med. Sci., May, 1905.
416. Kraemer. 1905. Amer. Med., Feb. 18, 1905.
417. Pilod and Codvelle. 1932. Compt. Rend. Acad. Sci. 194, 497-500.

had been removed by aspiration, growth not only did not take place, but the numerical content was greatly reduced so that the cultures became sterile within 24 hours. Tests showed that if filtered water was heated to 60°C.(140°F.) for 10 minutes it lost its toxic power. The origin of the toxic substances was ascribed to the development of water bacteria. After incubation for 33 days, this water was again filtered and found toxic for typhoid and coliform bacteria, and upon heating, it again lost its toxicity. The demonstration of the existence of bacteriophage in water has given new interest in this subject. Arnold [419] found bacteriophage present in Chicago River water in varying amounts. The concentration was in direct proportion to the amount of sewage. Arnold believed that such bacteriophage would influence the bacterial content of water.

Arloing and Sempe [420] described results which they secured with water of the Rhone and Saone rivers, using various species of organisms, *Escherichia coli*, *Salmonella paratyphi*, *Salmonella schottmülleri*, *Eberthella typhosa*, and *Eberthella dysenteriae*. The water of the Rhone and Saone rivers possessed inhibitory powers for the above bacteria. *Escherichia coli* seemed to be more sensitive than the other organisms. In general, the water of the Saone possessed greater inhibitory power than the water of the Rhone. Water from the latter, however, was more active against *Eberthella typhosa*. Arloing and Chavanne [421] extended these observations to other rivers. The results in each case show the presence of a lytic principle. Arloing, Sempe, and Chavanne [422] explained the antagonistic action of the waters, examination of which has just been reported, as due to a polyvalent bacteriophage. They were led to this explanation rather than to the presence of salt, etc., because dilution did not prevent lysis and increase of virulence occurred under conditions similar to those in which d'Herelle's principle was exalted.

The reaction of water was related to longevity of bacteriophage by Marginesu.[423] In alkaline water the phage against various pathogenic bacteria could always be detected. When the pH was 5.2, phages for *Escherichia coli* and Staphylococcus could be found but not that for *Eberthella typhosa* or *Shigella dysenteriae*. In water with a pH of 3.5 no bacteriophages were found. These observations were confirmed by observations in the laboratory. Chemical impurities from industrial plants were reported by Segre [424] to have little effect. He found various bacteriophages present.

In general those who have found bacteriophage in water have been able to relate it to evident fecal pollution. This was the experience of De Assuncao and Rodovalho,[425] Gildemeister and Watanare,[426] and Schloss-

418. Russell. 1902. Science 15, 364.
419. Arnold. 1925. Amer. J. Pub. Health 15, 950-52.
420. Arloing and Sempe. 1926. Compt. Rend. Soc. Biol. 94, 191-194.
421. Arloing and Chavanne. 1925. Compt. Rend. Soc. Biol. 92, 257.
422. Arloing, Sempe, and Chavanne. 1926. Bull. Acad. Med. 43.
423. Marginesu. 1932. Rev. in J. Amer. Water Wks. Assoc. 26 (1934), 1113.
424. Segre. 1913. Zentbl. gesam. Hyg. Bakt. Immunitäts. 22, 528.
425. De Assuncao and Rodovalho. 1934. Bull. Hyg. 9, 480.
426. Gildemeister and aWtanare. 1931. Zentbl. Bakt., Pt. 1, Orig., 122, 556-575.

mann.[427] Bacteriophage probably plays little role in purification of water (Gildemeister,[428] Stewart and Ghosal,[429] and Flu [430]).

Presence of bacteriophage in water was given sanitary significance by Pasricha and de Monte,[431] based on the assumption that presence of bacteriophage active against intestinal pathogens from the human intestines indicates contamination by individuals who harbor such bacteria. This assumption was supported by results of examination of 516 samples of water.

Pasricha and de Monte's (1941) Method Detecting the Presence of Bacteriophage in Water. Twenty-five ml. samples of water are collected in sterile containers. Each sample is added to 50 ml. of nutrient broth or peptone water to which are added one ml. each of young cultures of smooth strains of *Vibrio cholerae, Eberthella typhosa, Shigella dysenteriae,* Shiga and Flexner types. The mixtures are incubated for 48 hours, .1 ml. M. sodium hydroxide being added if necessary to maintain an alkaline reaction, and filtered through a diatomaceous earth filter. The filtrates are tested for bacteriophages by the drop method.

Viruses in Drinking Water. Viruses are not ordinarily spread by water. Information on this question, however, is not definite. If there are exceptions, the best known are those causing poliomyelitis and swimming pool conjunctivitis. Kling [432] reported finding the former in water. In view of this fact Levaditi, Kling, and Lépine [433] were led to investigate the effect of chlorination on the virus in water. They reported that four p.p.m., of chlorine destroyed the virus in cloudy tap water, while .4 p.p.m. was equally effective with clarified portions. As Kempf and Soule [434] stated, the above authors did not control pH and temperature nor did they determine the minimum effective chlorine concentration nor the shortest effective contact period. Kempf and Soule observed no virucidal action of chlorine in a concentration of .5 p.p.m. in one and one-half hours, a concentration in excess of that usually used in practice.

Bacteria in Bottled Waters. Bottled waters are used because of their special mineral content and because some people lose faith in their local water supply. The sanitary condition of bottled waters depends on the sanitary quality of water before bottling and also on methods employed during bottling. Both of these factors are carefully watched by the larger bottlers of mineral waters for advertising purposes, if for no other reason. Obst [435] conducted an examination of bottled waters from 110 American springs and 57 sources in foreign countries. The usual Standard Methods were used. Bacteriological analyses indicated an uncalled-for condition in these waters, since people are led to believe that bottled waters are clean and harmless. Some brands of water were found to contain *Escherichia*

427. Schlossmann. 1932. Ztschr. Hyg. 114, 65-76.
428. Gildemeister. 1932. Gesundheits-Ing. 55, 241.
429. Stewart and Ghosal. 1932. Indian J. Med. Res. 19.
430. Flu. 1941. J. Microbiol. and Serol. 7, 39-60.
431. Pasricha and de Monte. 1941. Indian Med. Gaz. 76, 492-493.
432. Kling. 1939. Internatl. Bull. Econ. Med. Res. and Pub. Hyg. A 40, 161.
433. Levaditi, Kling, and Lépine. 1931. Bull. Acad. Méd. 105. 190.
434. Kempf and Soule. 1940. Proc. Soc. Expt. Biol. and Med. 44, 431-434.
435. Obst. 1916. U. S. Dept. Agr. Bull. 369.

coli in such numbers that the water would not conform to any standard which could be imagined for public water supplies. Obst considered an extreme standard to be essential for such types of water. No water should be sold which gives any indication whatever of contamination at the source. Sanitary inspections at the source should be made to insure the proper care in the bottling establishments.

A few data on this subject were also published by Bauce and Caillon.[436] The hydrogen-ion concentration of 21 bottled mineral waters varied between 6.0 and 7.6. The number of bacteria per ml. varied from 0 to 10 in 10 samples, from 10 to 100 in five samples, from 100 to 1,000 in three samples, and 400,000 in one. Only one sample contained *Escherichia coli*. This same variation in bacterial content was observed by Kliewe and Lang.[437] Some harbored as many as 55,000 per liter. The State Departments of Health of New York [438] and Florida [439] reported that some bottled waters were bottled under quite unsanitary conditions. While the water as it came from the ground was satisfactory, examination after bottling revealed the presence of *Escherichia coli* in 10-ml. quantities. It is quite probable that what has been said above about bottled waters might not be true today.

Carbonated Waters. In carbonated water the bacteria must survive almost the same conditions as in the carbonated beverages. The viability of certain members of the colon-typhoid group in carbonated waters was studied by Koser and Skinner.[440] Carbonation caused sharp diminution in the numbers of *Escherichia coli*, *Eberthella typhosa*, and *Salmonella paratyphi*. At room temperature the destruction was more marked. Spore-forming bacteria were found to be quite resistant.

The effect of carbon dioxide under pressure on water bacteria was also tried by Colin.[441] *Escherichia coli* resisted a pressure of 25 kg. for more than five days. *Shigella dysenteriae* was destroyed in less than 15 hours at 15 kg., and in less than six hours at 20 kg. The cholera organism was destroyed in less than 10 hours at 10 atmospheres. Other organisms gave similar data. A pressure of 25 kg. on a sample of polluted Seine River water killed all of the bacteria except *Bacillus subtilis* in a few hours. Guillerd and Lieffrig [442] found that water artificially saturated with carbon dioxide showed practically no bactericidal action against *Escherichia coli* or *Eberthella typhosus*. Practically no reduction in numbers was evident after exposure of 40 minutes in their experiments.

BACTERIOLOGY OF ICE

In former times much natural ice was harvested and stored until used in the summer. When natural ice was widely used, questions were always

436. Bauce and Caillon. 1929. Arch. Inst. Pasteur, Tunis 18, 199-201.
437. Kliewe and Lang. 1931. Arch. Hyg. 105, 124-131.
438. Health News, New York State Dept. Health 9 (1932), 19.
439. Kennedy. 1936. Health Notes, Florida St. Bd. Health 28, 20.
440. Koser and Skinner. 1922. J. Bact. 7, 111-121.
441. Colin. 1915. Compt. Rend. Acad. Sci. 161, 652-55.
442. Guillerd and Lieffrig. 1935. Chem. Absts. 29, 7538.

raised with respect to its sanitary quality, for much of it was harvested from bodies of water of questionable sanitary condition.

Artificial ice is produced mostly by the can method. These are usually about the size of an ordinary cake, and, before freezing, are filled with distilled water; if ordinary water with a high mineral content is used, the cake of ice, after it has been frozen, will have a white core through the center. This is formed from the dissolved and suspended matter and will also contain the bacteria which were present in the original water.

The State of Connecticut [443] has inspected artificial ice plants for the purpose of enforcing sanitary code regulations adopted by the public-health council. While they admitted that the possibility of ice becoming contaminated and remaining so for a long period was slight, it was nevertheless desirable that ice should be obtained or made from safe water and under clean conditions.

Ice does not furnish the essentials of a good medium and consequently there is no multiplication of bacteria. The question resolves itself into determining how many bacteria may survive in such an environment. The following factors contribute to the inhibitory action on bacteria: temperature, lack of oxygen, and absence of moisture. Longevity of bacteria in ice has received some attention from bacteriologists and sanitarians. Frankland [444] reported data which were secured by Prudden. Cultures of *Serratia marcescens (Bacillus prodigiosus)*, *Bacillus proteus vulgaris*, *Staphylococcus pyogenes aureus*, a fluorescent bacillus, and *Eberthella typhosa* were put into samples of water and exposed to temperatures of —10°C.(14°F.) to —1.1°C.(30°F.) for 103 days. *Bacillus prodigiosus* decreased from 6,300 in four days to 3,000; in 37 days the number went to 22, and after 51 days, all of the cells had died. *Bacillus proteus vulgaris* disappeared in 51 days. At the end of 11 days there were 1,000,000 cells of *Eberthella typhosa* and 7,000 after 103 days. Alternate freezing and thawing were very detrimental to bacteria. Experiments with anthrax vegetative and spore cells indicated that the spores resisted for some time, while the vegetative cells were rather quickly destroyed. The cholera vibrio was reported to have been destroyed in from six to 10 days.

Chemical and bacteriological studies by Clark [445] with ice gathered in different localities in Massachusetts showed that ice contains less of both suspended and dissolved matter than the water from which it is formed. The same is true for bacteria, particularly if there is a considerable depth of water under the ice, and the water is quiet during the process of ice formation. When, in order to thicken ice, that already formed on a pond or river is flooded and the entire volume of water over the ice is frozen, bacteria will undoubtedly be retained in this ice. It was stated by Clark then when *Echerichia coli* and *Eberthella typhosa* were frozen in the ice they retained their vitality for a number of weeks, the exact limit not having been determined. It was also stated that if there was a considerable depth of water in portions of a somewhat polluted pond or river, and ice

443. Scott. 1933. The Connecticut Health Bull. **47**, 11-15.
444. Frankland. 1894. Microorganisms in Water, pp. 105-106.
445. Clark. 1901. Mass. St. Bd. Health, Rept., **509-524**.

was formed in these portions in comparatively quiet water with but little matter in suspension, such ice would probably be entirely satisfactory for domestic use, although considerable drainage may enter the body of water upon which it forms. On the other hand, ice formed in shallow portions of such ponds or rivers, even during still weather, or in any portion if there is a considerable movement of the water by currents or wind while it is forming, may be rendered by these conditions entirely unfit for domestic use.

Ice and Typhoid Fever. The general consensus of opinion among sanitarians is that ice is not an important epidemiological factor in the spread of typhoid fever. Reudiger [446] secured data with *Escherichia coli* and *Eberthella typhosa*. From this it is apparent that 99.9 per cent of the *Eberthella typhosa* die during the first eight days. Park [447] also reported experiments in which 20 cultures of *Eberthella typhosa*, after having been grown for 28 hours in agar, were placed in a room, the temperature of which was rather constant at 23°F. At the end of a week, only 14 per cent of the bacteria were alive, and at the end of 22 weeks, all of the cultures were dead. Watery suspensions of different bacteria were placed in small tubes and dropped into liquid air, exposures being from three minutes to two hours and 10 minutes. As a result of this pressure, the virulence of the organisms was only slightly decreased. Jordan, Russell, and Zeit [448] found that in filtered water *Eberthella typhosa* died rapidly. Two organisms were found after the first day, and none later. Hilliard *et al.*[449] reported that 99 per cent of *Escherichia coli* were destroyed by freezing in tap water for three hours. *B. subtilis* showed a less uniform reaction. No apparent difference was noticed by these investigators between alternate freezing and continued freezing. Hutchins and Wheeler [450] reported an ice-borne epidemic but Hill [451] believed the evidence to be inconclusive. The characteristics of the epidemic did not agree with those which Hill thought an ice-borne epidemic should have. Jordan [452] and Bartow [453] belittled ice as a cause of illness. Conway,[454] after a careful investigation, was led to conclude that an outbreak of typhoid fever at Elmira, N. Y., was due to the consumption of a superficial layer of natural ice harvested from a heavily polluted river, even though this ice was stored for between five and six months. Conway believed that a real danger existed in the use of polluted ice directly in drinks. Bacteriological analysis if the ice indicated pollution. There were 140,000 bacteria per ml. at 20°C.(68°F.), and 1,300 per ml. at 37°C.(98.6°F.). *Escherichia coli* was present in one-tenth ml. quantities.

446. Reudiger. 1911. Quart. J., Univ. North Dakota, 263-263.
447. Park. 1901. Science 13, 322-323.
448. Jordan, Russell, and Zeit. 1904. J. Infect. Dis. 1, 641-689.
449. Hilliard, Torission, and Stone. 1915. Science 42, 770-771.
450. Hutchins and Wheeler. 1903. Amer. J. Med. Sci. 126, 680.
451. Hill. 1910. Cold Storage and Ice Trade J. 40, 33-35.
452. Jordan. 1911. Idem 42, 31-32.
453. Bartow. 1916. Ill. State Water Survey Bull. 12, 183-188.
454. Conway. 1924. Amer. J. Pub. Health 14, 574-577.

Whether *Eberthella typhosa* might survive in ice would depend on various factors, such as number of cells present, age of the ice, and perhaps presence of organic matter. Results of experiments on longevity of *Eberthella typhosa* in ice are contradictory. Lascu [455] found that they would survive for months, while Thomas [456] took the opposite position. As is the case with foods in general, ice must be handled in a cleanly manner. Schulze and Karff [457] found evidence of pollution in ice which had been crushed and placed in unsanitary containers.

Methods for the Bacterial Examination of Ice. After ice has been sampled and the sample is melted, the methods of analysis, chemical and bacterial, are no different from those used in water analysis. The sampling of the ice for the bacteriological analysis does, however, require some special attention. Care must be exercised to secure a sample which is not contaminated. This may be accomplished in different ways. The block of ice should be carefully cleaned and washed with distilled water. Then, it should be copiously rinsed with sterile distilled water. After this it should be split, if it is a large block, and small pieces chipped off and transferred to sterile containers by means of sterile instruments. If this is carefully carried out, no contamination will result. The block may also be bored out with a sterile auger and the shavings collected in a sterile bottle. Greenfield [458] has described an instrument for sampling ice. It is constructed after the cheese sampler.

Longevity of Pathogenic Bacteria in Natural Waters. This is an important subject in sanitary work. The relative longevity of pathogenic bacteria and the various indicators of pollution must be known. In view of the various conditions under which experiments have been carried out, some confusion among results exists. This situation is not difficult to explain. This subject came to the fore in the so-called Illinois River case,[459] in which the City of St. Louis and the State of Missouri sued in the courts to prevent the City of Chicago from using the Illinois River for disposing of its sewage. The plaintiffs argued that pathogenic bacteria, such as *Eberthella typhosa*, could live in the Illinois River and eventually enter the St. Louis water supply. Several investigations were carried out to secure information on this possibility.

Jordan, Russell, and Zeit [460] studied this question in both pure and polluted waters. They suspended bacteria in collodion sacs in both pure and polluted waters. In pure Lake Michigan water, the bacilli did not die out until after a week, but three days seemed to be the limit for the polluted Chicago Drainage Canal water. Russell and Fuller [461] confirmed these results, using pure Lake Michigan water and sewage as the menstrua. In this experiment, the bacilli lived for about 10 days in Lake Michigan water and three days in sewage. Houston [462] has studied this question in England. He points out that one-ml. samples were used by the American workers in most of the cases, and from these small samples conclusions were drawn with regard to the longevity of *Eberthella typhosa*. When no

455. Lascu. 1922. J. Amer. Med. Assoc. 78, 1403.
456. Thomas. 1924. Science 60, 244-245.
457. Schulze and Karff. 1932. Munic. Sanit. 3, 453-454.
458. Greenfield. 1916. J. Bact. 1, 623.
459. Leighton. 1909. Water Supply and Irrigation Paper 194. U. S. Geol. Survey.
460. Jordan, Russell, and Zeit. 1904. J. Infect. Dis. 1, 641-689.
461. Russell and Fuller. 1906. J. Infect. Dis. Supp., 2, 40.
462. Houston. Various reports from Met. Water Bd.

organisms were found in one-ml. samples, it was stated that the organism had died out. Probably American bacteriologists have been too much accustomed to use small amounts of water in analytical work. Houston carried on experiments, using Thames, Lee, and New river waters, using 100-ml. quantities of the water as the maximum amounts examined. For 100-ml. quantities in 18 experiments, it required nine weeks for the total disappearance of *Eberthella typhosa*. Ninety-nine per cent of them disappeared in one week under laboratory conditions of the experiment. The above data of both American and English bacteriologists indicate the value of storage. The rate of death of *Eberthella typhosa* and *Escherichia coli* in pure natural water has been reported by Rahn and Hinds [463] to follow the monomolecular law. Under these conditions, the rate increased with the temperature. Oxygen was found to be harmful to *Escherichia coli* but beneficial to *Eberthella typhosa*.

In the laboratories of the Metropolitan Water Board of London (Whipple [464]), it was found that 99 per cent of the original number of *Eberthella typhosa* in river water died in one week, and of the remainder some lived for five to eight weeks. Uncultivated strains seemed to die more quickly; when the effect of temperature was studied, the following storage periods were necessary for the different temperatures given to reduce *Eberthella typhosa* organisms from 100,000 to three per ml.: five weeks at 32°C. (89.6°F.); four at 40°C.(104°F.); three at 50°C.(122°F.), and two at 64.4°C.(148°F.). Houston believed that storage for four weeks provided a reasonable margin of safety. Houston in the Second Research Report reported the results of attempts to isolate *Eberthella typhosa* from water. He examined, all told, 29,400 ml. from 156 samples of raw river water for the presence of this organism. This involved 7,329 colonies; all of the results were negative. Houston believed that *Eberthella typhosa* was not present in raw water in large numbers. These results were confirmed by investigations which were reported on the Fifth Research Report. In the Sixth Research Report Houston stated that "uncultivated" *Eberthella typhosa* tended to die in river water during storage more than the "cultivated" strains. He claimed that these data enhanced the importance of his statements about the value of storage. Wibaut and Moeus [465] attempted to find out why *Eberthella typhosa* disappeared from water. Specimens of water were inoculated and stored under different conditions. The organism disappeared from tap water, rain water, and swimming pool water in seven to 10 days. Their disappearance corresponded with a marked increase of a bacteria-eating protozoon. Less clear-cut results were secured when the cells were put into ground water. In one experiment, the cells of *Eberthella typhosa* remained for four weeks in spite of the presence of the protozoon. These authors concluded that other factors, besides the protozoon, also helped to explain the disappearance of the bacteria. For all practical purposes, Houston believed that a storage period of four

463. Rahn and Hinds. 1914. Canad. Engin. 26, 854-55.
464. Whipple. 1922. J. Amer. Water Wks. Assoc. 9, 208-225.
465. Wilbaut and Moeus. 1927. Pub. Health Engin. Absts., 1927.

weeks was adequate to render a water safe as far as *Eberthella typhosa* is concerned.

Houston also showed that temperature was a very important factor in the question of the longevity of *Eberthella typhosa* in water. He found that the lower the temperature, the longer the organism lived in water. The water in these experiments was artificially inoculated and stored at the several temperatures which were used. Greer [54] confirmed Houston's conclusions. He reported that *Eberthella typhosa* lived longer in colder water than in warm water. Various factors, such as hydrogen-ion concentration, sunlight, and temperature, among others, were said to influence the death of bacteria in water.

Presence of organic matter is important in longevity experiments. Vacek [466] found it to be important along with other factors. He artificially contaminated water from several sources with *Eberthella typhosa*, observing survival times varying from seven days with distilled water to 14 days with filtered water at 20°C.(68°F.). Water was believed to behave as a nutrient medium even though it contains only a little nitrogenous matter. Varying survival periods have been reported for this organism in water by Violle,[467] Ballantyne,[468] Warner,[469] Mouzet [470] and Heukelekian and Schuloff.[471] The latter observed disappearance of *Eberthella typhosa* to be rapid in sewage and polluted water. Several days' storage resulted in 99 per cent reduction with heavy initial infection. For short periods, they observed increases but these were overcome by rapid death rate later.

Schepilewsky [472] concluded that, as a rule, natural waters are able to free themselves quickly of bacterial contamination. The purification of the water from bacteria is largely dependent upon the rapidity of the growth of the protozoa.

The viability of *Vibrio cholerae* has also been investigated by Houston, using the same technique as for *Eberthella typhosa*. Ninety-nine per cent of the cholera organisms perished in three days under the laboratory conditions of the experiment. This is a much shorter period than required for *Eberthella typhosa*. Gelarie [473] studied the longevity of *Vibrio cholerae* in water of New York Bay. He stated that the survival of these organisms in water depends upon the strain which is used, the number of bacteria seeded, and other factors. The organisms were said to live in native bay water from seven to 45 days, and in sterilized bay water up to 285 days. In sterile tap water they lived for one to 18 days, and in native tap water from one to three days. In competition with the other water organisms the life of the cholera organisms was found to be short. Yasuhara [474] made

466. Vacek. 1932. Zentbl. Bakt., Pt. 2, 107, 485.
467. Violle. 1937. Presse Méd. 45, 1355.
468. Ballantyne. 1930. J. Bact. 19, 303-320.
469. Warner. 1933. Ztschr. Hyg., 115, 14.
470. Mouzet. 1936. Tech. Sanit. Munic. 31, 64.
471. Heukelekian and Schuloff. 1935-36. New Jersey State Bull. 589, 32.
472. Schepilewsky. 1910. Arch. Hyg. 72, 73-90.
473. Gelarie. 1916. Med. Rec. 89, 236-239.
474. Yasuhara. 1926. J. Pub. Health Assoc., Japan, 2, 1-3.

tests on the longevity of Yamamoto and Yamashita strains of cholerae vibrio in five different kinds of water by infecting 200-ml. portions and storing them outdoors, but shielded from the direct rays of the sun. The 1:00 A. M. temperature varied from 1 to 5°C. (33.8 to 41°F.). The type of water and the time of survival of the cholera organisms follows: (1) Sea water, Waka-no-ura Bay, 11 days; (2) mixture of sea and river water, Estuary water at Aogishi, 13 days; (3) river water, Kinodawa River, eight days; (4) tap water, Wakayame City water works, eight days; (5) well water, well at laboratory, eight days. It was suggested that if water is known to be contaminated with cholerae vibrio in winter, its use be suspended for at least two weeks. It was thought that this would give an ample margin of safety.

That generalizations should not be made is evident from experiments conducted by Moens [475] who found that the type of water was important. Presence of certain species of protozoa is also responsible for more rapid disappearance of *Eberthella typhosa*.

Mycobacterium tuberculosis. Possibility of dissemination of tuberculosis among human beings by water has not worried health officials. Briscoe [476] observed that tubercle bacilli could live more than a year (441 days) in running water. No difference in longevity of the human and bovine types could be noticed. Briscoe stated that water infected with *Mycobacterium tuberculosis* might infect man and that infected watering troughs might cause the disease in animals. Longevity of this organism was also shown by Brown, Petroff, and Heise [477] in river water infected by sewage. Viable acid-fast bacteria were found 2.9 miles down stream from the sewer outfall. They quoted Jessen and Rabinowitch,[478] who found the organisms 100 meters below a sewer outlet. Laboratory experiments have also shown appreciable longevity, especially in the dark. In Rhines' experiments, a strain of *Mycobacterium tuberculosis* (avis) was alive in both sewage and water after 93 days.

Tularemia from Water. Infected rodents are the usual sources of infection of tularemia. Karpoff and Antonoff [479] reported that it could be spread by water. The quantity of microorganisms in the infected water courses may sometimes be so considerable that their isolation does not meet with great difficulties. One hundred per cent of the guinea pigs infected with the water died and their organs showed characteristic pathological-anatomical changes. From the organs of all the guinea pigs were obtained cultures of *Pasteurella tularensis*. The cultures isolated from water did not differ in regard to virulence from those that were isolated from the suppurated lymph glands of patients. When these cultures were tested on guinea pigs, death followed in 100 per cent of cases and the organs showed changes characteristic of tularemic infection.

475. Moens. 1927. K. Akad. Wetensch. Amsterdam, Proc., Sect. Sci. 30, 444-454.
476. Briscoe. 1912. Ill. Agr. Expt. Sta. Bull. 161.
477. Brown, Petroff, and Heisc. 1916. Amer. J. Pub. Health 6, 1148.
478. Jessen and Rabinowitch. 1910. Jtschr. Tuberk. 16, 275; 1935. Amer. Rev. Tuber. 31, 493-497.
479. Karpoff and Antonoff. 1936. J. Bact. 32, 243-258.

Leptospira in Water. Hindle [480] found in London water an organism morphologically identical with *Leptospira icterohaemmorrhagiae*. He could not isolate it in pure culture. Guinea pigs which were inoculated with water containing the organisms died. Hindle believed that spirochetal jaundice may be added to the list of diseases which may be disseminated by bad water. Bauer,[481] by using a special medium, was able to isolate 12 strains of Leptospiras from 29 samples of water collected. He also obtained a number of different kinds of Spirochaetes. After Hindle's report, Houston of the Metropolitan Water Board, in the 20th Annual Report, was led to study the presence of Leptospiras in water. He reported their presence and studied the pathogenicity of certain strains which he isolated.

Tracing Pollution in Water Courses. Several methods have been used as well as different materials, such as sodium chloride, lithium salts, fluorescein, cultures of *Serratia marcescens (Bacillus prodigiosus)*, etc. Sanitarians frequently find it necessary to resort to one of these methods to determine the origin of pollution in water supplies.

Fluorescein. Dole [482] summarized his investigations on the use of fluorescein in the following statements: 1. In determining the sanitary value of a well or spring it is more important to study the underground flow than to analyze the water itself. 2. Foreign substances put into the aquifer and traced from point to point are of great value in this study. 3. With the fluoroscope one part of fluorescein can be detected in 10 billion parts of water. 4. Fluorescein is a particularly valuable flow indicator for fissured or cavernized rocks. 5. It is also available in gravels, where it has been used with success. 6. It progresses at a slightly lower rate than the water in which it is suspended. 7. It is not decolorized by passage through sand, gravel, or manure; it is slightly decomposed by calcareous soils. 8. It is entirely decolorized by peaty formations and by free acids, except carbonic acid. Trillat [483] claimed that fluorescein could be detected in dilutions of one part in 2,000,000,000 but that before the dye is used a study of the soils should be made with regard to the presence of matters which decompose it. Marboutin [484] came to somewhat similar conditions. Martel [485] showed that fluorescein, even in very concentrated solutions, decolorizes rather quickly after being kept in the sunlight. When it was kept in complete darkness, which would be the case in the earth, it did not change even after long periods. An anonymous article in the *Engineering News-Record* stated that one part of fluorescein in 40,000,000 parts of water may be detected with the naked eye and one part in 10,000,000,000 by means of a long glass tube. McCrae and Stokes [486] used fluorescein to good advantage for determining the source of *Escherichia coli* in wells. It was found that swamp water was getting into the wells through a fissure in the rock. It was shown that fluorescein penetrates soil and that it is devoid of harmful effects in the amounts used.

Uranin. Stiles, Crohurst, and Thomson [487] used the dye uranin for tracing the movement of water through sand. The conditions which would have to obtain would probably be quite like those for fluorescein.

Serratia marcescens (Bacillus prodigiosus). This organism was found to be an unreliable indicator since it so easily lost its red pigment-forming ability according to Hilgerman.[488]

480. Hindle. 1925. Brit. Med. J. 2, 57.
481. Bauer. 1927. Amer. J. Trop. Med. 7, 177.
482. Dole. 1906. U. S. Geological Survey, Water Supply Paper, 160.
483. Trillat. 1899. Compt. Rend. Acad. Sci. 128, 698-700.
484. Marboutin. 1901. Compt. Rend. 132, 365-368.
485. Martel. 1903. Compt. Rend. Acad. Sci. 137, 225-227.
486. McCrae and Stokes. 1907. J. Hyg. 7, 181-192.
487. Stiles, Crohurst, and Thomson. 1923. U. S. Pub. Health Serv. Hyg. Lab. Bull. 147.
488. Hilgerman. 1906. Arch. Hyg. 59, 150-158.

Gehrmann [489] reported that Alba Orlandi and Roudelli, who used a suspension of *Serratia marcescens*, found that cultures of this organism poured on the ground passed through soil 200 meters, and Pfuhl found that it took the same organism a short time to pass through 24 feet of gravel. Gehrmann also reported a place at which wells, 200 to 300 feet deep, too near an old canal, were subject to entrance of contaminated water; no experimental data were given. *Serratia marcescens* was used on a large scale in the famous litigation between the City of. St. Louis and the State of Missouri against the City of Chicago and the State of Illinois, over the pollution of the Illinois River with Chicago sewage. One hundred or so barrels of a broth culture of *Serratia marcescens* were poured into the drainage canal in order to show that objectionable bacteria might pass down the Illinois River and reach the intake of the St. Louis water supply.

Sodium Chloride. Salt was used by McCallie,[490] in Georgia, for the purpose of demonstrating the effects of discharging sewage into deep wells. A large amount of salt was put into a 124-ft. drilled well and the content of chloride in the water of the surrounding wells was determined. Increased content of chloride showed that there was underground connection between the wells and springs in the vicinity. Tanner [491] tried to use sodium chloride to determine how apparent pollution was reaching a city water supply in Illinois.

489. Gehrmann. 1914. Proc. Ill. Water Supply Assoc. 112-115.
490. McCallie. 1904. U. S. Geol. Survey, Water Supply Paper 110, 45-54.
491. Tanner. 1917. Ill. State Water Survey Bull. 13, 214-224.

REFERENCES

American Public Health Association, 1936. Standard Methods for the Examination of Water and Sewage. Eighth edition, 1936. New York, N. Y.

DIENERT, G. A., ETRILLARD, P., AND WANDENBULKE, F., 1936. Alimentation en Eau de Villes. Livre II. Procedés d'Analyses de Contrôle des eaux d'Alimentation et des Eaux usées. L. Eyrolles, Paris.

GAINEY, P. L., 1939. Microbiology of Water and Sewage for Engineering Students. Burgess Pub. Co., Minneapolis.

MASON, W. P., 1931. Examination of Water, Chemical and Bacteriological. Revised by A. M. Buswell. John Wiley and Sons, Inc., New York, N. Y.

* Ministry of Health, Great Britain, 1939. The Bacteriological Examination of Water Supplies. Repts. on Public Health and Medical Subjects, No. 71. H. M. Stationery Office, London.

PRESCOTT, S. C., AND WINSLOW, C. E. A., 1931. Elements of Water Bacteriology. John Wiley and Sons, Inc., New York, N. Y.

SINGER, E., 1931. Die Bakteriologische Untersuchung des Trinkwasser. Gustav Fischer, Jena.

THEROUX, F. R., ELDRIDGE, E. F., AND MALLMANN, W. L., 1937. Laboratory Manual for Chemical and Bacteriological Analysis of Water and Sewage. McGraw-Hill Book Co., New York, N. Y.

THRESH, J. C., AND BEALE, J. F., 1940. Simple Method of Water Analysis. J. and A. Churchill, London, Eng.

THRESH, J. C., 1933. The Examination of Waters and Water Supplies. Fourth edition. J. and A. Churchill, London, England.

* Metropolitan Water Board, London, England. Annual Reports and Reports of Research Work.

CHAPTER 5

MICROBIOLOGY OF MILK

Milk is an ideal substance for development of bacteria. It has adequate amounts of water, protein, and sugar. Bacteriologists use it in the laboratory as one of many culture fluids. The Milk Ordinance and Code of the United States Public Health Service [1] defines milk as follows: *Milk is hereby defined to be the lacteal secretion obtained by the complete milking of one or more healthy cows, excluding that obtained within fifteen days before and five days after calving, or such longer period as may be necessary to render the milk practically colostrum free; which contains not less than eight per cent of milk solids not fat, and not less than three and one-fourth per cent of milk fat.*

Reaction of Milk. Since the work on hydrogen-ion concentration, much progress has been made in knowledge of the reaction of milk. Milk is amphoteric to litmus.

Baker and van Slyke [2] found that the hydrogen-ion concentration of over 300 samples of fresh milk varied between pH 6.5 and 7.2. In 80 per cent of the samples it was more than pH 6.76. In general, the reaction of the milk from different quarters of the udder was the same. One hundred and sixty determinations of the hydrogen-ion concentration of fresh goats' milk gave a variation of pH from 6.7 to 6.4, the average being 6.53. Fresh goats' milk is somewhat more acid than fresh cows' milk and much more acid than human milk.

After determining the hydrogen-ion concentration of good, fresh milk, Baker and van Slyke attempted to use determinations of hydrogen-ion concentration for measuring undesirable changes in milk. They attempted this with brom-cresol-purple and stated that the color of this indicator was made lighter by acids, and by heating the milk above the usual temperatures of pasteurization. The color became darker in milk from diseased udders, watered or skimmed milk, or milk to which alkali salts had been added. A test for keeping quality could be made with a specimen collected under sterile conditions. This work was continued by Baker and Breed.[3] Decreased acidity in fresh milk was explained by infiltration of blood serum into the milk as secreted. A fairly close relationship was observed between decreasing hydrogen-ion concentration and increase in the number of leucocytes. Golding [4] used this method for detecting abnormal fresh milk. Sjollema and van der Zande [5] reported that milk from diseased udders did not differ from that from healthy udders. They believed that the leucocyte test was valuable. Baker and van Slyke [6] also studied the

1. Milk Ordinance and Code Recommended by the United States Public Health Service. Pub. Health Bull. 220 (1939), Federal Security Agency. Washington, D. C.
2. Baker and van Slyke. 1919. J. Biol. Chem. 40, 373-382.
3. Baker and Breed. 1920. J. Biol. Chem. 43, 221-235.
4. Golding. 1920. Abs. Bact. 6, 53.
5. Sjollema and van der Zande. 1922. Tijdschr. Vergelijk. Geneesk. 7, 169.
6. Baker and van Slyke. 1919. N. Y. Agr. Expt. Sta. Bull. 71.

reaction of milk and the bacterial count. Of 570 samples examined, 16 gave a lighter color than normal, of which 11 were found to contain over 10,000,000 bacteria per ml. These data suggested that the hydrogen-ion concentration of milk as determined with brom-thymol-blue could be used as a criterion of quality.

The Cooledge Brom-Thymol Blue Test. Another colorimetric method for determining hydrogen-ion concentration of milk as a method of control was proposed by Cooledge and Wyant,[7] Cooledge,[8] and Cooledge and Goodwin.[9] They suggested use of brom-thymol-blue under different conditions than those used by Baker and van Slyke [6] with brom-cresol-purple. They studied the rate of change of hydrogen-ion concentration of a brom-thymol-blue broth solution due to the bacteria and enzymes in .1 ml. of milk. The culture tubes were incubated at 37°C.(98.6°F.) and observed hourly for changes in pH values. With the same indicator, Schultz et al.[10] reported that where hydrogen-ion concentration was high, the bacterial counts were also high. At pH 6.6 the bacterial counts were high, averaging 16,000,000 and 100,000,000 bacteria per ml., at pH 6.5. These results were confirmed by Cooledge.[8] Schultz, Marx, and Beaver [11] applied the Cooledge test to market milks. The counts increased rapidly from about 3,000 per ml. with a pH of 6.8, to 100,000 with a pH of 6.5. Further increases in acidity were not accompanied by increase in counts. Acidity was not detected by taste until it had reached pH 6.0. Hastings and Davenport [12] did not find this test to be as reliable as the reductase test. On account of the interest in hydrogen-ion concentration methods for determining the sanitary quality of milk, Sommer and Hart [13] tried to determine whether the presence of acids in the ration of the cow influenced the reaction of the milk. Even 120 ml. of concentrated sulfuric acid a day did not alter it. This would seem to indicate that presence of acids in rations of the cow would not affect the pH methods of determining milk quality.

Cooledge,[14] comparing the bacterial count and changes in hydrogen-ion concentration, reported that the pH method seemed to be best for determining old milk. He believed that the pH score was more efficient in detecting slight changes in the milk than plating methods. The per cent efficiency of the methods as a whole in detecting slight changes in the history of the samples was as follows: In samples with bacterial count under 25,000, 45.8 per cent; between 25,000 and 100,000, 71.4 per cent; between 100,000 and one million, 85 per cent, and in samples with bacterial counts over one million, 97 per cent. The medium giving the highest average counts depended upon the predominant groups present in the sample studied, perhaps accounting for the divergent results obtained by

7. Cooledge and Wyant. 1920. J. Dairy Sci. 3, 156-166.
8. Cooledge. 1921. Mich. Agr. Expt. Sta. Tech. Bull. 52.
9. Cooledge and Goodwin. 1921. Mich. Agr. Expt. Sta. Spec. Bull. 112.
10. Schultz, et al. 1921. Abs. Bact. 5, 7.
11. Schultz, Marx, and Beaver. 1921. J. Dairy Sci. 4, 1-6.
12. Hastings and Davenport. 1920. J. Dairy Sci. 3, 353-366.
13. Sommer and Hart. 1921. J. Dairy Sci. 4, 7-11.
14. Cooledge. 1923. Mich. Agr. Expt. Sta. Bull. 124.

various workers. In 81 comparisons of the pH score with results of the reductase test and bacterial plate counts, the pH score checked as well with the number of bacteria per ml. as did the reductase rating, although neither is an absolute measure of the bacterial content. Devereux [15] reported good correlation between the brom-thymol-blue test and the methylene-blue reduction test. This work related the Cooledge test with another which is quite widely used in milk-control work.

Brom-Thymol-Blue Test in Milk (Cooledge and Wyant [7]). The technic and apparatus for this test were outlined in a bulletin from the Digestive Ferments Company. The following has been adapted from that bulletin:

Preparation of Media. Prepare in one flask, only as much medium as will be used in one test, by dissolving in the proportion of 1.8 grams Bacto Cooledge Broth, Dehydrated, in 100 ml. distilled water. Sterilize in the usual manner and store in the ice box. Larger quantities may be made, sterilized, and stored in flasks until needed.

When ready to use, check color to be sure the medium has a pH value very close to 7.0. This is done by removing 10 ml. with a sterile pipette into a sterile 1.8 x 16 cm. test tube, and comparing with the standard tube pH = 7.0 in the comparator. Broth without indicator should be used as a compensating blank. See *Preparation of Compensating Blanks.* A few drops of N/1 NaOH or HCl are then added if necessary.

This procedure is given only for emergency as no adjustment should be necessary. The sterile broth is then transferred in 10 ml. portions to sterile 1.8 x 16 cm. test tubes, using a sterile 10 ml. pipette.

Preparation of Compensating Blanks. To 100 ml. of ordinary nutrient broth is added one ml. of milk. This is distributed in 10 ml. portions in 1.8 x 16 cm. tubes and subsequently sterilized for 20 minutes at 15 pounds. These tubes may be held in the ice box for use. A few tubes of broth without indicator should be sterilized and stored for use as compensating blanks in adjusting pH of broth under *Preparation of Media.*

Preparation of Samples. The same care should be exercised in sampling milk for this test as is used in any other method. The test calls for the addition of .1 ml. milk to each tube of Cooledge Broth, but to reduce errors incident to this small measurement it is recommended that one ml. of milk be added to nine ml. of sterile dilution water, and one ml. of this mixture be added to the sterile Cooledge Broth.

If this medium is not available one may prepare his own medium as directed in the chapter on "Media."

Incubation. After the milk has been added the tubes are placed in a water bath or incubator at 37°C.(98.6°F.). Observations are made every hour to detect the first color changes due to activity of bacteria or enzymes in the sample. As soon as pronounced changes are noticed, hourly readings are made by placing the tubes containing the samples in the comparator and comparing with the standard tubes which are described below. Tubes must be cooled to 20°C. before readings are made, as it is quite necessary to have all readings made at a constant temperature.

Standards. The standards are the buffer solutions described by Clark and Lubs. Ten ml. portions are placed in the same 1.8 x 16 cm. tubes and .8 ml. of a .04 per cent aqueous solution of Brom Thymol Blue is added. The tube is then sealed and may be kept for a considerable period. The standards used in this test must have the following readings: pH 7.4, 7.2, 7.0, 6.8, 6.6, 6.4, 6.2, 6.0, and 5.8.

Wilson [16] observed that decoloration of the broth did not occur uniformly. While the lower part of the broth became yellow, the upper part remained blue. He found that sometimes the blue color was confined to the top and in some of the tubes the whole upper half might be blue. Consequently, readings of pH were unsatisfactory. Again, several tubes,

15. Devereux. 1929. J. Dairy Sci. 12, 367-373.
16. Wilson. 1935. Med. Res. Council, H. M. Stat. Office, p. 302.

after commencing to turn acid, reverted to alkaline and then once more became acid. The time required by these tubes to reach a pH of six was abnormally long. The experience of Wilson confirms that of others.

Souring of normal market milk is a complicated process subject to many different conditions. One of the most important is bacteria other than those which produce the acid. Cox and Whitehead [17] followed the action of four organisms commonly found in contaminated milk. *Escherichia coli, Bacillus subtilis,* a staphylococcus, and *Bacillus fecalis alkaligenes* were grown in milk with lactic streptococci and the acidity produced in a given time was determined. *Bacillus subtilis* appeared to stimulate acid production. *Escherichia coli* caused a decrease in acid production in some experiments and an increase in others. The staphylococcus had a slight stimulative effect. *Bacillus fecalis alkaligenes* had only a slight effect, which was barely beyond experimental error. Brown [18] had also reported similar results.

PROVISIONAL CLASSIFICATION OF MILK

Reading	pH	Score	Milk suited for
1 hour	5.8	20	Condemning
2 hours	5.8	25	
3 hours	5.8	30	
4 hours	5.8	35	Skimming for buttermaking
5 hours	5.8	40	" " "
6 hours	5.8	45	" " "
7 hours	5.8	50	" " "
8 hours	5.8	55	" " "
8 hours	5.9	60	Condensing
8 hours	6.0	65	"
8 hours	6.1	70	"
8 hours	6.2	75	"
8 hours	6.3	80	Milk plant supply
8 hours	6.4	85	Cheese making
8 hours	6.5	90	" "
8 hours	6.6	95	" "
8 hours	6.7	100	" "

Influence of Climatic Conditions on Souring of Milk. Milk sours so often during hot humid periods with thunderstorms that the change has been attributed to the lightning or thunder. Tolemei,[19] after subjecting fresh milk to currents of electricity of different intensities, found that, instead of hastening souring, it was actually retarded in some cases. Further experiments seemed to convince him that ozone formed by the electric current caused curdling. Gerstmann [20] claimed that lightning caused induction currents in the milk which decomposed the constituents soluble in water. Acid, suddenly formed in this manner, curdled the milk. Trillat [21] believed that reduced air pressure of thunderstorms caused the

17. Cox and Whitehead. 1931. J. Dairy Res. 2, 164-175.
18. Brown. 1913. Mich. Acad. Sci., Ann. Rept. 15, 71-73.
19. Tolemei. 1891. Milch Ztschr. 20, 519.
20. Gerstmann. 1896. Elektrotech. Ztschr. 1896, p. 74.
21. Trillat. 1912. Compt. Rend. Acad. Sci. 154, 372-374; 613-616.

development of gases which promoted growth of bacteria. High temperatures and humidity were said to favor the development of bacteria. Wernicke [22]also believed that the climatic conditions favored development of bacteria; his explanations were not very definite.

Relation of Bacterial Content of Milk and the Amount of Acid Formed. It was formerly believed that delay occurred in the formation of lactic acid by bacteria in milk. That a lag phase existed during which no acid was formed had been observed. Revis and Payne,[23] for instance, suggested that bacteria in milk developed ability to produce acid only after a certain period of growth. Such opinions are not held today. No reason in the first place obtains for assuming that acid is not formed at all phases of growth of bacteria in milk. During the early phases so little is formed that the biochemical methods used for its detection are not delicate enough. Rahn [24] and Baker, Brew, and Conn [25] computed the acid that might be formed by an average single cell in milk. In general, a fairly definite ratio existed between the acid produced and the number of bacteria. Heinemann[26] and Barkworth, Mattick, Taylor, and Williams[27] were able to show close relationship between temperature, numbers of bacteria, and amount of acid.

The types of bacteria are important. Some which are unable to attack lactose might develop without forming much acid. Schmidt [28] observed that production of acid in milk proceeded more rapidly at the surface than in the deeper layers. Cells of *Streptococcus lactis* were 85 times more numerous at the surface than in the deeper layers. It is readily seen that the question of relation of amount of acid formed to the number of bacteria present is an intricate one. Many factors are involved. In general, there must be a fairly close relationship, because acid is a product of metabolism. The greater the number of bacteria, the greater would be the amount of acid formed.

Coagulation by Rennin. It was believed for a long time that coagulation of milk was due only to acid. Fremy, in 1839, supposed that a special enzyme was present in the lining of calves' stomachs which formed acid from the lactose. Hammarsten proved that the production of acid from lactose was not the cause of coagulation by rennin, but that it was brought about by a special enzyme, which acted directly on casein.

The action of rennin is proteolytic, since it destroys casein. It might be regarded as a preliminary process in digestion. Bosworth [29] stated that probably the action attributed to rennin may be produced by any proteolytic enzyme. In the bacterial world, it has been known for some time that an organism which will split casein will also probably split gelatin and other proteins.

22. Wernicke. 1914. Mitt. Landw. Inst. Leipzig, No. 12, 97-129.
23. Revis and Payne. 1907. J. Hyg. 7, 216-231.
24. Rahn. 1911. Mich. Agr. Expt. Sta. Tech. Bull. 10.
25. Baker, Brew, and Conn. 1919. N. Y. Agr. Expt. Sta. Tech. Bull.
26. Heinemann. 1915. J. Infect. Dis. 16, 285-291.
27. Barkworth, Mattick, Taylor, and Williams. 1927. J. Min. Agr. 33, 997-1001.
28. Schmidt. 1925. Filchw. Forsch. 2, 432-449.
29. Bosworth. 1913. N. Y. Agr. Expt. Sta. Tech. Bull. 31.

"Sweet curdling" of milk causes considerable trouble in the dairy industry. Evaporated milk is frequently curdled by bacteria which form little or no acid, but which are able to thoroughly coagulate the proteins. Hammer [30] believed that these organisms were identical or closely related to *Bacillus subtilis*. Some evidence exists to show that the trouble is not always bacteriological.

Measurement of Volume of Cream on Milk. Harding [31] proposed the following method for measuring cream volume. The method of measurement consisted of filling round-bottomed test tubes, one inch in diameter, to a depth of 204 millimeters (8 inches) with the milk to be tested. These tubes of milk were immediately cooled in ice water; and when cool, were held at 4.5°C.(40°F.) for approximately 24 hours. The depth of the resulting cream layer was measured in millimeters, and each millimeter of cream represented .5 per cent of cream by volume. The volume of cream as determined in this way agreed closely with the volume of cream developed in milk bottles under similar temperature conditions. Dahlberg and Marquardt [32] used 100 ml. graduated cylinders and found them to be just as satisfactory as Harding's tubes.

Methods for Detecting Heated and Raw Milk. Food-control officials found it necessary to determine whether milk has been heated; for instance, city ordinances prescribe that milk shall be pasteurized. Laws in some countries demand that skimmed milk and buttermilk be heated to at least 85°C.(185°F.) before sale. It was for the administration of this law that Storch devised a method based on Babcock's discovery that fibrin in milk decomposes hydrogen peroxide, that cream is more active in this respect than whole milk, that skimmed milk is less active, and furthermore, that milk heated to 100°C.(212°F.) loses this property. Storch found that milk retained its property of reducing hydrogen peroxide up to 79°C.(174.2°F.). Grimes [33] improved Storch's technic. Other methods have been suggested by Bernstein,[34] Wilkinson and Peters,[35] Balaz,[36] Frost,[37] Hekma,[38] and van Slyke and Keeler.[39] The most recent and probably the best is the phosphatase test described in the chapter on "Pasteurization of Milk."

Duke's [40] Bacteriological Test for Pasteurized Foods. This method rests on the preparation of curves, showing the relation between the proportion of microorganisms surviving, and the temperatures to which these have been subjected. They are used to determine whether a solid or liquid has not, or has been pasteurized, and if the latter, at what temperature this was conducted. The test has been applied to milk and cheese, and should be adaptable to a wide range of products. The liquid under examination is well shaken to ensure an even distribution of the organisms present, and about five ml. are added to each of six sterile test tubes. One of these is kept at the ordinary temperature, while the remainder are placed in separate water baths at 50°C.(122°F.), 55°C.(131°F.), 60°C.(140°F.), 65°C.(149°F.), and 70°C.(158°F.) for 30 minutes. From each tube, one ml. of liquid is transferred to a tube of nutrient agar culture medium at 50°C.(122°F.) and dilutions of 1-10 and 1-100 are treated similarly, each portion of

30. Hammer. 1915. Iowa Agr. Expt. Sta. Res. Bull. 19.
31. Harding. 1921. Ill. Agr. Expt. Sta. Circ. 249.
32. Dahlberg and Marquardt. 1929. N. Y. Agr. Expt. Sta. Tech. Bull. 157.
33. Grimes. 1921. N. Y. Produce Rev. and Amer. Creamery 51, 592.
34. Bernstein. 1900. Ztschr. Fleisch. u. Milchhyg. 11, 80181.
35. Wilkinson and Peters. 1908. Rev. in Expt. Sta. Rec. 20, 1108.
36. Balaz. 1913. Chem. Ztg. 37, 554.
37. Frost. 1915. J. Amer. Med. Assoc. 64, 821-822.
38. Hekma. 1924. Rev. in Expt. Sta. Rec. 53 (1925), 206.
39. van Slyke and Keeler. 1920. N. Y. Agr. Expt. Sta. Tech. Bull. 78.
40. Duke. 1930. The Analyst 55, 14-19.

the inoculated medium being poured into a Petri dish, allowed to set, and incubated at 37°C.(98.6°F.) for three days. The numbers of colonies are then counted on each plate and the average of the three heated to the same temperature is taken and expressed as a fraction of the colonies developed from the unheated liquid calculated to 1,000. A curve is then drawn with the ordinates representing the number of colonies and the temperatures to which the liquids have been heated as abscissae. In the case of unpasteurized materials, the curve shows a steep decline immediately followed by an almost horizontal portion, while pasteurized foods in general, yield a surve rising irregularly to the pasteurizing temperature with a steep decline beyond this point. To avoid errors, owing to dilution, Duke is experimenting with Petri dishes nine inches in diameter, using 250 ml. of agar culture medium for each, and inoculating this with one ml. of the undiluted heated liquid.

Homogenized Milk. This is milk which has been forced through very small openings under high pressures. It so completely disperses the fat globules that they remain uniformly suspended throughout the milk without forming a cream layer on standing. Dispersion of the casein is also affected, for homogenized milk gives a soft curd in the stomach and is therefore recommended by physicians where curd tension is important.

Homogenized milk is defined in the Milk Ordinance and Code of the United States Public Health Service [1] as follows: *"Homogenized milk is milk which has been treated in such manner that after a storage period of 48 hours tests of the 100 ml. portion decanted from the top of a quart bottle of milk will not show a difference in fat content over tests of the remainder of the milk after thorough mixing exceeding 5 per cent of the total fat content. For example, on 4 per cent milk the difference shall not exceed 0.2 per cent."*

Relatively poor keeping quality of homogenized milk was one of its first problems, according to Tracy.[41] Bacterial numbers are usually higher in homogenized milk than in milk not so treated. This is due to breaking of clumps as well as pick-up of bacteria in the machine itself. Tracy found that it was possible to homogenize low-count pasteurized milk without materially increasing the count. The average of 13 days' observations showed a count of 1,213 for the milk in the vat and 1,990 for the first homogenized milk and 1,418 for the milk last homogenized. Fewer bacteria were reported to be present in pasteurized homogenized milk than in regular pasteurized milk by Hollingsworth [42] of the Canadian Health Department. Homogenization apparently permits a more efficient heat treatment; greater efficiency is thus obtained in the pasteurization process and more bacteria are killed.

BACTERIA IN MILK

Before bacteriological methods may be used for determining quality of milk, it is necessary to know the origin of bacteria which are found in milk. Unless these are known, proper interpretation of results of bacteriological analyses are not possible. Bacteria in milk are of interest for several reasons. They are used as indices of undesirable conditions of production by both health officers and research workers who are seeking more information about milk itself. It is necessary to know the reasons

41. Tracy. 1938. Twelfth Ann. Rept., N. Y. Assoc. Dairy and Milk Inspect. 69-84.
42. Hollingsworth. Undated. Observations About Homogenized Milk.

for high plate counts in milk if they are to be used in control of milk supplies.

Influence of Bacteria on Body of Cow on Number of Bacteria in Milk. At one time the surface of the cow was considered an important source of bacteria in milk. Consequently every attempt was made to prevent dirt from falling into the milk pail. Experiments carried out to determine the real origin of bacteria in milk showed that too much emphasis had been placed on the cow and her environment. Esten and Mason [43] reported that a gram of powder obtained by currying a cow was found to contain 207,-000,000 organisms. Despite such results later work indicated that utensils were the source of the great majority of bacteria.

Relation of Barn Conditions to Bacterial Content of Milk. Early dairy bacteriologists looked upon conditions in the barn as important sources of bacteria in milk. Important among them was barn air and the general construction of the stable. These various factors were studied at the New York and Illinois Agricultural Experiment Stations. Ruehle, Wilson, and Smith [44] probably were among the first to study the question seriously. They found that the importance of barn construction had been considerably overestimated and that, within rather wide limits, the condition of the stable exerted no measurable influence upon the bacterial content of the milk produced in it. Clipping the udder, flank, and adjoining portions of the cow seemed to increase rather than decrease the number of bacteria in the milk. The effect of brushing and combing at the rate of two cows per minute was practically the same as treatment with the vacuum cleaner at the rate of one cow per minute. When all utensils had been carefully steamed, cooling and straining the milk resulted in only a small increase in germ content, even when this was done under unfavorable conditions.

Another factor in the barn to which dairymen had always given considerable attention was the air. They were accustomed to feed after milking in order to avoid as much dust as possible during milking. Experiments again revealed that stable air contained few bacteria. Ruehle and Kulp [45] found that there were between 50 and 200 bacteria per liter in barn air during such barn operations as milking and feeding. When sterile water was "milked" in the station stable from an apparatus designed for the purpose, the bacteria in the liquid averaged only 12 per ml. with a maximum of 73. When a heavy dust was raised in the stable loft, the number of bacteria in the air was usually between 1,000 and 2,000 per liter. Under such conditions sterile water "milked" had an average bacteria content of 47.6. Ruehle and Kulp stated that between 100 and 1,000 cells per ml. would be added to milk when it was secured under very dirty conditions. It may be recalled that Winslow and Browne [46] reported the average number of bacteria in country air to be 56, in city street air 72, in office air 94, in factory air 113, and in air in school rooms 96 per cubic foot. Such data would indicate that bacteria are no more prevalent in

43. Esten and Mason. 1908-09. Conn. Agr. Expt. Sta. Ann. Rept., 1907-09.
44. Ruehle, Wilson, and Smith. 1913. N. Y. Agr. Expt. Sta. Bull. 365.
45. Ruehle and Kulp. 1915. N. Y. Agr. Expt. Sta. Bull. 409.
46. Winslow and Browne. 1914. Md. Weather Rev. 42, 452-453.

stable air than in the air of many other places. Results of investigations just reviewed would not justify indifference to the question of dust in the stable during milking. Earlier investigations than those just reviewed, Stocking's [47] for instance, showed a contribution of bacteria by dusty feeds while the cows were being milked which might, under some conditions, be significant. They might be significant if objectionable bacteria are contributed.

Prucha and Weeter,[48] studying the same problems, worked in three dairy barns of widely different degrees of cleanliness. Study of these three barns showed that even under wide extremes in barn conditions, it was possible to produce milk with fewer bacteria than 10,000 per ml. In a total of 1,665 samples taken from 138 cows during 1914 and 1915, the number of bacteria varied from three to 218,560 per ml. when determined by the standard agar plate. The average bacteria content of the milk from individual cows was low, but one cow was found whose milk showed a relatively high average of 35,131 bacteria per ml. The average bacteria content of the milk was over 10,000 only once in Barn I, only twice in Barn III, and in Barn II the highest average was only 2,224. These barns were two extremes in cleanliness. One was allowed to become very dirty, typical of what a dairy barn should not be. The other was what a dairy barn should be. The results of these investigations showed that factors other than barn conditions were responsible for the bacteria in milk.

Normal Bacterial Flora of the Udder. Investigations on the various sources of bacteria in milk logically start with the cow herself. As far as she is concerned, two possible sources exist, the udder interior and the exterior surface of her body. Very early in the history of bacteriology, milk was said to be sterile when it came from the udder. Chief among the proponents of this view was Lister, who assumed that the bacteria which he found were contaminants. Schulz,[49] however, reported that freshly drawn milk was not sterile and that a considerable number of bacteria might be present in first drawn milk. Toward the end of the milking period, however, the number might become smaller. The first portion of milk from a cow contained 50,556 bacteria per ml. when precautions were taken to rule out contaminating bacteria from the milker's hands, etc. Schulz and Barthel believed that bacteria might grow into the teat and that they were largely washed out during milking. Backhaus and Cronheim [50] believed that even with milking tubes, it was impossible to obtain sterile milk from the cow. Schulz's results were also confirmed by Moore,[51] who used the milk of nine cows. He believed that the characteristics of bacteria in milk were more important than were numbers. Ward [25] and Moore, after further study, again in 1902 arrived at similar conclusions.

47. Stocking. 1915. N. Y. Agr. Expt. Sta. Bull. 409.

48. Prucha and Weeter. 1917. Ill. Agr. Expt. Sta. Bull. 199.

49. Schulz. 1892. Arch. Hyg. 14, 260-271.

50. Backhaus and Cronheim. 1897. Ber. Landw. Inst. Univ. Königsberg 2, 12-23.

51. Moore. 1897. U. S. Dept. Agr., Bur. Anim. Indus., Ann. Rept., 12 and 13, 261-266; Soc. Prom. Agr. Sci. Proc. 1899, 110-113.

52. Ward. 1898. J. Appl. Micros. 1, 205-208; N. Y. Agr. Expt. Sta. Bull. 178.

The problem was attacked by Uhlmann [53] from another angle. Examination of over 800 sections of the teats of 35 cows revealed the presence of bacteria. Similar technic was used by Ward,[52] who examined the glandular tissue of apparently healthy udders of six cows, together with the foremilk just before they were slaughtered. He found that the same organism frequently occurred in the foremilk and in each of the three parts of the udder. D'Heil,[54] finding bacteria regularly present in the milk cistern and ducts, concluded that they gained entrance through the orifice of the teat. Glandular tissue which contained but a very few bacteria was believed to be bactericidal. Considerable attention has also been given to the types of bacteria found in fresh milk collected under carefully controlled conditions. Esten and Mason,[55] in the milk from a herd of 25 cows, found over 50 different species of bacteria. Over half of them had no effect on sterile milk when inoculated in pure cultures. Harrison and Cumming [56] reported a rather heterogeneous flora of bacteria in the udder and were not alarmed by the large number of bacteria which were found. Freudenreich's [57] experiments were carried out with every effort to rule out air contamination. Harrison and Savage [58] also reported the presence of bacteria in udder milk.

About this time a series of experiments was undertaken at the New York Agricultural Experiment Station, results of which answered many questions on origin of bacteria in milk. Harding and Wilson [59] reported an average of 428 bacteria per ml. in 1,230 samples of udder milk. Various factors, such as the age of the cow and the quarter of the udder from which the milk came, were suggested to be important influencing factors. A few years later Harding and Prucha,[60] from a similar investigation at the Illinois Agricultural Experiment Station, reported 964 bacteria per ml. in milk direct from the udder. The average number of bacteria per ml. per cow showed variation from 329 to 1,868. In some cases the milk from the same cow showed considerable variation in numbers of bacteria. In another investigation at Geneva, N. Y., Dorner [61] examined 993 samples of aseptically drawn milk from 132 cows in six herds, using standard agar plates, by the Burri quantitative film culture technic. The calculated average bacterial count of the milk from each herd showed great variations, the lowest obtained on Burri slants being 3,965 per ml., the highest 9,635 per ml., and the average 7,475 per ml. On standard agar plates, the average counts from individual herds varied between 530 and 4,390 per ml., the final calculated average being 2,775 per ml. It appears that a small number of samples containing relatively high numbers of bacteria is usually the source of the greater part of the bacteria in aseptically drawn milk. Dorner,[61] later at Liebefeld, Switzerland, reported an average bac-

53. Uhlmann. 1903. Rev. in Expt. Sta. Rec. 15, 1003.
54. d'Heil. 1906. Arb. Hyg. Inst., Berlin, No. 6.
55. Esten and Mason. 1908-09. Conn. Agr. Expt. Sta. Ann. Rept., 1907-08.
56. Harrison and Cumming. 1902. J. Appl. Micros. 5, 2029-2038.
57. Freudenreich. 1903. Centbl. Bakt., Pt. 2, 10, 401-423.
58. Harrison and Savage. 1912. Rev. Gen. du Lait, 9, 121-131.
59. Harding and Wilson. 1913. N. Y. Agr. Expt. Sta. Tech. Bull. 27.
60. Harding and Prucha. 1921. Ill. Agr. Expt. Sta. Bull. 231.
61. Dorner. 1930. J. Bact. 19, 44; Landw. Jahrb. Schweiz. 463-493.

terial content in fresh milk of 3,099 per ml. In South Dakota, Copeland and Olson [62] had previously found some 1,541 bacteria per ml. in fresh milk. Examination by the microscope method of 88 aseptically drawn samples of milk by Thornton and Strynadka [63] revealed the presence of many more bacteria than have just been reported. The average was 25,000 per ml. in 29 milks containing not over 500,000 leucocytes and 81,000 in 53 milks containing over 500,000 leucocytes per ml. That the microscope method showed more bacteria is to be expected.

Effect of Inoculating Bacteria Into the Udder and Feeding to the Cow. Demonstration of the presence of bacteria in milk from normal animals suggested to investigators a study of the behavior of saprophytic bacteria injected into the udder. Following injection of pure milk cultures of *Aerobacter aerogenes* into the udder, Appel [64] noticed swelling of the teats and marked changes in the milk. Injections of sterile milk and water, however, did not cause such results. Another experiment carried out by Pernot,[65] sought to determine whether bacteria commonly found in stagnant water could gain access to the milk supply through the cow. Pure cultures of *Pseudomonas fluorescens, Chromobacterium janthium,* and *Bacillus ramosus* were in turn added to the drinking water and given to a cow every morning for periods of 10 days. In no case were the bacilli found on plate cultures made from the milk each morning and evening. *Bacillus ramosus* was administered in cultures containing spores in abundance but was not found in either the milk or excreta. The same cow was then given each morning, for 10 days, 10 ml. of a bouillon culture of *Eberthella typhosa,* and for the five days following, 20 ml. of the culture without apparently affecting the health of the cow. In only two cases did colonies of *Eberthella typhosa* develop on plate cultures made each morning and evening from the milk, urine, and feces, and these were considered accidental inoculations. To determine whether *Eberthella typhosa* could enter the udder through the milk ducts, the teats were immersed in a pure culture, directly after milking and allowed to dry spontaneously. Twelve hours later the teats were disinfected and plate cultures made from the milk drawn under aseptic precautions. The experiment was repeated for five days; in no instance, during the experiments, or for a number of days after did cultures show presence of *Eberthella typhosa.* Similar experiments were made by Russell and Hastings [66] with *Bacillus acidi lactici,* an acid-producing liquefying bacillus isolated from Cheddar cheese, *Serratia marcescens,* and a yellow liquefying coccus isolated from foremilk. Agar cultures of these organisms were transferred to distilled water or normal salt solutions and introduced into the udder through a milking tube. The results furnished no evidence of the growth in the udder of any of the species used. In nearly every instance, the milk became abnormal, and occasionally the udder became inflamed and tense,

62. Copeland and Olson. 1926. So. Dak. Agr. Expt. Sta. Bull. 218.
63. Thornton and Strynadka. 1934. Internatl. Assoc. Dairy and Milk Insp. Ann. Rept.
64. Appel. 1900. Mölk. Ztg. 14, 277-278.
65. Pernot. 1902. Ore. Agr. Expt. Sta. Bull. 71.
66. Russell and Hastings. 1904. Wis. Agr. Exp. Sta. Ann. Rept., 164-168.

showing production of temporary garget. Ward [32] injected *Serratia marcescens* by means of a hypodermic syringe lengthened with a milking tube. He was able to find the organism in the milk for five days after its introduction, although it decreased regularly and disappeared on the sixth. Harrison and Cumming [56] inoculated udders with *Serratia marcescens, Bacillus exigum,* and *Pseudomonas fluorescens* by smearing the ends of the teats with cultures. The bacilli soon disappeared from the milk. Cultures were made from the livers and udders of three cows which had been dry for several weeks previous to slaughter. Bacteria were found in the livers of all three and in the udders of two cows. While the results are not considered sufficient to warrant a positive assertion they point toward infection by way of the blood or lymph rather than through the teat.

The experiments reported above involved nonpathogenic bacteria, but do show that bacteria can live for some time in the udder. They probably gain entrance in different ways. Similar experiments with pathogenic bacteria are reported elsewhere in this chapter.

Results of post-mortem examination of the udder must be interpreted with care. Curran [67] found that some bacterial types maintained in the udders of living cows at a fairly constant numerical level multiplied with great rapidity immediately after death and removal of the blood. Rapidly growing invasive types of streptococci were most affected. The udder floras of some cows did not increase appreciably during the post-mortem incubation period. Relatively inert, slow-growing micrococci and streptococci usually comprised this group. The suddenly increased multiplication of the udder flora that frequently attends withdrawal of the blood suggests that the circulatory system is directly or indirectly associated with the formation of the bactericidal substance in milk.

Relation of Utensils to Number of Bacteria in Milk. Failing to find among barn conditions explanations for the number of bacteria in milk, dairy bacteriologists continued their search for the answer. Since unsterile utensils were found to contribute most of the bacteria, many investigations have been carried out to learn how they should be handled. Pease [68] claimed that, where high counts had been obtained in a dairy which had operated for a long time, they were due to inefficiently cleaned apparatus, and incubation of bacteria occurred on moist surfaces of the cans, pails, etc. Prucha, Harding, and Weeter [69] reported some interesting data to substantiate this contention of Pease. With sterile utensils and sterile bottles, milk leaving the barn was found to contain 2,588 bacteria per ml. and the bottled milk 3,875. Where the utensils were simply washed and with only the bottles sterile, there were increases of 57,077 due to the pails, of 15,353 up to the clarifier, of 172,763 due to the clarifier, of 19,841 due to cooler and of 247,611 due to the bottler. Ayers, Cook, and Clemmer,[70] in a careful study of the factors involved in the production of a milk of low bacteria content, state as follows: *"Three simple factors were*

67. Curran. 1931. J. Infect. Dis. 48, 408-412.
68. Pease. 1916. Amer. J. Pub. Health 6, 563-568.
69. Prucha, Harding, and Weeter. 1915. Science 42, 353.
70. Ayers, Cook, and Clemmer. 1918. U. S. Dept. Agr. Bull. 642.

necessary for the production of milk with a low bacterial content, namely, sterilized utensils, clean cows with clean udders and teats, and the small top pail." A fourth factor, holding the milk at a temperature near 10°C. (50°F.) or lower, is necessary in order to keep the bacterial count low. Even cow manure was found to be of less importance in influencing the bacterial count than utensils. Prucha, Weeter, and Chambers [71] reported data which leave little doubt that the utensils are the important agents contributing bacteria to milk. This was strikingly illustrated by one experiment. When all of the utensils at the barn and in the dairy were thoroughly steamed, the bottled milk had uniformly only about 5,000 bacteria per ml. but when steaming was omitted the bottled milk frequently had 100,000 bacteria per ml. These authors stated that too much stress had been in the past laid on procedures which were of minor importance. According to Whiting,[72] the clumps of bacteria in milk noticed during examination with the microscope are due to utensils and not to growth. A study of 3,600 samples of unpasteurized milk showed clumps averaging 26.8 individuals per clump, the clumps decreasing in size as the total number of bacteria increased. Berry [73] also found that the dairy utensils were a more probable source of contamination of milk than dirty cows, dusty stables, or other imperfections in milk production. Sterilization of cans, for instance, increased the keeping quality of the milk between 20 and 30 per cent. Micrococci have been found to be especially prevalent in dairy utensils. Whiting [72] found them to be common on the dairy apparatus which he studied. Robertson [74] explained their prevalence on the fact that they survive the sterilizing procedures better than the other bacteria. Prucha and Harding [75] stated that the container could contribute as many as 100 bacteria per ml. without detriment to the milk, with which Proctor and Hoy [76] did not agree. They believed that not more than five cells per ml. should be allowed.

Construction of the milk pail has been found to influence the number of bacteria in milk. The smaller the top of the pail, the fewer bacteria reach the milk. This was nicely shown by Harding and Prucha [77]. In every case, considerably fewer bacteria were found in the milk collected in the closed-top milk pail. They reported that a small-top pail reduced the amount of dirt from 20 to 45 per cent over that getting into the milk when an open-top pail was used. As stated above, Ayers, Cook, and Clemmer [70] mentioned the small-top pail as one of the four important factors in the production of milk with a low bacterial count.

The milking machine has also made another opportunity for milk to pick up bacteria from utensils. The earlier literature on the subject has been reviewed by Ruehle, Breed, and Smith.[78] Investigations by Robert-

71. Prucha, Weeter, and Chambers. 1918. Ill. Agr. Expt. Sta. Bull. 204.
72. Whiting. 1923. N. Y. Agr. Expt. Sta. Bull. 98.
73. Berry. 1923. Ontario Bd. Health Ann. Rept. 42, 76-88.
74. Robertson. 1925. N. Y. Agr. Expt. Sta. Bull. 112.
75. Prucha and Harding. 1920. Ill. Agr. Expt. Sta. Bull. 230 and 254 (1924).
76. Proctor and Hoy. 1925. J. Hyg. 24, 419.
77. Harding and Prucha. 1921. Ill. Agr. Expt. Sta. Bull. 236.
78. Ruehle, Breed, and Smith. 1918. N. Y. Agr. Expt. Sta. Bull. 450.

son,[79] Bright,[80] and Breed and Bright[81] have resulted in information which should make the milking machine contribute fewer bacteria to milk. Fisher and White[82] attempted to use a commercial disinfectant. Large amounts had to be used.

Cleansing and Sterilization of Dairy Utensils. The fact that milk is such a good medium for development of bacteria makes it necessary to keep utensils in which it is handled as clean as possible. It has been found that they should be practically sterile. Prucha and Harding[83] and Ayers and Mudge[84] studied hot air as a method of sterilizing utensils. The former observed rapid development of bacteria in moist utensils. Cans which were quickly dried and kept dry contributed few bacteria to milk. Stewart[85] and Mattick and Hallett[86] stated that ordinary washing would not suffice. Drastic methods were necessary to remove bacteria from dairy utensils.

Chemical sterilization with chlorine compounds has become routine practice. Ruehle, Breed, and Smith,[78] Taylor,[87] and many others have contributed to the subject. This chemical substance is playing a role in milk sanitation comparable to that played in water purification.

SANITARY CONDITION OF GLASS MILK BOTTLES

While the glass milk bottle made possible vast improvements in marketing fluid milk, its use also introduced new problems in cleaning and sterilization. That these have not been easy to solve is indicated by many publications and committee reports. The main difficulty with the used glass milk bottle is to tell when it is clean, for results of different investigators have shown little relation between appearance of the washed and sterilized bottle and its bacterial content. A committee of the American Public Health Association (Holmquist, chairman)[88] tried to define clean and sterile dairy utensils. Milk bottles received some discussion. After analysis of results on the bacterial content of washed milk bottles the committee concluded that sterile containers in the surgical sense were not necessary. Sterility was defined as freedom from pathogenic microorganisms and a low number of other types. Barkworth[89] has also said that sterility in connection with washing dairy utensils makes allowances for a few bacteria. It would be ridiculous to require that *all* bacteria be destroyed when the few which might be left would be harmless. Furthermore, city ordinances frequently permit 30,000 bacteria per ml. in milk. A quart bottle would then receive in the milk placed into it some 29 million bacteria.

Results of various investigations on the bacterial content of washed milk bottles reveal a situation which would not ordinarily be expected. In the committee report referred to above, a state health department is

79. Robertson. 1924. N. Y. Agr. Expt. Sta. Tech. Bull. 105.
80. Bright. 1920. Idem Bull. 472.
81. Breed and Bright. 1921. Idem Bull. 488.
82. Fisher and White. 1927. Conn Agr. Expt. Sta. Bull. 144.
83. Prucha and Harding. 1920. Ill. Agr. Expt. Sta. Bull. 230.
84. Ayers and Mudge. 1921. J. Dairy Sci. 4, 79-90.
85. Stewart. 1906. Amer. Med. 11, 241-244.
86. Mattick and Hallett. 1923. Milk Indus. 3, 39-42.
87. Taylor. 1919. Internatl. Assoc. Dairy and Milk Insp. Ann. Rept. 8, 193-205.
88. Holmquist (Chairman). 1934. Amer. Pub. Health Assoc., Yearbook 1933-1934, p. 72.
89. Barkworth. 1941. Dairy Indus. 6, 35-37.

quoted as finding 22.6 per cent of 1,820 milk bottles containing in excess of 10 bacteria (colonies on plates) for each ml. capacity and 43.1 per cent in excess of one per ml., the standard which has been quite generally accepted in the United States. Layson, Huffer, and Brannon [90] also reported the bacterial content of glass milk bottles to be quite variable. They said that in any case of 12 bottles, two or three might be sterile while some of the remainder might contain as many as 180,000 to 200,000 bacteria per quart bottle. Some of the large numbers of bacteria might come from bottles which looked clean. Thirty per cent of milk jugs and 14.5 per cent of all bottles showed the presence of gas-forming bacteria. Such results as these indicate that problems relating to cleaning and sterilization of milk bottles have not yet been solved.

Insterility of washed and "sterilized" milk bottles has again been shown by Thomas and Jenkinson.[91] Glass bottles and paper containers taken at random from 24 farms and dairies during summer months showed that the paper bottles had many fewer bacteria than the most efficiently sterilized glass bottles. Hopkins and Kelly [92] found that supposedly sterile bottles (less than 100 bacteria per bottle) contained from 300 to 160 million bacteria per bottle. They emphasized the danger that might exist in unclean bottles. While large dairies may be able satisfactorily to clean glass milk bottles, the smaller ones may be less efficient, as pointed out by Koch.[93] Furthermore, smaller concerns may not have adequate laboratory service to check their procedures. They may be unable to enforce procedures which are known to be necessary whether they be methods involving heat sterilization or chemical substances. Furthermore, some bottles returned to a dairy may have been misused in such a manner that it would be difficult to remove the bacteria even by procedures which would ordinarily result in a satisfactory container. Such occurrences may be prevented by using a single-service container. If the bottle-washer is not operated correctly, Mattick and Hoy [94] believed that pathogenic bacteria might survive. Milk bottles have been incriminated in spreading communicable diseases. Hunt [95] observed such infection of a milk supply. Gibbs-Smith and Hobday [96] infected milk with *Eberthella typhosa* and recovered the organism from two of four bottles after superficial cleaning.

The puring lip may harbor many bacteria. In some cases, according to Dearstyne and Ewing [97] and Isaacs and Zeiber,[98] the number may be large. Single caps were found to be less desirable than double ones.

Paper caps have not been used without bacterial examination. Only saprophytic bacteria have been found in them and they are of no sanitary

90. Layson, Huffer, and Brannon. 1936. Milk Plant Mo. 25, 34-36.
91. Thomas and Jenkins. 1940. Welsh J. Agr. 16, 258.
92. Hopkins and Kelly. 1919. Amer. J. Pub. Health 9, 183.
93. Koch. 1932. Biol. Abs. 6, 824.
94. Mattick and Hoy. 1937. Natl. Inst. Res. in Dairying, Univ. Reading.
95. Hunt. 1911. N. J. Bd. Health Ann. Rept., 35, 101-113.
96. Gibbs-Smith and Hobday. 1928. J. State Med. 36, 660-664.
97. Dearstyne and Ewing. 1920. Amer. J. Pub. Health 10, 533.
98. Isaacs and Zeiber. 1932. Amer. J. Hyg. 16, 806-822.

significance. Paraffining of the discs, according to Rice,[99] forces the bacteria to the edge, where they may enter the milk more easily.

Bacterial Standards for Washed Milk Bottles and Containers. Bacterial standards have been suggested to determine whether washed and sterilized milk bottles are satisfactory. The "U. S. Public Health Service Milk Ordinance and Code" states that bottles shall be so cleaned that they shall not contribute more than one bacterial cell, or colony, per ml. to milk. The standard adopted by the International Association of Milk Dealers for satisfactory milk bottles was that they should not contribute more than 2,000 bacteria to a quart of milk. Shrader and Craig [100] recommended a standard of not more than 200 bacteria per bottle and that 80 per cent of the bottles of one dealer should conform to it. Parfitt [101] would allow 1,000 bacteria per bottle. In England Mattick and Hoy [94] believed that a standard of over 200 bacteria per bottle could be met by commercially washed bottles. The standard of not over 1,000 bacteria per bottle is generally accepted as good practice in the United States. Hoy [102] later confirmed this opinion.

Bacterial cleanliness of a vessel which has previously contained sour milk will, according to Neave and Hoy,[102a] normally contain less than 5 million recoverable bacteria per gallon capacity. Such a utensil was considered to be satisfactory when rinsings yielded not more than 5,000 organisms per gallon capacity, and not more than 50 coliform organisms and/or milk souring organisms per gallon capacity.

Levowitz's [103] Method for Determining Bacteriological Efficiencies of Milk Container Closures. A bacterial suspension of a suitable test organism is frozen into ice. The count of organisms in the ice is determined and this inoculated ice is mixed with normal ice after chopping it fine to yield a standard ice containing a fixed number of bacteria per gram. The organism selected for this work was *Serratia marcescens* and the concentration so arranged that 500,000 cells would be present in a gram of ice. This ice is then used to refrigerate a fixed number of containers, over 100 to reduce experimental errors. The iced containers are exposed to room temperature for four hours without agitation, followed by four hours of intermittent agitation. Such a procedure is comparable to commercial practice. After this the contents of the containers are examined for the test organisms by suitable laboratory methods.

Single-Service Paper Milk Container. The merits of such a container have been recognized for many years. Some health departments have insisted that they be used for homes in which cases of communicable diseases existed. Most of the early proponents, however, allowed economic problems to overshadow the health advantages. Early experience has been reviewed by Kilbourne.[104] These containers appeared on the American market early in the 1920's although they had been proposed many years earlier as very desirable. Relative costs of milk in glass bottles and paper containers have been studied by Bartlett.[105] The single-service container

99. Rice. 1930. Penn. Assoc. Dairy and Milk Insp. 1-18.
100. Shrader and Craig. 1923. Proc. World's Dairy Cong. 2, 1317-1324.
101. Parfitt. 1936. Milk Plant Mo. 25, 77.
102. Hoy. 1941. Proc. Soc. Agr. Bact.
102a. Neave and Hoy. 1942. Dairy Indus. 7, 200.
103. Levowitz. 1940. J. Milk Tech. 3, 41-43.
104. Kilbourne. 1920. Creamery 9, 25.
105. Bartlett. 1937. Amer. Prod. Rev. 85, 380-382.

meets most of the requirements of a satisfactory receptable for distribution of fluid milk. Health-department officials should encourage use of these containers for their bacteriological condition is vastly superior to that of the glass bottle even after the latter has been cleaned and sterilized by approved methods. It is not necessary to enforce stricter regulations for the single-service paper milk container than for the glass bottle. Contamination from human hands is much less possible with the former than the latter. Prucha [106] summarized the situation as follows:

"When the paper is so made that it is practically sterile, when it and the containers made from it are handled, packed, transported, and stored in such a manner that they will not become contaminated, and then the containers are properly paraffined at 185°F. for 30 seconds or longer, the paper containers will be fully as safe as any container which can be made. When it is remembered that, by the rinse test, the great majority of paper containers yield no microorganisms at all and that the great majority of those which do, show only one or two bacteria per bottle, the ideal package for fluid milk has just about been attained."

Paperboard, from which these containers are made, is made from virgin pulpwood. These containers are not made from chipboard which in turn is made from waste paper. Bacteriological problems in the manufacture of single-service paper milk containers are practically nil. The manufacture of paperboard involves cooking of the pulp at high temperatures, bleaching in strong chlorine solutions, and finally drying at high temperatures on the rolls of the papermaking machine. The United States Milk Ordinance and Code, 1939 edition,[1] stipulates that the stock from which paper containers are made shall not contain over 250 colonies per gram. When the paperboard is made into the final container it is paraffined at temperature which practically sterilizes it. The final product is well within the definition of sterility as it is used in the milk industry. Bactericidal effects of paraffination have been discussed by various investigators (Prucha,[106] Tanner and Lewis,[107] and Moss, Thomas, and Havens [108]). The last-mentioned investigators used *Escherichia coli* as a test organism and reported that a mean 99 per cent reduction of the *Escherichia coli* test organism owing to paraffining was obtained in about 10 seconds at 82.2°C.(180°F.), 20 seconds at 79.4°C.(175°F.), 35 seconds at 76.6°C.(170°F.), two minutes at 73.8°C.(165°F.), and four minutes at 71.1°C.(160°F.). These results indicate the greater mean bactericidal efficiency of the higher paraffin temperatures used. If paraffining is to serve as the bactericidal treatment for the surfaces of the paper container, the use of the higher temperatures studied appears essential, unless the immersion times generally used are considerably increased. After considerable study, Rice [109] concluded that most efficient waterproofing is obtained by treating paper containers with a high-melting-point wax, such as 56.1°C.(133°F.) to 57.2°C.(135°F.), applied at the lowest possible temperature, 65.5°C.(150°F.).

The United States Milk Ordinance and Code, 1939 edition,[1] requires that all single-service containers and container caps and covers shall,

106. Prucha. 1938. J. Milk Tech. 1, 4-5.
107. Tanner and Lewis. 1940. Oil and Soap 17, 26-30; Food Indus. 12, 57-58, 60-62.
108. Moss, Thomas, and Havens. 1941. Pub. Health Repts. 56, 944-956.
109. Rice. 1942. N. Y. Agr. Expt. Sta. Tech. Bull. 263.

prior to use, be given a bactericidal treatment equivalent to contact with paraffin for at least 20 seconds at at least 82.2°C. (180° F.), or for at least 35 seconds at at least 79.4°C. (175°F.), or for at least one second at at least 107.2°C. (225°F.). These regulations are based largely on the premise that paraffination may possess bactericidal properties in addition to waterproofing.

Sanitary Condition and Bacterial Content of Paper Milk Containers. The significance of this for paper milk containers may be weighed only in relation to the sanitary condition of the glass bottle. The problem for the latter has been discussed above. At a conference on "Sanitation of Paper Milk Containers"[110] in July, 1937, several requirements were agreed upon. The first was that only pure virgin mechanical or chemical pulp should be used. This was at no time to harbor more than 500 microorganisms per gram. Nonfermentable adhesives were also specified. Paraffining was to be done under conditions which would not impart flavors or odors to the paraffin or milk. Paraffined containers were to be shipped under conditions which would insure no abuse. Their bacterial content was to be determined by approved methods. In 1936 Rice[111] examined paper containers from four different manufacturers for their bacterial content by filling with sterile water, incubating at 37°C., for six hours, and then plating. He found a satisfactory condition but believed that bottles made and 'sealed in the factory were better than those made in the milk-bottling plant.

In a paper read before the Dairy Manufacturers' Conference at the University of Illinois in November, 1937, Prucha reported that examination of over 2,000 paraffined paper milk containers showed that about 50 per cent of them developed no colonies. The remaining 50 per cent developed only a small number of colonies. From a commercial standpoint, the number of bacteria in them was far below the standards suggested for milk bottles. This was confirmed by Rice[111] and Tanner.[112] The latter observed a high percentage of sterile containers and those which were not sterile harbored only a very few bacteria. *Escherichia coli* was not found once in 1,200 containers from each of which five ml. of rinse water were examined. The most recent work on this subject to which the author can refer is that of Rice[109] who examined 1,600 paper milk containers (Pure Pak type) by means of the broth-sterility test and found approximately 80 per cent of them to be sterile. The temperature of the paraffin bath used in the various treatments made practically no difference in the percentage of sterility among the several sets of containers.

Microorganisms in Milk Stored in Paper Containers. Several comparative investigations have been made on the bacterial content of milk stored in various containers. The point of interest here, however, is the relative number of bacteria in milk stored in glass bottles and paper milk containers. This question was studied by some of the earlier investigators.

110. Breed. 1937. The Milk Sanitarian 6, 11-13.
111. Rice. 1936. Penn. Assoc. Dairy and Milk Insp. Ann. Rept.
112. Tanner. 1938. Amer. J. Pub. Health 28, 587-592; J. Milk Tech. 2, 1-15.

Allyn [113] found that milk kept at 18.3°C.(65°F.) increased in acidity faster in glass than in paper containers. This observation was confirmed by bacterial counts. Three samples of milk kept at 32.2°C.(90°F.), 21.1°C. (70°F.), and 10°C.(50°F.) showed almost twice as many bacteria in glass bottles as in paper. Paper milk containers are used in foreign countries. Poulsen [114] studied a paper container which was sprayed with paraffin internally and externally just before filling. He stored milk in various ways as follows: (1) in paper containers which had been waterproofed with paraffin; (2) in well-washed glass bottles; (3) in glass bottles sterilized with steam; and (4) in chlorine-sterilized glass bottles. Milk stored in the single-service paper milk container was bacteriologically equal to that stored in glass bottles sterilized by steam or chlorine and was vastly superior, bacteriologically, to milk stored in well-washed glass bottles. The paper containers were tight and did not impart a taste to the milk.

Finally, mention may be made of the fact that the Ministry of Health in England, after a thorough investigation, approved a waxed paperboard single-service contained for fluid milk. This container made from pure bleached sulfite pulp and waterproofed with paraffin, has been used with satisfaction in England under the name of ''Perga'' Single Service Milk Container. This container was tested at the National Institute for Research in Dairying [115] and found to be satisfactory. The number of bacteria in the cartons was very low and *Escherichia coli* was absent. The bacteriological condition and the keeping quality of milk in the cartons were found to be equal to those of milk in sterile glass bottles. The flavor of milk was not changed. The ''Perga'' container is in all major details identical with those used in the United States. It is greatly to be hoped that use of such containers may become universal because they meet all salient requirements of a container for fresh fluid milk.

Methods for Testing Milk Bottles and Other Containers for Sterility. The present methods for examination of milk bottles for sterility are the results of many years of study. They are not entirely satisfactory but are probably as satisfactory as present experience and knowledge permit. Having shown that the glass bottle may harbor many bacteria and should be specially treated to make it clean and, perhaps, sterile, the next problem was to secure a method for examining it. Methods developed for research investigations might not be suitable for control laboratories where many bottles have to be examined. Hopkins and Kelly[116] placed bacteriological control of bottle sterilization on a par with control of milk. Horn, Rice, and Ramsey[117] made numerous tests by plating samples of sterile water used to rinse the bottles, and these results were compared with the counts upon a film of special agar gelatin medium rolled upon the inside of the bottles and incubated for 48 hours. No sufficiently significant differ-

113. Allyn. 1910. Milk Mangt. 3, 9.
114. Poulsen. 1936. Ugeskr. Laeger 98, 57-58.
115. Ministry of Agriculture and Fisheries, Agricultural Machinery Testing Committee, Certificates and Reports, No. 71, 1939. Gt. Brit.
116. Hopkins and Kelly. 1919. Amer. J. Pub. Health 9, 183.
117. Horn, Rice, and Ramsey. 1926. Penn. Assoc. Dairy and Milk Insp., 2nd Ann. Rept. 116-121.

ence was noted between the two methods. The principal factors developed were the dangers inherent in improperly cleansed bottles, the need for better care in cleansing than now obtained, and the tentative adoption of absolute sterility as the proper standard of bacterial content of milk bottles.

Parfitt [101] rinsed bottles with 100 ml. of sterile water. The bottle was taken from the line at the filling machine and capped with a sterile cap using sterile forceps. In the laboratory the cap was removed and 100 ml. of sterile water added to the bottle. A new sterile cap was placed on the bottle and the bottle shaken 25 times. Five ml. of the rinse water were added to a sterile Petri dish and nutrient agar added. The count secured after incubation at 37°C. (98.1°F.) for 48 hours was multiplied by 20. Cans were examined in somewhat the same manner. They were rinsed with a volume of water not less than $\frac{1}{20}$ the capacity of the can. The rinse water was plated in the usual manner. Parfitt suggested the agar disc method for examining surfaces of vats, pipe lines, and cans. This has been described in another chapter.

One of the first methods to receive wide acceptance was that proposed by the International Association of Milk Dealers.[118] The American Public Health Association [119] tentatively approved this procedure. One hundred ml. of sterile water were added to each bottle, capped, and shaken 25 times, making certain to wet the entire interior. One ml. portion of the rinse water was then added to each of two sterile Petri dishes after pouring, and incubated at 37°C. for 48 hours. The number of colonies on each plate multiplied by 100 equals the estimated number of colonies per bottle. Bottles were considered satisfactory when they contained less than one colony per ml. capacity. The American Public Health Association later approved an entirely new technic.[120] It had been pointed out by Fitzgerald of the American Can Company, that application of the above described procedure to paper milk containers left much to be desired in that such a small amount of rinse water was plated. He suggested in 1937 that 10 ml. be used and the entire amount plated in one large dish (140 mm. x 20 mm.) or distributed in three dishes of the size usually used in laboratories. Consequently Wheaton started to use this method in the laboratories of the American Can Company for examination of paper milk containers.

The eighth edition of *Standard Methods for the Examination of Dairy Products*, 1941, prescribed the use of 20 ml. of sterile tap or buffered distilled water in each bottle. After capping, the bottle is shaken so that all of the interior surface is rinsed. When low numbers of bacteria are expected, 10 ml. of the rinse water are distributed in three sterile Petri dishes. Should large numbers of bacteria be expected, one-ml. portions of the rinse water shall be added to each of two Petri dishes and .1-ml. portion to each of two Petri dishes. Standard agar medium shall then be added to the dishes. After the plates have been incubated at 32°C. (89.6°F.) for 48 hours, the colonies shall be counted. The enumeration of colonies from the plates gives the estimated number of bacteria per

118. Lab. Manual, Internatl. Assoc. Milk Dealers, 1933, 72-73.
119. Standard Methods of Milk Analysis, Amer. Pub. Health Assoc., Sixth Ed., 1934, 58-59.
120. Idem, Seventh Ed.

bottle. When 10 ml. of rinse water are distributed in three plates, the sum of the colonies on the plates multiplied by two equals the number of bacteria in the bottle; if one-ml. portions were plated in two dishes, the sum of colonies multiplied by 20 equals the number of bacteria in the bottle. Should smaller amounts be plated, appropriate factors must be used. The practice of using smaller quantities of rinse water has been accepted in England by Barkworth [89] and Mattick and Hoy.[94] Both of these investigators used 20 ml. of rinse water.

In addition to the methods just mentioned are several others which lend themselves more to research work than routine work. These are patterned after methods which have been used in different fields. They involve introduction of the medium, either melted fluid agar, plain broth, or sterile milk, into the container after which it is incubated in the bottle. These methods do not permit a numerical estimation of the microorganisms but merely indicate the presence of living organisms. When melted agar is added to the bottle, it may be allowed to coat the interior or may harden in the bottom. Incubation of the microorganisms occurs in the container.

A modification of this procedure was used by Mudge and Foard.[121] They introduced 20 ml. of sterile culture fluid, nutrient broth, into the closed container by means of a sterile needle. The container was then shaken and the rinse fluid counted as for glass bottles; or the percentage of sterile containers may be determined after incubation. The results may be reported as percentage of sterile containers.

It is indeed not difficult to summarize the paper milk container situation as far as its microbiological and public-health aspects are concerned. It constitutes one of the great advances in the distribution of safe and clean fluid milk to the public. Microbiologically it is far superior to the washed and sterilized glass bottle, some 80 per cent being sterile, according to Rice,[109] Tanner,[112] and others, by the broth-sterility test. Those which are not sterile yield only a few bacteria. The types of bacteria which have been identified have been found to be harmless aerobic sporeformers. Single-service containers are made from clean paperboard which is subjected to processes of heavy chlorination, cooking at high temperatures, and finally, drying on rolls at high temperatures. Each of these is a procedure with pronounced sterilizing value. Waterproofing the container by dipping in hot paraffin wax is the final bactericidal treatment. By and large the paper milk container is far superior to the glass bottle from the standpoint of the consumer, dairyman, and health officer even after the glass bottle has been subjected to the usual washing and sterilizing procedures. The public health aspects have been reviewed by Tanner [122] and Ball.[123]

Influence of Age and Temperature on Bacteria in Milk. Time and temperature are very important factors influencing the flora of milk. They cannot be separated. No single extensive investigation has been carried

121. Mudge and Foard. 1940. Amer. J. Pub. Health 30, 273-277.
122. Tanner. 1938. Dairy Indus. 3, 125-128, 165-170; 1939, J. Milk Tech. 2, 1-15; Amer. J. Pub. Health 28, 587-592; 1940, 30, 256-266.
123. Ball. 1942. J. Milk Tech. 5, 6-17.

out on the relation of temperature to development of bacteria in milk. Knowledge has to be pieced together from many different investigations, and in some cases, from data secured with quite diverse organisms.

Luxwolda [124] found that milk kept at low temperatures developed a large number of bacteria. These did not cause an acid reaction in the milk. At 20°C.(68°F.) lactic acid bacteria appeared and exerted a restraining action on the other forms. This restraining action was steadily diminished as the temperature was lowered. Reed and Reynolds [125] inoculated sterile flasks of milk with pure cultures and incubated them at four different temperatures for six weeks. As would be expected, the minimum time for maximum numbers of bacteria occurred at the higher temperatures of incubation. Conn and Esten [126] observed little regularity in the comparative development of different species of bacteria in milk. The number at any time was believed to depend more on temperature than on initial contamination. As to development of bacteria, two periods were recognized: the first in which the number of bacteria was less than 10 million per ml. lasting from 24 to 50 hours, according to whether the temperature was 20°C.(68°F.) or 13°C.(55.4°F.); and the second, in which the number of bacteria was above 10 million, lasting from the end of the first period until time of curdling. Some changes which occurred during the first period were described as follows: The number of bacteria in milk was not increased, but was frequently reduced during the first few hours after milking. At 20°C. most of the species began to increase in absolute numbers after the first six hours. *Bacillus acidi lactici* increased uniformly, the other lactic acid bacteria were irregular in their development, the Streptococcus group always increased, the liquefying bacteria practically always increased in absolute and sometimes in relative numbers, the species of Sarcina developed but little, and the miscellaneous species decreased slightly during the first period. At 13°C. the original period of no growth was increased, the number of bacteria at the end of 50 hours being no greater than that in milk at 20°C. after 18 hours. Rapid development of bacteria after 40 hours was most frequently due to the growth of the Streptococcus group rather than to the lactic acid bacteria. Development of miscellaneous species was favored by the lower temperature. Preliminary icing of milk for a period of 15 hours greatly reduced the number of bacteria, the number present at the time of curdling being much less than in samples not previously iced. Preliminary icing favored development of a number of miscellaneous species, but delayed development of *Bacillus acidi lactici*. Conn and Esten [126] made another report and gave descriptions of nine groups or types of bacteria and the relative development of these types in market milk at temperatures ranging from 1 to 37°C. Development of different types of bacteria in ordinary market milk was believed to be closely associated with temperature. The initial period, in which no increase in the total number of bacteria occurred was very short when the milk was kept at 37°C.(98.6°F.), but was six to eight

124. Luxwolda. 1911. Centbl. Bakt., Pt. 2, 31, 129-175.
125. Reed and Reynolds. 1916. Virginia Agr. Expt. Sta. Bull. 10.
126. Conn and Esten. 1902. Conn. Agr. Expt. Sta. Ann. Rept. 14, 13-80; 16 (1904), 27-28.

days when the milk was kept at 1°C.(33.8°F.). Following this period the bacterial content of the milk showed great diversity, depending upon the temperature. It was found that at 20°C.(68°F.) ordinary lactic acid bacteria developed rapidly and at the end of about 40 hours when the milk became curdled, *Bacillus acidi lactici* commonly constituted over 90 per cent of the total number of bacteria. At this temperature, other species were almost completely held in check by the lactic acid bacteria. At 37°C. (98.6°F.) the results were quite different. *Aerobacter aerogenes* commonly predominated over *Bacillus acidi lactici. Escherichia coli,* when present, also grew rapidly. At 10°C.(50°F.) all types of bacteria developed some-what uniformly after the first two or three days, none of the lactic acid types being favored. Neutral bacteria usually grew rapidly and liquefiers often became abundant. This temperature was not so favorable for devel-opment of lactic acid bacteria as 20°C.(68°F.). As the growth of other species of bacteria at this temperature was less retarded, the wholesome-ness of the milk was more under suspicion. Except as regards the rapidity of bacterial growth, there was but little difference between 10 and 1°C. Conn stated, "Milk is not necessarily wholesome because it is sweet, espe-cially if it has been kept at low temperatures. At the temperature of an ice chest, milk may remain sweet for a long time, and yet contain enormous numbers of bacteria, among which are species more likely to be unwhole-some than those that develop at 20°C.(68°F.). From this standpoint the suggestion arises that instances of ice-cream poisoning are perhaps due to the preservation of cream for several days at a low temperature, such treatment keeping the milk sweet, but favoring the development of species of bacteria that are, at higher temperatures, checked by lactic organisms."

Conn referred to an extreme case where the bacteria multiplied five fold in 24 hours, when the temperature was 10°C.(50°F.), and 750 fold in the same time when the temperature was 21.1°C.(70°F.). Milk kept at 35°C.(95°F.) curdled in 18 hours and at 10°C. in 148 hours. As far as the keeping property of the milk was concerned, low temperature was considered of more importance than cleanliness. Savage [127] also believed that temperature was more important than initial numbers. In milk kept at 35°C.(95°F.), the species developing most rapidly was the unde-sirable one, *Aerobacter aerogenes.* At a temperature of 21.1°C. this species developed relatively less rapidly in the majority of cases than *Bacillus lactis acidi,* the latter being very desirable in cream and cheese ripening. The bacteria in milk kept at 10°C. increased slowly and later consisted of very few lactic acid organisms but of miscellaneous types, including many forms that render the milk unwholesome. Pennington [128] found that milk stored at 0°C.(32°F.) underwent marked proteolysis, which was noticeable at the end of two weeks. She stated that proteolysis of casein was due primarily to bacteria, while lactalbumin was destroyed by the enzymes in the milk. The numbers of bacteria greatly increased

127. Savage. 1909-1910. Ann. Rept., Local Govt. Bd., Gt. Brit. 39, 474-503.
128. Pennington. 1908. J. Biol. Chem. 4, 353; 16 (1913), 331-368.

and this increase was most striking in the raw, untreated milk. The freezing-point was gradually lowered with the decomposition. Market milk held below 0°C. increased from 15,956 to 376,000,000 at the end of five weeks. These investigations tend to indicate that milk and other foods may not be held indefinitely even at low temperatures. Changes may eventually take place to render the food unfit for consumption. Pennington continued her investigations to determine which part is due to the enzymes of milk, and, finally, what results when both bacteria and enzymes act together. It was shown that proteolysis of casein is due primarily to bacterial action, while that of lactalbumin is due to the enzymes of the milk. Bacterial and milk enzymes, when active at the same time, cause a greater degree of proteolysis. The fermentation of lactose is largely, if not entirely, due to bacterial action.

Classification of Bacteria Found in Milk. Bacteria in milk are contributed to it by every agent with which it comes in contact. Consequently, attempts to classify the bacteria in milk may not be of great value. Conn et al.,[129] Kruse,[130] Orla-Jensen,[131] Löhnis,[132] Beijerinck,[133] and Rogers and Davis [134] are among those who have attempted to do this. Their classifications will not be reviewed here mainly because they are of historic interest now.

Ayers and Johnson's [135] Milk Tube Method. This is a useful method for grouping bacteria in milk. Five groups of bacteria are recognized depending on the changes induced in tubes of sterile litmus milk. The milk under study is plated in sufficiently high dilution to yield plates with individual colonies. Each colony is transferred to a tube of sterile litmus milk and incubated at 37°C.(98.6°F.) for 14 days. After this incubation period, the cultures fall into the following groups: (1) acid-coagulating, (2) acid-forming, (3) inert, (4) alkali-forming, and (5) peptonizing. This method has the advantage of grouping bacteria according to the changes which they bring about in the milk and not according to some name or charactersitic which may be unimportant as far as milk is concerned.

Alkali-Forming Bacteria in Milk. We are indebted to Ayers et al.,[136] for a study of the alkali-forming bacteria in milk. They are defined as bacteria which produce an alkaline reaction in litmus milk in 14 days, with no indications of peptonization. In the sterile litmus milk tube it appears within five days, sometimes in a shorter period. Ayers believed that the alkalinity was caused principally by the fermentation of citric acid salts to alkali carbonates. Other salts of the organic acids may undergo the same transition if they are present in the milk. Ammonia was found to play little or no role in establishing alkaline reactions. The bacteria which were responsible for these changes grew best aerobically between temperatures of 20°C.(68°F.) and 30°C.(86°F.). The thermal death points of these bacteria in milk were between 60°C.(140°F.) and 65.5°C.(149.4°F.). There was no indication of spore formation but a slimy growth on agar.

129. Conn, Esten, and Stocking. 1906. Conn. Agr. Expt. Sta. Ann. Rept. for 1906, 91-203.
130. Kruse. 1910. Allg. Mikrobiologie.
131. Orla-Jensen. 1919. Danske, Vidensk. Selks. Skr. Naturridenskog. Math. Afd. 8, 81.
132. Löhnis. 1907. Centbl. Bakt., Pt. 2, 18, 97-149.
133. Beijerinck. 1908. Arch. Néerland. Sci. Exact. et Nat. 12, 356-378.
134. Rogers and Davis. 1912. U. S. Dept. Agr., Bur. Anim. Indus. Bull. 154.
135. Ayers and Johnson. 1910. U. S. Dept. Agr., Bur. Anim. Indus. Bull. 126.
136. Ayers, Rupp, and Johnson. 1919. U. S. Dept. Agr. Bull. 782.

Bacteria that possess the property of breaking down protein with the consequent production of an alkaline reaction in milk were thoroughly studied by Storck.[137] He isolated them from raw milk by plating on China-blue lactose agar and incubation at 30°C.(86°F.). True alkali-forming bacteria were characterized after 48 hours by colonies surrounded by a clear zone easily recognizable under moderate magnification; there was no preliminary blue coloration. The alkali-forming bacteria belonged to the major groups of bacteria which are usually found in milk. These bacteria were considered undesirable in milk especially in the winter time when they might gain ascendancy over the acid formers and cause the milk to clot. Also, some of the alkali formers are able to split fat and cause rancidity in butter. On the other hand, these bacteria might be useful in the soft cheese industry because they could help decompose the casein.

Fat-Splitting Bacteria in Milk. These bacteria have received more attention recently than for many years. Long and Hammer [138] isolated *Pseudomonas fragi* repeatedly from various dairy products. It is widely distributed and grows well at low temperatures. It frequently grows with a characteristic odor which turns to a rancid odor with time. *Pseudomonas fragi* has never been isolated from pasteurized milk or cream directly from the vat but has been frequently isolated from bottled milk and cream which indicates contamination after pasteurization. Long and Hammer found the species so variable that it was difficult to characterize it. They isolated it from salted and unsalted butter in Iowa. More has been written about these bacteria in other places in this book. They seem to be assuming greater importance in the food industry.

"Fermentation Test" of Milk. This is an attempt to determine the predominant bacterium that is present in milk. The milk is kept in a sterile culture tube at 40°C.(104°F.) for several hours. Normal, clean, fresh milk, according to Van Oijen,[139] may then turn faintly sour in 12 hours, both in taste and odor, but in most cases will not curdle. If the milk is stored for a longer time, it may curdle and clot without appreciable extrusion of whey. The presence of undersirable bacteria will bring about other changes.

(*a*) Presence of strongly acid-producing bacteria produces a curd which is not homogenous. The milk curdles and shows large and small flakes.

(*b*) Gas production may take place, accompanied by a disagreeable odor. Presence of gas-producing bacteria, such as *Escherichia coli* and its relatives, is undesirable.

(*c*) Curds of different consistencies may be formed. These may be accompanied by bad odors, owing to presence of sporeforming bacteria. Such milk may not be adapted to condensing or dehydration.

STREPTOCOCCI IN MILK

Streptococci are widely distributed in milk and were once thought to be always related to undesirable conditions in the cow's udder which

137. Storck. 1936. Zentbl. Bakt., Pt. 2, 94, 295-330.
138. Long and Hammer. 1937. J. Dairy Sci. 20, 450; Iowa Agr. Expt. Sta. Res. Bull. 225.
139. Van Oijen. 1928. Proc. World's Dairy Cong., 697.

might cause illness in those who used the milk. Hueppe [140] reported *Bacillus acidi lactici* as the organism causing the souring of milk. In 1894-1895, Günther and Thierfelder [141] found another organism differing in characteristics from that described by Hueppe and thought it was the *Bacillus lactici acidi* of Leischmann. Kruse [142] claimed that *Bacillus acidi lactici* (Hueppe) belonged in the *Aerobacter aerogenes* group. He believed that the organism which caused the souring of milk was a streptococcus and, consequently, proposed the name *Streptococcus lacticus*. This name, according to Ayers, was substituted for *Bacillus lactici acidi*. It is well known that Lister was one of the pioneers in the study of the sour-milk bacteria, and proposed the name *Bacterium lactis* for the organism souring milk. Present-day investigators agree that this name should be used, on the grounds of priority. It seems to be replacing other names. After Heinemann [143] had investigated the bacteria which were said to be concerned with the souring of milk, he believed *Bacillus acidi lactici* to be a myth. The ordinary bacteria producing lactic acid fermentation in milk were said to be *Aerobacter aerogenes* and *Streptococcus lactis*. *Streptococcus lactis* was said to agree in morphological, cultural, and coagulative properties with pathogenic, fecal, and sewage streptococci; it could be demonstrated in cow feces, on the cows, and in the milk. These conclusions are at variance with the work of Ayers of a later date.

Frost and Engelbrecht [144] believe that milk freshly drawn from the bovine udder contains streptococci in a large percentage of the samples. Certain herds may also contain hemolytic streptococci closely resembling, if not identical with, those causing streptococcic sore throat and scarlet fever, but the vast majority of beta-hemolytic streptococci found in milk are either *Streptococcus mastitidis* or the pseudo-hemolytic. Non-hemolytic streptococci were said to be even more numerous than the hemolytic varieties. Frost and Engelbrecht reported that the alpha type of hemolytic streptococci was most common in milk from a number of herds producing certified milk in Wisconsin and northern Illinois as well as herds which were not producing certified milk. Among the strongly beta-hemolytic streptococci of the human type in milk they reported *Streptococcus pyogenes* and *Streptococcus epidemicus*. The former was said to occur typically in man and occasionally in milk. In 12,446 examinations they found it 18 times. They suggested that this organism might be the cause of scarlet fever. *Streptococcus epidemicus* was found 10 times in the same number of examinations. These two strains were said to differ from each other in that *Streptococcus epidemicus* is encapsulated. Frost and his colleague stated that they had found this organism in the certified milk herds during an eight-year period. During the time which they had been under observation, 10 cows were carrying this germ. Frost quoted the work of Edwards, of the Kentucky Agricultural Experiment Station, who

140. Hueppe. 1884. Mitt. K. Gsndhtsamt. 2, 367.
141. Günther and Thierfelder. 1894-95. Arch. Hyg. 25, 164-195.
142. Kruse. 1910. Allg. Mikrobiolgie, Vogel.
143. Heinemann. 1906. J. Infect. Dis. 3, 173-182.
144. Frost and Engelbrecht. 1934. Twenty-second Ann. Rept. Internatl. Assoc. Dairy and Milk Insp., 85-104.

reported a *Streptococcus epidemicus*-like organism in mares. The fermentation reactions, however, of this last strain were a little different from those which had come from streptococcic sore-throat outbreaks.

Streptococcus lactis. This organism, as just indicated, has been known under many different names. Study of the many papers which have been written on it indicates that a group of somewhat related streptococci are concerned. Many of the investigators speak about varieties of *Streptococcus lactis* established usually on the basis of some special property. Hammer and Baker [145] suggested several such species. Identity of species is indeed confused by the fact that fermentation reactions are not stable. This makes possible many fermentation varieties which confuse new investigators. Yawger and Sherman [146] reported cultures of *Streptococcus lactis* which gradually acquired ability to ferment lactose. According to Brown,[147] this organism grows rapidly in milk at fairly low temperatures producing a high acidity and is quite resistent to heat, usually surviving 60°C.(140°F.) for 30 minutes. Ayers, Johnson, and Mudge [148] did not find the organism in the mouths, udders, or feces of cows and believed that it gained entrance to milk from dairy utensils. Some workers have found *Streptococcus lacticus* to be indistinguishable from *Streptococcus fecalis* of the human intestines. It seems, therefore, that streptococci must not be accepted as indigenous to milk.

Considerable study has been given to the problem of the origin of *Streptococcus lactis*. According to the results of investigations by Rogers and Dahlberg,[149] Evans,[150] and Ayers, Johnson, and Mudge [148] *Streptococcus lactis* does not originate normally in the cow's udder.

Esten [151] could not find *Streptococcus lactis* in nature. When it was found it was considered to be accidental; however, it was found in the cow's mouth and intestinal tract. Any object which could be reached by the tongue of the cow was, therefore, believed to be a constant source of the organism. Barthel found it ever-present in the stable.

A recent attempt by Stark and Sherman [152] to answer this question seems to indicate that *Streptococcus lactis* lives normally on plants. They isolated 200 strains of *Streptococcus lactis* from various sources, such as fresh corn, navy beans, cabbage, wheat, garden peas, and head lettuce. Cultures from mature corn, aged heads of cabbage, lima beans, alfalfa, soil, and intestines of earth worms proved negative, but the number of samples examined was fairly small. The organism was not found in the mouths and throats of cows nor in bovine or human feces, though *Streptococcus faecalis* was isolated from all these situations. It would appear that certain plants constitute the natural habitat of *Streptococcus lactis* and that this organism finds its way into milk from these sources.

145. Hammer and Baker. 1926. Iowa Agr. Expt. Sta. Res. Bull. 99.
146. Yawger and Sherman. 1937. J. Dairy Sci. 20, 205-212.
147. Brown. 1932. Twentieth Ann. Rept. Internatl. Assoc. Dairy and Milk Insp., 269.
148. Ayers, Johnson, and Mudge. 1924. J. Infect. Dis. 34, 29-53.
149. Rogers and Dahlberg. 1914. J. Agr. Res. 1, 491.
150. Evans. 1916. J. Infect. Dis. 18, 437-476.
151. Esten. 1909. Conn. Agr. Expt. Sta. Bull. 59.
152. Stark and Sherman. 1935. J. Bact. 30, 639-640.

The serological grouping method of Lancefield,[153] which has proved of value for differentiation of hemolytic streptococci into more or less species-specific groups, was not successfully used by Sherman, Smiley, and Niven [154] for non-hemolytic streptococci except in these groups which included both hemolytic and non-hemolytic varieties, such as groups B and D. In group B (*Streptococcus mastidis* and its varieties) non-hemolytic strains may be serologically identified quite as satisfactorily as those which are hemolytic. In group D (enterococci), also, are found a number of closely related entities, the non-hemolytic *Streptococcus fecalis* and varieties and the hemolytic *Streptococcus zymogenes* and varieties.

Sherman and his colleagues further confirmed the serological identity of *Streptococcus lactis* by producing "species-specific grouping sera" for this organism. Variants may occur as shown by Sherman and Yawger.[155] Four cultures of an organism which did not ferment lactose but identical in all other respects with *Streptococcus lactis*, were isolated. One strain acquired the ability to ferment lactose after several months.

Identity of Streptococcus lactis (Streptococcus lacticus) and Streptococcus pyogenes. *Streptococcus pyogenes* of Rosenbach is a Gram-positive coccus, causing infection of man. It is very much like *Streptococcus lactis*—in fact, so much so that Heinemann,[156] after a comparative study, believed that they were identical. This was a most interesting statement in view of the position which *Streptococcus pyogenes* has as a pathogen for man. In the second paper, Heinemann [157] reported the results of an attempt to determine whether the virulence of *Streptococcus lactis* might be increased by successive passages through animals. Five strains of *Streptococcus lactis*, from different sources, and three of *Streptococcus pyogenes* were used. The conclusion was reached from the investigations that these two organisms are closely related, not only in morphological and cultural characters, but in pathogenic properties. The virulence of *Streptococcus lactis* was gradually increased by repeated passages through rabbits, so that after five or more passages, two ml. of a 24-hour-old broth culture were fatal in subcutaneous injections. The same amount injected intravenously was fatal to the first animal. The lesions of *Streptococcus lactis* in rabbits were the same as those produced by *Streptococcus pyogenes* in man. Ruediger,[158] however, reported that *Streptococcus pyogenes* could be separated from *Streptococcus lactis* by means of blood agar plates. The latter were said to produce small colonies surrounded by a large zone of hemolysis, whereas the former produced green or greenish colonies with little or no hemolysis. *Streptococcus pyogenes* was said to occur rarely in milk, and when it does occur, it indicates an inflamed condition of the udder. This latter opinion seems to be confirmed by the work of Baehr.[159] He found *Streptococcus pyogenes* in only two samples of milk examined;

153. Lancefield. 1933. J. Expt. Med. 57, 571.
154. Sherman, Smiley, and Niven. 1940. J. Dairy Sci. 23. 529-530.
155. Sherman and Yawger. 1937. J. Dairy Sci. 20, 83.
156. Heinemann. 1907. J. Biol. Chem., 603-612.
157. Heinemann. 1907. J. Infect. Dis. 4, 87-92.
158. Ruediger. 1912. Amer. J. Pub. Health 2, 107-109.
159. Baehr. 1910. Arch. Hyg. 72, 91-160.

one of them came from a cow with a diseased udder. On the other hand, *Streptococcus lactis*, as described by Kruse,[160] was present in a large percentage of samples.

Significant differences between these two organisms were also reported by Saito [161] and Sherman and Albus.[162] They reported differences in chain formation, ability to coagulate milk, and fermentation reactions, and especially a marked difference in ability to reduce stains. *Streptococcus lactis* reduced methylene blue, litmus, and indigo carmine very promptly, while the pyogenes group had no effect on the first named and decolorized the others very slowly and incompletely, and only after curdling had taken place. It was also observed that all the cultures of lactic acid bacteria grew at 10°C.(50°F.), while none of the other group developed at this temperature. Sherman and Albus believed that the two groups could be distinguished. Those who desire a comprehensive survey of the streptococci should consult the publication by Thomson and Thomson,[163] and the more recent publications of Sherman [164] and his colleagues. Kleckner [165] used more refined methods in trying to compare these two types of streptococci. He isolated 50 strains of each and made detailed studies on the growth and action in various media. Finally, immune sera were prepared and agglutination, cross-agglutination, and agglutinin absorption tests made. They showed no real difference between these two types of streptococci. Slight variations which occur are not of real importance since they may occur not only between two types but also among the members of the groups themselves. These slight variations perhaps are due to the fact that the organisms undergo changes according to environmental conditions. Since the lactic acid streptococci appear to be able to withstand conditions as they occur in the animal body, it is reasonable to assume that they should be found in the intestinal tract. As indicated here and also by other workers, there seems to exist no real difference between the fecal streptococci and those normally found in milk. Therefore, it is felt that the *Streptococcus lactis* ingested with milk and some milk products is of the same type as that found in the feces. From here they may enter the soil where only the most vigorous can survive and in turn enter milk through sources of contamination. In a study of the transformation of *Streptococcus fecalis* Starck [166] considered the following to be the critical differences between the two "forms": *Streptococcus fecalis*—heat resistant [30 min. at 63°C.(145.4°F.) in milk], late fermentation of pentoses (arabinose and rhamnose); *Streptococcus lactis*—non-heat-resistant, early fermentation of litmus milk not able to ferment pentoses.

A change of character from *lactis* to *fecalis* could be brought about by successive passages in certain media, e.g., milk, peptone milk, brewer's mash, mash with peptone, decoction of rye, etc., particularly with the last

160. Kruse. 1903. Centbl. Bakt., Pt. 1, Orig., 34,737.
161. Saito. 1912. Arch. Hyg. 75, 121-134.
162. Sherman and Albus. 1918. J. Bact. 3, 153-173.
163. Thomson and Thomson. 1927. Ann. Pickett-Thomson Res. Lab. 3, 1-306.
164. Sherman. 1937. Bact. Rev. 1, 3-97.
165. Kleckner. 1935. J. Lab. and Clin. Med. 21, 111-121.
166. Starck. 1936. Zentbl. Bakt., Pt. 2, 95, 284-310.

two media. To all these media it is necessary to add chalk. The change could also be brought about by passage through mash medium to which various digestive enzymes and bile has been added. This suggests that the transformation may take place in the alimentary canal and that some of the streptococci in the feces with the characters of *Streptococcus fecalis* are derived from *Streptococcus lactis* introduced with the food in the milk. According to Sherman, Mauer, and Stark [167] the *Streptococcus fecalis* group is a homogeneous one. They found no reason for subdividing it on the basis of results from fermentation tests.

These organisms were not considered to be identical by the committee which prepared the fifth edition of Bergey's *Manual of Determinative Bacteriology.* Both are listed as distinct species.

Streptococcus cremoris. This streptococcus was described in 1919 by Orla-Jensen.[168] It had probably been confused with *Streptococcus lactis.* Its normal habitat seems to be dairy products. Sherman [164] stated it does not grow as well in artificial media as does *Streptococcus lactis.* Yawger and Sherman [146] studied the physiological characteristics of 41 cultures of lactic acid-producing streptococci identified as *Streptococcus cremoris* and 25 cultures identified as *Streptococcus lactis* by methods described and gave definite evidence that these species can be clearly differentiated and that *Streptococcus cremoris* is entitled to rank as a separate species. An extensive description of this organism was presented. *Streptococcus cremoris* can be separated from *Streptococcus lactis* by the inability of the former to produce ammonia in four per cent peptone and by its inability to grow at 40°C.(104°F.) in the presence of four per cent sodium chloride and in broth at pH 9.2. It is also generally less tolerant to methylene blue than *Streptococcus lactis.* In a later publication Sherman, Smiley, and Niven [154] reported that *Streptococcus cremoris* seemed to be closely related serologically to *Streptococcus lactis.* Whether or not these two "lactic" organisms belong to the same serological group is not clear on the basis of our limited data. Most strains of *Streptococcus cremoris* react weakly with anti-lactis group sera. Some attempts to produce anti-cremoris group sera have failed. This finding of an apparently close serological relationship between *Streptococcus lactis* and *Streptococcus cremoris* appears to agree with results reported by others. Apparently pure strains of this organism may not be permanent, for Hunter [169] observed well marked variation in pure strains, especially in acid production and certain other characteristics. Klingmuller [170] could not distinguish between *Streptococcus mastitidis* and *Streptococcus cremoris.*

According to Ayers and Johnson,[171] the typical udder streptococcus of the cow is *Streptococcus mastitidis.* This streptococcus was said to be practically identical with *Streptococcus pyogenes*, when the ordinary cultural characters are considered. However, they can be separated by their

167. Sherman, Mauer, and Stark. 1937. J. Bact. 33, 275.
168. Orla-Jensen. 1919. The Lactic Acid Bacteria. Andr. Fred Host & Son, Copenhagen.
169. Hunter. 1939. J. Dairy Res. 10, 464-470.
170. Klingmuller. 1930. Milchw. Forsch. 10, 431-454.
171. Ayers and Johnson. 1922. J. Infect. Dis. 31, 40-50.

ability to split sodium hippurate. According to the same investigators, the characteristic streptococcus of cow feces is *Streptococcus bovis*. This streptococcus does not produce gas from dextrose, and is thus differentiated from *Streptococcus kefir*, which does form gas from dextrose and which ferments raffinose. Hammer [172] reported *Streptococcus paracitrovorus* as commonly present in milk. Ayers believed that this organism should be placed in the *Streptococcus kefir* group. Ayers, Johnson, and Mudge [148] stated that *Streptococcus kefir* predominated in milk with low acidity and *Streptococcus lactis* in milk with high acidity. Ayers,[173] before the World's Dairy Congress, summarized the results of his work in this field and reported a new species in the udder to which he gave the name *Streptococcus acidominimus*. He further reported that there was no reason for assuming that *Streptococcus mastitidis* was pathogenic for man and that it could be readily differentiated from human hemolytic streptococci.

Streptococcus liquefaciens. The 101 cultures which were isolated from dairy products by Long and Hammer [174] varied widely in their production of volatile acid, carbon dioxide, and acetylmethylcarbinol in skim milk. Diacetyl was not produced by any culture. Volatile acid production was not correlated with the fermentation of sucrose or the rapidity of reduction of litmus milk. The production of carbon dioxide and acetylmethylcarbinol did not vary directly with the volatile acid produced. Smaller amounts of these substances were formed at 37°C.(98.6°F.) than at 21°C. (69.8°F.). The addition of .2 to .4 per cent citric acid to skim milk generally reduced volatile acid production.

HEMOLYTIC STREPTOCOCCI IN MILK

Practically all investigations which have been made on the subject indicate that nearly all raw market milk may contain hemolytic streptococci, even of human origin, which is another strong argument for universal pasteurization. Gunnison *et al.*[175] found such streptococci in 134 specimens of raw market milk from as many different dairy farms. Most of these strains produced double zones of hemolysis in rabbit-blood agar. Their work confirmed conclusions which had been reached by other investigators in the same field. Sherman and Niven [176] examined a total of 313 samples of commercial milk, 68 raw and 245 pasteurized, for hemolytic streptococci. Narrow-zone hemolytic types in blood agar, the most typical form of *Streptococcus mastitidis* were not considered. Only 8.5 per cent of the pasteurized samples contained hemolytic streptococci, whereas broad-zone hemolytic types were obtained from 18 per cent of the raw samples. The cultures isolated were studied seriologically and physiologically and, on the basis of these results, six groups or species were recognized: *Streptococcus mastitidis* (Lancefield group B), the "animal pyogenes" (Lancefield group C), *Streptococcus durans* (Lancefield group D), and two other types which differ serologically and physiologically from any adequately

172. Hammer. 1923. Iowa Agr. Expt. Sta. Bull. 74
173. Ayers. 1923. Abs. Bact. 7, Abs. No. 32.
174. Long and Hammer. 1936. Iowa Agr. Expt. Sta. Res. Bull. 206.
175. Gunnison, Luxen, Marshall, and Engle. 1940. J. Dairy Sci. 23, 447-455.
176. Sherman and Niven. 1938. J. Infect. Dis. 62, 190-201.

described species of Streptococcus. The prevailing types of hemolytic streptococci in raw milk are *Streptococcus mastitidis* and the "animal pyogenes"; the most common forms in pasteurized milk are *Streptococcus durans* and *Streptococcus zymogenes*. While it is known that intramammary contamination is often gross Pullinger and Kemp [177] assumed that contamination by a human being is more likely to be slight or intermittent. They contaminated different grades of raw and heated milk with *Streptococcus pyogenes* and then stored the milk at various temperatures. These organisms multiplied readily in sterilized milk but in fresh raw milk they multiplied slowly only after from 48 to 72 hours. Similar results were secured in laboratory pasteurized milk. In all cases the organisms multiplied slowly at 15°C.(59°F.). Commercially pasteurized milk and raw graded milk bottled for distribution were said to sour too rapidly for multiplication of *Streptococcus pyogenes* following artificial contamination.

Streptococcus hermothermophilus. Sherman and Wing [178] described this organism as a new species. It differs from the pathogenic hemolytic streptococci in its higher maximum temperature for growth and a higher heat resistance. It differs from the types of human origin by hydrolysis of sodium hippurate and failure to ferment sucrose.

Streptococcus epidemicus. This is a pathogenic species first described by Davis [179] as the etiologic agent of septic sore throat. The fifth edition of Bergey's *Manual of Determinative Bacteriology*, published in 1939, considers this organism to be identical with *Streptococcus pyogenes.*

Streptococcus agalactiae. This is the name now applied to the Streptococcus causing bovine mastitis. Formerly the organism was called *Streptococcus mastitidis*. The literature on bovine mastitis is voluminous. Those who wish a good review of the more important contributions should consult Sherman's [164] review and Hansen's [179a] discussion of the identity of this species. Minett and Stableforth [180] believed that in addition to *Streptococcus agalactiae*, the organism of bovine mastitis, and *Streptococcus pyogenes* type, some of which may be responsible for human sore-throat outbreaks, other beta-hemolytic streptococci may be found in milk. Such streptococci are not as a rule numerous and may be found in the milk from individual cows. Of 150 individual cows from four herds whose mixed milk contained such streptococci they were cultivated from 29 quarters of 21 cows, but usually in quite small numbers. Samples from about 300 cows belonging to eight other herds failed to show these streptococci. They form two groups called here "low-acid" strains and *Streptococcus infrequens*. Their characters are described in detail. Although highly hemolytic they were nonpathogenic for laboratory animals and gave no results when introduced into the cows udder. The two groups could be distinguished from *Streptococcus agalactiae* and *Streptococcus pyogenes* by direct agglutination and the two groups from each other by agglutinin absorption methods.

177. Pullinger and Kemp. 1937. J. Hyg. 37, 527-538.
178. Sherman and Wing. 1935. J. Dairy Sci. 18, 657-660.
179. Davis. 1913. J. Amer. Med. Assoc. 58, 1852-1854.
179a. Hansen. 1935. N. Y. Agr. Expt. Sta. Tech. Bull. 232.
180. Minett and Stableforth. 1934. J. Dairy Res. 5, 223-232.

Pathogenic bacteria are influenced in milk as are other bacteria. Pullinger and Kemp [177] grew three strains of *Streptococcus pyogenes* in sterilized milk; considerable multiplication took place at 22°C.(71.6°F.) and 18°C.(64.4°F.) and also at 15°C.(59°F.), but at a much slower rate. With laboratory pasteurized milk, multiplication began only after 48 to 78 hours of storage at 18 to 22°C.(64.4 to 71.6°F.). With commercial pasteurized milk at 18°C. they diminished up to 48 hours, at 22°C. the milk soured within 48 hours but showed no tendency to streptococci multiplication.

In fresh raw milk the usual result was a diminution of *Streptococcus pyogenes*, and only multiplication, and that comparatively slowly, after 48 to 72 hours of storage at 18 to 22°C. The different strains used showed some differences in this respect, the newly isolated strain showing least multiplication. There was also no multiplication at 15°C. These are significant findings since they suggest that with chance contamination of milk from an infectious case or carrier there is no likelihood of rapid multiplication and a serious milk spread outbreak. It is suggested that infected cows play a major part in the spread of milk-borne *Streptococcus pyogenes* epidemics.

Procedures for Determining Hemolytic Streptococci in Certified Milk.[181] "Deep colonies in blood agar plates are necessary for the recognition and differentiation of streptococci. The surface inoculation of blood agar plates is not satisfactory. Blood agar plates poured as here recommended may also serve for determining the total bacterial count of milk and in fact, for Certified Milk, blood agar is sometimes a more suitable medium for this purpose than the agar recommended in Section 1 of the Appendix since Certified Milk is relatively free from all bacteria other than those which come from the udder and many of these grow best in blood agar. If blood agar is to be used for making total counts, use only 5% of blood in the agar.

"Samples of milk should be diluted 1:10 and 1:100 in sterile salt solution (0.85% NaCl). One ml. amounts of these dilutions shall be pipetted into sterile petri dishes. To the melted agar cooled to between 45° and 50°C., add 5% to 10% of sterile defibrinated horse or rabbit blood; less is known about the appearances when beef blood is used. The blood is immediately well mixed with the agar and 10 to 12 ml. are poured into the petri dishes containing the milk. The petri dishes shall be rocked immediately to insure uniform mixing of the milk with the medium. When the agar has solidified the plates shall be incubated in an inverted position at 37°C. The petri dishes shall be 9½ to 10 cm. in diameter and shall have glass tops; porous tops may not be used. The plates should be examined after incubation overnight and again after incubation for another day. Beta hemolytic streptococci, produce about the deep colonies clear colorless zones of hemolysis. When studied under the low power of the microscope beta zones of hemolysis should show no blood corpuscles remaining next to the deep colony. In the examination of blood agar plates it cannot be assumed that all colonies with beta zones are streptococci since certain strains of staphylococci, colon bacilli, and other organisms may also be hemolytic. Gram stained smears from the colonies or from subcultures from the colonies must be examined. For the identification of hemolytic streptococci two methods are available, the cultural method and the serological method.

"CULTURAL METHOD. For strongly presumptive diagnosis: (1) from the blood agar plates fish deep beta hemolytic colonies; (2) inoculate from the same colony or from a broth culture of the colony into (a) 1% dextrose broth, (b) sorbitol broth and (c) hippurate broth. Strains which are sorbitol-negative, hippurate-negative and which

181. By permission of the American Association Medical Milk Commissions, Inc., Methods and Standards for Production of Certified Milk, New. York, N. Y., 1940, p. 18.

attain a pH not lower than 4.8 in dextrose broth after incubation for 48 hours are to be suspected of being human pathogens (usually serological Group A, occasionally Group C). Such strains shall be sent promptly to the nearest Regional Laboratory of the A.A.M.M.C. for further study and, if possible, should also be studied by the local Commission Laboratory. Instructions as to details and for further study may be obtained from the Committee on Methods and Standards of the A.A.M.M.C. The hemolytic mastitis streptococci of serological Group B are sorbitol-negative and hippurate-positive. There are also many non-hemolytic mastitis streptococci. The so-called animal strains of hemolytic streptococci of serological Group C, less frequently a cause of mastitis, are sorbitol-positive and hippurate-negative, as are also those of Group E by the usual methods of testing. Hemolytic streptococci of serological Group D attain a final acidity of pH 4.0 to 4.5 in dextrose broth, are variable in their sorbitol and hippurate reactions, and are resistant to the temperature of pasteurization.

"SEROLOGICAL METHOD. When suitable Group-specific immune sera are available hemolytic streptococci may be rapidly identified by the precipitin method of Lancefield. A simplified technique makes possible the identification of the serological Group within 24 hours after the colonies are fished from the blood agar plate, and with a minimum of expense and labor. A description of the technique may be obtained from the Committee on Methods and Standards of the A.A.M.M.C. Since cultural study is necessary for the identification of species within the Groups, strains of streptococci found to belong to Groups A or C shall be sent to the nearest Regional Laboratory of the A.A.M.M.C. for further study.

"So far as is known only Group A hemolytic streptococci have caused milk-borne epidemics of septic sore throat or scarlet fever. If any cow should be found to harbor Group A hemolytic streptococci she shall be immediately and permanently removed from the herd. The milk from cows harboring Group C streptococci shall not be used in Certified Milk production, and such animals shall be segregated from the milking herd. Cows harboring streptococci of Group B shall be regarded as carriers of mastitis streptococci and potential sources of infection for other animals in the herd.

"Where facilities permit it is recommended that at least once a month samples of milk should be taken from groups of about 10 cows; that these samples should be diluted 1:20 with sterile salt solution (0.85% NaCl), plated in blood agar and studied for hemolytic streptococci. In case the presence of streptococci pathogenic for man is suspected in any of the group samples, milk from the individual cows of this group should be cultured and any cow found to harbor the organisms should be permanently removed from the herd. This same procedure is to be adopted if at any time there is any reason to suspect that pathoenic streptococci may have gained entrance to the milk supply or that any cases of milk-borne streptococcal disease have appeared among consumers of the milk, or that there may be present in the herd cows shedding large numbers of bacteria in their milk.

"Swabs from throats shall be sent promptly to the laboratory and there cultured by either of the following methods: (1) Place the swab into a test tube of about 5 ml. of broth and shake off the bacteria. One small loop of the broth suspension inoculated into a 10 or 12 ml. tube of melted blood agar prepared as described above, usually makes a proper dilution for a good plate which should contain not more than 100 to 200 colonies of all kinds. (2) Streak the swab across one edge of the solidified surface of a nutrient agar plate (preferably infusion agar without blood or dextrose, as described above). With the wire loop streak the material from the original streak over the remaining surface of the agar. Over the inoculated surface pour not more than 5 ml. of melted blood agar prepared as described above. After incubation of the plates deep colonies with beta zones of hemolysis are to be fished and the streptococci identified as described above."

Filterable or Virus Forms in Milk. On several occasions investigators have proposed the existence of filterable or virus forms of bacteria in milk and milk products. By dilution and plating methods, they estimated the numbers of these forms to vary from 10 million to a trillion per milliliter in raw milk, fermented milk, ice cream, cheese, and butter. Sherman and his colleagues [182] suggested that these forms might represent a cyclostage in the life history of ordinary bacteria. They relate no practical significance to these forms. Mudge [183] thought along the same line where he proposed in milk the existence of dormant "invisible spores" of thermophilic bacteria. Mudge believed that milk has a large number of organisms which are not demonstrable by ordinary means. The phenomenon is also involved in a cycle of growth forms in some of which the organism is easy to destroy; in others it is difficult to destroy. Mudge boiled milk showing no visible evidence of these spores for two hours and after such boiling found them in high dilutions. Boiling had no effect on the vegetation of the spores. Black and Brueckner [184] also reported evidence on this question.

Thermophilic Bacteria in Milk. During recent years thermophilic bacteria have assumed new significance in milk. Early bacteriologists observed these organisms in milk, but attached no significance to them. The earlier literature of this subject has been reviewed by Tanner and Harding [185] and Robertson.[186] Thermophilic bacteria are important in dairy bacteriology because they grow in pasteurizers and raise the counts of pasteurized milk as well as cause off-odors and off-flavors. These forms have been reported in milk by Gorini,[187] Weber,[188] Rabinowitsch,[189] Sames,[190] Morrison and Tanner.[191] Dotterer,[192] Yates and Glover,[193] Hungerford and Harding,[194] and many others whose work will be referred to below.

Thermophilic bacteria are known to exist widely in soil, water, dust, etc. It is easy to understand how they would get into milk. It is well established that they are not in milk as it comes from the udder, as shown by the work of Tanner and Harding [185] and Hansen.[195] Thermophilic bacteria are probably present in all milk, although some samples may have to be incubated at 55°C.(131°F.) to prove their presence. Ayers and Johnson [196] described a species to which they gave the name *Lactobacillus thermophilus.*

Tanner and Harding [185] reported thermophilic bacteria, though not numerous, in all samples of milk obtained after the milk had left the barn. Thermophilic bacteria are widely distributed in milk supplies of this country, as samples of milk, milk plates, and cultures, obtained from New York, Michigan, Illinois, Kansas, Missouri, and California, have been

182. Sherman, Safford, and Brueckner. 1931. Internatl. Dairy Cong. 1931, Sect. 2, 120-122.
183. Mudge. 1930. Cal. Dept. Agr. Monthly Bull. 19, 710-718.
184. Black and Brueckner. 1939. J. Bact. 39, 95.
185. Tanner and Harding. 1926. Centbl. Bakt., Pt. 2, 67, 330-347.
186. Robertson. 1927. N. Y. Agr. Expt. Sta. Bull. 130.
187. Gorini. 1895. Rev. in Centbl. Bakt., Pt. 1, Ref., 48, 206.
188. Weber. 1895. Arb. K. Gsndhtsamt. 17, 108.
189. Rabinowitsch. 1895. Ztschr. Hyg. 20, 154-164.
190. Sames. 1900. Idem 33, 313-362.
191. Morrison and Tanner. 1922. J. Bact. 7, 343-366.
192. Dotterer. 1923. Rev. in Abs. Bact. 8 (1924) 1836.
193. Yates and Glover. 1923. Internatl. Asso. Dairy & Milk Insp. Ann Rept. 12, 252-261.
194. Hungerford and Harding. 1924. Abs. Bact. 8. Abs. No. 52.
195. Hansen. 1929. N. Y. Agr. Expt. Sta. Tech. Bull. 158.
196. Ayers and Johnson. 1923. J. Dairy Sci. 6, 608-615.

found to contain them. A study of 73 cultures of thermophilic bacteria, isolated from milk, showed that all were motile, Gram-positive, sporeforming rods, which grew well at pasteurizing temperatures. Several were strict thermophiles, not growing at 37°C.(98.6°F.), while others were facultative thermophiles growing at 37°C., and some grew even as low as 20°C. (68°F.). Most of the cultures were facultative anaerobes, but many were strict aerobes; most of the cultures digested starch, produced acid and no gas from dextrose and saccharose, and produced no acid from lactose. The action in milk, although slow, led, in many cases, after many days to the production of a rennin curd and slight alkalinity. Many of the cultures seemed to be inert in their action on litmus milk. Thermal death-point determinations, made with a modified Bigelow and Esty technic, showed wide variations in heat resistance of spores formed at 55°C.(131°F.) on plain agar, suspended in neutral saline, and heated at 100 to 103°C.(212 to 217.4°F.). One strict thermophile formed spores which withstood boiling temperature for over six hours. Data were presented which show that thermophilic bacteria may be one of the causes of the appearance of pinpoint colonies on plates from pasteurized milk. This is due either to the effect of temperature on the growth of these forms or to the inherent tendency to form punctiform colonies on agar, even after long incubation time.

Yale and Breed [197] mentioned several factors which had been found to favor the development of thermophilic bacteria in milk: 1, presence of these organisms in the raw supply; 2, repasteurization of milk returned from milk routes; 3, prolonged holding at pasteurization temperatures; 4, cooking of milk solids on the walls of internal tube heaters and regenerative heater-coolers; 5, dead ends in pasteurization equipment; 6, filter cloths; and 7, development of thermophiles in the pasteurizer itself. Yale found faulty plant operation to be more important in development of thermophiles than the type of pasteurizing equipment. Eckford [198] found that thermophiles from milk and milk products were divided into two groups, i.e., obligate thermophiles, which developed from 42°C.(107.6°F.) to 63°C.(145.4°F.) or 75°C.(167°F.), with an optimum between 50°C. (122°F.) and 60°C. (140°F.), and thermotolerant organisms, which developed from 35°C.(95°F.) to 70°C.(158°F.) and 75°C.(167°F.), with an optimum between 50°C.(122°F.) and 60°C.(140°F.). Their cultural and other characteristics were described. Both groups had little or no proteolytic ability, and their fermentative activities were slight or absent. They had little or no effect as regards damage to milk or other foods. A thermophilic streptothrix was, however, isolated which was proteolytic, and may be of significance in the ripening of cheese. Distinction should probably be made between thermophilic and thermotolerant bacteria. The former grow best at higher temperatures while the latter are merely heat resistant. Both groups survived pasteurization and even 100 to 120°C. (212 to 248°F.) for 15 minutes. The obligate thermophiles were found to

197. Yale and Breed. 1930. Amer. J. Pub. Health 20, 1192-1198.
198. Eckford. 1927. Amer. J. Hyg. 7, 201-221.

multiply in milk from 42 to 63°C.(107.6 to 145.4°F.), but the thermotol-erant strains multiplied greatly at this high temperature and particularly at 55°C.(131°F.). They, therefore, may cause trouble in pasteurization plants by multiplying during the process and giving the milk a high count. They may cause pin-point colonies in plates from pasteurized milk at 37°C. (98.6°F.). They were not found by this author in canned milk, sweetened or unsweetened.

Robertson,[186] Clark and Dougherty,[199] Prickett and Breed,[200] and Prickett[201] have contributed to the subject. Prickett's report contains descriptions of species. Thermophilic bacteria are quite as important in other foods as in milk.

Mudge and Thorwaldson[202] stimulated thought in this field by claiming that thermophilic bacteria in milk may exist as invisible spores. These germinate and account for the large numbers of cells which are demon-strated to be present by plate counts. Work in other fields on filterable forms seems to lend support to Mudge's opinions.

Methylene Blue Reductase Test for Determining Thermophilic Bacteria in Milk. The use of the methylene blue reductase test for determining the relative number of bacteria in milk has been discussed in another paragraph in this chapter. Harding and Ward[203] stated that this test could also be used for determining the presence of ther-mophilic bacteria in pasteurized and raw milk. These investigators recommended in-cubation at 62.5°C.(145°F.). While they do not give the exact technique for carrying out the test, one may assume that it is like that used with the organisms growing about 37.5°C.(99°F.).

Thermophilic bacteria can be controlled by proper plant practices and by avoiding longer than necessary heating of milk. Hansen[204] stated that a bacteriological study of a dairy plant by means of the Breed micro-scope method or by plating usually revealed the source of these bacteria. Thomas[205] also related presence of thermophilic bacteria in milk to unsan-itary practices in the dairy. He found that plating on milk agar was the best method of enumerating them. They were present in most of the samples of raw milk produced under unsatisfactory conditions but in only three per cent of the clean raw samples. According to Gerhardt[206] elimination of dust is important in control of thermophilic bacteria in a dairy.

With one exception none who have worked with the thermophilic bac-teria has ever reported that they might be pathogenic. Hansen[207] grew the following thermophilic sporeforming bacteria in milk and fed some of the cultures to guinea pige: *Bacillus aerothermophilus* Weinzirl, *Bacillus calidus* Blau, *Bacillus coagulans* Hammer, *Bacillus kaustophilus* Prickett, *Bacillus michaelisii* Prickett, *Bacillus nondiastatious* Bergey, *Bacillus ther-moliquefaciens* Bergey, a strain of Cameron and Esty's group 80, and a

199. Clark and Dougherty. 1926. Diss. Catholic Univ., Wash.
200. Prickett and Breed. 1929. N. Y. Agr. Expt. Sta. Bull. 471.
201. Prickett. 1927. J. Bact. 15, 7.
202. Mudge and Thorwaldsen. 1930. J. Bact. 19, 47.
203. Harding and Ward. 1928. Pub. Health J. 19, 162-167.
204. Hansen. 1931. Internatl. Dairy Cong., England, Sect. 2, 10-19.
205. Thomas. 1937. Welsh. J. Agr. 13, 295-308.
206. Gerhardt. 1932. Proc. Ninth Ann. Short School, Texas Pub. Health Assoc. 83.
207. Hansen. 1932. N. Y. Agr. Expt. Sta. Bull. 196.

strain of their group 100. The animals increased normally in weight during and after the feeding experiment. None of the species tested produced detectable toxic substances. Feeding experiments with obligate and facultative thermophilic bacteria yielded only negative results with rabbits and guinea pigs.

Pin-Point Colonies on Agar Plates Made from Milk. These are minute colonies which appear on agar plates made from milk. Some of them are quite visible with the naked eye while others are visible only with the help of a lens. After they were recognized on agar plates, milk-control officials wondered whether they should be counted. If they were counted, many milk supplies would not pass requirements in cities where plate-count standards had been adopted. It was argued by some that they were of no sanitary significance and should, therefore, be ignored. This was a doubtful position to assume, for differences of opinion might occur as to what a "pin-point" colony is. They were first recognized as of importance on plates made from pasteurized milk and were related accordingly to the pasteurization process. Such a relationship is not necessary, for some pin-point colonies occur on agar plates seeded with other foods. Various explanations for their appearance are possible and have been made. These involve the organism itself as well as the conditions which exist on the plate. While some types of bacteria causing such colonies are thermophilic, it is known that mesophilic bacteria may also cause them. Diehm [208] suggested the term "minimo-visible" as more suitable than "pin-point" for those colonies which appear so small that they are just visible with a hand lens. The cultures which Diehm isolated were heat-resistant, but not thermophilic, since they would not grow at 60°C.(140°F.). Most of them were *Streptococcus lactis* varieties. Prickett and Breed [200] stated that the "pin-point" problem was a complex one, due to the variety of heat-resistant and thermophilic bacteria which may survive pasteurization. Many of these types may cause pin-point colonies on agar plates. These investigators believed that heat-resistant and thermophilic bacteria may be controlled, partially at least, by careful observance of the rules of cleanliness and certain corrective measures about the dairy.

Fay [209] explained "pin-point" colonies as due to thermotolerant organisms. In making counts of ice cream on standard plain agar large numbers of "pin-point" colonies on the low dilution plates (1-100) were noted, but not in proportionate numbers or none in higher dilutions (1-1,000). Replating of samples on sacchárose agar revealed the "pin-point" colonies in all dilutions and in proportionate numbers. Furthermore, replating on plain agar, containing in the higher dilution plates .001 ml. of sterilized ice cream, which supplied the same amount of sugar as was present in the lower dilution, resulted in the growth of the "pin-point" colonies in all dilutions. With a few exceptions, all pure cultures isolated from these "pin-point" colonies would withstand three or more pasteurizations at 62.18°C.(145°F.) for 30 minutes without decrease in number. All cultures

208. Diehm. 1927. N. Y. Prod. Rev. and Amer. Creamery 65, 338-341.
209. Fay. 1927. J. Bact. 13, 347.

were thermotolerant, but not highly thermophilic, since none grew above 45°C.(113°F.). Fay confirmed his earlier work and conclusions of other investigators, that these bacteria survive pasteurization temperatures but do not grow within this temperature range. He isolated and studied the characteristics of a number of individual bacteria of this thermotolerant group. They all failed to develop at temperatures above 47°C.(116.6°F.). It was noted that these strains develop, when plain agar plates are made from milk, only on low-dilution plates (*e.g.*, 1:100) and not in high dilutions. This is probably related to the fact that the addition of very small amounts of carbohydrate greatly facilitates their appearance on plates, the small amount of lactose carried over in a 1:100 milk dilution adding sufficient sugar. All the strains isolated were nonsporing organisms of various types. The survival of sporing forms which are heat-tolerant represents another phase of the problem not studied in this paper. On the practical side, Fay rejected compounding of media which would eliminate them, but preferred to look upon them as undesirable organisms, indicating improper care of the milk, and the aim should be their elimination by preventive measures. Swenarton[210] believed that "pin-point" colonies appeared with greatest frequency in the early spring. This was true for standard raw, standard pasteurized, and selected raw milk. Fifty of the 52 cultures isolated from typical plates were found to be streptococci. Since Swenarton probably picked these colonies from plates which had been incubated at 37°C.(98.6°F.) and not at 55°C.(131°F.), it is quite possible that he would not encounter thermophilic bacteria. Swenarton's organisms may not have been thermophilic.

Ayers and Johnson's[211] *Lactobacillus thermophilus* has been found to produce pin-point colonies under certain conditions. They found the organism to be the cause of pin-point colonies on plates made from the milk of one plant. Charlton[212] reported the same organism causing them in another plant.

Phelps[213] made a general survey of the pin-point colony findings in the routine milk samples from 82 dealers for about two and one-half years. The presence of pin-point colonies was not seasonal; no one type of organism was responsible for pin-point colony character after isolation and subculture. Pin-point colonies were found oftener in raw milk, suggesting that the true source of these organisms is ordinarily the raw milk. The appearance of pin points on laboratory plates often coincided with finding by the milk inspectors of either improper plant practices or a bad raw milk supply. Walts[214] found thermophilic bacteria to be often responsible for these colonies.

Utensils may be one source of bacteria which cause sporadic appearance of pin-point colonies. Robinson[215] traced one such instance to the can washer.

210. Swenarton. 1926. J. Bact. 11, 285-292.
211. Ayers and Johnson. 1924. J. Bact. 9, 285.
212. Charlton. 1932. J. Dairy Sci. 15, 393-399.
213. Phelps. 1932. Papers Milk Acad. Arts and Letters 16, 503.
214. Walts. 1940. Rev. in J. Dairy Sci. 23, A 108-109.
215. Robinson. 1941. Milk Dealer 30, 32.

Sporeforming Bacteria in Milk. Since these bacteria are not found in the cow's udder, they should probably not be present in milk which is being carefully handled. When they are present it means that dust has fallen into the milk or that it has even received more objectionable contamination, such as cow manure. Most sporeforming bacteria in milk are anaerobes and consequently bacteriological procedures are pointed at them more than aerobes.

Bacteriological methods devised for the control of milk supplies have involved aerobic bacteria almost entirely. A few attempts have been made to correlate the anaerobic bacteria content of milk with the conditions under which the milk was produced. Savage [216] found quite satisfactory agreement between the number of spores of *Clostridium sporogenes* and *Escherichia coli* in over 50 samples of fresh milk. A number of anaerobes including *Alcaligenes fecalis, Clostridium welchii, Bacillus ephemeros, Bacillus pseudotetani* and several unidentified species were isolated by Brown.[217] Hewlett and Barton,[218] however, found no correlation between low-grade milk and its content of total bacteria, *Escherichia coli* and *Clostridium sporogenes*.

The investigations of Barthel [219] led him to conclude that obligate anaerobic bacteria occurred but very rarely in common market milk. Those that were found were almost wholly of two species, Schattenfroh and Grassberger's nonmotile butyric acid bacterium and *Clostridium putrificum*. During the fall and winter months, the former occurred much more frequently than the latter, while the opposite was true during the spring and early summer. Obligate anaerobes were considerably more numerous during the summer months than in the fall or winter, as are also the total bacteria of the milk. No direct relation was found between the general hygienic condition of milk and appearance therein of obligate anaerobic bacteria. Barthel furthermore concluded that *Clostridium putrificium* and *Paraplectrum foetidum* (Weigmann) were identical. From examination of over 50 samples of market milk collected in Washington, Pryor [220] was able to confirm Flügge's original observation as to the presence of spore-bearing bacteria. In his experience the most important species was *Clostridium welchii*, which was believed to be universally present. Aerobic spore-bearing bacteria belonging in general to a group of gelatin liquefiers were also found. Such species did not develop normally in raw milk, nor in milk sold in Washington as "pasteurized," only the ordinary lactic acid bacteria being found. All these spore-bearing organisms had a profound effect upon milk, and when their development was not hindered by lactic acid bacteria, produced changes of decomposition and putrefaction which rendered milk unfit for food. How far they play a role in clinical conditions, especially in children, remains to be proved. Ford [221] has shown that the anaerobes in heated milk, which

216. Savage. 1909-1910. Ann. Rept., Local Govt. Bd., Gt. Brit., 39, 474-503.
217. Brown. 1909. Mass. St. Bd. Health Ann. Rept. 41, 632-667.
218. Hewlett and Barton. 1907. J. Hyg. 7, 22-31.
219. Barthel. 1910. Centbl. Bakt., Pt. 2, 26, 1-47.
220. Pryor. 1914. Bull. Johns Hopkins Hosp. 25, 276-278.
221. Ford. 1919. Amer. J. Dis. Children 18, 199-206.

bring about stormy fermentation, form poisons which cause death when inoculated into guinea pigs. Experiments with *Clostridium welchii* yielded the same results. The maximum toxicity, although variable, seemed to be reached in 24 hours.

While spores of anaerobic bacteria are not common in milk, Hussong and Hammer [222] described several abnormal conditions in dairy products caused by anaerobic bacteria. Several involved the appearance of gas in milk and one rancidity in pasteurized cream.

Standard methods of milk analysis do not provide for examination of milk for anaerobic bacteria. Several attempts have been made, however, to show that they may have sanitary significance.

Savage's Anaerobic Spore Test as an Indication of Contamination of Milk. The anaerobic spore-bearing bacteria have been associated with sewage pollution and contamination. British sanitarians have used the test especially in water analysis from which it was quickly adapted to other fields of work. While there are quite a number of anaerobes and the group is not clearly understood, the name *Clostridium sporogenes* has been generally applied to the organism concerned. As with all groups of indicators of pollution, it has its advantages and disadvantages. First of all, however, it is necessary to determine whether the group is always present in contaminated milks and absent in clean milks.

In applying the test to milk quite a number of investigators have been concerned. Savage added one ml., 10 ml., and 20 ml. to tubes of freshly sterilized milk and after heating at 80°C.(176°F.) for 10 minutes to destroy the aerobic vegetative cells, incubated under anaerobic conditions. Finally Savage modified his method by the use of small tubes four inches long and one-fourth inch in diameter. Into 10 of these tubes he placed two ml. of the milk and incubated anaerobically. He then established the following "standards":

> 0 or 1 tube positive = good milk
> 2, 3, or 4 tubes positive = unsatisfactory milk
> Over 5 tubes positive = bad milk.

Weinzirl's Anaerobic Spore Test as an Indication of Contamination of Milk. Weinzirl [223] has used the anaerobic spore test for determining the presence of manural matter in milk. He claims that this test is superior to either the counts of the bacteria or the visible dirt tests. The simplicity of the test, along with the apparatus, makes it one that is easily applied. The test is carried out as follows: One-half to one ml. of melted paraffin is placed in a 15 mm. test tube which is plugged with cotton and sterilized either by dry or moist heat. By means of a sterile pipette, five ml. of milk under test are placed in each of five tubes containing paraffin. The tubes containing the milk and paraffin are then placed in the Arnold sterilizer and heated to 80°C.(176°F.) for 10 to 15 minutes. This treatment melts the paraffin which rises to the surface, where it hardens on cooling and forms an anaerobic seal. The heat also expells oxygen absorbed by milk, thus rendering anaerobiosis more complete. All the vegetative bacteria are killed by the heat, only the spore forms remaining. The tubes are then incubated for three days at 37°C.(98.6°F.). If anaerobes are present, gas will be formed which will lift the paraffin plug in the tube. Two positive out of five tubes shows excessive pollution.

Procedures for Determination of Sporeforming Bacteria in Certified Milk.[181] The following test is a modification of that described by Weinzirl. Into clean, dry test tubes plugged with cotton, place about 2 ml. of petrolatum and sterilize them in the hot air oven at 160°C. or over for at least one hour, or until the cotton begins to turn brown. Ten ml. of each milk to be tested are pipetted into each of 10 of the above tubes. The tubes of milk are then heated in a water bath at 80°C. for 15 minutes. During this time

222. Hussong and Hammer. 1930. J. Bact. 19, 89-99.
223. Weinzirl. 1915. Amer. J. Pub. Health 5, 862-866; 11 (1921), 149-152.

the petrolatum melts and comes to the surface of the milk. The tubes of milk are then to be cooled and incubated for 72 hours. Gas formed in the milk raises the petrolatum up the side of the tube. Digestion is indicated by clearing of the milk. Certified Milk should rarely show gas formation, coagulation or digestion in any of the tubes. Other grades of milk, whether pasteurized or raw, usually show gas formation, coagulation or digestion in most of the tubes.

Ayers and Clemmer [224] found the Weinzirl test of doubtful value. They found no correlation between the number of positive tubes and the amount of manure. They stated that if the test was carried out with 10 tubes holding 20 ml. each, there was some indication of the methods of production. These conclusions of Ayers and Clemmer were confirmed by Hudson and Tanner,[225] who examined over 100 samples of milk brought to a commercial dairy. They compared the anaerobic spore test proposed by Weinzirl to the amount of dirt in the milk and the number of the bacteria as determined by the Frost plate. Cooledge and Goodwin,[226] however, found the Weinzirl test of value when used along with the pH score. Ritchie,[227] after using the anaerobic spore test for judging the quality of milk, concluded that its value was very slight.

Among anaerobic bacteria *Clostridium welchii* has a significant position. Since it is known to be the cause of severe infections in human beings, its presence in foods has been viewed with suspicion by some bacteriologists. This organism has been discussed in this book in several other places. Generally speaking its presence in foods is considered to be without significance. Whether this is the correct position to assume may not be known at present. North [228] searched for this organism in "certified," Grade A. and "market" grades of milk, using the old "sporogenes" anaerobic test applied directly to the milk but using 10 tubes of about 20 ml. each for each test. Few or no *Clostridium welchii* organisms were found in any of the 10 tubes of certified milk and in only one or two of the tubes of Grade A pasteurized milk. The market milk showed a positive reaction in from five to 10 tubes. These observations were made on a large number of samples from three cities. North believed that *Clostridium welchii* might be an important cause of diarrhea and other intestinal infections in children. On this question, however, no agreement of opinion exists.

Fungi in Milk. As might be expected various fungi have been found in milk supplies. As far as can be determined none of the higher fungi have been proven to come directly from the cow's udder. This would mean then that they have reached the milk from dirty utensils, dust in the atmosphere, and other sources. Among the more common fungi in milk is *Oospora lactis*. Its presence in milk has been reported by many different investigators. Neill [229] reported presence of common molds in dairies. Most of his attention to them was directed at their control and elimination which involved, in general, effective cleaning and washing.

224. Ayers and Clemmer. 1921. U. S. Dept. Agr. Bull. 940.
225. Hudson and Tanner. 1922. J. Dairy Sci. 5, 377-382.
226. Cooledge and Goodwin. 1921. Mich. Agr. Expt. Sta. Spec. Bull. 112.
227. Ritchie. 1916. Pub. Health 29, 270-274.
228. North. 1933. Med. Times and Long Island Med. J. 61, 359-363.
229. Neill. 1934. New Zeal. J. Agr. 48, 70-75.

Cummins, Kennelly, and Grimes [230] also reported the presence of numerous fungi in milk. Many of these species had not been reported before although their presence might be expected in view of the possible sources of contamination.

Another class of fungi which has caused considerable trouble in milk are the lactose-fermenting yeasts investigated by Hastings [231] and Ram-Ayyar.[232] These organisms attack lactose with abundant gas formation and thus are able to bring about fermentations in milk and dairy products. Nelson [233] separated the white yeast from dairy products into four groups. He did not consider them to be of any great importance in dairy products. Dombrowski [234] found yeasts to be present in all samples of milk and milk products. The species which he isolated fell into the Torula group more than into the Saccharomyces or Mycoderma group. The strains which he isolated were not limited to alcoholic fermentation but were found to produce colors and flavors undesirable in milk.

Body Cells or Leucocytes in Milk. Various body secretions contain cells discharged from tissue. Milk, therefore, may also contain such cells which originate from tissues with which it comes in contact in the cow's body. On account of similarity in appearance, they have been generally called leucocytes. When such cells were first observed in milk the question immediately arose as to their significance. Some of the earlier investigators believed that they possessed sanitary significance, and thus, a long line of experiments was made necessary to test the validity of this opinion. Stokes and Wegefarth [235] were among the first to look with suspicion on these cells for they called them "pus" cells. Breed [236] could find no evidence that they were harmful or that they indicated undesirable conditions in the udder. Russell and Hoffmann [237] reported a wide range in the cellular content of milks that were apparently normal and safe for use. Pennington and Roberts [238] believed that there was a relation between the number of leucocytes and the condition of the udder. Winkler [239] and Hewlett, Villar, and Revis [240] believed that cells found in normal milk were not leucocytes but young epithelial cells, and cells of the germinal layer. Prescott and Breed [241] and Breed [236] made extensive studies, results of which still confirmed Breed's earlier position that these cells were without sanitary significancé. They observed considerable variation in the numbers of leucocytes. Savage [242] could not confirm Bergey's [243] opinion

230. Cummins et al. 1929. Roy. Dublin Soc. Sci. Proc., Ser. 19, 311-319.
231. Hastings. 1906. Wis. Agr. Expt. Sta. Ann. Rept. 107-115.
232. Ram-Ayyar. 1928. Agr. Res. Inst., Pusa, Bull. 183.
233. Nelson. 1928. J. Dairy Sci. 11, 397-400.
234. Dombrowski. 1910. Centbl. Bakt. 28, 345-403.
235. Stokes and Wegefarth. 1897. Med. News 71, 45-48.
236. Breed. 1911. Arch. Hyg. 75, 383-392; N. Y. Agr. Expt. Sta. Bull. 380-568.
237. Russell and Hoffmann. 1908. Amer. J. Pub. Hyg. 18, 285-291.
238. Pennington and Roberts. 1908. J. Infect. Dis. 5, 72-84.
239. Winkler. 1908. Ztschr. Landw. Versuchsw. Österr. 11, 562-630.
240. Hewlett, Villar, and Revis. 1909. J. Hyg. 9, 271-278.
241. Prescott and Breed. 1911. J. Infect. Dis. 7, 632-640.
242. Savage. 1906. J. Hyg. 6, 123-138.
243. Bergey. 1904. Univ. of Penn. Med. Bull. 17, 181-183.

that a relation existed between leucocytes and streptococci. Breed [236] published a bulletin from which the following quotation is taken:

"In other words, the relationships between the number and types of leucocytes in milk and the conditions that give rise to variations in numbers and types of these cells are so complex that they cannot be summarized in any simple way. The only relationship that stands out sufficiently distinct to have been utilized in a practical way in routine microscopic examinations, is that excessive numbers of leucocytes predominantly of polynuclear types, accompanied by long-chain streptococci and particularly when phagocytes containing bacteria are present, indicate streptococcic udder infections with practical certainty. If one or more of the specified conditions are lacking, then the indications become less certain. On the other hand, milk containing small numbers of leucocytes of any kind and no indication of abnormal bacterial infection may certainly be regarded as normal so far as microscopic examination is concerned. When conditions intermediate between these two extremes are found, interpretation of microscopic findings are difficult and uncertain."

Breed [244] and Hucker [245] again stated that mere presence of epithelial cells in milk was not very significant from the sanitary standpoint. However large numbers (500,000 cells per ml.) from individual quarters indicates an abnormal, condition.

Wilson [16] found the leucocyte content of milk of little value in grading. The total number of cells was subject to great variation depending upon a number of factors whose exact importance it was difficult to determine. Prouty [246] stated that there was reason to believe that milk secreted from absolutely normal udders contained, as a rule, less than 100,000 cells per ml. In publications of various investigations, the number of cells which might be present in normal milk have been reported to vary from 225,000 to 930,000 per ml. Variations even occur between the different quarters of the same udder. He mentioned the fact that Breed had recorded an instance in which one udder gave milk containing 54 million cells per ml. without showing any evidence of active infection. Wilson believed that a uniform count might be of considerable value in the study of individual cows by veterinarians. Brucella infections did not increase the leucocyte content of milk according to Prouty.[246]

Stoke's [247] Method for Leucocytes in Milk. Centrifugal sediments from 10 ml. of milk are stained and examined under the one-twelfth oil immersion objective. The presence of cells in such a field was regarded by Stokes as justification for excluding an animal from a herd.

Reed's [248] Method for Leucocytes in Milk. 1. Fill 10 ml. centrifuge tubes with milk and heat for 10 minutes at 70-75°C.(158-167°F.).

1. Centrifuge the tubes at high speed for 10 minutes. Remove the upper layers of cream and milk with a pipette and refill the tubes with distilled water. Centrifuge again for three or four minutes.

3. Draw off all except one-half ml. of liquid in the point of the centrifuge tube. Wipe out the upper part of the tube with a bit of absorbent cotton fastened to the end of a glass rod. Mix thoroughly the remaining liquid and sediment.

4. Transfer a drop of this mixture to a clean Thoma-Zeiss blood-counting cell and place the cover glass over it. Count the cells under a one-sixth objective. If the num-

244. Breed. 1936. Tenth Ann. Rept., N. Y. State Assoc. Dairy and Milk Insp.
245. Hucker. 1936. Idem.
246. Prouty. 1934. J. Dairy Sci. 17, 75; J. Bact. 27, 293-301.
247. Stokes. 1897. Med. News 71, 45-48.
248. Reed. 1914. A Manual of Bacteriology. Ginn and Co., New York.

ber of leucocytes is low, the entire area of the cell should be counted, using a mechanical stage to move the slide. If their number is large, five or six small squares may be counted and averaged. The average number per small square multiplied by 200,000 will give the number of leucocytes per milliliter in the original milk .

Savage's Method for Leucocytes in Milk.[249] The ordinary Thoma-Zeiss blood-counting chamber is employed. Direct counting of the cells is impossible, owing to the opacity caused by the large amount of fat. One ml. of the milk is accurately transferred to a centrifuge tube (about 15 ml. capacity) of the usual pattern, and freshly filtered Toisson's solution is poured in to almost fill the tube. The two fluids are well mixed and then centrifugalized for 10 minutes. The cream is well broken up by a clean glass rod, to disentangle leucocytes carried to the surface, and the mixture centrifugalized for an additional five minutes. All the fluid is then removed down to the one ml. mark, great care being taken not to disturb the deposit. This can be conveniently and readily done by means of a fine glass tube connected to an exhaust pump. Theoretically, all the cellular elements present in the original one ml. of milk are now present in the one ml. of fluid. The deposit is thoroughly mixed (with a wire), and distributed through the one ml. A sufficient quantity is placed on the ruled squares of the Thoma-Zeiss apparatus, and the cover glass put on. The number of cells is counted in a number of different fields of vision, moving regularly from one field of vision to another. The diameter of the field of vision is ascertained before counting by drawing out the microscope tube until an exact number of sides of the squares spans a diameter of the field of vision.

The number of cellular elements per cubic millimeter of milk $= \dfrac{56{,}000y}{11d^2}$, where

$y =$ the average number per field of vision, $d =$ the number of squares which just spans the diameter. d is determined once and for all by marking the microscope draw tube so that only 20 fields have to be counted, and the figures substituted in the formula.

Doane-Buckley[250] **Quantitative Method for Estimating Leucocytes in Milk.** With this method 10 cc. of milk are centrifuged for four minutes in graduated sedimentation tubes, at an approximate speed of 2,000 r.p.m. The cream is lifted out with a cotton swab, care being taken to get as much as possible of the fat. It is then centrifuged one minute more and the cream again removed with a cotton swab. Any fat remaining in the milk interferes seriously with the counting, as, if there are more than a few globules they form a layer on the top of the liquid in the counting chamber, and, as the leucocytes settle to the bottom of the chamber, it is difficult to see through the fat. It is only with cows giving milk difficult of separation where this trouble is experienced, and with such animals considerable care is necessary in removing all the cream gathered at the top of the sedimentation tube. The method of removing the fat with cotton is the best one that has occurred to us, and it is the only part of the process that does not operate with entire satisfaction in every instance.

Following the removal of the cream, after the second centrifuging, the bottom of the tube will contain a portion of the sediment which is easily seen. This sediment may, in extreme cases of cows suffering from garget amount to as much as one cc. Ordinarily it will be considerably less than one-half cc. The amount varies considerably with the number of leucocytes, but not absolutely. The milk above this sediment is removed with a small siphon, which can be easily arranged with bent glas stubes drawn to a fine point and supplied with a small rubber end pinch cock. In using the siphon it is better to keep the point near the surface of the milk in the tube in order not to agitate the precipitated leucocytes and draw a number of them off with the milk. The milk in the tube may be siphoned within an eighth of an inch of the sediment in the tube. This will usually be below the one-half-cc. mark. Two drops ot saturated alcoholic solution of methylene blue are then added, thoroughly mixed with the sediment by shaking, and then set in boiling water two or three minutes to assist the leucocytes in

249. Savage. 1914. The Bacteriological Examination of Food and Water. Cambridge Univ. Press.
250. Doane. 1905. Md. Agr. Expt. Sta. Bull. 102; also Report of Committee of the Laboratory Section, Amer. Pub. Health Assoc., Amer. J. Hyg. 6 (1910).

taking the color. The contents of the tube can be boiled by holding it directly in the flame, but it has no advantage over the use of the water bath, and it is very likely to break the glass. After heating, some water is added to the tube to render the color less dense. Ordinarily filling the tube to the one cc. mark will be sufficient, and this quantity gives an easy factor for calculating the final results.

In putting this liquid containing the leucocytes into the blood counter considerable care is necessary, owing to the tendency of the leucocytes to sink to the bottom. At this place a capillary tube is used and the cover glass was held in one hand ready to cover the chamber as soon as the drop was transferred to the counting chamber. After placing the glass cover over the chamber, about a minute is allowed the leucocytes to settle to the bottom of the chamber. There are very few foreign bodies likely to be mistaken in counting for leucocytes. Ordinarily the polynuclear leucocytes predominate and the stained nuclei with the unstained surrounding cell show up very distinctly. A few small leucocytes with large nuclei may be found and these may be confounded with yeast cells until the worker becomes familiar with the distinction.

As regards counting we have taken a standard with a cubic centimeter as a basis quantity of milk, though we are, of course, aware that the corpuscles in the blood are enumerated with a cubic millimeter basis. We adopted the centimeter largely for two reasons. In counting bacteria in the milk the cubic centimeter is always the basis employed. Simply because the leucocytes were derived from the blood seemed to be no reason why the same basis for counting should be employed as was used with the blood, while to the ordinary bacteriological worker to whom this work will fall, if ever adopted to any extent, the cubic centimeter standard would be a little more easily comprehended because more frequently used. The blood counter holds 1/10 c. mm. and 1/10,000 cc. If 10 cc. of milk are used and the one cc. of fluid is in the tube after siphoning, and the coloring matter and the water used to dilute has been added, then the resulting number of leucocytes in the counting multiplied by 1,000 will be the total number of leucocytes per cubic centimeter in the milk. If a total of 75 leucocytes was counted in the chamber there would be 75,000 leucocytes per cubic centimeter in the milk.

In the actual counting under the microscope a square millimeter of the counting chamber will be found to be ruled off into 400 smaller equal squares. This facilitates an accurate and rapid count. Where the number of leucocytes is not great the entire field can be counted in a short time. Where there is a great number of leucocytes a few squares or sets of squares in different parts of the ruled surface will give approximately the number.

There are occasionally a few variations desirable from these rules, but it may be well to state that the details have been pretty carefully and thoroughly worked over and compared, and it is seldom that short cuts can be made if correct results are desired. The time and speed of centrifuging are placed as low as possible for accurate work. When there is one-half cc. or more of sediment, it is necessary to use more of the methylene blue for staining, as there will be too great a number of leucocytes to make a satisfactory count in the counting chamber, it is better to add water until there are two cc., or sometimes even more in the sedimentation tube.

This method of counting, while long in explaining, is in reality short and simple in application. Moreover, it is based on accurate measurements in every detail, and the results are correspondingly reliable.

The Stewart-Slack [251, 252] **Method for Examination of Centrifuged Sediments.** This method is included in the earlier editions of *Standard Methods for the Examination of Dairy Products*. It requires a "Board of Health" centrifuge and tubes. The latter are made from glass tubing one-fourth inch in diameter and are three inches long. The open ends are tightly closed with rubber stoppers. The samples of milk are collected and thoroughly stirred. The stoppered tubes are filled with two milliliters

251. Stewart. 1905. Amer. Med. 9, 486-488.
252. Slack. 1906. J. Infect. Dis. Sup. 2, 214-222.

of such milk and centrifuged. The sediment may be secured as follows: The stopper in the cream end of the tube is first removed. With the cream end down, the cream is removed with a wire and the milk poured out. The other stopper, to which the sediment will adhere, may then be carefully removed and the sediment transferred to a slide.

The sediment is spread in a drop of water over an area of four square centimeters on the glass slide by rubbing the end of the stopper in the drop of water. The film is gently dried, stained with methylene blue, and examined with the 1.9 mm. oil immersion objective.

If the number of bacteria or body cells per ml. of milk is desired, it will be necessary to standardize the field of the microscope in about the same manner as described for the Breed and Frost methods for counting the number of bacteria in milk. If the field has a diameter of .205 mm. it will require 3,000 fields to cover one square centimeter or 12,000 to cover four square centimeters in the entire film. This means that the number of cells seen at one time in one microscope field must be multiplied by 12,000 to secure the number in the entire film. If the diameter of the field happens to be .160 mm. there are then 5,000 fields per square centimeter and 20,000 in the entire film. At least 30 representative fields should be counted.

The interpretation of results is not easy. The character and types of leucocytes may be determined as well as their numbers. If body cells in milk are supposed to indicate bad conditions, they would be expected in much larger numbers during actual infections. To determine the relationship of the presence of streptococci and the number of body cells in freshly drawn milk to pathological conditions Hucker [253] studied a herd of 71 cows for 10 months. No streptococci were found in the milk from any quarter which was free from fibrosis (indurations). Such milk never showed cells in excess of 150,000 per ml., or gave a positive reaction to brom thymol blue. In other words, milk from the truly normal udders did not contain streptococci or an appreciable number of cells. Cells in excess of 150,000 per ml. and streptococci in the milk obtained from these herds indicated that the milk had been secured from udders containing a demonstrable amount of fibrosis. Not all fibrotic udders, on the other hand, showed streptococci or cells in the milk, when studied over a period of months. When more than 500,000 cells per ml. were found in any one quarter, streptococci were at some time noted in the same or some other quarter of the same udder during the lactation period. More than 500,000 cells per ml. in freshly drawn milk signified an infection in the udder.

While body cells may, under some conditions, indicate milk from diseased udders, they have been reported in milk from udders which were normal as far as could be determined. Some of them, of course, may have been abnormal, the condition not being pronounced enough to make itself apparent. Various standards have been proposed, the more recent ones being lower than the older ones. Rosell,[254] for instance, believed that a

253. Hucker. 1933. Amer. J. Pub. Health 23, 237-245.
254. Rosell. 1934. Sci. Agr. 15, 169.

body cell count greater than 250,000 per ml. indicated mastitis. According to Cherrington, Hansen, and Halversen [255] normal milk should have fewer than 50,000 cells per ml. while milk from infected udders would usually have more than 100,000. Many factors influence the body cell content of fluid milk. Formulation of any standard would have to consider all of them.

Bacteria which produce defects of appearance and flavor in milk belong to many different genera. Among the more important are fluorescent bacteria. Garrison [256] isolated 496 cultures from dairy products which were examined for their effects on various products.

Abnormal Flavors and Appearance in Milk. Like many other foods milk is quite liable to take up odors and flavors from materials with which it comes in contact. Besides these acquired odors are some which may result from bacterial changes in certain milk constituents. These are hard to define. since there may be several definitions for any one abnormality. The following headings include most of the abnormalities of this nature which may occur in milk. Certain individuals in the dairy industry have become quite expert in detecting abnormal odors in dairy products.

Soapy Milk. Fettick [257] isolated a bacillus which produced a soapy taste in milk. Finally the trouble was removed by thorough disinfection and cleaning of the utensils. Jaffa described a bacterium from milk under the name of *Bacterium sapolacticum*. It was said to cause a decided soap taste and produced the same flavor when inoculated into sterilized milk.

Moldy Flavor. Fellers [258] has reported the *Actinomycetes* as the cause of moldy flavor in milk as well as other foods.

Burnt Flavor. This flavor is often connected with pasteurized milk and has been mentioned as one of the objections to pasteurization. It is an indefinite characteristic. A bacterium was isolated by Sadler [259] which was similar to *Bacterium lactici acidi* (Leichmann), to which was attributed the ability to contribute a burnt flavor to milk. It was a facultative anaerobe. Such a flavor in milk would be difficult to define and standardize. It is reasonable that many different aromas and flavors could come under such a description. Hammer and Cordes [260] isolated an organism almost identical with *Streptococcus lacticus* which was said to be responsible for burnt taste in dairy products. They proposed the tentative name *Streptococcus lacticus* var. *maltigenes*. Butter and cream with the burnt taste did not reveal this organism on bacterological analysis. The burnt taste caused by bacteria should probably be distinguished from any alteration in flavor by pasteurization.

Turnip Flavor. This abnormal taste has been attributed to both the presence of turnips in the diet of the cow and to changes brought about by bacteria. The use of sodium nitrate to correct this flavor of milk has been mentioned by Reisz who told of the practice among dairymen of adding 10 grams of this chemical to 100 liters of milk, a practice which should not be allowed. Ritland [261] published a brief acocunt of a Norwegian experiment. Two cows which were on pasturage were fed turnips out of doors and milked in the stable, and later they were fed hay and turnips in the stable and milked out of doors, the object being to test the absorption of the turnipy odor. No grain was fed at any time. The amount of turnips fed was as high as 2.84 bushels per cow daily. Tests of the milk at different times by a number of persons failed to

255. Cherrington, Hansen, and Halversen. 1933. J. Dairy Sci. 16, 59.
256. Garrison. 1940. Iowa State Coll. J. Sci. 15, 72.
257. Fettick. 1912. Ztschr. Fleisch u. Milchhyg. 21, 389-392.
258. Fellers. 1922. J. Dairy Sci. 5, 485-501.
259. Sadler. 1911. Centbl. Bakt., Pt. 2, 29, 1-3.
260. Hammer and Cordes. 1921. Iowa Agr. Expt. Sta. Bull 68.
261. Ritland. 1899. Milch. Ztg. 28, 88.

reveal any turnipy flavor in the milk. The conclusion was reached that the characteristic taste often observed when turnips are fed is due entirely to the absorption by the milk of the volatile ingredients of the turnips.

Bitter Milk. Practically all dairy products may, at times, be bitter. Different explanations have been advanced. Wolff [262] classified the causes of bitter milk as follows:

(1) Certain foods,

(2) Physiological process in cows just before and after calving, owing to increase of magnesium sulfate in the milk,

(3) Action of lactic acid in milk on iron in poorly tinned vessels,

(4) Activity of bacteria and some of the higher organisms. It is not probable that any particular bitter substance is always present in bitter milk, but that a number of compounds may contribute this flavor to dairy products. He isolated seven different groups of bacteria from grass, clover, etc., which caused bitter tastes in milk.

During the early part of 1901, Harrison [263] investigated the cause of a bitter flavor in milk and cheese, the trouble being encountered in cheese factories in Ontario. A yeast was isolated from samples of bitter curd which was capable of producing a bitter flavor when added to sterile milk. From milk inoculated with this yeast bitter cheese was made in a number of experiments. The yeast, to which the name of *Torula amara* was given, was found in the milk from every farm supplying one of the cheese factories. It was not found in milk drawn into sterile dishes nor in the air of the stables but was found regularly in mixed milk, cheese, whey, and can washings. It was also found on the leaves of certain species of maple. The yeast was not destroyed in cans by washing with water at about 93.5°C.(200°F.), according to the usual farm practice. It grew well in whey in the presence of 1% acid, and acted energetically on lactose. Butter made from cream which had been sterilized or pasteurized and inoculated with the yeast was very inferior in quality, having in the case of pasteurized cans, a pronounced bitter, disagreeable taste.

Lochhead [264] isolated two motile rod-shaped bacteria which caused bitter milk. While one produced an evident bitter flavor, it was much more pronounced when the two organisms were grown together.

According to Trillat and Sauton [265] aldehyde and ammonia were found in milk having a bitter taste. *Bacillus subtilis* and *Bacillus lactis amari* when grown in milk in pure culture, caused characteristic bitterness and produced aldehyde and ammonia. It was stated that aldehyde came from the lactose. Certain other organisms, when inoculated into the milk, did not cause this flavor. Huyge [266] gave the cultural characteristics of a bacillus isolated from bitter milk. The organism was destroyed in whole milk by sterilizing at 105°C.(221°F.) for five minutes and in cream by heating at 90°C.(194°F.) for five minutes on three successive days. The thorough application of this method caused the disappearance of this trouble from the dairy under investigation. The investigations of Palmer [267] seemed to indicate that bitter flavor was due to lipase action. This fermentation proceeded rapidly at incubation temperature and was characterized by a liberation of fatty acids, including butyric acid, and an increase in the viscosity. A gelatin liquefying bacterium was responsible for the turnip flavor in a case of bitter milk studied by Orla-Jensen [268]. The same organisms caused rancid butter.

Hood and White [269] inoculated cultures of an organism quite like *Escherichia coli* into milk and produced bitter milk.

Tallowy Flavor. This is a common fault of fresh milk. Tracy, Ramsey, Ruehe [270] found that a relatively high temperature, 68 to 80°F., for the

262. Wolff. 1910. Centbl. Bakt., Pt. 2, 24, 231-233.
263. Harrison. 1902. Centbl. Bakt., Pt. 2, 9, 206-226.
264. Lochhead. 1924. Canada Expt. Farms, Div. Bact., Rept. 9-10.
265. Trillat and Sauton. 1908. Compt. Rend. Acad. Sci. 144, 926-929.
266. Huyge. 1906. Rev. in Expt. Sta. Rec. 18, 75.
267. Palmer. 1920. Missouri Agr. Expt. Sta. Bull. 172; J. Dairy Sci. 5 (1922), 201-211.
268. Orla-Jensen. 1925. Lait 5, 30-33.
269. Hood and White. 1931. Prorc. Internatl. Dairy Cong., Eng. Ed., 19-24.
270. Tracy, Ramsey, and Ruehe. 1933. Ill. Agr. Expt. Sta. Bull. 389.

first part of the storage period and bacterial development seemed to decrease the tendency for the occurrence of the tallowy flavor. Contamination with copper salts such as might result from utensils tended to favor the development of this condition. The score of butter made from cream stored for five days under different conditions before churning was higher when made from cream stored for one or two days at 20°C.(68°F.) and for three or four days at 4.4°(40°F.) than when stored for five days at 40°F., and the latter butter showed a very tallowy flavor. Living yeast cells retarded the development of tallowiness in milk, but dead yeast cells and the filtrate from suspensions of yeast had no effect on the development of tallowiness during a storage period at 40°F. Determinations of the oxidation-reduction potential of milk and cream indicated that the activity of bacteria and yeast tended to remove oxygen in their metabolic processes, and tallowiness resulted from the degradation of the fats. A shorter incubation period of 68°F. at the beginning of the storage period, although increasing the bacterial count, had a favorable effect in tending to prevent the tallowy flavor. Winter milk is consequently more liable to have a tallowy flavor than summer milk. Homogenization retarded the development of the tallowy flavor of milk due, it is suggested, to certain physical changes which make the detection of flavor more difficult.

In a study at the Pennsylvania Experiment Station,[271] it was shown that exposure of certain milk and milk products to sunlight ordinarily resulted in the development of off-flavors designated either as burnt or tallowy. These two appear to be distinct flavor changes, the former predominating in low fat products, the latter in high fat products. Paraffined paper milk bottles used in this study offered considerably more protection to skim milk, whole milk, and buttermilk against the development of burnt flavor than was afforded by clear glass bottles. However, paper bottles were no protection to whole milk or cream against tallowy flavors caused by sunlight. Blue and green colored paper bottles or blue and green cellophane wrappers on paper bottles retarded the development of both burnt and tallowy flavors. Off-flavors were detected first in the milk in glass containers, but the intensity of tallowy flavor in milk and cream was greater in the paper bottle.

Fishy Flavor in Milk. *Bacterium ichthyosmius*, according to Cusick,[272] will produce this offensive flavor. Samples of butter inoculated with this organism developed the flavor. It was stated that the organism formed trimethylamine which was responsible for the flavor. That bacteria may not be the sole cause of the fishy flavor in milk is emphasized by Johnstone.[273] Lecithin is said to be present in the milk of cows just freshened; under favorable conditions this lecithin combines with air to form choline; this choline then breaks down to trimethylamine. To prevent this form of fishiness in butter, the lecithin must be oxidized in the cream before the butter is made, or oxidation prevented after the butter has been made. Ruehle[274] reported the formation of a disagreeable sickish taste in milk; this was found to be due to a very short rod with which the abnormal condition could be reproduced upon inoculation into sterile milk.

271. Doan and Myers. 1936. Milk Dealer, 26 *et seq.*
272. Cusick. 1920. J. Dairy Sci. 3, 194-205.
273. Johnstone. 1923. Hoard's Dairyman 65, 446.
274. Ruehle. 1921. Mich. Agr. Expt. Sta. Quart. Bull. 3, 103-104.
275. Fettick. 1911. Ztschr. Fleisch. u. Milchhyg. 21, 280-283.

Fettick [275] studied a species of bacterium, thought to be the cause of a strawberry-like odor in milk. It was isolated from a sample of milk and appeared to have the properties of *Pseudomonas fragaroidea*.

Aromatic Odor. An amyl alcohol aroma of milk was found by Cunningham [276] to be caused by *Micrococcus caseolyticus*. The odor was especially noticeable when the cows were stabled but soon disappeared when they were pastured. The organism was said to originate from the floor of the stable. Washing and disinfecting the floor stopped the difficulty.

Malt Flavor. A micrococcus of the aureus type may cause an objectionable malt flavor in milk, according to Tracy and Ramsey.[277] When an organism of the *Bacillus subtilus* group was also present, a much more pronounced malt flavor resulted. Acid-forming bacteria retarded development of this flavor. The defect was found to be common in raw milk plants during summer. Utensils were a direct source of the large rods; the coccus forms were found in the udders of cows in suspected herds. Neither cocci nor the rods produced gas; they were proteolytic in action. Pasteurization of pure cultures of the cocci at 61.2°C.(142°F.) resulted in their death after 20 minutes, the rods surviving even higher temperatures. The malt flavor developed most rapidly in milk held at 29.4 and 37.8°C.(85 and 100°F.), although a more characteristic flavor was noted in milk held at 20°C.(68°F.). The defect failed to develop in milk held at 15.6°C.(60°F.) for three days.

Oxidized Flavor. This has become a common flavor defect of milk. Its cause is not bacterial so far as is known so it will not be discussed at length in this book. Barkworth [278] found that it could be induced by copper contamination, as did Webb and Hileman.[279]

Oiliness or Rancidity of Milk. This is largely of chemical origin. According to Mattick [280] oiliness in milk occurs during late autumn, winter, and early spring and is widespread. Search for a bacterial cause was not successful. At one farm replacement of an old cooler by a new one resulted in the disappearance of the taint. Bacteriological examination of the cooler gave no result, but it was noted that in the old cooler the tin plating had in part worn away and exposed the copper beneath. Laboratory experiments were made with fresh milk and a similar cooler. Milk passed over the cooler developed oiliness; at summer temperatures no oiliness was found. Oiliness is due to a reaction catalyzed by the copper; oxygen must be present.

During recent years, much has been done on bacterial decomposition of fats to fatty acids and glycerol. The former may have pronounced odors which would be most objectionable in milk. They would probably cause the condition known as rancidity. Bacteria which decompose fats are widespread and could be expected in dairy products. Methods for detecting them are given in Chapter 2, with a discussion of microorganisms involved. Hammer and his students at Iowa State College have

276. Cunningham. 1933. J. Dairy Res. 4, 197-205.
277. Tracy and Ramsey. 1931. J. Dairy Sci. 14, 457-462.
278. Barkworth. 1938. Dairy Industries 3, 7-8.
279. Webb and Hileman. 1937. J. Dairy Sci. 20, 47-57.
280. Mattick. 1927. J. Agr. Sci. 17, 388-391.

studied these organisms in milk and dairy products. Collins and Hammer [281] found several lipolytic bacteria in various materials, such as water, dairy products, and plant equipment. *Pseudomonas fluorescens* and *Pseudomonas fragi* were identified.

Further investigations on the distribution of *Pseudomonas fragi* by Morrison and Hammer [282] revealed its presence in 29 of 176 samples of milk delivered during the cool seasons to an Iowa plant; the organism was also found in many samples of soil, water, feed, and bedding and in swab cultures from different utensils. Presence of *Pseudomonas fragi* in such materials makes it easy to explain its origin in milk.

Blue Milk. This term indicates in a good way the change concerned. At one time it was one of the commonest color changes brought about by bacteria in milk and consequently received much study. Schultze [283] cited cases from which *Bacillus syncyaneum* could be isolated from milk which was taken under sterile conditions from the udders of eight cows. The infection was usually present in all of the quarters of the gland. Wolff [284] believed that the occurrence of blue milk should be ascribed to *Bacillus syncyaneum* and *Pseudomonas cyaneofluorescens*. The former bacterium formed small blue spots on the surface of milk which rapidly increased in size and extended downward. It was dependent upon the presence of lactic acid bacterium, without which the formation of pigment could not continue in strongly acid milk. There were other organisms capable of coloring milk blue. It was thought that though these microorganisms of blue milk are easily killed by pasteurization, the ordinary temperature of from 68 to 70°C. was low unless kept up for 30 minutes. Flies and water are common carriers of these organisms and are the sources of infection of milk. A more complete investigation was reported by Hammer.[285] Careful study of the organisms involved proved it to be *Bacillus cyanogenes*. The organism isolated was examined morphologically, culturally, and biochemically. In its action in milk the organism was found to produce a color in raw milk, in pasteurized milk, although the color produced was markedly influenced by the previous treatment of the milk.

Raw milk invariably developed a color sooner than pasteurized or sterilized milk and the color was also a brighter blue as a rule, being in some cases a sky blue. Pasteurized milk inoculated with the organism developed a more intense color than the sterilized milk, and in some cases (apparently influenced largely by the organisms surviving pasteurization) the color developed approximated that developed in raw milk.

Yellow Milk. This color change is less common than blue milk. One case was studied by Hammer [286] who reported morphological, cultural, and biochemical characteristics of two organisms, isolated in the dairy bacteriological laboratory and peculiar in their action on the cream layer of milk in producing a decidedly yellow color in it without breaking down the fat. One organism was named *Bacillus synxanthus*.

Red Milk. This also is a less common color change in milk. Some of the earliest observed cases of red milk were due to *Serratia marcescens (Bacillus prodigiosus)*. This organism is widely disseminated in nature and therefore is one of the commonest causes of this color change. A close relative of this organism *Serratia rubefaciens (Bacillus rubefaciens)* has also been found. There is no evidence that red milk is harmful.

Germicidal Action of Milk. The number of bacteria gaining entrance to milk is determined by conditions under which it is produced. After the bacteria are in the milk, their development is influenced by several factors. A number of investigators who made counts on fresh milk at

281. Collins andd Hammer. 1934. J. Bact. 27, 487.
282. Morrison and Hammer. 1941. J. Dairy Sci. 24, 9-18.
283. Schultze. 1911. Berlin Tierärztl. Wchuschr. 27, 90-95.
284. Wolff. 1913. Centbl. Bakt., Pt. 2, 38, 289-298.
285. Hammer. 1914. Iowa Agr. Expt. Sta. Res. Bull. 15.
286. Hammer. 1916. Idem, Res. Bull. 20.

frequent intervals reported a decrease in the number of bacteria which could grow on agar plates during the first few hours. In general, the lower the temperature at which the milk was held, the longer this period was. Investigations were then instituted to determine the reasons for the phenomenon. The earlier literature of the subject was reviewed by Rosenau.[287] Different explanations are possible. Some will be tabulated below with the names of the investigators whose work supports them.

1. Decrease in bacterial numbers is due to presence of specific antibodies.

This explanation was suggested by the fact that the blood, as well as other body fluids, contains bactericidal substances capable of destroying bacteria. Fokker,[288] who observed the phenomenon, leaned to this explanation. Woodhead and Mitchell[289] believed that milk contained opsonins which were detrimental to bacteria. The high opsonic index observed for milk was suggested to play a role in the protection of children from tuberculosis. Konig[290] believed that fresh milk contained substances of hemotogenous origin which gave it germicidal properties. Hesse[291] explained the reduction in numbers of bacteria on the basis of the presence of vital principles. Basenau[292] disagreed. Schenk[293] found a bactericidal substance in milk. Behring[294] thought that milk had bactericidal property similar to that possessed by blood. Meinicke[295] agreed for cholera organisms, but not for the members of the typhoid group. Moro[296] believed that a true bacteriolytic alexin was present in milk. Heinemann and Glenn[297] believed that their results supported the existence of agglutinins, which clumped the bacteria and caused a decrease in numbers. This view was also held by Rosenau.[287] The work of Chambers,[298] Meier,[299] Curran,[300] and Stek[301] probably supports this explanation also. Mazé[302] believed that alexins were present. The presence of antibodies is also supported by recent work by Henninger[303] and Jones and Little.[304] Jones and Simms[305] attributed germicidal action to the presence of a substance called "lactenin." Little[306] also believed in a specific substance in the milk of all cows which inhibited mastitis streptococci for a definite period. He believed it was an inherent factor because milk of young cows contained about as much of this substance as the milk of older cows, although

287. Rosenau. 1912. U. S. Pub. Health Serv., Hyg. Lab. Bull. 56, 427-453.
288. Fokker. 1890. Fortschr. Med. 8, 7.
289. Woodhead and Mitchell. 1907. J. Path. and Bact. 11, 408-414.
290. Konig. 1905. Milchw. Zentbl. 1, 49-68.
291. Hesse. 1894. Ztschr. Hyg. 17, 238.
292. Basenau. 1894. Arch. Hyg. 23, 170-183.
293. Schenk. 1904. Monatschr. f. Geburtsh. u. Gynäk. 19.
294. Behring. 1904. Therap. d. Gegenw. 4, 1-10.
295. Meinicke. 1904-05. Klin. Therap. Wchnschr. 4, 470-479.
296. Moro. 1907. Ztschr. Expt. Path. u. Ther. 4, 470-479.
297. Heinemann and Glenn. 1908. J. Infect. Dis. 5, 412-420.
298. Chambers. 1920. J. Bact. 5, 527-541.
299. Meier. 1919. Diss. Tech. Hochschule, Zurich.
300. Curran. 1931. J. Infect. Dis. 48, 408-412.
301. Stek. 1921. Schweiz. Zentbl. Milchw. No. 38-39.
302. Mazé. 1924. Compt. Rend. Acad. Sci. 178, 1434-1436.
303. Henninger. 1926. Arch. Hyg. 97, 183-194.
304. Jones and Little. 1927. J. Expt. Med. 45, 319-336.
305. Jones and Simms. 1930. Idem 51, 327-339.
306. Little. 1935-36. Rept. Internatl. Assoc., Dairy and Milk Insp. 115.

its concentration varied among different cows and even in the different quarters of the same cow. Support for the presence of definitely antibacterial agents in milk also was indicated by results of investigations by Dold, Wizemann, and Kleinen.[307] They observed an inhibitory effect of milk on bacteria which was attributed to the presence of "mutines" and "inhibines." With few exceptions growth of all of the bacteria tested was less on the raw than on the heated milk-agar plates. Whether these differences were of sufficient magnitude to justify the extensive conclusions reached by these authors is doubtful. Certainly there was little need for another set of names for agents which have been found in milk by many others before.

2. Presence of acid destroys the bacteria. This view was held by Weigmann and Zirn,[308] who studied the behavior of *Vibrio cholerae* in raw milk. Bardelli [309] believed that increased acidity explained the lack of growth. It is difficult to understand how this would function in the early history of milk after it has left the udder.

3. Decrease in bacterial numbers owing to death of bacteria which find milk unsuitable for development. This reasonable explanation was offered by Stocking.[310] It does not necessitate existence of specific bactericidal substances. Antagonisms between microorganisms would function here.

4. A phenomenon connected with transfer of organisms to a new medium. This places the explanation of the phenomenon on the same basis as the "lag phase." Coplans [311] pointed out that there is a period of latency when bacteria are transferred to new media. During this period, there is usually no increase in numbers. Sherman and Curran [312] believed that the explanation was in a better knowledge of bacterial growth curves.

These explanations are probably not the only ones which could be offered. They probably are the more important ones. The preponderance of evidence favors the existence of specific antibodies in the milk. The data, however, to support this view rest almost entirely on the fact that bacteria grow better in heated milk than in raw milk, which would seem to indicate that some thermolabile substance is destroyed.

Several different investigators believe that no germicidal action exists. Schottelius,[313] Kitasato [314] and Friedrich [315] agreed with Basenau [292] that milk was not germicidal for *Vibrio cholerae.* Moro denied the germicidal action of milk on *Eberthella typhosa, Escherichia coli,* and dysentery bacilli. Knox and Schorer [316] believed that the germicidal properties of milk had been greatly overemphasized. Confusion of the subject is partly due, according to Evans and Cope,[317] to different methods of working.

307. Dold, Wizemann, and Kleinen. 1937. Ztschr. Hyg. 119, 525-538.
308. Weigmann and Zirn. 1894. Centbl. Bakt. 15, 286.
309. Bardelli. 1909. Hyg. Viande et Lait 3, 249-265.
310. Stocking. 1904. Conn. Agr. Expt. Sta. Bull. 28.
311. Coplans. 1907. Lancet, 1074-1080.
312. Sherman and Curran. 1924. Soc. Expt. Biol. and Med. Proc. 22, 15-17.
313. Schottelius. 1896. Centbl. Bakt. 20, 897.
314. Kitasato. 1889. Ztschr. Hyg. 5, 491.
315. Friedrich. Arb. K. Gsndhtsamt. 13, 465.
316. Knox and Schorer. 1907. Arch. Ped., July, 1907.
317. Evans and Cope. 1908. Univ. Penn., Med. Bull. 21, 264-274.

Many of those who have studied the question have observed a specificity of the milk of certain cows for certain bacteria. Milk of various species also differs. Cozzolino[318] experimented with milk of asses, cows, goats, and human beings, finding the milk of the ass strongest and that of the goat weakest. Human milk was found to be especially active toward *Escherichia coli*. Klimmer's[319] work partially confirmed this. Heinemann reported that same bacteria were killed, while others were not, as did Evans and Cope, Chambers,[298] Meier,[299] Hanssen,[320] and others. Meier and Chambers found that the milk of various animals differed in intensity of germicidal property. Mazé related this to the time of year and "regimen" of the cow. Hanssen held the same opinion.

Slimy or Ropy Milk. This is an abnormal fermentation of milk caused by the growth of certain bacteria which form capsules. It should be sharply distinguished from stringy milk, which results from inflammatory infections of the udder. Much work has been done on ropy milk and, fortunately, most of the published work is in agreement. A fine historical survey was published in 1916 by Buchanan and Hammer.[321] Harding and Prucha[322] have characterized the trouble as follows:

The term ropy or slimy is applied to milk which has become noticeably more viscous than ordinary milk. When this ropiness is only slightly developed, it is ordinarily overlooked. It is sometimes noticed from the fact that the milk pours more slowly, or because the last portion drips from the container with the formation of an evident thread of milk.

Where the viscosity is more pronounced, the milk may be drawn out by means of a fork or similar object into threads. In extreme cases these threads may be fine and silky, and more than a foot long, though more frequently they break when only an inch or less in length.

In extreme cases, the milk takes on almost the consistency of a sticky, stiff dough, and a cup of it may be inverted without the milk being spilled.

Ropy milk should not be confused with the results of garget. Garget is an inflamed condition of the udder of the cow, and milk as it comes from such inflamed udders frequently contains white masses or strings of coagulated material. Milk which becomes ropy, on the other hand, comes from healthy udders and is normal when drawn, but the ropiness may appear at any time after twelve hours.

There are at least three common and distinct types of ropy milk: (1) the ropiness produced in milk drinks by the Bulgarian bacillus, (2) the ropiness in starter for buttermaking, resulting from the degeneration of the starter culture, and (3) the ropiness which appears in sweet milk.

Ropiness was one of the first abnormal fermentations observed in milk. Some people have become so accustomed to ropy milk that they prefer it to ordinary milk. Schmidt[323] showed that the fermentation could be brought about in sweet milk by adding a few drops of ropy milk. Adametz[324] isolated an organism, *Achromobacter metalcaligenes*, as the cause. Since that time Buchanan and Hammer,[321] Harding and Prucha,[322]

318. Cozzolino. 1900. Arch Kinderh. 33, 405.
319. Klimmer. 1903. Idem 36, 1.
320. Hanssen. 1924. Brit. J. Expt. Path. 5, 271.
321. Buchanan and Hammer. 1916. Iowa Agr. Expt. Sta. Res. Bull. 22.
322. Harding and Prucha. 1920. Ill. Agr. Expt. Sta. Bull. 228.
323. Schmidt. 1883. Landw. Vers. Sta. 28, 91-109.
324. Adametz. 1890. Centbl. Bakt. 8, 101-114.

Cole and Hadley,[325] Marshall,[326] Conn,[327] Hopp,[328] Sachmann,[329] Ward,[330] Gruber,[331] Burri,[332] Sato,[333] Dornic and Daire,[334] and many others have reported substantiating evidence.

Ward [335] isolated Adametz's organism in an outbreak of ropy milk, but had difficulty in locating the source of the organisms. No complaint followed the use of milk within a few hours. When it was allowed to stand, however, ropiness developed. Ward [330] believed that the bacteria got into the milk from water. He reported that the trouble could be stopped by adding one part of potassium bichromate to water. Tilmans, Konig, and Spiekermann [336] made ropy milk artificially with several bacteria and observed a marked difference in the type of rope. Hohl [337] isolated *Micrococcus pituitoparus* from straw. It caused ropiness in both raw and sterilized milk. An organism similar to *Bacterium güntheri* which produced ropiness in milk at 37°C.(98.6°F.) to 40°C.(104°F.), was isolated by Burri. Dornic and Daire isolated an organism forming rope from serum obtained in the manufacture of casein. The viscid substance formed was apparently a carbohydrate.

Harding and Prucha and Ward believed that rope-forming organisms were commonly present in milk. The former investigators stated that much ropy milk was overlooked because the consumer was not acquainted with it. Ward stated that the occurrence of ropy milk depended upon the following factors: (1) the necessary organism; (2) suitable temperature for multiplication; and (3) sufficient time for growth to a recognizable degree at the temperature to which the milk is subjected. Ward believed that ropiness was a constant possibility in milk, but that it is repressed by the conditions under which milk is usually handled. This means that the organisms are normal ones in milk, and when an outbreak of ropiness occurs the milk has been handled under conditions favorable for development of the capsulated organisms.

Many different species of bacteria may cause milk to become ropy. A comprehensive key of these bacteria was published by Buchanan and Hammer.[321] Typical organisms were described by Laxa [338] and Long and Hammer.[339] Laxa named his organism *Viscobacterium lactis faetidum,* while Long and Hammer used the name *Alcaligenes viscosus.* Even *Escherichia coli*-like bacteria have been isolated from ropy milk. Sadler and Middlemass [340] isolated *Escherichia neapolitana.* It was killed by heating

325. Cole and Hadley. 1909. Rhode Island Agr. Expt. Sta. Bull. 136.
326. Marshall. 1897. Mich. Agr. Expt. Sta. Bull. 140.
327. Conn. 1892. Bull. 9. U. S. Dept. Agr. Off. Expt. Sta.
328. Hopp. 1893. Cent. Bakt., 14, 174-177.
329. Sachmann. 1893. Rev. in Centbl. Bakt. 16, 122-123.
330. Ward. 1899. Science 13, 324.
331. Gruber. 1902. Centbl. Bakt., Pt. 2, 9, 784.
332. Burri. 1904. Centbl. Bakt., Pt. 2, 12, 192-204.
333. Sato. 1907. Centbl. Bakt., Pt. 2, 19, 27-40.
334. Dornic and Daire. 1907. Rev. in Expt. Sta. Rec. 18, 979.
335. Ward. 1901. N. Y. Agr. Expt. Sta. Bull. 165.
336. Tillmans, Konig, and Spiekermann. 1902. Ztschr. Untersuch. Nahr. u. Genussmtl. 5, 737.
337. Hohl. 1902. Rev. Gen. Lait., 1, 516-522.
338. Laxa. 1936. Centbl. Bakt., Pt. 2, 95, 125-130.
339. Long and Hammer. 1936. Iowa State Coll. J. Sci. 10, 261-265.
340. Sadler and Middlemass. 1926. Sci. Agr. 6, 297-302.

to 63°C.(145.4°F.) for 10 minutes. Escherichia-Aerobacter organisms were found by Sarles and Hammer [341] to produce various defects in dairy products. Among them was ropy milk caused by *Escherichia neapolitans*, *Aerobacter aerogenes, and Aerobacter cloacae.* Ropiness in pasteurized milk was due to contamination after pasteurization.

Microorganisms producing ropy milk probably originate in the various objects with which milk comes in contact. They reach milk from air and dust. Feeds were found to contribute them by Stark.[342] Thousands of ropy milk-producing bacteria were observed in alfalfa hay, clover hay, chaff, soybean meal, and cottonseed meal. Other feeds contained smaller numbers. In one outbreak studied by Kelly [343] the rope-producing bacteria were found to be contaminating pasteurized milk from pipes through which raw milk had passed. The trouble was aggravated by milk returned from wagons and stores. One lot contained 32,000 ropy-milk bacteria per ml.

Prevention of ropy milk is accomplished by constant attention to bacterial quality of raw milk, efficient pasteurization, sterilized utensils, and constant refrigeration. Milk may contain these bacteria without becoming ropy if it is kept cold. Once a dairy or milk-processing plant becomes infected by rope-producing bacteria they are eliminated by thorough cleaning of the plant in the bacteriological sense. This involves generous use of hot water and steam and even use of chlorine compounds as disinfectants. Perkins [344] and Harding and Prucha [322] advised use of calcium hypochlorite in a concentration of 12 ounces per 100 gallons of water. Apparently the efficiency of chlorine compounds varies. Johns [345] found the less alkaline hypochlorites to be very effective against five ropy milk and two bitter milk bacteria. Some Gram-positive bacteria were more or less resistant to such solutions.

Stark's [342] Method for Determining Presence of Ropy-Milk Organisms in Milk. Collect samples of incoming milk in sterile containers and incubate at 15.6°C.(60°F.) for 48 hours. After 24 hours test the samples by touching the top layer of milk, especially around the edge of the container, with a sterile toothpick. Those samples which show no evidence of ropiness at this time may be retested after 48 hours' incubation. The influence of various steps in processing of the milk may also be determined in the same manner.

Believing that Escherichia-Aerobacter bacteria cause more outbreaks of ropy milk than do other bacteria, Curtis [346] recommended formate ricinoleate broth for detecting these organisms in milk. Samples collected at various stages of plant processing and showing gas formation may or may not become ropy but samples showing no gas will rarely develop ropiness when placed at 15°C.(60°F.) to 18.3°C.(65°F.).

Medical Milk Commissions and Certified Milk. Medical Milk Commissions originated in 1890 when the Medical Society of New Jersey attempted to improve the quality of milk. A committee of this society studied the situation and later tried to induce the state to take over the work. This attempt failed because of lack of funds. Finally, plans were made by

341. Sarles and Hammer. 1933. J. Bact. 25, 461-467.
342. Stark. 1930. Proc. Ann. Conv., N. Y. State Assoc. Dairy & Milk Insp.
343. Kelly. 1933. N. Y. Agr. Expt. Sta. Bull. 631.
344. Perkins. 1923. Ontario Agr. Expt. Sta. 8, 187-190.
345. Johns. 1931. Sci. Agr. 12, 38-42.
346. Curtis. 1937. J. Dairy Sci. 20, 147-150.

physicians themselves to supervise milk production. A dairyman who already had high standards was interested and willing to cooperate. In this way the first Medical Milk Commission was formed, and the production of what is known as "certified milk" was begun. The first commission was known as "The Medical Milk Commission of Essex County, New Jersey." In order to protect the term "certified milk" from being degraded by dairymen not under contract with a Medical Milk Commission, it was registered in the U. S. Patent Office in 1904 (Lane [347]). It was not intended that the term was to be restricted to this one Medical Milk Commission, but that any Medical Milk Commission could use it. Certified milk, then, is milk produced under a legal contract between a Medical Milk Commission and a dairyman and conforms to certain requirements. Certified milk is well described in the following quotation which is taken from Lane's discussion.

The objects of this commission are to establish correct clinical standards of purity for cow's milk; to become responsible for a periodical inspection of the dairies under its patronage; provide for chemical and bacteriological examinations of the product, and the frequent scrutiny of the stock by competent veterinarians; to promote only professional and public interests.

The following are three general requirements or standards for the milk: (1) An absence of large numbers of microorganisms, and the entire freedom of the milk from pathogenic varieties; (2) Unvarying resistance to early fermentative changes in the milk, so that it may be kept under ordinary conditions without extraordinary care; (3) A constant nutritive value of known chemical composition, and a uniform relation between the percentage of fats, proteins, and carbohydrates.

Certified milk has been called the honor product of the industry and has been produced under exacting conditions which have been faithfully carried out. It is the only milk produced today under uniform national standards.[181]

Bacteriological Standards for Certified Milk. These have been critically reviewed by Brown.[348] The bacteriological standards require that it shall not contain more than 10,000 bacteria per ml. and that pasteurized, certified milk shall not contain more than 500 bacteria per ml. These counts are to be determined in a special agar, the formula for which is given in the chapter on "Media." Logarithmic and arithmetical averages were discussed by Brown who stated that the former minimized too effectively individual faults on particular occasions. The American Association of Medical Milk Commissions does not recognize judgment of certified milk by averages because it requires that certified milk have a uniformly low count rather than an average low count. Fewer than 10 coliform bacteria per ml. are permitted in raw certified milk; in pasteurized certified milk there shall be no such organisms. Provision is also made for examination of the milk for hemolytic streptococci and sporeforming bacteria. The former bacteria would give some information about the condition of the udder, for control of mastitis is essential in certified milk control. The spore test is of value in maintaining a clean milk. The methods of analysis adopted by the American Association of Medical Milk Commissions for

347. Lane. 1908. U. S. Dept. Agr., Bur. Anim. Indus., Bull. 104.
348. Brown. 1938. Amer. J. Pub. Health 28, 1053-1058; 29 (1939), 355-358.

examination of certified milk are given in other places in this book. The American Association of Medical Milk Commissions publishes them in a small pamphlet.[181]

Pasteurization of Certified Milk. Previous to 1935 certified milk was mainly raw milk. Pasteurization is required to make milk safe. Certified milk was probably clean but it was not necessarily safe milk. The American Association of Medical Milk Commissions,[349] at their annual meeting at Atlantic City, June, 1935, voted unanimously for permissive pasteurization of certified milk. Although certified milk has long been recognized as a superior product and has always been produced in accordance with uniform national standards, there has been opposition to its pasteurization. Investigations have shown that pasteurization does not impair the nutritional value of the milk.

Previous to 1935 pasteurized, certified milk had been recognized in Boston in 1928. According to Eustis[350] this has lowered the counts to 100 or under.

In Boston pasteurization of certified milk increased its sale and the demand for pasteurized, certified milk now exceeds that for unpasteurized, certified milk. This experience has been duplicated in other communities and it is to be expected that the more extensive adoption of the process will result in greater public appreciation of an already superior product.

Dirt or Sediment in Milk. Dirt is objectionable in any food. Estimation of the amount of dirt in milk has been suggested as a means for learning the conditions attending its production. The sediment test has evident limitations for the producer may strain his milk and remove most visible dirst. Wilson[16] did not consider the test to be of great practical value. In his comprehensive study of procedures for examination of milk, he made no observations on this test. *Standard Methods for the Examination of Dairy Products* of the American Public Health Association give suggested procedures for the test. The general procedure is to pass a pint of milk through a disc and to compare this disc with standard discs.

While cleanliness is to be desired in milk, the chief medical officer of the Ministry of Health of Health of Great Britain[351] has pointed out the important distinction which should be made between "clean milk" and "safe milk." In spite of the obvious and important distinction between "clean milk" and "safe milk," confusion often exists in the minds of some who are discussing quality of milk. This authority stated that "clean milk" is milk which has been produced and distributed with the minimum amount of extraneous contamination, such as manure from the cow's udder and flanks, dust from the cowshed and dairy, and dirt from the milker's hands, utensils, and milk containers. "Safe milk" is milk which contains no pathogenic organisms   The following paragraph summarizes this argument:

"It is clear therefore that cleanliness by no means connotes safety. It is true that when milk is handled carelessly the conditions which lead to dirty milk also favor con-

349. Amer. J. Pub. Health 25 (1935), 959-960.
350. Eustis. 1934. Twenty-third Ann. Rept. Internatl. Assoc. Dairy and Milk Insp., p. 121.
351. Ann. Rept. Chief Med. Officer, Min. of Health for 1934, H. M. Stat. Office 115-116.

tamination with any pathogenic organisms which may be in a position to gain access to the milk, such as streptococci from a milker with sore throat or organisms of the typhoid group which may have gained access to milk or milk vessels from persons infected with such organisms. It should, however, be noted that even a clean milk may be infected in this way, so that cleanliness is no guarantee of safety from adventitious human infection though in general it may be expected somewhat to reduce the possibility. Cleanliness is, of course, no safeguard whatever against infection conveyed to the milk from a diseased cow. Milk obtained from a herd infected with tuberculosis or contagious abortion is never safe no matter how cleanly it may be produced. Cleanliness, however, is important from an esthetic and commercial standpoint. Dirty milk is not only esthetically objectionable but it has also poor keeping qualities and for this reason alone reputable firms are anxious to obtain their supplies as clean as possible. While therefore cleanliness is desirable cleanliness is not enough. Safety is the really important consideration and in present circumstances the ordinary raw milk supply can never be regarded as safe. To ensure its safety, that is to say, its freedom from pathogenic organisms, suitable heat treatment such as that afforded by efficient pasteurization is essential."

Some early investigations were carried out to determine whether the results of a sediment or dirt test applied to milk could be used to determine the condition under which the milk was produced or handled. These results were also compared with the results of the plate count, for this was then the main method for examining milk. As might be expected the correlation was not always close, for various factors influenced the results of each test. The kind of dirt influenced the results secured with the sediment test and the types of bacteria, the results of the standard agar plate. Schroeder [352] found that the amount of dirt in fresh milk correlated well with the bacterial count. This was also borne out by the work of Reed and Reynolds.[353] On the other hand, Campbell [354] reported that the amount of dirt which appeared on the discs of the sediment tester was no criterion of the number or kind of bacteria in the milk. Ayers, Cook, and Clemmer,[70] when using fresh milk, found a relation between the amount of dirt and the bacterial count, as did Backhaus.[355] He stated that about 50 per cent of fresh cow dung, dissolved in the milk, could not be estimated by the sediment test. The bacterial count would probably be affected by this amount of foreign matter. Ayers, Cook, and Clemmer found that relatively large amounts of cow manure had to be picked up by milk to cause significant increases in the bacterial count. They found an average number of 50,000,000 bacteria per gram in fresh manure. On this basis, addition of .5 gram of wet manure to a pint of milk would increase the bacterial count 52,854 per ml.; other data were given for lesser amounts.

A number of sediment discs made from milk with known amounts of dirt were shown. It was brought out that .5 gram of wet manure represents a quantity far in excess of that found in the milk produced on an average farm; it was therefore believed to be evident that this excessive quantity of manure would only add 52,854 bacteria per ml. If .1 gram of manure were added to a pint of milk, that quantity would add only

352. Schroeder. 1914. Amer. J. Pub. Health 4, 50-64.
353. Reed and Reynolds. 1916. Virginia Agr. Expt. Sta. Tech. Bull. 10.
354. Campbell. 1916. U. S. Dept. Agr. Bull. 361.
355. Backhaus. 1897. Milch. Ztschr. 26, 357-359.

10,571 bacteria to each ml. It is evident then, that the bacterial count is not a means of measuring manurial pollution which would ordinarily occur. The same conclusions were reached by Harding, Prucha, Kohman, Weeter, and Chambers,[356] who compared dirt contents with bacterial counts.

The use of a small-top pail materially reduced the amount of dirt entering the milk, since practically all entered at the farm during the act of milking. The weight of such dirt was very small. Even when the cows were extremely dirty and were milked into an open-top pail, the dirt in the unstrained milk amounted to only about 10 mg. per quart. Under conditions comparable to those of the ordinary dairy, and when the small-top pail was used, the dirt in the milk was less than five mg. per quart. Under conditions similar to those which obtain in the better class dairies, the amount of dirt was not over 2.5 mg. per quart. The kind of dirt varies with the conditions of the animal. Hair and other material from the coat of the animal will fall into the milk unless the animal is kept clean. Thorough straining, however, removes such dirt to the extent of from 75 to 90 per cent. One must always admit the possibility of soluble dirt entering the milk; such dirt would not, of course, be removed by straining. Harding and his colleagues found a wide variation between the amount of dirt and the bacterial count. In dirt from extremely dirty cows, 1.55 billion bacteria per gram were found. Under the worst conditions, when the dirt in the milk amounted to 10.8 mg. per quart, the increase in the bacterial count of the milk was 17,000 per ml. Under the same conditions, except that the small-top pail was used, the increase in bacterial content owing to dirt was 13,000 per ml. Harding stated that the increase in content of bacteria owing to dirt would be overshadowed by other factors. He further stated that when the bacterial count is used to protect the consumer against undesirable milk, he will not be protected. It was stated that it was entirely possible for the dirtiest milk to pass the most stringent standards, based on bacterial counts, which have been established in connection with the supervision of municipal milk supplies. These investigators failed to take into account that bacteria multiply rapidly in milk. A count of 17,000 caused by dirt might soon cause so many bacteria to be present that the milk would not pass standards. Results of bacteriological examination of fresh cow manure have a bearing on such arguments. Prucha, Weeter, and Chambers [357] examined 27 samples of fresh cow manure, finding a variation of 434,000 to 73,200,000 per gram of dry matter. Allen,[358] in examination of 50 specimens found between 160,000 and 634,000,000 bacteria per gram in fresh moist feces and in dried specimens between 500,000,000 and 16,800,000,000. Such data would seem to indicate that the bacterial count might be significantly influenced by the addition of a little cow dung to milk.

356. Harding et al. 1921. J. Dairy Sci. 4, 430-447.
357. Prucha, Weeter, and Chambers. 1918. Abs. Bact. 2, 7.
358. Allen. 1923. J. Dairy Sci. 6, 479-482.

In another publication, Harding and Prucha [359] continued the discussion just reported. According to these investigators, the plate counts of dirt which may enter the milk may vary from 1,000,000 to 2,000,000,000 bacteria per gram (aerobic count). They classified the sources of dirt in milk as dust, feed, milk remnants, hair, dandruff, soil, and manure, most objectionable of which is manure. These investigators worked under average dairy conditions and also under filthy conditions in order to completely cover the subject. Small amounts of dirt were recovered from the milk and it seemed to have little influence in raising the bacterial count, as determined by the standard agar plate. Dirt from cows possesses an abundant bacterial flora, approximately one and one-half billion per gram. The data secured indicate that the enumeration of bacteria might not give information with regard to the dirt content of milk. However, in an added paragraph, the authors state that the count is, if properly determined, a satisfactory indication of keeping quality.

Ward [360] observed a close relation between the color of the cotton discs used in sediment tests and the conditions under which the milk was produced. He believed that sediment tests and temperature determinations of milk at delivery points would indicate those farms which needed attention. He also stated that examination of the dirt on the disc with a lens would indicate quite accurately what faulty conditions existed on the farm furnishing the milk.

Breed,[361] for the control of the milk supply of Geneva, N. Y. (15,000 population), urged the sediment test in preference to the bacteriological examination. He stated that high counts were due to (1) udders infected with streptococci; (2) poorly washed milk cans; (3) poorly sterilized milking machines; (4) improper cooling. One might consider that these very reasons indicate that the count is valuable for a good milk would not be produced under conditions such as these.

Methods for Estimating the Amount of Dirt in Milk. Even relatively small amounts of dirt may be observed by examination of the bottom of bottles which have been allowed to stand. Such a method does not have the precision desired in routine control methods. Various methods have been proposed. They were discussed by Schroeder [352] and grouped.

American Public Health Association Procedures for the Sediment Test on Milk. These are given in *Standard Methods for the Examination of Dairy Products*, seventh edition, 1939. Pint samples are considered as standard and are to be collected from well-shaken containers. The sample is passed through a cotton disc placed over an opening one inch in diameter. Sediment testers are available which will force the milk through the disc under air pressure. The disc secured on the sample is then compared with standard discs, directions for preparation of which are given. These may be secured in the book referred to above. The fifth edition of *Standard Methods of Milk Analysis* contained photographs of standard discs which had been made by filtering pint portions from two-quart amounts of milk to which 0, 5, 10, 15, and 20 milligrams of dry stable dirt had been added.

Mickle [362] criticized the directions given in earlier editions. He found

359. Harding and Prucha. 1921. Ill. Agr. Expt. Sta. Bull. 236.
360. Ward. 1918. Ann. Rept., Internatl. Assoc. Dairy and Milk Insp. 7, 54-60.
361. Breed. 1919. Rev. in Amer. J. Pub. Health 9, 627.
362. Mickle. 1928. Amer. J. Pub. Health 19, 172-178.

it impossible to use the standard discs as guides in Connecticut. He also believed that *Standard Methods* should specify some particular apparatus for making the test. He stated that the sizes of particles on the different standards varied greatly, and that the kind of dirt used in different laboratories varied in color to a greater extent than had previously been thought possible. Mickle suggested these changes in technic for determining dirt in milk:

1. The use of pint samples. Where absolutely necessary to use less, the size of sample to be stated plainly on the report.

2. The desirability of adopting one type of tester and, particularly, one grade of cotton disc. (Later on Mickle reached the conclusion that it was not always essential that the testers in use be uniform, providing a standard cotton disc is adopted. There are many valid objections against the use of one type of tester under the various conditions that obtain in the control laboratory, the milk-plant laboratory and the field test.)

3. All grading to be done against a photograph of standard discs prepared by a central agency and not against standards made by filtering milk to which different amounts of dirt have been added.

TABLE 3

Chart for Grading Visible Sediment in Milk According to Procedure Suggested by Mickle

Terms not to be reported	Terms to be reported	
Milligrams per unit	*Sediment score*	*Cleanliness ratings*
.00– .12	0	Clean
.13– .37	25	Fairly clean
.38– .62	50	Acceptable
.63– .87	75	Slightly dirty
.88–1.12	100	Dirty
1.13–1.77	125	Very dirty
1.78–3.75	250	Very dirty
3.76–5.00	500	Very dirty

4. The entire disc to be returned to the dairyman because of the difficulty of cutting many discs into two portions showing equal amounts of dirt.

5. No attempt should be made to grade as sediment any hair, piece of hay or straw, or large particle of dirt. Those should be reported separately.

6. Additional standards are recommended representing, respectively, .25, .50, .75, and 1.00 milligram of dirt per pint, as, otherwise, nearly all milk as sold to the consumer will be classed as "clean."

7. The descriptive terms in *Standard Methods* are not apt for use on bottled milk and should be changed. It is hopelessly confusing to have one standard for milk as sold to the consumer and another for milk as received at the milk plant.

8. Since the term "milligrams per pint" is not strictly accurate, is cumbersome, and is often misunderstood, it is suggested it be abandoned in place of the term "sediment score" (Table 3). No "sediment score" should be reported within closer limits than the eight figures given in the score. Samples should always be reported both in terms of the "sediment score" and by one of the descriptive terms for "cleanliness."

Mickle [363] later published the improved milk photographic sediment standards used in Connecticut, based on considerable work done by the

363. Mickle. 1932. Amer. J. Pub. Health 18, 926; Health Bull. Conn. State Dept. Health 42 (1928), 27; Amer. J. Pub. Health 19 (1929), 172-178; Internatl. Assoc., Dairy & Milk Insp. 18th Ann. Rept. 1929, 93-108.

Bureau of Laboratories of the Connecticut State Department of Health.

Results of any of the sediment tests which have been discussed apply only to invisible dirt. Other types of filth which might reach milk are not detected by the test. Committees of the International Association of Milk Sanitarians have shown the importance of the sample [363a] and compared various testers.

Clarification and Filtration of Milk. Clarification consists of passing the milk through a machine to remove the dirt and foreign matter. Hammer [364] quoted the following definition from *Hoard's Dairyman* in 1900: "Simply running the milk through a centrifugal separator for the purpose of removing the impurities, the spouts being so arranged that both empty into one vat, where the milk and cream are mixed before bottling." Severin and Budinoff [365] observed an increased bacterial count, owing to clarification. Hammer also reported that plate counts of clarified milk were usually higher than plate counts of unclarified milk. These were said to be due to disintegration of clumps of bacterial cells, and not to contamination from clarified slime. This explanation is now generally accepted. A later report by Hammer and Hauser [366] gave more data collected with a DeLaval clarifier, on the effect of clarification on the bacterial count of milk. Hammer noticed an increase in the number of bacteria, as in the former work. Fifty-two samples of milk with an initial count of under 100,000 were run through the clarifier. The great majority showed increases in counts, averaging 68 per cent. Clarification caused a decrease in tissue cell count, averaging 41 per cent. Armstrong [367] stated that the clarifier removed 30 times as many bacteria as the filter. He believed that too many factors are involved for the bacteria-removing qualities to be dependable.

The practicability of the clarifier for the removal of visible dirt from milk caused Dahlberg and Marquardt [368] to test the value of the filter. Visible insoluble sediment was completely removed by either filtration or clarification, but particles of sediment were revealed by microscopic examination in the filtered milk. They were absent in the clarified milk. Filtration seemed to have a variable effect on the bacterial counts, made by the plate, and direct microscopic methods. Clarification usually increased the number of colonies, as others have found (Baumgärtel and Struve [369]).

Lucas [370] *et al.* experimented with samples of milk, ranging in volume from 2,000 to 5,000 lb., which were run through clarifiers and filters at varying temperatures to determine the merits of these machines.

Of the samples clarified at 29.4 to 33.3°C.(86 to 92°F.), 71 per cent showed a bacterial increase of 28.1 per cent, 10 per cent showed no increase, and 19 per cent showed an average decrease of 11.7 per cent. When clari-

363a. J. Milk Tech. (1942) 281-297.
364. Hammer. 1916. Iowa Agr. Expt. Sta. Res. Bull. 28.
365. Severin and Budinoff. 1905. Centbl. Bakt., Pt. 2, 14, 470-472.
366. Hammer and Hauser. 1918. Iowa Agr. Expt. Sta. Res. Bull. 47.
367. Armstrong. 1937. Milk Sanitarian 6, 8-9.
368. Dahlberg and Marquardt.1924. N. Y. Agr. Expt. Sta. Bull. 104.
369. Baumgärtel and Struve. 1927. Milchw. Forsch. 4, 492-497.
370. Lucas *et al.* 1927. Mich. Agr. Expt. Sta. Tech. Bull. 84.

fied at 12.8 to 18.3°C.(55 to 65°F.), 62 per cent of the samples showed an average increase of 25.9 per cent, 14 per cent showed no change, and 24 per cent had an average decrease of 12.2 per cent. Of the samples filtered at 29.4 to 32.2°C.(85 to 90°F.), 26 per cent showed an average increase in bacterial count of 24.4 per cent, nine per cent showed no increase, and 65 per cent showed an average decrease of 19.3 per cent. When filtered at 12.8 to 21.1°C.(55 to 70°F.) 27 per cent of the samples showed an average increase of 24.7 per cent, 19 per cent showed no change, and 54 per cent showed an average decrease of 29.3 per cent. The clarifier showed some selective action in removing peptonizers, but the filter had no such effect. Filtration had no influence on keeping quality, but clarification slightly reduced it. Neither process affected creaming ability to any great extent. Of the visible dirt, the clarifier removed 99 per cent at all temperatures, and the filter was almost as efficient, especially at the low temperatures. Filtering milk at temperatures of 32.2 to 46.1°C.(90 to 115°F.) required a change of filter cloth every two hours. Washing the cloth reduced its efficiency.

Hastings [371] believed that clarification was undesirable, since a milk dealer could clarify and sell dirty milk. Hastings stated that the clarifier did not improve the milk to the extent claimed by health authorities. Landis [372] took issue with Hastings, claiming that clarification was a desirable step in the milk plant, since it did remove dirt.

The advantages and disadvantages of clarification of milk were stated as follows by the Commission on Milk Standards:

In its favor are the following points:

(a) It removes visible dirt.

(b) It removes inflammatory products, including many of the causative germs.

(c) It performs the work of the strainer, but in a much more efficient manner.

Against it are the following points:

(a) It removes the visible dirt, but not all disease-producing bacteria. and hence misleads the consumer as to the real purity of the milk.

(b) It does not remove urine or the soluble portions of feces; nevertheless, the milk appears clean.

(c) It adds another process required in handling milk, complicating the situation.

(d) It largely destroys the value of the dirt test, though not more so than good straining.

(e) It breaks up clumps of bacteria and distributes them through the milk.

(f) Exact nature of the material removed is not yet fully understood.

Grading of Milk Supplies. It is much easier to define high-quality milk than it is to determine whether it has been attained. The many methods

371. Hastings. 1917. J. Amer. Med. Assoc. 68, 899-901.
372. Landis. 1917. Ibid. 68, 1139.

which have been proposed for examination of milk are proof of this diffi-culty. Over the years that milk has been under scrutiny various systems of grading have been proposed, many of which were discarded soon after they were tried under practical conditions. Any answer to the question, "What is meant by quality in milk?"[373] must satisfy the chemist, bac-teriologist, nutritionist, and health official. The complexity of the problem is indicated by the fact that various systems of grading are used in larger cities and states. Practically all of them have had bacterial count stand-ards as part of the definition for each grade. In some cases these bacterial count standards have carried the greater part of the load in milk control.

The United States Public Health Service Milk Ordinance and Code[1] which was also approved by the Bureau of Dairy Industry was prepared to encourage greater uniformity of milk-control practice in the United States. This ordinance and code probably embodies the best information at present available on milk-control legislation and is subject to change as improvements are developed. Many communities have adopted this code, which has raised milk quality wherever it is in force. The entire bulletin of 160 pages should be examined. Seven grades of milk are provided, as follows: (See also tabulation on page 340.)

Certified milk—raw. Certified milk raw is raw milk which conforms with the re-quirements of the American Association of Medical Milk Commissions in force at the time of production and is produced under the supervision of the Medical Milk Com-mission of the Medical Society of.............................County, and of the State board of health or of the city or county health officer of...

Grade A raw milk. Grade A raw milk is raw milk the average bacterial plate count of which as determined under sections 1 (S) and 6 of this ordinance does not exceed 50,000 per cubic centimeter, or the average direct microscopic count of which does not exceed 50,000 per cubic centimeter if clumps are counted or 200,000 per cubic centi-meter if individual organisms are counted, or the average reduction time of which is not less than 8 hours: Provided, that if it is to be pasteurized the corresponding limits shall be 200,000 per cubic centimeter, 200,000 per cubic centimeter, 800,000 per cubic centimeter, and 6 hours, respectively; and which is produced upon dairy farms conform-ing with all of the following items of sanitation.

Grade A pasteurized milk. Grade A pasteurized milk is grade A raw milk, with such exceptions as are indicated if the milk is to be pasteurized, which has been pas-teurized, cooled, and bottled in a milk plant conforming with all of the following items of sanitation and the average bacterial plate count of which at no time after pasteur-ization and until delivery exceeds 30,000 per cubic centimeter, as determined under sections 1 (S) and 6.

Grade B raw milk. Grade B raw milk is raw milk which violates the bacterial stand-ard for grade A raw milk, provided that its average bacterial plate count, as determined under sections 1 (S) and 6, does not exceed 1,000,000 per cubic centimeter, or its average direct microscopic count does not exceed 1,000,000 per cubic centimeter if clumps are counted or over 4,000,000 per cubic centimeter if individual organisms are counted, or its average reduction time is not less than 3½ hours, and which complies with all other requirements for grade A raw milk except the provision for abortion testing of item 1r.

Grade B pasteurized milk. Grade B pasteurized milk is grade B raw milk which has been pasteurized, cooled, and bottled in a milk plant conforming with all of the requirements for grade A pasteurized milk, except the provision of lip-cover caps in item 20p, and the average bacterial plate count of which at no time after pasteurization

373. Harding *et al.* 1917. Ill. Agr. Expt. Sta. Circular 205.

and before delivery exceeds 50,000 per cubic centimeter, as determined under sections 1 (S) and 6.

Grade C raw milk. Grade C raw milk is raw milk which violates any of the requirements for grade B raw milk, and which shall be plainly labeled "cooking only."

Grade C pasteurized milk. Grade C pasteurized milk is pasteurized milk which does not meet the requirements of grade B pasteurized milk, and which shall be plainly labeled "cooking only."

Under this ordinance the health officer is instructed to announce the grades of all milk and milk products at least every six months. In some cities this is done every three months. This practice requires definite grading periods which are discussed as follows in the ordinance:

T. *Grading period. The grading period shall be such period of time as the health officer may designate within which grades shall be determined for all milk and milk products, provided that the grading period shall in no case exceed 6 months.*

Wide experience in the operation of this ordinance has indicated that it is undesirable to make the grading period shorter than 3 months. This is because most towns find it difficult to make inspections and analyses often enough to permit a shorter grading period.

On the other hand, the ordinance does not permit grading periods longer than 6 months. Experience has indicated that grading periods longer than 6 months result in inadequate supervision of the supply.

A grading period of 6 months does not imply an excessive enforcement cost. As a matter of fact, many of the cities enforcing this ordinance are grading every 3 months without prohibitive expense.

Examination of samples of milk and milk products during each grading period is provided as follows:

SEC. 6. *The examination of milk and milk products.* During each grading period at least four samples of milk and cream from each dairy farm and each milk plant shall be taken on separate days and examined by the health officer. Samples of other milk products may be taken and examined by the health officer as often as he deems necessary. Samples of milk and milk products from stores, cafes, soda fountains, restaurants, and other places where milk or milk products are sold shall be examined as often as the health officer may require. Bacterial plate counts and direct microscopic counts shall be made in conformity with the latest standard methods recommended by the American Public Health Association. Examinations may include such other chemical and physical determinations as the health officer may deem necessary for the detection of adulteration, these examinations to be made in accordance with the latest standard methods of the American Public Health Association and the Association of Official Agricultural Chemists. Bacterial plate count, direct microscopic count, reductase test, and cooling temperature results shall be given to the producer or distributor concerned as soon as determined if said results fall without the limits prescribed for the grade then held. Samples may be taken by the health officer at any time prior to the final delivery of the milk or milk products.

During the grading period the bacteriological condition of the milk is also determined by different methods:

S. *Average bacterial plate count, direct microscopic count, reduction time, and cooling temperature.* Average bacterial plate count shall be taken to mean the logarithmic average of the bacterial plate counts of the last four consecutive samples, taken upon separate days, irrespective of periodic grade announcements. Average direct microscopic count shall be taken to mean the logarithmic average of the direct microscopic counts of the last four consecutive samples, taken upon separate days, irrespective of periodic grade announcements. Average reduction time shall be taken to mean the arithmetic average of the reduction times of the last four consecutive samples, taken upon separate days, irrespective of periodic grade announcements. Average cooling temperature shall be taken to mean the arithmetic average of the temperatures of the last four consecutive samples, taken upon separate days, irrespective of periodic grade announcements.

Experience in cities which have adopted this ordinance has been satisfactory.[374] One cannot help but wonder whether the practice in New York City, discussed at the end of this chapter, is not a much better one.

Bulmer[375] believed that the U. S. Public Health Service Ordinance and Code was inadequate in so many ways that it failed where it was supposed to do good. While the ordinance contained a maze of detail as to how milk should be pasteurized, it did not consider safeguards for the product after pasteurization. Bulmer also pointed out that it provided for a multiplicity of grades. A vendor is allowed to have in his possession, for instance, grades A, B, and C of both raw and pasteurized milk at the same time. Sale of milks of certain grades would be controlled with difficulty under such conditions.

While several hundred small cities have adopted the standard ordinance, only a small number indeed of the large one have. Where it has been adopted by the latter, it has been profoundly modified. It is also very doubtful to the author of this book whether the average small community which glibly adopts this ordinance can afford the corps of inspectors, chemists, and bacteriologists which would be necessary to make it work. Any community which adopts such an ordinance and cannot afford to hire the experienced help which would be needed to enforce it, is living under a false security as far as its milk supply is concerned.

Another proposal for grading milk without use of bacterial count standards was made by Harding et al.[373] They recognized three grades of milk, special milk, table milk, and cooking milk. These were defined in terms of four elements of quality, food values, healthfulness, cleanliness, and keeping quality, as follows:

Grade	Element of quality	Degree of excellency
Special milk	Food value	Fat content as stated on package
	Healthfulness	Medical supervision of health of men and animals, or proper pasteurization
	Cleanliness	Sediment, not more than a trace
	Keeping quality	Excellent
Table milk	Food value	Fat content as stated on package
	Healthfulness	Properly pasteurized
	Cleanliness	Sediment, no more than a small amount
	Keeping quality	Good
Cooking milk	Food value	Fat content as stated on package
	Healthfulness	Boiled
	Cleanliness	May not be sufficient for table grade
	Keeping quality	May not be sufficient for table grade

374. Fuchs and Kroeze. 1930. Pub. Health Repts. 45, 1412-1421.
375. Bulmer. 1938. J. Milk Tech. 1, 10-13.

This proposal includes about all that should be involved in a definition of good milk. Park [376] took issue with some of the conclusions reached by Harding and his colleagues, because they were interested more in the farm than the infant. Park believed that the number of bacteria in milk should not be ignored. Harding and his colleagues believed that other things should be considered.

The problem to settle with respect to bacterial count standards is, What do they mean? Is a milk supply with a bacterial plate count of 75,000 per ml. more dangerous than one averaging 30,000 per ml.? Is pasteurized milk more healthful if it results from heating milk having a plate count of 200,000 per ml. than if it had a plate count of 1,000,000 per ml.? Sherman [377] has stated that he could see no reason for any difference in healthfulness of pasteurized milk made from raw milks of varied bacterial contents below 750,000 per ml. He further stated that there was no reason to fear "bacterial metabolic products" after pasteurization. Presumably he had in mind products which might result from disintegration of dead bacterial cells.

The present U. S. Public Health Service Standard Milk Ordinance and Code [1] provides for seven different grades of milk, all but three of which have bacterial count standards. Those in which no limit was established for bacterial content are Grade C raw and Grade C pasteurized. The advisory board has defended itself by stating:

"Public-health reason. It is widely accepted that the bacterial count of milk is an index of the sanitary quality of milk. A high count does not necessarily mean that disease organisms are present, and a low count does not necessarily mean that disease organisms are absent; but a high bacterial count does mean that the milk has either come from diseased udders, has been milked or handled under undesirable conditions, or has been kept warm enough to permit bacterial growth. This means, in the first two cases, that the chances of infection have been increased, and, in the last case, that any infection which has reached the milk has been permitted to grow to more dangerous proportions. In general, therefore, a high count means a greater likelihood of disease transmission.

"On the other hand, a wrong interpretation of the significance of low bacterial counts should be avoided, since low-count milk may be secured from tuberculous cows, may have been handled by typhoid carriers, and may even have been handled under moderately unclean conditions."

New York City established milk grading in 1911 and recognized several grades. Since differences in Grade A and Grade B pasteurized milk had become of so little sanitary significance, New York City adopted a regulation in September, 1940,[378] for a single grade designated as "Approved." Distribution of certified milk was not affected. According to one authority standards for this new grade of milk are higher than those for former Grade B, which comprised about 87 per cent of the total milk supply, but lower than former Grade A, which was purchased by about 12 per cent of local citizens. The new standards are as follows:

376. Park. 1918. J. Amer. Med. Assoc. 70, 720.

377. Sherman. 1939. J. Milk Tech 3, 41.

378. Amer. J. Pub. Health 30 (1940), 1111-1112.

Maximum number of
bacteria per
cubic centimeter

Approved Milk—after pasteurization and when delivered to consumer...... 30,000
Approved cream—after pasteurization and when delivered to consumer..100,000
Approved Milk—when produced in New York City or before pasteuriza-
tion at country plant...150,000
Approved Milk—before pasteurization after shipment from country
plant...400,000
Approved Cream—before pasteurization at country plant.........................250,000
Approved Cream—before pasteurization after shipment from country
plant...500,000
Certified Milk—pasteurized 500
Certified Milk—raw 10,000
Milk must contain at least 3.3 per cent butterfat and 11.5 per cent solids.
Light cream must contain at least 25 per cent butterfat.
Heavy cream must contain at least 36 per cent butterfat.

Rice and Pincus [379] justified this change in grading of milk for America's largest city. They stated that it was wise to discontinue grades of milk when the health significance of minor differences between grades had been illusory or non existent. This action caused much discussion. The question was asked whether continuance of specifications for Grade A milk were justified in view of the fact that such milk had to sell at higher price. Answers to such questions must rest on results secured in comparison of milks of different grades. Fortunately, in this case such a comparison between Grades A and B milk in New York City were made by Isaacs and Nussbaum.[380] Grade A milk was found to be a more uniform and cleaner product than Grade B milk.

· Following New York City the New York State Public Health Council voted to provide only one grade of pasteurized milk for the entire state after April 1, 1941, to be known as "Grade A Pasteurized." The bacteria content limit after pasteurization remains at 30,000 per ml. Others were stipulated.[381]

REFERENCE BOOKS

American Public Health Assoc., Standard Methods for the Exmaination of Dairy Products, eighth edition, 1941.
CHALMERS, C. H., 1939. Bacteria in Relation to the Milk Supply. Edward Arnold & Co., London.
DAVIES, W. L., 1939. The Chemistry of Milk. Chapman and Hall, Ltd., London.
ECKLES, C. H., COMBS, W. B., AND MACY, H., 1936. Milk and Milk Products. McGraw Hill Book Co., New York, N. Y.
HARVEY, W. C., AND HILL, H., 1937. Milk Products. H. K. Lewis and Co., Ltd., London.
HARVEY, W. C., AND HILL, H., 1937. Milk Production and Control. H. K. Lewis and Co., Ltd., London.
HAMMER, B. W., 1938. Dairy Bacteriology. John Wiley & Sons, Inc., New York, N. Y.
PARKER, H. N., 1917. City Milk Supply. McGraw Hill Book Co., New York, N. Y.
WILSON, G. S., 1935. The Bacteriological Grading of Milk. H. M. Stationery Office, London.

379. Rice and Pincus. 1941. J. Milk Tech. 4, 38-43.
380. Isaacs and Nussbaum. 1940. Supplement to Amer. J. Pub. Health, Sept., 1940, 2-22.
381. The Milk Dealer 30 (1939), 92.

CHAPTER 6

BACTERIOLOGICAL ANALYSIS OF MILK

In no other place in food technology has bacteriology played a role of greater importance than in the milk and milk products industries. Its methods and technics are used to appraise the conditions under which milk is produced and handled as well as to control the quality of various products made from it. Healthfulness and keeping quality are assured by constant vigilance of bacteriologists.

Methods for the laboratory examination of milk as well as other dairy products are embodied in *Standard Methods for the Examination of Dairy Products*, published by the American Public Health Association. These procedures are revised every five years or so. Other associations have, at times, published methods of analysis. These make available to the bacteriologist approved technic for determining the sanitary quality of milk. Another useful discussion of methods and apparatus is that by Robertson and Schacht.[1]

THE "BACTERIAL COUNT" OF MILK

Quality of milk for many years has been defined in terms of its bacterial count. While such "bacterial counts" were once believed to reflect quality, they have lost much of their significance today, for reasons which have been well stated by Wilson.[2] In order to avoid some of the criticism of "bacterial counts" new expressions have been proposed which, while perhaps somewhat more accurate, do not entirely correct the evil. Breed[3] believed the term "count" to be a misnomer and stated that no one had ever counted the bacteria in milk in the same manner that the number of people in a room had been counted. He looked upon the count as more of an estimate and used this term in place of "counts." His proposal was never widely adopted, for *Standard Methods for the Examination of Dairy Products* uses the words "count" and "counting," as well as "estimation of the count." Breed then mentioned some errors involved in using this technic, some of which are mentioned below. He also mentioned the fact that bacterial counts can and are frequently misused and that there is a general tendency to assume an accuracy for them which they do not possess.

The plate count has been analyzed from many angles by different investigators. One of the most recent, by Wilson[2] states:

The plate count is severely criticized. Ostensibly it measures the number of bacteria in milk, but in fact it does not. On account of the difference between various species of bacteria in their nutritional, respiratory, and temperature requirements, on account of the fact that many organisms may be dead, and most important of all on account of the gross irregularity in the distribution and clumping of the organisms in the milk, the plate count merely registers the number of bacterial units capable of mul-

1. Robertson and Schacht. 1931. N. Y. Dept. Agr. and Markets, Bull. 257.
2. Wilson. 1935. The Bacteriological Grading of Milk. Med. Res. Council, Spec. Rept. Ser. No. 206. H. M. Stat. Off., London.
3. Breed. 1927. Amer. J. Pub. Health 17, 604-606; N. Y. Agr. Expt. Sta. Bull. 567.

tiplying under the particular conditions selected. Since the average number of bacteria per clump is variable from one milk to another, and from time to time in the same milk, and since these clumps may disintegrate to a quite uncontrollable extent during the process of dilution, it follows that the figures yielded by the plate count are arbitrary, not strictly comparable from milk to milk, merely approximate and have no real significance.''

Wilson also pointed out that the technic is difficult to standardize and that the experimental error is large; an allowance of ± 90 per cent may have to be made. Rogers,[4] at a much earlier date, cautioned against using the plate count as a delicate criterion of quality. He stated that it was impossible to distinguish between original contamination and the unknown factor of bacterial multiplication.

Kilbourne[5] emphasized the danger in using the bacterial count as the only means of controlling a milk supply. He sent samples from the same lot of milk to different laboratories, and received results of analysis which were surprising. The variation was so great that, on first thought, one would be tempted to abandon the count entirely. Kilbourne, however, advised the use of other data along with the count. Tiedeman and Hohl[6] called attention to many of the shortcomings of the plate count and called on health officers to demand a revision or to discontinue its use. They further called attention to the fact that health officers have largely been forced to turn to sanitary inspections to determine the safety of milk. With respect to pasteurized milk, other methods have been introduced.

A few bacteriologists have supported the bacterial count. Probably their opinions would be accepted today largely in relation to the times when they were held. In earlier days, many more bacteria were found in milk than are generally found today. This is brought out by the standards which were once adopted by cities.

Hastings,[7] at the University of Wisconsin, discussed the bacteriological analysis of milk as follows:

The value of bacteriological analyses in the dairy industry has been established beyond all question. From the viewpoints of the producer, the distributor, and the ultimate consumer of milk, whether the home or the dairy manufacturer, the bacteriological examination of milk gives information concerning the product which can be obtained in no other way. The further extension of such work is certain to be to the advantage of all concerned.

Conn[8] has well stated the question. *"The bacterial analysis of milk is not to be taken as indicating in itself a condition of safety or a condition of danger, but only as a warning. Good, clean, fresh milk will have a low bacterial count, and a high bacterial count means dirt, age, disease, or temperature. A high bacterial count is, therefore, a danger signal, and justifies the health officer in putting a source with persistently high bacterial count among the class of unwholesome milk.''*

Both of these investigators spoke when milk harbored many bacteria. When Park and Holt[9] did their well-known work on the relation of the bacterial content of milk to infant health in New York City this was also the case.

4. Rogers. 1915. Cream and Milk Plant Mo. 4, 15-18.
5. Kilbourne. 1920. Ninth Ann. Rept., Internatl. Assoc. Dairy and Milk Insp., 101-111.
6. Tiedeman and Hohl. 1938. Amer. J. Pub. Health 38, 629-632.
7. Hastings. 1919. J. Dairy Sci. 2, 293-311.
8. Conn. 1916. Milk Dealer 6, 50-55.
9. Park and Holt. 1903. Med. News 83, 1066-78.

Park [10] found that the bacterial count checked quite well with the health of children fed milks with different contents of bacteria as well as the temperatures at which the milk was stored. He found that during the coldest weather the milk of New York City averaged 250,000 bacteria per ml. and during hot weather 5,000,000. Investigation showed that the milk in other large cities was in about the same condition. Attention was called to the fact that children in cities sicken on the milk in summer, but, as a rule, they improved when they were fed milk which was sterile or had few bacteria. Any intelligent farmer, with cleanliness and low temperatures, can produce milk with a count less than 100,000 bacteria per ml. Modern methods of milk production yield milk with far fewer bacteria than this.

A similar study of the effect of different grades of milk on infants was reported by Park and Holt. The study covered infant feeding in tenement houses during winter and summer. The observations were made by physicians. Bacteriological studies were made on the milk, and 239 varieties of bacteria were isolated. Without reviewing the experiments and data in great detail, we may state that the quality of the milk influenced the amount of illness and also the mortality. Those who received cheap store milk showed material ill effects.

Those who have supported the bacterial count have done so on the grounds that it reflects the conditions under which milk is produced. Opponents have pointed out that the true nature of foreign matter is not indicated. Harding,[11] for instance, stated that fairly large amounts of cow manure could be present in milk, without increasing the bacterial count to any marked extent. Allen [12] and Taylor,[13] however, did not agree with Harding.

One difficulty in using the plate count as a criterion of milk quality has been count standards. Savage [14] found the greatest objection here. While formerly there was little agreement among various city milk ordinances as to the permissible number of bacteria in milk, today they are in better agreement. An acceptable standard today is probably around 30,000 bacteria per milliliter, the count which appears in the United States Standard Milk Ordinance and Code.[15] Many cities have adopted this standard.

While plate-count standards have helped in the fields of milk sanitation and control, there is an increasing tendency to give them an importance which they probably do not deserve. If new methods for determining plate counts, such as a new plating medium and incubation temperatures which give much greater numbers of bacteria, can be accepted by official groups without changing standards which have accompanied the older technics which were replaced, something is wrong in milk control. How can the situation be explained to producers? Parker [16] in discussing this question,

10. Park. 1901. Science 13, 322-323; N. Y. Bull. Med. J. Hyg. 1, 391.
11. Harding *et al.* 1917. Ill. Agr. Expt. Sta. Circ. 205.
12. Allen. 1923. J. Dairy Sci. 6, 479-482.
13. Taylor. 1917. J. Dairy Sci. 1, 303-312.
14. Savage. 1923. Proc. World's Dairy Cong. 2, 1295-1301.
15. Milk Ordinance and Code Recommended by the United States Public Health Service. Pub. Health Bull. 220 (1939). Federal Security Agency, Wash.
16. Parker. 1941. Proc. Inst. Tech. 138-147.

suggested that it is time to analyze some efforts to improve milk, such as the continual demand on the part of a few dairy bacteriologists that plate-count standards be lowered. It is doubtful whether milk produced from healthy cows under adequate sanitary inspection is any more sanitary if its contains 15,000 harmless bacteria per ml. than if it contains 30,000 harmless bacteria. The great question is whether milk is clean and safe. Parker suggested that some attention should be given to qualitative methods in milk analysis—that the type of bacteria has some weight. If the present tendency to force lower and lower plate counts is not controlled, the public is going to be asked to pay for much effort in milk production which makes no contribution to better milk. Perhaps it was that fact which caused health authorities in New York City to provide for just one grade of milk, "Approved Milk."

Reporting of Bacterial Counts. *Standard Methods for the Analysis of Dairy Products* gives specific directions for reporting counts. While this advice was pointed mainly at milk, it may also be applied to other foods. Since the count is only an estimate of the bacterial population, it is recommended that the expression "number of bacteria per c.c." not be used. When the standard technic is used they recommend that the expression "Standard Plate Count, 20,000 per ml." be used rather than "20,000 per c.c." Wilson,[2] in his comprehensive analysis of the problems involved in milk analysis, also stated that care should be used in expressing results of use of the standard agar plate. To report the results as "the number of bacteria per ml." is wrong. The results should be reported as "the number of colonies developing per ml." or "the plate count per ml." should be used. Publication of counts from individual samples is also frowned upon. The United States Public Health Service Milk Ordinance and Code [15] recommends a logarithmic average of four samples as the count that shall be used.

The practice of publishing counts in newspapers is open to serious criticism. The public is not in position to properly interpret them (Prouty [17]) or even to know what the count means.

Limits of Error in Plate Count of Milk. These are due to many different factors, some of which are discussed below. To reduce them to a minimum bacteriologists have prepared "standard procedures" which have not eliminated all variations in counts. Some of them cannot be eliminated. Results of several comparative studies between laboratories have revealed some of the places where improvements could be made. Similar studies within one laboratory have revealed great variations because of the human element. Results of such comparative investigations must be interpreted with considerable care. In 1914, four laboratories in New York City decided to conduct a comparative test by which some of the factors leading to errors could be corrected. Conn acted as referee.[18] On certain dates he distributed to the laboratories a series of samples of milk, sometimes as many as 40 and as few as 15. He found that individual analyses, under the

17. Prouty. 1941. J. Milk Tech. 4, 32-34.
18. Conn. 1915. Public Health Repts. 30, No. 33.

best conditions, were subject to considerable variation, so that no single individual count could be relied on. An average of two or more plates should be demanded. Conn did point out that if standard procedures were used more consistent counts could be secured in different laboratories.

Hatfield [19] reported results of a similar comparative study of the methods of milk analysis made in four New York City laboratories. The greatest variations occurred in counts secured by plating raw milks. The studies were apparently not very extended, and involved mainly counts from plates. When the nature of the test was taken into account, and when the plates were not too highly seeded, Hatfield believed that counts made from the various dilutions could be expected to agree quite closely. Breed and Stocking,[20] in a similar comparative study, submitted samples of milk to several different analysts, working in laboratories situated within 50 miles of each other. The details of the study cannot be reported in this place. However, it was reported "that skilled analysts, using proper technique, ordinarily obtain reasonably accurate estimates of the number of living bacteria in cubic centimeter samples of milk by plate method *provided* the milk contains isolated organisms of a type capable of growth on agar under the conditions maintained." This is an interesting reservation, for different samples of milk may not have such bacteria or they may be present in different concentrations.

Slack [21] has also reported a study of results from different laboratories about and in Boston. Nine laboratories co-operated. The composition and reaction of the medium was found to be a factor of importance. After a conference of the workers, they decided to follow a uniform procedure. An important cause of variation in results was the reaction and composition of the medium. Quite wide variations in results were secured.

The Connecticut State Board of Public Health [22] also reported results of a co-operative study of duplicate milk samples plated simultaneously in nine laboratories. Considerable care was used in the preparation of the samples in order that this part of the work could not influence the results. Incubator temperatures were taken at the level of the plates in each laboratory twice daily during the test. Other details such as pH of media and occurrence of pin-point colonies were noted.

Co-operative investigations have been carried out by the New York State Department of Public Health and the Department of Agriculture and Markets.[23] The former had 80 sets of 10 identical samples of milk analyzed by 78 technicians in 74 laboratories. They found the results secured in the various laboratories to be in close agreement on normal low-count raw milk, on abnormal raw milk; pasteurized milk, however, showed variations. Further standardization of technic was recommended. The department conducted counting contests from which it was concluded that personal

19. Hatfield. 1918. Amer. J. Pub. Health 8, 913-915.
20. Breed and Stocking. 1920. N. Y. Agr. Expt. Sta. Tech. Bull. 76; J. Dairy Sci. 4 (1921), 39-72.
21. Slack. 1922. Boston Med. and Surg. J. 187, 500.
22. Ann. Rept., Conn. State Dept. Pub. Health 1937, 200.
23. Health News, N. Y. State Dept. Pub. Health 11 (1934). 5-6; 22nd Ann. Rept., Internatl. Assoc. Dairy and Milk Insp., 1934. 225-236; 1931, Ann. Rept., Dept. of Agr. and Markets, State of N. Y., for 1930, 98-102.

equation offered the greatest source of error. Some of the causes of error were (1) failure to know what to count, (2) failure to see the colonies, and (3) carelessness. More attention was focussed on the nature of the counting device than had been given it before. Wilson [2] reported about the same opinions.

In view of results reported in the literature by Conn [18] and Schacht and Robertson,[24] Wilson [2] made a few observations on the problem. His discussion with tables should be studied for the full details. They are quite instructive. In one experiment 12 plates were counted by 12 observers under the same conditions. The observers were individuals who had had some experience in bacteriological work. Several errors in counting were revealed. Personal bias and faulty counting apparatus were mentioned as especially important. Milk analysts should read Wilson's discussion.

The problem has been studied from another angle. Several investigations have been carried out to determine how nearly the counts secured on a long series of plates made as rapidly as possible from a sample of milk, would agree. Results of such experiments must be interpreted with great care. Considerable time is consumed in making such a series and the plates made at the beginning and end may be quite different. The reasons are obvious.

Wright and Thornton [25] made 2,330 counts of milk plates poured in duplicate series, 100 plates to the series, in order to determine how accurate plate counts could be. They reached the conclusion that quantitative plate counts were no more accurate than other methods available for judging the quality of milk. These investigators diluted 10 ml. of milk in 990 ml. of salt solution, used 10 ml. of agar in each Petri dish, and incubated the dishes in piles only three dishes deep. Great variation was found. Mudge and Lawler,[26] after a statistical analysis of a large number of plate counts, stated that statistical analyses were of no value. Albus [27] analyzed some of the difficulties which enter the making of a large series of plate counts as were made by Wright and Thornton, for instance. He called attention to the time factor that must be taken into account, for no matter how experienced the technician is, he cannot make 100 plates in the short time required to entirely overlook the fact that the bacteria may multiply in the dilution bottles. Consequently, Albus believed that the results of such experiments should be interpreted with the greatest care. Mudge and Lawler confirmed these opinions. They observed a significant rise in the number of colonies upon allowing the milk-water dilutions to stand. They stated that the dilution bottle was a hitherto unsuspected factor for variation in counts secured by the agar plate method.

Malcolm,[28] in similar work, used a simplified plating medium and a large number of parallel plates. It was shown that in a very high proportion of samples the plating method is unreliable if only one or two plates

24. Schacht and Robertson. 1931. J. Bact. 21, 22; Amer. J. Pub. Health 22 (1932), 80.
25. Wright and Thornton. 1927. J. Bact. 13, 22.
26. Mudge and Lawler. 1927. Idem 15, 7-50.
27. Albus. 1928. Idem 16, 269-277.
28. Malcolm. 1932. J. Dairy Res. 4, 91-104.

are poured for each dilution. It is suggested that in routine examination of unpasteurized milk the 1-10 dilution bottle and plates be omitted, and the 1-100 dilution, prepared by adding one ml. of the specimen to 99 ml. of sterile water be used. The 1-1,000 dilution bottle should be omitted, the 1-1,000 dilution plates being prepared directly from the 1-100 dilution bottle, using .1 ml. of inoculum measured by a special pipette. Five parallel plates should be poured for the 1-100 dilution and at least two for the 1-1,000 dilution. To obtain fairly accurate estimates, when the counts are in the neighborhood of 100,000 organisms per ml., at least five plates should be used for the 1-1,000 dilution.

One of the most thought-provoking discussions relating to plate-count problems is that by Wilson.[2] It should be examined by all who are analyzing the merits of plate counts of milk and other foods.

The Spreading Colony. These are troublesome in most milk-control laboratories. They render plate counts inaccurate or make it entirely impossible to secure them. Schacht[29] recognized three types of colonies which might be counted differently by different analysts. Two of them were the typical spreader while the third was the long chain of colonies. It was recommended that masses of spreading colonies be counted as units and not as individuals. The generally accepted explanation of spreaders is that they are caused by excessive moisture. The porcelain cover for the Petri dish was introduced to take up such moisture and prevent spreaders. Boerner and Robinson[30] stated that the condition of the surface of the agar influenced appearance of spreaders. They found that use of less than 10 ml. of agar medium in the dish restricted spreaders. Schacht found a relation between the amount of agar used in the medium and spreaders. One essential factor in control of spreaders is thorough mixing of the contents of the plate.

Factors Influencing Plate Counts of Milk. Arbitrary conditions have been established for determining the number of bacteria in milk by the agar-plate method. Unless these are strictly followed, variable results will be secured.

(a) *Media for Plate Counts.* Many different media have been used, the main characteristic of which was that they permitted more bacteria to develop. The earlier editions of *Standard Methods of Milk Analysis* specified plain nutrient agar as the plating medium. While it probably did not reveal all of the bacteria which were present in the milk, it yielded results which were the basis of real progress in milk sanitation.

Standard Methods for the Examination of Dairy Products, 1939 edition, provided for a new medium with a quite different composition from the old one. It is known as tryptone glucose-skim milk agar medium in the literature but is designated as nutrient agar in the standard methods just mentioned. This medium gives higher counts. That is about the only advantage it has. It is more complicated in composition and has the disadvantage that a material, skim milk, of somewhat indefinite nature is added. If, as Wilson[2] has stated, the plate count at best is subject to error of ± 90 per cent, the advantages of the new medium are not always apparent. Myers and Pence[31] eliminated the skim milk from their formula because it exerted a negligible effect on the count

29. Schacht. 1931. Ann. Rept., Dept. Agr. and Markets 1930, State of N. Y., 102.
30. Boerner and Robinson. 1930. J. Infect. Dis. 48, 372-380.
31. Myers and Pence. 1941. J. Milk Tech 4, 18-25.

and was merely troublesome. Furthermore it made the medium more turbid and occasionally caused a precipitate to be formed.

Van Horn [32] made media with Witte's peptone, Difco beef extract, and Liebig's meat extract. Comparative counts on these media gave more than three times as many on the media containing Difco beef extract, with pasteurized milk. With raw milk, however, the counts were only slightly higher.

A similar, but perhaps more comprehensive investigation of this subject was made by Supplee, Whiting, and Downs.[33] They compared three media and three incubation temperatures by making parallel counts on 100 samples of milk collected in Ithaca. The data are summarized in Table 2.

Attention was also given to the location of the Petri dishes in the incubator. They found that the lowest counts and the greatest variability were secured on plates which were placed in the interior of solid blocks of dishes. When the plates were exposed to warm circulating air, relatively high and uniform counts were secured.

Norton and Seymour [34] compared five different media using raw and pasteurized milk. Veal infusion media ranked first and meat extract and two dehydrated media second. Ayers and Mudge's [35] milk powder medium was less satisfactory. Norton and Seymour concluded that standard agar medium, dehydrated nutrient agar, and dehydrated peptonized milk agar were equally satisfactory.

The conclusions mentioned above indicate that standard technic should be strictly adhered to. Even slight departures will yield varying results. On this basis, we may explain some of the controversial situations which have arisen in the past.

TABLE 2

Influence of Medium and Incubation Method on Bacterial Counts of Market Milk
(After Supplee, *et al.*, 1921)

Incubation temperature		Incubation time	Relative counts		
			Plain agar 1%	Lactose agar 1%	Dextrose agar
C.	F.	Hours			
37°	98.6°	48	100.0	175.3	444.9
30°	86°	120	519.1	453.5	778.6
20°	68°	120	411.4	498.5	664.8

Lactose Agar. Milk sugar has been found by many to cause higher counts when added to plain agar. Sherman [36] reported that lactose agar gave 43 per cent more colonies than plain agar. Not only were increased counts secured, but the colonies were also larger which made counting easier. The average diameter of the 10 largest colonies on plates from one culture of *Lactobacillus lactis acidi* was 64μ on plain agar and 614μ on lactose agar. Sherman also found lactose agar to be of value for differentiating the type of organisms on the plates.

Milk Powder Agar. Ayers and Mudge [35] recommended the use of milk powder agar for accurate determination of bacteria in milk. The total counts were much higher than when meat-extract-agar was used. Borck [37] also found milk agar to be superior to meat extract agar. Parker and Byers [38] compared the standard agar medium for milk analysis and Ayers' milk powder agar. They found that the colonies on the milk powder agar were larger and more easily counted. With raw milk containing less than 10,000 bacteria per ml. there was no difference but when more than 50,000 bacteria

32. Van Horn. 1934. Abst. Bact. 8, 49.
33. Supplee, Whiting, and Downs. 1921. Cornell Agr. Expt. Sta. Mem. 43.
34. Norton and Seymour. 1927. Amer. J. Pub. Health 16, 35-39.
35. Ayers and Mudge. 1920. J. Bact. 5, 565-596.
36. Sherman. 1916. Idem 1, 481-492.
37. Borck. 1921. Centbl. Bakt., Pt. 2, 54, 127-129.
38. Parker and Byers. 1921. Ann. Rept., Internatl. Assoc. Dairy and Milk Insp., 46-52.

were present, higher counts were secured. With pasteurized milk higher counts were secured with the milk agar. Zoller and Eaton [39] modified Ayers and Mudge's milk powder agar. The counts on milk powder agar were always higher than on the standard agar. In a comprehensive comparison of different agar media Supplee and Flanigan [40] plated 100 samples of milk in seven different agars and incubated the plates for 48 hours at 37°C.(98.6°F.). Assuming that the average of all counts obtained on standard agar was 100 per cent, each of the averages from the other media showed the following relationships to the standard extract agar: previous standard infusion agar, 124.4 per cent; Bacto dehydrated agar, 114.7 per cent; Bacto dehydrated agar with milk, 153.2 per cent; dehydrated milk agar as prepared by the research department of a dry milk company, 167.6 per cent; Ayers' milk agar prepared with spray process milk powder, 170.9 per cent; Ayers' milk agar prepared with Just hot cylinder process milk powder, 177.2 per cent.

Skimmed Milk Agar. It is logical that sterile milk be added to the medium when organisms in milk are to be counted. A certain amount of milk always reaches the plates especially in low dilutions. Barkworth [41] analyzed three sets of experimental observations, viz., his own, those of Thomas,[42] and those of Provan, Dudley, and Thomas.[43] His tables show that use of one per cent milk agar gives a "significant" increase in colony numbers for both raw milk and pasteurized milk and this at all levels of count. With .01 and .001 dilutions of the pasteurized milk organisms which will not grow on standard agar showed marked growth on milk agar. Milk agar gives better colony growth and so aids rapid and accurate counting.

Studies at the National Institute for Research in Dairying, England, by Hiscox, Hoy, Lomax, and Mattick [44] showed that neither lactose nor other sugars tested, casein peptone, or yeast extract could satisfactorily replace milk as a means of correcting the discrepancies often observed between plate counts of the 1-100 and the 1-1,000 dilutions of milk on standard agar.

Thomas [42] also found that addition of one per cent skim milk to standard agar increased the colony count by ratios of 1.9 and 4.8 in samples of raw and pasteurized milks, respectively. With mastitis milk, parasitic streptococci were able to grow in pinpoint colonies on milk agar. Milk agar was much more suitable than yeast dextrose agar for the growth of thermophilic bacteria at 12.8°C.(55°F.) and particularly at 17.2°C.(63°F.).

Based on data obtained on approximately 760 samples of milk taken from the milk supply of 250 dealers representing winter, spring, and summer conditions, Safford and Stark [45] found that fermentable carbohydrates and other milk constituents in skim milk agar made a desirable medium to use in the routine control of market milk and other dairy products.

On 618 samples of pasteurized milk the skim milk agar counts averaged two to four times as large as the corresponding counts on standard agar. The counts on 137 samples of raw milk were only slightly larger. The colonies on the skim milk agar were much larger and could be counted with greater ease and rapidity than those on standard agar. The slight opacity of the medium prevented glare when artificial lighting devices were used. Acid-producing and protein-digesting types of bacteria could be differentiated on this medium, and it supported growth of the bacteria responsible for mastitis. The medium was simple and easy to make, and no more expensive than the standard agar.

Continuing this line of investigation, Safford and Stark [45] compared the bacterial counts of 190 samples of pasteurized milk plated on standard agar and on tryptone-glucose agar plus one-half and two per cent skim milk. Using arithmetical averages of

39. Zoller and Eaton. 1922. Ice Cream Trade J. 18, 59-61.
40. Supplee and Flanigan. 1923. Abs. Bact. 7, 250.
41. Barkworth. 1936. J. Hyg. 11, 847.
42. Thomas. 1937. Welsh J. Agr. 13, 287-295.
43. Provan, Dudley, and Thomas. 1936. Welsh J. Agr. 12, 130-135.
44. Hiscox et al. 1932. J. Dairy Res. 4, 105-121.
45. Safford and Stark. 1935. J. Dairy Sci. 18, 539-546; 1937. 20, 577-581.

percentage differences, the one-half per cent skim milk agar counts were 180 per cent higher and the two per cent skim milk agar counts 215 per cent higher than the corresponding standard agar counts. The two per cent skim milk agar also possessed superior differential value for bacterial types, which was considered especially advantageous in the bacterial examination of such products as butter, cheese, and starters.

Tryptone Glucose Skimmed Milk Agar. This is the standard plating medium in *Standard Methods for the Examination of Dairy Products,* eighth edition, 1936. Its adoption was mainly at the instance of Breed and his coworkers who reported a much higher count with it than was secured with the old standard agar medium. Bowers and Hucker [46] examined a large number of raw milk and pasteurized milk samples and compared the counts given after two days' incubation at 31°C.(87.8°F.) with standard agar (peptone-beef extract agar), tryptone-glucose agar, and tryptone glucose-skim milk agar. Compared with standard agar, tryptone-glucose agar increased the colony count in raw milk by approximately 34 per cent and in the pasteurized milk by 47 per cent. The addition of skim milk increased the counts by approximately four per cent for raw and eight per cent for pasteurized milk. The use of neo-peptone instead of tryptone did not increase the colony count nearly to the same extent. Bowers and Hucker recommended the use of tryptone-glucose agar, and thought the addition of skim milk to be unimportant. Bowers and Hucker assumed that their medium was an improvement because it gave a higher count than the standard plating medium then used. This may not be necessarily true. The best medium is that which indicates most accurately the sanitary condition of milk.

Tryptone glucose-skim milk agar was also compared with standard agar by Bradfield [47] at incubation temperatures of 32°C.(89.6°F.) and 37°C.(98.6°F.) using several types of milk. He also showed that higher counts were secured with the new medium. This was confirmed by Frayer [48] at the same station. He found that the new medium and lower incubation temperatures produced more luxuriant colonies in greater numbers. Also, on account of the opacity, visibility, especially of the smaller colonies, was increased. Yale,[49] working in the same laboratory in which the new medium was developed, confirmed what has been said above with respect to increased counts. He also apparently believed that a medium was better if it permitted more bacteria to grow on the plates. Whether the new medium and incubation temperature better reflected production conditions was not discussed. Abele,[50] Abele and Damon,[51] Phelan,[52] Lind,[53] Dixon,[54] and Marcus [55] all reported higher counts with tryptone glucose-skim milk agar than with the standard nutrient agar. Parker [56] has questioned the mathematical interpretations which Abele made from his data.

Powers [57] believed that a thorough comparison of glucose tryptone agar and plain nutrient agar should have been made before official adoption of the former. Seventeen laboratories in 10 states co-operated in making some 25,150 plate counts over a 12-weeks period. A statistical analysis of these plates was reported by Kelly.[58] Lowering of the temperature of incubation was said to be the greatest single factor in increasing plate counts irrespective of the culture medium used. In a later paper Kelly [58] reported that standard agar at 32°C. gives more uniform results between plants than tryptone agar at either 37°C. or 32°C. Grade A pasteurized milk seemed to be one of the few exceptions to this. There was greater variation in the results from different laboratories on the same sample of milk with the same medium than there was between

46. Bowers and Hucker. 1936. Amer. J. Pub. Health 26, 350-352.
47. Bradfield. 1937. Vermont Agr. Expt. Sta. Bull. 417.
48. Frayer. 1937. Idem Bull. 423.
49. Yale. 1938. Amer. J. Pub. Health 28, 148-154.
50. Abele. 1939. Amer. J. Pub. Health 29, 821-846.
51. Abele and Damon. 1939. Milk Tech. 2, 222-226.
52. Phelan. 1936. J. Dairy Sci. 19, 385-394.
53. Lind. 1940. J. Milk Tech. 3, 208-210.
54. Dixon. 1941. Idem 3, 210-214.
55. Marcus. 1940. Idem 3, 103-104.
56. Parker. 1941. Idem 4, 35-37.
57. Powers. 1936. Internatl. Assoc. Dairy and Milk Insp., Proc. Lab. Sect., 29, 28.
58. Kelly. 1936. Idem 50-75; 1937, 30, 25-33.

the results in the same laboratory using different media and temperatures. It would seem that laboratory procedures need to be standardized and that greater care to control conditions be exercised if satisfactory results are to be obtained.

Yale and Hickey[59] subjected 112 samples of ice cream to analysis with tryptone agar and the then standard nutrient plain agar. The results favored the former.

When tryptone glucose-skim milk agar was adopted as the standard medium, it was suggested in some quarters that new standards would be needed. This is probably not necessary. Abele stated that the average plate-count limits now fixed for milk and frozen desserts by ordinances and regulations need not be raised in order to avoid chaos in grades of milk and milk products. This virtually means that the plate count standard is suddenly lowered. If no change in plate count standards was needed when a medium was adopted which permitted many more bacteria to be counted, the old standards were wrong and too lenient. Perhaps, this again shows the weakness of plate counts and standards which are used with them in milk control.

Apparently introduction of the new medium will not interfere with development of pyogenic streptococci and organisms in milk from cows with mastitis. In one case Foltz and Bushnell[60] found more colonies on the new medium than when blood agar was used for examining milk from an animal responsible for an outbreak of septic sore throat.

(b) *Location of Plates in the Incubator.* Supplee, Whiting, and Downs[33] studied this because they believed that differences in temperature would result from piling plates in the smaller types of incubator. They found that when the plates were placed in the incubator so that there was free circulation of air, the counts were uniform. Every location in all incubators cannot be maintained at exactly the same temperature. Those plates which are near the source of heat may be hotter than those which are at a distance. Such conditions probably do not hold for the large incubators which are constructed in a small room. Where small incubators are used, those with water jackets are recommended since they permit more even heating of the incubation chamber. Wilson recommended such an incubator in his suggested technic for plate counting.

(c) *Temperature of Incubation.* Variations in the temperature at different places in incubators have been observed for a long time. These have been studied for their effect on plate counts. Widely divergent temperatures of incubation have also been studied. Breed and Pederson[61] tested incubators made to operate at 37°C.(98.6°F.) by packing them full of agar plates all prepared from a single sample of milk. Variations in counts were observed and attributed to temperature differences. They might have been and probably were due to the variations which are always observed when many plates are made from the same sample of milk. Prucha[62] showed this in some of his work on the sources of bacteria in milk. He made 100 plates from the same sample of milk. The lowest count was 110 and the highest 170. Sixty-two of the plates showed between 131 and 150 colonies. Breed and Pederson in one case prepared 800 plates from one sample of milk and apparently assumed that the counts should agree closely. Robertson[63] compared the standard temperature 37°C.(98.6°F.) with 21°C. (69.8°C.). At 37°C. for 48 hours, counts were secured which were accurate in only one-third of the cases. When the incubation temperature was increased to five days at 21°C., better correlations were secured. Robertson believed that another temperature than 37°C. should be adopted for standard methods. Supplee, Whiting, and Downs[32] studied incubation temperatures of 37°C., 30°C.(86°F.), and 20°C.(68°F.). Higher counts were secured at 30°C. and 20°C.

Later Pederson and Yale[64] carried out a similar investigation. Seventy-eight samples of dairy products were examined by making 75 duplicate plates from each sample. They were incubated at 21, 25, 30, 32, 35, 37, 39, 45, and 55°C. In general the results

59. Yale and Hickey. 1937. J. Dairy Sci. 20, 755-760.
60. Foltz and Bushnell. 1940. Idem. 23, 973-975.
61. Breed and Pederson. 1932. Amer. J. Pub. Health 22, 745-748.
62. Prucha. 1917. Ill. Agr. Expt. Sta. Bull. 199.
63. Robertson. 1921. N. Y. Agr. Expt. Sta. Bull. 86.
64. Pederson and Yale. 1934. Amer. J. Pub. Health 24, 477-494; 1936, 26, 344-349.

showed that the counts increased with temperature up to 32°C., and decreased as the temperature went above 32°C. The count secured at 37°C. was on the average one-half that secured at 32°C. Pederson and Yale therefore recommended incubation of agar plates at 32°C. for 48 hours instead of at 37°C. The authors did not prove that the recommended incubator temperature had a greater relation to production conditions but based their argument entirely on the fact that higher counts were secured. In 1940 Pederson and Breed [65] claimed that it appeared to be impossible to make a perfect incubator for milk-control work. At 37°C. the plate counts would be subject to considerable uncontrolled error. They, therefore, used this as an argument for changing the incubation temperature from 37 to 32°C. because the slight variations in temperatures would be insignificant. One could ask for more evidence that the temperature variations which would occur at 32°C. are so slight that they may be ignored.

(d) *Technic of Making Counts.* Much of the discussion about plate counts is based upon results of experiments involving 100 plates from the same sample of milk. These have indicated that under the best controlled conditions, great variations in numbers of bacteria are indicated. Albus,[27] however, has shown that these need not be as great as have been reported. Standard methods must be closely followed. The answers which Breed [66] secured to a questionnaire on technic indicated that much is to be desired. Even though detailed directions for examining milk bacteriologically are available many laboratories were permitting marked deviations. This was shown in a striking manner by Black of the U. S. Public Health Service in a paper before the American Public Health Association in St. Louis in October, 1942.

One of the greatest opportunities for error is in counting. The personal equation is an important factor. In order to reduce the possibility of error, *Standard Methods of Milk Analysis* provides that a lens magnifying two and one-half times shall be used.

The methods used for counting colonies are very important. Robertson and Schacht [67] compared some 20 different counting equipments and found that they caused marked differences in counts on the same plates by the same counters. Further observations along these lines have been made by Schacht and Robertson [24] who based their statements on the results of counting contests in which some 35 individuals participated. Some individuals proved to be good counters while others were not. The former showed wide differences when their duplicate counts were compared. Schacht and Robertson found that a properly constructed plate-counting device was important. Wilson [2] also analyzed the magnitude of various errors involved in the plate count. For instance, in one experiment 12 plates were counted by 12 individuals who had had considerable experience. It was apparent that counting of plates by different individuals is attended by a very large error. Even when the same plate was counted by experienced workers, the values obtained fluctuated around the mean by an average figure of 30 per cent. These were believed to rest on personal bias and personal variability which vary independently from one another. These are matters which cannot be readily adjusted.

Wilson [2] enumerated 10 principles which should be observed in correct counting of plates.

Archambault, Curot, and McGrady [68] described a counter, as did Wilson, which has become known as the "Quebec Colony Counter." This device makes for constant and even illumination and for accuracy. This counting device is recommended in *Standard Methods for the Examination of Dairy Products.*

(e) *Sampling.* As much care as possible must be used in taking the samples. They must also be properly prepared for analysis. This is indicated by the work of Torrey and Rahe.[69] Over 90 samples of bottled milk from New York City were examined in order to study the factors which influence the distribution of bacteria in the bottle.

65. Pederson and Breed. 1940. Amer. J. Pub. Health 30, 162-164.
66. Breed. 1927. Amer. J. Pub. Health 17, 604-606; N. Y. Agr. Expt. Sta. Bull. 567.
67. Robertson and Schacht. 1931. N. Y. State Dept. Farms and Markets, Bull. 257.
68. Archambault, Curot, and McGrady. 1937. Amer. J. Pub. Health 27, 809-812.
69. Torrey and Rahe. 1910. J. Infect. Dis. 7, 377-392.

Samples were taken with the pipette, the milk dipper, and by pouring from the bottle. The conclusions reached were as follows:

The upper two ounces of the cream of fresh bottled milk of fair quality contain on the average 50 to 100 per cent more bacteria than an equal amount of the lower cream. In older and more grossly contaminated milk the lower cream may embody as many as, or even more bacteria than, the upper layers. By removing these two top ounces from a milk bottle and using the remaining top milk (eight oz.) for the infant feeding, as Hess [70] has suggested, there generally results a reduction of from 30 to 50 per cent in the bacterial count.

The dominant controlling factor in the primary distribution of bacteria in a milk bottle is the upward "rafting" activity of the fat globules. A higher percentage of bacteria are brought to the surface layers in a milk rich in cream than one poor in that substance. At ice-box temperature the rate of increase of bacteria in the cream and that in the skim milk are practically identical. As the temperature is elevated the rate of multiplication in the skim milk outstrips that of the cream until at 30°C.(86°F.) it may be many times as rapid. In certain samples of rather highly contaminated milk the abrupt change in the temperature of the environment from 5 to 30°C.(41 to 86°F.) caused a striking bacteriolysis in both the cream and the skim milk. This was probably an expression of bacterial antagonism.

The sediment portion of the average bottle of fresh milk contains frequently fewer bacteria than any other region of the fluid. A marked excess of bacteria in the sediment indicates that the milk is old or that it has been kept in a warm place.

Methods of Averaging Bacterial Plate Counts. To avoid fictitious accuracy methods have been proposed for reporting plate counts which obviate use of the actual counts obtained. It is recommended that the counts obtained by a standard technic be reported as the "plate count" and not as the number of bacteria per milliliter. It is also better to average counts in some manner. Wilson [2] believed the arithmetic mean for averaging plate counts to be misleading. He agreed with Robertson and Schacht [67] that the geometric mean should be used. The former was believed to be permissible for averaging the numbers of colonies on a series of plates made at the same time, but the latter should be used in most other cases. Bigger and Griffiths [71] also proposed a weighted mean method of estimating the average bacterial count of a series of individual counts of milk. The weighted mean is calculated by finding the mean of a series as follows: (1) of the whole series, (2) of the whole series less the highest and lowest, and so on. This method is applicable to any series of three or more items, but the greater the number of items the more reliable are the results. The weighted mean impartially and equitably reflects the average bacterial content of milks.

A single plate count on a milk supply gives only meager information. This has been shown by series of plates poured from the same sample or dilution bottle and by plates prepared from different samples of milk. Wilson [2] stated that a margin of at least ± 90 per cent should be allowed on any count of raw milk based on a single plate; on two plates the allowance was ± 64 per cent and ± 52 per cent on three plates.

Practically no objection exists to averaging bacterial counts in some manner. The logarithmic average gives less weight to extremely high counts than the arithmetic average. The nature of bacterial reproduction

70. Hess. 1909. Ztschr. Hyg., 62, 395-400.
71. Bigger and Griffiths. 1933. J. Bact. 25, 253-260.

also suggests the logarithmic average. It has been found[72] that agar plate counts are just as variable as the microscope counts.

Another suggested method for this purpose was described by Leete.[73] It is known as the "three out of four" method; it was compared to the arithmetic average and logarithmic average methods for appraising the value of a series of standard plate counts when used in determining grades of milk, in degrading, and in revoking milk permits.

The method consists of taking a series of four consecutive counts; if three of the four counts are within the grade, the supply is considered officially satisfactory.

The study was made on 1,912 standard plate counts, and examples are cited showing the "three out of four" method to give a truer picture of the actual quality of the milk supply than either the arithmetic or logarithmic averages. The "three out of four" method is adaptable for milk-control administration.

The Standard Milk Ordinance and Code recommended by the United States Public Health Service, 1939,[15] suggested the following method for averaging bacterial counts:

"Averaging bacterial counts in determining grades. In grading milk supplies the average of the last four consecutive counts or reductase hours is used because less than this number has been found by experience not to give a dependable picture of the bacteriological condition of a milk supply. The averaging of bacterial counts in the determination of grades under this ordinance is done by the logarithmic instead of the arithmetic method. This is because the arithmetic method is sometimes unfair to the dairyman. Suppose, for example, the laboratory reports the last four consecutive counts to be 10,000, 10,000, 10,000, and 1,000,000. The one unusually high count may have been the result of accident and is not fair cause for degrading, yet if an arithmetic average is used the milk supply will be placed in grade B, whereas its most usual quality is grade A.

For this reason the logarithmic average is specified in connection with the enforcement of this ordinance. By its use high counts are "snubbed," so to speak, unless all counts are high, in which case the snubbing effect tends to disappear and the logarithmic average approaches the arithmetic average. For example, the same counts previously listed would yield a logarithmic average of 32,000, thus keeping the milk supply in grade A, where it obviously belongs.

"How to find the average bacterial count by logarithms. The logarithms of all bacterial counts from 1,000 to 300,000,000 are given directly in the following table.* The logarithms should be entered opposite the counts in the milk control ledger. To find the average bacterial count find the average of the logarithms and then find the bacterial count in the table which is opposite the average logarithm.

"Following is an example:

Counts	Logarithms
35,000	4.54
11,000	4.04
9,000	3.95
95,000	4.98
	[1] 17.51

[1] $17.51 \div 4 = 4.38$ average logarithm.

72. Ann. Rept., Dept. Agr. and Markets, State of N. Y., for 1929, 109-127.
73. Leete. 1935. Twenty-fourth Ann. Rept., Internatl. Assoc. Dairy and Milk Insp., 28.
* This table is given in the original report but not in this book.

"4.38 in the table is opposite 24,000, which is therefore the average bacterial count.

"If it is found that the average logarithm occurs opposite more than one bacterial count in the table, take the lowest bacterial count as the average.

"*Reductase test.* When the reductase test is used the procedure shall be as follows: Follow Standard Methods of Milk Analysis except that samples are to be examined at the end of each hour but not beyond 8 hours. The reduction time shall be expressed as the number of elapsed full hours when decolorization is first observed. Samples not reduced at the end of 8 hours are to be reported as reduced in 9 hours. For purposes of grading the simple arithmetic average (not the logarithmic average) of the last four consecutive samples is to be used."

Baker [74] also suggested a method for comparing estimates of numbers of bacteria in milk.

Burri's [75] Method for Enumerating Bacteria in Milk. This procedure was developed by Burri as a substitute for the plate method. He recognized many of the inconveniences which relate to the latter. From other work, Burri noticed the regularity of drops secured by using a loop for spreading material on cover glasses. He concluded that the platinum loop ought to serve as a measure for liquids in the same manner as the pipette. Observations showed that the values found in different weighings from a loop were nearly equal, seldom varying more than five per cent and never more than 10 per cent.

The procedure involves spreading, by means of a standard loop, .001 ml. of milk being examined, on an agar slant made with two per cent agar. Such an agar gives a surface which is sufficiently firm for spreading. Each tube contains about six or eight ml. of agar medium and is so slanted that a surface about three inches in length is secured. Before use the tubes should be dried a little to give a dry surface.

A standard loop must be used which will transfer as near .001 ml. of milk as possible. It may be made of platinum wire .3 millimeter in diameter and the loop so constructed that it will be one millimeter in diameter. Hucker and Haynes [76] advised that the loop be inserted not more than two or three millimeters into the milk. It should then be touched lightly at several places on the slant followed by transverse streaking.

Dorner and Demont [77] found that in general higher counts were secured with the Burri technic than with the plate method. They stated that it was to be recommended for use in Switzerland because of its rapidity, simplicity, and inexpensiveness. A less favorable report was made by Cunningham and Andrews.[78] They found that the percentage of error in determinations made by the smear-culture technic was markedly higher than in the determinations made by plating. Evidence is presented to show that the inaccuracy of the Burri method was partially due to errors involved in loop measurements and partly to the inferiority of conditions for growth on slopes as compared with those in plate cultures.

Hucker and Haynes [76] could not recommend the Burri agar slant method for accurate counting of bacteria in milk. It was said, however, to possess practical value for controlling the sanitary quality of milk and other products. Hucker and Haynes emphasized the value of the method in determining relative rather than actual numbers of bacteria in milk and its possible use for the control of certain plant procedures in processing milk and dairy products. Since Burri proposed the method, several others have mentioned its merits. Dorner [79] used the method in a study of the

74. Baker. 1931. J. Dairy Sci. 14, 477-482.
75. Burri. 1928. Proc. World's Dairy Cong. 690-697.
76. Hucker and Haynes. 1939. Amer. J. Pub. Health 29, 651-654.
77. Dorner and Demont. 1931. Lait 11, 909-923.
78. Cunningham and Andrews. 1934. J. Dairy Res. 5, 29-41.
79. Dorner. 1930. N. Y. Agr. Expt. Sta. Tech. Bull. 165.

number of bacteria in freshly drawn milk. It seemed to be more satisfactory than the agar plate. Kelly [80] also used it in investigations of ropy milk outbreaks.

It is doubtful whether results of the Burri method are any more inaccurate than those secured with the agar plate. Granted however, that they are not, the Burri technic is much simpler. Burri [81] again expressed his satisfaction with the test. As Weiser [82] stated, it is a method which is of value.

Myers and Pence [31] Procedure for Laboratory Examination of Milk. This is a simplified plating technic which employs, instead of the conventional culture dish, a culture tube which is oval in cross section; and substitutes a standard loop for the pipettes and dilution blanks normally employed. A standard .01 ml. or .001 ml. loopful of the laboratory pasteurized milk is mixed with sterile melted agar in the special culture tube and the tube is slanted so that the agar solidifies in a thin layer. The tubes are incubated and colonies counted in the usual manner. The counts obtained by this simplified procedure agree well with the standard agar plate count.

The American Public Health Association Procedure for the Plate Count of Milk.[83] This is the official method for bacteriological milk analysis in the United States. It is generally accepted by state and city health departments as the official procedure in their laboratories even though it is frequently not followed in detail. *Standard Methods for the Examination of Dairy Products,* in the latest edition. should be familiar to all who wish to be informed on accepted methods of milk analysis.

Medium. Previous to July 1, 1939, the standard agar medium was a simpler medium than is now official. The formulas of this medium as well as that of the new medium, official after July 1, 1939, are given in Chapter 26. The latter official medium is a tryptone glucose-meat extract-skim milk agar which, as discussed elsewhere in this chapter, gives a much higher count than the old medium. The reaction of the medium should be pH 6.6 to 7.0, preferably pH 7.0.

Dilutions. Dilution bottles should be so filled that after sterilization, they will contain 99 ml., or other amounts, of sterile water. A tolerance of two ml. of dilution water is allowed. When smaller amounts of dilution water are used, the tolerance should be proportionally smaller. After the sample has been added, the contents of each bottle should be thoroughly agitated.

The sample should be diluted so that. the plates made from it will have between 30 and 300 colonies. Where it is desired to determine whether the sample exceeds some official standard such as, 10,000 or 30,000 per ml., at least two plates per sample shall be poured. If the supply is known to have a uniform bacteria content so that a single plate will show between 30 and 300 colonies, but one plate need be poured.

Counting of Colonies. All colonies on the plate should be counted after incubation for 48 hours at 37°C.(98.6°F.). A tolerance of one to three hours is permitted. When it is impossible to count the colonies at the prescribed time, they may be held in a refrigerator at less than 10°C.(50°F.) for a period not exceeding 16 hours. All colonies should be counted, including those of pin-point size.

In counting the plates, illumination and a reading lens, four to five inches in diameter magnifying about one and one-half diameters, should be used. The Quebec Colony Counter was approved.

All plate counts obtained by the standard technic shall be reported in the form "Standard Plate Count, 20,000 per ml." rather than as "20,000 bacteria per ml. as obtained by standard methods." It is also advised that counts from individual samples of milk be not publicized.

80. Kelly. 1933. Idem Bull. 631.
81. Burri. 1939. Ann. Agr. Suisse 40, 192-197.
82. Weiser. 1940. Milk Dealer 29, 36; Amer. Milk Rev. 2 (1940), 157-8.
83. Amer. Pub. Health Assoc., Standard Methods for the Examination of Dairy Products, 8th Edition, 1941.

Another statement of methods of milk analysis is given in Bulletin 323 of the New York State Department of Agriculture and Markets.

Wilson's[84, 2] **Roll-Tube Method for Counting Bacteria in Milk.** This method involves replacement of Petri dishes by culture tubes. Instead of delivering the inoculum into a Petri dish and pouring 10 ml. of culture media over it, the inoculum is placed in a sterile culture tube (6 x ⅝ in.) containing two ml. of melted agar. After the contents have been mixed by gentle rotation, the tube is rolled rapidly under a stream of cold water so that the agar sets in a thin layer extending about one-third of the way up the tube. The tubes should be incubated mouth downward in an oblique position so that water of condensation will flow toward the plug. The preparation and use has been described by Donald.[85] Such methods would save much time and probably yield as accurate results as the plate method.

A method having much in common with the above method is the oval-tube method. These are really "flat" culture tubes which were introduced into bacteriology to facilitate study of growth on slant cultures. Myers and Pence[31] adapted this tube to the enumeration of bacteria in milk. A standard loop is used for inoculating the culture tube which contains about four ml. of melted agar medium.

Procedures for Bacteriological Examination of Milk of the Ministry of Health of Great Britain.[86] These procedures are precise and indicate exactly how milk shall be examined. The other parts are given on pages 371 and 382. Three grades are recommended.

Tuberculin Tested Milk, including **Tuberculin Tested Milk (Certified) : Accredited Milk.**—The milk when tested in accordance with the prescribed method must not decolourise methylene blue within 4½ hours if the sample is taken at any time from the 1st May to the 31st October; or within 5½ hours if the sample is taken at any time from the 1st November to the 30th April. The milk also must not contain coliform bacillus in 1/100 millilitre.[87]

Tuberculin Tested Milk (Pasteurised).—The milk must not contain more than 30,000 bacteria per millilitre.

Pasteurised Milk.—The Milk must not contain more than 100,000 bacteria per millilitre.

SAMPLING
Collection of samples.

2.[88] If the milk is in sealed bottles or cartons the sample should consist of one such bottle or carton, taken anywhere between the place of bottling and the consumer, and delivered intact to the laboratory for testing. Samples of other milk should be collected in sterile glass bottles of 2 fluid ounces capacity, provided with sterile caps or stoppers. Bottles should be filled as full as is practicable so as to permit the least possible amount of air to remain in them.

3. A convenient type of bottle in which to collect samples is one with a wide mouth having a screw thread on the outside of the neck, on to which fits a metal screw cap provided with an inner lining of rubber, or other suitable material which will withstand sterilisation by steam under pressure.

84. Wilson. 1922. J. Bact. 7, 405.

85. Donald. 1915. Lancet, Pt. 2, p. 1243; also 1916, Pt. 2, p. 423.

86. Reprinted by permission of the Controller of His Britannic Majesty's Stationery Office from Memo. 139/Foods (Jan., 1937) entitled *"Bacteriological Tests for Graded Milk,"* official copies of which may be purchased from The British Information Service, 30 Rockefeller Plaza, New York, N. Y.

87. It is not necessary that every sample should be submitted to both tests, and Licensing Authorities which require to have frequent tests made of samples of producers' milk may find it convenient to have most of the samples examined by the methylene blue test alone, reserving the coliform test for occasional use.

88. These numbers appear in the regular publication. They are retained to show the sequence of the several parts of the document which are reproduced in this book.

Sampling from Churns.

4. When collecting samples from churns it is important to ensure that a sample as nearly as possible representative of the whole content of the churn is obtained. The milk in the churn should be well mixed by means of a plunger, consisting of a perforated metal disc with a long metal rod as a handle. The plunger is inserted into the churn and plunged up and down in the milk at least ten times. A sample is then removed with a sterile dipper and delivered into a sterile sample bottle. The dipper should have a pouring lip and should be provided with a hooked handle to loop over the finger of one hand whilst the lid of the churn is removed with the other. Two or three plungers should be provided so that when one is in use the others can be sterilised in a vessel of boiling water. Dippers are best sterilised by hot air at 160°C. for two hours in a hot air oven. They can be conveniently packed and sterilised in a suitable metal container and a separate dipper should be used for each sample taken.

5. The time, date and place of taking each sample should be marked on the bottle containing it.

TRANSPORT AND STORAGE OF SAMPLES

A.—TUBERCULIN TESTED AND ACCREDITED MILKS.

6. The samples to be taken fall into two groups, viz.:—

(a) Samples of producer' milk (unbottled) taken while the milk is in the possession of the producer or before the container is opened by the dealer to whom it is consigned. In many areas the most convenient places of sampling may be the depots to which milk is delivered from a number of farms. (It is immaterial whether the special designation is used or not in relation to this milk.)

(b) Other samples (usually of bottled milk) in relation to which the special designation is used.

7. It is to be noted that the bacteriological conditions do not apply to milk in relation to which the special designation is not used (even though it is obtained from a licensed producer) when it has passed out of the possession of the producer and the containers have been opened by the dealer to whom it is consigned.

8. A sample of unbottled milk as described in paragraph 6 (a) must be kept at atmospheric (shade) temperature until 6 p. m. on the day of production if it is from a morning milking, and until 10 a. m. on the next day if it is from an afternoon milking.

9. A sample of bottled or other milk in relation to which the special designation is used (as described in paragraph 6(b)) should not be kept for the period set out in the last paragraph but it may be kept at atmospheric (shade) temperature for a period not exceeding two hours from the time of sampling. If it should not be practicable for the sample to reach the laboratory by the end of that period, it should be well packed in ice in a carrying-case.

10. In all cases if it is not convenient to begin the test at the end of the specified period (i.e. at 6 p. m. or 10 a. m. or two hours from the time of sampling as the case may be) the sample should be kept at 32° to 40° Fahrenheit. It should not in any event be so kept for more than 18 hours.

B.—PASTEURISED MILK AND TUBERCULIN TESTED MILK (PASTEURISED) (PLATE COUNT TEST).

11. On collection the bottles should ordinarily be transferred forthwith to a carrying-case and well packed in ice, and be kept in this condition until plated at the laboratory. This precaution may be dispensed with only if the bacteriologist considers it unnecessary on account of the proximity of the laboratory to the place in which the samples are collected.

C.—PLATE COUNT TEST FOR TUBERCULIN TESTED MILK (PASTEURISED) AND FOR PASTEURISED MILK

35. Samples should be examined for their bacterial content per 1 ml. in terms of numbers of bacterial colonies developing when measured quantities are mixed with nutrient agar and incubated in accordance with the following directions.

Apparatus required.

36. (1) *Dilution tubes*—as for the coliform test (paragraph 28 (*b*), see p. 371).

(2) *Pipettes*—1 ml. and 9 ml. pipettes as for the coliform test (paragraphs 13 (*e*) and 28 (*c*) above).

(3) *Petri dishes*—British Standard Specification No. 611, 1935.

(4) *Test tubes*—as for the Methylene Blue Test (paragraph 13 (*b*), see p. 382).

(5) *Water-jacketed incubator* at 37°C.

Diluent required.

37. As for the coliform test (paragraph 30, see p. 371).

Culture Medium required.

38.

Yeastrel (manufactured by Brewers' Food Supply Co., Ltd., Edinburgh	3 gm.
B.D.H. or equivalent Peptone	5 gm.
Washed shredded agar	15 gm.
Fresh whole milk	10 ml.
Distilled water	1,000 ml.

Dissolve the Yeastrel and peptone in distilled water in the steamer, and adjust the reaction at room temperature to pH 7·4, using phenol red as the indicator. Wrap the shredded agar in muslin and wash in running cold water for 15 minutes. Squeeze out the excess water and add the agar together with the freshly shaken milk to the broth. Autoclave at a pressure of 15 lbs. per square inch for 20 minutes, and filter through paper pulp in a Buchner funnel. Egg must not be used for clearing. The pulp is prepared by mashing up small pieces of "Postlip" or "White Heather" paper in water by means of a pestle and mortar. A single layer of Chardin filter paper should be laid on top of the Buchner funnel to prevent the pulp being sucked through, and the pulp itself should then be packed down evenly on top of it. The funnel should be inserted into an Erlenmeyer filtration flask fitted with a side piece. A filter pump should be applied to suck through the excess water, which should be poured off through the side piece. The filter, when ready for use, should have a total depth of about 1·5 mm. A pulp layer of suitable and approximately the same depth for any size of funnel may be obtained by pulping an area of dry "Postlip" filter paper equal to four times the square of the diameter of the funnel. With "White Heather" brand, 1 gm. of the dry paper is required for every 20 sq. cm. of funnel. Thus for a 25 cm. diameter funnel, 25 gm. of paper are required; for a 12·5 cm. funnel, 6 gm., and so on. The agar is taken directly from the autoclave and filtered hot, the whole apparatus being kept warm by a surrounding atmosphere of steam. The reaction of the filtrate is tested at 50°C. and adjusted, if necessary, to pH 7·0. The medium is tubed in 10 ml. quantities and autoclaved at a pressure of 15 lbs. per square inch for 20 minutes. The final reaction of the medium at *room temperature* should be pH 7·2.

Dilutions.

39. Dilutions of 1/10, 1/100 and 1/1000 of the milk sample, which has previously been thoroughly mixed in the way described for the Methylene Blue Test (paragraph 14 above), are to be made in the manner and with the diluent described for the Coliform Test (paragraphs 30, 31 and 32 above) except that an additional dilution, the 1/1000 dilution, is to be made from the 1/100 dilution.

Plating.

40. A fresh sterile 1 ml. delivery pipette should be introduced into the tube containing the highest dilution, with its tip not more than ½ to 1 inch below the level of the fluid. The fluid should be sucked up and down ten times, the contents discharged completely, a fresh 1 ml. quantity measured out, the pipette withdrawn, the tip touched against the side of the tube about ½ inch below the rim so as to remove any excess adhering to the outside, the contents blown out gently into the centre of a sterile Petri

dish, the tip of the pipette being held about ½ inch above the level of the glass, 3 seconds allowed to elapse, the tip of the pipette touched against the dish at a point some distance from the fluid already delivered, and the last drop blown out. The same pipette may be used for each dilution, provided the plates are inoculated in order from the highest to the lowest dilution. It is sufficient to suck the fluid up and down 3 times in each d:lution before measuring out the 1 ml. quantities for plating, except for the highest dilution which requires to be sucked up and down ten times for mixing purposes.

41. An alternative method which is somewhat quicker, is to inoculate the plates at the same time as the dilutions are made. After the 1 ml. quantity has been taken over to the next tube of diluent, the pipette may be used for inoculating the Petri dish corresponding to the dilution in which it has been washed out.

42. A sufficient number of tubes containing 10 ml. of standard milk agar are boiled up and cooled down to 45°C. The contents of one tube are delivered under sterile conditions into each Petri dish. Immediately the medium is delivered, mixing should be performed by a combination of rapid to-and-fro shaking and circular movements lasting 5 to 10 seconds, the plate being kept flat on the bench throughout the whole process. The exact procedure consists in 5 to-and-fro movements followed by 5 circular movements in a clockwise direction, succeeded by 5 to-and-fro movements at right angles to the first set followed by 5 circular movements in an anti-clockwise direction. After mixing, the plates should be allowed to stand for about an hour before being transferred to the incubator.

43. The time elapsing between the preparation of the dilutions and the pouring of the plates should not exceed 15 minutes.

44. The plates should be incubated bottom upwards for 2 days at 37°C. Water-jacketed incubators, preferably gas-heated, should be used, and the temperature in various parts of the incubator should be subject to frequent control. The plates may be piled in stacks, but unless a cellular incubator is used it is probably better not to make any stack more than 6 plates high. The incubator should be opened as little as possible during the two days.

45. A plate with more than 500 colonies should not be counted unless the plate made with the next higher dilution shows less than 30 colonies. If the plate made with the 1/1000 dilution contains more than 500 colonies it may be inferred that there are more than 500,000 colonies per 1 ml. of milk. A plate with less than 30 colonies should not be counted unless it is made with the 1/10 dilution in which case it may be inferred that there are 10 times the number of observed colonies per 1 ml. of milk. Plates should be counted within 4 hours of removal from the incubator. The best method of counting is with a specially constructed box allowing of examination of the plates by combined reflected and transmitted artificial light against a dark background with a hand magnifying glass of 4 inches focal length magnifying 2½ diameters.[89]

REPORTS

The results of the bacteriological examinations are recorded on forms provided for this purpose. They appear in the appendix of the original document.

Procedure for Determining the Total Bacterial Count of Certified Milk.[90] These prescribe a special medium but permit the new medium of *Standard Methods for the Examination of Dairy Products* if desired.

"1. Total Bacterial Counts. Total bacterial counts of Certified Milk shall be made by the agar plate method. The amounts of milk inoculated into these plates shall be 0.1 and 0.01 cc., or in such amounts as to insure plates containing more than 30 colonies and fewer than 300 colonies. The medium [90] used shall be as follows: agar, 1.5%; beef ex-

89. Suitable boxes have been described by Mattick and Hiscox, J. Scientific Instruments 10 (1933) and by Wilson.[2] Amer. Assoc. Med. Milk Commissions, Inc., Methods and Standards for Production of Certified Milk, New York, N. Y., 1940, p. 18.

90. Methods and Standards for Production of Certified Milk, Amer. Assoc. Med. Milk Commissions, Inc., New York, N. Y., 1940. Special media recommended may be purchased from Digestive Ferments Co., or Baltimore Biological Laboratory.

tract, 0.3%; peptone, 1.0%; sodium chloride, 0.5%; dextrose, 0.1% in distilled water. The final reaction after sterilization of the medium should be pH 6.8 to 7.2. The beef extract and the peptone used shall be such as to give the highest count and the largest colonies. Wilson Nutri-Peptone or a mixture of equal parts of Difco Proteose Peptone and Tryptone have been found satisfactory. Bacto peptone has been found to be less suitable than some other brands. The colonies in the plates shall be counted after incubation for 48 hours at 37°C. In other respects the methods described in *Standard Methods of Milk Analysis* shall be followed.

"The tryptone glucose milk agar recently adopted by the American Public Health Assoc. may be used if preferred."

The American Association of Medical Milk Commissions procedure of determining the presence of coliform bacteria in milk is given on page 373. This latter test was not approved for certified milk by Stuart et al.[91]

TABLE 3

Bacterial Count Standards Established for Milk and Milk Products

Milk Ordinance and Code Recommended by the United States Public Health Service, Pub. Health Bull. 220.

Grade	Log average plate count per c.c. not to exceed—	Log average direct microscopic count of clumps per c.c. not to exceed—	Log average direct microscopic count of individual organisms per c.c. not to exceed—	Arithmetic average reduction time in hours to be not less than—	
				Milk, etc.	Cream [2]
A consumed raw	50,000	50,000	200,000	8	7
B consumed raw	1,000,000	1,000,000	4,000,000	3½	2½
C consumed raw	(1)	(1)	(1)	(1)	(1)
A to be pasteurized	200,000	200,000	800,000	6	5
B to be pasteurized	1,000,000	1,000,000	4,000,000	3½	2½
C to be pasteurized	(1)	(1)	(1)	(1)	(1)
A pasteurized	30,000				
B pasteurized	50,000				
C pasteurized	(1)				

[1] No limit. [2] These arithmetic average reduction time limits represent twice the log average plate count limits corresponding to the figures in the preceding column.

Bacterial Count Standards. These are a part of practically all grading systems for milk. Each grade of milk has been given the maximum bacterial plate count which would be tolerated. If the milk could not meet this standard it was relegated to the next lower grade usually with some loss to the dealer. Such is the case, for instance, with Grade C, pasteurized milk in the United States Public Health Service Milk Ordinance and Code.[15] It is milk which violates any of the requirements for Grade B, pasteurized milk. If it meets all of the requirements with exception that it has over 50,000 bacteria per ml., it is Grade C milk.

Such standards have probably been helpful for they have been a whip in the hands of a health officer, with which a producer has been driven into line. Any one who has given the matter any thought and has honestly faced the facts, will have to admit the injustice that may be done both to

91. Stuart, Wheeler, and Griffin. 1938. J. Bact. 36, 411-418.

the producer and consumer. The gross errors in counting procedures must be considered.

The best example of bacterial count standards were those published in the United States Public Health Service Milk Ordinance and Code.[15] These are given in Table 3.

On several occasions, Parker [92] has pointed out the fact that the standard plate count is not a proper criterion of quality of milk. Any one who will make an effort to secure the facts and will face them cannot help but see the merits in Parker's position. It is time that bacteriologists woke up with respect to the use of plate counts. More attention must be given to types of bacteria than to numbers. Parker [92] stated that development of culture media to give only the maximum number of bacteria does not give a true picture of the numbers of bacteria in milk causing spoilage. He also pointed out that lowering bacterial counts has increased susceptibility to oxidized flavor in milk and surface taint in butter, owing to the upsetting of the balance in the normal bacterial flora. If the goal is zero it means reduction in quality with consequent reduction in consumption.

PRESCOTT-BREED METHOD FOR DETERMINING NUMBER OF BACTERIA IN MILK

This method is based on staining .01 ml. of milk spread in a film over one square centimeter on a clean glass slide after special treatment for removal of fat. *Standard Methods for the Examination of Dairy Products,* eighth edition, calls it the "Direct Microscopic Method." This method of counting microorganisms in a suspension by means of the microscope is of early origin. Wilson [2] mentioned methods proposed by Eberle,[93] Klein,[94] Hehewerth,[95] Eijkmann,[96] and Slack [97] as precursors. Slack's method, probably the first attempt to count bacteria in milk with the microscope, is virtually the method used today. It was used by Breed [98] and Prescott and Breed [99] for determining the number of body cells (leucocytes) in milk. Breed and Brew [100] and Brew [101] later analyzed its possibilities for determining the number of bacteria in milk.

Several other investigators about this time also became interested in the technic and published methods. They were probably stimulated to do this by publication of Prescott and Breed's [99] first paper in 1910. Skar's [102] method was practically identical except that the bacteria were stained in the milk. A study of the various contributions indicates that Prescott and Breed [99] were probably the originators of the present technic. Breed [98]

92. Parker. 1941. J. Dairy Sci. 23, 502-503; Amer. Milk Rev. 3, 128-130.
93. Eberle. 1896. Centbl. Bakt. 19, 2.
94. Klein. 1900. Centbl. Bakt. 27, 834.
95. Hehewerth. 1901. Arch. Hyg. 39, 321.
96. Eijkmann. 1904. Centbl. Bakt. 37, 436.
97. Slack. 1906. Centbl. Bakt., Pt. 2, 16, 537.
98. Breed. 1911. Centbl. Bakt., Pt. 2, 30, 337-340.
99. Prescott and Breed. 1910. Amer. J. Pub. Hyg. 20, 663-664; J. Infect. Dis. 7, 632-640.
100. Breed and Brew. 1916. N. Y. Agr. Expt. Sta. (Geneva) Bull. 49; J. Dairy Sci. (1917), 259-271.
101. Brew. 1914. Bull. 373.
102. Skar. 1913. Ztschr. Fleisch. u. Milchhyg. 23, 442-447.

stated that Prescott and Breed had observed during the previous year that the method could be used also for counting bacteria.

Despite most careful technic two important sources of error, according to Hanks and James,[103] hold for these methods which involve stained films: losses of bacteria from the slide during staining and faulty selection of areas for observation and counting. They recommended circular films and counting along two diameters at right angles to minimize the effect of abnormal distribution. Other factors were also discussed which suggest that microscope counts are subject to considerable error.

Relation of the Direct Microscope Count (Prescott-Breed Method) to the Standard Agar Plate Count. Introduction of this microscope method into bacteriological milk analysis made it desirable to know how results secured with it compared with those secured with the standard agar plate. Not all of those who have made such comparisons have realized just what was involved. Both methods are subject to such great errors that conclusions are almost meaningless. They are just about as valuable as would be a comparison of two measuring sticks, neither of which had any definite length and reporting the results in yards. In spite of the fact that both methods yield variable results, comparisons of results have been made.

Brew,[101] after a rather extensive study of the question, stated that the relative differences between the two counts were greater where the bacteria are few in number. In such a case, there is probably an error in the microscope count, since it is difficult to see how it is well adapted to milk with few bacteria. Brew found a greater difference when the individual bacteria on the smear are counted than when only groups of bacteria are counted. This is said to be due to the fact that a colony on a standard plate has developed either from a single bacterium or a group of bacteria. Goodrich [104] reported a marked correlation between the two counts. He thought that, for accurate work, more than one slide should be prepared. This is probably one of the major objections to Prescott-Breed microscope method. Breed and Brew [100] compared again the relation of the two counts when studying the application of the microscope method to the control of bacteria in market milk. No general agreement was observed. Brew observed little relation between the results obtained by the plate method and the direct microscope method of counting bacteria in milk, when used for determining the number of bacteria in single samples of fresh, unpasteurized milk. There was, however, a relationship between the two counts when series of samples are examined. Brew found the microscope count to be much higher, but more accurate. The relative differences were greater between the two counts where the bacteria were few in number. In samples of milk showing plate counts of less than 10,000 per ml., the count by the microscope showed approximately 44 times as many individual bacteria; or 17 times as many when the clumps and isolated bacteria were counted as units, individual cells in the clumps not being counted. Samples

103. Hanks and James. 1940. J. Bact. 39, 297-305.
104. Goodrich. 1914. J. Infect. Dis. 14, 512-519.

with 1,000,000 bacteria per ml. by the plate count showed about five times as many individual bacteria when the isolated bacteria and clumps of bacteria were counted as units. The number of these units was slightly less than the number of colonies given by the plate method.

Simmons [105] determined the bacterial content of milk by five different methods, among which were the direct microscope (Prescott-Breed) method and the standard agar plate. He believed from his work that the Prescott-Breed method was less reliable for low-count milks. Robertson [63] discounted Simmons' data and conclusions because he failed to take into account the effect of clumping and the possibility of making reasonably accurate counts on milks with fewer than 500,000 bacteria per ml. Breed and Stocking [106] also secured data with both methods. They believed that either method could be used for estimating the number of living bacteria.

Another comprehensive comparison was carried out in Breed's laboratory by Robertson. The ratio of individual microscope count to the agar plate count that occurred frequently, when the plates were incubated for five days at 37°C.(98.6°F.), was approximately four to one; when the plates were incubated for five days at 21°C.(69.8°F.), approximately two and one-half to one; when the plates were incubated five days at 21°C. with an additional two days at 37°C., approximately two to one. Since Robertson found these to be the most frequent ratios he stated that they were the most suitable ones for interpreting one count in terms of the other. As the incubation period is increased, the ratios between the two counts tended to become uniform.

Robertson found that the size of the clump indicated the quality of the milk. In good quality milk the clump was small, larger in medium quality milk, and small again in poor quality milk.

A fairly constant relation between the plate count and the Breed count of groups of bacteria in milk was reported by Kennedy.[107] The average relation between the plate count and Prescott-Breed group count shown by 70 comparisons was 1 to 13. No relation was found between the plate count and the Prescott-Breed count of total bacteria in milk. Milks with greater numbers of bacteria always give greater divergences between plate count and Prescott-Breed total count. Kennedy reported that the total count in milk could double without any appreciable increase in the group count, since the increase could appear in an increase of individuals in the groups. Allen [108] reported that the size of the groups of bacteria depended on time and temperature. Consequently, Allen thought that the relation of the plate count to the direct total count might vary with the conditions under which the milk had been kept. As was stated by Kennedy, Allen also found that the groups could undergo great increases in numbers of cells, without causing any change in the plate count.

Factors Influencing the Prescott-Breed Method for Enumerating Bacteria in Milk. As is the case with all methods of counting bacteria in milk

105. Simmons. 1919. J. Infect. Dis. 24, 322-336.
106. Breed and Stocking. 1921. J. Dairy Sci. 4, 39-72; N. Y. Agr. Expt. Sta. Bull. 75.
107. Kennedy. 1924. Abs. Bact. 8, 46.
108. Allen. 1924. Abs. Bact. 8, 16.

the Prescott-Breed method is influenced by many factors, a few of which are now discussed:

(a) *Bacteria in Clumps.* Individual bacteria may be counted or the clumps only. If a real attempt is being made to enumerate the bacteria in milk all cells should be counted, both the individual and those in clumps. Whether such a count would correlate well with the standard agar plate would be determined somewhat by the manner in which the sample was handled.

Whiting,[109] studying the number of bacteria in clumps of bacteria in market milk, found that they were somewhat dependent upon the species and the bacterial content of the milk. In low-count milk the clumps were smaller. The averages for all grades of Geneva milk were for clumps of streptococci, 26.8; *Streptococcus lactis*, 2.8; micrococci, 12.3; rods, 5.8; and yeast, 5.5.

(b) *Use With Low Count Milks.* One question about the method of estimating the number of bacteria by the direct microscope (Prescott-Breed) method has been whether it may be accurately applied to low-count milks. Different investigators have shown that with high-count milks, the Prescott-Breed method is sufficiently accurate and yields counts which are close to those secured by other methods. On low-count milks, however, there seems to be some difference of opinion. Brew and Dotterer[110] found that the agar plate counts were higher than the microscope counts of milk with few bacteria. They explained this as due to "unrecognized contamination" on the agar plates and to overlooking bacteria in the Prescott-Breed films. These are merely assumptions and should not be considered as explanations.

The question of clumps of bacteria in milk has been reported upon at greater length by Whiting.[109] He found very little uniformity in the average size of clumps. Each type of bacterium showed a tendency to occur in either small clumps *(Escherichia coli, Streptococcus lactis)* or large clumps, (long-chain streptococci). The average size of the clump was said to be dependent on the type of organism and the conditions under which it developed. The average size of the clumps in the milks which were studied in the investigation reported, was 11.1 cells per clump. Low-count milk with less than 10,000 bacteria per ml. rarely contained clumps with more than three cells per clump. As the grade of the milk became lower and the number of bacteria increased, the size of the clump also increased. This conclusion was not in accord with earlier conclusions of Brew and Dotterer. Whiting explained the discrepancy on the basis that the milks used by the latter investigators had a large number of lactic acid bacteria. In 1929, Brew[111] published another paper on the comparative accuracy of the direct microscope and agar plate methods. However, it was stated that both methods were sufficiently accurate to control public milk supplies.

Some samples of milk are preserved for analysis. Werner[112] made microscope counts on a series of samples preserved with formalin. It is interesting and important from the standpoint of laboratory analyses of milk to note that microscope counts on milk two to five days old, checked very closely ("perfectly") with counts made by the same method on fresh milk. This suggested to Werner the possibility of making counts from preserved samples at a central laboratory rather than in the field. In order to determine whether this formalin would in any way effect the grading of milk by the microscope count, Werner studied the effect of formalin in a strength of 500 to 1 in milk. In only three instances would the milk have been placed in a different grade by using the count on fresh milk and preserved milk. These data would seem to make the Prescott-Breed microscope method have greater possibilities in milk-control work. The work of Hastings and Davenport[113] refuted Werner's conclusions.

(c) *Use on Pasteurized Milk.* Since introduction of the Prescott-Breed method applicability with reliable results to pasteurized milk has been questioned. The question which has caused most trouble is whether the bacteria which are killed by pasteurization

109. Whiting. 1923. N. Y. Agr. Expt. Sta. Tech. Bull. 98.
110. Brew and Dotterer. 1917. N. Y. Agr. Expt. Sta. Bull. 439.
111. Brew. 1929. J. Dairy Sci. 12, 304-319.
112. Werner. 1917. J. Dairy Sci. 1, 284-289.
113. Hastings and Davenport. 1920. Idem 3, 494-501.

are stained, which would probably cause them to appear as living cells. Hastings and Davenport [113] reported that an irregular percentage of bacteria present in milk appeared in stained and countable form after pasteurization. The number of stainable bacteria decreased in six to 24 hours after pasteurization, so that in some cases, only three per cent of the original cells could be counted. This is probably due to marked variation in staining properties of bacteria which have been subjected to heat. In 16 series of counts they varied from 18 to 83 per cent of the counts on the corresponding raw milk. Pasteurization seemed to have no effect on the stainability or countability of *Escherichia coli* and *Staphlyococcus pyogenes aureus*. Cells of *Lactobacillus bulgaricum* were only faintly stained, but countable. Other bacteria gave varying results.

Ward and Myers [114] quoted results of examinations of milk by the Prescott-Breed method before and after laboratory pasteurization and observed that the heat treatment disintegrates as well as kills the bacteria, so they are no longer countable. In their opinion the opposite view was mainly due to the multiplication of thermophiles giving a high bacterial count after pasteurization. Their essential conclusion is that insufficient numbers of dead bacteria remain after pasteurization to impair the usefulness of direct microscope counts made on pasteurized milk. Mattick,[115] however, claimed that the Prescott-Breed microscope method did not distinguish living from dead bacteria and was, therefore, useless for pasteurized milk. He also believed that the small sample used was objectionable.

The work of Guittonneau and Brigando [116] also showed that the staining properties of bacteria in heated milk were altered. Hempler [117] found the microscope method of Prescott and Breed to be unsatisfactory for heated milk.

(d) *Small Samples Are Used.* This is another objection which has been made against the Prescott-Breed method. Mattick [115] and Strynadka and Thornton [118] both mentioned it.

Wilson [2] claimed that actual counts were not worth making by the Prescott-Breed method unless there is an average of at least one cell per field. Under such conditions at least 100 fields should be examined. As the average number of bacteria per field increases, the number of fields counted may be decreased.

Wilson [2] dealt at some length with the errors of the Prescott-Breed microscope count of bacteria in milk. The main errors were said to be due to difficulties in obtaining an adequate sample of milk, of measuring such a small sample of milk and spreading it over one square centimeter, failure of some bacteria to take the stain, and irregular distribution of bacteria over the microscope slide so that the counts of the fields vary greatly. Wilson doubted whether Breed's [98] statement that dead bacteria did not stain was true. In fact Barthel's [119] work was quoted to show that heating had comparatively little effect on the bacteria in milk. Wilson showed that when coliform bacteria grown in milk were exposed to 63°C. (145.4°F.) for 30 minutes, they stained as deeply as before. Use of a suspension of cells grown on agar and then added to the milk, showed that many cells did not stain. Wilson stated that the Breed count was not an indication of total organisms but merely the total number of stainable bacteria, whether alive or dead.

In order to gain an idea of the variations which might be observed in this method, four individuals made Prescott-Breed films on the same sample of milk. When the bacterial content was below 500,000 bacteria per ml., the coefficients of variations were very large. For low-count milks several hundred fields should be counted to secure comparable results. These conclusions agreed with those of Buice.[120] This latter investigator considered the Prescott-Breed microscope count to be unreliable for milk with less than 200,000 bacteria per ml.

(e) *Variation in Staining Reactions of Bacteria in Milk.* Accuracy of the Prescott-Breed method rests on the supposition that all bacteria in milk stain to the same degree.

114. Ward and Myers. 1937. Amer. J. Pub. Health 27, 898-905.
115. Mattick. 1930. J. Dairy Res. 111-135.
116. Guittonneau and Brigando. 1936. Lait 16, 156.
117. Hempler. 1940. Rev. in Biol. Abs. 14, 6.
118. Strynadka and Thornton. 1937. J. Dairy Sci. 20, 685-692.
119. Barthel. 1917. Ztschr. Untersuch. Nahr. u. Genussmtl. 15, 385.
120. Buice. 1934. Zentbl. Bakt., Pt. 2, 89, 387-398.

Whitehead [121] reported observations which indicate that this is not always the case. In experimental work on cheese he found that the addition of Gram-negative bacilli of the colon group to milk failed to be indicated by the Prescott-Breed method. Their presence was indicated, however, by the usual culture methods. According to Whitehead, the staining ability of bacteria in milk is greatly influenced by their age. Young cells seemed to stain readily while older cells did not. Whitehead suggested that his observations might explain some of the discrepancies between the standard agar plate count and the count secured by the Prescott-Breed method.

(f) *Considerable Skill Is Required.* The Prescott-Breed method is a technical procedure requiring considerable skill and experience. Breed and Stocking [122] stated that the chief limitations are the skill of the analyst and the patience necessary to examine a large enough amount of milk. If given enough time to examine a number of preparations, the skilled analyst can reach a fairly reliable index of the number of bacteria in milk. What constitutes a "skilled" analyst is an indefinite matter. Bacterial plate counts were said to be more regular in the hands of laboratory asssitants carrying out routine analyses of milk. About the same conclusion was reached by Conn, [18] who stated that considerable experience was needed by the analyst to distinguish between bacteria and dirt particles.

Others who have pointed out the limitations of the Prescott-Breed method are Hastings, [123] and Bryan, Turney, Fox, Begeman, Miles, and Bryan. [124]

Merits of the Prescott-Breed Method. While this method may not be entirely satisfactory for counting microorganisms in milk, it does have considerable value under some conditions. It is a good method for separating high-count from low-count milks. Stained films may be examined by trained workers, such as milk inspectors in the field, for rapid grading of different milks. As discussed below it gives information about the type of bacteria which are present, especially Streptococci. It is less expensive and more rapid than the agar plate method.

Detection of Abnormal Cow's Milk by Means of the Microscope. The inadequacies of microscope methods for determining the number of bacteria in milk may be somewhat compensated for by the fact that they might give valuable information concerning the presence of bacteria from diseased udders. In this way, a rapid method would be available for detecting presence of diseased cows in a herd, udders of which are shedding harmful streptococci. Practical application of such a procedure must rest on comprehensive observations on milk from cows definitely known to be shedding pathogenic streptococci and on well-trained microscopists. Forman and Shaw [125] secured samples of milk from cows showing clinical symptoms of mastitis. Samples of normal market milk and high-grade milk were also secured. The milk from infected udders contained many long-chain streptococci. Having established this, they then searched in market milk for these organisms and found them in 3.83 per cent of 261 samples examined. Results of a similar investigation were published by Breed, [126] who prepared 16 color plates. These were said to illustrate conditions in different grades of milk. They depend on the ability of the analyst to recognize streptococci solely by morphology.

121. Whitehead. 1930. J. Dairy Res. 2, 81-83.
122. Breed and Stocking. 1917. J. Dairy Sci. 1, 19-34.
123. Hastings. 1937. Milk Dealer 26, 100.
124. Bryan *et al.* 1938. J. Milk Tech. 1, 26-34.
125. Forman and Shaw. 1927. Pub. Health News, N. J., 12. 6.
126. Breed. 1927. Amer. J. Pub. Health 17, 604-606; N. Y. Agr. Expt. Sta. Bull. 567.

Hadwen and Gwatkin [127] made counts of bacteria and body cells from whole milk and from sediments obtained by centrifuging a large number of samples drawn directly from the udders. Sediments were preferred for examination because both sufficiently accurate counts and differential studies could be made from films prepared from them.

For defining normal milk a standard was established which was used in studying milk from individual cows. In a herd of 60 cows, milk of nine met the standard. Diphtheroids were present in 70 per cent of these animals. Special attention was given to types of leucocytes. Ring-shaped polymorphonuclear leucocytes were found in staphylococcic mastitis with cocci usually present in the film. Mononuclear leucocytes were numerous in streptococcic mastitis and existed in loose irregular clumps. Organisms were frequently so scarce that special methods had to be used to prove their presence.

The microscope method was also used by Turney et al.[128] for determining the source of bacteria found in low-quality milk. Photographs of stained films prepared according to the Prescott-Breed method were given as an aid in identifying streptococci and determining their origin and significance. Such methods have limitations as Ferguson [129] showed. Of 292 individual udder samples obviously unfit for use, only 50 contained streptococci in numbers sufficient to be detected by the Prescott-Breed method.

Prescott-Breed Method for Direct Microscope Count of Bacteria in Milk. This method is provided for in the eighth edition of *Standard Methods for the Examination of Dairy Products.*

Samples. Retail samples should be submitted in the original container. Wholesale samples should be collected in proper sampling bottles and kept iced if not preserved with a chemical preservative. A drop of 40 per cent formaldehyde solution for each 10 ml. of milk is recommended.

Apparatus. About the only special apparatus required are special pipettes and glass slides.

Pipettes. These are specially made for this work. The most convenient form is the straight capillary pipette calibrated to deliver .01 ml., the graduation mark being one and one-half to two and one-half inches from the tip. Such pipettes are now for sale by manufacturers, and can be easily obtained. The calibration should be tested by weighing with chemical balances the amount of milk discharged from the tube. Only a single pipette is needed in making a series of tests, provided this is kept clean while in use. In this kind of work cleanliness rather than sterilization is required. Clean towels may be used for wiping the exterior of these pipettes, while their bores may be kept clean by rinsing them in clean water between each sample. The small amount of water left in the tube may be rinsed out into the milk sample under examination. This method of procedure, while adding a small number of bacteria to each sample, introduces only a theoretical error, tests showing that such bacteria cannot subsequently be detected, and make no difference in the final result.

Standard Methods for the Examination of Dairy Products does not recognize use of standardized loops for measuring the samples in official control work.

127. Hadwen and Gwatkin. 1939. Canad. J. Res., Sect. D., Zool. Sci. 17, 225-244.

128. Turney et al. 1938. J. Milk Tech. 1, 26-34.

129. Ferguson. 1941. Cornell Vet. 31, 183-192.

Slides and Guide Plates. Slides may be of different sizes to suit the convenience of the bacteriologist. Whatever size is adopted may be used with a guide plate on which the proper round or square areas are marked (1 sq. cm.). The squares or circles may be marked on the glass slide with a wax pencil. For routine control work, a slide two by four and one-half inches, permitting 16 such areas, is especially convenient. Slides may be provided with etched or ground margins to permit marking and labeling.

Preparation of Films. One one-hundredth milliliter of milk or cream is deposited in one of the marked areas and carefully spread over it. If the glass slide is thoroughly clean, there will be no trouble. After the film has been made, it should be dried in a warm place within five minutes to prevent growth of bacteria.

a. Dip the slide in xylene, or other suitable fat solvent for removal of fat. This will require not less than one minute. Remove and dry.

b. Immerse the slide in the staining fluid.[130] Dip the slide in the staining fluid just long enough to stain it properly. Decolorize in alcohol if overstained and dry before examination. Old or unfiltered staining fluids are to be avoided, as they may contain troublesome precipitates. The slides remain in this solution for five seconds to one minute or longer, depending upon the effect desired, and are then rinsed in water to remove the surplus stain, and decolorized in alcohol. The decolorization takes several seconds to a minute, during which time the slide must be under observation in order that the decolorization may not proceed too far before they are removed from the alcohol. When properly decolorized the general background of the film should show a faint blue tint. Poorly stained slides may be decolorized and restained as many times as necessary, without any apparent injury. After drying the slides may be examined at once, or they may be filed away and preserved for further reference.

Standardization of the Microscope. The microscope to be used must be adjusted in such a way that each field of the microscope covers a certain known fraction of the total square centimeter's area. This procedure is simple, with the proper materials at hand. The microscope should have a 1.9 mm. (1/12 in.) oil immersion objective, and an ocular giving approximately the field desired, and should preferably be fitted with a mechanical stage. To standardize the microscope, place upon the stage a stage micrometer, and by the selection of oculars or adjusting the draw tube, or both, bring the diameter of the whole microscope field to .205 mm. When so adjusted, the microscope field will cover almost exactly 1/300,000 of a milliliter of the milk (actually 1/302,840). This means that if the bacteria in one field only are counted, the number should be multiplied by 300,000 to give the total number for a milliliter. If the bacteria in a hundred fields are to be counted, the total should, of course, be multiplied by 3,000.

Inasmuch as it is difficult to count bacteria lying near the margin of the microscope field, it is much better to have an eyepiece micrometer, with a circular ruling, eight mm. in diameter, and divided into quadrants. This will give, in the microscope field, a smaller area within which the bacteria may be seen most sharply, and which may be more easily counted. Such eyepiece micrometers are now manufactured by laboratory supply houses, and may be easily obtained. In the use of this eyepiece micrometer the inner circle, by the adjustment of the draw tube, should be made to cover a circle with a diameter of .146 mm. In this case this inner circle will cover 1/600,000 of a milliliter of milk, meaning, of course, that the number of bacteria in a single field should be multiplied by 600,000, or, if a hundred fields are counted, by 6,000, to obtain the number per milliliter.

The number of microscope fields to be counted will depend somewhat upon the kind of data that are desired. If this method is to be used simply for the purpose of dividing milk into grades, it will in most cases be unnecessary to do the actual counting, since a Grade A milk will show field after field without any bacteria at all, while a Grade C milk will show the field crowded with bacteria. In all doubtful cases, however, counting

---

130. *Standard Methods for the Examination of Dairy Products* indicates its preparation as follows: Add .3 gm. of certified methylene blue powder to 30 ml. of 95 per cent alcohol (ethyl or denatured). Add this to 100 ml. of distilled water. Buck's phenol methylene blue staining fluid (Amer. J. Pub. Health 16 [1926], 1049) may be used, if desired, to maintain sterility.

should be done, and there should never be less than 30 fields counted in order to have reliable results. Counting 30 fields is not so tedious a task as it would seem, since, in ordinary milk, the number of bacteria in each field is small, and the counting may be done very rapidly.

Counting. Counting the bacteria in such a film may be done in two ways: (1) the number of groups of one or more bacteria present; (2) the number of individuals. The second, of course, is really the correct count of the number of bacteria, but the former will give a count much closer to that obtained by the plate count, since the colonies upon the plate represent groups of bacteria rather than individuals, each group growing into a single colony only. Extensive tests have shown that there is a fair correspondence between the number of groups reported by experienced observers and the number of colonies that may grow in plates made from the same milk, although there are occasionally discrepancies of considerable extent. These discrepancies are caused by variations in judgment as to what constitutes a group, variations in the extent to which groups break up in the dilution waters when the smears are made, and the presence of dead bacteria or of bacteria which do not grow on the plates. Some experience is needed by the microscopist in determining just what should be counted. In high-grade milks, an inexperienced person is apt to fail to recognize differences between bacteria and other minute objects. This results, as a rule, in an overcount by inexperienced men. In milk containing many readily recognizable bacteria in each field the inexperienced man is apt to overlook some of them, giving an undercount. These difficulties are overcome, however, by training and experience.

Standard Methods for the Examination of Dairy Products provides for counting as follows:

Range of individual microscope counts	Number of fields to be examined if the field diameter measures	
	.206 m.m.	.146 m.m.
Under 30,000	60	120
30,000 to 300,000	30	60
300,000 to 3,000,000	15	30
Over 3,000,000	8	15

Beattie's [131] Modification of the Direct Microscope Method (Prescott-Breed Method) for Examination of Pasteurized Milk. Beattie suggested the following procedure for using the Breed microscope method for pasteurized milk. Her procedure is based on Proca's stain for differentiating between living and dead bacteria. The following procedure was used.

Glass slides ruled with two squares of four sq. cm. each were placed on the frame of an electric stove. The stove was leveled and freshly cleaned glass slides placed over the ruled slides. A 1/100 ml. milk pipette (Bausch and Lomb) was washed in cleaning fluid (sulfuric acid and potassium dichromate), rinsed twice in fresh water, and rinsed out with the milk sample. The rinsing water was in test tubes and a separate tube of water was used at each rinsing. The sample of milk was spread over the area marked on the slide by a stiff needle set in a metal handle. The needle was flamed between samples. The films were allowed to air dry but if longer than 10 minutes was required for the process, it was assisted by gentle heat from the stove. The dried films were immersed for 20 minutes in a mixture of equal parts of ether and alcohol. The films were then air dried and immersed from one to three minutes in a mixture of eight ml. concentrated carbol-fuchsin with 100 ml. Loeffler's methylene blue. This stain differs from Proca's in that 100 ml. of distilled water are omitted from the mixture.

The dried, stained smears were examined under the microscope by artificial light with a blue glass below the condenser. A 170 mm. tube length, oil immersion lens and No. 5 ocular gave a factor of 1,200,000. For each sample of milk 300 fields were counted, the sum of the organisms in these multiplied by 4,000 gave the number of organisms per milliliter.

131. Beattie. 1927. Amer. J. Pub. Health 17, 1031-1034.

Newman's Modification of the Direct Microscope Method (Prescott-Breed Method) of Counting Bacteria in Milk. Newman [132] believed that while the microscope method of Prescott and Breed was simple and direct, there was still a need for further simplification of the technic. Newman stated that most time and labor in the present method occurred in the treatment of the milk smear. He believed it possible to shorten this part of the technic by devising a combined procedure for extracting fat, fixation, and staining into one operation. I will quote from Newman's contribution:

"Preliminary work revealed considerable difficulty. The use of xylene, of course, precluded the use of Loeffler's methylene blue as a staining medium because the large amount of water which is contained in that dye solution is not miscible in fat solvents. However, a solution of powdered methylene blue dissolved in 95 per cent alcohol was found to combine readily with xylene. This combination gave excellent staining and fixation and the fat removal was entirely satisfactory, when freshly made. However, the preparation was not stable and after every hour or so required filtering to remove objectionable precipitates which would collect on the milk smear.

This difficulty was overcome by the addition of acetic acid. The acid not only effectively stabilized the solution but improved the fixation to a remarkable degree.

FORMULA I

Methylene blue, pwd.	2.0 gm.
Ethyl alcohol, 95%	60.0 ml.
Xylene, cp.	40.0 ml.
Acetic acid, glacial	6.0 ml.

"Dissolve methylene blue (certified) in warm (70°C. or 158°F.) alcohol, adding the powdered stain very slowly. Then add xylene and acetic acid. Filter and keep in tightly stoppered bottles.

DIRECTIONS FOR STAINING

"1. Milk smears are made on a glass slide in the usual manner. When dry, the slide is immersed in the above solution for ½ to 4 minutes. This simultaneously removes the fat from the milk, fixes the smear to the slide, and stains the bacteria and leucocytes.

(With the shorter immersion period the bacteria are well stained against a light blue background. However, when there are very few or no bacteria present on the smear, some workers prefer a four-minute immersion. This provides a more intensely blue background which facilitates focusing. There is little danger of overstaining. Slides may be allowed to remain in the solution for half an hour without injury to the smear or danger of overstaining.)

"2. Remove the slide from the solution and allow it to drain until the smear is thoroughly dry. In warm weather this seldom requires longer than half a minute.

"3. Wash thoroughly in water.

(It is very important that no water should ever be added to this or the following solutions. If by any chance water should come in contact with the smear before it has dried, the slide should be set aside until dry, then reimmersed for a moment in the solution (or in xylene), dried and then washed. If microscopic examination reveals particles of stain or of crystal-like material over the surface of the smear, the slide has been insufficiently dried and washed.)

"Comparative counts of raw and pasteurized milk, both with high and low bacterial content, revealed no apparent variation from the standard Breed method. The average counts obtained by the two methods agreed exactly.

"Recently another and more efficient fat solvent, tetrachlorethane, has been suggested as a substitute for xylene. (I wish to acknowledge the assistance of Mr. L. M. Lampert of the Dairy Laboratory, who also suggested the use of tetrachlorethane and

132. Newman. 1927. Mo. Bull. Calif. State Dept. Agr. 16, 1-7; 1926, Soc. Expt. Biol and Med. Proc. 24, 323.

pyridine which are incorporated in Formulæ II and III.) Not only does tetrachlorethane give better fat removal but there is the added advantage that it is an efficient solvent for methylene blue.

FORMULA II [133]

Methylene blue pwd.	1 to 1.12 gm.
Ethyl alcohol, 95%	54 ml.
Tetrachlorethane, (tech.)	40 ml.
Acetic acid, glacial	6 ml.

"Add the alcohol to the tetrachlorethane in a flask and bring to a temperature not to exceed 70°C.(158°F.). If it is desired to use methyl alcohol the temperature should not be raised to more than 55-60°C. or 131-140°F., add the warm alcohol mixture to the powdered methylene blue. Shake vigorously until the dye is completely dissolved, then slowly add the glacial acetic acid to the cold stain solution. Agitate the flask during the addition of the acid. Filter the entire volume through a 15 cm. filter paper. Keep in tightly stoppered bottle.

DIRECTIONS FOR USE

1. Prepare milk smear. When dry.
2. Immerse the smear in the solution and withdraw immediately.
3. Drain until dry (30 seconds).
4. Wash in water.
5. Dry and observe.

"The advantage of this formula lies in the complete elimination of the time factor in so far as exposure of the smear in the solution is concerned. In emergencies, the smear may be washed immediately after removal from the solution, although this procedure is not recommended.

"A great advantage in the use of tetrachlorethane lies in the fact that it is an excellent solvent for methylene blue. This not only permits the use of a much smaller amount of the dye but prevents any loss of dye through precipitation as the alcohol evaporates."

Breed,[134] after giving considerable study to Newman's procedure, found Formula No. 2 to be most satisfactory. Newman told Dr. Breed he was now adding 1.12 gm. of methylene blue instead of one gram originally recommended. This allowed deeper staining. Dr. Breed commented further as follows:

"Add alcohol to the tetrachlorethane in a flask and heat to a temperature not to exceed 70°C.(158°F.) (if it is desired to use methyl alcohol, the temperature should not be raised to more than 55-60°C. or 131-140°F.). Add the combined solution to the powdered methylene blue. Shake vigorously until the dye is completely dissolved. The original directions state that the glacial acetic acid should be added at this point, but Mr. Newman writes that it is better to *cool* the solution before adding acid and that the acid should be added *very slowly*. Further heating of the acid solution should be avoided. Filter and keep in a tightly stoppered bottle.

"This solution permits much more rapid staining than does No. 1 and yields a clear, well stained preparation. The smears readily wash off the slide unless they are dried before washing (Step No. 3). If dried too rapidly the smears present a spongy appearance. If the smear is dipped in 70 per cent alcohol, this trouble may be prevented.

"At this time it might be well to mention a simplification of the method of taking samples and preparing the slides that is entirely permissible where the counts obtained are to be used in education work only, or where preliminary results are used as a means of finding milk supplies that need more careful examination later. In these cases, samples may be dipped from the weight-vat with a dipper that is thoroughly rinsed in the milk that is to be sampled. The 0.01 cc. pipette is then inserted directly into this dipper and this amount of milk withdrawn. The smear is spread immediately on a slide and placed on a suitable warm and level drying plate. Satisfactory drying plates are readily

133. Newman stated that Formula II was used for routine grading of milk in California.
134. Breed. 1929. Amer. J. Pub. Health 19, 99-100.

made by placing an electric bulb in a tin box. In the majority of milk plants, connections can be made to some electric light fixture with a suitable extension cord.

"An experienced worker can prepare slides in this way with samples from each patron almost as rapidly as the milk is dumped and weighed. Ordinarily it is possible to stain the slides in spare moments so that the slides are ready for examination by the time all of the milk has been brought to the plant (usually 9 to 10 a. m.). Thus, it is quite possible to examine an average of 200 samples of milk per day with a great saving in the preparation of sample bottles, provision for icing samples and transportation to a suitable place for making the slides. A single worker using this simplified technic has collected and examined as many as 350 samples in one day."

Erb's [135] Modification of the Direct Microscope Method (Breed Method) of Counting Bacteria in Milk. Erb did not find the stains suggested by Newman to be entirely satisfactory. Considerable difficulty was experienced in obtaining completely defatted milk films within a reasonable time. Consequently Erb suggested another technic. The film of milk was prepared as usual. In order to prevent growth, the films should be dried within five to 10 minutes, but excessive heat must be avoided else the films will crack and peel from the slides. When the slides are dry, they are placed in a staining solution having the following composition:

> Ether (sulfuric).. 50 ml.
> Methyl alcohol (absolute).. 50 ml.
> Methylene blue (preferably certified).. 5 grams

Add the dye to the mixed alcohol and ether and filter through paper when dissolved. Store in a tightly stoppered bottle.

The slides should be placed in this staining solution for one minute. They should then be thoroughly but gently rinsed in water and dried in the air. They must then be examined in the usual manner.

Another microscope method was proposed by Rosan.[136] The method consists of spreading a platinum loopful (of a definite size and weight) of milk (previously heated with an equal volume of methylene blue and a little pyridin in a metal spoon) on a microscope slide, covering it with a cover glass, and counting the number of bacteria per microscopic field. The number of bacteria are calculated from this finding by means of a formula which is stated. The method is a rapid one.

Broadhurst and Paley's [137] Single-Dip Stain for Direct Examination of Milk. This stain was developed for making direct microscope counts of milk, employing the technic ordinarily used in direct microscope examination. Like the Newman stain, it combines fat extraction, fixing, and staining.

The advantage of this stain over other methylene-blue stains is that only the organisms and other cells take the deep blue stain, while the background stains a very faint pink. This permits the counting of all organisms and shows their characteristic formation. The nuclei of the white blood cells and tissue cells take a deep blue stain, while the cytoplasm takes a faint blue. The advantages are as follows:

1. The differential background permits the counting of all organisms and shows their formations.

2. This stain permits easy differentiation between bacteria and all other cells and foreign bodies, such as precipitated dye and amorphous bodies.

3. Eyestrain in routine work is eliminated because the organisms do not have to be searched for and are not hidden by darkly stained, congealed serum solids on the smear.

4. The serum solids on a properly made smear are stained a faint pink.

5. Preparation of the stain is simple, since the reagents are easily obtainable.

135. Erb. 1929. J. Lab. and Clin. Med. 14, 377.
136. Rosan. 1913. Milchw. Zentbl. 42, 333-334.
137. Broadhurst and Paley. 1939. J. Amer. Vet. Med. Assoc. 47, 525-526.

6. No decolorizing of a heavily stained smear is necessary, a procedure which sometimes decolorizes organisms as well as the background, thereby causing the possibility of low counts.

Preparation of Stain. To 54 ml. of 95 per cent ethyl alcohol is added .4 ml. of concentrated sulphuric acid (c.p.). This solution is mixed with 40 ml. of technical tetrachlorethane in a flask and heated to about 55°C. (no higher). Add the combined solution while hot to from one to 1.2 gm. of methylene blue dye, shaking vigorously until the dye is as completely dissolved as possible. Next, add eight ml. of a one per cent alcoholic solution of fuchsin (prepared by dissolving one gm. basic red fuchsin in 100 ml. of 95 per cent ethyl alcohol). The stain should be mixed well, cooled, filtered, and kept in tightly stoppered bottles.

In the preparation of the stain a pipette calibrated in .1 ml. should be used for measuring the sulphuric acid, since too much acid may result in too faint a background, while too little may cause difficulty in washing the blue out of the smear.

Directions for Use. 1. Prepare the milk smear by using .01 ml. of milk spread over one sq. cm. of surface, as is the general procedure for making bacteria counts by the direct microscope method. (Two sq. cm. may be covered, if it is desired.)

2. Dry the smear on a flat surface in a warm place within five minutes.

3. When dry, dip into the stain for about 15 seconds, or flood the smear for about 15 seconds; drain off excess stain and dry while flat in a warm place.

4. Wash in cold water until all the blue is washed out of the smear and the smear assumes a faint pink color.

5. Dry, and examine under oil immersion.

Because the organisms stand out so readily in contrast to the background, much higher counts are obtained by the use of this stain than with other methylene-blue stains. It should be noted that the method is actually the same as that employed by those using the Standard Methods of Milk Analysis, except that a different stain is used. Additionally, it may be well to remark that where a smear is unevenly made, *i.e.*, where some parts are thicker than others, it may be difficult to wash out all the blue from the thickened parts of the smear. However, this does not interfere in any way with the counting of the organisms and the easy differentiation of them. In the smear of two sq. cm., all the blue is washed out perfectly.

After two years' experience with this stain, Cohen [138] suggested that much care be used in cleaning the glass slides. After drying the milk films on the slide, the Broadhurst-Paley staining solution may be applied to it with a dropper and allowed to remain for about one minute. Drain and dry carefully and immerse in a glass of cold water holding the slide vertically without shaking. Lift the slide a few times from the water and the excess stain will run off the films. Repeat this in a glass of clean water. The slide may then be dried. The technician will know when the excess stain has been removed by almost entire absence of any color left in the second glass.

Broadhurst and Long [139] suggested a new stain for milk examination. It consisted of neutral red and brilliant green and was said to give as good preparations as the methylene-blue stain of Breed and Brew.

Knaysi and Ford's [140] Method of Counting Viable Bacteria in Milk by Means of the Microscope. The value of such a procedure is apparent to anyone who is concerned with bacteriological milk analysis. The procedure was given by the authors as follows:

1. One ml. of the well-mixed sample is measured into each of two clean test tubes, A and B.

138. Cohen. 1940. J. Milk Tech. 3, 204.
139. Broadhurst and Long. 1932. J. Bact. 23, 57.
140. Knaysi and Ford. 1938. J. Dairy Sci. 21, 129-141.

2. To each test tube is added .5 ml. of a dye mixture containing equal parts of .2 per cent methylene blue and .2 per cent Nile blue sulfate, and the contents of each tube are mixed well. The final concentration of each dye in the completed preparation will be .025 per cent. Knaysi and Ford showed that in such concentrations these dyes were not toxic to *Streptococcus lactis* and *Aerobacter aerogenes.*

3. To one of the tubes, say tube B, add a drop of .7-.8 N NaOH and mix. Tube A receives nothing.

4. To each tube add .5 ml. of the melted and tempered hardening agent which is an agar-gelatin mixture containing two per cent agar and eight per cent gelatin, and mix the contents of each tube. Before this is done, the tubes are placed for a few moments in the water bath alongside the melted agar-gelatin mixture. The temperature of the bath should be about 45 to 50°C.(113 to 122°F.). This prevents the instantaneous hardening of the mixture. The hardening agent is now present in the concentration referred to above, namely, .5 per cent agar and two per cent gelatin.

5. With a Breed pipette, measure out .01 ml. from tube A and place on the center of the right half of a clean glass slide, and immediately cover the droplet thus formed with a clean square cover glass 1.28 x 1.28 cm. The droplet spreads and forms a film occupying the space between the cover glass and the slide.

Do the same with tube B, placing the .01 ml. droplet on the center of the left half of the slide, etc.

6. Let the preparation stand or place it in the icebox for about two minutes so that the films harden.

7. Count the blue-stained bacterial cells in a certain number of fields of each film and calculate the bacterial content of each per ml. With a 6 x 97 combination, and using 1.28 x 1.28 cm. cover glass, the factor is about 1,000,000.

The stained cells from tube A represent the dead cells present originally in the milk. The stained cells from tube B represent the total bacterial content of the milk. The difference represents the viable cells present in the milk.

With ordinary market milk it is generally unnecessary to remove the fat. If it is desired to remove the fat, the milk sample should be warmed to 35°C. to liquefy the fat; heptane is then added and shaken vigorously for three to five minutes and centrifuged. A Babcock hand or electrically driven centrifuge is sufficient. The hydrocarbon-fat layer is then removed. A convenient way of removing this layer is by suction with a capillary glass tube attached to a water pump.

This method is based on observation of Knaysi [141] that the slightest shade of staining of the cytoplasm indicates death of the cell, while the cytoplasm of a viable cell is perfectly colorless. Knaysi and Ford found that pasteurization of milk does not render the killed bacteria invisible when their method was used. On the other hand, they confirmed earlier reports that pasteurization did render a certain percentage of the killed bacteria unstainable when the standard microscope method was used.

FROST'S MICROSCOPE METHOD FOR DETERMINING THE NUMBER OF BACTERIA IN MILK

This procedure is called the little plate method because of the fact that the microscope slide is used as a plate on which a mixture of agar medium and milk sample are incubated. Frost compared results secured with the standard agar plate with results secured with the little plate and observed good correlation. The bacterial content varied from 675 to 20,000,000 per ml. Hatfield and Park [142] reported the Frost method to be just as satisfactory as the standard agar plate for good-quality milk, such

141. Knaysi. 1935. J. Bact. 30, 193-206.
142. Hatfield and Park. 1922. Amer. J. Pub. Health 12; 478-487.

as Grade A, pasteurized. They said it might be less so with milk having over 1,000,000 bacteria per ml. or where unusual types of bacteria were present. Clarenburg [143] found the method to be dependable, the best results being secured when the little plates were incubated for 20 to 24 hours at approximately 28°C.(82.4°F.). Frost, however, incubated the plates for three to 12 hours. In a comparative investigation of several different methods for determining the quality of milk Simmons [105] found the Frost method to yield results which agreed satisfactorily with those secured with the standard agar plate and lactose agar plate. Results with the last-mentioned medium were higher and agreed well with those secured by the Frost method. Simmons believed the Frost method to be a satisfactory method for determining the number of bacteria in milk. Comparison of the Breed, Frost, and Allen methods by Hinton [144] showed good correlation in most cases, although divergent results were secured on some samples. Each method was said to have its advantages. Similar conclusions were reached by Bryan et al. [144a] who used the Frost method with milk, cream, and ice cream.

Wilson [2] gave some attention to the Frost little plate method. He stated that the procedure had some advantages over the ordinary plate method. However, he believed after considering all of the facts involved that the Frost method, as well as the Burri [75] method, gave an even less accurate estimate of the number of bacteria in milk than did the plate count. He could see no place in routine quantitative grading for either the Frost or the Burri method.

Frost's [145] Little Plate Method for Determining the Number of Bacteria in Milk. This method is really an adaptation of the standard agar plate so that the counts may be secured in a shorter time by means of the microscope. Professor Frost has stated the technic as follows:

APPARATUS NEEDED

Glass Slides. The apparatus needed consists, first of all, of glass slides. These must have marked off on them a definite area, of four square cm. It would seem best to have such areas permanently fixed, and slides can be purchased so marked. Since these are quite expensive, most workers will no doubt continue to use ordinary microscope glass slides (one by three inches) marked with a wax pencil. This grease border line has a distinct advantage since it causes the milk and agar to flow back and so the marked off areas are not overrun in making the "little plates." In order to have the areas accurate, it is best to use some mechanical means for the purpose of marking them. The apparatus is suggested as satisfactory, although it is possible to mark off the areas fairly accurately by tracing the lines over a paper pattern. It is economical to mark off two areas on each side.

Forceps. For handling the slides a good forceps is needed.

Warm Table. In order to prevent the hardening of the agar before it is thoroughly mixed with the milk, it is necessary to spread the little plates on a "warm table." A convenient form is a metal box surrounded with asbestos on all sides except the top and bottom. In it warm water (45°C. or 113°F.) is placed. At one end, tubulation to hold two test tubes of media are inserted at an angle of about 45 degrees.

Special Pipets. One pipet about 8 inches long made of capillary tubing is suggested. The tube should be sufficiently small so that about one-half inch will hold .01 ml. and

143. Clarenburg. 1925. Rev. in Expt. Sta. Rec. 54 (1926) 169.
144. Hinton. 1925. Abs. Bact., Abst. No. 105.
144a. Bryan et al. 1942. J. Dairy Sci., 25, 827-835.
145. Frost. 1921. J. Infect. Dis. 28, 176-184.

one-twentieth ml. would equal about two and one-half inches. If the pipet is marked in .01 ml., the same pipet can be used to make a direct count (Breed), as well as the little plate count. Such pipets are now stocked by most apparatus firms as "serological pipets."

Moist Chamber Cabinet. It is simply a rack to hold 48 slides and is provided with a space for water in the bottom and room on the sides for the moisture to circulate. The rack is made removable. This makes it possible to prepare all of the slides for microscopic examination without handling them individually.

Hot Plate or Drying Oven. It is necessary to dry the little plates rapidly, and this is best done by keeping them for about five minutes just below the boiling point of water. When the plates are handled individually, a metal box is used with a flat and level top in which water is kept at or near the boiling point. Where the slides are to be dried in the rack, an oven is necessary and an electric one is very satisfactory.

Staining Outfit. For the purpose of staining the individual slides a staining jar is needed. A good form is the Coplin jar. A tumbler or larger jar is needed for the wash water. In case the whole rack of slides is to be stained at once, a special container for the rack is needed.

MATERIAL NEEDED

Culture Medium. Ordinary nutrient agar is used. It is made and sterilized in the usual way (standard methods Am. P. H. Assn.).* One test tube of medium (five ml.) will be sufficient for about 50 samples.

Acetic Acid Solution. A 10 per cent solution of glacial acetic acid in 95 per cent alcohol.

Stains. Methylene blue and thionine are both satisfactory. Loeffler's methylene blue diluted with three times its volume of distilled water has been used most.

It is also possible to make a satisfactory stain by taking 10 ml. of a saturated alcohol solution of methylene blue to 400 ml. of distilled water.

The formula for the thionine stain is: thionine blue, one gm.; carbolic acid, two and one half gm., and distilled water, 400 ml.; filter. To this is added five per cent of glacial acetic acid. The slides are put in this stain without preliminary treatment with acid alcohol. We have found this the most satisfactory stain.

METHOD IN DETAIL

Melting Agar. A tube of agar is melted by placing it in boiling water. It is then placed in one of the tubulations on the warm table. The cotton plug is removed and a pipet which will deliver a small drop (about .05 ml.) is placed in it.

Filling the Warm Table. While the agar is melting, the warm table should be filled with water that has a temperature of about 45°C.(113°F.). It is necessary to note the temperature occasionally. If it gets down to 40°C.(104°F.), the agar is likely to harden, and if it gets much above 45°C.(113°F.), it is probable that some of the milk bacteria will be killed or at least devitalized to such an extent that they will not form colonies within the usual period of incubation.

Mixing the Milk. The bottle or sample should be shaken at least 25 times by tipping it from end to end slowly enough to avoid the formulation of a foam, since air bubbles would interfere with the accurate measurement of the sample in the pipet.

Sterilizing the Glass Slides. The glass slides, which have been properly marked, are sterilized in the direct flame. In order to do this, they are taken up in the forceps and passed through the flame, about three times, marked surface down, and once on the other side. About a half dozen are thus sterilized and placed on the warm table.

Pipetting the Sample. A special pipet has already been described. Approximate results can be obtained with any pipet that will measure a small quantity, as .05 ml., but since the accuracy of the count depends on the correct measurement of the sample, the construction and use of the pipet becomes a matter of great importance. It is necessary to use a pipet of small bore in order to measure accurately. This necessitates the use of heavy walled tubing. The end must be pointed, otherwise too much milk clings to the outside.

* The new plating **medium** now **official** in milk analysis could undoubtedly be used.

It is important, in using a pipet, not to dip it into the milk any farther than is necessary to avoid taking in air bubbles. The reason for this is that milk clings to the outside of the pipet and will run down and swell the sample. In any case, the tip of the pipet after it is filled should be brought in contact with the inside of the bottle above the milk to drain off the extra milk, or wiped with a piece of sterile filter paper or a sterile towel. Five one-hundredths (1/20) ml. of the sample of milk is placed in each area marked off on the glass slides, i.e., two equal portions from each sample are put in different squares on the same slide.

The milk portions should be put on only a few slides at once because they begin to dry before the agar is added to them, if allowed to stand on the warm table.

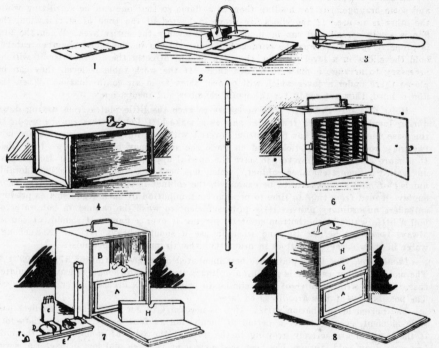

Fig. 3. Various apparatus used in Frost's Microscope Method of Milk Analysis.

1. Microscope glass slide with two areas of four sq. cm. each marked off with a wax pencil.
2. A guide for marking the slides.
3. Forceps provided with a stop which makes it possible to handle slides easily.
4. A "warm table." This is an asbestos covered metal box which holds about two liters of water and is used to keep the slides warm while the milk and agar are being spread to form the "little plates." It also serves to keep the tube of liquefied agar from solidifying. It has three tubulations, two at an angle for holding tubes of medium and the other for a thermometer.
5. A serologic pipet which delivers .01 ml.; .05 is the amount of milk usually used.
6. A "moist chamber cabinet." The "little plates" are kept in this while they are in the incubator. Water in the bottom keeps a moist atmosphere. The rack is made removable so that all of the slides can be dried (in an oven), fixed, and stained altogether, and thus avoiding the handling of each slide separately.
7. Field Outfit. The case is wood and is lined with an insulating material and when closed forms an incubator on the principle of a "fireless cooker." A is the "warm table" (Fig. 4) which is filled with water 42-43°C. B is the "moist Chamber cabinet" (Fig. 6) and contains the little plates. C is a cup which holds the agar tubes and in which they may be melted over the alcohol lamp D. E is a support for the cup and also holds the various articles in place when the case is packed. F is the cap to the alcohol lamp. G is the pipet case and H is a box in which are placed the glass slides, platinum loops, etc.
8. Carrying case packed ready to be closed. It then becomes an incubator. The outfit holds all the material necessary for making an analysis of 48 samples in duplicate.

Adding Agar and Spreading Film. As soon as possible after the milk has been put on the glass slides, a drop of agar should be added to each. An exact amount is not absolutely demanded, but it should be approximately .05 ml., and pipets should be selected that will deliver that amount in one or two drops. Practically the same amount should be used each time, otherwise the concentration of the agar will vary, and consequently, its consistency. This variation does not appear to affect the number of the colonies, but it influences their appearance.

The milk and agar must be thoroughly mixed and spread evenly over the four sq. cm. area. This is exactly done by means of a sterile platinum loop.

In order to spread the films as quickly as possible, it is desirable to have two loops and some arrangement for holding them in a flame so that one can be sterilizing while the other is in use. If the slides are properly heated at the time of sterilization, the film is easily spread and can be made to cover evenly the entire area. When the film is properly spread, it must be hardened. If the shelves in the moist chamber cabinet hold the slides in a level position, they can be put directly there, otherwise it will be necessary to arrange a place to harden them. If the work table is level, they can be placed there under a cover which will protect them from air contamination. When the film is hard, they are ready for the moist chamber and incubation.

Moist Chamber Cabinet. It is necessary to keep the little plates from drying down during incubation. For a few slides and as a makeshift Petri dishes can be used. In this case the Petri dish has the bottom covered with wet filter paper; on this are laid two glass rods or match sticks, and on these the slides may be placed, two to a dish. It is more convenient, however, to have the special apparatus designed for the purpose and called a "moist chamber cabinet," which has been described. When a considerable number of milk samples are to be examined, the cabinet is essential. It should be thoroughly cleaned from time to time to prevent contamination by such organisms as produce spreaders on ordinary plates. It is quite sufficient to wash the cabinet in hot water or boil a little water in the bottom of it by placing it over a flame. It should, of course, always be cooled before use, and when in use it should always have at least enough water in it to cover the bottom in order that the air may be kept moist.

Incubation. The little plates are best incubated at a temperature of 37.5°C.(99°F.). The moist chamber cabinet is put in an ordinary incubator, although a heavily insulated case, together with a source of heat, similar in principle to a fireless cooker, can be used. The possibilities of this are discussed later.

The period of incubation varies. If it is necessary to get results at the earliest possible moment, even so short a period of incubation as four hours will be satisfactory if the bacteria are actively growing in the milk at the time of sampling. If the milk has come from cold storage, has been pasteurized or is fresh and low in bacteria, seven or eight hours are necessary; if, on the other hand, there is no particular hurry about the results, the plates can be left in the incubator from one day to the next, i.e., 15 or 16 hours.

They can also be incubated at room temperature (20°C.). In this case it seems necessary to leave them for at least 24 hours. Even then the count seems lower than that obtained by incubating at 37°C., although this has not been fully established.

Drying Films. When the little plates are taken from the incubator, they should be dried at once. If they are allowed to dry at the room or incubator temperature, the films have a tendency to crack and to peel off or loosen in the staining process. It is best to dry the films down rapidly by putting them on a hot plate or in a drying oven at a temperature slightly below that of boiling water.

Recent trials indicate that it is possible also to put the wet films directly in the acetic acid alcohol or even the stain when it contains the acetic acid.

Staining. It is possible to stain the films so that the colonies are deeply colored, while the medium is almost wholly without color. The success of this process depends to a considerable extent on the treatment that the films receive before they are put in the stain. They must be properly dried as already indicated. They are then put in the acetic acid solution. This acts quickly but does not overact; hence, it should be applied for about one minute, but no harm is done if the exposure is a long one. The purpose of the acetic acid is to keep the agar from taking the stain. Any of the stains mentioned are satisfactory, and the time of exposure is about two minutes, although a longer exposure is not harmful. The thionine gives excellent results. The background is clearer than with methylene blue.

The slides should be thoroughly washed in tap water. When stained, the preparation should be dried, and for this purpose a drying plate is convenient; a temperature just below 100°C.(212°F.) is best.

Dilution of Heavily Contaminated Samples. If a milk is likely to have more than one million bacteria per milliliter it should be diluted before a little plate is made. When water blanks are used, as is the common practice with the Koch plate method, comparatively little milk is taken over into the culture. If the same method were followed with the little plates, the food conditions would be quite different in the direct plates and those diluted with water. In order, therefore, to have comparable conditions in all of the little plates, it is advised that sterile milk be used for dilution purposes instead of water. It is necessary to have tubes of sterile milk containing nine ml. To these is added one ml. of the milk to be counted, and then after thoroughly mixing the diluted sample is used in exactly the same way as the ordinary samples.

A simpler way, however, is recommended, especially for field work. This was suggested by W. D. Dotterer of the Bowman Dairy Co. A small fraction of a milliliter of the milk to be analyzed is used, .01 or .02 ml. and to this, on the side, a drop of sterile milk is added from a tube which is kept in the second tubulation on the warm table. To this is added the agar, and the whole is spread with perhaps more than usual care.

Counting Colonies. The counting is done under a compound microscope. If the colonies are large and few in number, the low power can be used, and this is best. If the colonies are small or numerous, the higher powers must be used. With the immersion objective, the oil is put on the dried agar. There is no objection to mounting them in balsam and using a cover glass. This is best if the high dry powers are to be used. At first it seemed necessary to count at least 20 fields widely distributed over the film in order to get a fair average. For this a mechanical stage was recommended. Further experience leads to the conclusion that, ordinarily at least, it is only necessary to count five fields. In this case the slide is put under the microscope and moved about to get a general idea of the distribution and then five representative fields are counted. In counting, several things should be kept in mind. First, all of the colonies within the fields should be counted and only half of those that touch the edge, say those on the right half of the periphery, while those touching the left edge of the field should not be counted. Second, with the highest powers single bacteria or small groups should not be counted, on those plates that have been incubated seven or eight hours or more. In plates incubated as long as that, practically all of the original live bacteria have grown into definite colonies. Here as elsewhere, experience and good judgment are necessary to get consistent results.

Calculating the Number of Bacteria per Milliliter of Milk. Having determined the number of colonies in a given number of fields of the microscope, or the number in an average field, it is necessary to multiply that number by some factor which will convert the figures representing the number of colonies per field of the microscope into figures which will represent the total number of bacteria per milliliter of the milk.

In order to do this it is only necessary to determine the area of the microscope field, for the value of all of the other factors is known, i.e., the area of the little plates (four sq. cm.) and the amount of milk used (.05 ml., .005 ml., etc.).

$$\left.\begin{array}{c}\text{The number of bacteria}\\\text{per ml. of milk}\end{array}\right\} = \frac{\text{No. colonies counted}}{\text{No. fields counted}} \times$$

$$\left.\begin{array}{c}\dfrac{\text{Area of little plates}}{\text{Area of the microscope field}}\end{array}\right\} \text{(or microscope factor)} \times$$

Reciprocal of the dilution of the milk.

Let:

Number of bacteria per ml. of milk $= X$.

Number of colonies counted divided by the number of fields counted, i.e., the average number of bacteria in a microscopic field $= C$.

The area of the little plates (four sq. cm. or 200 sq. mm.), divided by the area of the microscope field or microscopic factor $= M$. The reciprocal of the dilution of the milk $= D$.

Then $X = C \times M \times D$. The only unknown value in the second half of the equation is the area of the microscopic field. This must be determined not only for each microscope, but also for each combination of lenses.

The area of a disk equals the radius squared times 3.14159 (π), or the diameter squared times .7854 ($\pi/4$).

In order to determine the diameter of the field of a microscope a stage micrometer is necessary. This should be ruled to .1 and .01 mm.

By regulating the length of the tube, the size of the field may be varied. It would seem desirable, however, to use the ordinary tube length, otherwise there is always danger that the tube may not be properly drawn out and the count thus affected.

For the convenience of those who may not have a stage micrometer at hand, the following table is included, which gives the approximate diameters and the areas of the microscopic fields of an American microscope. This will give a value which will serve until there is an opportunity to have the diameter of the particular microscope carefully determined.

Diameter of Microscope Fields With Common Combination of Lenses and the Tube Pushed in (160) mm.

Objective (Equivalent focus)	Ocular	Diameter of field	Area of field
2/3 inch or 16 mm.	10 x	1.55 mm.	approximately 2 sq. mm.
1/6 inch or 4 mm.	10 x	0.31 mm.	approximately 0.08 sq. mm.
1/12 inch or 2 mm.	10 x	1.555 mm.	approximately 0.02 sq. mm.

In order to make correction for eyepieces of different magnifying power, multiply the area given above for the 10 x ocular by 1.4 for an 8 x by 1.5, for a 7.5 x, by 2 for a 5 x and 2.5 for a 4 x. With a 16 mm. objective and a 10 x ocular the area of the microscope field is approximately two sq. mm. In order to get the microscope factor, the area of the little plate (400 sq. mm.) is divided by the area of the microscope field (two sq. mm.). This gives 200. This figure multiplied by the denominator of the fraction of a milliliter of the milk used in making the little plate gives the factor necessary to convert the colonies in the field of the microscope into bacteria per milliliter of milk. The usual dilution is 1/20 ml.; this means that each colony in the field of the microscope represents 4,000 bacteria per milliliter.

The same figuring would show us that each colony under a four mm. objective would mean 100,000 bacteria per ml. of milk and one colony under the oil immersion would mean 400,000 bacteria per ml. of milk.

FIELD OUTFIT

Because of the small amount of material required to make the cultures and its simplicity, this method ought to be of special value in field work.

It is shown packed and its contents are exhibited in Fig. 3. It is a case about 13¾ inches long, 13½ inches high, and 9¾ inches wide. It is lined with an insulating material. In the particular case figured, the insulating material was made of flax straw. The important dimensions are the inside ones, 10¾ inches long, 11 inches high, and 6⅛ inches wide. The door is arranged to close tightly; this is accomplished by using a thick felt strip in the jamb. In this case are fitted the warm table A; the moist chamber cabinet B; a support for holding the needles and a cup for melting the agar over a flame, E; an alcohol lamp D; a cup for holding the medium and melting it C; a pipet case G; and a box for such articles as glass slides, needles, forceps, wax pencil, etc. The case is small and packed with material necessary for duplicate plates of 48 different samples. The weight is only about 20 pounds.

If one plate only were made, 96 samples could be analyzed. If the trip were to be long, a large number of samples could be analyzed by taking extra slides, pipets, and medium, provided one set of slides was incubated and dried down before the next set of plates was made. The dried plates keep indefinitely, either stained or unstained, in slide boxes.

To use the carrying case as an incubator, it is only necessary to fill the warm table with water at about 43°C.(109.4°F.), pack, and close the case. When the case is kept at ordinary room temperature, the heat of the water will bring the chamber up to about that of blood heat and hold it above 30°C.(86°F.) for at least 12 hours. In this case the colonies grow out satisfactorily in from eight to 16 hours.

Van Oijen's [146] **Modification of the Frost Method.** The technic suggested by Van Oijen is modified from that originally published by Frost. Barkworth described it as follows: "Using a capillary pipette holding .1 ml. of milk, .05 ml. is placed in each of two grids (each 20 x 25 mm.) previously marked off on a glass slide. The slide is placed on a warm table (47°C.). A similar quantity of agar medium, which has been melted and cooled to 47°C., is added, mixed with the milk, and after allowing to set, the slides are incubated 16 hours at 28°C.(194°F. stained, and washed and after final drying are ready for counting. The small colonies are counted under the lower power of the microscope (x 40). A special cover glass, ruled in one-mm. squares, is placed on the film, and the colonies per row or per square are counted. Good milk will have less than one colony per sq. mm."

Barkworth [147] found the Van Oijen modification to be more accurate than the plate-count method. He considered it to be a simple, accurate test for the bacterial content of milk. The results are secured from a considerable quantity of milk. Clarenburg [148] suggested that owing to overcrowding, the Van Oijen (modified) method might be best applied to milk containing over 200,000 bacteria per ml. Barkworth found that the colony counting error of Van Oijen test was about the same as that of the plate count. In the Van Oijen test a larger quantity of milk is used than in the plate test, and the author discussed in detail the extent to which this is the explanation of its increased accuracy. He concluded that probably this is not the sole factor and that it may be more accurate absolutely. Milk agar was used for the plate method to make the results more comparable, since in the slide incubation method the mixture is half milk. Better results were obtained by Clarenburg [148] when the little plates were incubated at 28°C.(82.4°F.) for 24 hours. Lorenz [149] concurred in this.

COLIFORM BACTERIA IN MILK

Since coliform bacteria have a well-established position as indicators of pollution in water and a few other foods, much study has been given to similar application in milk. Even though many results of investigations have been published, some disagreement exists among those who have studied the question. Many of the coliform bacteria isolated from milk do not originate in milk. They belong to the aerogenes section and come

146. Van Oijen. 1938. Tijdschr. u. Diergeneesk. 65, 865-884.
147. Barkworth. 1936. J. Dairy Res. 7, 244-257.
148. Clarenburg. 1935. Diss. Univ. of Utrecht.
149. Lorenz. 1937. Milchw. Forsch. 18, 265-279.

from sources which give them no sanitary significance. Wilson [2] reached this conclusion after a critical appraisal of this subject. Many of the premises which validate the coliform test for water do not hold for milk. Wilson, furthermore found poor correlation between results of the coliform test and sanitary inspection of the dairy, the plate count, reduction time, and keeping quality of the milk. Some conclusions are quite to the point, for mere presence of *Escherichia coli* is not objectionable. The organism itself would be harmless. It is what it indicates that interests the sanitarian. While the source of this organism is undoubtedly bovine feces, it must be admitted that under certain conditions, it might indicate contamination with human excreta.

The Standard Milk Ordinance and Code of the United States Public Health Service for 1939,[15] does not provide for use of the coliform test. *Standard Methods for the Examination of Dairy Products*, eighth edition, does include procedures for testing for the presence of coliform bacteria in milk. The American Association of Medical Milk Commissioners also provides for examination of Certified Milk for *Escherichia coli* because it considers the test to be more rigid.

Possibility of entrance of this organism is easy to explain. What happens after it has entered the milk is of great importance if it is to function as an indicator of pollution. Harrison and Vanderleck [150] attempted to ascertain the rate of increase of *Escherichia coli* under good, hygienic conditions, and to obtain precise information as to the restraining action of lactic-acid bacteria. At 37°C.(98.6°F.), the principal increase of organisms up to the time of curdling was due to *Lactobacillus lactis acidi*. *Escherichi coli* can increase much faster in beef broth than in milk because it is checked by the acid organisms in the latter medium. At 30°C.(86°F.) the temperature was still more favorable for *Lactobacillus lactis acidi*, which was practically the only microbe present when the milk curdled in 17½ hours. At 20°C.(68°F.), *Escherichia coli* and *Aerobacter aerogenes* increased slowly, the average time per generation for both organisms being 142 minutes. At 10°C.(50°F.) the results were irregular. The temperature was unfavorable for the *Escherichia coli* group, but there was a progressive increase of the lactic-acid bacilli. Malcolm,[151] also, showed that various members of the coliform group grew with different rates in milk. He followed development of 75 pure cultures of members of the coliform group in sterilized milk for 24 hours at 17°C.(62.6°F.). Certain species particularly *Aerobacter aerogenes* and *Aerobacter cloacae*, multiplied much more rapidly than *Escherichia coli*. Similar results were obtained with raw milk and mixed cultures. Different results were observed, however, when higher temperatures were used. At 22°C.(71.6°F.) members of the aerogenes-cloacae section of the coliform group grew faster than *Escherichia coli*. *Escherichia coli* was said to be predominant in bovine feces, the aerogenes-cloacae types occurring in small numbers; when bovine feces were inoculated into raw milk and incubated for 36 hours at 17°C.(62.6°F.), the

150. Harrison and Vanderleck. 1910. Rev. in Chem. Abs. 4, 1323.
151. Malcolm. 1939. J. Dairy Res. 10, 410-425.

coliform flora at the end of the incubation period were chiefly the aerogenes-cloacae types. Malcolm considered this to be important, for the latter organisms may be derived mainly from bovine feces.

These observations also explain the relatively higher incidence of the aerogenes-cloacae types in summer milk in Scotland. Such enrichment does not occur in winter, holding temperature of the milk being as a rule so low that there is little or no proliferation of any coliform types. The relative proportions of the various coliform types in winter milk tend to remain similar to those in the feces.

Presence of Coliform Bacteria in Milk. Results of many investigations which have not agreed have been reported. Ayers and Clemmer [152] reviewed the problem quite well from an historical viewpoint from which it was apparent that fresh milk, even when produced under the best conditions, always contained a few *Escherichia coli*. "In fresh milk, the colon count does not indicate the extent of direct manural contamination, but does indicate the general conditions under which the milk was produced." The differentiation of *Escherichia coli* and *Aerobacter aerogenes* types was of no material value in this examination. The authors stated, however, that future studies might make it of some value. In milk of unknown history, the only meaning which might be attached to *Escherichia coli* is that high *Escherichia coli* counts indicate that it was held above 10°C. (50°F.), rarely that it was produced under very abnormal conditions. Hunter, [153] after a study of the same question, arrived at the same conclusions. Hunter found the limits of colon bacilli in fresh cow feces to be 100,000 and 10,000,000 per gram, with an average of 1,883,333. Like Ayers and his co-workers, Hunter found the colon content of milk to depend on the temperature. There seemed to be a correlation between the colon content and the total content of bacteria. Of 169 cultures isolated from fresh feces 95.2 per cent represented the fecal type. The presence and significance of the colon-aerogenes group in milk has also been investigated by Finkelstein. [154] With milk that was initially contaminated in the barn, 100 per milliliter were found when care was used, and 588 per milliliter when no care was used. A temperature below 10°C.(50°F.) checked the growth of the members of this group. Above 15.5°C.(60°F.) there was rapid increase. Pasteurization, properly applied, destroyed practically all of the members of this group. The effect of pasteurization on *Escherichia coli* is discussed in a subsequent chapter.

Many factors may influence contamination of milk with *Escherichia coli* as Paley [155] has shown. All of them should be considered when the coliform test on milk is being weighed from the sanitary standpoint. For instance, Malcolm [156] found that *Escherichia coli* was more prevalent in milk in summer than in winter due largely to the influence of temperature. Samples which were positive contained 613 times as many bacteria as

152. Ayers and Clemmer. 1918. U. S. Dept. Agr., Bull. 739.
153. Hunter. 1919. J. Dairy Sci. 2, 108-129.
154. Finkelstein. 1919. Idem 460-482.
155. Paley. 1936. Milk Dealer 26, 38-39.
156. Malcolm. 1933-34. J. Dairy Res. 5, 15-28.

samples which were negative for *Escherichia coli*. A positive correlation was believed to exist between the average bacterial content of the milk, the proportion of coliform-positive samples, and the mean of the minimum and maximum atmospheric temperatures.

Methods for Detecting Coliform Bacteria in Milk. These have followed closely the methods used for the same purpose in water analysis. The same definition for the group has been followed, i.e., Gram-negative, nonspore-bearing, lactose-fermenting and growing aerobically in milk.

As Wilson [2] stated, two methods are available for estimating and determining the presence of coliform bacteria in milk. The first is the dilution method which consists of serial dilutions of the sample in suitable liquid medium. Lactose broth is the generally accepted medium in this country. The second method is a plating method which consists of inoculating a suitable solid medium with aliquot portions of the sample. The number of coliform colonies may then be counted.

The presumptive tests consist of the use of suitable media in which gas may be formed. These media may be either formate ricinoleate broth or brilliant green lactose bile. Gas formation in either of these media may be accepted as presumptive evidence of the presence of members of the coliform group.

The completed tests must prove that gas formation in the presumptive test was brought about by members of the coliform group and also to what section of the group they belong. Such media as Endo's agar or eosin methylene blue may be used. Poured plates of these media may be streaked from positive presumptive test fermentation tubes and incubated for 24 hours or less if possible. Typical colonies should be picked from one of these plates and studied to determine whether the characteristics mentioned above for *Escherichia coli* are fulfilled. Other tests, such as the citrate test and cellobiose fermentation, may also be applied.

Wilson found that both methods, as applied to milk, were open to serious objections. The first method had a very high sampling error and was unsuitable for the differentiation of members of the coliform group. Though the second method was ideal in theory, it was unreliable because a satisfactory medium has not yet been devised which will distinguish with certainty between coliform and non-coliform organisms or even between different types of coliform bacilli. His experience with several media indicated that fecal *Escherichia coli* grows as freely at 44°C.(111.2°F.) as at 37°C.(98.6°F.), whether in a solid or liquid medium. According to his experience no other type of coliform organism had this property. The McConkey broth medium gave more satisfactory results at 44°C. than did the modified Eijkmann medium described by Williams, Weaver, and Scherago.[157] Wilson stated that their experience with McConkey's medium, whether in the liquid or solid form, indicated that it never caused trouble by giving false positive reactions. He did admit, however, a slight inhibitory effect on growth of coliform organisms owing to presence of the bile salt. Comparative investigations showed that the count of coliform bacilli

157. Williams, Weaver and Sherago. 1933. Amer. J. Hyg. 17, 432.

on McConkey's medium was about 25 per cent less than that on heart extract medium without lactose or bile salt.

Wilson's experience with the citrate medium was quite successful. Evidence was also brought to suggest that in mixed cultures in raw milk at 22°C.(71.6°F.) *Escherichia coli* grew more rapidly than *Aerobacter aerogenes*; in McConkey broth the former organisms survived longer than the latter. Those who are interested in the details of laboratory technic should by all means read the discussion upon which these conclusions by Wilson were based.

Farrell [158] found brilliant green lactose bile broth, fuchsin lactose broth, and methylene blue-brom cresol purple broth to be the most efficient of the presumptive media for the detection of Escherichia-Aerobacter. The question was raised whether we possess a reliable medium for the detection of these organisms. Leahy [159] also reported that brilliant-green lactose bile was most suitable. Formate ricinoleate broth was also suitable for detecting coliform bacteria in milk and ice cream. Two types of media, liquid and solid, were examined by Bartram and Black.[160] Taurocholate agar, Wilson's hexamine agar, and Ritter's fuchsin-lactose broth gave poor confirmation of presumptive tests when compared with Endo's agar and brilliant green bile broth. Methylene blue brom cresol purple broth, formate ricinoleate broth, and desoxycholate agar yielded higher presumptive confirmation and a greater sample confirmation than Endo's agar or brilliant green bile broth. Methylene blue brom cresol purple broth gave perfect confirmation but proved somewhat inhibitive. Neutral red bile and violet red bile agar were the most satisfactory solid media and two per cent brilliant green bile the best liquid medium for isolation of *Escherichia coli* from raw, pasteurized, and certified milk. Violet red bile agar seemed to be a superior medium.

Direct plating on suitable solid media has yielded good results in the hands of some investigators. Brown and Gott,[161] using Endo's agar for locating sources of contamination, concluded that milk does not ordinarily contain *Escherichia coli*. They believed that presence of the organism indicated undesirable conditions in production of the milk. The count on Endo's agar was also said to be a good method for following the efficiency of pasteurization. Adams and Ward attached little value to the examination of milk for *Escherichia coli*, according to the methods proposed by Brown and Gott.[161]

More recently desoxycholate agar and violet-red bile agar media have been used with satisfactory results. Use of direct plating methods would, of course, save much time. McCrady and Archambault [162] stated that for the examination of dairy products containing a comparatively large number of coliform organisms the plating method would frequently be the method of choice. However, so-called "typical" colonies appearing in

158. Farrell. 1937. J. Dairy Sci. 20, 67.
159. Leahy. 1937. J. Bact. 34, 39.
160. Bartram and Black. 1936. Food Research 1, 551-561.
161. Brown and Gott. 1923. Amer. Food J. 18, 295-296.
162. McCrady and Archambault. 1934. Amer. J. Pub. Health 24, 122-128.

solid media pour-plates inoculated with milk may not be accepted as colonies of coliform bacteria unless a sufficiently thorough examination of a large number of colonies from representative samples has proved that they may be so accepted. The proportion of typical colonies on various solid media pour-plates which were confirmed varied from zero in some samples to 100 per cent in others.

Yale [163] also compared solid with liquid media for determining the presence of coliform bacteria in pasteurized milk. His results with culture media should be just as applicable to raw as to pasteurized milk.

Ten agar media were compared with respect to their value for plating .1- and one-ml. quantities of milk. Desoxycholate agar gave the best plates and was the only medium which showed promise where one-ml. quantities of milk were plated directly. Several bile salt agars were compared with desoxycholate agar (Baltimore Biological Laboratory) and bacto-violet red bile agar manufactured by Difco Laboratories. Both permitted the direct plating of one-ml. quantities of milk. Ingredients common to both are lactose, peptones, and neutral red indicator. From these studies based on 1,000 samples of raw milk from 85 producers colonies which are deep red in these media and are over one millimeter in diameter were found to produce gas in lactose broth in over 90 per cent of the cases. In a broad sense it was found that all red acid-forming colonies larger than .5 millimeter which grow on this media, either belong or are closely related to the coliform group. Positive results usually mean recontamination but quantitative results are not justified.

Moldavan [164] also recommended two per cent bile, brilliant green lactose peptone medium but the modification consists of using a plug of agar instead of estimating gas production by the use of a Durham tube. After the medium has been inoculated with one milliliter of milk and mixed, the agar in the form of two per cent is slowly poured in to make the gas seal. It is said to be quite airtight and to give quicker results than by the use of the older method.

Since Churchman's work on bacteriostasis, gentian violet has been added to the presumptive test fermentation tube media to inhibit the extraneous Gram-positive bacteria.

Kessler and Swenarton [165] made comparative tests of plain lactose broth, gentian violet lactose broth, and gentian violet lactose peptone bile to determine *Escherichia coli* in raw and pasteurized milk. Gentian violet lactose peptone broth was found most reliable. Gas production was found to indicate *Escherichia coli* in over 99 per cent of cases. Five per cent bile was used, but it was found that it could be reduced to one per cent with only a little loss of efficiency. No comparison was made between the value of these media and the lactose bile salt broth medium used by most English bacteriologists.

163. Yale. 1937. Amer. J. Pub. Health 27, 564-569.
164. Moldavan. 1935. Idem 25, 1032-1033.
165. Kessler and Swenarton. 1927. J. Bact. 14, 47-53.

Demeter and his colleagues,[166] when studying methods for detecting *Escherichia coli* in milk, reported that violet broth and the indol test in trypsin broth gave lowest results, and gas production methods gave lower counts than did plate methods. The inhibitive action of crystal violet was marked. In one case 15.3 per cent of the cultures did not produce gas in its presence. Fermentation of carbohydrates was considered to be important with acid formation more significant than gas production. Many of the lactose-fermenters which were isolated from milk were intermediates and many were of the *Aerobacter aerogenes* type.

Smit *et al.*[167] secured best results with MacConkey's medium and a modified Endo's broth. The latter was said to be slightly more advantageous; it permitted both development of color and gas formation. When *Escherichia coli* is present, this medium turns red. This medium allowed information on the quality of the milk in 24 hours.

The danger of using for this purpose culture media which were developed for use in water analysis was pointed out by McAuliffe and Farrell.[168] Many of the media which have been used for milk carry concentrations of bacteriostatic agents found to be desirable for water analysis. Assuming the possibility of these dyes being absorbed in milk solids, studies were made by McAuliffe and Farrell to determine a more desirable dye concentration to be used in milk analysis. Whole milk was added to lactose broth containing various dye concentrations (ratio: one part of milk to 10 parts of broth). This mixture was dialyzed through a semipermeable membrane and the amount of unabsorbed dye determined colorimetrically. Results with fuchsin lactose broth show that in order to have the recommended amount of dye available (one part in 66,500) for bacteriostatic action in the presence of milk solids, the concentration of basic fuchsin should be increased seven times (to one part in 9,500). A concentration of one part basic fuchsin in 13,300 parts lactose broth was found to be noninhibitive to a skim-milk suspension of pure cultures of the *Escherichia-Aerobacter* group. Similar investigations employing brilliant green lactose bile two per cent showed that the concentration of brilliant green in this medium should be increased two and one-half times, from one part in 75,000 to one part in 30,000. It is believed that lactose broth employing these higher concentrations of dyes offers a more selective means of detecting the *Escherichia-Aerobacter* organism in milk.

Savage [169] believed that the *Escherichia coli* test should be used in place of the bacterial count. He had previously studied this problem and published his results in 1909-1910. Further work since then had increased his respect for the *Escherichia coli* test. He mentioned several factors which favored the organism as an indicator of undesirable conditions in milk. It is a member of a rather restricted group, the members of which multiply uniformly in milk. Furthermore, the *Escherichia coli* test gives better indication of faulty conditions of production which we have, in the

166. Demeter, Sauer, and Miller. 1933. Milchw. Forsch. 15, 265-280; 16 (1934), 236-276.
167. Smit. Krol, and van Wijk. 1940. Antonie van Leeuwenhoek J. Microbiol. and Serol. 6, 1-10.
168. McAuliffe and Farrell. 1938. Amer. J. Pub. Health 28, 1217-1221.
169. Savage. 1923. Proc. World's Dairy Cong. 2, 1295-1301.

past, tried to detect by means of the plate count. Savage's opinions are, in general, concurred in by Neri and Simonetti.[170]

Savage stated: "For quick sorting out purposes, the following dilutions are convenient. They are added to tubes of lactose bile salt broth, and the results (positive acid and gas) are read off at once after two days' incubation at 37°C.(98.6°F.). With this medium, plating out and identification of the organism are not necessary:

Byre milk:

    1 cubic centimeter of milk inoculate 2 tubes.
    0.1 cubic centimeter of milk inoculate 2 tubes.

Vended milk:

    0.1 cubic centimeter of milk inoculate 1 tube.
    0.01 cubic centimeter of milk inoculate 2 tubes.
    0.001 cubic centimeter of milk inoculate 2 tubes.
    0.0001 cubic centimeter of milk inoculate 2 tubes.

Sorting standards such as the following may be used:

LACTOSE FERMENTERS OR COLI TYPE PER CUBIC CENTIMETER

Source of sample:
Byre (i.e., at cowshed):
    Winter (Oct. to Apr., inclusive); Summer (May to Sept., inclusive).
    Below reasonable standard if either or both 0.1 cubic centimeter tubes positive.

Vended:

    Winter Unsatisfactory if both of the 0.01 and 0.1 tubes are positive, and decidedly so if lower dilutions positive.
    Summer—Pass if only the 0.1 and 0.01 tubes positive; condemn if either or both 0.001 positive; between rather unsatisfactory.

Savage believed that these sorting standards applied only when no pasteurization or other form of heat had been applied. He stated also that the use of the *Escherichia coli* test on the lines recommended by him had been adopted by the Ministry of Health in connection with their graded milk requirements and standards.

Types of Coliform Bacteria in Milk. Whether the coliform test has any value in milk analysis or not, is largely dependent on the types which are found. Some members of the group may have little, if any, sanitary significance. If the test is to be of value, it must probably involve demonstration of the presence of *Escherichia coli* itself or other varieties as they may be shown to possess value as indicators of the conditions under which milk is produced and handled. Chambers[171] reported that 65.7 per cent of coliform bacteria in milk were of the *Escherichia coli* type. Seventy-one per cent of strains isolated by Malcolm[156] were of this variety in the winter and spring when the cows were in the stables. During the summer and autumn this percentage dropped to 40.4 per cent. Yale[172] also reported that the greater part of coliform bacteria from raw (64 per cent) and pasteurized (57 per cent) milk were of the *Escherichia coli* type. He

170. Neri and Simonetti. 1930. Ann. Ig. 40, 345-353.
171. Chambers. 1928. J. Hyg. 27, 295.
172. Yale. 1933. J. Dairy Sci. 16, 481-494.

identified many other members of the group also. Wilson [2] classified coliform bacteria from milk into four main groups: the *coli*, intermediate, *aerogenes-cloacae*, and irregular groups. He reported the citrate test to be one of the most reliable methods of differentiating the *coli* from the intermediate and *aerogenes-cloacae* strains. About 18 per cent of the fecal strains were found to be heat resistant. Wilson believed that the *coli* strains were derived directly or indirectly from excretal material, those of the intermediate group from soil, and the *aerogenes-cloacae* group from grains and foodstuffs.

The 310 cultures of the *Escherichia-Aerobacter* group isolated from 331 samples of raw milk by Bartram and Black [173] consisted of 57 per cent *Escherichia*, including twelve species, *Escherichia communior* predominating; 22 per cent *Aerobacter* of five species with *Aerobacter hibernicum* predominating; and 21 per cent intermediate of five species with *Citrobacter freundii* predominating. Only one of 34 pasteurized milk samples yielded *Escherichia-Aerobacter*. Of 15 cultures studied, one was *Escherichia*, one *Aerobacter*, and 13 intermediate, with *Clostridium decolorans* predominating. Eight cultures were isolated from 25 samples of certified milk, including four *Escherichia*, three *Aerobacter*, and one intermediate. This group of organisms as a whole was more significant than any one genus or species in indicating contamination. No correlation was apparent between the different media used and the genus or species isolated. Smit et al.[167] did not consider type differentiation to be important. Pure milk should be free of all types.

Significance of Coliform Bacteria in Milk. Use of these organisms as indicators of pollution in water, suggested that they might be used for the same purpose in milk analysis. The problem is to decide whether they bear any relation to the conditions under which the milk was produced. Opinion is not in agreement.

According to Zavagli [174] the presence of these organisms in milk is a normal condition, their numbers varying according to hygienic conditions. When precautionary measures are taken at time of production, the count should not exceed 100 per milliliter and milk to be used for market purposes should not contain more than ten per milliliter. About equal numbers of *Escherichia coli* (fecal) and *Aerobacter aerogenes* (non-fecal) types were found in market samples. The tests are of distinct value in determining the conditions under which milk has been produced. Since certain of these organisms survive pasteurization, their presence in milk does not necessarily prove that the process has not been properly conducted. The number surviving depends on the number and variety present, fat content of the milk, etc.; thus, Sherman and Wing [175] concluded that the test as now used in some places is of no particular value as an index to the sanitary conditions surrounding the production of raw milk. This applied to all milks except those which were so handled that bacterial growth was

173. Bartram and Black. 1937. Food Research 2, 21-26.
174. Zavagli. 1933. Hyg. u. Infektionskrank. 45, 110-134.
175. Sherman and Wing. 1933. J. Dairy Sci. 16, 165-173.

prevented. For high-grade raw milks containing less than 10,000 total bacteria per milliliter the coliform test may be a supplementary index of quality, and a standard of less than 100 per milliliter for such milk would not be unreasonable. For certified milk, the standard of less than 10 coliform organisms per milliliter is not unduly stringent. If all milk were promptly cooled to 7.22°C.(45°F.) and held at that temperature, this test might prove to be of more general value.

Kon [176] found that a large proportion of the organisms recovered from raw milk by direct plating were of the *Aerobacter aerogenes* type with a number of "intermediates" also present. *Escherichia coli* was largely predominant in feces, while the proportion of *Aerobacter aerogenes* was very small. On the basis of this study it may be assumed that many of the coliform types of organisms found in milk originate, not from feces, but from some external source, such as contaminated utensils or feed stuffs. Davies [177] could see little merit in the coliform test on milk. He concluded that while *Escherichia coli* in milk, as determined by the presumptive test, indicates faulty methods in production or keeping of milk, the test does not indicate gross contamination, as it fails to distinguish organisms introduced during contamination from those subsequently grown in the milk. Furthermore, as the presumptive test fails to discriminate between fecal and non-fecal contamination it affords no indication as to the nature of the contamination. Presumptive *Escherichia coli* in milk usually results from contamination from unsterilized utensils, fecal contamination, or the growth of organisms introduced in these ways. A high *Escherichia coli* content in freshly produced milk indicates faulty production and usually the use of unsterilized utensils. A high *Escherichia coli* content at time of delivery to the consumer, when milk has been produced under reasonably clean conditions, can nearly always be attributed to keeping it at a temperature favorable to bacterial growth. Moore and Fuller [178] also found the colon test to be of little value for judging conditions under which milk was produced.

Yale and Ellington [179] believed that the colon test had only slight value as a routine test on ordinary, fresh, raw milk. High numbers of coliform organisms may not be due to manural contamination, for these organisms may grow on the utensils. The coliform test was also condemned as an accurate method for estimating dirt.

In France, Pien, Bachimont, and Filhol [180] considered *Escherichia coli* in milk no less significant than in water. Pasteurization at 65°C.(149°F.) for 30 minutes destroys it; hence, quantitative determinations conducted on pasteurized milk afford valuable information for control purposes. The authors devised a method which they consider more adequate to detect small numbers of this organism than those commonly used. Large quantities of

176. Kon. 1933. J. Dairy Sci. 4, 206-212.
177. Davies. 1933. Vet. Rec. 13, 1046-1061.
178. Moore and Fuller. 1934. New Hampshire Agr. Expt. Sta. Tech. Bull. 57.
179. Yale and Ellington. 1936. Twenty-third Ann. Rept., Internatl. Assoc., Dairy and Milk Insp. 1935.
180. Pien *et al.* 1932-33. Lait. 903-914 *et seq.*

milk are first incubated at 37°C.(98.6°F.) for eight hours and one-milliliter portions are inoculated into peptone water and, after further incubation, tested for indol production. The acidity of the milk at the end of the preliminary incubation is also determined, and this value is used in estimating the number of *Escherichia coli* in the original milk.

Source of Coliform Bacteria in Milk. Whether coliform bacteria may be present in the cow's udder has not been studied much. Rowlands [181] believed that the presence of coliform bacteria in bulk milk, where other factors show general care in production, may occasionally be associated with an udder infection with these organisms which may be detected by examination of quarter udder samples. Coliform bacteria are comparatively rare in the udder but may be the cause of mastitis. A few cases have been recorded of coliform infection without any clinical manifestations.

Van Ketel [182] stated that the usual source of contamination is the feces, the body of the cow, or the feed and that the optimum temperature for growth is 37.5°C.(99.5°F.). The most obvious source of coliform bacteria would be cow feces. Kon,[176] however, believed that most of them came from external sources, such as utensils or feed stuffs.

Procedures for Determining Presence of Coliform Bacteria in Milk Approved by the Ministry of Health of Great Britain.[86] These are part of the entire procedure recommended for bacteriological examination of milk. References to other sections of the report refer to those sections which are quoted on pages 336 and 382.

27.[88] Samples should be examined in accordance with the following directions.

Apparatus required.

28.—(a) *Culture medium tubes.*—Test-tubes for holding culture medium conforming to the British Standard Specification 152/16, nominal 6" x ⅝", having an internal diameter of 13.5 ± 0.5 mm. should be used. Each tube should contain an inverted Durham tube conforming to the British Standard Specification 35/8, nominal 1⅜ x ⁵⁄₁₆", having an internal diameter of 7 ± 0.3 mm.

(b) *Dilution tubes.*—Test-tubes for dilution conforming to the British Standard Specification 152/19, nominal 6" x ¾", having an internal diameter of 16.5 ± 0.6 mm. should be used in the two-stage method of dilution described below.

Both culture medium tubes and dilution tubes should be plugged with cotton wool or preferably covered with closely fitting aluminium caps and sterilised in the way described under the Methylene Blue Test (paragraph 13 (b) page 382).

(c) *Pipettes.*—1 ml. pipettes of the type specified under the Methylene Blue Test (paragraph 13 (e) should be used.

9 ml. pipettes with the following specification should be used:—

Overall length	360 ± 10 mm.
Length of tapered portion forming jet	25 ± 5 mm.
Distance between graduation mark and tip of jet	200 ± 20 mm.
Length of tube of smaller bore at top of pipette	50 ± 5 mm.
External diameter of pipette	10.5 ± 0.6 mm.
External diameter of tube of smaller bore at top of pipette	6.0 ± 0.5 mm.
Wall thickness of tube of smaller bore at top of pipette	1.0 to 1.5 mm.
External diameter of jet to be at least	3.0 mm.

181. Rowlands. 1939. J. Hyg. 39, 454-462.
182. Van Ketel. 1913. Rev. in Expt. Sta. Rec. 32 (1915) 577.

The pipettes should be calibrated to deliver 9 ml. of water at 20°C., when held in the vertical position and allowed to discharge by gravity in 5 to 10 seconds, the tip being touched against the side of the vessel 3 seconds after the falling column of fluid has come approximately to rest. No pipette should have an error of more than ± 1 per cent., i.e., the volume of water delivered by a 9 ml. pipette should be between 8.91 and 9.09 ml.

The pipettes containing cotton wool plugs at their upper ends should be sterilised in the way described under the Methylene Blue Test (paragraph 13 (e) page 382).

Medium.

29. MacConkey broth made according to the following formula is to be used.

MacConkey Broth (Single strength).

Commercial sodium taurocholate	5 gm.
Lactose	10 gm.
Peptone	20 gm.
Sodium chloride	5 gm.
Distilled water	1,000 ml.

Steam for two hours and transfer to the ice-chest overnight. Filter in the morning through Chardin paper while still cold. Adjust the reaction to pH 7.4, using phenol red as the indicator. Add about 10 ml. of 1 per cent aqueous solution of neutral red.

Culture tubes with medium added.—Distribute the MacConkey Broth Medium in 5 ml. quantities into the culture medium tubes provided with Durham fermentation tubes. Plug the culture medium tubes with cotton wool or cover with aluminium caps and sterilise in an autoclave at a pressure of 10 lbs. per square inch for 15 minutes. or in a steamer for 30 minutes on three successive days. The medium in the finished culture tubes should be clear and should have a claret-red colour free from yellow or magenta.

Diluent.

30. Tap water may be employed if it has been shown that it is free from any marked germicidal activity. Distilled water, if it has been distilled in glass *and not in metallic stills,* is also permissible. Preferably one-quarter strength Ringer's solution should be used.

Ringer's Solution (Full strength).

Sodium chloride	0.2	gm.
Potassium chloride	0.42	gm.
Calcium chloride	0.48	gm.
Sodium bicarbonate	0.2	gm.
Distilled water	1,000	ml.

The one-quarter strength solution should be sterilised by autoclaving for 20 minutes at a pressure of 15 lbs. per square inch.

Method of carrying out the Test.

31. *Filling the dilution tubes with diluent.*—9 ml. of sterile diluent are measured by means of a 9 ml. pipette and delivered by gravity in the way already described (paragraph 28 (c) above) into each of the dilution tubes after these have been sterilised.

32. *Making the dilution.*—After the milk in the sample bottle has been thoroughly mixed as described under the Methylene Blue Test (see page 383) two successive 1/10 dilutions should be made in the sterile diluent in the dilution tubes in the following way. A sterile 1 ml. pipette should be introduced into the sample bottle of milk with its tip reaching not more than ½ to 1 inch below the surface of the milk. The milk should be sucked up and down ten times to the 1 ml. mark, and 1 ml. of milk should then be measured out, holding the pipette in the vertical position. The pipette should be withdrawn, the tip being touched against the neck of the bottle to remove

excess milk adhering to the outside; it should then be introduced into the first test-tube of the diluting series with the tip touching the side of the tube at a point about ½ to 1 inch above the level of the diluent. It is important that the pipette should not come into contact with the diluting fluid. The milk should then be blown out, 3 seconds should be allowed to elapse for drainage, and the remaining contents blown out. The pipette should then be discarded. A fresh pipette should be introduced into the 1 in 10 dilution, with its tip reaching not more than ½ to 1 inch below the surface of the diluent, the fluid sucked up and down ten times to the 1 ml. mark, 1 ml. measured out with the pipette in the vertical position, the pipette removed from the fluid, its tip being touched against the side of the tube about ½ inch below the rim so as to remove any excess adhering to the outside, the pipette transferred to the second tube of the diluting series, introduced with its tip touching the side of the tube about ½ to 1 inch above the level of the diluent, and the contents expelled in the manner described above.

33. *Inoculation and Incubation of the Culture tubes containing MacConkey Broth.*— Take a fresh 1 ml. pipette, introduce it ½ to 1 inch below the level of fluid in the 1/100 dilution of milk, suck up and down 10 times and then transfer 1 ml. portions to each of 3 culture tubes containing MacConkey Broth using the same technique as described under making of dilutions (paragraph 32 above). Incubate the culture tubes at 37°C. for 48 hours, and then examine for acid and gas production.

Standards.

34. The milk is regarded as satisfactory in respect to this test if two out of the three tubes are found to be free from acid plus gas after 48 hours' incubation.

Procedures for Determination of Coliform Bacteria in Certified Milk.[90] "The presence of these organisms in unpasteurized milk usually indicates uncleanly milking, contaminated utensils, or improper handling of milk. Rarely they may come from infected udders. Their presence in pasteurized milk indicates improper pasteurization or contamination of the milk after pasteurization. Properly pasteurized milk should contain no organisms of the coli-aerogenes group.

"The direct plating of one ml. of Certified Milk in desoxycholate agar is recommended, since this gives a direct enumeration of coli and aerogenes colonies of characteristic red color and makes unnecessary further confirmatory tests unless it is desired to differentiate coli from aerogenes organisms. The growth of all Gram-positive organisms is inhibited.

"The use of lactose broth in fermentation tubes is not recommended since it may give either false positives or negatives and requires the use of confirmatory tests for verification. If a liquid medium is used at least 10 tubes shall be inoculated with .1 ml. of the milk to be examined."

Stuart, Wheeler, and Griffin,[91] after a study of coliform bacteria from certified milk, concluded that a total coliform count was of doubtful value. Their strains were classified as Escherichia, intermediate, and Aerobacter. Their results showed wide differences in the relative proportion of these three types and no clear relation of source to type.

METHYLENE BLUE REDUCTION TEST
(REDUCTASE TEST)

It has been known for a long time that milk exerts a reducing action on dyes which are put into it. Since this action was believed to be due largely to bacteria, it was logical that attempts were made to use dye reduction as a measure of bacteria in milk. Much of the earlier work has been reviewed by Wilson [2] whose excellent analysis of this and other pertinent problems should be examined by all milk bacteriologists. In general, reduction of methylene blue is related to bacterial activity in the milk. Just what happens is probably not known even though many investigators have sought an answer to the question. Smidt[183] attributed reduction of the dye to an enzyme secreted in the milk to which he gave the name *aldehyde catalase*. Such explanations are opposed to the general opinion that reduction is due largely to bacterial activity or at least markedly influenced by it. Wilson has presented one of the best discussions of reducing systems in milk.

After many years' work on the reductase test, Barthel[184] suggested the explanation that decolorization of methylene blue in milk takes place in two phases: (1) The oxygen dissolved in the milk is consumed by the bacteria; (2) the methylene blue is decolorized by substances present in the milk itself. It has been shown since, especially by Virtanen,[185] that bacteria energetically reduce methylene blue. However, reduction in bacteria-free and oxygen-free milk must take place by means of substances in the milk itself; Virtanen showed that in such milk the reduction of methylene blue is brought about by citric acid acting as a hydrogen-donor, and milk salts serving as catalyzers. Milk contains about .27 per cent citric acid. Increasing the amount of sodium citrate in milk brings a corresponding shortening of the reducing time. Sodium succinate is also a hydrogen-donor, acting like citric acid.

The methylene blue reduction test may be used as a substitute for counting methods. Thornton[186] found it to be superior in both practice and research. This was also the experience of Nichols and Edwards[187] who recognized in the methylene blue reduction test a method for satisfactorily classifying milk according to bacterial quality. Not all who have studied the question concur in this opinion. Miles[188] considered the plate count to be superior for measuring keeping quality and commercial value of milk. The methylene blue reduction test was believed to be unsuited for examination of milk with few bacteria. According to Robertson and Frayer[189] this test will grade milk as good, medium, or poor but for determining the cause of poor milk one must use the microscope count. Thomas and Tudor[190] found the methylene blue reduction test to be a more lenient method of grading than a combination of the plate count and coliform test. A combination of the reductase test and coliform test was believed to be satisfactory.

Factors Influencing the Test. The actual conditions under which the methylene blue reduction test is carried out have a profound influence on the results secured with it. This has been revealed by various investigators. Some of these factors have not been appreciated by all who have published results of investigations. One of the first comprehensive investigations was

183. Smidt. 1906. Arch. Hyg. 58, 313-326.
184. Barthel. 1928. Die Methoden zur Untersuchung von Milch und Molkereiprodukten. P. Parey, Berlin.
185. Virtanen. 1923. Rev. in Abs. Bact. 7, Abst. No. 1358.
186. Thornton. 1934. Canad. Pub. Health J. 25, 284-294; 29 (1938), 270-276.
187. Nichols and Edwards. 1936. J. Dairy Res. 7, 258-270.
188. Miles. 1933. J. Min. Agr. 40, 414-419.
189. Robertson and Frayer. 1930. Vermont Agr. Expt. Sta. Bull. 317.
190. Thomas and Tudor. 1937. Welsh J. Agr. 13, 308-317.

by Hastings, Davenport, and Wright [191] who showed the effect of not following strictly the recommended technic.

Oxygen Content of the Milk. Davis [192] mentioned this as one of the three most important factors controlling the reduction of methylene blue. The oxygen content of milk was reported by Davis to be about 25 times the equivalent of the methylene blue in the oxidized form. Most of the activity of the bacteria is therefore spent in removing this oxygen by respiration, the methylene blue not being reduced until all of the oxygen is consumed. While some investigators have believed that dissolved oxygen might be one of the disturbing factors in the methylene blue reduction test, Thornton and Hastings [193] could not agree because the rate of diffusion of oxygen into milk is quite slow and would not influence reduction time. They did agree, however, with Barthel [194] that disappearance of methylene blue from milk takes place in two stages: (1) removal of dissolved oxygen by bacteria, and (2) reduction of the dye by constituents of the milk. The oxygen relationship was considered to be very important but normally produced milk is usually considered to be in oxygen equilibrium with the atmosphere. Preliminary shaking did not materially affect reduction times. Milk drawn from the udder anaerobically in Jackson's [195] experiments reduced methylene blue almost instantly, while the same milk exposed to the air usually requires over 10 hours for a similar degree of reduction. Jackson also observed that the oxidation-reduction potential of the anaerobically drawn milk is much lower than for the same sample after exposure to air.

Influence of Light. This factor may not have received the attention which is due it in bacteriological work. In the methylene blue reduction test it is very important. Whitehead,[196] for instance, found that light had considerable effect on the time required for reduction. When methylene blue was added to fresh milk of good quality and the mixture exposed to sunlight at 37°C.(98.6°F.) reduction was complete "in a short time" even as low as .5 hour, whereas, "in darkness at this temperature no reduction occurred in seven hours." That reduction was not due to an enzyme was shown by the fact that "it proceeds equally well in milk which has been heated to 100°C.(212°F.) for 30 minutes. When fat was removed from the milk, no reduction was secured. This ability was restored by addition of sodium oleate. Whitehead, therefore, believed that semilight catalyzes an oxidation-reduction reaction in which unsaturated fats are oxidized and methylene blue reduced. This catalytic effect of light was also observed by Jackson [195] and Frayer.[197] Both artificial and natural light were shown by Frayer to have this ability.

Influence of Bacterial Types and Numbers. It is obvious that the reducing activities of the microorganisms which happen to be present in the milk sample will greatly influence the results of the methylene blue reduc-

191. Hastings, Davenport, and Wright. 1922. J. Dairy Sci. 5, 438.
192. Davis. 1938. Dairy Industries 3, 214-215.
193. Thornton and Hastings. 1927. J. Bact. 13, 62; J. Dairy Sci. 13 (1930), 221-245.
194. Barthel. 1908. Ztschr. Untersuch. Nahr. u. Genussmtl. 15, 385-403; 34 (1917), 137-164.
195. Jackson. 1936. J. Dairy Res. 7, 31-40.
196. Whitehead. 1930. Biochem. J. 24, 579-584.
197. Frayer. 1934. Vermont Agr. Expt. Sta. Bull. 374.

tion test. In general, lactic acid-producing bacteria are active while other types are not. Fred[198] reported that reduction times depended on the organisms present. Hanke[199] stated that most bacteria have the ability to reduce the color, but the speed with which reduction is brought about depends on the nutrient media, the temperature, and the numbers of organisms present. Lactic acid bacteria are very important in the reductase test, since they are present in large amounts in milk. Hanke concluded that this test is not entirely satisfactory for determining the quality of milk, because it does not differentiate between the types of bacteria present, and various factors, such as antiseptics, may materially affect the results. Lactic acid-producing Streptococci were reported to be important in the test by Hastings, Davenport, and Wright.[191] They were more active than coliform bacteria.

Wilson[2] found evidence to the effect that milk produced under aseptic conditions from a healthy udder and having a plate count of less than 100 per milliliter at 37°C.(98.6°F.), contained a natural reducing system independent of any bacteria that may be present. Pure culture studies by Jensen[200] showed that reduction of methylene blue by lactic acid-producing Streptococci, Micrococci, and sporeformers was strongest in raw milk but more cells were needed. Alkali-forming bacteria caused slow reduction. Lactic acid-producing Streptococci caused most rapid reduction, while *Escherichia coli* and Micrococci exerted practically no influence. Another investigation along these lines by Hobbs[201] revealed presence of members of the coliform group and *Staphylococcus aureus* at time of reduction at about 37°C.(98.6°F.). In any given milk one type of organism tended to assume predominance. Hobbs isolated pure cultures and tested their reducing abilities in freshly drawn milk taken under aseptic conditions and having a plate count between 200 and 300 per milliliter. Contrary to findings of others Hobbs found a member of the coliform group to be the most rapidly reducing organism. This organism was followed by *Streptococcus lactis*, some of the fecal streptococci, *Staphylococcus aureus, albus* and other species. Hobbs believed this test to be a good index of the extent of bacterial metabolism in milk. Samples of milk examined by Davis and Lines[203] for physiological types of bacteria involved were shown to contain, on the average, 6.27 per cent acid coagulating bacteria, 55.82 per cent acid not coagulating, 11.59 per cent acid coagulating-gas proteolytic, 16.56 per cent acid proteolytic, 2.28 per cent alkali, and 2.83 per cent inert bacteria. A wide seasonal variation was evident in physiological types of bacteria in milk. Acid not coagulating bacteria were poor reducers of methylene blue but were prominent in most high quality milk. Proteolytic types of bacteria were good oxygen absorbers and played an important part in reduction of methylene blue. There was an associative action between bacteria which usually overshadowed individual variations of reduction power.

198. Fred. 1912. Centbl. Bakt., Pt. 2, 35, 391-428.
199. Hanke. 1925. Rev. in Chem. Abs. 21 (1927), 2942.
200. Jensen. 1937. Zentbl. Bakt., Pt. 2, 96, 234-257.
201. Hobbs. 1939. J. Dairy Res. 1, 35-38.
203. Davis and Lines. 1939. J. Dairy Sci. 22, 209-218.

Marked variations in physiological types of bacteria present in individual samples failed to have any material effect on reduction times.' Acid coagulating, alkali forming, and inert bacteria appeared to have an effect on reduction rates unless present in unusually large numbers. Guglielmo [204] also found milk free from *Escherichia coli* to give a longer reduction time than milk in which this organism was abundant.

Influence of Temperature of Incubation. Evidence is available to show that temperature is an important factor in reduction of methylene blue in milk. That is the reason for regulating to 37°C. and preferably using water baths instead of incubators. Wilson [2] compared the reduction times of identical milks at 35, 37, and 39°C.(95, 98.6, and 102.2°F.). Considerable difference in results was noticed. With Grade A raw and pasteurized milk reduction was most rapid at 39°C.; with other types of raw milk, it was most rapid at 35°C. The larger the content of saprophytic microorganisms, the more likely is the reduction time to be shorter at 35°C. than at 39°C.; larger proportions of parasitic and heat-resistant organisms reverse this situation. The higher temperatures accelerate the chemical reactions involved in reduction and reduce the amount of dissolved oxygen.

Braz and Hoy [205] also found that temperature was important and if not controlled would introduce large errors. In practice wide variations in temperature may occur. A series of tests showed that storage for 12 hours at 18.3°C.(65°F.) is equivalent to 18 hours at 15.5°C.(60°F.) A temperature of 4.4 to 10°C.(40 to 50°F.) has a considerable retarding effect on the test, but a storage temperature of 60°F. reveals a milk in its true character. This temperature was considered too high by Powell, Jenkins, and Thomas.[206] Holding at 4.4°C.(40°F.) in the winter retarded reduction while 15.5°C.(60°F.) was too drastic in summer. Johns [207] suggested a procedure which involved preliminary incubation at 12,8°C. (55°F.) for 18 hours followed by mixing of the contents of tubes not decolorized in six hours when subsequently incubated at 37°C.(98.6°F.). Both modifications shortened reduction time; the mixing reduced variations between duplicate tubes.

Chalmers [208] believed that examination of milk within four hours of the time of its production gave misleading indication of its keeping quality.

Testing milk by the methylene blue reduction test too soon after production does not permit distinction of good milk from bad milk. Time must elapse to permit sufficient growth of bacteria to make the reduction test of value. The "Guide to the Conduct of Clean Milk Competitions" of the Ministry of Agriculture and Fisheries of Great Britain has stipulated examination not sooner than 20 hours and not later than 30 hours after production.

Effect of Shaking the Tubes During Reduction. The main difference between the old and modified technics, is that of agitation. Wilson [2] stud-

204. Guglielmo. 1940. Gior. di Batteriol. e. Immunol. 24, 233-252.
205. Braz and Hoy. 1938. Rev. in J. Dairy Sci. 21, 803.
206. Powell *et al.* 1939. Welsh J. Agr. 15, 164-168.
207. Johns. 1930. Sci. Agr. 11, 171-190.
208. Chalmers. 1938. J. Dairy Res. 9, 351-353.

ied this question carefully before suggesting his new modified technic. He believed that the effect of inversion of the tubes is twofold, to mix the fat with the milk and thus maintain a more even distribution of bacteria, and to aerate the milk and increase its dissolved oxygen content. Wilson found that the first shortened reduction time; the second explanation (aeration) accelerated reduction in so far as it led to more rapid growth of bacteria in the milk. Consequently Wilson carried out comparative studies which prompted him to recommend inversion of the tubes during the reduction period. The observations of Johns [209] and Frayer [210] confirmed this opinion. On the other hand, Thornton [211] observed so little effect of inversion of the tubes that he did not recommend it. He found no reason for adopting the modified test on this continent. Johns pointed out that the methylene blue reduction test is based on the rate of oxygen consumption in the milk by bacteria during incubation. This rate cannot be measured with reasonable accuracy where varying proportions of the bacteria are removed from the main body of the milk during creaming process. Williams, Davies, and Thomas [212] shook stoppered tubes and correlated reduction time with off flavors. Immersion at half-hour intervals decreased reduction time of poor-quality milks by a few minutes only but of good milk by about 10 hours.

Amount of Methylene Blue. This has been found to have marked influence on the test. Fay [213] observed that, when varying amounts of dye solution were added the reduction time was directly related to the amount added. This relationship indicated the gross errors which would be introduced by careless measurement of the dye solution. This subject was discussed much earlier by Hastings, Davenport, and Wright.[191] They believed that one part of crystalline dye in 200,000 parts of milk gave a satisfactory color.

Relation of Reduction Time to Number of Bacteria in Milk. Since bacterial counts are one of the older methods for examining milk, they have been compared with reduction time to determine whether the simpler methylene blue reductase test could not replace the count. Barthel [214] concluded that it furnished a quicker means for judging milk than the fermentation test. He added .5 ml. of methylene blue solution in 10 ml. of milk, the mixture being covered with a few drops of liquid paraffin and placed in an incubator at 40 to 45°C. (104 to 113°F.). If the color disappeared in a few minutes, the milk contained 100,000,000 bacteria per ml., or more. If the dye was not reduced in three hours, the milk was said to be good market milk. Tromsdorff [215] stated that fresh, bacteria-free milk contained no reductase. Hoyberg,[216] believing that methylene blue might be reduced by various substances, stated that the test might have no relation to the

209. Johns. 1938. J. Dairy Sci. 227-237; Amer. J. Pub. Health 29 (1939), 239-247.
210. Frayer. 1937. Vermont Agr. Expt. Sta. Bull. 424.
211. Thornton. 1937. J. Dairy Sci. 20, 693-703.
212. Williams, Davies, Thomas. 1939. Welsh J. Agr. 15, 169-172.
213. Fay. 1930. J. Agr. Res. 40, 855-862.
214. Barthel. 1908. Ztschr. Untersuch. Nähr. Genussmtl. 7, 385-403.
215. Tromsdorff. 1909. Centbl. Bakt., Pt. 1, 49, 291-301.
216. Hoyberg. 1913. Ztschr. Fleisch. u. Milchhyg. 24, 107-112.

bacteria present. Rahn [217] believed that the test was useful only for mixed milks, and that it was subject to variation owing to temperature and other factors. Smith,[218] while believing that there was satisfactory correlation between the count and the results of the methylene blue reduction test, believed that it was not accurate for grading.

Hastings [219] stated that the reduction test determined the number of bacteria as accurately as could be done by any method. After considerable study, Hastings suggested the relation of the reduction time to the count. He examined the milk by the Breed method, the Frost little plate, and the standard agar plate. Tennent [220] also studied the relation between the agar count and the reductase test. Campbell [221] observed a relation between the results of the reductase test and the bacterial count.

Hastings, Davenport, and Wright [191] reported a continuation of Hastings' work on this test. They found no differences of any practical importance between the reduction times of dyes of domestic and foreign manufacture. Any impurities which might have been present were said to be diluted so much that they were of no significance. The temperature of 38°C.(100.4°F.) seemed to be as good as any other for a series of samples was found to be placed in the same order, no matter what temperature was used. The reduction test was stated to be only a rough indication of the general condition of the milk. The great heterogeneity of the flora of milk seemed to indicate that any one test should not be used for determining milk quality. This opinion was also expressed by Barthel.[194] Dahle and Martin [223] also observed a satisfactory correlation between the bacterial content and the methylene blue reduction test. This was not true, however, with low-count milks. Ellenberger, Bond, Robertson, and Moody [224] found the results of the reduction test more consistent than mere plate counts. Lerner and van Gelder,[225] Hiscox,[226] and Straub [227] were in agreement. Beutler,[228] however, did not agree with this conclusion. More recently a few others have found the reduction time to agree well with the plate count.

Fairer [229] concluded that both the bacterial count and reductase test yielded similar results; the former, being quantitative, may be of greater assistance to the producer. Sandberg [230] confirmed this. Faulds [231] found the methylene blue reduction test yielded 75 per cent of comparable results. It was more stringent in warm weather and less so in cold weather.

217. Rahn. 1920. Milchw. Zentbl. 49, 287-290.
218. Smith. 1922. J. Hyg. 21, 139-141.
219. Hastings. 1919. J. Dairy Sci. 2, 293-311.
220. Tennent. 1920. Queensland Agr. J. 13, 51-54.
221. Campbell. 1911. U. S. Dept. Agr. Bur. Anim. Indus. 28th Annual Rept., 195-224.
223. Dahle and Martin. 1925. Penn. Agr. Expt. Sta. Bull. 196.
224. Ellenberger et al. 1927. Vermont Agr. Expt. Sta. Bull. 264.
225. Lerner and van Gelder. 1926. Rev. in Chem. Abs. 21 (1927), 614.
226. Hiscox. 1926. Agr. Progress 3, 102-103.
227. Straub. 1926. Nederland. Tijdschr. u. Hyg. Microbiol. e. Serol. 1, 237-244.
228. Beutler. 1930. Chem. Weekbl. 27, 147-148.
229. Fairer. 1937. Med. Officer 58, 148-149.
230. Sandberg. 1938. Rev. in Chem. Abs. 32, 5089.
231. Faulds. 1937. Lancet, Apr. 17, 1937, 949.

A comparison of the plate count and methylene blue reduction test by Barkworth and Mattick [232] showed that 87 per cent of samples failed to pass both tests. The correlation between plate count and reduction time was lower in winter, although here a high correlation was found with high-plate count. Four laboratories testing common samples agreed on plate counts and reduction times at 37°C., but gave differences with the keeping quality test and the reduction test at 15.5°C.

Few investigators on this continent have studied the methylene blue reduction test as thoroughly as Thornton and his colleagues. He has used it in the field to determine reasons for non-compliance with milk regulations. In one experiment (Thornton [233]) he found that dirty utensils were the cause of the trouble. Marked extension of the reduction time was observed when utensils were sterilized. Discrepancies between reduction time and plate counts were observed; the former was believed to be a better measure of the conditions than the plate count. It is interesting to note that the standard of over five and one-half hours' reduction time was attained by no other effort than sterilizing utensils. This was also shown in investigations by Stott and Barkworth [234] and Nichols and Edwards.[187]

Some attention has been given to the possibility of using the methylene blue reduction test for detecting the presence of abnormal milk. Devereux and Bryan [235] found that it did. When only 10 per cent of mastitis milk was present reduction time was significantly reduced. They attributed this sharper reduction to presence of large numbers of leucocytes. Strynadka and Thornton [236] emphasized the need for careful reasoning on the relationship of leucocytes and reduction time. They believed that the abnormal udder conditions responsible for milk of high leucocyte content are also responsible for abnormally high concentrations of reducing substances in milk. Presence of such high concentrations of reducing substances would explain the rapid reduction of methylene blue without the aid of leucocytes. This is not a denial of the possibility that some leucocytes possess reducing properties, but the bulk of evidence indicates that leucocytes are rarely, if ever, the main or significant influence in the reduction of methylene blue.

Methylene Blue Tablets. Some difficulty is frequently experienced in the use of domestic varieties of methylene blue. Wall and Robertson [237] reported that the addition of a small amount of calcium carbonate, sodium carbonate, or sodium bicarbonate to the aqueous solutions of these samples made them more satisfactory. This was said to prevent dissolution of the film by the staining fluid. Barthel and Jensen [238] suggested that tablets of methylene blue, as put up by Blauenfeld and Tvede, be used as the standard product for reductase tests. The National Aniline and Chemical Co. has prepared similar tablets for the American trade. Grimes, Boyl, Barrett, and Reilly [239]

232. Barkworth and Mattick. 1938. Rev. in J. Dairy Sci. 21, 203.
233. Thornton. 1934. Canad. Pub. Health J. 25, 284-294.
234. Stott and Barkworth. 1937. Pub. Health 50, 297-301.
235. Devereux and Bryan. 1936. Quart. Bull., Mich. Agr. Expt. Sta., 18, 161-163.
236. Strynadka and Thornton. 1938. J. Dairy Sci. 21, 561-568.
237. Wall and Robertson. 1922. J. Bact. 7, 307-308.
238. Barthel and Jensen. 1912. Milchw. Zentbl. 41, 417-429.
239. Grimes *et al.* 1927. Rev. in Chem. Abs. 22 (1928), 120.

did not experience much trouble with various brands of dye. Stock solutions used in preparing dilute solutions were found to be stable for nine months. The longer the reductase time, the greater the variation between duplicate and triplicate tests. A large variation in the ratio of methylene blue to milk does not alter the grade of the milk, particularly if the milk is reduced in less than two hours. Fay [240] stated that the amount of dye solution used should be measured very carefully, as an error of .5 ml. caused a variation in time of reduction of from 30 to 47 minutes. Ellenberger and Moody [241] reported that certain refinements in technic were not as necessary as in other methods of milk examination. Methylene blue tablets were found to be heavily contaminated with rods by Mattick and Neave.[242] No effect was observed on the reduction test at 37°C.(98.6°F.). It would probably be good practice to examine the methylene blue solutions occasionally by plating and to store them in a cool place.

Variability among different lots of dyes has caused the necessity of attempting to standardize them in some manner. Thornton and Sandin,[243] after studying the purity of methylene blue dyes, recommended the use of methylene blue thiocyanate for use in the reductase test. They further recommend a concentration of one part of dye in 300,000 parts of milk Tablets have been available in the past for convenience to make preparation of the methylene blue solution easier. Thornton and Sandin, however, found them wanting. They recommended new tablets of methylene blue thiocyanate. The Committee of the Laboratory Section of the American Public Health Association on Examination of Dairy and Food Products approved this recommendation.[244] *Standard Methods for the Examination of Dairy Products* permits use of such tablets which have been approved by the Biological Stain Commission. One tablet is dissolved in 200 milliliters of freshly boiled distilled water. Conn [245] believed that American manufacturers could put out a very uniform product. He showed that the concentration of dye actually obtained with the chloride was near 1-700,000. Changing the strength of the dye solution has altered the reduction times. Johns [246] reported that the average increase in reduction time using the new methylene blue solution (thiocyanate 1-300,000) for summer milks is around 30 minutes. This was said to be due to the lower potential at which the dye-milk mixture reduces.

PROCEDURES FOR THE METHYLENE BLUE REDUCTION TEST

In view of the fact that the methylene blue reduction test is influenced by so many different factors, several different procedures have been proposed, in each of which some special factor, which was supposed to improve the test, has been emphasized. Probably the most profound change in technic has been inversion of the tubes containing the mixture of milk and dye solution at half-hour intervals, as proposed by Wilson.[2]

240. Fay. 1930. J. Agr. Res. 40, 855-862.
241. Ellenberger and Moody. 1930. Vermont Agr. Expt. Sta. Bull. 312.
242. Mattick and Neave. 1938. Rev. in Biol. Abs. 15 (1941), Abst. No. 11010.
243. Thornton and Sandin. 1935. Amer. J. Pub. Health 25, 1114-1117.
244. Breed. 1937. Yearbook, Amer. Pub. Health Assoc. 1937, 111-113.
245. Conn. 1937. Amer. J. Pub. Health 27, 793-795.
246. Johns. 1940. Canad. Pub. Health J. 31, 155-159; J. Dairy Sci. 23 (1940), 295-302.

American Public Health Association Procedure for the Reductase Test. Measure 10 ml. of milk with a sterile pipette or dipper into the test tubes in which the test will be made. Use sterilized apparatus. Add one ml. of methylene blue thiocyanate solution from a burette or with a one-ml. pipette. Stopper the tubes immediately and place them in the water bath at 37°C.(98.6°F.). After five minutes invert the tubes once, after which avoid agitation. The methylene blue reduction time is the interval between placing the tubes in the water bath at 37°C. and the disappearance of the blue color from the milk. Reduction should be considered complete when four-fifths of the tube has lost its color.

Procedures for Methylene Blue Reduction Test of the Ministry of Health of Great Britain. These are the official procedures for this test in England.[56] The other parts of the document are reproduced on pages 336 and 371.

12.[58] The reliability of the results of the Methylene Blue Test depends upon the strict observance of the directions given below.

Apparatus required.

13. (a) *Methylene Blue.*—Standard methylene blue tablets [247] must be used in carrying out the test. From these a standard solution of methylene blue is prepared in the following manner. The tablet is added to 200 ml. of cold sterile glass-distilled water in a sterile flask which is then shaken until the tablet is completely dissolved. After the tablet has dissolved the solution is made up to 800 ml. with cold sterile glass-distilled water and is stored in a cool dark place. If the solution is to be used for longer than a week, evaporation should be prevented by closing the flask with a rubber bung. The solution remains stable in the dark for a considerable time but no stock solution more than two months old should be used.

(b) *Test-Tubes.*—Test-tubes conforming to the British Standard Specification 152/16, nominal 6″ x ⅝″, having an internal diameter of 13.5 ± 0.5 mm. and an etched mark indicating 10 ml. are to be used. The test-tubes are plugged with cotton wool, or preferably covered with closely-fitting aluminium caps (23 mm. long by 17 mm. broad external diameter). They are sterilised before use in an autoclave at a pressure of 15 lbs. per square inch for 20 minutes or by exposure in a hot air oven to a temperature of 160°C. for two hours. If not to be used directly after sterilisation they should be kept in closed boxes to protect them from dust.

(c) *Rubber stoppers.*—These are supplied so made as to fit the test-tubes. They should be sterilised by immersion in boiling water for five minutes immediately before use.

(d) *Water Bath.*—A metal water bath fitted with a metal cover and containing a test-tube rack is required, in which the test-tubes containing the milk samples can be immersed. The water in the bath must be kept above the level of the milk in the test-tubes and its temperature, which must be between 37°C. and 38°C., should be maintained as nearly uniform as possible by means of a reliable automatic thermo-regulator. The interior of the bath must be completely dark.

(e) *Pipettes.*—1 ml. straight-sided blow-out delivery pipettes should be used for measuring the methylene blue solution, and these should preferably comply with the following specification:—

Overall length.. 300 mm.
External diameter.. 7.5 to 8.5 mm.
Internal diameter.. 2.6 to 3.0 mm.
Graduation... 1 mark only at 1 ml. level
Distance of graduation from tip.. 140 to 180 mm.
Distance of graduation from top...................................... 120 to 160 mm.

247. Traces of impurities normally present in methylene blue seriously affect the reliability of the test. It is essential, therefore, that only specially prepared standard methylene blue tablets should be used for this test. The names of manufacturers who supply such tablets may be obtained on application to the Ministry of Health.

The pipettes should be calibrated to deliver 1 ml. of water at 20°C. when the contents are blown out with the tip touching the side of the vessel, three seconds allowed for drainage and the accumulated drop then blown out. No pipette should have an error of more than ± 2 per cent.; that is, the amount delivered should be between 0.980 and 1.020 ml.

The pipettes should be plugged with cotton wool at the upper end, placed in a metal pipette tin or wrapped in Kraft paper and sterilised in a hot air oven at a temperature of 160°C. for 2 hours. The same pipette may be used for adding the methylene blue solution to successive tubes; it may conveniently be operated by a rubber teat.

If large numbers of tubes are being put up, it may be found convenient to add the methylene blue solution by means of an automatic all-glass 1 ml. delivery pipette.

Mixing of Milk in Sample Bottles prior to examination.

14. (a) A sample collected in a special sampling bottle should be treated in the following way. If the bottle is filled to the level of the stopper, it should be inverted 25 times by a rapid rotatory movement of the wrist in order to mix the cream uniformly with the milk. About one quarter of the contents of the bottle should then be poured away and the bottle shaken 25 times, each shake being an up-and-down movement with an excursion of about one foot, the whole shaking lasting about 12 seconds. If the bottle is not completely filled it can be shaken directly in the way just described.

(b) A sample in a sealed bottle or carton should first of all be inverted 25 times by a rapid rotatory movement of the wrist, the cap should be removed with sterile forceps, the whole contents should be poured rapidly into a sterile capped or stoppered bottle of larger capacity, and this should then be shaken in the way described above.

Method of carrying out the Test.

15. Thoroughly mix the sample of milk by inverting and shaking the sample bottle as described above and then pour the milk into a test-tube up to the 10 ml. mark. In doing this the stopper or cap of the bottle should be removed with aseptic precautions, the pouring-lip of the bottle thoroughly flamed with a bunsen burner, the cotton wool plug or the aluminium cap of the test-tube removed, the mouth of the test-tube flamed with a bunsen burner and the milk rapidly poured into the tube up to the 10 ml. mark. In pouring into the tube care should be taken to leave one side of the interior unwetted with milk. 1 ml. of methylene blue solution is then added to the tube from a pipette, care being taken that the pipette does not come into contact with any of the milk in the tube or with the wetted side of the interior of the tube. If this should occur the pipette must be immediately discarded. During delivery the tip of the pipette should be held against the dry side of the tube about ½ to 1 inch above the level of the milk and the methylene blue solution expelled by blowing with the mouth or by means of a teat on the pipette. After the lapse of 3 seconds the solution remaining in the tip of the pipette should be blown out, and the pipette withdrawn. The tube is then closed with a sterile rubber stopper held and inserted by sterile forceps or by the tips of the fingers on its extreme upper end. On no account must the fingers be allowed to come into contact with the mouth of the test-tube or with the end of the stopper which comes into contact with the test-tube. The tube is then inverted slowly once or twice, so that the whole column of contained air rises above the level of the milk, and placed within five minutes in the water bath.

16. With each batch the following control tubes should be put up: (a) 10 ml. of mixed milk [248] + 1 ml. of tap water; (b) 10 ml. of mixed milk + 1 ml. of methylene blue solution. Both control tubes (a) and (b) should be fitted with stoppers in the usual way and immersed for 3 minutes in boiling water in order to destroy the natural reducing system present in the milk. Comparison of the experimental tubes with control tube (b) will show when decolourisation is beginning and comparison with control tube (a) will show when it is complete.

248. The milk for the control tubes should consist of a mixture of milks preferably from several producers, so as to have an average fat content and color.

17. The tubes must be inspected at half-hourly intervals. At these inspections (1) any tube that has reached the end point (as defined below) should be removed from the rack, (2) any tube that shows commencing decolourisation should be left until the end point is reached and (3) all other 'tubes should be *inverted once*.

.18. The reduction (decolourisation) of the methylene blue is brought about by the combined action of the micro-organisms and of reducing substances that are naturally present in raw milk. Since these reducing substances are closely bound up with the fat globules, it is very important that the cream should be kept distributed as evenly as possible throughout the milk; if it is allowed to rise and collect at the top, reduction in the main body of the milk will be delayed. It is for this reason that half-hourly inversion of the tubes must be carried out. Any departure from this practice will result in an alteration of the reduction time and consequent invalidation of the result.

19. The milk is to be regarded as decolourised when the whole column of milk is completely decolourised up to within 5 mm. of the surface. The test is then finished. If a trace of colour persists at the bottom of the tube and does not extend upwards for more than 5 mm. it may be ignored. The time (within the prescribed limit) at which decolourisation is observed should be recorded. Where a tube is found not to be decolourised within the prescribed time, the sample satisfies the test.

Precautions in regard to the Test.

20. It is important that the methylene blue solution when not in use should be kept in the dark; it should at no time be exposed to sunlight.

21. The amount of methylene blue required for a day's work should be poured off from the stock bottle into a suitable glass container. On no account should the pipette used for transferring the methylene blue solution to the tubes of milk be introduced into the stock bottle. Moreover, if at any time during the filling of the tubes the methylene blue solution should become contaminated with milk carried into it by a pipette which has inadvertently come into contact with the milk, the methylene blue solution should be immediately discarded and replaced by a fresh supply.

22. It is essential that the interior of the water bath during the progress of the tests should be completely dark, since sunlight, diffused daylight and even artificial light catalyse the reduction of methylene blue. The tubes should not be exposed to direct sunlight during the half-hourly inspections.

23. The design and construction of the water bath including the thermo-regulator must be such as to ensure the maintenance of a uniform temperature of 37°C. to 38°C. during the test.

24. When a number of tests are being carried out it is convenient to place the test-tubes in a rack provided with a metal top to hold them in position so that at the half-hourly intervals all the test-tubes can be simultaneously inverted by merely inverting the rack.

25. The precautions against the adventitious contamination of the milk sample described in the method for carrying out the test must be carefully observed.

26. The sterilisation of the rubber stoppers for the test-tubes and their subsequent satisfactory manipulation can be facilitated by employing a simple rack for holding a large number of rubber stoppers immersed in a suitable vessel of boiling water.

Wilson's [2] Modified Method for Methylene Blue Reduction Test. After considerable study Wilson proposed a new technic for the reductase test, the main modification of which was inversion of the tubes at half-hour intervals.

It is important to use a standard methylene blue solution. At the moment standardization by chemical means seems impracticable, and the empirical method of comparison of each new batch with an accepted standard is unavoidable. In his own work Wilson used exclusively the standard Barthel-Orla-Jensen methylene blue tablets supplied by Blauenfeldt and Tvede of Copenhagen. One table is added to 200 ml. of warm, sterile, glass-distilled water in a flask, which is then shaken till the tablet is completely dissolved. After the solution has cooled down, it is made up to 800 ml. with cold, sterile, distilled water, and is stored in a cool, dark place, preferably in an icebox. If it is to be used for longer than a week or so, evaporation should be prevented by fitting the flask with a rubber bung. The length of time during which such a solution remains stable has not been determined, but we have observed no significant change within six months in the icebox. The addition of one ml. of this solution to 10 ml. of milk gives a final concentration of methylene blue of approximately 1/300,000.

Test tubes six inches by five-eighths inch external diameter are used, having a 10-ml. mark. The tubes are fitted with cotton-wool plugs and sterilized before use by auto-claving at 15 lb. per sq. in. for 20 minutes, or by exposure in the hot-air oven to a temperature of 160°C.(320°F.) for two hours.

Rubber corks should fit the test tubes. They are "sterilized" by immersion in boiling water for five minutes. Simple racks can be devised for holding large numbers of these corks, narrow ends downward, in a suitable bath of boiling water.

Metal water-baths fitted with metal covers and containing test tube racks are required. The water in the bath is kept above the level of the milk in the tubes, and its temperature is maintained at as constant a level as possible by means of a reliable automatic thermo-regulator. The interior of the bath must be *completely dark*, since both sunlight and artificial light catalyse the reduction of methylene blue. For raw milk the temperature of the water is kept at 37 to 38°C.(98.6 to 100.4°F.); for pasteurized milk an additional bath at 55 or 63°C.(131 or 145.4°F.) may be required.

One-ml. straight-sided, blow-out delivery pipettes, of the type specified, are used for measuring the methylene blue solution. They are plugged with cotton-wool at one end, placed in a metal pipette tin or wrapped in Kraft paper, and sterilized in the hot-air oven for two hours at 160°C. They are operated preferably by a rubber teat. If large numbers of tubes are being put up, an automatic delivery pipette may be used.

Technique for Examination of Raw Milk. Throughout the test it is desirable to employ the usual aseptic precautions. Samples are taken and mixed in the way already described and 10 ml. of milk from each sample are poured into a graduated test tube. In doing this, after the milk has been thoroughly mixed, the disc or cork should be removed with sterile forceps, the pouring lip of the bottle thoroughly flamed, the cotton-wool plug of the test tube removed, the mouth of the test tube flamed in a Bunsen, the milk rapidly poured into the tube up to the mark, and the cotton-wool plug immediately replaced. One ml. of methylene blue solution is then added to each tube by a pipette, care being taken that the pipette does not come into contact with any of the milk in the tube. During delivery the top of the pipette should be held against the side of the tube about one-half to one inch above the level of the milk, and the fluid expelled by means of a teat; after a wait of three seconds, the teat should again be compressed so as to expel the fluid remaining in the tip of the pipette. Each tube is then fitted with a sterile rubber cork picked up by means of a sterile forceps or the extreme tips of the fingers. On no account must the fingers be allowed to come into contact with the mouth of the test tube or the narrow end of the cork. The tube is then inverted slowly once, so that the whole column of air rises above the level of the milk, and placed within five minutes in the water-bath. At half-hour intervals the tubes are inverted once, the color of the milk being noted before inversion. Complete decolorization of the whole column, or complete decolorization up to within five mm. of the surface, is regarded as the end point. Any tube at the time of examination showing obvious signs of reduction should not be inverted, but should be left until the end point as defined is reached. All tubes that are not decolorized within an agreed time may be discarded.

Technique for Examination of Pasteurized Milk. The same technique is employed as for raw milk, but, if desired, duplicate tubes may be put up, one at 37°C., the other at 55 or 63°C. The 37°C. tube is inverted once every half-hour as usual, but the 55 or 63°C. tube, after the preliminary inversion before incubation, is not again inverted, since it is found that the reducing potential established in pasteurized milk by organisms of the thermoduric and thermophilic groups is often insufficient to decolorize methylene blue completely if half-hour aeration is practiced. Any tube not decolorizing methylene blue solution within an agreed time may be discarded.

Several investigators have made comparative studies with the older methods and that of Wilson.[2] Cinai [249] found the modified technic to be recommended in the control of the quality of pasteurized milk. According to Johns [209] the accuracy of the test is greatly increased by periodical inversion of the tubes during incubation. In addition, reduction time is generally shortened and decolorization is more uniform, especially with the better grades of milk. It is believed that these advantages more than compensate for the slight inconvenience entailed by this modification. Milks showing similar reduction times by the modified technic of Wilson show wide differences in standard reduction times. These appear to be associated with differences in the degree and rate of creaming. Reduction time is prolonged by approximately 20 per cent with the proposed stronger dye concentration. This is more than compensated for in all but the poorer grades of milk by the shortening of reduction time when inversion is practiced. Thomas [250] claimed that the Wilson modification decreased reduction time on the average of five hours. Williams, Davies, and Thomas [251] reported that the modified technic gave little average difference in reduction time from the old method for samples reducing within 5.5 hours. A very slight average increase in reduction time was obtained with the modified test in the case of the poorer qualtiy samples that reduced within three hours, but there was a marked decrease in reduction time with the better quality samples. Thornton [211] believed the only difference between the standard and the modified technic is that in the modified technic, the tubes are shaken at half-hour intervals. The present evidence does not warrant the replacement of the standard methylene blue reduction test by the modified test since the possible greater accuracy of the latter is offset by greater complexity of technic. Thornton believed that much had to be done yet to make the reductase test entirely reliable.

Results of a comparative study of the old and modified methods were also published by Matuszewski and Supinska.[252] The results obtained and their interpretation agreed with theoretical expectations. It was found that deviation in the reduction time, corresponding to a given initial number of bacterial cells, was smaller by the modified than by the old method and that the average time of reduction was shorter. The smaller variation in the reduction time, corresponding to a given number of cells at the beginning of the test, was due probably to a more uniform distribution of the bacteria in the milk following the inversion of the tube. It is suggested that the shortening of the reduction time in the modified test is due to the stimulation of bacterial growth. The average coefficient of multiplication in the old procedure was .66 and in the modified procedure was .885.

Methylene Blue Reduction Test Standards. Several different standards of milk have been proposed; it is probably pertinent to present them. Orla-

249. Ciani. 1939. Ann. Ig. 49, 290-308.
250. Thomas. 1938. Rev. in J. Dairy Sci. 21, 303.
251. Williams, Davies, and Thomas. 1939. Welsh J. Agr. 15, 169-172.
252. Matuszewski and Supinska. 1940. J. Dairy Res. 11, 43-50.

Jensen,[253] using Barthel's technic, proposed the following four groups of milk:

(1) Good milk which retains the color seven hours or longer, and which contains at the most 100,000 bacteria per ml.

(2) Fair milk which is discolored between two and seven hours and which, as a rule, has between 100,000 and 3,000,000 bacteria per ml.

(3) Poor milk which is discolered between one-fourth and two hours and which has from 3,000,000 to 20,000,000 bacteria per ml.

(4) Very poor milk which is discolored in less than a quarter hour and contains still more bacteria.

Müller [254] said that milk produced in a satisfactory manner required 10 hours for reduction; shorter times were secured with milk in process of delivery to the consumer. Fuller, DePew, and Huggins [255] found the reductase test to be a simple and inexpensive method for determining keeping quality. Milk requiring more than five and one-half hours for reduction was satisfactory milk.

Fuller and his colleagues suggested the following classification of milk by means of the reductase test:

Class 1.   Good milk, not decolorized in five and one-half hours.
Class 2.   Fair milk, decolorized in two and five and one-half hours.
Class 3.   Poor milk, decolorized in less than two hours.

de Gaspari and Sangiorgi [256] stated that if reduction occurred after two to four hours the milk was useable.

Standard Methods for the Examination of Dairy Products eighth edition, 1941, classified milk into the following groups by means of this test:

Class 1.   Excellent, not decolorized in eight hours.
Class 2.   Good, decolorized in less than eight hours but not less than six hours.
Class 3.   Fair, decolorized in less than six hours but not less than two hours.
Class 4.   Poor, decolorized in less than two hours.

THE RESAZURIN TEST

This is a dye reduction test quite like the methylene blue reduction test. It is carried out by adding $\frac{1}{10}$ ml. of a .05-per cent sterile aqueous solution of resazurin to 10 ml. of milk in 20-ml. culture tubes. These tubes are then incubated in the dark at 37°C.(98.6°F.) for one hour, according to instructions of Ramsdell.[257] Only one reading is taken according to the original technic, and the test is completed in an hour; the methylene blue test requires over five hours. On the basis of this test milk can be classified into four groups as regards sanitary conditions. Milks from diseased udders and from physiologically abnormal cows have significant effects on the reduction of this indicator, and hence the test aids in their detection. By observing the rate of color change in resazurin-milk mixtures over a period of hours of incubation, much information as to the kind and character of the flora may be obtained. Ramsdell [258] later

253. Orla-Jensen. 1910. N. Y. Prod. Rev. and Amer. Cream 29, 858-860.
254. Müller. 1906. Arch. Hyg. 56, 108-204.
255. Fuller *et al.* 1924. New Hampshire Agr. Expt. Sta. Circ. 23.
256. de Gaspari and Sangiorgi. 1915. Riv. d'Ig. San. Pub. 24, 220-232.
257. Ramsdell. 1936. Tenth Ann. Rept., N. Y. Assoc. Dairy and Milk Insp.; see also J. Dairy Sci. 18 (1935), 705-717.
258. Ramsdell. 1937. Milk Dealer 27, 90.

stated that the resazurin test is as trustworthy as the methylene blue test for evaluating the sanitary condition of milk. The test may be completed in one hour whereas the methylene blue test requires five hours. . Resazurin is more sensitive to reducing influence of abnormal milks and consequently more useful than methylene blue in detecting these types of milk. The resazurin test is more effective in detecting very poor milks than the methylene blue test, and with the short incubation period of one hour the flora approximates more closely the initial flora than when longer incubation periods are used, as with the methylene blue test. This opinion was confirmed by Keenan, Barrett, and Rutan [259] who stated that more information was gained in one hour's incubation with resazurin than with six hours' incubation with methylene blue. The former test is more sensitive to abnormal and pathological milks than is methylene blue.

Resazurin milk mixtures according to Warner [260] change color during incubation from the original blue to a pale violet, then to a rose pink and finally to a colorless state. If resazurin white is taken as the end point, no advantage results in its use over methylene blue. The resazurin violet and resazurin pink reduction times were considerably shorter than the methylene blue chloride reduction times. Warner's opinions in general seemed to be that no great advantage obtained for resazurin over methylene blue. Frayer [261] subjected samples drawn as aseptically as possible to the resazurin test, the methylene blue reduction test, and plate and cell counts. In the former test one ml. of a .005-per cent solution of resazurin was added to 10 ml. of milk and incubated for one hour at 37°C. In this series the resazurin test correlated poorly with the methylene blue reduction test and hardly at all with the plate count but showed fair correlation with the cell count of the near asceptically drawn samples. It was sensitive to the presence of cells and to the presence and activity of bacteria and very sensitive to strong sunlight or artificial light. Efficient initial cooling of milk retarded resazurin reduction. A supplementary microscope examination appeared necessary if the results of this test were used as a basis for corrective follow-up work. Especial attention was needed to determine the point in the range of the color changes which separates samples needing and not needing further inspection.

Collins, White, Turner, and Rice [262] found that uniform results could be secured when the technic was standardized. Good agreement of the resazurin test and the methylene blue reduction test were reported. There was a high agreement between the resazurin test to pink and the methylene blue test in selecting both poor and good quality milks. A resazurin test to pink in three hours is equivalent to a 5.5-hour methylene blue test.

Patrons' milk having a resazurin test to pink in three hours or more was found to have a bacterial count of less than 400,000 per milliliter. Five to six hours indicates less than 100,000 per milliliter.

259. Keenan et al. 1937 J. Milk Tech. 1, 22-35; J. Dairy Sci. 20, 705-709.
260. Warner. 1938. Dairy World 16, 18-22, 54-56.
261. Frayer. 1938. Vermont Agr. Expt. Sta. Bull. 435.
262. Collins et al. 1939. J. Milk Tech. 2, 236-244.

The resazurin and methylene blue tests were compared by Davies, Thomas, and Thomas [263] on 575 samples of accredited raw milk, with examination and inversion of the tubes at 30-minute intervals in both tests. The reduction of resazurin to the white stage correlated very well with, but was distinctly slower than, the methylene blue reduction; the average difference was 35 minutes. The reduction of resazurin to purple pink also gave a fair statistical correlation with methylene blue reduction, but about 10 per cent of the samples that reduced resazurin to this stage in one hour failed to reduce methylene blue in seven hours. The resazurin test can be utilized for advisory purposes, particularly when used in conjunction with microscopic examination, and samples that retain the original blue color for one hour at 37°C.(98.6°F.) can be considered satisfactory.

Johns, [264] however, believed that the resazurin one-hour test is not as reliable as the methylene blue reduction test. When incubation is continued to the pink stage, however, the accuracy of the test compares favorably with that of the methylene blue test, while the reduction time is shortened. Johns concluded that while the resazurin test is shorter than the methylene blue test, it is not as reliable as the modified methylene blue test, in that it places a larger proportion of high-count milks in the highest grades. If the resazurin test is continued to the pink stage, the comparison with the methylene blue test is favorable. The correlation between the resazurin color and the cell count was found to be much poorer with market milk than with individual quarter samples. Finally, it was concluded that further research concerning resazurin and its reactions in milk must be undertaken before the use of the test in milk control will be comparable to that of methylene blue tests. Johns and Howson [265] later advised a "triple reading" resazurin test which they said gave better results. They were more satisfied where the color number of each sample is recorded hourly. In view of the fact that this could not be done on a large number of samples Johns and Howson attempted to devise a simpler method which would combine the sensitivity of the "one-hour" test for abnormal milks with the greater accuracy of the "pink end point" for bacteria. Such a technic was proposed.

An incubation temperature of 18°C.(64.4°F.) instead of 37°C. was recommended by Davis and Watson.[266] The recommended time was three hours instead of the one hour at 37°C. Various reasons were offered to support this suggestion.

Dye for the Resazurin Test. As has been the case with most tests in which dye is used, attention must be given to the brand of dye used. Nelson [267] tested four brands and found only two to be satisfactory. Nelson, therefore, believed that resazurin would have to be standardized before the test can be generally adopted.

263. Davies et al. 1939. Welsh J. Agr. 15, 181-189.
264. Johns. 1939. Amer. J. Pub. Health 29, 239-247.
265. Johns and Howson. 1940. J. Milk Tech. 3, 320-325.
266. Davis and Watson. 1942. Milk Indus. 22, 37.

Ramsdell [257] recommended a .05-per cent solution of the dye. Collins *et al.* did not find this strength sufficiently accurate when speed is required and he followed the suggestion of Moldavan [268] that one ml. of a .005-per cent solution be used. Collins and his colleagues also found that an intermediate pink color could be read uniformly by various investigators. Consequently, a pronounced pink but not a vivid pink was used as the end point. Possibility of resazurin tablets and solutions containing significant numbers of bacteria was pointed out by Thomas and Thomas.[269] They recommended plating of the solutions occasionally. Advantages of storing the solutions in the refrigerator were also mentioned.

Collin's et al.[226] Technic for the Resazurin Test. Ten-ml. portions of the milk under examination are placed in sterile test tubes. The tubes are then brought to a temperature of 37°C.(98.6°F.) in a water bath for five minutes . One ml. of the fresh .005-per cent resazurin dye is then added by means of a 10-ml. pipette and the sample mixed by inverting. The tubes are then incubated at 37°C. either in an incubator or water-bath. They are read in medium light but away from direct or reflected sunlight.

Application of Resazurin Test for Determining the Quality of Pasteurized Cream.

According to Chilson and Collins [270] the resazurin test is a satisfactory and rapid criterion of keeping quality of cream. They did not find it always reliable for picking out high-count cream which had been stored at 4.4°C.(40°F.) for four or more days. A six-hour reduction time was said to be a criterion of high quality in pasteurized cream.

A valuable resumé of the resazurin test was prepared by Davis.[271] He discussed many problems which must be considered by those who use this test for grading milk.

REFERENCE BOOKS

Bacteriological Tests for Graded Milk. Memo 139/Foods (Jan., 1937). H. M. Stationery Office, London. May be purchased from the British Information Service, 30 Rockefeller Plaza, New York, N. Y.

Standard Methods for the Examination of Dairy Products, Eighth Edition, 1941. American Public Health Association, 1790 Broadway, New York, N. Y.

Milk Ordinance and Code Recommended by the United States Public Health Service. Pub, Health Bull. 220 (1939). Federal Security Agency, Washington, D. C.

Wilson, G. S., 1935. The Bacteriological Grading of Milk. H. M. Stationery Office, London, England.

267. Nelson. 1939. J. Dairy Sci. 22, 335-336.
268. Moldavan. 1938. Milk Plant Mo. 27, 58.
269. Thomas and Thomas. 1942. Dairy Indus. 7, 121-122.
270. Chilson and Collins. 1940. J. Milk Tech. 3, 334-340.
271. Davis. 1942. Food Manufacturer, November and December.

CHAPTER 7

PASTEURIZATION OF MILK

Few efforts to protect the public health have been so uniformly accepted by health officials and the consumer as milk pasteurization. Practically all milk in the large urban centers is pasteurized with possible exception of some "certified" milk; much of it is now pasteurized. Milk-borne epidemics have been greatly reduced in number. Microbiological problems of the process concern mainly destruction of bacteria in milk which cause disease and investigation of types which survive.

The Milk Ordinance and Code recommended by the United States Public Health Service [1] defines pasteurization as follows:

"The terms 'pasteurization,' 'pasteurized,' and similar terms shall be taken to refer to the process of heating every particle of milk or milk products to at least 143°F., and holding at such temperature for at least 30 minutes, or to at least 160°F., and holding at such temperature for at least 15 seconds, in approved and properly operated equipment; provided that nothing contained in this definition shall be construed as disbarring any other process which has been demonstrated to be equally efficient and is approved by the State health authority."

Many states have adopted virtually the same definition. The State of Illinois has adopted this same definition.[2] Frank,[3] who supervised preparation of the United States Public Health Milk Ordinance and Code, believed that an effective and practical definition of pasteurization should satisfy the following criteria: It must be effective with respect to the killing of any pathogens in milk and be practical with respect to enforcement by the health official, and its application by the dairy industry. Frank believed that these objects were attained in the standard code.

Perhaps other factors than merely destruction of pathogenic bacteria may be considered in the future for determining the temperature which shall be used for pasteurization of milk. When cream volume, phosphatase test, destruction of *Escherichia coli*, rennet coagulation time, and other factors were considered by Holland and Dahlberg [4] 76.7°(170°F.) seemed to be quite promising as a new standard for pasteurization.

Objections to Pasteurization of Milk. While many objections were once raised against milk pasteurization it is generally accepted today by the public. The few who question the process have not secured all of the facts or are unwilling to face them. Some of the more important objections, are as follows:

1. *Increases Cost.* Whether this argument against pasteurization has weight depends on the value placed on other factors. Any procedure which

---

1. Milk Ordinance and Code Recommended by the United States Public Health Service. Pub. Health Bull. 220 (1939), Federal Security Agency, Washington.

2. Illinois Dept. Pub. Health, Milk Plant Pasteurization Plant Law. Enacted 1939. 65 pp.

3. Frank. 1930. Amer. J. Pub. Health 20, 1105-1119.

4. Holland and Dahlberg. 1941. J. Dairy Sci. 24, A 103-104.

has for its object increased safety of foods is probably justified. Furthermore, any effort which tends to protect the unsuspecting portion of the
population, the children, is justified at significantly increased cost.

2. *May Conceal Inferiority.* While this is possible to a certain extent,
it is a criticism which does not have much weight. The dirt test, for instance, may be applied to pasteurized milk as well as to raw milk in order
to determine cleanliness. It is possible that old milk could thus be made
safe, but the enforcement of certain standards for milk which is to be
pasteurized prevents it. Most cities, by means of efficient inspection, are
able to enforce the required procedures to maintain a good raw milk. When
such milk is pasteurized, a double attempt has been made to make it safer.

3. *Interferes With Cream Rising and Whipping.* Considerable work
has been done to determine just what chemical changes are brought about
in milk by pasteurization. Rupp [5] reported that milk pasteurized by the
holder process at 62.8° C. (145° F.) underwent no appreciable chemical
change. He found that the acidity of pasteurized milk was slightly diminished. However, pasteurization by the holder process at 65.6° (150°F.) did
cause changes in the milk. Dutcher [6] has confirmed this.

Results of experiments by Kilbourne [7] indicated that when milk was
cleaned by a centrifugal clarifier the volume of cream in the milk is reduced
from two to three per cent. It was evident that volume of cream in bottled
milk is influenced by various factors, among which are temperature to
which it is heated, length of time it is held at the high temperature, temperature of the heating medium with which it comes in contact during
the heating process, clarification, type of apparatus used, and amount of
agitation to which it is subjected, especially when hot. This last factor
appears to be one of the most important. It is believed that, under the
most favorable circumstances, heating to 62.8°C. (145°F.) and holding for
30 minutes may be done without any injurious effect upon the cream line,
but it has been deemed best to reduce the required temperature to 61.1°C.
(142°F.) in order to allow for uncontrollable factors which may tend to
offset the volume of cream.

The layer of cream on milk in the bottle is important because the consumer uses it as an index of the richness of the milk. Harding [8] was
especially concerned with the effect of the new higher temperatures which
were being advocated. While 60 to 62.8°C. (140 to 145°F.) for 30 minutes
was generally recognized as the proper temperature, there was a growing
demand that 62.8°C. (145°F.) be accepted as the minimum. Harding found
that the volume of cream on bottled pasteurized milk was measurably less
when temperature of pasteurization was 61.1 to 62.2°C. (142 to 144°F.).
Higher temperatures caused greater decreases in cream volume; at 62.8°C.
(145°F.) it amounted to slightly more than 10 per cent by volume; at
63.3°C. (146°F.), it was 16.6 per cent; and at 64.4°C. (148°F.), decrease was
about 40 per cent. Harding's method of measuring this was to fill round-

5. Rupp. 1913. U. S. Dept. Agr., Bur. Anim. Indus. Bull. 166.
6. Dutcher. 1913. Penn. Agr. Expt. Sta. Bull. 181.
7. Kilbourne.1915. Creamery and Milk Plant Mo. 3, 11-20.
8. Harding. 1921. Ill. Agr. Expt. Sta. Bull. 237.

bottom test tubes one-half inch in diameter to a depth of eight inches with the milk. The tubes were then cooled and kept at 4.4°C.(40°F.) for 24 hours. The depth of the cream layer was measured in millimeters, each millimeter of cream representing .5 per cent of cream by volume. Marcussen[9] found that the average volume of cream on milk pasteurized at 62.8°C.(145°F.) was 13.325 per cent less than the average volume of cream on the same milk, pasteurized at 61.1°C.(142°F.). This subject was also studied by North *et al.*[10] in extensive experiments at Endicott, N. Y. They reported, in general, that with the standard holding period of 30 minutes a temperature below 62.8°C.(145°F.) during the holding period was without noticeable effect upon the cream volume. The effect first became noticeable at about 63.3°C.(146°F.) and of practical importance at about 63.8 to 64.4°C.(147 to 148°F.). Loss of cream line does not mean loss of fat. The fat is in the bottle, but does not come to the top, owing to dispersion of fat droplets. The same question was studied by Holland and Dahlberg[11] over the range in temperature from 60°C.(140°F.) to 79.4°C. (175°F.). A semilogarithmic relationship was found to exist between time and temperature in the case of cream volume, inactivation of phosphatase, and destruction of *Escherichia coli*. Much of the information on questions such as this one, is based on the old methods of pasteurization. Introduction of the newer methods of high temperature-short time methods made it necessary to review the subject to determine how they affected the cream line.

Results of experiments by Dahlberg and Marquardt[12] revealed that maximum cream layer was secured by heating to slightly less than 62.8°C. (145°F.) for a holding period of 30 minutes. Cooling should be promptly accomplished at 4.4°C.(40°F.) or below. The rate of cooling was found to influence creaming, whether slow or rapid creaming obtained. Creamline destruction was shown by Supplee and Jensen[13] to vary from six to 20 per cent through the temperature range of 71.1°C.(160°F.) to 82.2°C.(180°F.) and to increase rapidly thereafter for each degree rise in temperature.

4. *Modifies Taste.* Taste is undoubtedly modified by pasteurization. However, one must decide whether he would prefer to use a food product which is safe, although some of the methods which were employed to make it safe may have slightly altered the taste. Taste is a matter of education, anyway. The longer pasteurized milk is used, the less weight this objection will have. If pasteurized milk is used from childhood the taste of it will be the normal. Hammer and Hauser[14] prepared a table of the statements of various authorities on the effect of heat on the taste of milk.

5. *Less Wholesome.* This was a general criticism in early days when pasteurization was introduced. It was said that pasteurized milk had no

9. Marcussen. 1929. Creamery and Milk Plant Mo. 18, 24-32.
10. North *et al.* 1925. U. S. Pub. Health Service, Pub. Health Bull. 147.
11. Holland and Dahlberg. 1940. N. Y. Agr. Expt. Sta. Bull. 254.
12. Dahlberg and Marquardt. 1931. N. Y. Agr. Expt. Sta. Bull. 180; Bull. 189 (1932); and Bull. 223 (1934).
13. Supplee and Jensen. 1941. J. Milk Tech. 4, 5-7.
14. Hammer and Hauser. 1914. Iowa Agr. Expt. Sta. Bull. 154.

"life." When vitamins were discovered, some basis existed for this contention and many investigations were carried out to determine whether they were destroyed. Under any conditions the vitamin content of milk is variable and is influenced by the season of the year, the food of the cow, and the animal herself. Consequently it is a matter of no great concern whether pasteurization destroys vitamins. The literature on this question is voluminous and will not be reviewed in this book.

Results of comparative experiments in which raw and pasteurized milks were fed to animals have consistently shown that animals gain weight and develop just as well on the latter as on the former. Wilson [15] and his colleagues observed this with calves.

Finally, mention may be made of an analysis of results of a survey by Frank et al.[16] of over 3,700 children under six years of age as to weight, diet, and health history. This survey was conducted in over 39 cities in 10 states and involved two groups of children using raw and pasteurized milk. No information was gathered which reflected on the pasteurization process. In fact, a higher incidence of scarlet fever, diphtheria, intestinal disturbances, and rickets was observed in the children on raw milk.

6. *Pasteurized Milk Putrefies Rather Than Sours.* This was an early belief which has since been disproven. It was based on the fact that the lactic-acid-forming bacteria were nonsporeformers and therefore were susceptible to heat. The sporeforming bacteria, which are quite proteolytic, survive to peptonize the milk proteins. Products of this were supposed to be the causes of severe intestinal upsets. The explanation seemed to be logical but was soon proved false. As shown a little later in this chapter, lactic acid-producing bacteria can survive pasteurization. Despite results of many different experiments, these issues are constantly raised; for instance, Fearis [17] suggested that more inquiry is necessary as to the possible detrimental effects of the destruction of the lactic acid bacilli. He suggested possible multiplication of pathogenic bacteria freed from the restraining acid production, the absence of destruction of aerobic sporing organisms, such as *Bacillus subtilis* alleged to cause toxemia in infants, and the loss of oxygen in the milk from pasteurization.

Advantages of Pasteurization. Years of research and experience have furnished much evidence to support pasteurization of milk. All of the objections which have been or may be raised against the process may be met by one—that it makes milk safe.

1. *Makes Milk Safe.* Pasteurization destroys pathogenic bacteria in milk. Need for some method to rid milk of *Mycobacterium tuberculosis* caused health officers to resort to heating of the milk. Later as other pathogenic bacteria were found to occur in milk, it was found that they, also, were destroyed. Once these bacteria are destroyed, the pasteurized milk must be guarded against reinfection. The bacteriological evidence on

15. Wilson. 1938. Nature 141, 579-581; 1933, J. Soc. Chem. Ind. 52, 403T-406T; J. Dairy Res. 8, 203-217, 218-223; J. Hyg. 37, 243-253.
16. Frank, *et al.* 1932. Pub. Health Rpts. 47, 1951-1960.
17. Fearis. 1935. Lancet, April 27, 1935, 1015-1016.

this entire problem has been discussed in a companion volume, "Food Borne Infections and Intoxications."[18]

Epidemological evidence is available in abundance to support the statement that pasteurization destroys pathogenic bacteria in milk. Such diseases as typhoid fever and diphtheria, which were once scourges, have been greatly reduced. Milk pasteurization has had an important part in reducing these diseases. The former could probably be entirely stamped out were it not for the human carrier.

2. *Lowers Infant Mortality.* It is difficult to collect information on this point. It would also be difficult to plan an experiment and consequently, conclusions must be drawn from groups of infants which have received raw and pasteurized milk. The argument that milk pasteurization reduces infant mortality has been the center of much discussion. Some argument has arisen about causation of rickets or rachitis. Other argument has involved the changes brought about in the stomach by heated milk and raw milk. Brennemann[19] gave important data on this subject. He stated that raw milk was much more liable to cause the formation of indigestible hard curds in the stomach than pasteurized milk.

The results of feeding raw and pasteurized milk to infants was studied by Park and Holt[20] in New York City, who found that raw milk with a low bacterial content caused more cases of illness than the same milk given after pasteurization.

3. *Prolongs Keeping Quality.* While the real purpose of pasteurization of milk is not to make it keep longer, the heating involved does reduce the general bacterial population. This results in a product which will keep for a much longer time, especially when it is refrigerated. This is an important practical result of pasteurization. Prolonged keeping quality of pasteurized milk is an advantage gained with pasteurization even though it is not the original reason.

Pasteurization of Milk in the Final Package. After milk has been made safe by heat, the next problem is to keep it so by preventing reinfection. While opportunities for reinfection after bulk pasteurization are remote, they are possible as shown by Bray.[21] Consequently, possibility of pasteurization in the bottle has been studied. Carter,[22] North,[23] and Ayers and Johnson[24] all observed satisfactory reductions in bacterial content after pasteurization in the bottle. North used both submergence of the bottles and the shower-bath type of pasteurizer. Special caps are necessary and the tops of the bottles must be sound, else it will be difficult to secure tight seals. Carter found that a temperature of 65.6°C. (150°F.) for 30 minutes was best. Ayers and Johnson reported that a temperature of 62.8°C. (145°F.) for 30 minutes caused satisfactory bacterial reductions, but that bottles should be steamed for at least two minutes before being filled with

18. Tanner, F. W. 1933. Food-Borne Infections and Intoxications. The Garrard Press, Champaign, Ill., 439 pp.

19. Brennemann. 1916. J. Amer. Med. Assoc. 67, 1413-1419.

20. Park and Holt. 1903. Med. News 83, 1066.

21. Bray. 1922. Virginia Med. Mo. 48, 592-593.

22. Carter. 1911. J. Amer. Pub. Health Assoc. 1, 664.

23. North. 1911. Med. Rec. 80, 111-115.

24. Ayers and Johnson. 1914. J. Infect. Dis. 14, 217-241.

milk. When milk at an initial temperature of 10°C.(50°F.) was heated in bottles without agitation in water at about 62.8°C.(145°F.), the temperature of the milk in the top of the bottle reached 60°C.(140°F.) in about nine minutes before that in the bottom. Hammer and Hauser [14] found that milk pasteurized in bottles for 50 minutes at 62.8°C.(145°F.) was satisfactory. As temperatures higher than those just mentioned were used, the milk became less satisfactory.

Successful results were also reported by Weigmann,[25] Judkins and Downs,[26] Kufferath,[27] and Wright[28] as far as bacterial reduction is concerned. However, the difficulties of the process were pointed out. It is not only necessary to heat every particle of the milk to pasteurization temperature, but it is equally as important to cool the milk promptly. If it is not cooled, it may remain so long at incubation temperatures that bacteria will grow. Despite the advantages of bottle pasteurization, it has not been used to any extent.

Contamination after pasteurization must be prevented, as Bulmer [29] has pointed out. Pasteurization in the final package might make it more unlikely.

High Temperature-Short Time (Quick-Time) Pasteurization of Milk. This method involves heating milk to a higher temperature in shorter time than used in other methods. Most milk ordinances which permit flash or "high-short" pasteurization of milk place a minimum temperature at 71.1°C.(160°F.) for 15 seconds. This is the minimum stated in the United States Public Health Service Milk Ordinance and Code.[1] Higher temperatures are used for some other products. Flash pasteurization was not acceptable at one time to health officers because it was believed to be less efficient than the holding method. After much research, which has revealed that "high-short" pasteurized milk is safe, it is more generally acceptable. It has been accepted by committees of the American Public Health Association. Shrader [30] has reviewed in a fine report the bacteriological aspects of "high-short" pasteurization of milk. Supplee and Jensen [13] found that the dominant lethal factor in this method is temperature. The lethal value of elevated temperatures at a constant time of only a few seconds increases in a straight-line relationship up to 82.2 to 85°C.(180 to 185°F.) efficiency falling off rapidly at higher temperatures.

Yale and Breed [31] reported that high temperature-short time pasteurization was not as conducive to high counts of thermophilic bacteria as the long-time machines. Yale later reported results of experiments carried out in co-operation with the New York State Department of Health on the bacteria found in milk before and after pasteurization by a short-time pasteurizer at 71°C.(160°F.) for 15 seconds and after pasteurization by

25. Weigmann. 1914. Mitt. Deut. Milchw. Ver. 31, 149-165.
26. Judkins and Downs. 1918. Conn. Agr. Expt. Sta. Bull. 99.
27. Kufferath. 1921. Rev. in Abs. Bact. 7 (1923), 13-40.
28. Wright. 1923. So. Dakota Agr. Expt. Sta. Bull. 203.
29. Bulmer. 1938. J. Milk Tech. 1, 10-13.
30. Shrader. 1939. J. Milk. Tech. 2, 159-160.
31. Yale and Breed. 1932. Internatl. Assoc. Dairy and Milk Insp.,20th Ann. Rpt., 101.

the holder process at 61.7°C.(143°F.) for 30 minutes. Samples of the same milk were pasteurized under like conditions in the laboratory. The bacteriological counts determined on standard nutrient agar plates showed that pasteurization by the holder process was slightly more effective, the average count immediately following pasteurization being 17,200 per milliliter for the former as compared with 20,600 per milliliter for the latter. It was also of interest that the laboratory pasteurization methods gave approximately 50 per cent lower bacterial counts than when the milk was pasteurized under commercial conditions. Holding the milk for 24 hours 40 to 45°C.(4.4 to 7.2°F.) reduced the count of bottled pasteurized milk from 22,800 at the time of pasteurizing to 9,600 per milliliter at the end of the storage period. With the continued operation of the high-temperature pasteurizer the counts were increased from 22,000 for the first 25 minutes of operation to 34,000 after 30 to 90 minutes of operation. Foam collected from the layer on the surface of the milk of the pasteurizer yielded plate counts from two to 11 times higher than corresponding raw-milk samples. Yale [32] concluded from all of this work that high temperature-short time pasteurization produced as good a bottle of milk as did the 30-minute holding pasteurization, a conclusion in which Parfitt [33] later concurred.

The bacteriological problems relating to "high-short" pasteurization have been amply studied. A comprehensive investigation on high temperature-short time pasteurization was made by Mattick and Hiscox.[34] In their first series an old-type plant was used and the tabulated findings suggested that at the lowest tested temperature 70.4°C.(158°F.) and holding time of about 11.5 seconds tubercle bacilli in milk are killed, but that with this holding time if the temperature is below 71°C.(160°F.) the phosphatase test is positive, i.e., gives figures above 2.3 units. The second series with a modern plant of stainless-steel pressed plates showed still more definitely the high phosphatase figures at 71°C.(160°F.) or even 72.1°C.(162°F.) without holding. With even a few seconds holding, e.g., in a Stassane machine heated to 72.8 to 74.9°C.(163.4 to 167.2°F.) and held for 3.4 seconds, the phosphate test was negative. It was still negative at 66.9°C. (151.6°F.) but became positive at temperatures below this. The authors concluded that under practical conditions in a good plant a temperature of 72.1°C.(162°F.) for 15 seconds is satisfactory, offers a good margin of safety, and does not damage the cream line. Like approved "holder" types, accurate working is still somewhat at the mercy of the operator and indeed with high-temperature apparatus this is even more the case. Adequate control is especially necessary. They considered that this type of pasteurization should be permitted for pasteurizing by-products (skim milk, whey, etc.) under the Tuberculosis (Arrested Herds) Scheme 1938, and that there is also a case for serious consideration of "high temperature-short time" pasteurization as an official method alternative to the holder

32. Yale. 1933. N. Y. Agr. Exp. Sta. Tech. Bull. 207; Internatl. Assoc. Dairy and Milk Insp. 22nd Ann. Rpt., 62-69.
33. Parfitt. 1939. N. Y. State Assoc. Dairy and Milk Insp., 13th Ann. Rpt., 195-212.
34. Mattick and Hiscox. 1939. Med. Officer 61, 177-180.

process. A summary of information, especially bacteriological, was prepared by Dotterer [35] who believed that it could be accepted.

The Committee on Milk Supply of the Public Health Engineering Section of the American Public Health Association,[36] and the Committee on Milk Sanitation of the Conference of State Sanitary Engineers jointly considered the problems involved in high temperature-short time pasteurization. This method has not been approved because there seemed to be little assurance that every particle of milk will be heated to the required lethal temperature. The slightest lack of attention on the part of the operator might make it possible for improperly pasteurized milk to be supplied to the consumer. Development of a method which involved holding the milk for a short time at the lethal temperature, seemed to avoid some of the objections. Two types of these pasteurizers were in commercial use; in one the heating medium was hot water and in the other it was electricity. The first of the latter type was marketed under the name "Electropure." In view of the fact that this was quite a new pasteurizer, it was subjected to numerous and repeated tests by public-health authorities and private agencies before it was accepted. Some of the results of these investigations are presented below. These committees found this apparatus satisfactory, provided, certain recommendations which they prescribed were heeded. These were mainly mechanical and need not be listed here.

Various types of high temperature-short time pasteurizers were tested by joint committees of the American Public Health Association. These types were approved when certain recommendations of these committees were heeded. In the next Yearbook these same committees reported the York Plate pasteurizer to be efficient in destroying *Mycobacterium tuberculosis* and hemolytic streptococci. The results revealed an ample margin of safety in time and temperature when milk is heated to not less than 71.1°C. (160°F.) for not less than 15 seconds. The hemolytic streptococci survived heating without holding better than *Mycobacterium tuberculosis*. The bacteriological efficiencies of the method were reported at some length by Hileman and Leber [37] who compared the results with those secured by the older conventional methods.

Several special methods or pieces of apparatus have been developed. One of these, known as the Grindrod sterilizer, involved superheating milk under pressure with a finely divided jet of steam. Its efficiency was studied by Hucker and Hucker,[38] using milk cultures of pure strains of organisms of known heat resistance as well as uninoculated milk which had been allowed to develop a heat-resistant flora; 110°C. (230°F.) for one to two minutes eliminated all non-thermophilic organisms; thermophilic heat-resistant types were materially reduced at this temperature, but 115.5°C. (240°F.) for three to five minutes was required to free milk from them. The process may be adaptable to condensing and drying of milk. Its use

35. Dotterer. 1939. Internatl. Assoc. Milk Dealers, Assoc. Bull., 31st year, 13, 332; J. Milk Tech. 2 (1939), 197-198.
36. Amer. Pub. Health Assoc., Yearbook for 1931-32, 112-125; 1932-33, 89.
37. Hileman and Leber. 1941. J. Milk Tech. 4, 128-137.
38. Hucker and Hucker. 1929. N. Y. Agr. Expt. Sta. Bull. 155.

in the market-milk field may be confined to semitropical and tropical conditions where sterility is essential. This method destroys the cream line, gives a slight "boiled" flavor, and at the high temperature used there is a slight precipitation of albumin. Its advantages include the possibility of completely sterilizing milk, the rapidity of the process, and the removal of, in certain cases, the odors and flavors.

Another method of high temperature-short time pasteurization is termed stassanization which was compared to the holder method by Critien and Walker.[39] The stassanization temperature used for comparison is 75°C. (167°F.) with exposure for 16 to 22 seconds. No experiments are recorded, the authors apparently relying upon statements in various papers on the subject. They conclude that both methods are reliable as regards destruction of pathogenic bacteria but decide in favor of stassanization on the grounds of the slightly less alteration to the milk under this process and its greater economic advantages. They are careful to point out that this conclusion refers to the type of milk they have to deal with, i.e., goat's milk with few bacteria.

Destruction of pathogenic bacteria by the high temperature-short time method of pasteurization at 71.1°C.(160°F.) seems now to be well established. Workman [40] found this to be the case with many strains of pathogens causing the more important milk-borne diseases. Van Oijen [41] found that *Mycobacterium tuberculosis* was satisfactorily destroyed by the process discussed above as stassanization.

Dahlberg, Holland, and Miner [41a] successfully pasteurized milk by the "quick-time" method at 80.8°C.(177.5°F.) to 76.1°C.(169°F.) with the time interval above 60°C.(140°F.) varying from five to 24 seconds. Comparable pasteurization results were secured by the following:

Time above 60°C.(140°F.)	Highest temperature
5 seconds	81°C.(177.5°F.)
6 seconds	79.4°C.(175°F.)
12 seconds	76.6°C.(170°F.)
24 seconds	76.1°C.(169°F.)

Pasteurization by Electricity. Many attempts have been made to pasteurize milk by electricity. In 1894 Mason and others heated milk to 75.8°C. (168°F.), and at the same time subjected it to the effects of an electric current. Experiments at the University of Liverpool [42] showed that by means of specially constructed apparatus, not only could milk be sterilized, but that *Mycobacterium tuberculosis* therein could be destroyed. Satisfactory results were also reported by the use of a high tension current with a short period of exposure in New South Wales.[43] The advantages of not overheating, no coagulation, and the ability to use continuous flow, were reported. Members of the coliform group were destroyed. There was also

39. Critien and Walker. 1934. Ann. Rpt. on Health of the Maltese Islands during 1934.
40. Workman. 1941. Internatl. Assoc. Milk Dealers, Assoc. Bull. 22, 585-588.
41. Van Oijen. 1939. Tijdschr. Diergeneesk. 66, 1055-1075.
41a. Dahlberg *et al.* 1942. N. Y. Agr. Expt. Sta., Tech. Bull. 261; Internatl. Assoc. Milk Dealers, Assoc. Bull. 34, 174-178.
42. Dairy 25 (1913), 194.
43. Agr. Gaz. N. S. Wales 24 (1913), 1079.

a substantial reduction in all forms. No changes were induced in the milk. The same effects were reported by Kershaw.[44] In two cases, tuberculous milk was rendered free from living tuberculosis organisms and was regarded as a safe food. Lewis [45] reported that electricity was a satisfactory sterilizing agent for milk. The total bacterial count was reduced, *Escherichia coli* killed, and the milk was rendered noninfectious with organisms of tuberculosis. The University of Liverpool experiments were reported in full by Beattie and Lewis,[46] who carried out experiments for two purposes, to investigate the possibility of using the electric current as a sterilizing agent, and, if successful, to adapt it to large scale practice. They gave special consideration to the destruction of *Mycobacterium tuberculosis* and *Escherichia coli* and its allies. In the earlier experiments, direct current was used; it gave unsatisfactory results. There was evidence of destruction of bacteria, but the chemical changes in the milk were so pronounced that use of the direct current had to be given up. The initial experiments with the alternating current were sufficiently successful to justify further study. The details of the investigation may be left to a perusal of the original report. Beattie and Lewis stated that milk could be rendered free of *Escherichia coli* and *Mycobacterium tuberculosis* by the electrical method without raising the temperature higher than 63 to 64°C. They believed that this temperature effect was of too short duration to be the principal factor in explaining the action of the electric current. They observed a percentage reduction of 99.93 per cent, which caused a prolonged keeping quality. So little chemical change was caused that Beattie and Lewis referred to milk treated by electricity in their apparatus as "raw milk" free from pathogenic bacteria.

Anderson and Finkelstein [47] studied a patented electric pasteurizing apparatus installed at Camp Meade, Md. The milk was exposed to an alternating current of 2,300 volts. After being previously heated to 40°C. (104°F.), it was passed in rapid succession through four porcelain cups of about 200 ml. capacity, in each of which it came in contact with two electrodes and completed the circuit. The resistance of the milk to the passage of the electric current generated sufficient heat in about 20 seconds to raise the temperature to 70°C.(158°F.). A satisfactory reduction in the number of bacteria was noted when the machine was operated properly. The final product was equal to milk designated as Grade B pasteurized milk, and was often equal to Grade A milk sold in New York City. Practically all of the coliform organisms were destroyed. Treated milk kept well at from 5 to 10°C.(41 to 50°F.) for five days. The machine raised the temperature to about 30°C.(86°F.), irrespective of the initial temperature. Anderson and Finkelstein concluded that the heat generated was the active agent and not the current itself, because the bacterial content was not reduced when the initial temperature was below 25°C.(77°F.). Beattie

44. Kershaw. 1914. Engin. Mag. 47, 916-919.
45. Lewis. 1915. J. Bd. Agr., London, 21, 844.
46. Beattie and Lewis. 1920. Med. Res. Comm., Spec. Rpt. Series 49, 1-32; J. Hyg. 24 (1925), 123-137.
47. Anderson and Finkelstein. 1919. J. Dairy Sci. 2, 374-406.

and Lewis [46] still were of the opinion that the electricity itself and not the heat was the active agent in electrical pasteurization. Milk which was heavily seeded with *Mycobacterium tuberculosis*, when passed through the tube and treated with sufficient electric current to raise the temperature to 62 to 64°C.(143.6 to 147.2°F.), failed to infect guinea pigs; however, tuberculosis milk raised to but 60 or 62°C.(140 or 143.6°F.) produced slight infections. Generalized tuberculosis appeared in guinea pigs inoculated before treatment.

Milk was heated by Collumbein [48] to pasteurization temperatures by the resistance offered to a current of 3,000 volts. The count was reduced to a maximum of 25,000 per ml. As has been indicated in other fields of applied bacteriology, percentage reductions are meaningless, since with a 99.9 per cent reduction, the treated milk may have a high count, or contain pathogens.

Another study of the "electropure" pasteurizer was made by Robison.[49] This investigator stated that the following conditions were involved in the ideal process of pasteurizing milk:

1. Preservation of the cream rising phenomenon, or cream line.
2. Retention of the natural taste.
3. Preservation of the activity of natural vitamins.
4. Prolongation of the keeping quality.
5. Great reduction of total number of bacteria.
6. Destruction of pathogenic microorganisms.

The "Electropurifier" was put to a severe test by a milk heavily inoculated with *Mycobacterium tuberculosis* (5,000 cells per ml.). The results were practically perfect. One pig developed tuberculosis when given the infected "purified" milk, but it was stated that there was evidence of infection before the experiment started. As Robison stated, one would hardly ever expect to have a milk sample with 5,000 tubercle bacteria per ml.

On September 10, 1925, a dairy in Pittsburgh (Irwin, *et al.*[50]) requested permission of the Pennsylvania Department of Health to use the Electropure Process of milk treatment. The secretary of health appointed a committee to investigate the efficiency of the process, and on April 13, 1926, the committee report was presented. This report gave a description of the apparatus used and a record of the results obtained in the experimental plant. Milk inoculated with *Corynebacterium diphtheriae, Eberthella typhosa*, hemolytic streptococcus, *Mycobacterium tuberculosis* (bovine and human), *Escherichia coli*, and *Aerobacter aerogenes* was used in measuring the efficiency of the process. Temperatures of 65.6°C.(150°F.), 68°C. (155°F.), and 71°C.(160°F.) were used, and the retention period in the electric heater varied between eight and 10 seconds. It was their opinion, based on results of experimental work, that the process was a reasonably safe method for pasteurization of milk, and merited a thorough trial under commercial conditions, as well as continued investigation as to its efficiency in destroying the tubercle bacillus.

48. Collumbien. 1923. Lait 3, 332-334.
49. Robison. 1923. J. Ind. Eng. Chem. 15, 514-518.
50. Irwin *et al*. 1927. Penn. Assoc. Dairy & Milk Insp., 3rd Ann. Rpt. 143-146.

On December 21, 1926, the committee submitted its final report. This report gave the results of experimental work with *Escherichia coli* and *Mycobacterium tuberculosis*. Samples of treated and untreated milk were collected to determine the total number of bacteria and of *Escherichia coli* present. Samples were also collected from a dairy to show the results obtained by heating milk to 62.8°C.(145°F.) for 30 minutes in one type of horizontal-coil vat pasteurizer. It was the conclusion of the committee that the results of the work set forth in the final report confirmed the opinion given in the former report, namely, that the method known as the Electropure Process was a reasonably safe method for the pasteurization of milk. The bacteriological results obtained in a study of the process under commercial conditions confirm this opinion and supported the findings obtained under experimental conditions.

Prescott[51] also had an opportunity to observe electric pasteurization over about a year's time. Milk was pumped through the apparatus at such a speed that a 220-volt alternating 60-cycle current raised the temperature to 70 to 71.1°C.(158 to 160°F.) and at that speed 12 seconds were required to pass the milk through the treating chamber. The results showed great uniformity of treatment, normal taste and cream volume, and excellent keeping quality. The reduction of bacteria was highly efficient. No colon or tubercle bacilli were found among the surviving types.

The construction and operation of the "electropurifier," mentioned above, was described by Bailey.[52] The electric heater or, as it is called, the "electropurifier," contains an oblong chamber approximately three by four inches in cross section and 32 inches high, two opposite sides being of carbon and separated from each other by sides of hard rubber. There is an electrical connection on each of the carbon sides of the box, and a 60-cycle, 220-volt current is used in heating. Milk enters the bottom of the electric chamber and acts as a conductor for the current between the sides of the box. A temperature of 71.1°C.(160°F.) is used, and the time of passage of the milk through this machine is approximately 10 seconds. An automatic temperature control regulates the temperature of the milk leaving the heater by controlling the speed of the pump and, consequently, the rate of flow of milk, the electrical input to the machine being constant. Statements are made that there is no change in the flavor of the milk as it goes through the machine, and that a phenomenal bactericidal efficiency is obtained. It is said that no attempt is made to explain the action as there are different opinions regarding it, the various opinions being listed as heat alone, heat and electricity, and electrochemical action; the company believed that it is a "heat-plus" proposition.

Van Leersum[53] also found that the electric current was germicidal. The high frequency current was just as germicidal, whether carbon or copper electrodes were used. Demeter[54] reported the effectiveness of

51. Prescott. 1927. Amer. J. Pub. Health 17, 221-223.
52. Bailey. 1927. Ann. Rpt., Penn. Assoc. Dairy and Milk Insp., 165-68.
53. Van Leersum. 1926. Nederland. Tijdschr. Geneesk. 2, 234.
54. Demeter. 1927. Milch. Forsch. 4, 100-105.

electric pasteurization. Richter and Wendt [55] compared the amount of direct flow through two types of flash pasteurizers. The results showed that in one type of pasteurizer, which was cylindrical in shape, portions of the milk passed through in a few seconds, while other portions remained for as long as four minutes. The top of the other type of pasteurizer was larger in diameter than the bottom. The maximum and minimum time required for milk to go through this type was 70 and 15 seconds, respectively. In the latter type, the destruction of *Escherichia coli* was very complete. At the California Agricultural Experiment Station the Electropure process was reported to yield more effective destruction of bacteria in ice cream mix than the holder method. Carpenter [56] stated that the electrical method freed milk of viable tubercle bacilli. The milk which was used was heavily inoculated with *Mycobacterium tuberculosis* and contained from 2,400,000 to 4,000,000 cells per ml. According to Yale,[57] the high temperature, 72.2 to 73.3°C.(162 to 164°F.), attained in the Electropure pasteurizer caused a marked reduction in the thermophilic bacteria in milk. Devereux [58] reported the Electropurifier to be very efficient when operated at 71.1°C.(160°F.). This temperature was found to be reached when the milk had traveled about two-thirds of the distance, having been exposed to this temperature only 15 to 20 seconds. Milk inoculated with sporeforming bacteria, including *Bacillus anthracis*, was passed through the machine with a reduction of from 71.5 to 99.9 per cent of the spores. Tubes containing the same milk treated in a manner similar to steam sterilization showed a reduction in the sporeforming organisms of 0 to 13 per cent. Gelpi and Devereux [59] reported that the Electropure process gave greater destruction of spores of bacteria than pasteurization at 62.8°C. (143.8°F.). A series of commercial milk samples were treated by Stabler [60] in the Electropure apparatus and compared with specimens of the same milk treated in the laboratory at 62°C.(143.6°F.) for 30 minutes.

The Electropure laboratory unit was sterilized after each run in a manner not practicable under commercial conditions. The milk was electrically heated for five minutes. Under these rather artificial conditions the bacterial count for milk held at 62°C.(143.6°F.) for 30 minutes was practically identical (97.2 to 97.7 per cent reduction) with that with the Electropure unit heating the milk to 73°C.(163.4°F.). By both methods the surviving organisms included streptococci, sarcinae and micrococci, aerobic spore bearing bacilli and anaerobes, and no definite differences between the two methods were disclosed. No true *Escherichia coli* occurred in milk pasteurized by either method. When the electric temperature was 62°C.(143.6°F.) only a reduction of 98.3 per cent of organisms was obtained. Electrical pasteurization diminished the rate at which cream rises while not affecting the total cream content. Stabler's results were con-

55. Richter and Wendt. 1926. Milch. Forsch. 3, 200-208.
56. Carpenter. 1929. J. Infect. Dis. 44, 347-356.
57. Yale. 1930. J. Bact. 19, 46.
58. Devereux. 1930. Amer. J. Pub. Health 20, 1009-1010.
59. Gelpi and Devereux. 1930. J. Dairy Sci. 13, 368-371.
60. Stabler. 1931. Amer. J. Hyg. 14, 433-452.

cerned mainly with percentage reduction in bacterial numbers and to some extent with types. The effect of the process on pathogenic bacteria was not studied.

Holmquist [61] tested the Electropure process for the N. Y. State Department of Public Health in co-operation with the United States Public Health Service and the Department of Health of New York City. These tests extended over two weeks and were as stringent as they could be made. It was found from these tests that under normal operating conditions milk rendered highly infectious with *Mycobacterium tuberculosis* when heated in the Electropure apparatus operated at a mean temperature of 67.2°C. (153.9°F.) and held for a period of 12.4 seconds, was rendered noninfectious to guinea pigs. The pump-stop temperature during that run was 65.6°C.(150°F.). The next lower pump-stop temperature at which the apparatus was tested was 58.4°C.(138°F.). In other words, there were no test runs between the pump-stop temperature of 65.6°C.(150°F.) and 58.4°C.(138°F.).

These tests demonstrated to the satisfaction of the Public Health Council of the State of New York that this high temperature-short time process of pasteurization was equally as efficient, dependable, and safe as the so-called holding process of pasteurization, and it was approved by the Council and the State Department of Health on the condition that every particle of milk be heated to a temperature of not less than 71°C.(160°F.) and held at that temperature for not less than 20 seconds. This condition provided factors of safety of at least 3.3°C.(6.1°F.) and 7.6 seconds. Although this temperature factor of safety is approximately that generally accepted as satisfactory for the holding process of pasteurization, the time factor is negligible when compared with that required for the holding process. When dealing with temperatures around 71.1°C.(160°F.), however, seconds count more than minutes at temperatures from 61.1°C.(142°F.) to 62.78°C.(145°F.). The time factor has not received as much study as it should in this method of pasteurization. Using the Electropure Pasteurizer, Supplee and Jensen [13] worked with times of 15 seconds to as little as .8 second over a temperature range of 62.8°C. (145°F.) to 85°C. (185°F.) High bacteria effectiveness was observed for periods as short as .8 second.

Effect of Ultraviolet Light on Bacteria in Milk. Although ultraviolet light is lethal to microorganims, when it can reach them directly, it does not destroy all of them in milk. This is because the rays cannot penetrate opaque substances like milk. Besides this milk which has been subjected to irradiation with ultraviolet, has changed flavor and odor. Ayers and Johnson,[62] Schultz,[63] and Houghton and Davis [64] observed very low percentage reductions of viable microorganisms. Attempts to use ultraviolet rays for this purpose were also unsuccessful in the hands of Gerber and

61. Holmquist. 1931. Internatl. Assoc. Dairy and Milk Insp., 20th Ann. Rpt., 1932, 79-100; see also next paper.

62. Ayers and Johnson. 1913. Centbl. Bakt., Pt. 2, 40, 109-131.

63. Schultz. 1927. Ztschr. Fleisch. u. Milchhyg. 37, 131-135.

64. Houghton and Davis. 1914. Amer. J. Pub. Health 4, 224-240.

Hirschi.[65] Mancovitz [66] found it possible to destroy many bacteria in milk in less than 45 seconds' exposure to ultraviolet ray. Such milk, however, was unmarketable owing to off-flavors. Using an average time of 19 seconds, and average reduction in bacterial counts from 69,000 per ml. in the untreated raw milk to 4,500 per ml. in the treated milk was obtained. The taste and smell of the milk was not affected by the shorter time exposure.

The number of bacteria in low-count milks was not greatly changed in experiments by Wechel [67]; however, there were reductions in high-count milks. These were of little significance since they averaged 28 per cent. It was also found that the keeping quality of irradiated milk was improved even in milk of good quality where there was no appreciable effect of radiation on the bacteria count. By introducing cultures of *Streptococcus lactis, Escherichia coli,* or *Bacillus coagulus* into the milk it was found that the radiation as applied to milk had no selective action on the various organisms normally found in milk.

Intensity and spectral characteristics of the radiation employed greatly influence lethal effectiveness of ultraviolet rays (Supplee, Flanigan, and Jensen [68]). Using the "Sterilamp" of the Westinghouse Electric Mfg. Co., they found that greater bactericidal effect was obtained with a smooth-flowing milk film than with films flowing over corrugated cooler surface. Radiation in the 2,200 to 2,300 Å region gave erratic bactericidal results. Sublethal doses might cause stimulation. Percentage reduction in bacterial counts of raw mixed milk in excess of 90 per cent and frequently up to 95 to 98 per cent were obtained with a high degree of regularity by preferred methods of applying ultraviolet radiation of appropriate intensity and spectral characteristics.

Cooling of Pasteurized Milk. Pasteurized milk must be cooled promptly and well, else the bacteria which have survived will grow. If cooling is not adequate the milk may remain too long at a temperature which is incubation for bacteria. The difficulties involved are probably the main reasons why pasteurization in the final package has not been successful. Ayers, Bowen, and Johnson [69] reported that milk in containers not larger than quart bottles could be cooled by forcing cold air downward over them when the temperature of the air was 4.4°C.(40°F.) or lower. Brew [70] studied the subject of cooling under various conditions. He did not find air cooling efficient at temperatures above the freezing point.

In former years, it was suggested that cold shock after heating would destroy many bacteria which had survived any heat treatment. This has found little support in experiments of various kinds. Ayers and Johnson [71] promptly cooled milk which had been pasteurized in the laboratory at 62.8°C.(145°F.) and 71.1°C.(160°F.) for one-half hour. No evidence could be secured that prompt cooling had any effect on bacterial numbers.

65. Gerber and Hirschi. 1906. Molk. Ztg. 16-52.
66. Mancovitz. 1918. Milk Dealer 27, 33.
67. Wechel. 1935. Internatl. Assoc. Dairy and Milk Insp., 24th Ann. Rpt. 69.
68. Supplee, Flanigan, and Jensen. 1941. J. Dairy Sci. 24, 1055-1070.
69. Ayers, Bowen, and Johnson. 1916. U. S. Dept. Agr. Bull. 420.
70. Brew. 1929. J. Dairy Sci. 12, 304-319.
71. Ayers and Johnson. 1913. U. S. Dept. Agr., Bur. Anim. Indus. Bull. 161.

BACTERIA IN PASTEURIZED MILK

Bacteriologists once believed that sporeforming bacteria mainly survived pasteurization in milk. This idea resulted from observations on heating pure cultures of bacteria in other menstrua where most of them were destroyed. A different situation was later found to obtain for milk. Some of the earlier information resulted from experiments in which the milk was boiled. Under such conditions, sporeforming bacteria would probably be about the only types which would survive. When lower temperatures were used, nonsporeforming species were found. The literature on this subject has become voluminous. Ayers and Johnson [62] by means of their so-called "milk-tube" method were able to secure information which helped to correct some of the erroneous opinions which had been held previously. Owing to survival and development of nonsporeforming, lactic acid-producing bacteria, milk pasteurized at temperatures generally considered to be acceptable for destruction of pathogenic bacteria, soured in the normal manner. They found that the relative proportion of the groups of peptonizing, lactic acid-producing, alkali-forming, and inert bacteria in pasteurized milk was about the same as in raw milk. Ayers and Johnson, as did Weigmann [72] et al., observed lactic acid-producing bacteria with sufficiently high thermal death times to survive ordinary pasteurization procedures. Russell and Hastings [73] reported a micrococcus from milk which withstood 76°C. (168.8°F.) for 10 minutes. When studying the ability of streptococci to survive pasteurization, Ayers and Johnson [62, 71] stated that the "absolute" and "majority" thermal death points of the bacteria should be taken into account. They called attention to the fact that only relatively small amounts of the total volume of the pasteurized milk can be examined, and that this factor in technic is, therefore, very important when results are interpreted. The "majority" thermal death point is different from the "absolute" thermal death point. Prucha [74] attacked this problem in two different ways: first, the effect of pasteurization on the entire bacterial flora in milk; second, the different bacterial species found in milk were obtained in pure cultures and then subjected to the pasteurizing temperature. The results obtained corresponded, in general, with the results of previous investigators. Pasteurization reduced the bacterial count in the milk in general about 99 per cent. However, under certain conditions, the milk became heavily contaminated with bacteria that were resistant to the pasteurizing temperature. When that happened, pasteurized milk had high bacterial counts. The flora usually consisted of varying numbers of different species, each species varying in numbers from day to day. According to Prucha, various methods employed in connection with milk production and handling affect the number of bacteria and the percentages of different species. Not only the methods of operation, but also the weather and the climatic temperatures will affect the bacterial flora of milk. The source of these bacteria was not fully demonstrated in all cases. There was some evidence that they came from utensils. Incom-

72. Weigmann et al. 1916. Centbl. Bakt., Pt. 2, 45, 63-107.
73. Russell and Hastings. 1902. Centbl. Bakt., Pt. 2, 8, 462-469.
74. Prucha. 1927. Amer. J. Pub. Health 17, 356-359.

plete steaming of utensils permitted some organisms to survive, while those that are more sensitive to heat were completely destroyed. Heat-resisting bacteria did not grow very fast in milk when the milk was kept at lower temperatures. They did not seriously affect the keeping quality of the milk when the milk was kept at 15.6°C.(60°F.) or lower. However, the high counts in freshly pasteurized milk, whether the counts are due to thermophiles or to the heat-resisting bacteria or to the spore-producing bacteria, should always be considered to indicate neglect somewhere along the journey of the milk as it passes from the cow to the final container, the bottle. A later report was made by Brannon and Prucha.[75] Sterile milk was inoculated with the pure cultures and the milk was heated at temperatures between 55.5°C.(132°F.) and 62.2°C.(144°F.). Thirty of the organisms studied were greatly reduced in numbers as low as 55.5°C.(132°F.) with four or five exceptions. All nonsporeforming bacteria were destroyed at 61.1°C.(142°F.), but no sporeforming organism was completely destroyed at 62.2°C.(144°F.).

Results of experiments by Thurston and Olson [76] also showed that lactic acid-producing bacteria survived pasteurization of low-count milk during storage. Coagulation occurred at low acidities, probably owing to the production of a rennin-like enzyme by the bacteria. There was no tendency for peptonizing bacteria to overgrow other types in raw or pasteurized bottled milk held for four days at 2.2 to 13.3°C.(36 to 56°F.). The pasteurized bottled milk tended to develop a "cappy" flavor after two days' storage at the above temperatures. Prouty's [77] work on pasteurizing low-count milk confirmed again present-day knowledge on this subject. Based on a study of 75 corresponding samples, each of raw and commercially pasteurized milk, pasteurization at 61.6 to 62.8°C.(143 to 145°F.) for 30 minutes resulted in a decrease in the percentage of acid-forming bacteria from 29.4 to 18.8, a decrease in the percentage of the proteolytic group from 7.0 to 5.0, and an increase from 63.6 to 76.2 per cent in the alkali-forming and inert group. After 24 hours' incubation at 21.1°C.(70°F.) the group percentage in raw and pasteurized milks, respectively, were as follows: acid-forming, 92.1 and 12.4; alkali-forming and inert, 7.35 and 86.4. No significant differences existed in the proportion of the proteolytic group in the two kinds of milk. After 48 hours' incubation at 70°F. the group percentages in raw and pasteurized milks were as follows: acid-forming, 96.0 and 76.1; alkali-forming and inert, 3.96 and 23.7 per cent, respectively. The proteolytic group constituted less than one per cent of the flora of either type of milk. Twenty per cent of the pasteurized samples developed a pronounced bitter flavor without accumulation of more than .4 per cent acid.

Heat resistance of bacteria and the factors which influence it have been discussed in several other places in this book. In general, the same principles may be said to be involved in destruction of bacteria in milk by pasteurization that are involved when other foods are heated for destruc-

75. Brannon and Prucha. 1927. Ill. Agr. Expt. Sta. Ann. Rpt., 158-162.
76. Thurston and Olson. 1933. West Virginia Agr. Expt. Sta. Bull. 225.
77. Prouty. 1934. J. Dairy Sci. 17, 115-120; see also 15 (1932), 99-112.

tion of bacteria. The process is not a simple one but subject to many conditions. Among these the vigor and condition of the bacterial cells, themselves, have not received sufficient attention. In experiments by Sherman and Stark [78] age of bacterial cells influenced greatly their susceptibility to heat, young cells succumbing easily. Milks held at temperature at which bacterial growth takes place (e.g., 15.5°C.) show a greater percentage destruction of bacteria than occurs in similar milks when fresh or when held at a temperature (e.g., 4.4°C.) too low to allow multiplication of the bacteria involved. Some important milk bacteria (e.g., "ropy milk" types' may be entirely eliminated from milk by pasteurization when the cells are in a young and growing condition, while the old cells of the same organisms can withstand the process. Anderson and Meanwell [79] observed fluctuations in heat resistance of two streptococci strains at pasteurization temperatures, the most important being an increased resistance as the temperature for growth was lowered below the optimum. At these temperatures, one showed a progressive increase in resistance during the early logarithmic growth phase. Similar changes were shown by a second streptococcus isolated from pasteurized milk. Both cultures showed increased resistance as a result of 24 hours' cold storage. This was most marked when the low temperature was applied during the early logarithmic phase of growth. Both strains were *Streptococcus thermophilus* types; it is not known whether other strains behave in the same manner. The practical application is in relation to the usual practice of low-temperature storage of milk before pasteurization and its possible influence on increasing the heat resistance of the streptococci so held. Another factor to which less attention has been given is the influence of hydrogen-ion concentration of the milk. Mattick and Nichols [80] stated that the number of bacteria surviving decreases as the hydrogen-ion concentration decreases. This observation is in keeping with results secured when heat is applied to other acid foods.

The bacteria which may survive pasteurization are varied and may be arranged into the following groups:

1. Heat-resistant, nonsporeforming bacteria. These are said to be of two classes (Ayers [81]): first, those which have a low majority thermal death point in which only a few cells survive; and second, those which have a high majority thermal death point. Proper pasteurization at 62.8°C.(145°F.) for 30 minutes allows only a few of the first class to survive in large numbers but those of the second class may be present in large numbers. If there are large numbers of heat-resistant bacteria in the raw milk they will survive to appear in the pasteurized milk. These organisms can be of no great significance since they are nonpathogenic. Hucker,[82] when studying 180 strains of cocci which resisted pasteurization, found that *Streptococcus thermophilus* Orla-Jensen was the predominating coccus in freshly pasteurized milk. Various Micrococci encountered in pasteurized milk were believed to indicate use of dirty utensils by Hileman, Leber, and Speck.[83] Some of these organisms may be of interest in view of their ability to form products which are toxic by mouth. Breed (chairman)[84] reported variable re-

78. Sherman and Stark. 1929. J. Dairy Sci. 12, 385-393.
79. Anderson and Meanwell. 1936. J. Dairy Res. 7, 182-191.
80. Mattick and Nichols. 1935. J. Dairy Res. 6, 125-129.
81. Ayers. 1923. Proc. World's Dairy Cong. 1, 541-549.
82. Hucker. 1928. N. Y. Agr. Expt. Sta. Tech. Bull. 134.
83. Hileman, Leber, and Speck. 1941. J. Dairy Sci. 24, 305-315.
84. Breed (Chairman) . 1936. Amer. Pub. Health Assoc. Yearbook, 1936, 103-105.

sistances to heating in milk at 62.8°C.(145°F.) for 30 minutes. These organisms are frequently found on plates made from pasteurized milk. Investigation revealed that some micrococci of sanitary significance might survive pasteurization in milk at 62.8°C. (145°F.) for 30 minutes. Survival of streptococci is an interesting problem because of its possible significance. Some streptococci have been connected with pathologic conditions, while other species are considered to be very desirable. Ayers, Johnson, and Davis [85] reported that certain streptococci from pathologic sources survived heating in milk at 60°C.(140°F.) for 30 minutes.

Peiser [86] found in milk and cream pasteurized at 63°C.(145.4°F.) a number of strains of the *Bacterium lactis acidi* type, whose thermal death point in broth was below pasteurization temperature. The average thermal death point is in whole milk 5°C., in separated milk 2.5°C., and in whey .5°C., higher than in bouillon. These results indicate that the protection given to the suspended lactic bacteria by the casein and coagulated albumin of separated milk raises their thermal death point 5°C. These results have been confirmed by Ayers and Johnson [87] who studied the subject with a great number of *Streptococci*. The thermal death points of 139 cultures of streptococci isolated from cow feces, from the udder and the mouth of the cow, and from milk and cream showed a wide variation when the heating was performed in milk for 30 minutes under conditions similar to pasteurization. At 60°C.(140°F.), the lowest pasteurizing temperature, 89 cultures, or 64.03 per cent, survived; at 62.8°C.(145°F.), the usual temperature for pasteurizing, 46, or 33.07 per cent survived; and at 71.1°C.(160°F.), 2.58 per cent of the cultures survived; all were destroyed at 73.9°C.(165°F.).

The streptococci from the udder were, on the whole, less resistant and those from milk and cream more resistant to heat in general. This was confirmed by a very extensive investigation reported by Ayers and Johnson. [88] Streptococci isolated from milk, cow feeds, mouth of the cow, etc., showed wide differences in heat resistance when studied in milk. Ayers and Johnson stated that two classes of streptococci seemed to survive pasteurization: (a) Streptococci which have a low majority thermal death point, but among which a few cells are able to survive the pasteurizing temperature. This ability of a few bacteria to withstand the pasteurizing temperature may be due to certain resistant characteristics peculiar to a few cells, or may be due to some protective influence in the milk. (b) Streptococci which have a high majority thermal death point. When such is the case, the bacteria survive because the majority thermal death point is above the temperature used in pasteurization. This ability to resist destruction by heating is a permanent characteristic of certain strains of streptococci. Ayers and Johnson made their studies in milk under conditions which probably reflect those in actual pasteurization by the holder process.

Microscopic examination of bottled pasteurized milk by Way [89] showed large numbers of streptococci occurring usually in pairs and sometimes in chains of four or six. In raw milk the chains were longer. Agar plate preparations showed predominance of small "pin-point" colonies. After heating a specimen of milk containing 80,000 of these cells, their concentration was practically unchanged. They withstood 72.5°C.(162°F.) for one hour. These organisms were traced to cow feces and Way believed that large numbers of them indicated insanitary conditions.

Thermoduric Bacteria. These are heat-resistant bacteria which are not thermophilic. They survive pasteurization temperatures but do not develop at them. They are known to exist in the udder and also reach milk from utensils which harbor them. Hileman [90] prepared a review of the literature dealing with these forms. Maack [91] believed that they came from

85. Ayers, Johnson, and Davis. 1918. J. Infect. Dis. 23, 290-300.
86. Peiser. 1915. Science 42, 320.
87. Ayers and Johnson. 1914. J. Agr. Res. 2, 321-330.
88. Ayers and Johnson. 1924. J. Bact. 9, 279-300.
89. Way. 1925. Internatl. Assoc. Dairy and Milk Insp., 14th Ann. Rpt., 179-183.
90. Hileman. 1940. J. Dairy Sci. 23, 1143-1160.
91. Maack. 1941. Milk Dealer 30, 84-87.

utensils and apparatus which had not been thoroughly cleaned. Prucha and Maack [92] found many of these bacteria to be Gram-positive, coccus forms coming mainly from utensils. A new thermoduric bacterium, *Sarcina thermodurica* was reported by Wainess and Parfitt.[93] This organism resisted pasteurization and was isolated from milking machines and other utensils. Introduction of tryptone glucose skim-milk agar as the standard plating medium changed the picture for thermoduric bacteria, as pointed out by Hileman, Moss, and Stead.[94] They believed that a higher percentage of bacteria in raw milk are now appearing as thermoduric forms. Season and quality of raw milk contribute to variations in the number of thermoduric bacteria. Macy and Erekson [95] stated that thermo-tolerant organisms may be found in low-count as well as in high-count milk, but a higher proportion of the poorer quality milk will be difficult to pasteurize satisfactorily regardless of the season. Fewer bacteria survived laboratory pasteurization in winter than in summer, which Macy and Erekson believed was due to more thermoduric bacteria in summer milk. Both utensils and faulty cooling were said to be the cause. Careful washing of utensils was one method of meeting the problem of thermoduric bacteria.

Mallman, Bryan, and Fox's Procedure for Detecting Source of Thermoduric Bacteria in Milk. High counts of bacteria in pasteurized milk are often due to thermoduric bacteria and not improper pasteurization. While these bacteria are of no public-health significance, they do indicate unclean equipment and unclean practice in the dairy. After much study of the problem, Mallmann, Bryan, and Fox [96] suggested a standard of 40,000 bacteria per milliliter in milk incubated at 56 to 60°C.(132.8 to 140°F.) for two hours as the limit for objectionable numbers of thermoduric bacteria. The procedure was as follows:

1. Place five-ml. to 10-ml. samples of milk suspected of containing thermoduric bacteria in an incubator at a temperature of 58-60°C.(136.4-140°F.) and incubate for two hours.

2. By means of the microscope, with the usual procedure, count the bacteria which are present.

3. Samples showing more than 40,000 bacteria per milliliter contain thermoduric bacteria in excessive numbers.

Graham and Orme's [97] Procedure for Detecting Thermoduric Bacteria in Milk. This procedure consists of two steps, the first to check the efficiency of pasteurization in the plant being inspected and the second to detect the offending shipper. In the investigation of an outbreak, samples should be taken from all vats in the plant at the conclusion of the holding process and before cooling. Each sample is cooled in the sample bottle and taken to the laboratory. Here, the sample is divided and a portion repasteurized and original samples are then replated. Several dilutions should be used and incubation should be at 37°C.(98.6°F.). If thermoduric organisms are present there will be little or no reduction in the count on the plates from the repasteurized sample. In such cases individual samples are taken from each producer's milk and part of each of these subjected to laboratory pasteurization. Plates are then prepared using a dilution of 1:1000 for the raw milk and 1:100 for the pasteurized. The presence of thermoduric organisms will be indicated by a high count on the plates from the pasteurized

92. Prucha and Maack. 1940. J. Bact. 40, 157.
93. Wainess and Parfitt. 1940. Idem. 40, 157.
94. Hileman, Moss, and Stead. 1941. J. Dairy Sci. 24, 799-805.
95. Macy and Erekson. 1941. Internatl. Milk Dealers Assoc., Bull. 34.
96. Mallmann, Bryan, and Fox. 1941. N. Y. Assoc. Dairy and Milk Insp., 14th Ann. Rpt.. 167-178.
97. Graham and Orme. 1941. Canad. Pub. Health J. 32, 70-71.

samples. In such cases, further work will have to be done on the farm. Improperly cared for milking machines are often the cause of the trouble.

Marcus' [98] **Method for Determination of the Number of Thermoduric Bacteria in Milk.** Control of thermoduric bacteria in milk in the Boston area is accomplished with results of laboratory pasteurization experiments. Marcus stated that 10-ml. samples of milk are collected in 18-ml. aluminum screw-cap vials and placed in a water bath at 61.9°C.(143.5°F.) for 30 minutes. Addition of the cold-milk samples causes the temperature to drop. The holding period is computed from the time the temperature returns to 143.5°F. Counts are made with the standard plating medium with incubation at 32°C.(89.6°F.).

Myers and Pence [98a] **Method for Laboratory Examination of Raw Milk Supplies for Thermoduric Bacteria.** The technic of examination of raw milk for thermoduric bacteria was stated as follows: After a 5 ml. sample of milk in a screw-capped test tube has been pasteurized in the laboratory at 61.°C.(143°F.) for 30 minutes, it is vigorously shaken. With a standard loop, giving .001 ml. of milk (occasionally one giving .01 ml.) a loopful of the milk sample is transferred to the oval culture tube containing about 4 ml. of melted tryptone-glucose-extract agar, which has been previously sterilized and cooled to 45°C. The loop is moved back and forth through the agar to remove all of the milk from the loop. The agar medium and milk are then mixed by swinging the tube through a long arc. The tube is then laid on the table with the open end resting on a strip of wood or metal one-eighth inch thick, to cause the medium to flow to a point 2½ to 3 inches from the bottom on the tube. When the agar is solidified, the tubes are incubated at from 36° to 37°C. for 48 hours. The colonies are counted in the usual manner. Fischer and Johns [98b] found this procedure to be more satisfactory than others proposed for the same purpose.

2. **Thermophilic bacteria which grow well at pasteurization temperatures.** These bacteria have caused some interesting problems in dairy bacteriology. Some of them grow only at temperatures around 55°C.(131°F.) while others develop at lower temperatures also. The former would not develop on the standard agar plates incubated at 37°C.(98.6°F.) while some of the latter might. Introduction of a lower temperature of incubation, 32°C.(89.6°F.) will complicate the situation, particularly in respect to comparison of results with the new medium and those with the old one.

A standard plate count, as ordinarily determined, especially of pasteurized milk, probably does not reveal the presence of thermophilic and thermoduric bacteria. These organisms may be present in pasteurized milk in large numbers and yet not be revealed by the plate count. They are significant because they may attack some of the milk consistently, either fermenting lactose or decomposing proteins and producing off-flavors and bad odors. In view of this fact, many boards of health have not concerned themselves with these organisms. They have taken the attitude that since they do not develop under ordinary conditions their presence may be ignored. This is a questionable position because thermophilic bacteria are just as much a part of the bacterial population of milk as any other flora. Furthermore, the thermophilic bacteria may be a good index of undesirable conditions in the production of the milk. Another reason why they have been practically ignored is because they are nonpathogenic. The Connecticut State Board of Health, in its Annual Report for the year 1937, page 195, gives the results of a short survey to determine the presence of these organisms in market milk. Direct microscope counts by the Breed method and the standard agar plate were made on samples of pasteurized milk for about a year. For this purpose only large rods and sporeformers were counted, although it is known that other types of thermophilic and thermoduric organisms exist. Nearly 20 per cent of all samples examined contained these organisms. The bureau which did this work contended that detection of thermophilic bacteria in pasteurized milk by cultural and microscope methods was desirable and that such counts would contribute isformation obtainable in no other way as concerning plant practice.

98. Marcus. 1942. N. Y. Assoc. Dairy and Milk Insp., 15th Ann Rpt.
98a. Myers and Pence. 1941. J. Milk Tech. 4, 18-25.
98b. Fischer and Johns. 1942. Idem. 5, 269-275.

Rogers and Frazier [99] believed a high number of thermophilic bacteria in milk indicated one or more of the following: the pasteurizing plant may be receiving unusual contamination; it may be repasteurizing milk brought back from the wagons; the walls of the pasteurizer may have a thin layer of cooked milk in which thermophiles grow; the construction of the pasteurizer may be defective so that some of the milk fails to reach the pasteurizing temperature; there may be an excessive amount of foam which is not heated to temperature; or the vats may not be cleaned between runs. Ward, Adams, and McCutcheon [100] observed thermophilic bacteria predominating in nearly 50 per cent of the samples of pasteurized milk which they examined. In other samples they were present in lesser numbers. Thermophilic bacteria are probably the cause of one type of "pin-point" colony. Wright [101] claimed that these are largely *Streptococcus thermophilus* and are thermoduric. Ordinary standard media containing milk or lactose should be employed.

In view of the fact that the standard agar plate is not sufficient to show the real bacterial condition of pasteurized milk in routine milk-control work, Breed [102] recommended that his direct microscope method be used simultaneously with the agar plate. When large rod-shaped bacteria were revealed by the microscope, the probable presence of thermophilic bacteria was indicated.

Bacteria in pasteurized milk that stained well in methylene blue were usually found to be alive. The failure of obligate thermophiles to grow on plates as ordinarily incubated limits the usefulness but does not discredit the use of the standard agar plate in the official control of pasteurized milk. Some might wish to take issue with this statement. Introduction of high temperature - short time methods of pasteurization prompted inquiry about the behavior of thermophilic bacteria under these new conditions. This problem was studied by Yale and Kelly [103] in four plants using the Electropure process, two the Isotherm, two the precision, and one the York plate-type pasteurizer. The details of bacteriological technic need not be given here. It was found that the following plant practices were responsible for growth of thermophilic bacteria in the pasteurizing equipment: repasteurization, prolonged holding of hot milk in equipment as result of a shut-down, passage of hot milk through the same filter cloth for three hours or more, cooking of milk solids on to the walls of the regenerative heater and faulty sterilization of equipment.

The Milk Ordinance and Code of the United States Public Health Service [1] states as follows: "*Thermophiles*—If the pasteurization plant becomes infected with thermophilic organisms, it may prove that more intensive bactericidal treatment or a change in methods may be necessary. If the steam or hot water method has been in use, an attempt should be made to use higher temperatures and for longer periods (above 200° for more than 10 minutes)."

The methylene-blue reduction test has been applied to detection of thermophilic bacteria in pasteurized milk. Harding and Ward [104] observed a shortening of the reduction time by pasteurization and attributed this to the activity of thermophilic bacteria. Thomas [105] also found the methylene blue reduction test a sensitive test for detecting presence of thermophilic bacteria in milk. Thermophiles were detected in most samples of raw milk produced under unsanitary conditions but in only three per cent of the clean raw samples. These organisms were isolated from hay, straw, silage, bran, and cow manure. A brief description of the morphology and cultural characteristics of some thermophiles isolated from milk is presented. Meanwell [106] believed that decolorization in 30 minutes was a sign of trouble.

99. Rogers and Frazier. 1931. Amer. J. Pub. Health 20, 815-819.
100. Ward, Adams, and McCutcheon. 1934. Internatl. Assoc. Dairy and Milk Insp., 20th Ann. Rpt., 159.
101. Wright. 1936. J. Path. and Bact. 42, 31-44.
102. Breed. 1932. N. Y. Agr. Expt. Sta. Bull. 191.
103. Yale and Kelly. 1933. N. Y. Agr. Exp. Sta. Bull. 630; Bull. 156 (1929); Amer. J. Pub. Health 20 (1930), 1192-1198.
104. Harding and Ward. 1930. Internatl. Assoc. Dairy and Milk Insp., Ann. Rpt. 19, 135-143.
105. Thomas. 1938. Rev. in Expt. Sta. Rec. 78, 242.
106. Meanwell. 1939. Dairy Indus. 4, 283-285.

3. Non-thermophilic sporeforming bacteria. These organisms on account of the presence of spores resist pasteurization and appear in the heated milk. Such organisms were studied by Robertson, Yale, and Breed.[107] They observed occasionally large numbers of sporeforming rods by the microscope (Breed) method, which did not grow on plates in the same abundance as they appeared in the films for microscope examination. The source of these rods was found to be milk cooked onto the pasteurizers in which these organisms grew during the periods when the pasteurizer was empty. Cultures isolated from material scraped from the sides of the pasteurizers proved to be identical with the sporeformers isolated from the pasteurized milk. Of 140 cultures, 48 proved to be *Bacillus subtilis* Cohn, 29 were *Bacillus mesentericus* Trevisan, 22 *Bacillus vulgatus* Trevisan, 21 *Bacillus circulans*, Jordan, 10 *Bacillus albolactis* Migula, 2 *Bacillus laterosporus* Ford, 1 *Bacilus cereus*, Frankel and 1 *Bacillus mycoides*, Flügge, and five were not identified. This work showed that some of the commonest bacteria in nature may be responsible for high counts in pasteurized milk.

Flügge [108] was one of the first to believe that heated milk might contain bacterial spores and that these might later germinate. Three species of peptonizing bacteria were isolated from heated milk which caused the death of experimental animals. Since Flügge's milk was heated to the boiling point and not at temperatures ordinarily used for pasteurization, his conclusions ought not to be applied to modern pasteurization. Colwell and Sherman [109] reported that pasteurization at 60°C.(140°F.) seemed to restrain the peptonizing bacteria as much as the acid-forming bacteria. Ford and Pryor [110] attempted to confirm the earlier findings of Flügge to the effect that milk always contains heat-resistant spores of aerobic and anaerobic bacteria, which, by their development, can give rise to disagreeable and unwholesome changes in milk, converting it from a food of great nutritive value into an undesirable if not a dangerous article of diet. The results seemed to justify the warning that any milk heated to temperatures below the boiling point, might undergo undesirable changes if not kept cold.

The bacteria which resist pasteurization and appear in pasteurized milk were also studied by Marshall.[111] Prucha [74] pointed out that, under certain conditions, the milk may become contaminated with sporing bacteria, and then high bacterial counts after pasteurization will result. Figures are given of as many as 1,600,000 bacteria left in the pasteurized milk. Such results may occur with cows contaminated with numbers of spore-producing soil bacteria, occasionally with incompletely sterilized utensils, the more resistant strains surviving and multiplying in the moisture left in the vessels. The presence of these heat-resisting bacteria indicates some neglect in milk cleanliness precautions.

Bliss [112] found *Clostridium welchii* in 90 per cent of raw and pasteurized samples of milk in Baltimore. An interesting factor in connection with the pasteurization of milk was brought out by Sherman, Stark, and Stark,[113] who stated that the age of the cells had much to do with the results of pasteurization. Young cells were more easily killed than older cells. More data on this question are necessary before the significance of Sherman's conclusions may be fully appreciated.

Growth of Bacteria in Pasteurized Milk. Several investigators have reported that pasteurized milk is much more susceptible to decomposition by

107. Robertson, Yale, and Breed. 1926. N. Y. Agr. Exp. Sta. Bull. 119.
108. Flügge. 1894. Ztschr. Hyg. u. Infektionskrank. 17, 272.
109. Colwell and Sherman. 1908. J. Biol. Chem. 5, 247.
110. Ford and Pryor. 1914. Johns Hopkins Hosp. Bull. 25, 270-276.
111. Marshall. 1899-1900. Mich. Agr. Expt. Sta. Bull. 173.
112. Bliss. 1926. Amer. J. Hyg. 6, 5.
113. Sherman, Stark, and Stark. 1929. J. Dairy Sci. 12, 385-395.

bacteria than is raw milk. Allen [114] said that raw milk, as compared with pasteurized milk, exerts a powerful suppressing influence on multiplication of certain bacteria. Pasteurized milk was found to be more favorable to the attack of *Escherichia coli* and *Aerobacter aerogenes*. Allen emphasized the point that pasteurized milk, although it is safe for human consumption, should be handled with much care, since heating has decreased its resistance to many detrimental changes. Ayers and Johnson,[17] reported that the bacterial increase in clean raw milk and pasteurized milk was about the same when both were stored under the same conditions. Ford and Pryor [110] also expressed this opinion as did Cripps and Purvis.[115] Ayers and Johnson believed it to be manifestly unfair to conclude that bacteria increase faster in pasteurized than in raw milk, simply from a comparison of the ratios of bacterial increase. If pasteurized milk with a low initial count is compared with a raw milk of high bacterial content, then the ratios of increase may show that the bacteria in the heated milk do increase faster; on the other hand, if the same pasteurized milk is compared with a clean raw milk with a low count, then the ratios of increase will be found to be approximately the same. From the results of Ayers and Johnson's investigation, it is evident that bacterial increase in an efficiently pasteurized and a clean raw milk is about the same when the samples of milk are held under similar temperature conditions. This question of the relative growth of bacteria in raw and pasteurized milk can be properly settled only by a long series of comparisons of samples of milk with approximately the same bacterial count and similar bacterial group percentages. Andresen [116] has reported the existence in raw milk of a thermolabile agent which inhibits the paratyphoid organism.

Control of Pasteurization and Milk Pasteurizers. Since pasteurization was introduced to make milk safe and since it is one of the most important steps in processing fluid milk, it is subjected to official regulation and control. The reasons for this are obvious. Consumers must be assured that they are using properly pasteurized milk, else they use it with a false sense of security. Efforts to control and to supervise this process include inspection of and improvements in pasteurization apparatus, and application of tests to the heated milk to determine whether it has been satisfactorily treated. The former part of the problem has been considered at some length by the committees of the American Public Health Association. Necessity of changing certain features in the construction of pasteurizers was soon realized. These had to do largely with prevention of dead-ends or pockets in which some of the milk might not be heated to the pasteurization temperature and to inspection regularly of the thermometers. Necessity of frequently checking temperature recording devices used on pasteurization machinery has been pointed out by Tiedeman and Swanner.[117] When the New York State Department of Health began checking thermometers some of them were found to read 9.4°C.(15°F.) too high. This is more dan-

114. Allen. 1916. J. Infect. Dis., 19, 721-728; 21 (1917), 219-225.
115. Cripps and Purvis. 1915. J. Roy. Sanit. Inst. 36, 391-393.
116. Andresen. 1932. Ztschr. Hyg. u. Infektionskrank. 113, 530-540.
117. Tiedeman and Swanner. 1934. N. Y. Assoc. Dairy and Milk Insp., 8th Ann. Rept.

gerous than to have too high temperatures. Zeller [118] believed that the best guarantee of efficient pasteurization was careful supervision at the dairy and careful temperature control. He placed less confidence in tests applied to the heated milk because none had been developed at that time which could be relied upon. Of the enzyme reactions then available, he believed the Schardinger aldehyde-catalase test to be most satisfactory. Moore [119] found that the main difficulty in pasteurization practices rested on the failure to heat the milk to the necessary temperature or to holding it at the stated temperature for the required length of time. Similar conditions were found in New Jersey. In 85 per cent of the cases, the milk was not being held the full length of time. Such situations have been largely corrected by reconstruction of apparatus, the phosphatase test, and education of those who operate pasteurizers.

Owing to the fact that *Mycobacterium tuberculosis* was found in milk which was being sold as pasteurized, the Ministry of Health of Great Britain [120] found it necessary to more strictly control the process. This was done with the help of the phosphatase test. A large portion of the milk supplied schools in Reading, according to Milligan [121] was inadequately pasteurized. This has been the experience in other places and it indicates the need for regular and constant control.

Some have even advised that operators of pasteurizers be especially trained and made to feel their responsibility to the public. Cohee, Hostetter, Mitchell, Morgan, and Steele,[122] a committee of the Pennsylvania Association of Dairy and Milk Inspectors, recommended that those who supervise pasteurization in Pennsylvania be required to demonstrate their ability by passing an examination set by Pennsylvania State College. This has been proposed on several different occasions by Savage [123] in England. According to this authority granting of licenses to sell pasteurized milk rests with local authorities. Official requirements in England are (1) temperature between 62.8°C.(145°F.) and 65.6°C (150°F.) for at least 30 minutes with immediate cooling to not more than 12.8°C. (55°F.); (2) indicating and recording thermometers to be used and type of apparatus and thermometers and methods employed to be satisfactory to licensing authority; (3) temperature records kept for at least a month; (4) milk after pasteurization and before delivery shall not have more than 100,000 bacteria per milliliter. For laboratory control, two tests in addition to the plate count are recommended: (1) the coliform test— three 10-ml. tubes after milk is bottled, maximum allowable, one tube positive; (2) the phosphatase test—maximum allowable, 2.3 units Lovibond blue.

Bacteriological Methods of Control. It would be logical that these would be used first. Difficulties in examining milk for *Mycobacterium tuberculosis* caused bacteriologists to attempt to use colony counts as an index. This

118. Zeller. 1935. Münch. Tierärztl. Wchnschr. 86, 193-199.
119. Moore. 1924. J. Amer. Med. Assoc. 83, 1101.
120. Ann. Rpt. Chief Med. Off., Min. of Health 1936, 144.
121. Milligan. 1936. Med. Officer 55, 87-88.
122. Cohee *et al.* 1927 Penn. Assoc. Dairy and Milk Insp., 3rd. Ann. Rpt., 112-113.
123. Savage. 1936. Pub. Health 49, 260-263; J. Hyg. 33 (1933), 42-54; J. Roy. Sanit. Inst. 59 (1938), 1-8.

method resolved into "percentage reduction" in numbers of bacteria before and after pasteurization. This method has been largely abandoned for better ones. "Percentage reductions" may not always mean what they seem to. Hussong and Hammer [124] observed large variations in percentages of bacteria killed in samples of raw milk from different farms as well as in samples from the same farm. They believed that a close relationship of initial counts on raw milk to counts on pasteurized milk did not exist. In some cases the count on pasteurized milk exceeded the count of raw milk, indicating the presence of a heat-resistant flora. Unreliability of plate counts was also stressed by Tiedeman and Hohl.[125] They believed in the results of the phosphatase test.

Some bacteriologists have advised testing pasteurized milk for presence of coliform bacteria. Such recommendations rest on the belief that these bacteria are destroyed in milk at temperatures used for pasteurization, a question which is discussed at some length later in this chapter. Savage [126] believed that this method had merits.

The Ministry of Health of Great Britain has adopted the following requirements for control of pasteurization.

"On a sample of milk being taken at any time after pasteurization and before delivery to the consumer, the milk shall be found not to contain (a) more than 30,000 bacteria per cc., nor (b) any *Bacillus coli* in one-tenth of a cc."

After mentioning several that may be used, Leete [127] described a method that had been developed by the United States Department of Agriculture for testing the efficiency of pasteurization. For this purpose he proposed *Serratia marcescens (Bacillus prodigiosus)* as the efficiency indicator since it is nonpathogenic, easily isolated, easily killed, and is not widespread in natural waters. The exact technique was described as follows:

Leete's Method for Determining Efficiency of Pasteurizers. Twenty-four-hour old cultures of *Serratia marcescens (Bacillus prodigiosus)* are washed off in approximately 100 ml. of sterile water. Three slants are sufficient for a 4,000 to 6,000 pound machine. The water with the washed cultures is then shaken and filtered through filter paper. The method of making the test in detail under field conditions is as follows: Use of a pasteurizing plant is secured and the test is made either before or immediately after the regular run of milk. The holders, together with the necessary pumps, heaters, etc., are cleaned in the usual manner. The outfit is completely filled with ordinary tap water. Also, the supply tanks are filled with sufficient water to run the apparatus at its rated capacity for 30 minutes. A sufficient water supply is imperative. After the outfit has been filled, the pumps are started, or in the case of gravity-filled tanks the valves are opened. In this test it must be remembered that the water is run through at ordinary temperatures, rather than at pasteurization temperature. Constant checks upon the quantity of water passing through the machines are made at the outlet, in order to regulate the flow. This is done by actual measurement and timing. These checks are made at frequent intervals during the run. The rate of flow should always be constant and should correspond to the rated capacity of the holder. Samples of water for bacteriological analysis are taken at the supply tanks, at the inlet of the holder, or as near this point

124. Hussong and Hammer. 1931. Iowa Agr. Expt. Sta. Bull. 286.
125. Tiedeman and Hohl. 1938. Amer. J. Pub. Health 28, 629-632.
126. Savage. 1933. J. Hyg. 33, 42-54; J. Roy. Sanit. Inst. 59 (1938), 1-8.
127. Leete. 1923. Proc. World's Dairy Cong. 2, 212-218.

as possible, and at the outlet. These samples serve as bacteriological checks upon the water and apparatus.

The test organism is then introduced at the inlet to the holder and the time noted. In some types of machines it is impossible to introduce the culture immediately into the holder. The culture is then placed at the entrance to the heater. This should in no-wise detract from the accuracy of the test, for the time taken in passing through the heater is relatively short, and a portion of this time may be considered a part of the holding time, in that the milk while in the heater has reached the proper pasteurizing temperature.

Samples of the effluent are collected at the outlet, the time in each case being noted. These samples are for bacteriological analysis and must be taken aseptically. Sterile test tubes can be used for the collection of samples. The greater the number of samples taken, the more accurate will be the results. For ordinary purposes, samples taken at three-minute intervals for a period of 18 minutes, and then every minute up to 30 minutes will give accurate results. For additional study and information, samples should be taken up to 45 minutes. All samples taken, including the check samples, are then plated. One milliliter of each sample is plated directly on a plain agar medium. The plates are incubated at room temperature for 48 hours. At the expiration of this time a study of the plates is made. The holding time is computed as the elapsed time between introduction of the organism at the inlet and its recovery at the outlet. The identification of the test organism is easily made, microscopically, owing to its very character-istic luxuriant, bright red growth. In all cases, the check samples secured before the organism was introduced must be negative—that is, show no red colonies—if the test is to be relied upon.

Tanner and Windsor [128] found that the markedly low heat resistance of *Serratia marcescens (Bacillus prodigiosus)* might be a serious objection to the use of the organisms in this manner. None of the strains which they used survived nine minutes in milk heated to 62.8°C.(145°F.). Disappear-ance of the organism might occur in a much shorter holding period than 30 minutes, which is the accepted time in the continuous method. It is not easy, as Ayers [129] stated, to secure methods for controlling pasteuriza-tion. Bacterial counts are not satisfactory alone for they have decided limitations in themselves. It is probably equally difficult to secure an organism which may be used as an indicator of adequate pasteurization. McCrady and Langevin [130] also found plate counts inadequate for control of pasteurization apparatus. Since organisms of the coli aerogenes group are seldom found in properly pasteurized milk, it was suggested that their presence would indicate improper pasteurization.

After Leete's [127] method of testing pasteurizing machinery had been published, Goehrig [131] of the New Jersey State Board of Health used it for checking pasteurizers in that state. He reported some very interesting results. Up to the time of Goehrig's publication, 49 pasteurizing plants had been examined, 42 of which used the continuous flow system, while seven used the "vat" system, or the compartment type. He found that 19 of these plants showed a holding period of only three minutes; 12 showed a holding period of six minutes; while only four (two of the con-tinuous flow system and two of the vat system) showed a holding period of 30 minutes. Ninety per cent of the holders tested by this method allowed

128. Tanner and Windsor. 1929. J. Dairy Sci. 12, 202-210.
129. Ayers. 1923. J. Dairy Sci. 6. 608-615.
130. McCrady and Langevin. 1932. J. Dairy Sci. 15, 321-329.
131. Goehrig. 1925. Pub. Health News, N. J., 10, 220-226.

the milk to pass through in less than 30 minutes. Steps were immediately taken to remodel pasteurizers which would insure the holding of the milk for the full time, at the temperature required by law in that state (61.1 to 60°C.[142 to 140°F.] for 30 minutes).

The Phosphatase Test for Detection of Inadequately Pasteurized Milk. For some time there has been a need for a test which would reveal inadequately pasteurized milk both with respect to time and temperature. Many procedures have been proposed. Health officers have generally relied on inspection of pasteurization plants and machinery including temperature-time charts. Such procedures yield information only for the time when they were made. No, or little, information is given for between times or for the condition of the final product. Any test that is used must involve search for a normal thermolabile constituent of milk or for some added agent which is susceptible to heat. The phosphatase test seems to fulfill the requirements better than any test proposed heretofore. It is now widely used in America and England. Kay and Graham [132] have devised such a test which is based on the observation that the enzyme phosphatase is destroyed in milk at times and temperatures generally accepted as satisfactory for pasteurization of milk. Phosphomonoesterase is absorbed according to Kay [133] by the secreted milk from mammary tissue. Pasteurization at a temperature of 62.8°C.(145°F.) and 65.6°C.(150°F.) and immediately cooling to 12.5°C.(54.5F.) is just sufficient to inactivate the phosphatase. Lower temperatures will not do so. A known quantity of milk is allowed to act on an excess of well-buffered disodium-phenyl-phosphate for a given time and the amount of free phenol liberated by the enzyme is determined by the Folin and Ciocalteu's reagent. Delicacy is increased by extending the time.

Delicacy of the test was further shown by Koppejan [134] who stated that phosphatase disappears from milk on heating to 58°C.(136.4°F.), 59°C.(138.2°F.), 60°C.(140°F), 61°C.(141.8°F.), and 62°C.(143.6°F.) in accordance with a unimolecular reaction. It was removed completely by heating at 62°C.(143.6°F.) for 20 minutes, at 61°C.(141.8°F.) for 45 minutes, and at 60°C.(140°F.) for 75 minutes. A positive was secured by adding as little as .1 per cent of raw milk to pasteurized milk. Tiedeman [135] also showed that this small amount of raw milk could be detected.

The Kay and Graham [132] Phosphatase Test for Inadequately Pasteurized Milk. This is a simple test which indicates whether milk has been "legally" pasteurized. The enzyme *phosphatase* is destroyed under conditions which have been proven to adequately pasteurize milk; it is not completely destroyed if the milk is heated to lower temperature. According to Kay and Neave [136] the test is quantitative and the amount of undestroyed phosphatase is measured in terms of "blue units."

Two tests were proposed: first, a qualitative determination which distinguishes between heated and unheated milk; and second, a quantitative test in which the amount of phosphatase present may be determined and even minor variations in technic detected.

132. Kay and Graham. 1935. J. Dairy Res. 6, 191-203.
133. Kay. 1937. Proc. 11th World's Dairy Cong. 2, 500-502.
134. Koppejan. 1936. Chem. Weekbl. 33, 747.
135. Tiedeman. 1938. Amer. J. Pub. Health 28, 316-319.
136. Kay and Neave. 1935. Lancet, June 29, 1935, 1516-1518.

Pipette 10 ml. of buffer substrate into each of four test tubes of 20-25 ml. capacity. To two tubes (controls) add 4.5 ml. of diluted Folin's reagent. To all four tubes add .5 ml. of the milk to be tested. Mix well. Add a few drops of chloroform to the two samples (not to controls), cover to protect from dust, warm to 37-39°C. and keep in a 37°C. incubator for 24 hours.

Remove from the incubator, add 4.5 ml. of diluted Folin's reagent to the samples, mix, let stand three minutes. Filter all four tubes. Transfer five ml. of the filtrate to 13 mm. diameter test tubes, add one ml. of 14 per cent Na_2CO_3, mix, place in boiling water for five minutes and filter. The color of the filtrate is read in a Lovibond tintometer. Colors greater than 2.3 Lovibond units of blue indicate improper treatment.

REAGENTS

1. Buffer substrate. Dissolve 1.09 grams of disodium phenyl phosphate and 11.54 grams of "sodium veronal" in water saturated with chloroform and make up to one liter. Add a few drops of chloroform and keep in refrigerator.

2. Folin and Ciocalteu's phenol reagent. Dissolve 100 grams of sodium tungstate $Na_2WO_4 2H_2O$ and 25 grams of sodium molybdate, $Na_2MO_4 \cdot 2H_2O$ in 700 ml. water in a 1,500 ml. flask connected by a ground glass joint to a reflux condenser. Add 50 ml. sirupy (85 per cent) phosphoric acid and 100 ml. of concentrated hydrochloric acid. Reflux gently for 10 hours. Cool, add 150 grams c.p. lithium sulfate, 50 ml. water and a few (4-6) drops of liquid bromine. Boil without condenser for 15 minutes to boil off excess bromine. Cool, dilute to one liter, filter.

The finished reagent should have a golden yellow color with no greenish tint. Any reagent with a greenish tint should be rejected. Keep well protected from dust. Dilute one volume of this stock solution with two volumes of water before use.

3. A 14 per cent solution of anhydrous sodium carbonate, Na_2CO_3 c.p. (14 grams per 100 ml.).

The test is based on the fact that the enzyme hydrolyzes an added phenyl-phosphoric ester liberating phenol, which is readily detected by Folin's reagent. The blue color produced by small quantities of phenol readily lends itself to comparison with permanent standards prepared from inorganic solutions. The test has been approved by various investigators and is one of the important advances in dairy bacteriology. Gilcreas and Davis [137] after studying it with about 100 samples of milk representing varying conditions of temperature and holding time, believed that it should be a great aid in control of pasteurization. They stated (1936) that variations of five minutes or more in heating time were readily distinguished and addition of as small quantity as one-tenth of a per cent of raw milk gave a result indicative of incomplete pasteurization. Variations in temperature were also easily detected. The technic proved equally satisfactory in determining pasteurization by the ordinary process as by the high-temperature process. A correct evaluation of the character of the treatment to which milk has been subjected was made in 97 per cent of the specimens. According to Fasken and McClure [138] slight modifications are needed to make Kay and Graham's test suitable for examination of milk pasteurized at 61.7°C. (143°F.) for 30 minutes. The modifications are (1) four-hour incubation, with a limit of 1.8 blue units in place of 2.3, or (2) 24-hour incubation, with a limit of 5.0 blue units in place of 2.3.

137. Gilcreas and Davis. 1937. Internatl. Assoc. Milk Sanitarians, 25th Ann. Rpt., 15-39.
138. Fasken and McClure. 1940. Canad. J. Comp. Med. 4, 128-137.

The Scharer test was found slightly more sensitive than that of Kay and Graham.

Kay [139] pointed out that the method loses a certain amount of its precision if it is applied to milk which has been held at a lower temperature than 62.8°C.(145°F.). At the low temperature of 60°C.(140°F.), which is permitted in some parts of Canada, it is less precise and less capable of detecting small errors. Since, however, most of the enzyme is destroyed in 30 minutes at 60°C.(140°F.) it is still capable of yielding valuable results with some modifications. At 61.7°C.(143°F.) it is of material value but there is some loss of its extreme sensitiveness. The phosphatase test is also applicable to control of the high temperature-short time pasteurization process.

Gilcreas and Davis [140] found no significant variation in phenol concentration resulting when samples were incubated between 24 and 18 hours. but progressive inaccuracies were observed at shorter periods. Artificial color standards maintained an unchanged value for eight months. Reagents and buffer substrate tablets prepared commercially were found satisfactory. The phenol value obtained in the control test has, in general, been found to be negligible, but if abnormally high it should be substracted from the value obtained in the test in order to determine the phenol concentration corresponding to the degree of treatment of the milk. Unrefrigerated storage of samples for limited periods did not seriously affect the precision of the method. The technic has been applied to the examination of 780 samples collected from delivery trucks and labeled pasteurized. Adequate heat treatment was proven in 96 per cent of the samples, and this precision confirmed previous experience regarding the sensitivity of the test in determining minor, as well as significant, variations in procedures of pasteurization.

While Gilcreas [141] pointed out the great value of the phosphatase test he drew attention to certain difficulties which may obtain. If there is prolonged preheating or slight overheating, the phosphatase content of the milk may be reduced so that the laboratory test may fail to detect five minutes shortening of the holding time or even the addition of one-tenth of a per cent of raw milk. Slightly altered phenol values have to be adopted. If cream is separated from raw milk and then pasteurized, the phosphatase test adequately measures the reliability of the heat treatment. If, however, the cream is separated from pasteurized milk, either by gravity or mechanically, it tends to have an undue high phenol value with the phosphatase test although the initial pasteurization may have been adequate. Many figures are given to illustrate this point. While a full explanation is not available, examinations show a marked concentration of the enzyme in the cream fraction and there may not be complete inactivation at 61.7°C. (143°F.) for 30 minutes. It may become necessary to establish a separate code of readings for cream.

139. Kay. 1936. Canad. Pub. Health J. 27, 551-554.
140. Gilcreas and Davis. 1937. N. Y. Assoc. Dairy and Milk Insp. 11th Ann. Rpt., 83-100.
141. Gilcreas. 1939. Amer. J. Pub. Health 29, 158-162.

Several incubation periods of the milk plus substrate buffer solution were tested by Storrs and Burgwald.[142] They recommended a five-hour incubation period in testing milk supposedly pasteurized at 61.1°C.(142°F.) for 30 minutes, and a 24-hour incubation period be used where the legal limits of pasteurization are 61.7°C.(143°F.) for 30 minutes. The test was found to be applicable to milk pasteurized by the high temperature-short time method. In this case a 2.5-hour period of incubation was found to be proper for milk pasteurized at 71.1°C.(160°F.) for 10 seconds. When milk is required to be held 15 seconds at 160°F. the 2.5-hour incubation period is too short, and a 24-hour incubation period is too long. A 24-hour period was suitable, however, for milk held for 20 seconds at 160°F. There was no relation between butterfat content in mixed herd milk and the phosphatase content of raw milk and the blue color developed in the pasteurized milk.

The value of results secured with this procedure in actual pasteurization control was shown by Leahy [143] during a survey of 104 pasteurizing plants in the city of Rochester, New York; a total of 1,563 samples of milk, taken at different stages of the process, were collected from 157 vats, and 2,816 samples of milk from distributors. All samples were examined for improper pasteurization by a modified phosphatase test and for the presence of coliform bacteria employing formate-ricinoleate medium. In the course of a year's study, 50 plants were observed which gave no evidence of improper pasteurization. On the day of inspection, gross defects in pasteurization methods were disclosed in nine plants, routine samples from which were positive. The pasteurization in 24 plants was satisfactory on the day of inspection. Routine samples from these plants, however, were positive and there was evidence of faulty plant operation. With the exception of occasional minor imperfections, the pasteurization in 21 other plants was reliable, and routine phosphatase tests were rarely positive. Leahy found the phosphatase test to be invaluable for detection of improper operation in pasteurizing plants. He emphasized, also, that the test for coliform bacteria is equally valuable for the detection of recontamination by contact with unsterilized equipment at the plant. When both tests are employed simultaneously, they are of more value to the milk industry and public-health officials than any other combination of tests yet devised for milk control. Leahy suggested that the conventional bacterial count be discarded in their favor.

Results of similar investigations by Howell [144] all tend to confirm the value of the phosphatase test as an indicator of efficient pasteurization. Among a series of 216 samples of milk examined in the metropolitan borough of Hammersmith three failed to pass the test. It was discovered that in one case the sample had been taken by dipping a jug into the churn, the jug having just before been used for mixing and dividing a bottle of tuberculin-tested milk, though it had been cleansed between the samplings.

142. Storrs and Burgwald. 1938. J. Milk Tech. 1, 18-35.

143. Leahy. 1938. N. Y. Assoc. Dairy and Milk Insp., 12th Ann. Rpt.

144. Howell. 1939. Med. Officer 62, 218-219.

The second was very similar, the jug having been used for unpasteurized milk, then emptied and drained, but not wiped dry before being used again. No information was obtained regarding the third unsatisfactory sample.

Experiments were then made by which, first, one-third pint of pasteurized milk was placed in a jug which had previously contained raw milk and had not been drained or cleaned; second, in a jug which after being emptied of raw milk was drained for five minutes. Both were reported on as "raw or grossly underheated or contaminated with raw or improperly pasteurized milk." The Lovibond blue unit value was 10+ in place of a limit of 2.3 for properly pasteurized milk. When one pint of pasteurized milk was used in place of one-third of that amount the units were 3.7 and 3.1, respectively. Even a very thin film of milk remaining when a jug has been emptied and drained can thus be detected.

The phosphatase test in practical use has revealed situations which could have been discovered only with difficulty by other methods.[145] Raw milk as the cause of an outbreak of gastroenteritis was revealed by this test. Members of two camps became ill soon after meals at which the raw milk was served. The milk was supposed to have been pasteurized. Cans of raw milk were confused with cans of bulk pasteurized milk in a cooling room. The herds from which the milk used at the camps was obtained were found to contain cows with mastitis, six of which were slaughtered. The phosphatase test permitted accurate identification of the milk as raw milk. Otherwise this outbreak would have been attributed to contaminated pasteurized milk. The outbreak was attributed to a toxin in the raw milk. Excellent results with the phosphatase test have also been reported by Edwards and Nanji [146]; Kay and Neave [147]; Anderson, Herschdörfer, and Neave [148]; Smith [149]; and Geiger and Davis.[150]

Effect of Bacterial Growth on Phosphatase Test. Bacterial growth was mentioned by Leahy, Sandholzer, and Woodside [151] as a possible error resulting from hydrolysis of the bacterial nucleic acids. Tests were not advised on milk with microscope counts above 8,000,000 per ml. or standard plate counts above 2,000,000. Twenty-eight cultures of various bacterial species were tested for their ability to produce phosphatase when grown in milk. One strain of staphylococcus, five strains of Aerobacter, and three of Klebsiella were shown to produce a phosphatase reaction which showed slight activity at pH 9.0. Seven additional strains of various genera produced a false-phosphatase reaction. Similar observations were made by Hammer and Olson.[152] Pseudomonas produced most phosphatase in sterile milk. Members of this genus and other organisms produced phosphatase in butter. An important point in this connection is the ability of Pseudomonas to grow at relatively low temperatures. In general, it appears that there

145. N. Y. State Dept. Health, Health News 14 (1937), 121-122.
146. Edwards and Nanji. 1937. Analyst 62, 121-122.
147. Kay and Neave. 1937. Dairy Indus. 2, 5-7.
148. Anderson, Herschdörfer, and Neave. 1937. Analyst 31, 2694.
149. Smith. 1937. Canad. Pub. Health J. 28, 383-387.
150. Geiger and Davis. 1937. J. Amer. Med. Assoc. 109, 1363.
151. Leahy, Sandholzer, and Woodside. 1938. J. Bact. 38, 683; J. Milk Tech. 3 (1940), 183-188.
152. Hammer and Olson. 1941. J. Milk Tech. 4, 83-85.

is less danger of phosphatase production causing positive tests in cheese than in butter, as many phosphatase-producing organisms are inhibited by the acid nature of the cheese.

On the other hand, Neave [153] stated that the test was not affected by bacteria in milk which produced reducing substances. It was also unaffected by the presence in milk of bacteria which produced reducing substances or which hydrolyze the substrate, sodium-phenyl-phosphate, unless the organisms are present in large numbers. Paley [154] also stated that growth and presence of various bacteria which would be common in milk did not reactivate or increase the phosphatase enzyme to an extent where it would interfere with the test. Neither did old sour milk. Storage of pasteurized milk for five hours at 37°C.(98.6°F.) did not show reactivation of the enzyme. Results of an investigation by Barber and Frazier [154a] with cream revealed that a positive reaction to the phosphatase test developed in pasteurized cream after storage at from 4°C.(39.2°F.) to 10°C.(50°F.) for from 24 to 48 hours. Presence of phosphatase resulted from growth of Gram-positive. sporeforming bacilli in sterile skimmed milk. This is an important observation in appraisal of the phosphatase test. A false positive phosphatase test in properly pasteurized milk was also observed by Buck [154b] who attributed it to a thermophilic organism to which he gave the name *Lactobacillus enzymothermophilus*. The phosphatase was extracted from the organism with distilled water. The enzyme was destroyed by heating at 85°C.(185°F.) for one minute. Production of phosphatase in milk at pasteurizing temperatures of 61.1°C. (142°F.) to 62.2°C. (144°F.) was observed to begin after a 90-minute holding period. Temperature, size of inoculum and the holding period are important factors. Buck stated that bacterial phosphatase is different from milk phosphatase. Where the phosphatase test is used for pasteurization control, it must be shown that the positive test is due to milk phosphatase which has not been destroyed.

Several modifications have been proposed by various investigators to make the phosphatase test more suitable for certain conditions. These have been compared by Burgwald and Giberson [155] and by Kay, Aschaffenburg, and Neave.[156] The former found the laboratory tests to be of about equal value for detecting irregularities in pasteurization of milk. As little as 1°F. variation in temperature, five minutes' variation in holding time, and one-tenth of one per cent added raw milk to properly pasteurized milk is detectable. Scharer's standard of .5 p.p.m. of phenol as an indication of proper pasteurization of 61.7°C.(143°F.) for 30 minutes seemed to be a little low. His test, however, has the advantage over Kay and Graham's and Gilcreas and Davis' that it requires a much shorter incubation time, and is less expensive in that acid-washed filter papers are not required. Scharer's improved rapid field test is nearly as effective as are any of the laboratory tests and has the distinct advantage of time and cost of oper-

153. Neave. 1938. J. Dairy Res. 10, 475-484.
154. Paley. 1939. J. Milk Tech. 2, 251-254.
154a. Barber and Frazier. 1942. J. Dairy Sci. 25, 718.
154b. Buck. 1942. Amer. J. Pub. Health 32, 1224-1236.
155. Burgwald and Giberson. 1938. J. Milk Tech. 1, 11-24.
156. Kay *et al.* 1939. Tech. Commun. No. 1, Insp. Bur. Dairy Sci. 1939, 53 pp.

ation in its favor, together with the fact that it can be made directly in the plant in a few minutes' time. BQC* was found to vary in sensitivity, and might be a factor in preventing the Scharer tests from being as sensitive as either Kay and Graham or Gilcreas and Davis tests. A photelometer can be used in connection with any of these laboratory tests. Age of samples if kept so cold they do not sour has no effect on the test. Certain bacteria may be a factor with the Kay and Graham and Gilcreas and Davis tests if present in large numbers. This is rather remote, however, and the use of a control test would indicate the presence of any phenol-like substance which they might produce. Kay and his colleagues reported just about the same sensitivity. They found the test to be sensitive, accurate, and effective for controlling pasteurization by the holder process. The test in its appropriate modification is sufficiently sensitive to detect a drop in temperature of 1.0 to 1.5°F. if pasteurizing temperature is 61.7°C.(143°F.) for 30 minutes. If 62.8°C.(145°F.) for 30 minutes, a drop of 1.5°F. can be detected. They also reported that a reduction of 10 minutes in holding time could be detected but not five minutes with certainty. The presence of .2 to .25 per cent of raw milk in the pasteurized product and in many instances smaller amounts were detectable. These authors also found the test to be satisfactory for milk pasteurized for short times at high temperatures. In this bulletin are directions for the following modifications:

A. Kay-Graham Test A and Test B
B. Neave's Modification
C. Gilcreas and Davis' Modification
D. Scharer's Modification
    1. Laboratory Test
    2. Field Test
E. Leahy's Modification
F. Aschaffenburg and Neave's Modification.

Scharer's [157] Rapid Phosphate Test for Detection of Inadequate Pasteurization of Milk and Milk Products. In order to shorten as much as possible the Kay and Graham phosphatase test, Scharer proposed a rapid test. His procedure is as follows:

"The buffered substrate (white) tablet contains the phenyl phosphoric ester, magnesium to catalyze the enzyme reaction and adequate buffer to make 50 ml. of the buffered substrate solution—sufficient for 10 tests. The BQC (yellow) tablet contains 2.6 bromoquinone-chloroimide and a stabilizer—sufficient for 30 or more tests. These tablets should be kept under refrigeration if possible.

"The buffered substrate tablets available commercially may develop varying amounts of phenol under certain conditions of storage, such as exposure to light or heat. Since the extraction technique is extremely sensitive, it is necessary to work with a phenol-free substrate; therefore the following procedure is utilized to remove any phenol and is recommended in all cases:

"Crush buffered substrate tablet in test tube, dissolve in five ml. of distilled water. Add two drops of BQC solution. Allow five minutes for color development, then extract the indophenol with 2-2.5 ml. of normal butyl alcohol. Allow to stand until alcohol layer has separated at top of tube. Remove alcohol layer with medicine dropper and discard. Dilute remainder of solution to 50 ml. This solution is then phenol free. Dissolve the BQC tablet in five ml. of 95 per cent ethyl or methyl alcohol. DO NOT USE A DENATURED ALCOHOL. Transfer to dropping bottle delivering 50 drops per ml.

* BQC = Bromo-quinone chloroimide.
157. Scharer. 1938. J. Dairy Sci. 21, 21-34; J. Milk Tech. 1, 35-38.

METHOD

"Add one-half ml. of sample to five ml. of buffered substrate. Shake briefly. Incubate for 10 minutes in a water bath at 36.7°C.(98°F.). (If no water bath be available, incubate in pocket for somewhat longer period.) Remove from bath, add six drops of BQC solution. Shake well immediately. After five minutes compare color with opaque standards.

"Properly pasteurized milk will be a gray or brown.

"Properly pasteurized cream will be a gray or white. Raw milk or cream will be an intense blue. The appearance of any blue is indicative of improper pasteurization, the degree of intensity of color being proportional to the seriousness of the condition.

"If only a trace of blue is found it may be hard to distinguish. In this event add two ml. of normal butyl alcohol (neutral). Invert the test tube SLOWLY at least 10 times and allow to stand. Rapid inversion will result in an emulsion being formed but if correctly performed the alcohol will separate clearly and will have extracted the indophenol formed by the test.

"The appearance of any blue or blue-green in this alcohol layer is indicative of improper pasteurization. In the absence of a properly pasteurized milk to be used as a control a boiled milk may be substituted.

"The test has been standardized with milk pasteurized—under laboratory conditions satisfying legal requirements—namely, a preheating period of one to five minutes and a holding period of exactly 30 minutes at 143°F. Under commercial conditions varying time of preheating and filling and emptying of tanks should be taken into consideration.

CAUTION

"All equipment should be thoroughly washed and rinsed before reuse. Avoid the use of phenolic resin bottle closures anywhere in the test. The BQC reagent is sufficiently sensitive to demonstrate the leaching of phenol from the resin by water.

"Both solutions decompose with age and should be stored under refrigeration or prepared shortly before use.

"A reagent blank should be made by adding three drops of BQC to five ml. of substrate. If a blue color results the substrate solution should be discarded. If the butyl alcohol procedure is utilized this reagent blank should be extracted with the alcohol."

Errors in this rapid test may result from decomposition of reagents. Scharer[158] recommended that fresh reagents be prepared daily. A co-operative investigation by 18 laboratories on identical samples under supervision of Gilcreas[159] indicated that the Scharer technic should be perfected further to attain maximum accuracy.

Other investigators have been satisfied with its accuracy. Roger[160] found it, or slight modifications of it, satisfactory on some 18,000 lots of pasteurized milk. The modification consisted of using amyl alcohol for a color solvent instead of normal butyl alcohol. Amyl alcohol with highly colored milk did not give so much yellow color that readings were confused. Roger believed the Scharer test to be reliable. Asschaffenburg and Neave[161] found the test to be satisfactory. A few anomalies were found but were not considered to be significant. Some were due to the samples. Milk from animals suffering from mastitis tended to give abnormal results after pasteurization.

158. Scharer. 1939. Amer. J. Pub. Health 30, 1206-1210.

159. Gilcreas. 1939. J. Assoc. Off. Agr. Chem. 22, 497-507.

160. Roger. 1939. Internatl. Assoc. Milk Dealers, Ann. Rpt., 233; Amer. J. Pub. Health 28 (1938), 1325-1327.

161. Asschaffenburg and Neave. 1939. J. Dairy Res. 10, 487-497.

Since the phosphatase test is colorimetric, permanent standards have been suggested by several workers. Wyllie [162] found standard blue solutions and blue tinted glass to be satisfactory. Unlike Wyllie, however, Gilcreas and Davis [163] found permanent standards prepared from inorganic colored solutions to yield accurate results when the essential condition of depth of color solution and a blue glass plate for reading the colors are observed. Variations from these conditions and lack of sensitivity of the eye to detect color differences will lead to errors in the results. The General Electric Company has developed a simple photoelectric colorimeter for use with the phosphatase test. It is called the "Luximeter." It is calibrated in terms of milligrams of phenol per .5 ml. of milk and also in terms of the enzyme units used for reporting the results of the phosphatase test modified by the Department of Health of the City of New York. Comparison of results of tests made with this instrument and those obtained with the permanent color standards agree. Its use will eliminate possible error owing to the human element and to fading or other changes in color standards.

A photoelectric cell was used by Tracy and Hahn [164] for determining the amount of phenol color in the phosphatase test. A raw-milk contamination of as little as .1 per cent can be detected easily provided a properly pasteurized sample of milk is available for reference. The method also gives satisfactory results in the detection of irregularities that might exist regarding time and temperature of pasteurization. Mercuric chloride tablets are suitable preservatives for milk to be examined by the phosphatase test.

Application of Phosphatase Test to Other Dairy Products. Necessity of pasteurizing other dairy products has prompted study of the application of the phosphatase test to them. Scharer [157] modified his test for ice cream. Since ice cream is usually pasteurized at temperatures which will destroy the phosphatase, the test is chiefly of value for detecting addition of unheated standardizing materials to the mix. Vanilla powder, vanillin or coumarin, fruit products, synthetic fruit flavors, or nut meats may introduce phosphatase or phenolic compounds. Scharer [158] also reported results with pasteurized cream. Cream is higher in phosphatase activity than the milk from which it came. Cream pasteurized at 71.1°C.(160°F.) for 15 seconds shows considerable phosphatase activity. It also appears that a greater amount of phosphatase is present in cream separated after pasteurization of the milk than in cream separated before pasteurization. In applying the phosphatase test to butter, the serum is removed and the usual procedure applied to it. The enzyme is concentrated in the serum and yields higher results than if the melted butter were used. Only slight phosphatase activity was found in butter made from cream pasteurized for 30 minutes at 61.7°C.(143°F.), but butter made from flash-pasteurized cream showed considerable phosphatase activity. High phosphatase activ-

162. Wyllie. 1939. Canad. Pub. Health J. 30, 49; 32 (1941), 122-128.
163. Gilcreas and Davis. 1939. N. Y. Assoc. Dairy and Milk Insp., 13th Ann. Rpt., 67-78; J. Milk Tech 3, (1940), 14-18.
164. Tracy and Hahn. 1937. Proc. Internatl. Assoc. Milk Dealers 30, Lab. Sec., 57-79.

ity was found in butter made from raw cream even after prolonged storage periods. In applying the phosphatase test to cheese, the cheese is first dispersed in the buffer solution and the equivalent of .5 gram of the cheese is used in the test. The enzyme was detected even after 18 months' storage with undiminished activity in cheese made from raw milk, but was absent in cheese made from milk pasteurized by both the holding and short time-high temperature methods. Processed cheeses usually gave negative results with the phosphatase test. When ice cream mix was pasteurized in accordance with usual practice, negative results were obtained with the phosphatase test. Chocolate milk, vitamin D milk, condensed milk, goat milk, and the like require no special treatment to determine whether they have been properly pasteurized. The laboratory test as well as the field test may be applied satisfactorily to these products. The accuracy of the phosphatase test, according to Perry and Doan,[165] is not significantly affected by homogenization, storage under refrigeration up to six days, development of oxidized flavor, or reinforcement with vitamin D.

The Amylase Test as an Indicator of Inadequate Pasteurization. This test was proposed by Leahy[166] and is based on the destruction of amylase in milk by heat. The technic is as follows:

Ten ml. of a well-mixed sample of the milk to be examined are pipetted into a test tube with precautions to prevent contamination with raw milk or with salivary amylase. At a recorded time .5 ml. of a sodium chloride-starch reagent is added, and mixed well by pouring from one test tube into another and back again. The mixture is then incubated at 30°C.(86°F.) for four hours. The sodium chloride-starch reagent is prepared by dissolving .4 gram of soluble potato starch and 20 grams of sodium chloride in 100 ml. of distilled water. At the end of the incubation period, two ml. of a reagent consisting of equal volumes of glacial acetic acid and chloroform are added, followed by immediate shaking with the thumb over the mouth of the tube. The addition of this strongly acid reagent, which changes the pH to about 3.4, terminates completely the activity of any milk amylase present. Thereafter, at a convenient time the tube is centrifuged at high speed for about 15 minutes. The clear supernatant liquid resulting from this treatment is poured into a test tube and the stage of starch hydrolysis effected by the enzyme determined by the addition of a few drops of a dilute iodine solution, such as a .5 N iodine stock solution diluted to about .005 N strength. This dilution should be prepared just before use, as dilute iodine solutions decolorize rapidly.

The stage of starch hydrolysis indicated by the color developed upon adding the dilute iodine solution is used as a measure of the temperature at which the milk was heated during pasteurization. A distinct yellow color denotes a strong action of the enzyme and, therefore, indicates the presence of raw milk. A distinct starch-iodine blue color shows that no amylase action has occurred, thus indicating the presence of milk which has been pasteurized properly at 61.7°C.(143°F.) for 30 minutes. A purple, red, or orange color denotes intermediate degrees of activity, and therefore indicates either improperly pasteurized milk or the admixture of raw with properly pasteurized milk.

Gilcreas and Davis[167] found that this test differentiated unheated from heated milk but it was not possible to determine major variations in treatment. The amylase content varies with the breed, diet, and period of lactation of the cow, and occasionally fresh milk was examined which contained so little amylase that it reacted in the test as though heated.

165. Perry and Doan. 1941. J. Dairy Sci. 24, 369-382.

166. Leahy. 1934. Rochester, N. Y., Health Bur. Bull., Mar. 1934; Internatl. Assoc. Dairy and Milk Insp., 23rd Ann. Rpt., 23, 93-108.

167. Gilcreas and Davis. 1937. Internatl. Assoc. Milk Sanitarians, 25th Ann. Rpt., 15-39.

Effect of Pasteurization on Coliform Bacteria in Milk. Since these species are nonsporeformers and are generally destroyed by temperatures used in milk pasteurization, it was suggested that their presence in pasteurized milk indicated faulty procedures in the pasteurizing machine or contamination after pasteurization. Either of these situations would be objectionable. Results of many investigations have been reported and a survey of the literature leaves one in doubt about the pertinence of some of the conclusions which have been reported. Most strains of coliform bacteria are not sufficiently heat resistant to survive adequate pasteurization procedures when they are present in milk in reasonable numbers. When they are found, either excessive numbers were present in the raw milk or the milk was contaminated after it had been pasteurized. Attempting to determine whether *Escherichia coli* could be used as an index of adequate pasteurization, Swenarton[168] concluded that it could be used and proposed a standard—of all the .1-ml. portions examined not more than 20 per cent shall show the presence of *Escherichia coli*. Results of investigations by McCrady and Langevin[130] indicated that the plate count alone did not suffice for adequate control. Since coliform bacteria are seldom found in properly pasteurized milk, since even small numbers of them can be readily detected, and since they readily become established in open seams and fissures, and on unsterilized surfaces of equipment, the coliform test was considered to be a valuable supplementary control method. Large city plants, and probably small plants as well, can deliver to the consumer milk containing *Escherichia coli* in not more than 10 to 20 per cent of the one-milliliter portions.

On the other hand, Tiedeman[169] did not accept the coliform test as an index of adequate pasteurization, a position taken also by Frank of the United States Public Health Service. In France, however, Demigneux[170] stated that pasteurized milk in sealed containers should not contain *Escherichia coli* in one-ml. quantities when delivered to the consumer.

Gage and Stoughton[171] found that in 55 per cent of thermal death point determinations made with *Escherichia coli* the cultures withstood 80°C. (176°F.) for five minutes. Ayers and Johnson,[87] using 174 strains isolated from human and bovine sources and from dairy products, found, as a general rule, these organisms have a low majority thermal death point, but that resistant strains occurred which survived heating for 30 minutes at 62.2°C.(144°F.). At 60°C.(140°F.) slightly over 50 per cent of the cultures remained viable; at 62.2°C.(144°F.) only 6.89 per cent survived. They stated that 62.2°C.(144°F.) was a critical temperature for *Escherichia coli*, but that heating to 65.5°C.(150°F.) should certainly destroy it. In view of these results, they advanced the opinion that presence of *Escherichia coli* in pasteurized milk which has been held for some time is not an indication of inefficient processing but of the multiplication of the few cells which survived. However, large numbers of the organisms present in

168. Swenarton. 1927. J. Bact. 13, 419-429.
169. Tiedeman. 1936. Internatl. Assoc. Dairy and Milk Insp., 24th Ann. Rpt., 126.
170. Demigneux. 1937. Ann. Falsif. 30, 410-412.
171. Gage and Stoughton. 1906. Tech. Quarterly 19, 41-45.

milk immediately following pasteurization is evidence of inefficient and insufficient heating. Shippen [172] isolated from pasteurized milks 31 strains of organisms of the *Escherichia coli* type. These were subjected to a temperature of 60°C.(140°F.) for 15 minutes in sealed glass tubes; the survivors, identified by their action when inoculated into sterile litmus milk and then into lactose broth, were heated at 61°C.(141.8°F.) for 15 and 30 minutes and so on by increasing degrees of heat until they no longer survived. Cultures of the strains killed at the initial temperature were subjected to decreasing degrees of heat until they survived. Of the 31 strains, 11 remained viable after 60°C.(140°F.) for 15 minutes; of these, one was killed only at 68°C.(154.4°F.) in 15 minutes and at 65°C.(149°F.) for 30 minutes. No culture of *Aerobacter acrogenes* resisted treatment at 60°C.(140°F.) for 15 minutes. These results confirmed the opinions of workers cited above on existence of heat-resistant strains of *Escherichia coli*. Shippen concluded that the presence of *Escherichia coli* in pasteurized milk is not to be interpreted as an index of improper pasteurization nor of subsequent contamination.

Finkelstein [173] also found 62.2°C.(144°F.) to be a critical temperature for *Escherichia coli* in milk. Since Brown and Gott [174] had stated that Endo's medium could be used to detect *Escherichia coli* in milk and the presence of this organism indicated undesirable conditions, Adams and Ward [175] examined certified and pasteurized milk in Detroit, and found that many of the lactose fermenters which appeared on Endo's medium belonged to the coli section of the colon-aerogenes group. Prompted by the work of Twiss,[176] Tanner and Dubois [177] observed the effect of heat on several organisms of the colon-typhoid group, among which was a strain of *Escherichia coli*. The strains survived 15 minutes' heating under conditions employed. Seeleman,[178] using two strains, found that they were destroyed in less than 30 minutes at 60 to 63°C.(140 to 145.4°F.). In England, Jenkins [179] stated that an effectively pasteurized milk should not contain *Escherichia coli*, and that the organism was a valuable index of pasteurization efficiency. Some American investigators do not agree with this. Such a position seems justified by the results of an investigation by Johnson,[180] who found that the temperature of 62.8°C.(145°F.) for 30 minutes was the critical temperature for *Escherichia coli*, but that some strains did actually survive pasteurizing times and temperatures. Johnson brought out the difference between "absolute" and "majority" thermal death points for organisms. Experiments on *Aerobacter aerogenes* showed a wide discrepancy between these temperatures. Johnson said, "Since all nonspore-bearing bacterial cells are similar to *Aerobacter aerogenes* in this respect, it is quite important that the selection of an effective pasteuriza-

172. Shippen. 1915. J. Amer. Med. Assoc. 64, 1289-1291.
173. Finkelstein. 1919. J. Dairy Sci. 2, 460-482.
174. Brown and Gott. 1923. Amer. Food. J., 18, 295-296.
175. Adams and Ward. 1925. Amer. Food J. 20, 147-148.
146. Twiss. 1920. J. Infect. Dis. 26, 165-170.
177. Tanner and Dubois. 1925. J. Dairy Sci. 8, 47-53.
178. Seeleman. 1926. Milchw. Zentbl. 55, 117.
179. Jenkins. 1926. J. Hyg. 25, 273-284.
180. Johnson. 1926. Penn. Assoc. Dairy and Milk Insp., 2nd Ann. Rpt., 122-126.

tion temperature must be based on the 'absolute' thermal death point of pathogenic organisms, determined under laboratory conditions and in milk. Large scale efficiency tests are not necessary, and are apt to be misleading and wrongly interpreted so as to give a false sense of safety. Knowing the 'absolute' thermal death point of pathogenic organisms, the most valuable work for the future, in connection with pasteurization was predicted to be a study of the temperatures obtained in commercial practice, and the development of suitable instruments for determining that all of the milk in a given pasteurizing process is heated to a point which will provide a safe margin above the 'absolute' death point of pathogenic organisms.''

Sadler and Middlemass [181] found organisms like *Escherichia neapolitana* the cause of ropy milk. The strains isolated were killed at 63°C. in 10 minutes. Swenarton [168] studied 16 pasteurizing plants with respect to the *Escherichia coli* contents of the pasteurized milk. The pasteurizing temperature adopted as satisfactory is 61.7°C.(143°F.) for 30 minutes, with prompt cooling to 4.4°C.(40°F.). The term *Escherichia coli* is used broadly for lactose-fermenting (with gas), nonsporing aerobes. The test was found to be very helpful in checking up the performances of the different plants. Swenarton suggested the following standard: Five quantities each of .1 ml., to be examined, and not more than 20 per cent to show the presence of organisms of the *Escherichia coli* group. Apparently to guard against inequalities of sampling, etc., he adds, ''Occasionally three or more of the five equal .1-ml. portions constituting a single sample may show the presence of *E. coli*. This shall not be allowable if it occurs in more than (a) 10 per cent of the standard samples when 10 or more samples have been examined; or in (b) one standard sample when less than 10 samples have been examined.'' This standard is a more or less arbitrary one, based on the findings from the best plants examined.

Despite the fact that Tanner and Windsor [182] and Beavens [183] reported to the contrary, Swenarton [168] and McCrady and Langevin [130] have suggested the use of *Escherichia coli* determination as a reliable supplementary laboratory method for the control of pasteurization.

Coliform bacteria were present in about 94 per cent of raw-milk samples examined in Rochester, New York.[184] In every instance the number of colon bacilli decreased during the heating period, and only one per cent of the samples gave a positive test after the milk had been subjected to a temperature of 61.7°C.(143°F.) for 30 minutes. However, there was an increase during the bottling process. Conclusions were drawn that proper pasteurization destroys all of the coliform bacilli, that their absence from a sample of pasteurized milk gives evidence of not only proper pasteurization but also of proper sterilization of containers and utensils, and of proper technic in handling of the milk following pasteurization.

McCrady [185] later expressed the same opinion. The *Escherichia coli* test was stated to be a valuable adjunct to other methods for checking pasteuri-

181. Sadler and Middlemass. 1926. Sci. Agr. 6, 297-302.
182. Tanner and Windsor. 1929. J. Dairy Sci. 12, 202-210.
183. Beavens. 1930. J. Dairy Sci. 8, 94.
184. Rochester, N. Y., Health Bur. Bull., 1938, 2-4.
185. McCrady. 1936. Milk Inspector 5, 28-29.

zation. This same position has been defended by Slack and Maddeford,[186] who stated that presence of *Escherichia coli* in pasteurized milk indicated either inadequate pasteurization or contamination. Absence of typical colon bacilli in a given volume of milk does not necessarily indicate proper pasteurization or even that the milk has been pasteurized at all, but the presence of typical colon bacilli in small volumes of pasteurized milk indicates some fault in pasteurizing, cooling, or bottling which demands investigation and correction. A similar position was taken by MacLean.[187] During a period of 18 months in 1935 and 1936, using the brilliant green bile (Difco two per cent) as a presumptive test for *Escherichia coli*, samples taken daily during normal plant operation were examined. The average of 7,460 tests of one-ml. milk samples and 2,66 tests of 10-ml. samples showed 99.6 per cent and 96.6 per cent, respectively, as negative. The average of the corresponding highest prevailing average plate counts was 9,470. The use of one-ml. samples in duplicate and a single 10-ml. sample of pasteurized milk is recommended as a satisfactory modified technic for plant control. MacLean's experience was that when the three tubes constituting this technic are all negative, the plate count of the sample is almost invariably below 10,000 colonies per milliliter. He suggested that his technic might be used as a means of reducing the number of plate counts and yet obtain a more satisfactory insight into the degree of plant sanitation.

Seventy-five cultures of coliform bacteria were isolated from milk by Graham.[188] Only one strain survived in the milk pasteurized at 62.5°C. (144.5°F.) for 30 minutes. More survived when the cultures were mixed. Graham considered the *Escherichia coli* test as not perfectly satisfactory but as good as any other bacteriological test is likely to be. Forty-six per cent of samples of pasteurized milk were found to contain *Escherichia coli* by Moffat and Mackay.[189] It was concluded that at some time incompletely pasteurized milk had passed into the pasteurizer. Bartram and Black [190] found no pasteurized milk with total counts under 1,000 containing coliform organisms, counts of colon-positive being 413 times that of colon-negative samples.

Various media and technics have been used for determining coliform bacteria in milk. Guittonneau, Mocquot, and Eyrard [191] found the Dunham-Schoenlein medium most satisfactory. Ten-ml. portions of the medium were inoculated with 1 to .01 ml. of the milk to be tested and the tubes incubated at 41.5°C.(107°F.) for 48 hours. Indole was then determined by the Salkowski or Ehrlich method. The dilution of the milk at which indole is detected is a measure of the coliform content. This method was considered a (very) satisfactory method for determining contamination of pasteurized milk, especially the type of milk known as "certified" pasteurized milk.

186. Slack and Maddeford. 1932. Canad. Pub. Health J. 23, 574-578.
187. MacLean. 1936. Proc. 29th Ann. Conv. Internatl. Assoc. Milk Dealers, Lab. Sec., 3.
188. Graham. 1936. Canad. Pub. Health J. 27, 81-85.
189. Moffat and Mackay. 1938. Idem. 29, 283-287.
190. Bartram and Black. 1937. J. Dairy Sci. 20, 105-112.
191. Guittonneau *et al.* 1939. Lait 19, 113-139.

Yale [192] compared solid with liquid media. The two solid media chiefly employed were Bacto-violet-red bile agar and desoxycholate agar. Both were found satisfactory, and, in general, red acid-forming colonies larger than .5 mm. could be assumed to belong to the coliform group. Plates give quantitative results and are most useful in studying plants. For samples of unknown origin broth tubes are sufficiently accurate. Gunsalus and Stark [193] compared results with brilliant green bile and formate ricinoleate broths and concluded that the brilliant green bile broth gave a slightly greater number of positive presumptive tests than the formate ricinoleate broth, but the brilliant green bile broth gave slightly lower percentage confirmation. In some cases, the positive presumptives were shown to have been produced by anaerobic, spore-producing rods.

It is obvious that some strains of *Escherichia coli* may pass through the pasteurization process. Heat resistance of this organism in milk is probably not constant, as shown by Lembke,[194] but is an expression of their physiological state at the time of heating. Wilson [195] believed that the coliform test might have some merit as a test for adequate pasteurization. Interpretation, however, might be influenced by the possibility of recontamination or presence of heat-resistant strains. Wilson's own experience seemed to indicate that the coliform test is applicable only to those milks which contain an appreciable number of coliform cells before pasteurization. A similar position was taken by Breuckner.[196]

Barkworth [197] said that presence of coliform bacteria in pasteurized milk indicated a breach of plant hygiene. He suggested an Incubation Coliform Test which consisted of examination for coliform bacteria after incubation. This causes a few cells of coliform bacteria to develop into large numbers. Barkworth did not consider it necessary to identify the species. Resistant strains of coliform bacteria were of less importance to Rowlands and Provan [198] than the frequency of their occurrence in raw milk. If their occurrence is infrequent and the number surviving pasteurization is negligible in comparison with the number likely to be derived from contamination, then the test, when properly interpreted, can be applied as a measure of contamination during cooling and bottling.

The significance of results secured in the laboratory is difficult to determine. Practically any strain of *Escherichia coli* can survive pasteurization if the inoculum is large enough. Few of the investigators whose results are reviewed above paid any attention to numbers of cells which were present or to other factors which are known to be very important in heat-resistance work. If they had, it would have been difficult to know how many cells to have used, for the number ought to approximate normal contamination. When all information is analyzed, one is forced to maybe

192. Yale. 1937. Amer. J. Pub. Health 27, 564-569.
193. Gunsalus and Stark. 1938. Amer. J. Pub. Health 28, 832-834.
194. Lembke. 1937. Zentbl. Bakt., Pt. 2, 96, 92-109.
195. Wilson. 1935. (See list of reference books at end of chapter.)
196. Breuckner. 1939. Amer. Prod. Rev. 88, 838-839.
197. Barkworth. 1941. Dairy Indus. 6, Issues of May to Aug.
198. Rowlands and Provan. 1941. Idem, April and May issues.

consider presence of *Escherichia coli* in pasteurized milk as due to some break in plant hygiene, as Barkworth stated.

EFFECT OF PASTEURIZATION ON PATHOGENIC BACTERIA IN MILK

To make milk safe by destruction of pathogenic bacteria is the primary object of pasteurization of fluid milk. While not all pathogenic bacteria have been studied, it is quite probable that the results which have been secured with *Mycobacterium tuberculosis* hold for the others. Some results of investigations are contradictory owing, probably, to use of different strains under different conditions.

Effect of Milk Pasteurization on Mycobacterium Tuberculosis. It was the necessity of destroying this organism that forced health officials to pasteurize milk. Its heat resistance in milk determined the time and temperature that is used. *Mycobacterium tuberculosis* is contributed to milk by infected cows and consequently the milk must be treated to destroy the organism. Results of many experiments have been reported. There is some disagreement, as would be expected. Marshall [199] stated that 68°C. (154.4°F.) for 20 minutes destroyed the organism. In one series of five experiments, sterilized milk was infected with tuberculous material from different cows and then pasteurized by heating to 68°C. (154.4°F.), holding it at that temperature for 20 minutes, and cooling rapidly. In each experiment, one guinea pig for control was inoculated intra-abdominally with one ml. of the infected milk before pasteurization, and a number of guinea pigs were similarly inoculated with five ml. of the pasteurized milk. All of the control animals died from tuberculosis within a few weeks, while none of the 13 animals inoculated with the pasteurized milk developed the disease. As a temperature of 68°C.(154.4°F.) for 20 minutes did not produce a cooked flavor in the milk, and was shown by the experiments to kill the tubercle bacillus, Marshall argued that a lower temperature for pasteurization should not be adopted. Several experiments were also carried out in pasteurizing milk artificially infected with tuberculous material, at a temperature which would give the milk a cooked flavor. This was done by heating water surrounding small bottles of milk to the boiling temperature, removing the heat, and allowing the milk and water to stand for five to 30 minutes. Four guinea pigs inoculated with the unpasteurized milk developed general tuberculosis within a few weeks. The 12 inoculated with five times the quantity of pasteurized milk remained free from any trace of the disease.

Hammond [200] reported that heating of milk to a temperature of 71.1°C. (160°F.) for 15 minutes insured destruction of the tubercle bacillus, reduced the number of other bacteria, and did not give a cooked taste. In 1900, Russell and Hastings [201] reported the results of experiments which did much to help settle the question of time and temperature of pasteurization. In five series of experiments, milk was inoculated with pure cultures

199. Marshall. 1899-1900. Mich. Agr. Expt. Sta. Bull. 173.
200. Hammond. 1900. Ontario Agr. Coll. and Expt. Farm Rpt., 88-91.
201. Rusell and Hastings. 1900. Wis. Agr. Expt. Sta., Ann. Rpt., 147-170; Idem. for 1901, 185-194.

of the tubercle bacillus and heated at 60°C.(140°F.) in a commercial rotary pasteurizer. The time of heating in the different tests varied from five to 45 minutes. Control samples were unheated. The vitality of the organisms was tested by intraperitoneal injections into guinea pigs.

The conclusions from these series indicated that 10 minutes at 60°C. (140°F.) were sufficient to destroy the vitality of the tubercle organism so completely that large doses inoculated in the most susceptible portion of a very susceptible animal (guinea pig) failed to produce tuberculosis, while unheated samples of the milk and those exposed to 60°C.(140°F.) for five minutes produced the disease without exception.

In two series of experiments, a comparison was made of heating milk at 60°C. in the commercial pasteurizer and in open bottles placed in a water bath. In the latter case the milk remained in a quiescent condition and was exposed to the action of air which permitted a film to form on the surface. Where the milk was exposed in a quiescent condition, as in a glass tube or bottle, *Mycobacterium tuberculosis* was more resistant than where the milk was in a closed receiver and agitated. While *Mycobacterium tuberculosis* was destroyed in the commercial pasteurizer in 10 minutes, neither an exposure for this period, nor for 15 minutes, sufficed to destroy the same lot of organisms when the milk was treated in a quiescent condition at the same temperature in vessels to which the air had more access. It was recommended in order to thoroughly destroy any tubercle bacilli which it may contain, without in any way injuring its creaming properties or consistency, to heat it in closed pasteurizers for a period of not less than 20 minutes at 60°C.(140°F.).

Very high temperatures, 98°C.(208.4°F.) applied momentarily, did not always destroy *Mycobacterium tuberculosis*, according to Tjaden, Koske, and Hertel.[202]

According to Bang's [203] experiments with tuberculous milk heated in a closed metal vessel, heating at 60°C.(140°F.) for one minute or less permitted pronounced tuberculosis by inoculation into the abdominal cavity of rabbits. Milk kept at 60°C.(140°F.) for five minutes also caused tuberculosis, but to a less extent. Heating for 15 minutes reduced the effect still more, only half the number of animals becoming tuberculous. Milk heated to 65°C.(149°F.) for a moment caused rather slight, but still recognizable, tuberculosis. On heating at 65°C.(149°F.) for five minutes the bacilli were killed. The same result followed heating for a moment, to 70°C.(158°F.), 75°C.(167°F.), 80°C.(176°F.), and 85°C.(185°F.). Feeding experiments with milk heated to 60°C.(140°F.) for two minutes gave negative results.

In case of continuous pasteurization, Bang considered 80°C.(176°F.) the lowest safe temperature for destroying tubercle bacilli, and believed that the Danish pasteurization law could be modified without danger to allow pasteurization at this temperature in creameries, the Storch color test being used to ascertain whether the skimmed milk had actually been exposed to this temperature.

202. Tjaden, Koske, and Hertel. 1901. Arb. K. Gsndhtsamt. 18, 221.
203. Bang. 1901. Molkereinid. 14, 677-679.

Barthel and Stenstrom's [204] experiments were different in that naturally infected milk from a cow in the last stages of tuberculosis of the udder was used. The secretion from the anterior or badly affected half of the udder was mixed with the milk from the posterior quarters of the udder, which were not yet as badly attacked by tuberculosis. It was found that a temperature of 65°C.(149°F.) for periods of five, 10, and 20 minutes was not sufficient to destroy the tubercle bacillus. Milk maintained at 70°C. (158°F.) for periods of five, 10, and 15 minutes remained in each instance tuberculous. The same results were obtained with experiments at a temperature of 75°C.(167°F.). At a temperature of 80°C.(176°F.) the milk remained tuberculous after exposure for periods of one, five, and 10 minutes. The reaction of the milk was shown to be important. Another important contribution came from Smith,[205] who found that when tubercle bacilli were suspended in milk, they were destroyed in from 15 to 20 minutes at 60°C.(140°F.), the greater portion being killed in five to 10 minutes. Short periods of pasteurization showed that a temperature of 71.1°C.(160°F.) or above for one minute destroyed the virulence of bovine tubercle bacilli so that guinea pigs were not killed when inoculated with from two to five milligrams. Others have confirmed this work and these temperatures were accepted in the continuous process for some time. Smith's experiments were repeated by Hesse.[206] He repeated them on a large scale, and a large firm of milk dealers was prevailed on to try the experiment of heating their milk to 60°C.(140°F.) for 20 minutes. The milk was heated in large vessels to 60°C.(140°F.) and was kept at this temperature for exactly 20 minutes, after which it was cooled as quickly as possible to a temperature of 8°C.(46.4°F.). During the heating of the milk it was stirred continually to prevent the formation of a pellicle on the surface, or the cooling of the superficial layer of milk. Hesse also enclosed cultures of tubercle bacilli in glass tubes,[207] hermetically sealed, and placed these tubes in three vats of milk heated at temperatures of 60°C.(140°F.), 58°C.(136.4°F.), and 57°C.(134.6°F.), respectively. Inoculation experiments made on guinea pigs with the material contained in these vessels showed that all tubercle bacilli which were heated to a temperature of 60°C. were destroyed, while the guinea pigs which received the other cultures heated to temperatures of 58°C.(136.4°C.) and 57°C.(134.6°F.), respectively, developed cases of tuberculosis of a more or less generalized nature. It was believed that the sterilization of milk was best secured with the least changes in the composition and taste of the milk by subjection to a temperature of 60°C.(140°F.) for 20 minutes. Observations showed that by this treatment other organisms, including those causing cholera, typhoid fever and diphtheria, were also killed.

Levy and Bruns' [208] experiments were carried out at temperatures below 100°C.(212°F.). The tubercle bacilli were obtained from pathological

204. Barthel and Stenstrom. 1901. Expt. Sta. Rec. 13 (1901-1902) 886-887.
205. Smith. 1899. J. Med. Res. 4, 233.
206. Hesse. 1900. Ztschr. f. Hyg. u. Infektionskrank. 34, 347.
207. It is very probable that the temperatures attained in the interior of these tubes were lower than those of the milk in the vat.
208. Levy and Bruns. 1901. Hyg. Rundschau. 11, 669-675.

tissue of bovine origin. From these experiments, it was concluded that when milk is exposed in a water bath to a temperature from 65°C.(149°F.) to 70°C.(158°F.) for a period of 15 to 25 minutes, all bacteria contained in the milk are destroyed. Svensson's [209] experiments with an apparatus in which the milk was heated rapidly in a thin layer, to a temperature of 80°C.(176°F.) for two minutes, indicated that this was sufficient to destroy tubercle bacilli. This was not true, however, in experiments in which the temperature was 75°C.(167°F.). According to Russell and Hastings,[210] a temperature of 60°C.(140°F.) for 15 minutes is sufficient to destroy all nonsporulating pathogenic bacteria in milk without materially altering the flavor or appearance of the cream. When the method of pasteurization allowed the formation of a surface membrane, the destruction of *Serratia marcescens (Bacillus prodigiosus)*, *Mycobacterium tuberculosis*, and a micrococcus was not so efficient.

Rullmann.[211] however, reported that a temperature of 65°C.(149°F.) for 30 minutes was insufficient to destroy *Mycobacterium tuberculosis* in milk. According to Van der Sluis,[212] a temperature of 80°C.(176°F.) was necessary for its distribution. He found that cells artificially added to milk were more resistant than cells which were in the milk when it was excreted. Russell and Hastings,[210] in further work, inoculated milk with cultures of tubercle bacilli of human and bovine origin and subjected them in sealed tubes to different degrees of heat, for varying lengths of time, the main object, however, being to determine the time required to destroy the bacilli at 71.1°C.(160°F.), with a view to applying the results to the continuous pasteurization of milk. Five series of experiments were made in each of which the virulence of the milk was determined by intraperitoneal inoculation of guinea pigs. The conclusion was drawn that a temperature of 71.1°C.(160°F.) or above, for a period of one minute, sufficed to destroy the virulence of *Mycobacterium tuberculosis* (bovis), so that the disease was not produced in experimental animals, like guinea pigs, inoculated with cultures ranging from two to five milligrams.

It was noted, however, that these laboratory experiments had been conducted under conditions more carefully controlled than was possible in commercial practice, and while the results were believed to lay a proper foundation for a safe and efficient treatment of milk, it was suggested that variations in the conditions of exposure, and also variations in the organism itself, must be studied before this new limit for the efficient pasteurization of milk in machines of the continuous flow type could be accepted unreservedly.

The reaction of the milk had been observed by several to have an important bearing on the question. Barthel and Stenstrom [213] coagulated milk with acid and showed that, in such milk, *Mycobacterium tuberculosis* (hominis) was not easily killed.

209. Svensson. 1903. Rev. in Expt. Sta. Rec. 15 (1903-1904) 507.
210. Russell and Hastings. 1904. Twenty-first Ann. Rpt., Wis. Agr. Expt. Sta., 178-192.
211. Rullmann. 1903. München. Med. Wchnschr. 1342.
212. Van der Sluis. 1909. Centbl. Bakt., Abt. 1, 50, 378-401.
213. Barthel and Stenstrom. 1904. Rev. in Expt. Sta. Rec. 13 (1901-1902), 886-887.

Bartlett [214] confirmed the work of earlier investigators that the holder process of pasteurization between 61.1°C.(142°F.) and 64.4°C.(148°F.) for 30 minutes destroyed the tubercle bacillus in milk. Raw milk from large mixing vats showed greater frequency of the presence of bacteria. Brown [215] heated 25 strains of *Mycobacterium tuberculosis*, which were pathogenic for guinea pigs, and found that those heated to 60°C. for 20 minutes and to 70°C. for five minutes were noninfectious. The former heating period was recommended. This same question was studied by Macaulay,[216] who used the ability of tubercle bacilli to cause tuberculosis in guinea pigs as the criterion whether pasteurization at 63 to 65°C.(145.4 to 149°F.) for 30 minutes destroyed the tubercle bacillus in milk. He carried out his experiments in a pasteurizing plant, dealing with 150 gallons per hour. Fresh milk was inoculated with tuberculous sputum, this milk was then placed in a thin-walled, brass, cylindrical box, the cover of which could be tightly screwed down, making a tight joint. After sterilizing the outside of this box, it was lowered into the holder of the pasteurizer where it was left for the required time. Macaulay found that the tubercle bacillus was destroyed by pasteurization at 63 to 65°C.(145.4 to 149°F.) for 30 minutes. Oerskov [217] heated tubercle bacilli in small tubes containing two ml. of the infected milk. The milk was heated at 63°C. for different intervals. After heating, the milk was inoculated onto Petroff's agar. The organisms survived 40 minutes' heating at 63°C.(145.4°F.) but were killed in 45 minutes. Anderson [218] found that about one-third of the guinea pigs inoculated with tuberculous milk which had been pasteurized at 63°C. (145.4°F.) for one-half hour died. This was confirmed much later by Grinsted and Plum.[219] White [220] pasteurized naturally infected milk from cows with infected udders, and milk artificially inoculated with pure cultures, at 62.2°C.(144°F.) for 30 minutes, and found these conditions satisfactory for the production of a noninfective milk.

Brand [221] showed that pasteurization at 63°C.(145.4°F.) for 30 minutes killed all the pathogenic organisms but did not materially affect the keeping qualities. The findings were similar when human milk was pasteurized. An extensive study of the bacteriology of pasteurization was made by Jenkins.[179] He used a temperature of 62.2°C.(144°F.) for 30 minutes, with milk artificially infected with both the human and bovine types of *Mycobacterium tuberculosis*. Six experiments with culture strains tested under laboratory conditions at temperatures ranging from 62°C.(143.6°F.) to 63.3°C.(146°F.) showed killed or avirulent bacilli, as judged by guinea pig inoculations. Two experiments with naturally infected milk heated at 60°C. (140°F.) and 62.2°C.(144°F.) were equally satisfactory. One liter of tuberculous milk from a tuberculous cow was added to 50 gallons of milk

214. Bartlett. 1923. Amer. J. Pub. Health 13, 807-809.
215. Brown. 1923. Lancet, Pt. 2, 317-321.
216. Macaulay. 1925. Pub. Health 38, 297-301.
217. Oerskov. 1925. Bull. Inst. Pasteur, 23.
218. Anderson. 1925. Maanedsskr. Drylaeger 36, 177-189.
219. Grinsted and Plum. 1935. Maanedsskr. Drylaeger 46, 515-520.
220. White. 1926. Lancet, Pt. 1, 222.
221. Brand. 1927. Rev. in Pub. Health Rpts. 42, 2065.

and subjected to pasteurization in a commercial plant. Two guinea pigs, inoculated with the milk and cream, respectively, before pasteurization, developed tuberculosis, while pigs inoculated after pasteurization remained healthy (killed after six weeks).

The results of a comprehensive co-operative investigation of this question under conditions which approached those in practice were reported by North et al.[10] Their experiments were carried out in a factory which had been converted into a machine shop. Since it was impossible to obtain a sufficient amount of cultivated tubercle bacilli, the investigators had to resort to material from infected animals and human beings having severe tuberculosis lesions. Twenty-two tuberculous cattle were slaughtered and about 40 quarts of tuberculous material collected. About one gallon of discharges from 20 human being was also collected. These materials were then mixed, macerated and filtered, and diluted to make about 80 gallons. Certainly, such a procedure gave a potent inoculum with which to infect the milk. A number of tests were made with infected milk. Lack of space prevents a detailed review of the results.

They were finally summarized, and the statement made that the bovine type of *Mycobacterium tuberculosis* was destroyed in some tests in three types of improved commercial pasteurizers at 59°C.(138.2°F.) for 30 minutes. The authors mentioned regulations of the states of New York, Connecticut, and others that milk or cream shall be heated to a temperature of at least 61.1°C.(142°F.) and held at such temperature for 30 minutes or more. When taken in connection with the results of the tests just reported, North et al. believed that a temperature of 61.1°C.(142°F.) for 30 minutes gave an ample margin of safety. The report was criticized by several investigators who, as North and Park[222] stated, did not overlook the fact that in the first series of experiments the routine of operation and temperature control were not established and pathogenic bacteria were not killed. North et al. stated in their first report that this series was reported only as a matter of record.

In defense of the experiments and conclusions reported by North et al. in Public Health Bulletin No. 147, North and Park[222] claimed that the great variation in thermal death points reported for *Mycobcaterium tuberculosis* in milk was due to faults in the heating equipment and its operation by the investigators. They again reported their belief that there was no material difference in resistance to heat between bovine and human strains of *Mycobacterium tuberculosis*, or between different strains of either species, or between the tubercle bacilli in naturally infected milk, tissue lesions. or pure cultures. The authors stated that the volume of data reported in Bulletin No. 147 in tests made at 61.1°C.(142°F.) and at 59°C.(138.2°F.) exceeded in quantity, by a large margin, the volume of data reported in any of the previous investigations, the results of which have already been accepted by bacteriologists. They believed that sufficient care had been used to justify the conclusion that *Mycobacterium tuberculosis* was killed at 59°C.(138.2°F.) when heated at 30 minutes and that a standard of

222. North and Park. 1927. Amer. J. Hyg. 7, 147.

61.1°C.(142°F.) for 30 minutes was a proper standard for pasteurization. They further stated that temperature standards which injured the milk were not necessary for the protection of the public health.

Michel [223] showed that commercial pasteurization for 10 minutes at 63°C.(145.4°F.) or for five minutes at 65°C. is sufficient to completely destroy *Mycobacterium tuberculosis*. Meanwell [224] pointed out that apparent differences might be due in part to greater virulence of the organism in naturally infected milk. He also considered the possibility of latent infections, and in his experimental work kept guinea pigs 100 days or more. He pasteurized separately, in special laboratory apparatus designed to heat every particle of the milk to a uniform and accurately determined temperature, naturally infected milk from three cows known to be suffering from tuberculosis of the udder. The milk from cow No. 1 was abnormal in appearance, a flocculent mass separating out on standing. The milk from the other two cows was normal, although slightly darker in color at times.

The centrifugalized deposit and cream from pasteurized, naturally infected milk was injected into guinea pigs with the following results: Two pigs, out of 284 injected, developed tuberculosis with milk treated at 62.8°C.(145°F.) for 30 minutes, and 60°C.(140°F.) for 20 minutes, respectively, whereas 10 pigs, out of 12 injected, developed tuberculosis with milk treated at 59.5°C.(138.8°F.) for 20 minutes. Coagulated material collecting on the cooler in some of the experiments was ground up with saline and injected into guinea pigs with the following results: Two pigs, out of 44 injected, developed tuberculosis with material from milk treated at 62.8°C.(145°F.) for 30 minutes and at 60°C.(140°F.) for 20 minutes. None of the six pigs injected with this material from milk treated at 59.5°C.(138.8°F.) for 20 minutes, developed tuberculosis.

Zeller, Wedemann, Lange, and Gildemeister,[225] after extensive investigation on this subject, concluded that pasteurization, although bringing about a very great diminution of the infectivity of the tuberculous materials used in the experiments on animals, cannot be relied upon to kill off the organism completely. Important conclusions are that the continuous-flow type of pasteurizer is undesirable and that foam formation should be avoided as much as possible, because, in the milk foam, organisms are found to resist the conditions better than in the body of the milk. In a later publication these authors [226] reported more data. Milk heavily infected with tubercle bacilli and fed to animals was rendered practically though not absolutely safe by low-temperature pasteurization. Of 32 young guinea pigs fed unheated tuberculous milk, 29 developed lesions. Of 30 pigs fed low-temperature, pasteurized milk, 25 showed no lesions. Of 16 calves fed unheated, tuberculous milk, 15 developed lesions. Of 28 calves fed pasteurized milk, in 18 no lesions could be found.

223. Michel. 1927. Bull. Soc. Pharm., Bordeaux. 65.
224. Meanwell. 1927. Amer. J. Hyg. 26, 392.
225. Zeller *et al.* 1929. Ztschr. Fleisch. u. Milchhyg. 38.
226. Zeller *et al.* 1930. Arb. K. Gsndhtsamt. 61, 1-72.

*Thermal Death Times of Mycobacterium Tuberculosis in Milk
as Found by Various Investigators*

Investigator	Killed at	Not Killed at
Martin, 1882		80°C.
May, 1883	By cooking	
Sormani, 1884	Boiling, 5 min.	90°C., for 10 min.
Schill and Fisher, 1884		100°C.,
Voelsch, 1887		100°C., boiling twice.
Yersin, 1888	60°C., 10 min., no spores	
	60°C., 10 min., spores	
Bitter, 1890	68°C., 20 min.	
Bang, 1881	70°C., 5 min. (enfeebles)	
	60°C., 5 min. (enfeebles)	
	80°C., sometimes kills	
	85°C., always kills	
Bonhoff, 1892	60°C., 20 min.	50°C., 60 min.
Gancher and Ledeux-Lebard, 1892	60°C., 5 min. (attenuates)	
	70°C., 1 min. (kills)	55°C., 3 hr.
Forster, 1892	60°C., 6 hr.	60°C., 45 min.
	95°C., momentary	80°C., momentary
DeMan, 1893	55°C., 4 hr.	60°C., 1 min.
	60°C., 1 hr.	
Schroeder, 1894	60°C., 15 min.	
	50°C., 15 hr.	
	60°C., 8 hr.	
Woodhead, 1895	60°C., 45 min.	90°C., results contradictory
	70°C., 45 min.	
	10°C., 2½ min.	
Marshall, 1899	68°C., 28 min.	60°C., 10 min.
Th. Smith, 1899	60°C., 15 to 20 min.	70°C., 10 min.
Morgenroth, 1900	55°C., 3 hr.	100°C., momentary
Kobrak, 1900	58°C., 4 hr.	
Beck, 1900	100°C., 3 hr.	100°C.
		80°C., 30 min.
Galtier, 1900		85°C., 6 min.
Russell and Hastings, 1900	60°C., 20 min.	
Tjaden, Koske and Hertel, 1901	90°C., continuous	98°C., momentary heating
Herr, 1901	65°C., 15 min.	80°C., 5 seconds
Hesse, 1901	60°C., 20 min.	
Levy and Bruns, 1901	65°C., 15 min.	
Barthel and Stenstrom, 1901		70°C., 15 min.
Bang, 1902		60°C., 15 min.
Tjaden, 1903	85°C., 1 to 2 min.	
Rullmann, 1903	65°C., 30 min.	60°C., 30 min.
Svensson, 1903	80°C., 2 min.	
Rullmann, 1903		65°C., 30 min.
Van der Sluis, 1909	80°C.	
Barthel and Stenstrom, 1904	80°C., 1 min. (uncoagulated)	80°C., 1 min. (coagulated)
Russell and Hastings, 1904	71°C., 1 min.	
Zelenski, 1906		76°C., 20 min.
Rosenau, 1907	60°C., 20 min.	
Bartlett, 1923	61.5-65°C., 30 min.	
Brown, 1923	60°C., 20 min.	
Anderson, 1924	70°C., 5 min.	
Macaulay, 1925	63-65°C., 30 min.	63°C., 30 min.
Oerskov, 1925	63°C., 45 min.	63°C., 40 min.
Macheus, 1925	63°C., 30 min.	
North, *et al.*, 1925	61.5°C., 30 min.	
White, 1926	62.5°C., 30 min.	
Brand, 1927	63°C., 30 min.	
Jenkins, 1926	62-63.8°C., 30 min.	
Michel, 1927	63°C., 10 min.	
	65°C., 5 min.	
Meanwell, 1927	62.8°C., 30 min.	60°C., 20 min.
Scharr and Lentz, 1927		60-63°C., 30 min.
Katrandzieff, 1928	63°C., 30 min.	
Rautmann, 1927	63-65°C., 30 min.	

A similar experiment was made by Scharr and Lentz.[227] Samples of milk were taken before and after 30 minutes' treatment at 60 to 63°C.(140 to 145.4°F.) in a standard commercial pasteurizing plant. The samples were fed to young pigs daily for a period of three months, and at the same time, the centrifuged deposit from certain of the samples was injected into guinea pigs. Definite tuberculous lesions were not found in any of the pigs or in the guinea pigs, whether they had received raw or pasteurized milk. A further series of similar experiments was undertaken with milk artificially infected with tubercle bacilli. The guinea pigs did not develop tuberculous lesions, whether they had been injected with the raw or heated milk, but almost all the young pigs were shown at autopsy to have lymph glands infected with tubercle bacilli, including those that had received the pasteurized milk. They concluded that 30 minutes' heating of milk at a temperature of 60 to 63°C.(140 to 145.4°F.) does not suffice to kill all tubercle bacilli. The experiments of Katrandjieff [228] indicated that heating to 63°C.(145.4°F.) for 30 minutes was necessary.

Temperatures of 63 to 65°C.(145.4 to 149°F.), according to Rautmann,[229] could be relied upon to destroy the tubercle bacillus. Proscholdt [230] used these temperatures with milk which had been heavily seeded with tubercle bacilli. Control guinea pigs which received unheated inoculum developed tuberculosis, while pigs which received inoculum which had been heated at a temperature of 63 to 65°C.(145.4 to 149°F.) for 30 minutes, all remained healthy. In view of the various factors involved, Yanagisawa and Ida [231] believed a temperature of 63°C.(145.4°F.) was necessary for satisfactory pasteurization. Their conclusions were based on cultural tests and animal inoculations with both the human and bovine types of *Mycobacterium tuberculosis*.

The rate of death of this organism during pasteurization has not received much study. Corper and Cohn [232] found it to be logarithmic between the important range from 50°C.(122°F.) to 60°C.(140°F.).

It is most unfortunate that in most of the experiments, results of which are reported above, so few quantitative data were collected, and so little attention was paid to conditions of heating. The ample margin of safety, however, in selection of legal temperatures of pasteurization probably compensates for these defects in technic.

Proposals to pasteurize milk by the high temperature-short time method at 71.1°C.(160°F.) for 15 seconds made it necessary to determine that pathogenic bacteria would be destroyed. Workman [40] found it to be satisfactory with 17 strains of *Mycobacterium tuberculosis*. Other results are reported at other places in this chapter.

Eberthella Typhosa. At one time milk was a more important factor in spread of typhoid fever than it is today. While the number of milk-borne epidemics of typhoid fever has been lowered over the years, the curve

227. Scharr and Lentz. 1927. Ztschr. Fleisch. u. Milchhyg. 37, 202-205, 218-219.
228. Katrandjieff. 1928. Compt. Rend. Soc. Biol. 99, 1478-1481.
229. Rautmann. 1927. Ztschr. Fleisch. u. Milchhyg. 37, 185-189.
230. Proscholdt. 1928. Arch. Wiss. u. Prakt. Tierheilk. 58, 296-310.
231. Yanagisawa and Ida. 1935. J. Pub. Health Assoc., Japan, 11, 3-4.
232. Corper and Cohn. 1937. Amer. Rev. Tuberculosis 35, 663-677.

seems to have leveled off to about 30 epidemics a year in the United States. Many observations have been reported to prove the case for milk pasteurization with typhoid fever alone. This was well indicated by a striking report by Geiger and Kelly [233] traced to a large dairy employing 20 men and milking 300 cows. Ninety gallons of milk were delivered to a substation in Richmond and 600 gallons to a substation in Berkeley. Investigations indicated that the milk had been infected by a man who had been ill a week before consulting a physician. Later clinical and laboratory data indicated that the illness was typhoid fever. The milk from this dairy was not pasteurized for one city, but was so treated for another. The authors call attention to the fact that "this constitutes a unique and unparalleled experiment with human beings—accidental of course—but demonstrating conclusively that pasteurization of milk supplies is an efficient method for preventing typhoid fever from food." Other data in support of such a statement have been collected by Jordan.[234] Twiss [235] has stated that *Salmonella paratyphi* and *Salmonella schottmülleri* often survived pasteurization under experimental conditions. Krumwiede and Noble [236] denied this, and stated that 60°C.(140°F.) will destroy typhoid bacilli in milk in 20 minutes. They avoided possible error by completely submerging the container in the bath. The fact that the members of the colon-typhoid group are nonsporeformers might argue against their ability to survive pasteurization unless there were heat-resistant strains.

In the United States Naval Bulletin 19 (1923), 629-630, are reported results of experiments on thermal death points of *Eberthella typhosa* in heavily infected milk: at 54.4°C.(130°F.), some organisms survived one hour, but all cells were destroyed in from four to eight minutes at 61.1°C. (142°F.) to 62.7°C.(145°F.). In tests using large volumes of heavily infected milk, it was found that the organisms causing typhoid fever, paratyphoid fever, and diphtheria were killed in 10 minutes at temperatures between 60°C.(140°F.) and 62.7C.(145°F.). Some of the tubercle bacilli survived 10 minutes, but were destroyed after 20 minutes' heating at 61.1°C.(142°F.) and 62.7°C.(145°F.). A similar study was carried out by Tanner and Dubois,[237] who found that the usual methods of pasteurization would destroy the members of the colon-typhoid group if they were present in milk in not too large numbers. The laws of disinfection would indicate the possible survival of a few cells of these organisms if there were many cells in the raw milk. Anderson [218] studied the effect of heating milk to 63°C.(145.4°F.) for one-half hour on several strains of the typhoid, paratyphoid, and Gaertner group. He stated that *Escherichia coli* might be found which would survive this temperature and time. With most of the strains, such an exposure would destroy them. In four of the 15 cases in which streptococci were used in the experiments, the organisms were not killed by 63°C.(145.4°F.) for one-half hour.

233. Geiger and Kelly. 1916. J. Amer. Med. Assoc. 66, 263-264.

234. Jordan. 1912. J. Amer. Med. Assoc. 59, 1450-1457.

235. Twiss. 1920. J. Infect. Dis. 26, 165-170.

236. Krumwiede and Noble. 1921. J. Infect. Dis. 29, 310.

237. Tanner and Dubois. 1925. J. Dairy Sci. 8, 47-53.

Experiences of large cities during recent years has shown that pasteurization pays. Of course, there were probably other factors in part responsible for the steady decline in the typhoid death rate. Nauss,[238] in discussing milk-borne typhoid fever in Illinois, presented graphic evidence of the value of pasteurization. North et al.,[10] in their extensive study, heated strains from the typhoid-paratyphoid group. They stated that Eberthella typhosa was destroyed by momentary heating by a commercial heater to 60.6°C.(141°F.) and by one type of commercial holder at 55.5°C.(132°F.) for 30 minutes.

The data for the paratyphoid bacteria reflect quite well the facts for Eberthella typhosa. The conditions of the experiments seem to influence the results which are secured. For instance, Oerskov[217] heated milk in a test tube in a water bath at 63°C.(145.4°F.). It formed on the surface a ring composed of dried proteins. On account of this ring formation the paratyphoid bacillus may remain alive for 15 minutes to even two hours at the above temperature. However, if they are exposed to the action of the heat, they are killed in three minutes. The resistance of various strains heated to 63°C.(145.4°F.) in physiological salt solution, bouillon, and undiluted media was also determined. The strains studied withstood a temperature of 63°C.(145.4°F.) for from one to four minutes. The typhoid bacillus resisted only one minute; various strains of paratyphoid bacillus and Gaertner's bacillus two or three minutes; Escherichia coli 15 minutes. The pH has no influence between 6.0 and 8.0. Outside of these limits, the resistance diminishes.

Shigella dysenteriae (Bacterium dysenteriae). The characteristics of the dysentery organisms would indicate that they are just about as resistant to temperatures used in pasteurization as other members of the colontyphoid group. Doorenbos and Mulders[239] heated cultures of Shigella dysenteriae to 50°C.(122°F.) to 60°C.(140°F.) and found that they were made sterile. Note should be made, however, that such cells are more easily destroyed in water than in milk. The Shiga type was killed in one minute in water at 60°C.(140°F.), while six minutes were required to obtain the same result in milk. For the Flexner type, Doorenbos and Mulders stated that the time required was, respectively, one minute and 10 minutes; for the Leiden type, one minute and 20 minutes. Rosenau[240] stated that Shigella dysenteriae was somewhat more resistant to heating in milk than Eberthella typhosa. He stated that it sometimes withstood heating to 60°C.(140°F.) for five minutes. All cells were killed at 60°C.(140°F.) for 10 minutes; however, the great majority of cells were killed by the time the milk reached 60°C.(140°F.).

Pathogenic Streptococci. The possibility of infection with pathogenic streptococci in milk has made it necessary to determine whether such organisms are killed by pasteurization. Park[241] carried out an investigation on the thermal death point of a number of pathogenic streptococci from various sources in order to aid in the selection of a proper temperature for

238. Nauss. 1923. Ill. Health News 9, 238-244.
239. Doorenbos and Mulders. 1924. Tijdschr. Vergelijk. Geneesk. 10, 51.
240. Rosenau. 1912. U. S. Pub. Health Serv., Hyg. Lab. Bull. 42 and 56, 427-453.
241. Park. 1928. Amer. J. Pub. Health 18, 710-714.

commercial pasteurization. Previous to this time some work had been done, but not always with organisms of such sanitary significance. Ayers, Johnson, and Davis [185] reported that 60°C.(140°F.) for 30 minutes always destroyed 27 strains of pathogenic streptococci when heated in milk. A few other streptococci from similar sources survived this treatment and would, therefore, survive pasteurization. The number of cells heated in milk was not stated. Ayers and Johnson [87] also tested 139 cultures of streptococci from cow feces, the udder and mouth of the cow, and milk and cream. They stated that two classes of streptococci survived pasteurization: (a) Those which have a low majority thermal death point, among which are a few cells able to survive; (b) streptococci which have a high majority thermal death point. Some of the streptococci with which Ayers and Johnson worked were not killed in 30 minutes at 57.2°C.(135°F.), but none were able to withstand 60°C.(140°F.) for 30 minutes. These forms were not known to be pathogenic.

Park's [241] experiments were much to the point. He stated that in practically all cases, diseases transmitted through milk were caused by hemolytic streptococci. The strains which Park used came from septic sore throat, tonsillitis, scarlet fever, mastoiditis, glandular fever, erysipelas, and other sources. The details of technic used are given in a subsequent paragraph. Cultures from every one of 200 strains were killed by an exposure of 60°C. (140°F.) for 30 minutes. The majority of the strains were killed at 57.2°C. (136°F.) or less.

Davis [242] failed to find evidence that streptococci pathogenic for man could resist pasteurization temperatures (62.7°C.[145°F.)] for 30 minutes.). He tested 98 strains and 74 hemolytic, pathogenic streptococci and found a resistance of 30 minutes at 60°C.(140°F.). Twenty of the 74 hemolytic strains came from milk and were not virulent. They resisted 68.3°C.(155°F.) for 30 minutes. The efficiency of pasteurization depends on several factors: (1) the heating of every particle of milk to the pasteurization temperature, and (2) holding it at that temperature for fully 30 minutes; (3) prevention of reinfection.

Zeller et al.[225, 226] stated that streptococci from mastitis, although greatly diminished in numbers, were not killed completely. Such conclusions were also reached by Beckwith and Eddie.[243] Whether in milk or in ice cream mix, hemolytic streptococci were resistant to pasteurization temperatures.

Park's [241] Method for Testing Thermal Death Point of Streptococci in Milk. Fill sterile vials with 10 ml. of sterile milk and place in a water bath, the water of which is somewhat higher than the desired temperature. When the milk in the vials and the water in the bath have reached the desired temperature, .05 ml. of a blood broth culture of the strain to be tested is injected into the milk and the vial stoppered by a rubber cork already heated to the same temperature. The stoppered vial should then be submerged in the water for the desired time. It should then be removed and the contents poured into an ice cold bottle and packed in cracked ice. The bottle with its contents should then be placed in the incubator at 37.2°C.(99°F.) for 42 hours. After incubation the milk should be tested on blood agar plates for viable Streptococci.

242. Davis. 1918. J. Infect. Dis. 23, 559.
243. Beckwith and Eddie. 1924. J. Lab. and Clin. Med. 9, 316-321.

While most streptococci seem to be destroyed by pasteurization of milk, some have been reported occasionally to survive. This problem interested committees of the American Public Health Association [244] whose reports indicate that some streptococci are sufficiently heat resistant to survive pasteurization. Weakly hemolytic streptococci were reported by Slanetz [245] to be widely prevalent in pasteurized milk. He believed that the majority of these bacteria entered milk from the utensils. Since they were especially heat resistant, attention to utensils was recommended to eliminate them from the milk supply. Sixty strains were studied carefully, all of which could survive pasteurization temperatures. They formed alpha prime type of colonies on blood agar. Slanetz believed efforts should be made to keep such streptococci from milk. Whether these organisms survive or not depends on many factors, some of which were not considered by earlier workers. These have been reviewed in Chapter 2 under heat resistance of bacteria. Numbers of cells present and the time and temperature of heating are most important.

Corynebacterium diphtheriae (Bacterium diphtheriae). Milk has at times been the cause of diphtheria and, consequently, experiments were in order to determine whether pasteurization times and temperatures would destroy *Corynebacterium diphtheriae*. As early as 1894, Brieger and Fränkel [246] reported that this organism was killed at 55°C.(131°F.) in 45 minutes. Welch and Abbott [247] confirmed that result. Loeffler,[248] however, stated that the organism was killed at 60°C.(140°F.) in 30 minutes. Moore and Hemlet (1906) came to the same conclusions reached by Park.[241] Rosenau stated that *Corynebacterium diphtheriae* was susceptible to heat in milk, and that it usually failed to grow after heating to 55°C., but that some cells might survive heating at 60°C. More recent work by North *et al.*[10] seems to indicate that heating in a commercial heater to 53.9°C. (129°F.) for a very short time destroys the organism. Thus it seems that ordinary methods of pasteurization are probably able to destroy *Corynebacterium diphtheriae* in milk.

Brucella Species. These organisms are pathogenic for man and animals and may be transmitted in milk. It became necessary, consequently, to carefully determine whether they were killed by pasteurization. Rosenau [243] stated that, as far as evidence then available was concerned, a temperature of 60°C.(140°F.) for 20 minutes was more than sufficient to destroy the etiologic agent of Malta fever in milk. It was stated that the organism was not killed by 55°C.(131°F.) for a short time; the great majority of cells was killed at 58°C., and at 60°C. all were killed. In 1928 Carpenter and Boak [249] exposed cultures of human, bovine, and porcine species to temperatures of 60°C.(140°F.), 61.1°C.(142°F.), and 71.1°C. (160°F.) for various intervals of time. Tests for viability were made by cultures and animal tests, the guinea pig inoculation tests being more

244. Amer. Pub. Health Assoc. Comm. Rpts., Yearbooks 1933-1934 and 1935-1936.
245. Slanetz. 1938. New Hampshire Agr. Expt. Sta., Tech. Bull. 70.
246. Brieger and Fränkel. 1890. Berl. klin. Wchnschr. 27, 241.
247. Welch and Abbott. 1892. Johns Hopkins Hosp. Bull. 2.
248. Loeffler. 1887. Gesell. f. Heilkunde.
249. Carpenter and Boak. 1928. Amer. J. Pub. Health 18, 743-751.

reliable than the cultures. No cultures were viable after exposure to 60°C. (140°F.) for 20 minutes in milk. Later Boak and Carpenter [250] confirmed these results as did Zeller et al.[226] On the other hand, Bartram [250] stated that certain porcine strains of Brucella abortus might not be destroyed at 60°C.(140°F.) in 20 minutes, at 61.1°C.(142°F.) in 30 minutes, or at 62.7°C.(145°F.) in 15 minutes. Using a standard pasteurization outfit Murray, McNutt, and Purwin[252] found 62 to 63°C.(143.6 to 145.4°F.) when applied for three minutes to be sufficient to destroy both bovine and porcine varieties of the abortion organism. Their results indicated that the usual pasteurization temperature, as reported above, gave an ample factor of safety, providing the pasteurizer is operated in the proper manner. With the lid of the pasteurizer open, a much longer time exposure to this temperature is required and the results obtained are irregular and uncertain, in that viable organisms were recovered from the foam even after pasteurization for 30 minutes. The absolute necessity of a flush gate valve is also indicated, for in those experiments in which an ordinary faucet outlet was used viable organisms were obtained from the outlet after pasteurization for 30 minutes, whereas with the outlet closed by a stopper on the inside no living organisms remained after exposure for three minutes. The experiments emphasize the importance of carefully conducted operations in pasteurization if successful results are to be obtained.

Results of observations by Park, Graham, Prucha, and Brannon [253] on two strains of Brucella suis in artificially contaminated whole and skim-milk samples suggested that efficient pasteurization destroys it in milk, preventing milk-borne porcine brucellosis. In whole-milk samples, containing 500,000,000 Brucella organisms per ml., sealed in glass tubes, both strains survived 30 minutes at 56.7°C.(134°F.) but were destroyed in 20 minutes at 60°C.(140°F.), in 15 minutes at 61.1°C.(142°F.), and in seven mnutes at 62.2°C.(144°F.). They were more resistant to heat in milk samples in cotton stoppered tubes. Brucella suis remained viable for 30 minutes at 144°F. in milk containing 10,000,000 to 500,000,000 organisms per ml., but with the same time and temperature it was destroyed in milk containing 5,000 to 1,000,000 organisms per ml. Graham and Torrey [254] later reported that no organisms causing brucellosis were found in 68 samples of pasteurized milk collected in Illinois. These samples came from various types of pasteurizers. That pasteurization will take care of these organisms was also indicated by Wiseman.[255]

Park's [241] experiments with Brucella abortus and Brucella melitensis indicated that 10 minutes' exposure in milk at 60°C.(140°F.) were sufficient to kill these organisms. Zeller's et al.[225,226] cultures of Alcaligines abortus were apparently a little more resistant, for an exposure of 60 to

250. Boak and Carpenter. 1931. J. Infect. Dis. 49, 485-488.
251. Bartram. 1931. Cornell Vet. 21, 360-367.
252. Murray, McNutt, and Purwin. 1932. J. Amer. Vet. Med. Assoc. 80, 336-342; J. Dairy Sci. 15, 6-13.
253. Park, Graham, Prucha. and Brannon. 1932. J. Bact. 42, 461-471; Trans. Ill. Acad. Sci. 25 (1933), 155-156.
254. Graham and Torrey. 1936. J. Amer. Vet. Med. Assoc. 88, 614-623.
255. Wiseman. 1937. New England J. Med. 216, 977-978.

63°C.(140 to 145.4°F.) for 30 minutes was necessary. The results of experiments of this nature ought not to be compared too closely. They are subject to a number of factors, such as number of cells, reaction of the milk, etc. It seems evident, however, that *Brucella melitensis*, and probably *Brucella abortus*, is probably destroyed by the ordinary methods of pasteurization. According to Murray, McNutt, and Purwin.[252] *Brucella suis* is easily killed by pasteurization.

The high temperature-short time method of pasteurization at 71.1°C. (160°F.) was found by Workman [40] to be satisfactory for destroying Brucella organisms. Seventy-four strains were used.

Vibrio comma (microspira cholerae). Rosenau [240] stated that *Vibrio comma (Microspira cholerae)* was similar in heat resistance in milk to *Corynebacterium diphtheriae*. It was usually destroyed when the milk reached 55°C.(131°F.); only once did it survive 60°C.(140°F.) under the conditions of his experiments. Such results might be expected since this organism does not form spores.

Virus of Foot and Mouth Disease. The experiments of Zeller, Wedemann, Lange, and Gildemeister [225] revealed complete destruction of the virus of foot and mouth disease by heating milk at 60 to 63°C.(140 to 145.4°F.) for 30 minutes.

REFERENCE BOOKS

KAY, H. D., ASCHAFFENBURG, R., AND NEAVE, F. K., 1939. The Phosphatase Test for Control of Efficiency of Pasteurization. Imperial Bureau of Dairy Science, Shinfield, England.

KILBOURNE, C. H., 1916. The Pasteurization of Milk. John Wiley and Sons, Inc., New York, N. Y.

WILSON, G. S., 1935. The Bacteriological Grading of Milk. Med. Res. Council, Spec. Rpt., Series No. 206. H. M. Stationery Off., London, England.

CHAPTER 8

MICROBIOLOGY OF CREAM AND BUTTER

Microorganisms have an important role in the butter industry. Some are used to contribute desired flavor while others may cause deterioration and bad flavors. Quality depends on strict control of microorganisms, both those which are favored and those which are repressed. A few must be kept out of butter at all costs. Sorensen [1] stated that butter may be contaminated from impure water and be made to undergo serious spoilage. He recommended the use of chlorine-treated creamery waters. Linneboe [2] found that *Achromobacter putrescens* in water is often the cause of putrid butter. This organism was found in six out of 55 farm supplies. Other opinions on this question have been quoted in Chapter 4.

Microbiology of Cream. Owing to the fact that cream is frequently held on the farm and in creameries for long periods or shipped long distances, its microorganism content is important. The changes which may be brought about in it by various microorganisms will probably involve each of its constituents. When cream is not held at low enough temperature, some of these changes are quite undesirable. One of the more comprehensive investigations on microbiology of cream was carried out by Macy, Coulter, and Combs. [3] Raw cream in every instance was found to be quite heavily seeded with microorganisms. Seventy-seven per cent contained ten million bacteria or more per gram; 48.9 per cent of cream samples contained over 1,000 yeasts per ml. and between 10 and 100 molds per ml. Results after pasteurization were in striking contrast. Molds were completely destroyed and yeasts were eliminated in 71 per cent of the samples. Each constituent of cream is susceptible to attack by microorganisms with formation of specific substances which are involved in deterioration.

Microorganisms which attack fat in cream have received considerable study because the products of such attack may be most undesirable. These organisms may act on the fat in cream or in butter. Deterioration of cream accompanied by marked lipolytic action on the butterfat at refrigeration temperatures was reported by Anderson and Hardenbergh. [4] After several days the cream acquired a bitter flavor. The causal organism resembled certain members of the Achromobacter and Alcaligenes groups. It failed to grow above 35°C. (95°F.). Hydrolysis of fat was the main biochemical activity noted and was said to be of considerable economic importance. A new bacterium, for which the name *Bacterium lipidis* was proposed by Anderson, [5] exhibited powerful fat-splitting action, weak action on protein, and none on sugars. It grew rapidly at refrigeration temperatures. A sharp throat irritation resulted from swallowing cream containing the

1. Sorensen. 1940. J. Dairy Sci. 23, 423-435.
2. Linneboe. 1940. Sci. Agr. 21, 133-138.
3. Macy, Coulter, and Combs. 1932. Minn. Agr. Expt. Sta. Bull. 82.
4. Anderson and Hardenbergh. 1932. J. Bact. 23, 59.
5. Anderson. 1937. Ann. Conv. Internatl. Assoc. Milk Dealers, Lab. Sec., 19.

organism which was thought to be due to liberation of caproic, isocaproic, and caprylic acids from the milk fat. Spoilage of cream at low temperature is due mainly to hydrolysis of fat and protein which accounts for the rancid and bitter flavors. Lipolytic microorganisms are discussed in several other places in this book. They are becoming of great significance in the food industry.

The nitrogenous constituents of cream are also subject to attack by microorganisms. Powell[6] found acid coagulating organisms to predominate in fresh raw creams but they were replaced during storage by acid-forming and acid coagulating-peptonizing groups. In freshly heated creams the peptonizing groups increased from 25 per cent in cream held at 63.8°C.(155°F.) to 75 per cent in cream held at 85°C.(185°F.). Objectionable bitter flavors developed in raw creams shortly after storage. Flash pasteurization at 73.9°C.(165°F.) prevented the formation of these flavors during a 10-day storage period. In the late spring and summer flash pasteurization at 68.3°C.(155°F.) produced fine-flavored creams storable for 10 days. Pasteurizing temperatures above 73.9°C.(165°F.) imparted objectionable heated flavors to cream. Presence of both proteolytic and lipolytic bacteria might mean rapid deterioration of cream if it were not adequately refrigerated.

In view of meager information on the bacterial content of market cream, Robinton, Borman, and Mickle[7] examined 523 samples of raw and pasteurized cream; many were substandard according to "tentative standards." They recommended in addition to incubation at 37°C.(98.6°F.) for 48 hours, incubation at 8°C.(46.4°F.) for four days. Robinton, Borman, and Mickle were also inclined to minimize the importance of thermophilic bacteria in cream. A comparative study of methods later caused these investigators to conclude that the clump count under the microscope was the most satisfactory method, especially if, after pasteurization, the phosphatase test is made and if coliform bacteria are enumerated. They observed sporeforming bacteria in cream which survived pasteurization for 30 minutes and which developed rapidly in cream at 20°C.(68°F.). They do not develop on the old "standard methods agar" but can be counted by the microscope method. Pin-point colonies have been found on plates made from cream as well as on plates made from other dairy products. O'Droma[8] found them to be the cause of high counts and attributed them to *Streptococcus thermophilus*. The organism was slightly hemolytic and showed appreciable heat resistance.

Coliform Bacteria in Cream. While the sanitary significance of coliform bacteria in cream may be open to debate, these organisms are known to cause rapid and serious deterioration in cream. One hundred and twenty-eight strains of coliform bacteria isolated from cream by Pont,[9] when carefully differentiated by acceptable methods, proved to be 76.5 per cent

6. Powell. 1938. J. Dairy Sci. 21, 219-226.
7. Robinton, Borman, and Mickle. 1941. J. Milk Tech. 4, 253-257; Amer. J. Pub. Health Assoc. 32 (1942), 464-470.
8. O'Droma. 1940. J. Dairy Res. 11, 37-42.
9. Pont. 1935. Idem 6, 148-152.

typical *Escherichia coli*, 11 per cent *Aerobacter aerogenes*, and 12.5 per cent intermediates. The two latter groups were similar in their effect and produced more serious deterioration in quality than typical *Escherichia coli*. Crossley [10] also found coliform bacteria in clotted cream. They were believed to result from contamination during processing.

METHYLENE BLUE REDUCTION TEST FOR CREAM

Less attention has been given to the possibility of using the methylene blue reduction test for grading cream than for grading milk. Macy [11] carried out a most comprehensive investigation in which he found that a triple-strength methylene blue solution had to be used. Macy's results showed that the reduction time was inversely proportional to the number of bacteria in cream as determined by the agar plate and microscope methods. The test was said to be useful for sweet cream having acidity less than .21 per cent. It is not adaptable to sour cream. Rapid disappearance of color indicates a high number of bacteria. Barnum [12] used a triple-strength methylene blue solution for cream instead of the one recommended in *Standard Methods of Milk Analysis* then in use. Presence of fat did not significantly influence reduction time.

Macy's [11] Method for Methylene Blue Reduction Test on Sweet Cream. The procedures were given as follows:

APPARATUS NEEDED

1. Pipette or metal dipper having a capacity of ten (10) milliliters (10 cubic centimeters).

2. Burette, graduated to one (1) milliliter, and apparatus stand provided with burette clamps; or, pipette graduated to one (1) milliliter.

3. Test tubes, thick-walled, 5/8″ x 6″ or 5/8″ x 5″. (It is often convenient to grind an area 1/2″ square on the upper portion of the tube by means of an emery wheel so that each tube may be marked easily with a lead pencil. Such markings may be erased when the tubes are washed.)

4. Cork or rubber stoppers for each tube.

5. Water bath. (The size depends upon the number of tests made.)

6. Wire racks for test tubes. Single or double row type is advisable.

7. Alcohol lamp, gas burner, or electric hot plate.

8. Methylene blue tablets. Standard tablets are manufactured by the National Aniline and Chemical Company, Inc., New York City, and are available at creamery supply houses.

9. Thermometer. (Centigrade or Fahrenheit.)

10. Graduated cylinder.

COLLECTION OF SAMPLE

Collect a ten (10) milliliter sample of cream in weigh-room, directly from patron's can if possible, by means of a metal dipper or a pipette. Place sample in a clean, boiled or sterilized test tube. Number properly. Place boiled or sterilized stopper in tube. Set tubed sample in rack in ice water bath until all samples are collected or until methylene blue solution is added. Rinse dipper or pipette thoroughly in cold water and then in boiling water before taking the next sample.

10. Crossley. 1939. Agr. Prog. 16, 38-44.
11. Macy. 1934. Minn. Agr. Expt. Sta. Bull. 310.
12. Barnum. 1932. Internatl. Assoc. Dairy and Milk Insp. Ann. Rept. 21, 192-196.

As soon as possible after the samples are taken, add one milliliter of the methylene blue solution to each sample of cream. Mix thoroughly. (It is usually convenient to collect a number of samples before adding the solution in order to simplify and to expedite the reading of results. However, the samples must be kept cold during the interval before making the color test.)

The methylene blue solution is prepared by dissolving three methylene blue tablets in 50 ml. of boiling water. Then add sufficient cold water to bring the total volume to 200 ml. Three tablets are necessary for cream, while one is sufficient for milk.

Warm the cream samples to 37°C. (98.6°F.) immediately after adding the solution. (Record time when that temperature is reached. This is the starting point for observations on the time required for the disappearance of the blue color.) Keep tubes in water bath or incubator at that temperature until the samples are decolorized. (The alcohol lamp, gas burner or electric hot plate may be helpful in maintaining a constant temperature of the water bath.) The samples should be kept away from light during the period of observation.

READINGS

Observe the tubes at intervals of ten minutes or less during the first hour. After that readings may be made each half hour.

Record the time required for the blue color to disappear from each sample. This is called the "reduction time."

GRADING THE CREAM

The samples may be graded, on the basis of reduction time, according to the following classification:

GOOD: not decolorized in 5½ hours.

FAIR: decolorized in less than 5½ hours, but not less than 2 hours.

POOR: decolorized in less than 2 hours, but not less than 20 minutes.

VERY POOR: decolorized in 20 minutes or less.

Molds in Cream. Owing to the nature of cream it may contain a variety of fungi. *Oidium lactis (Oospora lactis)* is probably the best known species especially from sour cream. It grows on the surface with a characteristic velvety appearance. According to Elliker [13] it enters milk and cream in dust, dirt, manure, and from carelessly washed utensils. Some strains grow at as low as 4.4°C. (40°F.), others at as high as 37.7°C. (100°F.), but ideal temperatures approximate 23.8°C. (75°F.). It was found to be destroyed by proper pasteurization. Growth of *Oidium lactis* is favored by a slightly acid reaction but is retarded or inhibited by high acidity, lack of air, presence of salt, and possibly by propionic acid or its salts. Its presence in butter with yeasts and other molds indicates unclean utensils. Frequent delivery of cream prevents the mold problem because it does not have time to develop. When the cream is used for buttermaking, high mold content causes many molds in the butter. Fouts [14] found that *Oidium lactis* and bacteria were somewhat inhibited by butter-culture organisms in cream. *Mycotorula lipolytica*, however, showed increased growth in presence of such organisms. Even in high-acid cream lipolysis was extensive enough to be of considerable importance. Some of the fungi used were inhibited by addition of excessive amounts of lactic acid. Various opinions exist with respect to the possible significance of *Oospora lactis* in cream. Thom [15] considered the fungus to be a common and offensive contaminant

13. Elliker. 1941. Natl. Butter and Cheese J. 32, 8.
14. Fouts. 1940. J. Dairy Sci. 23, 303-306.
15. Thom. 1935. Fundamentals of Dairy Science. Associates of Rogers. Second ed.

which develops mostly in the cream layer of old milk. It causes serious deterioration especially when many lots of cream are blended. A few practical dairy technologists have expressed a different opinion. Parfitt and Galema,[16] however, believed that molds in sour cream produced products which were undesirable in the manufacture of butter. Better butter is made when they are absent.

Statements are common in dairy products literature that it is almost impossible to produce dairy products, cream in this case, without mold contamination. This may be true for very slight contamination but heavy contamination undoubtedly indicates carelessness either in cleaning utensils or in handling the product itself. Wildman [17] stated that farmers should be able to produce cream, even in the summer, relatively free from mold growth. Concerning the presence of mold mycelia in butter Wildman stated that an occasional mold spore in the cream would probably not cause mold mycelia to be present in sweet cream butter. He was unable to show the presence of mold mycelia in such butter of known history. However, in the case of butter churned from sweet cream of varying ages and degrees of soundness the facts were different. In a survey at several creameries producing butter from sour cream during the month of June Wildman found that the mycelia contents varied from 22 to 100 per cent, the latter being the highest obtainable by the method used. As he viewed the situation the problem was to determine the relation of the presence of mycelia in butter to the type of cream used. In general he found that unsound cream might be expected to be moldy. Products of sound sour cream involves strictly clean utensils, low temperatures, and fresh cream. Old cream during the summer was usually in the high-count range, while fresh cream naturally decreased the mold problem. Clean utensils and a storage temperature of 15.5°C.(60°F.), according to Elliker and Brown [17a] will keep mold development low in cream over a storage period of four days. Temperatures as high as 21.1°C.(70°F.) were said to be possible over a four-day period if utensils are kept scrupulously clean and milk or cream protected from dirt and dust.

Wildman's [18] Macroscopic Method for Estimation of Mold in Cream. In addition to the microscope method, Wildman proposed a macroscopic method which could be used by creamery operators for detecting moldy cream in those cases where the mold had been stirred into the cream.

Method "A":

EQUIPMENT AND REAGENTS

    (a) Teaspoon—five ml.
    (b) Methylene blue-borax solution—Dissolve 30 grams of sodium borate and 10 methylene blue tablets (as used for reductase test) in 1 liter of water.
    (c) Test tube—5-6".
    (d) Shallow tin pie pan—Approximately 7" in diameter.
    (e) Scalpel.

PROCEDURE

    Measure out five ml. of cream, preferably warm as for Babcock test sampling, in the teaspoon and place in the test tube . Add 15 ml. of hot (90°C.) methylene

16. Parfitt and Galema. 1931. Amer. Creamery and Poultry Rev. 71, 462-464.
17. Wildman. 1939-1940. Amer. Butter Rev. 1-2, p. 10.
17a. Elliker and Brown. 1942. Purdue Univ. Agr. Expt. Sta., Bull. 465.
18. Wildman. 1937. J. Assoc. Off. Agr. Chem. 20, 93-100.

blue-borax solution, using a portion to rinse all the cream from the teaspoon into the tube. Shake the mixture well and pour into the pie pan. Tip the pan back and forth until all mold present has agglutinated into blue-stained masses. (In samples containing much mold, the flocculation occurs immediately. In most cases of non-moldy sour cream, no blue flecks will form.) For purposes of comparison, collect the mold into a disk with a scalpel, and measure and designate the diameter roughly by the following scheme:

| Diameter of clot | Approximate area |
mm.	sq. mm.
9.5	70
5.5	24
3.5	9
2.5	4
1.0	1

At the present time the following simpler method of examination is used: Method "B":

EQUIPMENT AND REAGENTS

(a) Beaker—50 ml.

(b) Methylene blue-borax solution—Prepare as directed in Method "A."

(c) Perforated funnel—Made from perforated brass, No. 26 gage, having approximately 625 holes per sq. in., each hole being .02" in diameter. A circular disk 1.5" in diameter is cut, and from it is removed a 45° sector. The edges of the remaining disk are bent together until they meet, and are then soldered. To this funnel is soldered a .5" collar.

(d) Scalpel or dissecting needle.

PROCEDURE

Weigh out five grams of cream into the beaker and add 15 ml. of the hot methylene blue-borax solution. After agitating the beaker for three minutes, pour the mixture through the special perforated funnel. Add more hot methylene blue-borax solution to wash any mold clots into the apex of the funnel. By means of a dissecting needle, level off the top of the mold until it forms an inverted cone and then measure the diameter of the base formed thereby (mm.).

Significance of results secured with the above method was investigated by determining the mold content of 44 individual samples of butter churned from cream, the mold content of which had been determined with macroscopic methods. Cream with low mold content yielded butter with low count. Examination of many samples of cream showed higher mold content in the summer and fall months. In order to determine the effect of churning on the mold content of butter, a sample of moldy cream was churned. It yielded butter and buttermilk in the ratio of two to three. The mold count on the butter was 76 per cent, and only four per cent on the buttermilk. These results seemed to indicate that churning instead of reducing the amount of mold actually concentrated it in the butter.

Ropy Cream. Microorganisms causing ropiness in cream seem to be little different from those which cause the same defect in milk. Rodenkirchen[19] found ropy cream to be due to *Aerogenes aerobacter* and another species having much in common with *Sarcina aurantica*.

Canned Cream. In an outbreak of bitterness in canned cream the cause of the defect was found by McMaster[20] to be a short, sporeforming rod

19. Rodenkirchen. 1939. Zentbl. Bakt., Pt. 1, 144, 187.
20. McMaster. 1933. Ann. Rpt. Fruit and Veg. Res. Sta., Univ. of Bristol. 71-74.

which was similar to but not identical with *Bacillus cohaerens*. The spores when suspended in milk did not survive exposure to 115.5°C.(239.3°F.) for 12.5 minutes. Increasing the processing temperature prevented development of the bitterness. A bitter flavor and a thin consistency in canned cream was found by Nichok, Howat, and Jackson [21] to be due to three organisms, all belonging to the *Bacillus subtilis* group but showing various cultural differences. A large number of normal tins were inoculated with these three strains and the abnormal conditions reproduced, although the three strains were not equally effective. The changes did not readily occur at room temperatures, but occurred rather slowly at 25°C.(77°F.) (three weeks or longer), while most of the tins held at 32°C.(89.6°F.) and 37°C. (98.6°F.) showed thin contents with bitter taste at the end of two weeks. The organisms were always recoverable but often in surprisingly small numbers. The spores of these strains resisted temperatures up to 120°C. (240°F.) for as long as 40 minutes. Bitterness and thinning usually went together and chemical analyses showed that they were associated with breakdown of the protein.

Cream canning presents problems which are somewhat different from those of other dairy products. Loveless [22] studied the rate of heating and the viscosity of cream. The viscosity changed considerably during the first day after sterilizing, and continued to change at a decreasing rate over a period of many days. Variations in agitation seem to be the cause of variations in viscosity. The use of a preheating temperature of 140°F. (instead of 110°F. as generally used in commercial practice) produces an increase of about 50 per cent in viscosity after sterilization and reduces the tendency of the cream to form grains by coagulation of the protein, thus giving a smoother cream.

Whipped Cream Products. Whipped cream is a popular food on the American Market. Up to the present time it has been whipped mechanically with beaters, the success of the operation being dependent on numerous factors which have been reviewed by Sommer.[22a] Studies on the microbiology of cream by various investigators whose publications are listed elsewhere in this paper, and especially by Robinton, Borman, and Mickle [7] indicate that market cream may not always be a high-grade product.

A new method of whipping cream which departs from the older mechanical methods and contributes markedly to a sanitary product has been developed. This new method, best represented by "Instantwhip," involves charging the cream with an innocuous gas under pressure in a special container.[22b] The cream is whipped as it blows through the valve of the pressure bottle. Getz, Smith, Tracy, and Prucha [22c] stated that whipping takes place by physical-chemical rather than by mechanical means. This method involves use of nitrous oxide at 150 pounds pressure and results

21. Nichok, Howat, and Jackson. 1937. J. Dairy Res. 8, 331-346.
22. Loveless. 1935. Food 5, 52-58.
22a. Sommer, H. H. 1938. Market Milk and Related Products. Sommer. Madison, Wis.
22b. Getz. 1942. U. S. Patent 2,294,172. Aug. 25, 1942.
22c. Getz, Smith, Tracy, and Prucha. 1937. Food Research 2, 409-428.

in a product of about 300 per cent overrun. The sanitary features of such a product should be apparent to those who are familiar with the problems of handling whipped cream at many places where it is served. In a survey Prucha [22d] observed both insanitary handling and development of bad flavors in whipping cream, dispensed by hand dipping.

The following table summarizes some of the many data which Prucha published:

Average Logarithmic Bacteria Counts of Whipped Cream From Five Cities When It Was Served

City	Instant Whip	Hand-dipped
	Per gm.	*Per gm.*
City 1	770,000	5,100,000
City 2	44,000	700,000
City 3	225,000	1,190,000
City 4	200,000	5,400,000
City 5	No samples	590,000

It is evident that hand-dipped whipped cream has many more bacteria than whipped cream prepared and served by the new method. This is due largely to poorer raw materials, contamination during handling and serving, and the time which intervenes between manufacture and serving. A distinct advantage of whipped cream prepared according to the new method is the fact that it may be pasteurized in the closed special container. Such methods of pasteurization of a dairy product in the final container have been sought by dairy technologists for many years. Prucha [22e] has collected many data secured with *Eberthella typhosa, Shigella dysenteriae, Brucella meletensis,* and others, all of which show that pasteurization in the special closed container destroys all of these pathogenic bacteria and yields a dependable, safe product. Pressure of the gas itself also helps to destroy bacteria during storage and the cream was observed to keep much better under these conditions. This process may be looked upon as another distinct advance in distributing dairy products under safe and sanitary conditions.

Pasteurization of Cream for Butter Making. Cream is pasteurized before being made into butter to reduce the general bacterial flora before butter culture is added, to destroy microorganisms which would deteriorate butter, and to destroy pathogenic bacteria. Butter has been known to cause epidemics, and any step which would destroy disease-producing bacteria would help to make life safe. Pasteurization of cream may also destroy enzymes which might deteriorate butter. Hammer [23] observed that vat pasteurization of sour cream at $60°C.(140°F.)$ to $62.7°C.(145°F.)$ for 20 minutes sometimes left large numbers of living bacteria, although the percentage killed was high. Better destruction was observed by flash pasteurization at $82.2°C.(180°F.)$ to $85°C.(185°F.)$. Only small numbers of bac-

22d. Prucha. 1938. Dairy Manufacturers Conference, Manual. Dept. of Dairy Husbandry, Univ. of Ill., Urbana. Nov. 15-18, 1938. 177-188.
22e. Prucha. 1943. Personal communication.
23. Hammer. 1914. Iowa Agr. Expt. Sta. Bull. 156.

teria survived. Hammer's results in these experiments did not indicate as great benefits from pasteurization as later investigators reported. Butter made from raw cream showed as good keeping quality as butter from pasteurized cream. Hunziker et al.[24] reported that butter made from pasteurized cream brought a higher price than butter made from raw cream. Contrary to the results of Hammer, quoted above, Hunziker and his colleagues found the holding process of pasteurization at 62.7°C.(145°F.) to show greatest bacteria-killing power while the flash process at 85°C.(185°F.) gave erratic results. That keeping quality of butter is improved by pasteurization was shown by the fact that pasteurized cream yielded better butter.

It is not a simple matter to relate butter quality to any one factor, such as cream pasteurization. Wide variations in resistance of bacteria to heat influence the results of applying heat to cream. According to Parker and Brengman[25] optimum pasteurization methods for use under various conditions are not known. Besides reduction in the general bacterial flora by pasteurization of cream there is destruction of specific microorganisms which may cause development of bad butter. Prevention of development of fishy flavor in butter was accomplished by Platon and Olsson[26] by heating the cream to 85°C.(185°F.).

Resazurin Test for Determining the Quality of Pasteurized Cream. This test has been found to be satisfactory for judging the quality of various dairy products. Chilson and Collins[27] reported that it was satisfactory for determining quality in pasteurized 20 or 40 per cent cream. When such cream was stored for several days at less than 4.4°C.(40°F.) the resazurin reduction time did not indicate fully the increase in plate counts. Collins et al.[28] applied the resazurin test to raw cream. Samples which had resazurin pink tests of two hours or more had microscope counts averaging logarithmically 150,000 to 300,000 bacteria per ml. Jenkins[29] made the test by adding .1 ml. of a .05-per cent solution of resazurin dye to 10 ml. of pasteurized cream and incubating at 36.7°C.(98°F.). Cream with a reduction time of less than six hours often exceeded the legal limit for bacterial numbers (40,000 per ml.). Cream with a reduction time of from six to seven hours, had an average plate count of 17,000 bacteria per ml. and was free from customer complaints.

Phosphatase Test Applied to Cream. Most cream to be used for butter making is pasteurized by the "flash" method. Scharer[30] said there was some evidence to show that a greater amount of phosphatase is found in cream separated after pasteurization than when separation precedes pasteurization. He explained this by saying that inactivation of the enzyme was a logarithmic function of time and temperature, the enzyme not being

24. Hunziker et al. 1917. Indiana Agr. Expt. Sta. Bull. 208.
25. Parker and Brengman. 1938. Food Indus. 10, 66-67, 110.
26. Platon and Olsson. 1936. Meddel. Centralanst. Försöksv. Jordbruksområdet (Sweden) No. 468.
27. Chilson and Collins. 1940. J. Milk Tech. 3, 334-340.
28. Collins, White, Chilson, Turner, and Rice. 1939. J. Milk Tech. 2, 236-244.
29. Jenkins. 1940. Milk Dealer 30, 58-60.
30. Scharer. 1938. J. Milk Tech. 1, 35-37, July; 2 (1939), 16-20.

completely inactivated at 61.7°C.(143°F.) in 30 minutes, and that this small amount of enzyme is subsequently concentrated in the cream. Raw cream was said to contain several times the phosphatase found in raw milk. Cream heated to 71°C.(160°F.) for 15 seconds showed considerable phosphatase. The main object of an investigation by Shadwick and Parker[31] was to study the utility and limitations of the phosphatase test for this product. A laboratory flash pasteurizer was devised. Practically, there was no holding time as this was only about 30 seconds, including the heating time. On the basis of agar plate counts temperatures of 82.2°C.(180°F.) or above gave satisfactory (about 99 per cent) bacterial reduction. At 85°C.(185°F.) or higher temperatures negative phosphatase reactions were obtained with the original test or various modifications, such as the Scharer short method. At 180°F. negative results were obtained by the modified Scharer short method and by the methods of Kay and Graham requiring two and one-half and eight hours of incubation, but the results were doubtful using the 24-hour incubation period. At 79.4°C.(175°F.) positive phosphatase results were obtained with most methods and positive with all methods below 175°F. The authors discussed various factors which may possibly vitiate the phosphatase test findings, including the possible stimulation of phenol production in butter.

No relation was found by Parfitt, Brown, and Shadwick[32] of phosphatase value of butter to its yeast and mold count, total bacterial count, and keeping quality as measured by drop in score. Agreement secured between two laboratories on identical samples of butter was closer with the short methods than with the one-hour method. A higher percentage of phosphatase positive reactions was found in cream from flash systems of pasteurization than from plants using vat systems. However, some plants which were flash pasteurizing consistently yielded negative phosphatase reactions which indicate that the process was not at fault. Owing to possibility that the enzyme is concentrated in butter, and because of the lack of knowledge concerning its partition in butter from cream, further studies on this point are indicated. It has been found that under the conditions which butter is marketed a significant number of samples will react negative when fresh and positive after receiving treatment comparable to commercial methods of distribution.

Laboratory pasteurization of 20 and 35 per cent cream by Caulfield, Nelson, and Martin[33] at 61.8°C.(143.5°F.) for 30 minutes was not sufficient to secure negative phosphatase tests with all samples. Cream separated from milk pasteurized at 61.7°C.(143°F.) for 30 minutes was frequently positive for phosphatase. Pasteurization at 65.6°C.(150°F.) or higher for 30 minutes resulted in negative phosphatase tests. Most of samples collected in the field were negative.

The important observation was made by Barber and Frazier[34] that certain bacteria might render phosphatase-negative pasteurized cream posi-

31. Shadwick and Parker. 1939. Amer. J. Pub. Health 29, 482-489.
32. Parfitt, Brown, and Shadwick. 1940. Amer. J. Pub. Health 30, 240-246.
33. Caulfield, Nelson, and Martin. 1940. J. Milk Tech. 3, 245-254.
34. Barber and Frazier. 1942. J. Dairy Sci. 25, 718.

tive for this substance after storage for 24 to 48 hours at 4°C.(39.2°F.) to 10°C.(50°F.). This resulted from development of a Gram-positive, sporeforming bacillus in both sterilized cream and skimmed milk. Barber and Frazier believed that these observations explained the change in reaction of the phosphatase test from negative to positive on refrigerated pasteurized cream. Further information on this question is given on page 422.

Effect of Pasteurization on Coliform Bacteria in Cream. In a study of ice cream mixes, phosphatase was consistently more resistant to heat than some of the more resistant coliform bacteria (Nelson, Caulfield, and Martin [35]). These authors wanted to know whether this relationship held for cream. They believed that such knowledge was necessary for proper evaluation of the significance of coliform bacteria in pasteurized cream. Their experiments indicated that phosphatase was more resistant than the coliform bacteria which were studied. This would seem to indicate that cream which had been sufficiently heated to destroy phosphatase would also have been heated sufficiently to destroy coliform bacteria. Presence of coliform bacteria in cream which was negative for phosphatase would therefore be considered to have been contaminated after pasteurization.

Phosphatase Test Applied to Butter. According to Scharer [30] application of the phosphatase test to butter requires change only in preparation of the sample. In the case of butter, the sample should be melted at a temperature below 37.8°C.(100°F.) so as to effect a complete separation of the water serum. One ml. of this water serum is then pipetted directly into 10 ml. of the buffer substrate. The rest of the procedure is the same as for milk and cream except that less lead acetate solution is required for precipitation. Phosphatase is concentrated in this water serum and consequently yields higher results than the melted butter.

Scharer found only slight phosphatase activity in butter made from "holder" pasteurized cream. Butter made from "flash" pasteurized cream exhibited considerable phosphatase activity. Some brands of commercially processed butters consistently showed no phosphatase activity, while others showed as many as 500 units even though they were stated to have been made from pasteurized cream.

Parker [36] quoted Shadwick's work on the application of the phosphatase test to creamery butter in which it was shown that only butter samples taken at the churn could provide basis for attesting thoroughness of cream pasteurization. This was confirmed in a report to the American Public Health Association.

Hammer and Olson [37] observed formation of phosphatase in butter to such an extent during the long holding period that consideration must be given this fact when applying the test to butter. Application of the phosphatase test to sour cream butter is subject to various factors which are not involved when it is used to test products made from sweet milk. Other

35. Nelson, Caulfield, and Martin. 1939. J. Dairy Sci. 22, 535-541.
36. Parker. 1940. J. Milk Tech. 3, 264-268; Yearbook, Amer. Pub. Health Assoc., 1938-1939.
37. Hammer and Olson. 1941. J. Milk Tech. 4, 83-85.

factors than technic must be recognized as causes of variations in results. Brown [38] found a concentration of the enzyme in butter during butter making. This fact may cause a positive phosphatase test for butter even though the cream gave a negative test. In 10 per cent of samples examined Brown noticed an increase in phosphatase value during storage at 15.6°C. (60°F.) for 10 days. This increase also occurred at temperatures considerably below 60°F. At —17.8°C.(0°F.) the phosphatase values remained constant. Production of phosphatase by bacteria in butter was not observed by Brown.

Various factors may influence the phosphatase test on flash pasteurized cream and butter made from it. When Wiley, Newman, and Whitehead [39] used the Kay and Graham "long" phosphatase test on pasteurized cream and on serum from butter made therefrom, the butter gave much higher values than the cream from which it had been made. Addition of salt, galactose, or sucrose produced no immediate effect on the test, but after several hours, phosphatase values were considerably higher. The authors believed that a small amount of phosphatase might escape destruction during very short heat treatments. No evidence was secured to indicate that phenolic substances were formed by bacteria. Wiley, Newman, and Whitehead concluded that the phosphatase test could not be used on butter to determine whether the cream from which it was made had been properly pasteurized.

Bacteria in Cream and Cream Ripening. Cream is usually pasteurized and ripened before churned. Conn [40] stated that cream ripening was more complex than the souring of milk; he was in doubt whether one species produced what is known as ripened cream. In 1890 he isolated over 50 different species which were grouped for study. From this work, he concluded that selected strains to be used in starters greatly influenced the flavor of the butter. Similar conclusions were reached by Emmerling and Schrodt [41] and De Vuyst,[42] who worked with cultures obtained from Weigmann at Kiel. The latter investigator apparently thought that ripening was of lesser significance than some other bacteriologists believed. Conn [43] reported further results and announced discovery of *Achromobacter aromafaciens* (Bacillus No. 41) which was said to produce an aroma of high character and an excellent butter from cream ripened with it. This organism was isolated from a milk from Uruguay, which had become quite bitter. After showing that the organism produced flavor in butter characteristic of highest quality June butter, Conn studied the applicability of the organism in practical dairy work. Farrington and Russell [44] were unable to confirm Conn's work with Bacillus 41. Interest in the organism gradually diminished. Martiny [45] successfully used a culture of kephir for

38. Brown. 1940. J. Dairy Sci. 23, 510-511.
39. Wiley, Newman, and Whitehead. 1941. J. Council Sci. and Indus. Res., Australia 14, 121-128.
40. Conn. 1889. Conn. Agr. Expt. Sta. Bull. 4.
41. Emmerling and Schrodt. 1891-92. Expt. Sta. Rec. 2, 261.
42. De Vuyst. 1891. Expt. Sta. Rec. 2, 931.
43. Conn. 1893-94. Conn. Agr. Expt. Sta. Rept. 43-68; Bull. 12.
44. Farrington and Russell. 1896. Wis. Agr. Expt. Sta. Bull. 48.
45. Martiny. 1897. Ztschr. Fleisch u. Milchhyg. 3, 9.

ripening cream. The butter was pronounced to have a good flavor and keeping quality. Using commercial cultures, Vieth [46] could not always observe an unmistakable improvement, but believed that they might be of value in dairies where butter faults were present. Conn and Esten,[47] after a study of many bacteria from butter, believed that desirable flavor was connected with the presence of certain bacteria. Further work was reported by Hayward and McDonnell,[48] Eckles,[49] Heinemann and Class,[50] Mortensen,[51] Laxa [52] and others. Hammer and Baker,[53] who reported a comprehensive investigation on starters, observed that cream ripening was a symbiosis. While a single organism could be useful, the flavor was probably really due to a summation of the activities of several different species.

After considering the many papers which have been published on the question, one is forced to the conclusion that cream ripening has much to do with butter flavor. On this conclusion rests the use of starters which contain desirable bacteria.

Effect of Cream Ripening on Eberthella typhosa in Cream. The possible presence of *Eberthella typhosa* in cream stimulated considerable study to determine whether the organism could survive cream ripening. Northrup,[54] Potter,[55] and Krumwiede and Noble [56] could not observe pronounced action of the lactic acid-producing bacteria. The last-mentioned investigators believed that clean cream which soured slowly would be more dangerous if infected as an initial multiplication of organisms could occur. In artificially inoculated milk, Washburn [57] observed no decrease in numbers of *Eberthella typhosa* up to 20 days. Bruck [58] and Bolley and Field [59] also believed that cream ripening could not be relied upon to make infected cream safe. Confirmatory data were reported by Fraenkel and Kister,[60] Trillat and Fouassier,[61] and March.[62] The situation is not much different for Salmonella species (Kaiser [63]). Health officials are therefore justified in demanding clean cream and clean water supplies. Further data on this subject are given in the chapter on "Fermented Milks."

Butter Cultures or Starters. Such agents are added to cream after pasteurization for improving flavor. They are the result of much research for special strains which can contribute the desired flavor and aroma. Conn,[64] at the Connecticut Agricultural Experiment Station, was one of the first

46. Vieth. 1897. Milch. Ztg. 26, 519-521.
47. Conn and Esten. 1901. Centbl. Bakt., Pt. 2, 7, 743-752; 769-775.
48. Hayward and McDonnell. 1899. Penn. Sta. Bull. 44, 19.
49. Eckles. 1898. Centbl. Bakt., Pt. 2, 4, 731-734; 759-764.
50. Heinemann and Class. 1911. Expt. Sta. Rec. 25, 81.
51. Mortensen. 1922. Iowa Agr. Expt. Sta. Bull. 207, 87-96.
52. Laxa. 1917. Rpt. Dairy Inst. Polytechnical School at Prague.
53. Hammer and Baker. 1928. Iowa Agr. Exp. Sta., Res. Bull. 106, 133-156.
54. Northrup. 1911. Mich. Agr. Expt. Sta., Tech. Bull. 9.
55. Potter. 1909-1910. Conn. State Bd. Health, Rpt., 150-154.
56. Krumwiede and Noble. 1915. Collected Studies, Bur. of Labs., City of N. Y., 8, 311.
57. Washburn. 1908. U. S. Dept. Agr. Bur. Anim. Indus., 25th Ann. Rpt., 297-300.
58. Bruck. 1903. Dent. Med. Wchnschr., June 25, 1903, 460-462.
59. Bolley and Field. 1898. Centbl. Bakt., Pt. 2, 4, 881-887.
60. Fraenkel and Kister. 1898. München. Med. Wchnschr. 45, 197.
61. Trillat and Fouassier. 1916. Compt. Rend. Acad. Sci. 162, 849.
62. Marsh. 1918. Amer. J. Pub. Health 8, 590-593.
63. Kaiser. 1921. Centbl. Bakt., Pt. 2, 86, 554.
64. Conn. 1892. Office of Expt. Stations, Bull. 9.

in America to study these agents. He early stated that certain forms of fermentation were desirable in butter making. Conn isolated the organism known as B41; this organism was believed to be especially desirable in butter. Farrington and Russell [65] could not agree with Conn after making a comprehensive study of this organism. This culture produced results which seemed to be in direct opposition to those Conn attributed to it. About this same time Hayward and McConnell [66] also studied several butter cultures. The results were not absolutely convincing. In fact these authors believed that more attention should be given to cleanliness and careful selection of milk rather than to rely on pasteurization and "butter cultures," a conclusion stated also by Farrington and Russell. Experience since these early days has not justified such conclusions. Despite the fact that some manufacturers of butter have doubted the value of butter cultures, their use seems to be vindicated in higher scores of butter and better keeping quality. It is possible to make more uniform butter with a better flavor.

Bacteriophage in Dairy Starters. Some difficulties in dairy starters have been attributed to presence of bacteriophage. Bacteria of value in producing good aroma and flavor in dairy products seem to be just as susceptible to attack by bacteriophage as other species. Sutton [67] isolated a bacteriophage from whey which lysed the streptococcus in a milk culture. This agent has been found also in cheese-starter cultures by Whitehead [68] and his colleagues. Their work is discussed more fully below in Chapter 9. In Whitehead and Hunter's [69] experiments, bacteriophage showed a strain specificity toward lactic acid-producing streptococci, but some races exist which attack as many as four different strains.

Flavor of Butter. Many factors are involved in flavor of butter and much work has been done on the relation of bacteria to flavor. When bacteriological studies were first made on butter, Conn suggested that a distinction be made between "aroma" and "flavor." Butter may have a natural flavor from the cream from which it is made. Sweet cream butter would have a different flavor than sour cream butter made from cream which had been pasteurized and inoculated with desirable bacteria. Much more is probably known about the bacteria which deteriorate butter than about those which give it desirable characteristics.

Keith [70] isolated a micrococcus that produced a butter flavor and aroma when grown on milk or cream; he designated it is *Micrococcus butyri-aroma-faciens*. Another organism, named *Bacterium aromaticus butyri*, was isolated by Sewerin.[71] The aroma was produced in milk only when grown in symbiosis with lactic acid bacteria.

Hammer,[72] using a culture of *Streptococcus citrovorus* for ripening the cream, produced a butter which had a higher score than other butter. It

65. Farrington and Russell. 1892. Wis. Agr. Expt. Sta. Bull. 48.
66. Hayward and McConnell. 1892. Penn. Agr. Expt. Sta. Bull. 44.
67. Sutton. 1939. J. Aust. Inst. Agr. Sci. 5, 168.
68. Whitehead. 1940. J. Dairy Res. 11, 62-66.
69. Whitehead and Hunter. 1939. J. Dairy Res. 10, 403-409.
70. Keith. 1897. Tech. Quart. 10, 247-248.
71. Sewerin. 1904. Centbl. Bakt., Pt. 2, 11, 202-206.
72. Hammer. 1921. Abst. Bact. 6, No. 160.

was stated that while *Streptococcus lactis (Streptococcus lacticus)* played a very important role in cream ripening, it was the associated organisms which were really responsible for the desired flavor. A good starter is one in which a proper balance of these organisms is maintained. At Iowa State College, it was found that the sour cream butter scored higher than sweet cream butter, but after nine months' storage the sweet cream butter had a higher score Butter made from sour cream pasteurized at 76.7°C.(170°F.) by the continuous process, was better than butter made from cream pasteurized at lower temperatures. Pasteurization at higher temperatures also shortened the keeping qualities. Other data have been published by Brown, Smith, and Ruehle,[73] Ruehle,[74] Dahlberg,[75] and others.

Separation of the qualities of butter known as flavor and aroma may be very close and perhaps artificial. Van Beynum [76] believed that aroma results from combined action of lactic acid-producing bacteria and special aroma-producing bacteria. Good aroma production was related to utilization of citrates. A special aroma-producing bacterium was named *Streptococcus lactis aromaticus* by Joshi and Ram Ayyar [77] while Bogdanov [78] attributed aroma production to *Streptococcus lactis cremoris*. Since this work was done much more has been learned about the actual substances which are involved. Van Niel, Kluyver, and Derx [79] showed that aroma of butter was due to acetyl methyl carbinol. Having determined this, numerous investigations were carried out to determine what role microorganisms might play in formation of this substance. Later investigations showed that it was diacetyl formed from acetyl methyl carbinol which is the real flavor-aroma agent in butter. This was a marked advance. Slatter [80] considered these substances to be most important and studied their formation in both salted and unsalted butters. Homologues of diacetyl in butter cultures were not observed by Prill, Fabricius, and Hammer.[81] This indicated to them the importance of citric acid fermentation in flavor development. Not all who have worked on this problem agree as to the bacterial species which are involved. They are probably without doubt members of the lactic acid-producing group of bacteria, especially Streptococci. Wiley, Cox, and Whitehead [82] found *Streptococcus cremoris* to be important. Betacocci were found to produce acetyl methyl carbinol and to destroy it quite rapidly. Its destruction becomes of as much importance in the butter industry as its formation. Its reduction to 2, 3-butylene glycol by *Aerobacillus polymyxa* has been reported by Stahly and Hammer.[83] Michaelian and Hammer [84] reported that oxidation of acetyl methyl carbinol was due to the activities of citric acid-fermenting Streptococci rather

73. Brown, Smith, and Ruehle. 1920. J. Dairy Sci. 3, 375-405.
74. Ruehle. 1930. Mich. Agr. Expt. Sta., Tech. Bull. 102.
75. Dahlberg. 1923. Proc. World's Dairy Cong. 2, 966-972.
76. Van Beynum. 1934. Verslag. Landbounk. Onderzoek. 40, 355-407.
77. Joshi and Ram Ayyar. 1936. Indian J. Vet. Sci. 6, 141-150.
78. Bogdanov. 1937. Molochnaya Prom. 4, 5-9.
79. Van Niel,Kluyver, and Derx. 1929. Biochem. Zetschr. 210, 234-251.
80. Slatter. 1936. Natl. Butter and Cheese J. 27, 20 *et seq.*
81. Prill, Fabricius, and Hammer. 1939. Iowa Agr. Expt. Sta., Res. Bull. 268 and 290.
82. Wiley, Cox, and Whitehead. 1931. J. Council Sci. Indus. Res. 12, 232-238.
83. Stahly and Hammer. 1935. Proc. Iowa Acad. Sci. 42, 73-76.
84. Michaelian and Hammer. 1936. Iowa Agr. Expt. Sta., Res. Bull. 205.

than to direct chemical oxidation. These conclusions were amplified later by Michaelian, Hoecker, and Hammer,[85] Michaelian, Farmer, and Hammer,[86] and Hoecker and Hammer.[87] The last-mentioned investigators observed that some microorganisms favored formation of these agents while others caused a decrease in their content. Butter culture containing *Streptococcus diacetilactis* and *Streptococcus citrophilus* when added to cream caused an increase of flavor agents, while *Streptococcus citrovorus* and *Streptococcus paracitrovorus* often caused decreases. Importance of certain species of bacteria to good flavor and aroma production was well indicated.

Conditions under which cream is held apparently may have much influence on aroma production by these chemical substances. Oxygen has been shown to be important by several investigations. Virtanen, Mansikkala, and Tikka[88] and Virtanen[89] secured no acetyl methyl carbinol in thick layers of milk but large amounts in thin layers. Bubbling air through the cultures caused marked increases in the amount formed in experiments of Brewer *et al.*[90]

DETERIORATION OF BUTTER

Deterioration, in general, may be caused by various agents among which the microorganisms play a large part. Those which exhibit some marked characteristic, such as formation of a pigment or a special excretory product, have been especially troublesome. Abnormalities in butter resulting from activities of microorganisms may vary from slight imperfections to those which are so serious that they must be investigated. *Pseudomonas fluorescens* has been found by various investigators as the cause of spoilage (Prikryl[91] and Sadler, Vollum, and Cameron[92]). Large numbers of proteolytic bacteria, according to Flake and Parfitt,[93] are objectionable. They also believed that lipolytic bacteria might cause deterioration. Jacobsen[94] observed no relation of flavor deterioration to members of these groups.

Fishy Flavor in Butter. This is one of the most easily recognized abnormal flavors encountered in butter. Considerable work has been done on its microbiology. O'Callaghan[95] reported that *Odium lactis* caused it. Inoculation experiments proved it, since controls did not develop the fishy flavor. Pasteurization was found to kill the organism and allow the development of good flavor, 75.6°C.(168°F.) being sufficient. Cleanliness in and about the dairy was said to be necessary to prevent contamination of the milk. Rogers,[96] however, could not confirm O'Callaghan's statement that a fishy flavor could be produced by inoculation with *Oidium lactis*. A

85. Michaelian, Hoecker, and Hammer. 1938. J. Dairy Sci. 21, 213-218.
86. Michaelian, Farmer, and Hammer. 1933. Iowa Agr. Expt. Sta., Res. Bull. 115.
87. Hoecker and Hammer. 1941. Idem, Res. Bull. 290.
88. Virtanen, Mansikkala, and Tikka. 1936. Suomen Kemistilehti 9B, 28.
89. Virtanen. 1937. Proc. World's Dairy Cong. 2, 121-123.
90. Brewer *et al.* 1937. J. Bact. 33, 92.
91. Prikryl. 1921. Rev. in Abst. Bact. 6, 51.
92. Sadler, Vollum, and Cameron. 1926. Nat. Res. Council, Canada, Rpt. 16, 23.
93. Flake and Parfitt. 1938. J. Dairy Sci. 21, 545-551.
94. Jacobsen. 1938. Idem 21, 187-193.
95. O'Callaghan. 1901. Agr. Gaz. N. S. Wales 12, 341-345.
96. Rogers. 1909. U. S. Dept. Agr. Bur. Anim. Indus., Circ. 146.

biological study was made of farms, but no condition was found in the pastures and on the farms furnishing milk from which fishy butter was made which did not exist on some of the farms producing normal butter. This applied to the water supply as well as the flora of the pastures. These results seemed to exclude the possibility of any direct connection between the feed of the cows and the presence of the fishy flavor in the butter. Fishiness could not be produced in butter made under winter conditions by any combination of circumstances. Bacteriologically, the only peculiarity of the cream from the farms where the fishy flavor was developed was the presence of very active lactic acid bacteria. In all cases in which the records were complete it was found that those experimental butters which became fishy were made from high-acid cream. Fishy butter was made from cream acidified with lactic and acetic acids. However, cream with high acidity does not uniformly develop fishiness.

It was apparent that acidity, although having a determining influence on the fishy flavor, was not its sole cause. The effect of over-working butter was next investigated, and it was observed that fishiness occurred in a combination of high acidity and over-working. Further experiments in this line showed that over-working improved rather than impaired the flavor of the unripened cream butter. In the opinion of Rogers, fishy flavor was caused by a slow, spontaneous, chemical change to which acid is essential and which is favored by the presence of small amounts of oxygen. Rogers believed that fishy flavor could be prevented with certainty by making butter from pasteurized sweet cream. Butter made from pasteurized sweet cream with a starter but without ripening seldom if ever becomes fishy. Reakes, Cuddie, and Reid [97] isolated pure cultures of organisms from butter having a fishy flavor but failed to produce the effect experimentally. Butters of fishy flavor were found to contain a high percentage of acid, and it is, therefore, thought that a high acidity may be a contributing factor though not the direct cause of the trouble. According to Sommer and Schmidt [98] the conditions favoring the causation of fishiness in butter were high acidity in the cream, high salt content of the butter, over-working of the butter, and the presence of iron and copper salts. The real cause of the presence of this fishy taste rested on the formation of trimethylamine from lecithin. Johnstone [99] stated that the lecithin combined with air to form cholin which then decomposed to form, among other things, trimethylamine. Dyer [100] believed that fishy flavor of cold-stored butter was not due to oxidation of fat. Fishiness in butter was attributed by Davies [101] to oxidation of the choline residue of lecithin to yield trimethylamine.

Yeasty Flavor. This spoilage is characterized by the fact that yeasts have not been entirely to blame for the deterioration. Some of the trouble, according to Rosengren,[102] originated with the starter which was allowed to over-ripen. Rosengren studied one starter which produced yeasty butter, finding that *Lactobacillus lactis acidi* favored the development of the yeast. When the starter was stored below 20°C.(68°F.) the yeast grew abundantly. Many lactose-fermenting yeasts have been reported which are able to proliferate in cream. Among the better known are *Torula cremoris* and *Torula sphaerica*, isolated by Hammer.

97. Reakes, Cuddie, and Reid. 1912. New Zeal. Dept. Agr. 4, 1-6.
98. Sommer and Schmidt. 1923. Wis. Agr. Expt. Sta., Res. Bull. 57.
99. Johnstone. 1923. Hoard's Dairyman 65, 446.
100. Dyer. 1916. J. Agr. Res. 6, 927-952.
101. Davies. 1941. J. Indian Chem. Indus. and News Ed. 4, 1-15.
102. Rosengren. 1911. Meddel Centralanst. Försöksv. Jordbruksområdet, No. 46, 12; Expt. Sta. Rec. 25 (1911), 780.

Turnip Taste. This flavor has been attributed to the presence of turnips in the diet of the cow as well as to the growth of certain bacteria in the butter. Weigmann[103] found that the milk from cows fed on turnips had a peculiar odor and flavor. Apparently some volatile product from the turnips gets into the body fluids of the cow and thus affects the milk. This fault may be corrected by warming or aerating the milk. Besides this, certain organisms, as coli organisms, *Actinomyces odorifer*, *Penicillium brevicaule*, and lactic-acid bacteria, which are found in the feces of cows fed on beets or turnips, also produce the turnip flavor and aroma in butter made from milk or cream in which they are present. The turnip flavor of butter may be due to both of these causes together. Butter may have the turnip flavor and aroma, however, even when no turnips are fed, as coli bacteria causing the taste are found also on oats, barley, corn, rape, and other feed stuffs. Pasteurizing the milk, with subsequent aeration, is recommended as a means of preventing the development of the turnip flavor in butter. This work was continued by Weigmann and Wolff.[104]

Cheesy Flavor. This defect was shown by Herreid, Macy, and Combs[105] to be caused by microorganisms in the raw cream. While pure cultures of the several bacteria would not always produce this off-flavor, they usually did when used together in mixed cultures. Gram-negative, rod types of bacteria predominated in the mixed and pure cultures capable of producing the Cheddar cheese type flavor. This flavor in cream or unsalted butter occurred most typically at temperatures of 10°C. (50°F.) or below. Creamery water supplies were sometimes contaminated with bacteria capable of producing the off-flavor, and sterile cream butter may be infected through contact with such water. The plasma of cream contained the substrates necessary for the development of the causative flora producing the cheesy flavors and aromas.

Metallic Taste. This term depicts sufficiently well the flavor indicated. Ruehle[106] reported the appearance of metallic flavor in butter from cream to which iron or copper lactate had been added and also by the use of cream containing organisms of the *Bacillus subtilis* group. He believed that the bacteria produced the flavor by decomposition of the casein. On account of the fact that this organism and its close relatives are spore-formers, it will survive pasteurization. Consequently the presence of the organism in milk from which butter will be made is of more significance than its presence in milk which will be used in a short time. Houston[107] reported that *Bacillus subtilis* caused bitter butter. It is very probable that the same off-flavor may have been described in different ways by investigators.

Musty Flavor. Musty flavor was attributed by Randell[108] to an unnamed member of the genus Achromobacter as the causal organism. The organisms may have originated in the creamery from unsterilized equipment. Musty odors are often related to development of molds but bacteria have been found to be just as important, if not more so.

Rancidity of Butter. This is a term which includes many abnormalities of edible fats and oils. Investigation of rancidity from a scientific viewpoint is rendered more difficult, according to Lea,[109] by the fact that

103. Weigmann. 1908. Landw. Jahrb. 261-309.
104. Weigmann and Wolff. 1909. Centbl. Bakt., Pt. 2, 24-25.
105. Herreid, Macy, and Combs. 1934. Minn. Agr. Expt. Sta., Tech. Bull. 97.
106. Ruehle. 1921. Mich. Agr. Expt. Sta., Quart. Bull. 3, 103-104.
107. Houston. 1921. Irish Agr. Organ. Soc., Ann. Rpt., 9-52.
108. Randell. 1936. J. Aust. Inst. Agr. Sci. 2, 23-26.
109. Lea. 1939. Rancidity of Edible Fats, Spec. Rpt. No. 46, Food Invest. Bd., H. M. Stationery Office. London.

ultimate standards to which all data must be referred are based on taste
and smell, the most elusive and least clearly defined of the five senses. He
further pointed out that the term "rancidity" has been employed in the
past, either in the general sense to indicate deterioration in odor and flavor
without attempt to specify the cause, or as applying to some particular
type of spoilage. In the latter case, it has usually been applied to hydrolytic changes produced in butter and similar fats by action of enzymes or
microorganisms while "tallowiness" has been used to denote oxidation.
The deterioration is quite often characterized by a butyric acid odor.
Guthrie [109a] reviewed the literature and reached the conclusion that rancidity as defined by butter judges, is rarely found. He believed that many
alterations in flavor were explained as rancidity when better descriptions
could have been given. Studies on butter rancidity were made quite early.
Amthor [110] believed that rancidity was due to bacteria which produce alcohol from lactose. Simultaneous cleavage of the fats occurs which yields
acids for ester formation. Another claimed that rancidity, in some cases,
was due to intensive development of "bouquet." Orla-Jensen [111] believed
that the changes which took place in rancid butter involved the fat mainly.
These changes were said to be oxidative and hydrolytic. While Orla-
Jensen considered the various causes of rancidity, he gave special attention
to the bacteria which might be involved. This portion of the paper may
be reviewed at greater length.

It was shown that several forms of microorganisms commonly occurring in butter
were capable of decomposing the butter, with the formation of volatile fatty acid and
esters. This, Orla-Jensen believed, was sufficient proof that the rancidity of butter may
be due to microorganisms, and that the hypothesis of the action of a milk enzyme is
very improbable. It was thought very possible, however, that the microorganisms effect
the cleavage of the fat by means of an enzyme (steapsin) which they form. Orla-
Jensen added to filtered and sterilized butter a quantity of an old milk culture of the
organisms to be tested which had been passed through a Chamberland filter. Samples
of butter were treated in this way with cultures of *Pseudomonas fluorescens (Bacillus
fluorescens liquefaciens)* and of *Oidium lactis*. These experiments showed that the acid
number increased, i.e., that the rancidity progressed, and it was concluded that this was
due to enzymes (steapsin).

The microorganisms which, under ordinary conditions, caused rancidity
are *Oidium lactis, Cladosporium butyri, Pseudomonas fluorescens (Bacillus
fluorescens liquefaciens)* and occasionally *Serratia marcescens (Bacillus
prodigiosus)* also. All of these cleave the butter-fat. Some of these organisms are introduced into butter by contaminated water.

Volatility of acids formed in rancid butter is not necessarily related to
degree of rancidity. Fouts [112] observed considerable variation in total fatty
acids in sterile cream inoculated with *Oospora lactis, Mycotorula lipolytica,
Pseudomonas fluorescens*, and *Achromobacter lipolyticum*. Mold growth in
butter causes both an acid-oxidative rancidity and a ketonic rancidity,
according to Davies.[112a] The former is due to molds containing lipases

109a. Guthrie. 1917. J. Dairy Sci., 1, 136-138.
110. Amthor. 1899. Ztschr. Analyt. Chem. 38, 10-20.
111. Orla-Jensen. 1902. Centbl. Bakt., Pt. 2, 8, 11-16.
112. Fouts. 1940. J. Dairy Sci. 23, 307-314.
112a. Davies. 1941. J. Indian Chem. Soc. 4, 179-183.

and being able to metabolize glycerol; the latter, on the other hand, was said to be due to molds developing on the surface of the butter. Microorganisms causing rancidity in dairy products seem to be regular contaminants. With proper enrichment procedures, Garrison and Hammer [112b] observed fluorescent bacteria to be widely distributed in milk, cream, ice cream, and butter and also in water from a dairy barn and its surroundings. Selected cultures produced off-flavors in butter. Salt had variable effects on the strains.

Putrid Butter. Eckles [113] examined samples of butter having a strong disagreeable taste and a putrid odor. Three kinds of bacteria were isolated which produced very bad effects on the milk and were thought to be the cause of the putrid butter. The principal difference between the spoiled butter and the sweet butter was a large number of gelatin liquefiers in the spoiled butter. Eckles stated that the milk was contaminated in some manner before it was delivered to the creamery. Better sanitation stopped the trouble.

Pseudomonas fluorescens was found to be the cause of putrefactive flavor in pasteurized creamery butter by Shutt. [114] The organism came from water. Cultures of this organism in ordinary media possess a strong odor. Filippini [115] also stated that the fluorescent bacteria were active agents in butter spoilage. Whether they produce true rancidity may be questioned.

Surface taint has caused some trouble in the butter industry and has been related to microorganisms by Derby and Hammer [116] who found many more bacteria on the surface of butter than in the interior. While the defect was not produced by inoculating a normal product with tainted butter, it was reproduced by inoculating pasteurized cream with tainted butter and churning the cream. *Achromobacter putrefaciens* was believed to be the causal organism and is probably identical with *Pseudomonas fluorescens*. Some years later Claydon and Hammer [117] isolated the organism from putrid butter by means of the Burri film-culture method. It was about the only organism obtained which reproduced the defect on inoculation. Forty-one strains of this organism studied by Wolochow *et al.*[119] were observed to be quite pleomorphic and variable in activity. The organism was strongly proteolytic.

Later work by Long and Hammer [118] indicated that *Pseudomonas putrefaciens* syn. *Achromobacter putrefaciens* was commonly present in certain dairy products It was isolated from raw, sweet milk and cream and from normal and putrid salted butter but not from sour cream or highly ripened, unsalted butter, where the sensitivity of the organism to acid may have resulted in its destruction. It was obtained from a sample of moist soil but not from three samples of dry soil; from stream, lake, and roadside water collected in various states; from creamery water supplies; and from the floors and sewers in dairy plants, particularly from sites that tended to remain moist.

112b. Garrison and Hammer. 1942. Iowa State College J. Sci. 16, 363-377.
113. Eckles. Iowa Agr. Expt. Sta. 40, 53-64.
114. Shutt. 1929. Sci. Agr. 9, 316-320.
115. Filippini. 1922. Policlinico. 29, 755.
116. Derby and Hammer. 1931. Iowa Agr. Expt. Sta., Res. Bull. 145.
117. Claydon and Hammer. 1939. Idem, Res. Bull. 267.
118. Long and Hammer. 1941. Idem, Res. Bull. 285; J. Dairy Sci. 24 (1941), 921-924.

In studies of dairy equipment, *Pseudomonas putrefaciens* was obtained from parts of a butter printer in a plant that was having difficulty with putrid butter. This printer had probably been infected from the butter, since the butter contained the organism before printing. The organism was also obtained from three of four churns that were examined by culturing material from around bolt heads, from between staves, from the junction of staves and ends, etc. These churns were in plants that were encountering putrid butter. Finally, it was obtained from the lining of a leaky milk vat immediately after the vat was taken out of service.

Wolochow, Thornton, and Hood[119] were unable to identify the precursor of surface-taint substance. The strain of *Pseudomonas putrefaciens* which they investigated grew at 20°C.(35.6°F.) and at 32°C.(89.6°F.) but not at 37°C.(98.6°F.). It did not survive 54.4°C.(130°F.) for 10 minutes. When grown in skim milk it produced a typical putrid odor. There was some suggestion that outbreaks of surface taint in butter followed institution of high-temperature heat treatment of churning cream. *Pseudomonas putrefaciens* is widely distributed in Alberta (Canada) waters and is found also in the United States and Australia. Later work by Dunkley, Hunter, Thornton, and Hood (1942) indicated the substance causing the trouble was related chemically to isovalerianic acid.

The fluorescent bacteria have also been related to butter defects as they have to defects in other foods. Garrison and Hammer[120] observed that selected cultures of these bacteria produced various off-flavors in milk and cream held for 18 days at 5°C.(41°F.). Rancidity was not detected although lipolytic cultures were included in those which were used. While various off-flavors were observed, putrid and rancid butter were especially common. The fluorescent bacteria were found to be widely disseminated in water and in various dairy products.

Skunk-Like Odor in Butter. This is one of the unusual odor defects observed in butter. Claydon and Hammer[121] observed development of a skunk-like odor in three samples of butter held at 21°C.(69.8°F.) to test its keeping quality. When the defective butter was inoculated into pasteurized sweet cream and the cream churned, the defect was reproduced. The causative organism, *Pseudomonas mephitica*, was isolated and described. On inoculating the pasteurized cream used for churning, the defect developed in unsalted butter made from cream having pH values from 5 to 7.5. Salt had an inhibitory effect on the production of the defect but thorough working of the salted butter was necessary to prevent its appearance. The skunk-like odor was produced in unsalted butter by inoculating small amounts of culture into water used to wash the butter.

Microbial Discoloration of Butter. Several bacterial species have been isolated which impart abnormal colors to butter. Olson and Hammer[122] mentioned developments of pink color in butter for which no specific microorganisms could be isolated. Consequently they suggested that the deteri-

119. Wolochow *et al.* 1942. Sci. Agr. 22, 227-286, 347-355, 438-447, 461-464.
120. Garrison and Hammer. 1942. Iowa State Col. J. Sci. 16, 363-377.
121. Claydon and Hammer. 1939. J. Bact. 37, 251-258.
122. Olson and Hammer. 1933. Iowa State Col. J. Sci. 7, 487-491.

oration might be chemical in nature. A violet color in butter was attributed by Deshauses and Novel [123] to a bacterium named *Bacillus janthinus* var. *butyricus*. A similar deterioration was reported by Morgan,[124] who reported the cause to be *Chromobacterium violaceum*. A pink color was attributed to *Rhodococcus rosaceus*, a green color to *Pseudomonas fluorescens*, and a bright orange color to an unidentified rod-shaped organism.

An organism causing a dark discoloration in butter containing .38 to .55 per cent salt was isolated by Hiscox.[125] At 15°C.(59°F.) a brownish color developed and diffused through the medium. At lower temperatures this was mixed with a ,blue-black pigment insoluble in water, brine, chloroform, ether, ethyl, and methyl alcohol, butterfat, and dilute sulphuric and acetic acids, but soluble in formalin. During growth of the organism the blue-black pigment was excreted from the cells and deposited as irregular aggregates of platelets varying considerably in size and shape. The nature of the source of the nitrogen influenced the development of this pigment, proteose appearing to be inhibitory. The brown pigment produced at higher temperatures may probably be attributed to the action of ammonia produced by the organism.

The organism, a rod with rounded ends, nonsporing, actively motile, and Gram negative, was regarded as a species of Pseudomonas. In litmus milk it produced alkalinity with bleaching and digestion at all temperatures up to 30°C.(86°F.). At 1 to 3°C.(33.8 to 37.4°F.) the action was very slow, a dark ring developing to a depth of about one-half inch. No growth was obtained on standard agar, yeast-dextrose agar, beerwort agar, bean agar, and potato. The first two media became satisfactory for growth with the addition of one-half per cent NaCl. With five per cent NaCl growth became very scanty. The causal organism of a blackening of butter was identified as *Pseudomonas nigrifaciens* by White.[126] This halophilic bacterium produced reddish-brown spots on the surface of the prints. Plant sanitation and use of enough salt to result in seven per cent in the serum was recommended. *Pseudomonas nigrifaciens* does not survive minimum pasteurization temperatures of 76.7°C.(170°F.) for 10 minutes used in Canadian creameries.

Jamieson's [127] "Butter-Shake" Method for Identification of Bacteria Which Deteriorate Butter. This method was proposed for determining whether bacteria were the causative agents in butter deterioration. Jamieson referred to his technic as the "Butter-Shake Method." It was devised principally for testing the effects of pure cultures on butter but was also used for determining whether waters were suitable for use in creameries. Butter of clean flavor and low microanalytical count is melted to a creamy consistency and poured aseptically in 20-ml. amounts into special wide-mouthed, screw-capped glass vials four inches high and one inch in diameter, gaving a 45-ml. capacity. These are then chilled quickly and held at freezing temperature until used. The butter used in this test should be prepared under exacting conditions. The required amount may be easily made in a bacteriological laboratory from whole milk and refrigerated cream using sterile glass churns, water, salt, and other materials and utensils. The butter in

123. Deshauses and Novel. 1939. Mitt. Lebensmtl. Untersuch. u. Hyg. 30, 2-7.
124. Morgan. 1931. New Zeal. J. Agr. 41, 315-318.
125. Hiscox. 1936. J. Dairy Res. 8, 238.
126. White. 1940. Sci. Agr. 20, 638-645.
127. Jamieson. 1943. Food Research 8, 62-66.

the vials may be inoculated with the pure culture by use of a sterile graduated pipette. The butter may be left in the solid form until all vials have been inoculated and labeled, after which it may be melted at a temperature of not over 40°C.(104°F.). Higher temperatures may produce undesirable textures. Thorough distribution of the inoculum throughout the butter is attained by vigorous agitation for 20 minutes on a shaker set to hold as many vials as are required for any test. The butter cultures with the vial caps loosened one-half turn are then incubated at the desired temperature for the time most favorable for development of off-flavors. For removal of samples for flavor determination, strips of 20-gauge stainless steel, five inches by five-eighths inch, and preferably shaped longitudinally to a half-round are effectively used.

Microbiology of Butter. On account of the raw materials, the methods of manufacture, and the fact that bacteria are added in large numbers to the cream before churning, the microbiology of butter has different import from that of other dairy products. This is one of the few dairy products, the bacterial plate count of which has not been attempted as an index of manufacturing conditions. The microbiology of butter has been studied by many investigators. Of these, Sawyer, Rahn, and Farrand,[128] and Fettick[129] reported rather large numbers of bacteria. Sawyer, Rahn, and Farrand could not find a characteristic flora, but believed that variable numbers of bacteria in butter were probably due to many different factors, such as bacteria in the cream, amount of salting, temperature of storage, etc. Torré[130] reported a bacterial content of fresh butter of from 36,000 to 7,000,000. Maximum numbers of bacteria were attained in from 13 to 14 days, after which there was a slow decline in numbers.

Rosenau, Frost, and Bryant[131] studied 25 samples of butter, scoring from 80 to 98, representing the market supply of Boston. The average number of bacteria per gram was determined by emulsifying the butter in warm water. The average number for the 25 samples was 5,700,000 per gram; the lowest number was 8,600 and the highest 41,000,000. There was no particular relation between the number of bacteria and any other constituent determined, such as salt, reaction, moisture, etc. The number of bacteria diminished markedly with age; in one sample 85.8 per cent in two weeks, in another 93.7 per cent in four weeks, and in another 95.6 per cent in six weeks. It was suggested that the number of bacteria may, therefore, be used as an index of the age of the butter. *Escherichia coli* was found in only six of the 25 samples, and then only in small numbers. It seems that *Escherichia coli* soon dies out in butter. Streptococci were found in 14 samples, but no special relation between their presence and virulence as tested upon guinea pigs could be made out. *Clostridium welchii* were not found in any of the samples. Tubercle bacilli were demonstrated in two of 21 samples tested for these organisms and from butter of apparently first quality. Pasteurization of cream intended for butter is recommended. Brown, Smith, and Ruehle[132] also reported relatively high numbers of bacteria in butter over a year old. After 275 days' storage,

128. Sawyer, Rahn, and Farrand. 1908. Mich. Agr. Expt. Sta., Tech. Bull. 1.
129. Fettick. 1908. Centbl. Bakt., Pt. 2, 21, 32-44.
130. Torré. 1922. Ann. Ist. Sper. Caseif. Lodi. 1, 57-70.
131. Rosenau, Frost, and Bryant. 1914. J. Med. Res. 30, 69.
132. Brown, Smith, and Ruehle. 1920. J. Dairy Sci. 3, 375-405.

lactic acid bacteria were noticeable, and in one case, were found after 462 days' storage.

Much study has been given to the relation of salt to butter quality. From two to four per cent of salt is added to butter which, when dissolved in the 15 per cent of water found in butter, gives a brine of about 30 per cent concentration. Fettick,[129] after inoculating pure cultures into sterile butter, found that several molds, *Pseudomonas fluorescens*, and lactic acid bacteria grew in three per cent of salt. *Escherichia coli, Bacillus subtilis, Aerobacter aerogenes,* and some torulae multiplied in six per cent concentration. Fettick concluded that three per cent of salt should be used in butter. Rahn, Brown, and Smith [133] found that salted butter kept better than unsalted, and Thom and Shaw [134] reported that two and one-half to three per cent of salt was necessary to repress mold growth. Much larger amounts of salt, according to Giltner and Baker,[135] do not restrict development of all microorganisms. Some bacteria were able to withstand 20 per cent of salt. Streptococci were found to be sensitive to salt, while staphylococci and micrococci were not. The greater part of the yeasts and torulae in butter cannot withstand as much salt as the cocci. Eight per cent of salt was believed to limit the physiological activities of most bacteria. Continued cultivation of some organisms on salt agar increased the salt tolerance. Pont [136] reported an ill-defined relation between microorganism content of butter and market gradings. Changes in flavor under storage conditions seemed to have little relation to microbial activity.

Reports of numbers of bacteria in butter do not tell much unless the manner of their distribution is considered. Rahn and Boysen [137] did this when they related the number of bacteria to moisture dispersion. Moisture in butter is distributed as droplets varying in size between one μ to over 100 μ in diameter. Most of them are less than five μ in diameter. Between 10 and 18 billion droplets per gram were found in butter. The largest number of bacteria in butter ever recorded in literature is 57 billion per gram. Comparison of this figure with the number of droplets would indicate that there are not enough bacteria to supply each droplet with one cell. Even with the most uniform distribution, only one droplet in 200 could contain a bacterium; the remaining 199 droplets would be devoid of bacteria. This statement is based on a much higher number of bacteria than would usually be found in butter. Rahn and Boysen [137] and Rahn [138] found the amount of infected moisture in butter to vary from 4.8 to 41 per cent of the total moisture in the samples. Lactic acid formation in butter proceeds much more slowly than in its buttermilk, and final acidity is also much lower, proving that actually part of the moisture in butter must be sterile, but the acidity that rises above the computed concentration indicates some diffusion of acids. In butter, with 100,000 bacteria per

133. Rahn, Brown, and Smith. 1909. Mich. Agr. Expt. Sta., Tech. Bull 2.
134. Thom and Shaw. 1915. J. Agr. Res. 3, 301-309.
135. Giltner and Baker. 1915. Mich. Agr. Expt. Sta. Rpt. 209.
136. Pont. 1939. J. Aust. Inst. Agr. Sci. 5, 202-207.
137. Rahn and Boysen. 1928. J. Dairy Sci. 11, 446-470.
138. Rahn. 1928. Sci. Mo. 27, 206-211.

gram, 88 per cent of the moisture is sterile; with 10,000 bacteria, 99 per cent is sterile; and with 1,000 bacteria, 99.9 per cent is sterile. This last butter cannot be attacked noticeably by bacteria. These deductions do not apply to molds, which can force their way from one droplet to another through the surrounding walls of fat.

Washing of butter, according to Rahn and Boysen, resulted in an uneven distribution of food and bacteria, the smallest droplets containing undiluted buttermilk but very few bacteria, the largest droplets containing most bacteria but practically nothing but the wash water of the butter. This accounts for the better keeping quality of washed butter. Working of the butter breaks the moisture into smaller droplets. The practical aspects of this were investigated by Long and Hammer.[139] In experimental unsalted butter, made from pasteurized cream inoculated with pure cultures of bacteria, growth of bacteria at 21°C.(69.8°F.) and at 5°C.(41°F.) was most rapid in underworked butter. Distribution of organisms in fresh butter was regular; after holding at 21 or 5°C., long enough to allow considerable growth, the distribution in the underworked and moderately worked butter was usually irregular, that in thoroughly worked butter was more regular. When the butter contained an organism capable of producing a flavor defect, the period required for its appearance at 21 or 5°C. increased as the working was increased. The pH values of the serum of butter made with butter culture decreased more rapidly at 21°C. and reached lower final values in underworked than in thoroughly worked butter, while moderately worked butter gave intermediate values. Acid numbers on the fat of butter containing a lipolytic organism and held at 21°C. indicated that underworking resulted in higher values than through working.

Bacteria in butter come from many different sources. Olson and Hammer [140] found the churn to be a fertile source. Agar disk counts on the internal surface of many churns varied. Churns which were thoroughly cleaned with hot water contained few living bacteria. Many bacteria in butter come from the air. Protection of churns from such contamination increased the keeping quality of butter.

Coliform Bacteria in Butter. Coliform bacteria may at times be present in milk and cream. They may reach butter from contaminated cream or they may be present in wash water. Hammer and Yale [141] found them to contribute off-flavors. Salting seemed to inhibit them for they grew well in unsalted butter. Escherichia species did not produce off-flavors but Aerobacter species did in both salted and unsalted butter. The same observations were made by Rice [142] on Australian butter. French butter, according to Dienert [143] also contained members of this group. He found their concentration to be inversely proportional to the acidity. In view of the sanitary significance of these bacteria Dienert believed they might indicate unwholesome conditions of manufacture and handling.

139. Long and Hammer. 1938. Iowa Agr. Expt. Sta., Res. Bull. 246.
140. Olson and Hammer. 1933. Idem, Res. Bull. 159.
141. Hammer and Yale. 1932. J. Dairy Sci. 15, 199-208.
142. Rice. 1938. Queensland Agr. J. 50, 708-715.
143. Dienert. 1932. Lait 12, 1055-1058; Bull. Acad Méd. 107, 969-971.

Survival of Pathogenic Bacteria in Butter. This subject has been discussed in the author's *Food-Borne Infections and Intoxications*. Just one report of results will be mentioned here since it concerns more common bacteria which might get into butter. Berry [144] inoculated butter with a broth culture of each organism, both on the surface and throughout the mass. A specially modified MacConkey's medium was employed, and the number of pathogens was counted in poured plates. *Streptococcus scarlatinae* was grown on poured blood agar plates. The experiments indicated a rapid decrease in numbers during the first few days. The periods of maximum survival for the various organisms under observation were *Salmonella enteritidis*, 228 days; *Salmonella schottmülleri*, 212 days; *Salmonella paratyphi* A, 117 days; *Eberthella typhosa*—Mississippi, 22 days; *Eberthella typhosa*—Talledega, 110 days; *Salmonella suipestifer*, 49 days; *Shigella dysenteriae*, 18 days; *Streptococcus scarlatinae*, 17 days. These results indicate that butter must be regarded as a potential source of infection.

Carbonated Butter. Proposals have been made in the past that carbonation of various foods would bestow on them various benefits. None of these claims seems to have been confirmed. Hunziker [145] disclaimed them and stated that carbonated butter is subject to all the ailments to which normal butter is subject, if made from unpasteurized cream. He denied that carbonation would preserve vitamins or that it protected vitamins; that harmful bacteria would be destroyed; that it is free from flavor defects; or that carbonation improves the flavor. This position was also taken by the Iowa Agricultural Experiment Station.[146] Results of experiments by Prucha, Brannon, and Ruehe [147] in general were in agreement. Carbonation of sweet cream at first caused a slight reduction of bacteria and retarded development of acidity. It did not prevent bacterial growth which later occurred at practically the same rate as in uncarbonated cream, though the types of bacteria were somewhat different. Quality of butter was not improved by churning in presence of carbon dioxide. Carbonation of dairy products was without effect. It influenced keeping quality in some cases but to a slight extent.

MICROBIOLOGICAL EXAMINATION OF BUTTER

The methods which have been developed for microbiological examination of butter are quite like those which have been devised for other foods. Various organizations have proposed methods among which may be mentioned the American Dairy Science Association, the American Public Health Association, and the American Butter Institute.[148] All of these organizations have had committees which have studied procedures. Besides these reports there are results of studies by individuals, such as those of

144. Berry. 1927. J. Preventive Med. 1, 429-442.

145. Hunziker. 1922. J. Dairy Sci. 7, 484-496.

146. Iowa Agr. Expt. Sta., Ann. Rpt. for 1925, 42; Res. Bull. 95 (1926), 179-207.

147. Prucha, Brannon, and Ruehe. 1925. J. Dairy Sci. 8, 318-329; Ill. Agr. Expt. Sta. Bull. 368.

148. American Butter Institute, Laboratory Manual of Analysis for the Butter Industry.

Parfitt [149] and Moir and Russell.[150] The purposes for making laboratory examinations usually determine the type of examinations made. Moir and Russell used with satisfaction a microplate method for bacterial analysis of butter. It was believed to be superior to older methods because time was saved and the results were just as satisfactory.

British Standard Methods for Microbiological Examination of Butter.[151] This is a concise method of analysis; it is quoted as it appears in the original publication.

A. GENERAL.   5

Method of Sampling.

"1. It is essential that a sample properly representative of the bulk shall be taken. After determining the results of samples composed of 3, 6 and 12 cores, the Committee has concluded that a sample composed of 3 cores taken at appropriate points from a package of butter (reaching to the centre and including the surface portion) is reasonably representative of the bulk. The total sample shall be not less than 2 oz. (*See* also B.S. 809.) The sample shall be transferred to a suitable sterile container.

"As the micro-organisms present at the surface of the package are often of importance, the surface layer may be examined separately. For this purpose the surface shall be removed to a depth of ¼ in. by means of a sterile scraper and tested in the same way as the bulk sample.

"All analyses shall be carried out within six hours of sampling or the temperature of the sample shall be reduced to 40°F. and the examination carried out within 48 hours.

Treatment of Sample.

"2. For the purpose of examination the sample shall be quickly melted at a temperature not exceeding 45°C. by immersing the bottle for a short time in a water bath at 50°C. thoroughly mixed by shaking 50 times with an excursion of one foot in about one minute and a quantity of 10 ml. transferred without delay to 90 ml. of diluent in a suitable bottle of approximately 200 ml. capacity, using pipettes and diluent at 45°C. This will give a dilution of 1 in 10.

"The diluent and butter shall be shaken together 25 times with an excursion of 1 foot in about one minute, in order to obtain a homogeneous suspension.

"Subsequent dilution shall be made by transferring 1 ml. quantities of dilutions to 9 ml. quantities of diluent in test tubes at room temperature.

Apparatus.

"3. (a) Test Tubes (152 mm. x 16 mm., B.S. 625).
    (b) Pipettes (B.S. 700).
    (c) Petri dishes (B.S. 611).
    (d) Stoppered 200 ml. bottles.

Diluent.

"4. Dilutions of the butter under test are made in quarter-strength Ringer's Solution, containing 0.1 per cent agar to stabilize the emulsion.

Ringer's Solution.		
(full strength)	Sodium chloride	9.0 g.
	Potassium chloride	0.42 g.
	Calcium chloride	0.24 g.
	Sodium bicarbonate	0.2 g.
	Glass distilled water	1 000 ml.

149. Parfitt. 1934. Amer. J. Pub. Health 24, 303-308.
150. Moir and Russell. 1939. J. Dairy Sci. 10, 310-325.
151. Reprinted by permission from British Standards No. 895—1940, *British Standard Methods for the Microbiological Examination of Butter*. April, 1940. (Official copies may be obtained from the American Standards Association, 29 West Thirty-Ninth St., New York, N. Y.)

"Dissolve the constituents in glass distilled water, or other distilled water free from toxic metals.

"Dilute the full strength Ringer's Solution 4 times with glass distilled water, add 0.1 per cent washed fibre agar, heat to dissolve, sterilise by autoclaving for 15 min. at 120°C. and fill out 9 ml. quantities into test tubes (152 mm. x 19 mm., B.S. 625).

Plating and Counting.

"5. (a) *Dilutions of Butter to be examined.*—It will be appreciated that it is not possible to state what numbers or levels of dilutions shall be plated, as the number of organisms varies greatly from butter to butter. For routine purposes, dilutions need seldom exceed 1/10 000, as all counts greater than 5 000 000 indicate heavy contamination "An indication of the dilutions generally suitable is given with each medium.

"(b) Pouring the Plates.—Within 10 minutes of preparing the dilutions transfer 1 ml. quantities of each dilution to the plates; add 10 ml. of the medium, cooled to between 45° and 48°C., and mix with the dilution by rotary movements in a horizontal plane. After pouring the plates as quickly as possible with the minimum of exposure to light, cover with a black cloth and allow to harden for 30-60 minutes.

"(c) *Incubation.*—Invert the plates and transfer to an incubator which shall maintain the desired temperature within the range ± 1°C. Anhydric incubators are not recommended.

"(d) *Counting.*—After incubation for the specified time, count the colonies with the aid of a specially constructed box permitting the examination of the plates by combined reflected and transmitted artificial light against a dark background. A lens of 4 in. focal length magnifying 2½ diameters shall be used.[152]

"To facilitate counting, the plate may be divided into quarters by lightly ruling with a grease pencil.

"Mark the colonies with ink or grease pencil without using the lens; then scan the plate with the lens and complete marking. Record the colonies as they are marked by means of a tally counter.

"All plates considered to have colony numbers between 30 and 500 shall be counted.

"The count shall be computed from the number of colonies on that countable plate which contains the highest concentration of butter.

B. MEDIA FOR THE DIFFERENTIAL ENUMERATION OF VARIOUS MICRO-ORGANISMS IN BUTTER.

"The media described below shall be used as required for estimations of the numbers of organisms of different types which may be desirable for general or special purposes.

Yeasts and Moulds.

"1. The yeast and mould count may be regarded as an index of the care used in preparation of the butter.

"The work of the Committee has shown that there is no statistically significant difference between the counts obtained on:—

    (i) Beerwort agar
    (ii) Malt extract agar   } the pH value being 3.5, the
    (iii) Dextrose agar   plates being counted after incu-
    (iv) Yeast salt agar   bation for 3 days at 25°C.

"In order to make it possible for workers in all countries to make use of those constituents of media which are most easily obtained the composition of the above media is given below:—

    (a) *Preparation of Media.*
       (i) *Diluted Beerwort.*

---

152. Counting devices are recommended which involve combined reflected and transmitted artificial light against a dark background. Such devices are described by Wilson in Med. Res. Council Special Rpt. Series, No. 206, p. 102; Standard Methods for the Examination of Dairy Products, Eighth Edition, 1941, also describes one.

"Heat unhopped wort as received from the brewery to 100°C. for 1 hour, filter through pulp, allow to cool to 20°C. and add an equal volume of tap water. After thorough mixing, fill out the medium into flasks and sterilise by steaming for half hour at 100°C. on each of three successive days.

(ii) *Malt Extract.*

"Mix 100 g. of malt of high diastatic value with 1 000 ml. of tap water and hold at 50° to 55°C. until no colour reaction is obtained with iodine. Then raise the temperature to 100°C., filter the mixture and sterilise by steaming at 100°C. for 30 min. on each of three successive days. Alternatively, a 3 per cent solution of commercial malt extract (approximately 80 per cent of malt solids), free from preservatives, shall be used.

(iii) *Dextrose Broth.*

Dextrose	20 g.
Peptone [153]	10 g.
Commercial beef extract or yeast autolysate [154]	5 g.
Tap water	1 000 ml.

"Dissolve the constituents in hot tap water and raise to 100°C. Filter and make up the volume to 1 000 ml.

Experiments have shown that the type of peptone used in media for yeast and mould counts does not appear to influence the result.

(iv) *Yeast Salt Broth.*

Ammonium nitrate	1 g.
Ammonium sulphate	1 g.
Dipotassium hydrogen phosphate	4 g.
Potassium dihydrogen phosphate	2 g.
Sodium chloride	1 g.
Dextrose	1 g.
Commercial yeast autolysate	1 g.
Tap water	1 000 ml.

"Dissolve the constituents in hot tap water and raise to 100°C. Make up the volume to 1 000 ml.

"(b) *Addition of Agar.*—Add 20 g. of washed fibre agar per 1 000 ml. of medium, dissolve by raising to 100°C., and sterilise by autoclaving at 120°C. for 15 minutes.

"(c) *Adjustment of Media.*—*Media i, ii and iii.*—Add citric acid (10 per cent solution, previously autoclaved as in (b), aseptically to the medium at 90°-100°C. to bring the pH value to approximately 3.5, using bromphenol blue as an external indicator. (Diluted beerwort requires about 20 ml. per 1 000 ml.)

"A previously prepared buffer mixture is then added as follows:—

> For every 1 000 ml. of medium dissolve 12.8 g. of citric acid monohydrate and 7.2 g. of potassium citrate monohydrate in 50 ml. water and sterilise by autoclaving for 15 minutes at 120°C. Then add this buffer aseptically to the medium, which has been adjusted to approximately pH 3.5, both being at a temperature of 90°-100°C.

Medium iv.

"Adjust the pH value of the yeast salt medium to 3.5 by the addition of 5.7 g. of citric acid monohydrate per 1 000 ml. autoclaved as in Media (i), (ii) and (iii)

(c). No buffer is required.

All media.

"After thorough mixing, fill out the medium aseptically into sterile test-tubes in 10 ml. quantities. Further sterilisation is not required and shall not be attempted.

153. The products of British Drug Houses, Hopkins & Williams, Fairchild, Allen & Hanbury, Parke-Davis, Difco, and Gurr were used in the Committee's experiments.
154. For beef extract, Lemco and for yeast autolysate, Yeastrel and Marmite were used in the Committee's experiments.

"(d) *Pouring of plates.*—Melt the medium and cool to between 45° and 48°C. as soon as possible, as prolonged heating at 100°C. will destroy the gelling properties of the medium.

"(e) *Dilution.*—It is normally sufficient to plate 1 ml. quantities of the 1/10, 1/100 and 1/1 000 dilutions.

Lipolytic (Tributyrin-splitting) Organisms.

"2. Lipolytic organisms are defined as organisms whose colonies produce zones of clearing in tributyrin agar.

"There is evidence that a high proportion of organisms splitting tributyrin also split butter fat. As the rate of zone production in tributyrin is much faster than in butter fat the former has been adopted, as it permits the results to be obtained more quickly.

"The Committee's work has shown that nile blue sulphate butter fat agar is inferior to tributyrin agar in that it gives smaller and fewer colonies.

(a) *Preparation of Medium.*

Tributyrin Agar :

Washed fibre agar.. 15 g.
Peptone [153] .... 5 g.
Commercial yeast autolysate [154].. 3 g.
Tributyrin... 10 g.
Tap Water .... 1 000 ml.

"The Committee's work has shown that the type of peptone used in media for the count of lipolytic organisms does not influence the result.

"Dissolve the constituents in tap water by raising to 100°C. Add the tributyrin and emulsify in an efficient emulsifying machine at a temperature of 45° to 50°C. The emulsion shall show no macroscopic globules and shall be stable. Adjust the pH value to 7.5 by the addition of HCl or NaOH with the aid of a comparator, using phenol red as indicator. Fill out in 10 ml. quantities and sterilise by steaming at 100°C. for 30 minutes on each of three successive days.

"(b) *Dilutions.*—It is normally sufficient to plate 1 ml. quantities of the 1/10, 1/100, 1/1 000 and 1/10 000 dilutions.

"(c) *Incubation.*—Incubate the plates at 30°C. for three days.

"(d) *Counting.*—On this medium, colonies with well-defined clear zones extending at least 1 mm. from the edge of the colony shall be considered to be lipolytic.

Caseolytic Organisms.

"3. These are defined as organisms whose colonies produce permanent zones of clearing in an opaque medium containing casein after flooding with a protein precipitant. Most micro-organisms attacking casein also hydrolyse fat.

(a) *Preparation of Medium* [155]

Stock Solution A—Calcium chloride (fused)... 1.5%
Stock Solution B { Disodium hydrogen phosphate ($Na_2HPO_4 \cdot 12H_2O$)...... 1.05%
{ Potassium dihydrogen phosphate (KH_2PO_4).... .... 0.35%
Stock Solution C—Tryptone (Difco) 5%

"Soak 3.5 g. Hammarsten's casein in 150 ml. of distilled water for 15 minutes. Add 72 ml. saturated lime water and shake until the casein has dissolved. About three hours shaking in a mechanical shaker is usually sufficient. Then add 0.35 g. of potassium citrate. Add 50 ml. of stock solution C, filter and make up to 300 ml. Add 10 ml. of stock solution A and 10 ml. of stock solution B, and make up to 500 ml. Adjust the pH value to 7.0 if necessary, using bromthymol blue as indicator. Tube in 5 ml. quantities, sterilise for 15 minutes at 120°C.

155. Frazier and Rupp. 1928. J. Bact. 16. 57.

"Make up 5 ml. quantities of 3 per cent agar in distilled water and sterilise separately.

"(*b*) *Pouring of Plates.*—Pour the broth first, followed immediately by the 3 per cent agar, and mix the solutions well. The temperature at the time of pouring shall be 45° to 48°C.

"(*c*) *Dilutions.*—It is normally sufficient to plate 1 ml. quantities of the 1/10, 1/100, 1/1 000 and 1/10 000 dilutions.

"(*d*) *Incubation.*—Incubated plates at 30° C. for three days.

"In order to distinguish zones due to caseolysis from those due to solution of the protein by alkali formed by the organisms, flood the plates with a freshly prepared 1 per cent solution of tannic acid. If an enumeration of the total number of organisms (excluding organisms requiring sugar) is required, counting shall be done before flooding the plates.

Saccharolytic Organisms.

"4. *Chiefly lactic acid bacteria.*—To assess the number of streptococci and other sugar fermenting organisms which in some methods of butter manufacture indicate faulty methods of pasteurisation a milk serum medium may be employed. In addition to permitting growth of lactic streptococci many other common contaminants of butter, such as micrococci and coliform organisms will grow, and the count on this medium may be considered to approximate to the 'Total Count.'

(*a*) *Preparation of Medium.*

(i) *Milk Serum.*—Warm 1 000 ml. of fresh whole or separated milk to 40°C., add 70 ml. of 7 per cent citric acid monohydrate per 1 000 ml. slowly with stirrings, stand for 1 hour and filter overnight. Sterilise the filtrate (approximately 600 ml. at pH 4.7) by heating to 100°C. for ½ hour. Adjust to pH 6.8 before use (600 ml. requires about 40 ml. N NaOH).

(ii) *Milk Serum agar.*

Milk Serum (pH 6.8)	1 000 ml.
Peptone	5 g.
Commercial yeast autolysate	5 g.
Dextrose	5 g.
Agar	15 g.

"To the milk serum add the other constituents, heat to 100°C. to dissolve, readjust the pH value to 6.8, using bromthymol blue as an indicator and fill out into tubes in 10 ml. quantities. Sterilise by autoclaving for 10 minutes at 120°C.

"(*b*) Dilutions.—It is normally sufficient to plate 1 ml. quantities of the 1/10, 1/100, 1/1 000 and 1/10 000 dilutions.

Coliform Organisms.

"5. There is evidence that the presence of coliform organisms indicates faults in manufacture and handling and that they affect keeping quality.

"(*a*) *Preparation of Medium.*

Sodium taurocholate (commercial)	5 g.
Lactose	10 g.
Peptone	20 g.
Sodium chloride	5 g.
Tap water	1 000 ml.

"Mix the constituents, steam for 2 hours and keep in an ice chest overnight. Then filter through Chardin paper whilst still cold. Adjust the pH values to 6.8, using bromthymol blue as indicator. Add 5 per cent of 0.04 per cent aqueous solution of bromcresol purple. Distribute in 6 ml. quantities in B.S. test-tubes (152 mm. x 16 mm., B.S. 625) provided with Durham fermentation tubes (35 mm. x 8 mm., B.S. 625). Plug with cotton wool, sterilise in the autoclave at 120°C. for 10 min., or in the steamer at 100°C. for 30 minutes on three successive days.

NOTE.—Laboratories not wishing to duplicate media may use the medium described on p. 8, Memo. 139, Foods 1937, Ministry of Health. (See page 372 of this book.)

"(*b*) *Dilutions*.—Dilutions of 1/10, 1/100 and 1/1 000, each in triplicate, shall be used when an estimation of coliform organisms (presumptive) is required. If acid and gas are observed in two tubes at any dilution the result shall be regarded as positive at that dilution."

Butter Examination With the Burri Film Technic. The technic of the Burri film has been given on page 334 of this book. Long and Hammer [156] examined butter bacteriologically with an adaptation of the Burri smear culture technic which consists of picking small amounts (approximately 1/20,000 gram with a needle and spreading each on the surface of a dry agar slope. The bacteria in various types of butter were often found to be very irregularly distributed, both from the standpoint of numbers and colony types. The colonies on the slopes were well differentiated since they all developed on the surface of the agar. In some instances colony types were found on slopes which were not evident on plates.

Plate Counts of Butter. These have not been of as much value as have plate counts of milk. Pont [157] analyzed the experimental error in plate counts of butter and found just about what has been found to be true for plate counts of other foods. The plate count was not always found to be a reliable index of bacterial population. In some cases wide variations were found. Before using plate counts in research projects, this report should be carefully studied.

MICROSCOPE METHODS OF BACTERIOLOGICAL BUTTER ANALYSIS

The advantages of microscope methods over the older plate methods have prompted attempts to use them for determining the number of bacteria in butter. Hedrick [158] found microscope methods to be fairly accurate for distinguishing butter made from excellent cream, but not reliable for lower grades. He explained this difference on the basis that low-grade butter is not always due to bacterial action. Hedrick used the Fay method for preparing cream slides. He was able to satisfactorily grade cream and butter.

Hammer and Nelson's [159] Method for Microscope Bacteriological Examination of Butter. This method was used by the authors for following the changes resulting from storage of butter under different conditions. Hammer and Nelson stated that the methods of sampling butter proposed by the Special Committee on Bacteriological Methods of Analyzing Dairy Products of the American Dairy Science Association, were satisfactory. They outlined their method as follows:

1. The entire sample of butter or enough of it to yield 10 ml. of the melted product for centrifuging, is put into a beaker so that it can be readily melted and mixed. A 250-ml. beaker of the conical type is preferred, although beakers of various capacities

156. Long and Hammer. 1938. Iowa State Col. J. Sci. 12, 441-450.
157. Pont. 1941. J. Dairy Res. 12, 24-34.
158. Hedrick. 1938. J. Dairy Sci. 21, 553-558.
159. Hammer and Nelson. 1931. Iowa Agr. Expt. Sta., Res. Bull. 137.

and shapes are convenient. The melting and mixing are carried out by placing the beaker in a water bath at a temperature of from 50 to 55°C. and slowly agitating the butter, using a thermometer as a stirring rod, until the temperature reaches 45°C. (113°F.).

2. Ten ml. of the melted fat at a temperature of 45°C. are transferred to a 30-ml. separatory funnel, using a pipette that has been warmed by passing it through a flame. The size of the portion centrifuged is of no great importance, but a standard volume seems advisable and one of 10 ml. has some advantages over smaller amounts. These advantages are (1) enough serum collects to permit the removal of the serum without including any considerable percentage of fat, and (2) the volume of serum secured provides ample material for plating in case the microscope picture makes this advisable.

Centrifuging is carried out using a funnel support intended for a separatory funnel of a different shape from the one employed. A rubber stopper around the upper part of the funnel rests against the wall of the support and the funnel is carried in this way. Very little funnel breakage has been encountered and most of this has involved the tip of the funnel which projects into the lower portion of the support.

The centrifuging should throw out the serum completely without causing a separation in the serum itself. When centrifuging has been done properly the fat layer will be clear and uniform throughout. With a centrifuge in which the stop-cocks of the funnels were 14½ inches apart with the machine in operation, centrifuging one minute at a speed of 1,000 R.P.M. was found to be entirely satisfactory for the types of butter used. Samples of butter of different characters behave differently, and some types are easily over-centrifuged so that there is a separation in the serum. When this occurs a solid pack of material at the bottom of the funnel may make it very difficult to start a flow through the stop-cock and, of course, it becomes imperative to remove the serum very completely, and then thoroughly mix it, if a representative portion is to be secured for spreading on the slides. In general, centrifuging of butter made from a poor quality of cream must be carefully done or there will be a separation in the serum; presumably, this is due to the content of particles of casein or some casein derivative that readily centrifuges out. With butter made from good-quality sweet cream the centrifuging can be greatly in excess (either time or speed) of that suggested without any undesirable effect.

3. Immediately after centrifuging, the funnel is removed from the centrifuge and the serum drawn off; unless this is done before the fat begins to congeal, a great deal of difficulty is encountered. The serum should be removed very slowly so that the plane between the fat and serum is kept as flat as possible. When the serum is drawn off rapidly the portion along the wall of the funnel tends to lag and the fat is pulled down to the stop-cock when there is still a considerable percentage of the serum in the funnel. The serum is removed as completely as possible without including objectionable amounts of fat.

A short test tube makes a very satisfactory container in which to collect the serum since portions of the serum can be easily removed from it with a Breed pipette.

4. The collected serum is thoroughly agitated, and portions are removed to microscope slides with a Breed pipette. Ordinarily .01 ml. of the serum is spread over one, four, or eight sq. cm. If the area is larger than one sq. cm., sterile skimmilk, free from stainable bacterial cells, or water is added with a loop to facilitate even distribution. The spreading is conveniently done with a transfer needle bent at an angle of 90 degrees. When skim milk or water is to be used it should be put near the .01 ml. of serum and thoroughly mixed with the serum before an attempt is made to cover the desired area.

The area over which the .01 ml. of serum should be spread depends on the bacterial content of the butter and the information desired. If a study of the morphologic types of organisms present is the main consideration, it is an advantage to have the organisms rather numerous in each field while if an estimation of the number is desired, the organisms should not be so numerous that counting is difficult. With butter having a very high bacterial content, counting may be facilitated by spreading the .01 ml. of serum over an area larger than eight sq. cm.

A card with the desired area laid out in black and surrounded by a broad red border is a great aid in the making of spreads that are reasonably exact in area and reasonably uniform in thickness. If a portion of the background is white the desired results are not so easily secured.

The slides are rapidly dried on a level surface and are well protected from flies and dust.

5. Both the regular methylene blue stain described in "Standard Methods of Milk Analysis" (10) and Newman's one-solution technic (5) are satisfactory for staining preparations of the serum secured from butter.

6. The examination of the stained smears under the oil immersion lens shows the general morphologic types and the general number of organisms present.

7. The number of organisms per ml. of butter may be estimated by (1) determining the average number per field, counting as many fields as seems desirable for the purpose in mind; (2) calculating the number per ml. of serum from the area over which .01 ml. of serum was spread and the diameter of the microscope field, and (3) dividing by 9 to change from a basis of one ml. of serum to a basis of one ml. of butter. Steps 2 and 3 may be combined for routine work.

Fay's [160] **Microscope Method for Examination of Butter.** This method was devised by Fay to eliminate some of the difficulties involved in use of the .01-ml. capillary pipette and the centrifuge and to provide a method which would lend itself to routine examination of many samples.

The butter to be examined is melted by heating to 45°C.(113°F.) for a period not to exceed 15 minutes, after which it is agitated sufficiently to insure a homogenous sample.

(a) On a standard 1 x 3 inch, chemically clean, glass slide place .1 ml. of the melted butter, one drop of xylol, and one drop of Mayer's egg-glycerine mixture. To prepare Mayer's solution equal parts of egg albumin and glycerine are mixed, thoroughly beaten, and filtered through cotton. One per cent sodium salicylate should be used as a preservative, and the solution kept in a refrigerator when not in use. Mayer's solution is used to aid in fixing the smear to the slide.

(b) With an "L" shaped platinum needle stir the butter, Mayer's solution, and xylol together until the mixture is opalescent and homogenous, then spread evenly over the entire area of the slide. It is important that the mixing of the ingredients be properly done before spreading the smear over the area of the slide. Proper mixing requires from two to three minutes.

(c) Allow the preparation to dry, and at the same time coagulate the albumin by placing the slide on a flat bottle of hot water at approximately 80°C.(716°F.) for 10 to 15 minutes.

(d) Fix the smear in 70 per cent alcohol for 10 to 20 seconds, and allow to dry.

(e) Immerse in xylol two minutes, and allow to dry.

(f) Stain in methylene blue for one minute, then wash by dipping the slide once in each of two vessels of water. Allow to dry in the air.

(g) Examine under an oil immersion lens, the field of which has been standardized to a diameter of .157 mm. The average number of microorganisms per field multiplied by 1,000,000 gives the number per milliliter of melted butter.

If it is desirable to enumerate objects large enough to be seen with the lower magnifications of the microscope, standardize the diameter of the field of the high dry objective to .351 mm. and of the low power objective to 1.57 mm.; multiply the average number of objects observed per field by the factors 200,000 and 10,000, respectively, to give the number per milliliter of melted butter. The method described in this paper has been found to be equally advantageous for the microscope examination of heavy cream.

Demeter's [161] **Microscope Method for Counting Bacteria in Butter.** The following method was proposed after considering other similar methods. Three grams of butter

160. Fay. 1938. J. Dairy Sci. 18, 9.
161. Demeter. 1937. Deut. Milch. Ztg. 36, 1190-1191.

are weighed into a centrifuge tube marked 3, 6, and 9 ml. Seven ml. of xylol are added and the tube closed with a well-fitting stopper. It is then shaken for about five minutes and placed in an incubator at 40 to 45°C. (104 to 113°F.) for 45 minutes. After thorough shaking again the tube is centrifuged in an ordinary fat-centrifuge for one to two minutes. The supernatant solution of fat in xylol is poured off and five per cent sodium hydroxide solution poured in up to the mark 3. The tube is then corked and shaken until a homogeneous solution is obtained. Following the usual technic with a .01-ml. pipette slides are prepared and stained by Newman's method, with a contact time of six to eight seconds. The count of each gram of butter is obtained by multiplying the mean number of bacteria per field by 300,000. For poor-quality butter water is added to mark 6 or mark 9 and a factor of 2 or 3 used for determining the count.

The Frost little-plate method and certain modifications has also been found to be satisfactory for butter. Moir and Russell [150] recommended the microplate method of Johns [162] for counting bacteria in butter. By staining the cultures as recommended, the results were available within 24 hours. Moir and Russell described their method in full.

YEASTS IN BUTTER

Yeasts are widespread in nature and are to be expected in butter. Their presence in butter has a two-fold interest for bacteriologists. They may indicate faulty handling of cream and inefficient pasteurization and they may cause objectionable changes in the cream which result in bad flavors and odors. Both of these problems have received much study. Lactose-fermenting yeasts are common in cream and if allowed to develop, cause a frothy fermentation. Many such yeasts have been described in milk, cream, and milk products.

Yeasts were found by Dombrowski [163] in all samples of milk and milk products. Torulae were more frequent than Saccharomyces and Mycoderma. The activities of the yeasts were not limited to alcoholic fermentation. Some were found to produce colors and flavors, while others showed no fermentative activity whatsoever. Hammer [164] mentioned some of the difficulties in studying yeasts in butter and other dairy products and identification with species in the literature. His comments may be extended to the identification of yeasts from all sources. Similar observations were made by Hastings [165] for milk, whey, butter, and cheese. Yeasts were found to be widely distributed in Swiss, brick, and Cheddar cheese factories. They were also present in about one-fourth of the samples of butter examined and in 29 out of 51 samples of milk. The main sources of infection were believed to be the soil and accumulations of dirt protected from drying. This type of yeast was not considered of economic importance except in certain branches of dairying. In Swiss and brick cheese factories infection with lactose-fermenting yeasts have, in several instances, caused considerable trouble. The danger from infection with this organism is not apt to occur in Cheddar cheese making. Bochicchio [166] observed spoilage of Grana cheese by a yeast which fermented lactose. The yeast was checked

162. Johns. 1928. Sci. Agr. 8, 353-368.
163. Dombrowski. 1910. Centbl. Bakt., Pt. 2, 28, 345-403.
164. Hammer. 1926. J. Dairy Sci. 9, 507-511.
165. Hastings. 1906. Wis. Agr. Expt. Sta., Ann. Rpt., 107-115.
166. Bochicchio. 1894. Centbl. Bakt., 15.

by a temperature of 55°C.(131°F.) to 60°C.(140°F.), so that infected utensils could be readily cleaned with boiling water. The name suggested by the author for this yeast was *Lactomyces inflans caseigrana.*

Effect of Pasteurization on Yeasts in Cream. Yeasts are not as resistant to heat as bacteria and consequently it has been suggested that their presence in butter might indicate that pasteurization was inefficient. Dougherty [167] and Wells [168] have both demonstrated that most yeasts are destroyed at 61°C.(141.8°F.). Dougherty found only three species which survived this temperature under the conditions under which she worked. Hunziker *et al.*[169] stated that the efficiency of pasteurization of cream at 73.9°C.(165°F.) for 30 seconds in killing yeasts and molds was 78 per cent, while at 85°C. (185°F.) for 30 seconds or 62.8°C.(145°F.) for 30 minutes the efficiency was 99.9 per cent. Lund [173] found that nearly all yeasts were destroyed at 62.8°C.(145°F.) in 30 minutes. Macy, Coulter, and Combs [172] found that yeasts were destroyed in 71 per cent of cream samples by pasteurization. Bouska and Brown [170] stated that if butter which purports to have been made from pasteurized cream contains hundreds of yeasts or molds they would hesitate to say that pasteurization had fulfilled its usual hygienic or commercial requirement, nor would they agree that it could be marked as pasteurized.

Stiritz,[171] on the other hand, reported that the yeast and mold counts cannot be regarded as an index of efficient pasteurization. However, Stiritz was willing to accept a standard of 30 colonies per ml. as the maximum number allowable for a butter prepared under suitable conditions. No information was yielded by the yeast and mold count on the question as to whether the butter was made from raw or pasteurized cream. After pasteurization the churn was said to be a source of contamination. This has also been reported by others.

Prevalence of Yeasts in Butter. Much of the butter formerly made in the United States contained many yeasts. This was due largely to lack of adequate methods of refrigeration and to faulty processing of the cream. Pasteurization of the cream reduced the yeast content of the butter but did not eliminate them.

Samples of butter examined by Lund [173] showed from 350 to 4,000 yeasts per ml. in the unpasteurized cream butter. In pasteurized cream butter the yeast count varied from 60 to 5,000, except in one sample which contained 5,000,000. The yeast content of butter was said to come from contamination in the churn. In a later paper, Lund [174] stated that pasteurization would reduce the Oidium counts, but the yeast counts often were high. Again he stated that the yeast contamination resulted from the churn and not from the fact that the yeasts survived pasteurization. Lund ex-

167. Dougherty. 1920. Thesis, Univ. of Ill.
168. Wells. 1917. Vermont Agr. Expt. Sta. Bull. 203, 13-14.
169. Hunziker *et al.* 1917. Indiana Agr. Expt. Sta. Bull. 208.
170. Bouska and Brown. 1921. Wis. Univ. Studies Sci., No. 2, 131-138.
171. Stiritz. 1922. J. Dairy Sci. 5, 362-371.
172. Macy, Coulter, and Combs. 1932. Minn. Agr. Expt. Sta., Tech. Bull. 82.
173. Lund. 1918. N. Y. Prod. Rev. and Amer. Creamery 48, 282 et seq.
174. Lund. 1922. Sci. Agr. 2, 332-340.

amined, in one case, seven specimens of creamery butter made from raw cream, and four from imperfectly pasteurized cream. An average yeast count of 1,700 per ml. was reported. Ten samples of butter from pasteurized cream gave a yeast count of 1,182. Further work by Lund [175] on butters submitted in a scoring contest revealed a high yeast count, and confirmed his former statements; he considered the churn to be the most insanitary piece of apparatus in the modern creamery. Sandelin [176] found torulae to be common in butter. He classified the strains which he studied, according to the substances which they attacked. Bouska and Brown [170] reported that the butter from creameries using a pure starter and thorough steaming of equipment had a low yeast content and kept better. Since contamination with yeasts may result from the churn, Stiritz [171] believed that yeast and mold counts of finished butter could not be taken as an efficiency index of pasteurization, or as a method for determining whether butter has been made from raw or pasteurized cream. North and Reddish [177] studied the presence of yeasts in samples of butter scoring 93 or over by Redfield's microscope method. They found yeasts to be more evenly distributed than Oidia. Redfield [178] made similar observations on butter of slightly lower grade. Redfield reported that, in general, low-grade samples of butter showed high counts of yeast, but this was not always the case, indicating that other factors were also responsible for deterioration. Redfield believed that there was some relation of high yeast counts to the condition of the cream used in manufacture of the butter. Neither salt content nor acidity affects yeast growth in fresh cream butters (Gilmour and Curess-Callaghan [179]). Growth increased as the temperature was higher but was stopped at $-7°C.(19.4°F.)$.

Significance of Yeasts in Butter. Yeasts in butter have about the same significance in butter that molds have, *i.e.*, bad "housekeeping" in the creamery. Their presence may be due to cream which has been mistreated, to insanitary utensils and apparatus, and to lack of refrigeration of both cream and butter. Dust owing to poor ventilation may also be a contributing factor. Lund's experience with the yeast count indicated that it could be used for determining whether butter had been made from raw or pasteurized cream. Macy [180] believed that the yeast and mold counts reflected the care which had been used in making the butter.

Relation of Yeast Count to Keeping Quality of Butter. While a number of investigations have been carried out on this subject, the conclusions which have been reached are neither convincing nor in agreement. Lund [181] found large numbers of yeasts in butter but could not definitely relate them to keeping quality. Bouska and Brown [170] believed that a butter with few yeasts and mold was a safer hazard for long shipments and storage.

175. Lund. 1921. N. Y. Prod. Rev. and Amer. Creamery 51, 510-511.
176. Sandelin. 1920. Centbl. Bakt., Pt. 2, 51, 429.
177. North and Reddish. 1921. J. Dairy Sci. 4, 510-520.
178. Redfield. 1922. J. Dairy Sci. 5, 14-21.
179. Gilmour and Curess-Callaghan. Dept. Agr. J. (Ireland) 31, 226-231.
180. Macy. 1937. Proc. Tenth Ann. State Col. Wash. Inst. Dairying, 20-24.
181. Lund. 1920. Creamery and Milk Plant Mo. 10, 30.

Their experience showed that creameries with low yeast and mold count butter, had better commercial reputations. These, in general, were the conclusions reached also by Grimes,[182] Shutt,[183] and North and Reddish.[177] Anyone familiar with the physiology of the yeasts would expect some of them, at least, to be injurious to butter. The differences of opinion on this question may be easily explained by the fact that different species may have been predominant in the specimens which were used by the several investigators. If the predominating species were injurious, yeasts were said to harm butter. This problem probably ought to be approached from the pure culture viewpoint.

Because of differences of opinion among investigators with respect to the proper medium for counting yeasts Parfitt [184] compared several different ones. The results of the study showed that whey agar prepared by rennet coagulation produced the lowest yeast and mold counts. The differences between the dehydrated agars prepared by a commercial concern were slight. In order to secure comparative yeast and mold counts it was found that either dehydrated whey, malt, or wort agars should be used. Shadwick [185] found that proper adjustment of reaction of media to pH 3.5 was necessary in order to eliminate bacteria which otherwise confuse observations on yeasts. Potato dextrose agar, especially the dehydrated product of the Digestive Ferments Company, gave better results than did dehydrated malt, peptonized milk, whey or wort agars. Other factors were investigated by Hood and White.[186] No significant differences in counts were attributed to pH from 3 to 4.6 of agar medium incubated for five days at 25°C.(77°F.). White and Hood recommended a pH for the plating medium of ± 3.5. Temperature of incubation should be 25°C.(77°F.). They believed standard times and temperatures should be used.

Redfield's [187] Method for Counting Yeasts in Butter. Redfield modified Breed's microscope method for estimating yeasts and Oidia in butter and cream. He described his technic as follows:

Butter: By means of a small butter trier, three or four cores from different portions of the butter sample are transferred to a six by one inch test tube, usually about half filling the tube. The butter is melted at 45°C.(113°F.) and allowed to stand at temperatures between 45°C.(113°F.) and 40°C.(104°F.) until the fat is separated in a clean layer with mixture of curd and whey or brine at the bottom of the tube. With a sterile one ml. pipette the curd and whey are thoroughly mixed by drawing the liquid back and forth in the pipette. Then one ml. of this mixture is transferred to a clean watch glass, care being taken to thoroughly wipe all fat from the outside of the pipette with a clean towel before discharging the pipette into the watch glass. With a Breed Pipette .01 ml. of the mixture is transferred to a microscope slide, carefully spread over an area of two or four sq. cm. depending on the quality of the butter, diluting if necessary with distilled water to obtain uniform smears. After drying in the air, extracting with xylol, and fixation with 95 per cent alcohol, the smears are stained with saturated aqueous methylene blue after which they are washed with water and then with 95 per cent alcohol and dried in air.

182. Grimes. 1923. J. Dairy Sci. 6, 427-445.
183. Shutt. 1929. Sci. Agr. 9, 316-320.
184. Parfitt. 1933. J. Dairy Sci. 16, 141-147.
185. Shadwick. 1938. Food Research 3, 287-298.
186. Hood and White. 1931. J. Dairy Sci. 14, 463-476.
187. Redfield. 1922. J. Dairy Sci. 5, 14-21.

Counting is done with a combination of lens and draw-tube length to give a factor of 500,000. The diameter of the field should be .16 mm. to give this factor. Redfield recommended counting at least 100 fields except in very high count products.

Shutt's [188] **Method for Determining Yeasts in Butter.** Shutt, in a personal communication to the author, outlined the following procedure for determining yeasts in butter:

Apparatus required:

Sterile screw-top jars, sterile butter irons, [189] sterile water blanks of 90 ml., sterile Petri dishes, sterile pipettes, 10 ml. and one ml.

Sampling. With a well-boiled and cooled butter iron remove a plug of butter from the print or solid and transfer the plug, less the top half-inch, to the sterile jar. If sample must be held it must be kept in cold storage for not longer than 36 hours.

Method of Analysis. Place the water blanks and the samples of butter in a warming chamber at 41°C.(105.8°F.) until the water blanks are warm and the butter is melted. Shake the butter well.

Transfer 10 ml. of the melted butter, with a warmed pipette, to a 90 ml. warm water blank and shake 25 times. Make further dilutions if required.

Transfer one ml. of each dilution including original butter to Petri plates and pour with acidified malt extract agar.

Incubate all plates at 25°C.(77°F.) for four days.

Count all yeast colonies and record.

American Public Health Association [190] **Procedures for Determination of Yeasts and Molds in Butter.** Since butter cultures are added to cream to be made into butter, a plate count cannot be used for determining its sanitary condition. Consequently, in search for a microbiological method which could be used, bacteriologists have considered yeasts and molds as possible indicators of faulty conditions of manufacture. If these organisms are used in this manner it must be on the premise that they should be present in significant numbers in bad butter and absent in good butter made from adequately pasteurized cream.

The first instructions concern collection and handling of the sample. A sterile trier is recommended for taking two or three samples from each lot. These are transferred to sterile sample bottles and kept below 40°C.(104°F.) before analysis. Where many samples are to be collected, a single trier may be used if it is wiped clean, dipped in alcohol, and the latter ignited between each sample.

The sample jar with samples, just before analysis, is placed in warm water between 40 and 45°C. (104 and 113°F.) to melt the butter. The time should not exceed 15 minutes.

Dilutions are made in sterile water in dilution bottles using sterile 11-ml. pipettes. These are warmed by drawing into them some of the warm dilution water (40 to 45°C.) and letting it run back into the bottle. Then place 11 ml. of the melted sample in the 99-ml. dilution bottle. Plate as for milk with such dilution that fat in the dishes will not interfere with colony counting.

The medium is dextrose-potato-agar and the plates should be incubated for five days at 21 to 25°C. (69.8 to 77°F.). At the end of this time count the number of yeast and mold colonies.

British Standard Methods [151] **for Determination of Yeast and Molds in Butter.** These procedures are not very different from those recommended by the American Public Health Association. After the sample has been collected and melted at a temperature not exceeding 45°C.(113°F.) a 1-10 dilution is made by transferring 10 ml. of melted sample to 99 ml. of sterile water. This mixture is then well shaken. Subsequent dilutions are to be made by transferring one ml. of this 1-10 dilution to nine ml. of sterile water at room temperature.

188. Shutt. 1924. J. Dairy Sci. 7, 357-360.
189. While it is desirable to use absolutely sterile butter irons, Shutt stated that the irons could be boiled and cooled when samples are collected away from the laboratory. This would insure freedom from yeasts and molds even though all bacteria might not be killed.
190. Amer. Pub. Health Assoc., Standard Methods for the Examination of Dairy Products, Eighth Edition. 1941. New York, N. Y.

Plates are poured in the usual manner using either beerwort agar, malt extract agar, dextrose agar, or yeast salt agar media. The plates should be counted after incubation for three days at 25°C.(77°F.).

Johns' Method for Determining Yeast Count of Butter. This is described below on page 495.

Yeast Count Standards for Butter. These should be established only after adequate observations on good and poor butters. Only a few have made suggestions. Based on study of conditions of production and yeast and mold counts Parfitt [191] proposed standards as follows. Less than 50 yeasts and molds per milliliter of butter representing good conditions of manufacture; 51 to 100 ml. representing fair conditions; 101 to 500 per ml. representing poor conditions; and over 500 per ml. representing very poor conditions of manufacture.

Brandt [192] graded butter with the yeast count as one criterion of quality. Samples held for five to six days at 10 to 12°C.(50 to 53.6°F.) containing more than 150,000 yeast cells and more than 400,000 bacteria were graded as poor.

Olson and Hammer's [193] Agar Disc Method for Studying Contamination From Metal Surfaces. This method was developed for studying the microbial condition of the surface of churns. The method should also be useful for studying other surfaces.

a. After melting and cooling to approximately 43°C., the special medium (about 10 ml.) is poured on a small area of the surface to be examined and allowed to solidify. The medium that has been used is beef-infusion agar made with 2.5 per cent of air dried agar so that the disc will be strong enough to permit handling. Other media can be employed and perhaps are advisable for some purposes.

b. The agar disc is picked up with a sterile spatula and tipped into a sterile petri dish so that the portion of the disc that was in contact with the surface being examined is toward the top of the dish.

c. The disc is incubated at 21°C. for four days, although if the disc is so heavily seeded that there is danger of the colonies fusing, the incubation period is shortened. The incubation conditions can be varied for special purposes.

d. The colonies developing on a measured area (usually 20 to 30 sq. cm.) are counted and the results expressed as the number per square centimeter. With very heavily seeded discs, either approximate counts or estimates are accepted.

Wildman's Agar Slice Method for Detection of Mold and Yeast on Utensils. The Hammer-Olson method just described for determining presence of microorganisms on surfaces was not considered by Wildman [194] to be suitable for conditions under which Wildman was working. He used slices of agar medium described below. The slice may be placed on the surface to be examined, picked up, and stored in a suitable container for further observation.

METHOD

Preparation of Materials: Straight-edged test tubes of a convenient size (three-fourths inch to one inch, outside diameter) are selected and a small opening made in the bottom of each. The tubes are then corked, cotton-plugged tightly in the small opening, both ends wrapped with tin foil, and sterilized with dry heat. After sterilization, the tubes are filled with sterile, acidulated, potato-dextrose agar (2.5 per cent agar), corked, and quickly unverted. The tin-foil wrappings are replaced and held with rubber bands.

A supply of small petri dishes, or metal salve boxes, and double-edged razor blades are sterilized. Salve boxes (one-fourth ounce) fitted with small squares of glass held

191. Parfitt. 1937. Rev. in J. Dairy Sci. 20, 449.
192. Brandt. 1939. Molk. Ztg. 52, 262-264.
193. Olson and Hammer. 1933. Iowa Agr. Expt. Sta. Bull. 300.
194. Wildman. 1940. J. Milk Tech. 3, 162-163.

in place by means of paraffin have proved satisfactory for holding the agar slices during observation periods. New razor blades may be sterilized in the original carton and each blade broken in two lengthwise before unwrapping. Used blades may be wrapped and used again.

Operation: A tube of solidified agar is prepared for use by removing the small cotton plug aseptically and replacing the tin-foil cap. The agar core is allowed to slide out of the tube approximately one-eighth inch and a disc is sliced off with a sterile blade. The disc may adhere to the blade after slicing. In order to facilitate its placement in the utensil under test, it may be pushed to the extreme end of the blade with a sterile edge of the test tube. The slice should be pressed down with the blade in order to secure contact of slice and utensil, after which the disc is removed by sliding the blade between disc and utensil and placed in the salve box contact side up. The disc should be examined at 24-hour intervals since yeast or *Oospora lactis,* when present, develop rapidly but may be overgrown later with air-borne molds. A wide-field binocular microscope of the Greenough type, having a magnification of 20-30, has been found to be a useful aid in the examination.

Precautions should be taken at each step to insure freedom from contamination of agar core, ends of tube, and agar slice.

Wildman used this method in an investigation of relative abundance of *Oospora lactis* on utensils used in production of cream.

MOLDS IN BUTTER

Mold counts of butter have become an important part of laboratory control. High mold counts reveal unsatisfactory plant processing methods and sanitation. Hood [195] listed the main sources of molds as inefficient pasteurization and raw cream recontamination; dead ends in pipes; improperly cleaned and sterilized vats, pumps, pipes, and churns; impure water; improperly treated parchment linings; unseasoned butter boxes; and damp storage. Attention must be given to all of these if butter is to be produced with a low mold count. Cream may be a rich source of molds. Even though they are killed by pasteurization, the cream may be contaminated again or the butter contaminated during preparation for distribution.

Effect of Pasteurization of Cream on Molds. Mold spores are, in general, less resistant to heat than spores of other microorganisms. Thom and Ayers [196] were among the first to give serious study to the effect of pasteurization on molds in cream. They used spores from cultures of various molds, including several species of Penicillium, Aspergillus, and Mucors, with, in some experiments, the addition of *Oidium lactis* and one strain of Fusarium. These experiments were made to test the temperatures used in pasteurization by the holder process, and the effects of dry heat. In the holder process of pasteurization, in which milk was heated to from 48.9 to 65.6°C.(120 to 150°F.) and maintained at these temperatures for 30 minutes, the *Mucor racemosus* group and *Rhizopus nigricans*, which are found more frequently than all others of the Mucor group combined, were destroyed at 54.5°C.(130°F.); a few withstood 57.2°C.(135°F.), and two, one of them an undescribed soil organism, survived 60°C.(140°F.) for 30 minutes. Among species of Aspergillus, however, the strains of *Aspergillus flavus, Aspergillus fumigatus,* and *Aspergillus repens* all survived 62.8°C.

195. Hood. 1941. Canad. Dairy and Ice Cream J. 20, 29.
196. Thom and Ayers. 1916. J. Agr. Res. 6, 153-166.

(145°F.) for 30 minutes; and *Aspergillus repens* and *Aspergillus fumigatus* both survived 65.6°C.(150°F.). These three species are always found in forage and feeding stuffs; hence, milk is more or less subject to contamination with them. *Apergillus repens* grows very poorly in milk, however, and the examination of a great many cultures of milk and its products has shown that the actual development of *Aspergillus flavus* and *Aspergillus fumigatus* is comparatively rare. Pasteurization of milk at 62.8°C.(145°F.) may, therefore, be regarded as destroying mold spores completely enough to render them a negligible factor in the further changes found in the milk.

In the flash process of pasteurization, where milk was heated to from 62.8 to 79.4°C.(145 to 175°F.) for a period of 30 seconds, the spores of all the molds tested were destroyed with the exception of many spores of one form and occasional spores of three more forms. At 79.4°C.(175°F.) only occasional spores of two forms developed.

When the heating process was performed in dry air for a period of 30 seconds at 93.3°C.(200°F.), 31 out of 42 forms of Penicillium and seven out of 24 forms of Aspergillus were destroyed, but none of the cultures of the Mucors. A temperatures of 121.1°C.(250°F.) over a period of 30 minutes killed all the forms of Penicillium species tried, but left an occasional living spore in one species of Aspergillus and three out of six Mucors.

Careful study of the cultures showed that the first effect of heating was to delay germination. At times, heating to a degree just under the death point delayed germination almost the full length of the usual growing period of the species. There is, frequently, a survival of a few spores where a majority die. There may be, therefore, a difference of as much as 20°C. (36°F.) between the temperature at which an occasional culture is completely killed and that at which cultures of that species are uniformly killed. These results resemble those obtained in determining thermal-death point of bacteria. Macy and Combs [197] stated that in 40 per cent of the supposedly pasteurized cream, the mold has not been destroyed. Approximately 90 per cent of the dry parchment and cloth circles carried mold spores. Pipes, churns, pumps, liners, starter, and salt were important sources of mold contamination of butter.

The good effects of pasteurization may be offset in a large way if cream is contaminated afterwards by careless handling. Molds in Canadian butter made from pasteurized cream was attributed by Hood and White [198] to this. Unclean utensils played a role here. According to Lund,[199] butter made from unpasteurized cream may contain from 10 to 7,000 spores per ml. Spores of *Oidium lactis* were destroyed by exposure to 54.4°C.(130°F.) for 30 minutes. Lund, therefore, believed that the presence of these organisms could be used as an index of efficient pasteurization. Nicholls,[200] on the other hand, observed that *Oidium lactis* might survive pasteurization for short periods at 76.7°C.(170°F.). Results of investigations by Gibson and Tanner and Hofer, reported in Chapter 3, indicate that most strains

197. Macy and Combs. 1927. Minn. Agr. Expt. Sta. Bull. 235.
198. Hood and White. 1939. Canada Dept. Agr., Pub. 570, 1-21.
199. Lund. 1919. Dairymen's Assoc. Ontario, Ann. Rpt., 90-94.
200. Nicholls. 1919. Rev. in Abs. Bact. 4, 294.

would be destroyed by pasteurization as usually carried out. Lund [175] found less than 10 colonies of *Oidium lactis* in 63.5 per cent of Canadian and 70 per cent of Ontario butter made from pasteurized cream.

Significance of Molds in Butter. Presence of large numbers of molds in cream indicates bad handling. Should they grow to any extent bad flavors and odors result. Vandaveer and Wildman [201] associated high acidity of cream with a high mold-mycelium count; sweet cream or a good sour cream usually produced butter with a zero or low mold-mycelium count, while butter made from a high-acid cream almost invariably had a high mold count. This was considered to prove conclusively that decomposed or unfit cream was used. Macy [202] concurred in this opinion. The above discussion refers to mold spores which may develop into mycelia if the butter is not stored properly.

Adams and Parfitt [203] believed that mold-mycelia fragments in butter are an index of the length of time of storage, temperature of storage, and oxygen relationship of the cream from which the butter was made. Mold mycelia in butter is not an direct index of the organoleptic quality of the cream from which the butter was made. A higher percentage of mold mycelia than of bacteria is retained in the butter. In general, the retention is 20 to 30 per cent. Of the manufacturing operations studied none was found to influence significantly the mold-mycelia content of butter. Thom and Shaw [204] believed that the presence of the species Alternaria, Oidium, and Cladosporium indicated low salting. Excess of curd favored the development of molds; well-washed butter was less subject to development of mold. To prevent the development of molds, Thom and Shaw believed that butter should be carefully packed and stored under proper conditions.

Mold and yeast counts have been believed by some to be related to keeping quality of butter. Macy and Ritchie [205] found the relationship to be indefinite since counts of these microorganisms were not reliable indices of keeping quality under all conditions. Similar conclusions were reached by Vernon,[206] who observed only slightly better keeping quality of butter with low yeast and mold counts. Vernon believed that it was the activity of the mold which was important. Some molds grow in butter and produce products which affect quality, while others may be present only as viable spores and have no effect on quality. In the mold count both types receive equal emphasis. Vernon [206] believed, further, that an attempt might be made to learn something about the activities of molds in butter—whether they were lipolytic or caseolytic. The mold counts as determined today are indications of bad practice in handling cream and methods of making and handling the butter. Lower counts indicate good "housekeeping." Groth [207] gave moisture much significance and, therefore, sug-

201. Vandaveer and Wildman. 1940. J. Assoc. Off. Agr. Chem. 23, 263-709.
202. Macy. 1941. The Circle, 3-6.
203. Adams and Parfitt. 1939. J. Dairy Sci. 22, 367-374.
204. Thom and Shaw. 1915. J. Agr. Res. 3, 301-309.
205. Macy and Ritchie. 1929. J. Dairy Sci. 12, 351-366.
206. Vernon. 1937. Dairy Industries 2, 255-256.
207. Groth. 1937. Amer. Creamery and Poultry Prod. Rev., p. 702.

gested good ventilation and even drying of air in creameries. In addition attention should be given to many little things in the creamery, all of which are good practice under any conditions. *Oidium lactis* is a fungus prone to be prevalent in butter. Redfield [187] found it to be especially prevalent in low-grade butters. He believed the churn to be the source of the fungus. Samples of butter with lower yeast and mold counts keep a little better than those with higher counts (Vernon [208]). The count, however, may not be all that is involved. The activity of the fungus is just as important. Some molds grow in butter and produce products which cause bad odors and flavors while others have no effect on quality. Both types receive the same consideration in the mold count. Qualitative counts are fast receiving attention due them. The present yeast count is only an indication of plant methods.

Species of Molds Found in Butter. As would be expected these are quite varied and represent most of the common genera. Cream and butter pick up molds from every agent with which they come in contact. Various species have been identified by Boekhout and van Beyum,[209] Olson and Hammer,[210] and Grimes *et al.*[211]

Factors Involved in Mold Growth in Butter. These are several in number, such as salt content, hydrogen-ion concentration, presence of casein, and water content. Most of them have been investigated at one time or another. Development of *Penicillium glaucum* is stopped according to Voitkevitch [212] in nutritive media at 27 per cent concentration of sodium chloride and 83 per cent relative humidity, while a 12-per cent concentration of sodium chloride, and 92 per cent humidity have the same effect on *Oidium lactis*. The quantity of spores inoculated into butter does not affect the rapidity of their development; high humidity favors their development. Salting butter decreases the percentage but does not prevent the development of molds. High acidity of the butter correlates with increase of molds. An attempt was made by Thornton and Wood [213] to relate mold growth on the surface of butter to condensation moisture on the surface. They considered it improbable that mold growth started in incorporated moisture of salted and unsalted butter. *Cladosporium* sp. was isolated from butter showing interior type of molding.

Sources of Mold in Butter. Results of many investigations indicate that molds may reach butter from many different sources. Some have suggested that the mold content of butter might be accepted as the sole measure of its sanitary qualities, with which Wood and Thornton [214] disagreed.

Thorough sanitation seems to be the best solution of the mold problem. Macy and Combs,[197] Hood and White,[215] Macy and Ritchie,[205] and Macy [216]

208. Vernon. 1934. New Zeal. J. Sci. and Technol. 15, 237-247; Dairy Industries 2, 133-135; 255-256.
209. Boekhout and van Beyum. 1931. Rev. in Biol. Abs. 6 (1932), 1142.
210. Olson and Hammer. 1937. Iowa State Col. J. Sci. 11, 207-212.
211. Grimes *et al.* 1930. Sci. Proc. Roy. Dublin Soc. 19, 549-569.
212. Voitkevich. 1938. J. All-Russian Cong. Bot., Leningrad 201; Rev. in Biol. Abs. 5, 1749
213. Thornton and Wood. 1935. Canad. J. Res. 12, 295-305.
214. Wood and Thornton. 1935. Idem. 12, 286-294.
215. Hood and White. 1925. Canada Dept. Agr. Pamphlet 92, N 5, 15.
216. Macy. 1930. J. Dairy Sci. 13, 266-272.

supported this opinion. Mendelsohn, McCoy, and Long [217] believed that a mold-free butter could be made in a well-operated creamery.

Cream. This has been shown to be a fertile source of many of the molds in butter. Field surveys by Macy and Combs [107] revealed that raw cream is usually heavily contaminated with molds even though it may seem to be sweet and fresh. In 40 per cent of the supposedly pasteurized cream, molds had not been destroyed. About every article with which the cream comes in contact may contribute molds to it. Adams and Parfitt [203] also showed the close relationship which may exist between mold content of cream to mold content of the butter made from it. From 20 to 30 per cent of the mold mycelia in cream is retained in the butter.

Parchment Paper. This article has often been blamed, and probably rightfully in many cases, for surface defects, especially mold spots, of butter. Vernon [218] stated that surface taint of butter has been termed "parchment flavor" by some in trade circles. Although methods of manufacture should give a practically sterile paper, contamination during cutting, packing, and shipment is possible. Under proper conditions these molds may develop on the paper and infect butter wrapped in it. Should certain ingredients be incorporated in parchment for any purpose, growth of molds may be enhanced. Glycerol, according to Vernon, stimulates spore formation and is a good food for molds. Its hydroscopic nature assists development of molds and limits the value of low temperatures in repressing them. Glycerol-treated parchment molds sooner and to a greater extent than glycerol-free paper. Salt-softened parchment does not inhibit mold growth unless high concentration, not commercially possible, is used. Parchment treated with five or 10 per cent salt solution is attacked by some common molds more easily than untreated papers. Where parchment has been carefully studied, as it has been at the University of Minnesota by Macy [219] and his colleagues, it has been found to be a troublesome source of molds. In some of their experiments, butter produced under aseptic conditions was wrapped in contaminated and sterilized parchment. Part of it was stored at 12.8°C.(55°F.) and the remainder at 4.4°C.(40°F.). Some was also stored in moist stagnant air which greatly favored mold development. No molds appeared even after 90 days on the butter wrapped in treated parchment. Butter wrapped in untreated parchment molded in 48 to 70 days at 12.8°C.(55°F.) and in 60 to 90 days at 4.4°C.(40°F.). The parchment became contaminated from dust and careless handling. Attempts to solve this problem in the early days involved boiling in water for 10 minutes or a brine containing three to five pounds of salt per gallon. The paper was then left in this container until used. Reports of exhaustive experiments were reported a year later by Macy and Pulkrabek.[220] The treatment just recommended was enlarged upon and other methods involving use of chemicals were discussed. It was apparently

217. Mendelsohn, McCoy, and Long. 1922. J. Lab. and Clin. Med. 7, 208-214.
218. Vernon. 1936. Dairy Industries 1, 125-126.
219. Macy. 1927. Creamery and Milk Plant Mo. 16, 38, 40.
220. Macy and Pulkrabek. 1928. Minn. Agr. Expt. Sta. Bull. 242.

more difficult to control surface molding when the butter itself was the source of the fungi.

Macy and Olson [221] reported marked inhibition of molds on butter deliberately contaminated with mold spores by wrapping in parchment paper which had been treated with sodium or calcium propionate. The inhibition was much more pronounced with salted butter. Parchment is now available for this purpose. One is known as "Mycoban," treated parchment containing six per cent of calcium propionate on the basis of the dry weight of the paper. Creameries also treat paper to be used for lining tubs. Vast amounts of butter are packed today in such paper.

Butter Boxes. These are wooden boxes used for butter in bulk. They are subject to attack by molds, for the wood holds moisture and may even become saturated with various substances which molds like and need in their metabolism. Vernon [222] recognized these boxes as important sources of molds.

The most important source of infection is thought to be the condensation water accumulating in boxes of butter after removal from cold storage. As a rule, the temperature conditions obtaining in transport and storage are sufficiently low to prevent fungal development, but on removal from storage after four months the molds are capable of almost immediate resumption of growth. Glycerine and salt are frequently used to treat parchment wrappers for Australian and Danish butters, respectively; both were found (contrary to expectation in the case of salt) to increase susceptibility to mold infection. Experiments carried out in New Zealand by Riddet and Neill [223] showed that molds (*Pullilaria pullulans, Cladosporium herbarum, Penicillium expansum, Mucor* sp., and a red-staining type) originating in butter boxes may infect the surface layer of butter packed therein and cause extensive damage. Mold growth on the boxes was stimulated by defrosting the butter at high atmospheric temperature in air of high humidity, by admitting air to the inner surface of the box, and by the use of sapwood in place of heartwood and of rotary-cut instead of sawed wood. The "springing" of the sides away from the ends of boxes during handling and the consequent admission of air stimulated mold growth. Swedish pine impregnated with wax was less susceptible than white pine, but imparted a taint to the butter. Immersion of the wood in .1 per cent sodium salicylanilide solution for 10 minutes gave very promising results in preventing infection.

Churn. The churn has been found to be a prolific source of molds and other microorganisms if it is not thoroughly and properly cleaned. Observations were made on two churns by Macy, Combs, and Morrison,[224] one of which had been used for 10 years in a creamery where considerable difficulty with mold had been experienced and the other in the experiment station creamery where it had been in daily use for seven years. A large

221. Macy and Olson. 1939. J. Dairy Sci. 22, 527-534.
222. Vernon. 1936. Dairy Industries 1, 56-58.
223. Riddet and Neill. 1936. New Zeal. J. Agr. 53, 129-139.
224. Macy, Combs, and Morrison. 1931. J. Dairy Sci. 14, 398-403.
225. Morrison, Macy, and Combs. 1931. Idem, 404-415.

number of samples collected from the first churn showed the presence of many molds and a wide variety of species while those from the second churn were relatively free from molds; those which were found were members of only five genera. Having determined this situation, Morrison, Macy, and Combs studied procedures for removing them from churns. Steam and hot water when used regularly were found to yield satisfactory conditions. Little success was secured with such disinfectants as sodium hypochlorite, alkaline crystalline hypochlorite, and chloramine-T. The same conditions in churns were observed by Olson and Hammer.[193] Wide variation in their microbiological condition existed with bacteria usually more numerous than yeasts and molds. Striking reductions in number of microorganisms were accomplished with hot water. Yeasts and molds were largely eliminated. Solutions of sodium hypochlorite and chloramine preparations seemed to be less satisfactory. Bendixen[226] found that quite stringent methods had to be used to rid churns of molds. Chemical disinfectants cannot be added to butter but may be used on utensils.

Water and salt are other agents which may contribute molds to butter. Mold spores are ubiquitous and may easily be picked up by water. Unless salt is handled in a cleanly manner, it may harbor large numbers of mold spores. It should not be stored in bulk on the floor as it once was in many preservation plants. Sweepings and dust contribute various microorganisms in large numbers.

Prevention and Control of Molds in Butter. Damaging outbreaks of moldy butter have prompted many investigations as to cause and means of prevention. The investigations of Hood and White[198] revealed two possible methods of preventing moldy butter: (1) preventing ingress of molds into butter during manufacturing and (2) preventing development in case they have entered. Among those who early emphasized the need of strict cleanliness in the creamery was Hastings.[227] Practically all who have worked on this problem have stressed strict sanitation as the bacteriologist defines it.

Various investigators have reported that salt may be used to inhibit molds in butter. Thom and Shaw[204] stated that species of Oidium, Alternaria, and Cladosporium cannot develop in butter containing 2.5 per cent of salt. Consequently, they believe that occurrence of any of these forms in butter meant low salting. About the same species were reported by Morgan[228] in unsalted butter. They observed germination of spores, however, in much more concentrated salt solutions than others have reported. Distinction should be made between concentrations of salt in butter and in brine. Mold spores may be exposed to fairly high concentrations of salt in butter because it concentrates in the water phase only. Development of *Penicillium glaucum* occurred in Voitkevich's[212] experiments at 27 per cent concentration of salt and 83 per cent relative humidity, while 12 per cent concentration and 92 per cent relative humidity had the same effect

226. Bendixen. 1937. J. Dairy Sci. 20, 15-25.
227. Hastings. 1916. Wis. Buttermakers' Assoc. Proc. 16, 145-152; Creamery and Milk Plant Mo. 9, 34-37.
228. Morgan. 1929. New Zeal. J. Agr. 39, 38-46, *et seq.*

on *Oidium lactis*. Salting of butter reduced mold growth but did not prevent it. High humidity was a factor which favored it.

METHODS FOR DETERMINING MOLDS IN BUTTER

Examination of butter for molds may involve either cultural methods for actually enumerating the living fungi which are present in examination of the butter for mold mycelia. Mere presence of molds which will develop in culture media and on plates may not have much significance unless they are present in large numbers or possess most undesirable characteristics which will affect the color and flavor. Examination for mold hyphae is usually a microscope technic based largely on the Howard method for demonstrating molds in tomato products. Results of this examination tell whether the cream and butter have been mishandled either by being held at too high temperatures, held in dusty creameries, handled in unclean apparatus, or wrapped in mold-infested parchment. Other factors may also be involved. The Howard method reveals the presence of mold filaments which have resulted from careless practices. Some of the other methods tell whether mold spores are present which may develop into hyphae.

Johns' [162] **Method for Determining Mold and Yeast Count of Butter.** This method is an adaptation of the Frost little-plate method for determining the number of bacteria in milk as described on page 354. After considerable preliminary work, Johns gave the following detailed description of technic:

Samples of butter are obtained by drawing three or four plugs with a sterile trier discarding the top one-half inch in each case, and transferring the remainder to a sterile sample jar. Jars are set in a water bath at 40-45°C.(104-113°F.) until melted. When completely melted, sample is shaken vigorously for 30 seconds, and a 10-ml. portion withdrawn with a sterile warmed pipette. After removing the butter from the outside of the pipette with a sterile cloth or paper, the contents are delivered into a dilution bottle containing 40 ml. of sterile water warmed to 45°C.(113°F.). (A 250-ml. Erlenmeyer flask may be substituted for a dilution bottle; or two ml. of butter may be added to eight ml. of water in a 16 × 150 mm. test tube. These substitutes are less convenient for shaking and mixing.)

While the samples are melting, an area of two by four cm. is marked out upon clean microscope slides with a wax pencil. A small metal box or tank, insulated upon the sides and bottom, is filled with water at 45°C.(113°F.); this is used as a "warm table" to prevent hardening of the agar medium before it can be mixed with the diluted butter being plated. A tube of previously melted wort agar acidified with sterile lactic acid to pH 3.5 to 4.0 is placed in the water through a hole in the top of the warm table, to maintain the proper temperature.

Duplicate slides are flamed and placed upon the surface of the warm table. The dilution bottle is shaken vigorously for 30 seconds, and a one-ml. pipette, graduated in tenths, filled to the upper graduation. After wiping off the exterior with a sterile cloth or paper, .2 ml. is delivered on to the marked area of each slide. Four drops of agar are added to each, thoroughly mixed with the diluted butter, and spread evenly over the area with a sterile needle. The microplates are removed to a cold level surface and covered to protect them from air contamination while hardening. When hardened they are transferred to a sterile moist chamber for incubation. (A convenient form of moist chamber is listed by the Central Scientific Co. for milk analysis with the Frost technique.) An incubation period of 12 to 18 hours at 25°C.(77°F.) has been found most suitable, and fits in well with ordinary laboratory routine. Where a shorter period must be used, it is advisable to raise the temperature to 30°C.(86°F.); conversely, with a period in excess of 18 hours, a lower temperature is desirable.

At the conclusion of the incubation period the microplates are removed and "dried down" upon a metal sheet placed over boiling water. This should take between five and 10 minutes. When dried the microplates are immersed in a thionin solution made up as follows:

Thionin—1 gram
Carbolic acid—2½ grams
Distilled water—400 ml.

Filter, and add five per cent of glacial acetic acid. No preparatory fixation is necessary, as the acid in the solution prevents the agar from staining too deeply. Slides are stained for three minutes, then carefully washed, dried, and examined under the 16 mm. objective. The microscope should be so adjusted that the area of the field with this objective will be 2 mm². The technique described enables counts up to 50,000 molds and 1,000,000 yeasts per ml. to be obtained from 1.5 dilution.

COUNTING OF COLONIES

With the majority of samples analyzed, the counting of 20 fields on the microplate gives sufficient accuracy for routine work, where rapidity and convenience are more important than extreme accuracy. Tests, where various numbers of fields have been counted, have rarely shown any significant change through the counting of more than 20 fields. The case of low-count butter provides an exception; here it is advisable to increase the number to 40. Also should the yeast count exceed 50 colonies per field, the counting of 10 fields will suffice. After a rapid preliminary survey to determine the evenness of distribution of the colonies, 20 representative fields are counted, preferably with the aid of a mechanical stage. Counts on duplicate microplates are then averaged, and molds and yeasts per ml. of butter calculated from the formula.

$$\frac{A}{B} \times X \times Y \times Z = N$$

where   A = number of colonies observed
B = number of fields counted
X = reciprocal of dilution
Y = reciprocal of quantity plated
Z = microscopic factor
N = number of molds (or yeasts) per ml.

For example, if the average of duplicate microplates showed 10 molds and 30 yeasts on 20 fields we would have

$10/20 \times 5 \times 5 \times 400 = 5,000$ molds per ml.
$30/20 \times 5 \times 5 \times 400 = 15,000$ yeasts per ml.

This calculation can be greatly simplified by determining the number of molds (or yeasts) per field $\dfrac{(A)}{B}$ and multiplying by 10,000 $(X \times Y \times Z)$ to obtain the number per ml. of butter (N). Where 40 fields are counted, the lower limit is $< 1/40 \times 5 \times 5 \times 400 = \, < 250$ per ml.

This lower limit could be reduced to < 125 ml. by employing an ocular which would give a field with a diameter of 2.25 mm. One was not available for the work reported here, but there seems no reason why it should not prove satisfactory.

Johns found that mold counts obtained by the Frost little-plate method were about twice as great as those obtained by the standard-plate method.

Shutt's [186] **Method for Determining Molds in Butter.** This procedure was submitted to the author in a personal communication. The apparatus required is the same as listed for determination of yeasts in butter.

Sampling. With a well-boiled and cooled butter iron remove a plug of butter from the print or solid and transfer the plug, less the top half-inch, to a sterile jar. If sample must be held it must be kept in cold storage not longer than 36 hours.

Method of Analysis. Place the water blanks and the samples of butter in a warming chamber at 41°C.(105.8°F.) until the water blanks are warm and the butter is melted. Shake the butter well.

Transfer 10 ml. of the melted butter, with a warmed pipette, to a 90-ml. water blank and shake 25 times. Make further dilutions if required.

Transfer one ml. of each dilution, including the original butter, to Petri plates and pour with acidified malt extract agar.

Incubate all plates at. 25°C.(77°F.) for two to four days.

Count all mold colonies as follows:

Number of Oidium colonies

Number of Penicillium colonies

Number of miscellaneous mold colonies.

Mold Mycelia in Butter. Food-control officials have long wanted a method which would indicate whether or not butter had been made from cream which was unfit. Many believe that this need has been filled by a method which involves determining the number of mold mycelia in butter. An investigation by Vandaveer and Wildman [201] on the significance of mold mycelia in butter churned from cream of known histories resulted in the following conclusions: (1) Decomposition flavor characteristics occur when cream is exposed to adverse conditions of time, temperature, and sanitation. (2) The presence and growth of molds in cream are associated with the development of decomposition flavor characteristics. (3) There is a correlation between mold mycelia content of butter and the acidity of the cream from which it is churned; sweet cream or good sour cream produces a butter of a zero or a very low mycelia count, while butter made from high-acid cream almost invariably has a high mold-mycelia count. (4) A high mold-mycelia count in butter shows conclusively that decomposed or unfit cream was used.

Wildman's [231] Microscope Method for Estimation of Mold in Butter. Wildman's technic resulted from an extended study of the problem. In the first experiments the butter was heated and the fat removed by decantation. To the remaining curd and serum sufficient 50 per cent glycerol solution was added to bring the volume back to that of the original butter used, after which a drop of the thoroughly mixed sample was mounted on a Howard counting chamber and the mold filaments counted as in the Howard method for tomato products. Necessity of long manipulation to remove the fat was eliminated by use of gasoline. At this stage certain samples of butter showed numerous mold filaments in all fields. To reveal any significant differences between samples, it was necessary to dilute the serum-glycerol mixture with seven parts of glycerol solution. It was unnecessary to remove the fat in this case because the globules were so diluted that they did not interfere. Finally, a gum solution was substituted for the glycerol. Wildman stated the method as follows:

EQUIPMENT AND REAGENTS

(a) Measuring spoon—¼ teaspoon.

(b) Pipette—10 ml.

(c) Gum solution—Make up one liter of a .75 per cent solution of carob bean gum with two per cent of added formaldehyde as a preservative. Use the clear supernatant solution, free from cells, left when the cellular elements in the gum gradually settle out. (A similar solution made with gum tragacanth may also be used for this purpose.)

229. White and Hood. 1931. J. Dairy Sci. 14, 463-476.

230. Clerkin. 1929. Dept. Agr. J. (Dublin) 28, 199-207.

231. Wildman. 1937. J. Assoc. Off. Agr. Chem. 20, 93-100.

PROCEDURE

Weigh out one gram of butter by means of the one-fourth teaspoon measure. Measure out seven ml. of hot gum solution and, with the spoon bottom side up over a 50 ml. beaker, pour two or three ml. of the hot solution over the spoon. (This quantity is usually sufficient to loosen the butter and cause it to slide into the beaker.) Use the remainder of the seven ml. of solution to rinse the remaining fat from the spoon.

Stir until the solution is well mixed and fat globules are .1-.2 mm. in diameter. The stirring necessary to obtain a uniform sample must be determined by experience.)

Mount a portion of the mixture on the mold-counting slide and estimate the mold by the Howard method. Report no field as positive unless the combined length of the two longest filaments exceeds one-sixth of the diameter of the field.

For applying this method to cream, Wildman first churned it, and used the above method. Since a small sample of butter is used, the question naturally arose as to whether a single sample could be representative of the total amount of butter in the churn. Investigation of this indicated that the results were close on various samples, indicating that molds were evenly distributed in a churn.

Wildman [232] later reported that a stain was not necessary for detecting presence of mold filaments when proper illumination was obtained. In certain cases addition of one or two drops of a five-per cent solution of crystal violet to the gum-butter mixture, if the butter is melted, was helpful. Wildman called attention to the possibility that carob bean gum and gum tragacanth might be impossible to secure. Study was being given to the possibility of using pectin and algin solutions but official recommendations were not made because further investigations were necessary. Prevention of mold growth in stored samples was prevented by a saturated atmosphere of formaldehyde. Disks of filter paper saturated with formaldehyde were fastened in the lids of the sample jars.

If mold counts are to be made on butter as an index of undesirable conditions in manufacture, much control work must be done to determine the incidence of these fungi in commercial butter. Wildman [232] examined 65 samples taken at random. These samples were said to represent an accurate cross section of the butter market. He also counted the molds in 53 samples that were taken from lots seized for mold or filth. It was found that the bulk of the seizure samples contained from 50 to 90 per cent while the bulk of the random samples varied from 0 to 30 per cent.

Mold Count Standards. If the laboratory examination of butter is to include examination for molds with approved or standard methods, some standards must be available with which to judge quality. Hood [195] suggested that pasteurized butter should contain less than 25,000 bacteria and less than a total of 50 molds and yeasts.

Sediment in Butter. This has become an important subject in view of the position taken by the United States Food and Drug Administration toward foreign matter in butter. Both cream and butter are being scru-

232. Wildman. 1937. J. Assn. Off. Agr. Chem. 20, 468; 25 (1942), 609.

tinized carefully for such matter. Parfitt [233] pointed out some of the difficulties when sediment tests are made on cream and butter. Such foreign matter in cream indicates carelessness on the part of the producer. Parfitt could find no relation between the amount or kind of sediment in butter and the number of living yeasts and molds.

The sediment test has been thoroughly investigated by a Research Committee of the American Butter Institute [234] and found to be satisfactory for cream and butter. The American Butter Institute has adopted the Connecticut Official Milk Sediment Standards for interpreting results of sediment tests applied to cream and butter.

Parfitt's [233] Method for Determining Sediment in Cream and Butter. *Using Lintine Disks*—Weigh into a 400-ml. beaker 100 gm. ± .1 gm. of the butter to be examined. Add 200 ml. of .03 to .05 N. hydrochloric acid. Heat the mixture over a water bath to 74°C.(165.2°F.), stirring thoroughly to insure complete mixing. Run through a milk sediment tester. Rinse out the tester with at least 120 ml. of 83°C.(181.4°F.) filtered water. Mount and examine the soiled lintine disk.

Using Filter Papers (Horrall)—Weigh into a 400-ml. beaker 100 gm. ± .1 gm. of the butter to be examined. Add 150 ml. of .03 normal hydrochloric acid (3.2 ml. of 35-37 per cent hydrochloric acid diluted to 1 liter with distilled water) and place this mixture in an 83°C. water bath. Heat until butter is melted. Stir the mixture but once and let it stand until the milk fat rises. Place the filter paper (Max Dreverhoff No. 86, or equivalent) in a seven-cm. Buchner funnel containing a 50-mesh copper screen (diameter of which is slightly less than the series of holes in the funnel), seal the paper by suction, and warm the funnel with distilled water at 83°C. After sealing, pour the prepared samples of butter very slowly on to the paper, permitting the fat to pour on to the filter paper first. If the filter clogs, pour distilled water at about 83°C. slowly on the paper until it filters freely; repeat this if necessary until the sample is filtered, then wash the beaker, funnel, and paper free from fat using hot distilled water. With a pair of tweezers place the filter paper in a Petri dish, or similar container, to prevent contamination.

Greene's [235] Method for Determination of Extraneous Material in Butter. Various types of foreign matter may reach butter if it is not carefully handled during manufacture. Greene (1935) devised a method which has been of value in detecting the presence of filth in form of insects and other extraneous materials in butter.

Method. Weigh out 100 grams of the butter from each sub-division in a 400-ml. beaker. To this add 150 to 200 ml. of borax solution made by dissolving 40 grams of borax in one liter of water (stronger alkaline solutions must not be used as they are destructive to hair). Heat on electric hot plate to boiling. Filter at once through a seven-cm. Buchner suction funnel equipped with a rapid filter paper, wash the paper with gasoline to remove any remaining grease and then with hot water. When a butter contains mold, either finely divided or in clumps, it may close the pores of the paper so that as many as 10 separate papers are required in extremely moldy butter to filter one sample.

After investigating brands of filter paper supplied by different dealers and manufacturers, the most efficient found was No. 86, seven cm., made by Max Dreverhoff and supplied by Heil Corp., 210 S. 4th St., St. Louis, Mo. As an aid in filtering, a circle of copper screen, 50 mesh, is cut about 6.5 cm. in diameter and fashioned to lie in the bottom of the funnel. The paper is then placed over this making sure that the paper and screen are centered to make a tight seal and not allow any material to pass under around the edges. The paper may be moistened with water to hold it in place before pouring the butter solution into the funnel.

233. Parfitt. 1937. Amer. J. Pub. Health 27, 341-345.
234. Parfitt (Chairman). 1938. J. Milk Tech. 1, 44-47; (Aug. 1937, issue of J. Dairy Science has the complete report).
235. Greene. 1935. Food Industries. Sept. 1935.

By the above described method, the curd is changed by the borax solution into a soluble caseinate and therefore all of it readily passes through, leaving no deposit on the filter paper. When mold is present in the butter, it is retained on the filter paper either in a finely divided condition or in large clumps which sometimes resemble undissolved curd, but if this material is scraped off, placed on a microscope slide with a drop of oil or glycerine, and pressed out quite thin, the mold filaments may be seen. An estimation is made of the total square area that would be occupied by the mold clumps if they were all moved in together. Search should be made of the sides of the Buchner funnel to insure that no mold, insects, or other foreign material has been retained there. In connection with distinguishing the material as mold, the analyst must bear in mind the distinguishing characteristics between mold and paper since occasionally fragments of the latter have been found.

Attention is called to the fact that in those cases where a slimy residue is recovered on the filter papers which is suggestive of mold, it is our practice to always verify this by making examinations of a small portion of the substance under a compound microscope. This caution is observed because it has sometimes been found that such residues are in the main composed of curd with but little mold present. The reason for this variation in different samples we have not yet been able to answer to our full satisfaction, but the fact remains and this method of verification has been followed to avoid erring on such a condition.

The filter paper is examined with a wide-field binocular microscope. with lenses giving a magnification of approximately 15-20 X. A lower magnification may be used to find larvae but the 20 X is recommended for other material. Hairs, fragments of insects, and other contaminants except mold are removed with a needle, placed in a drop of glycerine on a slide, and covered with a cover glass for further examination.

Margarine. This is not strictly a dairy product, but on account of its close relation to butter and the fact certain dairy products are used in its manufacture, brief mention may be made of it.

Two quite distinct types of margarine are made in America; one is prepared from animal fats and perhaps is more commonly known as "oleo" while the other is prepared from certain vegetable oils and known as "nut margarine." These artificial butter substitutes are prepared in somewhat the same manner. They consist of soft oils and hard oils which are crystallized after careful purification. These oils are mixed in the proper proportions in churns where they are churned from 15 to 20 minutes. Longer churning gives a higher grade product. After churning, the batch is crystallized by means of cold-water spray or other methods, and conducted to vats where it is allowed to stand at a constant temperature to ripen. This ripening produces a better flavor. When the flavor has been sufficiently developed in the ripening process, the margarine is thoroughly worked on kneading tables to adjust the water content and also bleach the product. It is sold in packages and in bulk.

That rancidity of margarine is due to microorganisms seems very probable (Jacobson [236]). The use of rancid cocoanut oil may cause rancid margarine, but this is not the sole explanation. If the oil or margarine contains small amounts of water, molds may develop and bring about undesirable changes. *Penicillium glaucum* has been found in rancid margarine, also Aspergillus sp. Margarine keeps when sufficient salt is used to make a brine in each water droplet. Other preservatives will also cause

236. Jacobson. 1913. Folia Microbiol. 5, 94-102.

the margarine to keep. Stokoe [237] did not believe that bacteria played any role in rancidity of water-free fats. A culture of an organism from rancid margarine was inoculated into many fats and oils. After 14 days, there was only the slightest increase in free fatty acids. Stokoe divided rancidity of margarine into three groups:

1. Fats becoming rancid with tallowy flavor and odor without change of color caused, like tallowness of butter, by an oxidation process. According to the views of the English chemists, the glycerin which is first split off is oxidized to glyceric acid.

2. Rancid fat with aromatic but not disagreeable odor but with an offensive taste. These occur only in margarine that contains cocoa fat or palm oil, and consequently, is not observed in butter. This type of rancidity is caused by *Penicillium glaucum*. Ketones are the volatile substances produced.

3. Rancid fats with a change in the color and small change in the odor and flavor. The changes observed are (1) gray or blue-black coloring caused by Aspergillus species; (2) red coloration by *Serratia marcescens (Bacillus prodigiosus.)*

Fresh, well-prepared margarine, according to Hoffmann, contains principally lactic acid bacteria of the diplococcus type, since milk is used in its preparation. If milk which has become too sour is used, the long-chain streptococci will predominate. This prevents the production of the delicate butter flavor. The more water present in the margarine, the less the keeping qualities.

Great variety was found by Horovitz-Vlasova *et al.*[238] in the bacterial flora of margarine in addition to the acid-forming organisms introduced in the milk. There are bacteria and fungi coming from the air or the wrapper and capable of causing spoilage. Scrupulous cleanliness in manufacturing is essential to good keeping quality in margarine; experiments show that, like butter, it is stable for weeks or even months to pure cultures of the lactic organisms but quickly becomes rancid if contaminated with Pencillium, Oidium, or *Bacillus fluorescens liquefaciens* since neither prior acidification, salting, nor cold storage is sufficient to stop the growth of these fungi. Oxidative spoilage, causing a tallowy consistency, is accelerated by air, light, and moisture; hence margarine should be well pressed, wrapped in good parchment paper, packed in fungus-free tubes, and kept in a scrupulously clean room. Margarine made with soybean milk instead of cow milk shows the same behavior. Diacetyl is recommended for imparting butter aroma.

Margarine should be free from pathogenic bacteria since it is made from safe raw materials. No tuberculosis organisms in 150 samples of margarine were found by Eber.[239] Presence of tubercle bacilli in this product would not be probable.

A fungus causing spoilage of margarine, to which the name of *Marginomyces bubaki* was given, was reported by Laxa.[240] This fungus caused greenish-black spots in the margarine. The fungus could be controlled by more careful methods of manufacture.

237. Stokoe. 1921. Chem. Umschau 28, 132.
238. Horobitz-Vlasova *et al.* 1932. Schriftenzentbl. biochem. Forschungsinst. Nahr.—Genussmtl. 2, 303-311.
239. Eber. 1908. Wiener Klin. Wchnschr. 21, 1203.
240. Laxa. 1930. Centbl. Bakt., Pt. 2, 81, 392-396.

REFERENCE BOOKS

GUTHRIE, E. S., 1923. The Book of Butter, a Text on the Nature, Manufacture, and Marketing of the Product. The Macmillan Co., New York, N. Y.

HUNZIKER, O. F., 1940. The Butter Industry. Published by the author, La Grange, Ill.

TOTMAN, C. C., McKAY, G. L., AND LARSEN, C., 1939. Butter. John Wiley and Sons, Inc., New York, N. Y.

CHAPTER 9

MICROBIOLOGY OF CHEESE

In the United States the term "cheese" unqualified is generally understood to mean Cheddar cheese, American cheese or American Cheddar cheese. Many other kinds are known, some of which, formerly imported, are now made in large amounts in the United States. According to Doane and Lawson,[1] there are probably 18 distinct varieties of cheese known under some 400 different names. These are usually of local origin and bear names of towns or communities.

Cheese may also be classified in other ways. Rennin curd cheeses are made from curd secured by the action of rennin while acid curd cheeses are secured by the artificial or natural souring of milk. Those who are interested in a discussion of the hundreds of varieties of cheese may consult the bulletin by Doane and Lawson,[1] who remarked that attempts to classify cheeses have usually been unsatisfactory. Some of the international problems of cheese nomenclature have been discussed by Swaving[2] and Porcher.[3]

The Food and Drug Administration in accordance with provisions in the Food, Drug, and Cosmetic Act of 1938[4] defined Cheddar cheese as cheese made from cow's milk containing not more than 39 per cent of moisture, and its solids containing not less than 50 per cent of milk fat. The rest of the definition concerns its method of manufacture.

Pasteurization of Milk for Cheese Making. Differences of opinion exist over the question whether cheese can be made from pasteurized milk. Pasteurization should have the same functions here that it has for other dairy products. It should improve the quality of cheese by eliminating defects caused by undesirable microorganisms in raw milk. Furthermore it should make cheese safer by destroying pathogenic bacteria in the milk, should they be present. Cheese from raw milk, in Lane and Hammer's[5] experiments, was better in both quality and texture. Their work involved cheese made from raw milk, from pasteurized milk, and from a mixed milk composed of 90 per cent pasteurized and 10 per cent raw. Raw-milk cheese had good flavor while pasteurized-milk cheese had a tough, rubbery texture. Some of the cheeses in their experiments were inoculated with *Lactobacillus casei*, certain strains of which, when added to pasteurized milk used for making Cheddar cheese, had a desirable effect on protein decomposition, flavor, and uniformity of cheese. For Swiss cheese, Babel and Hammer[6] found it desirable to add propionic acid-forming bacteria to pasteurized milk to secure good flavor and eye formation. Price[7] believed that all

1. Doane and Lawson. 1932. U. S. Dept. Agr. Bull. 608.
2. Swaving. 1923. Proc. World's Dairy Cong. 2, 760-61.
3. Porcher. 1923. Proc. World's Dairy Cong. 2, 762-764.
4. Federal Register, Jan. 9, 1942.
5. Lane and Hammer. 1935. Iowa Agr. Expt. Sta., Res. Bull. 183.
6. Babel and Hammer. 1939. Iowa Agr. Exp. Sta., Res. Bull. 264.
7. Price. 1938. Natl. Butter and Cheese J. 29, 16 *et seq.*

of the more common types of cheese made in the United States could be
made from pasteurized milk with the exception of Swiss.

Pasteurization in Phillips'[8] experiments improved the quality of cheese
made from poor milk but had little effect on cheese made from good milk.
Pasteurizing gassy milk at 80°C.(176°F.) produced better cheese than
if raw milk had been used. Here is an instance when undesirable bacteria
were destroyed. Murray[9] had previously reported the same experience.

The other aspects of this subject concern health hazards of cheese made
from raw milk. While it is probably not as true today as formerly, raw
milk may contain *Mycobacterium tuberculosis*, an organism which may live
for many months in cheese. Other pathogenic bacteria, such as *Eberthella
typhosa*,[10] have also been found. The fact that pasteurization makes cheese
safe would be a strong argument in its favor. *Standards of Identity for
Cheddar Chesee*[4] states that milk from which it is made *may* be pasteurized.
This important public-health effort is left as optional, even though epidemics of typhoid fever and undulant fever have been traced indisputably to
cheese.

Phosphatase Test Applied to Cheese. This test for adequate pasteurization was applied to cheese by Scharer.[11] On account of the acidity and
high protein content of cheese, the sample should be neutralized and diluted
as follows: Triturate 20 gm. of cheese in 20 ml. of the buffer and 20 ml. of
water. Use a one-ml. portion and proceed as for milk. Scharer detected the
enzyme after 18 months' storage with undiminished activity in cheese made
from raw milk. It was absent in cheese made from milk pasteurized by
both "holder" and high temperature-short time methods. Pasteurized,
processed, packaged cheese was, in general, negative for phosphatase. Other
types of cheese were frequently positive. Presence of the enzyme phosphatase in cheese was believed by Sharer to indicate use of raw or improperly
pasteurized milk or cream.

Cheddar Cheese. This cheese derives its name from the village in England where it was first made. In the United States it is called American
cheese and is probably the most popular variety. More has been written
about the role of microorganisms in preparation of this cheese than any
other variety.

Ripening of Cheddar Cheese. By means of this process Cheddar cheese
acquires those characteristics by which it is so well known. The most important agents are bacteria with, perhaps, milk enzymes having small part.
It is a complicated process, as Davis[12] has shown. Some of the early
investigators attributed a role in the ripening process to enzymes from the
cow also.

Many investigations have been carried out to determine the influence
of various factors on the activities of bacteria. The bacteriological aspects

8. Phillips. 1928. J. Dairy Sci. 11, 292-298.
9. Murray. 1923. Agr. Gaz. N. S. Wales 34, 559-566.
10. Tanner, F. W. 1932. Food Borne Infections and Intoxications. Garrard Press, Cham
paign, Ill.
11. Scharer. 1939 J. Milk Tech. 2, 18.
12. Davis. 1935. Chem. and Ind. 54, 631-635.

of the subject were reviewed by Hucker.[13] Several different explanations have been given to explain the appearance of the characteristic flavor. Baier [14] did not connect any specific bacterium with cheese ripening, while Orla-Jensen [15] attributed it to the action of the enzyme casease, very similar to tryptase. Studies by Shirokih [16] on products formed by bacteria in milk caused him to believe that the peptonizing bacteria played an important role in cheese ripening. One does not read the literature of the subject long before encountering the name of Freudenreich.[17] From extensive experiments reported in 1897, he stated that lactic acid-producing organisms were important, for cheese would not ripen when liquefying bacteria were used alone. Weigmann [18] denied the statements of Freudenreich; he did admit, however, that they played an indirect role in providing an acid medium. Freudenreich [19] replied to Weigmann's criticisms and explained the controversy on the ground that he had used hard cheese, while Weigmann used soft cheese. Weigmann reported more data which seemed to show that cheese ripening was a symbiotic phenomenon in which a number of different types of bacteria played a role. This opinion was based on data secured from experiments with Titsler cheese. Harrison [20] and Chodat and Hofman-Bang,[21] in general, believed that lactic acid bacteria were of indirect importance, and that they did not have the importance with Freudenreich attributed to them. The latter believed that ripening was due to the digestive action of rennin in the presence of acid.

Harding [22] also carried out some experiments to determine whether lactic acid bacteria played a role in ripening of Cheddar cheese. In the introduction of his bulletin, brief explanations are given concerning three theories of cheese ripening: (1) that ripening is due, mainly, if not entirely, to lactic acid bacteria; (2) that ripening is brought about by liquefying bacteria; and (3) that the breaking down of the casein is largely due to the enzymes naturally present in milk. In factory milk lactic acid bacteria were said to be always present, and at the time of souring commonly make up more than 95 per cent of the total number. The rapid development of the lactic acid bacteria checks the growth of other species, owing to the conversion of milk sugar into lactic acid. The action of this acid has been found in practice, and shown experimentally, to hasten the curdling action of rennin. Investigations have shown that lactic acid combines with paracasein to form two salts, one the unsaturated paracasein monolactate, insoluble in water but soluble in dilute salt solutions, and the other the saturated paracasein di-lactate, insoluble in both water and dilute salt solutions. That paracasein monolactate was formed in cheese curd by lactic acid bacteria was shown experimentally as follows:

13. Hucker. 1921. Abs. Bact. 5, 287-303.
14. Baier. 1897. Milch. Ztg. 26, 177-179.
15. Orla-Jensen. 1897. Exp. Sta. Rec. 9, 289-290.
16. Shirokih. 1896. Selsk. Kroz. Lyesov. 98, 263-288.
17. Freudenreich. 1897. Centbl. Bakt., Pt. 2, 3, 47-54.
18. Weigmann. 1898. Landw. Vers. Sta. 51, 1-14.
19. Freudenreich. 1899. Centbl. Bakt., Pt. 2, 5.
20. Harrison. 1901. Trans. Canadian Inst. 7, 103-134.
21. Chodat and Hofman-Bang. 1901. Ann. Inst. Pasteur 15, 36-48.
22. Harding. 1903. N. Y. Agr. Expt. Sta. Bull. 237.

Fresh milk was curdled by rennin in the presence of ether to prevent bacterial growth, and the curd was washed with water to remove the greater part of the sugar. After sterilization, portions of the curd were inoculated with lactic acid bacteria, with and without the addition of sugar. Without the addition of sugar, only very small quantities of paracasein monolactate were formed, while with the addition of sugar considerable amounts were produced. In normal cheese during the first week after it is made, it was stated that from one-half to three-fourths of the nitrogen was found in the form of paracasein monolactate. In forming the amount of monolactate ordinarily present, the bacteria use up an amount of sugar equal to two to four per cent of the weight of the cheese. The presence of the monolactate was considered essential to the digestive action of the rennin enzyme. The action of rennin was not believed to extend much beyond the formation of peptones, leaving the formation of the simpler nitrogenous compounds characteristic of a ripened cheese to be explained in some other manner.

The statements above on the ripening of cheese are based almost entirely on experiments with Cheddar cheese. Some investigators have studied the types of microorganisms in cheese after its preparation. Harding and Prucha [23] isolated and studied more than 300 pure cultures of bacteria from Cheddar cheese by means of the group number on the descriptive chart of the Society of American Bacteriologists. When these strains were studied, they fell into 33 groups. *Lactobacillus lactis acidi* made up over 99 per cent of the total bacterial count. Hastings, Evans, and Hart [24] conducted a similar investigation. They stated that *Lactobacillus lactis acidi* was very important and summed up the role of these microorganisms as follows:

1. They favor the curdling process.
2. They favor the expulsion of whey.
3. They permit the fusing of curd particles.
4. They activate the pepsin in the rennin extract.
5. They have a protective action against the putrefactive bacteria.

They stated that development of *Lactobacillus lactis acidi* was followed by the growth of members of the *Lactobacillus bulgaricus* group which reach numbers comparable with those of the first group within the first month of ripening. Since they develop after the sugar has been fermented, they must have some other source of carbon and of energy than milk sugar. Another interesting observation was that enzymes play quite a role in cheese ripening since acid was formed in the absence of living cells. These authors believed that the constant presence in large numbers is the only certain proof that a group of organisms is important in cheese ripening.

Protein decomposition is important in cheese ripening because the products formed are responsible for cheese flavor. Raw-milk cheese, according to Lane and Hammer,[25] undergoes a more rapid and extensive decomposition than cheese made from pasteurized milk. After two months flavor

23. Harding and Prucha. 1908. N. Y. Agr. Expt. Sta., Tech. Bull. 8.
24. Hastings, Evans, and Hart. 1912. U. S. Dept. Agr., Bur. Anim. Indus. Bull. 150.
25. Lane and Hammer. 1935. Iowa Agr. Expt. Sta., Res. Bull. 183.

scores were higher in the cheese from raw milk while that made from pasteurized milk was characterized by lack of flavor and a tough, rubbery body. Sherwood [26] also investigated this question to determine whether pasteurization at various temperatures was sufficient to modify proteolytic action of enzymes when bacterial action was inhibited by two per cent of chloroform. Pasteurization seemed to reduce proteolytic activity of both enzymes and bacteria.

Use of pure-culture inoculation of Cheddar cheese gave inconsistent results in the hands of Harris and Hammer.[27] Thirty-four cultures of Micrococcus originally isolated from Cheddar cheese were used. Strains of micrococci apparently belonging to the same species differed in their effects on flavor. When used in small numbers, certain strains of propionic acid bacteria improved the flavor of pasteurized milk Cheddar cheese, while others had no definite effect; when used in large numbers all the strains improved the flavor, and some of them produced a distinct sweet flavor somewhat resembling that of Swiss cheese. It might be possible to improve the flavor of pasteurized-milk Cheddar cheese by adding to the milk various organisms other than the usual cheese cultures.

Off-Flavors in Cheddar Cheese. These may be due to development of various microorganisms. Whitehead's [28] experiments showed that representative strains of organisms of the coliform group had a deleterious effect on the flavor of Cheddar cheese when added to the milk just before the start of the manufacturing process. Even when present in large numbers they did not produce gas holes if an active culture of lactic streptococci was used as a "starter." This indicates that metabolism was so modified by association with the starter that while they grew they produced little or no gas. In this study they had no influence on the texture of the cheese, nor did they appreciably affect the production of acid by the starter in the milk or curd. Since they did not cause decolorization of annatto in a colored cheese, it did not seem likely that they were responsible for mottling in cheese. These organisms may come from a variety of sources. Albini [29] examined several kinds of cheese for the presence of bacteria belonging to the coli-aerogenes group, with a view to determining the sources and degree of impurity. His investigations led to the conclusions that in most cases the organisms are not in the milk from which the cheeses are made but are introduced in the process of manufacture. Those cheeses which in the process are subjected to the prolonged action of salt contain far fewer of these organisms than others. Albini utters a plea for better surveillance of cheese dairies and for wider application of more modern methods of manufacture. The grading of all cheeses by the Dominion of Canada Department of Agriculture during 1930 showed about one per cent to be rancid. This condition was reproduced by Hood and White [30] by adding undesirable bacteria to the cheese milk. Milk containing manure, dust, or

26. Sherwood. 1936. J. Dairy Res. 6, 204-217.
27. Harris and Hammer. 1940. J. Dairy Sci. 23, 701-708.
28. Whitehead. 1930. J. Dairy Res. 2, 76-80.
29. Albini. 1939. Settimana Med. Palermo. 27, 805-808; 810-811.
30. Hood and White. 1931. Canada Dept. Agr. Bull 146, 1-16.

feed may contain many butyric acid or rancidity producing bacteria. Low-grade milk was found to be the cause of much rancidity.

The development of acidities greater than pH 5 at four days after making the cheese, according to Phillips and Price,[31] may contribute to the production of bitter flavor. Acid development in the bitter cheese was much more rapid than in the low-acid groups, but slower than in the high-acid group. Excess acidity in the curd may be brought about by use of a very active starter, and by using milk in which too much acid has been permitted to develop. Differences in moisture content in curd has no relation to bitterness. Limiting of acidity during the curd-making operations is recommended as an aid in improving cheese quality.

Canned Cheese. Rapid molding of cheese in some seasons and the desire to hold it over long periods prompted attempts to can it. Pernot[32] was among the first, if not the first, to successfully hold cheese in cans. He shipped cans of cheese long distances by sea and land and found it able to stand up. His cheese "cured" in the cans. Rogers[33] described a method of canning Cheddar cheese, the essential feature of which method is a valve which permits escape of gases formed during ripening without allowing ingress of air. The cheese ripens normally without loss of moisture, formation of rind, or growth of mold. The increased cost of cheese in this package is largely offset by elimination of loss through evaporation, necessity for paraffining, and care of the cheese in the curing room. Use of this can means that some of the ripening process occurs in the can, which makes it necessary to have a ventilation valve.

Bacteriophage in Cheese Making. Most cheese makers have culture problems, explanations for which have not been available. Among them is slow acid formation, the solution of which has usually been to secure new cultures. Cheese makers in New Zealand who use a single strain of bacteria have found some of them to be contaminated with bacteriophage which destroys all of the bacteria. Whitehead and Hunter[34] believed bacteriophage to be of common occurrence under dairy-manufacturing conditions. Bacteriophages which they isolated showed a strain specificity but some races attacked as many as four strains. They also observed that chlorine and permanganate destroyed the phage. Whitehead and Hunter had previously attributed failure of single-culture starter in Cheddar cheese manufacture to bacteriophage in air-borne, fine whey particles. Special rooms had to be used where air-borne infection could not occur. Johns[35] demonstrated bacteriophage in a starter in Canada. It attacked all of 10 bacterial species in the starter. Thorough sterilization and cleaning of equipment helped. Johns was able to reproduce the trouble experimentally. Strict sanitation in the factory and proper handling of starters seem to be involved in prevention of phage troubles.

31. Phillips and Price. 1936. Wis. Agr. Expt. Sta., Ann. Rpt., 75-76.
32. Pernot. 1905. Oregon Agr. Expt. Sta. Bull. 78.
33. Rogers. 1932. J. Dairy Sci. 15, 185-189.
34. Whitehead and Hunter. 1939. J. Dairy Res. 10, 120-132; 403-409; 11 (1940), 62-66; 12 (1941), 63-70; J. Path. and Bact. 53 (1941), 440-441.
35. Johns. 1941. Canad. Dairy and Ice Cream J. 20, 18; Canad. J. Res. 19C, 49-58.

Cottage Cheese. This is a simple cheese widely made in rural districts of the United States. It varies widely in flavor and texture because it is made in small batches and because of varying tastes among consumers. Starter may be added to assist in curdling. The curdled milk is heated to about 37.8°C.(100°F.) and allowed to remain at this temperature for 30 minutes after which the whey is drained. The curd may be washed, salted, and used as it is or after it has been mixed with cream. Microbiology of cottage cheese follows quite closely that of the milk from which it is made and the starter which may be used. Diehm [36] analyzed some 10 samples purchased at different places. The greatest number of colonies appeared on plates made from a sample which had been stored uniced. The smallest number came from an iced sample. More colonies developed at 37°C. (98.6°F.) than at room temperature. *Streptococcus lactis* was the predominating organism. *Oospora lactis* was also present. Ellenberger [37] found storage conditions to be important in keeping cottage cheese of high quality.

Blue or Blue-Veined Cheeses. These are cheeses which are in general ripened by the action of molds belonging to the genus Penicillium. The most common and probably the oldest is Roquefort cheese originally prepared in France from goat's or sheep's milk. It differs from Camembert cheese in being ripened throughout by the mold *Penicillium roquefortii*. The air spaces are surrounded with vegetation of this mold which gives Roquefort cheese its blue-green appearance. This mold digests the curd quite completely. This cheese is made by pressing alternate layers of curd and mold powder into five- or six-pound bricks, punching them full of holes to allow entrance of air, and allowing them to ripen under controlled atmospheric conditions. The inoculum of *Penicillium roquefortii* may be gotten into the curd in different ways. Hussong and Hammer [38] grew the mold on bread which was ground into a powder when dry. Only a small amount of this powder was found to be necessary by Lane and Hammer [39]; .01 per cent produced satisfactory mold growth in cheese. The inoculum was best mixed with the curd to secure good distribution. Lane and Hammer found that homogenized milk offered some advantages, for the volatile acidities and acid numbers on cheese fat were considerably greater in cheese made from such milk. Attempts by Hammer and Bryant [40] to find the chemical substance which is responsible for the flavor of Roquefort cheese indicated that it might be methyl-n-amyl ketone formed by the mold from caprylic acid.

Thom [41] stated cheeses of the same quality were made in Europe from mixtures of cow's and sheep's milk or cow's milk alone. He noticed remarkable uniformity in cultures from the interior of cheeses. Usually a single species of Penicillium existed along with a few typical lactic acid-

36. Diehm. 1927. N. Y. Prod. Rev. and Amer. Creamery 65, 338-341.
37. Ellenberger. 1919. Vermont Agr. Expt. Sta. Bull. 213.
38. Hussong and Hammer. 1935. J. Dairy Sci. 8, 599-602.
39. Lane and Hammer. 1938. Iowa Agr. Expt. Sta., Res. Bull. 237.
40. Hammer and Bryant. 1937. Iowa State Col. J. Sci. 11, 281-285.
41. Thom. 1906. U. S. Dept. Agr., Bur. Anim. Indus. Bull. 82.

producing species. By means of the mold, then referred to as the Roquefort Penicillium, Thom was able to make good cheese with cow's milk. Thom, Currie, and Matheson [43] later enlarged on this and described in more detail preparation of this type of cheese in America. Salt was observed to inhibit microorganisms which were not desired, such as *Oidium lactis*. Thom's observations on the function of *Penicillium roquefortii* were in general confirmed by Evans [43] who found *Streptococcus lactis* and *Penicillium roquefortii* to be essential for making Roquefort cheese. The former decomposed the lactose to produce the acidity necessary for cheese making. After two or three weeks these organisms disappear. The flora then consists mainly of cheese streptococci and *Lactobacillus bulgaricum*, organisms which are found in all kinds of cheeses. These bacteria play no role in ripening of Roquefort cheese. The mold is most important. Currie [44] found the mold to be well provided with enzymes for producing compounds concerned with flavor. While most investigators gave the mold most credit for the proper decompositions, Dvorak [45] believed that a symbiosis of the lactic acid-producing bacteria and mold was involved.

Blue-veined cheeses are subject to deterioration; Lane and Hammer [39] mentioned two types, lack of development of good flavor and black discoloration. The former was said to be due to lack of development of the mold. One type of black discoloration was attributed by Bryant and Hammer [46] to growth of *Hormodendron olivaceum*, particularly in punch holes and cracks in the surface. Gas formation was said to be of little importance in blue cheeses. Trials with a culture of *Aerobacter aerogenes* showed that inoculation of milk which resulted in very gassy Cheddar cheese caused no, or only insignificant, numbers of gas holes in blue cheese. Production of good blue cheese depends on use of a good strain of *Penicillium roquefortii* and elimination of contamination microorganisms which might bring about abnormal protein decomposition.

Camembert Cheese. This cheese originated in the village in France from which it derives its name. It is a soft cheese made with rennin from cow's milk. Camembert is made in smaller units than other cheeses and is provided with a hard exterior, or rind of hard cheese covered with molds, and a soft interior. *Penicillium camemberti* along with bacteria and molds is the important fungus. Early bacteriological work on Camembert cheese in the United States was carried out by Conn, Thom, Bosworth, Stocking, and Issajeff [47] and Thom.[48] The first object is to secure good production of lactic acid, during which lactic acid-producing bacteria predominate. Following this period, lactic acid concentration decreases and the mold makes itself evident. In three to five weeks, much of the curd has been decomposed with appearance of characteristic odor and

42. Thom, Currie, and Matheson. 1914. Conn. Agr. Expt. Sta. Bull. 79.
43. Evans. 1918. J. Agr. Res. 13, 225-233.
44. Currie. 1914. Idem 2, 1-14.
45. Dvorak. 1917. Rev. in Expt. Sta. Rec. 44 (1921), 575.
46. Bryant and Hammer. 1940. Iowa Agr. Expt. Sta. Bull. 283.
47. Conn *et al.* 1905. U. S. Dept. Agr., Bur. Anim. Indus. Bull. 71; also published as Bull. 35, Conn. Agr. Expt. Sta., 1905.
48. Thom. 1906. U. S. Dept. Agr., Bur. Anim. Indus. Bull. 82.

flavor. Thom stated that *Penicillium camemberti* was the only mold studied up to that time which could produce the desired changes in curd soured by lactic acid without producing objectionable flavor. In spite of this Thom did not exclude *Oidium lactis* or bacteria from having a part. Other fungi might produce undesirable flavor.

Other than the necessary mold, *Penicillium camemberti*, many bacteria and yeasts are present in Camembert cheese. Esten and Mason [49] stated that 99 per cent or more of the bacteria in the interior of Camembert cheese were of the lactic acid-producing type. That yeast forms an important part of the surface flora of Camembert cheese is indicated by results of investigations by Guittonneau, Keiling, and de Laval.[50] Among the various species isolated were those which fermented lactose with production of alcohol and esters. Many of the yeasts which were isolated are peculiarly fitted to grow in symbiosis with lactic acid-producing bacteria and to constitute an important part of the surface flora. The more practical problems relating to manufacture of Camembert cheese were studied by Thom.[51]

Brick Cheese. This is an American cheese the real origin of which is not known. Doane and Lawson [1] stated that it is about half way between Limburger and Emmentaler with a strong sweetish taste, elastic texture, and many round eyes or holes. Brick cheese is a rennin curd cheese. Varied microorganisms were found by Filipovic [52] in it. Anaerobes outnumbered aerobes. Frazier and his students have studied American brick cheese. They made it by the conventional method with *Streptococcus lactis* and *Streptococcus thermophilus* starters used singly and in different combinations. When used alone neither of the starters produced brick cheese of satisfactory quality. *Streptococcus lactis* starter produced a cheese with a sour flavor and a short, crumbly body, while *Streptococcus thermophilus* produced a fermented flavor with open texture. From results of investigations of Garey, Foster, and Frazier [53] good brick cheese depends on proper amounts of starter and proper processing of the cheese during manufacture.

Swiss or Emmentaler Cheese. This is a hard, dry cheese with a mild flavor and many large holes throughout the cheese mass. It is now widely manufactured in the northern United States. It is well known that as good cheese of this type can be manufactured in America as abroad. Von Freudenreich [54] observed many lactic acid-producing bacteria with few liquefying forms. At this time nothing was known as to the origin of the holes in Swiss cheese. Jensen [55] attributed them to carbon dioxide formed by the lactic acid bacteria under certain conditions. Von Freudenreich and Jensen,[56] however, later showed that calcium lactate was fermented

49. Esten and Mason. 1915. Conn. Agr. Expt. Sta. Bull. 83.
50. Guittonneau *et al.* 1939. Lait- 19, 338-353.
51. Thom. 1909. Conn. Agr. Expt. Sta. Bull. 58 and 59.
52. Filipovic. 1923. Centbl. Bakt., Pt. 2, 58, 9-41.
53. Garey, Foster, and Frazier. 1941. J. Dairy Sci. 24, A267.
54. Von Freudenreich. 1897. Landw. Jahrb. Schweiz. 11, 85-101.
55. Jensen. 1898. Centbl. Bakt., Pt. 2, 4, 217-222.
56. Von Freudenreich and Jensen. 1906. Ann. Agr. Suisse 7, 243-252.

by certain bacteria to propionic acid and carbon dioxide. The bacteria were described. They were found only in small numbers in Swiss cheese examined by Eldredge and Rogers.[57] Three morphological groups of bacteria were arranged. They stated that the essential bacteria of Emmentaler cheese were evidently not ubiquitous. Sherman[58] isolated *Bacterium acidi-propionici* (d) as the essential bacterium for production of eyes and characteristic flavor of Swiss cheese. This was proved in factory experiments.

Some European workers found that *Lactobacillus bulgaricum* produced good commercial Swiss cheese, an observation not concurred in by Sherman.[59] Matheson[60] used it in starters and secured good eye-formation and flavor. So-called "stinker cheeses" were suppressed. Sherman seemed to confirm this statement that undesirable fermentations could be suppressed. Frazier, Burkey, Matheson, and Watson[61] showed that use of starters containing *Streptococcus thermophilus* in addition to the usual *Lactobacillus casei* or *Lactobacillus bulgaricus* bettered the quality, with marked improvement in eye-formation, texture, and flavor. There was, however, a tendency to produce more checking and gas. Three strains of *Streptococcus thermophilus* produced different results in cheese. Use of pure cultures of *Streptococcus thermophilus* in cheese is recommended as part of the pure culture method. What happens to these bacteria in the cheese is largely determined by the temperature at which the cheese is held. Frazier, Burkey, Boyer, Somers, and Matheson[62] stated that the temperature at dipping 50 to 51°C.(122 to 123.8°F.) prevented increase in numbers of bacteria for several hours, although the pH decreased rapidly. *Streptococcus thermophilus* increased in numbers within three or four hours after dipping. Coliform bacteria may grow in the press and cause gasiness. Results of further investigations by Frazier, Johnson, Evans, and Ramsdell[63] on manufacture of Swiss cheese under factory conditions indicated a good product could be secured with a *Lactobacillus helveticus* starter in combination with *Streptococcus thermophilus*.

Eighteen strains of propionic acid-forming bacteria were used by Babel and Hammer[6] in manufacture of Swiss-type cheese from pasteurized milk. Several of the cultures were consistent in flavor production while others were variable. In general, cultures which developed actively gave the best flavors. None of the cultures consistently gave good eyes. In several series the control cheeses, made without added propionic acid bacteria, developed a good flavor; propionic acid-producing bacteria were found in these control cheeses in large numbers. The commonest defect in the cheese was poor eye-formation. Large numbers of coliform bacteria were more objectionable from the standpoint of flavor since eyes were small

57. Eldredge and Rogers. 1914. Centbl. Bakt., Pt. 2, 40, 5-21.
58. Sherman. 1921. J. Bact. 6, 379-391.
59. Sherman. 1924. Proc. World's Dairy Cong., Wash., 287-290.
60. Matheson. 1924. Idem 290-299.
61. Frazier *et al.* 1933. J. Dairy Sci. 16, 387-399.
62. Frazier *et al.* 1935. J. Dairy Sci. 18, 373-388.
63. Frazier *et al.* 1935. Idem 503-510.

and numerous. Anaerobic sporeforming bacteria produced bad flavors and odors, that of butyric acid being conspicuous.

Gas Formation in Swiss Cheese. Formation of gas in Swiss cheese has been found by Weiser [64] to be due to lactose fermenting yeasts and facultative anaerobic bacteria of the *Clostridium perfrigens* group. Accompanying formation of gas was lack of characteristic eye-formation, poor body, bitter flavor, and sometimes off-odor. Hostettler and Sahle [65] attributed this defect to coliform bacteria. A nonpathogenic strain of *Clostridium welchii* was isolated as the cause of this defect by Albus.[66]

Limburger (Limburg) Cheese. This cheese also derives its name from a village in which it was marketed. It is known as Limburg or Limburger, either name being accepted. It is a rennin cheese made from cow's milk, praised by many and condemned by as many more. While earlier dairy bacteriologists studied the microorganisms on cheese of this type, it remained for Wolff [67] to initiate fundamental investigations at the dairy research institute at Kiel, which finally resulted in isolation of an organism, *Bacterium denigrans*, which was believed to be the special bacterium for making Limburger type cheese. Weigmann [68] later renamed the organism *Bacterium linens*, under which name it is known today although it has many more characteristics of members of the genus Corynebacterium. Wolff's work revealed the fact that better ripening of Limburger cheese resulted when a lemon-yellow, short rod was used along with *Bacterium linens*. Steinfatt [69] confirmed Wolff's work in fine manner and published results to show that *Bacterium linens* should probably be classed with Corynebacterium. He also showed the relationship which other lactobacilli may have to manufacture of Limburger cheese along with *Bacterium linens* and to formation of good flavor and aroma.

Limburger cheese in the past has been generally made from raw milk. Use of pasteurized milk introduced new problems. Yale,[70] however, found that Limburger cheese of good quality could be made from pasteurized milk if proper manufacturing methods are followed. Milk pasteurized at 62.8°C.(145°F.) yielded good cheese. Kelly [71] observed a definite sequence with advance of the ripening period. Budding yeast cells appeared after two or three days, becoming abundant in four to five days when the surface became slimy. Uniform distribution of the organisms in the slime over the surface was accomplished by rubbing the cheeses with the hands. Short slender rods *(Bacterium linens)* appeared about the sixth or seventh day, rapidly increased in numbers, and were uniformly distributed over the surface about the eighth day. Undoubtedly these organisms are responsible for the reddish color which appears on the cheese at this time. The slime on the surface also became heavier or thicker at this stage. Yeast

64. Weiser. 1941. Natl. Butter and Cheese J. 32. 20.
65. Hostettler and Sahle. 1940. Schweiz. Milchztg. 66, 435-460.
66. Albus. 1928. J. Bact. 15, 203-206.
67. Wolff. 1909. Milchw. Centbl. 5, 145; 7 (1911), 296-303.
68. Weigmann. 1924. Pilzkunde der Milch.
69. Steinfatt. 1929. Milchw. Forsch. 9, 1-50.
70. Yale. 1940. N. Y. Agr. Expt. Sta., Tech. Bull. 253.
71. Kelly. 1937. J. Dairy Sci. 20, 239-246.

cells decreased in size from the 10th to the 18th day and finally disappeared entirely. It is believed that other types of organisms, while present from time to time, do not have any important part in the ripening of Limburger cheese.

Processed Cheese. The advent of certain types of cheese which may be quickly characterized as loaf cheese, into the American market has introduced pasteurization of cheese. The cheese is allowed to ripen naturally and is pasteurized just before it is placed on the market. This process gives the advantage of blending and thus an improvement or equalization of flavor and quality. Robinson,[72] who has discussed this question, stated that the keeping quality was also lengthened. To prove this, Robinson stored equal portions of pasteurized and unpasteurized cheese in a 37°C.(98.6°F.) incubator. After 20 days they were examined. All of the unpasteurized cheeses except one were swelled and spongy in texture. The pasteurized cheeses were in good condition. The methods of carrying out the pasteurization need not be reviewed here, except to state that the cheese is ground, heated in a jacketed container with agitation, and then filled into the container. Different cheeses may be pasteurized; different temperatures are used, however.

. Defective processed cheese having a bleached appearance, crumbly texture, and a penetrating putrefactive odor caused by a *Clostridium coagulans*-like organism was studied by Griffiths.[73] This organism was believed to have come from milk of low quality.

One possible defect of processed cheese is gas formation resulting from development of microorganisms originating in the raw milk. Palmer and Sly [74] described the gas holes as generally in the form of slits in the cheese which becomes soft and spongy. In some cases the package may be distended. Palmer and Sly believed that proper processing temperatures were the best methods of preventing the defect. A minimum temperature of 73.9°C.(165°F.) was considered to be necessary for Cheddar cheese. The critical processing temperature was said to be 60 to 68.3°C.(140 to 155°F.). Below this temperature microorganisms causing spoilage can survive. Presence of .25 per cent of potassium nitrate seemed to inhibit gas formation. Palmer and Sly did not study the microorganisms involved. Albus and Ayers [75] stated that washing of pimientos to remove fermentable sugars, would prevent gas formation in processed cheese to which they had been added. Anaerobic bacteria have also caused gaseous spoilage of cheese. Csiszar [76] found that spores of *Clostridium sporogenes, Clostridium putrificum,* and *Bacillus saccharobutyricus* were destroyed only by temperatures which were too high to make a satisfactory product.

Rusty spots on Cheddar cheese are caused by chromogenic varieties of at least two distinct varieties of lactobacilli, *Lactobacillus plantarum* var. *rudensis* and *Lactobacillus brevis* var. *rudensis*, according to Pederson and

72. Robinson. 1923. Proc. World's Dairy Cong. 1, 273-276.
73. Griffiths. 1939. Queensland Agr. J. 52, 186-191.
74. Palmer and Sly. 1941. Dairy Indus. 6, 241-243.
75. Albus and Ayers. 1928. J. Dairy Sci. 11, 175-178.
76. Csiszar. 1933. Milchw. Forsch. 15, 201-227.

Breed.[77] They stated that these organisms were commonly present in the nonchromogenic form. The conditions under which pigment is formed are unknown. *Propionibacterium rubrum* van Niel was the cause of similar defect, according to Lubow.[78]

Rancidity of Cheddar Cheese. A small percentage of cheese in Canada was found to be rancid or slightly so by the Department of Agriculture. Hood and White [30] reproduced the defect by addition of certain bacteria to the milk from which the cheese was made. These bacteria were isolated from poor-quality milk, improperly sterilized equipment, poor starters, bad water, and from factories in poor sanitary condition. Most rancid cheeses were traced to such factories.

Swelling of Emmentaler Cheese. Following introduction of Emmentaler cheese into the curing room or salt bath, an undesirable fermentation accompanied by gas formation may take place. Protuberances and crevices may form on the surface. Hostettler, Binz, and Sahle [79] found *Escherichia coli, Aerobacter aerogenes,* and *Bacillus casei delta* (Freudenreich) to be the cause. To prevent the defect, use of a strong, acid-producing rennet starter was recommended. Whitehead [80] observed that coliform bacteria even in large numbers formed no gas in Cheddar cheese if an active culture of streptococci was used as a starter. Coliform bacteria did have a deleterious effect on flavor.

Mold Growth on Cheese. Control of mold growth on foods has always been a problem. It has stimulated various investigators to seek a harmless substance which could be used for preventing development of molds. Results of experiments with certain fatty acids by Hoffman, Schweitzer, and Dalby [81] showed that some were fungistatic. Among these propionic acid has received considerable study and has been shown to be valuable for control of molds in several different foods. Miller,[82] Irvine and Sproule,[83] and John [84] all found propionic acid, or its soluble salts, to be quite inimical to molds on cheese. In Miller's experiments immersion of cuts of cheese in eight-per cent solutions of propionic acid increased the mold-free life of the cheese at 15.6°C.(60°F.) from the usual three to five days to 12 to 38 days, depending on the cheese and the method of treatment. Solutions of 14 to 16 per cent of the calcium or sodium salt were required to produce the same effect. Strong solutions of propionic acid up to 40 per cent failed to completely eliminate molds. Propionic acid is not, therefore, a germicide but an antiseptic or fungistat. Quite similar results were secured by Irvine and Sproule, who finally recommended a mixture of 10 per cent calcium propionate and 10 per cent propionic acid in the ratio of five to one. Mold inhibitive properties of propionic acid when

77. Pederson and Breed. 1941. N. Y. Agr. Expt. Sta., Tech. Bull. 259.
78. Lubow. 1938. Zentbl. Bakt., Pt. 2, 107-115.
79. Hostettler, Binz, and Sahle. 1940. Rev. in Chem. Abs. 35, 2989.
80. Whitehead. 1930. J.Dairy Res. 2, 76-80.
81. Hoffman *et al.* 1939. Food Research 4, 539-545.
82. Miller. 1940. Proc. Inst. Food Technol. 153-158.
83. Irvine and Sproule. 1940. Canad. Dairy and Ice Cream J. 19, 19.
84. Mallmann. 1941. Food Indus. 13, 41-42, 54.

added to milk or cream or when used as a dip for parchment butter wrappers and for cheese were observed by Willingham.[84a] It was ineffective when added to the exterior of cottage cheese; when mixed with the cheese it was effective. Propionic acid and its salts imparted a slight odor and flavor to dairy products but this was not objectionable.

According to Smith [84b] ultraviolet light failed to control mold growth on cheese. He used a 15-Watt low-pressure burner emitting in 2500-2600 Å region. Irradiation of cheese immediately before paraffining, did not eradicate mold. The thickness of coating materials on cheese was found to greatly reduce penetrating power of the rays.

METHODS FOR MICROBIOLOGICAL EXAMINATION OF CHEESE

Methods for microbiological examination of cheese are not unlike those used for other dairy products after the cheese has been prepared for culturing. The first task is to secure a representative sample and prepare it for analysis. In the past this latter problem was solved by grinding it in a sterile mortar with sterile sand and water, a procedure which was open to criticism because of the possibilities of contamination from the air. More recently introduction of electrically driven mixers has made it possible to thoroughly mix samples for analysis under conditions which do not permit contamination of the sample.

Harrison [86] reported that emulsions of ripe Cheddar cheese prepared with hand emulsifiers gave plate counts nearly 10 times as high as emulsions prepared by grinding in a mortar, the method which has been quite generally used. He recommended taking several plugs of cheese which, when added to one another and prepared for analysis, would give better information on the bacterial content of the cheese.

Hucker's [87] Method for Microbiological Examination of Cheese With the Microscope. The procedure quoted here is taken from his original publication. The samples of cheese were embedded by the usual histological technic and sectioned with a Minot rotary microtome. In sectioning, the microtome was so adjusted as to give sections five microns thick. The sections were stained by the Gram method and with an aqueous solution of methylene blue.

In order to determine the effect of the embedding process upon the cheese, small measured cubes of cheese were subjected to the routine procedures. Only a slight shrinkage was found, indicating that the volume of embedded cheese when examined is approximately the same as that of the fresh sample.

MICROSCOPIC EXAMINATION

The preparations were examined with an oil immersion lens and a high power ocular, the most satisfactory combination being a 1.9 mm. fluorite objective with a numerical aperture of 1.32. Where a thick coverslip was used it was necessary to have a three mm. apochromatic objective with a numerical aperture of 1.4. Greater depth can be secured with compensating oculars than with the ordinary Huygenian oculars.

The method, although at first used only for determining the types of organisms present in the samples and as a check on the usual plate method, was found useful as

84a. Willingham. 1941. Iowa St. Coll. J. Sci. 16, 152.
84b. Smith. 1942. J. Dairy Sci. 25, 525-528.
85. Johns. 1941. Canad. Dairy and Ice Cream J. 20, 36.
86. Harrison. 1938. Rev. in J. Dairy Sci. 21, 303.
87. Hucker. 1921. J. Agr. Res. 22, 93-100.

a means of determining the number of organisms present. In order to make such a computation, the microscope was so standardized as to allow an estimate of the number of organisms per gram when only a small amount of the original section was examined. This computation is quite similar to that used in the direct method of counting bacteria in milk described by Breed and Brew. This was accomplished by measuring both the diameter of the microscopic field and the thickness of the section from which the amount of cheese actually seen in each field examined was determined. Knowing the volume and specific gravity of the cheese examined, the total number of organisms per gram can readily be computed. With the diameter of the field measuring .14 mm. (140 μ), the microtome so adjusted as to cut sections of a thickness of .005 mm. (5 μ), and a specific gravity of 1, the amount of cheese examined per microscopic field would be 1/13,000,000 gm.—that is, each organism observed in a single microscopic field represents 13,000,000 per gram.

This factor may be computed by the following formula, in which any measure may be substituted:

$$\frac{1,000}{r^2 a} b = \text{factor per gram}$$

In the above formula

r = the radius of the field examined in millimeters as determined by actual measurement.
a = the thickness of the section in millimeters.
b = the specific gravity of the cheese.

The radius of the field, as has been stated, is determined by measurement with a stage micrometer and varies with the magnification and with the type of ocular used. However, it was found advisable to adjust the draw tube of the microscope so that the field would be of the greatest possible diameter without losing definition, as the greater the diameter of the field the less the increment of error in the total counts.

The thickness of the section is controlled by adjusting the microtome to cut sections of a desired and known thickness. If all the adjustments on the microtome are firm and a sharp knife is used, sections can be cut of uniform thickness with surprising accuracy. The thickness of the sections can also be measured with the fine adjustment screw on the microscope. Although not perfect, this method of measurement serves as a check upon the accuracy of the sectioning. The measurement is accomplished by focusing with the graduated fine adjustment screw on both the upper and lower surfaces of the section and noting the differences in the readings between the two levels. The difference can be read in microns where graduations are given on the fine adjustment screw.

To convert the per milliliter counts into numbers per gram, the specific gravity of the cheese must be considered. As the specific gravity of all samples has been assumed to be approximately 1, the counts are interchangeable. This assumption in regard to the specific gravity is arbitrary, but the variations in the specific gravity of Cheddar cheese are so slight that the total count is not affected to any appreciable degree. Accurate determinations did not seem practicable, as the specific gravity varies with the fat content and with the moisture and general consistency of the cheese.

With the measurements and adjustments used in this laboratory the per-gram formula resolves itself into the following:

r = .07 mm. (70 μ).
a = .005 mm. (5 μ).
b = 1.0.

$$\frac{1,000}{3.1416 \times .0049 \times .0005} \times 1 = \text{approximately } 13,000,000.$$

It is evident that this microscopic technic is subject to the limitations of any direct method of examination, many of which are unavoidable and are due to mechanical limitations or to the human error, which enters in when counts or estimat are made.

Wisconsin Curd Test for Detection of Objectionable Microorganisms in Milk for Cheese Making. This technique was proposed for detecting undesirable microorganisms in milk from which cheese was to be made. It is a simple, direct method of detecting the presence of such organisms as those which form gas. The test is made by collecting pint samples of the milk in sterile bottles. The temperature of the milk is then changed to 32.2°C.(90°F.) and 10 drops of rennin extract are added to each sample. After coagulation, the curd is cut with a sterile knife and the whey poured off. The curd is then incubated at 37°C.(98.6°F.) for about 12 hours, after which it is examined. The curd at the end of this time should be solid and have a satisfactory odor. Presence of gas-forming microorganisms will be indicated by gas bubbles in the curd. The test is especially suitable for studying the presence of undesirable organisms among the milk of various producers selling to a cheese factory.

REFERENCE BOOKS

Thom, C., 1925. The Book of Cheese. The Macmillan Co., New York, N. Y.

CHAPTER 10

MICROBIOLOGY OF FROZEN DESSERTS, ICE CREAM, AND SIMILAR PRODUCTS

Frozen desserts of various types have been used by man for ages. The varieties of these products have increased greatly during recent years in the United States. Washburn[1] reviewed the history of frozen and iced products which were probably forerunners of modern ice cream. For many years little official attention seems to have been given to sanitary qualities of these products even though they are consumed in large quantities during all seasons of the year and may be made from ingredients with questionable sanitary origin. Fabian[2] defined "frozen desserts" as follows: They shall "include ice cream and the various kinds of ice cream, such as parfait, nut, fruit, bisque, mousse, puddings, and custards as well as sherbets, ices, milks, and special forms of desserts in which there is a combination of any two or more of the above kinds of desserts or any flavored and/or colored, sweetened water (such as popsicles), natural fruit, vegetable, or other juices with or without milk solids in which sufficient heat has been removed from the liquid mixture so as to convert it into a semisolid or solid mass with or without agitation."

The Frozen Desserts Ordinance and Code Recommended by the United States Public Health Service[3] defines these products as follows:

"Frozen Desserts: A frozen dessert is any clean frozen or partially frozen combination of two or more of the following: milk or milk products, eggs or egg products, sugar, water, fruit or fruit juices, candy, nut meats, or other harmless and wholesome food products, flavors, color, or harmless stabilizer, and shall be deemed to include ice cream, frozen custard, ice milk, milk sherbet, ices, and similar products."

The ordinance then defined many of the terms used in this definition in order that control officials would know just what products were indicated. The ordinance was so worded a health officer could also control products similar to frozen desserts but which would not ordinarily be considered to come within the usual definitions of such products as ice cream, milk sherberts, and ices. The above-mentioned ordinance, which is recommended for adoption by municipalities, provides for a balanced program for control of frozen desserts. Besides the requirement for bacteriological analysis of the products, the plants in which they are made are put into three grades, A, B, and C.

As Fabian[2] has shown, many different ingredients may be added to frozen desserts. Many of them may carry bacteria which may negate the effects of pasteurization. The microbiology of some of these materials is discussed elsewhere in this book. As Prucha[4] and Tracy[5] have stated,

---

1. Washburn. 1910. Vermont Agr. Expt. Sta. Bull. 155.
2. Fabian. 1939. J. Milk Tech. 2, 75-83.
3. Frozen Desserts Ordinance and Code Recommended by the U. S. Public Health Service, May 1940 edition, Washington, D. C. Published in J. Milk Tech. 3 (1940), 44-52; 4 (1941), 26-31.
4. Prucha. 1939. J. Milk Tech. 2, 127-129.
5. Tracy. 1939. Idem, 118-126.

most of the ice cream today is made from pasteurized mix, but such ingredients as flavoring extracts, fresh fruits, berries, candies, syrups, and nut meats are added to the mix at the time of freezing and therefore do not receive the protection of pasteurization. It has been found that they may harbor a large bacterial population which may contaminate the pasteurized ice cream mix. This particular study was not for the discovery of pathogenic organisms but for the general sanitary quality of the articles. It involved a thorough investigation of their preparation as well as their use. As a result of the investigation it has been suggested that since these ingredients cannot be put into the mix prior to pasteurization, there should be sanitary laws for the preparation of such articles before use. Proper inspection and regulation should be assumed by the health authorities to assure a sanitary product.

Many of these agents are not now pasteurized. Recommendations have been made that many of them should be heated before addition to the ice cream.[6]

Origin of Microorganisms in Ice Cream. The ultimate sources of bacteria and other microorganisms in ice cream are the various raw materials from which it is made, the utensils in which they are handled, and any contamination which may reach the product during manufacture. The materials from which ice cream is made have been examined bacteriologically by different investigators. Some of the results are given below. Hall and Needs [7] and England [8] believed that as much as possible should be done to keep the bacterial content low. Such statements are without great significance when no attention is given to type and groups of organisms. These investigators believed that only pasteurized dairy products should be used. England stated that bacteria in ice cream came from (1) equipment, (2) plant operator, (3) ingredients added to mix after pasteurization, and (4) retail dispensing of ice cream. Usually the personal factor is the most difficult to control. While every effort has been made to keep the bacterial count low and to make ice cream mix safe by pasteurization, little attention has been paid until recently to the bacteria in materials which may be added. The Frozen Desserts Ordinance and Code of the United States Public Health Service [3] prescribes as follows for various products to be used in manufacture of frozen desserts:

"The following tentative standards are recommended for ingredients not derived from milk. Egg products should have an average bacterial plate count not exceeding 200,000 per ml. or per gram. Sugar, stabilizers, fruits, nuts, chocolate, cocoa, colors, extracts, maple syrup, vanilla powder, fruit or lactic acids, candies, baked confections, or other flavoring materials should have an average bacterial plate count not exceeding 10,000 per ml. or per gram, a yeast count not exceeding 100 per ml. or per gram, and a mold count not exceeding 100 per ml. or per gram. The use of synthetic flavors and artificial colors should not be permitted unless they have been

---

6. Fabian (Chairman). 1938. J. Milk Tech. 1, 20-31.
7. Hall and Needs. 1935. Med. Officer 53, 155-157.
8. England. 1938. Ice Cream Field 32, 31-32, et seq.

certified as harmless by the Food and Drug Administration, U. S. Department of Agriculture.''

Possible means of ridding many of the above-mentioned substances of great numbers of bacteria were reported by Brown.[9]

Cream. This may be the source of many bacteria in ice cream. It may be shipped for long distances and may be stored under conditions which permit development of bacteria. Pasteurization destroys many of these bacteria. In a study of pasteurization of ice cream mix, Hammer and Sanders[10] used cream with from 81,500 to 24,700,000 bacteria per ml. with 56 per cent of the samples exceeding 1,000,000. They believed that such cream represented in a good manner the cream generally used in ice cream. Bahlman,[11] as did Fay and Olsen,[12] found that the cream was the most important source of bacteria. Comparatively few bacteria were contributed by the other ingredients. Compulsory pasteurization of ice cream mix in several states tends to reduce the number of bacteria going into the ice cream.

Sugar. The microbiology of sugar will be discussed in a later chapter. It is probably of minor importance as a source of bacteria in ice cream. Olson and Fay[13] and Ellenberger[14] both reported quite low numbers of bacteria, i.e., around 200 per gram.

Egg Products. Microbiology of eggs is discussed in a later chapter. The Frozen Desserts Ordinance and Code Recommended by the United States Public Health Service, May, 1940,[3] Edition, states that egg products should have an average bacterial plate count not exceeding 200,000 per ml. or gram.

Gelatin. Fabian and Cromley[15] found that gelatin might contain many bacteria. The counts on a goodly number of samples varied from 850,000 to 4,000,000 per gram. Parfitt[16] also reported some data from the bacteriological analysis of gelatin. In general, his counts were much lower than those reported by Fabian. Tracy, Ruehe, and Brannon[17] reported the pH of 48 samples of gelatin varied from 4.05 to 7.35. In most cases the gelatins with a low H-ion concentration had a high bacterial count. Fay[18] in a study of 34 samples of gelatin failed to find any relation between the reaction and the bacterial count. The bacterial counts ranged from less than five per gram to 20,000, and the reactions between pH 4.8 and 6.6. The keeping quality test failed to check with the relative bacterial counts. The high acidity of some of the samples had a marked deterring action on the rate of growth of the microorganisms, but in no case did the reaction completely inhibit growth when a mixed microorganism population was added. Gelatin, contaminated in the drying alleys and having a high acidity, would show very little growth. On the other hand, a nearly neutral reaction would show growth. In interpreting a low bacterial count of gelatin, one of the factors to be taken into consideration is the reaction. A low bacterial count was believed to be a fairly good index to gelatin of good sanitary quality, although the factors affecting bacterial destruction and growth, such as acidity, must be taken into consideration.

The above data do not indicate that gelatin contributes a significant number of bacteria to ice cream. Fay and Olson[12] reached this conclusion. Hammer,[19] however, stated that gelatin might add large numbers of bacteria and that it was not a factor to be ignored.

The organisms predominating in raw material from which gelatin is made are aerobic sporeforming bacteria and various ordinary fungi. Henoch[20] found that the flora is

9. Brown. 1937. Ice Cream Field 31, 9-13; next issue, 27-29.
10. Hammer and Sanders. 1919. Iowa Agr. Expt. Sta., Bull., 186.
11. Bahlman. 1914. Amer. J. Pub. Health 4, 1009-1015.
12. Fay and Olson. 1924. Kansas Agr. Expt. Sta. Circ. 103.
13. Olson and Fay. 1925. J. Dairy Sci. 8, 415-444.
14. Ellenberger. 1919. N. Y. Agr. Expt. Sta. (Cornell) Memoir 18.
15. Fabian and Cromley. 1923. Mich. Agr. Expt. Sta. Bull. 60.
16. Parfitt. 1923. J. Dairy Sci. 6, 278-282.
17. Tracy, Ruehe, and Brannon. 1927. Ill. Agr. Expt. Sta., Ann. Rpt., 158-162.
18. Fay. 1928. J. Dairy Sci. 11, 313-324.
19. Hammer. 1913. Iowa Agr. Expt. Sta. Bull. 134.
20. Henoch. 1937. Chem. Zentbl., 1937-II, 1717-1718.

greatly reduced during the boiling of the bones, especially on the outer surface. The inner portion may still contain bacteria. Subsequent maceration and treatment with hydrochloric acid destroys bacteria. The entire manufacturing procedure is a fight with bacteria, especially the proteolytic species. Thexton [21] stated that in 1935 the Canadian Federal Department of Health passed regulations stipulating that the total bacteria count of food gelatin must not exceed 10,000 per gram with the absence of coliform bacteria from .01 gram. A survey of the bacteriological quality of gelatin imported since these standards were adopted, revealed that gelatin manufacturers have been able to satisfy them in the great majority of cases.

Parfitt's Fermentation Test of Gelatin for Ice Cream Making. Weigh 10 grams of gelatin aseptically into 100 ml. of sterile distilled water containing a gram of lactose. Heat carefully at 50°C.(122°F.) to hasten solution of the gelatin. Transfer with sterile pipettes to sterile tubes and incubate at 28°C.(82.4°F.) for 18 hours and 20°C.(68°F.) for 36 hours.

Flavoring Materials. Since these are generally alcoholic solutions, they were once believed to be sterile. When fresh fruits are used for flavors many microorganisms of diverse types may be introduced. Fabian [22] suggested a standard of not over 5,000 bacteria per gram for flavoring sirups and fruits. According to results published by Prucha [23] such a standard would cause complications at present. Tracy and Brown [24] found that flavoring materials could be heated before use. Experiments with flavoring extracts pasteurized at 62.8°C.(145°F.) for 30 minutes indicate that if doubt exists as to the sanitary quality of the extract, heating can be resorted to without decreasing the value of the flavor of ice cream. The trials indicate that vanilla extract subjected to this treatment can be used satisfactorily.

Information on this problem is not limited to recent investigations. Hammer,[25] as early as 1912, reported the presence of bacteria in vanilla extract. He analyzed five samples of vanilla extract and found only 2,300 bacteria per ml. in the most heavily contaminated sample.

Coloring Materials. Little bacteriological work seems to have been done on colors used in frozen desserts. Smallfield [26] and Prucha [23] found these materials to carry many bacteria. The dry, powdered colors, according to Smallfield's results, contained but a few thousand microorganisms while the liquid colors contained as many as 198,000,000 bacteria per ml. in some of them. Prucha found some to be heavily seeded, and in some others coliform bacteria were present. Survival of *Eberthella typhosa* and *Staphylococcus aureus* in three different coloring materials for two weeks was observed by Brown.[9] Results of a more comprehensive investigation by Boyles [27] has, in general, confirmed the conclusions just presented. He examined 98 samples of dyes, the total microbial content varying from 10 per ml. to 26 million. Twenty-six of the 98 samples examined contained over 400,000 per ml. and 17 harbored coliform bacteria. Molds, clostridia, and thermophilic bacteria were absent. Presence of large numbers of bacteria and coliform bacteria indicated that some of the dye solutions had been prepared under insanitary conditions. The older solutions frequently had greatest number of microorganisms.

Nut Meats and Fruits. The great amount of bacteriological work which has been done on nut meats indicates that they might seed the ice cream mix with many bacteria, some of which have been found by Prucha [4] to be members of the coliform group. These products are discussed in a later chapter in this book. Tracy [28] mentioned the fact that while the mix is pasteurized and utensils are carefully cleaned, the results of these new standard procedures are largely nullified by addition of many materials which may be

21. Thexton. 1939. Canad. Pub. Health J. 30, 24.
22. Fabian. 1930. Ice Cream Field 16, 16 and 102.
23. Prucha. 1936. 26th Ann. Conv. Internatl. Assoc. Ice Cream Manfrs., 40-45.
24. Tracy and Brown. 1936. Idem.
25. Hammer. 1912. Iowa Agr. Expt. Sta. Bull. 134.
26. Smallfield. 1933. Ice Cream Trade J. 29, 41.
27. Boyles. 1941. J. Assoc. Off. Agr. Chem. 24, 794-798.
28. Tracy. 1939. J. Milk Tech. 2, 118-126.

of questionable sanitary quality. Brown [9] greatly improved the sanitary quality of nut meats for frozen desserts by immersing them in boiling sugar solution after which they were dried in an oven. In view of the conditions which Tracy revealed, he believed that some treatment was necessary to rid nut meats of the microorganisms. Fifty per cent of specimens he collected from ice cream plants carried *Escherichia coli.* He tried several methods. Hot sucrose solutions (25-75 per cent) at 82°C.(180°F.) or boiling, and hot butter at 97.4°C.(208°F.) or boiling were the best. Efficacy of these procedures was shown by using inoculated nut meats.

Condensed Milk. The microbiology of this product is discussed in Chapter 11.

Fruit Products. Both fresh and frozen fruits may be used. Fresh fruits may yield a better flavor, but many believe today that frozen fruits may be just as satisfactory. Fellers and Mack,[29] Joslyn and Cole,[30] and Sarber [31] have supported their use. As shown elsewhere in this book, frozen fruits are not sterile and may carry many bacteria, yeasts, and molds. Should they be added to ice cream mix, the count may be materially raised.

Homemade Ice Cream. More adequate methods of refrigeration in the home have stimulated greater use of homemade ice cream and similar products. Little was known about the bacteriological quality of such products until Foltz and Martin [32] published results of examination of many samples collected in Manhattan, Kansas. The bacteriological quality of homemade ice cream averaged lower than commercial ice cream examined. Foltz and Martin believed that this was due to use of unpasteurized products in some cases. When pasteurized milk and cream were used, an average bacterial count of 17,000 per ml. was secured which compared favorably with the counts of commercial samples. Presence of coliform bacteria in a few samples which showed high counts was assumed to indicate bad contamination of the product.

Machinery and Utensils. The machinery may increase the bacterial count in two ways: it may contribute bacteria to the mix, and may break up the clumps. Fabian [33] studied this question very thoroughly and suggested means for cleaning and sterilizing machinery. These procedures need not be reviewed here, but should be read by those who control and operate ice cream plants. It is quite important that pasteurized mix should not be contaminated by dirty utensils. The lines and apparatus must be thoroughly steamed to prevent seeding the mix and thus negating the effects of pasteurization. Similar advice was given by Fay and Olson.[12]

In order to make certain that the freezer was unimportant in the contamination of ice cream, Ellenberger [14] ran 500 ml. of sterile water through it. Plate counts on this water varied from 10 to 55 colonies per ml, with an average of 28. Thus it was shown that the freezer would not contribute significant numbers of bacteria. Hammer,[34] however, agitated sterile water in a freezer and in five tests secured counts of 3700, 300, 1195, 8050, and 141,500 per ml., indicating that the freezer under some conditions may be important. Fay and Olson [12] reported that thorough washing and cleaning of all equipment with live steam were essential factors in the production

29. Fellers and Mack. 1929. Fruit Prod. J. 9. 8-11.
30. Joslyn and Cole. 1938. Ice Cream Trade J. 34, 16.
31. Sarber. 1939. Ice Cream Field 33, 22-25.
32. Foltz and Martin. 1941. Food Research 6, 31-38.
33. Fabian. 1927. Mich. Agr. Expt. Sta., Spec. Bull. 159; Tech. Bull. 83.
34. Hammer. 1921. Univ. of Wis. Studies in Science 182-199.

of ice cream with a low count. Utensils seem to have the same relation to the bacteria content of ice cream that they do to milk.

Prucha [35] believed that utensils should be exposed to a temperature of at least 76.7°C.(170°F.) for at least 15 minutes or 93.3°C.(200°F.) for five minutes in a steam cabinet or a jet of steam for one minute. Chlorine solution with at least 50 p.p.m. of chlorine applied one minute would also be satisfactory. If hot water is used, the utensils should be immersed for two minutes.

Another utensil which has been much studied from the bacteriological viewpoint is the container in which ice cream is distributed. Paper ice cream containers have replaced metal containers in many cases for their advantages are obvious. They parallel those which obtain for the single-service paper milk container. Bacterial counts by Speck and Black [36] of open-top ice cream containers obtained from retail stores varied widely and apparently correlated with storage conditions, air and dust contamination being most important. Cylindrical containers closed during manufacture with tight crown tops had consistently low counts. Paper ice cream dishes in nests and inverted at the ice cream bar until used gave low or negative counts. Containers at one ice cream plant sampled directly from the original package from the paper manufacture gave high counts, a condition not found in a different brand sampled at another plant. Some typical organisms isolated were species of micrococci (11 strains), Alkaligenes (3), Sarcina (2), Bacillus (1), and Achromobacter (1). The presence of some of these organisms in containers directly from a manufacturer suggested contamination during manufacture by polluted water. Inoculations, using five per cent of the liquid in which the swabs were disentangled, into brilliant green lactose peptone bile, failed to reveal the presence of coliform bacteria.

Speck and Black [36] found the swab method more practical for the examination of open-top paper containers than rinse methods. They swabbed the surface with one moist and one dry swab. After use, the swab was thoroughly broken and disentangled in a 40 ml. dilution blank. This technic would be especially suitable for open-top containers but might have decided limitations with containers that are practically closed.

Speck and Black's [36] Method for Bacteriological Examination of Paper Ice Cream Containers. This procedure consisted of swabbing the interior of the container with sterile swabs. The swabs were made by winding cotton onto the end of a six and one-half inch wooden applicator to a thickness of one-fourth inch and a width of one inch. The swabs were wrapped in pairs in brown paper and sterilized at 120°C.(248°F.) for 30 minutes in the autoclave. Standard nutrient agar adjusted to a pH of 7 was used for plating. Plates were poured in duplicate and incubated at 37°C.(98.6°F.) for 48 hours. Two swabs held in the same hand, the first moistened from the 40-ml. water blank and the second dry, were used to swab the inside of the container thoroughly. Both swabs were then broken into the 40-ml. dilution blank and shaken until disentangled. One-ml. portions were then plated. The average counts were reported as bacteria per container.

35. Prucha. 1937. Ice Cream Trade J. 33, 25.
36. Speck and Black. 1937. Food Research 2, 559-566; 567-580.

Ice Cream Scoops. Ice cream is usually dispensed by means of scoops. These have been found to be a source of bacteria in ice cream in retail stores. Krog and Dougherty [37] examined over 200 samples taken from the surface of ice cream sold in bulk. High counts were secured when the vendor's scoop was used and only moderate counts when the sample was collected with a sterile spoon. With subsurface samples (at least one inch below) equally high figures were obtained using the vendor's scoop and very low figures with a sterile spoon. The scoops are usually kept in a vessel containing cold water and samples of such water showed exceedingly high counts. That the scoop and the way it was kept is largely responsible for the high counts was shown by further figures with the scoops kept on dry racks and rinsed in either hot or cold running water before and after each usage. Studying the same subject Geiger [38] found that 124 scoops had bacterial counts under 10,000 per ml., 226 had over 100,000, and 97 had over 1,000,000 per ml. Abele [39] examined the water in which the scoops were placed. A study of 40 samples of such water revealed that the bacterial content of the water ranged from 600 per ml. to 20,000,000 per ml. The average count from five receptacles into which a small stream of water was constantly flowing was 9,500 per ml., the extremes being 600 and 77,000 per ml. Hopkins [40] and Fabian and Hook [41] found, at fountains where the dippers were kept in running water, the total bacterial count as well as the coliform count of the water to be less than where still water was used. Eighty-one per cent of the samples of still water had a plate count in excess of 100,000 bacteria per ml. while only 18 per cent of the samples of running water exceeded 100,000 bacteria per ml. Ten of the 18 per cent of samples of running water which exceeded 100,000 ml. were probably high because the water was running too slowly through the receptacle containing the dippers.

A general relationship between the total bacterial count and the coliform bacteria content of retail ice cream exists when the count exceeds 100,000 bacteria per ml. Below this, the relationship is less marked. However, there seems to be no direct correlation between the Escherichia-Aerobacter content of the ice cream being served and the dipper water. Further information on this question was published by Horn.[42] Most of the results just quoted are counts only. Little attention was given to types of bacteria. Do these counts always indicate what they are supposed to?

The Ice Cream Mix. When the various ingredients to be used in a frozen dessert have been combined and are ready to be frozen, the mixture is spoken of as the "mix." The Frozen Desserts Ordinance and Code recommended by the United States Public Health Service, May, 1940, Edition,[3] defines the term as follows:

C. *Mix.* Mix is the unfrozen combination of all ingredients of a frozen dessert with or without fruits, fruit juices, candy, nut meats, flavor, or harmless color.

37. Krog and Dougherty. 1937. Amer. J. Pub. Health 27, 1007-1009.
38. Geiger. 1938. Calif. and West Med. 49, 357.
39. Abele. 1938. Ice Cream Rev. 22, 74.
40. Hopkins. 1940. Sanitarian 3, 86-87.
41. Fabian and Hook. 1936. Proc. 36th Ann. Conv., Internatl. Assoc. Ice Cream Manfrs.
42. Horn. 1936. 24th Ann. Rpt., Internatl. Assoc., Dairy and Milk Insp. 249-256.

It frequently happens that there are fewer bacteria per ml. in the mix than in cream. This is probably due to dilution of the cream with other constituents which are considerably freer from bacteria. It is possible that the sugar added to the mix may kill some of the bacteria. Since the ice cream mix contains milk products and since many of them are liable to contain living *Mycobacterium tuberculosis,* manufacturers and public health officials have found it desirable to pasteurize it. The Public Health Council of the State of New York, for instance, passed a law, effective April 1, 1929, to the effect that ice cream mix should be pasteurized at 65.5°C.(150°F.). Other states have similar laws although there is a little variation in the temperature and time.

Pasteurization of Ice Cream Mix. This is necessary in order that ice cream may be a safe food. Ice cream mix is a different product from fluid milk and presents more problems; consequently times and temperatures are higher for ice cream mix than for milk.

Fabian's [43] summary of epidemics caused by ice cream suggested that pasteurization of the mix should be thoroughly studied. While the temperatures now used in milk pasteurization are well supported by adequate experimental data, such is not the case for ice cream mix. Recommended times and temperatures vary widely. Those who are familiar with the problems involved appreciate why this is the case. Some bacteriological work has been done on the problem but whether it is reliable from the bacteriological viewpoint is open to question.[44]

Fabian and Cromley [15] and Hammer and Sanders [10] both reported significant decrease in bacterial content by pasteurization at 65.6°C.(150°F.) for 30 minutes. Fay and Olson [12] stated that the bacterial content of the mix, after pasteurization, depended on the number originally present. Pasteurization at 62.8°C.(145°F.) for 30 minutes, followed by homogenization, resulted in counts of less than 100,000 bacteria per gram in the finished product, even with raw mixes containing as high as 34,000,000 bacteria per gram.

The subject has also been studied by the committee on dairy products and eggs of the American Public Health Association (Schrader [45]). A survey of methods used by 500 ice cream companies revealed the use of temperatures and holding periods ranging from 60°C.(140°F.) for 30 minutes, up to 85°C.(185°F.) for 10 minutes. Experiments on a commercial ice cream mix, inoculated with pathogenic bacteria, showed that 62°C. (143.5°F.) for 30 minutes allowed an ample margin of safety. A further report confirming this work by Oldenbusch, Frobisher, and Schrader [46] is mentioned later. Brannon [47] believed that 65.5°C.(150°F.) to 71.1°C. (160°F.) would destroy all pathogenic bacteria in ice cream mix.

Significance of the presence of coliform bacteria in many food products, especially milk and dairy products, is still a controversial subject.

43. Fabian. 1926. Amer. J. Pub. Health 16, 873-879.
44. J. Milk Tech. 3 (1940), 61-63. (Editorial).
45. Schrader. 1930. Amer. J. Pub. Health 20, 492-494.
46. Oldenbusch *et al.* 1930. Idem. 20, 615-618.
47. Brannon. 1941. Ice Cream Rev. 24, 28.

As is the case with fluid milk, a few bacteriologists believe that the organisms in ice cream mix mean faulty processing including pasteurization. Accordingly it was necessary to know something about the resistance to heat of coliform bacteria in ice cream mix. Fabian and Coulter [48] reported that the thermal death point of 33 cultures of *Escherichia coli*, seven of *Aerobacter aerogenes,* and four of unidentified lactose-fermenting organisms isolated from water showed variation when heated in ice cream mix at 60°C.(140°F.), 62.8°C.(145°F.), and 65.5°C.(150°F.) for 30 minutes. Four determinations were made at 60°C.(140°F.), the number surviving expressed in per cent being 51.2, 39, 36, and 57, respectively. When the temperature was increased to 62.8°C.(145°F.) the number surviving decreased to 22.7, 6.8, 2.2, and 22.7 per cent, respectively. At 65.5°C. (150°F.) the number surviving still further decreased to 0.0, 2.4, 2.4, and 9.1 per cent, respectively, while at 68.3°C.(155°F.) no cultures tested survived. A larger number of cultures, when heated to corresponding temperatures, survived in ice cream and skim milk. Different ingredients used in making ice cream failed to show any protective action. These data indicate that the critical temperature for the Escherichia-aerogenes group in ice cream is about 65.5°C.(150°F.). Previous work by Fabian [49] with coliform bacteria had shown that 68.3°C.(155°F.) was necessary to kill all of the cultures. Dubois and Martin [50] reported that exposures to 62.8°C. (145°F.) for 20, 25, and 30 minutes; to 65.6°C.(150°F.) for 20, 25, and 30 minutes; to 71.1°C.(160°F.) for 10, 15, and 20 minutes; to 76.7°C. (170°F.) for 2, 5, and 10 minutes; and to 82.2°C.(180°F.) flash, yielded results differing insufficiently to be measured by plate counts. In mixes made from previously pasteurized dairy products the flora after pasteurization was about evenly divided between peptonizing and alkali-forming and inert groups of bacteria; in mixes made from previously pasteurized dairy products the flora after pasteurization consisted largely of slow acid-forming bacteria. In only one case did rapid acid-forming bacteria survive the exposures. The predominating types of organisms surviving pasteurization (slow acid formers) were small Gram-negative rods which grew well at 26.7°C.(80°F.) but not at 37°C.(98.5°F.). Presence of coliform bacteria along with a negative phosphatase reaction, according to Nelson,[51] indicates contamination after pasteurization. Several strains were found to survive pasteurization at 62.8°C.(145°F.) for 30 minutes, and phosphatase tests were positive. At 65.6°C.(150°F.) they were destroyed in 10 minutes, but 30 minutes were necessary for destruction of phosphatase.

One of the important factors involved in pasteurization of ice cream mix is the effect which ingredients of the mix may have on survival of microorganisms. Sugar in higher concentrations is known to cause them to survive longer. Beavens,[52] Fay,[53] and Fabian and Coulter [48] have

48. Fabian and Coulter. 1930. J. Dairy Sci. 13, 273-287.
49. Fabian. 1931. Canad. Dairy and Ice Cream J. 10, 21.
50. Dubois and Martin. 1933. J. Dairy Sci. 16, 435-443.
51. Nelson. 1939. Ice Cream Rev. 22, 69-70.
52. Beavens. 1930. J. Dairy Sci. 13, 91-93.
53. Fay. 1934. J. Agr. Res. 48, 453-468.

shown this. Results of investigations by others have been mentioned in other chapters.

Various opinions have been expressed as to what pasteurization of ice cream mix is. Armstrong [54] believed that 67.2°C.(153°F.) was required. He mentioned the recommendations of the International Association of Milk Sanitarians that 68.3°C.(155°F.) for 30 minutes should be used or 82.2°C.(180°F.) for 16 seconds, or higher in each case.

The Frozen Desserts Ordinance [3] proposed by the United States Public Health Service includes the following definition of pasteurization:

Pasteurization: The term "pasteurization," "pasteurized," and similar terms shall be taken to refer to the process of heating every particle of mix to at least 68.3°C. (155°F.) and holding at such temperature for at least 30 minutes in approved and properly operated equipment, providing that nothing contained in this definition shall be construed as debarring any other process which has been demonstrated to be equally efficient and is approved by the state health authorities.

Effect of Pasteurization on Pathogenic Bacteria in Cream. Although much work has been done on the thermal death time of nonpathogenic bacteria in milk, much less has been done to determine the longevity of pathogenic bacteria at pasteurization temperatures. In order to secure information on this question Oldenbusch, Frobisher, and Shrader [46] suspended two strains of *Eberthella typhosa*, two of beta type hemolytic streptococci (one from scarlet fever and one from septic sore throat), and one culture of *Mycobacterium tuberculosis* of the bovine type in cream with 50 per cent butterfat content. This had been previously sterilized in an autoclave for 30 minutes at 15 pounds' pressure. The determinations were carried out by placing 9.9 ml. of cream into each of a series of small bottles. Just before the experiment, the bottles of cream were heated to the five temperatures which were used between 57.2°C.(135°F.) and 62.8°C.(145°F.). Samples were taken at various intervals and subjected to bacterial examination which would reveal viability of the organism under study. The streptococci did not survive heating in cream at 57.2°C. (135°F.) for five minutes nor at 60°C.(140°F.) to 61.2°C.(142°F.). *Eberthella typhosa* heated at 57.2°C.(135°F.) were killed in less than 10 minutes, at 60°C.(140°F.) in less than five minutes, and at 61.2°C.(142°F.) to 62.8°C.(145°F.) in less than three minutes. Tubercle bacilli in cream were killed in less than 20 minutes when heated to 57.2°C.(135°F.), in less than 10 minutes at 60°C.(140°F.), in less than seven minutes at 61.2°C. (142°F.) to 62°C.(143.5°F.), and in less than three minutes at 62.8°C. (145°F.). Failure to produce infection in guinea pigs was interpreted as meaning that the organisms had been killed. The authors, therefore, concluded that 30 minutes heating in cream at 62°C.(143.5°F.), recommended by a committee of the American Public Health Association for the pasteurization of milk, allows an ample margin of safety for the pasteurization of cream and commercial ice cream mix.

Effect of Homogenization on the Number of Bacteria in Ice Cream. Ice cream mixes are generally homogenized to yield a more thoroughly mixed

54. Armstrong. 1940. Ice Cream Rev., April 1940, 41-42.

product. The mix is forced through a very small opening under high pressure. The procedure apparently affects the bacterial count. Fabian [55] stated that homogenization tends to reduce the size of the clumps. The bacterial contamination in the homogenizer was said to be of the same type as is normally found in milk. The clumps of bacteria were broken up and the count was increased. Fay and Olson [12] observed an increase in the count 18 times and a decrease 10 times from homogenizing the mix. Similar results were also reported by Hammer and Sanders [10] who cautioned that the homogenizer must be carefully cleaned else it would seed the mix with more bacteria.

The Phosphatase Test Applied to Ice Cream. This test which has enjoyed such a wide application to milk has also been used to control pasteurization of ice cream mix. Nelson [56] said the phosphate test could be effectively used for detecting the efficiency of pasteurization of ice cream mixes. Careless handling after pasteurization was believed to be indicated by presence of coliform bacteria. Hahn and Tracy [57] found Scharer's modification of the phosphatase test to be possible for detection of variations in the time and temperature of pasteurization of ice cream mixes provided they were not colored or flavored. Use of all raw or partially pasteurized milk products in building a mix had no effect on the final phenol value if the mix was pasteurized at 65.6°C.(150°F.) or above. However, at 63.8°C.(147°F.) or below, the mix made from raw milk products gave a considerably higher final phenol value than did the mix made from partially pasteurized milk products. Subjecting raw milk and ice cream mix made from all raw milk products to the same heat treatment by heating to 65.6°C.(150°F.) or above and holding for 30 minutes resulted in the same final phenol value for both milk and mix. Temperatures below 65.6°C.(150°F.) resulted in a higher final phenol value for the ice cream mix than for the milk. The condensing process decreased the amount of phosphate enzyme present. Increasing the serum-solid content of the mix had no effect on the final phenol value when the mix was pasteurized at 65.6°C.(150°F.) for 30 minutes. Storage of pasteurized, unflavored, and uncolored ice cream at —28.8°C.(—20°F.) over a period of two weeks did not alter appreciably the phenol value. Storage of such ice cream for 12 weeks resulted in marked decreases in the phenol value of all samples except those made from mix samples taken 20, 25, and 30 minutes after reaching 65.5°C.(150°F.). Samples heated to a lesser degree than 20 minutes at 65.5°C.(150°F). showed a sufficient phenol value for the sample to be considered under-pasteurized. Pure vanilla had no effect on the phenol value, while artificial and imitation vanilla compounds caused a slight increase and coumarin and vanillin caused appreciable increase in the phenol value. The addition of coloring material to ice cream mix in many instances affected the phenol value unless the coloring matter was precipitated with the protein upon the addition of lead acetate. Test runs

55. Fabian. 1925. J. Dairy Sci. 8, 246-269.
56. Nelson. 1939. Ice Cream Rev. 22, 46 et seq.
57. Hahn and Tracy. 1939. J. Dairy Sci. 22, 219-227.

on commercial samples of ice cream mix gave indication of complete pasteurization in all but one case.

Scharer [58] believed that the pasteurized mix should show no phosphatase activity. This would probably mean adequate pasteurization for destruction of pathogenic bacteria because observations by Caulfield and Martin [59] indicated that sugar protected the enzyme against incubation at temperatures of 61.1°C. (142°F.) to 62.7°C. (145°F.) in 30 minutes. At temperatures around 65.5°C. (150°F.) the enzyme was destroyed regardless of presence or absence of sugar.

Bacterial Content of Ice Cream. Results of many investigations are available in the literature. In general, bacterial counts have been used to judge the conditions under which the ice cream was made and handled. The count alone was probably of much greater significance in former times than it is now. Other methods have been proposed to either supplement the count or replace it. Wiley [60] and his colleagues reported many bacteria in ice cream manufactured in the District of Columbia. Fabian [61] believed that the count could be kept below 100,000 per gram. However, Ayers and Johnson [62] never found summer samples to be below this limit. Only 14.28 per cent of the winter samples were below this limit. Palmer [63] reported bacterial contents between 20,000 and 8,000,000,000 per ml. The cream and utensils contributed most of the bacteria. Ice cream samples collected in London by Rawlinson [64] showed gross contamination. Olson and Fay [13] and Fabian [65] agreed that bacterial numbers could be kept down by careful methods of manufacture. The former accepted Fabian's proposed standard of not over 100,000 bacteria per gram. Hammer [19] reported an average of 19,920,000 bacteria per ml. in ice cream collected on the Des Moines market. He also believed that low-count ice cream could be produced if proper care was used.

Bacteriological examination of 63 samples of ice cream by Chalke [66] gave counts varying from 3,000 or less to over one million per ml., while *Escherichia coli* was present in seven cases in .001 ml., in 21 in .01 ml., in four in .1 ml., and one case only in 1.0 ml. An analysis of the findings shows that the small vendor is worst offender, the most "cold mix" samples are heavily contaminated while "pasteurized-mix" nearly always yielded low bacterial figures, that visiting and education work can be very effective and result in a marked lowering of the bacterial content, and that many possible sources of contamination have to be considered.

Effect of Aging on Bacteria in Ice Cream Mix. Fay and Olson observed little change in the bacterial content of ice cream mix when stored below 7.2°C. (45°F.) for 16 to 24 hours. Hammer and Goss [67] also reported no

58. Scharer. 1939. J. Milk Tech. 2, 19.
59. Caulfield and Martin. 1939. J. Dairy Sci. 22, 261-270.
60. Wiley. 1912. U. S. Pub. Health Serv., Hyg. Lab. Bull. 41, 249-312.
61. Fabian. 1927. Mich. Agr. Expt. Sta., Spec. Bull. 159.
62. Ayers and Johnson. 1915. U. S. Dept. Agr. Bull. 303.
63. Palmer. 1923. J. Dairy Sci. 6, 278-282.
64. Rawlinson. 1927. Lancet 211, 1267.
65. Fabian. 1929. Amer. J. Pub. Health 19, 596-600.
66. Chalke. 1939. Med. Officier 61, 249-252.
67. Hammer and Goss. 1917. Iowa Agr. Expt. Sta. Bull. 174.

increase in numbers of bacteria of mix aged for days at 0°C.(32°F.). Similar results were secured by Peterson and Tracy [68] but Fabian and Cromley [15] reported that aging at 2°C.(35.6°F.) did increase the plate count. These increases were not regular nor were they significant. Mueller and France [69] attempted to ascertain whether or not the aging temperature of 20°C.(68°F.), considered desirable when gelatin is used in the manufacture of ice cream, had an unfavorable effect on the bacterial count of the finished product.

It was found that aging a pasteurized mix for six hours at 68°F. whether followed by aging for 18 hours at 3.3°C.(38°F.) or not, had no significant effect on the increase in the number of bacteria. On the other hand, aging an unpasteurized mix under similar conditions resulted in a material increase in the number of bacteria present. There was no definite increase in bacterial count until after the tenth hour in ice cream mixes aged for 24 hours at 68°F. Aging a mix for 24 hours at 38°F. did not cause a material increase in the number of bacteria.

Effect of Freezing on the Number of Bacteria in Ice Cream. From the nature of the freezing process, one would expect an increase in the number of colonies on plates made from ice cream over the number on plates made with the mix before freezing. Ellenberger [14] found this to be true in almost every case. He observed an average increase of 48 per cent. Gordon, Prescott, Heinemann, and Pease [70] reported similar observations. The increase in the number of bacteria may be explained in the same manner that it is explained by passing milk through a clarifier—to the breaking up of clumps of bacteria during the beating of the mix. Similar increases in the colony count of ice cream owing to freezing have been observed by Fay and Olson [12] and Fabian and Cromley.[15]

Effect of Hardening and Storage on the Number of Bacteria in Ice Cream. When ice cream comes from the freezer it is soft and plastic and must be hardened before storage. It is run into five- or 10-gallon containers or worked into novelties and placed in the hardening room at low temperatures. Hardening alone would probably not destroy many bacteria. Hammer and Goss [71] and Fay and Olson,[72] however, reported decreases in numbers of viable organisms which amounted to as much as 75 per cent in some cases. In a few cases the former investigators observed increases in bacterial counts after hardening. These were believed to be due to manipulation of the sample rather than actual development of bacteria. Fay and Olson's results agreed quite well with those of Hammer and Goss in that hardening and storage for a few days resulted in a decrease of living bacteria.

Most ice cream is stored for varying lengths of time and several investigators have studied the effect of storage on the bacterial content. Esten

68. Peterson and Tracy. 1922. J. Dairy Sci. 5, 273-281.
69. Mueller and France. 1934. Mass. Agr. Expt. Sta. Bull. 314.
70. Gordon, Prescott, Heinemann, and Pease. 1914. Publication of the National Association of Ice Cream Manufacturers, p. 37.
71. Hammer and Goss. 1917. Iowa Agr. Expt. Sta. Bull. 174.
72. Fay and Olson. 1924. J. Dairy Sci. 7, 330.

and Mason [73] reported no marked change in the bacterial content of ice cream kept frozen for at least a month. By the use of litmus lactose gelatin plates, they noticed little change in the percentage of acid-forming and liquefying bacteria. Other investigators, however, have reported decreases in the number of bacteria. Stiles and Pennington [74] stored ice cream for 34 days. They observed in some cases small increases in the number of bacteria during the first three days, after which there was a decrease to the 14th day; a marked increase occurred on the 27th day, followed by a sharp decline to below the original count on the 34th day. Now and then an investigator has reported increases in bacterial numbers during storage. Ellenberger [14] was one of these. Hammer [34] and Hammer and Goss [67] could not observe a tendency for the number of bacteria in ice cream to increase. There was rather a general tendency for the number of bacteria to decrease. Fabian and Cromley [15] made the same observation.

Effect of Season on Number and Types of Bacteria in Ice Cream. Ayers and Johnson [62] found that the average number of bacteria in ice cream is lower during the winter months. A summary of their results is given in the following table:

Item	Summer series (94 samples)	Winter series (91 samples)
Average number of bacteria per ml.	37,859,807	10,388,222
Maximum number.	510,000,000	114,000,000
Minimum number.	120,000	13,000

These authors, as did Ellenberger [14] also, determined the percentage of groups of bacteria in ice cream by the Ayers' milk tube method. Their data are tabulated below:

	Ayers' samples		Ellenberger's experimental samples
	Summer	Winter	
	Pct.	Pct.	Pct.
Acid coagulating	49.82	30.84	46
Acid forming	20.72	38.03	29.4
Inert bacteria	13.98	4.81	22.7
Alkali formers	1.86	5.42	0.6
Peptonizers	13.62	20.90	1.3

Ellenberger also studied the influence of pasteurization of the cream on the percentage distribution of the above groups. The most noticeable difference was that in all except one sample the pasteurized cream group showed but few inert bacteria as compared with the raw cream group. There was at the same time an increase in the total acid group.

Distribution of Bacteria in Ice Cream. Since statements were made that bacteria were very unevenly distributed in ice cream, Ayers and Johnson [75]

73. Esten and Mason. 1915. Conn. Agr. Expt. Sta. Bull. 83, 128-134.
74. Stiles and Pennington. 1907. U. S. Pub. Health Serv., Hyg. Lab. Bull. 41.
75. Ayers and Johnson. 1917. U. S. Dept. Agr. Bull. 563.

collected samples from different places in cans of ice cream. Contrary to the general opinion, they found that the bacteria were quite evenly distributed and that analysis of one sample yielded results which represented the condition of different portions of the same gallon. Furthermore, storage for 11 days in a commercial ice cream cabinet did not cause uneven distribution of the bacteria. A goodly number of samples taken from commercial freezers yielded counts which checked within the usual limits of error of bacteriological analyses. These investigators observed no greater variation in counts when the plates were incubated at 37°C. (98.6°F.) for 48 hours than when incubated at 30°C. (86°F.) for five days.

Homemade Ice Cream. For various reasons, homemade ice cream may contain more bacteria than commercial ice cream. This is due to factors not given as much attention by the homemaker as by the commercial ice cream maker. One hundred samples from 40 homes were examined by Folz and Martin.[76] The logarithmic average standard plate count of all samples was 171,000 per ml. and the logarithmic average coliform count was 70 per ml. Both standard plate count and coliform count were much higher on those samples frozen with salt and cracked ice in tub freezers than were the samples frozen in the freezing units or pans of mechanical refrigerators. Samples frozen from pasteurized dairy products were much lower in both counts than those from unpasteurized dairy products. The bacteriological quality of homemade ice cream averaged lower than that of somples of commercial ice cream collected in a survey made somewhat earlier, more of the homemade samples being found in the high-count groups. This was undoubtedly due largely to the use of unpasteurized milk products in the making of the mix.

Bacteriology of Sherbets and Ices. These have usually shown a much lower bacterial content than ice cream and frozen desserts. Results of only a few investigations have been reported even though these products have enjoyed considerable popularity. Fay[77] examined 21 samples of orange sherbet and found less than 200 bacteria per gram in 10 per cent of the samples, between 200 and 100,000 per gram in 80 per cent of the samples, and more than 100,000 per gram in 10 per cent. Hammer and Goss[71] had previously examined 17 water sherbets which showed bacterial counts between six and 7,800 per ml. Quite different results were secured by Gundel[78] on sherbets made in Germany. He believed that ices and ice cream might become contaminated during manufacture by various agents. Total counts of from 8,000 to 14,500,000 per ml. were secured on samples obtained from trade sources (street vendors, hotels, and restaurants). More than half of the samples contained more than one million bacteria per ml. *Escherichia coli* content was variable but many samples were positive for the organism in .001-ml. quantities or less. Gundel believed that more attention should be given to these products.

76. Foltz and Martin. 1941. Food Research 6, 31-38.

77. Fay. 1928. J. Dairy Sci. 11, 404.

78. Gundel. 1937. Deut. Med. Wchnschr. 63, 1158-1163.

BACTERIAL EXAMINATION OF FROZEN DESSERTS

Many investigators have suggested methods for this purpose. Most of them have involved use of the bacterial plate count as an index of quality and general conditions under which ice cream has been made. As time has progressed and new methods have been developed for other dairy products, especially fluid milk, they have been applied to ice cream. Three methods for determining quality of ice cream were used by Weinzirl and Harris[79]: (a) total count of bacteria (48 hours at 37°C.[98.6°F.]); (b) tests for members of the coliform group, and (c) the anaerobic spore test. They believed that the total count revealed the results of contamination and subsequent multiplication of bacteria introduced but that it did not distinguish between the two. The test for members of the coliform group functions much like the total count but was somewhat more specific in indicating unsanitary conditions. The anaerobic spore test was believed to show unsanitary conditions only. It fails to distinguish between the spores added in the sugar and those resulting from unsanitary conditions.

Control of any food product ought to involve use of every method which will give helpful information. Results of only a few investigations in which various methods were compared have been published. Martin, Nelson, and Caulfield[80] examined 318 samples collected from over 300 ice cream manufacturers in Kansas for the standard plate count; the minimum amount of samples containing coliform organisms; the phosphatase test; the butterfat test; the weight per gallon; and the flavor, body, and texture, and color and package scores. Standard plate counts of 100,000 or less per ml. were obtained on 59.8 per cent of all samples. A slightly higher percentage of samples from counter freezers than from wholesale manufacturers were in the lower count range. Only 17 of the 313 samples gave a positive phosphatase test. However, these authors stated that 126 other samples would have been considered under-pasteurized, if suitable controls had been run. These would have been under-pasteurized or contaminated with unpasteurized dairy products. Failure of results of various methods of examination to agree, prompted Martin, Nelson, and Caulfield[80] to conclude that it was difficult to determine the true quality of a sample by a few tests.

Somewhat the same approach to the problem was made by Yale and Hickey[81] who examined samples collected in a small city in central New York State. Both total and coliform counts were determined for 77 process samples from seven local plants, 137 ice cream samples from 12 retail stores, and 36 dipper-water samples from 18 establishments. Enumeration of coliform bacteria was more sensitive than either standard nutrient agar or tryptone agar counts in revealing contamination by ice cream dippers and dipper waters. Three of the manufacturers had all standard agar plate counts of store samples under 100,000 per gram. Yale and Hickey believed the greatest need for improvement in sanitation to be in dispensing bulk ice cream.

79. Weinzirl and Harris. 1928. J. Dairy Sci. 11, 284-291.
80. Martin, Nelson, and Caulfield. 1939. J. Dairy Sci. 23, 146.
81. Yale and Hickey. 1937. N. Y. Agr. Expt. Sta. Tech. Bull., 248.

Influence of Temperatures of Incubation on Bacterial Counts. The nature of ice cream suggested to some of the investigators that more information should be available on the effect of temperatures of incubation on the colony counts. The average count of plates incubated at 30°C. (86°F.) for five days was almost two and one-half times the count on plates incubated for two days at 37°C.(98.6°F.). In no case did plates incubated at 37°C. show as many colonies as those incubated at 30°C. The counts on plates incubated at 20°C.(68°F.) averaged three times as great as those on plates at 37°C. The results of this comparative study seemed to indicate that the incubation of plates for seven days at 20°C. tended to show the true number of bacteria in ice cream. Ayers and Johnson [75] compared the incubation of plates at 37°C. for two days and at 30°C. for five days. They observed that the incubation of plates at 37°C. for 48 hours did not give counts which showed any greater variation than those obtained by incubation at 30°C. for five days. The count obtained from plates incubated for five days at 30°C. was practically double that from plates incubated at 37°C. for 48 hours. These investigators observed less variation when dilutions were used which gave about 200 colonies on the plates.

The Committee on Bacteriological Methods of Analyzing Dairy Products of the American Dairy Science Association, which prepared a report on methods of ice cream analysis, made indefinite statements about incubation of the plates. They stated that a "more complete" count would be obtained by incubating the plates for 48 hours at 37°C. followed by one week at room temperature. Plate counts probably do not indicate the actual number of bacteria in ice cream or ice cream mix. Fabricius and Hammer [82] reported that when standard agar was used as the plating medium, serious discrepancies were found in the counts secured by plating different dilutions, especially the 1 to 1,000 and 1 to 10,000 dilutions. When one per cent of sucrose was added to the medium, these discrepancies did not occur. The presence of sucrose also frequently made the colonies so much larger that they were more easily counted. Various types of organisms were found to be responsible for pin-point colonies on plates poured with ice cream dilutions.

Satisfactory sampling is one obstacle in bacteriological examination of ice cream. Data in the past have, in general, been based on the gravimetric and volumetric basis. Fay [83] compared the data secured by both methods. The errors which might be introduced by gravimetric methods are more apparent than real. Fay concluded that just as reliable data could be secured with the volumetric as with the more tedious gravimetric sample. He also believed that a 10-ml. would be preferable to one-ml. sample.

Influence of Plating Medium on Bacterial Content of Ice Cream. Substitution, in the seventh edition of *Standard Methods for the Examination of Dairy Products 1940*, of dextrose-tryptone-glucose skim milk agar for the nutrient agar which had been used for many years prompted investi-

82. Fabricius and Hammer. 1931. Iowa Agr. Expt. Sta. Bull. 285.
83. Fay. 1930. J. Dairy Sci. 13, 40-47.

gations in which the two media were compared. As far as ice cream is concerned, the change was made without information as to how the new medium would work with ice cream. Abele [84] presented a few data which prompted him to conclude that standards for ice cream would not have to be changed, even though the new medium would reveal many more bacteria. This would seem to indicate that plate count standards do not mean much.

Many comparative studies were made in which the old plating medium was compared with the new one mentioned above.

Robertson [85] reported results of comparisons made in five different ice cream plants of bacteria counts obtained by use of standard nutrient agar then in use and with tryptone-glucose agar at both 32°C.(89.6°F.) and 37°C.(98.6°F.). The latter was found to give definitely higher bacteria counts than standard nutrient agar. The higher count with tryptone-glucose agar is thought to be a more accurate criterion of the actual number of organisms present in ice cream than is the count secured with standard nutrient agar. As to the incubation temperature, duplicate counts from the same dilution waters have been shown to be from 30 to 50 per cent less variable at 32°C. than at 37°C. Similar results were reported by Foltz and Martin [86] who made bacterial counts on 279 samples of commercial ice cream using standard nutrient agar and 37°C. incubation temperature, and tryptone-glucose-skim milk agar incubating the plates at 37°C. and 32°C. The logarithmic average of the standard agar counts at 37°C. was 96,500, and the counts obtained on tryptone agar at 37°C. and 32°C. incubation temperatures were 137 and 192 per cent, respectively, of the standard agar count. The arithmetic average of the standard agar count was 5,490,000, and the counts obtained on tryptone agar at 37°C. and 32°C. were 132 and 156 per cent, respectively, of the standard agar count. The mean and median ratios of tryptone agar count at 32°C. to the standard agar count at 37°C. were 4.11 and 1.52, respectively. The mean ratio of the tryptone agar count at 37°C. to the standard agar count at 37°C. was 2.46 and the median ratio was 1.25.

White [87] covered about the same ground by making comparative total bacterial counts of 82 samples of ice cream on standard nutrient agar, standard nutrient agar plus one per cent sucrose, and two types of tryptone-glucose-milk agar, to one of which five ml. of fresh skim milk per liter were added just previous to tubing, while in the other the skim milk was already incorporated in dehydrated form. Bacto dehydrated media were used and plates were incubated at 37°C. for 48 hours. With the majority of samples, higher counts were obtained on the media containing sugar than on standard nutrient agar. The use of sugar media did not have as great an effect on total counts when few bacteria were present in the ice cream as when the counts were high. The presence of sugar tended to increase the size of the colonies, decrease the number of pin-point colonies, and give better

84. Abele. 1940. J. Milk Tech. 3, 24-32.
85. Robertson. 1936. Proc. 36th Ann. Conv., Internatl. Assoc. Ice Cream Manfrs., 132; J. Milk Tech. 2 (1939), 84-86.
86. Foltz and Martin. 1938. J. Dairy Sci. 21, 289-294.
87. White. 1938. Sci. Agr. 19, 69-80.

agreement in the counts on different dilutions, especially those of 1:1,000 and 1:10,000. There was no significant difference in the total counts on tryptone-glucose-milk agar when the skim milk had been added in different form. A more constant proportion of the bacterial flora in ice cream capable of developing colonies was obtained on standard nutrient agar plus one per cent sucrose and on tryptone-glucose-milk agar than on standard nutrient agar.

Several other media were compared by Babel [88]: (1) tryptone-glucose-skim milk agar, standard nutrient agar plus one per cent sucrose, and standard nutrient agar for determining the total bacterial count of ice cream; (2) brilliant green lactose peptone bile, formate-ricinoleate broth, Leifson's desoxycholate agar, and Bacto violet red bile agar for detecting the presence of the coliform group in ice cream; and (3) for determining the number of yeasts and molds, thermoduric, thermophilic, and sporeforming organisms in ice cream and their relation to the total count. The analysis of 192 samples of commercial ice cream for total bacteria showed tryptone-glucose-skim milk agar to be superior to standard nutrient agar or standard nutrient agar plus one per cent sucrose. Tryptone-glucose-skim milk agar gave higher total counts and colonies of greater size than did the other two media. Standard nutrient agar plus one per cent sucrose gave, on the average, slightly higher counts and colonies of greater size than did standard nutrient agar.

Violet red bile agar was superior to sodium desoxycholate agar in the detection and enumeration of members of the coliform group of organisms on ice cream.

Violet red bile agar and sodium desoxycholate agar are superior to formate-ricinoleate broth or brilliant green lactose peptone bile in detecting the presence of the Escherichia-Aerobacter group of organisms in ice cream.

No significant difference was found in a comparison of formate-ricinoleate broth and brilliant green lactose peptone bile in their ability to detect the presence of the Escherichia-Aerobacter group of organisms in ice cream.

The most frequent ratio occurring between thermophilic, thermoduric, and sporeforming bacteria in relation to the total count was 1 to 1:10.

Strawberry ice cream contained the largest number of sporeforming organisms when compared with vanilla or chocolate. Chocolate ice cream had the highest ratio of spores to total bacteria, indicating few sporeforming organisms.

A direct relation was secured between the total bacterial count and the yeast and mold count of ice cream. The yeast and mold count usually increased with an increase in the number of total bacteria.

METHODS FOR BACTERIOLOGICAL EXAMINATION OF ICE CREAM

These methods are much like those for the examination of milk. Special attention must be given to the sample since, if it is not representative, results of analysis will be misleading.

88. Babel. 1936. Ice Cream Trade J. 32, 35.

Determination of Streptococci in Ice Cream. (Wiley[89]). The method for the detection of streptococci in ice cream has been used by Wiley and his coworkers as follows: The melted sample should be centrifuged for half an hour in a Stewart lactocrite with a speed of approximately 3,000 r.p.m. This apparatus, which consists of a flat aluminum pan holding 20 tubes of one-ml. capacity and stoppered at the outer end with a specially constructed rubber plug, causes the sediment not only to be thrown to the end of the tube but drives it against the rubber plug with such a force that it is almost quantitatively adherent to the plug. Accordingly, if one removes the rubber stopper and by rubbing on a glass slide and over an area of known surface attaches the sediment, one can obtain, on staining and examining the film microscopically, an approximation of the number of organisms and leucocytes in one ml. of the liquid. Because of the débris in the ice cream, which ordinarily renders the usual method of centrifuging milk and cream samples quite impracticable, the above method was resorted to so far as the detection of the presence of streptococci was concerned. It was found eminently satisfactory.

Fay's[90] Method for Enumerating Bacteria in Ice Cream. Remove and discard a one-fourth inch layer of ice cream from the surface of the container in order to eliminate surface contamination. The sample for analysis is then taken with a sterile butter sampler. The cores should be removed from the entire depth of the ice cream, one from the center and one from the edge of the can. These cores should be placed in a sterile bottle which is submerged in water at 45°C.(113°F.) for five to 10 minutes until the ice cream is melted. A gravimetric sample is then obtained by adding 10 grams of melted ice cream directly to a 90-ml. dilution blank of sterile physiological sodium chloride solution. Appropriate dilutions may then be made from this and plates made in accordance with "Standard Methods for Bacteriological Examination of Milk."

Ellenberger's[14] Method for Determining Number of Bacteria in Ice Cream. Remove the surface of the ice cream to a depth of one-half inch with a sterile spoon and then remove a sample with a sterile butter trier. Transfer the sample to an ordinary dilution bottle and allow to stand at room temperature. Thoroughly mix by shaking and then transfer about one ml. to a sterile weighing bottle and weigh. Dilutions are calculated from this weight and the number of bacteria is expressed per gram.

Newman's[91] Procedures for Bacteriological Examination of Frozen Desserts. The following procedures were developed in a successful system of control of frozen desserts in the State of California over many years.* The former outline of bacteriological technic by Smith, Newman and Nielsen[91a] is superseded by the present one herein reviewed in some detail; it is an integral part of the regulatory control of these products.

Considerable preliminary work was done in Newman's laboratory to determine whether samples should be gravimetric or volumetric. Since it was found that one ml. of various melted ice creams might vary in weight from 0.5 to 1.5 grams and that the weight of one ml. portion of a sample might vary considerably from weighings of subsequent portions, depending on the temperature at which the sample was held and the interval between weighings, Newman adopted the gravimetric method described by Smith, Newman and Nielsen.

NECESSARY EQUIPMENT

Newman listed several special pieces of equipment besides those usually found in a bacteriological laboratory.

a. Butter boats, made of monel metal, stainless steel, sheet nickel, etc. (one for each sample). Newman uses butter boats made of monel metal supplied by Mojonnier Bros. Company of Chicago.

b. Rimless test tubes 4¾" by 4¾" (one for each sample).

c. Dilution bottles, 6 oz. prescription ovals for the 99 ml. water blanks; the mouths of these bottles have an opening sufficiently large to allow a butter boat to slide freely

89. Wiley. 1912. U. S. Pub. Health Serv., Hyg. Lab. Bull. 41, 251-311.
90. Fay. 1923. J. Dairy Sci. 6, 283-291.
91. Smith, Newman, and Nielsen. 1928. Calif. State Dept. Agr., Mon. Bull. 17, 239-246.
* Newman's paper in which this technic is described contains several illustrations which will not be reproduced in this book.

into the bottle (one required for each sample). Occasionally it may be necessary to alter the width of the butter boat to fit the opening of the dilution bottle. This may be done by squeezing the sides of the boat with pliers.

d. Water bath for tempering agar medium before pouring.

e. Suitable analytical balance or scales.

f. Colony counting chamber with adequate illumination of the Petri dish.

COLLECTION OF SAMPLES

The samples are taken with a sterile metal spatula or spoon. The former is an all metal (one piece) stainless steel, heavily plated dinner knife ground to furnish a blade three to four inches long. The end is square and sharpened in a chisel fashion. Prior to taking each sample, the spatula is washed and then sterilized by heating in the flame of an alcohol lamp. The surface layer of the ice cream is always removed before sampling bulk ice cream because this surface would not be bacteriologically representative of the entire product and, also, because in many instances the surface may be covered with frost crystals which would affect the analysis for fat and solids determinations.

Samples are placed in sterile two-ounce, screw-capped wide-mouth bottles. The aluminum caps of these bottles have lacquered paper liners which are replaced each time the bottles are to be sterilized. This amount of sample has been found to be adequate for both bacteriological and chemical analysis. After the samples have been sealed, and labeled for identity, they are placed in insulated shipping cases containing pads of frozen brine. Samples are thus kept in their original frozen condition despite exterior high temperatures. When the case has been filled it is placed in the hardening room of an ice cream plant over night to refreeze the brine and thoroughly chill the samples. The next morning the brine pads and cover are replaced and the case expressed to the laboratory. Such samples arrive at the laboratory completely frozen even though they may have been shipped hundreds of miles. Included in the shipping case are the inspector's record cards containing all necessary information for the analyst as well as signed statements of the manufacturer that the samples were taken in his presence and in proper manner.

METHOD OF PLATING

1. Each sample is maintained in a frozen condition until ready for plating. Then

2. Samples are placed in a water tempering bath maintained at not more than 40°C., and for a period of not longer than five minutes. As a rule most samples are ready to pipette in from one to two minutes or less. Warming samples to a temperature above 40°C. is unnecessary and should be avoided.

3. When the frozen dessert has melted, shake the sample 25 times in accordance with the directions described for shaking dilution bottles in Standard Methods for the Examination of Dairy Products.

4. Remove the cotton plug from a test tube, holding the tube in a slanting position so that the butter boat slowly slides down toward the opening against the plug. The movement of the boat is controlled by the plug as the latter is withdrawn. Allow about one-half inch of the boat to project out beyond the opening of the tube. Place the tube on one pan of the balance. Discard the cotton plug. Place a counterbalance on the opposite pan and check for exact balance. Add a one gm. weight to the counterbalance.

5. Measure exactly one gm. of the liquid dessert into the butter boat by means of a sterile one ml. pipette. With short practice this may be done very easily, accurately and rapidly.

6. With one hand, remove the wine bottle cap from a 90 ml. dilution bottle. Tilt the bottle slightly to receive the boat. With the other hand, carefully remove the test tube from the balance pan; then using care not to spill any of the sample allow the boat to slide down, end first, into the dilution bottle. Replace the dilution bottle cap. If desired the dilution may be marked with an identification number before proceeding with the next sample.

7. Shake the dilution bottle and then plate according to the method described for milk in the latest edition of Standard Methods for the Examination of Dairy Products.

8. Not more than 25 minutes shall elapse between the time the first frozen sample is placed in the water-bath and the agar medium is poured into the last plate.

9. The temperature and time of incubation of the plates shall be that specified for milk in Standard Examination of Dairy Products.

10. In counting incubated plates it is essential to use a colony counting chamber providing adequate illumination from beneath the plate. It is important, also, to use a magnifying glass or hand lens of sufficient power (such as 3½× opticians lens) to clearly differentiate between small bacterial colonies and other small objects which may simulate colonies. Particularly is this necessary for some ice milks, some of the mixes and for many of the various ingredients which enter into their manufacture. This subject is treated at some length in the original paper.

11. Counts shall be reported as "Standard Plate Count No....., Bacteria Per Gram."

American Dairy Science Association Bacteriological Methods for the Examination of Ice Cream. Through its committee on bacteriological methods the American Dairy Science Association formulated a complete set of bacteriological procedures useful in controlling the quality of dairy products. A preliminary report [92] was published for ice cream; parts of this report are reproduced below with permission of the chairman of the committee. The complete report should be available to all analysts concerned with the bacteriological examination of ice cream.

Sampling. The sample may be either weighed or measured. The gravimetric method was recommended for research and public-health work.

Media. The media recommended by the committee for ice cream analysis were the standard agar, preparation of which is described in *Standard Methods of Milk Analysis of the American Public Health Association,* and Ayers and Mudge's milk powder agar, which is described in Chapter 26.

Making the agar plates. After placing one ml. of the desired dilutions in Petri dishes, 10 ml. of agar should be admitted to each plate under aseptic conditions. If the agar is in flasks, care should be taken to pour the same amount of agar into each plate. The number of plates poured will depend upon the accuracy desired. Ordinarily, duplicate plates should be prepared from each dilution, although this may not be necessary in routine work.

Incubation. The Standard Methods of Milk Analysis recommends incubation of plates for 48 hours at 37°C.(98.6°F.); still other laboratories use one-week incubation at room temperature. If results are to be compared with the results of another laboratory, the incubation time and temperature should be the same in both laboratories.

Plates should be inverted during incubation to prevent spreaders. The atmosphere in the incubator should be kept moist so as to prevent the drying of the media. Care should always be taken not to stack plates in piles of more than three, in order to insure equal incubation of all plates. Plates should not be disturbed during incubation, otherwise the water of condensation will flow across the plate and cause growth on the surface of the agar.

Counting the colonies. A convenient method of counting the colonies is to invert the plate and mark each colony with ink or a wax pencil as it is counted, at the same time keeping count with a tally meter in the other hand. This method greatly increases the accuracy of counting by preventing confusion of the count, owing to interruptions or to counting the same colony twice. All plates in a series should be counted at as nearly the same time as possible. After counting the colonies with the naked eye, all plates should be carefully examined with a hand lens (3½ ×) to detect colonies too small to be seen with the naked eye. Occasionally, it may prove necessary to examine the plates under the low power of a compound microscope to determine the true nature of apparent colonies.

Bacteriological Methods of Examination of Frozen Desserts Recommended by the Ordinance and Code of the United States Public Health Service.[3] These follow quite closely those recommended in the milk ordinance and code, parts of which are reviewed

92. J. Dairy Sci. 10 (1927), 460-478.

* Bacteriological Methods of Examining Ice Cream. Jour. Dairy Science. 10 (1927) 460-478.

earlier in this book. In this ordinance a grading period is not longer than six months. During this time at least four samples of frozen desserts and pasteurized mix from each plant are collected. Samples from retail vendors may be examined as often as desired. These samples must be protected from contamination and kept below 10°C.(50°F.) until examined. Bacterial plate counts and microscope counts are to be made in conformity with *Standard Methods for the Examination of Dairy Products* of the American Public Health Association. The 1934 edition, instead of the current one, is indicated because of lack of information on applicability of the tryptone-dextrose-skim milk agar as a plating medium in place of the older standard agar medium. Until this question is settled the 1934 *Standard Methods* is to be used.

The Ordinance and Code Recommended by the United States Public Health Service prescribes as follows for bacterial examination of frozen desserts:

"*Reporting bacterial plate counts.* The number of routine samples which must be examined in many cities makes the use of more than two dilutions per sample impracticable. For this reason it has become general practice to make only two dilutions. In all except known high-count milk or frozen desserts the dilutions used are 1-100 and 1-1,000; on the latter 1-1,000 and 1-10,000. The following special rules for reporting counts are now being used:

"(1) When the higher plate count is more than twice the lower, record the lower count.

"(2) When the higher plate count is not more than twice the lower, apply the Standard Methods rules for counting, which may be summarized as follows: (a) If there are plates with 30 to 300 colonies, use all of them and no others; (b) otherwise use that nearest 300.

"(3) In case one plate cannot be counted because of a spreader covering more than half the plate, the result is to be reported as unsatisfactory unless the count of the other plate is within the grade then held by the supply in question.

"(4) Report bacterial plate counts to the nearest 1,000, unless the count exceeds 100,000, in which case report to the nearest 10,000, or unless the count exceeds 1,000,000, in which case report to the nearest 100,000.

"(5) If all plates show no growth the result shall be reported as unsatisfactory.

"A good method by which control officials may judge laboratory technique and the correctness of reporting is to have the laboratory enter its results upon the following form of laboratory record form.

"The State representatives should determine the following data each grading period as a part of the State records:

"(1) Average of the count ratios of those samples for which both dilutions show between 30 and 300 colonies. This should not be over 2.0.

"(2) Per cent unsatisfactory counts (spreaders). This should not be over 2 per cent.

"(3) Per cent incorrectly recorded counts. This should be practically 0.

"These three figures are measures with which to judge the work of the laboratory.

"All counts should be recorded on the ledger record as soon as reported by the laboratory.

"*Averaging bacterial counts.* In determining grades (or compliance with the minimum requirements) of milk supplies and frozen desserts manufacturers, the average of the last four consecutive counts or reductase hours is used because less than this number has been found by experience not to give a dependable picture of the bacteriological conditions of a supply. The averaging of bacterial counts under this ordinance is done by the logarithmic instead of the arithmetic method. This is because the arithmetic method is sometimes unfair to the manufacturer or producer. Suppose, for example, the laboratory reports the last four consecutive counts to be 10,000, 10,000, 10,000, and 1,000,000. The one unusually high count may have been the result of accident and is not fair cause for degrading or permit revocation, yet if an arithmetic average is used, the supply would not comply with grade A standards, although its most usual quality is grade A.

"For this reason the logarithmic average bacterial count is specified in connection with the enforcement of this ordinance. By its use high counts are "snubbed," so to speak, unless all counts are high, in which case the snubbing effect tends to disappear and the logarithmic average approaches the arithmetic average. For example, the same counts previously listed would yield a logarithmic average of 32,000, thus keeping the supply in grade A, where it obviously belongs.

"*How to find the average bacterial count by logarithms.* The logarithms of bacterial counts from 1,000 to 300,000,000 are given in the table on the following page.[93] The logarithms should be entered opposite the counts in the control ledger. To find the average bacterial count find the average of the logarithms and then find the bacterial count in the table [93] which is opposite the average logarithm.

Following is an example:

Counts	Logarithms
35,000	4.54
11,000	4.04
9,000	3.95
95,000	4.98

$$4 \overline{\smash{)}17.51}$$

4.38 = average logarithm

4.38 in the table is opposite 24,000, which is therefore the average bacterial count.

"If it is found that the average logarithm occurs opposite more than one bacterial count in the table, take the lowest bacterial count as the average.

"*Reductase test.* When the reductase test is used the procedure shall be as follows: Follow Standard Methods except that samples are to be examined at the end of each hour but not beyond 8 hours. The reduction time shall be expressed as the number of elapsed full hours when decolorization is first observed. Samples not reduced at the end of 8 hours are to be reported as reduced in 9 hours. For purposes of grading the simple arithmetic average (not the logarithmic average) of the last four consecutive samples is to be used.

"*Bacterial and reductase test standards.* Section 7 of this ordinance establishes limits of average bacterial plate count in the case of frozen desserts, pasteurized mix, and pasteurized or otherwise heated ingredients derived from milk, and of average plate count or average direct microscopic count or average reduction time in the case of raw ingredients derived from milk. When average direct microscopic counts are used the limits are the same as for average plate counts if clumps are counted, but four times as high if individual organisms are counted. The limits are doubled for cream used as an ingredient of frozen desserts."

American Public Health Association Procedures for Determining the Number of Bacteria in Ice Cream. These are embodied in *Standard Methods for the Examination of Dairy Products,* a new edition of which is published at intervals of a few years. The agar plate method of making counts for routine control of frozen ice cream is recommended. Where it is possible, the microscope method is also recommended to give results with which to supplement the plate counts. Detailed procedures are given for handling the sample. These will not be recorded here for most of them would be used only by an analyst who has the right to be making such analyses.

The plating medium recommended is tryptone-glucose-skim milk agar, unfortunately designated as "nutrient agar," the name used for the plating medium for many years. The agar recommended in the 1939 edition of *Standard Methods for the Examination of Dairy Products* is the new medium approved for milk analysis. The Advisory Committee which prepared the Frozen Desserts Ordinance and Code Recommended by the United States Public Health Service, May, 1940 Edition, indicated that in enforcement of that ordinance, the old plating medium should be used. Consequently, they advised use of the 1934 edition of *Standard Methods of Milk Analysis* until it could be determined whether new standards would have to be established.

<hr>

93. In the printed ordinance is a table to be used for computing logarithmic averages of bacterial counts.

Alternative Bacterial Standards Established by Section 7 for Frozen Desserts, Pasteurized Mix, and Ingredients Derived from Milk

Product, heated or unheated, grade of plant [94]	Log. average plate count not to exceed	Log. average direct microscopic count not to exceed		Arithmetic average reductase hours not less than
		Clumps	Individual organisms	
FROZEN DESSERTS AND PASTEURIZED MIX				
Grade A plants.................................	50,000	....	....	....
Grade B plants.................................	100,000	....	....	....
Grade C plants.................................	No limit	....	....	....
CREAM AS INGREDIENT				
If pasteurized:				
Grade A plants.................................	100,000	....	....	....
Grade B plants.................................	500,000	....	....	....
Grade C plants.................................	No limit	....	....	....
If raw:				
Grade A plants.................................	400,000	400,000	1,600,000	5
Grade B plants.................................	2,000,000	2,000,000	8,000,000	2½
Grade C plants.................................	No limit	No limit	No limit	No limit
MILK AND INGREDIENTS DERIVED FROM MILK				
If pasteurized, condensed, powdered, etc.:				
Grade A plants.................................	50,000	....	....	....
Grade B plants.................................	250,000	....	....	....
Grade C plants.................................	No limit	....	....	....
If raw:				
Grade A plants.................................	200,000	200,000	800,000	6
Grade B plants.................................	1,000,000	1,000,000	4,000,000	3½
Grade C plants.................................	No limit	No limit	No limit	No limit

94. The Grade A specifications listed here are identical with the minimum requirements in the non-grading form of this ordinance.

Fabian's [95] Microscope Method for Counting Bacteria in Ice Cream. The only additional apparatus required is an analytical balance. Slides used in this work should be exceptionally clean if the best results are to be obtained. The slides are placed on the balance and counterpoised; .01 gram of ice cream is then weighed upon each end of the slide as quickly as possible in order to reduce the error owing to evaporation. A platinum loop has been found to work very well for putting the ice cream on the slide. The .01 gram of ice cream is then spread uniformly over an area of one square centimeter, using a clean needle. This area may be conveniently measured by placing the slide upon the guide plate or any surface ruled in square centimeter areas. After the film is spread, the slide should be placed upon a warm surface for drying. The drying should not be too rapid for this may crack the film and cause it to peel from the slide. However, the drying should be completed quickly (within 10 minutes) or growth may take place.

After the film has been prepared as above described, the slides are ready for the staining process. They are first dipped in xylol or other suitable fat solvent for five minutes to remove the fat. Longer exposure is necessary for ice cream than for milk, owing to the larger amount of fat present. The xylol is then drained off and the slide again placed on a warm surface to evaporate the remainder of the xylol. The slides are next immersed in 70 to 95 per cent grain or denatured alcohol for about 20 minutes.

95. Fabian. 1925. J. Dairy Sci. 8, 246-269.

The alcohol is poured off and the slide again placed on a warm surface. The film is then stained 30 seconds with Loeffler's methylene blue, prepared as follows: saturated alcoholic solution of methylene blue, 30 ml. caustic potash (.01 per cent solution), 100 ml. Care should be taken in selecting the methylene blue. Fresh preparations of the stain from a satisfactory source should be used.

The film is then ready to be decolorized. This may be done by first draining off the excess stain, and placing the slide in 70 to 95 per cent alcohol. The length of time it should remain in the alcohol is a matter of judgment and experience; usually dipping the slide in and out once or twice is sufficient. In case the decolorization is carried too far, the preparation may be re-stained without apparent injury. The film should be warmed again after it has been decolorized; this seems to be necessary for best results.

In routine practice staining jars may be used to good advantage. Place four jars in a row, containing xylol, 95 per cent alcohol, Loeffler's methylene blue, and 95 per cent alcohol, respectively. The preparation of four slides may be started and carried through the whole procedure at the same time, and these followed by four more, thus saving considerable time.

The Frost Little Plate Method for Counting Bacteria in Ice Cream. This technic described fully on page 354 was observed by Bryan et al.[95a] to yield counts comparable to those obtained with the standard agar plate.

Fay's [96] Microscope Method for Examination of Ice Cream and Other Dairy Products. This is another modification of the microscope method for counting bacteria in dairy products. Fay believed that the weighing procedures involved in securing .01 gram of sample on a slide, as proposed in the Fabian method reported above, introduced possibilities for error besides being too tedious and time consuming for practical conditions. Fay, therefore, placed .1 ml. of the sample on a clean slide and added two to four drops of sterile water. The mixture was then spread evenly over the entire surface of the slide. The film was allowed to dry and was then stained in the usual manner. If the diameter of the microscope field has been standardized to .157 mm. the bacterial count may be determined by multiplying the average number of cells per field by the factor 1,000,000.

Examination of Ice Cream by the Burri Film Technic. Results of examination of several other dairy products with Burri's [97] method are given in other places in this book. Long and Hammer [98] applied it to ice cream.

Small portions (.02 mg.) selected from firm ice cream are spread over the surface of a dry agar slant using a low-power binocular microscope to aid in keeping the portions of fairly uniform size and to avoid scraping from a large area. The number of colonies developing from the various portions indicates the distribution and general bacterial content. Variation in the weights of the portions picked is greater than with butter. The data list the number of colonies on agar slants smeared with the interior of package ice cream, interior and surface of dipped ice cream including those with counts over 100,000 per ml., and a comparison of the counts on ice cream by this Burri technic and the plate method. There was no close agreement between the two methods, counts being generally higher with the Burri technic. The primary advantage of the Burri technic is the use of few slants and the opportunity to study distribution of the organism in the product.

Bacterial Standards for Ice Cream.

These are largely plate counts and in the past have varied widely. Efforts have been made to relate plate counts to conditions of production. While such a relationship may exist under some conditions, it may have no such relationship under other conditions. In some cases, it seems that about all plate counts are good for is to confuse an ice cream manufacturer and make him believe that his

95a. Bryan et al. 1942. J. Dairy Sci. 25, 827-835.
96. Fay. 1933. Idem 16, 311-313.
97. See Chapter 6 for discussion and references.
98. Long and Hammer. 1940. Iowa State Col. J. Sci. 14, 163-177.

product may have too many microorganisms with no effort whatever to find out what they are and whether they have any significance. *Standard Methods for the Examination of Dairy Products*, 1939 edition, in a discussion "Interpretation of Agar Plate Counts" covers these points quite well. In one place it is stated:

"In this connection it should be borne in mind that there is an unavoidably high percentage of error in the agar plate method of estimating the number of bacteria in ice cream; also that ice cream having a high plate count does not necessarily contain pathogenic bacteria; and that an ice cream having a low agar plate count is not necessarily free of pathogenic bacteria. Laboratory analyses should always be combined with sanitary inspections before definite conclusions are drawn."

It is also stated that a high count in ice cream means not necessarily an insanitary product but more properly a neglected product. This is not necessarily true, for the committee which prepared these "standard methods" has admitted that there is "an unavoidably high percentage of error in the agar plate method of estimating the number of bacteria in ice cream."

The whole question is whether bacteria plate counts are indices of quality. What is "quality" in ice cream? Nothing more than excellence of character which involves many factors. Bacterial content is only one of them and, at best, is of questionable value in some cases.

Many standards have been proposed for so-called control of ice cream. They vary widely as do most such standards for other dairy products. *Standard Methods for the Examination of Dairy Products*, while giving seven pages of instructions for ice cream analysis which are offered as "standard methods," makes no suggestions as to "standards." Some of the difficulties in establishing such standards have been reviewed by Anderson,[99] who was not opposed to them but believed that they had great limitations and must be used most carefully. They will not guarantee freedom from pathogenic bacteria but may contribute to a more hygienic product when used along with other proposals which were made. Bardsley [100] recognized two grades of ice cream designated as A and B. To qualify as Grade A, coliform bacteria must be absent in .1-ml. amounts and the total number of bacteria shall not exceed 200,000 bacteria per ml. at 22°C.(71.6°F.) or 37°C.(98.6°F.); enterococcus must be absent in .01 ml. and spores of *Clostridium welchii* must be absent in 10 ml. For Grade B ice cream the requirements are absence of coliform bacteria in .01 ml., not over 500,000 bacteria per ml., absence of enterococci in .01 ml., and absence of enterococci in 10 ml.

In 1932, Fabian [101] reported a range of 100,000 to 800,000 per gram. He considered a standard of 100,000 per gram as a reasonable bacterial standard. This was supported by experience in ice cream plants of varying sanitary conditions. As chairman of the Committee on Ice Cream Sanitation of the International Association of Milk Santarians [102] Fabian

99. Anderson. 1935. J. Roy. Sanit. Dist. 55, 592-599.
100. Bardsley. 1938. J. Hyg. 38, 527-546.
101. Fabian. 1932. Amer. J. Pub. Health 22, 353-359.
102. Fabian (Chairman). 1939. J. Milk Tech. 2, 193-196.

studied the standards of 12 states. They varied from 75,000 per gram in California to 500,000 per ml. in two other states. In the case of one state the standard is 100,000 per ml. for plain and 500,000 per ml. for frozen desserts with fruits and nut meats. The reason for such standards is not easy to see. If plate counts mean anything at all in ice cream sanitation, why should there be leniency with a nut and fruit product, especially when Tracy and Prucha [103] found that 50 per cent of samples of nut meats harbored *Escherichia coli*? Newman [91] stated that the first standard in California was not more than 150,000 per gram but in August, 1937, it was reduced to 75,000 per gram and the law was broadened to include sherbets.

Graaff [104] reported the requirements of the ice cream decree, based on the Netherlands food law to be: negative Storch reaction; no more than 100,000 organisms per ml.; and no viable coliform bacteria in .1 ml. or less. The vanilla ice cream for sale in Utrecht gave the Storch reaction in 25 per cent of cases, about 35 per cent of the tested samples had more than 100,000 organisms per ml.; and about 46 per cent had a coliform titer of .01 to .001 ml. The streptococcus titer, useful in indicating age of ice cream and care taken in preparation and storage, was determined, results indicating that for ice cream of good quality the titer should not be more than .001 ml.

In England, Benson [105] suggested both chemical and bacteriological standards for ice cream as follows: Bacteriological—(1) not more than 100,000 bacteria per ml. and no coliform bacillus in .1 ml., also all ice cream mixes must be subject to efficient pasteurization. Chemical—(1) ice cream to contain not less than six per cent butterfat and not less than 18 per cent milk solids total. A standard of not over 100,000 colonies per ml. was also approved by Thomas *et al.*[106] He also believed that coliform bacteria should not be present in .1 ml.

The United States Public Health Service,[3] in its frozen desserts ordinance which is recommended for adoption to states and communities, prescribes limits of bacterial content of frozen desserts of 50,000 per ml. of melted product for Grade A plants, 100,000 per ml. for Grade B plants, and no limits for Grade C plants. These standards are significant, for they are used with careful plant inspection. This ordinance is probably the best statement of procedures which should be followed in making certain that proper products are distributed to the consuming public. Fabian [101] stated many years ago that whatever method is adopted for this purpose it should

1. Be concerned with the type of raw materials;
2. Refuse to permit reprocessing of ice cream mix;
3. Define pasteurization as at least 65.6°C.(150°F.) for 30 minutes;

103. Tracy and Prucha. 1936. Ice Cream Trade J. 32, 17, 18 and 20.
104. Graaff. 1932. Pharm. Weekbl. 69, 1124-1132.
105. Benson. 1933. J. Roy. Sanit. Inst. 53, 542-547.
106. Thomas *et al.* 1938. Welsh J. Agr. 14, 261-277.
107. England. 1938. Ice Cream Field 32, 31-32 *et seq.*

4. Provide a maximum standard of not over 100,000 bacteria per gram;
5. Prescribe medical examination of all who handle the product;
6. Require licensing of manufacturer after inspection;
7. Provide for regular inspection.

England [107] and Anderson [99] believed that inspections of methods of manufacture were very important. Their suggestions were quite similar to those quoted above from Fabian. Anderson recommended pasteurization at 71° C. (160° F.) and storage of the mix before pasteurization below 4.44° C. (40° F.) for not over two days.

Sediment Tests on Frozen Desserts. The sediment testing of milk and butter has been generally accepted. This test has done much to improve the products just mentioned. Appearance of dirt on a disc is visual evidence that anyone must admit. One important objection is that straining may be resorted to to remove the visible dirt. This was also admitted in *Standard Methods of Milk Analysis* of the American Public Health Association. Parker [108] recommended that a half-pint sample of mix or frozen dessert be used in the sediment test. Detailed instructions were prepared by a joint committee of the American Public Health Association [109] for determining sediment in various constituents of frozen desserts.

Coliform Bacteria in Frozen Desserts. Attempts have been made to determine the value of coliform bacteria content with nearly all dairy products. While these organisms have been found in ice cream, little agreement exists as to their significance. Examination of results of many investigations on this question probably indicate that the coliform test alone is not acceptable.

Ayers and Johnson [75] found organisms forming gas from lactose present in one-tenth ml. in 88.33 per cent of 120 samples of ice cream. The average number of gas formers in the entire series of samples was 16.298 per ml. Ellenberger [14] made plates with ice cream samples with Endo's medium, since the presence of *Escherichia coli* in dairy products has been looked upon with suspicion. This technic indicated no increase in members of the *Escherichia coli* group, but on the contrary a decided falling off during storage. Rawlinson [64] found 22 samples of ice cream in London which contained over 10,000 coliform organisms per ml. while *Clostridium sporogenes* was present also in large numbers. This investigator believed that the presence of so many coliform organisms was a danger signal. The *Escherichia coli* count of ice cream was believed to be specific in indicating unsanitary conditions of manufacture by Weinzirl and Harris.[79] It is doubtful whether *Escherichia coli* could have more significance in ice cream than it has in milk. Until that question is settled, the use of *Escherichia coli* as an index of unsatisfactory conditions in ice cream manufacture is open to considerable question. This position seems to be justified by data

108. Parker. 1939. J. Milk Tech. 2, 87-90.
109. Amer. Pub. Health Assoc. Yearbook, 1937-1938, 49-51.
110. Anzulovic. 1932. J. Bact. 23, 56.

reported by Fabian and Coulter.[48] Anzulovic[110] attempted to determine whether *Escherichia coli* could survive in ice cream. Seventy-three samples of ice cream were found to contain from 200 to 157,000 bacteria per ml. in some of which *Escherichia coli* was present. Two cultures of *Escherichia coli* survived 62.8°C.(145°F.) in milk and 13 survived 62.8°C. in ice cream mix. At 65.5°C.(150°F.) one culture survived three out of four trials and at 68.3°C.(155°F.) the same culture survived one out of four trials. The ingredients of the mix, especially the sugar, showed some preservation action on the microorganisms.

In order to have more information on heat resistance of coliform bacteria in ice cream, Myers and Sorensen[111] considered it desirable to establish the thermal resistance in ice cream for especially resistant strains of organisms within the coliform group. Two different strains of *Escherichia coli* and one of *Aerobacter aerogenes* were used. One strain of *Escherichia coli* survived for a period of 20 minutes at 60°C.(140°F.) and for five minutes at 62.8°C.(145°F.). The strain of *Aerobacter aerogenes* survived 10 minutes at 140°F. and for five minutes at 145°F. Neither organism would, therefore, survive pasteurization at 140°F. for 30 minutes. However, the second strain of *Escherichia coli* was much more heat resistant. It survived for 118 minutes at 60°C.(140°F.), for 55 minutes at 62.8°C. (145°F.), for 24 minutes at 65.6°C.(150°F.), but for only 9.5 minutes at 68.3°C.(155°F.). On the basis of these results a pasteurization temperature of 68.3°C.(155°F.) for 30 minutes is recommended to insure complete destruction of coliform bacteria in ice cream mix. Aging ice cream mix at 7.2°C.(45°F.) for 24 hours had no appreciable effect on the thermal resistance of *Escherichia coli*. In a discussion of the work by Myers and Sorensen, Parfitt reported results which he had collected at Purdue University. Sixty-seven cultures of *Escherichia coli* and *Aerobacter aerogenes* were selected and pasteurized in ice cream in capillary tubes. No coliform organisms were found which survived 62.8°C.(145°F.) for 30 minutes. Stark and Patterson,[112] who isolated 505 pure cultures of coliform organisms from water, also found that all the organisms isolated were destroyed at 62.8°C.(145°F.) for 30 minutes.

Results of Myers and Sorensen show clearly the need for uniform regulations as to time and temperature of pasteurization of ice cream mixes. If mixes are pasteurized at 68.3°C.(155°F.) for 30 minutes and coliform organisms are found in the finished products, more accurate interpretation can now be placed upon these results than was possible previously. Paley and Isaacs[113] found a strain of *Escherichia coli* to be about twice as resistant to heat in ice cream mix as in milk.

To secure information on the significance of the presence of coliform bacteria in ice cream, Yale[114] studied the quality of bulk ice cream sold in Geneva, New York. The count of coliform bacteria proved to be a

111. Myers and Sorensen. 1936. Proc. 36th Ann. Conv., Internatl. Assoc. Ice Cream Manfrs. 7.
112. Stark and Patterson. 1936. J. Dairy Sci. 19, 495.
113. Paley and Isaacs. 1941. J. Dairy Sci. 24, 421-447.
114. Yale. 1936. Proc. 36th Conv. Internatl. Assoc. Ice Cream Manfrs.

fairer measure of quality than the standard plate count since the freshly pasteurized mix in practically all cases was free from coliform organisms. Thus, the presence of coliform organisms is primarily an index to handling of the product subsequent to pasteurization. Discriminating manufacturers should include tests for coliform organisms in finished products since their presence is always undesirable and indicative of some faulty condition. Relatively high coliform counts in the case of ice cream with low-standard plate counts are significant, and line-run samples will usually show contamination either from ingredients or from equipment. The coliform plate count is more sensitive in detecting contamination from the vendor's dipper than is the standard plate count.

Since there are instances where total counts indicate faulty conditions but coliform counts do not, a test for the coliform group should supplement rather than supplant the standard plate count. In discussing Yale's work, Fay stated that coliform counts have some value as an index to pasteurization efficiency, especially if high temperatures are employed. If the usual thermal exposure of $62.8°C.(145°F.)$ for 30 minutes is employed, the interpretation of the test must be made with caution. The test has some value as an index to the contamination of ice cream subsequent to pasteurization, especially if the freshly pasteurized product is known to be free from colon types. Tests for coliform bacteria, Yale believed, serve as an index to the general sanitary conditions surrounding production of ice cream; in this capacity he believed it to be a poor substitute for the bacterial plate count. Yale thought that the coliform test had special merits for demonstrating contamination of small magnitude, such as from the ice cream scoop.

Thomas, Jenkins, and Evans [106] also believed that coliform bacteria had value in bacteriological ice cream analysis and that they should be absent in ice cream in .1-ml. amounts. That it may be present in large numbers in some samples was shown by Fournelle and Macy.[114a]

Carbonated Ice Cream. The freezing of ice cream with incorporated carbon dioxide instead of air, was proposed by Heath [115] who claimed the following advantages:

1. Carbon dioxide is cleaner than air.

2. Vitamins are destroyed by oxidation. Carbon dioxide protects the vitamins.

3. Carbon dioxide is not a flavor saver but a flavor intensifier.

4. Ice cream with incorporated carbon dioxide replacing the air "becomes atmospherically compressed to a greater degree during hardening than ordinary ice cream."

5. A volume of carbon dioxide in Heathized ice cream requires over 35 per cent more heat to raise it one degree than a similar volume of air.

6. The employment of carbon dioxide is imitating nature more closely than to imprison air in foods.

These claims naturally caused scientific investigations to be instituted to determine their validity. Prucha, Brannon, and Ambrose [116] studied the

114a. Fournelle and Macy. 1912. J. Dairy Sci., 25, 475-487.
115. Heath. Creamery and Milk Plant Mo. 9, 56.
116. Prucha, Brannon, and Ambrose. 1922. Ill. Agr. Expt. Sta. Circ. 256.

effect of carbon dioxide on the bacterial life in carbonated ice cream. One lot of freshly frozen ice cream prepared from a mix having 620,000 bacteria per ml. had 703,000 bacteria per ml. in the plain mix and 765,500 per ml. in the carbonated cream. At the end of 58 days, there were 530,000 in the plain and 742,000 in the carbonated products. A sterile ice cream mix was also seeded with typhoid bacilli so that each milliliter had 24,700,000 cells. Counts were made for 12 days. The results are tabulated below:

Samples	Plain ice cream	Carbonated ice cream
Mix	24,700,000	
Freshly frozen	50,050,000	50,700,000
5 days old	8,180,000	9,380,000
12 days old	10,465,000	6,896,000

The National Association of Ice Cream Manufacturers also had an investigation made for them by Rettger of Yale University. Rettger [117] could find no evidence that carbon dioxide exerted bactericidal action in ordinary commercial ice cream. With *Bacillus cereus* in ice cream, there was a more pronounced decrease in numbers than in the plain ice cream. Rettger explained this on the basis of the extreme susceptibility of this organism to increased acidity. The process, however, could not be regarded as making ice cream safer. Winslow, in the same report, presented experimental data to show that carbonation, according to the Heath process, did not materially affect the rate of melting of ice cream. Smith of Yale University could find no evidence that carbon dioxide in ice cream preserved the vitamins.

The proposal that ice cream was badly contaminated by the incorporation of foul air into it caused Fabian [33] to study the question. Fabian found that, contrary to the prevailing opinion that large amounts of air entered the freezer, only very little entered. He found that bacterial contamination from the air was insignificant. Fabian found a considerable variation in the bacterial content throughout the year. The argument, then, for substitution of the air with inert gases is groundless.

Survival of Pathogenic Bacteria in Ice Cream. Epidemics caused by ice cream and survival of pathogenic bacteria in it have been discussed in the author's *Food-Borne Infections and Intoxications.* They will not be discussed here. While freezing may greatly reduce the viable bacteria in ice cream, the product is by no means sterilized. Pathogenic bacteria may live for a long time, far beyond the time that the product would ordinarily be stored. It is necessary, then, to keep the ingredients clean and free from suspicion. This is borne out by the number of outbreaks of communicable diseases caused by ice cream.

117. 1922. Natl. Assoc. Ice Cream Manfrs. Spec. Bull.

REFERENCES

American Public Health Association. Standard Methods for the Examination of Dairy Products. New York, N. Y.

DAHLE, C. D., 1927. A Manual for Ice Cream Makers. Ice Cream Field, New York, N. Y.

FISK, W. W., 1923. The Book of Ice Cream. The Macmillan Co., New York, N. Y.

FRANSDEN, J. H., AND MARKHAM, E. A., 1915. The Manufacture of Ice Creams and Ices. Orange Judd Co., New York, N. Y.

MOJONNIER, T., AND TROY, H. C., 1925. The Technical Control of Dairy Products. Mojonnier Bros. Co., Chicago, Ill.

SHERFY, C. B., 1928. Bibliography on Ice Cream Up to and Including the Year 1926. Bibliographic Contributions, No. 17, U. S. Dept. Agr., Washington, D. C.

SOMMER, H. H., 1938. The Theory and Practice of Ice Cream Making. Published by the Author, Madison, Wis.

TURNBOW, G. D., AND RAFETTO, L. A., 1928. Ice Cream. John Wiley and Sons, Inc., New York, N. Y.

CHAPTER 11

MICROBIOLOGY OF CONCENTRATED MILKS

Various types of concentrated milks are now widely used. Extraction of water and the processes which are used to remove it, cause these various products to differ greatly in appearance. These concentrated products owe their reputation to the fact that they may be kept for long periods under proper conditions.

The Standard of Identity [1] for sweetened condensed milk is as follows:

Sweetened Condensed Milk—Identity. (a) Sweetened condensed milk is the liquid or semi-liquid food made by evaporating a mixture of sweet milk and refined sugar (sucrose) or any combination of refined sugar (sucrose) and refined corn sugar (dextrose) to such point that the finished sweetened condensed milk contains not less than 28.0 per cent total milk solids and not less than 8.5 per cent of milk fat. The quantity of refined sugar (sucrose) or combination of such sugar and refined corn sugar (dextrose) used is sufficient to prevent spoilage.

Microbiology of Sweetened Condensed Milk. Much has been published on this subject, but it is not always easy to determine just what type of product was used; consequently, the results reported by different investigators ought not to be compared too closely. Much of the work on the microbiology of condensed milk has been done on swelled or otherwise spoiled cans, and far less on cans which could be considered to be normal.

One of the first reports indicating that condensed milk was not sterile was by Kossowicz,[2] who isolated *Bacillus sinapinagus, Pseudomonas fluorescens,* and *Serratia marcescens.* The next year Dold and Stewart [3] reported from 700 to 120,000 bacteria per ml. in eight samples of full cream, and 10 of machine-skimmed sweetened milk, purchased on the open market. Streptococci were isolated from eight specimens. *Clostridium sporogenes* and *Escherichia coli* were absent. Attempts to demonstrate the presence of *Mycobacterium tuberculosis* were not successful. Non-heat-resisting forms were found in condensed milk by Klein [4] also. Eight samples, discussed in his first report, showed the presence of Micrococci. In the second report all of the 32 shop samples of 11 different brands were reported to contain from 13 to over 2,000 bacteria in one-tenth gram, a rather large number; all but four contained Streptococci in one-tenth gram, and 14 showed the presence of gas-forming aerobic bacteria (Savage and Hunwicke [5]). Large numbers of bacteria were also observed by Heggs [6] in 11 samples purchased on the open market. The counts varied from 230 to 70,490 per ml. on gelatin. Streptococci were found in all specimens of condensed milk examined by Gordon and Elmslie.[7] They

---

1. The Federal Register, July 2, 1940.
2. Kossowicz. 1909. Ztschr. Landw. Versuchw. Österr. 11, 719-729.
3. Dold and Stewart. 1910. Bull. Soc. Chim. Belg. 24, 225-231.
4. Klein. 1901. J. Hyg. 1, 78-95; Pub. Health, 22 (1909), 222.
5. Savage and Hunwicke. 1923. Gt. Britain Food Invest. Bd. Spec. Rpt. No. 13.
6. Heggs. 1906. Quoted by Savage and Hunwicke.
7. Gordon and Elmslie. 1911. Quoted by Savage and Hunwicke.

were not identified. From their experimental data, it is probable that *Escherichia coli* was present. Proteus organisms were found in three samples. Andrews [8] believed that organisms multiplied in condensed milk, and that a few survivors might mean many hundreds later. It is interesting to note that many of the viable bacteria in condensed milk are nonsporeforming species. That the condensing process affects the bacterial population seems to be borne out by the investigations of Delepine [9] and Ruehe.[10] Delepine observed that a bacterial content of 38,000,000 bacteria might be reduced to less than 50. *Mycobacterium tuberculosis* was apparently destroyed, because the finished milk failed to produce lesions in guinea pigs when it was inoculated into them. Continuous observations were made by Ruehe during the condensing process. Becterial counts were made of the raw milk, and of the processed milk after preheating, concentration, and superheating. Some of the samples were modified by skimming, by the addition of some concentrated milk, and by changes in other conditions. The results showed that the processes through which milk goes in being condensed, tend to lower the bacterial content of the finished product, the maximum, minimum, and average final counts being, respectively, 36,400, 480, and 6,289 bacteria per ml., though the initial milk had counts in some cases of over 100,000,000. High bacterial counts in condensed milk are suggested as due to contamination after manufacturing or to improper storing.

The lower bacterial content of condensed milk was due to longer process times and higher temperatures by Park, Schroeder, and Bartholow.[11] They were of the opinion that inferior grades of milk were frequently used for condensing. Bacteria were found in all of 85 cans of condensed milk, the number varying from 500 to 8,000,000. *Escherichia coli* was present in eight of 17 brands. Thirty brands of Japanese condensed milk, examined by Nishizaki and Wakita,[12] were found to be free from *Escherichia coli*. Beveridge,[13] when investigating the keeping properties of condensed milk in the tropics, reported that increase of acidity by bacterial fermentation may enhance the change of color. Sporeforming bacteria were said to be the cause of the trouble. Weinzirl,[14] in his investigation of the bacteria in various canned foods, included a few cans of milk. Twelve cans were examined, of which 10 were not sterile. The organisms which were isolated were aerobic sporeformers *(Bacillus mesentericus* and *Bacillus subtilis)*. Haarnagel [15] made colony counts on 48 samples of condensed milk from America, Germany, Denmark, and Switzerland. The colony counts varied from 0 to 242,000 per ml. Only one can was sterile. Both sporeforming and nonsporeforming bacteria were found. Attempts to show the presence of tubercle bacilli were not successful.

8. Andrews. 1913. J. Path. and Bact. 18, 169-178.
9. Delepine. 1914. J. Soc. Chem. Indus. 34, 297.
10. Ruehe. 1924. Cornell Agr. Exp. Sta. Mem. 76, 3-18.
11. Park, Schroeder, and Bartholow. 1915. N. Y. Med. J. 102, 1073-1083.
12. Nishizaki and Wakita. 1914. J. Pharm. Soc., Japan, No. 329, 1133.
13. Beveridge. 1914. J. Royal Army Med. Corps, 22, 1-8.
14. Weinzirl. 1919. J. Med. Res. 39, 349-413.
15. Haarnagel. 1921. Rev. in Abs. Bact. 8 (1924), 317.

One of the most complete investigations and discussions of the microbiology of sweetened condensed milk was published by Savage and Hunwicke.[5] They worked with English, American, and Canadian brands. All of their samples were full cream, and none were of the machine-skimmed variety. Of 15 market samples and 34 factory samples which were sound or not known to be spoiled they found great variations in bacterial content. For instance, one can, packed in the United States, had a count of 100 and 175 colonies per gram, while another specimen showed 400,000 and 460,000 per gram. According to Gehri,[16] Swiss condensed milk is not sterile, but may contain as many as 9,000 cells per ml. Haarnagel[15] reported many bacteria in condensed milk from Germany, America, Denmark, and Switzerland. Thus condensed milk, packed in various countries, seems uniformly to contain many bactéria. However, it should be pointed out that since these investigations were reported, the entire subject of processing canned foods has been studied and procedures perfected. It is probable that the situation with respect to viable bacteria is quite different today. Greater attention is also paid to sanitation in food preservation. This means a smaller bacterial load imposed on the process. Such a situation seems to be borne out by the results of a bacterial examination in the author's laboratory of 300 cans of condensed milk packed in 1928. The great majority of them were sterile.

Types of Organisms in Sweetened Condensed Milk. Sweetened milk is not always sterile although it probably contains fewer viable microorganisms today than formerly.

Yeasts. Yeasts have been reported by several investigators; Savage and Hunwicke[5] stated that swelling of cans of sweetened condensed milk was almost invariably due to yeasts. However, the mere presence of yeasts could not be considered as evidence that the cans would swell. The biological properties of the yeasts must be considered. Even the ability of yeasts to grow in 50 per cent sugar solutions is not conclusive evidence that they will cause swells to develop. Savage and Hunwicke's inoculation experiments showed that 70 per cent of the yeasts from swelled cans of milk caused swelling of cans into which they were injected. The factors which seemed to influence yeast growth were sugar concentration (35 to 40 per cent) and oxygen supply.

Gas-Forming Aerobic Bacteria. Savage and Hunwicke[5] found them present in two normal cans and five swelled cans. The strains which they isolated were *Escherichia coli*. They were not inhibited by the amount of sucrose present. The organism did not grow but ultimately died out. The two strains found in the sound cans were from cans packed by the same factory. The contents of these cans were quite sound, and would probably have remained so and the strains have died out. Nishizaki and Wakita)[12] found 30 samples of Japanese condensed milk to be free from *Escherichia coli*. Certainly a microorganism with such low heat resistance would not, ordinarily, be expected in a food which has been processed.

Aerobic Sporeforming Bacteria. Of the 30 sound cans of sweetened condensed milk examined by Savage and Hunwicke,[5] aerobic sporeforming bacteria were found in 26. Sixty-three out of 76 total samples showed these organisms. These investigators believed that they would have been found in the rest of the cans if larger amounts had been examined. These forms are, probably, always present, even in sound cans. While they did not ordinarily cause swelling of cans, they were believed to be able to cause decomposition changes. Savage and Hunwicke suggested that these organisms could not grow

16. Gehri. 1928. Mitt. Lebensmtl. Untersuch. u. Hyg. 19, 89-101.

in the milk on account of anaerobic conditions and the concentration of the milk. However, experiments in which air was blown into the milk did not result in growth.

Thayer [17] made a bacteriological examination of samples of condensed milk which had spoiled from 12 to 24 hours after condensing and canning and found *Bacillus subtilis*. A sterilizing temperature of 125°C.(257°F.) for 15 to 20 minutes is recommended where the diffiulty is encountered. Delepine also observed sporeforming bacteria in condensed milk.

Thermophilic Bacteria. These bacteria which thrive at high temperatures have been shown to be present in sweetened condensed milk. Weinzirl [14] found a thermophilic organism in one can. Savage and Hunwicke [5] examined 76 cans of condensed milk and found 36 of them to contain these forms. Of 30 sound cans of milk, 17 contained thermophiles. They found these bacteria as abundant in the commercially sound cans as in the swelled cans. They believed them to be widely disseminated in condensed milk. The characteristics of all of the thermophiles from condensed milk were given in tabular form. All of the strains were sporeformers which did not form gas. The presence of these bacteria in condensed milk would suggest that it should be stored with the same care which is given other foods in which viable thermophiles may grow.

Anaerobic Bacteria. While anaerobic bacteria would be expected in condensed milk, they are conspicuous by their absence. Savage and Hunwicke isolated anaerobic bacteria from only two cans. One came from a can which was slightly swelled; the other came from a can which gave some evidence of fermentation, although Savage and Hunwicke reported that there was no evidence of pressure from gas. Yeasts and gas-forming bacteria were not present. Lack of development of the anaerobe in condensed milk was attributed not to the presence of so much sucrose, but to unfavorable physical conditions consequent on condensation. These investigators mentioned the interesting observation that, although *Clostridium welchii* is present in raw milk, it was not found once in condensed milk. It seemed apparent to Savage and Hunwicke that anaerobic bacteria are not significant in spoilage of condensed milk. Another investigator who isolated anaerobic bacteria was Haarnagel. He isolated anaerobic sporeforming organism which formed butyric acid as well as an anaerobic diplococcus.

EVAPORATED MILK

Evaporated milk is the product resulting from the evaporation of a considerable portion of the water from milk or from milk with adjustment, if necessary, of the ratio of fat to nonfat solids by the addition of, or by the abstraction of, cream. It contains not less than 7.8 per cent of milk fat nor less than 25.5 per cent of total milk solids; provided however, that the sum of the percentages of milk fat and total milk solids be not less than 33.7 per cent.

The Standard of Identity for evaporated milk [1] under the Food, Drug and Cosmetic Act of 1938 is as follows:

Evaporated Milk—Identity—Label statement of optional ingredients. (a) Evaporated milk is the liquid food made by evaporating sweet milk to such point that it contains not less than 7.9 per cent of milk fat and not less than 25.9 per cent of total milk solids. It may contain one or both of the following ingredients: (1) Disodium phosphate or sodium citrate or both, or calcium chloride, added in a total quantity of not more than .1 per cent by weight of the finished evaporated milk. (2) Vitamin D in such quantity as increases the total vitamin D content to not less than 7.5 U.S.P. units per avoirdupois ounce of finished evaporated milk. It may be homogenized. It is sealed in a container and so processed by heat as to prevent spoilage.

Results of many investigations published several years ago indicated a high degree of unsterility in cans of the product. In all probability this

17. Thayer. 1912. Vermont Agr. Expt. Sta. Bull. 170.

is not the situation today because better plant sanitation and better processing have made it possible to destroy microorganisms in canned foods Gordon and Elmslie [7] examined four apparently sound cans of unsweetened condensed (evaporated) milk. None of the cans was sterile. *Escherichia coli*, anaerobic bacteria, and streptococci were not found. Aerobic organisms, however, were present. Andrews,[8] contrary to the data of Gordon and Elmslie, found evaporated milk to be invariably sterile. Thirty-seven cans examined by Park, Schroeder, and Bartholow [11] were found to be infected. The lowest number of bacteria found was 300 bacteria per ml. and the highest 50,750 per ml. with an average count of 7,000 bacteria per ml. *Escherichia coli* was present in four cans. Savage and Hunwicke commented on the fact that cans of evaporated milk, containing this lactose-fermenting organism, remained sound. They examined 104 cans of evaporated milk. Eighty-five per cent of the shop samples and 76 per cent of the factory samples were found to be sterile. The organisms were quite diverse in characteristics. All of 25 cans examined by Weinzirl were sterile. These data seem to support the general opinion that evaporated milk is much better bacteriologically than condensed milk. This is due to the fact that the former can be given a cook which is more adequate.

A comprehensive study of 315 presumably sound and 150 presumably defective samples of evaporated milk, 252 samples of sound canned cream, 115 specials, and 80 samples of sweetened condensed milk was made by Nichols.[18] Of the evaporated milk samples presumably sound only 16 or five per cent were not sterile; with the defective cans 59 were not sterile (39 per cent). Canned cream presumably sound showed 50 (20 per cent) not sterile and the specials, selected for some abnormality, showed three per cent not sterile. The non-sterile sound (commercially sterile) tins of cream were mostly associated with the introduction of large 12-ounce cans. Spoilage caused by nonsporeformers was generally shown by a blown condition (here called "swells"), or by curdling or by both together. Many kinds of bacteria were isolated but strains of the genus Escherichia were the commonest producers of gassy spoilage. Aerobic sporeformers were isolated in about 80 cases from both sound and unsound cans. Of these 69 per cent were *Bacillus subtilis* strains and 15 per cent were *Bacillus licheniformis*. Some were associated with spoilage, clot, bitter flavors, etc., but others were from apparently sound tins. Cans inoculated with these strains showed in some cases no defects even up to 18 months; in others, defects appeared. A bitter flavor associated with thinness developed in some cases. Aerobic sporeformers were isolated from both evaporated milk and from canned cream. Only two cultures of anaerobic sporeformers were isolated from sound tins. Some evidence was produced that *Bacillus licheniformis* may produce a slight "swell" in canned dairy products. Defects in the sweetened condensed milk samples were due to yeasts when the defect was a "swell." "Buttons" were due to various molds, while progressive thickening was due to various causes.

18. Nichols. 1939. J. Dairy Res. 10, 231-249.

Microscopical examination of 154 cans of four leading brands of evaporated milk purchased on the open market by Deming and Davis [19] showed only an occasional organism in eight cans. In only one case was the number of organisms considerable. Cultural studies were essentially negative except for one can from which was isolated an anaerobe growing at 55°C. (131°F.). The authors conclude that evaporated milk as purchased on the open market is not only free from pathogenic bacteria but may be considered practically sterile. Bacteriologically, this product is regarded as a safe food for infant feeding. Recent investigations have revealed that these products are better bacteriologically today than they were a few years ago. This is due to greater attention to plant sanitation and to better methods of processing.

SPOILAGE OF CANNED CONCENTRATED MILKS

Several different types of spoilage have been encountered in canned milks. The bacteriology of some of them has not been thoroughly worked out. In others, the causal organism was isolated and studied at considerable length. A few of the common types of spoilage will now be discussed.

Formation of "Buttons" in Sweetened Condensed Milk. These are hard, reddish-brown lumps of curd. Rogers, Dahlberg, and Evans [20] found that they were due to the growth of *Aspergillus repens* and perhaps other molds on the surface of the milk, after the can had been sealed. On account of the lack of oxygen, the growth of the mold was quite restricted, and it died out in about two weeks. The mold hyphae then broke up and on old cans of milk there were no appearances, whatever, of mold growth. The button is probably formed from the casein by enzymes. Rogers recommended sealing the cans under a vacuum of at least 20 inches, since the mold cannot develop in such concentrations of oxygen. Knudsen [21] reported ''button'' formation in condensed milk by *Aspergillus glaucus* and *Catenularia fuligenea*. Savage and Hunwicke, whose report has been rather fully reviewed, did not make routine observations for molds in canned milk. While they were observed a few times, these men believed a greater incidence would have been noted if special attention had been given them. Dixon and Sugden [22] observed molds as the cause of ''buttons'' in two samples which were found to be abnormally thick and to contain a number of reddish, button-like masses. The changes in the milk were evidently caused by the growth of molds induced by storage at too high a temperature. Both samples contained invert sugar, probably produced as a result of the activity of molds. Harris [23] isolated *Monilia nigra* from cans of condensed milk which showed button formation. They were found mainly at the ends of the can. Harris [23] isolated the organism using a medium of dextrose, lactic acid, and yeast water. *Monilia nigra* is a yeast-like organism producing filaments readily, developing a black pigment within 24 hours after the colony is large enough for microscope examination, and not forming ascospores. Its cultural and other characters are described in detail. Inoculations into tins of condensed milk with closure of the cans gave rise to colonies in only one out of six cans.

Buttons are a cause of much trouble in condensed milk. They are caused by molds which are widely disseminated in nature. This makes it possible for them to reach the condensed milk easily, for they may be in the cans when they are filled or in the sugar. The latter may be an important factor if it is not kept scrupulously clean and free from dirt.

19. Deming and Davis. 1931. Arch. Ped. 48, 42-47.
20. Rogers, Dahlberg, and Evans. 1920. Rev. in Abs. Bact. 6, 366.
21. Knudsen. 1922. Idem 6, Abs. No. 1889.
22. Dixon and Sugden. 1930. Analyst 55, 749-751.
23. Harris. 1933. Zentbl. Bakt., Pt. 2, 88, 58-61.

Putrefaction of Canned Concentrated Milk. This type of spoilage is no different from that induced in practically all nitrogenous materials. The proteins are hydrolyzed by certain bacteria which survive the process and later attack the milk. Anaerobic sporeforming bacteria, such as *Clostridium putrificum* or members of the Proteus group, may be the causal organisms. The changes induced are very much like those of true putrefaction. A few cases have been observed in the author's laboratory. Savage and Hunwicke stated that anaerobic sporeforming bacteria were not important in spoilage of canned milk.

Bitterness in Canned Concentrated Milk. This type of spoilage in canned milk was studied by Hammer.[24] A condensory which lost a portion of its pack over a period of time eventually coped with the trouble by increasing the process. Bacteriological examination showed the presence of a sporeforming, facultative organism to which the name *Bacillus amarus* was given. One is impressed by the possibility that this organism is really a member of the *Subtilis-Mesentericus* group. Spitzer and Epple[25] found an organism much like *Lactobacillus panis* as the cause of bitterness in evaporated milk. The organism was killed in between eight and 10 minutes at 121.5°C.(250°F.). The organism decomposed proteins to peptones and amino acids. The bitter taste was probably due to these compounds. Savage and Hunwicke examined three old cans of milk from a lot said to be bitter. They were sterile, however.

Gaseous Fermentation of Canned Concentrated Milks. Various lactose-fermenting organisms may cause this spoilage in canned milks. Pethybridge[26] investigated the occasional occurrence of spoiled cans of condensed milk in the product of one factory and found the cause to be yeasts. They were not introduced into the milk with the cane sugar used nor were they inhibited in their activity by increasing concentration of the cane sugar. The source of the yeasts was apparently the original milk supply. As the destruction of the yeasts by heat during the manufacture of condensed milk was not practicable, more careful attention was paid to the condition of the milk supply and a considerable improvement followed the rejection of dirty milk. Cassedebat[27] could isolate no viable organisms from swelled cans. He believed therefore, as did Dodge[28] that spoilage was not due to bacteria. The possibility of auto-sterilization of canned foods was not appreciated then, as it is today. Hammer[29] found a budding fungus in cans of hard swelled canned milk to which the name *Torula lactis-condensi* was given. One important contribution in this work of Hammer is that yeasts may cause this type of spoilage. Statements appear in many texts that yeasts rarely ferment lactose. The fermentation of this disaccharide would seem to be common if one took time to study the literature. In a later publication Hammer[24] announced two more varieties of yeasts, under the names of *Torula cremoris* and *Torula sphaerica*, which cause the foamy fermentation of lactose. While these yeasts caused no trouble in canned milks, they might, perhaps, do so. Other investigators have also found yeasts to cause spoilage. Savage and Hunwicke[5] believed yeasts to be common causes of spoilage. The work of Hammer quoted above, was confirmed by Knudsen,[21] who reported two types of yeasts from swelled cans of sweetened condensed milk. Both yeasts fermented glucose, fructose, and sucrose but not galactose, maltose, or lactose. Ascospores were not formed. No changes were induced in milk, but the addition of a fermentable substance was followed by an active fermentation and coagulation. It was killed by a few minutes' exposure at 55°C.(131°F.). Dutch sweetened condensed milk contained another species. Yeasts were found to be important in condensed milk but of practically no importance in evaporated milk.

Bacteria able to ferment lactose may also be responsible for gaseous fermentation of condensed milks. Rogers and Clemmer[30] found *Aerobacter aerogenes* types of organism growing in condensed milk, containing from 40 to 45 per cent of cane sugar. Since

24. Hammer. 1919. Iowa Agr. Expt. Sta. Res. Bull. 52.
25. Spitzer and Epple. 1920. J. Dairy Sci. 3, 486-492.
26. Pethybridge. 1906. Econ. Proc. Roy. Dublin Soc. 1, 306-320.
27. Cassedebat. 1892. Rev. Hyg. 14, 749.
28. Dodge. 1905. J. Infect. Diseases, Suppl. 1, 353-354.
29. Hammer. 1919. Iowa Agr. Expt. Sta. Res. Bull. 54.
30. Rogers and Clemmer. 1918. Abs. Bact. 2, 6.

it would not grow in milk containing 40 per cent of cane sugar in true solution, they concluded that there was a crystallization of sugar in the can of milk. They believed that infection occurred between the pan and filling machine. Jandin[31] isolated a "Bacillus A" which rapidly inverted the sucrose in milk, and caused a vigorous gas formation. Another organism like this, except that it formed acid and coagulated the milk was also isolated. These gas-producing bacteria probably originate in the raw milk. They have been studied by many different investigators because they are, in general, quite undesirable bacteria in milk products. In fresh milk they are killed readily by temperatures of 58.5-63.5°C.(137-146°F.) in 10 minutes (Harrison[32]). In condensed milk, however, the situation is quite different. Crystallization of sugar in condensed milk was offered as a reason for the growth of gas-forming bacteria by Rogers and Clemmer.[30] They isolated an organism which formed sufficient gas to burst the cans. It was able to endure from 40 to 45 per cent of sugar.

A gas-forming streptococcus to which the name *Streptococcus distendens* was given, was isolated by Hammer[33] from swelled cans of condensed milk. Small quantities of gas were produced along with considerable quantities of volatile acids from some of the constituents in the milk.

Nichols[18] reported that members of the Escherichia group were the most common causes of gaseous spoilage.

Coagulation of Canned Concentrated Milk. This is a common type of spoilage, and has caused much concern among those who pack evaporated milk. It is due to a number of causes. Milk with too high an acidity in the beginning may be the cause of it. The presence of certain types of microorganisms may also be the cause. In support of this there are several publications. The contents of a can which has undergone this spoilage, when emptied into a dish, will stand up and retain the shape of the can, especially if it has not been shaken. The milk may have an "off" flavor, but may not be sour. Some cans have a fruity odor and a slightly bitter taste. Considerable bacteriological work has been done on the spoilage.

Grieg-Smith[34] isolated an organism which was distinguishable from *Staphylococcus pyogenes albus* only by its nonpathogenicity for mice. Activity of the organism was increased by calcium carbonate. Thayer[17] noticed spoilage of condensed milk 12 to 14 hours after sterilization which was evidenced by a "chug" in the cans upon shaking. Thayer isolated an organism which was believed to be *Bacillus subtilis.* He suggested that the trouble be corrected by raising the temperature and time of processing. Similar organisms were reported by Kelly.[35] Three types of bacteria were isolated which reproduced the spoilage when inoculated into sound cans. The bacteria were identified as *Bacillus cereus, Bacillus simplex,* and *Bacillus megatherium.* One of the most detailed reports in the literature is by Hammer[36] who isolated, from coagulated canned milk. a bacterium to which he gave the name *Bacillus coagulans.* He was able to reproduce this condition in sterile cans by injections of the new organism. Cordes[37] also isolated an organism believed to be identical with *Bacillus coagulans* Hammer. Koch's postulates were fulfilled, indicating that the organism was able to produce the decomposition. The organism was found to resist killing by heat at 80°C.(176°F.) for 10 minutes. Cordes also studied the effect of heating in the autoclave. The cells survived heating for two minutes at 106.1°C.(223°F.), between 100°C.(212°F.) and 106.1°C.(223°F.) for three minutes, and between 89.5°C.(193°F.) and 106.1°C.(223°F.) for 12 minutes. Rice and Downs[38] have also explained the thickening of sweetened condensed milk on. the basis of bacterial action. The specific organism was a coccus which was isolated from the equipment. Growth was prevented by keeping the sugar content up to a concentra-

31. Jandin. 1922. Rev. in Abs. Bact. 8, 320.
32. Harrison. 1905. Centbl. Bakt., Pt. 2, 14, 359-374.
33. Hammer. 1927. Iowa State Col. J. Sci. 2, 1-7.
34. Grieg-Smith. 1909. Linn. Soc. of N. S. Wales Proc., Pt. 1, 34, 107-113.
35. Kelly. 1926.
36. Hammer. 1915. Iowa Agr. Expt. Sta. Res. Bull. 19; J. Bact. 23 (1932). 301.
37. Cordes. 1928. J. Dairy Sci. 11, 46-51.
38. Rice and Downs. 1923. J. Dairy Sci. 6, 532-47.
39. Downs. 1925. J. Dairy Sci. 8, 344-369.

tion at which the coccus cannot grow. Downs,[39] after a study of various organisms isolated from thickened milk, reduced all of them to one general type, of which two distinct varieties were found. Downs stated that the production of acid alone was not responsible for thickening. He believed that thickening was caused by a rennin-like enzyme formed by certain bacteria. The organisms were not named. They were not heat resistant. An organism identified as *Bacillus cereus* was isolated by Hammer and Hussong[40] from three cans of milk from one batch in which coagulation trouble had occurred. In evaporated milk, in tubes providing access of air, this organism curdled milk rapidly and produced objectionable odor and flavor, but in cans incubated at 37°C.(96.8°F.) coagulation was slow with no change in odor or flavor unless the holding period was prolonged. Owing to the fact that the organism was isolated from only three cans, Hussong and Hammer did not consider it to be the primary cause of coagulation.

While many of the publications on the subject indicate that coagulation may be due to development of certain bacteria, several others suggest other causes. For instance, Rogers[41] and Sommer and Hart[42] studied the relation of coagulability to acidity and temperature of processing. Increase in acidity did not always accompany lowered coagulation temperatures. Each milk seemed to have a definite hydrogen-ion concentration at which it was stable.

Another outbreak of coagulated canned milk was described by Sarles and Hammer.[43] The strain of *Bacillus coagulans* which was isolated was quite like the original. The coagulated milk had no odor of putrefaction.

Abnormal Flavors in Concentrated Milks. Flavor in any food product is an indefinite characteristic, but one, however, which must be taken into account. The element of flavor is especially important with the dairy products where, through training, the consumer has become accustomed to a certain taste. Unfortunately, there is no standard with which to compare such abnormalities, and they are, consequently, known under a variety of names. Those who are familiar with these flavors are adept in identifying them.

Fishy Flavor. Fishy odors and flavors have been noted in practically all dairy products. Hammer[44] described an investigation of "fishy" evaporated milk and suggested the name *Escherichia ichthyosmia (Bacterium ichthyosmius)*. Spores were apparently not formed, since they were not observed in the stained preparations, and no growth was secured after heating for 10 minutes at 80°C.(176°F.). It is not at all improbable that the explanation of fishiness in milk by Sommer and Smith,[45] that it was due to the formation of trimethylamine from lecithin, might hold for the formation of the fishy flavor in concentrated milks.

Common aerobic sporeforming bacteria, *Bacillus mycoides* and *Bacillus mesentericus*, were said to cause fishy milk by Cecelia.[46] Hammer's organism was not found in a single instance.

Rancidity of Sweetened Condensed Milk. As used by Rice,[47] who reported a study of rancidity of sweetened condensed milk, the term refers to a flavor resembling that of butyric acid. Twenty commercial samples of rancid condensed milk were found to have a high acidity, a low bacterial content, and to give the peroxidase reaction. Condensed milk prepared in a vacuum pan became rancid when small amounts of unheated milk were made a part of the batch. Raw milk did the same thing in condensed milk of regular manufacture. The active agent was said to be lipase which is destroyed by heat in the regular manufacture of condensed milk in the factory. When unheated milk

40. Hammer and Hussong. 1932. J. Dairy Sci. 15, 220-29.
41. Rogers. 1921. Canner, 52, Pt. 2, 165 and 166.
42. Sommer and Hart. 1926. Wisc. Agr. Expt. Sta. Res. Bull. 67.
43. Sarles and Hammer. 1932. J. Bact. 23, 301-314.
44. Hammer. 1917. Iowa Agr. Expt. Sta. Bull. 38.
45. Sommer and Smith. 1923. Wisc. Agr. Expt. Sta. Res. Bull. 57.
46. Cecilia. 1940. Lait 20, 385-390.

gets into the batch through some error, the enzyme hydrolyzes part of the butterfat to fatty acids to which the evidences of rancidity are due.

Tallowiness of Sweetened Condensed Milk. This flavor, according to Rice [47] who studied its development, resembles to a considerable degree the flavor of tallowy butter and powdered whole milk. The production of this flavor is probably a chemical phenomenon and not a biological one. Rice stated that it was due to the action of oxygen of the air in the container on the butterfat of the milk, the action being catalyzed by a little copper.

Clostridium botulinum in Condensed Milk. The possibility of growth and toxin-formation by *Clostridium botulinum* in canned milk was investigated by Schoenholz, Esty, and Meyer. [48] Five cans were inoculated with toxin-free spores and stored either at room or incubator temperatures. The contents of one can was tested after 10 days and proved to be slightly toxic to guinea pigs. The appearance was normal. The contents of three other cans after 122 days were coagulated and gave off a strong odor of butyric acid and were very toxic for guinea pigs. Other inoculations into canned milk caused these investigators to reach the following conclusions: (1) spoilage in canned milk after inoculation with *Clostridium botulinum* may be quite irregular; (2) the number of cells introduced apparently makes little difference; (3) the milk appearing normal may be weakly toxic; (4) introduction of soil increased spoilage, but did not increase toxin-formation. They also stated that evidence was secured indicating that toxin, once formed in milk, might deteriorate in the milk. One outbreak of botulism caused by commercially canned milk was reported by the Botulinus Commission (Geiger, Dickinson, and Meyer [49]). The outbreak was not proven toxicologically or bacteriologically.

Canning of Condensed and Evaporated Milks. Concentrated milks have been canned for many years. They have presented problems which have not been easy to surmount, although great progress has been made. The heat which is applied to the cans in the retort probably destroys nearly all of the bacteria in some cans and all of them in others. The heat also brings the milk to the desired consistency. Processers in the past have been prone to relate consistency with sterility, although there is no relation between these two factors. Bigelow [50] and his colleagues in the Research Laboratories of the National Canners Association have devoted much study to the question of heat penetration into evaporated milk during processing. The introduction of cookers in which the cans may be agitated during processing has greatly improved the sterility of the product.

Vacuum Packed Milk. This process was described by Willison. [51] It was believed that the removal of air would prevent the development of yeasts and molds and thus reduce one of the greatest causes of spoilage. The milk is drawn from the cooler or holding tank into the vacuumizing tank to undergo a violent agitation under high vacuum. The agitation releases occluded air which is then drawn off by the vacuum. As a result of this

47. Rice. 1926. J. Dairy Sci. 9, 293-305.
48. Schoenholz, Esty, and Meyer. 1923. J. Infect. Diseases 33, 289-327.
49. Geiger, Dickson, and Meyer. 1922. U. S. Pub. Health Serv., Pub. Health Bull. 127.
50. Bigelow. 1922. Canning Age, 11-13.
51. Willison. 1924. Canning Age, Oct. 1924.

the body of the milk is reduced to a thinner consistency. The vacuumizing took place just before the milk went to the fillers. The belief that removal of air from the cans would reduce spoilage is in keeping with the opinions of Savage and Hunwicke, who stated that entrance of air favored the development of yeast cells which were quiescent.

BACTERIOLOGICAL EXAMINATION OF CONDENSED AND EVAPORATED MILK

The technic for examining these products is quite like that described for canned foods in Chapter 23.

Bacteriological standards have been proposed at various times for condensed milk. Coutts did not favor them but suggested that special attention be given the conditions under which the milk for condensing was produced as well as the conditions under which it was condensed. Savage and Hunwicke also agreed that the bacterial standards would not be of much assistance. They believed, however, that no condensed milk should contain *Escherichia coli.* The presence of this organism was believed to indicate the presence of nonsporeforming bacteria or that contamination of an undesirable character had reached the milk. They were unable to make suggestions with regard to the presence of streptococci on account of the fact that so many streptococci are of no significance.

The cans should be incubated if they have just been packed or may be opened immediately if they are old. After incubation the same procedures may be followed that are described in Chapter 23.

Examination of Stained Centrifugalized Deposit (Savage and Hunwicke [5]). A little of the milk is taken and centrifugalized with water to get rid of fat and other products. If clotted it is first mixed with water and filtered, and the filtrate centrifugalized. If necessary the deposit is remixed with water and again centrifugalized. A little of the deposit is spread on a coverslip, fixed, and stained in the ordinary way. While this gives an idea of the number of bacteria and yeasts present in the milk it does not, of course, distinguish between the living and the dead.

Savage and Hunwicke's Technic for Examination of Condensed Milk for Bacteria. The following procedures were suggested:

1. Pour a few drops of alcohol over the top of the can and burn off.

2. Open with a can opener sterilized in the same manner, or better still, by boring a small hole with a ⅜-inch drill, sterilized by burning alcohol.

3. Remove a considerable quantity of condensed milk with a sterile glass tube (about ¼-inch bore) not contracted at the tip. Add this to a weighed, sterilized, stoppered flask.

4. Add a large drop to surface of glucose agar in a petri dish and distribute over the surface.

The flask should then be weighed to determine the amount of milk which should not be less than five grams. A simple calculation will give the amount of sterile water to be added to bring the dilution to one to four. For example, if five grams is the amount of milk, the diluted milk should be 20 ml.

Add two ml. of the diluted milk to the culture tubes of plain broth, glucose yeast water, and glucose litmus broth in the double tube. The glucose agar plate and the yeast water should be incubated at 21°C.(69.8°F.) (or better, 25°C.[77°F.] if available) for yeasts, the other tubes at 37°C.(98.6°F.), the meat broth anaerobically for anaerobes, the glucose litmus for aerobic gas-formers, aerobic sporeformers, and bacilli.

Part of the diluted milk may be centrifugalized and stained directly.

DEHYDRATED MILK

This product has much less water than the other concentrated milk products and, therefore, has somewhat different characteristics. Under certain conditions milk powder has distinct advantages. No question need exist as to its sanitary qualities, although Prickett [52] said that factors are involved in controlling the sanitary quality of dried milk which are additional to those used in ordinary milk control. Since dried milk is frequently made from surplus milk, the sanitary quality of the fluid milk from which it is made may be poor. Experts with this product have stated that the plate count of dry milk may not indicate the quality of raw milk from which it is made. Prickett recommended the microscope method of analysis using a 1 to 10 dilution of the milk powder.

Leary [53] stated that "the fact that milk is a fluid, and further, that it is a good culture medium, is responsible for its transmission of disease; and the removal of water from milk makes it a poor culture medium and largely does away with its perishable qualities." While drying greatly reduces the bacterial content, dried milk is not sterile. Two processes are used for dehydrating milk. Leary described them as follows: In the roller process, the milk adheres to the surface of the hot rolls heated by steam to between 110 and 140°C.(230 and 284°F.); as the roll revolves the milk is scraped off in the form of a moist powder, the whole procedure requiring not over a few seconds. In the spray process, the milk is atomized under great pressure into a chamber where it encounters currents of warm air. The warm air removes the water from the milk. In order to prevent caking and cause more rapid solution in water, the milk is usually concentrated before atomizing.

Considerable study has been given to the bacteriology of dehydrated milk. Some of these reports will be reviewed even though the data and conclusions are contradictory. In the examination of six different kinds of dried-milk preparations, Prachfeld [54] found from 4,000 to 69,000 bacteria per gram. The nature of the organisms indicated that they entered the milk after drying. Hoffmann [55] obtained results from inoculation experiments with guinea pigs, showing that *Mycobacterium tuberculosis* (bovis) was destroyed in the manufacture of milk powder by the Just-Hatmaker process. Kossowicz [56] found that drying reduced the bacterial content to some extent. *Bacillus sinapivagus*, *Serratia marcescens*, and *Pseudomonas fluorescens*, however, were not destroyed. Dried milks may become reinfected if not kept in closed vessels. Ten per cent solutions of the powder showed aerobic bacterial growth at 22°C.(71.6°F.) ranging in numbers from 100 to 757,000 per ml., and at 37°C.(98.6°F.) from 1,000 to 892,000 per ml. The results for the most part, however, ranged under 10,000 per ml. in each case. The presence of streptococci, *Salmonella enteritidis*, and *Escherichia coli* was recorded in many of the samples. There

52. Prickett. 1939. J. Milk Tech. 2, 133-137.
53. Leary. 1922. Boston Med. and Surg. J. 186, 591-597.
54. Prachfeld. 1908. Ztschr. Fleish. u. Milchhyg. 18.
55. Hoffmann. 1906. Arch. Hyg. 59, 216-223.
56. Kossowicz. 1908. Ztschr. Landw. Versuchsw. Österr. 11, 719.

was no evidence of tuberculosis in guinea pigs inoculated from these samples. According to Supplee and Ashbaugh,[57] a bacterial content of over 1,000 per gram in milk powder made by the Just process indicates recontamination, since the bacteria are usually fewer in this product than in milk dehydrated by the spray process. The number of bacteria in the milk before drying does not influence the number in the dried milk. Bacteria were said to die off during storage, approaching constancy after two to four months. Even large numbers of bacteria in the powder were said to have little influence on keeping quality if the moisture content is kept below that usually allowed in commercial powders. Fuller and France [58] reported negative results when milk dried by the roller and spray processes were examined for *Mycobacterium tuberculosis*.

Very interesting are the statements of Kossowicz,[59] that only sanitary milk should be used in making powdered milk. He stated that even nonsporebearing bacteria survived drying by the Hatmaker ".drying roller" process. The spray process was stated to yield a product with bacteria; even more were found in the milk concentrated in a vacuum and dried slowly at low temperatures. The high bacterial content of a dehydrated milk is also borne out by Delepine's [60] work in England. In the Journal of State Medicine [61] it was stated that in milk powder made by the Hatmaker process the numbers of bacteria were reduced from 70 to 120 million per ml. to 70 to 120 per ml. Experiments also indicated that *Mycobacterium tuberculosis* was destroyed by this process. The accessory substances seem to be reduced during dehydration.

Reduction in the total number of bacteria, according to Delepine, was almost entirely due to the death of Streptococci, Staphylococci, Sarcinae, bacilli of the *Escherichia coli* type, Streptothrices, yeasts, etc. At none of the stages of preparation was the milk ever found completely sterile. Some living tubercle bacilli of bovine origin were found to have survived treatment of drying milk over heated, revolving cylinders, while the drying of milk in a current of hot air had even less effect on tubercle bacilli. These bacilli were capable of producing tuberculosis in guinea pigs, but the course of the disease was much slower than when the same amount of untreated tuberculous milk was used. There is room for more work on the effect of different methods of drying on *Mycobacterium tuberculosis*. That the initial number of bacteria in the milk, before drying, has much to do with the number in the dry milk, is suggested by data reported by Hunwicke and Jephcott.[62] Desiccation of milk by the roller process which had been inoculated with *Escherichia coli, Aerobacter cloacae, Sarcina lutea, Staphylococcus albus*, a long chain streptococcus, and an encapsulated organism producing a red pigment, practically sterilized it. The only milk containing bacteria after drying and reconstituting was one

57. Supplee and Ashbaugh. 1922. J. Dairy Sci. 5, 216-228.
58. Fuller and France. 1933. Mass. Agr. Expt. Sta. Bull. 293.
59. Kossowicz. 1911. Ztschr. Landw. Versuchsw. Österr. 15, 737-754.
60. Delepine. 1914. J. Soc. Chem. Indus. 34, 297.
61. J. State Med. 30 (1922), 540-546.
62. Hunwicke and Jephcott. 1925. J. Dairy Sci. 8, 206-14.

which originally had 2,000,000,000 bacteria per ml. and, after drying, four per ml. Milk inoculated with *Bacillus subtilis* and *Bacillus mycoides* showed a greater number of surviving cells. Similar results were secured by Dick and Dick.[63] They stated that many of these bacteria would appear in the food of infants prepared from milk powder, if the milk was not boiled. Schrader, Ewing, Korff, and Conn [64] examined 100 samples of milk powder from widely different sources. They were examined for total count, *Escherichia coli* count, Breed count, and for *Mycobacterium tuberculosis* by animal inoculation. All of the samples were negative for *Mycobacterium tuberculosis*. The counts by the standard plate and the Breed method were variable. These authors believed that there was still opportunity for improvement in handling milk powder. Macy [65] used drum and spray-dried milk powders, in the fresh condition, and after storage for up to six years. Original counts per gram on spray samples varied from 4,400 to five and one-half million, averaging over 50,000; on drum samples 40 to 79,000, averaging below 500. There was a decrease of over 90 per cent on one year's storage, and a greater decrease with increase of storage temperature up to 37°C.(98.6°F.) with spray process powders. He also said that the types of bacteria present in the dried milk vary with the drying process.

According to Supplee and Bixby,[66] dry milk, made by the Just roller process, rarely has a bacterial content of over 1,000 per gram. Many undesirable bacteria were destroyed by this process. On account of the conclusions reached by Dick and Dick[63] that undesirable streptococci might not be killed, Supplee and Bixby dried milk which had been artificially inoculated with hemolytic and green-producing streptococci. All were destroyed.

Four hundred seasonal samples of spray-dried milk powder examined by Nichols [67] from factories in England and Scotland showed wide variations in bacterial content and methylene blue reduction times. Plate counts varied from 1,400 to 149,000,000 per gram and reduction times from three to 14 hours. Variations in quality of milk powder from the same plant was attributed to processing methods and presence of heat-resistant microorganisms, such as thermoduric and thermophilic bacteria. After aging at room temperature for 12 months, the mean reduction in bacterial content was 95 per cent. Heat-resistant streptococci predominated in the milk. Crossley [68] also found large numbers of microorganisms. He thought that the plate count could be used as an index of the quality of raw milk from which the milk powder was made. Thermophilic bacteria were reported to be present in skim-milk powder by Sorensen.[69]

MICROBIOLOGICAL EXAMINATION OF MILK POWDER

Less attention has been given to methods for the bacteriological examination of milk powder than has been given to methods for examination of

63. Dick and Dick. 1927. Amer. J. Diseases Children 34, 1040.
64. Schrader, Ewing, Korff, and Conn. 1928. Amer. J. Hyg. 8, 386-397.
65. Macy. 1928. J. Dairy Sci. 11, 516-526.
66. Supplee and Bixby. 1929. Amer. J. Diseases Children 37, 1016.
67. Nichols. 1939. J. Dairy Res. 10, 202-230.
68. Crossley. 1938. Rev. in J. Dairy Sci. 21, 303.
69. Sorensen. 1938. Food Indus. 3, 421-427.

other products. After the powder has been reconstituted, the regular methods for examination of fluid milk may be used. Miller and Prickett [70] and Prickett [71] believed that the sanitary condition of milk powder could be ascertained by determining the "standard plate count" per gram, a similar count with plates incubated at 55°C.(131°F.), a microscope count, a mold count, and a sediment test. Prickett [71] placed considerable confidence in the microscope count because it enumerated both living and dead bacteria and thus gave more information concerning the previous history of the powdered milk. Although the standard plate count was said to be beset with several difficulties which were discussed by Prickett, it was considered to be an important step in bacteriological control of this product.

Comprehensive observations were made by Curtis and Hileman [72] on media and incubation temperatures which might be used for making bacterial counts of dry skim milk. In this work 254 samples of spray-process, dry skim milk were plated on standard agar and tryptone-dextrose skim milk agar recommended by Bowers and Hucker. The plates were incubated at 37°C.(98.6°F.) and at 32°C. (89.6°F.) for 48 hours. The tryptone agar and lower incubation temperatures both resulted in higher counts. The medium was more important in a greater increase in count than was lowering the incubation temperature. This was said to be contrary to results obtained on other dairy products for usually lowering of the incubation temperature has resulted in the greater increase. Curtis and Hileman explained this by the fact that the methods of making dry skim milk might result in a richer flora of heat-resistant bacteria, growth of which would be favored by the tryptone agar. Other dairy products are stored at low temperatures which would probably result in a flora which would grow better at lower temperatures.

Bacterial Standards for Milk Powder. Quality of raw milk from which milk powder is made or of the final product itself is probably not indicated by the number of bacteria in it as determined by the plate count. The method of manufacture determined to a great extent the number of microorganisms that may survive. For "Extra Grade" dry skim milk the Dry Milk Institute suggests no more than 15,000 bacteria per ml. of reconstituted milk; for "Standard Grade" no more than 50,000 per ml. whether these milks are made by the spray process, vacuum drum process, or atmospheric roller process.

American Dairy Science Association [73] **Procedures for Examination of Milk Powders.** These procedures resulted from actions of the committee on bacteriological methods of analysis and have been used as the basis for statements of procedure by later workers.

Samples. It is important that all apparatus be clean and sterile and that the sample be taken as speedily as possible. Samples should be taken at points beneath the surface in order to avoid those which may have been unduly contaminated. If the lot to be sampled is a large one, it is better to remove portions from different points throughout the mass. Such portions should be combined in a larger container and thoroughly mixed. Sterile spoons or spatulas may be used.

70. Miller and Prickett. 1933. Milk Plant Mo. 22, 24-29.
71. Prickett. 1939. J. Milk Tech. 2, 133-137.
72. Curtis and Hileman. 1937. Food Research 2, 73-80.
73. Down (Chairman). 1932. J. Dairy Sci. 15, 383-389.

Standard Agar Plate. The procedures recommended by the American Public Health Association for determining the plate count of fluid milk are used. For the one-to-ten dilution, 10 grams of milk powder are added to 99 grams of sterile water in a dilution bottle; or, if desired, five grams of the powder may be added to 45 grams of water. Dilutions for plating should be made so that plates with not less than 30 or more than 300 colonies per plate are available for counting. If lactic acid, milk-powder preparations are being analyzed, N/10 lithium hydroxide should be used as diluent to facilitate dissolving the sample. The plates should be incubated for two days at 37°C.(98.6°F.), as recommended in the standard procedures of milk analysis. Other temperatures may be used in special work, such as incubations at 55°C.(131°F.), to determine the number of thermophilic bacteria which are present. In counting, great care should be exercised to distinguish between colonies and débris on the plates. Doubtful objects should be scrutinized with a lens to determine whether they might be bacterial colonies.

The Microscope Count. This may be done either by the Frost method or by the Prescott-Breed method. If the Frost method is used, the little plates should be incubated for from 12 to 16 hours at 37°C.(98.6°F.). The committee did not believe that the latter was an adequate method for determining the bacterial content of milk powder. It was said to be of supplementary value in conjunction with plating procedures.

Examination for Hemolytic Streptococci. These organisms should be determined by use of blood agar plates prepared by adding .5 per cent of sodium chloride and from two to five per cent of defibrinated blood to standard nutrient agar medium. These plates should be incubated for two days at 37°C. Suspicious colonies should be examined by the Gram stain to determine presence of streptococci.

Examination for Thermophilic Bacteria. For routine work plates should be prepared with standard nutrient agar medium. They should be incubated for 48 hours at 55°C.(131°F.). In order to prevent drying, at least 15 ml. of medium should be used in each plate.

Examination for Yeasts and Molds. When it is desired to examine milk powder for yeasts and molds, procedures devised for butter may be used.

Reporting of Results. These should ordinarily be per gram of dry powder. If desired they may be transformed to the fluid basis by dividing by the factor used in reconstitution. This is usually eight parts of water to one part of powder.

Thompson, Slemmons, and Fleming's [74] Method for Bacteriological Examination of Dry Skim Milk. The authors of this method constituted the Standards Committee of the American Dry Milk Institute. They proposed the following method:

A. Completely disperse 10 grams of a well-mixed powder in 100 ml. of sterile, distilled water. It is suggested that this be done by weighing 10 grams directly into a six-ounce sterile bottle containing 100 ml. of sterile water and furnished with a sterile rubber stopper. It is important that the mixture be thoroughly shaken so as to make sure that the powder is completely dispersed.

B. After reconstitution as in A, follow the procedure as outlined for the microscope colony count (plate method) as published in the Standard Methods of Milk Analysis of the American Public Health Association. It is important to note that the final count is to be expressed as the plate count per milliliter of the reconstituted solution. The American Dry Milk Institute established two grades of dry milk: "extra grade" and "standard grade." The former should not contain over 30,000 bacteria per ml. and the latter not over 100,000 bacteria per ml., whether "spray dried," "vacuum drum dried," or "roller dried." This technic was adopted as official by the American Dry Milk Institute.

American Dry Milk Institute [75] Procedures for Bacteriological Examination of Milk Powder. Completely disperse 10 grams of the sample in 100 ml. of sterile distilled water. This may be done by weighing two grams directly into a six-ounce bottle containing 100 ml. of sterile water and furnished with a rubber stopper. Shake the bottle vigorously to break lumps and assure distribution of bacteria. After this the standard procedure for examination of milk as given in *Standard Methods for Examination of Dairy Prod-*

74. Thompson, Slemmons, and Fleming. 1930. J. Dairy Sci. 13, 319-335.
75. The Grading of Dry Milk Solids. Amer. Dry Milk Inst., 221 No. LaSalle St., Chicago, Ill.

ucts should be followed. Further dilutions of the reconstituted milk should be made so that plates may be counted which have not less than 30 or more than 300 colonies per plate. The results are to be expressed as the number of bacteria per ml, of reconstituted milk.

Microbiology of Infant Foods. An important baby food is milk powder, the microbiology of which is discussed here. Dick and Dick [63] showed that the use of milk powder for the preparation of feedings for infants permitted many bacteria to be ingested. A feeding prepared at one institution from a sample of protein milk contained 22,000 bacteria per milliliter, of which 11,000 were green-producing streptococci. A similar feeding prepared at another institution from another sample of protein milk contained 9,000 bacteria in one ml. with 7,000 green-producing streptococci. Results of an extensive investigation on infant foods were published by Hucker and Hucker.[76] Samples of prepared infant foods secured from the manufacturers and on the open market contained living bacteria varying from 10 to over 600,000 per gram of dried material. The principal organisms were spore-bearing types, many of which were thermophiles. Hucker and Hucker stated that no hemolytic streptococci should be permitted nor should the total count be more than 10,000 per gram. Careful attention to plant sanitation and other factors permitted manufacture of products which were consistently below this standard. Giblin and von Pourtales [77] examined 200 samples of dried-milk preparations used in infant feeding. The total count varied from 1,000 to 10,000 per gram. No pathogenic streptococci nor tubercle bacilli were observed, indicating that the standards suggested by Hucker and Hucker were being met.

Of 20 brands of powdered infant foods studied by Mattoon,[78] average total colony counts made on standard agar ranged from 37 to 98,000 per gram after 48 hours' incubation at 37°C.(98.6°F.). The majority of organisms found were sporeformers, ranging from seven to 29,900 per gram, though micrococci, streptococci, nonsporeforming rods and a few sarcinae, yeast, and molds were found. Gelatin liquefiers varied from 0 to 34,000 and the number of chromogens from 0 to 8,900 per gram. No coliform colonies were noted. Average total counts of hemolyzing colonies were from 0 to 19,800 per gram, though individual counts as high as 160,000 were obtained: Viridans and beta hemolytic streptococci were found in five different products, and their presence was questioned in two others. In one product these organisms numbered as high as 160,000 per gram. Cultures obtained from this sample were not pathogenic for guinea pigs.

REFERENCE BOOKS

BAUMGARTNER, F., 1920. The Condensed Milk and Milk Powder Industries. Jackson Press, Kingston, Ontario.

HUNZIKER, O. F., 1935. Condensed Milk and Milk Powder. Published by the Author. LaGrange, Illinois.

PORCHER, C., 1929. Dry Milk. Olsen Pub. Co., Milwaukee, Wisconsin.

76. Hucker and Hucker. 1929. N. Y. Agr. Expt. Sta. Bull. 154.
77. Giblin and von Pourtales. 1929. Idem 41, 1100.
78. Mattoon. 1932. Amer. J. Diseases Children 44, 16-24.

CHAPTER 12

FERMENTED MILKS

Milk has been fermented for ages by nomadic people. Fermented milks were first used for their food values. Gradually, they have been used for whatever therapeutic value they might possess. Interest in this latter use, and indeed in the entire subject of intestinal bacteriology, was greatly aroused by Metschnikoff's book, *The Prolongation of Life*, in which it was stated that senility was related to autointoxication in the digestive system. He believed that the evil consequences from constipation are due, mainly, to retention of fecal matter and undigested food residues in the intestines. Toxic substances and even putrefactive bacteria were believed to be absorbed into the blood. He observed the numerous instances of old age among people of the Balkans, and resorted to the unique explanation for which he is so well known today. A discussion of this subject with the literature has been prepared by Rogers.[1] Since Metschnikoff published his interesting conclusions, many others have studied the subject. While, in general, the beneficial results of ingestion of fermented milks have been confirmed, not all of Metschnikoff's conclusions have been accepted. Metschnikoff's reputation undoubtedly suffers from unwarranted interpretations which have been made of some of his statements.

Considerable confusion exists today in this field. This may be explained, perhaps, by the fact that there is no certainty that some investigators really had the organism which they said they were using. It is probable that Metschnikoff may have had one organism at one time, another at another time, or perhaps mixtures of types.

Cohendy,[2] one of the first to show that feeding of milk containing *Lactobacillus bulgaricus* was beneficial, reported that the organism could be implanted, in this manner, in the intestines; a conclusion which was not confirmed by investigators. He further reported, however, that the diet had much to do with the sojourn of the organism in the intestines. Cohendy and Belonovsky[3] believed that *Lactobacillus bulgaricus* remained in the intestines for some time. This has since been disputed by Rahe[4] and others.

It was believed that if intestinal putrefaction could be prevented, senility and premature death could be inhibited. Metschnikoff, therefore, advised the drinking of large amounts of sour milk which would contain both lactic acid and the organisms producing it. Putrefactive bacteria would then be checked because it is well known that they cannot thrive in an acid environment.

Rettger[5] and his colleagues at Yale University, who have done much work on this subject, showed in 1915 that sweet as well as sour milk

1. Rogers. 1916. U. S. Dept. Agr. Bull. 319.
2. Cohendy. 1906. Compt. Rend. Soc. Biol. 60, 558-560.
3. Belonovsky. 1908. Milchw. Zentbl. 41, 449-454.
4. Rahe. 1915. J. Infect. Diseases 16, 210-221.
5. Rettger. 1915. J. Expt. Med. 21, 365-388.

functioned alike in altering the intestinal flora. Furthermore, sour milk containing *Lactobacillus bulgaricus* was no more beneficial than milk with the ordinary lactic acid bacilli. Working with white rats, they found that lactose would give the same results. From this, Rettger [6] reasoned that it was the lactose in the milk that exerted the effects which were attributed to sour or sweet milk. This lactose created the optimum conditions for the proliferation of the aciduric group of bacteria. Cheplin and Rettger [7] later reported that lactose was quite as beneficial as sour milk in the diet. They also claimed that Metschnikoff and his collaborators probably worked with *Lactobacillus acidophilus,* believing that they had *Lactobacillus bulgaricus.* Cheplin and Rettger found that a milk diet would completely suppress the ordinary flora of the intestines and establish a flora made up of *Lactobacillus acidophilus.* The work was, in general, confirmed by Torrey,[8] working with dogs. Not all sugars were able to alter the flora to the same degree. Sucrose, maltose, and glucose gave far less striking changes in flora to the aciduric type than did lactose and dextrin. Glucose and maltose, even in large amounts, exercised no transforming effect on the types of bacteria which were present in the intestinal tract. Torrey did report the interesting observation that there was a difference in flora when boiled milk or unboiled milk was used. With unboiled milk, *Escherichia coli* and streptococci predominated while with boiled milk streptococci and *Lactobacillus acidophilus* outnumbered the other organisms. With regard to the proteins causing a putrefactive flora, it was found that mammalian tissue caused the most pronounced change to an obligate putrefactive flora.

LACTIC ACID BACTERIA AND INTESTINAL THERAPY

The lactic acid bacteria are those which produce appreciable amounts of lactic acid in the fermentation of sugars. Rettger [9] distinguished the following three main groups:

1. *Escherichia coli* and *Aerobacter aerogenes.*
2. *Streptococcus lactis,* Lister *(Streptococcus lacticus),* Kruse.
3. *Lactobacillus caucasicus,* Beijerinck *(Bacterium caucasicum),* Kern.

The members of these three groups are materially different from one another. The coli-aerogenes types grow well on laboratory media, producing many different products. These organisms are prevalent in some milk but are not as important as the species in the other groups.

In contrast with the members of the coli-aerogenes group, *Streptococcus lactis,* Lister *(Bacterium lactis acidi,* Leichmann, *Streptococcus lacticus,* Kruse, *Micrococcus lacticus,* Migula) is commonly present in milk. It brings about changes which are quite well understood and which, under some conditions, are quite desirable. It functions, for instance, in producing desirable flavor and aroma in cream ripening.

The third group, the *Lactobacillus caucasicus,* Beijerinck group, is the one of main interest at this time. This organism has been used to designate

6. Rettger. 1917. Sci. Mo., July, 1917.
7. Cheplin and Rettger. 1921. Abs. Bact. 5, 20.
8. Torrey. 1919. J. Med. Res. 39, 415-447.
9. Rettger. 1923. Proc. World's Dairy Cong. 2, 1136-1144.

the group because Massol, Moro, and Tissier had not named their organisms when Beijerinck named his. In this group may be placed the well-known organisms:

Lactobacillus caucasicus (Kern), Beijerinck (*Bacillus caucasicus*, Kern).
Lactobacillus bulgaricus (Grigoroff), Holland (*Bacillus bulgaricus*, Grigoroff).
Lactobacillus acidophilus (Moro), Holland (*Bacillus acidophilus*, Moro).
Lactobacillus bifidus (Tissier), Castellani and Shalmers (*Bacillus bifidus*, Tissier).

Rettger has stated that these organisms cannot be easily separated by common laboratory tests. All three types *(Lactobacillus bulgaricus, Lactobacillus acidophilus,* and *Lactobacillus bifidus)* are strongly Gram-positive, are rod-shaped, often grow in long filaments, etc. All three types are distinctly pleomorphic. The growth on ordinary culture media is delicate. They differ, as stated below, in their normal habitat. It is quite possible that some of the confusion in the literature on these intestinal forms may be explained on the basis that the investigators were not certain of the identity of the organisms which they were using. Cruickshank and Berry[10] found a wide range of morphologic appearance of aciduric bacteria in feces from adults and infants. They believed that the name *Lactobacillus acidophilus* covered a considerable group of organisms and that numerous strains might exist in one sample of stool. Considerable confusion may arise in the use of such terms as acidophile. Close distinctions are frequently not made, and specific terms are made to cover much more ground than they should. Schlirf,[11] for instance, stated that some forms should be called acid tolerant rather than acidophilic. Perhaps it is better to use the actual names of species and thus avoid the use of collective terms.

Lactobacillus bulgaricus (Bacterium bulgaricum). This organism was isolated from sour milks, especially those milks common in the countries of southern Europe. Rettger[9] stated that the organism was isolated in Massol's laboratory by Grigoroff[12] at the behest of Metschnikoff. Bergey et al.[13] gave Grigoroff credit for isolating the organism. Metschnikoff believed that the well-being of the Bulgarians and other Balkan peoples was due to the almost constant use of sour milk. The beneficial action of sour milk was ascribed to one organism *Lactobacillus bulgaricus.* Metschnikoff believed that when this organism was taken by the mouth it replaced other types which were far less desirable, such as those which brought about intestinal putrefaction. It is, without doubt, a very desirable organism but one which has been confused with other closely related species. It has probably received credit for results actually due to *Lactobacillus acidophilus.*

Lactobacillus bulgaricus has a voluminous literature of its own, all of which cannot be reviewed here. An extensive comparative study of *Lactobacillus bulgaricus* and *Lactobacillus acidophilus* was carried out by Kulp and Rettger.[14] They made no attempt to include various lactobacilli other than varying strains designated under the above names. The first problem

10. Cruickshank and Berry. 1924. J. Hyg. 24, 241.
11. Schlirf. 1926. Centbl. Bakt., Pt. 1, 99, 129-145.
12. Grigoroff. 1905. Rev. Suisse romande 25.
13. Bergey *et al.* 1939. Manual of Determinative Bacteriology, Fifth Edition. Williams and Wilkins, Baltimore, Md.
14. Kulp and Rettger. 1924. J. Bact. 9, 357-394.

was to find a medium on which the organisms could be grown. Their efforts to solve the question resulted in a casein-digest medium. For securing acidophilus strains, they used the discovery of Rettger and his associates that the feeding of lactose or dextrin would cause a transformation in the intestinal flora to the aciduric types, and since *Lactobacillus acidophilus* is an intestinal form, it would thus appear. *Lactobacillus bulgaricus* strains were secured from the Bureau of Animal Industry and several other sources. They found close resemblance between the members of the *Lactobacillus acidophilus* and *Lactobacillus bulgaricus* types. The strains used were fairly representative of the organisms found in fermented milks and in the intestines of man and animals, characterized by the production, in part or altogether, of sea-urchin-like colonies in agar and in gelatin media. The *Lactobacillus bulgaricus* type appeared to be more constant than the *Lactobacillus acidophilus* type in this respect. The morphology of the two groups was quite similar.

The one outstanding difference between the two types was their habitat. In no case in the course of this investigation had an organism been isolated from feces which had the characteristics of a typical *Lactobacillus bulgaricus* strain. Herter and Kendall,[15] Rahe,[4] and Rettger and Cheplin [16] proved that *Lactobacillus bulgaricus* cannot be implanted in the intestines of man or animals. In the course of an unfinished experiment, they were not able to recover a non-maltose-fermenting *Lactobacillus bulgaricus* from the feces of white rats after two weeks' feeding of large milk cultures of *Lactobacillus bulgaricus* plus lactose. On the other hand, the ingestion of milk or broth cultures of *Lactobacillus acidophilus,* or the use of a high lactose or dextrin diet alone (Rettger and Cheplin), brought about a transformation of the intestinal flora to such an extent that *Lactobacillus acidophilus* became the predominating organism. Therefore, they concluded that the normal habitat of *Lactobacillus acidophilus* is the intestine of man and animals.

Origin of *Lactobacillus bulgaricus* can only be a matter of conjecture. Was it always a saprophyte living in milk, possibly coming from soil? Or, may it not be a degenerate form of *Lactobacillus acidophilus,* requiring milk as food because of long acclimatization to this medium? Rettger and Cheplin accept the latter explanation for reasons which cannot be given in detail here. They center around the nutrient properties of milk.

Several of those who have studied these organisms have suggested that many of the older names be dropped. Heinemann and Hefferan [17] and Makrinoff [18] would place them all in the *Lactobacillus bulgaricus* group. White and Avery [19] believed them to be identical with *Lactobacillus caucasicus.* The great difficulty of identifying members of the lactobacillus genus was emphasized again by Hunt and Rettger.[20] They stated that, at

15. Herter and Kendall. 1909. J. Biol. Chem. 7, 203-236.
16. Rettger and Cheplin. 1922. Arch. Int. Med. 29, 357-367.
17. Heinemann and Hefferan. 1909. J. Infect. Diseases 6, 304-318.
18. Makrinoff. 1910. Centbl. Bakt., Pt. 2, 26, 274-388.
19. White and Avery. 1910. Centbl. Bakt., Pt. 2, 25, 161-178.
20. Hunt and Rettger. 1930. J. Bact. 20, 61-83.

times, there are greater differences in fermentation reactions of two given strains of the same organism than are seen between two individuals of different species. Hunt and Rettger pointed out that the soil and grain strains of lactobacilli do not ferment lactose while *Lactobacillus bulgaricus* and *Lactobacillus acidophilus* do. Sherman and Hodge [21] regarded it as significant that freshly isolated *Lactobacillus bulgaricus* grew at 60°C. (140°F.) and showed vigorous growth at 55°C.(131°F.), whereas old laboratory cultures had a maximum temperature of about 50°C.(122°F.). *Lactobacillus bulgaricus* rarely grew at 15°C.(59°F.), whereas *Lactobacillus acidophilus* usually did.

Characteristics of Lactobacillus acidophilus and Lactobacillus bulgaricus. The characteristics of these organisms merge to such an extent that it is difficult to distinguish one from the other. During the past few years several methods have been suggested for separating the two organisms. Kulp and Rettger [14] believed that the action of the organisms on maltose, sucrose, and levulose might be of value. *Lactobacillus bulgaricus* did not ferment levulose; *Lactobacillus acidophilus* did. *Lactobacillus acidophilus* fermented maltose and sucrose. Day and Gibbs,[22] however, reported that fermentation of maltose, sucrose, and levulose did not differentiate these organisms. Kulp [23] suggested that tolerance for indol or phenol might be used for differentiating these species. *Lactobacillus bulgaricus* was said to be only slightly tolerant to these compounds, which may explain why it does not live in the intestine. Albus and Holm [24] observed that *Lactobacillus bulgaricus* would not grow in a medium the surface tension of which had been reduced to less than 40 dynes, but *Lactobacillus acidophilus* showed good growth in the same medium when the surface tension was depressed to 36 dynes. They then suggested that this was a plausible explanation for failures to implant *Lactobacillus bulgaricus* in the intestines. Kopeloff and Beerman [25] confirmed the work of Albus and Holm. They used sodium ricinoleate as a surface tension depressant, with six strains each of *Lactobacillus acidophilus* and *Lactobacillus bulgaricus*. Day and Gibbs, however, were unable to concur in these conclusions. They stated that no instance was found in which inhibition of growth could be attributed to lowered surface tension. Sodium ricinoleate was found to exert a toxic action towards the two microorganisms, but this action could not be used as a means of differentiation.

Possibility of using the kind of lactic acid formed by members of the genus lactobacillus has also been suggested as a means of differentiation. Curran, Rogers, and Whittier [26] were able to establish two groups of lactobacilli on the basis of the kind of acid formed, temperature characteristics, colony type, carbohydrate fermentations, and inhibition by phenol and indol. About one-half of the strains used agreed with what is usually

21. Sherman and Hodge. 1936. Science 84, 208; J. Bact. 40 (1940), 11-22.
22. Day and Gibbs. 1928. J. Infect. Diseases 43, 97-107.
23. Kulp. 1926. J. Amer. Med. Assoc. 98, 833-835.
24. Albus and Holm. 1926. Abs. Bact. 9, 142.
25. Kopeloff and Beerman. 1925. Soc. Expt. Biol. and Med. Proc. 22, 318.
26. Curran, Rogers, and Whittier. 1933. J. Bact. 25, 595-621.

574 THE MICROBIOLOGY OF FOODS

considered to be *Lactobacillus acidophilus*. They showed a high positive correlation in production of inactive lactic acid, formation of R or fuzzy colonies, failure to grow above 46°C.(114.8°F.) or as low as 20°C.(68°F.), fermentation of raffinose, and failure to ferment mannitol. As a rule these cultures formed more carbon dioxide and a larger proportion of volatile acids and grew in higher concentrations of phenol and indol than the strains in the other group. A large percentage of the strains of known intestinal origin were in the *Lactobacillus acidophilus* group. The results reported by these investigators show again what a labile group of organisms we are dealing with. Kopeloff and Kopeloff [27] related the types of lactic acid produced to the types of form, R or S, which might be present. The R form of *Lactobacillus acidophilus* produced inactive lactic acid. The R form of *Lactobacillus bulgaricus* produced inactive lactic acid in the first six fractions, while the seventh yielded the dextrorotatory enantiomorph. The latter represented one-sixth of the total zinc salt. The S forms of both *Lactobacillus acidophilus* and *Lactobacillus bulgaricus* produced dextrorotatory lactic acid. It is suggested that some of the inconsistencies reported in the literature might be due to the use of cultures containing mixtures of R, S, or intermediate forms.

A few attempts have been made to determine whether *Lactobacillus bulgaricus* can survive in cultures with other lactic acid bacteria. Vas,[28] for instance, cultured *Lactobacillus bulgaricus* with *Streptococcus lactis* and studied the amount of acid formed. The amount of acid necessary to coagulate milk was the same in each case, but when grown together the organisms stimulated each other, producing the necessary degree of acidity for coagulation much sooner. Rogers [29] found that when milk was inoculated simultaneously, both would grow, but when a heavier *Streptococcus lactis* inoculation was used or if the organism was allowed to grow for a while before *Lactobacillus bulgaricus* was put in, the latter organism did not thrive immediately, but after a few days it began to develop. The inhibiting factor was removed by heating and by filtering through clay or plaster of Paris filters.

Development of *Lactobacillus bulgaricus* in milk is greatly influenced by other bacteria which may be present. When Rogers[29] inoculated sterile milk with equal amounts of *Streptococcus lactis* and *Lactobacillus bulgaricus*, the latter predominated. If the inoculation of *Streptococcus lactis* is two to three times as great as *Lactobacillus bulgaricus* only slight development of the latter occurs. When a mixed culture is held for a few days *Lactobacillus bulgaricus* finally develops. Antagonism of these organisms was further shown by growing a culture of *Lactobacillus bulgaricus* in a collodion sac placed in a culture of *Streptococcus lactis*.

Implantation of Lactobacillus bulgaricus in the Intestines. There is no field in microbiology where more unwarranted assumptions have been made than in the exploitation of the uninformed with *Lactobacillus bulgaricus*

27. Kopeloff and Kopeloff. 1937. J. Bact. 33, 331-334.
28. Vas. 1926. Lait 4, 625-638.
29. Rogers. 1928. J. Bact. 16, 321-325.

preparations. Fortunately, the researches of Rettger and his colleagues at Yale University have largely cleared this field. Cheplin and Rettger [7] failed in every instance to implant *Lactobacillus bulgaricus* in the intestines. They secured these results with both rats and men. This was confirmed by Smith.[30] Kopeloff [31] tried to implant *Lactobacillus bulgaricus* into the intestinal tract of 12 psychotic women, some constipated, the rest not. Over a period of 10 to 15 days, daily doses of *Lactobacillus bulgaricus* milk (?) containing 50,000,000 viable cells per ml. were used. In 10 subjects no *Lactobacillus bulgaricus* cells were isolated from the feces. A negligible number was found in the feces of one patient; these finally disappeared entirely. While no implantation was observed, Kopeloff was reluctant to state that such implantation was impossible, since the number of cells in the milk was considerably lower than the number used in acidophilus milk. Kulp [23] carried out experiments to determine the viability of *Lactobacillus acidophilus* and *Lactobacillus bulgaricus* in the human intestine. Several strains of each species were employed. The organisms were ingested as milk cultures, the subjects taking one to three pints daily during each experiment. Whole, sweet, and *Streptococcus lactis* soured milk were fed previous to these experiments as control diets. The results appear to justify the conclusion, that typical *Lactobacillus acidophilus* is viable in the intestine, while typical *Lactobacillus bulgaricus* is not. Emphasis was placed on the point that isolations of *Lactobacillus acidophilus* should be thoroughly tested upon normal individuals, before these cultures are advocated for therapeutic use. Failure to implant *Lactobacillus bulgaricus* may be due to the fact that this organism cannot tolerate indole and skatole as shown by Kulp, or an unsuitable surface tension of intestinal contents.

Lactobacillus acidophilus. This organism was isolated by Moro in 1900 and was named *Bacillus acidophilus*. Unlike *Lactobacillus bulgaricus*, it is a normal inhabitant of the intestines, and can be made to proliferate there by use of an appropriate diet. The experiments on which this statement is based were carried out mainly in Rettger's laboratory at Yale University with a sufficient number of confirmatory papers from other laboratories to justify acceptance of the conclusions. Frost and Hankinson [32] published an annotated bibliography on this organism.

Implantation of Lactobacillus acidophilus in the Intestines. The early work by Cheplin and Rettger [33] was done with white rats. They observed that the addition of two grams of lactose daily to the basal ration of bread and meat caused a pronounced transformation. *Lactobacillus acidophilus* replaced practically all other types. One gram brought about only a partial change. Combination of lactose with culture produced good transformation. According to Rettger and Cheplin,[34] *Lactobacillus acid-*

30. Smith. 1924. Brit. Med. J. 948-950.
31. Kopeloff. 1925. Soc. Expt. Biol. and Med. Proc. 22, 393.
32. Frost, W. D., and Hankinson, H. 1931. Lactobacillus acidophilus: An Annotated Bibliography. Davis-Green Corp., Milton, Wis.
33. Cheplin and Rettger. 1921. Abs. Bact. 5, 20-21.
34. Rettger and Cheplin. 1921-1922. Soc. Expt. Biol. and Med. Proc. 19, 72-76.

ophilus may be implanted in the intestines by oral administration of various preparations, as follows:

1. Ingestion of 300 to 400 grams of lactose or dextrin daily.
2. Daily ingestion of 300 ml. of whey broth culture of *Lactobacillus acidophilus*.
3. Daily ingestion of a combination of 150 grams of lactose and 150 ml. of bacterial culture.
4. Daily ingestion of 500 to 1,000 ml. of acidophilus milk.
5. Daily ingestion of 500 ml. of acidophilus milk and 100 grams of lactose.

They stated that the acidophilus milk, of the methods mentioned above, was the best. The milk method stimulated change in bacterial types within the intestines more quickly and perhaps more effectively than feeding the carbohydrate or the whey broth culture. They reported that in two men 500 ml. of acidophilus milk brought about marked alteration in the flora within two to three days. All of the subjects responded to 1,000 ml. of the milk, and a change in the flora of the intestines was produced more quickly and perhaps more effectively. No success was attained in attempts to implant *Lactobacillus bulgaricus* in the human intestinal tract thus supporting the conclusions of the experiments with rats. The hydrogen-ion concentration of the intestines was not changed and consequently this could not be offered as an explanation of the change in flora. The change in type of predominating organisms could be followed culturally. This work was extended by Rettger and Cheplin to pathological cases. One quart of acidophilus milk a day caused a response in an aggravated case of constipation within a week. The same beneficial results were secured in cases of chronic diarrhea, colitis, sprue, and dermatitis. Cannon [35] and Gompertz and Vorhaus [36] also reported beneficial results from using culture of *Lactobacillus acidophilus*. Cases of chronic constipation and diarrhea were greatly benefited. In a later paper, Gompertz and Vorhaus reported further improvement after the use of acidophilus milk. This was attributed solely to decreased activity of bacteria of the coliform group. They believed, however, that broth cultures were the best way of giving *Lactobacillus acidophilus*. This was said to be more pleasant for the patient and more accurately controlled by the physician. They called attention to the fact that indiscriminate use of *Lactobacillus acidophilus* in all sorts of ailments would tend to discredit it and send it to the same oblivion that *Lactobacillus bulgaricus* now has. Some believe that this time has already come. Kopeloff and Cheney [37] also reported confirmatory observations. Less favorable results, however, were reported by Bassler and Lutz.[38] Bass and Jones [39] wondered whether acidophilus milk had therapeutic value even though it is possible to change the intestinal flora with it. If it is used, they believed that best results are secured when the milk is taken with meals in order to heavily seed the food with viable bacteria. A glass of the milk with each meal was said to be enough. In from four to 10 days a high degree of transformation took place which was main-

35. Cannon. 1921. J. Infect. Diseases 29, 369.
36. Gompertz and Vorhaus. 1921. J. Amer. Assoc. 80, 90.
37. Kopeloff and Cheney. 1922. J. Amer. Med. Assoc. 79, 609.
38. Bassler and Lutz. 1922. J. Amer. Med. Assoc. 79, 607-608.
39. Bass and Jones. 1933. New Orleans Med. and Surg. J. 76, 116.

tained as long as the milk was continued. When lactose alone was used, daily ingestion of large amounts resulted in rapid increase of *Lactobacillus acidophilus* in due course of time; if the quantity was sufficient, all other bacteria in the intestinal flora were reduced to a negligible number. In some instances, however, more than 300 grams of lactose per day were required to establish *Lactobacillus acidophilus* as the predominating organism. Unfortunately, such a quantity of these sugars is too large to be continued over long periods of time, hence the practical application of this method must be very limited. The investigations of Bass on the use of cultures of *Lactobacillus acidophilus* for therapeutic purposes, including a large number of experiments on 23 different human subjects, yielded results which practically agreed with those of Rettger and Cheplin.

According to Stark, Gordon, Mauer, Curtis, and Schubert,[40] ingestion of lactose, sweet milk plus lactose, or acidophilus milk with or without added lactose had no material effect upon the numbers of lactobacilli normally growing in the human intestinal tract. However, the types of lactobacilli in acidophilus milk were found in large numbers in fecal specimens from a majority of subjects ingesting this milk but disappeared in two to six weeks after stopping consumption of acidophilus milk even though continuing to take sweet or sour milk with three per cent added beta lactose. The number of coliform bacteria were not greatly changed until acidophilus milk had been taken for three months or more, when a slight decrease occurred. Streptococci and sporulating anaerobes decreased under acidophilus milk therapy. A definite decrease in indol content of the feces occurred in those subjected to acidophilus milk or to sweet milk plus lactose. Moisture content of the stools was increased during ingestion of acidophilus milk but reverted to its original level in four to six weeks in constipated subjects who ceased consuming the milk. Changes in the average weight of the stools occurred in a similar manner owing in part to consumption of lactose in the milk. Yeasts and sporulating aerobes were unaltered. The pH varied little from the average for human feces, which is 7.3. Good implantation of *Lactobacillus acidophilus* after taking whey cultures, was observed by Brown and Redowitz.[41] They recognized the value of laboratory examination of stool specimens to determine whether implantation had occurred.

Having observed the improvements in health following implantation of *Lactobacillus acidophilus* in the intestines, Kopeloff [42] attempted to determine whether the essential nature of this phenomenon was physical, chemical, or bacteriological. The following points were established:

1. *Lactobacillus acidophilus* therapy was not a physical phenomenon since patients receiving sterile milk were not relieved of constipation.

2. *Lactobacillus acidophilus* therapy is apparently not a strictly chemical phenomenon since patients receiving *Lactobacillus acidophilus* milk, which has been pasteurized to kill all living forms, were not relieved of constipation.

40. Stark *et al.* 1934. Amer. J. Pub. Health 24, 470-472.

41. Brown and Redowitz. 1935. Penn. Med. J. 39, 73.

42. Kopeloff. 1923. J. Amer. Med. Assoc. 80, 602-604.

3. It is essentially a bacteriological phenomenon since patients were relieved of constipation by the ingestion of milk fermented by *Lactobacillus acidophilus*.

4. Relief from chronic constipation has persisted for six months after *Lactobacillus acidophilus* milk feeding was stopped.

5. Viable *Lactobacillus acidophilus* cells were isolated from the feces six months after the ingestion of the milk.

The work of Torrey and Kahn [43] would seem to indicate that *Lactobacillus acidophilus* exerts an antagonistic action on proteolytic bacteria. They placed cubes of coagulated egg albumen in cultures of anaerobic bacteria. Cultures to which *Lactobacillus acidophilus* was added did not attack the coagulated egg white. Even when *Lactobacillus acidophilus* was put into older cultures proteolysis was inhibited. Torrey and Kahn found that different strains of *Lactobacillus acidophilus* possessed different abilities to inhibit proteolysis. The conclusions reported have been quite well confirmed by Cruickshank.[44]

Unfermented Acidophilus Milk. An unfermented acidophilus milk containing a high concentration of viable *Lactobacillus acidophilus* and yet similar in taste and physical properties to fresh milk, and having only a negligible quantity of free lactic acid was used by Myers.[45] The product is virtually a sweet whole milk in which viable cells of *Lactobacillus acidophilus* have been suspended in large numbers (in excess of 100 million per ml.). Growth of the organisms is held in check by keeping the milk cold. Since *Lactobacillus acidophilus* has a growth temperature limit at about 20°C.(68°F.) development of acid over a period of two to three days is prevented if the milk is held below 10°C.(50°F.). Data are presented to show that these organisms suspended in unfermented milk are capable of being implanted in the intestinal tract of white rats and of man. Experiments in which a number of individuals drank daily a quart of unfermented acidophilus milk were made to test out the effectiveness of such feeding in bringing about transformation of the intestinal flora. In the ten experiments on human subjects, successful implantation of *Lactobacillus acidophilus*, as determined by the plate method, was obtained in each case. In 12 of the 16 experiments a predominant *Lactobacillus acidophilus* flora was obtained by regular consumption of approximately one quart of unfermented acidophilus milk per day, no other modification of the ordinary diets of the subjects having been made.

Permanence of Results of Acidophilus Therapy. Since it has been quite definitely shown that implantation of *Lactobacillus acidophilus* in the intestines is largely dependent on the diet, one is not surprised to find that implantation may not be permanent. Kopeloff [46] found that the organisms remained for some time in the intestines after their ingestion in cases of diarrhea and constipation had been discontinued. One case was cited in which the benefits persisted for two years, three cases for over a year, and ten for three to six months. Other data on this question are given in

43. Torrey and Kahn. 1923. J. Infect. Diseases 33, 482-497.
44. Cruickshank. 1928. Brit. J. Expt. Path. 9, 318-26.
45. Myers. 1931. Amer. J. Pub. Health 21, 867-872.
46. Kopeloff. 1925. Soc. Expt. Biol. and Med. Proc. 22, 293.

contiguous paragraphs. That the results of acidophilus therapy may be greatly influenced by the particular strain used seems to be indicated by the work of Sanborn,[47] who observed that a foreign strain of *Lactobacillus acidophilus* ingested in acidophilus milk almost completely suppressed the native strains. However, when the milk therapy was stopped, the foreign strain disappeared rather quickly. Under appropriate dietary conditions, the native strains frequently developed to greater concentration than before milk therapy.

Preparation of Acidophilus Milk. Much confusion has probably been caused by the use of preparations which were not properly prepared. Unless Rettger's technique for preparing acidophilus milk is followed, one cannot expect to secure the results which Rettger and his colleagues reported. This was emphasized by Rettger[48] in a paper before the American Public Health Association. He criticized many modifications which have been made in the preparation of the milk. He called attention to the fact that the use of such preparations would not yield results which could be compared with those resulting from the use of properly prepared milk.

Cheplin and Rettger's Acidophilus Milk. Cheplin and Rettger[7] proposed the following procedure for the preparation of *Lactobacillus acidophilus* milk. Stock strains of the organism, preferably a mixture of strains, are grown sufficiently long in milk to produce light curdling in 24 hours. Usually this results from a shorter incubation period, hardly ever over 24 hours. Sweet milk is thoroughly sterilized under pressure after which it is inoculated with a mixture of pure cultures of *Lactobacillus acidophilus* and incubated at 37°C.(98.6°F.) for 12 to 24 hours. Strains which have been growing in milk for a time have to be used, since the freshly isolated strains are often inactive. After coagulation, the milk should be stored in the refrigerator.

Prucha and Brannon's[49] Modified Acidophilus Milk. These authors have described their acidophilus milk as follows: Skimmed milk of good quality is pasteurized in a glass-lined vat at 79.4°C.(175°F.) for 30 minutes, cooled to 37.8°C.(100°F.) and allowed to stand for three or four hours, repasteurized under the same conditions, cooled to from 37.8°C.(100°F.) to 38.9°C.(102°F.). It is then inoculated with a strong active culture of *Lactobacillus acidophilus* using at least three per cent of inoculum. When an acidity of .5 to .6 per cent is reached the milk is cooled to 15.6°C.(60°F.) and cream is added to give a fat content of one per cent with five to 10 per cent of a good lactic acid starter to improve the flavor. The milk is then passed through a homogenizer and over a cooler.

Eggston and Norman's[50] Modified Acidophilus Milk. These investigators claimed to have produced an acidophilus milk which was white in color, of a nonlumpy consistency, practically odorless, and in which the fat content could be regulated to suit the patient. One pint of tap water was placed in a liter flask. If one wished a sweet-tasting milk, a heaping tablespoon of lactose was added to the water which was then autoclaved for 20 minutes under 25 pounds pressure. The water was cooled and a pound tin of unsweetened evaporated milk was added to the flask using aseptic conditions. The mixture was then inoculated with ten ml. of a stock culture of *Lactobacillus acidophilus*, shaken, and incubated for 24 hours at 37°C.(98.6°F.). A soft curd was formed, slightly separated from the whey at the top. This was shaken and kept cool. The fat content may be varied by altering the amount of water.

Carlsson, Wertz, and Broadhurst's[51] Modifications of Acidophilus Milk. Carlsson, Wertz, and Broadhurst reported favorable results obtained with 16 subjects with two

47. Sanborn. 1931. J. Infect. Diseases 49, 37-89.
48. Rettger. 1929. Amer. J. Pub. Health 19, 771-776.
49. Prucha and Brannon. 1926. Ill. Agr. Expt. Sta., Ann. Rpt., 95-96.
50. Eggston and Norman. 1922. N. Y. Med. J. 115, 683-685.
51. Carlsson, Wertz and Broadhurst. 1923. Teachers' Coll. Rec. 24, 497-502.

modifications of acidophilus milk. One was a mixture of *Lactobacillus acidophilus* and ordinary compressed yeast, obtained by inoculating autoclaved milk with pure cultures of these two organisms. The product was highly acid, often two to four times as acid as milk inoculated with acidophilus only. In the other modification, the milk was also autoclaved, before inoculating with acidophilus, until a caramel color and taste developed. This was used while still sweet, subjects who disliked sour milk finding it palatable. The results show that smaller doses than those heretofore recommended are successful when fresh, vigorous cultures are used, favorable results being obtained in such intestinal complications as constipation and "gas, headache, constant sleepiness."

Hughens' [52] **Procedure for Preparation of Acidophilus Milk.** Hughens used materials and equipment which are found in bacteriological laboratories. He gave the following technic:

1. Fill the number of 500 or 1,000 milk bottles which are to be planted half full of water.

2. Place temporary cotton stoppers in the bottles.

3. Wrap the number of corks necessary in a piece of muslin.

4. Sterilize the bottles of water and the package of corks by steam under 15 pounds pressure for 30 minutes.

5. Remove the water and the package of corks from the sterilizer and allow to cool.

6. Evaporated milk is provided for the completion of the culture medium.

7. Each can of evaporated milk as it is used is flamed on one side of the top until it is hot enough to be sterile. When the heat expands the milk until there is a cracking noise, the can is shaken and the heat again applied. After the edge of the can has been sterilized a pointed instrument, which has been rendered sterile by flaming, is plunged through the sterile area in the top of the can. The hole made answers for an air hole. The can is turned to the opposite side and another area sterilized. The opening made on this side by the sterile pointed instrument is made large enough so that the milk will pour freely. A screw driver, old scissors blade, or file may be used for puncturing the cans.

8. The top of the bottle is flamed, and with a flamed pair of thumb forceps the temporary cotton stopper is removed and discarded. The top of the bottle is again flamed. The stopper of the culture is removed, the top of the bottle flamed, and about one ounce of the culture is poured directly into the bottle which has just been prepared. Fill the bottle with evaporated milk and stop with a sterile cork stopper.

9. After the bottles have been treated as described, place them in an incubator at 37°C.(98.6°F.) for 24 to 36 hours, the time depending upon the degree of sourness desired. Usually around 30 hours makes a palatable milk. A good product will show a smooth white clot and there will be no gas formation.

10. Place the milk in a refrigerator where it will keep palatable for a considerable time.

Rice's Method for Preparing Acidophilus Milk in the Home. Rice [53] reported a method for preparation of acidophilus milk on a small scale. The milk should be free from those bacteria which naturally occur in fresh milk. This can be obtained by boiling market milk for a long time, or unsweetened evaporated milk may be used. The evaporated milk is particularly desirable since it is always ready for use, and it is sterile. The *Lactobacillus acidophilus* culture may be secured at drug stores. This organism grows best at 32.2°C.(90°F.) to 40.6°C.(105°F.) although it grows to considerable extent at room temperature. The procedure requires the use of a thermos bottle which has been thoroughly sterilized. Wipe the top of a one-pound can of evaporated milk free from dust and pour boiling water over it. Open the can and pour contents into a pan that has been scalded. Fill the can with boiling water and pour into the evaporated milk. Cool the mixture to about 105°F. Add two or three ounces of commercial *Lactobacillus acidophilus* culture, mix, and transfer to the thermos bottle. Cork and let stand for 24 hours, or until the milk has a pleasantly sour taste. Transfer to a clean milk bottle and place in the refrigerator. Succeeding cultures of acidophilus are prepared

52. Hughens. 1924. U. S. Naval Med. Bull. 21, 548-549.
53. Rice. 1928. Amer. J. Pub. Health 18, 1105.

by using about a teacupful of milk culture previously made to inoculate diluted evaporated milk for the next turn. Thirteen to 17 hours are quite sufficient for succeeding cultures. Milk kept in a refrigerator must be used within 48 hours because the organisms rapidly die out at such low temperatures. Typical acidophilus milk has a fine grained curd and is not "stringy" as is that produced by *Lactobacillus bulgaricus*. The fact that the commercial culture is much less active than the prepared milk culture used for inoculation shows how much greater must be the therapeutic value of the latter.

Knaysi's [54] Method for Preparing Acidophilus Milk. Knaysi stated that this method overcame some of the difficulties inherent in other methods. He believed that the great problem was elimination of rapidly developing sporulating bacteria. His method consists in incubating skimmed milk at 37 to 47°C.(98.6 to 116.6°F.) for two and one-half to three hours, heating to as near the boiling point as possible for 30 minutes, followed by prompt cooling to 37 to 40°C.(98.6° to 104°F.). The milk is then inoculated with a culture of *Lactobacillus acidophilus* and allowed to coagulate.

Storage of Acidophilus Milk.

Biological products are usually stored in the refrigerator. Acidophilus milk is no exception. Kopeloff [42] made daily determinations of the number of viable cells in milk kept in a refrigerator at 9°C.(48.2°F.). There was a 50-per cent reduction in one day, a 75-per cent reduction in two days, and 90 per cent in three days. Kopeloff, therefore, believed that acidophilus milk should be stored at room temperature instead of in an icebox. This would not result in such a rapid decrease in the number of viable cells. Different conditions of storage might easily explain the various results which have been secured in the examination of these products. Black,[55] on the other hand, stated that *Lactobacillus acidophilus* milk cultures may be stored at refrigerator temperatures for several days without deterioration in the number of living cells. Less reduction in numbers occurred at 9°C. or even 0°C.(32°F.) than occurred at 37°C.(98.6°F.). Black believed that cultured milk could be held at 4.4°C.(40°F.), or below, for several days without materially affecting the content of viable cells. All strains with which Black worked acted in the same manner. Kulp,[56] in general, confirmed Black's work. To insure satisfactory viability for two days to a week, Kulp suggested a storage temperature of 5°C.(41°F.), provided the acidity was not above .65 per cent. To insure viability for a longer time, Kulp stated that the number of foreign bacteria must always remain at a negligible figure; rigid precaution against excessive acidity must be observed; the storage temperature should range between 12 and 16°C.(53.6 and 60.8°F.), the optimum viability temperature for *Lactobacillus acidophilus* in milk being 16°C. when the initial acidity is .65 per cent. Kopeloff, Etchells, and Kopeloff [57] stored acidophilus milk prepared with an R and an S strain of *Lactobacillus acidophilus* with initial acidities of six-tenths and one per cent at 4 and 20°C.(39.2 and 68°F.). The viability of these two strains differed. The R strain, the only one of proved therapeutic value, lost its viability more rapidly at 4°C. than at 20°C. The original count was diminished approximately 90 per cent after three days in the icebox. The S strain lost its viability less rapidly but storage in the icebox was more detrimental

54. Knaysi. 1932. J. Dairy Sci. 15, 71.
55. Black. 1931. J. Dairy Sci. 14, 59-72; 198-208.
56. Kulp. 1931. Amer. J. Pub. Health 21, 873-883.
57. Kopeloff, Etchells, and Kopeloff. 1934. J. Bact. 28, 489-500.

than at room temperature. It is recommended that acidophilus milk be kept in a cool place, but not in an icebox.

Attempts have been made to incorporate *Lactobacillus acidophilus* in various dairy products. In one of them Prouty and Bendixen [58] incorporated the organism in sherbet and determined its ability to survive. The number of viable cells after five days' storage at —17°C. (1.40°F.) was a few million per ml. with one culture, but several hundred million with three others. Higher titratable acidity caused more rapid decrease in living organisms, but sugar concentration seemed to have no effect. Prouty and Bendixen stated that sherbet with high numbers of *Lactobacillus acidophilus* could be prepared by keeping acidity below one per cent and using resistant strains.

Other Lactobacillus Acidophilus Preparations. Effort has been made to incorporate *Lactobacillus acidophilus* in materials other than milk. Rettger, in whose laboratories acidophilus milk was originated, believed that milk was the best medium in which to distribute the organism. One of the first to sound a note of warning in the use of various products containing *Lactobacillus acidophilus* was Bass.[59] He considered it advisable to warn against making the same kind of mistake with *Lactobacillus acidophilus* that was made with *Lactobacillus bulgaricus*. Enthusiastic workers were reporting most striking therapeutic results from the administration of broth cultures of *Lactobacillus acidophilus* in teaspoonful doses, only a small fraction of the amount of culture that others had found necessary to change noticeably the intestinal flora. Commercial interests placed on the market *Lactobacillus acidophilus* in the form of tablets, capsules, and liquids. Bass examined some of these preparations to determine the number of viable *Lactobacillus acidophilus* contained therein. In the instance of tablets, none of those examined was found to contain as many as 1,000 viable bacteria of any kind per tablet. If it should be granted that all the viable bacteria present were *Lactobacillus acidophilus*, it would take more than 1,000,000,000 tablets, or more than 20 tons, to contain as many bacilli as are contained in 1,000 ml., or the usual daily dose, of acidophilus milk, the quantity found, by most investigators at least to be necessary to transform the flora. Bacteria were more numerous in the commercial liquid cultures examined. If they were all *Lactobacillus acidophilus*, a patient would have to drink seven or eight gallons daily to get as many as he would in 1,000 ml. of the acidophilus milk culture. Only fresh cultures produced according to the proper bacteriological methods should be used. The Council on Pharmacy and Chemistry of the American Medical Association [60] attempted to take a conservative position on these products. This bureau has considered acidophilus milk and broth cultures and concentrates of *Lactobacillus acidophilus* not acceptable unless the number of viable organisms is clearly stated on the package. This is not enough. The number of cells must be known to survive when the consumer purchases

58. Prouty and Bendixen. 1932. J. Dairy Sci. 15, 413-419.
59. Bass. 1923. J. South. Med. Assoc. 16, 1-7.
60. J. Amer. Med. Assoc., 1926, 87, 172-174.

the package. Certain other products are not accepted unless adequate evidence that they will induce implantation is presented. Results of an extensive study of these products were reported by James [63] from the laboratories of the Bureau of Chemistry. James' results would indicate that some of these products were worthless. The milk cultures showed the greatest number of viable cells, the whey cultures next, and the solid cultures the lowest. In some cases, James was unable to find *Lactobacillus acidophilus*. He examined 107 samples of which only 15 were sufficiently pure or had a sufficient number of viable cells to have possible value. Examination of tables in James' paper showed counts of milk cultures on whey galactose agar which varied from 450,000 to 4,750,000,000 per ml. Broth cultures showed a variation between 0 and 250,000,000. Cheplin, Post, and Wiseman [61] also claimed that the tablets of *Lactobacillus acidophilus* were useless for transforming the flora. Kopeloff, Cohen, and Beerman [62] observed that only five of the eight products examined gave any information on the label as to the number of viable organisms. But three of these fulfilled their claims. Three of the specimens examined contained *Lactobacillus acidophilus* as the predominating organism. Only one product contained the specified number of living cells identical with known stock cultures of *Lactobacillus acidophilus*. These results bear out the findings of James [63] and Bass.[59] Kopeloff and his colleagues recommended that the labels carry more complete information about the product.

James' [63] Method for Examining Lactobacillus acidophilus and Bulgaricus Preparations. James used the following methods in his work on commercial preparations:

1. Liquid (broth or milk) cultures:

(a) One milliliter of the culture was inoculated directly into each of two tubes containing 20 ml. of litmus milk. The largest amount of culture inoculated was one ml.

(b) One milliliter of the culture was added to nine ml. of sterile water, and one ml. of this dilution was inoculated into the first set of plates. Different platings were made in triplicate with dilutions to 1:100,000,000. The largest amount of culture plated was .1 ml.

2. Solid (tablet or powder) preparations:

(a) Three tablets (or the powder from three capsules) were dissolved in 30 ml. of sterile water.

(b) One milliliter of this dilution was then added to each of two tubes containing 20 ml. of litmus milk. The largest amount of culture inoculated was .1 ml.

(c) One milliliter of the dilution used in a was seeded in the first set of plates. Higher dilutions were then plated. All platings were made in triplicate. The largest amount of culture plated was .1 ml.

3. Semisolid or jelly cultures:

(a) Cultures liquefying at 40°C.(104°F.). These usually had a consistency resembling that of petrolatum. A sterile glass tube (inverted 10 ml. pipette with full size opening) was thrust to the bottom of the jelly and the subsample thus obtained blown into a sterile tube. The tube and subsample were placed in a 40°C.(104°F.) bath, where the jelly was melted and could be handled with a previously warmed pipette. After thorough mixing, one ml. was transferred to nine ml. of warmed sterile water and vigorously shaken.

(b) Cultures not liquefying at 40°C.(104°F.). These consisted of solidified agar in which bacteria were suspended. The agar was molded in cubes, each wrapped sep-

61. Cheplin, Post, and Wiseman. 1923. Boston Med. and Surg. J. 189, 405.
62. Kopeloff, Cohen. and Beerman. 1928. J. Amer. Med. Assoc. 91, 1187-1192.
63. James. 1927. J. Amer. Med. Assoc. 89, 89-92.

arately. One cube being considered as one dose, it was selected as the unit. Each cube was thoroughly ground in a sterile mortar, after which 10 ml. of sterile water were slowly added, with continued grinding until an even suspension was obtained. Sterile dry sand was used when necessary, but sparingly in order to avoid rupturing the bacteria.

Kopeloff, Cohen, and Beerman's[62] **Method for Examining Lactobacillus acidophilus Preparations.** The following data were recorded: name, date received, date of examination, date of manufacture, date of expiration, number of acidophilus bacilli guaranteed, character of vehicle, color, taste, consistency, acidity (titrated with tenth-normal sodium hydroxide) and Gram stain (Kopeloff and Beerman modification).

The determination of the number of viable acidophilus bacilli was made by plating all milk samples on the same batch of whey agar and casein digest agar. Aqueous suspensions were plated on meat infusion (instead of whey) agar and casein digest agar. The concentration of agar in all mediums was 1.2 per cent and the pH from 6.8 to 7.0. One per cent lactose was always added. The plates were incubated at 37°C. (98.6°F.) for three days ordinarily, and a parallel series was incubated in the presence of five to 10 per cent carbon dioxide gas.

Before plating, the following dilutions were made: 10 milliliters of the original sample were added to 90 ml. of physiological sodium chloride solution, making a dilution of 1:10. Subsequent dilutions of 1:1,000, 1:100,000 and 1:1,000,000 were made. One milliliter of dilutions 1:10 and 1:1,000 were plated in quadruplicate, while dilutions of 1:100,000 and 1:1,000,000 were plated in sextuplicate. Then one-half of the plates were incubated atmospherically at 37°C.(98.6°F.) and the other half in five to 10 per cent of carbon dioxide. A preliminary examination of atmospherically incubated plates was made at the end of 24 hours to determine the number of contaminants present. Control plates were always included. At the end of three days' incubation, all plates were counted with a magnifying lens and the numbers of acidophilus bacilli and contaminants appearing on the plates from the two highest dilutions were recorded.

THERAPEUTIC USE OF ACIDOPHILUS MILK

Considerable success has been attained with the acidophilus preparations, especially acidophilus milk. Rettger and Cheplin[16] reported interesting results following administration of these preparations.

Psychoses. In general Kopeloff and Beerman[64] were able to show improvement over their original condition following administration of acidophilus milk to psychotic individuals. The constipated cases were greatly benefited and the non-constipated had a greater number of normal defecations. Julianelle and Ebaugh[65] recommended acidophilus milk for psychotic patients because it tended to better physical well-being. They observed no change in the psychoses. About the same conclusions were reached by Brown and Borden.[66]

Constipation. This is one of the first ailments to be treated with acidophilus therapy. Gompertz,[67] Cheplin and Wiseman[68] and Mizell[69] reported fairly prompt response. Rettger and Cheplin[16] used two obstinate cases of constipation which responded readily to treatment. Cheplin, Fulmer, and Barney,[70] Kopeloff and Cheney,[37] and Cheplin[71] published further conclusions.

64. Kopeloff and Beerman. 1925. Soc. Expt. Biol. and Med. Proc. 22, 318.
65. Julianelle and Ebaugh. 1923. Arch. Neurol. and Psych 9, 769.
66. Brown and Borden. 1929. U. S. Vet. Bur. Med. Bull. 5, 583-584.
67. Gompertz. 1923. J. Amer. Med. Assoc. 80, 90-92.
68. Cheplin and Wiseman. 1921. Boston Med. and Surg. J. 185, 627.
69. Mizell. 1923. South. Med. J. 16, 835.
70. Cheplin, Fulmer, and Barney. 1923. J. Amer. Med. Assoc. 80, 1896-99.
71. Cheplin. 1923. Abs. Bact. 7, No. 246.

The subject is somewhat confused by statements by Smith and Kulp,[72] and Kast, Short, and Croll,[73] that if urinary indican is accepted as an index of intestinal putrefaction, acidophilus therapy has no effect. Some patients showed increased amounts of indican and phenols in their urine during treatment. Kahn,[74] however, reported the opposite. Segal's[75] conclusions agree with those of Smith and Kulp,[72] while Fisher's[76] agree with Kahn's. It is difficult, therefore, to reach conclusions on the subject. Later work by Weinstein et al.[77] reported some success with acidophilus milk in one-quart quantities daily. The cultures used for preparation of the milk were known to possess high viability. In some cases the organism remained in the intestines for 12 to 16 weeks after the milk treatment had been discontinued. Most favorable results were said to be secured by using the milk over long periods.

Diarrhea. Cheplin and Rettger[16] reported improvement in patients suffering from diarrhea following administration of acidophilus milk. Patients treated by Gompertz[67] developed formed stools after *Lactobacillus acidophilus* had been implanted.

Epilepsy. Since the gastrointestinal tract has been under suspicion in epilepsy, Kopeloff, Lonergan, and Beerman[78] fed acidophilus milk to epileptics to determine any effect this might have on the number of convulsions. Fifteen epileptics were used in one experiment. They were given one liter of acidophilus milk a day for 42 days with beneficial results. Ingestion of sterile milk did not influence the number of convulsions. Neither did the ingestion of six grams of kaolin daily for one month. But when the same quantity of *Lactobacillus acidophilus* milk, one liter reinforced with 300 grams of lactose, was administered for two months, there was a striking reduction in the number of convulsions in five patients. Three patients remained the same and one showed a slight increase in the number of convulsions. In the two-month period following administration of *Lactobacillus acidophilus milk* the patients had an increased number of convulsions. It appeared therefore, that the treatment was not sufficiently prolonged to confer permanent benefit. The work of Lynch[79] did not confirm the beneficial effects of acidophilus therapy in epilepsy. The number of defecations was increased whether the bacteria were given in milk or blocks.

Typhoid and Paratyphoid Carriers. Smith[80] gave *Lactobacillus acidophilus* to typhoid and paratyphoid carriers; after transformation, from 80 to 90 per cent of the flora became *Lactobacillus acidophilus*. Excretion of *Eberthella typhosa* and the paratyphoids was not influenced by acidophilus milk administration.

Lactobacillus bifidus (Bacillus bifidus). This organism was discovered by Tissier and named *Bacillus bifidus*. It is a normal intestinal form and very pleomorphic. In most of the cultures Y and T forms are common. Kendall and Haner[81] stated that variants of the type are common as determined by morphological characteristics and sugar-fermenting powers. They found the organism to be more pleomorphic in artificial cultures than

72. Smith and Kulp. 1922. Soc. Expt. Biol. and Med. Proc. 20, 44.
73. Kast, Short, and Croll. 1922. Soc. Expt. Biol. and Med. Proc. 20, 45.
74. Kahn. 1926. J. Lab. and Clin. Med. 12, 226.
75. Segal. 1924. J. Metabolic Res. 5, 293-351.
76. Fisher. 1919. Conn. Agr. Expt. Sta. Bull. 104.
77. Weinstein et al. 1933. Arch. Int. Med. 52, 384.
78. Kopeloff, Lonergan, and Beerman. 1925. Soc. Expt. Biol. and Med. Proc. 23, 25.
79. Lynch. 1928. Amer. J. Med. Sci. 176, 547.
80. Smith. 1924. Brit. Med. J. No. 3334, 948-950.
81. Kendall and Haner. 1924. J. Infect. Diseases 35, 89-104.

in the feces. Adam [82] believed that the peculiarities of the cells of *Lactobacillus bifidus* were due to their metabolism. Kling [83] observed an antagonistic action of *Lactobacillus bifidus* on a number of intestinal forms, such as *Escherichia coli, Aerobacter aerogenes,* and *Staphylococcus aureus.* This action could not be explained on the basis of heat labile bactericidal substances, such as those found by Eijkmann and called "autotoxins." According to Brown and Bosworth [84] the stools of normal breast-fed infants showed a complete dominance of *Lactobacillus bifidus.* When cow's milk is fed, the stools show larger numbers of cocci and Gram-negative bacilli than are usually found in stools of breast-fed babies. These organisms may persist for as long as four weeks. With regard to the source of *Lactobacillus bifidus* Brown and Bosworth stated that "the bifidus organisms which are present in or on the mother's nipple are an important source of the bifidus organisms found in the nursling's intestines." Lauter [85] also stated that intestinal infection of the infant is by mouth. *Lactobacillus bifidus* was said to appear in the stool about two and one-half days after birth. About the same conclusions were reached by Boventor [86] who stated that this organism was the predominating one in stools of newborn babies. He also gave instructions for cultivating the organism. Weiss and Rettger [87] stated that *Lactobacillus bifidus* may constitute from 90 to 95 per cent of the intestinal flora of breast-fed infants. It remains the predominating organism as long as breast milk is the sole diet.

The taxonomic relationships of this organism have been a matter of discussion among bacteriologists for some time. It has been placed in one genus and another until now it seems to be fairly firmly established as a member of the genus Lactobacillus. Weiss and Rettger [87] were of the opinion that *Lactobacillus bifidus* should be considered a variant of *Lactobacillus acidophilus.* Only slight differences between the two organisms were observed and these could be accounted for by normal variation within the species or type. Rettger and Weiss [88] agreed with Eggerth [89] that the Gram-positive, nonsporeforming anaerobes of the human intestine do not belong to the group Bacteroides and that this name should be retained for the Gram-negative organisms.

Buttermilk. This is one of the commonest fermented milks and is usually prepared during the churning of sour cream for butter in which process it is a by-product. Owing to the great interest in artificial or cultured buttermilks these products have appeared on the market. Popular discussions have done much to stimulate interest in fermented milks. Not enough buttermilk could be produced in cities to supply the demand. Consequently, dairies are preparing artificially inoculated and soured milk. Such fermented milks often have a better flavor than buttermilk. Some

82. Adam. 1922. Ztschr. Kinderheilk. 33, 308-312.
83. Kling. 1914. Ann. Inst. Pasteur 28, 797-806.
84. Brown and Bosworth. 1922. Amer. J. Diseases Children 23, 243.
85. Lauter. 1921. Centbl. Bakt., Pt. 1, Orig., 86, 579-582.
86. Boventor. 1938. Idem 142, 419-430.
87. Weiss and Rettger. 1934. J. Bact. 28, 501-518.
88. Weiss and Rettger. 1937. Idem 33, 423-434.
89. Eggerth. 1935. Idem 30, 277-299.

buttermilk may possess an undesirable flavor, owing to the presence of foreign bacteria. The Secretary of Agriculture promulgated the following definition of buttermilk in Food Inspection Decision No. 210, issued April, 1927:

Cultured buttermilk is the product obtained by souring pasteurized skimmed, or partially skimmed milk by means of a suitable culture of lactic acid bacteria. It contains not less than eight and five-tenth per cent (8.5%) of milk solids not fat.

The Milk Ordinance and Code of the United States Public Health Service (1939) defines it as follows:

F. *Buttermilk.* Buttermilk is a product resulting from the churning of milk or cream, or from the souring or treatment by a lactic acid or other culture of milk, skimmed milk, reconstituted skimmed milk, evaporated or condensed milk or skimmed milk, or milk or skimmed-milk powder. It contains not less than eight per cent of milk solids not fat.''

The microbiology of buttermilk is probably not greatly different from that of butter. Many of the organisms originally in the milk or added in the starter probably appear in the buttermilk.

Reid's [90] **Method for Making Buttermilk Beverages.** Reid conducted the following investigations at the University of Missouri to produce buttermilk drinks which will not whey off. Five one-pint samples of milk with an acidity of .16 per cent were heated to 87.8°C.(190°F.) for 40 minutes to destroy all bacteria present, cooled to 21.1°C.(70°F.), inoculated with one per cent of a culture of *Streptococcus lacticus* and *Bacterium acidi lactici*, and held until coagulation started, which took place in seven hours. They were then cooled to 5.6°C.(42°F.), held until the next day, and examined. Samples were also prepared in the same manner as above, except that before heating gelatin was added to four of them in the following amounts: .25, .55, .75, and one per cent, respectively. These samples were scored the next day and again after aging six days. After standing one day, the check sample had an acidity of .7 per cent and was free from gas and whey. Before shaking, the body was medium firm and the aroma medium full, clean, and pleasant. After shaking, the body was smooth, velvety, and fairly firm and the flavor clean and desirable. After standing six days, there was a decided wheying off, the body was weak, the aroma improved, and the flavor unchanged. Addition of gelatin prevented wheying off but had no effect on flavor or aroma. Amounts of .1 and .25 per cent gelatin gave best results.

Busa. This is a fermented milk prepared in Turkestan. It contains, according to Chekan,[91] up to .78 per cent of lactic acid and up to 7.1 per cent of alcohol by weight. Chekan stated that the alcoholic fermentation of rice was induced by *Saccharomyces busae asiaticae* and a bacterium named *Bacterium busae asiaticae*. The yeast grows better in the presence of organic matter. Chekan stated that it ferments maltose best; sucrose, dextrose, levulose, lactose, and dextrin next best; inulin very slightly; and mannitol, arabinose, and starch not at all. The optimum pH for growth is 6.4 to 6.7. The lactic acid bacillus grows better when in root extract agar and when stabbed. The maximum acid production is 1.1 per cent. It ferments dextrose, galactose, maltose, sucrose, levulose, lactose, and arabinose strongly and mannitol, dextrin, and starch weakly. The best sources of nitrogen are peptone, phaseolin, gelatin, and alanine. The optimum pH is 6.7.

90. Reid. 1928. N. Y. Prod. Rev. and Amer. Creamery 65, 628
91. Chekan. 1922. Centbl. Bakt., Pt. 2, 78, 74-93.

Cieddu. This is a fermented milk made in Italy and, according to Rosini,[92] corresponds to kumiss, kefir, and a few other fermented milks. He stated that it was antagonistic to pathogenic microorganisms in the intestines. Samarini [93] reported that bacteriological examination of fresh cieddu (Sardinian fermented milk) showed the presence of only two forms of microorganisms, one a variety of *Bacterium lactis acidi* and the other a variety of *Bacillus casei* of Freudenreich.

Dadhi. Dadhi is a product made in India by curdling milk through the growth of certain lactic acid-forming bacteria. It is prepared by heating fresh milk to boiling, allowing it to cool to about 36.7 to 37.8°C.(98 to 100°F.), and adding a small quantity of dadhi from an earlier batch. Upon standing overnight in a covered container a smooth, homogeneous curd with an acid taste is produced. Examination of dadhi films by Ram-Ayyar [94] showed the presence of very long rods, short rods joined in pairs, cocci, and yeast cells. In summer, 24 hours after inoculation, dadhi contains long rods *(Streptothrix dadhi)* almost exclusively, the acidity of the product at the end of that time being one to 1.4 per cent, calculated as lactic acid, when the milk is kept at 36.7°C.(98°F.). In winter, the chief agent responsible for curdling is the short, rod-type organism which grows well at 20°C.(68°F.) and produces .5 to .7 per cent acid in 24 hours. The product of low-temperature fermentation is known as "sweet dadhi." A nonsporeforming yeast of the Torula type is always associated with both types of lactic acid organisms in dadhi. This yeast grows only in curdled milk of acid reaction and consumes the lactic acid produced by other organisms. It grows well in media containing sucrose or glucose and does not produce alcohol from any sugars. Lactic acid-forming bacteria live longer when associated with this yeast because of its ability to prevent the accumulation of toxic quantities of acid.

Kefir. This is one of the best-known fermented milks prepared by the inhabitants of certain of the Balkan countries. Little if anything is known about its origin. Many investigations have been carried out on it to determine the causes of the fermentation and whether it is possible to prepare it by pure-culture inoculation. Among the earliest of these was that of Kern.[95] The first complete investigation of the fermenting agents of kefir was made by Freudenreich,[96] the eminent Swiss dairy bacteriologist. He found a yeast, *Saccharomyces kefir*, which lived symbiotically with two bacteria, *Dispora caucasica* and Streptococcus A. *Saccharomyces kefir* when isolated by itself did not act on lactose. Jandini [97] also found a yeast and several bacteria in the fermenting organisms of kefir. *Torula kefir* was isolated by Beijerinck,[98] and Nikolajewa [99] believed that a Torula which fermented lactose, sucrose, and dextrose was essential to formation

92. Rosini. 1913. Rev. in Exp. Sta. Rec. 30 (1914), 276.
93. Samarini. 1907. Ann. R. Staz. Sper. Caseif. Lodi 95-98.
94. Ram-Ayyar. 1918. Agr. J. India 23, 107-110.
95. Kern. 1882. Bot. Ztschr. 40, 263-264.
96. Freudenreich. 1897. Centbl. Bakt., Pt. 2, 3, 47-54 .
97. Jandini. 1914. Bull. Soc. Pharmacologie 21, 356-363.
98. Beijerinck. 1908. Arch. Néerland. Sci. Exact. et Nat. 12, 356-378.
99. Nikolajewa. 1908. Centbl. Bakt., Pt. 2, 21, 429-430.

of good kefir. *Torula ellipsoidea* was also isolated. *Bacterium caucasicum*, the organism mentioned by Beijerinck, was also observed. Essaulow [100] isolated, from kefir grains of various origins, a Saccharomyces, *Bacillus acidi lactici,* and *Bacillus subtilis* in every case. Other microorganisms isolated from kefir grains were believed to be contaminants and to cause trouble in the fermentation. Neither of these three microorganisms alone can produce anything like kefir. *Bacillus subtilis* did not appear to have any part in preparation of kefir grains; it was believed to produce a network which supported the other two microorganisms. Alcohol, carbon dioxide, and peptone were recognized in kefir. Work of this nature was carried on also by Kuntze.[101] Two sporeforming species belonging to the butyric acid-producing group were regularly found. One was believed to be a variety of *Bacillus esterificans* while the other was designated *Bacillus kefir.* According to Kuntze, the characteristic kefir fermentation is due more to these butyric acid fermentations than to lactic acid-producing fermentations or to activities of yeasts. A more heterogeneous flora of microorganisms was found in kefir by Kornblum.[102] They were grouped as follows:

1. *Streptococcus lacticus* Kruse, of which three types were isolated. 2. Nonsporeforming oval yeasts resembling *Saccharomyces kefir* and *Torula lactis* Adametz; three types of yeasts were also isolated. 3. *Oidium lactis,* a harmful contaminant of kefir which produces a rancid, bitter taste in old cultures. In none of the kefir-milks examined could Kornblum find the microorganisms mentioned above reported by earlier workers. The mixed flora of the fermenting agents of kefir was again brought out in the results of investigations by Starygina and Khaldina [103] who believed the main elements of the microflora of kefir to be the lactic acid-producing Streptococci, lactic acid-producing rods, yeasts, and a small number of peptonizing bacteria. The latter are apparently quite important. Samtsevich [104] found them to be important. They produce a good consistency and flavor. A few investigators have studied the possibility of using pure cultures for making kefir. Kornblum [102] secured satisfactory results with the microorganisms which he isolated without *Bacillus caucasicus.* By varying the amount of the different organisms kefir of various qualities could be produced. Starygina and Khaldina [103] also found pure cultures possible. A composite starter was prepared also by Palladina, Krotova, and Maejukewitsch [105] consisting of various bacteria and yeasts.

Kumiss (Kumys). Preparation of this fermented milk has been described in some detail by Rubinsky.[106] This beverage is obtained by the fermentation of mare's milk and is consumed by the inhabitants of The Steppes. Three to 10 parts of the fresh milk are pitched with one part of kumiss and, during the next day or two, the liquor is stirred for about 15

100. Essaulow. 1895. Rev. in Exp. Sta. Rec. 8, 169.
101. Kuntze. 1909. Centbl. Bakt., Pt. 2, 24, 101-122.
102. Kornblum. 1932. Acta Soc. Bot. Poloniae 9, 421-466.
103. Starygina and Khaldina. 1934. Microbiologia 3, 88-102.
104. Samtsevich. 1934. Idem 3, 103-109.
105. Palladina *et al.* 1935. Milchw. Forsch. 17, 25-38.
106. Rubinsky. 1910. Centbl. Bakt., Pt. 2, 28, 161-219.

minutes at intervals of two to three hours with specially made wooden sticks. In the course of 12 to 24 hours "new" kumiss is obtained; after a further period of 12 to 20 hours "medium" kumiss, which is the most general type of the beverage, is formed; "strong" kumiss is formed in 56 to 72 hours after pitching, as a result of the more advanced acidification and fermentation. "Medium" kumiss (which also serves for medicinal purposes) contains one to two per cent of alcohol and .6 to .8 per cent of lactic acid, while "strong" kumiss contains on the average 2.3 per cent of alcohol and 1.1 per cent of lactic acid. The contents of carbon dioxide and protein are .6 to 1.3 and 2.3 to 2.6 per cent, respectively. Four kinds of microorganisms were almost always found in kumiss, viz., the kumiss yeast, the kumiss bacterium, *Streptococcus lactis*, and *Bacillus acidi lactici*, Hueppe; of these the two latter are not specially characteristic of kumiss. The kumiss yeast is a bottom-fermentation yeast; it decomposes lactose and casein and produces the ester-like, aromatic substances of kumiss. The Kumiss bacterium is nonmotile, forms no spores, and has a temperature optimum of 30 to 35°C.(86 to 95°F.). There is a symbiotic relation between the two organisms. The kumiss fermentation is not a controlled one and probably depends much on accidental infection of the raw materials with the necessary organisms.

The results of studies on the bacteriology of kumiss are in fair agreement. Practically all indicate that it is a mixed fermentation carried on by yeasts and bacteria to which many different names have been given. Most of these, however, are members of the lactic acid group and the confusion is no more apparent here than in the other branches of dairy bacteriology. A few of the reports which have been made may be reviewed at some length.

Schipin [107] found three kinds of microorganisms in all examinations of kumiss, namely, Saccharomyces, *Escherichia acidi lactici*, and the kumiss bacillus. The last-mentioned organism decomposed lactose with a lactic and alcoholic fermentation. Quite similar conclusions were reached by Ginsberg.[108]

According to Batschinskaja-Raitshenko,[109] kumiss as prepared in Ufa contains a lactic acid organism to which he gave the name *Bacterium orientale*. This organism was considered to be identical with the one isolated from kumiss by Berdnikoff and Rubinsky. The organism seemed to be one of the active members of the lactic acid group of bacteria. The yeasts were of two types. None of them formed ascospores, and consequently the author called them *Torula kumiss I and II*. Both the bacterium and one of the yeasts are necessary for the production of kumiss. According to Belokopytowa and Smirnowa,[110] properly prepared kumiss generally has three groups of microorganisms: *Lactobacillus bulgaricus*, Torula, and *Lactobacillus lactisacidi* (*Bacterium lactis acidi*, Leichmann).

107. Schipin. 1900. Centbl. Bakt. 6, 775-777.
108. Ginsberg. 1910. Biochem. Ztschr. 30, 1-24; 28.
109. Batschinskaja-Raitshenko. 1912. Rev. in Exp. Sta. Rec. 26, 779.
110. Belokopytowa and Smirnowa. 1929. Centbl. Bakt., Pt. 2, 79, 185-194.

Normal microflora of kumiss, according to Voitkevich,[111] is represented by lactic acid bacteria of the *Lactobacillus bulgaricus* type and yeasts of the genus Torulopsis. Preparation of the inoculum, described by Haldena,[112] is a somewhat tedious procedure. As is the case with other fermented milks, kumiss is quite bactericidal for pathogenic bacteria. This was ascribed by Kazberynk[113] to its content of lactic acid. He worked with *Bacillus paratyphi abortus equi*.

Leben. This fermented milk used by the Egyptians resembles kefir. It is prepared from the milk of the buffalo, goat, and cow. The fermentation is started by pitching boiled milk with dried leben. After about six hours or somewhat longer in winter, according to Khoury and Rist,[114] the beverage is ready. It contains a white, flocculent material in suspension and has a pleasant, fresh taste and a peculiar aroma. According to Khoury and Rist, five groups of microorganisms are involved in the leben fermentation, three bacteria and two yeasts. They claimed that better leben is secured when the yeasts are put into the mlk first. Neither of the budding fungi (a yeast species and Mycoderma species) fermented lactose. These fungi are able to ferment only the products of lactose after it has been hydrolyzed by the bacteria.

Mazun. Mazun is a fermented milk made in Armenia from cow's, goat's, and buffalo's milk. Its bacteriology has been studied by Emmerling,[115] Weigmann, Gruber, and Huss,[116] Düggeli,[117] and others. A temperature of 30°C.(86°F.) was found to yield the best mazun. As with other fermented milks, a mixed flora of microorganisms has been found to be present. Düggeli[117] reported different microorganisms in it. Yeasts and lactic acid bacteria were common. Rod-shaped bacteria like *Streptococcus lactis (Bacterium güntheri)* were present. The yeasts which were present fermented lactose with acid formation along with alcohols and some aromatic bodies. These microorganisms were said to be necessary for the preparation of good mazun. One of the yeasts seemed to have much to do with the development of an agreeable odor. Weigmann, Gruber, and Huss[116] reported the presence of a lactose-fermenting, pastorianus-type yeast. They also reported the presence of *Bacillus mazun* and *Bacterium mazun*, both of which formed acid and coagulated milk.

Taette. This is a soured milk which has been prepared for centuries by peoples in the northern countries in Europe. It is a viscous, thick, coagulated milk with an agreeable acid taste. Olsen-Sopp[118] made a microbiological study of this fermented milk and isolated the following organisms:

1. A streptobacillus corresponding to *Bacillus acidi lactis longus*, already described by Gerda Trosilli. This species was not easily cultivated. On gelatin it formed small, round colonies .6 to .8 mm. in diameter. The temperature limits were 3°C.(37.4°F.) and 35°C.(95°F.), the optimum being around 15°C.(59°F.).

111. Voitkevich. 1934. Mikrobiologie 3, 398-408.
112. Haldena. 1939. Molochno-Maslodel' naya Prom. 6, 10-14.
113. Kazberynk. 1940. Rev. in Chem. Abs. 36, 2584.
114. Khoury and Rist. 1902. Ann. Inst. Pasteur 16, 65.
115. Emmerling. 1898. Centbl. Bakt., Pt. 2, 4, 418.
116. Weigmann, Gruber, and Huss. 1907. Idem 19, 70-87.
117. Düggeli. 1905. Idem 15, 577-600.
118. Olsen-Sopp. 1912. Idem 33, 1-54.

2. *Lactobacillus Taette,* very much like the yoghurt lactobacillus. This was a large rod, having an optimum temperature of 35°C.(95°F.).

3. Two yeasts. *Saccharomyces major Taette* and *Saccharomyces minor Taette.* These two species were separated by the fact that the former was much larger than the second, and also on the basis of ascospore formation. The latter never formed ascospores.

4. *Torulae.* These were not always present.

5. Mucedinaceae. *Monilia lactis Taette* and *Oidium lactis.* When these organisms were found they indicated an old product and an unsatisfactory one.

Olsen-Sopp stated that *Saccharomyces major* and *minor Taette, Lactobacillus Taette,* and *Bacillus acid lactis longus* were necessary for the production of Taette. Heinemann [119] also investigated this fermented milk. He stated that this favorite food in Scandinavia was made by inoculating sweet cow's milk with the leaves of butterwort *(Pinguicula vulgaris),* which causes the milk to become thick and slightly stringy, with a slight cheesy taste and odor. A microscope examination of the samples showed streptococci in large numbers, mostly in diplococcus form. Two species of yeast were abundant, one being oval and the other a large organism with square ends, often forming long filaments. There were also some bacilli resembling *Escherichia coli* in shape and size, which proved to be Gram negative. There were a few large bacilli, resembling that group commonly found in milk, which forms larger amounts of acid than ordinary lactic acid bacteria. The streptococcus could not be distinguished microscopically from *Streptococcus lactis,* but its action on sterile milk differed in that it coagulated but slowly; after coagulation the coagulum was stringy, similar to the coagulum formed by *Lactobacillus bulgaricus* but in a smaller degree. The oval yeast gave the microscope picture of *Saccharomyces cerevisiae.* It ferments lactose and saccharose with violent gas production, levulose slowly, and maltose not at all. Cultures of this yeast in liquid beerwort impart a somewhat stringy consistency to the medium. The other yeast proved to be *Oidium lactis,* which is always present in milk and in this milk is probably responsible for a slight cheesy taste and odor.

Yogurt (Yoghurt). This fermented milk differs from other varieties by having a much higher content of acid and thicker curd. Yogurt requires more work in preparation than the other varieties. It is boiled and often reduced in volume about one-half. The fermentation is started by the use of a former batch of the product.

Kern [120] was led to investigate the morphology of the fermenting agent of yogurt and called it *Dispora caucasicum,* a name of inaccurate taxonomy. Other bacteriological studies were reported by Beijerinck,[121] Freudenreich,[122] Khoury and Rist,[114] and Cohendy and Grigoroff. Kuntze [123] called attention to the great variability of the bacteria found in yogurt and matzoon by different observers. From his own researches he thought

119. Heinemann. 1911. Science 33, 630.
120. Kern. 1881. Bull. Soc. Imper. d. Naturalistes de Moscov, No. 3.
121. Beijerinck. 1908. Arch. Néerland. 13, 356.
122. Freudenrich. 1897. Centbl. Bakt., Pt. 2, 3, 47-54.
123. Kuntze. 1908. Centbl. Bakt., Pt. 2, 21, 737-768.

that some, if not all, of these species described as new were only varieties of species previously known. Hastings and Hammer [124] examined many samples of milk from different sources which were incubated at 37°C. (98.6°F.) and in all cases developed a greater acidity than could be accounted for by the presence of *Lactobacillus lactis acidi*, indicating that the causal organism, a bacillus closely related to *Lactobacillus bulgaricus* and *Bacillus casei E*, has a wide distribution. According to Guerbet, yogurt is identical with leben which has been studied by Rist and Khoury. They claimed that a streptobacillus decomposed the lactose into glucose and galactose. These sugars were fermented by yeasts to alcohol. Guerbet stated that the alcohol came from this bacillus. Duchacek [125] made tests of several strains of *Lactobacillus bulgaricus*, one strain coming from a commercial medicinal source and another which was recognized as the true *Lactobacillus bulgaricus*.

The latter strain was found to be much more sensitive but was readily killed by acids and would develop only in certain culture media which contained sugars. The other strain was much less sensitive and, in contrast to the true *Lactobacillus bulgaricus*, readily digested proteins. Attention was directed to the difficulty of completely sterilizing milk, to the ease with which the true *Lactobacillus bulgaricus* is destroyed and the great possibilities of such destruction taking place in commercial preparations, and to the predominance in these of other strains of bacteria which remain owing to incomplete sterilization. Boersma [126] reported that the growths known as yogurt plants are true kefir grains consisting of *Lactobacillus caucasicus B*. Yeast did not contribute to the structure of these grains even though they were present. Live yogurt bacteria were reported in dry tablets eight years old, by Klebs,[127] and in milk cultures five and six years old. Their strength seemed to have been diminished and it required several transfers to bring them back to an active condition. In the old cultures, numerous coccus-shaped forms existed as well as in the first subcultures. After several transfers these dropped out and the usual rods appeared. Weil [128] believed that the preparation of yogurt should recognize the typical flora, absence of contaminations and pathogenic bacteria, and the proper methods of preparation. The flora was said to consist of *Lactobacillus bulgaricus* which produced the acid and desirable aroma and a coccus. *Lactobacillus bulgaricus* and *Streptococcus lacticus thermophilus* were used by Rosell.[129] He experienced little trouble in making yogurt.

Kuban. Bogdanoff [130] observed that kuban fermented milk was characterized by lactic acid and alcoholic fermentations. The flora consisted of a lactic acid-producing streptococcus much like *Streptococcus hollandicus*, a lactic acid-producing, rod-shaped bacterium like *Lactobacillus bulgaricus*,

124. Hastings and Hammer. 1910. Centbl. Bakt., Pt. 2, 25, 419-426.
125. Duchacek. 1915. Biochem. Ztschr. 70, 269-293.
126. Boersma. 1918. Rev. in Abs. Bact., Feb. 1921.
127. Klebs. 1922. München. Med. Wchnschr. 69, 1285-1286.
128. Weil. 1926. Centbl. Bakt., Pt. 2, 69, 321-337.
129. Rosell. 1933. Canad. Pub. Health J. 24, 344-347.
130. Bogdanoff. 1934. J. Dairy Res. 5, 153-159.

and three types of yeast. All of these bacteria worked together. Care must be used in heating the milk.

Survival of Pathogenic Bacteria in Fermented Milks. Should these products be made from raw materials which are not clean and sanitary or should they be improperly handled, it is desirable to know whether common pathogenic bacteria could survive in them. Results of investigations which bear on this problem have been discussed in Chapter 9. It has been found, in general, that high acid content is detrimental to such bacteria as *Eberthella typhosa* and members of the genus Salmonella. Kazaryan[131] observed that .1 per cent of lactic acid hindered the development of the bacteria just mentioned; greatest resistance to this acid was exhibited by *Salmonella schottmülleri* and coliform bacteria. While these bacteria were inhibited they were not destroyed, which makes it possible for the fermented milk studied by Kazaryan to disseminate disease. Sircana,[132] working with yogurt, found *Eberthella typhosa* to neither grow nor survive. He believed, therefore, that fermented milk was not a dangerous vehicle for pathogenic bacteria. Nicholls, Nimalasuriya, and de Silva[133] considered fermented milk to be safe even where sanitation was primitive. *Eberthella typhosa* and *Shigella dysenteriae* inoculated into whey of fermenting milk did not survive beyond three hours.

Less information seems to be available about longevity of *Mycobacterium tuberculosis* in sour milk. Kliewe and Schuppener[134] observed *Mycobacterium tuberculosis* (hominis) to survive for seven days and the bovine variety for 20 days. Milk from which fermented milks are made may come from tuberculous cattle. Broers and Ten Sand[135] reported that guinea pigs several days old, which had been inoculated with kefir, developed tuberculosis. Cells of *Eberthella typhosa* did not resist the kefir fermentation very long, being destroyed after 48 hours. Similar conclusions have been reached by others who studied the question for cream ripening.

REFERENCE BOOKS

RETTGER, L. F., AND CHEPLIN, H. A., 1921. A Treatise on the Transformation of the Intestinal Flora With Special Reference to the Implantation of Bacillus Acidophilus. The Yale University Press, New Haven, Conn.

METSCHNIKOFF, E., 1907. The Prolongation of Life. New York City.

KOPELOFF, N., 1925. *Lactobacillus Acidophilus.* Williams & Wilkins Co., Baltimore, Md.

RETTGER, L. F., 1935. *Lactobacillus acidophilus* and Its Therapeutic Application. Yale University Press, New Haven, Conn.

FROST, W. D., AND HANKINSON, H., 1931. *Lactobacillus Acidophilus:* An Annotated Bibliography to 1931. Davis-Green Corp., Milton, Wis.

BURKE, A. D., 1938. Practical Manufacture of Cultured Milks and Kindred Products. Olsen Pub. Co., Milwaukee, Wis.

131. Kazaryan. 1936. Ztschr. Microbiol. Epidemiol. 17, 684-691.
132. Sircana. 1937. Ateneo. Parmense 9, 15-21.
133. Nicholls *et al.* 1939. Ceylon J. Sci. D, 5, 17.
134. Kliewe and Schuppener. 1937. Zentbl. Bakt., Pt. 1, Orig., 139, 180-183.
135. Broers and Ten Sand. 1907. Nederland. Tijdschr. v. Geneesk., 50, 1854-1857.

CHAPTER 13

INTESTINAL MICROBIOLOGY

Food microbiologists have a legitimate interest in intestinal microbiology. Severe intestinal infections and intoxications may be caused by microorganisms in foods; they may also function in digestion by aiding decomposition of various complex substances. Kelemann[1] stated that bacterial enzymes decomposed much of the sucrose in the alimentary tract of animals and made it available as simpler sugars. It has been known for some time that various bacteria in the intestines may also synthesize vitamins. One of the recent reports on this latter subject is by Burkholder and McVeigh[2] who showed the formation of B-vitamins by various bacteria.

Intestinal Flora in Childhood. At birth the alimentary tract is sterile but becomes infected in a few hours. Bacteria enter through both the mouth and the anus. Some of these bacteria may be harmful, while others are either beneficial or harmless. Dreyfus[3] found that the intestinal tract of the newly-born infant on different milk diets was sterile up to the 15th or 20th hour. At about 20 hours, infection sets in and increases up to about the third day. After the fourth day, the flora becomes fixed. When the child is put on a mixed diet, there is a change, the extent of which depends on the amount of milk which is left. Heineman[4] suggested that, at this time, the gastric secretion is small and the stomach offers no serious obstacle to the passage of bacteria through it into the intestines. This first infection is undoubtedly a heterogeneous one which becomes more homogeneous as those types which find the conditions in the intestines unsuitable, drop out. The high carbohydrate diet of the infant, rich especially in lactose, causes *Lactobacillus bifidus* to establish itself. As the diet is extended *Escherichia coli* enters, since it can live either in the presence or absence of lactose. Hauschild[5] also reported gram-positive cocci, yeasts, sarcinae, and aerobic sporeformers in the intestines of normal infants. *Escherichia coli* was absent. In cases of toxicoses, the cocci were replaced by gram-negative cocci. *Escherichia coli* was found in cases of diarrhea. Bosworth, Wilder, Blanchard, Brown, and McCann,[6] in seeking an explanation for the formation of large amounts of acetic acid in the stools of infants receiving a commercial dry milk, isolated strains of *Aerobacter aerogenes* which decomposed citric acid, forming water, carbon dioxide and acetic acid. *Lactobacillus bifidus* formed a mixture of acetic and oxalic acids. Other bacteria which fermented citrates were isolated

1. Kelemann. 1922. Bratislav Lekarske, Listy 2, 163-165.
2. Burkholder and McVeigh. 1942. Natl. Acad. Sci. Proc. 28, 285.
3. Dreyfus. 1927. J. Amer. Med. Assoc., 89, 895.
4. Heineman. 1925. J. Biol. Chem., 2, 612.
5. Hauschild. 1922. Ztschr. f. Kinderheilk., 31, 399-406.
6. Bosworth, Wilder, Blanchard, Brown, and McCann. 1922. Amer. J. Dis. Children, 23, 323-337.

but not identified. The close relationship between bacteria in the intestines and those in the food was also shown by Ford, Blackfan, and Batchelor.[7] They found that the bacteria with which the food of children is infected are about the same as those found in the feces. They found *Bacillus cereus* and *Bacillus albolactis* most commonly present, while *Bacillus mesentericus* and *Bacillus pseudotetanus* were also found. Ford and his colleagues found that pasteurized milk, protein milk, buttermilk and farina used in children's diet were seeded with sporebearing bacteria, the spores of which were capable of withstanding the heat used in their preparation. It was believed that the presence of sporebearing, gram-positive bacteria in the intestines was due to such bacteria in the food. They believed that both the food and the stools should be studied when reaching conclusions in intestinal bacteriology.

The multiplication of gram-positive bacteria in the intestinal tract of infants was favored by the addition of fats and certain sugars; lactose was especially active. The amount and nature of the fatty acids and soaps in the intestines determine the relative abundance of gram-positive and gram-negative bacteria. Thus it is seen that there are two distinct periods in the life of a child as far as the intestinal flora is concerned, the first when it is receiving almost entirely a milk diet and the second when that is supplanted by a more extended diet which not only introduces a varied flora but encourages such a flora by a wider variety of food materials.

Effect of Diet on Intestinal Flora. Students of the subject of intestinal bacteriology have accepted the dictum that the character of the bacterial flora is determined by the diet. It is believed that the ingestion of foreign bacteria, even in large numbers does not displace the common intestinal types. In order to cause a microorganism to take up its abode in the intestines for an appreciable time, a suitable diet must be ingested and an organism used which is preferably an intestinal species. This is further indicated by the fact that from the great variety of bacteria which gain entrance to the alimentary tract, only a few species are able to establish themselves.

Much work has been done by various investigators from which facts have been well established with regard to changes induced in the intestines by variations in the diet. The changes in the flora resulting from various diets have been measured in terms of certain large groups and rarely in terms of any one of few organisms. These groups which have thus been used may be enumerated as follows:

  I. Putrefactive group
       Escherichia coli, Clostridium welchii.
  II. Aciduric group
       Lactobacillus bulgaricus, Lactobacillus acidophilus, Lactobacillus bifidus
  III. Amylolytic group
       Glycobacter amylolyticus, and others.

7. Ford, Blackfan, and Batchelor. 1917. J. Amer. Med. Assoc., 68, 1776.

Herter and Kendall,[8] working with monkeys, studied the effect on the intestinal flora of sudden changes in the diet. After the flora from a distinctly protein diet had been established, the diet was changed to one of milk and sugar. After this change they were able to detect a change in the intestinal flora and mental condition of the animal. Also in the urine, putrefactive products were quite evident. In the intestines, the acidophilus group of organisms was changed to a proteolytic group. This was one of the first papers from which definite conclusions could be drawn. The authors suggested that in a disease where either the acidophile or putrefactive group tended to become established, a rapid alteration in the diet would tend to prevent either group of bacteria from becoming established. Herter,[9] in a later paper, reported the same conclusions.

The relation of diet to intestinal flora was also studied by Cannon[10] with white rats. When kept on a stock diet of oats and carrots, at the end of two weeks the colon-acidophilus ratio was 1 to 99; on a protein diet consisting almost exclusively of raw meat there was a colon-acidophilus ratio of 99 to 1. When variations intermediate between these two diets were used, varying colon-acidophilus ratios were secured. Grain foods, lactose, and dextrin led to a predominant aciduric flora, while animal proteins led to a predominance of organisms of the gas-producing proteolytic types, both aerobic and anaerobic. Vegetable proteins accelerated the appearance of a distinct antiputrefactive effect, favoring development of *Lactobacillus acidophilus*. These results were also obtained with two human adults. Hudson and Parr[11] also reported quite similar results. Torrey,[12] as did Cannon, also found that mammalian tissue was the only one which encouraged to any extent the growth and activity of the obligate putrefactive bacteria within the intestines. Four years before, Torrey[13] observed the results of a high calorie diet on the fecal flora of typhoid patients. When large amounts of lactose were fed, there was a change to a flora in which *Lactobacillus acidophilus* predominated. That the factors which control the intestinal flora are varied is suggested by the work of Torrey and Rahe,[14] who found that certain undesirable strains of *Escherichia coli* could be removed from the intestinal tracts of dogs by means of large doses of autogenous bacteria.

One hundred and seventy-three rats were fed 12 different diets by Porter and Rettger.[15] On the stock diet the "normal" bacterial flora of the young white rat was simple, especially in the upper segments of the alimentary tract, the flora being made up largely of *Lactobacillus acidophilus* type of aciduric microorganisms. Bacteria became increasingly more abundant in the lower sections of the small intestines and cecum

8. Herter and Kendall. 1910. J. Biol. Chem., 7, 203.
9. Herter. 1910. Internatl. Beitr. Path. u. Ther. Ernährungsstör. Stoffw. u. Verdauungskrank., 1, No. 3, 275-281.
10. Cannon. 1921. J. Infect. Dis., 29, 369.
11. Hudson and Parr. 1924. J. Infect. Dis., 34, 621-624.
12. Torrey. 1919. J. Med. Res., 49, 415-447.
13. Torrey. 1915. J. Infect. Dis., 16, 72.
14. Torrey and Rahe. 1920. J. Immunol., 5, 133-143.
15. Porter and Rettger. 1940. J. Infect. Dis. 66, 104-110.

where an appreciable number of coliform bacteria were found. Yeast-like fungi were observed in all segments in small numbers. This "normal" flora was said to be altered throughout the intestinal tract by food or starvation, but was fairly stable irrespective of the diet. Various salts were observed by Eppright, Valley, and Smith[16] to alter the intestinal flora. On low salt intakes the usual aciduric intestinal flora with *Lactobacillus acidophilus* was replaced by a flora consisting of coliform and proteus types and *Streptococcus fecalis*. The Osborn and Mendel salt mixture maintained a flora rich in *Lactobacillus acidophilus* and restored the resistant aciduric bacilli previously altered by ingestion of a diet deficient in inorganic salts.

Effect of Fasting and a Low-Protein Diet on Intestinal Flora. Blatherwick and Hawk[17] studied the effect of fasting and a low- and high-protein intake on the bacteria in the intestines by determining the amount of bacterial nitrogen in the feces, according to the method mentioned elsewhere in this chapter and the output of urinary indican. They found no relation between output of bacteria in the feces and the amount of indican in the urine. By means of a seven-day fast, the bacterial nitrogen excreted by a 76-kg. man was reduced from 1.571 to .101 gm. The actual weight of excreted bacterial substance was reduced from 14.336 to .920 gm. per day. The output of bacterial nitrogen and bacterial substance was about the same during a fast and on a low-protein intake. Ingestion of a high-protein diet caused an increase in the above amounts. Unfortunately a qualitative study of the bacteria in the feces was not made, and to secure such information it is necessary to consult the work of others. Herter and his colleagues, the work of whom has been summarized by Herter,[18] have given definite proof that a protein diet favors the proteolytic group. Rettger and his colleagues, on the other hand, have studied the effect of milk and carbohydrate feeding. The experiments were made with laboratory animals and man. Hull and Rettger[19] found that lactose, when taken by adults along with their usual food, caused a shift in the flora to the acidophilic group of bacteria. *Lactobacillus acidophilus* and *Lactobacillus bifidus* appeared, with the former more abundant. The most practical diet, however, to produce these results, was a combination of milk and lactose. *Lactobacillus bulgaricus* was not found, which is in accord with the work of others. For a more complete discussion of this subject, see Chapter 12.

Fasting has a decided effect on intestinal bacteria. As quoted above, Blatherwick and Hawk,[17] during fasting, noticed a decided reduction in the amount of bacterial nitrogen and bacterial substance. Sisson[20] found that, after periods of starvation, there is a definite decrease in the number of bacteria in contrast to the usually large number. No change in the kind

16. Eppright *et al*. 1937. J. Bact. 34, 81-97.
17. Blatherwick and Hawk. 1914. J. Amer. Chem. Soc., 36, 147.
18. Herter. 1907. The Common Bacterial Infections of the Digestive Tract and the Intoxications Rising from Them. The Macmillan Co., New York.
19. Hull and Rettger. 1915. J. Bact., 2, 47-71.
20. Sisson. 1917. Amer. J. Dis. Children 13, 117-127.

of organism after starvation was noted. The greatest decrease in the number of bacteria was noticed in the duodenum. Sisson regarded the condition produced by starvation as one of relative amicrobism. When Poppens [21] studied the effects of fasting on the bacterial flora of the stomach and duodenum, using dogs fed bread and meat until 14 hours before the operation, the bacteria found varied in type. Cannon and McNease [22] reported that a meat diet caused a neutral reaction in the contents of the cecum and colon; they were foul-smelling and contained indol. The flora was of a gas-producing variety and proteolytic with *Lactobacillus acidophilus* at a minimum. The addition of lactose caused a distinct change in the reaction of the contents of the cecum and colon. Cushing and Livingood reported relative amicrobism following a fasting period of 24 hours. Sisson [20] also observed a reduction in the bacterial content, the greatest reduction occurring in the duodenum. Fasting never brought about a condition of complete sterility. The above results were, in general, confirmed by Schnorbusch.[23]

Effect of Copious Water Drinking on Intestinal Flora. The influence of copious water drinking on the intestinal flora has not been studied as much as other factors. Fowler and Hawk [24] noticed a decrease in the total nitrogen appearing as bacterial nitrogen. The following weights of fecal bacteria were excreted per day during the periods mentioned:

Preliminary	5.327 gm. per day
Water period	4.579 gm. per day
Final period	3.280 gm. per day

Hattrem and Hawk,[25] by means of copious water drinking, obtained a decrease in putrefaction and stated that it was probably due to a decrease in the activities of indol-producing bacteria following accelerated absorption of products of protein digestion. Copious water drinking (1000 ml.) caused a decrease of indican in the urine which was accompanied by an increase of etheral sulfates. The drinking of distilled and softened waters were found by Sherwin and Hawk [26] to cause a decrease in intestinal putrefaction as measured by urinary indican. It is possible that the character of water used for drinking influences the type of microorganisms, but few data are available upon which to base conclusions.

Effect of a High-Protein Diet on Intestinal Flora. A high-protein diet has been found to induce the predominance of bacteria which can utilize proteins. After Metschnikoff propounded his interesting theory on the relation of the intestinal flora to longevity and well-being, many investigations were instituted to prove the truth of his statements. Among the early investigators to study the question was Herter.[18] Torrey [12] fed dogs a protein diet over a long period of time and, furthermore, studied the transforming ability of animal as compared with vegetable proteins. A

21. Poppens. 1921. Amer. J. Med. Sci., 161, 203.
22. Cannon and McNease. 1923. J. Infect. Dis. 32, 175-180.
23. Schnorbusch. 1937. Deut. Arch. Klin. Med., 181, 55.
24. Fowler and Hawk. 1910. J. Expt. Med., 12, 388-410.
25. Hattrem and Hawk. 1911. Arch. Int. Med., 7, 610.
26. Sherwin and Hawk. 1914. J. Amer. Chem. Soc., 36, 1779-1785.

considerable number of dogs were kept for a varying length of time on boiled beef heart. A putrefactive flora of a pronounced and uniform type appeared. Under these conditions, the flora was dominated by the gram-positive, sporebearing, anaerobic bacilli to the same extent that *Lactobacillus bulgaricum* dominates when a diet of lactose of dextrin was fed. The *Clostridium welchii*-like organisms were found throughout the intestines and were in almost pure culture in the small gut. On this meat diet *Escherichia coli (Bacterium coli)* was markedly suppressed, and *Lactobacillus acidophilus* and *Bacteroides bifidus (Bacillus bifidus)* practically eliminated. Bacteria producing hydrogen sulfide from peptone were markedly numerous, especially members of the proteolytic group. Different results were secured with a fish diet. A high fish diet did not encourage the growth of sporebearing bacteria, of either aerobic or anaerobic type. Instead of *Clostridium welchii*-like flora as occurred when beef heart was fed, Torrey observed an *Escherichia coli* flora. *Clostridium welchii, Lactobacillus acidophilus*, and streptococci were present in small numbers or entirely absent. A fish diet also seemed to favor a flora of organisms which formed hydrogen sulfide from proteins more than any other diet. Torrey,[27] in a later report, published the results of experiments on the same subject carried out with human beings. Two of the subjects were kept on an exclusive meat diet for over a year. Change from a mixed to a whole-meat diet caused an abrupt drop in the total bacteria amounting to about 50 per cent. In one subject it reached 76 per cent during the 13th month. This decrease was attributed to the suppression of lactic acid-producing types, Enterococci and Streptococci and to a lesser extent, *Escherichia coli*. Free spores and sporeforming bacteria remained at about the same level. Spirochaetes disappeared. The interesting observation was made that the high-meat diet did not induce greater proteolytic activity than a mixed diet. Furthermore, no evidence was gathered that a long-continued exclusive meat diet favored the development of putrefactive conditions in the colon. Such conclusions are somewhat different from the general opinions which are prevalent on this question. Although milk casein is animal protein, it did not seem to create putrefactive conditions to the same degree as did meat. Vegetable proteins were said to stand in strong contrast to animal proteins, especially meat, in that they did not offer the slightest encouragement to the growth of intestinal putrefactive types of bacteria. This is an interesting observation which was confirmed by Cannon.[10] Cannon stated that his experiments agreed with those of Torrey in that vegetable proteins not only reduced the relative proportion of proteolytic types, both aerobic and anaerobic, but also encouraged the overgrowth of a non-gas-producing aciduric flora. Animal proteins, on the other hand, such as meat, fish, and eggs, led to an enormous overgrowth of gas-forming proteolytic types. Hull and Rettger [28] had reported in 1917 that a high-protein diet of meat or other proteins increased the indol-producing bacteria and other organisms of the putrefactive type. The

27. Torrey. 1930. Soc. Expt. Biol. and Med. Proc. 28, 295; J. Infect. Dis. 49 (1931), 141-176.
28. Hull and Rettger. 1917. J. Bact. 2, 47-71.

contradictory conclusions which have been reached by those who have studied this subject are not easy to explain. It is very probable that other factors than the one under study may have had some effect.

Influence of Hydrogen-Ion Concentration on Intestinal Flora. The actual acidity of the intestinal contents of the cecum and colon, according to Cannon and McNease,[22] is one of the important factors influencing the bacterial flora. With a high-protein diet the reaction of the contents of the cecum and colon was pH 7.0 to 7.1; the addition of lactose may lead to a pH in the cecum of 4.6 with 6.2 in the lower colon. The simplification of the intestinal flora varied directly with the hydrogen-ion concentration. A pH of 7.0 is characteristic of a gas-forming proteolytic type; an increasing acidity causes a diminution in proteolytic forms and their replacement by aciduric types. Hull and Rettger,[28] however, did not observe a relation between the character of the intestinal flora and the reaction of the intestine. They found, as a rule, the highest acidity in the duodenum and the lowest at the ileocecal valve. Robinson[29] determined the hydrogen-ion concentration of the feces from several human subjects by means of the electrometric method. The reaction was found to vary ordinarily between pH 6.5 and 7.5 although occasional isolated values were observed which were outside of this range. However, the normal fecal reaction of healthy men was between pH 7.0 and 7.5. Robinson made the interesting observation that drinking one quart of *Lactobacillus acidophilus* milk and *Lactobacillus bulgaricus* milk daily did not change the reaction of mixed feces. Cheplin and Rettger[30] made the same observation. Hudson and Parr,[11] however, found that a change in the intestinal flora from a heterogeneous, gram-negative type to a simplified gram-positive type was also accompanied by a change in the reaction from nearly neutral to distinctly acid.

Investigations seem to indicate that the reaction of the intestines does not vary within wide limits. It is perhaps difficult to decide whether the reaction determines the type of the bacterial flora or whether the flora is responsible for the reaction. Long and Fenger[31] studied the reaction of intestinal contents of both men and animals. Arnold[32] found cocci and *Escherichia coli* seldom present in the upper part of the small intestine as long as there was a predominance of acid-reacting substances. The subject was discussed again by Arnold and Brodny.[33] A change in the bacterial flora of the duodenum and upper jejunum was noticed when the normal reaction of the contents was changed from slightly acid (pH 5 to 6) to a neutral or alkaline reaction (pH 7 to 8). The reaction of this region was also said to depend to a great extent on normal gastric secretory function.

No correlation was observed by Weinstein, Weiss, and Gillespie[34] between pH in the small intestine and its *Lactobacillus acidophilus* content

29. Robinson. 1922. Abs. Bact., 6, 157.
30. Cheplin and Rettger. 1921. Abs. Bact. No. 58.
31. Long and Fenger. 1917. J. Amer. Chem. Soc., 39, 1278.
32. Arnold. 1927. Amer. J. Pub. Health 17, 918-921.
33. Arnold and Brodny. 1926. Amer. J. Hyg., 6, 672-683.
34. Weinstein *et al.* 1938. J. Bact. 35, 515-525.

in white rats on three different diets; in the colon there was some degree of correlation. The nature of the diet and the portion of the intestines examined are important in determination of the average pH and content of *Lactobacillus acidophilus*. Hydrogen-ion concentration and the volatile acid content of the intestines, according to Bergeim,[35] must not be overlooked in investivations on intestinal flora. He studied the effect of formic, acetic, butyric, and lactic acids on growth of yeast and *Escherichia coli* over the range of pH and acid concentration likely to occur in the intestines. Above pH 6.5, these acids had little effect. Below pH 4, the pH itself became important. In the pH range of 5 to 6 where pH itself was not inhibitory, the fatty acids, even in low concentrations, had a marked effect on growth. In this range acetic and butyric acid were the most effective and lactic acid had little influence. *Lactobacillus acidophilus* was very resistant. Bergeim believed that volatile acids could not be disregarded when studying the effect of acidity on the intestinal flora.

Effect of Intestinal Absorption on Intestinal Flora. Dragstedt[36] and his colleagues reported that in cases of complete obstruction or stasis in the passage of the intestinal contents, a proteolytic flora is induced irrespective of the diet of the individual. It was stated that carbohydrates, such as dextrin and lactose, were probably absorbed in the upper part of the intestines and therefore exerted no influence on the character of the flora in the lower parts of the intestinal tract.

Relation of Vitamin-Deficient Diets to Bacterial Flora. Creekmur[37] studied the intestinal flora of rats on a normal diet and one deficient in Vitamin A. In most of the animals, on the deficient diet streptococci disappeared completely. There seemed to be no change in the proportions of bacteria fermenting glucose, lactose, and sucrose or in the proportion of H_2S forming bacteria. The feces of the animals on the deficient diet became dry and hard with a distinct decrease in the total number of bacteria. The addition of vitamin A in the form of a few drops of cod liver oil daily produced a normal condition. Animals on vitamin-deficient diets are probably abnormal; the bacterial flora would be markedly influenced by many factors.

Relations of a Milk Diet to Intestinal Flora. The effect of milk on intestinal flora has been rather extensively discussed in Chapter 12, where the use of fermented milks in the diet was taken up. Hull and Rettger,[28] as a part of the extensive investigations of Rettger on the effect of diet on intestinal bacteria, studied the influence of milk. They stated that the beneficial action of milk in changing the flora to one in which acidophilic bacteria predominated was due mainly to its lactose content. Bergeim's[38] work on ferric oxide as an index of intestinal putrefaction seemed to indicate that milk tended to depress the formation of reducing substances by bacteria in the intestines. This subject is discussed further in Chapter 12, where the influence of fermented milks on intestinal bacteria is reviewed.

35. Bergeim. 1940. J. Infect. Dis., 66, 222-234.
36. Dragstedt. 1922. Idem 31, 209-214.
37. Creekmur. 1922. Idem 461-467.
38. Bergeim. 1924. J. Biol. Chem., 62, 45-60.

Effect of Carbohydrates on Intestinal Flora. Sugars, when added to the diet, uniformly have favored the growth of acidophiles. Torrey [12] found that when lactose and dextrin were added to the diet of dogs, acidophiles increased in numbers. Rettger and his collaborators have shown the same thing. Hull and Rettger,[28] using white rats, studied the effect of carbohydrates on the character of the intestinal flora. This was a continuation of Rettger's [39] work on the same subject. *Lactobacillus acidophilus* (Moro) and *Bacteroides bifidus* (Tissier) were said to be common inhabitants of the intestinal tract of white rats and man, although their numbers may vary greatly. They claimed that diet was the most important factor determining bacterial flora. Lactose fed in two- to three-gram quantities brought about a complete transformation in the flora in two to three days. Milk required a longer time and did not cause as complete a transformation. It is well known that *Lactobacillus acidophilus* is commonly present in the intestinal tract and in various other places in the body. Naujoks [40] isolated it from the vaginal secretions as well as in two-thirds of his pregnancy cases. It was said to be identical with *Bacillus vaginalis minor*. The organism appears in the rectum of breast-fed infants in from four to seven days, and in the mouth after seven days. Lauter,[41] studying *Bacteroides bifidus*, believed that intestinal infection was by mouth. The value and importance of milk rests on its content of lactose, which is absorbed slowly from the intestines. Foods which are made up of starch stimulate the establishment of an aciduric flora. Bread, however, which contains cooked starch, had little effect. Lactose in amounts from 250 to 300 grams per day brought about a marked change in the flora of the human intestinal tract. These results were confirmed by Cruickshank [42] in feeding experiments on rats. A diet with high-carbohydrate content produced a simplified flora in the intestines of rats but failed to effect a radical transformation to an aciduric flora. Lactose and dextrin, when added to a diet of bread, meat, and oats, quickly changed the intestinal flora to aciduric types. Saccharose had a much less marked effect. Maltose, glucose, galactose, and levulose produced no change. Acidophilus milk caused a change to an aciduric flora and the change was more marked when lactose was added. Cruickshank believed that the value of acidophilus milk in the diet was not due to its bulk or acidity but to the combination of the living microorganism with the unfermented lactose in the milk.

Implantation of *Lactobacillus bulgaricus*, even by feeding large quantities, was not successful. Torrey [12] confirmed these discoveries with dogs. Not all carbohydrates had the same value in stimulating the appearance of an aciduric flora. He placed the sugars in the following order: dextrin, lactose, saccharose, maltose, and dextrose. With unboiled milk *Escherichia coli* and streptococci predominated, while with boiled milk streptococci and *Lactobacillus acidophilus* were favored. Bass [43] reported the

39. Rettger. 1915. J. Expt. Med., 21, 365-388.
40. Naujoks. 1923. Centbl. Bakt., Pt. 1, Orig., 86, 582-584.
41. Lauter. 1921. Idem 86, 579-582.
42. Cruickshank. 1928. Brit. J. Expt. Path., 9, 318-326.
43. Bass. 1923. South. Med. J., 26, 1-7.

same results with lactose feeding. Daily ingestion of sufficiently large amounts of lactose caused a change to a *Lactobacillus acidophilus* flora. In some cases, more than 300 grams of lactose per day were required to cause a shift in the flora. Since such amounts of lactose are too large to be continued over a long period, this method has certain limitations. The results of feeding acidophilus milk were in accord with the statements of Rettger and others. Cheplin and Rettger [44] emphasized again the intimate relation between the chemical constitution of the diet and the nature of the bacteriological flora. The addition of two (2) grams of lactose or dextrin to albino rats, being fed a diet of beef and bread, stimulated the proliferation of *Lactobacillus acidophilus*. The organism completely dominated the intestinal flora in six days. *Lactobacillus bulgaricus* could not be implanted so easily or so completely and these workers suggested that Metschnikoff and his colleagues, when reporting the results of sour milk therapy, really observed *Lactobacillus acidophilus* and not *Lactobacillus bulgaricus*. Even when large numbers of *Lactobacillus bulgaricus* were added to the diet, the organism could not be established in the intestine.

As might be expected from the above discussion, Hull and Rettger [28] noticed that the presence of "corn-starch" in the diet appeared to foster the amylolytic bacteria; the ingestion of grain was said to favor the development of fusiform bacteria. Perhaps the real reason why a large amount of lactose or dextrin in the diet leads to such a predominance of *Lactobacillus acidophilus* is not known. Some have suggested that it was due to the fact that lactose persists so much farther along the alimentary tract. It is not entirely absorbed or fermented before the large intestine is reached. One may wonder why an undesirable fermenter of lactose does not flourish instead of *Lactobacillus acidophilus*. Kendall [45] suggested that feeding liberal amounts of lactose to infants might lead to an excessive development of *Clostridium welchii*, an inhabitant of the alimentary tract. In opposition to this is the experience of Cheplin and Rettger and others who have always reported a decrease if not entire elimination of *Clostridium welchii* and *Escherichia coli* as well. Kopeloff and Cohen [46] put the investigation of the problem on a practical basis by using 45 human subjects. Without enumerating details of technic, the conclusions which they reached may be given. The ingestion of 10 grams of lactose did not transform the intestinal flora; 50 grams daily, however, transformed the flora in four out of 15 subjects. Ingestion of 100 grams of lactose daily transformed the flora in three out of 15 subjects. The presence of *Lactobacillus acidophilus* before lactose feeding did not seem to aid in transforming the flora. These experiments were carried out over a period of three to eight months.

Addition of lactose and *Lactobacillus acidophilus* to a well-balanced diet caused an increase in cocci at the expense of gram-positive and gram-negative bacilli in the ileum, according to Paulson.[47] This indicated that there may be some alteration in the flora of the ileum and that *Lacto-*

44. Cheplin and Rettger. 1920. Soc. Expt. Biol. and Med. Proc. 6, 423-426.
45. Kendall. 1911. J. Med. Res., 25, 117-187.
46. Kopeloff and Cohen. 1930. J. Amer. Med. Assoc., 94, 1833-1885.
47. Paulson. 1929. Bull. Johns Hopkins Hosp., 45, 315-330.

bacillus acidophilus is washed down or may multiply to some extent in the human ileum. According to Sanborn,[48] the alteration of the intestinal flora by a high-carbohydrate diet is largely dependent on the flora already established.

Dried fruits may be presumed to be rich in carbohydrates and therefore function in influencing the bacterial flora as do carbohydrates. Such was the finding of Weinstein and Weiss [49] when they fed banana powder, apple powder, and raisins to white rats on a high-protein diet. *Lactobacillus acidophilus* predominated in the intestines. Prunes had little effect. They attributed the effect of dried fruits to their sugar and mineral salts content.

Effect of a High-Fat Diet on Intestinal Flora. Since fewer bacteria are able to split fat than proteins, one would not expect a high-fat diet to cause much change. Such was the case when Torrey [12] fed butter to dogs. No new types of bacteria were introduced, but some species normally present were somewhat suppressed. The streptococci seemed to be especially influenced. The numbers of *Escherichia coli (Bacterium coli)* were frequently reduced, but aciduric bacteria of the *Lactobacillus acidophilus* type were least affected.

BACTERIA IN THE MOUTH

All kinds of bacteria enter the mouth in food and drink. Consequently, if all of these transient types are considered in studies on the mouth flora, the flora would be quite heterogeneous. However, study of the question narrows the flora to certain species which are always present.

Bloomfield [50] found that bacteria and fine dust particles disappeared in a very short time. He found that they neither remained nor spread over the mouth. Carbon particles seemed to be removed in from 15 to 30 minutes. He found that the tonsils were normally so protected by the pillars that the particles from the mouth were swept by without infecting them. The upper part of the pharyngeal wall was also untouched. This would seem to indicate that many of the bacteria in food hurry through the mouth and do not contribute to its flora.

Appleton, Klein, and Palmer,[51] after developing a method for measuring the rate of elimination of bacteria from the mouth, used it to follow elimination of a test organism,*Serratia marcescens.* They observed that this organism eventually disappeared when introduced into the human mouth. The rapidity depends on various factors.

Filamentous bacteria have also been found in the mouth by Bibby and Berry [52] who divided some 83 strains into seven groups. Six of them had distinct characteristics. Most of them had characteristics of the genus Leptotrichia. Most of them were classed as *Leptotrichia buccalis.*

Germicidal Action of Saliva. Data available on this subject are neither conclusive nor extensive. Huggenschmidt,[53] from a study of the various

48. Sanborn. 1931. J. Infect. Dis., 49, 37-39.
49. Weinstein and Weiss. 1937. Idem 60, 1.
50. Bloomfield. 1920. Amer. Rev. Tuber. 4, 247; Bull. Johns Hopkins Hosp., 33 (1922), 145.
51. Appleton *et al.* 1938. Amer. J. Hyg., 28, 213-231.
52. Bibby and Berry. 1939. J. Bact. 28, 263.
53. Huggenschmidt. 1896. Dental Cosmos.

factors which contribute to the protection of the sputum, mechanical action of the saliva, action of the mucous membrane and bacterial antagonism, concluded that the mechanical action of the sputum was the most important factor. Sanarelli [54] filtered saliva through a Chamberland filter and tested the bactericidal action of the filtrate. He believed that saliva did possess a germicidal action quite similar to that exhibited by other body fluids, such as blood, aqueous humor, etc. The speed of the reaction depended upon the initial number of bacteria introduced into the saliva. If a small number of cells (three or four hundred) were introduced, all were killed in a short time, but when a few thousand cells were introduced, there was usually a decrease followed by an indefinite increase. With *Corynebacterium diphtheriae* and the Pneumococcus no germicidal action was noticed. They were found alive after 28 and 40 days. The cause of the germicidal action was not determined. Gordon [55] carried out his experiments on this subject in culture media, and found a germicidal action against the Meningococcus, which he attributed to the antagonistic effect of other bacteria in the saliva. These were supposed to be mixed streptococci. Van der Reis [56] could observe no bactericidal activity in saliva against a number of bacteria in test-tube experiments. *Escherichia coli (Bacterium coli)* sprayed into the mouth remained for many days. This last statement is not in accordance with the conclusions of Bloomfield. In fact, van der Reis claimed that this organism had colonized on the tonsils.

The subject was studied by Barnes [57] with fresh saliva sterilized by filtration. Loopfuls of broth cultures of the organisms were inoculated into about .4 ml. of saliva. No germicidal effect could be observed with the pneumococcus, streptococcus, staphylococcus, or influenza bacillus. Indeed the staphylococcus and pneumococcus were favored.

The saliva of various animals, dogs, cats, rabbits, monkeys, and goats, was studied by Clairmont. The saliva seemed to exert a mechanical action more than a real germicidal effect. Whether saliva is shown to exert bactericidal action is determined by the conditions under which the experiments are carried out. If the investigator uses a very delicate organism, one which is quite susceptible to unfavorable conditions, he might conclude that lack of growth is due to destruction of cells by the saliva. On the other hand, it might be due to unfavorable conditions of culture.

Weigmann and Noeske [58] observed inhibition by human saliva of growth of *Corynebacterium diphtheria, Bacillus subtilis,* and *Bacillus anthracis.* The activity of the saliva of different individuals varies greatly. Short exposure to boiling and 30 minutes' heating at 56°C.(132.8°F.) destroys it. The property was also said to be destroyed by filtration and centrifugation. The property soon disappears from saliva. Piasecka and Zeyland [59] observed an inhibitory action of saliva on *Mycobacterium tuberculosis.* In

54. Sanarelli. 1891. Centbl. Bakt., 10, 817-825.
55. Gordon. Brit. Med. J., I, 849-851.
56. Van der Reis. 1921. Rev. in J. Amer. Med. Assoc., 76, 1714.
57. Barnes. 1909. Trans. Chicago Path. Soc., 7, 249-254.
58. Weigmann and Noeske. 1937. Ztschr. f. Hyg. u. Infektionskrank. 119, 413-424.
59. Piasecka-Zeyland. 1937. Tubercle 24-27.

contradiction to the results of Weigmann and Noeske, they did not observe that heating at 56°C. destroyed it. They attributed this action to unknown factors. The antibacterial activity of saliva was attributed by Van Kesteren, Bibby, and Berry [60] to at least two antibacterial factors, one of which was said to resemble lysozyme. Each of these agents acted more specifically on certain microorganisms.

THE STOMACH

The bacteriological aspects of the stomach have been concerned mostly with its diseases. The bacteria of the stomach gain entrance with the food and drink. The germicidal action of the saliva may probably be neglected as a factor influencing the number of bacteria passing through the mouth. The types of bacteria found in the stomach are undoubtedly determined by the kind of food taken in and the types of microorganisms in this food. Henneberg [61] analyzed 17 fresh stomachs and found the following organisms: *Oidium lactis*, Torula, *Saccharomyces Minor*, *Lactobacillus beijerinckii (B. beiejrinskii)*, Sarcinae, lactic acid bacteria, and certain other forms. Aronovitch, Coleman, and Einhorn have published similar data for the stomach. Kopeloff [62] reported that many of the bacteria in the stomach resulted from swallowing saliva. Dukes [63] tried to find out whether bacteria were digested in the stomach. He reported that bacteria did not absorb proteolytic enzymes for they seemed to be protected by means of a lipoidal envelope.

Germicidal Action of Gastric Juice. The gastric juice is the normal secretion of the stomach. It contains between two to three per cent solids and about .2 per cent of free hydrochloric acid, which is the most powerful of any acid combination in the stomach. A condition of hyperacidity exists when a decidedly greater amount of hydrochloric acid is present than normally, and hypoacidity when the amount of acid is below normal. During conditions of hypoacidity fermentation may be active with the formation of lactic and butyric acids. Some hold that gastric ulcer and gastric catarrh may be due to reduced acidity.

That the gastric juice is germicidal was noticed by Spallanzani in 1734. When he moistened meat with gastric juice, it did not putrefy. Meat which was not so treated but which was moistened with other substances, such as water, developed a putrid odor very quickly. He opened a snake 18 days after it had swallowed a lizard and while the lizard was partly digested, it had not decomposed. Other experiments by this early scientist demonstrated that putrefaction could be stopped by gastric juice.

Somewhat the same technic was used by van der Reis. [56] After feeding *Serratia marcesens (Bacillus prodigiosus)* he was able to isolate it from the stools, which would indicate that it had not been killed in the stomach by the gastric juice. He also dipped pieces of bacon and apple seeds in cultures of *Serratia marcesens (B. prodigiosus)* and staphylococcus, tied

60. Van Kesteren *et al.* 1942. J. Bact. 43, 573-583.
61. Henneberg. 1922. Centbl. Bakt., Pt. 2, 55, 243-281.
62. Kopeloff. 1921. Soc. Expt. Biol. and Med. Proc. 19, 110-112.
63. Dukes. 1922. Brit. Med. J., II, 3194.

threads to them and had them swallowed. Bacteria could be cultivated from them when they were withdrawn two hours later. The experiments were repeated before, during, and after meals. The hydrochloric acid was said to have received undue credit for destroying bacteria in the stomach. William Beaumont, when studying the gastric secretion of Alexis St. Martin, also suggested that gastric juice checked putrefaction.

Koch [64] fed cholera vibrios to dogs and after a few hours found that they had been destroyed. He stated that cholera vibrios were destroyed in the stomach under normal conditions, and that if they passed through, it was due to some abnormal condition. Falk secured no action on *Mycobacterium tuberculosis*. Kurloff and Wagner [65] noticed a selective action of the gastric juice. Cholera vibrio, *Eberthella typhosa*, and *Pseudomonas aeruginosa (Pseudomonas pyocyaneus)* were destroyed, but *Mycobacterium tuberculosis, B. anthracis,* and *Clostridium tetani* (spores) were not affected. Strauss and Wurtz [66] showed that anthrax bacilli were killed in 15 minutes, and that the destructive factor in the gastric juice was the hydrochloric acid. The same conclusion was reached by Kabrhel.[67] Hamburger [68] first called attention to the fact that some of the acid was bound and that the free acid had a stronger germicidal effect. This was proven by testing the action of a solution of HCl with one of the same strength containing peptone. Kianowsky [69] showed a direct relation between the number of bacteria in stomachs and the amount of acid. With patients possessing a faulty acid secretion many bacteria were found. Cadeac and Bournay [70] found that *Pseudomonas aeruginosa (Pseudomonas pyocyaneus)* was destroyed after six hours and that *Bacillus anthracis* and *Mycobacterium tuberculosis* were not killed. Pettenkofer [71] reported some startling work which was carried out in 1893. This was done soon after the great epidemic of cholera in Hamburg and Altoona. He proposed the X, Y, Z theory for cholera where X = bacterium; Y = host or soil; Z = environment. He stated that X without Y and Z would not cause cholera. So thoroughly did these workers believe in this theory that Pettenkofer and Emmerich drank pure cultures of the cholera vibrio. Each mixed 1 ml. of a broth culture with 100 ml. of 1 per cent sodium bicarbonate solution and drank it. Pettenkofer did not change his usual manner of living and, after having diarrhea for four days, came back to normal. Emmerich's case ran a longer time. In this case the sodium bicarbonate neutralized the HCl of the gastric juice. The bacteria thus passed through the stomach and produced the usual results.

Stern [72] did not regard the gastric juice as such a barrier against bacterial invasion as some of the former workers. He regarded persons with

64. Koch. 1884. (Berlin) Klin. Wchnschr., Nos. 31 and 32.
65. Kurloff and Wagner. 1889. Centbl. Bakt., 7, 448-450.
66. Strauss and Wurtz. 1889. Arch. Med. Expt., et d'Anat., Pathol. No. 3.
67. Kabrhel. 1890. Ztschr. f. Hyg. u. Infektionskrank. 10.
68. Hamburger. 1890. Klin. Med., p. 425.
69. Kianowsky. 1891. Centbl. Bakt., 10, 236-237.
70. Cadeac and Bournay. 1893. Centbl. Bakt. Orig. 16, 572.
71. Pettenkofer. 1892. München. Med. Wchnschr. 1892. No. 96.
72. Stern. 1908. Centbl. Bakt. I, 47, 561.

hyperacidity as fortunate from this standpoint, but in no way absolutely protected. Bile was found to decrease the bactericidal action of the gastric juice. When proteins were present, cholera vibrios were found to live a long time. Pepsin was found to strengthen the action of the acid. Hansen [73] infected food with *Escherichia coli* and secured only a slight decrease of bacteria in the stomach. Schultz-Schultzenstein [74] found the gastric juice to be more germicidal than hydrochloric acid solution of the same strength. Gregersen [75] reported some of the more recent work on this subject. He studied the action of the acid in the juice and whether any other factors were important. In general, he found that without free acid, bacteria in the stomach were not killed. As the amount of free hydrochloric acid increased, the time required for destruction of bacteria was reduced. Experiments by Bartle and Harkins [76] indicated no germicidal activity in concentrations of "free" hydrochloric acid below .04 per cent, but when .08 per cent was present a well-marked germicidal action was evident.

Hajos [77] studied the germicidal action of gastric juice under different conditions. The bactericidal power was believed to be due to the free hydrochloric acid. Normal gastric juice killed old cells of bacteria of the colon-typhoid group in about 15 minutes. Bacteria introduced into the stomach along with solid foods were killed more quickly than those coming into the stomach with liquid foods such as milk or water. Foods in the latter group pass out of the stomach more quickly than the solid foods. People with hypoacidity are more prone to intestinal infections. The work of Schönbauer [78] would indicate that the germicidal action of the gastric juice might be due to combined activity of both pepsin and hydrochloric acid. According to Kopeloff, [79] the bacterial content of the saliva has much significance in interpreting bacteriological data from the stomach. Kopeloff reported that the bacterial condition of the stomach at any time is dependent on the saliva swallowed previous to analysis. In a later paper, this same author stated that the stomach acted as a receptacle for bacteria and that it was not a focus of infection.

Aronovitch, Coleman, and Einhorn [80] used the Einhorn intestinal tube and were able to investigate the bacteria in the intestinal contents much more thoroughly than did others. They were able to secure material 135 inches from the lips. In this report, they confined their work to the stomach, duodenum, and jejunum. Using eight subjects, they secured the following data: In the stomach the number of viable organisms and spores was low with the exception of one case in which the spore count was high. The type of organism was not especially significant. Acid was usually formed in dextrose and milk. In the duodenum, 28 inches from the lips, the number of viable organisms and spores was uniformly small, although

73. Hansen. 1912. Centbl. Bakt., 62, 89-126.
74. Schultz-Schultzenstein. 1908. Centbl. Bakt. Orig. 30, 785.
75. Gregersen. 1916. Centbl. Bakt. Orig. 77, 353-361.
76. Bartle and Harkins. 1925. Amer. J. Med. Sci., 169, 373.
77. Hajos. 1922. Wien. Arch. Int. Med., 3, 453.

79. Kopeloff. 1922. J. Infect. Dis., 30, 613-622.
80. Aronovitch, Coleman, and Einhorn. 1922. Soc. Expt. Biol. and Med. Proc. 20, 97-99.

there was a slight tendency to increase in numbers. The organisms expected were found. There appeared at this point a greater diversity of types than in the stomach. In the jejunal contents, the results on the various patients seemed to be a little more irregular. The numbers seemed to increase.

Data secured with *Mycobacterium tuberculosis* are especially interesting in this connection. Fernbach and Rullier [81] mixed tuberculous sputum with gastric juice and, after incubation under controlled conditons, injected into guinea pigs. The animals which received the digested sputum did not develop tuberculosis, showing that the organisms were destroyed by elements in the gastric juice. The intestinal juice from a dog is not capable of digesting tubercle bacilli, according to Mylius and Sartorius.[82] After 24 hours of contact, the bacilli are less easily stained. There was also a slight decrease in the Much granules. Similar conclusions were reached by Inkster and Gloyne.[83]

Later work by Johnson and Arnold [84] showed that free acid in the stomachs of dogs destroyed bacteria. During periods of acid deficits, the number of living bacteria became quite large. Rawles and Chapman [85] found this to be the case with *Escherichia coli*. An excessive number of *Escherichia coli* were found in the feces of individuals suffering from achlorhydria. When there was even a trace of free hydrochloric acid in the stomach, coliform bacteria were greatly reduced.

Results of investigations just reported indicate that the gastric juice shows bactericidal properties for most bacteria. That it does not destroy all of them is indicated by the fact that pathogenic species, such as *Eberthella typhosa,* pass through to cause severe infections. Furthermore, it is conceivable that bacteria imbedded in food particles would be protected. Water passes through the stomach quickly and bacteria in it would thus survive. The gastric juice would also be so diluted that its acid would be too weak to destroy bacteria.

Germicidal Action of Intestinal Secretions. Many of the body fluids are known to possess definite germicidal properties. Investigations have also been carried out to determine whether there are germicidal properties connected with intestinal secretions or mucosa. Soli [86] reported experiments on rabbits which demonstrated a specific germicidal action of the intestinal epithelium. The germicidal action varied in intensity and in different parts of the intestines, being strongest in the jejunum. Schutz [87] placed *Pseudomonas aeruginosa (Bacillus pyocyaneus)* in the intestines of cats and observed a destruction of cells which was attributed to a germicidal action.

Mylius and Sartorius [82] could observe no dissolution or digestion of *Mycobacterium tuberculosis* by normal duodenal fluid. After exposure to

81. Fernbach and Rullier. 1924. Rev. Tuberc. 5, 99.
82. Mylius and Sartorius. 1924. Ztschr. f. Immunitäts f. u. Expt. Ther. 39, 12.
83. Inkster and Gloyne. 1921. Brit. Med. J., II, 3181.
84. Johnson and Arnold. 1932. Soc. Expt. Biol. and Med. Proc. 29, 501-502.
85. Rawles and Chapman. 1939. Rev. Gastroenterol. 6, 317-320.
86. Soli. 1921. Pediatria 29, 97.
87. Schutz. 1909. München. Med. Wchnschr., 56. 1683-1685.

duodenal fluid for 24 hours, the cells of *Mycobacterium tuberculosis* lost some of their ability to retain the stain which would indicate that the organisms were changed in some manner. Löwenberg [88] demonstrated a bactericidal action of duodenal secretion on *Eberthella typhosa (Bacterium typhosum)* and *Shigella dysenteriae (Bacterium dysenteriae)*. Löwenberg claimed that the cells of these organisms might pass through the bowel so quickly that they would not be exposed to the action of the juices. Direct contact under conditions which obtained in their experiments, prompted Day and Gibbs [89] to report that fresh pancreatic juice killed bacteria tested, with exception of *Staphylococcus aureus*, in 48 hours. In only one instance was digestion of the cells observed. While *Mycobacterium tuberculosis* was killed by the pancreatic juice, no evidence of dissolution nor loss of acid fastness was observed. Pancreatic secretion secured directly from the pancreatic duct by aid of secretin was consistently sterile.

Arnold and Brodny [33] made an appendicular fistula in each experimental animal, and cultures of *Serratia marcescens* or *Pseudomonas aeruginosa* were administered by mouth in various excipients, such as a watery suspension of lampblack or buffered milk solutions. The time of arrival of these organisms in the caecum, their maximal concentration in this region, and their period of persistence were studied by the removal of samples of intestinal contents from the fistula at suitable intervals. Full protocols of the experiments were given. The following conclusions were reached: Bacteria introduced (in watery suspension) into the empty stomach of a dog, 12 to 18 hours after a meal, do not reach the caecum. Bacteria introduced with alkaline buffered milk reach the caecum in large numbers over a relatively long period of time. Bacteria introduced with acid buffered milk sometimes reach the caecum, but in small numbers and over a relatively short period of time. Bacteria introduced into the stomach in an acid buffered aqueous solution seldom reach the caecum. When suspended in alkaline buffered aqueous solution, the bacteria reach the caecum in almost the same concentration as in the original ingested suspension. The "auto-disinfecting" mechanism of the upper part of the small intestine is dependent upon the presence of acid buffered material in its contents. This reaction is insured in the healthy animal by normal gastric secretory function. When neutral or alkaline buffered material enters the duodenum, this bactericidal power is lost and the bacterial content of such material is passed into the caecum.

Arnold [32] observed an auto-disinfecting process in the upper half or two-thirds of the small intestine that destroyed bacteria ingested and prevented the large intestinal flora from extending upwards. Arnold stated that certain changes in diet as well as climate could cause a loss of this bacteria-killing power. Arnold [32] reported that when the hydrogen-ion concentration was between 5.5 and 6.5 a substance was produced which inhibited the growth of aerobic bacteria.

88. Löwenberg. 1926. Deut. Med. Wchnschr. 52, 1767.
89. Day and Gibbs. 1930. J. Infect. Dis., 46, 26-30.

Relation of Bacteria to Life. This has been a much-debated question. Pasteur [90] believed that bacteria were essential for normal life. Nuttal and Thierfelder [91] reared guinea pigs under aseptic conditions which had been delivered by Caesarian section. These increased in weight, but not as regularly as normal pigs. From these data, the authors concluded that bacteria were not necessary for normal development. Schotellius [92] hatched chickens in a sterile environment and from the data which he secured concluded that chicks could not live in absence of bacteria. He stated also that sterilizing the grain may have destroyed some essential substance. He had no knowledge of vitamins. Levin [93] found the intestines of most Arctic animals completely sterile. He drew no conclusions, but his work is of interest on account of normal growth without bacteria. Metschnikoff[94] grew tadpoles on sterile bread and water and secured no transformation into frogs in either the sterile or unsterilized tadpoles. The non-sterile grew larger than the sterile. Portier [95] observed that larvae of certain Lepidoptera lived aseptically. Moro [96] confirmed the work of Schotellius, which has been mentioned above. He used turtles instead of chicks. Bogdanow [97] concluded that bacteria were necessary for normal development because sterile larvae of Diptera did not do as well as those kept in an unsterile environment. Wollman [98] criticized the work of Bogdanow, stating that his sterilization was carried out at too high a temperature. He concluded from work on flies that bacteria were not necessary for normal development. Cohendy [99] thought that the digestive processes could proceed without bacteria but that they aided digestion. Life was thought to be possible without bacteria but bacteria are not indispensable. Kuster removed a kid by Caesarian operation from the mother and maintained it in a sterile condition for 14 days.

Kianizine [100] produced data which he thought weakened the argument of Cohendy. With chickens, Kianizine believed that bacteria were of great aid in digestion. They carried on analytic and synthetic processes which were of much value to the host. Further work was reported in 1916 by the same author. He made guinea pigs breathe sterile air and eat sterile food and found that, even after a few days, they were greatly weakened. The bad results from the deprivation of bacteria was thought to be due to reduced oxidation and accumulation of leucomaines in the body. Loeb and Northrup [101] attempted to determine the ability of flies to synthesize their body proteins without the aid of microorganisms. Larvae grown on sterile media (banana) did not do well, while those placed in a sterile yeast cul-

90. Pasteur. 1885. Compt. Rend. Acad. Sci., 1885, p. 66.
91. Nuttal and Thierfelder. 1895, 1896, 1897. Ztschr. Physiol. Chem., Vols. 21, 22, and 23.
92. Schotellius. 1899, 1908. Arch. Hyg., 34, 210-243; 67 (1908), 177-208.
93. Levin. 1899, 1904. Ann. Inst. Pasteur, 13, 558; Arch. f. Phys., 1904, 249.
94. Metchnikoff. 1901. Ann. Inst. Pasteur, 15, 631.
95. Portier. 1905. Compt. Rend. Soc. Biol., p. 605.
96. Moro. 1905. Jahrb. Kinderheilk. p. 589.
97. Bogdanow. 1908. Rev. in Ann. Inst. Pasteur, 26, 106.
98. Wollman. 1911. Ann. Inst. Pasteur, 25, 79.
99. Cohendy. 1912. Ann. Inst. Pasteur, 26, 106.
100. Kianizine. 1916. J. Physiol., 50, 391-396.
101. Loeb and Northrup. 1906-17. J. Biol. Chem., 27, 309.

ture developed normally. It was thought that yeasts were essential for this species of fly, although the essential element could not be isolated.

It is difficult to appraise the results reported in these early publications. The question may always be raised as to whether they had sterile conditions in their experiments. It has also been suggested that their methods of sterilizing foods may have destroyed vitamins and that failure to observe normal development was due to this factor. There is always the indefiniteness of what is normal development and growth. Perhaps the more recent experiments by Reyniers [101a] will help to settle the question. He reared a *Macacus rhesus* monkey under sterile conditions for 30 days when an accident allowed the the animal to become infected with bacteria.

Number of Bacteria in Feces. Different investigators are not in agreement on this question. This may be due, in part, to different methods of analysis and to the variations in samples. The securing of concordant results is hardly to be expected. The data which are on hand vary from 5 to 50 per cent. Strassburger [104] stated that one-third of the feces of an individual on a normal diet was bacteria. The quantity of daily dried bacterial wastes in adults was as follows:

(a) Eight grams under normal conditions.

(b) In dyspeptic intestinal conditions on an average of 14 grams and even as much as 20 grams.

(c) In chronic constipation 5.5 grams and, at times, even as iittle as 2.6 grams.

The total number of bacteria eliminated by an individual in one day was believed by Strassburger to be 128,000,000,000. Among the determinations which have been made by different investigators are the following, collected by Mattill and Hawk.[105]

	Daily Excretion of Dry Bacteria grams	Pct. of Dry Bacteria
Strassburger	8.0	24.3
Berger and Tsuchiya	3.023	12.60
McNeal, Latzer, and Kerr	5.34	26.90
Mattill and Hawk	8.27	27.97
Sato	8.54	24.39
Schittenhelm and Tollens		42.00
Lissauer		8.67
Tobaya		11.22

Osborne and Mendel [106] found that about 70 per cent of the nitrogen in feces of animals was caused by bacteria. MacNeal, Latzer, and Kerr [107] found most of the bacteria to be dead; the relative number of viable bacteria in human feces to the total count was estimated to be 1 to 3,000.

101a. Reyniers. 1942. J. Bact., 43, 778.
102. Damon. 1921. J. Biol. Chem. 48, 379.
103. Wollman. 1921. Compt. Rend. Soc. Biol. 85, 801-803.
104. Strassburger. 1902. Ztschr. f. Klin. Med., 46, 413.
105. Mattill and Hawk. 1911. J. Expt. Med., 14, 433-443.
106. Osborne and Mendel. 1914. J. Biol. Chem., 18, 177.
107. MacNeal, Latzer, and Kerr. 1909. J. Infect. Dis., 6, 123-169; 571-609.

Vitamin Synthesis by Intestinal Microorganisms. If intestinal micro-organisms are able to synthesize vitamins in the intestinal tract, the animal has an additional source of these necessary agents. This subject has interested microbiologists since the early days of vitamin investigations. Pacini and Russell [108] discovered from observations of clinical observers that in certain infections growth was produced apparently by the infection. In typhoid fever, for instance, the patient might grow one to even several inches in height. Pacini and Russell then stated that this increase in height might be due to the formation of accessory substances by the bacteria. The experimental data were interpreted to prove this contention. Rats on a deficient diet were given typhoid bacilli extract immediately after which there was a gain in weight. Development of scurvy in guinea pigs on a ration of heated oats plus 200 ml. of sterilized milk inoculated 48 hours before with *Lactobacillus bulgaricus* was thought to indicate, according to Wollman,[109] that the organism did not synthesize vitamin C. Similarly, development of polyneuritis in pigeons on a diet of sterilized rice inoculated with "Amylomucor" was also thought to indicate that this mold did not synthesize vitamin B. Evidence was found by Fulmer and his colleagues [110] that bakers' yeast synthesized vitamin B. Addition of two per cent of the yeast grown on a synthetic ration proved sufficient to promote rapid growth in animals declining on the basal ration. About this same time Damon [111] observed no synthesis of vitamin B by *Salmonella schott-mülleri, Escherichia coli,* or *Bacillus subtilis.* Administration of sterilized cultures of these bacteria as the sole source of vitamin B to rats on an otherwise adequate diet, did not stop a continued loss of weight. Further work with *Bacillus adherens,* Friedländer's bacillus, Pfeiffer's bacillus, *Bacillus ramosus capsulatus,* and the "timothy grass bacillus" yielded negative results with exception of Pfeiffer's bacillus and the "timothy grass bacillus," both of which, in amounts equivalent to five per cent of the diet, caused resumption of growth or maintained the animals at constant weight. Three members of the acid-fast group were found to produce vitamin B. Harden and Zilva [112] reported that yeasts grown on synthetic media contain vitamin B but not in as large amounts as those grown on wort. Scheunert and Schieblich [113] observed formation of vitamin B by *Bacillus vulgatus.* Prompt increase in body weight and elevation of temperature to normal of pigeons in a state of nutritive decline when cultures of *Bacillus vulgatus* were fed, were thought to indicate synthesis of vitamin B. Similar observations were made by Zajdel and Funk [114] and Sunderlin and Werkman [115] using various common bacteria and yeasts which would

108. Pacini and Russell. 1918. J. Biol. Chem. 34, 43-49.
109. Wollman. 1921. Compt. Rend. Soc. Biol. 85, 801-803; 86 (1922), 832-833.
110. Fulmer, Nelson, and Sherwood. 1921. J. Amer. Chem. Soc. 43, 186-199; J. Biol. Chem. 46 (1921), 77-81.
111. Damon. 1921. J. Biol. Chem. 48, 379-384; 56 (1923), 895-902; J. Path. and Bact., 27 (1924), 163-169.
112. Harden and Zilva. 1921. Biochem. J., 15, 438-439.
113. Scheunert and Schieblich. 1922. Centbl. Bakt., Pt. 1, Orig., 38, 390-398; Biochem. Ztschr., 139, 47-65.
114. Zajdel and Funk. 1925. Compt. Rend. Soc. Biol. 93, 1527.
115. Sunderlin and Werkman. 1928. J. Bact. 16, 17-33.

be found in the intestinal tract. Results of experiments by Schieblich [116] showed the importance of the culture medium in experimental work on this subject. Vitamin D synthesis by *Azotobacter chroococcum* was observed by Greaves.[117] Similar observations were made for *Clostridium butyricum* and *Staphylococcus albus* but not for *Mycobacterium tuberculosis, Escherichia coli,* and a Corynebacterium, which contained neither sterol nor vitamin D. Several common species of bacteria were reported by Burkholder and McVeigh [2] to produce biotin, riboflavin, thiamine, and niacin in a synthetic medium. Microbiological methods of assay were used. They used *Escherichia coli, Proteus vulgaris, Aerobacter aerogenes, Alcaligines fecalis, Bacillus mesentericus,* and *Bacillus vulgatus.* The quantity of vitamins formed was small and they were contained in the bacterial cell. If this is shown to be the case, a logical argument is available for showing that intestinal bacteria are beneficial, if not necessary for the animal.

Destruction of Vitamins by Intestinal Microorganisms. Another important aspect of intestinal microbiology is the action of microorganisms on vitamins. Much effort is expended to determine vitamin contents of various foods and the effects of processing procedures on them. These foods are fed to animals with the general assumption that, with the help of control animals, some idea may be secured as to the effects of vitamins in foods on development and growth. Complicating this work is the possible effects of intestinal microorganisms, some of which have been shown to decompose vitamins in the intestines. While most of the work has been done with ascorbic acid, it is possible that microorganisms act on other vitamins. This situation is a little confused at the present time probably on account of the fact that not all species act on vitamins in the same manner. Consequently variable results would be expected. They would be determined by the species present in the intestines. Young and James [117a] observed that two intestinal species *Escherichia coli* and *Aerobacter aerogenes* decomposed vitamin C under both aerobic and anaerobic conditions. Members of the genera Alcaligines and Proteus failed to attack the vitamin and produced a substance which protected the vitamin from atmospheric oxidation, but this substance did not function in the presence of vitamin C decomposing bacteria. Glucose and lactose in the nutrient medium also "spared" the vitamin from oxidation by fecal cultures and pure cultures of *Escherichia coli.* The vitamin disappeared from the medium as soon as the sugar had been used. Earlier investigations had shown that bacteria might decompose ascorbic acid, some of which were reviewed by Young and James. Esselen,[117b] on the other hand, had stated that he could find no evidence which would indicate that bacteria are destructive of ascorbic acid and that loss of this factor in food could not be attributed to bacterial action. Esselen based his conclusions on results of an investigation in which 45 different strains, representing 39 species, were used.

116. Schieblich. 1933. Biochem. Ztschr. 259, 19-26.
117. Greaves. 1935. J. Bact., 30, 143-148.
117a. Young and James. 1942. J. Bact., 44, 75.
117b. Esselen. 1939. Food Research 4, 329-334.

Action of Bile on Bacteria. This juice is poured into the intestine just below the pylorus. It is a thick liquid with a decidedly bitter taste. It is made up of salts of glycocholic and taurocholic acids, pigments (bilirubin, biliverdin, etc.), fats, phosphatids, and inorganic salts.

The bile, like most of the other body fluids, is probably sterile when secreted. Toida [118] found that bile of man and dogs was normally sterile, and that it was not a satisfactory medium for all becteria. It was only slightly suited to *Staphylococcus pyogenes aureus* and *Pseudomonas aeruginosa (Ps. pyocyaneus)*. *Streptococcus pyogenes* and *Dip. pneumoniae* were better adapted to it. The bactericidal action was found to vary with the origin. Just below the point of entrance into the intestine, the bacterial flora is much simpler. *Escherichia coli* is often the predominating form.

The regulation of carbohydrate fermentation by bile has been studied by Roger.[119] The hydrolysis of starch was increased up to 30-40 per cent, but when smaller amounts (10 per cent) were used there was a retardation. Heating the bile did not destroy its activity. Moderate amounts of bile (5-20 parts per 100) retarded the action of intestinal bacteria on glycogen. Larger amounts were erratic, causing sometimes a retardation and sometimes an increase in the action. The same was found to be true with regard to glucose. Pure cultures of *Escherichia coli* were inhibited in their action on glucose, moderate amounts exerting a more consistent retarding effect than larger amounts.

Bile also exerts a retarding effect on putrefaction. Roger [120] found that the intensity of the biuret reaction of protein media inoculated with intestinal bacteria in the presence of different amounts of bile, showed that the attack on proteins was retarded. This retardation was evident up to concentration of 20 per cent, after which the retardation decreases. Roger [121] regarded the bile as a factor tending to diminish the production of bacterial enzymes and neutralizing toxins. Boudielle [121] reported that bile, as well as bile salts, had an inhibiting action on the fermenting power of *Escherichia coli* on glucose. Moderate amounts had more pronounced effects than greater amounts. Lagane [122] added bile to bouillon cultures and noticed no retardation in growth of intestinal bacteria. He claimed that it favored the development of *Escherichia coli* at the expense of other species.

Whether the bile is a germicide seems hardly to have been settled. However, most of the data which have been accumulated seem to show that bile exerts a selective action. Toida found that under normal conditions the bile was sterile. In this connection, it is interesting to remember that gall stones may be started by bacteria and that very often typhoid carriers liberate the bacilli in the bile. In these instances the bile seems to exert no bactericidal action, but perhaps a selective action.

118. Toida. 1914. Rev. in Chem. Abs. 8, 2558-2559.
119. Roger. 1912. Arch. Med. Expt. et Anat. Path. 24, 461-488; Compt. Rend. Soc. Biol. 72 (1913), 544-545; *et seq;* Ann Inst. Pasteur 29 (1915), 545-550.
120. Roger. 1913. Compt. Rend. Soc. Biol. 73, 274-276.
121. Boudielle. 1913. Idem 72, 783-785.
122. Lagane. 1914. Idem 73, 242-243.

Bile was shown to have a dissolving action upon pneumococci by Nicolle and Adil-Bey,[123] and earlier by Neufeld. Sodium choleate, the bile salts, and other similar preparations were also found to possess the same action. Farnet [124] reported that fresh bile dissolved typhoid bacilli and Marbais [125] stated that the disappearance of dysentery bacilli from stools of patients was closely correlated with the flow of bile into the intestinal tract. These were regarded as having been destroyed by the bile. To test this Marbais inoculated ox bile which had been heated to 120°C.(248°F.) with different strains of dysentery bacilli. Even 48 hours in contact with the bile failed to kill the bacilli. Van der Reis [126] found bile collected from diseased persons and animals very soon after death to be sterile. A bactericidal action of bile on the pneumococcus and *Bacterium putrificans* was found. *Streptococcus pyogenes* was also inhibited while *Escherichia coli (Bacterium coli)* and *Salmonella schottmülleri (Bacterium paratyphosum B)* seemed to be favored. Less favorable results were secured with *Serratia marcescens (Bacillus prodigiosus)*, *Bacterium dysenteriae*, Flexner, the enterococcus and *Eberthella dysenteriae (Bacterium dysenteriae)* Shiga-Kruse. Knorr,[127] however, found a somewhat destructive action on the Shiga-Kruse type of *Salmonella dysenteriae (Bacterium dysenteriae)*. A small inoculation was generally destroyed, while a heavy inoculation was able to survive and develop. Type Y of the pseudodysentery bacilli was found to resist, which perhaps explains why this organism is so frequently found in the feces. This subject has also been discussed at other places in this book, especially in Chapter 4.

Autointoxication. This has been one of the most interesting subjects in connection with intestinal bacteriology. The term autointoxication was introduced to signify the ill effects following an undue amount of putrefaction in the intestines. Proteins were split to compounds which would diffuse into the blood and cause headache, malaise, and, indirectly, according to Metschnikoff, senility. This latter investigator, who proposed his well-known sour milk therapy, believed that these protein-split products were at the foundation of premature death. This has been referred to again in the chapter on Fermented Milk Products. Very interesting, in this relation, is the paper of Alvarez,[128] in which it is claimed that this so-called "autointoxication" is used as a refuge for "etiologic uncertainty" —the same idea which Jordan has expressed with regard to "ptomaine poisoning." Alvarez claimed that there is little evidence to support the theory of intestinal toxemia. A complete review of the subject was prepared by Alvarez [129] in 1924.

Proteins are decomposed in the intestines by putrefaction into their constituent amino acids, which are, in turn, decomposed according to well-known chemical processes. The amino acids are decomposed by deaminiza-

123. Nicolle and Adil-Bey. 1907. Ann. Inst. Pasteur 21, 20-25.
124. Farnet. 1907. Arch. Hyg., 60, 134-143.
125. Marbais. 1918. Compt. Rend. Soc. Biol. 81, 1136.
126. Van der Reis. 1921. Centbl. Bakt., I., Orig., 86, 337-346.
127. Knorr. 1921. Centbl. Bakt., Pt. 1, Orig., 87, 339-345.
128. Alvarez. 1919. J. Amer. Med. Assoc. 72, 8-13.
129. Alvarez. 1924. Physiol. Rev. 4, 352-393.

tion, decarboxylation, and oxidation. Some of them yield end-products which must be detoxified before excretion. The indican reaction is probably the best known for determining the presence of intestinal putrefaction, although Bergeim [38] suggested another method.

Changes in Bacterial Content of Stored Normal Feces. These changes may be of considerable importance in diagnostic work involving examination of stools. As far as normal feces is concerned, Jordan [130] found that the number of bacteria increases during the first few days of storage. He further observed a decline in numbers after two weeks, although this decline was not universal. The actual number after two or three months' storage was often less than the initial number in the fresh stool, but this was not always the case; in more than one-third of the experiments the colony count was higher at the end of the storage period than at the beginning. The initial changes were followed. Increase in numbers was found to be due almost entirely to an increase in numbers of *Escherichia coli (Bacterium coli)*. This increase was often enormous, amounting to two to three hundred times the original number. Jordan observed these changes at wide limits of temperature: 37, 20, and 10°C. (98.6, 68, and 50°F.).

Attention was also given to the longevity of *Eberthella typhosa (Bacterium typhosum)*, since it had never been studied with modern methods. He found considerable difference in the longevity of *Eberthella typhosa* on different stools. The longest survival period observed by Jordan seems to have been 62 days. This is decidedly longer than that reported by previous investigators.

BACTERIAL STUDY OF FECAL MATERIAL

Specimens of feces for bacteriological examination should be collected in wide-mouth bottles and taken to the laboratory as soon as possible. Marked changes in temperature should be avoided.

Torrey's Technic for the Bacteriological Examination of Fecal Material. The following technic was devised by Torrey [131] for the general study of the intestinal flora. His description is quoted:

PRELIMINARY PROCEDURE

Clinical Material. This should be examined as soon as possible after collection, certainly within two or three hours. The manner of obtaining the material is dependent on the purpose in view. If a bacterial analysis of the rectal region is desired a normal movement may be examined or the material obtained through the aid of a proctoscope, with or without a preliminary catharsis and irrigation, but if that from higher colonic levels is required, some such cathartic agent as epsom salts, phenolphthalein, or citrate of magnesia should be given and the speciment selected from the second or third movements, or better still from the result of a high irrigation with sterile water. Particularly, in cases of colitis it is important to obtain some mucus. This should be well washed in sterile salt solution and part spread on a slide for staining and microscopic examination and part streaked on the purple agar plate medium. (See Chapter 27.) If an examination of material from intestinal segments removed at operation is to be made, some of the lumen content is collected and with it scrapings from the gut wall. This

130. Jordan. 1926. J. Infect. Dis., 38, 306.
131. Torrey. 1926. Idem 39, 352-369.

should be placed in test tubes with rubber stopper and packed in ice prior to examination.

Reaction. The reaction of the material may readily be ascertained by the use of weak, aqueous (neutral) dilutions of the Clark and Lubs indicators, brom-cresol purple, brom-thymol blue or phenol red, according as the reaction is acid, nearly neutral or alkaline. A little of the material, about the size of a pea, is picked up on a glass rod or inoculation loop and rubbed into suspension in a tube containing about 10 ml. of the proper indicator and, after standing for a few minutes to allow for settling or after centrifuging, the color obtained is compared with known H-ion standards. This test should be made as soon as possible after the collection of the specimen.

Preparation of Fecal Suspensions. In order that an examination may have comparative value as regards quantitative bacterial findings, it is necessary to adopt some standard for the degree of density of the primary fecal suspension. The use of a nephelometer of the McFarland type, as recommended by Rettger and Cheplin, has its advantages, but as this or a similar instrument is not generally available, the following simple procedure is recommended and is believed to be sufficiently accurate for the purpose in view:

A small amount of the well-mixed fecal specimen taken up on a glass rod with a small prong at the end, is evenly suspended in about 20 ml. of salt solution in a test tube with an inside diameter of 16 and 17 mm. This is allowed to stand for several minutes to permit the coarse particles to settle and is decanted into another similar tube. A heavy mark with a wax pencil (black preferable) is then made about half way up on the outside of the tube and the density of the suspension adjusted, either by rubbing up more material or by adding salt solution until the mark is just discernible as a faint shadow in looking through the tube toward a strong light. This is labeled tube 1 and from it dilutions are prepared in a series of eight tubes, each containing 9 ml. of salt solution and 1 ml. of the preceding dilution. Tube 9 contains accordingly a 1:100,000,000 dilution of the primary suspension in tube 1. If the latter has been properly prepared, tube 3 will show only a faint cloud, just discernible when viewed in a good light against a dark surface. In the examination of material from the small intestine, the primary suspension is generally much lighter—about equal to the density of tube 2 of the above series.

Five ml. are next removed from each of the dilutions 1, 3, 5, 7, and 9 and are placed in narrow (10 mm. inside diameter) tubes. These are heated in a water bath at 80°C. (176°F.) for 10 minutes, thereby killing all but the strong heat-resistant organisms (chiefly sporebearers, although some streptococcal and *B. aerogenes* types may survive).

Microscopical Examination. Except for special purposes, such as the examination of infant stools, of material from different segments of the intestine, and following the degree of implantation of *B. acidophilus*, gram-stained films of fecal material generally give little or no definite information and may be omitted. If carried out, one of the alkaline modification of the original gram method such as that of Kopeloff and Beerman is recommended. This technic gives a much sharper differentiation than the original method. Mucus spread thinly on slides and air dried, may be stained with this method, with carbol thionin (Lyon-Smith), or with a tubercle bacillus stain, if such a procedure seems called for.

CULTURAL PROCEDURES

Brom-Cresol Purple Lactose Agar. The preparation of this medium has been described in Chapter 26.[132]

Large petri dishes (120 mm. in diameter) are used and plates prepared with the above medium. At least three are desirable for an examination and after the agar has cooled and hardened they are surface-seeded respectively with a large loop (.4 cm. in diameter) of fecal suspensions in tubes 4, 3, and 2. The loop of material should be drawn across one side of the plate and then distributed thoroughly over the whole surface of the medium. If after seeding there is any evidence of moisture on the medium

---

132. Torrey stated that the Difco brand could be used if desired but that the reaction should be adjusted to pH 7.4; he also stated that the medium prepared from fresh meat gave a better differentiation as well as a greater variety of bacterial types.

surface, it should be dried off by partial uncovering and exposing the plate face downward in the incubator for a few minutes.

These plates are incubated for 24 to 48 hours at 37°C.(98.6°F.) and then kept at room temperature for two to three days longer for further study. *Staphylococcus aureus* colonies are particularly conspicuous after this period. They bring to development practically all of the aerobic types in the flora and nothing is to be gained by enrichment with ascitic fluid or a similar agent. This medium has marked differential value and if seeded in accordance with the above directions these plates give quantitative information as well. The *B. coli-aerogenes* group develop as yellowish colonies with a yellow zone. *B. mucosus* forms mucoid colonies with color unchanged or slightly yellowish; *B. typhosus* and *B. dysenteriae* colonies, thin, translucent, smoky hue, with medium unchanged; *B. paratyphosus* (intermediate) group like *B. typhosus* or medium darker purple with blue centers in colonies *(B. morgani, B. alkaligenes)*; *B. proteus*, irregular spreading contours, dark reddish purple zone; *B. pyocyaneus* group, yellow colonies with greenish purple zone. For a general analysis of the flora for specific purposes representative colonies may conveniently be fished and seeded on Russell double agar slants and then carried through differential mediums. A great variety of coccus types develop on these plates. These may be differentiated by fishing representative type colonies and streaking on plain blood agar plates (pH 7.4). The effect on the blood agar, chromogenesis, morphology, and reaction to the gram stain, seeding into differential sugars (lactose, sucrose, salicin, raffinose, and mannitol) and into litmus milk and gelatin stab will generally serve for identification.

Virulence tests for *E. coli* or *B. paratyphosus*-like types may be made by seeding into meat infusion peptone broth (pH 7.0) and incubating for 24 hours. Dilutions of the cultures are made in sterile salt solution to 1:15 and 1:50. Two white mice (20 to 25 gm.) are then inoculated intraperitoneally, one with .5 ml. of the 1:15 and the other with .5 ml. of the 1:50 dilution. As regards the colon types, if the strain is avirulent neithere will die, if moderately virulent the first, but not the second, will die within 48 hours, and if exceptionally so, both mice will die within that period. After inoculation with paratyphoid-like types the mice should be observed for four or five days to cover a more prolonged incubation period.

Reduced Oxygen Tension Plates. The medium for these plates is nutrient glucose agar (meat or liver infusion, 1 per cent peptone, 1.5 per cent agar, .5 per cent glucose, (pH 7.4) to which 10 per cent fresh, defibrinated, sterile blood has been added just before the plates are poured. Deep petri dishes (20 mm.) should preferably be used. Oxygen tension reduction is obtained by *B. subtilis* growth on an opposed agar plate in accordance with the technic recently described by Herrold [133] for gonococcus culture. This was in turn a modification of a method described [134] some years ago in which the Wherry and Oliver technic [135] was adapted to plate cultures.

Two sterile bottoms of deep petri dishes are selected which are exactly of a size. Into one the blood agar medium is poured and when hard is surface-seeded with diluted fecal suspension, drying off, by inverting in the incubator, any obvious surface moisture after seeding. Into the other dish about 10 ml. of a firm nutrient agar, seeded with *B. subtilis* (a type producing a thick growth, such as *B. cereus*, is preferable) is poured. When hard it should be dried off in the incubator until no moisture is visible. These two bottoms are then fitted together and bound with 1-inch wide adhesive tape, and this in turn is covered with broad elastic bands.

One blood plate should be surface-seeded with a large loop (4 mm. diameter) from dilution tube 4, and one from dilution tube 3. They should be incubated for at least 48 hours with the blood agar side uppermost. This method will at times bring to development a surprisingly large variety of organisms, some of which have not been recovered in any other way. *B. bifidus* and *B. acidophilus*, grow particularly well and may be recognized by the brown or chocolate color and morphology of the colonies. At times

133. Herrold. 1921. J. Amer. Med. Assoc., 76, 225.
134. Torrey. 1917. J. Bact., 2, 435.
135. Wherry and Oliver. 1916. J. Bact., 19, 288.

the colony count for these plates is many times that for aerobic plates seeded from the same fecal dilution and on the same medium.

Cooked Meat Medium. This medium is prepared according to the original description by Robertson,[136] except that peptone is added and the reaction adjusted to pH 7.2.

Just before seeding, the seven tubes necessary for the examination are placed in the Arnold for 15 minutes and then cooled to 45°C.(113°F.). One tube is next seeded with 1 ml. of unheated dilution 5 of the specimen, placing the tip of the pipette rather deep in the meat, and one tube with 1 ml. of the unheated suspension 1. Five other tubes are seeded respectively with 1 ml. from dilutions 9, 7, 5, 3, and 1, heated at 80°C.(176°F.). The height of the meat column in each tube is then registered by a wax pencil mark on the glass, and all are capped by running about 5 ml. of melted, warm, sterile, yellow vaseline on the surface of the fluid in each tube. They are then incubated at 37°C.(98.6°F.) and are examined after 1, 3, and 6 or 7 days. At each observation the degree of digestion is measured in millimeters as shown by the decrease in the meat column height, the amount of gas noted (elevation of the vaseline cap) and also changes which may have occurred in the color and composition of the meat as indicated in the table. The tube seeded with the unheated fecal suspension 1 yields information particularly in reference to the putrefactive propensities of the whole flora. If the decrease in the meat column height amounts within a week to 1.5 to 2 cm. an unusually marked putrefactive propensity is indicated; if between 1 and 1.5 cm. a fairly marked; and less than 1 cm. a moderate to slight tendency. The digestion is very largely due to the sporebearing anaerobes.

Microscopic Examination of the Feces. Direct microscopic examination of the feces may give valuable information on the microbiological relationships in the intestines. Iodophile bacteria are colored blue with iodin.

Methods for Determining the Number of Bacteria in Feces. There are many factors which complicate such determinations. The accurate enumeration is not easy and consequently, a number of different methods have been proposed. It is difficult to separate the bacteria from the other material in feces, and this complicates the counting of the bacteria by either the microscope or chemical methods. Plating out on agar or gelatin would be inadequate. Only living bacteria could be counted and several types of plates would have to be prepared in order to count both the aerobic and anaerobic forms.

MacNeal's (et al.) Modification of the Winterberg Method. The first employment of the Thoma-Zeiss blood-counting chamber for bacteriological technic was made in the one-cell dilution method of obtaining a pure culture. By this method the number of cells per unit volume could be ascertained and the dilution per unit volume of a suspension with one cell in two to five drops required to obtain a suspension with one cell in two to five drops calculated. In this way the first pure bacterial culture was obtained. Henrich Winterberg was the first to use this method of bacterial counting, and to test its accuracy both as regards suspensions of varying dilutions and in comparison with the microscopic plate-counting method. He considers the method more accurate than the plate-counting method, but as a quantitative procedure he would consider it unimportant. He says his determinations were too low. Winterberg's counts were made with suspensions of living bacteria in bacteria-free distilled water.

The method, as used by MacNeal, Latzer, and Kerr, is as follows: a portion of the 1:100 suspension of feces is diluted 10 times, and a portion of this is drawn up to the mark 1 in the capillary of a dilution pipette, ordinarily used in estimating the white blood cells. This is diluted to the mark 11 with a dilute solution of methylene blue in physiological-salt solution. (The staining solution consists of methylene blue, 1 gm.; glycerine, 25 ml.; distilled water, 75 ml. A few drops of this are mixed with

136. Robertson. 1916. J. Path. and Bact., 20, 327.

10 ml. of .8 per cent salt solution until the mixture is well colored, but not too opaque. This mixture is used as the diluting fluid. A little practice will show the proper depth of color to be employed.) The suspension is thoroughly mixed in the bulb by shaking and rolling in the usual manner. Several drops are blown out and then a very small drop is placed in the center of the circular elevated portion of the slide, which has been previously thoroughly cleansed by washing in distilled water and alcohol. A clean, thin, ground cover slip is made slightly moist by breathing upon it and is immedia'tely placed upon the slide. Slight pressure upon it causes the Newton color rings to appear, and these remain after the pressure is removed, if the preparation has been properly made. The slide is allowed to stand one to two hours to allow the bacteria to settle. Then the bacteria in 50 small squares upon the scale are counted microscopically, the No. 7 Leitz objective and No. 3 ocular being used. The calculation is simple as an example will show:

"Example. B252, Subject H, July 15, 1908. Fifty squares contain 400 bacteria. Therefore the average per square is 8.0 bacteria. One small square = 1/4000 c.mn. One c.mn. contains 8 × 4000 = 32,000 bacteria. One milliliter contains 32,000 × 1000 = 32,000,000 bacteria. Pipette dilution is 1:10. 32,000,000 × 10 = 320,000,000 bacteria per milliliter of 1/1000 suspension. One milliliter of 1/000 suspension is equivalent to 1 mg. feces. Therefore, there are 320,000,000 bacteria per milligram feces.

"Counting by this method is an exacting process and much practice is required to see all the bacteria present. Careful adjustment of the light is important and best results have been obtained by illumination with Welsbach light; constant focusing through the different layers is necessary. Perhaps the greatest source of error is the difficulty of distinguishing accurately the bacteria. Skill in this is acquired only by practice. The method has the advantage of simplicity. The results of the authors seem to conform to those of Winterberg in that high dilutions give a relatively high count."

MacNeal's (et al.) [107] **Modification of the Eberle-Klein Method for Determining the Number of Bacteria in Feces.** Eberle, working in Escherich's laboratory, was the first to determine the quantity of fecal bacteria by counting them in stained films. His experiments were carried out with normal infants' stools. Cover-glass preparations were made from fecal suspensions of known dilution and, after being completely dried, were stained with freshly prepared aniline water fuchsin, then washed in water, air-dried, mounted in Canada balsam, and counted. The method was very much improved by Alex, Klein, and Hehewerth. Klein had noticed that vegetative bacteria were more sensitive to disinfectants in a moist than a dry state, and this led him to believe that bacteria would also be stained more readily in a moist condition than after drying. Therefore, he allowed the dye to act while the bacteria were suspended in a liquid and the cover-glass preparation was made, dried, and fixed, only after the bacteria were stained. Later the same investigator modified the method still further, using gelatin to fix the stained bacteria to the cover glass. The aqueous solution of gelatin and the stained bacterial emulsion were put upon the cover-glass separately, then fixed and spread. When dry, the preparation was immediately mounted in Canada balsam without flaming.

The procedures as employed by MacNeal, Latzer, and Kerr have been considerably modified. In the addition of the gelatin to the bacterial suspension, in spreading the films, in selecting the fields to be counted, and in counting individuals, rather than groups, as units, the technic differs from Klein's method. Of the 1:100 suspension of the feces prepared as described above, 2½ ml. are transferred to a clean, dry bottle, ½ ml. of melted nutrient gelatin and 2 ml. of aniline water gentian violet added, and the whole thoroughly mixed and allowed to stand for three to five minutes. Then by means of a platinum loop, the carrying capacity of which has been determined with great care, a loopful of the mixture, well shaken. immediately before, is transferred to a clean, flamed 20 mm. square No. 1 cover glass and deposited near the center of the glass. Immediately another cover glass of the same size is accurately placed on top of the first so that the two glasses are in contact over about three-quarters of their surfaces and the sides evenly fitted together. As soon as the liquid has spread evenly between the two cover glasses, they are quickly slipped apart and allowed to dry. The technic here is the same as ordinarily used in the preparation of cover glass blood films. If the preparation does not appear evenly spread, the process is to be repeated with two or more cover glasses until a satisfactory result is obtained. The films are next accurately measured by a millimeter rule and then, without further treatment, mounted in Canada balsam upon one slide so that one diagonal of each rectangular film is parallel with the long axis of the slide. By laying the slide over the coordinate paper these diagonals are readily brought into the same line parallel with the edge of the slide.

The covers must be so mounted that these diagonals, now in a straight line, are those which crossed each other as the two cover glasses were originally put together in preparing the films. When properly made, each diagonal measures almost exactly 25 mm.

For counting the bacteria in the preparation, the Leitz 1/12 oil immersion objective and the No. 3 ocular fitted with an Ehrlich ocular square to restrict the field to a convenient size and a mechanical stage graduated in millimeters are employed. Beginning at the end of the diagonal of one cover glass the bacteria are counted in each of 25 fields 1 mm. apart along this diagonal. In a similar way 25 fields are counted on the diagonal of the second cover glass, making a total of 50 fields, the average of which may be considered as representative of both films. The size of the square field is accurately measured by a stage micrometer. From the data then at hand, the number of bacteria per milligram feces is calculated.

"Example. B252, Subject H, July 15, 1908. In the preparation made, as described, each film measures 16.5×17.55 mm., total film area therefore, 33×17.5 mm.; the field employed measured 0.0445 mm. square; the amount carried by the loop 2.01 mg.; the number of bacteria counted in 50 fields was 559 and the original 1:100 suspension was used (diluted to 1:200 by dye and gelatin). From these data, Bacteria per milli-

$$\text{gram feces} = \frac{559 \times 33 \times 17.5 \times 200}{50 \times 0.0445 \times 0.0445 \times 2\text{-}01} = 324{,}000{,}000.$$ In this fraction all the members except the size of the films and the number of bacteria counted may be kept constant and the calculation simplified by the use of logarithmic tables.

"With apparatus and reagents ready and the 1:100 suspension prepared, this entire estimation can be completed in about 40 minutes. The results cannot be considered very accurate as the platinum loop does not carry an exactly constant quantity. There is also sometimes great difficulty in distinguishing micrococci from other fine particles in the preparations. The concentration of the bacterial suspension also influences the final result. The estimation is in general relatively higher when dilute suspensions are counted as we have observed in applying it to enumeration of bacteria in pure cultures."[107]

Steele's Modification of the Strassburger Procedure for the Quantitative Enumeration of Fecal Bacteria. Steele described the method as follows: The possibility of separating the bacteria from the rest of the feces depends on the fact that the bacteria are so nearly of the same specific gravity as distilled water that they cannot be centrifugalized out of a watery suspension of the feces, but remain suspended in the supernatant fluid. Taking advantage of this, the bacteria can be removed by washing with the centrifuge. Then, if the specific gravity of the wash-water is lowered by the addition of large amounts of alcohol, the relation of the bacteria to the fluid is changed to such an extent that the microorganisms can be readily centrifugalized out, separated, and weighed. Unless the period of passage of the feces has been ascertained to be normal, it is better to mark the beginning and end of each period of examination by carmine. The end of the Schmidt diet is not necessary. The whole stool is saved. Unless the feces are liquid they are rubbed up with a known amount of distilled water until they are smooth and semiliquid and as homogeneous as it is possible to make them.

Two portions of 5 ml. are measured off with a pipette of large caliber, using for this purpose an ordinary 5-ml. pipette with the tapering end cut off, and with the necessary correction made at the upper mark. One of these portions of 5 ml. is put into a porcelain dish and dried over a water bath and later in a drying oven, in order to determine the dried weight. The addition of a little alcohol and thorough mixing will hasten the process of drying and prevent caking of the feces.

The second portion is washed free from bacteria. This is done as follows: The wash-water is .5 to 1 per cent HCl solution in distilled water. The acid increases the solubility of the salts and soaps of the feces. One hundred ml. of this solution is employed at the beginning of the washing. The feces are thoroughly mixed with the wash solution and then centrifugalized. The use of the water motor or electric centrifuge is almost essential. Each tube is centrifugalized for about 1½ minutes, then the cloudy supernatant liquid is poured through a layer of gauze. This fluid contains the bacteria in suspension. All of the mixture (the wash-water and the feces) is centrifugalized the same way, and then the residue in the tubes is shaken up with more of the wash-water and centrifugalized again. This is repeated until the supernatant liquid after the centrifugalizing is transparent, showing that approximately all the bacteria have been washed out. If a smear is made of the residue at this point, it will be found that the bacteria are not entirely washed away, but are evidently very much reduced. They occur singly, while in the unwashed feces they are in great lumps and masses. The suspension of bacteria is then mixed with a liberal portion of alcohol, and evaporated down slowly at a temperature of 40 to 50°C. (104 to 122°F.) until it amounts to not more than 50 ml. in all. This takes approximately 24 hours. It is then mixed with at least twice its volume of alcohol, preferably absolute alcohol, although this is not absolutely necessary. This lowers the specific gravity of the fluid to such an extent that now the bacteria readily centrifugalize out. The mixture is then centrifugalized until the supernatant liquid is quite clear. This takes 30 minutes or more for each tube. The residue, which consists of the bacteria, is washed with pure alcohol and is shaken up with ether to remove the fat; then it is again washed with alcohol. All of this washing is done by means of the centrifuge. The bacteria are next washed out of the tube with a little alcohol and evaporated to dryness and dried in the oven at moderate heat, dried in the desiccator, and weighed. Smears of the final preparation show that it consists of bacteria with a very few minute particles of other material. These particles are only visible with high power, and are very few in number, perhaps two at each field of the 1/12-inch objective. They stain with methylene blue; Strassburger suggests that they are cellulose, which they may well be. At any rate, the error arising from the inclusion of these small particles in the dried weight of the bacteria must be very small, and is probably balanced by the bacteria that it is not possible to wash out of the residue in the first washing. During the preparation of the bacteria the first portion of 5 ml. has been dried and weighed. We then know the dried weight of 5 ml., the weight of the dried bacteria in 5 ml., the original volume of the stool, and the volume after the addition of a known amount of water. It is then easy to calculate the data that we desire, namely the volume of the stool, its dried weight, the weight of the dried bacteria, and the percentage of bacteria in the dried weight.

Mattil and Hawk's [105] **Method for Quantitative Determination of Fecal Bacteria.** The method is a simplification of MacNeal's adaptation of the Strassburger procedure. About 2 grams of feces are accurately weighed and placed in a 50-ml. centrifuge tube. To the feces in the tube a few drops of .2 per cent hydrochloric acid are added, and the material is mixed to a smooth paste by means of a glass rod. Further amounts of the acid are added with continued crushing and stirring until the material is thoroughly suspended. The tube is then whirled in the centrifuge at high speed for one-half to one minute. The suspension is found sedimented in more or less definite layers, the uppermost of which is fairly free from larger particles. The upper and more liquid portion of the suspension is now drawn off by means of a pipette and transferred to a beaker. The sediment remaining in the tube is again rubbed up with a glass rod with the addition of further amounts of dilute acid, and again centrifugalized for one-half to one minute. The supernatant liquid is pipetted off and added to the first, the same pipette being used for the one determination throughout. A third portion of the dilute acid is then added to the sediment, which is again mixed by stirring and again centrifugalized. All the washings are added to the first one and, during the process, care is taken to wash the material from the wall and mouth of the centrifuge down into it.

Finally, when the sediment is sufficiently free from bacteria, the various remaining particles are visibly clean, and the supernatant liquid, after centrifugalization, remains almost clear. This is removed to the beaker in which are now practically all of the bacteria present in the original portion of feces, together with some solid matter not yet separated. In the centrifuge tubes there is a considerable amount of bacteria-free solid matter.

The suspension is now transferred to the same centrifuge tube, centrifugalized for a minute, and the supernatant liquid transferred to a clean beaker by means of the same pipette. The tube is then refilled from the first beaker and thus all the suspension centrifugalized a second time. The beaker is finally carefully washed with the aid of a rubber-tipped glass rod, the second sediment in the centrifuge tube is washed free of bacteria by means of this wash-water and the successive portions of the dilute acid, and the supernatant liquid, after centrifugalization, is added to the contents of the second beaker. The second clean sediment is added to the first. The bacterial suspension now in the second beaker is again centrifugalized in the same way and a third portion of bacteria-free sediment is separated. Frequently a fourth serial centrifugalization is performed—always if the third sediment is of appreciable quantity. At all stages of the separation, small portions of the dilute hydrochloric acid are used, so that the final suspension shall not be too voluminous. Ordinarily it amounts to 125 to 200 ml. At the same time, the final amount of fluid should not be too small, as shown by Ehrenpfordt, ʰecause the viscosity accompanying increased concentration prevents proper and complete sedimentation.

To the final bacterial suspension an equal volume of alcohol is added and the beaker set aside to concentrate. A water bath at 50 to 60°C.(122 to 140°F.) is very satisfactory. After two or three days, when the liquid is concentrated to about 50 ml., the beaker is removed and about 200 ml. of alcohol are added. The beaker is covered and allowed to stand at room temperature for 24 hours. At the end of this time the bacterial substance is generally settled, so that most of the clear supernatant liquid, of dark brown color, can be directly siphoned off without loss of solid matter. The remainder is then transferred to centrifuge tubes, centrifugalized, and the remaining clear liquid pipetted off. The sediment consists of the bodies of the bacteria, and is transferred to a Kjeldahl flask for nitrogen determination. This is the bacterial nitrogen. Where a determinaton of bacterial dry substance is desired, the sediment of bacteria is extracted by absolute alcohol and ether in succession, transferred to a weighed porcelain crucible, and dried at 102°C.(215.6°F.) to constant weight. This dried sample is then used in the nitrogen determination. Our procedure differs from that of MacNeal in that the bacterial dry matter is not determined. A saving of about seven days' time and of considerable labor is accomplished by this omission.

Inasmuch as it has been shown by various investigators that such bacteria as are present in the feces contain on the average about 11 per cent of nitrogen, the values for bacterial nitrogen as determined by our method may conveniently serve as a basis for the calculation of the actual output of bacterial substance.

CHAPTER 14

MICROBIOLOGY OF FRUITS AND FRUIT PRODUCTS

Fresh fruits may possess a varied flora of microorganisms, the number and types of which are determined by conditions under which fruits have been grown. Nature has provided many of them with protective coverings which shield the fruits from microbial decomposition as long as they are intact. Once the covering is broken, however, microorganisms enter readily. Presence of much acid and sugar in fruit juices makes them especially suitable for yeasts and molds.

Microorganisms on Fresh Fruits. Microorganisms on fresh fruits have a several-fold interest for food technologists. They may be spoilage organisms which must be destroyed in any preservation process to which the food may be subjected later, or they may be organisms which are desirable if the fruits or their juices are to be fermented. Lastly, they may be pathogenic and introduce health hazards later if the fruits are eaten raw and without washing or sterilization. Various investigators have reported results of investigations on the general flora of microorganisms present. As would be expected many different species and types are found. Some of the earlier work was carried out by Hansen,[1] Delbrück,[2] and others with grapes because it was necessary to know what effect the general flora might have on fermentation of the grape juice. Yeasts were reported by Hansen to be commonly present in the soil of vineyards where they spent the winter. While they were also found in the soil of beech and oak groves, they were not as common as in the soil of vineyards. They reached the grape by means of dust and insects. Smeall[3] found various microorganisms on fruits. On dates which were in boxes from Iraq and Tunis *Bacillus subtilis* and allied species were found; about half of the samples showed streptococci. Yeasts were found on the grapes. Cherries had a general flora quite like that of the other fruits examined.

Mold spores are commonly prevalent on citrus fruits and are responsible for spoilage. Mechanical injury and spore loads, according to Tomkins,[4] should be kept at a minimum. Molds are especially troublesome on citrus fruits on which they develop with ease when the resistance of the fruit is lowered owing to age or injury.

Microorganisms in Inner Structures of Fruits. Most information on microorganisms in fruits concerns the outside surface, for it is that area which would most likely be heavily contaminated. One or two investigators (Romwalter and Kiraly[5]) have reported presence of microorganisms in the inner structures of fruits, seeds, and plant tissue as well as in the sap. Similar results were reported by Niethammer.[6]

1. Hansen. 1881. Compt. Rend. Lab. Carlsberg 1, Pt. 4.
2. Delbrück. 1892. Veröffentl. K. Gsndhtsamt. 42, October 19.
3. Smeall. 1932. Brit. Med. J., Nov. 19, 1932, 917-919.
4. Tomkins. 1936. J. Soc. Chem. Ind. 55, 66T-70T.
5. Romwalter and Kiraly. 1939. Arch. Mikrobiol., 10, 13-25.
6. Niethammer. 1939. Idem, 87.

Presence and Survival of Pathogenic Bacteria on Fruits. Since many fruits are eaten without sterilization, experiments have been carried out to determine whether pathogenic bacteria could survive for significant periods. This subject is especially important in places where sanitation is not practiced or where night-soil may be used as a fertilizer. Numerous reports have also been published on the presence of pathogenic bacteria on fruits and their possible relationship to disease dissemination. Ehrlich,[7] Abbott,[8] Rommel,[9] Ressel,[10] Neumann,[11] Clauditz,[12] and Sartory and Fillasier,[13] all reported that fruits may carry not only indicators of pollution but even pathogenic bacteria. The last-mentioned investigators studied fruits exposed for sale on Paris street stands and found that they carried a large number of organisms, the principal species being *Penicillium glaucum, Rhizopus nigricans, Staphylococcus aureus, Bacillus termo, Bacillus subtilis,* and *Micrococcus candicans.* Washing removed a large proportion of the bacteria; lower numbers were found in the second and third wash waters as compared with the first. The authors concluded that sale of fruits intended for consumption without cooking should be subject to regulation. Abbott[8] found pathogenic bacteria and organisms of sanitary significance on grapes and berries exposed for sale on sidewalk stands. The danger of disease dissemination by raw fruits is probably not as great in America as it is in countries where the great epidemic diseases are rampant. Vasquet-Colet,[14] who investigated the subject for three epidemic diseases, typhoid fever, cholera, and dysentery, found that *Vibrio comma* survived on human food for as long as six days.

Cholera epidemics in India have been related by Bharucha and Bharucha[15] to consumption of watermelons. While the whole fruit was sterile, cut slices sold on the open market were contaminated with dust organisms. The maximum survival of the organism in artificially inoculated watermelon was six days. Growth appeared in watermelon juice as acid as pH 4.7.

The survival time for the etiologic agents of the other two diseases was not much different. Garcia[16] reported the results of a short study of common fruits (apples, lemons, oranges, and bananas) since these fruits are usually eaten raw. *Escherichia coli* was always present. The Medical Officers of Health of Cardiff, Wales,[17] have twice found *Bacillus anthracis* on hides bound around orange boxes shipped from Spain. This organism might thus reach the fruit. Johnston and Kaake[18] found members of the colon-dysentery group on fresh fruits purchased on the Toronto market. These are generally accepted as the cause of summer diarrhea in

7. Ehrlich. 1901. Arch. Hyg., 41, 152.
8. Abbott. 1910. Texas State Bd. Health Bull. 4, 16-18.
9. Rommel. 1902. Wchnschr. Brau., p. 176.
10. Ressel. 1907. Univ. of Berlin, Dissertation.
11. Neumann. 1910. Deut. Med. Wchnschr., p. 2046.
12. Clauditz. 1904. Hyg. Rundschau 14, 865.
13. Sartory and Fillasier. 1909. Compt. Rend. Soc. Biol. 66, 445.
14. Vasquet-Colet. 1924. Philippine J. Sci., 24, 35-40.
15. Bharucha and Bharucha. 1938. J. Univ. Bombay, 6, 35-40.
16. Garcia. 1911. Penn. Health Dept., Ann. Rpt., Pt. 2, 1022-1024.
17. J. Amer. Med. Assoc. 80 (1927), 1627.
18. Johnston and Kaake. 1935. Amer. J. Pub. Health 25, 945-947.

children and are therefore of some hygienic significance. *Shigella dysenteriae*, Sonne, artificially inoculated into a tomato, was recovered after two but not after six days and from apple after six but not after eight days. Further information on the longevity of pathogenic microorganisms on fruits was reported by McCleskey and Christopher [19] whose experiments involved strawberries inoculated with aqueous suspensions of pathogenic bacteria just before freezing. Their results are given later in this chapter. Giuffrida [20] found no *Mycobacterium tuberculosis* on fruits. Such bacterial agents of disease are probably not as widespread in nature as those mentioned above.

The conditions which obtain on the surface of fruits are, apparently, not inimical to the organisms of typhoid fever and cholera. In addition to the facts quoted above are the conclusions of Murillo [21] and Ko.[22] The former sprayed fruits with cultures of *Vibrio comma* and *Eberthella typhosa*. Juice from half-ripe fruit exerted a stronger action than fully ripened fruit. The vegetable acids were ranked as follows in their action: tannic, citric, tartaric, and malic. Lemonades were decidedly germicidal. The juices from some oranges, mango, and watermelon were devoid of action. Alliot [23] confirmed these results for lemon juice and white wine. Under the conditions of his experiments the minimum time for lemon juice to kill *Eberthella typhosa* was 15 minutes; *Salmonella paratyphi*, 15 minutes; and *Salmonella schottmülleri*, 20 minutes. In this connection should be mentioned the experience of certain investigators that lemon juice in home-canned vegetables exerts a destructive action on *Clostridium botulinum* and its toxin. However, others have not confirmed this.

Morel and Rochaix [24] employed the thread method of Koch for studying the effect of certain vegetable essences on bacteria. The following essences were used: lemon, thyme, orange, bergamot, juniper, clove, citron, lavender, mint, eucalyptus, and several others. Threads impregnated with the above organisms in pure culture were suspended over three ml. of these essences in test tubes. The vapors from lemon, thyme and orange were most effective. A long contact was necessary. These results are in accord with that of Thöni,[25] who found that the bacterial content of fresh lemonade progressively decreased. Guyot [26] reported a viscous fermentation of this product.

Conn-Cholodny's Method for Microbiological Examination of Fruits and Vegetables During Storage. This procedure, developed for use in the field of soil microbiology, was adapted to examination of fruits by Shtrobindev and Driabina.[27] The surface of the fruit is first sterilized with alcohol and a cut is made with a sharp sterile knife through the section to be investigated, such as a spoiled portion surrounded by healthy tissue. A clean, sterile microscope slide is then inserted into the cut after first spreading the sides; the fruit is then pressed against the slide and the crack sealed with sterile

19. McCleskey and Christopher. 1941. J. Bact. 41, 98-99.
20. Giuffrida. 1938. Gior. Batteriol. e. Immunol. 21, 506-510.
21. Murillo. 1919. Plus-Ultra, Madrid 2, 115.
22. Ko. 1917. Rev. in Chem. Abs. 13. 462.
23. Alliot. 1919. Compt. Rend. Soc. Biol. 82, 457-459.
24. Morel and Rochaix. 1921. Compt. Rend. Soc. Biol. 86, 933-934.
25. Thöni. 1911. Centbl. Bakt., Pt. 2, 29, 616.
26. Guyot. 1927. Compt. Rend. Soc. Biol. 97, 857-859.
27. Shtrobindev and Driabina. 1935. Microbiologïa (Russia) 4, 379-384; Biol. Abs. 11, 145.

collodion. After incubation of the fruit for seven to 21 days, the slide is removed, dried, and stained. From examination under the microscope the type of microflora may be determined.

Washing and Disinfection of Fruits. While washing removes many microorganisms from the surface of fruits, it is frequently not enough. Sterilizing treatments may be desirable for destruction of harmful microorganisms. Champion and Van de Velde [28] studied especially the significance of *Escherichia coli*. Strawberries, lettuce, and carrots, when rinsed in .2-per cent solution of chloride of lime, were reasonably well disinfected. After exposure to this solution for 30 minutes, *Escherichia coli* was destroyed and the total number of bacteria greatly reduced. The organoleptic properties were not altered. Herfarth [29] placed fruits in a solution containing 4.5 grams of chloride of lime per liter and allowed the solution to act. With stronger solutions shorter times were required for sterilization. The disinfectant may be easily removed from the fruits by careful washing.

Many attempts have been made to rid apples of undesirable bacteria before pressing. Parville [30] used formaldehyde for this purpose, while Alliot and Gimel [31] used chloride of lime.

The practice in the Orient of fertilizing the soil in which vegetables and fruits are grown with human excreta caused Mills, Bartlett, and Kessel [32] to study the sanitary features of foods grown under such conditions. Several fruits and vegetables from the market were examined for sterility of the interior structures; all were found to be sterile. Fruits first sterilized in chlorine water and then immersed in broth containing *Escherichia coli* were found to have viable organisms on their surfaces after exposure for at least 15 days under dry or moist conditions. The bruised areas of fruits and the cut ends of vegetables after similar exposure contained viable organisms, but the main portions remained sterile. Attempts to sterilize fruit contaminated in this way were successful in the case of chlorine water, 10 parts per million for 15 minutes, and boiling water for 10 to 20 seconds, and were partially successful in the case of soap and water and chlorine water, three to six parts per million. Matsuoka and Shiraiwa,[33] when experimenting with the chlorine compounds as disinfectants for fruits, found that long times and too high concentrations were required when the fruits were cut up. However, the surfaces of apples were effectively sterilized by 30 minutes' exposure to a solution containing 50 p.p.m. of available chlorine. Lombardo [34] treated apples, pears, grapes, peaches, lettuce, celery, and fennel with various disinfectants for different lengths of times. Some were inoculated with pure cultures of *Eberthella typhosa*, *Vibrio colerae*, and Salmonella species. Satisfactory disinfection was secured with chlorinated lime (20.7 per cent available chlorine) after 30 minutes' treatment with a 1.5-per cent solu-

28. Champion and Van de Velde. 1921. J. Amer. Med. Assoc., 7, (1921) 1511-12.
29. Herfarth. 1921. Cent. Bakt., Pt. 1, Orig., 86, 33-44.
30. Parville. 1906. Amer. Soc. Hart. Allier., 296-301.
31. Alliot and Gimel. 1909. 1909. Compt. Rend. Acad. Sci., 149, 532-534.
32. Mills Bartlett, and Kessel. 1925. Amer. J. Hyg., 5, 559-579.
33. Matsuoka and Shiraiwa. 1927. Sci. Rpt. Govt. Inst. Infect. Dis., 6, 223-235.
34. Lombardo. 1927. Ann. Igiene 3, 298-306.

tion. Excess chlorine was removed by washing the fruits and vegetables in dilute sodium thiosulfate. Formalin was also satisfactory in five-per cent solution. After 30 to 40 minutes' treatment the materials were washed in clean water. Pathogenic microorganisms were destroyed, and taste and appearance were not changed. Chlorinated lime was also found to be satisfactory by Vendramini.[35] After treatment with one-per cent solution and rinsing in clean water, strawberries which had been soaked in a suspension of *Eberthella typhosa* were disinfected. Several different types of wine were also tested with unsatisfactory results. None of the wines sterilized the strawberries in 30 minutes and some failed to do so in three hours. There seemed to be little relation between the alcohol and acid content of the wine and disinfecting power. Lemon juice failed to sterilize the strawberries in one hour.

Hot water may also be used for disinfecting some fruits where slight changes caused by it are of no consequence. Ommyoji[36] stated that grapes suffered no deterioration by passage through water at 80°C.(176°F.), but the bacilli on them were killed; on pears with decayed spots, they were not killed.

Role of Sugar in Preservation of Fruits. Sugar sirups play a large role in fruit preservation. They not only bring out fruit flavors but inhibit development of microorganisms. When heat is also used most microorganisms are destroyed. In studying this, Bitting[37] observed no preservative effects of sugar until the amount of sugar had reached 25 grams per 100 ml. of bouillon. For studying the restraining action of sugar against molds, solutions were prepared containing amounts of sugar up to 200 grams per 100 ml. of bouillon. The growth of the molds became slower up to 170 grams per 100 ml. and above that amount it required two months to secure growth. Yeasts were not able to survive 80 grams of sugar in 100 ml. Barnard[38] studied the subject directly for fruits. First, sirups were prepared by both the hot and cold methods, containing 8, 10, 12, 14, and 16 pounds of sucrose per gallon of water. A few lots of the 10- and 12-pound sirups developed mold in a week. Then crushed fruits were prepared, as for soda-fountain use, by adding one part of fruit to two parts of simple sirup. Barnard reported that fruits in sufficiently heavy sirups would keep for some time if kept cold. Experiments of a similar nature were made by Grove[39] on jams, jellies, and preserves. When 50 per cent of sugar was present, yeasts and bacteria did not develop. In a 45-per cent concentration growth took place if the acidity was below .8 per cent, but was completely stopped when it was over 1.2 per cent. Addition of 1.5 per cent of salt also stopped the development of yeasts and bacteria. A sugar concentration of 65 per cent was required to stop the growth of *Penicillium glaucum*, and there was feeble growth after a month of 70

35. Vendramini. 1939. Gior. Batteriol. e. Immunol., 22, 795, 805.
36. Ommyoji. 1931. J. Oriental Med., 14.
37. Bitting. 1909. U. S. Dept. Agr., Bur. Chem. Bull. 119.
38. Barnard. 1909. Pharm. Era. 42, 199-201.
39. Grove. 1918. Rev. in Expt. Sta. Rec., 42, 114.

per cent concentration. Tarkow, Fellers, and Levine [40] observed more inhibitory action of glucose than sucrose in equal concentrations. Mixtures of these sugars showed an inhibitory action intermediate between that of each sugar when used alone. A greater number of sugars were studied by Erickson and Fabian.[41] Their order of activity with the organisms used was fructose, dextrose, sucrose, and lactose. Thermophilic bacteria were more susceptible to the action of sugar than *Streptococcus lactis* and *Streptococcus liquefaciens*. Yeasts were more resistant than bacteria. Lactose had no preserving value with the yeasts studied. These authors also studied the effects of acids alone and in combination with these sugars.

The high moisture and sugar content of jellies, jams, and marmalades makes them quite susceptible to spoilage by yeasts and molds. Various factors influence the type and rapidity of such spoilage. Bitting [42] used two yeasts and two molds in experimental packs to determine the effect of such variables as vacuum, temperature, acidity, and type of closure. Yeasts developed in a vacuum as high as 25 inches and were normal in appearance. *Oidium lactis* was not harmed by this vacuum but the Aspergillus species was inhibited. Bitting said that a temperature of 65.5°C. (150°F.) was sufficient to inhibit yeasts when the glasses were reversed for two minutes. However, with heavy yeast infection, heating to 71°C. (160°F.) was not sufficient for sterilization. Acidity to two per cent or more aided greatly in sterilization.

Drying of Fruits. Dried fruits are by no means devoid of microbial life. They do not undergo spoilage, however, as long as the moisture content is kept low. How low it must be depends on many factors. Prescott [43] found few dry foods to be sterile. Long storage, however, caused the number of microorganisms to become much lower. Mold spores were more prevalent than other organisms. Yeasts are commonly found in dried fruits. According to Clague [44] the microbial content of dried foods may vary from a few thousand per gram as a maximum on dried fruits up to several millions per gram on dried vegetables. Greater reductions in the bacterial load were noticed with fruits than with vegetables. The fruits examined by Clague were prunes, raisins, and apricots. These were used because they represented the dried fruits usually sold on the market. Numbers of organisms on the prunes were very low, 80 bacteria per gram being the highest count obtained. Molds were present on all samples but yeasts were found on only one sample. A maximum number of bacteria on dried apricots was 850 per gram; yeasts were not encountered on any of the samples, and molds were demonstrated on only one sample. The low number of microorganisms on the apricots may be explained by the fact that they had been sulfured. More molds were found on raisins than on prunes or apricots. The steaming applied to raisins to make it possible to remove the seeds, probably accounts for the few microorganisms present.

40. Tarkow, Fellers, and Levine. 1942. J. Bact., 44, 367-372.
41. Erickson and Fabian. 1942. Food Research 7, 68-79.
42. Bitting. 1925. Canning Age, April 1925, 413-417; 440.
43. Prescott. 1920. J. Bact. 5, 109-125.
44. Clague. 1936. Food Research 1, 45-59.

Dried fruits may, under proper conditions of moisture content and temperature, undergo several types of spoilage. Essu and Cruess [45] found yeasts to be the cause of "souring" of prunes and dates. The spoilage was controlled by heating in a sealed container so that all parts of the container and contents reached 60°C.(140°F.). Mrak and Baker [46] found a white sugar-like substance on dried fruit to be rich in yeasts. These fungi may cause deterioration. Many belong to the genus Zygosaccharomyces.

Pasteurization of Dried Fruits. On account of the fact that dried fruits harbor so many microorganisms, Fellers [47] carried out experiments to determine whether such fruits as figs, raisins, and prunes could be heated to pasteurization temperatures without injuring their texture or flavor. He observed a percentage reduction in the number of organisms from 93 to 99 per cent. In the case of dates, large commercial continuous pasteurizers are now in use. Several thousand cases of dates are processed daily. The laboratory experiment showed that temperatures of 71.1°C.(160°F.) to 85°C.(185°F.) at humidities of 70 to 100 for 30 to 90 minutes were effective on the different dried fruits.

A few inoculation experiments were also made. Dates, figs, raisins, and prunes were coated with cultures of *Escherichia coli* and subjected to various pasteurizing treatments. In all cases where the relative humidity was 75 per cent or more, a 30-minute exposure to 71.1°C.(160°F.) was sufficient to destroy all the organisms. Approximately 40 such tests were made. Using *Eberthella typhosa* on dates, a single experiment showed complete destruction of the organisms after exposure to 76.7°C.(170°F.) for 25 minutes, or 71.1°C.(160°F.) for 30 minutes, at a high (unmeasured) humidity. Since the *Escherichia coli* is considered more resistant than the *Eberthella typhosa,* such findings are significant.

Fellers also carried out a few experiments to study the effect of storage on dried fruits heavily inoculated with *Escherichia coli. Escherichia coli* died out in 15 days on prunes and in 30 days on raisins, dates, and figs. To eliminate pathogenic microorganisms which might be introduced during packing and to destroy spoilage microorganisms Clague and Fellers [48] attempted to use heated humidified air for pasteurizing fruits. Using *Escherichia coli* as index of pasteurization efficiency, the following effective minute processes were obtained: 87°C.(188.6°F.) for 20 minutes at 96 per cent relative humidity or above; 82°C.(179.6°F.) for 30 minutes at 75 per cent relative humidity; 71°C.(159.8°F.) for 50 minutes at 90 per cent relative humidity; 66°C.(150.8°F.) for 60 minutes at 100 per cent relative humidity; and at 63°C.(145.4°F.) no effective pasteurization time under 80 minutes. Sporeforming bacteria and molds constituted a considerable part of the microbic flora on raw dried dates. While pasteurization did not always reduce the number of bacteria, it did destroy larvae and eggs of insects. Strains of *Escherichia coli* were found to be more

45. Essu and Cruess. 1933. Fruit Prod. J., 12, 144-147.
46. Mrak and Baker. 1940. Proc. Third Internatl. Cong. Microbiol., 1939, 700-701; J. Bact. 36 (1938), 317-318.
47. Fellers. 1930. Amer. J. Pub. Health 20, 175-181.
48. Clague and Fellers. 1933. Arch. Mikrobiol. 4, 419-426.

resistant than related pathogenic forms. Pasteurization destroyed virulent *Mycobacterium tuberculosis* swabbed on the dates.

Clague's [44] Method for Bacteriological Examination of Dried Foods. Two methods were used. The first was to take whole pieces of fruit and aseptically cut off portions until a 10-gram sample had been obtained. A tared, sterile petri-dish cover was placed on a balance and the sample cut into it until 10 grams had been obtained. This sample was then transferred to 90 ml. of sterile water.

The second procedure was to place five whole prunes or pieces of other fruits in 100 ml. of water. After shaking the bottle well by hand, one ml. was plated directly, or diluted further; thus, one ml. was considered as representing 5/100, or 1/20, of the total number of microorganisms per piece of fruit. By weighing the fruit the count per gram as well as per piece may be secured by this method.

The procedure with powdered fruits was to weigh 10 grams directly into a sterile wide-mouth bottle.

Use of Sulfur Dioxide for Preserving Fruits. Sulfur dioxide has been used for a long time in dried fruits for preserving color, and for preserving other fruit products in some countries. Atkinson and Strachan [49] and Fisher, Mrak, and Long [50] have discussed some of the mechanical problems which are involved. Only its bacterial properties will be considered here. In solution it has an appreciable toxic effect on microorganisms, as shown by a number of reports. Fernbacher [51] reported that several species of yeasts were affected by sulfur dioxide. Fermentation by Frohberg yeast was stopped by 7.5 mg. of sulfur dioxide in 100 ml. of medium, while with Saaz and Logos types 6.8 and 9.2 mg., respectively, were required. According to Hailer,[52] yeasts are more sensitive to sulfur dioxide than are molds and bacteria. He stated that the concentrations required to kill are for molds 1/150, for yeasts 1/186, and for bacteria 1/520 gram molecules per liter. According to Cruess,[53] yeasts differ in their reaction to sulfur dioxide. Wild yeasts and molds were inhibited, while the true wine yeasts were not. Such data indicate the futility of making general statements about the effect of bactericidal agents on microorganisms. One paper by Moreau and Vinet [54] may be mentioned because in it was pointed out the fact that it is free sulfur dioxide which acts on microorganisms. Moreau and Vinet pointed out that sufficient fresh sulfur dioxide must be added to permit a residual uncombined amount to be available for action as an antiseptic.

A new use of sulfur dioxide has developed during recent years in the shipping of fresh grapes. Winkler and Jacob [55] have discussed the subject. The purpose of using sulfur dioxide in this manner is to delay deterioration caused by development of molds and other spoilage-producing microorganisms. Jacob reported that in 1928, 15,000 carloads of grapes were treated. He stated that a concentration of 50 parts of sulfur dioxide per million parts of grapes (.005 per cent) will delay the development of molds and other microorganisms, so that the rate of deterioration is about one-half

49. Atkinson and Strachan. 1941. Fruit Prod. J., 21, 5-8 *et seq.*
50. Fisher *et al.* 1942. Idem, 175-176 *et seq.*
51. Fernbacher. 1901. Brauerei J., 11, 516.
52. Hailer. 1911. Chem. Ztschr. Répert., 1911, p. 215.
53. Cruess. 1912. J. Ind. Eng. Chem., 4, 581-585.
54. Moreau and Vinet. 1928. Ann. Sci. Agron. 46, 583-603.
55. Winkler and Jacob. 1925. Hilgardia 1, 107-131.

that of similar untreated grapes, stored under similar conditions. Most of the grapes were treated after they had been loaded in refrigerator cars. Sulfured fruits may contain objectionable amounts of hydrogen sulfide if yeast fermentation occurs. Sage [57] recommended pasteurization if active yeasts are present.

Preservation of Fruits by High Pressures. Some food preservation methods affect the flavor. Consequently, experiments were carried out to determine the effect of high pressures on the bacteria in fruit and other food products. Could they be destroyed in this manner, the flavor of the product would probably not be affected or altered. Not many experiments have been carried out with food products. Consequently, it is probably not amiss to review the results of a few experiments with pure cultures.

Regnard [58] stated that yeasts could stand a pressure of 1,000 atmospheres for one hour without being destroyed. Melsens [59] used pressures of 8,000 atmospheres and noticed no diminution in the vitality. This early work has been checked by some work in America which seems to have been carried out to determine whether foods could be preserved by pressure. Hite, Giddings, and Weakley [60] studied the effect of pressure on bacteria in canned fruits and vegetables. The bacteria which caused spoilage of sweet, ripe fruits could be destroyed by pressure. One hundred thousand pounds for 10 minutes stopped the fermentation of grape juice. Apple juice which was subjected to 60,000 to 80,000 pounds for 30 minutes remained sweet. These authors kept apple juice which had been subjected to 90,000 to 120,000 pounds for five years. Inconsistent results, however, were secured with blackberries and raspberries. Tomatoes also gave such results. The work indicated that more study is necessary to overcome some of the difficulties of the process in its application to food preservation. Bridgman [61] reported that egg white became somewhat stiffened when it was exposed to 75,000 pounds per square inch for 30 minutes at 20°C. (68°F.). This conclusion may have significance in attempts to explain how bacteria are killed by pressure. Larson, Hartzell, and Diehl [62] found that direct pressure of 6,000 atmospheres would kill nonsporeforming bacteria when applied for 14 hours. It required 12,000 atmospheres for the same length of time to kill the sporeformers. This has much significance in the sterilization of foods by this method, since the sporeformers cause much of the trouble in spoilage. In an atmosphere of carbon dioxide, 50 atmospheres for 1.5 hours killed nonsporeformers. High pressures have not been used for food preservation on account of the uncertainty of results and the mechanical difficulties of applying them.

FROZEN FRUITS

As is the case with other frozen foods, the types and numbers of microorganisms on frozen fruits is determined largely by those in the raw

56. Jacob. 1929. Calif. Agr. Expt. Sta. Bull. 471.
57. Sage. 1931. The Analyst 56, 451-452.
58. Regnard. 1884. Compt. Rend. Acad. Sci.
59. Melsens. 1870. Compt. Rend. Acad. Sci., 70, 629, 632.
60. Hite, Giddings, and Weakley. 1914. W. Va. Agr. Expt. Sta. Bull. 146.
61. Bridgman. 1914. J. Biol. Chem., 19, 511-512.
62. Larson, Hartzell, and Diehl. 1918. J. Infect. Dis., 22, 271-279.

products and the methods of freezing and storage. In general, yeasts and molds make up a larger part of the flora of frozen fruits than of frozen vegetables. This fact determines to a considerable extent the type of spoilage which may occur in the defrosted fruit. The bacterial flora may be quite heterogeneous. Tanner and Wallace [63] studied certain phases of methods of preservation using temperatures of —16°C.(3.2°F.), —40°C. (—40°F.), and —79°C.(—110.2°F.). In general, the degree of cold had little effect on the death rate of bacteria.

A few experiments with *Clostridium botulinum* in several vegetables and a few fruits showed that spores of this organism survived freezing at —16°C.(3.2°F.) for 14 months. The toxin also showed no decrease in strength when stored at —79°C.(—110.2°F.) for the same time. Vegetables to which detoxified spores were added before freezing at —14°C. (6.8°F.) for 14 months, became toxic in three to six days when allowed to thaw and stand at room temperature. Toxin formation was observed in a few instances in inoculated, thawed, frozen fruits despite a hydrogen-ion concentration which has been found to be protective in canned fruits. Formation of toxin under these conditions was probably made possible by the development of other microorganisms which created conditions favorable for *Clostridium botulinum*. A similar situation in home-canned Bartlett pears was reported by Meyer and Gunnison.[64]

Frozen fruits are not sterilized; they must, therefore, be prepared under conditions which prevent entrance of *Eberthella typhosa*, Salmonella organisms, etc. Special attention must be given to the water supply. Tanner and Wallace [63] inoculated the clear juice and juice and cherries with the organisms just mentioned. When the organisms were frozen in the clear juice, no viable cells could be found after two weeks at —14°C.(6.8°F.). However, when held at —16°C.(3.2°F.) in the presence of both cherries and juice, they remained alive for five months. Such results emphasize the need of establishing the purity of a water supply used in preparing frozen fruits. The danger rests in considering them in the same category as canned fruits. Cruess and Overholser,[65] Woodruff,[66] and many others have discussed other aspects of the subject.

Some of the small fruits which are preserved by freezing, such as strawberries and cherries, are handled mainly by hand and are thus subject to contamination. In order to ascertain the survival period of pathogenic bacteria, McCleskey and Christopher [19] heavily inoculated sliced strawberries with about five million cells per gram and held them at —18°C. (—.4°F.). The following survival periods were observed:

Eberthella typhosa... 6 months
Staphylococcus aureus... 5 months
Salmonella aertrycke.. 1 month
Salmonella schottmülleri... 1 month
Salmonella paratyphi... Not recovered

63. Tanner and Wallace. 1931. Soc. Expt. Biol. and Med. Proc. 29, 32-34.
64. Meyer and Gunnison. 1929. J. Infect. Dis., 45, 135-147.
65. Cruess and Overholser. 1925. Canning Age.
66. Woodruff. 1930. Ga. Agr. Expt. Sta. Bull. 163.

Using unsliced but sweetened strawberries, *Eberthella typhosa* was still present in small numbers after 14 months' storage at —18°C.(—.4°F.).

Fruits are in the same category as are vegetables with respect to decrease in microbial numbers during storage. The number of viable organisms decreases markedly but not to the point of complete sterility. Smart[67] reported viable bacteria, yeasts, and molds in sealed tins of frozen strawberries which had been stored at —9.4°C.(15°F.) for three years. Lochhead and Jones[68] studied the problem with strawberries and raspberries. They were packed in paraffin-lined, one-pint cartons. The strawberries were packed in a sugar sirup of 55° and the raspberries in a sirup of 45° Balling. After packing, the fruits were stored at —17.8°C.(0°F.) and kept frozen until examined. Samples were removed for examination over 37 weeks. Great variations were noted in freshly packed materials, as have been reported by others. Such variations are explainable, for the raw materials may be of varying age and carry different amounts of soil. The variations which Lochhead noticed became largely obliterated during storage. Pronounced differences in microbial content owing to methods of packing were not observed. Frozen fruits were found to harbor a considerable number of yeasts and molds. Members of the coliform group were few in number as was also the case with anaerobic sporeformers. Smart[69] observed that less than two per cent of the microorganisms found on fresh blueberries survived storage of seven months at —9.4°C.(15°F.). While the types which are found in blueberries do not affect the healthfulness of the product, they are sufficient to cause spoilage in a few hours at room temperature. Prompt handling, freezing, and storage should give a frozen product offering no problems to the packer or consumer. A high number of bacteria probably indicates inefficient washing.

Berry's[70] observations on microorganisms in frozen berries showed that microorganisms died out more rapidly in the temperature zone between —9.4 to —6.7°C.(15 to 20°F.) than at —20.5°C.(—5°F.). Growth of microorganisms was noticed in non-airtight containers at —3.8 to —2.2°C.(25 to 28°F.) in contrast with a rapid decrease in numbers in sealed containers. Berries in airtight containers at storage temperatures as high as —3.8°C.(25°F.) did not spoil; strawberries, however, did not keep well at this temperature. The observation that microorganisms die out more rapidly at —9.4°C.(15°F.) than at lower temperatures had been previously reported by Prescott, Bates, and Highlands.[71] Berry[72] suggested that this might be due to formation of lethal amounts of carbon dioxide from respiration of the berries when they are frozen more slowly. Results of experimental work did not confirm this.

67. Smart. 1934. Phytopathology 24, 1319-1331.
68. Lochhead and Jones. 1936. Food Research 1, 29-39.
69. Smart. 1937. Food Research 2, 429-434; 4 (1939), 287-292.
70. Berry. 1933. Canning Age, October, 445-447; The Glass Pack Age, April 1932, 251-254.
71. Prescott *et al.* 1932. Amer. J. Pub. Health 22, 257-262.
72. Berry. 1932. Western Canner and Packer 23, 17-18; Amer. Soc. Hort. Sci. Proc. 33, 224-226.

Application of the Howard Microscope Method for Detecting Spoilage in Berry Products. Unless berries are handled promptly, they are susceptible to deterioration by molds. Several common species are involved. In view of results secured with the Howard method for detecting excessive mold growth in tomato products, Needham and Fellers [73] investigated its use on berry products. They soon found that these products should not be held more than one day under ordinary cannery conditions. High mold count in fresh or canned blackberries or strawberries indicates a high percentage of soft or moldy fruit. High yeast counts indicated spoiled and fermented fruit; and in general, high mold and high yeast counts occurred together. Highest mold counts were obtained when the pulp alone was sampled. Juice contained only very little mold. Counts obtained on the entire contents of the can (both pulp and juice) were somewhat lower than those on pulp alone, but should be determined preferably to those on pulp alone. Blackberry jelly contained little mold, yeasts, or spores regardless of the condition of the raw product. In strawberry and blackberry jams the mold count increased in proportion to the mold in the raw material, while the yeast count had a slight tendency to decrease. Preliminary experiments indicated that blackberries or strawberries containing 5 to 10 per cent of decayed or moldy berries by weight gave 40 per cent or more positive mold fields in the combined pulp and juice. Moderately high mold count may be obtained on soft, mushy, or overripe fruit showing no readily visible evidence of mold, especially with blackberries.

Before the Howard method may be used on a large scale on fruits, a standard technic must be developed.

Wildman's [74] Method for Examination of Canned Raspberries and Blackberries for Mold. This procedure was devised to detect the presence of primary spoilage in berries before they are packed.

(1) Examination is made on the basis of a No. 2 can. Where larger cans are to be examined, pour the contents into a large pan, and take a No. 2 can sample at random.

(2) Select a quart Mason jar with glass top and fill one-fourth full with water. Pour in sample, and water, and rinse several times with water until color has disappeared from juice. Avoid as much breakage of fruit as possible.

(3) Finally, cover berries with water, add 10 gm. of fresh anhydrous sodium sulfite and 10 ml. of concentrated hydrochloric acid. Allow to stand over night.

(4) Fill a white bottom pan about three-fourth inch deep with water. Pour about one-fourth of the berries into a 15-mesh sieve, allow to drain, and transfer to the white bottom pan.

(5) Examine berries for mold. Moldy berries are generally somewhat darker in color. Consider only as moldy those berries which have exterior mold filaments covering at least three drupelets. The presence of exterior mold can be detected with an ordinary hand lens by turning the suspicious berries over slowly in the water and examining the outline of the berry against the white pan. The work is less tedious by the use of a wide field binocular microscope, such as is used in the examination of butter, held over the pan by a suitable arm and support.

(6) Place moldy and passable berries in separate dishes and keep covered with water until examination is completed. Finish examination, using portions of about one-fourth of the sample. Drain moldy berries on sieve, transfer to tared watch glass, drain off excess liquid by turning watch glass on edge and holding berries with hand, and weigh. Weigh passable portion similarly and compute percentage.

73. Needham and Fellers. 1925. J. Assoc. Off. Agr. Chem., 8, 312-337.
74. Wildman. 1941. Private communication.

In Tentative U. S. Standards for Grades of Fruit Preserves (or Jams)[74a] tolerances have been proposed for various fruit preserves. Fruit preserves or jams that consist of a single variety of fruit may contain mold filaments not exceeding the maximum percentage of positive fields shown in the following table. When they consist of a combination of fruits they may contain mold filaments not exceeding the maximum percentage of positive fields for the predominating variety:

Apple	20	Huckleberry	30
Apricot	4	Loganberry	30
Blackberry	30	Nectarine	4
Blueberry	30	Orange	12
Boysenberry	30	Peach	4
Cherry	10	Pear	4
Crabapple	20	Pineapple	4
Cranberry	30	Plum*	20
Damson plum	20	Quince	4
Dewberry	30	Raspberry	20
Elderberry	30	Red currant	12
Fig	20	Rhubarb	10
Gooseberry	30	Strawberry	10
Grape	40	Tangerine	30
Grapefruit	12	Tomato	4
Greengage plum	20	Yellow tomato	30
Guava	4	Youngberry	4

* Other than Greengage and Damson.

Spoilage of Processed Fruits by Byssochlamys fulva. This mold has become a problem in processed fruits in England and the United States. It is a very resistant species, according to Olliver and Smith,[75] readily cultivated on various media. Tissues of processed fruit are readily disintegrated even under reduced oxygen pressure. Olliver and Rendle [76] found it on fruit in the fields and believed it to be present in soil. Its ascospores resisted 86 to 88°C.(186.8 to 190.4°F.) for 30 minutes in many fruit sirups. Further information on heat resistance of *Byssochlamys fulva* has been given by Gillespy,[77] who found the maximum heat resistance of the ascospores to be at about pH 5; resistance at pH 3 was considerably greater than at pH 7. The protective effect of sucrose in solution was greater at 90°C. than at 85°C. Survival time for 10 per cent of the ascospores, when heated in fruit sirups, exceeded 45 minutes at 90°C.(194°F.). Enzyme activity continued in stored bottles even long after the fungus had died out.

An unusually heat-resistant mold which grew in a high vacuum has been reported by Williams, Cameron, and Williams.[78] The species was isolated from canned blueberries where it grew on the surface as in the form of small plaques. Growth apparently did not occur below the surface.

74a. The Canner, May 29, 1943, 17-18.
75. Olliver and Smith. 1933. J. Botany 72, 196.
76. Olliver and Rendle. 1934. Chem. and Indus., 53, 166T-172T.
77. Gillespy. 1937. Rev. in Chem. Abs., 33, 2605.
78. Williams, Cameron, and Williams. 1941. Food Research, 6, 69-73.

At 82°C.(180°F.) 9.7 minutes were required to destroy conidia, while the sclerotia required 1,000 minutes. The logarithmic order of death did not seem to hold. The mold was able to develop in high vacuum above 25 inches.

Spoilage of Canned Pineapple. Losses from spoilage of canned pineapple have been small. Occasional outbreaks have made it possible to determine the causal organisms. Spiegelberg,[79] in several publications, has summarized the literature and made significant contributions. The pH of canned pineapple ranges from 3.5 to 4.7, depending on the pH of the raw fruit. Examination of sound cans showed that many contained viable microorganisms consisting of two types of sporeformers which survived the process but which were unable to develop in the cans. Oxygen and pH were said to be the chief factors which limited growth of these organisms. One organism grew with scum formation on culture media while the other did not. The butyric organism produced spores and thus showed some resistance to heat. Processes used in commercial practice were said to be generally satisfactory. With a pH of 4.4 to 4.5 and below, the standard of 87.8°C.(190°F.) in the fruit after the cooking process was adequate to insure sterility, but with a pH of 4.5 and above a temperature of 93.3°C. (200°F.) or above was required to eliminate arrested swells. Even with these temperatures butyric acid-forming organisms persisted. When the pH was 4.4 butyric spoilage was entirely absent even with substandard cooks; low pH and lower cooks permitted other types of spoilage to appear.

FRUIT JUICES

The increased use of unfermented fruit juices in America has necessitated constant study of the various methods of preservation. Application of heat, or pasteurization, has been the most satisfactory method of preservation even though the flavor is always altered. In order to minimize the change in flavor, as low a temperature as possible is used. Other methods of preservation are constantly proposed. Some of these newer methods have involved attempts to extract sterile juice from the fruits or impregnation of the juice with some such gas as carbon dioxide.

The technology of fruit juices and related products has been comprehensively treated by Charley and Harrison.[80] Special attention was given to pasteurization preservation. A Committee of the American Public Health Association [81] recommended that some control should be applied to this industry. They believed that a need existed for quality standards.

Grape Juice. This is the unfermented juice of the grape. It enjoys wide sale in the United States. The best grapes are used in its manufacture and in this respect grape juice may differ from apple juice. In the preparation of apple juice, frequently the cull apples or windfalls are used. Grapes are usually as clean as apples, since they grow on vines above the ground and are harvested before they are too ripe to handle. Therefore,

79. Spiegelberg. 1934. Pineapple Quarterly for 1934 and 1935.

80. Charley and Harrison. 1939. Tech. Commun. No. 11, Imp. Bur. Hart. and Plantation Crops, Kent, England, 104 pp.

81. Amer. Pub. Health Assoc. Yearbook, 1940-1941, 101-105.

they probably carry fewer bacteria than do apples. Cruess [82] and others have described the manufacture of grape juice.

Grapes are washed and crushed, which consists of breaking the skin but not pressing the fruit flat. After being stemmed, they are cooked in aluminum kettles at 63°C.(145°F.) with constant stirring. They are then pressed under a pressure of about 170 tons. The juice is heated to 72°C. (160°F.), and skimmed. It is then run into glass-lined carboys and allowed to stand in tiers for several months, during which time the argol settles out. The juice is then filtered off and is ready for bottling. Sugar is added to the extent of one pound for every five gallons of juice. The bottles are pasteurized at 77°C.(170°F.) for 30 minutes. The temperatures of pasteurization suggested by Bioletti [83] were considerably higher for bottles. Cruess and Hintze [84] recommended lower temperatures of pasteurization than those mentioned.

Pederson and Tressler [85] have published results of many experiments on preparation and pasteurization of grape juice. Pederson [86] stated that relatively few organisms, primarily molds and bacteria, survive the heating of Concord grapes for extraction. A large number of organisms are introduced in the pressing operations. These apparently are not the result of growth in the juice but are due to contamination from equipment. These organisms, which are mainly yeasts, are apparently more resistant to heat than the yeasts natural to the grape. All organisms are killed in the pasteurization before filling carboys. The juice in carboys is occasionally spoiled by mold growth. The source of this contamination may be mold spores on the corks used for closure or mold spores on corks which had been pushed into the carboys when previously used. The latter source of contamination can be overcome only by removal of these corks. The former may be overcome by dipping the corks in hot paraffin immediately before use. Pederson stated that lower temperatures could be used. A temperature of 71.1°C.(160°F.) is apparently sufficient, although 73.9 to 76.7°C.(165 to 170°F.) would be safer, especially for carboy juice made from Concord grapes. The majority of yeasts and bacteria are killed at temperatures well below 62.8°C.(145°F.). The molds are more resistant but are apparently unable to withstand temperatures much above 68.3°C. (155°F.).

Grape juice has been cleared of its objectionable turbidity by means of enzymes, by Willaman and Kertesz.[85] Molds grown on appropriate media produce an enzyme which converts most of the pectin of grape juice into other soluble substances. A portion of the pectin comes down as a flocculent precipitate which occludes other suspended matter. By simple filtration this precipitate is removed, leaving a brilliantly clear juice. Production of the enzyme from *Penicillium glaucum* and practical use of the process is described in detail.

82. Cruess. 1920. Calif. Agr. Expt. Sta. Circular 220.
83. Bioletti. 1914. Calif. Agr. Expt. Sta., Ann. Rpt., 190-191.
84. Cruess and Hintze. 1914. J. Ind. Eng. Chem., 6, 302-304.
85. Pederson and Tressler. 1936. N. Y. Agr. Expt. Sta. Bull. 676.
86. Pederson. 1936. Food Research 1, 9-27, 87-97.
85. Willaman and Kertesz. 1931. N. Y. Agr. Expt. Sta. Bull. 178.

Apple Juice. In America this is the fresh, unfermented juice of the apple. It is sometimes called apple cider, sweet cider, or cider and is to be distinguished from the English product which has undergone fermentation. The apples from which the juice is expressed are frequently those which cannot be sold as eating or cooking apples. The use of such apples is probably not objectionable if they are sound and clean. When old, partly-spoiled apples are used, a low-grade juice is secured. Today more attention is paid to the condition of the raw materials. The apples are washed and thereby much foreign matter is removed. Truelle [86] stated that if cider apples are washed and the water filtered, an ill-smelling filtrate is secured. He believed that this residue would have given a bad taste to the cider. He recommended that baskets of apples, about to be pressed, be placed in a stream of water for a while, and then allowed to dry—a practice commonly followed in Germany, Austria, and Switzerland. The subject was also studied by Müller-Thurgau and Osterwalder,[87] Vaton,[88] and Alliott and Gimel.[89] Alliott and Gimel studied the effect of several disinfectants in the wash water and reported that calcium hypochlorite, in a strength of 40 to 60 grams per hectoliter, gave best results. Sufficient bacteria were destroyed to leave a clearer field for *Saccharomyces mali*. Apple juice prepared in this manner was a better product. Perrier [90] soaked apples in water containing .5 per cent of formaldehyde for 15 to 24 hours. After washing in fresh water, the apples were pressed with apparatus which had been washed with formaldehyde water. Samples of juice from apples treated in this manner resisted fermentation for a considerable time. When pitched with yeast, such juice fermented normally.

It is quite probable that more attention could be paid in America to cleaning apples than is now given them. Disinfectants have not been used to any extent, if at all. The present procedures, founded as they are on a rule-of-thumb basis, could well derive benefit from the results of bacteriological and chemical researches.

Use of too-high temperatures of pasteurization causes marked changes in flavor of apple juice. Cruess and Aref [91] studied the possibility of using lower temperatures than ordinarily used. Since molds cannot develop in canned juice even though they may not be killed by the heat, because of absence of oxygen owing to its combination with metals in tin plate, all that needs to be done is to kill the yeasts. Cruess and Aref's results showed that it was practicable to pasteurize at as low a temperature as 56.1°C.(133°F.). In large scale experiments 57.2°C.(135°F.) and 60°C. (140°F.) kept juice in No. 1 tall cans perfectly. When pasteurized at the latter temperature, the flavor was quite like that of fresh, unheated juice.

Possibility of Communicable Disease Dissemination by Apple Juice. Before apples are washed, the purity of the water should be established. So

86. Truelle. 1899. Mess. Agr. 4th Ser., 10, 164.
87. Müller-Thurgau and Osterwalder. 1917. Landw. Jahrb. Schweiz. 29, 537-568.
88. Vaton. 1922. l' Alimentation Moderne, July 1922.
89. Alliott and Gimel. 1909. Compt. Rend. Acad. Sci., 149, 532-534.
90. Perrier. 1905. Idem 140, 324-325.
91. Cruess and Aref. 1933. The Canner, Dec. 30, 1933, 38-40.

far as the author can determine, experiments have not been carried out, in America, to determine the behavior of *Eberthella typhosa*, for instance, in fresh apple juice. A few investigations have been reported in Europe.

Bodin [92] reported that this organism was destroyed in two to 18 hours. Paque,[93] however, reported 24 cases of typhoid fever caused by sweet cider. The apples were washed in polluted water. A similar epidemic, it was stated, had been caused a few years before. Discussions by several hygienists indicated possible dissemination of typhoid fever by beer with low alcoholic content. Paque then carried out experiments to determine how long the members of the typhoid group could live in cider. *Eberthella typhosa* and *Salmonella paratyphi* were destroyed in a week. *Salmonella schottmülleri* was more resistant. It was able to live a week. Paque believed that cider 15 days' old would be safe. He stressed the necessity of using clean water for washing the apples.

Spoilage in canned fruit juices and in other similar products may be reduced by attention to several steps in the canning operation. Microorganisms may be eliminated by using sterile cans. Bitting [42] found this to be the case with jams and marmalades. Her conclusions might hold for canned fruit juices which are often packed without heat processing after the cans have been filled with hot juice and closed. Pearce [94] pointed out the value in this connection of inverting the can in order to sterilize its entire interior. When this method is relied on, the juice must not be allowed to cool between closure and inversion.

Clarification (Filtration) of Apple Juice. Desire for a clear product has caused large commercial pressers of apples to clarify the juice by one method or another. Filtration through various materials was the first method used. This procedure may also be looked upon as a method of preservation, since a great many bacteria and yeast cells are thus removed. One of the present methods is to mix from one-half to two per cent of "filter cel" with the cider. This is then passed through a filter press. In large quantities of apple juice, about 300 pounds of "filter cel" are used per 5,000 gallons of juice. After filtration the apple juice may be bottled or stored in glass-lined or wooden tanks. Grove [95] reported a study of the use of various possible substitutes for filtration. None of the various attempts were successful. Grove stated that filtration was the best method for removing yeast and bacterial cells from cider, as did Carpenter and Walsh.[96] The Dominion Bacteriologist of Canada [97] tested the efficiency of the Seitz filter for removal of organisms before bottling. Experiments were made at pressures of 10 and 24 pounds per square inch. Sterile filtrates were found to be possible at pump pressures up to 24 pounds. This pressure was greater than that considered possible by Carpenter, Pederson, and Walsh who regarded 10 pounds per square inch as the

92. Bodin. 1898. Ann. Inst. Pasteur 12, 458-464.
93. Paque. 1923. Rev. Hyg. 45, 165-169.
94. Pearce. 1939. The Canner, Feb. 11, 1939, 11-12.
95. Grove. 1915. Univ. Bristol Agr. and Hart. Res. Sta. Ann. Rpt. 51-52.
96. Carpenter and Walsh. 1932. N. Y. Agr. Expt. Sta. Bull. 202.
97. Progress Report of the Dominion Agricultural Bacteriologist, for the Years 1934, 1935, 1936. Ottawa, 1938, p. 34.

maximum safe pressure. Even when the filter was in use for five hours, there was no evidence that microorganisms grew through the filter.

Pasteurization of Apple Juice. Application of heat to destroy microorganisms seems to be the safest method for preserving apple juice, even though the taste may be altered. Freezing is possible under certain conditions but this method is not convenient at all times. Spoilage of apple juice may be due to fermentations caused by yeasts or other changes caused by bacteria. Infection of the juice is easily explained. Diehm [98] stated that minimum heat treatment to destroy mesophilic bacteria is 15 minutes' heating at 70°C.(158°F.), 10 minutes at 80°C.(176°F.), and five minutes at 90°C.(194°F.). Gore [99] was able to preserve fresh apple juice satisfactorily by pasteurization. The juice was heated to 65 to 70°C.(149 to 158°F.), and kept for six months without fermentation. He stated that it could also be sterilized in tin containers, although 65°C. for 30 minutes was not quite sufficient for all varieties which were tested. Tin containers are not to be recommended, however, for this product. Apple juice today is heated under vacuum to remove air and then pasteurized. The best treatment for cider in glass containers consisted of heating for one hour at 65°C. or one-half hour at 70°C. Cruess and Irish [100] reported that apple juice could be sterilized by a temperature of 65.5°C.(150°F.) for 30 minutes. Carbonated juice was said to require 76.7°C.(170°F.) for 30 minutes. Wiegand [101] advised great care in preheating apple juice before bottling if marked alterations in taste were to be avoided. Preheated juice was filled directly into sterilized cans within one-quarter of an inch of the top. The cans were heated in an exhaust box at a temperature of not over 71.1°C.(160°F.) to drive out surplus air. Exhausting of No. 2½ tins for not less than five minutes was advised and from six to eight minutes for No. 10 tins. Processing in open-bath cookers at 71.1°C. for 20 minutes for No. 2½ cans and for 30 minutes for No. 10 cans, was advised. Prompt cooling to 32.2°C.(90°F.) was also recommended.

Bottling of fermented apple juice is carried out in England as described by Grove.[102] Some of his conclusions could be applied in America to preparation of fresh juice. He advised that iron containers be avoided, if possible, since too much iron might cause darkening of the product. Juice from tart apples was successfully flash-pasteurized and canned at 71.1°C. (160°F.) or higher although a cooked flavor might be imparted (Pederson and Tressler.[103]

Preservation of Fresh Apple Juice With Chemical Reagents. Prohibition of the sale of fermented beverages in the United States stimulated investigations on the preservation of fruit juices by other means than low temperatures. Several investigators turned to the chemical compounds

98. Diehm. 1932. Fruit Prod. J., 11, 359-362.
99. Gore. 1906. U. S. Dept. Agr., Yearbook, 1906, 239.
100. Cruess and Irish. 1923. Calif. Agr. Expt. Sta. Bull. 359,
101. Wiegand. 1922.
102. Grove. 1928. Brewing Trade Rev., 42, 407.
103. Pederson and Tressler. 1938. Ind. Eng. Chem., 30, 954-959.
104. Gore. 1922. U. S. Dept. Agr., Bur. Chem. Bull. 118.

which had been suggested for other foods. Gore [104] reported that sodium benzoate in quantities of .03 to .15 per cent checked alcoholic fermentation but that acetic acid fermentation developed with an alteration in flavor. The latter statement would indicate that the alcoholic fermentation had progressed appreciably. Scott and Will [105] reported that, for commercial purposes, .2 per cent of sodium benzoate was required for efficient preservation, although this amount would not prevent the acetic acid fermentation. Apparently Acetobacter are not very susceptible to the action of sodium benzoate. According to Rice and Markley [106] and Tanner and Strauch,[107] fermenting yeasts are not especially susceptible to sodium benzoate; this finding was later confirmed also by Diehm.[98] Rice and Markley found that sodium benzoate would not do much good if there were many yeasts present, or if the juice was not kept cool. With warm juice as much as .5 per cent of sodium benzoate was necessary. Similar conclusions were reached by Tanner and Strauch, who worked with a number of pure yeast cultures. They observed marked differences among yeasts in resistance to sodium benzoate. They showed, furthermore, that fresh apple juice to which .1 per cent of benzoate had been added by law, would ferment. Cruess and Richert [108] reported that hydrogen-ion concentration greatly influenced action of sodium benzoate on microorganisms.

They observed a much stronger action at pH values of 2.5 to 4.5 than at 5 to 9. The concentrations of benzoate required to prevent the growth of *S. ellipsoideus, S. cerevisiae,* a mucor mold, two penicillium molds, three strains of mycoderma yeast, a lactic acid bacterium, a vinegar bacterium, *E. coli, B. subtilis,* and *Cl. sporogenes* were greatly affected by the pH of the medium. Much more sodium benzoate was required at pH values near neutrality, *e.g.,* pH 5 to 8 than at those in the acid range, 2.5 to 4.5.

Preservation of Apple Juice by Cold Storage and Freezing. Freezing has been considered to be a possible method for preserving apple juice for several decades. Gore [109] was one of the first to study the matter seriously. He found that when freshly expressed juice was chilled immediately to 0°C.(32°F.) it remained without noticeable fermentation for an average of 50 days. Gore stated that the juices suffered no deterioration but, on the other hand, became more palatable. Descours-Descares [110] studied two methods of freezing. One involved a slow but uniform lowering of the temperature to —3 or —4°C.(26.6 or 24.8°F.) in 24 hours. The ice is drained off just below zero. The other method involved freezing at —6 or —7°C.(21.2 or 19.4°F.) with slow motion. This latter method gave very fine crystals which were drained and washed just below freezing. Development of freezing apparatus should greatly stimulate interest in this method of preservation. The microbiological features of the method are probably no different from those which are reported above in the discussion of freezing of fruits. Microorganisms tend to disappear rapidly in frozen

105. Scott and Will. 1921. J. Ind. Eng. Chem., 13, 1141-1143.
106. Rice and Markley. 1921. N. Y. Agr. Coll. Expt. Sta., Cornell Univ., Bull. 44.
107. Tanner and Strauch. 1926. Soc. Expt. Biol. and Med. Proc. 23, 449-450.
108. Cruess and Richert. 1929. J. Bact., 17, 363; Ind. Eng. Chem., 24 (1932), 648.
109. Gore. 1910. U. S. Dept. Agr., Bur. Chem. Circular 48.
110. Descours-Descares. 1900. Compt. Rend. Acad. Sci., 130.

apple juice. In experiments by Berry and Diehl,[111] in which apple juice containing 2,000,000 microorganisms per ml. was used and it was stored at —5, —9.4, and 6.7°C.(23, 15, and 20°F.), over 90 per cent of the bacteria were destroyed in one month. At —2.2°(28°F.) many of the samples showed alcoholic fermentation in one month. The microbial content was lowered still further by prolonged storage.

Ropy Apple Juice (Sweet Cider). Slime or rope producing bacteria are responsible for losses in various foods. They are probably harmless, but so change the consistency of the foods that they are no longer desired. These organisms are, in general, unable to grow in the presence of acid. Consequently, acids are often added to foods to prevent their development. They cause this same change in apple juice before it becomes too acid for their development. They may also develop in some cider which is undergoing alcoholic fermentation. Grove [112] carried out some inoculation experiments with organisms which were known to cause rope. About a year elapsed before rope developed. A sediment appeared at the bottom of the bottle, most of which consisted of the rope-producing organisms. Kayser [113] isolated four different microorganisms from ropy cider. Their characteristics were somewhat divergent and need not be reproduced here. The significant statement was made by Kayser that ropiness might be due to other factors than the mere presence of bacteria.

Off-flavored apple-juice caused by development of a special microorganism has been reported by Warcollier and Tavernier.[114] The unnamed bacterium imparted a raspberry-like flavor.

Orange Juice. Much effort is being expended on methods of preparation and preservation of orange juice. The nature of the juice suggests that it is just as susceptible as the juices of all other fruits to the attacks of bacteria and yeasts. It is rich in organic acids, mineral salts, and carbohydrates, all of which, with the high amount of water, make a good medium for the development of microorganisms. The use of heat is ruled out by the alterations in flavor which it causes. Despite this a palatable orange juice is being packed and has been widely accepted. Townsend and Esty [115] stated that two minutes at 76.7°C.(170.°F.) were adequate for commercial sterility of California orange juice with a pH of about 3.7, sterilized prior to canning; to destroy contamination from cans and lids, a short treatment after sealing is necessary. For juice filled at 170°F., two minutes at this temperature subsequent to closing should be satisfactory on sealed cans. If the filling temperature is below 170°F., two minutes at 79.4°C. (175°F.) should be used.

Orange juice has been preserved by freezing. This method of preservation brings about minimum change in flavor. Juice from sound oranges is a sterile product, and effort is made to keep the bacterial content as low as possible. Enzymes act to bring about deterioration and every effort is

111. Berry and Diehl. 1934. Amer. Soc. Hart. Sci. Proc. 32, 157-159.
112. Grove. 1919. Univ. Bristol, Agr. and Hart. Res. Sta., Ann. Rpt., 14-15.
113. Kayser. 1911. Compt. Rend. Acad. Sci., 152, 1422-1424.
114. Warcollier and Tavernier. 1937. Chim. et Indus. 38, 179E.
115. Townsend and Esty. 1939. Ann. Rpt. to the Res. Committee, Natl. Canners Assoc., for 1938, Washington, p. 27.

made to remove oxygen. The juice is frozen to a slush and finally hardened in an air blast at —23.3°C.(—10°F.). Few, if any, data have been reported on the effect of such treatment on microorganisms that might be present. By analogy, we might expect a decrease in the number of viable microorganisms but not a condition of absolute sterility. Thawed, frozen orange juice is a perishable product.

Grapefruit Juice. This juice is now being put up in bottles and tin cans as are other fruit juices. The juice is pressed from the grapefruit in a manner similar to apple juice. According to Chace,[116] the fruit is cut into halves or quarters depending on the size of the press used. After pressing, the juice should be strained and pasteurized immediately at a temperature of 75 to 80°C.(167 to 176°F.). This seems to be a very important step in the preparation of grapefruit juice since quality of the product may be greatly harmed. The best method is to heat a thin film of the juice while it is in motion in a coil heated to the desired temperature. The juice should be conducted into carboys which are filled, leaving only sufficient room for the sterile cork. These carboys are then stored in a cool room for one or two months at not above 10°C.(50°F.) in order that sedimentation may take place. The clear supernatant liquid is decanted for bottling. Often the juices should be sweetened before bottling if the content of acid is above one per cent. Before bottling the juice is pasteurized again and run into the bottles which are capped and allowed to cool.

Freezing of Fruit Juices. This has been found to be a suitable method for preserving fruit juices without changing the flavor to any extent. Freezing has also been used to concentrate fruit juices; the ice is removed by filtration. Juices and sirups containing about 50 per cent of sugar have retained their flavors well in the frozen condition. The problems involved are more technical than microbiological. Most of the results of investigations on freezing fruits are applicable to fruit juices, although it is probably easier to destroy bacteria in the juice than in the fruit. McFarlane[117] observed greater destruction of microorganisms in unsweetened juice than in juice-sucrose media stored at —17.8°C.(0°F.). Survival in juice-sucrose media varied with sucrose concentration. In some cases 50 and 60 per cent of sucrose did not protect. It is evident from McFarlane's discussion that preservation of fruit juices by freezing involves many factors.

Sterilizing Values of Fruit Juices. Owing to acids and other constituents, fruit juices are inimical to many bacteria. Most attention has been given to pathogenic bacteria. Douglas[118] was inclined to attribute the lethal effect of fruit juices to their acid contents. He stated that two teaspoonfuls of lemon juice would kill two billion cells of *Eberthella typhosa* in less than 10 minutes. He pointed out that such acidity is quickly neutralized in the body. From investigations with 16 fruit juices and 19 condiments Sogo[119] found "Yuzu" juice to possess the strongest sterilizing

116. Chace. 1921. Calif. Citrogr. 5, 264-267.
117. McFarlane. 1942. Food Research 7.
118. Douglas. 1930. Lancet 219, 789-791.
119. Sogo. 1934. Bull. Agr. Chem. Soc., 10, 166-176.

power among such fruit juices as lemon, mandarin, orange, and straw-berry juices. Juices of Japanese medlar, peach, pear, and sweet cherry had weak sterilizing powers. He attributed the sterilizing power of fruit juices to the fatty acid content. According to Lasseur and Renaux [120] agglutination of *Bacillus pyocyaneus pyocyanogenes, B. chlororaphis, B. prodigiosus, B. balticus,* and *B. subtilis* (Neisser, Marburg, and Michigan strains) by lemon juice is due to acidity, not to a precipitin. As pH approaches 6, by dilution or by neutralization of the juice, agglutinating power disappears. Heating or filtration of juice does not affect agglutinat-ing power. Lemon juice does not agglutinate *B. mesentericus niger, B. megatherium,* or *B. caryocyaneus.* Curves are given for precipitation of *B. chlororaphis* and *B. prodigiosus* by lemon juice, citric acid, citric acid plus Na citrate and HCl, at pH .5 to 6.

Fresh juices of grapes with pH values of 2.6 to 3.2 also showed definite bactericidal properties against *Eberthella typhosa,* according to Rochaix and Jacqueson.[121] *Escherichia coli, Salmonella paratyphi A* and *B,* Shiga dysentery bacillus, and *Vibrio cholerae* were killed in grape juice at periods varying from 15 minutes to three hours. The Shiga bacillus was more resistant than other organisms to the action of grape juice. The agent responsible for the destruction of bacteria is not mentioned, al-though the several constituents of grape juice are discussed.

Experiments by Beard [122] showed an appreciable inhibition of the bac-tericidal effect of acidity at low temperatures. In orange juice the survival period varied from 50 hours for staphylococci to 170 hours for strains of *E. typhosa* and *S. dysenteriae.* This suggests the possibility of infection by this group of organisms in highly acid foods preserved only by storage at such temperatures. This possibility of infection is increased by the fact that such foods are frequently served with little storage—indeed freshness is often made a selling point. Danger is probably decreased by the fact that massive infection of the product would be relatively rare. It follows that preparation and handling of such foods should be subject to as rigid regulations and inspection as are applied to other types of food. The or-ange juice, after inoculation, was stored at —4°C. (24.8°F.).

Dates. The saccharine nature of this fruit would suggest the possible presence of microorganisms. Dates are usually sold in small packages or in large boxes. Hunwicke and Grinling made a bacteriological study of dates, after having been prompted to do so by illness in a child who had partaken of dates. Eleven samples were examined, four of which were ''block'' or bulk dates, while the other seven were dates from smaller packages. The ''block'' dates were all free from intestinal bacteria, but coliform bacteria were isolated from all but one of the boxes. They were all of the *Escherichia coli* type. When dates are repacked in Europe, a solution of glucose is sprayed over them; this probably favors bacterial growth. These data tend to suggest that dates may be contaminated. Con-

120. Lasseur and Renaux. 1934. Trav. Lab. Microbiol. Faculte Pharm. Nancy, 7, 171-191.
121. Rochaix and Jacqueson. 1938. Rev. Hyg. 60, 241-250.
122. Beard. 1932. J. Prev. Med. 6, 141-144.
123. Hunwicke and Grinling. 1928. Lancet. May 26, 1928.

vincing conclusions could only be reached, however, after more extended experiments. Fellers [47] reported the results of a large number of analyses of American dried fruits. None of the samples had undergone spoilage. Ten-gram samples of the fruits were placed in 90 ml. of distilled water in rubber-stoppered dilution bottles. Bacteria, yeasts, and molds were found to be present in considerable numbers. Eight of 79 samples contained lactose-fermenting bacteria. None was identified as *Escherichia coli*, although several closely resembled *Aerobacter aerogenes*. Fellers remarked that yeasts were conspicuous by their absence. This was probably due to the fact that plain agar was used; had agar with dextrose been used, yeasts would probably have developed.

Souring of Dried Dates. This deterioration is characterized by a soft, dark-colored and matted together appearance and a peculiar aromatic odor and poor flavor. Fellers and Clague [124] found far more yeasts than bacteria to be present. Six types of sugar-tolerant yeasts were isolated which reproduced the spoilage when inoculated into sound dates. Although yeasts, mainly Torulae and Willia species were largely responsible for souring, Acetobacter were often present on secondary invaders. While souring was not produced when the moisture content was blow 25 per cnt, 23 per cent was suggested as a safe moisture maximum. Pasteurization, as discussed elsewhere in this book, effectively destroyed all date souring yeasts.

Souring of Figs. According to Caldis [125] souring is a term used to describe many different kinds of spoilage. He suggested that "fig fermentation" would be a better name were it not for the fact that the name souring has become so firmly intrenched. The first change consists of a change in color from pink to colorless. A pink liquid exudes through the eye. Gas bubbles appear throughout the pulp which becomes watery and loses its firmness. Fig souring is primarily an alcoholic fermentation. Later, acetic acid bacteria may oxidize the alcohol to acetic acid. Caldis isolated several strains of yeasts which were inoculated into normal figs. It was shown that insects disseminated the spoilage organisms.

The white substance generally considered to be sugar, which often covers dried prunes and figs during storage before processing and occasionally in cartons, was found by Baker and Mrak [126] to be a mixture of yeast cells and sugar crystals. The sporulating yeasts which were isolated were members of various genera. Especially interesting were the species which could develop in heavy concentrations of sugar. No obligate osmophilic yeasts were encountered. The cultural details will not be given in this book. Most of the species were reported by Mrak, Phaff, Vaughn, and Hansen [126] to be Saccharomyces or Candida.

REFERENCE BOOKS

Cruess, W. V., 1938. Commercial Fruit and Vegetable Products. McGraw-Hill Book Co., New York City.

Marris, T. N., 1933. Principles of Fruit Preservation. Chapman Hall, London.

124. Fellers and Clague. 1932. J. Bact., 23, 53; Fruit Prod. J., 21 (1942), 326-327.
125. Caldis. 1930. J. Agr. Res., 40, 1031-1051.
126. Baker and Mrak. 1938. J. Bact., 36, 317.

CHAPTER 15

MICROBIOLOGY OF VEGETABLES AND VEGETABLE PRODUCTS

Vegetables and vegetable products are of interest to the bacteriologist on account of the possible relation of the bacteria which they carry to disease dissemination or decay. Considerable attention has been given to the relation of vegetables to disease dissemination. In America they are probably not very significant in this respect because fertilization of crops for human food with night soil and sewage is prohibited. It would be wrong, however, to state that vegetables could not carry harmful bacteria, because they are frequently handled under unsanitary conditions or inadequately washed.

Microorganisms on Fresh Vegetables. Since vegetables are grown in or near the ground, they may carry a heterogeneous flora of microorganisms. These organisms may be of interest on account of their ability to infect human beings or their relation to decay. Furthermore, the numbers of microorganisms are important if the vegetables are to be preserved. The greater the number, the greater will be the load on the preservation process.

Wurz and Bouges [1] showed that vegetables grown in infected soils or watered with infected water could transmit pathogenic bacteria. Kozyn [2] examined a number of samples of vegetables. Three had *Clostridium tetani* on their surfaces. Sixty samples showed no *Eberthella typhosa*, though the surface was more or less infected with intestinal bacteria. Generally speaking, bacteria were not found in the interior of the vegetables. *Escherichia coli* was found by Bessel [3] on 59.6 per cent of fruits and vegetables, which were purchased on the open market. It was thought that contamination resulted from storing the vegetables where contamination was possible and from handling. Neumann [4] reached the same conclusions, working with many of the common fruits and vegetables. Bacteria seem to stick so firmly to fruits and vegetables that even vigorous washing and rinsing do not remove them (Clauditz[5]). Microorganisms may persist for some time on fruits if the surface is unbroken. In some cases the juices may be germicidal.

Another phase of this question concerns the relation of vegetables from sewage farms to public health. Broad irrigation or sewage farming is used by several large cities for disposing of sewage wastes. Typhoid fever is said to increase every year from July to October in Paris. A goodly portion is attributed to vegetables raised on sewaged land.[6] While it was the original plan to use land fertilized in this manner for orchards and

1. Wurz and Bouges. 1901. Arch. Med. Expt. et Anat. Path., 13, 575.
2. Kozyn. 1907. Rev. in Expt. Sta. Rec., 20 (1908-1909), 64.
3. Bessel. 1907. Dissert., Berlin.
4. Neumann. 1910. Deut. Med. Wchnschr., p. 2046.
5. Clauditz. 1904. Hyg. Rundschau., 14, 865.
6. J. Amer. Med. Assoc. 80 (1923), 1628.

pastures, the excellent yields caused some to be used for market garden-
ing. An investigation of the crops raised on the sewage farms showed the
following: peas, beans, potatoes, artichokes, leeks, cauliflower, carrots,
turnips, sorrel, and spinach, all of which are usually eaten after cooking.
There were also such vegetables as lettuce, dandelions, endive, onions,
parsley, and radishes, which are most frequently eaten uncooked. It was
stated that stringent laws were necessary to control the crops which should
be raised on sewage farms (Marchoux[7]). This subject was investigated
experimentally by Remlinger and Nouri.[8] Their work indicated that the
danger from this source was probably exaggerated. The results showed
that none of the various pathogenic organisms used were taken up internally by the plants, and that the only possible source of danger was
from organisms adhering to their surface. It was found that the only
organisms which were retained by plants grown under conditions similar
to those on well-managed, sewage-irrigation farms were *Bacillus anthracis*
and *Clostridium tetani*, but, as the authors pointed out, the former organism is very rare in sewage water and the ingestion of *Clostridium tetani*
is harmless. Water cress, however, was believed to have caused an epidemic
of typhoid fever.

Kurk[9] studied the microbiology of vegetables bought on the open market in Chicago. His attention was principally directed to finding members
of the coli-typhoid group, streptococci, and anaerobic bacteria. He examined such foods as water cress, lettuce, celery. etc. *Escherichia coli* was
found on 22 out of 29 samples, streptococci on three samples: 28 of the
specimens contained bacteria which formed gas in lactose. Kurk could
not correlate the condition of the store with his bacteriological results. The
investigation was not an extensive one, but probably gives some idea of
real conditions. The vegetables may be contaminated either by being grown
in filthy soil or by careless handling after harvesting. In order to secure
data with regard to the longevity of *Eberthella typhosa,* in the soil growing
fruits and vegetables, Murillo[10] incorporated the organisms in garden soil
by spraying the low-growing fruits with a suspension. After 36 days,
virulent organisms were still found. They lived 55 days in sterile sand.
Such data indicate that salads and other dishes prepared from uncooked
vegetables may spread disease. Experiments with *Vibrio comma* were
equally conclusive up to three weeks. On the other hand, Rucker[11] did
not find many *Escherichia coli* on fruits. Melick[12] found that the longevity
of *Eberthella typhosa* in the soil depended on the source and the strain,
the time varying from 29 to 58 days. Under natural conditions, radishes
were infected after periods of 28, 35, and 37 days, and lettuce after 21 days.
There was no evidence that the organisms entered the interior of the plant,
but ordinary washing did not remove them. Creel[13] studied the same

7. Marchoux. 1923. Rev. Hyg., 45, 300-304.
8. Remlinger and Nouri. 1910. Hyg. Gen. et Appl., 1910. 421-426.
9. Kurk. 1918. Amer. J. Pub. Health, 8, 660-661.
10. Murillo. 1919. Plus-Ultra, Madrid. 2, No. 9, 115.
11. Rucker. 1911. Ann. Rpt. Comm. Health., Penn., Pt. 2, 1022.
12. Melick. 1917. J. Infect. Dis., 21, 28-38.
13. Creel. 1912. Pub. Health Rpts., 27, 187-193.

question, and reported that plants growing in soil carried on their leaves and stems organisms which existed in the soil. *Eberthella typhosa* was recovered from leaves which were apparently free from dirt. Under conditions which were most favorable to *Eberthella typhosa* infection lasted for 31 days, a period which is sufficiently long for lettuce and radishes to mature. Melick mentioned a number of instances where vegetables have caused disease. Wary [14] reported an epidemic of typhoid fever in a London suburb, supposed to have been caused by eating water cress grown in beds fertilized by sewage. Pixley [15] reported two cases of the same disease from eating uncooked rhubarb. Morse [16] believed that 49 cases of typhoid in an insane asylum came from eating celery. The celery beds had received hospital sewage. Another outbreak occurred in Philadelphia where 18 out of 19 persons who ate water cress [17] sandwiches became ill with typhoid fever. A visit to the farm yielded data which seemed to incriminate the cress. According to Mills, Bartlett, and Kessel,[18] bacteria may be present on the surface of fruits and vegetables kept under moist conditions for 15 days or more. If the fruits and vegetables are covered to prevent a rapid evaporation of moisture, the survival period may be longer than 15 days. They carried out experiments to determine methods for elimination of pathogenic bacteria from these foods. Chlorination, for instance, was efficient for the pathogenic bacteria but did not affect cysts and ova. Alcohol was also ineffective for protozoan cysts and helminth ova. Neither was potassium permanganate an efficient disinfectant. These investigators reported that burning alcohol on the surface of vegetables or pouring boiling water over them did not destroy pathogenic bacteria. They found that after fruits and vegetables were dipped into boiling water for 10 seconds pathogenic bacteria, protozoan cysts, and ova were destroyed. This then seems to indicate that the simple procedure of boiling may be the satisfactory method for the treatment of these foods. This conclusion was confirmed by Ommyoji [19] and Lu.[20] Exposure to boiling water for a few seconds destroyed *Eberthella typhosa* in cabbage, carrots, and a few other vegetables.

A more recent investigation of the subject was made by James [21] with head lettuce. With fresh untrimmed lettuce the number of bacteria was much higher on the surface than in the interior of the head, but with increasing length of storage under ordinary room conditions, the bacterial count in the interior increased much more rapidly than on the outside. The bacterial count of lettuce stored at the temperature of 21°C. (69.8°F.), and under controlled humidity was much lower and the lettuce remained in good condition much longer. Lettuce heads which had been trimmed and washed in the market were much more highly con-

14. Wary. 1903. Lancet, 1903, p. 1671.
15. Pixley. 1913. N. Y. Med. J., 98, 1913.
16. Morse. 1899. Mass. Bd. Health Ann. Rpt., 1899, p. 761.
17. Expt. Sta. Rec., 30 (1914), 64; Med. Rev. 81 (1917), 1-10. Article by Lewis.
18. Mills, Bartlett, and Kessel. 1925. Amer. J. Hyg., 5, 559-579.
19. Ommyoji. 1931. J. Oriental Med., 14, 30.
20. Lu. 1931. J. Oriental Med. 14.
21. James. 1925. Amer. Food J., 20, 302-304.

taminated throughout the head than unwashed lettuce, and similar results were obtained with washed lettuce stored at 20°C.(68°F.). The practice of washing lettuce before storing in the refrigerator was considered unwise as favoring more rapid bacterial growth.

The behavior of pathogenic bacteria in water and soil in nature has some bearing on the possible contamination of vegetables grown in infected soil or washed or freshened with infected water. Bitter secured some data on the behavior of *Escherichia coli, Eberthella typhosa,* and some of the paratyphoid bacilli in dry and moist soil. The above organisms lived for eight days in dry soil while in the moist soil they were present at the end of 60 days. A more recent contribution to our knowledge on this subject has come from Beard.[22] Massive inocula of *Eberthella typhosa* were made into four types of soil placed in unglazed flower pots suspended over lysol trays and exposed out-of-doors to rain at any time and sun for about two-thirds of the day. Survival depended largely on moisture and was longest in the wet season and was much longer in adobe and adobe-peat-moss loam (six to seven weeks) than in sand (four to seven days). Without reviewing all of Beard's observations, it may be said that the type of soil and other conditions largely determine the results which are secured.

Other work has been done by Pfuhl,[23] Graucher and Deschamps,[24] Uffelmann,[25] Robertson,[26] and Stimson.[27] Typhoid bacteria, according to Murillo,[10] were still active and virulent from 30 to 36 days after they had been incorporated in garden dirt or after low-hanging fruits had been sprayed with these organisms. On the basis of these data Murillo stated that salads and raw fruits and vegetables were important in the spread of typhoid fever in Spain. Experiments with *Vibrio comma (Microspira cholerae)* were equally convincing. Evidences of contamination were reported on water cress by MacDonald.[28] Water cress was suggested as the cause of sporadic outbreaks of typhoid fever which are always found but which cannot be traced to any definite source. Bacterial standards of purity have not been established for water cress or other vegetables. Mihaeloff[29] also showed the contaminated condition of some fresh vegetables. Coliform bacteria were found in 68 cases, *Eberthella typhosa* in eight, *Salmonella paratyphi* in six, and *Salmonella schottmülleri* in six. *Shigella dysenteriae* and *Microspira cholerae* were present in one case each. Mihaeloff suggested washing of vegetables in flowing water for five minutes and in chlorine solutions.

Escherichia coli on Fresh Vegetables. The position which this organism holds as an indicator of pollution in various foods and beverages prompted Slocum and Boyles[30] to determine the incidence and significance of this

22. Beard. 1940. Amer. J. Pub. Health 30, 1077-1082.
23. Pfuhl. 1902. Ztschr. Hyg. u. Infektionskrank. 40, 3555-60.
24. Graucher and Deschamps. 1889. Arch. Med. Expt. et Anat. Path. 1, 33-44.
25. Uffelmann. 1899. Centbl. Bakt., Orig., 5, 497-502.
26. Robertson. 1898. Brit. Med. J., Pt. 1, 421-424.
27. Stimson. 1907. Hyg. Lab. Bull. 35, 177-191.
28. MacDonald. 1938. Med. Officer 59, 101-102.
29. Mihaeloff. 1934.
30. Slocum and Boyles. 1941. Food Research 6, 377-385.

organism on vegetables which were irrigated with water of questionable purity or raised on polluted soil. Vegetables irrigated with sewage-polluted water had a considerably higher incidence of coliform bacteria on their surfaces than those irrigated with nonpolluted water. The former harbored from 100 to 10,000,000 cells per 100 grams on all vegetable samples which were irrigated with impure water. Slocum and Boyles then decided to learn the incidence of *Escherichia coli* on market vegetables. *Escherichia coli* was present on 31.5 per cent of samples and coliform bacteria on 78.3 per cent. These organisms were found in higher percentages on vegetables which grow below the ground than on the edible portions growing above the ground. No difference in incidence of these bacteria was observed on vegetables raised on different areas. The question to answer is whether these results indicate that such pathogenic bacteria as *Eberthella typhosa* can also appear on fresh vegetables. That soil bacteria including *Escherichia coli* do not prevent development of *Eberthella typhosa* seems to be indicated by experiments by Pfuhl.[31] Mair [32] found that *Eberthella typhosa* could survive in natural soils in large numbers for about 20 days, and in small numbers for 70 to 80 days. Survival in sterilized soil was said to be much shorter.

Sterilization of Vegetables. Under some conditions, it may be necessary to sterilize vegetables. Different methods have been studied. Champion and van de Velde [33] studied chlorinated lime for this purpose. They gave special attention to *Escherichia coli,* pathogenic bacteria, and the total number of all forms. Chloride of lime showed satisfactory action on vegetables. Lettuce and carrots rinsed in .2 per cent solution were reasonably well disinfected but not sterilized. *Escherichia coli* was destroyed by this concentration and the total number of bacteria was frequently reduced to zero. Herfarth [34] also used bleaching powder for ridding vegetables of undesirable bacteria. Matsuoka and Shiraiwa,[35] however, believed that the required amounts of chlorine and the times were too long, owing to a rapid consumption of chlorine by the vegetable tissue when the vegetables were cut up. About 500 p.p.m. for 10 hours were required. Surfaces of apples or radishes were effectively sterilized in 30 minutes' exposure to a solution containing 50 p.p.m. of available chlorine. Results of another investigation on the same subject were reported by Suzuki,[36] who used chloride of lime in strengths between three and 200 p.p.m. *Eberthella typhosa* was killed in 15 minutes. *Eberthella dysenteriae* and *Vibrio comma* were killed in less than five minutes in solutions having three p.p.m. of available chlorine. Experiments with vegetables showed that *Eberthella typhosa* was not killed in 40 minutes in solutions having 200 p.p.m. of chlorine. This was said to be due to lack of penetration. Such data indicate that chlorine disinfection of vegetables might not yield a safe food in

31. Pfuhl. 1899. Centbl. Bakt., Pt. 1, 26, 49-51.
32. Mair. 1908. J. Path. 8, 37-47.
33. Champion and van de Velde. 1921. J. Amer. Med. Assoc., 76, 1511-12.
34. Herfarth. 1921. Centbl. Bakt., Pt. 1, Orig., 86, 33-44.
35. Matsuoka and Shiraiwa. 1927. Sci. Rpt. Gov. Inst. Infect. Dis., 6, 223-35.
36. Suzuki. 1930. J. Pub. Health Assoc., Japan, 6, 8.

all cases. This conclusion seems to have been confirmed in Japan by Bannai and Habu.[37] They could not satisfactorily disinfect such vegetables as greens, radishes, turnips, and spinach with bleaching powder, irrespective of its concentration or length of exposure.

Potassium permanganate has also been employed for disinfecting vegetables used in salads without cooking. Bernard [38] first washed them in clear water and then soaked them for one-quarter hour in a one to 2,000 potassium permanganate solution. He inoculated chopped green salad leaves with *Escherichia coli* and staphylococci and exposed them to the action of various strengths of potassium permanganate for periods of 10, 30, and 60 minutes. The permanganate strengths varied from one to 10,000 to five to 100. Under these conditions, even after one hour, the test organism was recovered. In strengths of over one to 1,000 the appearance of the salad was spoiled. Bernard concluded that this compound could not be used; such conclusion was also reported by Gohar.[39]

Public Health Significance of Sewage Sludge Used as a Fertilizer. An important factor in epidemiology is the longevity of pathogenic bacteria in nature, for upon such longevity rests the ability of various agents, such as foods, to disseminate communicable diseases. Chief among such agents may be fresh vegetables which are eaten raw. The possibility of such foods causing food-borne infections directs attention to the methods by which they may be infected. Before considering the modes of infection, however, information on the actual presence of *Eberthella typhosa* in sewage and the actual significance of fresh vegetables in disease dissemination should be reviewed.

The nature and origin of sewage would suggest that it would contain *Eberthella typhosa*. This organism might be present even though there were no recognized cases of typhoid fever. The missed case and the carrier make it possible for this organism to be present most of the time. Results of bacteriological examination of sewage have borne out this suggestion. Sir Alexander Houston in several Research Reports from the Metropolitan Water Board reported isolation of *Eberthella typhosa* from sewage. Wilson and Blair [40] showed that Belfast sewage contained *Eberthella typhosa* constantly over a period of three years. One milliliter of sewage contained at least one cell of *Eberthella typhosa*. Gray[41] found *Salmonella schottmülleri* in seven of 20 specimens of sewage from the city of Edinburgh. Seventeen of the samples, including all of the positive ones, were from one district. Gray used the Wilson and Blair direct-plating method and reported it to be superior to enrichment methods. Further review of literature on this subject need not be attempted here.

The significance of fresh vegetables is related to the use of night soil, sewage, and sewage sludge as fertilizer. This subject has been significant with respect to sewage farming, in which an attempt was made to utilize

37. Bannai and Habu. 1930. J. Pub. Health Assoc., Japan, 6, 3-6.
38. Bernard. 1937. Bull. Soc. Path. Exot., 30, 712-714.
39. Gohar. 1937. J. Trop. Med. and Hyg., 40, 115-117.
40. Wilson and Blair. 1927. J. Hyg. 27, 374.
41. Gray. 1929. Brit. Med. J., Jan. 26, 1929, p. 3551.

the constituents of domestic sewage as fertilizer. In some cases the water was desired. From the beginning, health officers looked with suspicion on the practice and rightfully so, if for no other reason than decency. It is true that in some oriental countries human excrement is used as fertilizer but such a practice need not be permitted in this country. The primary problem of sewage disposal is to get rid of the waste matter. The temptation in sewage farming has been to let fertilization of crops become the paramount object with less and less attention to the sewage disposal feature. Among many objections and technical difficulties is that which is before us in this discussion—the possible health hazards which may be involved in the use of fresh vegetables which have been fertilized with sewage or sewage sludge. Any method of sewage treatment which results in sludge presents serious problems of sludge disposal for some communities.

Good epidemiological evidence seems to exist in the literature to the effect that fresh vegetables may and have caused communicable diseases and that the sanitary condition of the soil from which they are harvested, is important. Bundesen [42] believed that more attention should be given to raw foods. Water cress, on account of the conditions under which it is cultivated, was viewed with considerable suspicion. It is well known that *Eberthella typhosa* may survive for long periods in the soil. Murillo [10] found these organisms to be active and virulent in garden dirt after 30 to 36 days. In sterile sand, they survived for 55 days. Galvagne and Calerin [43] studied this question in a privy vault, in a barrel, and in soil. The organism survived in the privy vault for 30 days, in the barrel 25 days, and in feces spread upon soil, after 10 days on the surface and 40 days in the deeper layers. Mair [32] could isolate the organism after 84 days from soil. Levy and Kayser [44] observed a survival period of over five months in a naturally infected privy vault. This included 14 days during which the infected feces had lain as fertilizer in a garden. Firth and Horrocks,[45] after a very comprehensive study, concluded as follows:

1. That there was no evidence to show that the *Eberthella typhosa*, when placed in soil, displays any disposition or ability to either increase in numbers or grow upward, downward, or laterally.

2. That *Eberthella typhosa* can be washed through at least 18 inches of soil by means of water, even when the soil is closely packed down and no fissures or cracks are allowed to exist.

3. That *Eberthella typhosa* is able to assume a vegetative existence in ordinary and sewage-polluted soil and survive therein for varying periods, amounting in some cases to as much as 74 days.

4. That the presence or absence of organic nutritive material in the soil appears to be a largely negligible factor, since *Eberthella typhosa* can survive in a soil indifferently well, whether it be an organically polluted soil or a virgin soil, and whether it receive dilute sewage or merely rainwater.

42. Bundesen. 1925. J. Amer. Med. Assoc., 85, 1285.
43. Galvagne and Calerin. 1908. Ztschr. Hyg. u. Infektionskrank. 41, 185-208.
44. Levy and Kayser. 1903. Centbl. Bakt., 33, 489.
45. Firth and Horrocks. 1902. Brit. Med. J., II, 936-943.

5. That an excess or great deficiency of moisture in soils appears to be the dominant factor affecting the chances of survival of the enteric bacillus in, or at least the possibility of recovering it from, soil.

6. That from fine sand allowed to become dry, *Eberthella typhosa* can be recovered on the 25th day after inoculation.

7. That from fine sand, kept moist with either rain or dilute sewage, *Eberthella typhosa* cannot be recovered later than the 12th day after fouling; this inability to recover the organism is due probably not so much to its death as to its being washed down into the deeper sand layers by liquids added.

8. That in peat, *Eberthella typhosa* appears to die out rapidly, as the microbe cannot be recovered from it after the 13th day; but this soil is so porous that it is quite possible the microorganisms were washed down into the deeper parts and consequently were not recoverable from the place of inoculation.

9. That from ordinary soil kept damp by occasional additions of rainwater *Eberthella typhosa* can be recovered up to and on the 67th day.

10. That from a similar soil kept damp by occasional additions of dilute raw sewage, *Eberthela typhosa* is recoverable up to the 35th day.

11. That from a similar soil kept damp by occasional additions of dilute sterile sewage the *Eberthella typhosa* is recoverable up to the 74th day.

12. That in a similar soil, after heavy rainfall, Eberthella typhosa at once disappears from the surface layers.

13. That from a similar soil, allowed after inoculation to become so dry as to be readily blown about as dust, the enteric typhoid infective material can be readily translated from dried soil and sand by means of winds and air currents.

14. That in a sewage-polluted soil recovered from beneath a broken drain, *Eberthella typhosa* is able to survive up to the 65th day.

15. That *Eberthella typhosa* is able to survive in surface soil on exposure to 122 hours of direct sunshine, extending over a period of 22 consecutive days. That from a piece of infected serge *Eberthella typhosa* is recoverable after the fabric has been exposed to 50 hours of direct sunshine spread over a period of 10 days.

Results from an investigation by Kligler [46] are also pertinent to this discussion. He made observations to determine danger of soil pollution and its relation to the spread of intestinal diseases. He reported that bacteria causing typhoid fever and dysentery succumb rapidly in nature. Both organisms died out in one to five days in septic tanks. The survival period of these organisms in soil was greater than in badly polluted materials. In moist natural soil with a pH of 6.6 to 7.4 typhoid and dysentery bacteria were recovered up to 70 days. In the same soil dry, they were not recovered after two weeks. It is quite obvious from Kligler's work that the character of the soil and other factors greatly influence the results that would be secured.

46. Kligler. 1921. Rockefeller Inst. Med. Res. Monog. No. 15, p. 75.

Longevity of pathogenic bacteria in soil is influenced by different factors. Among the important ones are character of the strain used, hydrogen-ion concentration of the soil, nature of competing bacteria, amount of moisture, penetration of light and air, and others. Sufficient data have been recorded in the literature to justify the conclusion that polluted soil may infect vegetables grown on it. Whether the problem is serious, however, depends on many factors. Any material, therefore, which may contribute pathogenic bacteria to soil becomes of considerable sanitary significance. Sewage sludge is in this category, because sewage from which it comes is known to contain pathogenic bacteria.

That sewage sludge should be applied with considerable caution to land on which crops to be eaten raw are to be grown has been recognized for many years. Wolman,[47] however, stated that if it is held in a sludge digestion tank for a period of not less than 10 days, its application to soil may be practiced without detriment to public health through the possible dissemination of vegetable-borne diseases. Wolman suggested regulations that would prevent delivery to farmers of sludge which had been digested for less than 10 days. He further suggested that the sludge should be used on ground only before crops are planted and not sprinkled over or brought into direct contact with growing vegetables. The origin and type of the sludge undoubtedly has considerable bearing on the results which may be secured. Whether Wolman's conclusions would apply to all types of sludge could be determined only by comprehensive investigations. New methods for isolating bacteria have been developed in the past few years. Use of these methods might reveal the presence of bacteria where the older methods gave negative results. The later paper by Ruchhoft [48] would suggest that it is now time for more work on the subject.

Ruchhoft reported isolation of *Eberthella typhosa* from activated sludge. Investigations of artificially inoculated aeration mixtures were then made. Five and one-half hours' aeration caused a decrease in viable *Eberthella typhosa* cells from 750,000 to 103,000 per milliliter. Four strains of *Eberthella typhosa* were used in experiments on longevity in activated sludge. At 20 to 22.2°C.(68 to 72°F.) one of the strains died rapidly; two others survived for eight to 10 days; the fourth, the Rawling's strain, was isolated after 13 to 14 days. Ruchhoft concluded that "wet activated sludge cannot be considered innocuous. At times it may be quite infectious. Caution should be observed when it is used as a fertilizer for truck gardens."

The application of sewage sludge to soil on which vegetables that may be eaten raw are grown, should be practiced with caution. While results of longevity studies on pathogenic bacteria in sludge would probably be greatly influenced by the nature of the sludge and the conditions under which it is stored and handled, sufficient data have been recorded to indicate the presence of viable *Eberthella typhosa* cells in sludge. At best the sludge should be added to the soil in the late fall, winter, or early spring.

47. Wolman. 1924. Engin. News-Rec., 92, 198-202.
48. Ruchhoft. 1934. Sewage Works J., 6, 1054-1057.

Wolman's advice that it should not be added to growing crops is probably sound. Sanitary districts and others concerned with the sale of sewage sludge to farmers might well consider the possible health hazards involved.

The Committee on Sewage Disposal of the American Public Health Association [49] recommended that fresh sewage sludge should be used only on forage crops and ploughed in promptly after application. It was recommended that sludge not be added to root crops or low-lying leafy vegetables which are eaten uncooked.

Penetration of Vegetables by Microorganisms. There is very little evidence that bacteria are able to penetrate very far into plant tissue. Careful experiments on this subject seem to indicate that bacteria die out rapidly when introduced into plants. Mills et al.,[18] after a study of the literature, were in accord with the above statement. They found that particulate matter corresponding in size to bacteria and protozoan cysts did not freely penetrate the substance of either fruits or vegetables; such matter remained on the surface or attached to portions which are usually removed when the vegetables are prepared for the table. Neither was the cut end penetrated to any appreciable extent. The skin of fruits and vegetables, then, like the skin of animals, is a barrier preventing infection. However, injured fruits and vegetables allowed the entrance of bacteria. Mills stated that bacteria might endure under such conditions for seven to 42 days. Data from experiments by Clauditz[5] and others on this subject are given in the paragraph above.

Preservation of Vegetables by Dehydration. The object of drying vegetables is to reduce the water content to such a point that bacteriological and chemical changes are prevented. Nichols, Powers, Gross, and Noel,[50] who made an extensive study of commercial dehydration, stated that fruits and vegetables with low amounts of sugar should not have more than five to 10 per cent of moisture; moisture in products with much sugar should not exceed from 15 to 20 per cent to assure best keeping qualities. Looking at the matter from another angle dehydrated foods may be considered as concentrated solutions in that there is a large amount of organic material and a very low amount of water. Prescott[51] stated that dehydrated vegetables generally contain less than 10 per cent of water. Cruess[52] described the dehydration of fruits and vegetables in California. We are indebted to the investigations of Prescott et al.[53] for much of our knowledge on the bacteriology of dehydrated foods. The bacteria on such foods are made up of those which have survived the process and those which have been contributed during handling and packing. Prescott found that few, if any, of the foods, were sterile. During long storage the number was reduced slowly. Mold spores were commonly present but yeasts were invariably absent. Bacteriological data reported by Prescott indicated a variable bacterial content. One sample of mixed vegetables had a plain agar count of

49. Engin. News-Rec. 119, 906.
50. Nichols et al. 1925. U. S. Dept. Agr. Bull. 1335.
51. Prescott. 1920. J. Bact., 5, 109-125.
52. Cruess. 1921. Amer. J. Pub. Health 11, 6-12.
53. Prescott, Nichols, and Powers. 1922. Amer. Food J. 17, 11-16.

1,600,000, a glucose agar count of 2,000,000, and a litmus lactose agar count of 2,000,000. Prescott also inoculated vegetables heavily with some of the undesirable organisms. When these vegetables were dried, most of them were killed. Prescott, Nichols, and Powers published further data on the subject. Moisture content was found to be one of the important factors and if its concentration was kept below a critical concentration the microorganisms did not change.

Clague [54] examined samples of dried vegetables which were received from manufacturers. The counts were determined on the gram basis. Numbers of microorganisms were much higher than on fruits, the numbers exceeding 500,000 per gram except on dill and garlic. Molds and yeasts were scarce on vegetables.

Prescott's [51] Method for Determining the Number of Microorganisms in Dried Foods. Ten grams of the sample, well broken up with aseptic precautions, were weighed into a tared sterile dish and later transferred into an Erlenmeyer flask containing 200 ml. of sterile tap water. After thorough mixing in order to get all of the particles wetted, the sample is placed at 37°C.(98.6°F.) for two hours to allow the tissues to come back to normal condition and permit an easy separation of bacteria. At the end of this time the sample is again agitated and aliquot portions are removed for culture. Plate cultures with glucose agar should be used. Incubation should be at 37°C. for 40 to 48 hours.

The microorganisms of dried foods are probably not different from those found in other foods. The flora is probably predominately sporulating since the heat treatment is sufficient to destroy the vegetating forms. Since bacteria require so much water, they probably do not function much in the spoilage of dehydrated vegetables. Insect infestation is a common cause of spoilage. The moth *Plodia interpunctella* is one of the commonest moths found in dehydrated vegetables. It is also responsible for the spoilage of other foods, such as cornmeal, oatmeal, and numerous ground breakfast foods. The infection is said to have its origin in the adult laying its eggs on the dehydrated food after drying and before it has been packed into the final container. Consequently, the packing rooms should be assiduously guarded from the moths.

Clague's [54] Method for Determining the Bacterial Content of Dried Vegetables. Two 10-gram portions of each sample are weighed into two wide-mouth dilution bottles containing 90 ml. of sterile water. The samples are shaken 100 times by hand and further dilutions made. Duplicate plates are made from each dilution using tomato agar, plain nutrient agar, and dextrose agar. These plates are incubated at 30°C.(86°F.) for 48 hours.

FROZEN VEGETABLES

A wide variety of vegetables are preserved by quick-freezing. The general bacteriological problems have been discussed in Chapter 1 as well as the effect of freezing on the microorganisms causing food poisoning. Based on considerable experience, Tressler [55] mentioned three criteria for judging quality of frozen vegetables: bacterial count, catalase and peroxidase tests, and determination of ascorbic acid content. A bacterial count under 80,000 per gram shows that the product was blanched at a high enough temperature to destroy all of the bacteria on the surface of the vegetables, that the blanched product was quickly cooled in clean water, and that it was properly handled before and after freezing. Tressler stated

54. Clague. 1936. Food Research 1, 45-59.
55. Tressler. 1938. Refrig. Engin. 36, 319-321.

that careless handling would result in a product with at least 100,000 or even 200,000 bacteria per gram. Lochhead and Jones [56] observed a wide variation in bacteria content of frozen vegetables soon after packing. During storage, however, this was obliterated. Coliform bacteria decreased during the first six weeks of storage to an insignificant number, while anaerobic sporeforming bacteria persisted somewhat. Defrosting at room temperature resulted in a marked increase in bacteria content while defrosting in the refrigerator resulted in a much smaller increase. Smart [57] reported that defrosted vegetables were unfit for food after 24 hours at 30°C.(86°F.). The types of bacteria in commercially frozen vegetables were without any significance so far as health is concerned. In this connection Berry [58] gave lactic acid-producing bacteria considerable importance because they survived freezing well and would develop conditions unfavorable to *Clostridium botulinum.*

General statements probably should not be made about the bacteria content of various frozen vegetables. The method of preparation and the soil from which they are harvested would have some influence.

Commercial machine-shelled peas show high infection with bacteria.[59] Blanching does not sterilize peas. They should be frozen as soon as possible after blanching.

Spoilage of quick-frozen vegetables may be of different types caused by various microorganisms. Bacteria have been found to be the main cause of spoilage in vegetables, while yeasts and molds may be the cause in fruits. Souring of quick-frozen vegetables was attributed by Sanderson and Fitzgerald [60] to *Streptococcus fecalis* which was believed to exist in the pod and on the kernels of corn examined aseptically. They believed that frozen vegetables would be sour to the point of inedibility before microorganisms forming enterotoxins could develop. Whether this would be the case must be determined experimentally.

Survival of Bacteria in Frozen Vegetables. Results of investigations in various parts of the United States and with various frozen vegetables indicate wide variations in numbers and types of microorganisms. Reasons for this are obvious since the flora of the raw products and processing methods and conditions would have considerable effect.

Smart and Brunstetter [61] reported that organisms in only three genera failed to survive freezing for three to 15 months when the foods were held at —9.4°C.(15°F.). All molds and yeasts survived. While lima beans were a good medium for development of microorganisms, the authors believed that no difficulty need be anticipated with keeping quality or

56. Lochhead and Jones. 1936. Food Research 1, 29-39.

57. Smart. 1939. Food Research 4, 293-298.

58. Berry. 1933. Science 77, 350.

59. Morris and Barker. 1936. (Gt. Brit.) Dept. Sci. and Indus. Res., Food Invest. Bd., Ann. Rpt. for 1935, p. 149.

60. Sanderson and Fitzgerald. 1940. Third Internatl. Cong. Microbiol., 1939, p. 710.

61. Smart and Brunstetter. 1936. The Canner. Aug. 15, 1936, 14-16.

healthfulness. Smart [62] found approximately 10,000 to 300,000 micro-organisms on fresh washed mushrooms. Steam blanching resulted in marked reduction in the number of viable bacteria. The bacteria in four packs were reduced from 275,000 to 720 per gram by blanching for five minutes in steam. About two-thirds of these surviving bacteria died out during six months' storage of the mushrooms in the frozen state. Members of the coliform group survived blanching but were not present after six months' freezing at —9.4°C.(15°F.). Sporeforming bacteria, molds, and yeasts did survive. Smart reported a marked ability of yeasts to survive low temperatures. Because of survival of many types of micro-organisms, Smart advised against eating frozen mushrooms in the raw or semiraw state.

Bacteriological studies on freezing peas, by Diehl, Campbell, and Berry [63] showed that shelled raw peas may harbor 1,000,000 microorgan-isms per gram, and that after about six hours at 21.1°C.(70°F.) the num-ber increases rapidly. While scalding at 93.3 to 98.9°C.(200 to 210°F.) for one minute kills some 99 per cent of the microbial flora, scalded peas permit very rapid growth of survivors and spoil fully as readily as raw peas. Microbial growth in both raw and scalded peas is largely prevented for 48 hours by a temperature of 0°C.(32°F.). The lower limit for micro-bial growth appears to be between —9.4 to —6.7°C.(15 to 20°F.). The usual storage temperature of frozen-pack peas of about —17.8°C.(0°F.) reduces the microbial population greatly in a few months. According to Lochhead and Jones,[64] micrococci (including staphylococci) comprised a much larger percentage of the organisms in frozen than in freshly packed products. Though 20°C.(68°F.) permitted development of greater num-bers than 37 or 4°C.(98.6 or 39.2°F.), organisms developing at 37°C. were proportionately the most resistant and those developing at 4°C. were the least resistant to freezing. This is due to the fact that as the tempera-ture of incubation is increased micrococci comprise a higher proportion of the organisms developing. Attention is directed to the importance of the Micrococcus group of bacteria in relation to the proper handling of frozen vegetables. The microorganism content of fresh spinach and kale used by Smart and Brunstetter [65] was high, the lowest count being 1,200,000 or-ganisms per gram. Scalding, freezing, and storage at —9.4°C.(15°F.) for about one year reduced this count more than 99 per cent. The microbial content of the frozen greens was characterized by a great diversity of types (genus names and some names of species are listed for organisms frequently isolated from fresh and frozen spinach and kale). While the counts were low in numbers and types present were those ordinarily found in fresh vegetables and in no way affect the wholesomeness of the product, there were enough viable microorganisms in the frozen greens to cause spoilage in a few hours at room temperature. When proper care is taken in handling good-quality spinach and kale and when when prompt cooling

62. **Smart.** 1934. The Canner, April 7, 1934.
63. **Diehl** *et al.* 1936. Food Research 1, 61-71.
64. **Lochhead and Jones.** 1938. Idem 3, 299-306.
65. **Smart and Brunstetter.** 1937. Idem 2, 151-163.

and freezing are practiced, high microbial counts should not be encountered in the frozen packs of these products.

More results were reported by Smart [66] on peas, beans, and sweet corn. Smart made a comprehensive study of the microbial content, quantitative and qualitative, before and after freezing of 18 varieties of peas, 35 varieties of sweet corn, 14 varieties of green and wax beans, and eight varieties of lima beans, all grown in the East. The microbiological examination included studies on both the fresh and frozen vegetables except for peas which were studied only in the frozen state. The microbial content of the fresh vegetables used in this experiment was high and varied considerably in different lots. Scalding and storage of these vegetables at —17.8°C. (0°F.) for five to seven months reduced the microbial content of sweet corn 94.6 per cent, green and wax beans 99.8 per cent, and lima beans 97.2 per cent. The average microbial content of frozen sweet corn was higher than that of the other vegetables studied. This might have been due in part to a higher initial contamination, which was associated with ear-worm infestation in the fresh corn; or to the greater protection sweet corn afforded the microorganisms which contaminated it, against the killing effects of low temperature, than was afforded by either green or lima beans. The sugar content, which is higher in sweet corn than in green or lima beans, was suggested as a possible protective factor. In spite of the great reduction of microorganisms resulting from scalding and freezing storage of vegetables the frozen products contained sufficient viable forms to bring about spoilage in a few hours at room temperature. The types of microorganisms frequently isolated from both fresh (except peas) and frozen vegetables are listed and were found to be those normally present on vegetables which would in no way affect the healthfulness of the frozen products provided they were kept frozen until they were used. Frozen foods, which are still essentially fresh foods, should be subjected to at least the same care in observing proper sanitary control during their preparation and storage as has been found necessary in handling fresh foods.

Nickerson's [66a] Modified Little Plate Method for Counting Bacteria in Frozen Vegetables. The Frost little plate procedure was modified by Nickerson to aid in plant sanitation in packing frozen foods. Three distinct changes were made in the procedure as given in Chapter 6.

1. The incubation period of four to eight hours was lengthened to 16 hours.

2. A new staining procedure was used.

3. A slide was developed which greatly facilitated the work.[66b] This slide limited the culture to a definite area, prevented washing off of the agar film during staining, and allowed more thorough mixing of culture and medium. Errors, resulting from the use of a glass marking pencil

66. Smart. 1937. Food Research 2. 515-528.
66a. Nickerson. 1943. Food Research.
66b. The slide was developed by M. G. Hallenback, formerly with the Birdseye Laboratories at 3 Commercial Street, Boston, Mass.

to confine the culture to a definite area and caused by mixing of pencil wax and culture, were entirely eliminated by use of the new slide.

The new slide was provided with a central elevated portion, of definite area, which served as the surface supporting the culture. Slides of this type were made either by grinding away the area around the raised portion or by fusing a piece of glass, of definite area, upon a larger glass strip.

A number of the special slides are cleaned in dichromate-sulfuric acid solution, thoroughly rinsed with water, wiped dry, and sterilized with dry heat in a closed metal container.

Small batches of nutrient agar are sterilized in homeopathic vials plugged with cotton. The vials are heated to melt the agar, after which the cotton plug is replaced with a sterile rubber stopper fitted with a medicine dropper and bulb. During preparation of cultures, the agar is kept molten by suspending the vials in a beaker of water kept at 45°C. (113°F.). Extension clamps are used to hold the vials.

Ten grams of the sample to be examined are placed in 90 ml. of sterile dilution water and thoroughly shaken. A sterile slide is placed on the warming table (metal plate regulated to 45°C. by clamping on a ring stand above a hot plate) and .1 ml. of the dilution water is delivered to the raised portion. The measuring pipette used (capacity $\frac{1}{10}$ milliliter) is lined with dilution water several times by filling and emptying the pipette, and the lower portion is wiped with a sterile kleenex before the culture sample is delivered. Four drops of molten nutrient agar (33.5 grams bacto-nutrient agar to 1,000 ml. of distilled water) are then placed on the raised portion of the slide and the material thereon mixed. Mixing is accomplished by running a sterile wire through the culture 15 times, first backwards and forwards then from right to left to right. The culture is spread to the edges of the raised portion by slanting the needle and following the edge of this area.

The slides, prepared as indicated in the foregoing, are marked for identification and placed in a moist chamber for incubation. After 16 hours' incubation at 25°C.(77°F.) cultures are removed, heated on a hot plate at about 80°C.(176°F.) until dried, treated with a one-per cent aqueous ferric sulfate solution for 20 seconds, washed, and treated with a .5-per cent aqueous solution of hematoxylin for 15 to 30 seconds. The agar film is then washed and dried.

The prepared slides are examined with the microscope, using a 16-mm. objective, to detect bacterial colonies. A blood cell counter greatly facilitates this work, since it provides means of recording both number of fields and number of colonies counted with minimum trouble.

Since .1 ml., from the equivalent of 100 ml. of dilution water, containing the bacteria from 10 grams of product, was used, the number of bacteria per gram of product is determined by the following formula:

$$100 \times \frac{\text{Area of little plate}}{\text{Area of microscopic field}} \times \frac{\text{Number of colonies found}}{\text{Number of fields counted}}$$

Since 100 fields were counted on all slides. the formula resolved to:

$$\frac{\text{Area of little plate}}{\text{Area of microscopic field}} \times \text{Number of colonies found.}$$

VEGETABLE JUICES

These products were developed largely on account of the success attained by fruit juices. They have never been as popular on account of carelessness in manufacture and over advertising. Some were hailed as foods while others were looked upon merely as beverages. The term ''vegetable-wines'' was used by a few of the pioneers. Some of the early efforts to prepare these products have been described by Cruess *et al.*[67] and Tressler.[68] Since vegetable juices are nonacid in character, some care must be used in processing them in glass jars or cans.

Two cases of typhoid fever traced to freshly prepared carrot juice prompted Geiger [69] to investigate the preparation of such products. Freshly prepared carrot juice was found to be slightly acid, pH 6.5 to 6.7. The bacterial content of fresh juice varied between wide limits, the greater number of organisms coming from the surface of the carrot and from steps in processing. Geiger believed that more care in washing and preparing the carrots for juicing should result in a virtually sterile product. Using elaborate precautions, however, a minimum count of 2,800 colonies per ml. was secured. The maximum count observed was three million colonies per ml. It is difficult to evaluate these figures since no standards exist for vegetable juices. Furthermore, Geiger believed that satisfactory standards could probably not be established.

The Department of Public Health of San Francisco passed regulations for pasteurization of vegetable juices. It was recognized, of course, that such regulations would not put completely sterile juices on the market but would greatly reduce the bacterial content and destroy pathogenic bacteria if they should be present. Experiments show that coliform organisms were usually eliminated and always sharply reduced. Experiments with a freshly isolated strain of *Eberthella typhosa* in all cases, even with liberal inoculations, showed that *Eberthella typhosa* did not die in the raw juices, indicating that it probably was not germicidal. Extended investigation would be needed to demonstrate conclusively that pasteurization at 60°C.(140°F.) for 30 minutes is not adequate and that 61.1 or 61.7°C. (142 or 143°F.) for 30 minutes would be preferable as a lower limit.

Chlorination was not found to be satisfactory. Even with carefully scrubbed hands, with carrots immersed in 200 p.p.m. chlorine, and with the use of completely sterilized apparatus, the bacterial count was appreciable and spoilage was not delayed. Despite these results, Geiger believed that chlorine sterilization might be given more study.

67. Cruess, Thomas, and Celmer. 1937. Fruit Prod. J., 16, 324; Cruess and Yerman. 1938. Idem 196-198; 210.
68. Tressler. 1937. Idem 196-198; 210.
69. Geiger. 1939. Amer. J. Pub. Health 29, 1244.

CHAPTER 16

MICROBIOLOGY OF TOMATO PRODUCTS

Tomatoes and tomato products are widely used in most countries. The fruit itself is used fresh or canned and has been shown to be a good food. Many tomato specialties are also available which add to the flavor of other foods. Various bacteriological problems arise in preparation of these products, and those people experienced in the use of the microscope are called on to determine whether satisfactory raw materials have been used. The laboratory procedure involved, known as the Howard mold-count method, is discussed later in this chapter. It has had a large part in improving tomato products and has won the confidence and respect of those processors who desire to pack only high-grade products. Among the many publications which have been issued on tomato products, that by Bigelow, Smith, and Greenleaf [1] is especially useful.

CANNED TOMATOES

Owing to the fact that tomatoes are generally sufficiently acid, less trouble has been experienced in preserving them than most other foods. This is indicated by lower cooks used in processing as well as fewer outbreaks of spoilage.

Strict enforcement of regulations by government food-control officials has made it necessary for canners to devote special attention to sorting and trimming in order to avoid trouble. Decayed portions owing to several types of rot must be removed if the finished product is to comply with the regulations. If the packer uses sound, ripe fruit a high-quality product will be obtained which will easily meet the new government tolerance of not over 50 per cent of microscope fields showing mold.

After careful preparation in the canning factory, tomatoes are filled into various sized cans which are carefully exhausted before closing. If this is not done difficulties of "swells" and "springers" may develop later.

Processes for canned tomatoes have been published by Bigelow.[2] These processes have been found to be satisfactory if cooling is adequately carried out. Heat-penetration studies on canned tomatoes have been reported by Magoon and Culpepper [3] and by Bigelow, Bohart, Richardson, and Ball.[4] The latter investigators stated that tomatoes packed together in such a manner as to interfere with the free movement of convection currents materially influenced heat penetration. Rotation of the cans makes it much easier for heat to penetrate. Canned tomatoes are cooled by two different procedures—air-cooling and water-cooling. The former is slower than the latter, which means that the temperature of an air-cooled can of

1. Bigelow *et al.* 1941. Tomato Products, Pulp, Paste, Catsup, and Chili Sauce. Natl. Canners Assoc., Washington, D. C., Bull. 27-L, Revised.
2. Bigelow. 1926. Natl. Canners Assoc. Circ. 15-L.
3. Magoon and Culpepper. 1922. U. S. Dept. Agr. Bull. 1022.
4. Bigelow *et al.* 1920. Natl. Canners Assoc. Bull. 16-L.

tomatoes will continue to rise for some time after the cans have been removed from the cooker. Heat is removed from the can much more quickly by water cooling. It should be pointed out that the process must be increased if water cooling is practiced.

Experience of the industry indicates that the center of the can of tomatoes should be brought to 87.8° C. (190° F.) if the cans are water-cooled, and to 76.7°C.(170°F.) if they are air-cooled. Some of the confusion over processing temperatures has been due to the two methods of cooling. Air-cooling is less efficient than water-cooling and the temperature continues to rise in the can after it has been removed from the bath consequently water-cooled cans must be cooked a little longer or at a higher temperature. The real object of processing canned tomatoes is to attain a minimum temperature which will insure sterilization. Canners are frequently tempted to lower process time and temperature in an attempt to secure a product with better quality. Siegel [5] observed that a 45-minute process gave a high-grade product and that it was hazardous to reduce processes.

Types of Spoilage in Canned Tomatoes. Canned tomatoes are not subject to much spoilage. The chemical and physical nature of the product makes sterilization relatively easy. They have an appreciable hydrogen-ion concentration which aids materially in their sterilization. Generally nonsporulating bacteria are found to be present. This is indicated also by the fact that the process times and temperature are much lower than those used for other foods.

Hydrogen Swells. These result from attack of the metal of the can by the acids in the fruit. Hydrogen swells are usually sterile when subjected to bacteriological examination.

Bacteriological Swells. The organism, *Lactobacillus lycopersici*, which causes this spoilage is discussed in a subsequent paragraph in this chapter. This organism is probably not the only one which may cause this type of spoilage, but it is among the most important.

Flat-Sour Spoilage. This spoilage is known in the trade as "flat-sour" spoilage although it is probably a misnomer. Bacteria have been isolated which materially alter the flavor of canned tomato juice and tomatoes. The microbiology of this spoilage is discussed under Tomato Juice later in this chapter.

Thompson [6] recommended incubation of samples to determine the efficiency of the process given canned tomatoes. He believed that such samples should be collected systematically each day.

TOMATO JUICE

This is one of newer tomato specialties which now enjoys wide acceptance by the public. Nothing is added to the fresh juice except salt. In view of the fact that it is a product, color and flavor of which are most important, great care is exercised to secure the right variety of tomatoes

5. Siegel. 1942. Canning Age, Jan. 1942.
6. Thompson. 1928. Canning Age, Convention Digest, 256-258.

and to pick them just when they make good juice. If they are picked too green, color suffers; and if they are picked too ripe, the flavor is not good. This product was defined a few years ago by food and drug control officials as "the unconcentrated, pasteurized product consisting of the liquid with a substantial portion of the pulp, expressed from ripe tomatoes with or without the application of heat and with or without the addition of salt." Under the Food, Drug and Cosmetic Act of 1938, a newer definition will probably be heard.

The manufacture of this product has reached a high level in America today, owing largely to results of scientific investigations. These have resulted in a product with good flavor and color and one rich in the vitamins present in natural tomatoes.

Processing Tomato Juice. Tomato juice is generally processed in boiling water under conditions which will bring the center of the can to 82.2°C. (180°F.). Agitation during processing has been found to increase markedly the rate of heat penetration into the can. Under some conditions the center of the can should reach 87.8°C.(190°F.) in order to allow satisfactory sterilization. In view of possible presence of relatively heat-resistant spoilage bacteria in tomato juice, trend in processing tomato juice has been to raise the temperature instead of lower it. Wessel and Benjamin [7] studied the problem with experimental packs and stated that "flash" processing in a tubular heat exchanger for a time and temperature equivalent to the thermal death-time of the contaminating organism, rapidly cooling to 87.8°C.(190°F.) before filling and processing the closed cans for a brief time at 100°C.(212°F.) to destroy nonresistant bacteria which might enter during filling, might be used commercially. Merrill cautioned against lowering processes for tomato juice when it is indicated that higher processes have little appreciable effect on general quality. He pointed out that lower process times and temperatures do not have the effect on quality that is attributed to them. His statements were based on results of experiments using both high and low filling temperatures and high and low processes. The low temperatures ranged from 63.9 to 68.3°C. (147 to 155°F.), while the high temperatures ranged from 76.7 to 93.3°C. (170 to 200°F.). As far as quality was concerned experienced canning technologists could find little difference between tomato juice processed at 100°C.(212°F.) for 20 to 35 minutes or at 112.8°(235°F.) for from 10 to 30 minutes.

Flat-Sour Spoilage of Tomato Juice. This is a bacterial defect of tomato juice which has been encountered since the juice has been packed, according to Pearce and Ruyle.[9] Although the spoilage has been known for many years, it has had more attention since Berry [10] discovered the causal organism to which he gave the name *Bacillus thermoacidurans*. Berry described the organism quite thoroughly. Only those characteristics of interest to processors of tomato juice will be given here. A concentration of 10

7. Wessel and Benjamin. 1941. Food Indus. 13, 40-42.
8. Merrill. 1941. Fruit Prod. J., 20, 176-177.
9. Pearce and Ruyle. 1938. The Canner 86, No. 12, Pt. 2, Convention Issue, 68-72.
10. Berry. 1933. J. Bact., 25, 72.

million spores per ml. gave a span over one logarithmic cycle on semi-log paper of 14.5°F. in tomato juice pH 4.5 and 17°F. in phosphate buffered water pH 7.0 with an extrapolated "F" value (destruction time in minutes at 250°F.) of .33 minutes in tomato juice and 3.8 minutes in phosphate buffered water.

This organism was isolated from off-flavored canned tomato juice. While the spoilage eventually ends in "flat-sour" type of spoilage an off-flavor is noticeable some time before a change in pH occurs. Berry believed that soil was the source of the organism.

Results of observations on packs of tomato juice (2,058 cans) and other acid foods (132 cans) showed a decrease in pH of all cans. The off-flavor appeared more quickly at 37°C.(98.6°F.). Heavier inoculations produced higher incidence of spoilage. Processing for 10 minutes at 100°C.(212°F.) gave 28 per cent more off-flavored cans than processing for 20 minutes at this temperature. *Bacillus thermoacidurans* produced the off-flavor in Indiana tomatoes but not in California tomatoes.

As the name of the spoilage indicates, the cans do not swell and considerable experience indicates slight if any loss of vacuum. This makes it impossible to separate spoiled from unspoiled cans because deterioration is not apparent until the can is opened and the contents examined. The organism, *Bacillus thermoacidurans*, is a little fastidious in its growth habits as revealed by results of investigations by Stern, Hegarty, and Williams.[11]

Non-thermophilic spore-forming anaerobic bacteria have been found as causes of spoilage in certain acid canned foods (pineapple and tomatoes). *Clostridium pasteurianum* was isolated from canned pineapple by Spiegelberg, Townsend, and Woerz and Lenane.[11a] The latter found them in canned tomatoes from different sections of the country.

Pearce and Ruyle [9] believed that multiplication in the canning plant was the crux of the problem of control. Consequently, cleanliness and elimination of all sources of contamination are first among whatever efforts are made to control the trouble. Pearce [12] again emphasized the seriousness of this type of spoilage. He reported discovery of viable spores of the spoilage organism in cans which had not undergone change in flavor at the time of sampling. Such results raised the question as to the significance of these dormant spores and what conditions of storage might favor their development. Williams [13] also recognized the necessity of strict cleanliness in the canning factory in order to reduce possibilities of contamination. While regular bacteriological technic has been used in most of the work on this trouble, Cameron [14] suggested another method. A few cans of tomato juice were taken from the line at the beginning of the day's pack and another set after the plant has been running for two or three hours. We may quote Cameron for details:

11. Stern, Hegarty, and Williams. 1942. Food Research 7, 186-191.
11a. Woerz and Lenane. 1943. The Canner, Feb. 6, 1943, 11-12; 24.
12. Pearce. 1940. The Canner 90, No. 12, Pt. 2, Convention Issue, 49-51.
13. Williams. 1940. Idem 48-49.
14. Cameron. 1935. The Canner, July 20, 1935.

"*Sampling Procedure.* A. Take 24 cans **daily** at the beginning of the pack or as soon thereafter as the filling temperature reaches 82.2°C.(180°F.) or 87.8°C.(190°F.). Under no circumstances should samples be taken before 180°F. is reached, because it is necessary to destroy all bacteria not in the spore form. Invert the cans and allow them to air cool. Apply suitable codes and set aside for daily observation.

"B. Take 24 cans after the line has been operated for from two to two and one-half hours without extended shut-down periods. Invert cans and treat otherwise as indicated under "A." When the samples are taken, make certain that the filling temperature is at least 180°F.

"C. If there are two or more lines, it is not suggested that 24 cans be taken from each line. A total of 24 cans from all lines at each sampling period should be sufficient.

"*Observations for Spoilage.* Make daily observations. If spoilage contamination is high, a significant number of swells should appear within two or three days, although, in some instances, it is possible that only flat-sour spoilage may occur. At the end of ten to fourteen days, open flat cans and taste to determine whether there is flat-sour spoilage. If no swells occur in samples from the first period, open one-half the number of the samples at the end of five days to determine whether flat-sour spoilage has occurred. Record the occurrence of swells and flat sours on a card especially drawn up for that purpose.

"*Interpretation of Results.* If spoilage is low (below 25 per cent) in samples from the first sampling period and materially lower or absent in the second sampling period, the condition of the equipment and the efficiency of the clean-up may be regarded as satisfactory.

"If there is high spoilage in the first samples followed by low spoilage or its absence in the second samples, there is the indication that there has been an overnight development of spoilage bacteria which infects the product during the first part of the day's run. In other words, this contrast means that at the start of the pack there are bacteria in the equipment which are gradually washed out by the tomato juice. The cleaning of the equipment should be carefully supervised, and all utensils and pipe lines should be thoroughly flushed with water before beginning the day's run. Hot water may be used for flushing and is preferable to cold water because it will serve the double purpose of cleaning out the machinery and at the same time heating it to a point where a proper filling temperature may be had from the outset. At night, however, the clean-up should consist of first flushing with hot water and following with cold water until all equipment is cooled.

"Significant spoilage in both the first and second lots of samples indicates that there is a persistent source of contamination and the canner should make a detailed search for "pockets" in the equipment. If he cannot improve the situation by his own efforts, he should consult some qualified laboratory.

"*Process.* If unprocessed cans show little or no spoilage, this is not to be taken to mean that the process may be reduced with safety. A favorable condition at any part of the pack carries no insurance that this condition will be maintained throughout the pack. Where the condition of the unprocessed test cans is favorable, however, the canner may be satisfied that his process has provided a high factor of safety against spoilage.

"The following open bath processes are suggested for tomato juice. These processes should be adequate where precautions are taken to keep contamination at a low level.

Processes at 212°F.

Size of Can	Time at 212° F.
No. 1	15 minutes
202	20 minutes
No. 2	25 minutes
No. 10	40 minutes

"In the event of high spore contamination, these processes may not be adequate. There are no data upon which to base process suggestions that would apply to all conditions of contamination. The initial temperature should be 170° to 180°F. To insure this temperature, the juice should be filled at about 190° F.''

Stern, Hegarty, and Williams'[11] **Procedure for Isolating Bacillus thermoacidurans from Spoiled Tomato Juice.** The laboratory technic involved in isolation of *Bacillus thermoacidurans* from spoiled tomato juice was studied by Stern, Hegarty, and Williams. The technic finally adopted was to open the can aseptically and to place one ml. of the juice in each of three sterile Petri dishes, pouring into each dish approximately 20 ml. of proteose peptone acid agar medium. After hardening, the plates should be incubated at 55°C.(131°F.) for 48 hours. Preliminary to this work organoleptic examinations should be made on the juice.

TOMATO PUREE (PULP)

This is prepared by concentrating tomato juice to a fraction of its original volume. This results in economy in shipping and storage. Arengo-Jones and Grant[15] stated that a solid content of 22.5 per cent could be obtained without greatly influencing flavor or color. They also reported the rate of heat penetration into canned purée to be very low.

Tomato puree is packed in several sizes of cans, depending largely where the product is going to be used. It is filled into cans between temperatures of 76.6°C.(170°F.) and 82.2°C.(180°F.). If processed at all, it is done in boiling water. The larger cans are generally not processed. Enough heat is present in the product to sterilize them.

Characteristics of tomato purée (pulp) and various methods for examining it have been received by Bigelow, Smith, and Greenleaf.[1]

TOMATO PULP

This is much like tomato juice, the main difference being consistency. This latter quality is secured by concentrating the juice in glass-lined tanks or similar containers. Effort is also made to preserve color and prepare a juice which will not settle. The manufacture of tomato pulp as well as methods of examining it have been reviewed well by Bigelow, Smith, and Greenleaf.[1]

Catsup. This is probably the commonest tomato product; it has received considerable attention from those who are engaged in the enforcement of the Food and Drugs Act. The methods of manufacture are outside the scope of this book.

Catsup must be bottled hot if it is to keep. Much trouble results in the factory from careless and haphazard methods of temperature control. In these days of delicate control apparatus, there is no need to use obsolete methods, such as placing a thermometer in a few bottles to determine the temperature. Ayers and Osborne,[16] prompted by fermentation and spoilage troubles in bottled catsup, used thermocouples for determining the temperatures in the bottles. Wide variations existed at different points within the container. The temperature in the center of the catsup was nearest the filling temperature; at other points it fell below the filling temperature. The differences in temperature of the contents of a given container varied with the temperature of the container when it was filled with hot catsup. In commercially filled catsup bottles the temperature on

15. Arengo-Jones and Grant. 1939. The Canner, October 21, 1939.
16. Ayers and Osborne. 1927. Glass Container 6, Nos. 3 and 4.

the inner surface of the cap never reaches a point high enough to have pasteurizing value. This is true regardless of whether the container is upright or on its side. A short heat treatment for hot filled bottled catsup after capping was effective in raising the temperature sufficiently to prevent spoilage. Catsup should be filled at temperatures above 77°C. (170°F.), capped, and processed for at least five minutes at 88°C.(190°F.).

Spoilage of Tomato Catsup. The chemical constitution of tomato catsup makes it susceptible to the attack of various microorganisms. Those which attack carbohydrates seem to be most important; at least the deteriorations in which sugar is attacked are most common. They result in both a change in state, owing usually to gas formation, and a change in flavor. "Black neck" in the bottle is a chemical decomposition resulting from formation of iron tanates.

Spoilage by Yeasts. Fermenting yeasts have caused much trouble in tomato products. Many of these cases have not been reported in the literature. A case of this type of spoilage was reported by Ayers.[17] The bottles when opened showed considerable pressure and in one bottle it was over 30 pounds per square inch. When the bottles were opened the catsup was forced out quite violently in a manner well known to those who have examined spoiled foods in tin or glass containers. A yeast was isolated which could form gas in catsup of different brands. Ayers found that the yeast was not destroyed at a temperature of 60°C.(140°F.), for five minutes but was when heated 10 minutes, in tomato juice. Ayers called attention to the fact that the temperature of the catsup as it leaves the filling machines is not the true temperature after it is in the bottle. The final temperature is influenced by the temperature of the bottle. He gave the following data:

A 9½-ounce bottle which was at room temperature at about 24°C.(75°F.) was filled with tomato catsup at a temperature of 76.8°C.(170°F.). The temperature at the top of the bottle immediately after filling was only 68.3°C.(155°F.). Such data indicate that the bottles should be hot when filled. Ayers' experiments indicated that when the process of bottling hot without subsequent holding was depended on, a filling temperature as high as 82.2°C.(180°F.) would not stop yeast fermentation if the infection occurred at the time of bottling and if the bottles were at room temperature.

Spoilage of Catsup by Bacteria. Bacteria have also been incriminated in the spoilage of catsup. Mickle and Breed[18] experienced difficulty at first in isolating viable bacteria from spoiled tomato catsup, but when fresh samples and proper media were used, colonies appeared on the plates. Tomato juice and tomato pulp broth were found to be most satisfactory. An organism, *Lactobacillus lycopersici*, was isolated and described. This organism had been encountered by many who had worked on tomato products spoilage. For instance, investigators at the Research Laboratory of the National Canners Association showed that spoilage in tomatoes was due to the survival of a non-sporulating organism which may be repeatedly recovered from swelled canned tomatoes. While the organism does not form spores, it is sufficiently heat resistant to survive some processes. Esty stated that the organism was distributed throughout sections in which tomatoes are raised and also in and about factories which have been packing tomato products. It was further stated that the presence of this non-sporulating organism in canned tomatoes was not always proof that it could survive sterilization applied to the cans. Defective cans were suggested as one method by which the organism could get into the can. Esty also stated that the presence of yeasts in canned tomatoes probably indicated a defective container. *Lactobacillus lycopersici* is much like *Bacillus pleofructi*. However, Mickle and Breed believed they were sufficiently different to justify a new name for the organism which they isolated from catsup. They discussed the organisms as follows:

17. Ayers. 1926. Glass Container 5, No. 4.
18. Mickle and Breed. 1925. N. Y. Agr. Expt. Sta., Tech. Bull. 110.

"However, the typical strains of *B. pleofructi* isolated from fruit juices were pleomorphic, showing as coccobacilli in broth and agar cultures and as long slender rods in fruit juices. They were also distinctly capsulated. Thirteen of the sixteen cultures produced acid in litmus milk, ten of them sufficient to curdle. Three aberrant strains resemble *L. lycopersici* more closely in that they produced no change in litmus milk.

"The two organisms resemble each other in showing the general characters of lactobacilli. They differ from the usual lactobacilli in that they produce gas abundantly under proper conditions. They are alike in that they produce this gas most abundantly in the fruit juices from which they are isolated, while they ordinarily fail to produce gas in sugar broths."

This microorganism was observed by Esty[19] of the National Canners Association. *Lactobacillus lycopersici* was also described later by Pederson[20] who studied 11 strains besides the original one isolated by Mickle and Breed. Pederson described six other bacteria as agents in the spoilage of tomato produces as follows:

Lactobacillus lycopersici, Lactobacillus gayoni, Lactobacillus pentoaceticus, Lactobacillus mannitopoeum, Lactobacillus plantarum, Leuconostoc pleofructi.

They are completely described in Pederson's original paper. None of the species were resistant to heat and should, therefore, be easily killed when proper methods of manufacture are used. Pederson devised a key for identification of these organisms without a study of all characteristics.

Windred[21] mentioned an organism from tomato pulp which caused sliminess. It resembled *Bacillus ruminatus* Gottheil.

Gaseous spoilage of tomato products was also studied by Jones.[22] The organisms found to be responsible were Lactobacilli in all cases; three species were found— *Lactobacillus gayoni, Lactobacillus lycopersici*, and a species closely related to the latter. These organisms were found to be readily killed by heat, one minute at 75°C. (167°F.) being sufficient even when they were growing in concentrated tomato pulp. Jones, therefore, pointed out the necessity of using clean methods of manufacture.

Preservation of Catsup. The various substances added to catsup have been studied to determine whether they might have bactericidal properties as well as flavoring properties. At other places in this book, the agents discussed below are discussed in other relations. Probably no one substance will function as a preservative alone.

Salt. Salt is added to catsup to improve the flavor. Bitting[23] tested its effect on preservation. He added 5, 10, 15, 20, 25, and 30 grams of salt to 100 ml. portions of catsup which were then inoculated with mold. Five grams of salt seemed to have no effect. In the culture containing 10 grams growth appeared as quickly as it did in the control, but was not as extensive. In the 15-gram solution or culture, growth was retarded for four days. With the 20-gram culture, growth was five days slower than the normal; after that, there was only slight development. The results with the 25-gram culture were not materially different from those with the 20-gram culture. No development occurred in the 30-gram culture.

Bitting also made inoculations with a yeast. The 5-gram culture caused slight inhibition while the 10-gram solution allowed a thin film to form in two days, which ordinarily developed as a rather thick film in 24 hours. No development of the yeast took place in the 15-gram salt medium.

19. Esty. 1925. The Canner 60, 94-96.
20. Pederson. 1929. N. Y. Agr. Expt. Sta., Tech. Bull. 150.
21. Windred. 1928. Roy. Soc. N. S. Wales, Proc., 62, 341-349.
22. Jones. 1936. Canad. Canner and Food Mfr., 7, 9-14.
23. Bitting. 1909. U. S. Dept. Agr., Bur. Chem. Bull. 119.

Analyses of 18 brands of catsup by Pederson and Breed [24] showed a salt content which varied from 1.6 to 3.7 per cent.

Sugar. Bitting tested the effect of sugar on both the mold and yeast in tomato bouillon. No effect was noticeable until the concentration of sugar had reached 25 grams per 100 ml. In this concentration growth appeared as readily as in the lower concentrations but was less abundant. In the 25- to 40-gram concentrations there was less development as the amount of sugar was increased. In the 70- and 75-gram media, growth was delayed one day. In the 80-, 85-, and 90-gram media, growth was delayed two days. Bitting prepared heavier solutions. When the concentration reached 170, 180, 190, and 200 grams, development of molds was very slow.

The yeast could not develop in concentrations above 80 grams per 100 ml. Pederson and Breed [24] found sugar to be ineffective as a preservative in catsup. Even 35-per cent concentrations inhibited certain types only. Combinations of sugar and salt proved effective; 15 per cent of sugar and 3.5 per cent of salt stopped growth of all organisms used except the yeast. According to Pederson and Breed, the sugar content of 18 brands of catsup varied between 15 and 26.3 per cent.

Spices. These are added to catsup mainly to improve the flavor. However, some of them possess bactericidal properties. Bitting [23] investigated this property in tomato bouillon using water infusions, acetic acid extracts, and oil extracts of spices. Bitting's experiments with water extracts showed that cinnamon and cloves were the strongest antiseptics. These checked growth when used in small amounts; three ml. of the cinnamon extract and one ml. of the clove extract were required to inhibit the growth of the mold. Mustard, paprika, and cayenne pepper also inhibited growth but five ml., the highest concentration used, did not stop growth. Ginger, mace, and black pepper had no effect. Bitting secured slightly different results with the yeast. Cinnamon showed the strongest action; cloves came next. After these came cayenne and black pepper. Ginger, mustard, and mace had no effect.

Since acetic acid extracts of spices are frequently used in catsup, Bitting used such extracts of allspice, celery, cloves, coriander, garlic, and black pepper. These extracts were added to tomato bouillon; one set of tubes was inoculated with the mold and the other with the yeast. No growth of mold occurred with allspice and cloves; the celery extract checked growth considerably. Coriander and garlic were not very active. The yeast seemed to be just a little more resistant. The oil extracts were also tried, but were believed to be unsuitable since too large an amount would have to be used. The delicate tomato flavor was interfered with.

Vinegar and Acetic Acid. According to experiments by Bitting, 30 per cent of 50-grain distilled vinegar added to tomato bouillon checked the growth of mold. As the concentration increased, the extent of inhibition was also increased. Acetic acid was much more active. One-half of one per cent gave about the same inhibition as 30 per cent of vinegar.

24. Pederson and Breed. 1926. N. Y. Agr. Expt. Sta. Bull. 538.

Sodium Benzoate. This compound is permitted as a preservative in catsup. In 1909 Bitting studied its preservative ability in tomato bouillon inoculated with a yeast and a mold. Tomato gelatin was prepared with .1, .5, 1, and 2 per cent of sodium benzoate. There was no development of the mold in the presence of 1 and 2 per cent of benzoate; in the presence of .5 per cent, growth was retarded, but normal in the presence of .1 per cent. Experiments with catsup containing 1/16, 1/12, and 1/10 of 1 per cent were also made. These concentrations checked growth of the mold and even caused distortion of the filaments of the mold. Irregular results were secured as far as complete inhibition of growth was concerned. Bitting was led to conclude that sodium benzoate gave uncertain results as a preservative. Pederson and Breed [24] reported that .2 per cent of sodium benzoate was required to stop the growth of all bacteria used in their studies. However, certain types were less resistant. A yeast isolated by Ayers was quite resistant. Tanner and Strauch [25] previously reported that yeasts were quite resistant to sodium benzoate.

Effect of Combinations of Ingredients as Preservatives in Catsup. Pederson and Breed [24] studied this problem and suggested a number of formulas. They discussed the matter as follows:

Combinations of sugar and salt were found to be much more effective in preventing spoilage than a combination of either one with acid. In fact, with the addition of 25 per cent of sugar to the medium, the acid required to stop growth of the organism could be lowered only about .1 per cent. Four per cent of salt had no more effect than the sugar in lowering the quantity of acid required. On the other hand, 10 per cent of sugar and 3.5 per cent of salt inhibited growth of the majority of organisms, while 15 per cent of sugar and 3.5 per cent of salt inhibited growth of all except the one resistant yeast. The addition of a small quantity of acetic acid, that is, from .3 to .4 per cent, lowered these figures but slightly. Combinations of 15 per cent of sugar, 3 per cent of salt, and .3 per cent of acid; of 15 per cent of sugar, 2.9 per cent salt, and .4 per cent acid; or of 10 per cent sugar, 3.5 per cent salt, and .4 per cent acid were all found to be effective in preventing growth of the bacteria.

HOWARD AND STEPHENSON'S METHOD FOR MICROANALYSIS OF TOMATO PRODUCTS

The original statement of this procedure by Howard [26] and by Howard and Stephenson [27] has been modified several times. Much has been written for and against the method. It may leave much to be desired when compared with other methods of analysis, but when the procedure for arriving at the technic is studied, its merit is also obvious. The method has played an important role in raising the standard of tomato products and forcing out of business those manufacturers who were unwilling to use the best methods of manufacture.

This method for the examination of catsup which has been in use since 1911, [28] probably because no one has proposed a better one to replace it, is based on examination of tomato products for yeasts, molds, and bacteria, and it is thus assumed that

25. Tanner and Strauch. 1926. Soc. Expt. Biol. and Med. Proc. 23, 449.
26. Howard. 1911. U. S. Dept. Agr., Bur. Chem. Circ. 68.
27. Howard and Stephenson. 1917. U. S. Dept. Chem., Bull. 581.

such microorganisms indicate decayed fruit was used or the method of manufacture is faulty. This latter possibility was found to be the case in an instance quoted by Howard and Stephenson. A manufacturer was using ripe, fresh tomatoes and still secured high counts of microorganisms in the final product. They resulted from faulty methods in the factory and not from the presence of rot in the tomatoes. The method may thus serve the manufacturer as well as the consumer.

Association of Official Agricultural Chemists'[28] Procedure for the Howard-Stephenson Method. The section numbers in the procedure are those in the original publication.

30   APPARATUS

(a) *Compound microscope.*—Equipped with good objectives and oculars, giving magnifications of approximately 90, 180, and 500 diameters. For convenience of use the lenses should be adjusted so as to be parfocal. A mechanical stage is highly desirable. It is essential that the combination giving the low magnification be capable of adjustment to give an area of the field of view of 1.5 sq. mm. (a circle whose diameter is 1.382 mm.). With the higher powers the working distances must be ample to allow the free use of the blood-counting cell.

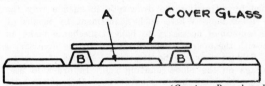

(*Courtesy Bausch and Lomb Optical Co.*)

FIG. 3. Side View of the Cell.

The flat circular area A, the contact areas B, and the 33 x 33 mm. cover glass, are optically worked. These areas should be thoroughly cleaned before using the cell. Cotton batting dipped in strong hydrochloric acid is used in cleaning the surfaces. Rinse thoroughly with distilled water, then with alcohol, and finally with acetone. All particles of lint or dust must be removed with a camel-hair brush.

Place a drop of the fluid to be tested on the circular disc A. Spread it evenly over the disc in order to avoid squeezing out the more liquid parts around the edge of the disc. Rest the cover glass against the edge of one of the contact areas B, and tilt it gently down onto the liquid. It is important to note that no liquid should be allowed to penetrate between the contact areas and the cover glass, since this would interfere with the proper contact between these surfaces. The use of too much fluid is to be avoided for this reason.

The cell has been constructed to give a depth of 0.1 mm. of fluid when the cover glass is in sufficiently close contact with the areas B so that Newton's rings may be observed. The rings appear between the surfaces in contact. These colored bands, or rings, are accurate criteria of the proper contact. Inability to obtain them is an indication of insufficient cleaning of the contact surfaces.

In making a mold count it is necessary to have a field of 1.5 sq. mm. area, that is the diameter of the field should be 1.382 mm. This may be obtained by using a 16 mm. objective and a 10X eyepiece, adjusting the draw-tube length to give the correct field size. For ready calibration a circle 1.382 mm. outside diameter is etched on the right hand rail. Using the objective and eyepiece mentioned the microscope is focused on the etched circle. The draw tube is then adjusted until the circumference of the microscope field coincides with the *outside* of the circle.

(b) *Drop-in cross-ruled disk.*—For estimating lengths of mold filaments, an ocular drop-in disk cross-ruled in sixths of the ocular diaphragm opening is desirable.

(c) *Blood counting cell.*—Preferably ruled in the Thoma or the old Neubauer system of rulings. The so-called "improved" system of Neubauer may be used if the depth of the chamber is 1/10 mm. and care is taken to select the proper sized area for counting.

(d) *Howard mold-counting cell.*—Constructed like a blood-counting cell but with unruled central disk about 19 mm. in diameter.

28. Official and Tentative Methods of Analysis of the Association of Official Agricultural Chemists, Fifth edition, 1940.

29. Bonney. 1942. Assoc. Off. Agr. Chem. J. 25, 464-465.

28   MOLDS

In making mold counts of tomato juice, catsup, and puree, use the product as is, but with tomato pastes mix first with H_2O so that the tomato solids will give a sp. gr. of 1.035. If the paste contains salt or other substance that influences the sp. gr. materially, take this into consideration in making the dilution.

Clean the special Howard cell so that Newton's rings [30] are produced between the slide and the cover glass. Remove the cover and place a small drop of the well-mixed sample upon the central disk; using a knife blade or scalpel, spread the drop evenly over the disk, and cover with the glass so as to give an even spread to the material.

It is of the utmost importance that the drop be taken from a thoroly mixed sample and spread evenly over the slide disk. Otherwise, when the cover slip is put in place the insoluble material, and consequently the molds, may be more abundant at the center of the mount. Avoid using a drop that is much greater than is sufficient to fill the space between the center disk and cover slip. Discard any mount showing uneven distribution, absence of Newton's rings, or liquid that has been drawn across the moat and under the cover glass.

Place the slide under the microscope and examine with such adjustment that each field of view covers 1.5 sq. mm. This area, which is of vital importance, may frequently be obtained by adjusting the draw-tube in such a way that the diameter of the field becomes 1.382 mm. Where such adjustment by means of the draw-tube is not possible, it is sometimes necessary to have a mechanic make an accessory drop-in ocular diaphragm with the aperture accurately cut to the necessary size. The diameter of the area of the field of view can be determined by use of a stage micrometer, or by employing the rulings on the blood-counting cell. In order to use the latter method it is necessary to bear in mind that a square whose diagonal is 1.382 mm. has sides of approximately .977 mm. Hence the mm. scale on the blood-counting cell can be used by such adjustment that the circle of the field of view cuts off the necessary amount from each corner of the mm.-ruled square. When the instrument is properly adjusted, the quantity of liquid examined per field is .15 c.mm. (.00015 cc.).

Examine at least 25 fields from each of two or more mounts taken in such manner as to be representative of all sections of the mount. Observe each field, noting the presence or absence of mold filaments and recording the result as positive or as negative, as the case may be. No field should be considered positive unless the aggregate length of not more than three of the filaments present exceeds approximately ⅙ of the diameter of the field. Calculate the proportion of positive fields from the results of the examination of all the observed fields and report as percentage of fields containing mold filaments.

Realizing the necessity of some study of tomato histology, Howard prepared "Outlines For Instruction in Tomato Microscopical Methods" in which much preliminary work is outlined. Accuracy in using the Howard method for tomato products requires some experience on known samples as well as rigorous attention to details. Here are some of the factors which must be closely attended.

Standardization of Microscope Field. The microscope field must be carefully standardized to an area of 1.5 square millimeters. To meet this requirement, the field must have a diameter of 1.382 mm. The best method to accomplish this is probably with a stage-micrometer. While applying the Howard count for molds and yeasts and spores

---

30. These are rainbow colored rings produced at the point of contact when polished plates of glass are pressed against each other. In a letter to the author Dr. Howard commented as follows about Newton's rings: "In talking with various users of the method, and observing others in its employment, I find that some are not as careful, in obtaining the Newton's rings as they should be . . ."

31. Since difficulties were anticipated in securing blood-counting cells with the old Neubauer ruling, Bonney [29] proposed substitution of this last paragraph under procedures for counting "Yeasts and Spores" and "Bacteria" by the Howard method for the description of technic as previously given.[47]

to frozen fruit products, Needham and Fellers[32] used a compound binocular microscope and found many advantages. Since a field 1.382 mm. in diameter is specified, it was found that a Bausch and Lomb binocular microscope of 163 mm. tube length with a 10× ocular, a 16 mm. objective, gave a field 1.422 mm. in diameter. The error in the diameter of the field is less than three per cent.

Mounting Specimens on the Mold-Counting Chamber. Clean and polish both the chamber and cover glass until a good display of Newton's rings is obtained when they are in contact.

The great dependence on an arbitrary procedure for the control of tomato products and the differences in results which are obtained with even slight modifications in technic has been shown by Howard.[33] The standard procedure as stated by Howard reads: "Remove the cover and place by means of a knife blade or scalpel, a small drop of the sample on the central disk." In order to determine whether the instrument used to place the drop of sample on the disk had any influence on the results, Howard used various ones, such as a large scalpel, a medium scalpel, a platinum loop, a pipette, and a forefinger of the operator. Such a series of examinations was made by three microscopists. The results indicated that a considerable percentual variation occurred with the methods of working used. It was stated that the pipette method of delivering a drop of sample to the slide was not satisfactory. Medium and large scalpels were most satisfactory in that the smallest variations in mold counts were secured when these were used.

Clean the slide and *spread* the drop over the disc as evenly as possible with the point of the scalpel before putting the cover glass into position, which, in this case, should be done quickly. Make sure that Newton's rings are present. If the specimen thus mounted does not seem to the naked eye to be uniform but has streaks or uneven patches in it, this condition, if slight, can sometimes be overcome by tapping the center of the cover two or three times gently with a pencil point or the wooden top of the scalpel handle. This tapping operation should not be extensive or the consistency of the entire sample will be changed; much of the cellular fibrous material will work out toward the edge, leaving only the fine granular and liquid portion of the main part of the disc. Test this by tapping the cover glass 30 to 40 times and compare the resulting mount with one properly made. The effect of tapping varies greatly with the thickness of cover glass used. Cover glasses are made in several different thicknesses, of which the following seem most common: 1 mm., .6 mm., and .4 mm. Although the thick form is not as easily broken as the others, the medium one is preferable for general rountine work. A properly mounted specimen should be practically free from air bubbles.

The size of the drop should be so taken that when the cover slip is in place the disc will be just about covered by the specimen without any very appreciable proportion having been squeezed out into the moat surrounding the disc. No mount is proper for use if Newton's rings are not visible when the mounting is completed.

Howard[33] suggested the use of the net micrometer for making mold counts. This was considered desirable for the instructions that no field should be considered positive unless the aggregate length of the filaments present exceeds approximately one-sixth of the diameter of the field, left too much to the analyst. Two of Howard's colleagues, Stephenson and Makenison, suggested having the mold counting chamber ruled in squares of .23 mm. on a side (1/6 of 1.382 mm., the diameter of the field in view).

32. Needham and Fellers. 1924. Science 59, 341.
33. Howard. 1922. Assoc. Off. Agr. Chem. J. 6, 50-51.

Mold filament counting usually seems obscure to the novice. This situation clears considerably with instruction by competent mold counters and experience. Risk of loss by seizure of the product should indicate the desirability of using only trained counters. Various structures in the tomato and mold filaments have similar appearances and it is not easy for an inexperienced microscopist to distinguish them. Haynes [34] mentioned the following six characters which help to distinguish mold filaments from tomato filaments:

1. *Segmentation:* Some mold filaments are segmented. Tomato filaments are never segmented.

2. *Granulation:* Mold filaments are granular. Tomato filaments are clear, vitreous, or fibrous.

3. *Parallelism of the Sides of the Cell Wall:* The sides of the cell walls are always parallel in mold hyphae. In tomato filaments the sides of the filament often appear constricted or expanded.

4. *Comparison of Focal Plane or Side Walls:* The two side walls of mold hyphae are always in focus at the same level while the side walls of other filaments may come into focus at two different levels. This results from the fact that hyphae are cylindrical or tubular filaments while the tomato filaments are ribbon-like.

5. *Character of Branching:* Branching occurs at sharp angles among mold hyphae while it may be rather indefinite among other filaments.

6. *Appearance of Ends of Filaments:* The ends of mold hyphae are blunt, never flared or pointed as they may be on tomato filaments.

29   YEASTS AND SPORES

Fill a graduated cylinder with H_2O to the 20 ml. mark and add the sample till the level of the mixture reaches the 30 ml. mark. Close the graduate, or pour the contents into an Erlenmeyer flask, and shake vigorously for 15-20 seconds. To assure thoroness the mixture should not fill more than ¾ of the container in which the shaking is performed. For tomato sauce or pastes, or products running high in the number of organisms or of heavy consistency, use 80 ml. of H_2O with 10 ml. or 10 g. of the sample. In the case of exceptionally thick or dry pastes, it may be necessary to make an even greater dilution.

Pour the mixture into a beaker. Thoroly clean the counting cell so as to give good Newton's rings. Stir thoroly the contents of the beaker with a scalpel or knife blade and after allowing to stand 3-5 seconds remove a small drop, place it upon the center disk of the blood-counting cell, and cover immediately with the cover glass, observing precautions to secure production of Newton's rings and avoiding the overflowing of the liquid so as to run in between the cover and supporting surfaces of the slide. Allow the slide to stand not less than 10 min. before beginning to make the count. It is customary to make the count with a magnification of about 180 to 220 diameters.

If a counting cell [31] ruled by the Thoma or old Neubauer system is used, count number of yeast and mold spores on one-half of ruled squares on disk (this amounts to counting the total number in 8 of the blocks, each of which contains 25 of the small ruled squares, or a total area examined of .50 sq. mm.). (If a counting cell having a depth of chamber of 1/10 mm. but ruled by some other system is used, care must be taken that the total area examined is .50 mm.) Total number thus obtained equals number of organisms in 1/60 c.mm. (1/60,000 ml. of original product) if a dilution of 1 part of sample with 2 parts of water is used. If a dilution of 1 part of sample with 8 parts of water is used, multiply the number by 3. In making the counts, the analyst should avoid counting twice the organisms that rest on a boundary line between two adjacent squares.

34. Haynes. 1941. Canning Age, August 1941, 438-439; 458.

30   BACTERIA

Determine the number of rod-shaped bacteria from the mounted sample used in 28, but before examination allow the sample to stand not less than 15 min. after mounting. Use a magnification of about 500 diameters.

If a counting cell [31] ruled by the Thoma or old Neubauer system is used, count and record number of bacteria having a length greater than 1½ times their width, in an area including 5 of the small squares. Count number in 5 such areas, preferably 1 from near each corner of ruled portion of slide and 1 from near the center. Since each of these groups has an area of .0125 sq. mm. the total area examined is .0625 sq. mm. (If a counting cell having a depth of chamber 1/10 mm. but ruled by some other system is used, five .0125 sq. mm. areas from different parts of the slide should be examined so that the total area counted covers .0625 sq. mm.) Determine total number of rod-shaped bacteria in the .0625 sq. mm. area examined and multiply by 480,000. This gives the number of this type of bacteria per ml. If a dilution of 1 part of sample with 8 parts of water, instead of 1 part of sample with 2 parts water, is used in making up the sample, then total count obtained must be multiplied by 1,440,000. The bacteria sometimes exhibit slight motion and thus may present

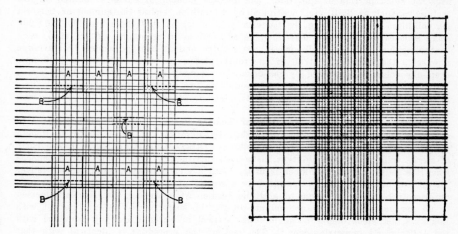

FIG. 4. Showing Thoma and Improved Neubauer Hemacytometer Rulings.

A. Thoma. One sq. millimeter divided by lines into twenty spaces in each direction, each space equalling 1/20 sq. mm. To facilitate counting every fifth space is subdivided by a line through the middle. (After Howard and Stephenson, 1917.)

B. Neubauer. The improved Neubauer ruling has been recently introduced. The square millimeter in the center is divided into 25 squares each in turn being subdivided into 16 squares of 1/400 square millimeter area. There are, therefore, 400 of these small divisions in the center, grouped into 25 units of 16 smaller squares. This subdivision is accomplished by a "split" fifth line which appears through the microscope as a distinct but transparent boundary for each of the 16 smaller squares.

momentarily an end view instead of a side view. For this reason it is necessary to keep them under observation long enough to establish their true character. Thus far it has proved impracticable to count the micrococci present as they are likely to be confused with other bodies frequently present in such products. See page 678 for explanation of calculations.)

The above is a complete statement of the Howard-Stephenson method. During the many years that it has been used, various suggestions have been made to make it easier to use. Some of these are discussed below.

Explanation of Calculations. Fig. 4 has been prepared to make somewhat clearer the explanation of the areas denoting the yeast and spore and bacterial counts. The light lines in the figure show the arrangement of rulings on the entire slide. The squares (*A. A.* etc.), and rectangles (*B, B,* etc.) designated in the figure by the heavy lines indicate the portions used for the yeast and spore and for the bacterial counts, respectively. The eight large equares, *A, A,* etc., are the squares used for yeast and spore counts. Each of these squares has 25 of the small squares. The sum of organisms counted in the eight squares marked *A, A,* etc., is the number in 1/60 c.mm. if a dilution of one part of product to two parts of water is used.

Yeast and Spore Count. The ruled square on the slide is 1 mm. on each side and the cell is 1/10 mm. deep. The volume of the ruled part is therefore 1/10 c.mm. The ruled area is divided into 16 large squares and the number of organisms is counted in eight of these, which is equivalent to 1/2 of 1/10 c.mm., or 1/10 c.mm. If a dilution of one part of the product to two parts of water is used 1/) of 1/20 c.mm., or 1/60 c.mm. as representing the actual amount of original stock in which organisms are counted, is obtained.

Bacterial Count. The rectangles, *B, B,* etc., each including five of the smallest squares, represent the areas used in making the bacterial count. Similar rectangles of equal area might be selected, the object being to count five such areas well distributed over the ruled portion of the slide. The *average* number of bacteria counted on five rectangles, such as *B, B,* etc., multiplied by 2.4 million, equals the number of bacteria per milliliter. In calculating the bacteria, it is observed that there are 400 (20×20) small squares on the slide. The numbers of bacteria in rectangles (*B, B,* etc.), each containing five of these small squares, are counted and an average made. This average represents the bacteria in 1/80 of the total ruled area. Since the cell is 1/10 mm. deep, the volume represented by the organisms counted is 1/80×1/10 or 1/800 c.mm. With the usual dilution of one part of product to two parts of water the actual volume in which the number of organisms is determined is 1/3 of 1/800 cm. or 1/2400 c.mm. or 1/2,400,000 ml.

Vincent's Method for Examination of Tomato Paste. Vincent[35] has attempted to overcome the errors of the Howard method by adapting the Breed smear to tomato products. The method is described as follows: ''The catsup is diluted with two parts of sterile water, since this dilution has proven satisfactory in counting most specimens when the Zeiss counting chamber is used. With a sterile pipette calibrated to deliver .01 ml. the diluted catsup is deposited on a second glass slide and evenly spread over an area of 1 sq. cm. by means of a sterile needle. After drying, the slide is immersed in 95 per cent alcohol for one minute to fix the smear, dried in air, stained with Loeffler's methylene blue for two minutes, washed in water, dried and examined with the 1/12 in. oil immersion lens.'' The rest of the procedure is identical with that outlined under Breed's microscopic method for counting bacteria in milk. The microscope is standardized to bring the diameter of the field to .205 mm. Thirty fields are counted and the average for one field is multiplied by three on account of the dilution of the catsup. This result is then multiplied by 300,000, which represents the number of bacteria per milliliter.

Vincent compared this microscopic count with the count secured with the Zeiss blood counter. The latter count was always much smaller than the former. Vincent believed that the cocci should be counted since they probably take as important a part in the spoilage of tomatoes as the rods.

This method has not received official recognition.

Bertarelli and Marchelli's[36] Method for Controlling Tomato Products. These two Italian investigators made a comparative study of the Howard and Vincent methods for the control of tomato products. They believed the Vincent method to be superior although both methods were open to considerable error. They proposed the following method:

Two milliliters of the product are made up to 50 ml. with distilled water, shaken thoroughly, and filtered through four thicknesses of muslin. The residue is carefully washed with another 50-ml. portion of distilled water and the filtrate collected in the

35. Vincent. 1918. J. Bact., 3, 183-185.
36. Bertarelli and Marchelli. 1920. Ann. d'Ig. 30, 309-322.

beaker containing the original filtrate. The combined filtrate is estimated to contain all but about 20 per cent of the bacteria originally present and in estimating the bacterial count a correction is made for this. By careful manipulation, 1/200 ml. portions are dropped from a pipette on glass slides, spread over the surface with a platinum wire, fixed with alcohol-ether, stained with Loeffler's methylene blue, and subjected to microscopic count in the usual manner.

Miller's[37] Modification of the Howard and Stephenson Technic. Another modification of the Howard and Stephenson technic was suggested by Miller. He suggested preliminary heating of the material (20 ml. of tomato juice or 5 ml. of paste diluted to 30 ml.) successively with from 2 to 4 ml. of Loeffler's alkaline methylene blue and 2 ml. of Ziehl-Neilsen's carbol-fuchsin. After reducing any excess of stain with 5 to 10 drops of formaldehyde the material is diluted with 60 to 120 ml. of water and shaken well. It is then used for preparation of slides according to the usual technic. Artificial light should be used for the examination of the slides.

Smith's[38] Methods for Detection of Mold in Various Products to Which Tomato Sauce Has Been Added. These methods were devised for detecting presence of mold filaments in several products to which tomato sauce has been added. Owing to the fact that the technic differs for the various products, Smith gave the procedure for the following three groups. Since different samples of products within the same group vary in consistency, the analyst's ingenuity must be used when applying the method to certain samples.

TOMATO SOUP WITH OR WITHOUT CREAM

The chief difficulty with examination of this product is the large amount of starchy material, such as cracker crumbs and flour, which may be present. In the case of heavy soups, it is best to place the can in hot water for several minutes until thoroughly warmed. This facilitates stirring and measuring the soup. With thinner products this preliminary heating is unnecessary. Place 10 ml. of thoroughly mixed soup in a large centrifuge tube, 50 ml. or larger is best, and add three ml. of a concentrated solution of potassium hydroxide—a little more will do no harm. (If desired, from 10 to 15 ml. of methyl ethyl ketone may be added at this point to remove the fat. After stirring thoroughly, the ketone, which rises to the top and is stained red, is poured off. Since the potassium hydroxide saponifies the fat, the ketone is usually unnecessary.) Stir for a few minutes until the starch in the soup has been dissolved and the tissues cleared. Now add sufficient water to fill the tube and centrifuge. In heavy soups the gelatinizing of so much starch sometimes interferes with the proper settling of the solids during centrifuging. If the liquid remains cloudy it may be necessary to discard the sample and start again with only five ml. of soup and proceed as usual with the usual three ml. of potassium hydroxide. When the supernatant liquid is clear and the solid particles have settled out, the liquid should be poured off and examined for mold fragments. If no mold filaments are found in the supernatant liquid, add enough water to the residue in the centrifuge tube to bring it to the original volume of soup, mix, and count by the usual Howard technic. If desired, a few drops of gentian violet may be added. This stains the mold filaments and facilitates counting.

Since the KOH has been found in time to etch the mold-counting slide and cover glass, it is best, if much mold counting is to be done, to neutralize the alkali with a few drops of 50 per cent phosphoric acid. This is done after the supernatent liquid is discarded and before the water is added to bring the volume up to the original 10 ml.

PORK AND BEANS, SPAGHETTI WITH TOMATO SAUCE, SPAGHETTI WITH MEAT BALLS OR MEAT, RAVIOLI, CHILI CON CARNE, AND TAMALES

All of these products are treated essentially the same. The unopened can is placed in hot water and heated until the contents are thoroughly warmed. This preliminary heating thins the tomato sauce so that it will separate more readily from the solid portions of the product. The can is then opened and the contents dumped into a rather

37. Miller. 1920. J. Ind. Eng. Chem., 12, 766-769.
38. Smith. 1940. Personal communication from Dr. B. J. Howard.

coarse sieve, a six-mesh one has been found satisfactory. With some products the sauce runs through at once, but in the case of some beans and spaghetti it may taken 10 or more minutes. It should drain at least until a major portion of the liquid part has been drained through. Mix the sauce thoroughly, place 10 ml. in a centrifuge tube, and proceed as for tomato soup. In counting products containing meat care should be used not to confuse mold filaments and muscle fibers which bear a superficial resemblance to each other although the muscle fibers are usually much thicker and the striations are often visible.

SARDINES OR OTHER FISH WITH TOMATO SAUCE

This product presents difficulty owing to the large amount of fat or oil. Since the sauce as made apparently contains little added oil, that found present in the finished product comes from the fish themselves. For this reason it is possible to discard the oil without removing any of the constituents of the original sauce. The can is heated in boiling water and the sauce drained off as in other products. The sauce is then thoroughly mixed and a portion placed in a centrifuge tube. This is centrifuged until the oil rises to the surface. The oil is discarded and 10 ml. of the remaining sauce is treated with three ml. of KOH just as in the other products. With herring tidbits or other products when there is but little oil, it is not necessary to remove it. Care should be used in the examination to differentiate between mold filaments and muscle fibers from the fish.

United States Department of Agriculture Standards for the Howard Method. The Government officials first stated standards for the Howard procedure [39] as follows: Not more than

Molds in 25 per cent of the microscopic fields.
Yeasts and spores—25 in 1/60 milliliter.
Bacteria—25 million per milliliter.

In 1916, the Bureau of Chemistry became a little more lenient and stated that there would be no condemnation unless the following were exceeded:

Molds in 66 per cent of the microscopic fields.
Yeasts and spores—125 in 1/60 milliliter.
Bacteria—100 million per milliliter.

On May 14, 1931, the Food and Drug Administration stated that the mold standard of 1916 was unjustifiably liberal. They stated that proceedings would be recommended against tomato products if mold filaments were present in more than 50 per cent of the microscopic fields. Government food-control officials believed that this new standard was a just one in view of the great improvements which had been made in the tomato-products industries. On July 27, 1938, it was announced in connection with tomato juice that pending consideration of a further lowering tomato juice would be regarded as adulterated when mold filaments are present in more than 25 per cent of the fields. Since these announcements material improvements have been effected by the industry. In the light of these advances, these mold-count limits are now unjustifiably liberal.

During the 1940 packing season, and pending consideration of further reductions after this season, actions under the Act will be instituted against tomato catsup, puree, and paste if mold filaments are present in more than 40 per cent of the microscopic fields, and in the case of tomato juice if

39. Howard. 1912. U. S. Dept. Agr.. Yearbook for 1911, 297-308.

mold filaments are present in more than 15 per cent of the microscopic fields.

Comminuted tomato products are often used in the fabrication of other food products, such as tomato soup, beans with pork, spaghetti sauce, etc. The use of comminuted tomato products with mold counts in excess of the above limits in the manufacture of other foods constitutes adulteration. Action has been and will continue to be taken against foods in which illegal comminuted tomato products have been used. Soon after promulgation of this standard, the Food and Drug Administration was petitioned to raise the tolerance from 15 per cent to 20 per cent of microscopic fields. The Administration appraised the situation and concluded that in the case of tomato catsup, purée, and paste, it was not unreasonable to expect canners to meet the mold tolerance of 40 per cent of microscopic fields announced in 1940. In the case of tomato juice, the tolerance was placed at 20 per cent of microscopic fields. Adequate allowances were to be made in applying the tomato-juice tolerance to those articles which have been homogenized. Comminuted tomato-juice products exceeding these mold-count tolerances cannot be used as ingredients of manufactured foods such as tomato soup, spaghetti sauce, etc., since this would constitute adulteration.

The Howard method has been criticized from many sides. It has inherent weaknesses, but they do not seriously invalidate the method. It has been stated that the method has been responsible for distinct improvement in quality of certain tomato products. It has enjoyed the approval of many of the largest manufacturers who have been interested in a high-grade product. A few of the criticisms may now be presented.

Prescott, Burrage, and Philbrick[40] condemned Howard's method of enumerating mold hyphae, yeast cells, mold spores, and rod-shaped bacteria in tomato products. Among the various sources of error were mentioned the low magnification used on unstained preparations making it almost impossible for the analyst to differentiate between particles of plant tissue and the desired microorganisms. These authors mentioned the fact that no attention was given to the coccus types which may be important in the spoilage of tomato products. Prescott and his colleagues also mentioned the indefinite directions which were often given. Bitting and Bitting.[41] in a little monograph entitled ''Ketchup,'' gave many objections to the Howard method of controlling tomato products. Some of these may be enumerated as follows: (See also Darling.[42])

1. Too indefinite directions concerning the putting of material into the counting chamber, the amount of shaking, the cleanliness of apparatus, sterility of apparatus, etc.

2. The use of different units of volume for reporting results.

3. Impossibility of differentiating between bacteria and bits of debris.

4. Arbitrary selection of rod bacteria for counting since cocci may be confused with other bits of material.

5. Yeasts and spores are counted together. They cannot be separated from each other nor from many other particles.

40. Prescott, Burrage, and Philbrick. 1917. Abs. Bact., 1, 51.
41. Bitting and Bitting. 1925. Ketchup. Pub. by authors, Lafayette, Ind.
42. Darling. 1922. N. Y. Agr. Expt. Sta. Bull. 91.

6. In counting mold hyphae no distinction is made between large masses in the field and one thread.

7. No real relation exists between the organisms counted and the decomposition, for mere numbers of organisms are not always coincident with putrefactive activity.

Bitting and Bitting also pointed out that certain steps in the process of manufacture might influence the number of organisms which may be counted. A pulp may vary from an unevaporated tomato juice to a concentration which is represented by an evaporation of a volume of water up to 60 per cent and catsup may vary from a watery consistency to one which will scarcely flow from the bottle. They stated that a method which did not take into consideration the concentration would be deficient for judging the quality of a food. For example, a tomato juice with 10,000,000 bacteria per milliliter when evaporated to one-half its volume might have more than twice that number. A thin pulp with 10,000,000 bacteria per milliliter might easily be worse than a heavier one with 30,000,000 or 40,000,000 cells. These authors stated that it would, therefore, be impossible to concentrate any pulp to the consistency of a paste and have it pass the standards. Vincent maintained the above objections. Another critique on the Howard method was published by Darling.[42] He was apparently more concerned with the shortcomings of the methods as an analytical procedure than with its use as a control method in a different field. In spite of the accuracy of probably all of Darling's criticisms, the Howard method serves a useful purpose today in keeping the tomato-products industry on a high level.

Despite shortcoming which are obvious to microscopists, the Howard-Stephenson method for determining whether decayed unfit fruit has been used or whether bad practices have existed in the factory, or both, has had a great part in bringing the tomato-products industry to its present high position. This method has helped to get rid of manufacturers of tomato products who have not cared to pay much attention to the condition of tomatoes which they were using. Seizures by the government have cost them much money. It is necessary to be certain that the analyst is competent and understands the procedures for if he does not the packer is working under a false sense of security. Schools are conducted each summer at several places where potential analysts may be trained by those who are competent and who have had experience in counting microorganisms under the microscope. The Department of Agriculture of the Dominion of Canada [43] found the Howard-Stephenson count of value in improving quality of tomato products. While working with manufacturers, a progressive lowering of the mold count was observed during the years 1933 to 1936.

Tice [44] used the Howard method in the control of tomato products manufactured in the state of New Jersey. He stated that he found a direct relationship between the methods of manufacture or character of the initial materials used in tomato products and the microscopical results secured by Howard's method. He stated that, "The average of the counts

43. Lochhead. 1938. Prog. Rpt. to the Dominion Agr. Bacteriologist for the Years 1934, 1935, and 1936. Ottawa, Canada, p. 33.

44. Tice. 1918. New Jersey State Board of Health, Ann. Rpt.

on tomato pulp, soup stock or catsup taken from stock which appeared to be acceptable from a visual inspection, were as follows: Molds in 19 per cent of the fields, yeasts and spores 20 per 1/60 c.m.m., bacteria 34,000,000 per cc." He continued, "Our experience has been similar to that of B. J. Howard of the Bureau of Chemistry, United States Department of Agriculture, that in factories where sufficient sorting is in effect, thorough washing is employed and where promptness in handling is observed, the mold count is of greater importance in judging the condition of the raw stock than counts on the other organisms. High counts of yeasts and spores are usually indicative of secondary spoilage."

Insect Fragment Count of Tomato Products. The Federal Food, Drug and Cosmetic Act prohibits shipment in interstate commerce of a food which consists in part or wholly of filthy, decomposed, or putrid animal or vegetable substance. Such a food is adulterated and subject to seizure and destruction. Tomato products which are made from worm and insect infested tomatoes are judged to be adulterated. Consequently, the manufacturer must make certain of clean raw materials and the control officer must develop methods for detecting this sort of adulteration. This effort places a new burden on the manufacturer. The Federal control officials [45] have stated that the canner must know the degree of infestation of the fruit which he is processing and must use sufficient care in the factory to cope with it.

The insects which cause most trouble are the tomato fruit worm and the tomato pin worm. The former, in sweet corn-producing areas, is known as the corn ear worm. The latter, as its name indicates, burrows into the fruit, leaving a pinhole.

Howard's [46] Method for Determination of Insect Fragments in Tomato Products. The following method is fundamentally a method devised by Mr. J. D. Wildman for the recovery of small insects from vegetable greens:

APPARATUS AND MATERIAL REQUIRED

One two-liter Erlenmeyer flask.

One rubber stopper of such size as will just allow it to be crowded down into the interior of the flask. The stopper must be supported by means of a suitable stiff rod (⅛-inch diameter) about three inches longer than the height of the flask.

One Büchner funnel and seven cm. rapid action filter paper with a rather hard finish.

One six-cm. disk cut from a piece of 60-mesh wire screen.

One wide angle field, Greenough type, binocular microscope giving magnifications of about 10× to 30×.

USEFUL ACCESSORIES

One fine point indelible pencil for indicating on the filter paper the location of each insect part as located.

One metal ring 8½ cm. in diameter strung with very fine wire or human hair to form a grid with the strands about 7 mm. apart. This is set over the filter paper which has been placed in a Petri dish for convenience of examination. It serves as a guide in systematically searching the paper over for insect fragments.

One fine teasing needle made by inserting the eye end of a No. 12 sewing needle into a suitable soft wood handle. This is used for manipulating the insect fragments on the filter paper when necessary to secure more suitable view for identification.

45. Harrison. 1937. Canning Age, May 1937.
46. Howard. Private communication.

A miniature coffer dam has proven a valuable aid in order to prevent any portions being lost by being drawn over the margin of the filter disk. A medium soft rubber ring about $\frac{3}{16}$ inch thick is cut of such diameter as to just fit into the Büchner funnel and cover a marginal strip of the filter paper about $\frac{1}{4}$ inch wide. This rubber gasket is held down firmly in place against the paper by a suitable glass cylinder slightly longer than the inside depth of the funnel and kept in place by a thin spring brass yoke clamp which has an inch hole in the center through which the stem of the funnel passes, allowing it to come up and rest against the cone of the funnel. The two arms are bent up in such manner that the ends press down upon the upper edge of the glass cylinder. In order to remove it, it is only necessary to spring the ends back to release the glass collar. The width of the portions forming the arms should be such as will furnish a good moderate pressure without being so strong as to endanger breakage. (See Fig. 2.)

TECHNIQUE OF METHOD

The stopper, by means of the supporting rod, is pressed down into the Erlenmeyer flask. In the case of purée, catsup, etc., 200 ml. of the product to be tested is placed in the flask and 20 ml. of gasoline added. The product and gasoline are then thoroughly shaken together. Water from the tap at about room temperature is run into the flask in such manner as to produce vigorous agitation until the contents rise in the neck of the flask to about the point to which the stopper can be raised. Allow contents to stand for five to 10 minutes, occasionally giving the contents a gentle rotary motion by means of the stopper and rod to facilitate the lighter portions coming to the top. Finally, slowly raise the stopper until it fits firmly into the neck of the flask so as to entrap the gasoline portion and a narrow strip of the aqueous sub-layer, the latter being not over $\frac{3}{16}$ inch deep. (See Fig. 1.) The analyst should avoid entrapping more of the aqueous layer than is needed since, by so doing, an amount of tomato cellular material may be retained that will interfere with filtering and render more difficult the subsequent finding of insect parts. As a guide in this respect it is well to determine by experiment and mark on the neck of the flask the point to which the watery layer should be brought to attain the best results. After the stopper has been raised into place, about 10 or 15 ml. of water is added to the entrapped portion to slightly increase its volume. Carefully pour the entrapped portion onto the filter, underneath which has been placed the wire screen disk. Rinse out the neck of the flask to remove any remaining insect fragments and add to the material on the filter paper. Remove the filter paper and examine the residue under the microscope for insect parts, recording the number of fragments of each kind found and spotting their location by use of the indelible pencil. While search for fragments is being made, it is advantageous to keep the filter paper fairly moist.

In the case of paste, 50 or 100 ml. of product is used, according to concentration. Before the gasoline is added, the test sample is mixed with 200 to 300 ml. of water. After the test has been completed, the results are calculated back to a 200-ml. basis according to the amount of test portion used.

Because of the difficulty of avoiding entrapping so much cellular material as to make the filtering difficult, some preliminary tests have been made in entrapping a somewhat larger amount and pouring it into a 500-ml. Erlenmeyer flask fitted with stopper and rod similar to the large flask. In the small flask a second treatment of the first portion is made before it is thrown on the filter paper. This procedure will reduce the cellular material retained and, from some preliminary tests made, no very appreciable number of insect fragments is lost.

Wilder and Joslyn's [47] **Method for Estimating Worm and Insect Fragments in Tomato Products.** After much study these authors recommended the following procedure:

REAGENTS

Sulfuric acid.—12 N.

Potassium permanganate solution.—Dissolve 100 grams of $KMnO_4$ in 1 liter of warm water and filter.

47. Wilder and Joslyn. 1937. Assoc. Off. Agr. Chem. J. 20, 648-655.

APPARATUS

Separatory funnel.—1 liter.
Graduated cylinder.—250 ml.
Graduated cylinder.—50 ml.
Filter paper.—7 cm.
Petri dish.—10 cm. diameter.

PROCEDURE

Put 200 ml. of the tomato sauce, juice, or catsup (or 100 ml. of tomato paste) into the separatory funnel. Add 35 ml. of gasoline, stopper, invert, and shake. Open the stopcock slowly to release the pressure. Close the stopcock and shake well until the gasoline is thoroughly emulsified. Open the stopcock to release pressure, close, and invert. Add 200 ml. of the sulfuric acid solution. Move in a rotary motion until the gasoline is well mixed.

Effect on the Total Number of Fragments Found of Varying the Amount of Gasoline (Modified Procedure)

Ml. of Gasoline	Number of Fragments
25	50—42—46
35	54—59
50	53—57—55

Add 150 ml. of the permanganate solution in 50 ml. portions to prevent excessive foaming. After the addition of each portion move the funnel vigorously in a rotary motion until all traces of the permanganate and the manganese dioxide have disappeared. After the last addition, fill the funnel with water and allow to stand for 1 minute.

Drain off the lower layer of water and pulp until the bottom of the gasoline layer is about 2 inches from the stopcock. Add 200 ml. of water, allow to stand for 20-30 seconds, and then drain as before. Add 100 ml. of water and drain again as soon as the gasoline has risen to the surface. If all pulp is not gone, repeat the washing until the water layer is free of pulp.

When the washing is completed, drain off the water until the bottom of the gasoline layer is about one-half inch from the stopcock. Filter the remaining water and gasoline through the filter paper, washing the inside of the funnel well with water. Examine the filter paper under the microscope for worm and insect fragments in the usual manner, as described by Howard.

Microanalysis of Tomato Pulp, Purée, Sauce, and Paste by the Howard Method.[48] The following procedure is the Howard method for these tomato products. It serves the same purpose here that the original method does for canned tomatoes and juice.

APPARATUS

(a) *Compound microscope.*—Equipped with good objectives and oculars, giving magnifications of approximately 90, 180, and 500 diameters. For convenience of use the lenses should be adjusted so as to be parfocal. A mechanical stage is highly desirable. It is essential that the combination giving the low magnification be capable of adjustment to give an area of the field of view of 1.5 sq mm. (a circle whose diameter is 1.382 mm.). With the higher powers the working distances must be ample to allow free use of the blood-counting cell.

(b) *Drop-in cross-ruled disk.*—For estimating lengths of mold filaments, an ocular drop-in disk cross-ruled in sixths of the ocular diaphragm opening is desirable.

(c) *Blood-counting cell.*—Ruled in the Thoma or the old Neubauer system of rulings. The so-called "improved" system of Neubauer is not suitable for this purpose.

48. Methods of Analysis, Assoc. Off. Agr. Chem., 1940 edition, 522-524.

(d) *Howard mold-counting cell.*—Constructed like a blood-counting cell but with unruled central disk approximately 19 mm. in diameter.

MOLDS

In making mold counts of tomato products, use the material as is except that clean, mold-free gum may be added to thin products to assist in making more uniform mounts; in the case of tomato products of such heavy consistency as to make observation of mold filaments difficult, mix water to make total tomato solids of diluted product 8.37 to 9.37 per cent. If the product contains salt or other substance that increases solids content materially, take this into consideration in making dilution.

Clean the special Howard cell so that Newton's rings are produced between slide and cover glass. Remove cover and place small drop of the well-mixed sample upon central disk; using knife blade or scalpel, spread drop evenly over disk, and cover with the glass so as to give an even spread.

It is of the utmost importance that the drop be taken from a thoroughly mixed sample and spread evenly over the slide disk. Otherwise, when cover slip is put in place the insoluble material, and consequently the molds, may be more abundant at center of mount. Avoid using a drop that is much greater than is sufficient to fill space between center disk and cover slip. Discard any mount showing uneven distribution, absence of Newton's rings, or liquid that has been drawn across moat and under cover glass.

Place slide under microscope and examine with such adjustment that each field of view covers 1.5 sq. mm. This area, which is of vital importance, may frequently be obtained by so adjusting the draw-tube that the diameter of the field becomes 1.382 mm. When such adjustment is not possible, it is sometimes necessary to have a mechanic make an accessory drop-in ocular diaphragm with the aperture accurately cut to necessary size. The diameter of area of field of view can be determined by use of a stage micrometer, or by employing the rulings on the blood-counting cell. In order to use latter method it is necessary to bear in mind that a square whose diagonal is 1.382 mm. has sides of approximately .977 mm. Hence the millimeter scale on the blood-counting cell can be used by such adjustment that the circle of the field of view cuts off necessary amount from each corner of the mm.-ruled square. When the instrument is properly adjusted, the quantity of liquid examined per field is .15 c.mm. (.00015 ml.).

From each of two or more mounts examine at least 25 fields taken in such manner as to be representative of all sections of the mount. Observe each field, noting presence or absence of mold filaments and recording result as positive or as negative, as case may be. No field should be considered positive unless the aggregate length of not more than three of the filaments present exceeds approximately ⅙ of diameter of field. Calculate proportion of positive fields from results of examination of all observed fields and report as percentage of fields containing mold filaments.

YEASTS AND SPORES

Fill graduated cylinder with H_2O to 20-ml. mark and add sample till level of mixture reaches 30-ml. mark. Close graduate, or pour contents into Erlenmyer flask, and shake vigorously 15-20 seconds. To assure thoroughness the mixture should not fill more than ¾ of container in which shaking is performed. For tomato sauce or pastes, or products running high in number of organisms or of heavy consistency, use 80 ml. of water with 10 ml. or 10 gm. of sample. In case of exceptionally thick or dry pastes, it may be necessary to make even greater dilution.

Pour mixture into beaker. Thoroughly clean blood-counting cell so as to give good Newton's rings. Stir thoroughly contents of beaker with scalpel or knife blade and after allowing to stand 3-5 seconds remove a small drop, place it upon the central disk of the blood-counting cell, and cover immediately with cover glass. Discard any mount showing uneven distribution, absence of Newton's rings, or liquid that has been drawn across moat and under cover glass. Allow slide to stand not less than 10 minutes before beginning to make the count. It is customary to make the count with a magnification of 180-220 diameters.

Count number of yeasts and mold spores on ½ of ruled squares on disk (this amounts to counting the number in 8 of the blocks, each of which contains 25 of the small ruled squares). Total number thus obtained equals number of organisms in 1/60 c.mm. (1/60,000 ml. of original product) if a dilution of 1 part of sample with 2 parts of H_2O is used. If a dilution of 1 part of sample with 8 parts of H_2O is used, multiply the number by 3. In making the counts, the analyst should avoid counting twice the organisms that rest on a boundary line between two adjacent squares.

BACTERIA

Determine the number of rod-shaped bacteria from mounted sample used in "Yeast and Spores," but before examination allow sample to stand not less than 15 min. after mounting. Use magnification of approximately 500 diameters.

Count and record number of bacteria having a length greater than 1½ times their width in an area including 5 of the small squares. Count number in 5 such areas, preferably 1 from near each corner of ruled portion of slide and 1 from near the center. Determine total number of rod-shaped bacteria in the 5 areas and multiply by 480,000. This gives number of this type of bacteria per ml. If a dilution of 1 part of sample with 8 parts of H_2O instead of 1 part of sample with 2 parts of the H_2O is used in making up the sample, then total count obtained in the 5 areas must be multiplied by 1,440,000. The bacteria sometimes exhibit slight motion and thus may present momentarily an end instead of a side view. For this reason, it is necessary to keep them under observation long enough to establish their true character. Thus far it has proved impracticable to count the micrococci present as they are likely to be confused with other bodies frequently present in such products.

Linden's[49] Method for Examination of Canned Tomato Products. This procedure proposed by Linden is recommended for tomato products and other products with a similar acidity. Linden stated that modifications in treatment could include: (a) Before being cultured, samples submitted for examination for incipient or advanced spoilage should be examined microscopically in order to obtain some information as to the types of organisms present. Gram's stain is useful as most spoilage organisms in this class of foods are Gram-positive. Determination of pH may be useful, but is of limited value as only slight reaction changes occur in these products. (b) Normal appearing cans submitted for examination for commercial soundness or keeping quality should be incubated at 30°C. if less than 14 days has elapsed since the product was packed. Additional incubation at this temperature to insure at least 14 days' incubation is desirable. When no 30°C. incubator is available, incubation at an average room temperature of 25°C. may suffice. (c) Samples examined for the presence of other than spoilage organisms require incubation at 37°C. in culture media suitable for the detection of organisms capable of causing spoilage of non-acid foods. Products such as tomato pastes, purées, and ketchups are often used as packing media (sauces) for non-acid products and may be responsible for spoilage under these changed conditions of pH. The following method is recommended:[50]

CULTURING PROCEDURE

A. PHYSICAL EXAMINATION AND PREPARATION OF CAN

1. Note and record all marks of identification, either embossed on the can or appearing on the label.

2. Remove the labels. Record any physical defects such as improper closure, leaks, bad seams, buckling, or other abnormal conditions such as springers, flippers, or swells.

3. Scrub the entire surface of the container with a brush, using soap and warm water, and wipe off the surface with 70% alcohol prior to opening.

4. If possible, open the end of the container that does not bear the cannery code marks. For sterilization at the site of opening, expose the container top over the flame of a Bunsen burner, using a rotary motion to obtain an even distribution of

49. Linden. 1938. Assoc. Off. Agr. Chem. J. 21, 454-457.
50. Assoc. Off. Chem. J. 21 (1938), 72.

heat and to prevent scorching of contents. (This procedure also tends to minimize the danger of contamination from inrush of air when the container is opened.) Do not subject hard swells to heating before opening. (It is suggested that swollen containers that exhibit considerable pressure be chilled before they are opened to reduce spurting.) After cleansing swollen cans, apply the treatment described by Fellers.[51] (As an alternative it is suggested that after the mechanical cleansing with soap and water the container be thoroughly cleaned with 70% alcohol. Phenolic solutions may interfere with the organoleptic examination of the can contents because they tend to mask the odors.)

B. Removal of Sample

1. *Opening of container.*—After sterilizing the site of opening, make an entrance with an appropriate type of opener, which has also been sterilized by direct flaming. For products of heavy consistency, such as tomato paste, preferably use openers of the spiral or circular type, which cut around a central puncture. (Openers that cut around the can seam are less desirable because of greater surface exposure and danger of contamination.) When fluid products are sampled, make the opening by a suitable metal punch of appropriate diameter to insure an aperture that will permit free access of the sampling pipet. Further details on sampling devices are discussed by Tanner.[52]

2. *Inoculum.*—Sample liquid or semi-liquid food products with sterile untapered pipets or inverted tapered pipets of suitable capacity. (The untapered pipets should have minimum dimensions of 350 mm. in length and 5 mm. inside diameter.) Sample solid or semi-solid food products with sterile spatulas, long-handled spoons, or other instruments, as suggested by Tanner, depending on the character of the food under examination. Use pipets only for products of such viscosity as to permit transfer of the inoculum into the culture media by gravity. As suggested by Tanner, use a sample consisting of a minimum of 15 grams or 15 ml. of the food material and divide it into aliquots for duplicate culturing in each of the different culture media used in the examination.

3. *Sampling of product fractions.*—When representative inocula are desired from both the liquid and solid parts, transfer the solid component of the sample to the culture medium with forceps sterilized by flaming and use culture media in large test tubes (100×25 mm.) or in wide-mouthed jars or bottles.

C. Culture Media

Because of their acid nature many products in this class are subjected to the limited processing designed only to prevent spoilage. This is done to preserve the color, flavor, and texture of the foods. In some instances the products are filled into the cans while hot and receive no further heat processing. Two main groups of microorganisms encountered in the spoilage of this class of canned food products are the aciduric bacteria and the yeasts. Viable bacteria capable of producing spoilage in non-acid foods but rendered inactive in acid foods have frequently been responsible for the reporting of false positive results in examinations for spoilage in acid canned foods. Use the following media adjusted to a reaction below *p*H 5.0 for the detection of spoilage organisms:

1. *Aciduric spoilage bacteria.*

Acid ·Meat Medium [53]

Dstilled water...1000 ml.
                                                                      grams
Ground fresh lean beef.. 500
Proteose peptone... 5
C. P. NaCl... 5
C. P. Dextrose... 10

51. Fellers. 1936. Assoc Off. Agr. Chem. J. 19, 430.
52. Tanner. 1936. Idem 432.
53. Modified acid meat medium for tomato products and other acid canned foods—to 1,000 ml. of broth as above add 11 gm. citric acid and 12 gm. of potassium citrate. This will give a pH of 4.4 to 4.5 (private comm. from Linden).

Infuse the beef-water mixture overnight in the refrigerator. Heat in Arnold or boil for 30 minutes. Strain through several layers of cheese cloth and press out broth, retaining the meat press cake. Add distilled water to the infusion to make up to 1 liter. Add the peptone and heat in Arnold or boil 10 minutes. Filter, and add salt. Acidify with C. P. lactic acid to pH 4.7, add the dextrose, and filter. Distribute the pressed-out beef remaining from the infusion into medium sized test tubes (150× 20 mm.), approximately 2 grams into each tube, and add 10 ml. of the broth. Sterilize in the autoclave at 15 lbs. pressure for 15 minutes (final reaction should be pH 4.8. Prior to using, boil the tubed medium for 10 minutes to expel absorbed oxygen and cool promptly in a water bath.

As an alternative enrichment medium use digest-yeast-tomato juice, described in last year's report,[54] modified by the addition of 0.5 per cent proteose peptone and adjusted to pH 4.8-5.0 with C. P. lactic acid.

The preparation of plate cultures is optional, and when desirable add 2% agar to the broth formula given above, dissolve by heating, filter, and adjust reaction to give final pH 5.0. Sterilize in an autoclave at 15 lbs. pressure for 15 minutes.

2. *Bacteria inhibited below pH 5.0.*—Use a medium essentially the same as the acid meat medium with reaction adjusted to pH 7.2. (This medium, when rid of excess free oxygen by boiling and prompt cooling just prior to use, has been found satisfactory for the growth of anaerobes, aerobes, and facultative bacteria.

3. *Yeast spoilage.*

Clarified malt extract medium.[56]

Dry malt extract (Difco).. 100 grams
Distilled water ....:.................. 1000 ml.

Dissolve the powdered malt extract in the water by heating in an Arnold sterilizer, or on the water bath. Adjust to pH 4.7 and cool to 50°C. Add slowly 100 ml. of a 5% suspension of Bentonite (colloidal clay) and mix vigorously. Hold at 50 to 75°C. for 30 minutes, then filter through a fluted paper filter until clear. Heat the filtrate in the autoclave 10 minutes at 15 lbs. pressure, and filter through paper to remove any precipitate formed. Distribute into tubes or flasks. For a plating medium, dissolve by heating, 2% agar-agar in the clarified broth, and filter if necessary through cotton and cheese cloth. To avoid further precipitation sterilize at 10 lbs. pressure for 15 minutes and cool promptly. (Bacto Malt Extract Broth can now be obtained in convenient dehydrated form and may be substituted for the above medium.)

4. *"Flat-sour" spoilage bacteria.*

Medium for detection of "flat-sour" organisms

The bromocresol purple dextrose tryptone medium, recommended by Cameron in his Report on Culture Media for Non-Acid Products [56] has been found useful in the detection of thermophilic bacteria occurring in acid canned foods.

D. INCUBATION

Incubate all cultures for the detection of spoilage organisms for at least 72 hours at 30°C. For the detection of non-aciduric bacteria, incubate at 37.5°C. for at least 48 hours. For the occasional "flat-sour" spoilage encountered in such products as tomato juice, incubate for thermophilic anaerobes at 56°C. for at least 48 hours.

E. CULTURE STUDY

Use the Manual of Methods for Pure Culture Study of Bacteria of the Society of American Bacteriologists as a guide for study of microorganisms obtained in the cultural procedure described.

54. Cameron. 1937. J. Assn. Off. Agr. Chem. 20, 429-432.

55. Assoc. Off. Agr. Chem. J. 19 (1936), 445.

56. Cameron. 1936. Assoc. Off. Agr. Chem. J. 19, 433.

REFERENCE BOOKS

BIGELOW, W. D., SMITH, H. R., AND GREENLEAF, C. A., 1941. Tomato Products, Pulp, Paste, Catsup, and Chili Sauce. Nat. Canners' Assoc., Washington, D. C. Bull. 27-L.

BITTING, A. W., 1909. Experiments on the Spoilage of Tomato Ketchup. U. S. Dept. Agr., Bureau Chem. Bull. 119.

BITTING, A. W., AND BITTING, K. G., 1915. Ketchup. Murphy-Bivins Co., Press, Lafayette, Indiana.

HIER, W. G., 1919. The Manufacture of Tomato Products. Published by the author. Denver, Colorado.

HOWARD, B. J., 1911. Decomposition and its Microscopical Detection in Some Food Products. U. S. Dept. Agr. Yearbook, 1911, 297-308.

HOWARD, B. J., 1911. Tomato Ketchup Under the Microscope With Practical Suggestions to Insure a Clean Product. U. S. Dept. Agr., Bureau Chem. Circular 68.

HOWARD, B. J., AND STEVENSON, C. H., 1917. Microscopical Studies on Tomato Products. U. S. Dept. Agr., Washington, D. C., Bull. 581.

CHAPTER 17

MICROBIOLOGY OF BREAD

The use of bread by man goes back to earliest times. Many different kinds have been made. Wittmack [1] examined Egyptian bread 4,400 years old with the microscope and observed remains of yeast cells and bacteria indicating that it was fermented. Bacteria similar to butyric acid bacteria were particularly noticeable. Starch was largely gelatinized. Unchanged starch grains were found, however, which gave characteristic reactions with iodine. More recent reports on examination of some old breads have been made by Grüss, [2] who isolated several yeasts.

Bread sold in America is a clean food because it is wrapped. In 1913, the National Association of Master Bakers took the position that wrapping bread in waxed or paraffin paper was not to be recommended as it held the moisture upon the surface of the bread and produced injurious effects upon the quality of the product, It was stated that the wrapping of bread in porous paper, which allows a gradual loss of moisture and ventilation, may be used with satisfactory results generally, except in the cases of Vienna and rye bread, the wrapping of which impairs the crispness and flavor of the crust. The sanitarian, however, has a different interest. Young [3] pointed out the ease with which unwrapped bread may be contaminated as it is carried about. Bread in some foreign countries may not be as clean a product as in America. Wibaux [4] inspected 100 bakeries in the Lille region and found very unsatisfactory conditions. He believed that tuberculosis was a disease which might be disseminated by pastries since the temperatures at which they were baked might not be sufficient to sterilize them. Introduction of machinery in the baking industry in France is greatly changing the hygienic qualities of French bread, just as it did in America.

TYPES OF BREAD

The various kinds of bread may be classified in different ways. One convenient grouping is leavened and unleavened bread. Leavened bread is "raised" by the formation of gas resulting from chemical reactions (baking powder) or biological fermentation. The first bread baked by man was probably little more than pulverized grains and other materials mixed with sufficient water to yield a sticky dough, molded, and baked. Later, it was learned that desirable characteristics were obtained by allowing the dough or sponge to ferment. In the early days fermentations were induced in one batch by using a little fermented dough from a previous baking. Many times this procedure resulted in undesirable changes, caused by foreign organisms which overgrew the desired fermenting agents. An

1. Wittmack. 1896. Sonder. Abdruck. Sitzber. Gesell. f. Naturf. Freunde Sitzber. Berlin, No. 5.
2. Grüss. 1930. Tagesztg. Brau. 38, 774-776.
3. Young. 1908. Rev. in Expt. Sta. Rec., 22, 264.
4. Wibaux. 1921. Rev. d'Hyg., 43, 178-184.

example of unleavened bread would be the Mexican *tortilla* or crackers, as used in the United States.

"**Sauerteig.**" This bread is made by seeding the sponge or dough with fermenting microorganisms from a portion saved from the previous baking. Owing to formation of acids from microbial fermentation and appearance of a well-established characteristic odor, it is called "sauerteig" or sour dough. This method is used for making many of the coarser whole-meal breads. The bacteria in "sauerteig" according to such investigations as Lehmann [5] and Wolffin, are varieties of *Aerobacter levans (Bacterium levans)* and *Escherichia coli*. Levy [6] believed that the bacteria all fell into the coliform group. He concluded that in the case of spontaneous fermentation and fermentation caused by leaven, *Bacillus coli albidoliquefaciens* and *Bacillus coli luteoliquefaciens* were present in addition to a typical *Escherichia coli*, all of which produced acid and gas. Porosity was said to have been caused by these three organisms. When leaven was used, yeast was said to be the main fermenting agent. Holliger [7] believed that *Aerobacter levans* was not identical with *Escherichia coli*. He stated that *Aerobacter levans* may be isolated by means of a two-per cent dextrose bouillon. It may be distinguished from *Escherichia coli* by gelatin liquefaction, which takes place in about 12 days. *Aerobacter levans* may also be distinguished by formation in dextrose broth of a gas with two-thirds carbon dioxide and one-third hydrogen, while *Escherichia coli* shows the reverse. Data have also been reported by Wolffin,[8] Burri and Holliger,[9] Teichert,[10] Kossowicz,[11] and others.

About 200 lactic acid bacteria were isolated by Knudsen [12] from the dough from 20 Danish bakers. Some of them formed only lactic acid, while others formed acetic acid, alcohol, and carbon dioxide. The latter strains were said to give sour dough and bread their special aroma. One strain referred to as *Betabacterium* was considered to be the specific organism of "sauerteig." It was always found in the meal, but only in small numbers. In order to have it gain ascendancy over other forms, ideal conditions had to be maintained. In order to make certain that the organisms are present, some old dough should be put in; infection may also occur from the apparatus. Levy and Wolffin classified the various forms of bacteria in "sauerteig" as forms of *Aerobacter levans* in addition to *Escherichia coli*, which was generally found to be present.

Lactic acid is not the only acid formed in this fermentation. Seliber [13] observed another but did not identify it. The aroma and flavor of these breads was reported by Komm and Lehmann [14] to be due to biacetyl and acetone, the same substances which have been found in dairy products. A

5. Lehmann. 1894. Centbl. Bakt., 15, 350-354.
6. Levy. 1904. Arch. f. Hyg., 49, 62-112.
7. Holliger. 1902. Centbl. Bakt., Pt. 2, 9, 305-312.
8. Wolffin. 1894. Arch. f. Hyg., 21, 268-307.
9. Burri and Holliger. 1909. Centbl. Bakt., Pt. 2, 23, 99-105.
10. Teichert. 1906. Centbl. Bakt., Pt. 2, 17, 376-378.
11. Kossowicz. 1911. Ztschr. Landw. Versuchswesen, 12, 771.
12. Knudsen. 1924. Kgl. Vet. Landbohojskole.
14. Komm and Lehmann. 1939. Ztschr. f. Untersuch. der Nahr. u. Genussmtl., 78, 458-469.

heterogeneous flora was observed by Seliber, Bychkovskaia, and Volfson [15] in dough from Leningrad bakeries. Many of the bacteria were acid formers. Such results suggest that this dough fermentation is a symbiosis rather than a pure-culture matter. However, these authors seemed to secure good results with pure cultures as leavening agents. They believed they had isolated "true sour dough bacteria." Results of experiments by Nikolaev [16] were quite similar. Combinations of the right bacteria and yeasts gave high-quality bread. Bacteria from wheat and rye leaven were similar. Most of the species were organic acid producers.

Black Bread. This is a coarse whole-meal bread, usually leavened with "sauerteig." Its microbiology probably differs little from that of "sauerteig," discussed above. Coarse wheat or rye flour is usually used. Perhaps the results of a bacteriological investigation of sour rye bread, reported by Budinov [17] are pertinent. Only one bacterium *(Bacillus mesentericus pani viscosi II)* was found to be common to both samples, but representatives of the following groups were identified: (1) peptonizing bacteria which turned the dough from a thick to a more plastic state; (2) yeast, which caused the dough to rise; and (3) lactic or acetic bacteria, on which the sour taste and smell of the black bread depend. Cultivation of the isolated forms on sterilized dough was not successful, owing to the difficulty of obtaining sterilized flour. For complete sterilization of flour, one-half hour's heating in an autoclave under two atmospheres of pressure was necessary; this treatment, however, changed the flour and made it unsuitable for dough.

Another coarse bread prepared by the Indians of Brazil (Lieske [18]) is also apparently leavened by a mixture of yeasts and bacteria. This bread is known as "jamin-bang." The fermentation is made up of an acid and alcoholic fermentation and is affected by organisms on maize or in the river water in which the grain is soaked. Two yeasts and a bacterium were isolated by Lieske. Lindner, who discussed this fermentation, considered the occurrence of a bottom-fermentation yeast in the tropics as unusual.

Self-Rising (Salt-Rising Bread). This bread has been made for generations in America. As suggested in the name, the fermentation is a spontaneous one, since no leavening agent is added. Kohman,[19] who reviewed the literature quite thoroughly, reported some interesting experimental work.

Some believe that the fermentation is due to wild yeasts which enter the dough from the air. In support of this are investigations of Mitchell,[20] Bailey [21] and others. That it is a bacterial fermentation is supported by the work of Heinemann and Hefferan [22] and Kohman.[19]. The middle ground, that both yeasts and bacteria are concerned, was taken by Leh-

15. Seliber *et al.* 1933. State Inst. Expt. Agron., Bur. Agr. Mikrobiol. Bull., U. S. S. R., 5, 259-275; Rev. in Biol. Abs. 10 (1936), 8842.

16. Nikolaev. 1935. Rev. in Biol. Abs. 9, 387-1815.

17. Budinov. 1908. Centbl. Bakt., Pt. 2, 10, 458-463.

18. Lieske. 1914. Wchnschr. f. Brau., 31, 122-123.

19. Kohman. 1912. J. Ind. Eng. Chem., 4, 20-30; 100-106.

20. Mitchell. 1908. Office Expt. Sta., U. S. Dept. Agr. Bull. 200.

21. Bailey. 1914. Sanitary and Appl. Chem., p. 168.

22. Heinemann and Hefferan. 1909. Science 29, 1011.

mann,[23] Peters,[24] and perhaps Harrison.[25] Lehmann isolated an organism which he called *Aerobacter levans (Bacillus levans)*. Heinemann and Hefferan isolated a bacillus from corn meal which had many of the characteristics of *Lactobacillus bulgaricum (Bacillus bulgaricus)*. They proved that the organism came from the corn meal and believed that, the large amount of acid formed by this bacillus (1.65 per cent) from milk, united with the inorganic salts to form carbon dioxide. The extensive work of Kohman [19] indicated that bacteria were the important agents in the fermentation. Kohman stated that the leaven in salt-rising bread was not yeast, as stated in literature on the subject, but consisted of certain species of bacteria which aerate the bread by decomposing some of its constitutents, principally sugar, into gaseous products. He did not favor the opinion that the carbon dioxide resulted from acids and sodium bicarbonate. The microbic flora involved varied greatly, depending upon the temperature to which the meal was subjected in setting the "batter." The organisms that predominate in the batter when it is made by stirring the meal into boiling milk or water are only occasionally found upon plates made from batters that were not subjected to temperatures which destroy nonsporebearing organisms. The chief source of the bacteria is not the air and utensils, as has been suggested in the literature, but the corn meal used in making the batter. One organism was isolated which in pure culture produced the gas necessary to properly aerate bread. This bacterium seemed to be a member of the *Escherichia coli* group and was never found in batters that were heated to 75°C.(167°F.). It in all probability, belongs to the same group as the organism described by Wolffin and Lehmann which they called *Aerobacter levans*. This organism could be propagated in liquid media such as milk or could be grown in batter and subsequently dried, to be used in the preparation of bread. When the liquid used in making the batter was sufficiently hot to bring the temperature of the batter to 75°C.(167°F.) or higher certain sporebearing organisms prevailed which readily produced the gas necessary to aerate bread. These bacteria soon lost their gas-producing power when kept in liquid media or when transferred to fresh media at intervals of 12 to 24 hours. From this fermenting batter no culture was isolated that retained its ability to produce gas when kept in the liquid state. A dry product consisting for the most part of starchy material was prepared, however, which could be used at will in making uniform bread. Bread made with leaven, *i.e.*, the "sauerteig" method differed from salt-rising bread in that the leavening is due to yeasts and not to bacteria. It is a question then whether gas-forming bacteria, which are present, are desirable or not. The two breads differ also in that salt-rising bread is made from fresh materials each time, while in making leavened bread a portion of the dough is saved to start the fermentation of the next baking. The gases produced by the "salt-rising" bacteria, as found in these experiments, consisted of nearly two-thirds hydrogen and rather

23. Lehmann. 1894. Centbl. Bakt., 15, 350-354.

24. Peters. 1889. Bot. Ztg., 47, 405, 240, and 435.

25. Harrison. 1902. Ontario Agr. Bull., 118.

more than one-third carbon dioxide and no hydrocarbons. The losses of materials, owing to decomposition and volatilization of some of the constituents, are much smaller in salt-rising bread than in bread made with yeast, and the losses in the latter vary with the amount of fermentation to which it is subjected. The difference in the losses of materials in the preparation of the two kinds of bread is to be explained by the fact that (1) there is no alcohol found in the former; (2) owing to inherent difference in the nature of the fermenting agents involved, it is subjected to far less fermentation; and (3) the gases are much lighter.

Woodward [26] believed that the fermentation occurring in salt-rising bread may be due to the presence of one or more organisms accidentally in the corn meal from which the batter used in starting the bread is made, or introduced in some similar way. The organisms isolated were not yeasts but belonged to some other group. Koser [27] reported a very interesting investigation of a commercial "bread starter" advocated for the preparation of salt-rising bread. Bacteriological examinations seemed to indicate that his leavening agent was *Clostridium welchii*. The organism in the starter was compared with an authentic strain of *Clostridium welchii* and both the authentic strain and that isolated from the starter were used for making bread. The bread prepared with the strain of *Clostridium welchii* of known authenticity could not be distinguished from that prepared with the starter. The commercial starter contained 1,000 organisms per gram. Bread from bakeries using this starter was found to contain considerable numbers of viable spores. Koser stated that in view of the possible pathogenicity of *Clostridium welchii*, it might be better to employ an organism the use of which was beyond question from the public-health standpoint. This is another illustration of the fact that some of the pathogenic anaerobes may not be harmful when taken by mouth. This organism which was found in a bread starter is known to be commonly present in the intestinal tract and in foods. Albus,[28] for instance, has reported *Clostridium welchii* as the organism responsible for the gassy fermentation of Niszler cheese. Koser estimated that the sponge at one stage of its preparation might contain from 1 to 100 million cells of *Clostridium welchii* per gram. His work further suggests that perhaps those who have tried to find the real agent responsible for the "self-rising" bread fermentation, have erred by not looking for anaerobic bacteria.

Microbiology of Flour and Meal. Microorganisms in flour and meal have much to do with the bacterial content of bread. As would be expected, the flora of flour has been found to be heterogeneous. Thom and LeFevre [29] found common molds such as *Aspergillus repens*, *Penicillium luteum*, *Penicillium oxalicum*, *Aspergillus flavus*, *Aspergillus tamari*, *Aspergillus niger*, and others, to be present in corn meal. Various yeasts were also found. As long as the moisture was kept below 13 per cent, the molds did not develop, but above 15 per cent, *Aspergillus repens* began to be active.

26. Woodward. 1911. J. Home Econ., 3, 100-101.
27. Koser. 1923. J. Infect. Dis., 32, 208-219.
28. Albus. 1924. Abs. Bact. 8, 13.
29. Thom and Le Fevre. 1921. Abs. Bact., 5, 10.

Similar observations were reported by Bailey and Thom,[30] Bell,[31] Street,[32] and McHargue.[33] Arnoldow [34] found that practically all kinds of bacteria and molds would develop when the water content was above 17 per cent. *Aspergillus fumigatus* was found by Sartory and Sartory [35] in flour with a musty odor. Kühl [36] isolated butyric acid bacteria from abnormal flour.

The bacterial content of flour may be high. Turley[37] reported counts which varied from 310,000 to 5,200,000 bacteria per gram. Results of a comprehensive investigation on this subject have been recently reported by Amos and Kent-Jones [39a] These authors studied at some length, the technic that should be employed. Freshly milled patent flour contained less than 20,000 bacteria per gram, straight-run flour less than 50,000, and lower grades less than 300,000, growing at 37°C. (98.6°F.). Storage of flour resulted in a lowering of the content of microorganisms, but the rate depended on the amount of water present and the temperature. Especially interesting was the report that *Escherichia coli* of fecal origin was present in flour. It was suggested that the organism might originate in the water used for washing the whole wheat. This was proven by analyzing the water used for this purpose, in several mills. Members of the *Bacillus mesentericus* group are almost always present. Holtman [39] observed a reduction in microbial content of flour during milling. Most flours on the market contained fewer than 8,000 microorganisms per gram.

Kent-Jones and Amos [38] reported results of a comprehensive examination of flour. Preliminary examinations by them revealed the presence of from 2,000 to 200,000 bacteria per gram developing at 37°C. They distinguished between bacteria developing at 37°C. (blood-heat) and those organisms developing at lower temperatures ("cool") mainly as a matter of convenience. When freshly and normally milled, patent flour showed less than 20,000 bacteria developing at 37°C. per gram straight-run flour less than 50,000, and lower grades up to 300,000 or more. Bacteria growing at lower temperatures were usually present in greater numbers. During storage both types of organisms decrease the rate depending on the moisture content and the temperature of storage. The types of bacteria were not especially significant, with exception of *Bacillus mesentericus* which causes "ropy bread." These investigators, then, reported a great variation in numbers of bacteria in flours. Results of another extensive investigation by Barton-Wright [40] also indicated a reduction in viable microorganisms in stored flours. His work was on two different low-grade English flours stored in bins with two different moisture contents. He used the Kent-

30. Bailey and Thom. 1922. Oper. Miller. 25, 368-371.
31. Bell. 1909. Amer. Miller. 37, 280-281.
32. Street. 1903. New Jersey Agr. Expt. Sta., Ann. Rpt., 123-147.
33. McHargue. 1920. J. Ind. Eng. Chem., 12, 257-262.
34. Arnoldow. 1908. Chem. Abs. 2, 1017.
35. Sartory and Sartory. 1926. J. Pharm. d'Alsace Lorraine 53, 58-59.
36. Kühl. 1911. Chem. Ztg. 35, 1321-1322.
37. Turley. 1922. Baking Technol. 1, 327-329.
38. Amos and Kent-Jones. 1931. Analyst 56, 572-586.
39a. Kent-Jones and Amos. 1930. Analyst. 55, 248-268.
39. Holtman. 1935. J. Bact. 30, 359-361.
40. Barton-Wright. 1938. Cereal Chem. 15, 521-541.

Jones and Amos method for microbial analysis substituting a synthetic medium for the organic medium used by the former investigators. Barton-Wright did not secure the high counts reported by Kent-Jones and Amos, the highest being 57,000 per gram. During storage bacterial numbers always decreased while fungal numbers increased. The later increased to a maximum when the moisture content was 16 per cent or over. Mustiness was due to fungi and not bacteria. Over 90 per cent of the fungi belonged to the genus Penicillium.

Rancidity of flour, according to Gustafson and Parfitt [41] is not related to total numbers of bacteria either in the case of plain or self-rising flours. The total number of bacteria was practically the same in both types of flour. Storage caused the number of bacteria to decrease.

The conditions under which flour is stored have much to do with behavior of bacteria in it. Among the more important is humidity. Barton-Wright and Tomkins [42] observed that flour exposed to relative humidities between 80 and 90 per cent was attacked by Penicillium sp.; bran under the same conditions was attacked by Penicillium and Aspergillus sp. at room temperatures. No mold growth was observed in flour of 16 per cent moisture content, the equilibrium moisture content at 75 per cent relative humidity. Critical moisture content for mold growth increases as the temperature decreases. Mold growth was prevented when flour was exposed to relative humidity of 79 per cent at 20°C.(68°F.) when moisture content of the flour was 16 per cent, to a relative humidity of 82.5 per cent at 15°C.(59°F.) when the moisture content was 16.5 per cent, and to a relative humidity of 85 per cent at 5°C.(41°F.) with a moisture content of flour of 17.4 per cent. Wheat flour over several years was found to contain no canned food spoilage bacteria by Yesair and Reed.[43] Not many samples were examined, however.

McWhorter's [44] Method for Counting Spores. This method was described by Mc-Whorter for enumerating spores and may be applied to various food products. The method requires two persons, an observer and a recorder, but is very rapid and eliminates some of the experimental error. Select a thin, round cover glass and with India ink rule across it two parallel lines a millimeter or less apart. In the middle of the cover draw a third line perpendicular to and joining the first two, thus forming a narrow letter H in the center of the cover. Drop the cover onto the "stop" of an ordinary 10 × eyepiece as though inserting a micrometer disc. Such a cover, unlike an ordinary micrometer disc, does not perceptibly interfere with definition, a factor of importance when observing hyalin spores. Place the slide, which should be prepared so as to give a fairly uniform distribution of spores, in position on a mechanical stage having convenient right and left movement. Arrange the eyepiece containing the cover slip so that the parallel lines coincide with the right and left movment of the stage. With a three or four mm. lens, select, in the region well to the left of the center of the preparation, a field showing abundant spores. Suppose there are five kinds of spores in the mount; assign a letter to each kind. Move the slide from left to right so that the spores appear to be slowly travelling along between the two lines. Call off to the assistant the proper letter for each spore passing by the vertical line within the

41. Gustafson and Parfitt. 1933. Cereal Chem. 10, 233-238.
42. Barton-Wright and Tomkins. 1940. Idem 17, 332-342.
43. Yesair and Reed. 1939. Natl. Canners Assoc., Ann. Rpt. to the Research Committee for
43a. Yesair and Cameron. 1942. The Canner 94, No. 13, Pt. 2., Convention Number 92-93. 1938, 13-16; see also later reports.
44. McWhorter. 1926. Science 63, 211.

parallel lines. Let the assistant record the letters on plotting paper conveniently divided off into 50 or 100 squares. This method will enable a record to be made almost as fast as one can talk. Of course, simply counting the letters will give the percentage of each type of spore. This procedure will obviously eliminate some of the experimental error common in "field counts," and is much faster.

Kent-Jones and Amos' [38] **Method for Bacterial Examination of Flour.** A wide-mouthed, glass-stoppered bottle of eight-ounce capacity; two narrow-mouthed, glass-stoppered bottles of four-ounce capacity; and a 100-ml. measuring cylinder are thoroughly cleaned. The measuring cylinder is plugged with cotton-wool and then, together with the bottles, is placed in the hot-air sterilizer. One one-ml. and two five-ml. pipettes are cleaned, plugged with cotton-wool, and inserted in a metal container, which is then also placed in the hot-air sterilizer. The sterilizer is then raised to a temperature of 150°C.(302°F.) and maintained thus for one hour. A .5 per cent solution of sodium chloride in distilled water is prepared and sterilized by steaming for two hours. By means of the measuring cylinder, 100 ml. of the sterile salt solution (after cooling) are measured into the eight-ounce bottle, and 45 ml. into each of the four-ounce bottles. Ten grams of purified sand are ignited strongly in a platinum capsule and poured, while hot, into the bottle containing the 100 ml. of the salt solution.

Ten grams of the flour are weighed out on a sterile watch glass and transferred, by means of sterile paper, to this same bottle. The bottle is then shaken vigorously for two minutes. When the bulk of the sand has settled (it settles very rapidly), one of the sterile five-ml. pipettes is used to transfer five ml. of the suspension to one of the bottles which contain 45 ml. of the salt solution. The bottle is then shaken vigorously. Then, by means of the remaining sterile five-ml. pipette, five ml. of the liquid are transferred to the remaining bottle, which is vigorously shaken. Finally, one ml. of this liquid is transferred, by means of the sterile one-ml. pipette, to a sterile Petri dish. A 10-ml. tube of sterile nutrient agar is melted in boiling water, allowed to cool to 45°C.(113°F.), the plug removed, the neck of the tube "flamed," and the contents of the tube poured into the Petri dish. The agar and the extract are mixed by rocking the dish, which is then placed on a flat surface while the agar solidifies. The dish is then placed, in an inverted position, in a blood-heat incubator (37°C.). A count is taken at the end of 48 hours.

Barton-Wright [44a] used formation of a pellicle on nutrient broth as the method of estimation instead of counting. Otherwise his technic conforms so closely to that of Kent-Jones and Amos that it need not be given in detail here.

Hoffman's Method for Estimating Bacteria in Flour. Hoffmann,[45] in order to determine the number of bacteria in flour, shook 7.5 grams in 300 ml. of sterile water for one-half hour. After this the mixture was plated in the usual media.

Toxins for Yeasts in Flour. According to different investigators, agents exist in flour which retard the action of yeast as a leavening agent. Brewers' yeast is especially susceptible while distillers yeast is less so. Baker and Hulton [46] tried to find why brewers' yeast when used in bread making, did not produce a degree of fermentation equal to that produced by distillers' yeast. When comparative tests were made with both brewers' and bakers' yeast and wheat flour, using distilled water as a menstruum, practically no fermentation took place in the case of brewers' yeast while distillers' yeast fermented well. When tap water was employed however brewers' yeast fermented without any trouble. Experiments were then conducted

44a. Barton-Wright. 1943. J. Soc. Chem. Ind., 62, 33-37.
45. Hoffmann. 1896. Wchnschr. f. Brau., p. 1153.
46. Baker and Hulton. J. Soc. Chem. Ind., 28, 778-784.

with inorganic salts, potassium sulfate and others in distilled water. Here it was found that fermentation occurred with brewers' yeast and that these salts had a protective or antitoxic effect towards the toxins contained in the wheat flour. The use of these salts produced no acceleration of fermentation with bakers' or distillers' yeast. The effect produced by tap water was probably brought about by the presence of acid calcium carbonate. Brewers' yeast cultivated three times in distillers' mash took on some of the characteristics of bakers' yeast. Baker and Hulton believed that the yeast acquired an immunity to the toxins in the flour. Thus there is an explanation why brewers' yeast did not give good results with raw flours.

In another paper the same investigators reported the results of experiments carried out with invert sugar, aqueous flour extract, invert sugar and flour, aqueous flour extract and flour, distillers' wort (rye and maize), cold aqueous extract of distillers' malt, and unboiled malt wort prepared from brewers' malt. It was found that potassium sulfate was without effect as far as the actual acceleration of fermentation was concerned with invert sugar solutions and that its function is only that of a protective agent against toxins. A distilled water extract of the toxin was destructive to yeast and this toxicity could be held in check by the addition of potassium sulfate. Fermentation of a sugar solution by brewers' yeast was stopped by adding flour, but if potassium sulfate was present fermentation proceeded. Brewers' yeast was acted upon strongly by the rye flour toxin, but the latter was not so soluble as the toxin of wheat. Fermenting an aqueous solution of flour by brewers' yeast and adding flour checked fermentation. Bakers' yeast fermentations were not affected. A malt distillers' wort containing rye flour and maize was toxic to brewers' yeast, but this toxicity could be destroyed by boiling. High temperatures destroyed the toxicity of the malt but the process of germination did not. The toxicity in the flour may also be partially destroyed by heating at a temperature of 100°C.(212°F.) for some hours. Baker and Hulton sought to simulate the toxic action of the flour toxin by adding potassium cyanide to the fermentation but found that potassium sulfate exerted no protective effect.

After summarizing the work already published on this subject, LeCourt [47] described his own researches on the localization of the toxin in the wheat and the various attempts to isolate it. The poison appeared to accompany the glutenin portion of the seed protein without being glutenin itself. The question was discussed as to whether the toxin was of a protein nature. Hayduck [48] concluded that it was, since it was destroyed by trypsin digestion—a fact verified by LeCourt, who, however, considered this no proof, since if it is admitted that the poison is a product of degradation from the nontoxic protein, it must also be admitted, as Willstätter has shown for enzymes, that the poison consists of a collodial support and an active chemical group and that toxicity disappeared when the colloidal support was destroyed. Numerous attempts to adsorb the toxin on kaolin, norit, alumina, and hydrate of iron were described. It was noted that the

47. LeCourt. 1927. Diss., Paris; Ann. Brasserie 26.
48. Hayduck. 1908. Allg. Ztschr. f. Bierbrau u. Malzfabrikat 36, 505-507, 513-516.

toxicity of wheat flour towards yeast was only manifested in the presence of fermentable sugars and was a function of their concentration. Among the conclusions of LeCourt may be mentioned the following: In the presence of sugar the poison acts rapidly on bottom fermentation yeast at 2°C.(35.6°F.), but at 27°C.(80.6°F.), it acts slowly, both on bottom yeast and bakers' yeast. Certain races of yeast exist, which, even when cultivated in wort, remain insensitive to the action of the toxic substance of flour. By washing the glutenin with acidulated water it was found possible to remove the poison from it. Wheat flour toxin acts in very small doses and is comparable in this respect to enzymes. It has no action on zymase but in the presence of sugar kills yeast fairly rapidly, the toxicity, however, being diminished when the acidity of the medium is increased. All salts are able to neutralize the toxicity at sufficient concentrations. Hayduck's early work on this subject was confirmed by LeCourt who found that the toxic substance was definitely associated with glutenin. It was very potent and only a very small amount was necessary to destroy the action of yeasts.

More definite information on these bodies in flour has appeared in recent literature. Stuart and Harris [48a] reported isolation of a crystalline substance of protein-like nature from wheat flour which showed marked fungicidal activity for *Saccharomyces cerevisiae* causing death of cells in concentrations of 0.005 mg. per ml. and higher. Similar results were secured with pathogenic fungi *Debaromyces nadiformis* and *Endomycopsis albicans*. This activity was believed to be restricted to yeasts and yeast-like fungi. These results help to explain the yeast-killing activity of wheat flour, much of the literature of which has been reviewed above. Failure of dough to rise is thus explained. That these agents may exert their activity on yeast enzymes was suggested by Kneen and Saudstedt.[48b]

Soy Bean Flour and Meal. This is known to harbor many microorganisms, some of which are spoilage organisms for foods to which it is added. Thermophilic bacteria contained therein have caused spoilage of meat preparations. Those who recommended its addition to foods which are to be preserved in any of several ways must consider this possibility. Samples analyzed by Kaberg, in the author's laboratory for canned food spoilage bacteria, were found to vary greatly in content of flat sour-producing sulfide spoilage, and thermophilic anaerobes. Practically all of the samples had flat sour-producing bacteria; two samples were entirely free, however. Sulfide spoilage bacteria were few in number and thermophilic anaerobes were present in only two samples. One manufacturer claimed to have developed a process which eliminated most of the thermophilic species. In processing soybean oil meal the temperature may reach 132.2°C.(270°F.) for a short time while the flour may reach 115.6°C(240°F.). This might not sterilize the products but would destroy many nonsporeforming species.

Microbiology of Other Meals and Flours. Many of these products are added to various foods which are processed in different ways. Few results

48a. Stuart and Harris. 1942. Cereal Chem. 19, 288-300.
48b. Kneen and Saudstedt. 1943. J. Amer. Chem. Soc. 65, 1247.

of general bacteriological examination have been published. Most of the investigations have been carried out for some definite purpose as is the case in the canning industry where it is important to learn whether spoilage bacteria are present. The various types are discussed in Chapter 19 where the generally accepted procedures are also given. Yesair and Reed [43] used them on sugar, starch, cracker meal, cracker flour, wheat flour, corn flour, tapioca flour, and a few other types. The percentage of satisfactory samples was high. Flat sour-producing bacteria were the only types found to be present. Yesair and Reed believed that such materials should be subject to regular laboratory control before they were used. Corn flour was observed by Yesair and Cameron [43a] to contain more thermophilic bacteria than wheat flour. They believed that satisfactory flours could be secured for addition to canned meats and other non-acid canned products.

Yeast Cells in Bread Doughs. The function of yeast cells in dough is to produce gases which leaven it. Whether yeast increases in numbers in dough or whether it remains constant in numbers respiring enough to produce leavening gases, has been argued by baking technologists. According to Hoffman, Schweitzer, and Dalby [49] whose method is quoted below, Lindet [50] tried to answer the question using the standard agar plate. Owing to clumping of yeast cells, the results secured with this method are usually too low. Geere and Geere [51] proposed a microscope method while Simpson [52] used a hemacytometer.

Activity of yeast cells in dough depends somewhat on the conditions under which they are stored before use. Thiessen [53] observed better activity over a longer time when pressed yeast and dried yeast were stored at 4.4 to 10°C. (40 to 50°F.) than when stored at room temperature of 21.1 to 23.9°C. (70 to 75°F.). Pressed yeast retained its activity for several months when frozen and resumed almost normal biological activity when used under favorable conditions. Only a small percentage of dead cells was present but this increased on longer storage.

Hoffman, Schweitzer, and Dalby's [49] Method for Counting Yeast Cells in Bread Dough. The method was given by the authors as follows:

PROCEDURE

Take a 20-gram sample of dough, place in a two-liter beaker, add 1,460 ml. of distilled water, five ml. of chloroform, and 10 grams of sodium chloride. The chloroform is added to prevent further growth of the yeast cells while the counts are being made, but, inasmuch as it does not mix with the solution, no account need be taken of it when considering the dilution. The salt is added to bind and hold the gluten in a ball and thus prevent its disintegration during the washing process.

Wash the starch and yeast cells from the gluten by hand for a period of at least 10 minutes, taking care to incorporate all shreds and particles of the original 20-gram sample.

Place the gluten ball in a graduated cylinder and add distilled water to a volume of 500 ml. Again wash the gluten ball in this volume of water for another period of

49. Hoffman *et al.* 1941. Cereal Chem., 18, 337-342.
50. Lindet. 1910. Compt. Rend. Acad. Sci., 150, 802-809.
51. Geere and Geere. 1922. U. S. Patent No. 1,431,156.
52. Simpson. 1936. Cereal Chem., 13, 50-54
53. Thiessen. 1942. Idem 19, 773-784.

10 minutes, in order to remove the yeast cells enmeshed therein, and add this solution to the first wash water. Thoroughly agitate this yeast and starch suspension, which now totals 1,960 ml., and transfer 49 ml. to a 200-ml. flask and stopper to prevent evaporation. Add one ml. of standard Carbol Fuchsin solution, made up according to the directions given in the U. S. Pharmacopoeia, to the 49 ml. of the suspension in the Erlenmeyer flask. This gives a final dilution of 20 grams of dough in 2,000 ml. of solution, or a 1-to-100 dilution.

Allow the stained solution to stand four or five hours or, if convenient, overnight, before the counts are made. This permits the color to stain the yeast cells thoroughly. When examined under the microscope at the end of that period, it will be found that the yeast cells have taken on a deep, dark red color, while the starch cells are only colored a faint pink. Any small particles of gluten material will also be colored a dark red but they can easily be differentiated from the yeast cells because of the regular contour and the cellular structure of the latter. Likewise, it is possible to distinguish yeast cells from small or similarly shaped starch cells by the fact that the latter are always clear and translucent and show no cellular structure.

During the time that the 50-ml. portion of the "starch-yeast" suspension is being stained, place the gluten ball remaining from the two washings in the graduate and add distilled water to bring the volume to 188 ml., which is about one-tenth the volume of the main suspension. It is better to work with more concentrated solutions in this case because of the very small number of yeast cells still remaining in the gluten ball. Add .2 ml. of concentrated hydrochloric acid to the solution and allow to stand overnight. At the end of the overnight period the gluten will be dissolved almost completely, and upon shaking a collodial suspension of the gluten is obtained, while the yeast cells are unchanged. To 47 ml. of this suspension add three ml. of Carbol Fuchsin solution and let stand overnight. It is necessary to use considerably more of the staining solution in this case because the collodial gluten seems to prevent the yeast cells from readily taking the stain. Even with this amount, the cells are colored only a faint pink, instead of a dark red, as in the case of the "starch-yeast" suspension. However, the minute gluten particles remain colorless in this solution and show no cellular structure.

For this work in our laboratory a Thoma-Zeiss haemacytometer is used, and the counting chamber is a Thoma-Levy modification of the Burker apparatus with two Neubauer rulings. Immediately before the actual counting, the flasks containing the stained solutions are shaken vigorously to bring into suspension all particles and cells which may have settled out. With a stirring rod, drops are removed and one placed on each of the Neubauer rulings and one on the intervening moat. The plano-parallel cover glass is placed in position with the thumb and forefinger and then one end of it is rapidly lifted up and down several times in order to expel any air bubbles and also to insure a uniform distribution of the solution. It is essential that this precaution be taken. The prepared slide is now allowed to set for a few minutes before the counting is started in order that the yeast cells may settle out upon the ruled surface of the counting chamber. The counts are made with the high-power four-mm. objective.

Each Neubauer ruling of the Thoma-Levy counting chamber is divided into nine large squares of one mm. each. The number of yeast cells in such a square is counted and an average taken of from eight to 12 such counts. Since there is a space of only .1 mm. between the cover glass and the ruled disc, it is necessary to multiply this average count by 10 to find the number of yeast cells in one cubic millimeter of the solution. This figure must be multiplied by 1,000 to convert to milliliters, and again by 100 because of the dilution of the solution. Consequently, when the average count is multiplied by 1,000,000 the number of yeast cells present in one gram of the original dough is obtained.

Each of the larger square-millimeter squares in the Neubauer ruling is further subdivided into 16 small squares. One of these small squares completely covers the field of the microscope when the four-mm. objective is used. In actual practice, therefore, the number of yeast cells in each small square is counted and the number put down in its corresponding place in a table representing the larger square-millimeter square. The sum of 16 such counts gives the number of cells in a square millimeter. It has been found preferable to count the cells in one or not more than two sq.-mm. squares, after which the counting chamber is cleaned and a fresh slide prepared. This prevents errors owing to evaporation of the solution, and it is for this same purpose that a drop of the solution was placed in the moat. In counting, the cells lying on the lines above and to the right are counted, never those on lines below or to the left. Yeast buds mature speedily in the dough into normal cells and exert the same influence on the dough as do the parent cells. For this reason, in counting, each bud that is large enough to be unmistakably recognized as such is counted as a single cell.

AN EXAMPLE OF COUNTING

Each square represents a square millimeter on the Neubauer ruling. Thus, the 16 sets of figures inside the square represent the number of yeast cells in the 16 small divisions into which each square millimeter of the ruling is subdivided. Illustrated yeast-cell counts follow:

4	2	3	3
6	7	12	11
7	5	7	8
6	7	5	7

Total 99 per sq. mm.

7	2	6	1
5	9	8	3
8	6	10	4
3	7	5	5

Total 89 per eq. mm.

4	4	8	4
6	2	7	4
6	8	3	10
4	3	7	4

Total 84 per sq. mm.

Number of Yeasts Cells in Square Millimeters of Neubauer
Ruling "Starch-Yeast" Suspension

Individual Counter No. 1 No. of cells	Individual Counter No. 2 No. of cells
99	106
89	89
84	83
87	81
124	96
90	87
110	74
85	113
104	113
103	127
91	107
123	99
Average 99.1	98.0
Average of both counters 98.5	......

CALCULATION OF NUMBER OF YEAST CELLS PER GRAM OF DOUGH

The total number of yeast cells per gram of dough is obtained by adding the number of yeast cells found in the "starch-yeast" suspension and the number found in the "gluten-ball" solution, which is divided by 10 before being added to the count obtained from the "starch-yeast" suspension. For example, if 98.5 cells per sq. mm. were found in the "starch-yeast" suspension, and 18.8 cells per sq. mm. in the "gluten-ball" solution, the total count would be 98.5 plus 1.88, which is 100.4 cells per sq. mm. Multiplied by 1,000,000 the result is 100,400,000 yeast cells per gram of dough.

Hoffman, Schweitzer, and Dalby [49] found that yeast definitely grew in dough, the greatest growth occurring between the second and fourth hour in a straight-dough formula. Optimum baking results were secured with 1.75 per cent of yeast based on the flour. Ammonium chloride and calcium sulfate showed a nutritive effect on yeast.

Neumann and Knischewsky's [54] **Method for Counting Yeast Cells in Dough.** Turley [55] outlined the method as follows: Remove 15 grams of dough from the batch and place in 150 ml. of water. The gluten separated by washing 25 ml. of this suspension was mixed with 25 ml. of iodine solution (150 ml. water, 1 gram KI, and .005 gram I), and diluted to 400 ml. with distilled water. One drop of this suspension was placed on the ruled area of a yeast counting apparatus or hemacytometer.

Turley's [55] **Method for Counting Yeast Cells in Dough.** In order to obtain representative sample, collect 20-gram pieces of dough from different parts of the batch and place in a covered dish. Weigh one gram sample of the dough by taking bits from the different samples which were collected.

Place the sample in a 600-ml. beaker with 200 ml. of distilled water (acidified with .1 ml. normal hydrochloric acid) at a temperature of 65°C.(149°F.). Add .5 gram of soluble pepsin and hold at 65°C. for 15 minutes. This may be done on a water bath. At intervals, the digestion may be aided by breaking up the bits of dough with a rod. Digestion is complete in 15 minutes. The digestate should then be thoroughly stirred and 10 ml. withdrawn with a 10-ml. pipette graduated in tenths. Of the amount withdrawn 4.8 ml. are transferred to a 20-ml. beaker and .05 ml. of melted phenol added. Hold for one minute at 65°C. with stirring. Allow the phenol to act for an additional two minutes. Then add .15 ml. of Loeffler's methylene blue and allow to act for one minute. Then thoroughly stir the sample and transfer a drop to the ruled area on a counting chamber. Count and record the yeast cells in a row of 20 squares. Computation is made in the usual manner.

Simpson's [56] **Method for Counting Yeast Cells in Fermenting Dough.** This is a modification of Turley's method. The dough from 20 grams of flour is rapidly cut into small pieces, put into a 600-ml. conical flask with 400 ml. of .05 N hydrochloric acid containing .2 per cent of pepsin scales, and placed in a water bath maintained at 40°C. (104°F.). The flask is repeatedly well shaken during digestion which generally takes from 45 minutes to one hour; and the shaking is continued until all pieces of dough have been dispersed. A few drops of brom-thymol blue indicator are added, the liquid is titrated with normal sodium carbonate solution to a greenish-blue color. The flask is placed in a boiling water bath, being shaken at first until the temperature of its contents comes to 90°C.(194°F.), after which it is left in the bath for another five minutes. After cooling to 65°C.(149°F) 10 ml. of a five-per cent dilution of diastatic malt extract (about 100° Lintner) are added, digestion being continued for 10 minutes at 65°C. After cooling to room temperature one ml. of one per cent methylene blue solution is added, the flask well shaken, and its contents transferred to a 500-ml. graduated flask, the washings from the conical flask being used to make up 500 ml.

After appropriate dilution of an aliquot portion, the yeast cells are counted with a haemacytometer in the usual manner.

Not much has been published on the influence of the particular species of yeast on bread flavor. Wardall [57] used 33 pure strains of yeasts and could observe no difference in the flavor of bread leavened by them. She regarded the time of incubation as too short for the development of any special flavor. This subject could well be studied again. The availability of commercial compressed yeast, produced under rigid conditions, has made the manufacture of bread more uniform. The baker finds it necessary to have an active, uniform supply of yeast.

54. Neumann and Knischewsky. 1909. Rev. in Centbl. Bakt., Pt. 2, 25 (1910), 314.
55. Turley. 1924. Cereal Chem., 1, 261.
56. Simpson. 1936. Cereal Chem., 13, 50-54.
57. Wardall. 1910. J. Home Econ., 2, 75-91.

DEFECTS OF BREAD

Bread, like other foods, may undergo a number of deteriorations, some of which may be due to defective raw materials, while others may result from infection after the bread has been made and baked.

Veikko [58] found the spoilage in barley bread was in part due to *Bacillus mesentericus,* the maximum temperature of growth of which was 50°C.(129.2°F.) and to other organisms with a growth temperature of 62°C.(143.6°F.). Microorganisms which liquefied gelatin caused most rapid spoilage of bread. A comprehensive discussion of defects of bread has been published by Nikolaev.[59] Morison and Collatz [60] reported that cut surfaces of ropy bread present a strong odor which is decidedly unpleasant and not unlike that of decomposed or overripe melons. The center of the crumb is soft and discolored. This discoloration is of a brownish hue and the softened portions can be drawn out into long threads from four to six inches in length when touched with a glass rod or other instrument.

ROPE IN BREAD

This may be a troublesome defect of bread. It has been prevalent during times of emergency when coarse and more uncommon flours have been used. The literature has become quite voluminous and is in fair agreement as to the cause and methods of prevention. One of the first to study the problem was Laurent [61] who isolated a bacterium from ropy bread in Belgium, to which he gave the name *Bacillus panificans.* It was a sporeforming organism which survived the temperatures attained in bread during baking. The organism was isolated from many different materials, including cereals and soil. Laurent reproduced the defect by inoculating the organism into dough and was probably the first to show that addition of vinegar to bread prevented development of the organism. Kratschmer and Niemilowicz [62] reported *Bacillus mesentericus vulgatus* as the cause of ropy bread in Vienna. It was probably the same organism described by Laurent. These observations have been confirmed in the United States by subsequent investigators. *Bacillus mesentericus* is a strict aerobe which grows well on ordinary media. It is actively proteolytic. Vogel [63] isolated organisms to which he gave the names *Bacillus mesentericus pani viscosus* I and II. Russell [64] reported that *Bacillus mesentericus vulgatus* was the causal organism. Russell found that after the loaf had been baked for an hour and a half that the center had not reached a temperature high enough to destroy the organism. He further believed that the organism was present in the yeast. Eckles,[65] by means of thermometers, confirmed Russell's statements about the temperatures reached in baking. The highest temperature attained by the loaf was 97C.(206°F.) after about an hour's baking. *Bacillus*

58. Veikko. 1938. Rev. in Chem. Abs. 32.
59. Nikolaev. 1932. Rev. in Biol. Abs. 9, 605.
60. Marison and Collatz. 1921. Amer. Inst. Baking Bull. No. 5.
61. Laurent. 1885. Brussels Acad. Roy. de Belg. Bull., Ser. 3, 10, 765.
62. Kratschmer and Niemilowicz. 1889. Vierteljahrschrift Nahr. u. Genussmtl. 4, 305.
63. Vogel. 1897. Ztschr. f. Hyg. u. Infektionskrank. 26, 398.
64. Russell. 1898. Wis. Agr. Expt. Sta., 15th Ann. Rpt., 110.
65. Eckles. 1899. Iowa Acad. Sci. Proc., 165-173.

panis was isolated by Fuhrmann [66] as the etiologic agent in ropy bread. Honig [67] believed the rope to be derived mainly from the outer membrane of the cells themselves. Watkins'[68] investigation pointed to *Bacillus mesentericus* as the cause of the trouble. Breads containing much bran were believed to be especially susceptible to rope.

The work of the investigators just referred to was confirmed by Juckenack,[69] Kreis,[70] Svoboda,[71] Harrison [72] and Fisher and Halton [73] Experiments by Allen [74] in which some 15 aerobic sporeforming bacteria quite similar to *Bacillus subtilis* were inoculated into bread doughs, showed that all of them produced rope in 30 hours when the bread was stored at 25°C.(77°F.). In one case where the oven was held at 204°C.(399.2°F.) the center of the loaf did not reach 100°C.(212°F.).

Source of Bacteria Causing Ropy Bread. While almost every ingredient used in bread making may contribute spores of rope-forming bacteria, under present commercial practice, flour, yeast, and malt are the main sources. Flour practically always harbors these bacteria as shown by results of various investigators. Powdered milk has also been reported to contribute rope-producing bacteria to the sponge.[76]

Methods for Prevention of Ropy Bread. This involves keeping the spores of *Bacillus mesentericus* out of the dough, or preventing their development if they are present. General cleanliness in the bakery is, of course, desirable. Ashby and Prickett,[76] in addition, suggested destruction of the spores of *Bacillus mesentericus* with germicides. Among those which may be used vinegar, hypochlorites, and formaldehyde were suggested. Vinegar in concentrations as low as one per cent was said to be germicidal toward rope-producing bacteria in the vegetative stage. When spores are present even vinegar containing as much as 2.5 per cent of acetic acid did not destroy them. Ashby and Prickett reported that hypochlorite solution containing 1,000 p.p.m. of available chlorine destroyed the most resistant spores.

Prevention of rope in bread has, in general, been accomplished by addition of acetic acid, .3 to .7 pound per sack of flour (280 lb.). Fisher [77] stated that this was equivalent to three and one-half to eight and one-half pounds of white vinegar per sack. He stated that two pounds of acid calcium phosphate per sack would completely prevent rope while one and one-half pounds would prevent it for five or six days. Watkins stated that the minimum amount of acid to prevent rope was three pounds per sack. Lactic acid had to be used to the extent of .6 pound. After studying

66. Fuhrmann. 1905. Centbl. Bakt., Pt. 2, 14, 385-399.
67. Honig. 1902. Fuhling's Landw. Ztg., 51, 823-827.
68. Watkins. 1906. J. Soc. Chem. Ind., 25, 350-357.
69. Juckenack. 1900. Ztschr. f. Analyst. Chem., 39, 73.
70. Kreis. 1893. Ber. That. Chem. Lab. Basel-Stadt.
71. Svoboda. 1901. Österr. Chem. Ztg., 4, 417.
72. Harrison. 1903. Brit. Food J., 5, 240.
73. Fisher and Halton. 1928. Cereal Chem., 5, 192-208.
74. Allen. 1919. Abs. Bact. 3, 4.
75. Food Indus., July, 1937, p. 406.
76. Ashby and Prickett. 1938. Idem July 1938.
77. Fisher. 1934. Northwest. Miller and Amer. Baker 11, 24-27.

various possible preventatives of rope in bread, Bunzell, Forbes, and Sherman [78] stated that 100-grain white vinegar in amounts of .66 per cent (3.82 pints per 600 pounds of flour) was more than adequate to prevent development of rope. Results of extensive experiments have been reported by Kirby, Atkin, and Frey.[79] They found that vinegar and calcium acid phosphate prevented development of rope at a pH of about 5 to 5.15, whereas tartaric acid must be used in quantities to give a higher acidity—a pH of about 4.7. Kirby and his colleagues were led to state that vinegar must possess some specific substance inimical to rope-producing bacteria other than its effect on acidity. Kirby, et al. also showed that vinegar was quite effective against molds on bread when it was applied to the surface of the loaf. When it is added to the dough, it is volatilized during baking and perhaps neutralized by bread constituents. Further information on the effect of acids on these organisms may be found in publications by Thomas,[80] Cohn, Wolbach, Henderson, and Cathcart,[81] Weimershaus and Svenson,[82] and Stuchlik.[83]

The other method of fighting rope in bakery products is through plant sanitation and destruction of the spores in the bakery with germicides. Ashby and Prickett,[76] after ruling out those which could not be used because of toxicity, odor, and color, mentioned hypochlorites, vinegar, and formaldehyde as possible ones. Hypochlorites were found to be good for regular use and formaldehyde for emergency use. Vinegar was objectionable because of its corrosive effect on metals.

Morison and Collatz [60] studied the influence of certain acids and acid salts on development of rope in bread and on the quality of the bread so treated. The acids used were acetic, lactic, hydrochloric, and sulfuric. The salts used were potassium dihydrogen phosphate and acid sodium sulfate. The source of the rope-producing organisms was a badly infected flour. Bread made from this flour was incubated in a moist chamber at 37°C. (98.6°F.) for three days. The bacterium responsible for ropy bread is generally conceded to be Bacillus mesentericus. Many strains are strongly proteolytic on gluten media prepared from washed gluten. The gluten is reduced, according to Morison and Collatz, to a slimy mass which gives off the characteristic odor. These investigators used acetic acid in amounts from 10.4 to 1.04 ounces per barrel of flour with a varying pH from 4.8 to 5.4. When used at the rate of 10.4 ounces (.33 per cent) rope development was prevented but the quality of the bread was poor. When 5.2 ounces (.17 per cent) of acetic acid was used, the bread was of good quality but rope developed in five days. At lower concentrations of acetic acid, rope developed more quickly. The experiments with lactic acid in larger amounts (22.21 ounces of 70 per cent lactic acid or about .5 per cent of anhydrous lactic acid) prevented rope development but yielded bread of

78. Bunzell, Forbes, and Sherman. 1932. Arkady Rev., July and September.
79. Kirby et al. 1936. Food Indus., Sept. 1936.
80. Thomas. 1938. Ztschr. f. Gesam. Getriedew. Muhlen u. Bakereiwesen. 25, 174-181.
81. Cohn et al. 1918. J. Gen. Physiol. 1, 221-230.
82. Weimershaus and Svenson. 1938. Jahresber. des Inst. Backerei, 76-80.
83. Stuchlik. 1935. Rev. in Chem. Abs. 29, 3738.

poor quality. Results with sulfuric and hydrochloric acids were generally unsatisfactory. Sodium acid sulfate (20.67 ounces to 196 pounds of flour or 66 per cent) produced a poor bread with inhibition of rope. Lower amounts gave better quality bread but rope developed sooner. Attempts to use combinations of above-mentioned salts were generally unsatisfactory.

In a comparative study of calcium acid phosphate and calcium propionate, O'Leary and Kralovec [84] found the latter to be from two to three times as effective as the former. Rope formation became more important as the number of bacteria increased from six to 1,300 per gram of flour. More than 1,300 spores per gram did not increase the rate of development of rope. These were well-controlled experiments.

Hoffman and his associates [90] proposed standards for spore counts of bread ingredients. Bread baked with six bacteria per gram of flour (twice Hoffman's standard adjusted to the formula used) developed symptoms very slowly. At one-third Hoffman's standard, no rope devoloped in 10 days. The pH of bread did not influence the rate of rope development if the inoculum used was high. With lower inoculum, the rate of development varied markedly when pH 5.37 was compared with pH 5.87. The inhibitory effects of both calcium acid phosphate and calcium propionate were found to be influenced by the amount of inoculum used and by the pH of the bread. Calcium propionate was found to be two or three times as effective as calcium acid phosphate. The difference in retarding effect between the two rope inhibitors was greatest at high pH values.

Watkins' [68] Method for Detecting the Organisms in Flour Which Cause Ropy Bread. The test is rapid and Watkins stated that there is little possibility of a sound flour failing to pass the test because they do not yield appearances of ropiness in the time proposed as a limit. Ten large test tubes (six inches by one inch) are thoroughly boiled in water for one hour, washed and drained. When drained, sterilize in the oven at 232°C.(449.6°F.) for three hours. The tubes should be thoroughly sterilized. Cool and then place into each tube a finger of bread three inches by one-half inch, but from the center of the same two-day-old loaf. The average weight of each loaf should be five grams. Moisten with distilled water and plug the tubes. Sterilize by boiling in water on three successive days. To test the flour, two grams are well mixed with water and placed in boiling water 30 minutes. To the series of 10 tubes add successively from one to seven ml. of the flour mixture, leaving three tubes to serve as checks. Number the tubes in rotation. Incubate at 28°C.(82.4°F.) and at the end of 24 hours examine for ropiness.

Kornauth's [85] Method for Detecting Organsims in Flour Which Cause Ropy Bread. This is a modification of Kühl's method and is carried out as follows: 280 grams of flour, 140 ml. of salt water, and .6 gram of yeast are made into a loaf. After baking, the loaf should be stored at 25°C.(77°F.) for 48 hours. If the organisms causing ropy bread were present in the flour, the loaf will have a characteristic odor. Several loaves should be made at the same time with sound flour as a check.

Lloyd's [86] Method for Detecting Ropy Bread Organism in Flour. Lloyd and his colleagues used the following method:

1. 300 ml. of distilled water are placed in a 500-ml. flask which is plugged with cotton and sterilized in the autoclave.

84. O'Leary and Kralovec. 1941. Cereal Chem. 18, 730-741.
85. Kornauth. 1912. Arch. f. Chem. u. Mikros. 5, 267-270.
86. Lloyd. 1921. J. Hyg. 19, 380-393.

2. 100 grams of flour are weighed out and shaken into sterile water with constant stirring.

3. The flask containing the water is well shaken.

4. Tubes containing from 10 to 20 ml. of nutrient agar are melted, four of these being allowed for each sample of flour.

5. Four ml. of the flour emulsion are removed from the flask with a sterile graduated pipette, one ml. being placed in each of the four tubes of melted agar which are placed in boiling water for 20 minutes.

6. The contents of each tube are then poured into sterile Petri dishes which are incubated at 38°C.(100.4°F.) for 24 hours.

Brahm's [87] Method for Detection of Organisms in Flour Causing Ropy Bread. To 300 ml. of sterile water in a 500-ml. flask add 100 grams of flour or meal and shake thoroughly. Then add one ml. of this suspension or emulsion to tubes of liquefied agar and heat in boiling water for 20 minutes. After this, pour the contents of the tubes into sterile Petri dishes. After 24 hours' incubation, colonies of *Bacillus mesentericus* should develop. Less than 12 colonies per ml. indicate a satisfactory flour; between 12 and 50 colonies indicate a flour which is unfit for bakery purposes.

Voitkevich's [88] Method for Detecting Rope-Forming Bacteria in Flour. Inoculate .2 gram of suspected flour into 10 ml. of sterile water; pasteurize at 75°C.(167°F.) for 10 minutes. Inoculate the contents of the tube into a loaf and incubate at 33°C. (91.4°F.) for 40 hours. The presence of *Bacillus mesentericus* is indicated by changes in the appearance of the loaf, as well as by microscope examination. Voitkevitch observed a striking seasonal prevalence of ropy bread; 35 per cent of 612 samples examined in summer and 10 per cent of 131 samples in winter showed the organism.

Bunzell and Forbes' [89] Method for Testing Ropiness of Bread. This method was devised for determining with considerable accuracy the incidence of rope-forming organisms in bread. The method is based upon the formation of the enzyme catalase by bacteria in the bread. It is necessary to assume that the bacteria which survive baking are members of the mesentericus group. Bunzell and Forbes devised an apparatus with which catalase activity could be measured.

Hoffman, Schweitzer, and Dalby's Method for Estimating Rope-Producing Bacteria in Flour. A dilution method was suggested by Hoffman, Schweitzer, and Dalby [90] for estimation of spores of rope-producing bacteria in flour and other materials. Two hundred grams of the material to be examined are transferred aseptically to a 250-ml. glass-stoppered bottle. About 10 grams of sea sand are added; then add 96 ml. of distilled water to the dilution bottle. This provides a dilution of 1 to 48 and may be used to determine presence of spores up to 200 per gram. Shake the dilution bottle vigorously 50 times, each excursion being about one foot up-and-down. Immediately after the sand has settled pipette 4.8 ml. of the 1 to 48 dilution into another 250-ml. glass-stoppered bottle containing 95.2 ml. of distilled water. This provides a dilution of 1 to 1,000 and is used to determine the presence of spores in numbers between 250 and 20,000 per gram. Pipette the following amounts of the 1 to 48 dilution into culture tubes containing sterile broth:

Ml.	Dilution	Ml.	Dilution	Ml.	Dilution
4.8	1-10	1.2	1-40	.48	1-100
2.4	1-20	0.8	1-60	.32	1-150
1.6	1-30	0.6	1-80	.24	1-200

Shake the 1-1,000 dilution 25 times as previously described. Prepare a third dilution of 1 to 100,000 from the 1 to 1,000 dilution. Use this dilution for determining the presence of spores between 25,000 and 100,000.

87. Brahm. 1921. Ztschr. f. Gesam. Getriedew. 13, 105-113.
88. Voitkevich. 1926. Rev. in Biol. Abs. 3 (1929), 1388.
89. Bunzell and Forbes. 1930. Cereal Chem. 7, 465-472.
90. Hoffman *et al.* 1937. Ind. Eng. Chem., 29, 464-467.

Pipette the following amounts of the 1 to 1,000 dilution into culture tubes containing nutrient broth:

Ml.	Dilution	Ml.	Dilution
4.0	1-250	.2	1-5,000
2.0	1-500	.1	1-10,000
1.0	1-1,000	.05	1-20,000
0.4	1-2,500		

Shake the 1 to 100,000 dilution 25 times and pipette the following amounts of this dilution into culture tubes containing nutrient broth:

Ml.	Dilution
4.0	1-25,000
2.0	1-50,000
1.0	1-100,000

Heat the tubes of nutrient broth in the steam sterilizer for 30 minutes at 100°C. (212°F.). The time is considered from the time the temperature of the sterilizer reaches 100°C. Incubate the tubes for 48 hours at 37.5°C.(99.5°F.). Examine them at the end of 48 hours for the presence of surface growth. Presence of a pellicle or any surface growth constitutes a presumptive test for the presence of rope-producing spores. Record the results as plus or minus for each dilution. The number of rope-producing spores per gram of material tested is taken as the reciprocal of the highest dilution giving positive results. Then the results should be recorded as indicating the number of spores equal to the number of spores equal to the reciprocal of the dilution next lower than the highest one giving a positive result. The quantitative estimation is not complete unless the two highest dilution tubes show negative results.

A long series of dilutions are ordinarily unnecessary in routine examinations for sorting our suspicious samples. The 1 to 48 dilution is adequate. Strict bacteriological technic must be observed throughout the test; all glassware and media must be sterile and the work must be carried out in dust- and draft-free laboratories.

Amos and Kent-Jones' [91] **Method for Counting Spores of Rope-Producing Organisms in Flour.** This is a modification of a method from Hoffman. It was outlined by Amos and Kent-Jones as follows:

Method. The details of the method finally adopted are as follows: The bottles, pipettes and measuring cylinder are sterilized by heating at 150°C.(302°F.) for two hours. The .5 per cent sodium chloride solution is sterilized by boiling in a plugged flask for one hour. Four hundred ml. of the sodium chloride solution are measured into a sterile 16-ounce glass-stoppered bottle and 100 ml. into a sterile eight-ounce glass-stoppered bottle. Twenty grams of purified silver sand are heated to redness in a platinum capsule for some minutes, and then poured, while hot, into the liquid in the 16-ounce bottle. Twenty grams of the flour are weighed out on a sterile watch glass and transferred by means of sterile paper to the 16-ounce bottle. This bottle is then shaken vigorously for two minutes. Volumes of two ml. and one ml., respectively, of the suspension are then added immediately, by means of a sterile one-ml. pipette, to five ml. tubes of the broth (for preparation of the broth, see later). The bottle is reshaken once or twice and, by means of a sterile pipette, 20 ml. of the suspension are added at once to the liquid in the eight-ounce bottle, and this bottle then well shaken. By means of a fresh sterile one-ml. pipette, volumes of 4, 3, 2.5, 2, 1.7, 1.5, 1.3, 1.2, and 1 ml., respectively, of this dilution are then added to five ml. tubes of the broth. The bottle is shaken once or twice before the withdrawal of each of the above quantities. Each tube is taken individually, the contents thoroughly mixed, and the tube at once placed in a bath of boiling water, so that the level of the water is above the level of the liquid in the tube. The tubes are allowed to remain in the bath for 20 minutes, and during this time the water is kept boiling. On removal of the tubes from the bath their contents are thoroughly mixed and they are then

91. Amos and Kent-Jones. 1931. Analyst. 56, 573-585.

placed in an incubator kept at 37°C.(98.6°F.). The contents of the tubes are well mixed three or four times during the first 24 hours' incubation. At the end of 48 hours' incubation the tube is reported as positive or negative according to whether the contained broth shows a pellicle or not. The number of rope spores per gram is taken as the reciprocal of the smallest fraction of a gram of flour giving a positive result. If, as sometimes happens, a negative result is obtained with a quantity of flour greater than the smallest amount giving a positive result, then the number of spores per gram is taken as the reciprocal of the quantity next greater than the smallest amount giving a positive result. The quantity of flour corresponding with the various volumes used is as under:

2	ml. of primary suspension—1/10 gm.	flour
1	ml. of primary suspension—1/20 gm.	flour
4	ml. of 20:100 dilution—1/30	gm. flour
3	ml. of 20:100 dilution—1/40	gm. flour
2.5	ml. of 20:100 dilution—1/48	gm. flour
2	ml. of 20:100 dilution—1/60	gm. flour
1.7	ml. of 20:100 dilution—1/70	gm. flour
1.5	ml. of 20:100 dilution—1/80	gm. flour
1.3	ml. of 20:100 dilution—1/92	gm. flour
1.2	ml. of 20:100 dilution—1/100	gm. flour
1	ml. of 20:100 dilution—1/120	gm. flour

If the flour contains more than 120 spores per gram a further dilution is made.

Cleaning of Used Tubes. The tubes are heated in a steam sterilizer for at least 30 minutes. The plugs are then removed, the contents discarded, and the tubes well washed out with hot water, a test-tube brush being employed. The tubes are then placed in a bath of mercuric chloride solution (1:1,000) and allowed to remain there for some hours. On removal from this bath, the tubes are washed out 10 times with water, drained, plugged, and heated at 150°C. for one hour and a half.

Preparation of Nutrient Broth. Ten grams of B.D.H.* bacteriological peptone, 5.4 grams of "Difco" beef extract, and 9 grams of A. R. sodium chloride are dissolved in a liter of distilled water, and the pH adjusted to 7.2 to 7.3. The solution is boiled and filtered, and the filtrate made up to one liter. The medium is distributed in five-ml. quantities in sterile test-tubes of five-eighth-inch diameter and sterilized for 10 minutes on three successive days in a steam sterilizer. In order to make certain of the complete absence of rope spores in the sterilized tubes of broth, they are placed in a blood-heat incubator for 48 hours; any of the tubes that show pellicle formation are discarded.

Amos and Kent-Jones [91] reported the presence of *Bacillus subtilis,* an organism almost identical with the rope-producing bacteria in flour. It may cause trouble in examination of flour for rope-producing bacteria because it grows quite like the latter. It does not however, cause ropy bread. To distinguish the organisms Amos and Kent-Jones suggested preparation of agar slant cultures from pellicles. The form of growth permits distinction between these two organisms. *Bacillus mesentericus vulgatus* was said to form a greyish-white growth which is at first moist and "blister-like," later becoming dried and unwrinkled. *Bacillus subtilis* gives a whitish, spreading growth; the edges of which, viewed under the low power of the microscope, appear as an interwoven mass of fine hairs.

The organisms causing ropy bread are present in all flours. Neumann and Knishchewsky [92] found them in all specimens irrespective of the grade.

* British Drug House, Ltd.

92. Neumann and Knischewsky. 1910. Ztschr. Gesam. Getriedew. 3, 187-191; continued in later numbers.

They also observed the effect of acids on these spoilage organisms. Henderson,[93] Williams,[94] and Zeckendorf [95] also added acids. Hydrogen-ion concentration is then very important in the baking industry, as shown by Sorensen.[96] Others who have studied this question are Kayser,[97] Perotti and Comanducci,[98] Beattie and Lewis,[99] Henderson,[100] Cohn et al.,[101] Seligmann,[102] Lloyd,[103] Beatty,[104] Fisher and Halton,[73] and Amos and Kent-Jones.[38] The last-mentioned found ropy bread organisms in much of the bread in England. This is also true for bread and flour in America. Many samples were examined in the summer of 1923 in the author's laboratory by Miss Strauch and later in 1928-1929 by Mr. Beier. All contained many spores of rope-producing bacteria. Hoffman, Schweitzer, and Dalby [90] examined hundreds of flour samples of patent, clear, rye, and whole-wheat flours, the spore counts of which were as high as 150 per gram, although many samples were free. For about 10 years after this work was done, spores of rope-producing bacteria have been less frequent in flour. This condition was attributed to better methods of harvesting and milling grains. Kent-Jones and Amos [38] also found many rope-producing bacteria in flour. Three varieties of these organisms were reported. They also reported the presence of Bacillus subtilis in flour. This organism is almost identical with Bacillus mesentericus but is not involved in rope formation.

While flour is generally considered to be the source of spores of rope-producing bacteria in bread, it is now known that malt, yeast, and other materials may also contribute these organisms. Hoffman, Schweitzer, and Dalby [90] mentioned appearance of rope in bread even when spore-free flour was used. This prompted counts on all ingredients of bread. Spores of rope-producing bacteria were found in yeast and malt in significant numbers but were absent in other ingredients, such as sugar, milk, shortening, and water. Daily examination of yeast shipments yielded spore counts as high as 20,000 per gram. This condition prompted the manufacturers of pressed yeast to product a product which has 10 or fewer spores per gram of yeast.

Malt extracts have also been dangerous potential sources of rope-producing bacteria. Hoffman et al. reported as many as 10,000 spores per gram. Here again the manufacturers of malt so improved their product that it is now relatively free of spores.

Tentative standards for interpretation of spore counts of flour and other materials were reported by Hoffman et al. Counts of 20 per 100 grams of flour, 100 per gram of yeast and malt, and 10 per gram of other

93. Henderson. 1918. Science 48, 247.
94. Williams. 1912. Biochem. Bull., 1, 529-534.
95. Zeckendorf. 1913. Natl. Assoc. Master Bakers, Proc., 16, 66-78.
96. Sorensen. 1926. Ann. Brass. Dist. 25, 65-71; 81-84.
97. Kayser. 1911. Soc. Sci. d'Hyg. Aliment. Bull., 349-357.
98. Perotti and Comanducci. 1918. Atti. della R. Accad. dei Lincei 27, 258-261.
99. Beattie and Lewis. 1917. Lancet, Pt. 2, 211-212.
100. Henderson. 1918. Science 48, 247.
101. Cohn. 1918-1919. J. Gen. Physiol. 221-230.
102. Seligmann. 1919. Centbl. Bakt. I, Orig., 83, 39-50.
103. Lloyd. 1921. J. Hyg., 19, 380-393.
104. Beatty. 1928. J. Roy. Army Med. Corps, 50-214-215.

ingredients are considered objectionable. These suggested standards are quite rigorous.

After developing a procedure for determining the number of rope-producing bacteria in flour, Amos and Kent-Jones [91] found that the content of these bacteria in flour, unless particularly high, is of little significance in outbreaks of rope formation in commercial practice. While it is helpful to supply a flour with few such bacteria, of greater importance are the systems of fermentation, baking, and bread cooling. In fact, Amos and Kent-Jones believed that the importance of these factors was not sufficiently recognized in the trade. When ropy-bread troubles appeared, they advised a short system of fermentation, a liberal quantity of yeast, avoidance of a low temperature in the dough, and avoidance of slack doughs. Amos and Kent-Jones did recognize some slight value in knowing whether flour was heavily ladened with spores of rope-producing bacteria. The baker might have an abnormal flour or might not be doing something which should be done. O'Leary and Kralovec,[84] on the other hand, believed the number of spores in the flour to be important, even from as few as six spores up to 1,300 per gram of flour.

Effect of Baking on Spores of Rope-Producing Bacteria in Bread. Spores of *Bacillus mesentericus* are not destroyed by baking but are reduced somewhat in numbers. Kent-Jones and Amos [98] found viable spores in normal loaves. Their procedure was to remove small samples of bread aseptically from the center of loaves and to incubate them in sterile tubes containing a little moist wool at 37°C.(98.6°F.).

Sour Bread. The abnormality is due to the production of acids in the dough. This usually occurs in dough which has been allowed to ferment or rise too long. Different explanations have been offered to explain sour bread. An old theory had it that the alcohol formed in the bread by the yeast was oxidized to acetic acid. While it is a reasonable explanation, there is little evidence to support it. Jago and Jago [105] stated that sour bread was due to bacterial fermentations, chief among which is the lactic acid fermentation. The bacteria which bring about these fermentations are introduced either in the yeast or flour or by dirty utensils. Sour bread is probably due to bacterial fermentation instead of yeast. The bacteria leave acids while the yeast forms carbon dioxide.

Chalky Bread. This was first observed by Lindner [106] and is characterized by the formation of white spots. The white spots were found to consist in part of a fungus to which the name *Endomyces fibuliger* has been given. This organism has received quite intensive study by Guilliermond, Lindner, and others. It is known to form typical white-chalky colonies on various media. Saito [107] also found the species on bread. The defect is not common.

Red Bread. This defect is due to the growth on bread of organisms forming a red pigment, chief among which *Serratia marcescens (Bacillus prodigiosus)* is known. The appearance of red bread caused consternation among early people. The formation of a deep shell-pink color in bread in eastern Ontario was attributed by Reed [108] to bakery infection with *Monilia sitophila*.

105. Jago and Jago. 1925. (See reference book list at end of this chapter.)
106. Lindner. 1907. Wchnschr. f. Brau. 24, 36.
107. Saito. 1912. Ztschr. f. Gärungsphysiol. 2, 151-153.
108. Reed. 1924. Phytopathology 14, 346.

MOLD ON BREAD AND BAKERY PRODUCTS

This is a significant bread defect, especially in warm humid weather. Pirrie [109] stated that 100 million loaves of bread a year are not saleable because of mold. This is a vast amount of wasted food. Bread is not the only bakery product which becomes moldy. Pirrie believed that losses owing to mold in bakery products are serious. Those who tend to belittle this problem are either uninformed or indifferent to the great loss of good food.

A general discussion of the bread-mold problem was published by Skovholt [110] and Glabau. [111] This latter author has reviewed the more general aspects of the problem.

The baker, himself, has also contributed to his mold problems by wrapping the loaves and by slicing them. The former maintains the moisture content of the loaf at a concentration favorable to mold development while the slicing machine helps to spread mold spores over bread surfaces. The saws distribute mold spores from the surface of the loaf over fresh-cut surfaces. Therefore, sliced bread has been observed to mold more than unsliced bread in the loaf.

Moldy bread was studied as early as 1885 by Smith [112] who isolated several species of common molds as its cause. Welte [113] also isolated *Rhizopus nigricans, Aspergillus nidulans,* and *Penicillium glaucum.* Herter and Fornet, [114] who isolated and described nine species, believed that the conidia were in the flour and gained entrance to the bread in this manner. Moisture was one of the determining factors in the development of molds on bread. It is very doubtful whether molds in bread are harmful to the health of those who consume it. Brocq-Rousseau, Forgeot, and Urbain [115] isolated a number of fungi from moldy bread, but could not prove that they were pathogenic. Prescott, Streider, and McClellan [116] believed that the incidence of mold on bread was proportional to the sanitation of the bakery. When better sanitary procedures were introduced, moldy bread was checked. Infection of the loaf was said to take place after the loaf left the oven. Rhizopus, Penicillium, and Aspergillus species were especially abundant. Frazier [117] in agreement with Herter and Fornet, believed that the flour was the source of the mold spores. He studied two flours used in the making of bread which became moldy, both of which had many mold spores. Discontinuance of these flours caused no further trouble. Wrapping caused more mold because moisture was retained, which in turn allowed the spores to germinate.

Various species of molds will develop on bread as many have shown. Herter and Fornet [114] described 11 species belonging to the genera Asper-

109. Pirrie. Private communication.
110. Skovholt. 1933. Minn. Agr. Expt. Sta. Bull. 296.
111. Glaubau. 1939. Bakers Weekly, Aug., Sept., and Oct., 1939.
112. Smith. 1885. Analyst. 10, 181-183.
113. Welte. 1895. Arch. f. Hyg., 25, 104.
114. Herter and Fornet. 1919. Centbl. Bakt., Pt. 2, 49, 148-173.
115. Brocq-Rousseau *et al.* 1921. Rec. de Méd. Vét.. Dec. 15, 694-708.
116. Prescott *et al.* 1922. Baking Technol. 1, 230-235.
117. Frazier. 1923. Wis. Agr. Expt. Sta. Bull. 352; Baking Technol. 2 (1923). 184-187.

gillus, Penicillium, Mucor, and Rhizopus. After baking, development of these molds in bread is influenced by various factors. One of the most important is humidity, studied by Skovholt and Bailey.[118] Relative humidities of 80 per cent or more in air are required for appreciable mold growth on bread crust within the usual interval of time between production and consumption. Introduction of milk solids into bread increased slightly its hygroscopicity. Attempts to use carbon dioxide in control of molds on bread yielded results of no practical value.

Moldy bread is a greater problem during warm and humid seasons. While the temperature relations of all species of molds are not identical, most of them grow more rapidly at higher temperatures.

Origin of Mold Spores in Bread. Published reports indicate that mold spores may be present in materials from which bread is made or come from utensils and air in the bakery. The latter is undoubtedly one of the main sources of mold. All air is more or less ladened with various microorganisms or their spores. City air is probably much more heavily laden than is country air. Since this subject is discussed more fully in another chapter in this book, it will not be discussed here. Mold spores may be brought into the bakeshop in various ways, on the street clothes of workers, on baskets and crates in which bread is handled, and by drafts of air from the outside. Mold infection is a difficulty which develops after the bread has left the oven.

Bread probably collects its load of mold spores on the cooling racks and in the wrapping machines. Both of these are exposed to the air. Wrapping and slicing of bread have contributed greatly to the mold problem even though they are considered marked advances in other ways. The former has retained moisture so important in mold growth, while the saws on the slicing machine distributed molds throughout the crumb.

Flour in some cases has been a fertile source of mold spores. Frazier[117] studied one outbreak of moldy bread in which the flour contained as many as 11,000 mold spores per gram. When use of this flour was discontinued, the trouble stopped. The bread made from this flour showed mold in the loaf within one and one-half and two hours after leaving the oven. By the time it reached the consumer, the whole loaf was moldy.

Effect of Baking Temperatures on Mold Spores. Mold spores are not especially resistant to heat, as indicated in various places in this book. They are killed by temperatures much lower than those used in baking. Morison[119] reported that conidia and ascospores of Monilia species isolated from moldy bread survived heating for 30 minutes at 50°C.(122°F.) but were destroyed by heating at 60°C.(140°F.) for 20 minutes or at 70°C. (158°F.) for 10 minutes. Loaves baked from infected dough for 30 minutes at 220°C.(428°F.) showed no evidence of mold development after five days' incubation. The work of Prescott, Strider, and McClellan[116] would also suggest that microorganisms are killed in the loaf by baking because the center of the loaf reached a temperature of 97°C.(206.6°F.) which

118. Skovholt and Bailey. 1933. Cereal Chem., 10, 446-451.
119. Morison. 1933. Cereal Chem., 10, 462.

would destroy microorganisms. Brouilett [120] believed that mold spores are killed in baking and quoted Skovhold and Bailey to the same effect. While this may be generally the case, some conditions might exist which would allow them to survive. Frazier's work would indicate this.

Control of Mold on Bread. Control of molds on bread involves elimination of their spores in flour and other materials or control of them in the bread. It also involves elimination in the bakery. The problem is not simple but involves several possible methods of attack. Improvements in general sanitation of the bakery were suggested by some of the earlier authors, and while this has helped to reduce mold trouble, it has not entirely solved the problem. Related to these efforts is attainment of bacteriological cleanliness which means much more than ordinary cleanliness. Machines must be scrubbed and washed and walls and floors thoroughly cleaned. Germicidal paints are being tried on the former with some success.

Vacuum cooling of baked goods has been given considerable importance as one possible method of protecting them from undesirable organisms. The bread is cooled partially at room temperature after which it is subjected to a vacuum of from 28 to 29 inches.

The modern methods of air-conditioning also play a role in protecting bread from mold spores. Air is washed and changed so that foreign matter is continually being removed.

The mold problem has been so troublesome that various types of methods have been attempted to combat it. These have involved, in addition to those just mentioned, ozonizing the air, passing the baked goods through fungicidal vapors, and use of so-called inhibitors of which quite a few have been proposed.

A more recent attempt to control bread mold has involved use of rays from the quartz lamp. This proposal is in keeping with the efforts which have been made in practically every part of the food industry, to control microorganisms. Owen [121] found that the exposure of the bread-slicing unit to ultraviolet light during slicing operations greatly reduced development of molds. These rays sterilized the saws and inactivated mold spores. Read [122] exposed freshly baked bread heavily infected with the mature spores of the more common species of Aspergillus, Penicillium, Rizopus, and Mucor for varying lengths of time at a given distance to ultraviolet radiations from three types of mercury vapor lamps and from the open C_4 type of carbon lamp with carbons of different materials in the core. Some doubt may exist with respect to the practicability of this method for controlling "rope" in bread because of the relatively long exposure times required. They are not only expensive but might cause undesirable changes in the bread.

The carbon lamp gave better results than the mercury vapor lamp, and there was considerable variation in the effectiveness of the different car-

120. Brouilett. 1933. Amer. Soc. Bakery Engin. Bull. 91.
121. Owen. 1932. Food Indus. 4, 208-210.
122. Read. 1934. Cereal Chem. 11, 80-85.

bons. The most effective destroyed heavy spore infection on the surface of the loaves in 45 seconds at a distance of eight inches with the lamp operated by the direct current at 75 and 60 volts. Wrapping the infected loaves in transparent sheeting, such as cellophane and Sylphwrap, did not decrease the fungicidal potency of the radiation. This process of sterilization is being used on a limited commercial scale to prevent the occurrence of mold on certain special breads. While exposure of bread to ultraviolet rays may reduce the number of viable microorganisms, it does not remove all of them. This is probably due to the fact that the rays have little if any penetrating power, as well as to the unevenness of the surface of the loaf.

The chemical substances which have been proposed at various times are added to the dough and are, in general, known as inhibitors. The most important of these are certain harmless organic acids, acetic and propionic, or their salts.

Acids have also been used for controlling development of molds on bread. Kirby, Atkin, and Frey,[123] using five different species of molds, observed that the effect of acidity on growth must be considered not only from the standpoint of hydrogen-ion concentration but the specific effect of the kind of acid used. At the same pH different acids varied in their effect. Fatty acids were much more toxic than mineral acids and such organic acids as lactic, citric, tartaric, and maleic. Molds, like yeasts, have a wide growth optimum with respect to pH. They seem to grow well at all pH values at which commercial bread is produced. Kirby, Atkin, and Frey believed that if a baker increases the pH of his bread to approximately 5.0 for the purpose of controlling rope, he will not increase his mold problem. If he uses acetic acid or other fatty acids of this series he would not only control rope but would also retard development of molds. A film of dilute acetic acid such as vinegar covering the surface of the loaf of bread was said to be very effective in preventing development of mold.

Mold Inhibitors in Bread. These are substances which are added to the product to repress development of mold spores which have survived baking or have reached the product after baking. Glabe [124] has stated that a good mold inhibitor must be potent in low concentrations, must be nonpoisonous to man, must not decompose in baked products, must not produce deleterious results during baking, and must have no effect on taste and odor. Such requirements restrict the chemical substances which may be used to a few. Sodium and calcium propionates have had wide use under the name Mycoban. More recently sodium diacetate (Badex) has been proposed.

Propionic acid as such, or its calcium or sodium salt, has also been proposed as a mold preventative in bread. Little doubt exists as to its retarding effect on development of molds of these compounds. Macy [125] reported prevention of mold development in butter by wrapping in parchment treated with sodium or calcium propionate. Miller [126] reported the

123. Kirby, Atkin, and Frey. 1937. Cereal Chem. 14, 865-878.
124. Glabe. 1941. The Bakers' Digest, p. 221-223.
125. Macy. 1939. J. Dairy Sci., 22, 527-534.
126. Miller. 1940. Proc. Inst. Food Technol. 2, 153-158.

same results with cheese treated with solutions of propionic acid. Mold growth was not entirely eliminated but was greatly retarded. These results were supported by those from experiments by Irvine and Sproule.[127] Both of these investigations indicated marked action of calcium propionate on molds in cheese. This was confirmed for bread by O'Leary and Kralovec.[128]

Is Moldy Bread Hazardous to Health? The answer is unquestionably "no." Mold spores are widespread in nature and are eaten in large numbers. No evidence has ever been produced to dispute this fact. Herter and Fornet,[114] after an extensive investigation of the molds from moldy bread, stated that such bread was harmless. Owing to the musty flavor and appearance, it would ordinarily be excluded from the diet.

Bacteriology of Bread. Even though bread is baked in hot ovens, it is not necessarily sterile. Probably the better heated and controlled ovens of the present day are turning out bread which is more satisfactory bacteriologically than ever before. A careful bacteriological study of various breads sold today is needed to determine whether results which have been reported in the literature still represent the situation. As early as 1894, Lawrence-Hamilton [129] recognized the need for technical control in the baking industry. He studied the temperatures attained in the interior of the loaf and found that they were considerably below the temperatures of the ovens. Belli [130] and Marchand found living bacteria in bread, the number being proportional, in general, to the size of the loaf. The size of the loaf would influence the efficiency of heat penetration.

Investigators in foreign countries have studied the possibilities of pathogenic bacteria surviving the baking process. Roussel,[131] Auché,[132] Fenyvessy and Denies [133] and Gaujoux [134] all studied the effect of baking on *Mycobacterium tuberculosis* in dough. All of the evidence seemed to indicate that the organism was destroyed. Auché used a number of other pathogenic bacteria, finding that they were also destroyed.

Wrapping bread is a practice with considerable hygienic value. Jacobs, LeClerc, and Mason [135] and Howell [136] reported that the bacterial content of bread was determined largely by the conditions under which it was produced, and wrapping.

Considerable attention to bread hygiene still seems to be necessary in France, according to papers by Violle [137], Fouassier[138] and Aubertin, Daugoumeau, Leuret, and Piechaud.[139]

While properly baked bread will probably be free from pathogenic bacteria, the danger of dissemination of pathogenic bacteria is always

127. Irvine and Sproule. 1940. Canad. Dairy and Ice Cream J., 19, Nov. 1940.
128. O'Leary and Kralovec. 1941. Cereal Chem., 18, 170-740.
129. Lawrence-Hamilton. 1895. Rev. in Expt. Sta. Rec., 7, 793.
130. Belli. 1906. Gior. R. Soc. Ital. Ig., 28.
131. Roussel. 1908. Rev. in Chem. Abs. 2 (1908), 1168.
132. Auché. 1909. Compt. Rend. Soc. Biol., 66, 800-802; Brit. Med. J., 1910, 771-772.
133. Fenyvessy and Denies. 1911. Ztschr. f. Hyg. u. Infektionskrank. 69, 223-224.
134. Gaujoux. 1911. Rev. d'Hyg., 33, 1176-1180.
135. Jacobs, LeClerc, and Mason. Amer. J. Pub. Health 4, 721-732.
136. Howell. 1912. Amer. J. Pub. Health 2, 321-324.
137. Violle. 1930. Rev. d'Hyg., 52, 409-425.
138. Fouassier. 1930. Rev. d'Hyg. 52, 329-362.
139. Aubertin et al. 1938. Compt. Rend. Soc. Biol., 127, 64-66.

present. The American practice of wrapping each loaf of bread was considered by Fouassier to be impracticable on account of the large size of French loaves. The introduction of breadmaking machinery has greatly reduced the possibility of infection from those who kneaded the bread by hand. It is quite generally agreed that maintenance of a temperature of 100-102°C. (212-215.6°F.) for at least 10 minutes, should be adequate to destroy pathogenic bacteria. La Rosa,[140] however, stated that same pathogenic bacteria might survive baking. Whether this would be the case depends largely on temperatures attained in the loaf during baking. On this question, results of experiments by Stout and Drosten[141] may be quoted.

The time-temperature curves showed in all cases three general periods. During the first 10 minutes there was a rapid rise of temperature within the loaf which was more marked in the ovens of high than low temperature. This was followed by another 10 minutes in which the temperature rose at a slower rate, and finally there was a period of from nine to 12 minutes of constant temperature. The two extremes of oven temperature did not produce good loaves. In no case did the temperature within the loaf exceed 100 or 101°C. Under the experimental conditions this temperature must have been maintained for at least a period of nine minutes to produce a loaf of satisfactory doneness.

Relation of Bread to Illness. In America bread has not been incriminated in many outbreaks of illness. The nature of bread would indicate that it may be infected when handled by a carrier just are are other foods. Hansen[142] reported an outbreak of typhoid fever which was believed to have been caused by bread. The evidence is not as convincing as one would desire. Louste and Godlewski[143] made a similar report for an outbreak of dysentery involving 31 cases and six deaths. When medical officers enforced rules of hygiene, the outbreak terminated. Silberschmidt also gave evidence that bread may carry pathogenic bacteria. In experiments by Alves[144] bread was contaminated after baking with *Eberthella typhosa, Shigella dysenteriae*, Shiga, and Flexner. These organisms were recoverable by cultural methods at periods varying from two to 30 hours after contamination.

Clostridium botulinum in Bread. Few experiments have been carried out with organisms in bread. Edmondson, Thom, and Giltner[145] inoculated enough bread dough with toxin-free spores of *Clostridium botulinum* to make one loaf. This was put through the usual procedures and finally baked in an oven held at 220°C. (428°F.) for 35 minutes. Another loaf was inoculated just after it had been worked and before being placed in the pan for the second rising. This second loaf was baked as was the former. *Clostridium botulinum* could not be recovered. One would not

140. La Rosa. 1928. Ann. d'Hyg. 38, 23-33.
141. Stout and Drosten. 1933. Ind. Eng. Chem., 25, 428-430.
142. Hansen. 1913. Ill. Water Survey Bull. 11, 384-430.
143. Louste and Godlewski. 1919. Bull. Soc. Med. de Hop., 43.
144. Alves. 1935. So. African Med. J., 9, 191-192.
145. Edmondson *et al*. 1923. Amer. Food J., March.

expect the spores of *Clostridium botulinum* to be destroyed by the temperatures attained in bread during baking.

Yeast Foods in Breadmaking. While the materials used for making bread are sufficient to permit good growth and fermentation by the yeast, better results are secured when certain inorganic salts are added. Addition of phosphates greatly stimulates gas formation in dough and Vandevelde and Masson [146] observed improved results by the use of salt mixtures. The subject has been studied at considerable length in recent years in America by Kohman [147] and his colleagues and Hoffman.[148] Kohman's work apparently had its origin in the effect of different natural waters on fermentation in dough as noticed by a large baking company. He showed that the use of small quantities of ammonium and calcium salts and potassium bromide brought about a saving of 50 to 65 per cent in the amount of yeast required. Hoffman also showed the benefits of using ammonium chloride. The result of these investigations was the appearance on the market of Arkady Yeast Food,'' a product said to contain calcium sulfate 25, ammonium chloride 9.7, potassium bromate .3, sodium chloride 25, and patent wheat flour 40 parts. Street [149] confirmed the experiences of those quoted above. He was able to see no objection to the addition of the material to bread. Other studies on these products were reported by Elion [150] and Masters and Maughan,[151] although their products were not of such importance in breadmaking as those discussed above.

Macaroni. This is such a dry product that microbial spoilage is rare. Occasional purple streaks on macaroni, as reported by Falkova and Mishutin,[152] were due to a member of the genus Monilia. It was not pathogenic; the spores found in the paper wrappers were destroyed in 40 minutes at $100°C. (212°F.)$; older colonies were destroyed in 60 minutes at $160°C. (320°F.)$.

REFERENCE BOOKS

JAGO, W., JAGO, W. C., 1925. The Technology of Bread Making. Northern Pub. Co., Liverpool. 638 pp.

BENNION, E. B., 1940. Breadmaking: Its Principles and Practice. Second Edition. Oxford Univ. Press, England.

PELSHENKE, P., 1939. Untersuchungs methoden für Brotgetreide, Mehl and Brot. M. Schaefer, Leipzig. 288 pp.

146. Vandevelde and Masson. 1907. Rev. in Koch's Jahresber. 18, 297.
147. Kohman. 1916. J. Ind. Eng. Chem. 8, 781-789.
148. Hoffman. 1917. Idem 9, 148-151.
149. Street. 1917. Comn. Agr. Expt. Sta. Bull. 200.
150. Elion. 1928. Ztschr. f. Angew. Chem. 41, 230.
151. Masters and Maughan. 1920. Biochem. J., 14, 586-602.
152. Falkova and Mishutin. 1940. Microbiology (U. S. S. R.) 9, 54-57.

CHAPTER 18

FERMENTED FOODS

Foods are fermented for various reasons. Preservation and improvement of flavor are the main ones. Vegetables, such as cabbages, cucumbers, and even lettuce, have been preserved by fermentation for many decades. Although flavor is changed, differences of opinion might exist as to whether it is actually improved. The products of fermentation are usually acids which inhibit microorganisms that are food destroyers. In some cases these acids exert a selective action. Cream is fermented (ripened) in order to stabilize and improve the flavor. Butter made from ripened cream keeps well.

VINEGAR

Vinegar is one of the oldest fermentation products used by man. One of the first substrates fermented to yield vinegar was wine. Our modern word for vinegar comes from the two French words for sour wine, *vin-aigre*. Luckow,[1] who discussed the earlier history of the vinegar fermentation, showed how closely studies on this fermentation were associated with early advances in the study of microbiology. Pasteur's contributions were among the first to throw light on the foundations of the fermentation. He showed that living microorganisms were important. Hansen's[2] publication, *Recherches sur les Bacteries Acetifiantes,* was the first modern publication on the subject. In some of his pioneer work he showed that oxidation of alcohol to acetic acid was not carried out by one species but that several, to two of which he gave the names *Mycoderma aceti* and *Mycoderma pasteurianum,* were involved. These names were later changed to *Bacterium aceti* and *Bacterium pasteurianum,* and still later to names given below.

Fermentation vinegar is more than a solution of acetic acid or other organic acids. In addition, there are substances which contribute to odor, flavor, and color. The amount of acetic acid in market vinegar is prescribed by law.

In the remote past, very little attention was given to the preparation of the apples from which the juice was pressed. No serious attempt was made to sort defective fruit, nor were the apples washed. Under such conditions, the juice was not only of poor quality, but contained a rich flora of undesirable microorganisms. Vaton[3] stated that in Germany, Switzerland, and some other countries it is the custom to wash the apples used for the manufacture of vinegar, but that in France opinion is divided on the matter. Vaton subjected cider apples of different kinds to a washing process, to ascertain the nature and amount of the matters removed. Twenty kilos of each kind were employed. The impurities formed a nauseous mass containing dry matter ranging in amount from two to 26 grams. The aver-

1. Luckow. 1927. Centbl. Bakt., Pt. 2, 72, 39-66.
2. Hansen. 1895. Carlsberg Lab. Compt. Rend. des Trav., 3, 182-216.
3. Vaton. 1922. L'Alimentation Modern, July, 1922.

age amount was 7.258 grams, consisting of sugar, tannin, pectic and protein materials, and ash. The loss of sugar by washing, per metric ton of apples, would scarcely amount to 281 grams, a negligible quantity. If washing is prolonged, the loss becomes greater. It is advisable, therefore, not to leave the apples for too long a time in the water and not to subject them to excessive movement. Apples should be dried after washing. The necessary operations can be carried out by means of machines, which should be found in every well-equipped cider mill. Vandecaveye [4] stated that washing and sorting of the apples had little effect on the fermentations. This would seem to indicate that not all undesirable organisms were removed by washing. It was stated, however, that too much emphasis could not be placed on clean utensils. Certainly, clean fruit would have some advantage.

Alcoholic Fermentation. The fermentation of saccharine substances to vinegar involves two fermentations, alcoholic and acetic. The former is brought about by yeasts which are known to be widely distributed in nature and would, therefore, be present on the surface of fruits, the juices of which would constitute the substrate. The time required to complete the alcoholic fermentation depends on such conditions as temperature, composition of the juice, vigor of the yeast, air supply, etc. The most favorable temperature is about 30°C.(86°F.). The substrate should be protected from dirt and insects.

Less work has been done on the use of pure cultures of yeasts in the vinegar industry than in some of the other industrial fermentations. Perhaps it has not been needed, but it is quite probable that pure cultures would improve the product.

Acetic Acid Fermentation. The acetic acid fermentation follows the alcoholic and yields the vinegar. This oxidation of alcohol to vinegar seems to be a reaction carried on especially by the acetic bacteria. Since the making of vinegar is a process carried on by microorganisms, every attempt is made to furnish them with optimum conditions for working. The temperature limits for maximum vinegar formation seem to be 20-35.5°C. (68-96°F.). Beyond these limits, the reaction is slow. The substrate must not contain over 15 per cent of alcohol, while from 11 to 13 per cent allows greatest growth of the vinegar bacteria. On the other hand, a content of alcohol which is too low does not allow good development of the acetic bacteria. The chemistry of the acetic acid fermentation has been found to be just as complicated as the chemistry of alcoholic fermentation.

The chemical oxidation of alcohol in the presence of platinum black was first observed by Edmund Davy in 1821. This caused the early workers to believe that the reactions in the quick vinegar process occurred in the same manner. In 1864, Pasteur [5] proved that the real promoters of this change were organisms, which grew in a delicate film over the surface of the beech shavings used in the process.

Neuberg and Windisch [6] and his colleagues have done much to explain the chemical mechanism of the acetic acid fermentation. It is generally

4. Vandecaveye. 1926. Wash. Agr. Expt. Sta. Bull.
5. Pasteur. 1864. Ann. de l'École Normal. Suppl. 1.
6. Neuberg and Windisch. 1925. Biochem. Ztschr. 166, 454.

admitted that the oxidation of ethyl alcohol to acetic acid takes place in two stages, the oxidaton of ethyl alcohol to acetaldehyde and the oxidation of the latter to acetic acid. Using Neuberg and Nord's method of fixation, which was so successful in the alcoholic fermentation, Neuberg and Windisch [6] showed that acetic acid bacteria as well as a few others could act on the acetaldehyde, transforming it into equimolecular proportions of acetic acid and ethyl alcohol. This transformation took place in the absence of air, as well as in the presence of air. If it were merely a simple oxidation of acetaldehyde, it would only take place in presence of air. According to Neuberg's conceptions the acetaldehyde formed by oxidation of ethyl alcohol is transformed not by a direct oxidation, but by a process of "dismutation," into acetic acid and alcohol by a Canizzaro reaction; for each two molecules of aldehyde which enter the reaction, one is transformed by oxidation to acetic acid, while the other goes by reduction to ethyl alcohol. Identical results were secured with *Acetobacter ascendens, Acetobacter pasteurianus,* and *Acetobacter xylinum.* Myrback, von Buler, and Sandberg [7] examined the acetic acid bacteria and found that they dismute acetaldehyde rapidly, and that this property was destroyed by boiling. The heated extract contained a cozymase which activated fermentation by cozymase-free yeast. Kluyver and Donker [8] also presented a scheme to show how ethyl alcohol might be formed.

The bacteria which change ethyl alcohol to acetic acid belong to the genus Acetobacter. Their action is influenced greatly by other microorganisms which may be present, according to Vaughn.[9] The type of yeast is important.

METHODS OF MAKING VINEGAR

While the chemistry and bacteriology of vinegar making is the same, several different methods have been developed to bring about those changes.

Orleans Method. Vinegar was made in Orleans, France, by mixing vinegar with wine in tanks. As the fermentation progressed, the surface of the liquid was covered with a pellicle composed of fermenting organisms. These grew in contact with air using oxygen for oxidizing alcohol to acid. When acetic acid had reached a concentration of between 12 and 14 per cent, the fermentation stopped only to be renewed by some process which will remove the acid. Usually more wine is added after the volume of the solution has been decreased. This process unless carefully done will disturb the pellicle over the surface and therefore upset the system for a time. To obviate this difficulty, a board covering is now used upon which the "mother of vinegar" is supported in such a manner that it is not destroyed when the tank is regenerated with new wine. Sour wine with not over 10 per cent of alcohol is used. When it contains more than 10 per cent, it must be diluted with weaker wine.

Domestic Method. The generator in this method consists of a tight barrel with a capacity of 190 liters more or less. The raw material may be

7. Myrback *et al*. 1928. Ztschr. f. Physiol. Chem., 175, 316-320.
8. Kluyver and Donker. 1924. Verlags. Akad. Wettenschappen Amsterdam 33, 895-914.
9. Vaughn. 1938. J. Bact. 36, 337-357.

wine, but in America it is usually fresh apple juice. The cask is partly filled so there is air space to allow good oxidation.

Quick Vinegar Process. In this process every possibility for furthering oxidation of the alcohol is sought. The alcohol containing liquid is allowed to flow slowly in a thin layer over a stratum on which are Acetobacter. The bacteria oxidize the alcohol to acid. The contrivance used for this purpose is called a "generator." This generator is analogous in many ways to a furnace because in both a strong oxidation is going on. The generator is an upright wooden tank from three to four feet in diameter and eight to 10 feet high. A false bottom exists about 10 inches from the base on which is placed porous material, such as beech wood shavings, corn cobs, etc., until the generator is nearly full. At the top of the generator is a tilting device which discharges the alcoholized material in either direction. As it flows through the generator Acetobacter oxidize the alcohol. Wüstenfeld [10] found that acetification began rather promptly in the upper layers and reached its highest rate in the lower layers.

A new generator must be gotten in shape by acidulating the shavings (or other material) and establishing a rich flora of Acetobacter. During operation the effluent must be analyzed for acid and alcohol and the temperature carefully kept under control. If it is allowed to become too high, the bacteria may be killed. Analytical data on such vinegar were published by Hartman and Tolman.[11] When Acetobacter in a vinegar generator are harmed and fail to act normally, they are said to be "poisoned." Popper [12] studied such cases. In one, he found that failure to acetify was due to an asphalt paint used for dressing the walls. He advised against the use in or around generators of any agent which would harm the bacteria.

Since oxidation of alcohol in making vinegar has much in common with the aeration method of treating sewage, Fowler and Subramaniam [13] were interested to determine whether increased oxidation of alcohol would result from forcing air through the substrate. Good oxidation resulted, although strict attention had to be given to amount of air which was used. They could observe no benefits from presence of "activated silt." The method seems to be worthy of more study.

Various Types of Vinegar. Almost any substrate which contains sufficient sugar and nitrogenous food materials may be fermented to acetic acid. Besides those mentioned in the early paragraphs in this section, several others may be briefly discussed here. Chace and Poore [14] described orange vinegar in a study of possible uses for citrus by-products. A generator was described. Poore [15] described a method for making orange vinegar in the home without a generator. Fabian [16] published formulas for making vinegar from honey. According to Hofmann,[17] honey vinegar has been made

10. Wüstenfeld. 1916. Chem. Zentbl., Pt. 2, 702-703.
11. Hartman and Tohman. 1917. J. Ind. Eng. Chem. 9, 759-762.
12. Popper. 1924. Fruit Prod. J., and Amer. Vinegar Indus. 4, Sept., 1924.
13. Fowler and Subramaniam. 1923. J. Indian Inst. Sci., Pt. 8, 6, 147-163.
14. Chace and Poore. 1920. Citrus Indus. 1, 12.
15. Poore. 1920. J. Ind. Eng. Chem. 12, 1176-1179.
16. Fabian. 1926. Mich. Agr. Expt. Sta. Circ. 85; Ext. Bull. 149 (1935).
17. Hoffmann. 1905. Pharm. Weekbl. 42, 704-705.

in Holland on a commercial scale for a long time. According to Von Loesecke,[18] bananas may be used, and Pernot [19] suggested prunes as a fermentable substrate. Vinegars made from these materials would possess flavors and aromas somewhat different from apple vinegar, but would probably be just as satisfactory. Low-grade honey was used for vinegar manufacture by Fabian.[16] A satisfactory formula consisted of from 40 to 45 pounds of extracted honey, 30 gallons of water, two ounces of potassium tartrate, and two ounces ammonium phosphate. The solution was sterilized and pitched with yeast for the alcoholic fermentation. When this was finished it was inoculated with Acetobacter for the acetic fermentation. Bhagwan and Sarin [20] used dates as raw material for vinegar making. The fruit was cooked and the juice pressed out for fermentation.

Microbiology of Vinegar Manufacture. The microbiology of vinegar has received much study. Some of the earliest investigators in microbiology studied it and secured data which in light of present knowledge and information, are quite accurate. Persoon in 1822 recognized the plant nature of some of the fungi concerned in acetic acid fermentation. Pasteur [5] proved that acetic acid resulted from development of microorganisms, and not from chemical reactions alone. Hansen reported isolation of several acetic acid bacteria to which he gave the names, *Bacterium pasteurianum*, *Bacterium Kützingianum*, and *Bacterium aceti*. He classed Pasteur's *Mycoderma aceti*, and *Bacterium aceti* with *Bacterium pasteurianum* and *Bacterium kützingianum*. Later on, Brown [21] isolated a new organism to which he gave the name *Bacterium xylinum*.

Identification of acetic acid bacteria is complicated by the fact that many names appear in the literature of the subject for the same species. Bergey's *Manual of Determinative Bacteriology*, Fifth Edition, lists 15 species in the genus *Acetobacter*. Five more species are listed as probable members of the genus. Henneberg,[22] Rothenbach,[23] Hoyer,[24] Mason,[25] and Beijerinck [26] attempted to systematize the group. Henneberg [27] recognized two groups of vinegar bacteria, "culture" and "wild." *Bacillus orleanse* belonged to the first group as did *Bacillus xylinoides*. To the second group belonged *Acetobacter xylinum*, *Bacillus vini acetate*, and *Acetobacter ascendens*. These bacteria were said to be characterized by type of films formed on media. The so-called "culture" acetic acid bacteria (*Bacillus xylinoides* and *Bacillus orleanse*) and the "wild" species *Acetobacter ascendens* (*Bacillus ascendens*) were reported to develop in as much as 10 to 12 per cent of alcohol. Henneberg stated that acetic acid bacteria which had not been grown in wine vinegar would have to be acclimated to the high acetic

18. Von Loesecke. 1929. Ind. Eng. Chem. 21, 175-186.
19. Pernot. 1902. Oregon Agr. Expt. Sta. Bull. 73.
20. Bhagwan and Sarin. 1936. Ind. Eng. Chem. 28, 814.
21. Brown. 1886. J. Chem. Soc. 49, 176-187.
22. Henneberg. 1898. Ztschr. Deut. Essig Indus., No. 19 and 20; Centbl. Bakt. 4, Pt. 2, 4, 14.
23. Rothenbach. 1899. Wchnschr. f. Brau. 16, 41.
24. Hoyer. 1899. Deut. Essig Indus.
25. Mason. 1924. Bull. Biotech. 2, 75-77.
26. Beijernick. 1898. Centbl. Bakt., Pt. 2, 4, 209.
27. Henneberg. 1907. Deut. Essig Indus., No. 32 and 33.

acid and alcohol content of the substrate. Inoculation should be effected in such a manner that the film particles float on the surface of the liquid.

The acetic acid bacteria are very pleomorphic. They grow on the surface of suitable media with a film of pellicle. The cells of this film are held together by a mucilaginous substance equivalent to, if not a true, capsular material. This constitutes the so-called "mother-of-vinegar." Perold [28] stated that involution forms usually appeared under undesirable conditions, but that this was not always the case. He even stated that they were of service in identification of cultures.

According to Grove,[29] who examined from 30 to 40 acetified ciders, *Acetobacter xylinum* is the most common species. Acetification abilities of several cultures which were isolated differed considerably and was markedly affected by temperature. It was much slower at 15°C.(59°F.) than at 25°C.(77°F.).

The oxidizing ability of Acetobacter, according to Mezzadroli[30] may deteriorate and even become nil. When propagated on unsuitable media, they became more pleomorphic and lost their ability to acetify. He recommended Pasteur's medium as useful for maintaining cultures. Acetobacter seem to be just as resistant to unfavorable conditions as other bacteria. For instance, Hansen [31] reported that they continued to exist for over nine years in lager beer, five to six in "double" beer, and two years in sucrose solution. They died in 16 months in water. Therefore, Hansen suggested keeping them in lager beer. In an earlier paper Hansen [2, 31] had shown that dry storage of Acetobacter showed greater longevity. Sealed in glass tubes and stored at 2°C.(35.6°F.) the cells survived for more than a year. Beijerinck [26] stated that this method of storage might influence the activity of such organisms.

Pure Cultures in Vinegar Fermentation. Pure cultures have not been used in the vinegar industry to the same extent as in other industries. It has been shown however, that they are helpful, although there are many conflicting conclusions. Henneberg,[27] using pure cultures of acetic acid bacteria, was able to secure a clear product with 11½ per cent of acetic acid. He was convinced that undesirable bacteria could be suppressed with pure cultures and a better bouquet developed. Cruess [32] stated that some manufacturers in California prepare a starter by inoculating fresh juice with pressed yeast. This is used in turn to inoculate larger batches of juice. Small-scale studies by Cruess and his collaborators showed that good results were obtained by using pure cultures of yeast in vinegar making. Cruess believed that the wild yeasts could be overgrown by a culture of selected yeast with a consequent increase in alcohol production. Grove,[33] who used pure cultures to secure a more regular and cleaner fermentation and perhaps an improvement in the flavor and aroma, believed that sterile sub-

28. Perold. 1909. Centbl. Bakt., Pt. 2, 24, 13.
29. Grove. 1916. Agr. and Hort. Res. Sta., Univ. Bristol, Ann. Rpt., 16-17.
30. Mezzadroli. 1921. Pure Products 5, 216-218.
31. Hansen. 1900. Carlsberg Lab. Compt. Rend. des Trav. 5, 39.
32. Cruess. 1923. The Canner, Aug. 11. 1923.
33. Grove. 1914. Agr. and Hort. Res. Sta., Univ. Bristol. Ann. Rpt. 27-29.

strate should be used. Satisfactory methods, however, for securing sterile juice are difficult to secure for large-scale production. Although the flavor might be affected, Grove proposed heating the substrate. Ultraviolet light was also suggested, but this would probably not be effective on highly colored juices. He found little difference in the rate of fermentation of inoculated juices and those allowed to ferment naturally. Similar results were reported by Tanner and Vogele.[34] On the other hand, Mezzadroli[30] and Vandecaveye[4] reported favorable results after the use of pure cultures. The few conflicting data may be explained by the fact that personal equation might enter in determining whether vinegars were improved by inoculation or not.

Bottling of Vinegar. Complete fermentation may yield a vinegar which is stable. However, if it is not completely fermented, trouble may result from slow fermentations which may continue when the vinegar is bottled. Therefore, the bottles are often pasteurized at temperatures around 68.3°C. (155°F.). This ought to kill the organisms which are directly concerned in vinegar fermentation.

DEFECTS OF VINEGAR

Besides the usual defects, such as low-acid content and abnormal flavor and color, vinegar is subject to other spoilage.

Vinegar Eels. These are small forms of animal life which live in the finished vinegar. They also exist in fermenting vinegar where they interfere with acetification. Paserini[35] observed better "mother" formation where no eels were present. Where eels were present the mother settled, bringing about a decomposition of acetic acid. Sacher[36] reported that heating to 45°C.(113°F.) for a few minutes killed the organism. Sunlight also killed them but its use was unsatisfactory if further action of Acetobacter was desired.

Loss of Acid. Any organism which can decompose acetic acid may cause a loss of acid. Janke[37] reported that algae (*Prototheca* sp.) brought about such an oxidation. Wüstenfeld[38] found that the algae could be destroyed by ultraviolet light and a temperature of 30°C.(86°F.).

Black Vinegar. This is due to iron and tannin in proper ratios. The usual source of iron in vinegar according to Campbell,[39] is the appliances. As little as .01 per cent of iron will cause black vinegar.

Vinegar Analysis for Food Preservers. It is always necessary for those interested in food preservation to know the strength of vinegar which is being used. The chemist is able to use methods and apparatus which give accurate results. Some of them have been adapted to use by persons untrained in chemistry.

The Leo Tester. This apparatus is distributed by concerns which handle supplies for vinegar makers. Cruess[40] described its use and stated that it gave results accurate

34. Tanner and Vogele. 1925. Ill. Agr. Expt. Sta. Ann. Rpt., p. 149.
35. Paserini. 1920. Soc. Ital. per lo Studio Aliment. Bol. 2, 1-5.
36. Sacher. 1914. Chem. Ztg. 38, 1021-1022.
37. Janke. 1923. Centbl. Bakt., Pt. 2, 305-310.
38. Wüstenfeld. 1911. Deut. Essig Indus. 15, 243-244.
39. Campbell. 1928. The Glass Packer. 1, 15-16.
40. Cruess. 1923. The Canner, Sept. 2, pp. 46-49.

enough for factory control. An exact volume of vinegar is measured into a bottle by means of a small marked glass tube. A pinch of baking soda (sodium bicarbonate) is added and the cork at once placed tightly in the bottle. The acid in the vinegar reacts with the soda and liberates carbon dioxide. This forces water from a second bottle upward into a vertical glass cylinder marked in grains. The first bottle is gently shaken until the water ceases to rise. The reading is in grains. A good cider vinegar must test at least 40 grains; distilled vinegar 85 to 110 grains.

Titration Method. Measure 10 ml. of the vinegar into an Erlenmeyer flask, add 50 ml. of distilled water and titrate with normal sodium hydroxide with phenolphthalein as the indicator. Titrate to a red color. To determine the per cent of acid multiply the burette reading by .6 when sodium hydroxide is used. If desired, the sodium hydroxide may be tenth normal, in which case the vinegar should also be diluted in a volumetric flask. Place 10 ml. of vinegar in a volumetric flask and dilute to the mark with distilled water.

Rysavy and Hac [41] described a special pipette which delivered 18.012 ml. of vinegar; when titrated with normal sodium hydroxide, the reading on the burette was in per cent.

Preserving Action of Vinegar. The preserving action of vinegar as such is probably of little practical importance. While it may delay the appearance of molds it is apparently of only incidental value. It probably has some value when used with other substances. Bitting [42] reached this concluson after studying its preserving action in catsup. He apparently used commercial distilled vinegar and not cider vinegar made from apple juice. When 30 per cent of 50-grain distilled vinegar was added to tomato bouillon, mold development was checked and the extent to which it was checked increased with increased amounts of vinegar. In this concentration development was delayed two days. One-half of one per cent solution of glacial acetic acid in tomato bouillon accomplished what 30 per cent vinegar did; no development occurred when the quantity of one per cent solution of glacial acetic acid was increased to two per cent. Bitting observed that with increased amounts of vinegar in the tomato bouillon, more sugar and spice had to be added to overcome the pungency of the acid and insure good flavor. More recent investigations by Levine and Fellers [43] indicated that bacteria could not grow in bouillon adjusted to pH 4.9 with acetic acid. *Saccharomyces cerevisiae* did not grow at pH 3.9 and *Aspergillus niger* was inhibited at pH 4.1. Thermal death times of bacteria were decreased by presence of acetic acid while they were not altered for yeasts and molds. Levine and Fellers apparently based their thinking mainly on pH. That other factors may be involved was suggested by Ash.[44] He suggested that the acetate radical might be more important than what pH produced. The preservative effect of .75 per cent of acetic acid was said to be equal to .1 per cent of sodium benzoate.

In addition to the factors mentioned above others which are present in vinegar may exert an inhibitive action on microorganisms. Vinegar is known to contain propionic acid which has been shown to inhibit development of molds. This might explain the inhibitive action of vinegar for preventing development of mold in bread.

41. Rysavy and Hac. 1909. Chem. Ztg. 33, 57.
42. Bitting. 1909. U. S. Dept. Agr. Bur. Chem. Bull. 119.
43. Levine and Fellers. 1940. J. Bact. 39, 499-514; 40 (1941), 255-269.
44. Food Indus. 14 (1942), November, p. 40.

SAUERKRAUT

In Food Inspection Decision 196, August 1925, the following definition and standard for sauerkraut as adopted by the Joint Committee on Definitions and Standards, composed of representatives of the United States Department of Agriculture, the Association of American Dairy, Food and Drug Officials, and the Association of Official Agricultural Chemists, at its meeting July 13 to 17, 1925, was reported:

Sauerkraut is the clean, sound product, of characteristic acid flavor obtained by the full fermentation, chiefly lactic, of properly prepared and shredded cabbage in the presence of not less than two per cent (2%) nor more than three per cent (3%) of salt.

It contains, upon completion of the fermentation, not less than one and one-half per cent (1.5%) of acid, expressed as lactic acid. Sauerkraut which has been rebrined in the process of canning or repacking contains not less than one per cent (1%) of acid, expressed as lactic acid.

Sauerkraut is prepared by salting shredded cabbage. Alternate layers of cabbage and salt are packed into containers and allowed to ferment. About three pounds of salt are used for each 100 pounds of cabbage. The salt withdraws the juice from the cabbage tissue. A brine results in which the acid-forming bacteria thrive. They ferment sugars to organic acids which act as preserving agents and prevent action of putrefactive bacteria. The fact that sauerkraut is a fermented food makes it possible to have various grades and flavors. Fred and Peterson [45] found low titratable acids and higher alcohol contents in inferior sauerkraut. Good kraut always showed numerous lactic acid bacteria with an occasional yeast cell while abnormal kraut showed different kinds of bacteria and large numbers of yeasts.

During the early fermentation of sauerkraut, large amounts of gas are given off. Preuss, Peterson, and Fred [46] found that it resulted from bacterial action and not from yeast growth or plant cell respiration. It consisted almost entirely of carbon dioxide.

The nature of the fermentation is controlled by the type of cabbage content of salt, temperature of fermentation, and activity of the ferment-started normal fermentations; sugars of cabbage were said to be converted to lactic and acetic acids, alcohol, mannitol, and carbon dioxide. The fermentation was continued and completed by certan lactobacilli, such as *Lactobacillus plantarum* and *Lactobacillus brevis*. It is, then, the sugar in the cabbage which is the source of organic acids so important in preservation of the cabbage tissue. These vary in the cabbage according to season, variety, and stage of maturity. If too little is present to permit sufficient acid to be formed, spoilage may result. Some investigators have added sugar to the cabbage in order to prevent this. Fellers, Clague, and Levine [48] added from one to two per cent of glucose or sucrose, or mixtures of these sugars, to raw vegetables before fermentation and after it had been in progress for some time. This greatly increased the number of bacteria but did not increase final acidity. However, if the sugars were added after the

45. Fred and Peterson. 1924. The Canner. March 8, 1924.
46. Preuss Peterson, and Fred. 1929. Ind. Eng. Chem. 20, 1187-1190.
47. Pederson. 1939. J. Bact. 39, 87.
48. Fellers, Clague, and Levine. 1939. Idem, p. 88.

acidity had reached one per cent, final acidity was materially increased. Fellers and his colleagues believed that added sugar might be useful in promoting rapidity of fermentation which in turn, would decrease the possibilities of spoilage owing to growth of bacteria and yeasts. High final acidities were believed to promote keeping and to have no effect on flavor.

The time required for fermenting cabbage to become sauerkraut depends on many factors. Pederson [49] showed that the lower the temperature at the time of filling the vats, the slower is the rate of fermentation. Temperature of the building also has some effect on fermentation. In view of these facts the time required for a vat of cabbage to ferment cannot be predicted. Another factor of importance is washing of the cabbage. Keipper, Peterson, Fred, and Vaughn [50] reported that it was desirable. In the laboratory, 84 per cent of sauerkraut made from washed cabbage graded ''good to fancy,'' whereas only 19 per cent of that from unwashed cabbage reached this grade. Under factory conditions, the increase in quality obtained by washing amounted to 17 to 50 per cent. Washing removed many undesirable microorganisms. Chlorine in the water was found to be undesirable because of objectionable flavors which resulted. While inoculation with pure cultures was slightly beneficial, it was not considered to be of any great practical value.

Microbiology of Sauerkraut. Since sauerkraut is a fermented product, its microbiology has been much studied. Yeasts were important in the fermentation of cabbage along with gas-forming bacteria. Wehmer [51] believed that lactic acid fermentation was most significant. Besides yeasts (*Saccharomyces mycoderma* I and II) and lactic acid bacteria he found a small rod *Bacillus brassicae*. Wehmer [51] believed that acid formation in kraut resulted from action of this organism. It was not well characterized but LeFevre believed it was identical with *Lactobacillus cucumeris (Bacterium cucumeris fermentati)* of Henneberg and *Lactobacillus pentoaceticus* of Fred, Peterson, and Davenport.[52] Preuss, Peterson and Fred,[53] however, did not agree with LeFevre that *Lactobacillus pentoaceticus* and *Bacterium brassicae* were identical. Conradi [54] isolated a Lactobacillus sp. as the organism responsible for sauerkraut fermentation, while Henneberg [55] isolated an organism to which he gave the name *Lactobacillus fermentatae (Bacillus brassicae fermentatae)*. Butjagin,[56] Gruber [57] and Henneberg [58] also made contributions.

In America, Round [59] believed that bacteria alone, and not yeasts, were the active fermenting agents. Respiration of plant tissue cells was also ruled out. Steamed cabbage inoculated with a known starter from another

49. Pederson. 1930. New York Agr. Expt. Sta. Tech. Bull. 168.
50. Keipper, Peterson, Fred, and Vaughn. 1932. Ind. Eng. Chem. 24, 884-889.
51. Wehmer. 1905. Centbl. Bakt.. Pt. 2, 14, 682-713; 781-800.
52. Fred, Peterson, and Davenport. 1920. J. Biol. Chem. 42, 175-189.
53. Preuss, Peterson, and Fred. 1929. Ind. Eng. Chem., 20, 1187-1190.
54. Conradi. 1897. Arch. f. Hyg. 29, 56-95.
55. Henneberg. 1909. Ztschr. f. Spiritusindus. 26, 322.
56. Butjagin. 1904. Centbl. Bakt., Abt. II, 11, 540.
57. Gruber. 1909. Centbl. Bakt. II, 22, 555-559.
58. Henneberg. 1917. Deuts. Essig. Indus. 20, No. 21 and 22.
59. Round. 1916. J. Bact. 1, 108; 1917. Abs. Bact. 1, 50.

actively fermenting tank produced no gas. while a jar of the brine and cabbage developed gas in 12 hours. Round belittled the idea that salt was essential in exact amounts. From two to three per cent of salt exerted little influence on the fermentation. He stated that the function of salt was to extract water from the cabbage; the cabbage to which water had been added instead of salt fermented as well as when salt had been added. *Escherichia coli* was found to be present in large numbers at first. When the brine reached from seven to eight per cent acidity, coliform bacteria dropped out. The organisms which produced high concentration of acid were closely related to *B. brassicae* (Wehmer) and *Lactobacillus cucumeris (Bacillus cucumeris fermentatae)* (Henneberg).

Various species of bacteria were also reported by Pederson [49] from examination of three normal and five inoculated krauts. *Leuconostoc mesenteroides, Lactobacillus pentoaceticus Lactobacillus cucumeris,* and *Lactobacillus plantarum* were found to be commonly present. The first organism mentioned was reported to be largely responsible for early development of acidity. Lactobacilli were said to complete the fermentation. Acids formed in the kraut were shown to be very important by Nelson and Beck.[60] Their work indicates the error in giving lactic acid all of the credit for preservation of kraut.

Products formed during a normal fermentation and the influence of inoculation on these products and the quality were examined by Brunkow, Peterson, and Fred [61] Inoculation seemed to increase the number of bacteria. This varied from 500,000 to 91,000,000 per ml. of brine. A better product was secured by inoculation. *Lactobacillus lactis acidi (B. lactis acidi)* gave consistently better kraut. Large numbers of yeasts were said to cause red kraut. Two per cent salt seemed to yield the best product. Above three per cent gave a tough and salty product. The chief products were found to be lactic acid, acetic acid, and ethyl alcohol. Temperature of fermentation was reported by Martin, Peterson, Fred, and Vaughn [62] to greatly influence the quality. The most favorable temperature was reported to be between 15.6°C. (60°F.) and 18.3°C. (65°F.). Higher temperatures favored the production of soft and pink kraut. During the first few days of fermentation, a rise of 3 to 5°F. above the temperature of the surrounding air was noticed.

Use of Pure Culture in Sauerkraut Fermentation. The fermentation of cabbage to sauerkraut is greatly influenced by the presence of certain microorganisms whether they are added or not. Since undesirable bacteria give abnormal flavors, attempts have been made to override them with cultures of desirable bacteria. The evidence on the value of such cultures does not always agree. Reference will not be made to the earlier work in Germany on this subject but only to those papers which have been published in very recent years in America. Fred and Peterson [45] believed that inoculation always yielded a better sauerkraut. Besides improved flavor and aroma,

60. Nelson and Beck. 1918. J. Amer. Chem. Soc., 40. 1001-1005.
61. Brunkow, Peterson, and Fred. 1921. J. Amer. Chem. Soc., 43, 2244-2255.
62. Martin, Peterson, Fred, and Vaughn. 1929. J. Agr. Res. 39, 285-292.

inoculated sauerkraut fermented more rapidly with a great saving of time. LeFevre [63] did not recommend the use of pure cultures of *Lactobacillus brassicae*. Considering the experience of the industry as well as the results of research work one is convinced that sauerkraut of good quality may be made without artificial inoculation. However, inoculation might give improved fermentation under some conditions. Such was the case in experiments conducted by Peterson, Fred, and Viljoen [64]. Addition of selected pure cultures of bacteria to vats of fermenting cabbags gave superior sauerkraut. While over 80 per cent of inoculated sauerkraut had good color, only some 25 per cent of the uninoculated was in this class. Indifferent results were secured by Pederson at the New York Agricultural Experiment Station with pure culture inoculation. In his first experiments, 72 different sauerkrauts were made, all but 25 of which were inoculated with pure cultures of some one of the following bacteria: *Streptococcus lactis, Leuconostoc mesenteroides, Lactobacillus buchneri, Lactobacillus pentoaceticus, Lactobacillus delbrücki Lactobacillus cucumeris, Lactobacillus plantarum*, and two other cultures. Normal sauerkraut completed its fermentation at 21.1 to 29.4°C.(70 to 85°F) in two to three weeks when it attained an acidity of 1.5 per cent or more. Inoculation with pure cultures of *Streptococcus lactis* improved quality and did not affect the by-products. Inoculation with *Lactobacillus brassicae, Lactobacillus cucumeris*, and *Lactobacillus plantarum* was detrimental to good fermentation; inoculation with *Lactobacillus pentoaceticus* resulted in sauerkraut of fair quality but abnormal in flavor. Pederson's results showed that much care must be taken in selecting the culture to be used and that it is best to attempt to duplicate the normal flora of the cabbage. Pederson also used mixed cultures of *Streptococcus lactis, Leuconostoc mesenteroides, Lactobacillus pentoaceticus*, and *Lactobacillus cucumeris*. This was said to be of doubtful value.

Sauerkraut is subject to several abnormal fermentations. These may be due to presence of undesirable bacteria in the fermentation vats or to introduction of such forms after fermentation has started. A spoilage of sauerkraut, studied by Peterson and Fred [65] was found to be due to yeasts. Deterioration followed the first fermentation and occurred after the sauerkraut had been repacked for shipment. The acids were low and allowed acid-utilizing yeasts to develop.

Pink Sauerkraut. This is a defect which practically every sauerkraut manufacturer has had to battle. The trouble is connected with uneven salting. Butjagin [56] and Wehmer [51] were among the first to attribute pink kraut to the presence of microorganisms. Henneberg [58] secured pink kraut after adding 1.2 per cent of lactic acid to shredded cabbage. Fred and Peterson,[66] by chemical analysis, could observe no difference between normal and pink kraut. Bacteriological examination revealed the presence of bacteria and a yeast which formed a red pigment in the presence of air. Temperatures of 22°C.(71.6°F) and 28°C.(82.4°F.) seemed to permit greatest

63. LeFevre. 1928. U. S. Dept. Agr. Circ. 35.
64. Peterson, Fred, and Viljoen. 1925. Canning Age, Sept., p. 777.
65. Peterson and Fred. 1923. Centbl. Bakt., Pt. 2, 58, 199-204.
66. Fred and Peterson. 1921. Deut. Essig Indus. 20, 194.

growth. The deepest pigment was formed at 22°C. The yeast was able to live in high concentrations of salt and thus have a free hand in producing its pigment. Pederson and Kelly [67] also found yeasts involved in formation of a pink color in sauerkraut. Growth of the yeasts seemed to be encouraged by over salting or any condition which interfered with normal development of the bacteria.

LeFevre's Method for Determining the Salt Content of Pickle or Sauerkraut Brine with the Salinometer (Salometer). The following instructions are taken from LeFevre's bulletin:

The salt strength of brine is determined by means of a salinometer, which should form a part of the equipment of every sauerkraut factory. The salinometer scale is graduated into 100°, which show the range of salt concentration between 0°, the reading of pure water at 15.55°C.(60°F.), and 100°, which indicates a saturated salt solution (26½ per cent). In a pure salt solution the salinometer shows accurately the percentage of salt. As sauerkraut brine, however, is not a pure salt solution but contains much other soluble material, a salinometer reading can be regarded only as a measure of its total solids. This may vary greatly in different samples, depending not only on the quantity of salt added but upon the moisture content and the soluble constituents of the cabbage. Under ordinary conditions when 2.5 per cent of salt has been added a salinometer reading of about 17° is obtained.

LeFevre's Method for Determining the Amount of Acid Formed in Pickle and Sauerkraut Brine. The following technic is taken verbatim from LeFevre's publication:

For determining the acidity of the brine in a tank of sauerkraut a small sample should be taken by suction through a glass tube. This sample should be obtained at least two feet below the surface and from the sides of the tank. Brine obtained by opening the bottom vent should not be used, as it may differ from the above and is not a representative sample. Brine from the middle of the tank would best represent the average acidity in the tank. If possible, a hole should be provided in the tank for obtaining this brine.

The acidity of sauerkraut may be determined with sufficient accuracy by titration of the brine against an alkaline solution of known strength. A normal solution of sodium hydroxide is generally used. The test gives no information regarding the kind of acid in the brine but determines only the quantity of normal alkali which is required to counteract its acidity and produce neutrality. The quantity of normal alkali used to produce neutrality multiplied by the appropriate figure for the acid gives the number of grams of acid per 100 cubic centimeters of brine. This factor for lactic acid is 0.09. Although the acid in sauerkraut is not entirely lactic, it is mainly lactic, and it is therefore calculated as lactic acid.

Grams of acid per 100 cubic centimeters of brine is not quite the same as by weight, but it is nearly the same and is often referred to as percentage.

The methods of making titrations differ slightly in detail, but any of them may be easily followed. Although not the simplest, the following method is perhaps the best.

With a pipette transfer exactly five cubic centimeters of the sample of brine to a 100-cubic centimeter Erlenmeyer flask. Add to this 45 cubic centimeters of distilled water and three or four drops of a phenolphthalein solution. Then run in slowly from a burette a one-twentieth normal solution of sodium hydroxide. While this is running shake the flask constantly and watch it carefully. As soon as a permanent faint pink tint is produced throughout the solution the neutral point has been reached and no more should be added. It is important that the addition of alkali stop at the first appearance of the pinkish tint. Read to a fraction on the burette the number of cubic centimeters required to neutralize the brine. Multiplying this number by 0.09 gives the grams of acid, calculated as lactic, in 100 cubic centimeters.

If it is desired to use a one-tenth normal sodium hydroxide solution start with 10 cubic centimeters of brine and 40 cubic centimeters of distilled water and proceed as before.

67. Pederson and Kelly. 1938: Food Research 3, 583-588.

The acidity may be tested more simply and the result may be read directly in percentage of lactic acid by the following method: Use a one-ninth normal solution of sodium hydroxide (1 part normal sodium hydroxide solution to 8 parts distilled water), place 10 cc. of brine in the flask, add 40 cc. of distilled water, and proceed as before. The number obtained divided by ten gives the percentage of lactic acid in the brine.

Microbiological Examination of Fermented Foods. Such examination is of no great importance as a routine procedure. It may be desirable at times to examine canned sauerkraut for sterility or raw sauerkraut for special microorganisms. The Committee on Microbiological Examination of Foods of the American Public Health Association recommended use of tryptone-glucose-yeast extract agar as a plating medium. The Frost little plate method described on p. 355 was also recommended.

Canned Sauerkraut. Much kraut is canned today in America. According to McConkie [68] it may undergo two types of spoilage. One, caused by bacterial activity which results in "swells" with formation of carbon dioxide and hydrogen, is due to understerilization and later development of microorganisms which have survived the process. Canners have learned that more attention to acidity of the kraut before canning, to the exhaust, and to processing will yield a product which will keep well. The other type of spoilage to which canned sauerkraut is susceptible is the hydrogen springer or swell. Kraut is processed in cans for about 15 minutes at 100°C.(212°F.) for No. 2 cans and for 40 minutes at the same temperature for No. 10 cans.

Analysis of over 100 samples of sauerkraut from over 70 different packers by Pederson [69], showed that at least one-third did not conform to the regulations of the U. S. Federal Food and Drug Administration. Some was unfit for consumption, defects being pink color and unpleasant odors and flavor. The analytical methods used were determination of salt, total acid, volatile and nonvolatile acid (by difference), alcohol, and such inspection points as length of cut, texture, color, odor, and flavor. A supplemental microscope examination of the juice for yeasts was often helpful. Secondary fermentations are usually caused by yeasts. These methods and findings from them are not sufficiently worked out to enable definite standards to be set up but are advanced as valuable sorting procedures. Pederson [69] observed that good kraut was also good as far as chemical composition was concerned.

Lettuce Kraut. Attempts have been made by the California Agricultural Experiment Station [70] to use lettuce as a raw material for kraut manufacture. Natural fermentation yielded a good product although use of starters of *Lactobacillus pentosus* gave a superior flavor. In general the changes which were observed paralleled those which have been observed for cabbage kraut. Addition of dextrose to the lettuce either before or during the fermentation had little or no effect upon total acid produced. The most prevalent organisms found in lactic acid fermentations of lettuce were *Lactobacillus plantarum* (Orla-Jensen) Bergey *et al.*, and *L. brevis* (Orla-Jensen) Bergey *et al.*, and some nonsporulating, film-forming yeasts.

68. McConkie. 1927. Canning Age, Convention No., 240-241.
69. Pederson. 1934. Amer. J. Pub. Health 24, 229-234; New York Agr. Expt. Sta. (1940) Bull. 693.
70. Hohl and Cruess. 1940. Inst. Food Tech. Proc., 159-166. Hohl. 1942. Food Research 7, 309-312.

Occasional cultures of *L. buchneri* (Henneberg) Bergey *et al.* and *Leuconostoc mesenterioides* (Cienkowski) Van Tieghem were also isolated.

CUCUMBER PICKLES

Cucumber pickles are made by placing fresh cucumbers in brine until certain changes have occurred. Most of the latter result from bacterial action and everything is done to further the activity of desirable bacteria and repress that of spoilage types. Many kinds of pickles and specialties described by Fabian and Switzer [71] are manufactured.

Pickles have been made for a long time in the home, but in more recent years they have been made by large manufacturers. The industry is now profiting from application of scientific methods. The methods used by large manufacturers differ somewhat from those which are used in the home. The pickle manufacturer uses fermentation to develop the chemical compounds which make the pickles keep. The homemaker would find such a method too cumbersome for small quantities of cucumbers; consequently, she tries to prevent fermentation, resorting to heat and antiseptics, such as spices and vinegar, to control bacteria. The fermentation method is probably best for the manufacturer and the sterilization method best for the home. Under the conditions which obtain in commercial manufacture of pickles, the cucumbers are brought to salting stations, where they are dumped into large tanks, often without washing or cleaning. The tanks are sometimes placed in the open, where they are exposed to dust and dirt. It is possible that cleansing of the cucumbers might be advantageous, since it would reduce to a minimum extraneous bacteria which would enter the tanks. The fewer such bacteria, the lighter would be the load on the factors involved in preservation.

In the pickle industry salt concentrations are usually not given in per cents but in degrees. Zero degrees is water and 100° is a saturated solution of salt in water, *i.e.*, 26.395 per cent. For comparison, the following data are given:

Degrees	%NaCl	Degrees	%NaCl
10	2.64	60	15.80
20	5.82	70	15.80
30	7.80	80	21.06
40	10.57	90	23.76
50	13.19	100	26.40

It is very necessary that the strength of the brine be carefully watched during fermentation. Usually a hydrometer known as a ''saltometer'' is used. This is graduated in degrees from 0 to 100 showing the saturation at 60°C.(140°F.). Hasbrouck [72] has found the Baumé hydrometer satisfactory. Data for preparing a brine of any strength are given in the table.

Hasbrouck [72] did not approve the use of the saltometer because saltometers may be too inaccurate. He advised that salting be done according

71. Fabian and Switzer. 1941. Fruit Prod. J., 20, 136-140.
72. Hasbrouck. 1910. Pure Food 6, 509-514.

to temperature. As the temperature rises the concentration of the brine should be raised, since at higher temperatures bacterial activity is accelerated.

Pounds of salt per gallon of water	Degrees on saltometer	Pounds of salt per gallon of water	Degrees on saltometer
5	0.11	55	1.42
10	0.22	60	1.57
15	0.33	65	1.72
20	0.45	70	1.89
25	0.58	75	2.07
30	0.70	80	2.24
35	0.83	85	2.42
40	0.97	90	2.60
45	1.12	95	2.78
50	1.27	100	2.98

The pickling season begins in the middle or late summer and lasts until frosts kill the vines. In the beginning and at the end of the season, when only a few cucumbers are delivered to the factory they may be put into smaller containers, while in the middle of the season they are salted in large tanks, holding 1,000 to 15,000 bushels. According to Campbell, the size of the tank may vary from eight to 14 feet while the height is usually about eight feet. If the cucumbers are to be salted in a barrel, they may be put into a 20-per cent brine (equal to 80°). In such a strong solution they will naturally float, and have to be forced under the surface by means of boards which are weighted down or nailed down. With large tanks the procedure may be a little different. The tank is started with about six inches of brine to which cucumbers and salt are added in the average proportion of five to six pounds of salt per bushel of cucumbers. The strong brine draws the water from the cucumber, which causes them to shrivel for a time, but in a day or two they are plump again. When the tank is full, enough water is added to cover the cucumbers which are pressed or "keyed down" below the surface of the brine. The cover holding them down consists of heavy boards with cracks to let the fermentation gases escape.

The manufacturer tries to fill a tank as quickly as possible. While the cucumbers are not covered with brine and exposed to air, they are apt to spoil. After the tank or barrel has been "keyed down," the fermentation starts, and very little has to be done to the cucumbers. The brine remains clear for a few days, depending on the temperature, and turns cloudy just before active fermentation begins. During this preliminary stage the brine is becoming saturated with materials taken from the cucumber. When the fermentation starts, gas bubbles arise through the cracks slowly at first, and then very rapidly. Rahn [73] stated that in a factory which came under his observation a large tank was filled very late in the season. A sudden change in the weather stopped fermentation. The following May, after a few warm days, fermentation started again and continued for two weeks.

73. Rahn. 1913. The Canner and Dried Fruit Packer, Nov. 20, p. 27.

Besides gas formation, which is a criterion of fermentation, there are other evidences that changes are taking place. The cucumber changes in color. The fresh pale green color is replaced by a darker olive green. A manufacturer can follow the progress of curing by examining a cross section of the cucumber in cure. As curing progresses, the white opaque appearance is changed from the outside toward the center to a transparent green. When the white appearance is entirely replaced, curing is complete, and the cucumber is too heavy to float. LeFevre[74] reported a marked loss in weight which was not regained for over a month.

The pickles remain in this brine until they are to be sold or manufactured into sweet, sour, dill, and other kinds. Then they are sorted according to size, whether by hand or by machine, and washed in brine or water. As long as they remain in brine, they keep very well, and occasionally a factory may hold pickles of a certain size for several years. If the tanks are not under roof, they have to be filled up after long drought and salt may have to be added after heavy rains. The brine is tested by a salometer and is ordinarily kept at 40° (10 per cent salt). Some manufacturers prevent this trouble by putting the tanks under roof, but this brings another difficulty, namely, the scum or film. On brine pickles under roof there forms invariably a heavy, gray, wrinkled scum which becomes very thick and has to be removed once in a while since, as the manufacturer says, it makes the pickles slippery if it settles. This thick scum is due to the growth of yeasts, a group of microorganisms detrimental to the pickle industry.

Salt plays a great rôle in restricting development of proteolytic bacteria which would destroy the cucumbers. Fabian, Bryan and Etchells [75] found that while at first they were more abundant than acid-producing bacteria, they were gradually killed by the brine, more rapidly in a brine of 40° salometer than in a 30° brine.

The composition of cucumbers has been determined by Heinze,[76] who showed that from the point of food value the pickle does not hold a prominent place. The cucumber in the fresh condition is composed mostly of water, about 96 per cent, and four per cent of solids. These solids seem to be mostly sugar and proteins in about equal amounts. Heinze also reported results of analyses for dill pickles.

The curing process consists mainly of an acid-gas fermentation. As much as one per cent of lactic acid has been found in the brine in some cases. The rapidity of fermentation, according to Campbell,[77] depends on the concentration of the brine. Some have attempted to secure earlier fermentations by adding a little sugar to the brine. (Aderhold.[78])

From a gaseous fermentation occuring during salting, Etchells [79] isolated some 29 strains of bacteria. Most of them were closer in characteristics to *Aerobacter cloacae* than to *Aerobacter aerogenes*. The optimum

74. LeFevre. 1920. U. S. Dept. Agr. Farmers' Bull. 1159.
75. Fabian, Bryan, and Etchells. 1932. Mich. Agr. Expt. Sta. Tech. Bull. 126.
76. Heinze. 1903. Ztschr. f. Untersuch. der Nahr. u. Genussmtl. 6, 529-544; 577-578.
77. Campbell. 1920. The Canner 51, 45-47.
78. Aderhold. 1899. Centbl. Bakt., Pt. 2, 5, 511-525.
79. Etchells. 1941. Rev. in Biol. Abs. 16 (1942),12957.

temperature was near 35°C.(95°F.) with a possible range from 5 to 45°C. (41 to 113°F.). More gas seemed to be formed in heavier brines.

Microbiology of Brine Pickles. Fermentation of brine pickles is known to be caused by microorganisms. Bacteria are also known to cause undesirable changes such as softening, blackening, etc. When a normal fermentation has been secured the pickles will keep if the manufacturer holds them under the proper conditions.

The undesirable results of the presence of film yeasts on the surface of pickle tanks have been recognized for some time. They decompose the acid and make it possible for putrefactive bacteria to develop. Rahn,[73] Riley,[80] and Brown [81] showed that film yeasts were acid consumers.

Despite the fact that fermentation of pickles is an old industry, much research may yet be done and must be done before it can be considered a controlled fermentation. There is great need for combined microbiological and chemical investigations. To date, most of the work has been microbiological in nature, with almost no attention to the chemical products which are formed by these microorganisms. Investigations must be instituted before the fundamental causes of softening, loss of color, hollow pickles, etc., will be clearly understood. The question of the value of pure cultures has not been sufficiently studied to justify the extensive conclusions at which some investigators have arrived.

One of the troubles in cucumber fermentation is formation of a scum over the surface of the pickle brine. In this are many pseudo-yeasts which eat the acid and thus lower the preservative value of the pickle brine. Rahn[82] suggested that ultraviolet light might be used to control this scum. Daily radiation for 30 minutes kept the surface of brine free from Mycoderma. Growth of these Mycoderma is influenced by salt content of the brine.

Authentic cultures of Debaryomyces and Mycoderma obtained from ordinary culture collections by Mrak and Boner [83] had a much lower salt tolerance than those obtained from pickle brines. Strains of Debaryomyces isolated from food brine could resist a salt concentration of 24 per cent and those of Mycoderma, 15 per cent. Other factors than film yeasts may also disturb the acid balance of brine tanks in pickle curing. Fabian, Bryan, and Etchells [75] stated that lime or sodium bicarbonate ,by neutralizing the acidity produced by the acid-forming bacteria, creates a condition favorable for proteolytic bacteria, but should never be added to fermenting cucumbers and should be reduced to a minimum by every possible means. Very hard water is also undesirable, and only high-quality salt should be used. Acetic acid, to control cucumber fermentation, was found unnecessary, but a small amount was apparently beneficial in 30° salometer brine. Acetic acid added to high-test brines, such as 40° salometer, seemed detrimental since it apparently delayed fermentation. "A high acetic acid content in the presence of a high salt concentration is an undesirable combination."

80. Riley. 1914. Science 39, 954.
81. Brown. 1917. Abs. Bact. 1, 104-105.
82. Rahn. 1931. The Canner 73, 42-44.
83. Mrak and Bonar. 1939. Zentbl. Bakt., Pt. 2, 100, 289-294.

Environmental conditions influence markedly the course of the cucumber fermentation. Among them temperature plays an important role. Fabian, Bryan, and Etchells [75] found the acidity of a barrel of cucumbers kept outdoors to be nearly twice as high as that of a barrel kept indoors, the acidity disappearing much more rapidly from the barrel kept indoors. Barrels outdoors had a more gradual fermentation with a higher acid production, and the acid persisted much longer. It was found necessary to be more careful about the salt concentration in the case of outdoor tanks than it is with indoor tanks. The top layer of cucumbers from an unweighted barrel showed signs of spoiling within 24 hours as evidenced by soft spots on the surface—a possible explanation of layers or areas of soft pickles in a vat of pickles otherwise prime.

In view of the fact that organic acids formed from sugar by microorganisms are the important preserving agents in pickle brine, some investigators have suggested that larger amounts of these acids might be formed if sugar were added to the brine. Fabian and Wickerham [84] found that addition of two pounds of sugar per barrel increased the number of bacteria at the beginning of the fermentation. This was considered to be desirable because it would result in prompt acid formation.

Contrary to results of others, Veldhuis, Etchells, Jones, and Veerhoff [85] found that addition of sugar to fermenting cucumbers caused no significant change in brine acidity. Apparently no increase in fermentative activity of microorganisms was caused. On the other hand, they reported a large increase in proportion of bloaters during production of either salt stock or dills.

The gases evolved from pickle fermentations have been shown by Veldhuis and Etchells [86] to be mainly carbon dioxide and hydrogen. A study was made of the gases evolved during vat fermentations in salt brines of 20, 30, 40, 60, and 80 per cent saturations, with subsequent increases in brine concentration to 70 per cent saturation in six weeks. Carbon dioxide was found in the gases from all fermentations. Hydrogen was produced in considerable amounts from all fermentations in 60 per cent saturated brines and in smaller amounts of some fermentations in 20, 30, and 40 per cent saturation. Hydrogen was also produced in 80 per cent brines, but the gas evolution was slow. Organisms capable of producing hydrogen were isolated from brines.

Pure Cultures in Pickle Fermentation. The evidence on the value of pure-culture inoculation on pickle fermentation is not clear cut. Kossowicz [87] reported that bacteria isolated from pearl onions and garlic markedly facilitated acidification of pickles and prevented softening. LeFevre [88] found pure cultures to yield good results because they favored the initiation of an active fermentation. He believed that the organism *Lactobacillus brassicae* was the cause of pickle fermentation. LeFevre could observe no

84. Fabian and Wickerham. 1935. Mich. Agr. Expt. Sta. Tech. Bull. 146.
85. Veldhuis *et al.* 1941. Food Indus., Oct. and Nov., 1941; Food Research 5 (1940), 533-547.
86. Veldhuis and Etchells. 1939. Food Research 4, 621-630.
87. Kossowicz. 1909. Ztschr. f. Landw. Versuchsw. Österr. 12. 757.
88. LeFevre. 1920. The Canner 50, 230-232; Chem. Age 30 (1922), 34.

benefit from acidulating fermenting cucumbers with lactic acid. The use of pure cultures in pickle fermentation should be considered from two viewpoints, whether they are necessary or whether they improve the product. They may not be necessary but it would probably be wrong to deny that they might improve the quality.

If pure cultures are not used, the pickle maker may attempt inoculation of a large tank by dumping a barrel of fermenting cucumbers into it. One must be certain, however, that the starter is a good one, else a weak fermentation may result.

DETERIORATION OF BRINE PICKLES

Some manufacturers have suffered serious losses owing to microbial activities and improper handling. Most of them may be attributed to abnormal fermentations.

Slippery, Soft, and Mushy Pickles. While many different reasons have been given for appearance of this type of spoilage, microorganisms and abnormal fermentation are the most reasonable explanation. Some manufacturers find layers of soft pickles in tanks. The tank may be so large that it is not filled quickly. Some of the cucumbers may not be forced under the brine until the tank has been filled. Fresh cucumbers float in the brine. In this manner, spoilage bacteria may grow and soften the cucumbers before the preservation agencies owing to fermentation can function. Softening is probably stopped as soon as an active fermentation is started. Softening may also develop after curing. This is a slow process. When it appears the pickles are usually worked up into some of the special types, such as sour, spiced pickles, etc.

Softening may be due to decomposition of acid by film yeasts. Joslyn [89] classed such yeasts with Mycodermae. Wehmer [51] described two species under Mycoderma I and Mycoderma II. Janke [90] attempted to find some method of preventing the development of these organisms. They were found to be sensitive to acetic acid; at 30°C.(86°F.) .6 per cent inhibited them. Allyl mustard oil was suggested for controlling these organisms in pickle tanks. While it prevented development of Mycoderma, it is not used to any extent. One of the earliest reports on the subject was published by Aderhold,[78] who believed that spoilage was due to the activities of *Escherichia coli*. Kossowicz [87] disagreed, and quite conclusively from Aderhold's paper, that this organism was not the cause of spoilage. Aderhold reported that his plates showed large numbers of liquefying bacteria. Kossowicz believed that Aderhold was wrong in not considering these liquefiers. Several years later, in his contribution to Lafar's *Handbuch der technischen Mykologie*, Aderhold still held to his original idea that *Escherichia coli* caused soft pickles. Kossowicz's investigations were made at the request of a pickle packer who had had frequent trouble with softening of fermented pickles. He proved experimentally that *Escherichia coli* did not spoil pickles and that several aerobic- spore-forming bacteria

89. Joslyn. 1927. Fruit Prod. J. and Amer. Vinegar Indus. 6, 22-23.
90. Janke. 1923. Amer. Vinegar Indus., March, 1923, 17-18.

did. Further work was published in 1909. LeFevre [91] isolated 50 organisms, 16 of which caused softening to a greater or lesser degree. *Bacillus vulgatus* showed the highest salt and acid tolerance. LeFevre believed that a wide range of bacteria could decompose cucumbers. In several publications, he stressed the necessity of keeping unfit stock out of brine tanks. Kossowicz [92] and Aderhold [78] recommended prompt fermentation if defective pickles were to be avoided. Kornauth and Zanluchi [93] believed that *Bacterium güntheri* was the organism to be favored and that this species was identical with some of the bacteria reported by others. This type of spoilage, according to Fabian, Bryan, and Etchells, [75] is accompanied by marked morphological evidence of decomposition of tissue. An organism from spoiled pickles isolated by Fabian and Johnson [94] corresponded to *Bacillus mesentericus fuscus*; it was capable of causing "slips" in six to 12 hours and "mushy" pickles within 12 to 24 hours. This organism grew well in concentrations of salt up to and including nine per cent and more slowly up to 11 per cent.

Floaters. Pickles which, owing to some cause, float on the surface of the tank are known as "floaters." They may be caused by hollow spaces in the pickle or even to gas formation by bacteria which gain entrance through abrasions. LeFevre, [91] who carried out extensive investigations for the Bureau of Chemistry, found that most floaters were hollow. He also stated that improper salting might cause floaters. Floaters may be prevented by using stock which does not run to hollow cucumbers and the prevention of infection of the cucumber by careless handling. There seems to be no real explanation for floaters. The varying density of the brine in the pickle tank might explain it. Another opinion offered to explain floaters has it that the skin of the cucumber may be made tough and intact so as to prevent the exit of gases which, when retained, buoy up the cucumber. That salting modifications may greatly influence formation of floaters was also indicated by Jones, Etchells, Veerhoff, and Veldhuis. [95] Relatively large numbers of floaters were secured when brines of high salinity were used during the early portion of the curing period in salt stock production. Floater formation was said to be related to gaseous fermentation. This was probably confirmed by Etchells and Jones [96] who observed, by microscope examination, presence of many dead yeast cells in brine from a batch of pickles among which were many bloaters.

Black Pickles. Old brine pickles are apt to turn black if the acidity is low. The blackening is accompanied by a strong odor of hydrogen sulfide; the black color is probably nothing but iron sulfide formed from the iron in the water with the hydrogen sulfide. The hydrogen sulfide is in all probability formed from the gypsum in the water. Most waters contain a little gypsum and iron. Bacteria liberating hydrogen

91. LeFevre. 1921. The Canner 52, 207.
92. Kossowicz. 1913. Ztschr. f. Gärungsphysiol. 2, 78-80.
93. Kornauth and Zanluchi. 1913. Ztschr. f. Landw. Versuchsw. Österr. 16, 1034-1043.
94. Fabian and Johnson. 1938. Mich. Agr. Expt. Sta. Bull. 157.
95. Jones *et al*. 1941. Fruit Products J., 20, 202-206.
96. Etchells and Jones. 1941. Idem 20, 370.

sulfide from gypsum are found commonly in soils and in mud at the bottom of rivers and lakes. Especially Spirillum forms are noted for that. Tanner [97] has shown that many common bacteria and yeasts are able to reduce sulfur compounds with the formation of hydrogen sulfide. Fabian and his colleagues also found that small quantities of iron compounds together with the formation of hydrogen sulfide in the brine caused black pickles. It occurred only in nearly neutral or alkaline brines, began at the top of the brine, was accompanied by an odor of hydrogen sulfide with or without the odor of other putrefactive products, and was retarded, though not prevented, by a one-inch layer of mineral oil on the surface of the brine. Softening appeared not to be related to brine blackening except in that both required a neutral or alkaline brine for development. Combined softening and blackening were accompanied by a strong ammoniacal odor. Addition of a sugar, dextrose or sucrose, to the brine after the active fermentation has ceased seemed to be beneficial when pickles were stored for any length of time. There is a sufficient number of acid-producing bacteria left to cause a considerable increase in the acidity.

Bacillus nigrificans was isolated by Fabian and Nienhuis [98] as an organism causing black pickles. It is a spore-forming rod which produces blackening by a water-soluble pigment. Conditions favoring blackening are presence of a carbohydrate, absence of an excessive amount of nitrogenous material, and a neutral or slightly alkaline brine.

Ropy Brine. Capsulated bacteria cause trouble in several foods preserved by methods which require activities of certain bacteria. Thirteen cultures of bacteria, isolated by Fabian and Nienhuis from four samples of ropy brine from Michigan and Wisconsin, were divided into two groups on the basis of morphological, cultural, and physiological characteristics. Group I (seven cultures) consisted of bacteria which were short and generally motile, gram-negative, encapsulated rods not fermenting any of the carbohydrates tested. Group II (six cultures) consisted of bacteria which were motile, gram-negative rods, somewhat longer than those of Group I: three members of this group were encapsulated. The 13 cultures produced the greatest amount of ropiness in a brine of low acidity and salinity; rise in temperature also favored ropiness. The rough forms of the two groups studied produced little or no ropiness, as compared with the smooth forms. Ropiness is most easily controlled by increasing the salt concentration about twice as fast as normal.

Hollow Pickles. Hollow pickles are the cause of considerable loss in some factories, while others do not seem to have this trouble at all. The reasons given by manufacturers are very different. Season, temperature, too fast fermentation, too strong brine, too weak brine, imperfect growth are possible explanations. It seems to be true that the cucumbers of the late season show more tendency to become hollow than the first crop. This tends to show that the trouble lies in the structure of the cucumber perhaps rather than in the method of fermentation. LeFevre [74] stated that

97. Tanner. 1918. J. Amer. Chem. Soc. 40, 663-669.
98. Fabian and Nienhuis. 1934. Mich. Agr. Expt. Sta. Tech. Bull. 140.

hollow pickles were due to too long an interval between harvesting and curing.

After the pickles are removed from the brine tanks, they are made into different varieties, such as dill, sour, spiced, etc. Some are canned and given a process to destroy bacteria and prevent respiratory changes.

Pasteurization of Pickles. In order to reduce and eliminate deteriorative changes in stored pickles, they have been pasteurized in order to destroy microorganisms. Jones, Etchells, Veldhuis, and Veerhop [99] observed persistence of many microorganisms in pickles stored for a considerable time and a low number of bacteria in pasteurized pickles. In unpasteurized pickles acid-forming bacteria and yeasts predominated while these species were destroyed by pasteurization. The bacteria found in the latter were resistant sporeformers. The same results were reported by Etchells and Ohmer,[100] who pasteurized pickles at 71.1°C.(160°F.) for 20 minutes or 73.9°C.(165°F.) for 15 minutes. Little or no increase was noted during storage. Similar conclusions were reached by Etchells and Goresline.[101] Jars of pickles pasteurized at 71.1°C. for 20 minutes retained their fresh appearance and most of their crispness during several months' storage. Pasteurization temperature of 71.1°C. was sufficient in Etchells' and Jones'[101a] experiments to destroy both acid-forming bacteria and yeasts irrespective of the inoculum used. Acidity was an important factor in destruction of microorganisms by pasteurization.

Preservation of Vegetables by Salting. Owing to scarcity of tin and rubber at the time this is written, attempts are being made with considerable success, to preserve various vegetables by salting. Brine concentrations of 40°, 60°, and 80° salometer have been used. The microbiological changes are apparently quite similar to those observed in making cucumber pickles.[101b, c]

OLIVES

Olives have been used by man since earliest times. Besides the olive itself, its oil has been pressed for human food. The industry was developed in Greece and Spain and was later introduced into California.

The method of pickling olives as it is practiced in Greece and Spain today has much in common with the methods used in California. These have been described by Kaloyereas [102] and Trabut.[103] Cruess,[104] who reviewed the history, technology, and preservation of olives, credited the old Mission Fathers with introduction of various fruits, some of which are known today as "Mission" varieties. Olives are picked when firm and ripe and are shipped to the factory in light brine in barrels. Cruess stated that they are handled much like cucumbers, the same type of lactic fermen-

99. Jones *et al*. 1941. Fruit Products J., 20, 304-305.
100. Etchells and Ohmer. 1941. Idem 334-337.
101. Etchells and Goresline. 1940. Idem 19, 331-335; 24 (1942), 330-332.
101a. Etchells and Jones. 1943. Food Research 8, 33-44.
101b. Fabian and Blum. 1943. Fruit Prod. J. 22, 228-236; 273-275.
101c. Etchells and Jones. 1943. Idem 242-246.
102. Kaloyereas. 1928. Idem April, 1928, 14-16.
103. Trabut. 1913. Soc. Natl d' Agr. de France, Bull. 72, 69-70.
104. Cruess. 1927. The Canner, July 30; Food Indus. 1927, Jan., 170-174.

tation being induced, during which time the fruit becomes firmer and the sugars change to lactic acid. This author stated that the terms "curing" or "processing" are now used in preference to the older term "pickling." The changes which occur during the curing process have been discussed by Lesley, Cruess, and Kaloyereas.[105] These will not be reviewed in this book because they were mainly chemical in nature. Cruess [106] stated that the olives are put into 50-gallon barrels and salted with from five to 10 pounds of salt. The olives are fermented in about the same manner as are brine pickles. Differences of opinion apparently obtain with regard to the value of pickling. Cruess believed that if it is necessary to hold olives, they should be placed in a strong brine which will prevent all fermentation. He advised starting the olives in a five-per cent brine and increasing the concentration to 10 per cent. Such treatment will prevent shriveling and sliminess and keep the olives free from molds. Ripe olives are often put into a lye solution to remove a bitter principle. After removal of the lye by soaking, the olives are put in dilute brine, after which they are sorted and canned. A temperature of 115.6°C.(240°F.) for 60 minutes is used for processing both in glass and in tin. In California, this step in olive canning is under the supervision of the State Board of Health. After processing, the cans and jars are cooled in water.

More extensive investigations of the ripening of olives were reported by Cruess.[107] As far as the use of high temperatures is related to the merchantable qualities of olives, Cruess found that there was no difference. It seemed that olives which were sterilized at 115.6°C.(240°F.) and 121.7°C. (250°F,) possessed as good taste and flavor to the average consumer as those sterilized at 100°C.(212°F.) for 40 minutes.

The floral changes occuring in fermentation of Manzanillo olives was found by Vaughn and Douglas [108] to be quite similar to those in the fermentation of sauerkraut, with the important exception that gas-forming species of Lactobacillus apparently play no role in olive fermentation. During the early stages of olive fermentation coliform and other gram-negative bacteria predominate. They are soon crowded out by Leuconostoc types. These in turn are replaced by Lactobacillus plantarum which carry the fermentation to completion. Vaughn and Douglas observed both film-forming and non-film-forming species of yeasts which were believed to have a role in flavor and aroma formation.

Olives are subject to several deteriorations as are other fermented foods. Bioletti [109] stated that overripe olives often became soft during fermentation, especially in lye solutions. Salt is used in the lye to prevent it. Kossowicz [110] believed Escherichia coli to be the cause of softening of green olives stored in brine. A lactic acid fermentation stopped the spoilage. On the other hand, West, Gilliland, and Vaughn [111] did not find this organ-

105. Lesley, Cruess, and Kaloyereas. 1927. The Canner, Sept. 17.
106. Cruess. 1920. Calif. Agr. Expt. Sta. Ann. Rpt. 48-49.
107. Cruess. 1920. The Canner, Jan. 24.
108. Vaughn and Douglas. 1941. J. Bact. 41, 93-94.
109. Bioletti. 1914. Calif. Agr. Expt. Sta. Ann. Rpt., 199-200.
110. Kossowicz. 1908. Rev. in Expt. Sta. Rec., 20 (1908-1909), 77.
111. West, Gilliland, and Vaughn. 1941. J. Bact. 41, 341-342.

ism to be important in olive spoilage. In fact no true *Escherichia coli* were found. Aerobacter made up about 70 per cent of the cultures examined while the rest were intermediates. Tracy[112] also failed to report *Escherichia coli* among several coliform species isolated from spoiled olives. The species isolated were *Escherichia neopolitana, Escherichia pseudocoloides, Escherichia iliaca, Aerobacter cloacae*, and occasionally several other members of the genus. Fermentation tanks were believed to be contaminated by dust and water supplies.

As is the case with pickles, olives are subject to another type of spoilage yielding what are known as "floaters." Alvarez[113] found three types of bacteria involved. During fermentation the olives became covered with blisters which caused them to rise to the surface. Even though no spores were formed the bacteria which were believed to cause floaters were resistant to salt, heat, acids, and alkali. To prevent this deterioration frequent cleaning of the vats was recommended.

Tracy[114] believed that good results followed the use of starters in factory tests on olive curing. The bacteria used were originally isolated from holding solutions although Tracy suggested that sediment from holding solutions might be used if they were carefully handled. Large numbers of cells are necessary, about one-half billion per milliliter of brine, before fermentation is initiated. It was suggested that, if olive sugar could be fermented to acid before coliform bacteria could ferment it, no spoilage would occur in the holding brines. Furthermore, flavor would probably be improved.

Pasteurization procedures have been introduced for ripe olives in process in order to prevent attack by bacteria which may develop between lye treatments. The temperature and time is determined by the amount of time which the olives will stand. Too much heat will result in olives with a soapy taste because of reaction of the lye with the oil in the olive. Cruess[115] stressed the necessity of experiments to determine the time and temperature which could be used.

Canning of Olives. After being cured, sorted, and graded the olives may be packed in either metal or glass containers. The cans are exhausted for a few minutes near the boiling temperature until the center of the can reaches a temperature of 85°C.(185°F.). They are then closed and processed.

Processing of canned olives in California is done according to regulations of the Cannery Inspection Division of the California State Department of Public Health. Each retort is provided with temperature recording devices and a record kept for every batch cooked. The process times and temperatures are based on results of investigations conducted by the University of California. Glass containers are closed under vacuum and are processed in water at 115.6°C.(240°F.) for 60 minutes. Since introduction of this process, spoilage has been eliminated and botulism prevented.

112. Tracy. 1934. J. Bact. 28, 249-264; The Canner, Sept. 26, 12-13.
113. Alvarez. 1926. J. Bact. 12, 359-365.
114. Tracy. 1936. The Canner, Sept. 26, 12-13.
115. Cruess. 1936. The Canner, Oct. 17, 19-20.

Warth [116] summarized spoilage of brine-packed olives as follows:

a. Molds owing to faulty fruits.
b. Bacteria, mostly of the lactic acid type, manifesting themselves as colonies in the form of tiny white spots on packed fruit.
c. Sediment and cloudiness. This may be caused by deterioration of the product or packing under undesirable closure.
d. Yeasts owing to contamination.
e. Staining of cap liners. The liner of a cap will undergo decolorization through careless methods of packing or imperfect sealing.

Clouding of Olive Brine in Glass Jars. Clouding of olive brine accompanied by white flaky deposits is not an uncommon occurrence in bottled olives. Clouding of green olive brine may be due to calcium and magnesium salts in the water used in making the brine or to presence of microorganisms. Among the latter are the so-called film yeasts and bacteria which are able to withstand the conditions in the olive brine. If curing of the olives is carried to completion before any attempt is made to pack them in glass or tin containers, little, if any, trouble will be experienced with clouding. If, on the other hand, curing is not complete, it will continue in the fresh brine in the containers and of course, be accompanied by clouding. Various means have been attempted to prevent such trouble. Reduction of the oxygen content by filling the jar completely and vacuum sealing is one remedy. Pasteurization [117] is another, for it has been found that short heating at 54.4°C.(130°F.) will easily destroy the yeast.

Ayers, Barnby, and Voigt [118] considered the function of Mycoderma in this type of spoilage. Bottles of olives frequently show the presence of film on the surface. In order to prevent the appearance of this film, Ayers and his colleagues studied the effect of concentration of salt, exclusion of oxygen, and application of heat. It was found that salt concentration could not be relied upon to control development of the yeast and still have a merchantable product. The data secured by Ayers were in accord with those secured by Cruess,[119] showing that growth of Mycoderma was not prevented by eight per cent of salt and that at least 18 per cent was necessary to stop its growth. Exclusion of air was found to prevent development of the yeast. It was found that vacuum packing of the olives restricted the fungus. The next step was to determine whether heat could be used to destroy the organism. In a four-per cent brine, the organism was not destroyed by heating at 130°F., for five minutes. However, in this concentration or brine it was destroyed in five minutes. It is very interesting to note, however, that when the salt concentration was 14 per cent, the temperature required to destroy the yeast was slightly lowered. The authors believed that heating of the bottles of olives after packing might be of value in practice.

116. Warth. 1937. The Canner, Aug. 21, p. 30.
117. The Glass Pack Age, April, 1934, 257-258.
118. Ayers *et al.* 1928. Glass Container 7, No. 10; Food Indus. 2 (1930), 61-64.
119. Cruess. 1930. Calif. Agr. Expt. Sta. Bull. 498.

Ripe Olives. After being picked the olives are put into wooden barrels or tanks in brine of at least 25° salometer. After several weeks, the olives are subjected to a lye treatment to destroy the natural bitterness. Following this treatment they are thoroughly washed in water to leach out the lye. They are then packed in brine with two to three per cent of salt. After standing for a few days, they are ready for packing in glass or tin containers. Some are sold in bulk. Under regulations of the California State Department of Public Health [120] all bulk ripe olives must be held in kegs or barrels in a brine solution containing at least two and one-half per cent of salt (10 per cent brine).

TEA

Tea is prepared by fermentation processes which are probably not microbiological to any extent. More important are enzymes in the leaf. Green tea is prepared by roasting the leaves soon after picking to prevent fermentation, while black tea is allowed to stand during which time a slow drying process occurs. Mann [121] and Newton [122] believed the important enzyme in the tea leaf to be an oxidase and that the leaf should be handled so as not to harm it. Most investigators, among whom are Tunsdall,[123] Straub and Deuss,[124] Bernard,[125] Evans,[126] and Tatarskaya,[127] are agreed that microorganisms are not involved in normal tea curing. Straub and Deuss tried to use pure cultures of yeasts but observed no improvement in flavor. Bernard, however, isolated a yeast from Java tea which seemed to improve the flavor. Since it is possible to produce fermentation in completely sterilized leaf, Evans reasoned that microorganisms are not essential. On the other hand, rapid development of microorganisms took place at temperatures higher than those which allow fermentation of the leaf. Yeasts were harmless but any development of bacteria or molds resulted in dark or yellow liquors with characteristics of over-fermented tea. Tatarskaya also believed microorganisms to have no function in tea fermentation. They are always present on leaves, as shown by Itano and Yasuhiko,[128] who followed their development under different conditions. Bacteria and fungi were observed to survive the entire process although their number decreased toward the end.

Molds were observed by Nakazawa et al.[129] to spoil tea leaves destined for black tea. Members of the genera Aspergillus, Penicillium, and Rhizopus were isolated. When they grew on tea leaves the extractive was soon rendered unpalatable. Dry heat used in preparation of the leaves and strict cleanliness aided in controlling these fungi.

120. Calif. State Dept. Pub. Health Weekly Bull., 9, 39.
121. Mann. 1901. J. Asiatic Soc., Bengal 70, 154-166.
122. Newton. 1901. Expt. Sta. Rec. 13, 921.
123. Tunsdall. 1924. Trop. Agr. 62, 131-134.
124. Staub and Deuss. 1912. Rev. in Expt. Sta. Rec. 32, 111.
125. Bernard. 1910. Bull. Dept. Agr. Indes. Neerland. No. 36, 42.
126. Evans. 1931. Tea Quarterly 3, 27-33.
127. Tatarskaya. 1936. Rev. in Chem. Abs. 31 (1937), p. 8057.
128. Itamo and Yasuhiko. 1936. Rev. in Biol. Abs. 11, 1532.
129. Nakazawa et al. 1936. J. Agr. Chem. Soc., Japan 13, 805-814.

Germicidal Action of Tea Infusion. *Eberthella typhosa,* according to Dold,[130] was not destroyed in 80 days in .25 per cent infusion of black tea or in .50 per cent cocoa solutions. In four per cent green tea, it lived for 20 days. These data indicate that pure water must be used for these beverages. Ropiness in tea reported by Greene, Judd, and Marx [131] confirms this statement. Ropiness was found to be due to *Aerobacter aerogenes* which came from the water supply.

COCOA AND CHOCOLATE

These products are prepared by grinding the seed of the cacao plant. The seeds are enclosed in a woody shell which is removed by a special fermentation. The beans are piled into boxes where they undergo a spontaneous fermentation which loosens the shell. Bainbridge and Davis [132] described the process as it is carried out in the West Indies and South America. The beans in the fermenting box become warmer as fermentation continues. After five or six days the temperature may reach 45 to 50°C. (113 to 122°F.). The first stage is accompanied by a vigorous growth of *Saccharomyces apiculatus* and *Saccharomyces anomalus.* The second stage is an alcoholic fermentation by true Saccharomyces. Development of Acetobacter is the third stage. Later aerobic, sporeforming bacteria may develop. This fermentation results in an improved flavor. Fermentation thus serves two purposes. (Wigman.[133]) *Saccharomyces theobromae* was isolated by Preyer [134] and Lambert.[135] Loew [136] also believed that yeasts were important. They were believed to develop in the juices which came from the pulped tissue.

After discussion of literature and review of methods used in different parts of the world, with studies on predominating yeast flora at different stages of fermentation, Lilienfeld-Toal [137] emphasized the value of pure-culture control, and found that in all parts of the world the same yeasts are concerned. The two species invariably present are *Saccharomyces ellipsoideus* var. *tropicus* and *Schizosaccharomyces bussei.* Other yeasts are present, but play no role. Steinmann [138] isolated four kinds of yeast from the sweating boxes on several estates in central Java: Mycoderma, which grew when the temperature was kept below 30°C. (86°F.); a true wine yeast of *Saccharomyces ellipsoideus* group, occurring later when the temperature of the beans has become between 25 and 40°C. (77 and 104°F.); an ascospore forming variety; and finally an Apiculatus type. On some estates, the temperature during the first 24 hours is below 30°C. (86°F.) since the fermentation is carried on in houses which are not protected from cool air at night. On estates where closed houses are used, the temperature is higher. A rather heterogeneous flora of microorganisms was

130. Dold. 1921. Ztschr. f. Hyg. u. Infektionskrank 92, 30.
131. Greene, Judd, and Marx. 1940. Amer. J. Pub. Health 30, 680-682.
132. Bainbridge and Davis. 1912. J. Chem. Soc. 101, 2209-2221.
133. Wigman. 1908. Rev. in Expt. Sta. Rec. 14 (1902-1903), 46.
134. Preyer. 1901. Tropenpflanzer 5, 157-173.
135. Lambert. 1911. Bull. Sci. Pharmacol. 18, 574-587.
136. Loew. 1908. Rev. in Centbl. Bakt. II, 21, 533.
137. Lilienfeld-Toal. 1927. Beitr. z. Tropenplanz. No. 1.
138. Steinmann. 1928. Arch. Algem. Landw. Syndic. Batavia, 3, 71-80.

reported by Busse, Henneberg, and Zeller.[139] The fermentation process was said to start with yeasts and bacteria. During fermentation, increase in temperature makes the conditions favorable for acid-tolerant, thermophilic, sporeforming bacteria. Attempts to use pure cultures of organisms for hastening fermentation were not successful. *Thermobacterium mobile* was suggested for supplementary fermentation before manufacture by Borghi *et al.*[140]

Spoilage of cacao beans, especially when moist, may be induced by molds. Several groups of molds were described by Bunting,[147] all of which came from cacao beans. Most of them were ordinary species which are present in air and dust. Five species of Actinomyces were isolated by Ciferri from cacao beans which gave off a moldy or earthy odor. They were found either on the rind of the fruit or in the fermentation receptacles whence they contaminate the beans. Acid from the fermentation inhibits but does not kill them. Ciferri believed that proper handling would control these fungi.

Inhibition of Microorganisms by Chocolate. Some evidence has been published to indicate that chocolate may be inhibitive if not germicidal for microorganisms. Tanner and Snyder [143] observed shorter survival times of bacteria in chocolate fudge than in plain fondant. Cathcart and Merz [144] reported growth of *Staphylococcus aureus* to be effectively inhibited by fillings made with natural chocolate and natural cocoa. The inhibitive substance was believed to exist in the non-fat portion of the cocoa.

COFFEE

The beverage coffee is an extract of berries from the coffee tree *Coffea arabica*. The coffee berries grow in clusters or rosettes, each berry containing a soft pulp surrounded by a membrane. Inside the pulp are two coffee beans surrounded by a parchment membrane. In order to prepare the coffee beans for commerce, the extraneous pulp must be removed. This is done in one of two ways, by a *dry method* or *wet method*. In the former method the berries are spread in thin layers for exposure to sun and air for three weeks. This thoroughly dries them so that the extraneous material may be removed by hulling machines. In the latter, the wet method, the berries are softened by soaking in large tanks in water for 24 hours. The berries are then passed through pulping machines which remove the outer covering and pulp. This leaves the two berries within the parchment covering. The beans are then allowed to ferment in large tanks which further softens the membrane about the berries. They are then dried and finally "hulled" or shelled.

Fermentation of coffee has a primary purpose in removing the slimy "saccharine matter" from the parchment. Beckley [445] found that the active

139. Busse, Henneberg, and Zeller. 1929. Tropenpflanzer Beihefte. 26, 1-87.
140. Borghi *et al.* 1939. Off. Internatl. du Cacao et Choc. Bull. Off. 9, 341-344.
141. Bunting. 1929. Gold Coast Dept. Agr. Bull. 16.
142. Ciferri. 1927. Centbl. Bakt. Pt. 2, 71, 80-93.
143. Tanner and Snyder. 1940. Inst. Food Tech. Proc., 307-321.
144. Cathcart and Merz. 1942. Food Research 7, 96-99.
145. Beckley. 1931. Kenya Colony Dept. Agr. Bull. 8, 1-10.

agent in the cleaning was an enzyme in the "saccharine matter" and that microorganisms are not strictly essential to the process. However, use of certain bacteria was found of value in hastening cleaning, through fermentation of fermentable sugars formed by decomposition of the "saccharine matter." In addition, a favorable level of acidity was maintained. Beckley believed that, providing proper precautions are taken, inoculation with favorable bacteria will save time in fermentation and will improve the quality of the coffee.

Germicidal Properties of Coffee Infusion. A few investigators have suggested that coffee infusions possess germicidal properties. Crane and Friedlander [146] stated that ground coffee, when mixed with yolks and whites of eggs and with chopped beef, prevented decomposition. Coffee infusion exposed to air became covered with mold growth but never turbid with bacteria. A 10-per cent infusion prevented development of *Eberthella typhosa, Escherichia coli,* and *Bacillus anthracis.* They did not ascertain to what constituent of coffee the germicidal action should be attributed. Dold,[147] using six per cent infusions of coffee, observed *Eberthella typhosa* to be killed in one to three days, the resistance varying with the strain. Aging of the infusion caused it to lose some of its germicidal properties. *Salmonella schottmülleri* was a little more resistant, surviving for 14 to 15 days.

Soy and Related Fermentations. Soybean sauce is a dark brown-black fluid prepared in the Eastern countries by the fermentation of soybeans. The subject was well reviewed by Church.[148] The manufacture of the soybean sauce, called "shoyu" in Japan, involves first of all a preliminary mold fermentation followed by ripening in brine. After the soybeans have been cooked and mixed with prepared wheat they are inoculated with a mold-starter called "tane-koji." This is a rice preparation heavily overgrown with the mold. The species of mold varies somewhat. Miss Church stated that the species was *Aspergillus flavus* Link; occasionally *Aspergillus oryzae* or species between these two are used. This preliminary mold fermentation is carried out in shallow wooden trays which in Japan are stored in rooms, in cold weather they may be heated. The soybeans are first soaked for about 20 hours with frequent changes of water in order to prevent souring. A rapid fermentation occurs from the growth and activities of a sporeforming, rod-shaped organism. To prevent this, the water is changed frequently. After soaking, they are cooked until soft enough to be pressed flat between the thumb and finger. After cooking, the beans are spread out to cool. Wheat is crushed unevenly and roasted to a dark brown color. The boiled beans and roasted wheat are then mixed thoroughly so that the beans are separated from one another by the wheat. The mixture is then inoculated with mature rice koji, a pure culture of the mold, or some previously molded material. The inoculated mass is then placed in koji trays and placed in the koji room maintained at about 25°C.(77°F.). The mix-

146. Crane and Friedlander. 1903. Amer. Med. 6, 403-407.
147. Dold. 1921. Ztschr. f. Hyg. u. Infektionskrank. 92, 30.
148. Church. 1923. U. S. Dept. Agr. Bull. 1152.

ture is stirred at intervals and is matured between 24 and 48 hours. When the mixture has sufficient growth of mold, it is emptied into a tube of brine of a strength of 20-22° Baumé. Each tube is inoculated on the first day with Zygosaccharomyces sp. The budding fungi of "shoyu-moromi" were studied by Takahashi and Sano.[149] They found two varieties of film-forming Zygosaccharomyces which were varieties of *Zygosaccharomyces salsus*. Since they differed from this species by fermenting saccharose, raffinose, and alpha-methylglucoside, Takahashi and Sano suggested the name *Zygosaccharomyces salsus* var. *saccharosum* I and II.

Under American conditions Church secured a satisfactory product. Similar sauces were also made from peanut press cake.

Sixteen aerobic bacteria and 12 anaerobes, isolated by Tshimaru[150] from soy mash, were found to grow in 10-per cent salt solution. Half of them grew in a 20-per cent solution. In manufacture of soy, the bacteria accelerated hydrolysis of protein and polysaccharides by the mold (Aspergillus). Several bacteria were named which were especially useful in soy manufacture. Most of them are well-known diastatic species.

Some evidence has been published to show that soy sauce may be inimical to bacteria. Worcestershire sauce, an important constituent of which is soy sauce, was reported by Tetsumoto[151] to have a strong sterilizing action.

POI

This, according to Allen and Allen,[152] was one of the chief foods of the old Hawaiians, and is used today in the Hawaiian Islands. It is made by pounding the steamed roots of the taro plant *Colocasia antiquorum* var. *esculenta* into a smooth paste with addition of small quantities of water. While it may be eaten immediately, it is most desired after it has fermented several days. Allen and Allen reported the flora of various samples of poi with an acidity not greater than pH 4 to consist largely of bacteria and yeasts. The bacteria were mainly coliform types. Poi that was older than three days or with acidity greater than pH 4 showed few coliform bacteria but many bacteria growing as pin-point colonies. Bilger and Young[153] believed that the fermentations involved in poi manufacture were carbohydrate decompositions with various fatty acids resulting.

CITRON

This is prepared in Corsica by fermentation for use in confections. Hollande and Chadefaux[154] described a yeast as important in the fermentation to which he gave the name *Saccharomyces citri medicae*; a bacterium, *Bacillus citri medicae* was also an important fermenting agent. Citron prepared in Corsica by this method had a superior aroma caused by esterification by yeast of the essence of citron. Hollande and Chadefaux[154]

149 Takahasi and Sano. 1922. J. Co. Agr., Imp. Univ.. Tokyo. 7, 119-155.
150. Tshimaru. 1933. J. Agr. Chem. Soc., Japan 9, 859-904.
151. Tetsumoto. 1934. Idem 10, 123-127.
152. Allen and Allen. 1932. J. Bact. 23, Abs. No. A 12; Hawaiian Agr. Expt. Sta. Bull. 70.
153. Bilger and Young. 1935. J. Agr. Res. 51, 45-50.
154. Hollande and Chadefaux. 1924. Bull. Sci. Pharmacol. 31, 458-471.

suggested that the citron could be sterilized by steam and a pure-culture fermentation instituted. In the United States this fermentation has been studied by Fellers and Smith,[155] who confirmed the work of Hollande and Chadefaux as far as fermenting organisms are concerned. Acetic acid production in 15 days averaged from six to seven grams per liter. In preserving citron 35 per cent of glucose with sucrose yielded a peel with excellent flavor, color, and texture. A moisture content of 17 to 19 per cent in the candied peel prevented yeast fermentation or mold growth.

155. Fellers and Smith. 1936. J. Agr. Res., 53, 859-867.

CHAPTER 19

MICROBIOLOGY OF SUGAR AND SUGAR PRODUCTS

Sugar is so necessary in present day cookery and nutrition that its place and importance is recognized only when some event arises to reduce its availability. On account of the nature of the substance and the methods necessary to purify it, sugar is especially subject to the attacks of yeasts, molds, and bacteria. These microorganisms cause much spoilage and the spending of much money to check their activities. The character of the raw materials, beets, cane juice, and maple sap, from which sugar is made, explains the sources of many bacteria. They are usually heavily seeded with microorganisms from the air,,water, soil, etc. These start through the process of sugar manufacture in the juice, and many of them which are sporeformers are able to persist for some time.

Of all the sugars, cane sugar, prepared from the succulent stems of the sugar cane *(Saccharum officinarum)*, is probably the most satisfactory, although beet sugar is becoming an important article. The preparation of cane sugar for the market is a process too long for detailed discussion in a book of this nature. However, the main step is extraction of juice from the cane, which is usually accomplished by crushing and squeezing the cane stalks between rollers. Under the most ideal conditions from seven to 10 per cent of the weight of cane will be secured as sugar. Extraction of the juice by diffusion is not followed so much with cane as with beets. After crushing, the next step is purification of the juice. When it comes from the rolls, it contains all of the materials which were in the juice when it was pressed out of the cane cells. The juice begins to change just as soon as it is out of the cells of the plant and this should be stopped. Lime is added to neutralize the acids and stop inversion. The mixture is then allowed to settle. The juice which flows from the separators is concentrated to a thick sirup previous to the final concentration and crystallization. Great advances have been made in this step by vacuum pans and other devices for driving the concentration process more rapidly. The vacuum pan is used in the crystallization which leaves the sugar as crystals suspended in a noncrystalline sirup or molasses.

Gum Formation in Sugar Manufacture. This is a very troublesome deterioration which causes considerable loss to sugar manufacturers. The same slimy fermentation so often met with in other sugar-containing substances is encountered in making sugar. Many organisms have been described. The usual rod-forming, sporebearing bacteria have been found. Glaser[1] described *Bacterium gelatinosum betae*, while other organisms have been mentioned by Maassen,[2] Schöne,[3] and others.

1. Glaser. 1895. Centbl. Bakt., Pt. 2, 1, 879-880.
2. Maassen. 1905. Idem 15, 66; 16, 236.
3. Schöne. 1904. Ztschr. Ver. Rubenzuckerindus. 54, 1060.

The air of sugar mills was shown to be seeded with the microorganisms which cause decomposition of the sugar, by van der Bijl [4] who reported the presence of the following: *Aspergillus flavus, A. parasiticus,* Monilia sp., Cladosporium sp., *Penicillium divaricatum.* Gum formation was early recognized by Greig-Smith.[5] He called the gum levan. Kopeloff, Perkins, and Welcome [6] identified levan formed by the enzymes produced by *Aspergillus sydowi.* In order to study the mechanism of levan formation, these investigators set up sucrose solutions of varied concentrations and analyzed them for sugars and gum. The latter was thought to be formed from dextrose and levulose by levanase from mold spores. These sugars are formed from sucrose by invertase. In the absence of nascent glucose little gum was formed.

Violle [7] reported that the organism responsible for formation of gum in sugar was much like *Streptococcus lacticus.* Large capsules were formed which caused the bacteria to adhere in very large masses. Capsule formation, however, seemed to depend upon the medium on which the organism was propagated. A viscous material was formed in the sugar; saccharose seemed to be the only sugar in which this material was formed. This material was precipitated by alcohol. The experiment of Owen [8] indicated that gum formation was favored by a slightly alkaline environment. He also found that at least one per cent of moisture had to be present. Pederson [9] believed that this spoilage could be prevented by greater cleanliness and more rapid handling of the cane and juice previous to and during heating. He isolated many species (over 300) among which was *Leuconostoc mesenterioides.* It occurred in many of the samples.

MICROBIOLOGY OF RAW SUGAR

Much work has been done on the microorganisms in raw sugar. Owen [8] summarized most of the earlier literature. Gayon [10] observed that changes which took place in stored sugar were fermentations favored by moisture and high temperature. In 1878 he reported that they were accompanied by decrease in sucrose content and increase in dextrose and levulose content. Many microorganisms were found in these samples, activities of which could be checked with certain chemical compounds. The subject has been reviewed also by Church.[11] Owen [12] classified the organisms occurring in sugar into three groups—mold fungi, yeasts, and bacteria. They are named in the order of their importance in connection with sugar deterioration.

Molds. The species that have been found are quite varied and represent almost all of the well-known genera. Payen [13] observed presence of fungi

4. van der Bijl. 1922. So. African J. Sci. 18, 232-233.
5. Greig-Smith. 1902. Internatl. Sugar J. 4, 430-433; 481-485.
6. Kopeloff, Perkins, and Welcome. 1921. J. Agr. Res., 20, 637.
7. Violle. 1922. Ann. Inst. Pasteur., 36, 439-454.
8. Owen. 1914. Centbl. Bakt., Pt. 2, 42, 335-378.
9. Pederson. 1937. J. Bact. 35, 74.
10. Gayon. 1880. Compt. Rend. Acad. Sci., 91, 993-995.
11. Church. 1921. Sugar 23, 413-414.
12. Owen. 1925. Facts About Sugar, 20, 178-179; 442-444; 705-707.
13. Payen. 1851. Compt. Rend. Acad. Sci., 33, 393.

and connected them with spoilage. Contributions to the subject were made by Kamerling,[14] Shorey,[15] Greig-Smith,[16] Schöne,[17] Scott,[18] Amons,[19] and others. According to Owen,[20] possibility of molds causing spoilage in sugar was first mentioned by Shorey.[15] Owen, however, gave more information on this question. Different species of molds were isolated as follows: *Aspergillus niger, Asp. fumigatus,* and quite a number of Aspergillus-like fungi. These were carefully tested for their action on sugar solutions. In almost every case strong deteriorating action of the fungi was noticed in the sugar solutions in which these fungi were inoculated. These molds possessed a strong active invertase. Kopeloff and Kopeloff[21] reported a long list of mold fungi from sugar. Many of the common varieties, including those which verge into the yeasts, were isolated. Van der Bijl[22] isolated four varieties of fungi and three bacteria from samples of sweating South African sugar. The fungi included Aspergillus, Stemphylium, Sterigmatocystis, and *Hormodendron cladosporoides.* With the exception of Stemphylium all were capable of growing in sugar solutions of 63° Brix. Tubes containing inoculated solutions were placed in boiling water for 15 minutes which was sufficient to destroy the organisms. The bacteria seemed to belong to the subtilis-mesentericus group. This was indicated by their thermal resistance, ability to form gum, and their low nutritive requirements. Browne[23] isolated four organisms from Cuban sugars, *Torula communis, Monilia nigra, Monilia fusca,* and *Bacterium invertens.* Browne mentioned a number of possible sources of undesirable organisms in sugar.

Yeasts. Some difference of opinion exists over the significance of these fungi. Owen believed them to be of minor importance. Tempany and D'Emmerez de Charmoy,[24] however, believed them to be very important as spoilage organisms. The term yeasts will be loosely applied here to include fungi which are like yeasts. Jorgensen[25] reported Torulae in several refined sugars. Owen[20] isolated 17 cultures of Torulae as well as *Schizosaccharomyces octosporus* from sugar. In general, the forms isolated seemed to be without significance in the sugar industry.

Torulae do bring about some change in the sugar. Browne[23] mentioned the odor of esters formed where sugar was stored. Torulae bring about a reduction in the content of reducing sugars and a corresponding increase in polarization.

Owen[26] observed an antagonistic action between molds and Torulae in sugar. When the latter organisms were present, the former could not

14. Kamerling. 1899. Proefsta. Suikerindus. in West Java. Kagok, 97-104.
15. Shorey. 1898. J. Soc. Chem. Ind., 17, 555-558.
16. Greig-Smith. 1902. J. Soc. Chem. Ind., 21, 1-17.
17. Schöne. 1908. Deut. Zuskerindus. 33, 638.
18. Scott. 1912. Internatl. Sugar J., 14, 582-586.
19. Amons. 1917. Arch. Suikerindus. 25, 1225-1231.
20. Owen. 1918. La. Agr. Expt. Sta Bull. 162.
21. Kopeloff and Kopeloff. 1919. J. Ind. Eng. Chem. 11, 845-850.
22. van der Bijl. 1920. So. Africa Dept. Agr. and Forestry, Sci. Bull. 18.
23. Browne. 1918. J. Ind. Eng. Chem. 10, 178-190.
24. Tempany and D'Emmerez de Charmoy. 1922. Mauritius Dept. Agr. Bull. 24.
25. Jörgensen. 1911. Microorganisms and Fermentation. Chas. Griffin & Co., Ltd., London, 1911.
26. Owen. 1911. La. Agr. Expt. Sta. Bull. 125.

invert any sucrose. By virtue of these observations, Owen proposed to inoculate sugar with Torulae in order to keep down the undesirable fungi.

Bacteria. Many different species of bacteria have been found in sugar. They are abundant in raw sugar and persist through many of the steps in its manufacture. Owen has studied this subject and was probably the first to propose a connection between the number of bacteria and deterioration.

Deterioration of Raw Cane Sugar in Storage. An account of the nature of raw sugar it is susceptible to attack by various microorganisms. Owen [26] observed most of the bacteria in raw sugars to be sporeformers having many characteristics of members of the subtilis-mesentericus group. Greig-Smith [27] isolated a bacterium to which he gave the name *Bacillus levaniformans* because it formed a gum-like substance. Owen classified the organism as a *Bacillus subtilis*-like species. In an investigation conducted by Tempany and D'Emmerez de Charmoy [24] on factors involved in spoilage of raw sugar in Mauritius, moisture content was found to be very important. Moisture may result from that left in the sugar and that absorbed during storage. Tempany and his colleague quote Lewton Brain and Noël Deer as placing the critical concentration of water at one per cent which, if exceeded, will allow development of spoilage microorganisms. Tempany and D'Emmerez de Charmoy described the deterioration in Mauritius as follows:

The bags of sugar appear to sweat, which feature is usually the first to call attention to the deterioration. Examination of the sugar from such bags showed that it was damp and sticky, and in the later stages became liquefied and sirupy. Tempany and his collaborator stated that deterioration usually began in the outermost layers of sugar in the bags and proceeded inwards. Those bags which were in position to have contact with sources of moisture, were also the first to spoil.

Tempany and D'Emmerez de Charmoy [24] examined sugar from deteriorated bags bacteriologically. Three types of fungi were found to be present—torulae, molds, and bacteria. Contrary to statements of Kopeloff and in agreement with those of Amons, there seemed to be no relation between the number of microorganisms and the degree of deterioration. It was believed that Torulae were more responsible for deterioration of sugar than were other fungi. The species studied by Tempany and D'Emmerez de Charmoy had the following characteristics:

"On agar, containing 50 per cent of sugar, the colonies are only visible with a lens 48 hours after inoculation. These colonies are sometimes of the same size, and sometimes of two different dimensions. Those included within the agar are hardly visible to the naked eye, whilst those growing on the surface reach a diameter of .3 to .5 mm. They are at first transparent but later on become almost opaque. Under a low power of the microscope, the colonies are rounded and somewhat granular in appearance. When examined with direct light they are white and absolutely opaque.

"Under a high power the Torula is seen to affect two forms—a giant and a rounded one, the small form being about half the size of the large. The small cells are always

27. Greig-Smith. 1901. Linn. Soc. N. S. Wales, Proc. 26, 602.

found in much greater numbers, and are less regular in shape, being somewhat ovoid or acuminated at one end. They vary in diameter from 2.6μ to 7μ with an average diameter of 4.5μ to 5μ. The granulations are numerous and exhibit very rapid vibrating motion. Budding is rather scarce although apparent signs of some are conspicuous. There are never formed strings of any appreciable length.

"In sugar solutions, with or without the addition of nutrient media, and whether grown in pure culture or not, the cells are much smaller than on agar, more transparent, and show scarcely any vacuoles.

"When stained with Grubber's medicinal pure Methylene Blue, the plasma takes a pale blue color and the metachromatic corpuscles stain pink or darker if the time of staining is prolonged.

"In 10 per cent sugar solutions the growth of the Torula is less rapid than it is in 50 per cent solution. Turbidity is not noticeable before 48 hours, after which the ferment begins to settle, the liquid becoming clear again after a few days. A fair amount of sediment is obtained. Effervescence is never produced; only a few bubbles of gas escape during fermentation and this never before 48 hours after inoculation.

"On sweet potato, the organism grows readily and forms a rather thick white shiny layer which spreads over nearly the entire surface of inoculation, without however covering the other sides of the slant."

It was believed that the sugar became infected with the spoilage organisms between the centrifuge and the bag. The Mauritius sugar was said to be practically sterile. Tempany and D'Emmerez de Charmoy believed it to be an impossibility to keep sugar sterile and prevent all deterioration. While they made cautious statements, it was suggested that the size of the grains might have something to do with spoilage.

Less has been done on the microorganisms which may destroy beet sugar. Mares [28] found various fungi and yeasts. Included were species to which the names *Aspergillus betae* and *Penicillium candido-roseum* were given. These fungi were especially common on the beets. Spores were hardy and survived various processes involved in extraction of the sugar and were present in the finished sugar. One species of yeast fermented sucrose very rapidly.

Microbiology of Refined Sugar. Knowledge of the microbiology of refined sugar has been greatly stimulated by investigations on the origin of spoilage bacteria in canned foods. Earlier investigations on the subject were concerned especially with the microorganisms which were deteriorating finished sugar by fermentation or inversion.[29] Attention was first called to this problem during the 1925 packing season when a serious spoilage of canned peas was reported to the National Canners Association. Examination of spoiled cans by Cameron, Williams, and Thompson [30] revealed the presence of both "swells" and "flat-sours." During the next packing season, in 1926, a laboratory was established at the factory where the spoilage had occurred during the previous season, in order to make a thorough investigation of the source of the thermophilic spoilage bacteria. Results soon showed that contamination occurred mainly in the factory either from machinery or ingredients added to the cans. When

28. Mares. 1928. Ztschr. Zuckerindus. Cechoslovak. Repub., 45/46, 493-502.
29. Clark and Tanner, Jr. 1939. Food Manufacture 14, 387-389; 15 (1940), 39-44.
30. Cameron, Williams, and Thompson. 1928. National Canners Association Bull. 25-L.

the brine was placed under suspicion, the several ingredients were examined separately. Water and salt contained no thermophilic bacteria while sugar was always positive for their presence. It was then necessary to show that other samples of sugar also contained these canned-food spoilage bacteria. Cameron and Williams [31] believed that all cane sugar contained them in variable numbers. In some samples the number was as high as 100 spores per gram. Thermophilic anaerobic bacteria were commonly found but those causing sulfide spoilage were somewhat uncommon. Samples of beet sugar were quite free from thermophilic bacteria causing flat-sour spoilage; thermophilic anaerobes (spores), however, were more prevalent in beet sugar than in cane sugar. Beet sugars contained no sulfide-spoilage bacteria. James [32] confirmed the work of Cameron and Williams in examination of 197 samples of commercial sugars. Aerobic bacteria, thermophilic anaerobes, sulfide-spoilage, and flat-sour-producing bacteria were found to be present. Spores of flat-sour-producing bacteria were abundant. These results caused considerable controversy. Ingersoll [33] was reluctant to believe that refined sugars were as contaminated with spoilage bacteria as reported. He claimed that Cameron and Williams had reached false conclusions in their investigation of the 1926 outbreak of spoilage referred to above. Ingersoll argued that since canning factories had operated for a long time without undue spoilage traced to sugar, sugar could not have been the source of thermophilic bacteria. On the other hand, Bigelow [34] and Williams [35] each expressed his belief that certain sugars could be incriminated. Cameron [36] also took issue with Ingersoll who later apparently accepted the situation. This indicated to Cameron and Yesair [37] that plant equipment was not always the sole source of spoilage microorganisms. They reported as many as 2,000 spores of flat-sour-producing bacteria in some sugar. Even though a canner had sterile equipment he would still be marketing a non-sterile product. This would lead to spoilage if his cans were not adequately cooled.

This condition was not limited to American sugars because Homans [38] found all three groups of spoilage bacteria in European sugars. More sulfide-spoilage bacteria were found in them than in American sugars. Owen and Mobley [39] suggested that attention be given to other bacteria in sugar than the thermophiles. They believed that nonacid-producing thermophiles might also be significant.

The results just discussed prompted sugar refiners to attempt to produce more bacteriologically satisfactory sugars. The sources of infection had to be determined and methods found to prevent development during manufacture. The problem was studied by Cameron and Bigelow,[40] Owen

31. Cameron and Williams. 1928. Centbl. Bakt., Pt. 2, 76, 28-39.
32. James. 1928. Food Indus. 1, 65-69.
33. Ingersol. 1930. Food Indus. 2, 325 and 563.
34. Bigelow. 1930. Idem 2, 417.
35. Williams. 1930. Idem 2, 463.
36. Cameron. 1930. Idem 2, 473.
37. Cameron and Yesair. 1931. Idem 3, 265.
38. Homans. 1933. Tijdschr. algem. tech. ver. Bielwortels 29, 29.
39. Owen and Mobley. 1937. Ind. Eng. Chem. 24, 1042-1044.
40. Cameron and Bigelow. 1931. Idem 23, 1330-1333.

and Mobley,[41] and Calton.[42] Calton summarized the information as far as the sugar mill is concerned:

1. Filtration plays one of the most important roles in removal of thermophiles and thermophilic spores.

2. Accumulation may occur before and after filtration.

3. Crystallization, although less effective than filtration, excludes a large degree of contamination from the sugars.

4. Contamination is confined to the crystals' surface and is greatest in clumps of crystals.

5. Contamination of sirups bears no relation to purity.

6. Flat-sour thermophiles can grow in concentrations as high as 40 per cent raw sugar sirup; growth and acid production are rapid in concentrations up to 25 per cent.

Owen and Mobley found that the microorganism content of sugar was quite variable from month to month, the heaviest infection occurring in April and the lowest in September. This may be due partly to humidity as suggested by King and Suerte.[43] That sugar refiners were able to cope with the situation is proven by many results of investigations since the above experiments were made. Great improvement is evident.

Sugar of foreign manufacture contains the same general types in variable number. McMaster[44] and Barton[45] found them in English sugars. These sugars did not seem to be as heavily seeded as American and French sugars. Twenty samples of Formosan sugar, examined by Hirabayashi[46] contained not over 100,000 bacteria. Fungi were also present.

Beet sugar is quite similar in thermophilic bacteria content to cane sugar. It is prepared from the root of *Beta maritima* which thrives in more northern latitudes than sugar cane. After careful washing the beets are sliced; sugar is taken from the slices by diffusion. A large and varied flora is undoubtedly carried into the diffusors. Orth[47] reported 20,000 bacteria per milliliter in this water. In view of the fact that the temperature in the diffusors is quite near that which favors bacterial growth, these bacteria may cause significant losses of sugar. Samples from 13 sugar factories in Idaho, examined for thermophilic bacteria by Halversen,[48] were within the limits established by the National Canners Association.

Detecting and Estimating Numbers of Thermophilic Bacteria in Sugar. As soon as it was established that sugar might harbor bacteria which could cause spoilage of canned foods, methods were developed for detecting them and estimating their numbers. The first statement of such a procedure was made by Bigelow[49] and Cameron[50] of the

41. Owen and Mobley. 1933. Facts About Sugar 28, 382-385.
42. Calton. 1936. Ind. Eng. Chem. 28, 1235-1238.
43. King and Suerte. 1930. Sugar News 11, 434-449.
44. McMaster. 1934-35. Univ. Bristol, Fruit and Vegetable Preservation Research Station, Campden, 58-64.
45. Barton. 1938. Food Manufacture 13, 23-26.
46. Hirabayashi. 1934. Soc. Trop. Agr. J. 6, 534-541.
47. Orth. 1899.
48. Halversen. 1935. Idaho Agr. Expt. Sta. Bull. 220.
49. Bigelow. 1931. Canning Age, April, 1931, 291-292; The Canner, April 4, 1931, 19-20.
50. Cameron and Bigelow. 1931. Ind. Eng. Chem. 23, 1330-1333.

National Canners Association Research Laboratory in 1931, revisions of which have been published at intervals since then. A recent statement of procedure is as follows:[51]

12   SAMPLING

Take ½ lb. samples from each of 5 bags or barrels of shipment or of lot in question. Send these samples to laboratory in clean sealed cans, or other appropriate containers.

(The adequacy of this sampling will vary in relation to size of shipment or lot, and if there is any significant variability in the shipment, this fact will become evident, in the majority of cases, thru individual tests on 5 samples.)

13   PREPARATION OF SAMPLE

Place 20 g of sugar in a sterile 150 ml Erlenmeyer flask marked to indicate a volume of 100 ml. Add sterile H_2O to the 100 ml mark. Bring rapidly to boiling, and boil 5 min. Replace evaporation with sterile H_2O.

14   CULTURE MEDIA

(a) *Dextrose tryptone agar.*—For use in detection of flat sour bacteria.

This medium is prepared as a standardized, dehydrated medium and is marketed under the name of Bacto-dextrose Tryptone Agar by the Difco Laboratories, Inc., Detroit, Mich. Because of its standardization, its use in this form is recommended. It may, however, be prepared according to following formula: Tryptone, 10 g; dextrose, 5 g; agar, 15 g; bromocresol purple, 0.04 g; and H_2O, 1000 ml.

(b) *Liver broth.*—For detection of thermophilic anaerobes not producing H_2S (*Cl. thermosaccharolyticum*), putrefactive anaerobes, and other mesophilic anaerobes.

Mix chopped beef liver with H_2O in proportion of 500 g to 1000 ml. Boil mixture slowly 1 hour, adjust to ca pH 7.0, and boil an additional 10 min. Then press boiled material thru cheese cloth and make liquid to 1000 ml. To broth add 10 g of peptone and 1 g of dipotassium phosphate. Adjust reaction to pH 7.0. In tubing, introduce ½-1" of previously boiled ground beef liver into the tube.

Before using, unless it is freshly prepared, exhaust medium by subjecting to streaming steam at least 20 min., and after inoculation, stratify it with 2-2½" layer of plain nutrient agar (common formula), which has been cooled to 50°.

(c) *Sulfite agar (modified).*—For detection of thermophilic anaerobes producing H_2S (*Cl. nigrificans*).

Prepare according to following formula: Tryptone, 10 g; Na_2SO_3, 1 g; agar, 20 g; and H_2O, 1000 ml.

At time of tubing place a clean iron strip or nail in tube. No adjustment in reaction is necessary. Prepare medium at frequent intervals (1 week), and if Na_2SO_3 is used in soln also prepare it at frequent intervals (1 week).

CULTURE TECHNIC
15   DETECTION OF FLAT SOUR SPORES

Into each of 5 Petri dishes pipet 2 ml of the boiled sugar soln. Cover, and mix inoculum with the dextrose tryptone agar. Incubate plates at 55° for 36-48 hours, and to prevent drying of the agar, humidify the incubator. The combined count from the 5 plates represents the number of spores in 2 g of original sugar. Multiply this count by 5 to express results in terms of number of spores per 10 g of sugar.

These colonies are characteristic. A colony is round, measures 2-5 mm in diameter, presents a typical opaque central "spot," and is usually surrounded by a yellow halo in a field of purple. This halo may be insignificant, or missing, where certain low acid-producing types are concerned, or where the plate is so thickly seeded that the entire plate takes on a yellow tinge. The typical subsurface colonies are rather compact and may approach the "pin point" condition.

If there is doubt as to the identity of the sub-surface colonies, a decision can usually be made after observing the nature of the surface colonies. If they show

51. Reprinted by permission from Official and Tentative Methods of Analysis of the Association of Official Agricultural Chemists, Fifth Edition, copies of which may be purchased from the Association in Washington, D. C.

reasonable purity of flora, it is safe for practical purposes to assume that the sub-surface colonies have been formed by similar bacterial groups. It is emphasized that where the plate is heavily seeded, there may be loss of accuracy as regards counts, and colony structure and size may be atypical. If plates are so heavily seeded as to make counting impracticable, a second sample of the sugar may be plated, dilutions of the original solution being used.

Whether atypical subsurface colonies are flat sour organisms may often be determined by streaking from the colonies to agar plates so that their surface characteristics may be noted.

No immediate significance is attached to the presence of "non-spoilage" thermophiles; i.e., aerobic spore-formers, actinomyces, etc., although when present in large numbers they carry significance with regard to the general bacteriological quality of the sugar. The total thermophilic spore count may be obtained from the dextrose tryptone agar plates.

16   DETECTION OF THERMOPHILIC ANAEROBES NOT PRODUCING H2S

(Under the conditions stated, thermophilic anaerobes are manifest thru the splitting of agar and the presence of acid. At times a cheesy odor is noted. The method is considered suitable as a qualitative test but quantitatively it provides only a means of rough estimation. The method does not permit expression of results in terms of numbers of spores per unit weight of sugar.)

Divide 20 ml of the sugar soln approximately equally among 6 liver broth tubes and stratify the liquid medium with plain nutrient or yeast water agar. After agar has solidified, preheat to 55° and incubate at that temp. for 72 hours.

17   DETECTION OF THERMOPHILIC ANAEROBES PRODUCING H2S
(SULFIDE SPOILAGE ORGANISMS)

(In sulfite agar the sulfide spoilage organisms are detected thru the formation of characteristic blackened spherical areas. Owing to solubility of H2S and its fixation by the iron, no gas is noted. Certain of the thermophilic anaerobes (not producing H2S), methods for the detection of which precede, give rise to relatively large quantities of H, which splits the agar and reduces the sulfite, thereby causing general blackening of the medium. This condition, however, is readily distinguishable from the restricted blackened areas mentioned previously. The blackened areas may be counted to obtain quantitative results.)

Divide 20 ml of the sugar soln approximately equally among 6 freshly exhausted tubes containing the sulfite agar. Incubate at 55° for 72 hours.

18   REPORTING RESULTS

Report flat sour and sulfide spoilage results as number of spores per 10 g of sugar. Report thermophilic anaerobes (not producing H2S) as number of tubes positive and number negative in the following manner: + + + — — —.

Microbiology of Refined Starch. The role of sugar as a source of spoilage bacteria in canned foods prompted investigations on starch which is also added to some foods, such as cream-style corn. Cameron [52] and Clark and Tanner [53] found spoilage bacteria in starch and studied methods for detecting them. The latter used the method proposed by the National Canners Association with a few modifications. Analysis of 20 samples of starch confirmed results of experiments by Owen and Mobley [54] who found an average of 131 flat-sour-producing spores; 50 per cent of the portions from each sample contained spores of thermophilic anaerobes and 33 per sent sulfide-spoilage organisms. Clark and Tanner found an average of

52. Cameron. 1937. Food Indus. 9, 182-183.
53. Clark and Tanner. 1937. Food Research 2, 27-39.
54. Owen and Mobley. 1932. Ind. Eng. Chem. 24, 1042.

193 flat-sour-producing spores; 50 per cent of the portions were positive for thermophilic anaerobes and only 5.5 per cent of the samples showed sulfide spoilage bacteria.

Owing to the thickening properties of starch Clark and Tanner found that the method given above for sugar analysis was impractical without modification.

Clark and Tanner's [53] **Procedure for Determining the Number of Spoilage Microorganisms in Starch.** This procedure is based on the one given above for sugar examination.

Preparation of Sample: Ten grams of starch are weighed into a sterile flask. Enough water is added to make up to 100 grams. This mixture is thoroughly stirred and pipetted into the media for detecting the various groups of organisms.

Detection of Flat-Sour Spores: Twenty ml. of the starch suspension are pipetted into 100 ml. melted dextrose brom-cresol-purple agar or dextrose tryptone brom-cresol-purple agar, the mixture being stirred as the starch suspension is added. This agar starch mixture is then heated with frequent shaking until the starch flows, and is then placed in the Arnold sterilizer for 30 minutes with occasional shaking. Place equally among six Petri dishes. Incubate at 55°C.(131°F.) for 36 to 48 hours.

Thermophilic Anaerobes: Twenty ml. of starch suspension are distributed equally among six tubes of liver infusion broth which have been previously heated to 100°C. (212°F.). After reheating and agitating to distribute the starch thoroughly and prevent excess foaming, they are placed in the Arnold sterilizer for 30 minutes, cooled and stratified with plain agar. They are then incubated at 55°C.(131°F.) for five days.

Sulfide Spoilage Spores: Twenty ml. of starch suspension are distributed equally between six tubes of melted "sulfite" agar. The medium and starch are shaken thoroughly to distribute the starch and then heated in the Arnold sterilizer for 30 minutes. After heating thoroughly agitate, allow to harden, and incubate for five days at 55°C.(131°F.).

In order to determine whether these procedures were capable of giving comparable results in different laboratories, Cameron [55] submitted to 21 laboratories four samples of sugar representing varying degrees of contamination. Results indicated that the method was satisfactory. A few borderline samples gave trouble.

Standards for Sugar and Starch. Bigelow [49] included the National Canners Association standards for sugar in the report of analytical methods for its examination. Owen and Mobley [56] criticized these standards because they included only thermophiles. Since the microbial flora of refined cane sugars includes mesophilic and thermophilic sporeforming bacteria, yeasts, and molds, they believed the presence of any of these groups in large numbers was objectionable. Sugars are used in many ways, as in soft drinks, where a heavy microorganism contamination is undesirable. They proposed the following in addition to the National Canners Association standards for thermophiles.

1. The percentage of mold infection in any lot of sugar should not exceed 20.
2. Number of mold spores should never exceed 10.
3. Not more than 20 per cent should contain viable yeast cells.
4. Maximum of 50 yeast cells per gram.

55. Cameron. 1940. Assoc. Official Agr. Chem. J., Aug., 1940, 608-613.
56. Owen and Mobley. 1935. Facts About Sugar 30, 451-452.

5. Maximum number of bacteria other than thermophiles (already controlled) should not be over 50 and the maximum total count should be 100.

Owen and Mobley's standards have not received wide acceptance, especially by the National Canners Association, which still uses the following standards for thermophilic bacteria:

Total Thermophilic Spore Count: For the five samples examined there shall be a maximum of not more than 150 spores and an average of not more than 125 spores per 10 grams of sugar or starch.

Flat-Sour Spores: For the five samples examined there shall be a maximum of not more than 75 spores and an average of not more than 50 spores per 10 grams of starch or sugar.

Thermophilic Anaerobes: These shall be present in not more than three (60 per cent) of the five samples, and in any one sample there shall not be more than four (65 per cent) positive tubes.

Sulfide-Spoilage Spores: These shall be present in not more than two (40 per cent) of the five samples and in any one sample to the extent of not more than five colonies per 10 grams. This is equivalent to two colonies in the six tubes.

Effect of Storage on Thermophilic Bacteria in Sugar. Since this might be one way of meeting the problem if storage resulted in the death of spoilage bacteria, several bacteriologists analyzed stored sugar at intervals. Hall[57] did observe decrease in these spoilage bacteria in stored refined beet sugar. While the number of spoilage bacteria exceeded the standards in some cases, storage for several months often raised the quality to canning grade. In more work in which beet sugar was again used, Hall observed that thermophilic food-spoilage in beet sugar stored in paper, burlap, toweling, and glass containers generally decreased in numbers during storage for eight and 20 months. The type of container did not seem to influence survival of organisms in sugar during storage. Decreased spore counts probably resulted from dehydration caused by drying of sugar during manufacture or from the presence in sugar of hygroscopic impurities. Hall and Keane[58] found that many of the spores (47.8 per cent) of *Bacillus stearothermophilus* in sugar could be killed by ultraviolet light (2537Å). Hall's results were confirmed by Clark and Tanner, Jr.[29] Ten samples of sugar used in previous experiments were examined after six months' storage in sealed tin cans. The original counts on these samples were all within the limit set by the National Canners Association, ranging from 50 to 75 thermophilic flat-sour spores per 10 grams of sugar. The average for the 10 samples was 70. After storage no thermophilic flat-sour organisms could be isolated from three of the 10 samples. Counts ranged from 0 to 30 with an average of 15, or a reduction of from 40 to 100 per cent, the average reduction being 75 per cent. Thus the bacteriological quality of this sugar was improved by storage. An increase in the number

57. Hall. 1939. Food Research 4, 259-267; J. Bact. 35, 75.
58. Hall and Keane. 1939. Ind. Eng. Chem., 31, 1168-1170.

of spores never was observed. No attempt was made to determine the factors which cause the decrease.

The significance of bacteriological examination of and standards for sugar and similar substances is indicated by results which have been published in annual reports to the Research Committee of the National Canners Association. Extensive outbreaks of spoilage in certain canned foods have been proven to have been caused by contaminated sugar. To show the significance of sugar in canning Cameron and Yesair [59] packed three lots of corn as follows: one containing no sugar, the second with sugar considered suitable for canning, and the third with unsuitable sugar highly contaminated with thermophilic bacteria which spoil canned foods. The following results were secured:

Spoilage in No. 2 Cans of Corn Due to Presence of
Thermophilic Bacteria in Sugar
(After Cameron and Yesair, 1931)

Process at 121.1°C. (250°F.)	Per cent spoilage in corn with		
	No sugar	Sugar A	Sugar B
70 minutes	0	0	95.8
80 minutes	0	0	75.0
90 minutes	0	0	54.2

Sugar A—Suitable for canning nonacid products. "Flat-sour" count, 60 spores per 10 gms. of sugar.

Sugar B—Unsuitable for canning nonacid products. "Flat-sour" count 2,500 spores per 10 gms. of sugar.

Such results indicate the importance of using suitable sugar in canning non-acid products. Cameron and Williams [60] reported more convincing results on this subject.

MOLASSES AND SIRUPS

Many different kinds are available on the American market. They vary in quality from those which are by-products in the sugar-refining industry to those which are prepared from high-grade saccharine materials for special purposes. Much trouble has been caused by deterioration of molasses and sirups in barrels. In order to prevent such deterioration in sirups to be used on the table, they are processed in tin and glass containers.

While concentrated sugar solutions may function as preservatives, they are not sufficiently reliable to make it unnecessary to add any other preservative. Usually heat in addition is used. The sirups themselves are subject to spoilage by microorganisms. The raw sirups contain a wide variety of microorganisms among which are various yeasts. Hall, James, and Nelson [61] isolated *Zygosaccharomyces nussbaumeri*, *Zygosaccharomyces major*, and *Clostridium saccharolyticum* from cured Barbados molasses.

59. Cameron and Yesair. 1931. The Canner, March 21, 15-16.

60. Cameron and Williams. 1937. Ann. Rpt. to the Research Committee of 1936, Natl. Canners Assoc., Washington, D. C.

61. Hall, James, and Nelson. 1937. J. Bact. 33, 577-585.

Canning of Molasses and Sirups. The problems encountered in canning sirups are probably simpler than those encountered with vegetables. The raw material may be highly contaminated with many microorganisms which possess, in most cases, quite low heat resistance. This is especially true for yeasts which cause fermentation of sugar solutions. While these organisms possess low heat resistance according to the usual methods for determining it, they are frequently quite resistant when heated in sirups. It is known that heavy sirups are difficult to sterilize by heat. Much more heat is required to destroy microorganisms in sirups than in water. Rahn [62] showed this with yeasts. Since then others have confirmed it, using bacteria. Owen [63] made the same observation when studying causes of spoilage of canned sirup and molasses. Cultures in heavy sirup were reported to be more resistant to heat than in low concentration sirups. He also reported greater heat resistance in corn than in cane sirup. Further information on this subject is given in other places in this book.

Spoilage of Canned Sirups. This may be caused by both bacteriological and chemical processes. Microorganisms involved are those which can survive the processes given canned sirups and develop in heavy sugar sirups. Many cans of swelled cane molasses and mixtures with corn sirup were examined by Owen.[63] Even though the characteristics of the spoilage might have suggested fermentation by microorganisms the cause in many cases was not microbial. Torulae were bound to be the cause of fermentation spoilage. Thermal death times were determined by inoculating tubes of sterile cane sirup with a platinum loopful of growth from an agar slant culture. These tubes were heated in a water bath for varying lengths of time at different temperatures. The tubes were then incubated to permit viable cells to develop. Two of the cultures were found to be more heat resistant than the others. One withstood 76.6°C.(170°F.) for five minutes and the other 79.7°C.(175.5°F.) for 2.5 minutes. Owen then classified his cultures on the basis of their heat resistance, the variation between the two end groups being —3.8°C.(25°F.). Yeasts were observed to decrease progressively in numbers in sirup in which fermentation had occurred. This was shown to be due to carbon dioxide, resulting from fermentation.

The other type of spoilage to which canned sirups are especially susceptible is what Owen [63] called "spontaneous decomposition." It is to be distinguished from true fermentation by yeasts, although living yeast cells may be present in small numbers. A complicating factor is that composition of the gas is about the same in both cases. German technologists called this deterioration "Schaumgärung" or "frothy fermentation." Lueck [64] said it was especially common in such products as canned sirups, malt extract, and certain fruits packed in sirups. In general, it has all the evidences of bacterial spoilage but no bacteria.

Development of molds on the surface of sirups in bottles has caused some trouble. Investigation of one sirup packing plant by Ayers and

62. Rahn. 1928. Canning Age, Aug., 1928, 705-706.
63. Owen. 1926. Facts About Sugar, Oct. 2, 1926, 946-949; Food Indus. 1 (1929), 156-158.
64. Lueck. 1925. Canning Age, Dec., 1925.

Barnby [65] revealed the necessity of filling bottles with hot sirup at a temperature of at least 87.7°C.(190°F.), then sealing at once with cork shells and glass stoppers which have been steamed for 20 minutes at atmospheric pressure. Following sealing, the bottles should be laid on their sides in order that the neck and stoppers will be subjected to as high a temperature as possible. Ayers and Barnby gave curves showing the rate of cooling of sirups in bottles. The temperature and time required to destroy mold spores in sirup was 73.8°C.(165°F.) for five minutes for the conditions under which they worked.

Maple Sugar and Other Products. This carbohydrate is secured from the genus *Acer*, the sap of which is collected after tapping and concentrated by heating. The sap contains from two to three per cent of sucrose with traces of invert sugar. During the early part of the season the sap is clear and sweet, but as the season progresses, especially at the end, it becomes cloudy and may possess bitter principles. This is often called green sap and does not make good sirup or sugar. Besides the content of sucrose, sap contains other bodies which function in supplying the tree with food.

Great improvements have been introduced into the manufacture of maple sugar. Introduction of the evaporator allowed concentration of each day's run of sap, giving a better and clearer sugar and sirup, since the older boiling method made it necessary to hold the sap from large runs until it could be boiled down in the pan. This gave time for the development of bacteria.

The effect of microorganisms on the keeping quality of sap was studied by Edson.[66] He sterilized bottles of sap by the intermittent method and kept it for months, the flavor remaining unchanged during that time. That which was not sterilized became cloudy and soured very quickly. Edson carefully collected sap under sterile conditions and stated that the souring of sap was not due to auto-decomposition but to the ingress of extraneous organisms; sap collected under aseptic conditions remained sterile. Souring of sap was found to be due to many common bacteria, a few yeasts, and molds.

Sour Sap. This type of spoilage probably includes all decompositions which do not have pronounced characteristics such as a strong color or strong odor. Chemical composition of sap makes it an ideal medium in which microorganisms develop. On nutrient agar, Edson found as many as 141,420,000 bacteria per milliliter in sap. In sweet maple sap the number was much lower. Utensils were found to be important in spreading infection.

Stringy Sap. Edson isolated several organisms which caused a stringy consistency when inoculated into sterile sap. The causal organism was named *Bacillus aceris* since it did not seem to possess characteristics similar to any other described organism. It was capsulated and to this its ability to cause ropiness may be attributed.

Green Sap. Sap which possessed a greenish or brownish-green color was found to contain bacteria of several different types. The organisms were subjected to very careful study later by Edson and Carpenter [67] and found to be members of the *Pseudomonas fluorescens* group. This type of sap is commonly called "buddy" sap

65. Ayers and Barnby. 1926. Glass Container, July, 1926.
66. Edson. 1910. Vermont Agr. Expt. Sta. Bull. 151.
67. Edson and Carpenter. 1912. Vermont Agr. Expt. Sta. Bull. 167.

since it is believed by some to be related to the development of the tree in the spring. The green color, however, is due to microorganisms and not to any natural process in the tree.

Red Sap. This color was imparted to sap by bacteria which formed a red pigment. They were said to be widely distributed in the sugar woods. Along with these organisms were yeasts and yeast-like fungi.

Standard maple sirup keeps quite well but it must have between 65 and 67 per cent sugar solids. Such sirup will weight 11 pounds to the gallon. When sugar content exceeds this amount crystallization may occur. Maple sirup spoilage has been shown to be caused by several types of microorganisms. Fabian and Buskirk [68] isolated bacteria from the sap of *Acer saccharum* which, when inoculated into sterile sap or into dilute maple sirup, produced ropy maple sirup upon concentration of the sap to the consistency of sirup. Since these bacteria were isolated from the sap from which the ropy maple sirup was produced in the sugar bush, they were considered responsible for the condition. Morphological, physiological, and cultural characteristics of the bacteria responsible for this condition, corresponded in all essential details to those of *Aerobacter aerogenes*. Addition of acetic acid sufficient to cause approximately the acidity found in fermented sap did not influence the consistency of the evaporated sap. The addition of a similar quantity of lactic acid did influence the consistency of the sirup. Neutralizing the acidity of fermented sap somewhat reduced the ropy condition of the concentrated sap.

Yeasts were found to cause fermentation of maple sirup by Fabian and Hall.[69] On the basis of morphological, cultural, and physiological characteristics, they were divided into seven groups as follows: *Saccharomyces aceris-sacchari; Saccharomyces behrensianus* (Behrens) Klocker; *Saccharomyces monacensis* Hansen; *Zygosaccharomyces mellis* Fabian and Quinet; *Zygosaccharomyces barkeri* (Barer) Sac. & Syd.; *Zygosaccharomyces japonicus* Saito; and *Zygosaccharomyces nussbaumeri* Lochhead & Heron. Vegetative cells were killed in nutrient broth at 55°C.(131°F.) in five minutes and in maple sirup in five to 10 minutes at 60°C.(140°F.). In most cases ascospores were killed in nutrient broth at 65°C.(149°F.) in five minutes and in maple sirup at 75°C.(167°F.) in five minutes. The moisture content of freshly made maple sirup was 26.3 to 36.5 per cent. Samples of fermented maple sirup contained 32.7 to 34.6 per cent moisture.

Canned Maple Sirup. Maple sirup has been sold in tin cans for many years but the cans were never sealed as cans for other foods have been. After studying the problem Fellers [70] believed there should be no difficulty. Plain cans kept maple sirup about as well as did enameled cans. Fellers found, for instance, that U. S. Grade No. 1 sirup, which has a light amber color, was still classified in the same grade after eight months of storage. There was a tendency for heated sirup to become darker. Processing in boiling water produced a slight darkening which was not serious. One of the significant observations by Fellers, was that if the sirup is filled

68. Fabian and Buskirk. 1935. Ind. Eng. Chem. 27, 349-350.
69. Fabian and Hall. 1933. Zentbl. f. Bakt., Pt. 2, 89, 31-47.
70. Fellers. 1935. The Canner, April 20, 1935, 13-14.

into the cans at 93.3°C.(200°F.) or above, no further processing was necessary. As small headspace as possible should be left in the can in order to reduce the amount of free oxygen present.

Spoilage of Maple Products by Molds. Development of molds in maple products, if allowed to continue, soon results in off-flavors. Fellers [71] reported that Aspergillus species grew well in tub maple sugar containing from five to 12 per cent of moisture. Such maple sugar often becomes moist and semiliquid owing to the inverting action of invertase on a part of the sucrose. The "sweating" or runny condition of maple sugar was attributed by Fellers to this action. Both mold growth and invertase action are accelerated by high temperatures. Mold spores are unable to survive the concentration methods used in making maple sugar and probably get into the sugar from utensils after it has been made. Fellers recommended the Howard method for determining whether molds are present in the sugar.

HONEY

Honey is probably the first sweetening agent used by man. It is frequently mentioned in the scriptures and the types of yeast cells found in bread from Egyptian tombs indicate that honey was probably used in its manufacture. Undiluted honey is quite resistant to decomposition by ordinary microorganisms. If it is diluted with water some microorganisms may start to decompose it. As Fabian and Quinet [72] suggested, organisms take up their abode on the surface where perhaps water from the air has diluted the honey. These organisms also become accustomed to a higher concentration of sugar and in time are able to induce an active fermentation.

Microorganisms in Honey. While comb honey may contain a few microorganisms, White [73] and Sackett [74] have reported it to be sterile most of the time. The former, according to Sackett, isolated Bacillus A *(Bacillus mesentericus)*, *Bacterium acidiformans*, and *Saccharomyces rosens* from combs. Sackett examined comb honey from many different sources and found it to be uniformly sterile.

Schweizer [75] found practically all Swiss honeys to be free from bacteria, as were also several of French origin. Many Swiss honeys as well as several foreign brands were examined bacteriologically. It was concluded that a bacteriological examination does not show the origin of the honey. Fehlmann [76] reported the presence of *Pleurococcus vulgaris*, a green alga, in honey in Switzerland. This organism is apparently able to withstand the concentrated carbohydrate solution in honey. Sartory and Moreau [77] examined honeys from various sources and found *Bacillus subtilis, Bacillus megaterium, Bacillus aerophilus, Sarcina lutea, Micrococcus radiatus, Staphylococcus pyogenes, Penicillium glaucum, Rhizopus nigricans, Sac-*

71. Fellers. 1933. J. Bact. 25, 67.
72. Fabian and Quinet. 1928. Mich. Agr. Expt. Sta., Tech. Bull. 92.
73. White. 1906. U. S. Dept. Agr. Bur. Ent., Tech. Bull. 14.
74. Sackett. 1919. Colorado Agr. Expt. Sta. Bull. 252.
75. Schweizer. 1928. Mitt. aus dem Geb. der Lebensmtl. Untersuch. u. Hyg. 19, 117-125.
76. Fehlmann. 1911. Idem 2, 179-208; 220-271.
77. Sartory and Moreau. 1911. Ann. des Falsif. 4, 259-263.

charomyces cerevisiae, Mucor racemosus, Aspergillus gracilis, Sterigmato-cystes nigra, pink yeast, etc. Among various microorganisms a yellow bacillus was isolated which produced a coloring matter at an optimum of 30°C.(86°F.) slightly soluble in absolute alcohol. Its color was changed to a yellow-brown by the addition of alkali, but when acidified it resumed its original shade. The bacillus was placed in a class with *Bacillus luteus* and *Bacillus flavus.*

Longevity of Microorganisms in Honey. This has been investigated mainly for pathogenic bacteria. One investigator was prompted to study the problem because he saw bees crawling over human excrement. It seemed desirable to know how long objectionable bacteria could survive in honey. Little information if any was available on this question until Sackett[74] reported results of quite extensive experiments with new fall honey and fall honey six months old. In the former *Eberthella typhosa* survived for only 48 hours. In dilutions above 50 per cent, it was dead after 24 hours. After four days it was alive only in the control which contained no honey. In the second series, *Eberthella typhosa* was not present in the pure honey after 24 hours and was absent from dilutions above 50 per cent in 10 hours. After 24 hours it had disappeared from 30, 40, and 50 per cent dilution; and after 48 and 72 hours it was no longer present in the 20 and 10 per cent dilutions. *Salmonella schottmülleri* was very sensitive. It disappeared from pure honey in 48 hours and from dilutions above 30 per cent in 24 hours. In the second series, it was dead in 24 hours in pure honey and after 10 hours in all dilutions above 20 per cent. *Salmonella paratyphi* in the first series, exhibited about the same resistance as *Salmonella schottmülleri*. It was dead after 24 hours in pure honey and in all dilutions above 30 per cent. *Eberthella dysenteriae* could not survive in pure honey nor in dilutions above 40 per cent after 10 hours. In the second series it was dead after 10 hours in pure honey and had disappeared in five hours from all dilutions above 20 per cent. Sackett's results are somewhat different from what would be expected, for pure honey is a very highly concentrated sugar solution. Sackett discussed the situation as follows:

The failure of the organisms to die out as readily in concentrated honey as in the dilutions was rather interesting. A possible explanation of this suggests itself in the physical state of the sugar particle in the honey. Assuming the honey to have been a saturated solution, and this appears to have been the case, there is a probability that it was a colloidal solution with low osmotic pressure. In such a solution plasmolysis would take place relatively slow. When water was added, as in the dilutions, some of the colloidal sugar passed over into molecular solution, the osmotic pressure increased, and plasmolysis became more active.

Sackett's results were confirmed in general by Schett.[78] He found that pathogenic bacteria did not survive long times in honey. While Schett did not attribute this to a definite germicidal action, others have said that such action was observed and have described the germicidal substance. Such a substance was said to exist by Prica.[79] Neither acidity nor sugar content could explain the bactericidal action. The active principle was

78. Schett. 1937. Ztschr. f. Hyg. u. Infektionskrank. 120, 155.
79. Prica. 1938. Ztschr. f. Hyg. u. Infektionskrank. 120, 437-443.

filterable, resistant to sunlight, withstood heating to 90°C.(194°F.) for one hour, but was partially destroyed by boiling for five minutes. Whether it came from flowers or bees was not determined. Prica [79] carried out his experiments with *Escherichia coli* and *Staphylococcus aureus*. Work by Bahr [80] also seemed to indicate presence of a germicidal substance in honey. "Linden-tree," clover, and sage honey from New Zealand and California showed greater effectiveness against "Ratinbacillus" *(Salmonella enteriditis)* than manufactured honey. Heat seemed to decrease the strength of the substance.

Fermentation of Honey. Honey is susceptible to fermentation by various microorganisms. These may be incorporated in the honey by the bees or may come from contaminated utensils. In some cases the bees contaminate the honey in the comb with yeasts so that it ferments and disrupts the cells. Bees are known to harbor yeasts. One of the best known organisms in this respect is *Zygosaccharomyces mellis acidi* Richter. The honey from which Richter [81] isolated this yeast had undergone an alcoholic fermentation. Klöcker [82] isolated *Zygosaccharomyces prioranus* from a bee. White [73] isolated several species of yeasts from bees. Ewert [83] stated that yeasts were present in honey and could cause spoilage. Nussbaumer [84] found several species of Zygosaccharomycetes in numerous samples of honey, the sources of which were unknown. Fabian and Quinet [72] isolated 25 yeasts from honey, both normal and abnormal. These investigators put their yeasts into five groups, as follows:

Group	I.	*Zygosaccharomyces japonicus*, Saito
	II.	*Zygosaccharomyces Barkeri*
	III.	*Zygosaccharomyces mellis*, Fabian and Quinet
	IV.	*Zygosaccharomyces prioranus*
	V.	*Torula mellis*, Fabian and Qinet.

Vegetative cells of Zygosaccharomyces were killed at 50°C.(122°F.) for 10 minutes in broth; vegetative cells of Torulae were killed at 50°C. in 15 minutes. In honey, vegetative cells of Zygosaccharomyces were killed at 60°(140°F.) in five minutes and Torulae at 60°C.(140°F.) in 10 minutes. Honey is quite hydroscopic and may absorb enough water to ferment. Fabian and Quinet found the critical concentration to be about 21 per cent. They believed that honey could absorb enough water at the surface to allow fermentation to begin. Yeasts then gradually become accustomed to the higher sugar concentration and eventually grow throughout the honey. Very interesting are the data reported by Lochhead and McMaster,[85] that sugar-tolerant yeasts were found to be present in all of 191 samples of Canadian honey. The number varied greatly, however, with an average count of 1,000 per gram. Yeast infection was believed to be a factor directly affecting fermentation of honey. Although the yeast count tended

80. Bahr. 1934. Berlin. Tierärztl. Wchnschr. 50, 321-324.
81. Richter. 1912. Mycol. Centbl. 7, 67-76.
82. Klöcker. 1907. Handbuch. tech. Mykol. 4, 141-191.
83. Ewert. 1925. (Quoted from Fabian and Quinet.)
84. Nussbaumer. 1910. Ztschr. f. Untersuch. der Nähr. u. Genussmtl.
85. Lochhead and McMaster. 1931. Sci. Agr. 11, 351-360.

to increase with increasing moisture content, fermentation was not considered to be merely a function of the latter.

At the University of Wisconsin, Marvin [86] studied the yeasts in fermented honey. Five strains were isolated, all of which were able to grow in concentrated solutions of honey. Marvin reported that undesirable flavor of fermented honey was due to alcohol, nonvolatile acids, and carbon dioxide. Marvin further reported that honey which was to be sold in small containers should be heated to 71.1°C.(160°F.) and sealed while hot. Prompt cooling was advised in order not to affect the color. Unheated honey should be stored below 11.1°C.(52°F.) to prevent fermentation. Marvin believed that crystallization of honey made it more possible for yeasts to ferment it, which was later confirmed by Marvin, Peterson, Fred, and Wilson.[87] The fermentation process was said to be slow and to extend in some cases over several years. About equal quantities of carbon dioxide and alcohol (rarely over five per cent) together with nonvolatile acids are the chief fermentation products. They stated that fermentation of honey could be prevented by heating it to 71.1°C.(160°F.), pailing while hot, and, after cooling, storing below 11.1°C.(52°F.). Townsend [68] believed that lower times and temperatures could be used than would be expected.

A number of pure yeast cultures were isolated from fermented honey by Lochhead and Heron.[69] Early work indicated the presence of osmophilic yeasts which could not develop in low concentration. They showed, in a striking manner, the differences in tolerance to honey of species responsible for fermentation of honey and ordinary species. Four pure cultures of yeasts were isolated for intensive study. Two of them were believed to be new species and were named *Zygosaccharomyces nussbaumeri* and *Zygosaccharomyces richteri*. The descriptions of these two species are given by the authors. In order to determine the possible origin of sugar-tolerant yeasts, Lochhead and Heron examined 34 kinds of flowers commonly visited by bees during a season. Eleven different yeasts which were able to ferment high concentrations of honey were isolated and described. Two of them proved to·be identical with types found in fermented honey. Another type was identical with Fabian and Quinet's *Torula mellis*. Examination of the hives for sugar-tolerant yeasts indicated a constant and early infection. Soil from about the hives were found by Lochhead and Farrell [90] to harbor the above-mentioned organisms. Ordinary field soil is not a primary source of infection of honey, for sugar-tolerant yeasts are not regarded as members of the normal soil microflora. Sugar-tolerant yeasts, in apiary soils, are able to remain viable through the winter in frozen soil, but are cold-enduring rather than psychrophilic. From the soil 166 cultures of sugar-tolerant yeasts belonging to Zygosaccharomyces and Torulae, were isolated and classified. These were found to represent seven types considered as six species with one subspecies, three being types found in fermented honey.

86. Marvin. 1927. J. Econ. Ent. 21, 363-370; 23 (1928), 431-438.
87. Marvin *et al.* 1931. J. Agr. Res., 43, 121-131.
88. Townsend. 1939. J. Econ. Ent. 32, 650-654.
89. Lochhead and Heron. 1929. Canad. Dept. Agr. Bull. 116.
90. Lochhead and Farrell. 1930. Canad. J. Res. 3, 51-64.

A study of the predominant sugar-tolerant yeasts infecting 163 samples of normal Canadian honey, by Lochhead and Farrell,[91] led to recognition of eight species, comprising the genera Zygosaccharomyces, Schizosaccharomyces, and Torula. The frequency of their occurrence varied greatly, *Zygosaccharomyces dichteri* being by far the most commonly encountered. The yeast predominating originally is not necessarily the most abundant type for fermentation. Analysis of samples fermenting within 14 months showed species of Zygosaccharomyces only to be most abundant, while *Zygosaccharomyces richteri*, in addition to being the predominant type infecting a large majority of samples, was able, even in certain cases where it was originally outnumbered, to develop and apparently assume the leading role in fermentation. Later work by Lochhead [92] in which 128 samples of normal honey were examined, showed the presence of sugar-tolerant yeast in all cases, confirming a previous study of 191 samples. Yeast counts were one to 1,000,000 per gram. The tendency of honey to ferment within one year increased with increased yeast infection. The view that the amount of yeast infection, apart from moisture, is a factor directly affecting fermentation was confirmed. Although the honeys varied in their content of so-called "bioactivator," capable of stimulating the activity of osmophilic yeasts, this factor is not considered significant in affecting the spoilage of honey under practical conditions. Fermentation is conditioned essentially by the moisture and yeast infection of honey, and a zone of probable safety with respect to these factors is indicated.

Heat resistance of strains of yeasts isolated from honey by Lochhead and Farrell [93] was determined by Stephens [94] by heavily inoculating sterile honey. Since investigations had revealed no more than 100,000 yeast cells per gram in Canadian honey, Stephens tried to approximate this number. Owing to ability of some species of yeasts to withstand considerable heat in honey, and absence of any necessity to destroy all living cells, Stephens suggested the term "commercial sterility" for use in honey pasteurization. Based on experimental data, Stephens stated that it would require one hour and 40 minutes to five hours and 30 minutes to reduce the count to less than 10 yeast cells per milliliter at 50°C.(122°F.) depending on the species and the initial inoculation. Curves in Stephen's paper show that rates of death of different species vary greatly. At 60°C.(140°F.) the time necessary to obtain "commercial sterility" would be less than 30 minutes. Stephens believed that to attain "commercial sterility" by flash pasteurization a temperature near 80°C.(176°F.) would have to be used, the exact temperature depending on the time necessary to bring the honey to that temperature.

Effect of Preservatives on Fermentation of Honey by Yeasts. Investigations by Lochhead and Farrell [95] have resulted in information on this subject. Various preservatives were used, but since sodium benzoate is the

91. Lochhead and Farrell. 1931. Canad. J. Res. 5, 655-672.
92. Lochhead. 1933. Zentbl. f. Bakt., Pt. 2, 88, 296-302.
93. Lochhead and Farrell. 1931. Canad. J. Res. 5, 665-672.
94. Stephens. 1942. Sci. Agr. 22, 705-720.
95. Lochhead and Farrell. 1931. Canad. J. Res. 5, 529-538; Food Research 1 (1936), 517-524.

only one in the group which is permitted in foods, only the results secured with it need be given. It was found to exert a repressing effect on the growth of yeasts and to be without effect on the flavor of the honey. Later these investigators reported that in 80 per cent honey solution containing 64 per cent of sugar, .05 per cent of sodium benzoate, calculated as benzoic acid, was the lowest effective concentration for killing the osmophilic yeast, *Zygosaccharomyces nussbaumeri* within 26 weeks. For inhibition of fermentation a concentration of .04 per cent was sufficient. With sodium hydrogen sulfite ($NaHSO_3$), .02 per cent, calculated as sulfur dioxide, was the minimum lethal concentration as well as the lowest which inhibited fermentation during the same period. The effect of these substances in retarding fermentation by mixed strains of *Zygosaccharomyces nussbaumeri* is increased with increasing sugar concentration. When added to freshly extracted honey .025 per cent of sodium benzoate and .01 per cent of sodium sulfite (Na_2SO_3) were effective in preventing fermentation during storage.

CANDY

Candy is a product which may easily be contaminated by indifferent methods of preparation but especially from insanitary conditions of handling. The prevalent custom of wrapping smaller pieces has contributed to a much safer and cleaner product. The Food and Drug Administration [96] has studied the conditions which obtain in the confectioner's industry. They recognize that candies may be objectionable owing to improper storage conditions, remanufacture of returned goods, and manufacture from unfit material. The Bureau recognized improper storage conditions as one of the important common sources of adulteration.

Microorganisms in Candies and Confections. The types and numbers are influenced by such factors as microbial content of raw materials, methods of manufacture, and vending. Our information comes mainly from a few investigations, results of which have been published.

Tanner and Davis [97] investigated the sanitary condition of candies purchased on the open market. Coliform bacteria were not encountered in any of 30 specimens examined. Bacteria in candy were said to be in a dormant condition. Sporeforming bacteria predominated. On account of these facts, candy which might be contaminated by a carrier could be a source of danger. The number of bacteria per gram was found to be variable and probably dependent on conditions in the factory, methods of manufacture, and especially the raw materials and flavors used. As Bachman has reported, Tanner and Davis found a distinct germicidal action in such varieties as cinnamon drops and mint candies. These species have been found to destroy bacteria.

A more comprehensive study of this question was reported by Weinzirl,[98] who examined 1,138 specimens purchased on the open market. Coliform bacteria were found on 2.5 per cent of the samples. Many of

96. Food and Drug Administration Ann. Rpt., 1938, p. 10; also for 1939, p. 14.
97. Tanner and Davis. 1922. Amer. J. Pub. Health 12, 605.
98. Weinzirl. 1927. Amer. J. Pub. Health 17, 708-711.

these instances occurred with candies containing unsterile ingredients, such as nuts. The bacteria belonging to the coliform group were mostly atypical. Typical *Escherichia coli* or *Escherichia communior* were found but twice in 525 samples. Weinzirl stated that danger of candy carrying disease-producing bacteria can readily be eliminated by sterilizing the materials from which it is made and by using sanitary devices for handling. These data indicate that candy may carry undesirable bacteria and that it should be handled with the same care that is given to other foods. Such was the suggestion of Greaves.[99] She analyzed 200 samples of candy and found the bacterial content to vary with (1) type of store from which it was obtained, (2) type of candy, (3) wrapped or unwrapped condition, and (4) nature of the centers of the candy. Poorly kept stores, conducted by careless individuals, dispensed candy with a high bacterial content, and in a large percentage of cases acid-producing organisms were present. Sanitary conditions of the store and clerk were more important factors in determining bacterial contamination than type of store. Handmade candies were usually found to be higher in bacterial content than machine-made candies. Soft and nut-containing candies were usually higher in bacterial content than were hard candies and those free from nuts. Careless methods of displaying candies increased the bacterial content. Candies which dry rapidly decrease in bacterial content quite rapidly when exposed to light and air. More bacteria were found in the centers than on the surface. Quite similar results were secured by Ciampi[100] and Driml[101] from examination of these products made in foreign countries.

About the same bacteriological condition was found to exist in candies purchased on the American market by Tanner and Snyder[102] during the year 1939. Coliform bacteria were not found in any of the samples examined. Wrapped products usually had fewer bacteria as did hard candies which are heated to high temperatures during manufacture. Those products to which raisins, fruits, and nuts are added may have have many bacteria. Tanner and Snyder examined many samples of various kinds of candies for mesophilic and thermophilic bacteria growing aerobically and anaerobically. The chocolate products contained, in general, more microorganisms.

Longevity of Microorganisms in Candy. Cummins[103] investigated the death rate of different pathogenic bacteria in candy. Information of a general nature was given regarding the importance of the confectionery industry and its sanitary aspects. Only chocolate-coated candies were used. The methods of their manufacture were discussed briefly in so far as they influenced the sanitary quality of the finished product. A few data were given, showing the bacterial content of various raw materials used in the manufacture of chocolates. In the experiments a mixture of sugar, chocolate, and milk powder was prepared. After being sterilized,

99. Greaves. 1930. Western Hosp. Rev. 15, 32-37.
100. Ciampi. 1933. Igiene Moderna, May 25, 175.
101. Driml. 1929. Spisy Lekarske Masarykovy. Univ. Brne 7, 1-36.
102. Tanner and Snyder. 1940. Proc. Inst. Food Tech., 307-321.
103. Cummins. 1915. Amer. J. Pub. Health 5, 1148-1163.

portions of this were inoculated with cultures of different types of bacteria. The inoculated portions were stored at approximately 20°C. (68°F.) and samples were taken from them at stated intervals for bacteriological examination.

The organisms used were *Eberthella typhosa, Escherichia coli, Hemophilus pertussis,* and *Mycobacterium tuberculosis.* A study of the effect of hand and machine methods of dipping chocolates upon the bacterial content showed that in almost every instance machine-dipped chocolates contained fewer bacteria than hand-dipped ones. Little or no increase in the number of bacteria originally present took place in the case of machine-dipped chocolates. In general, it was found that the raw materials, especially chocolate, are the sources of a large number of the bacteria present in chocolate candies. The experiments with *Hemophilus pertussis* showed that within a few hours after inoculation, these organisms ceased to be present in the candy. In the opinion of the author, there was little possibility of the transmission of whooping cough by candy infected in the factory. Although the results obtained with *Mycobacterium tuberculosis* were regarded as unsatisfactory, they indicated slight possibility of surviving for a long time in chocolate. After a long period of storage, it was possible to isolate *Eberthella typhosa* from the inoculated candy; the results indicated that there was a possibility of typhoid fever being transmitted by infected candy in case a worker should be a carrier. It was found also that members of the coliform group survived for a long time, and the results of the experiments indicated that after being inoculated into candy these organisms would probably find their way into the body through this source. The death rate of the organisms seemed to be somewhat related to the amount of water present in the candy. In a candy of high water content the bacteria died out faster than in one with low water content.

Longevity studies were also made by Tanner and Snyder,[102] using fondant and fudge. They observed a regular decrease in viable bacteria which were inoculated into fondant and fudge. Since they died faster in the latter, it was believed that chocolate might have had a repression effect on the bacteria which were used. Candies to which nuts and similar fillings were added often contained many bacteria. *Escherichia coli* was not found in any market samples.

Bursting or Explosion of Chocolate Creams. This deterioration of chocolate-coated creams was studied by Church, Paine, and Hamilton.[104] They believed that constitution of the fondant made possible the growth of spoilage organisms. This was described as a cream or a sirup enveloping closely packed particles of microscopic crystals of sucrose and fragments of coagulated egg white. Each sugar crystal was said to have a thin film of sirup about it. The small particles of egg white furnish protein for the bacteria which may be present. Many inoculations were made into fondant and chocolate creams. This work resulted in conclusions that yeasts tolerant of high percentages of sugar in sirup, are capable of caus-

104. Church *et al.* 1927. Ind. Eng. Chem. 19, 353.

ing bursting of chocolate-coated creams and that bursting is primarily due to formation of minute quantities of gas in the cream through microbial activity. The yeasts obtained from exploded commercially-manufactured confections were of different types. Church, Paine, and Hamilton believed that some means must be devised in candy factories to develop a cream containing sirup of high density.

Weinzirl [105] quoted an article in the Western Confectioner, July, 1920, by J. P. Hill, as stating that explosion of chocolate-coated candy was due to *Escherichia coli*. Weinzirl found *Clostridium sporogenes* to be the chief cause of the trouble, but that yeasts could also cause it. He could find no evidence that *Escherichia coli* was involved. The source of the infection was found in egg albumen which was being used. Weinzirl [106] stated that sugar itself was the source of anaerobes also. Thirty-three samples were analyzed; anaerobes were reported in 85 per cent of the 330 gram samples tested. Five types of anaerobes were found: *Clostridium sporogenes, Clostridium putrificum, Clostridium aerofetidum* and two unidentified strains. Sugar seemed to be a source of the organisms causing explosions of chocolate candy. Hill [107] isolated a saccharolytic anaerobe thought to be *Cl. multifermentans* from 11 out of 24 samples of chocolate creams which had spoiled through cracking. The organism was also isolated three times from mazetto cream, a commercial preparation used in confectionery as a foundation for cream fillings, and three times from egg albumen. The inoculation of 15 samples of unspoiled chocolate creams with a pure culture of the organism caused splitting in nine cases. The cultural and morphological characteristics of the organism were outlined. According to Philbrick,[108] one cause of cracked or blown chocolate creams was a facultative anaerobic bacillus capable of fermenting dextrose. The bacillus probably entered through some one of the ingredients, but it was difficult to establish which was the infecting material as the spoilage was often not apparent until the materials had been consumed in the factory process. On the other hand, examination of the molding starch generally showed the presence of the organism. In this manner, the starch acted as a secondary infecting agent long after the original had been eliminated by use. The infected starch should be discarded to effect a complete and final elimination of the infection. Starch was also said to be the source of gas-forming bacteria by Stapp[109] who studied the cause of bursting chocolate-covered confections. Besides molds, sporeforming rods which fermented glucose, fructose, and cane sugar were present.

Paine, Birckner, and Hamilton [110] stated that only a small amount of gas was needed to break the chocolate. When this does occur, a sirup exudes through the opening. When considerable gas is formed, the entire center may protrude. They stated that the density of the sirup in fondant

105. Weinzirl. 1922. Absts. Bact. 6, 26.
106. Weinzirl. 1926. J. Bact. 11, 100.
107. Hill. 1925. J. Bact. 10, 413-420.
108. Philbrick. 1925. J. Bact. 12, 275-278.
109. Stapp. 1927. Mitt. Ges. Vorratsschultz 3, 67-68.
110. Paine, Brickner, and Hamilton. 1927. Confectioner 7, 28-29.

may vary widely, but that it was possible to produce a sirup of sufficiently high density to inhibit the growth of even those yeasts which are tolerant of high sugar concentrations. This is apparently the only alternative since it seems to be impossible to get rid of the undesirable bacteria. Paine and Hamilton [111] suggested the use of invertase for controlling inversion of a part of the sucrose after the goods are made. It was found that fermentation of even highly sugar-tolerant yeasts could be controlled in a practical manner by increasing the solids concentration of the sirup portion to about 79 per cent with invertase.

111. Paine and Hamilton. 1924. U. S. Patent 1,502,207.

CHAPTER 20

MICROBIOLOGY OF FISH AND SHELLFISH

Flesh of various animals which live in the sea has become an important food in most nations. Better methods of preservation are making it possible for inland communities to be supplied with sea foods. Owing to the fact that fish muscle is susceptible to both enzymic and bacterial decomposition, problems of preservation have required much study. Related to these problems of preservation are those of sanitation to insure not only a product which has no gross evidence of decomposition but which is free from contamination with undesirable bacteria. Fishermen try to accomplish these ends by icing the fish immediately after they are caught and handling as carefully as possible. Increased markets resulting to some extent from more satisfactory methods of preservation, have made it necessary to use fishing grounds farther and farther removed. This means longer trips and longer holding periods.

Many fish are now gutted at sea soon after they are caught. Fitzgerald and Conway [1] pointed out that this practice contaminates all surfaces of the opened fish with many bacteria; special care is therefore necessary to hold the fish in good condition. Such surface contamination may be removed by thorough washing and scaling when the fish is filleted. Wash water may contain from one to two parts per million of chlorine to keep the water sterile. Fitzgerald and Conway believed this to be about the only reason for using chlorine in wash water. *Escherichia coli* was not removed from whole fish by soaking in chlorine wash water for two minutes. Scaling and washing removed many bacteria. One gains the impression that sanitation of a plant in which fish is prepared for the market, involves generous use of water and chlorine compounds. Gibbs [2] reported that on English fishing boats, calcium hypochlorite has been incorporated into the ice used for holding fish. This compound used in this manner was said to have marked germicidal and preservative action. One part in 400 parts of water before freezing seemed to be most active. This compound has also been used as such in the fish industry. Harrison and Sadler [3] found calcium hypochlorite in ice to be beneficial in destruction of a fluorescent organism which caused spoilage. Chen and Fellers [4] prepared sodium hypochlorite electrolytically. Experiments with eulachon (Columbia river smelt) and halibut showed that immersion in sodium hypochlorite containing .6 per cent of available chlorine for five minutes materially reduced the number of bacteria and enhanced the keeping quality. Solutions with less than .2 per cent of available chlorine were ineffective. Eulachon were unaffected as to color, odor, and taste; halibut, however, became yellowish, and attempts to prevent it were negative. Sodium hypochlorite

1. Fitzgerald and Conway. 1937. Amer. J. Pub. Health 27, 1094-1101.
2. Gibbs. 1923. Bd. Gt. Brit. Canadian Fisherman 10, 99.
3. Harrison and Sadler. 1929. Food Indus., 1, 308-312; Biol. Bd. of Canada Bull. 12.
4. Chen and Fellers. 1926. Univ. of Wash., Pub. Fisheries 1, 205-27.

ice containing .6 to .2 per cent of available chlorine acted like sodium hypochlorite when it melted. Chen and Fellers believed that the use of such ice was beneficial and should have wide application.

Production and distribution of crustacean meats has become a great industry. Hunter [5] has pointed out how many sources of contamination exist in the picking, handling, and packing which might be dangerous to human beings. Aside from sanitary inspections Hunter favored bacteriological procedures and development of a standard method of procedure. He reported that the Food and Drug Administration accepted the presence of *Escherichia coli* as satisfactory evidence of danger to health. Ordinary cooking, according to Nickerson, Fitzgerald, and Messer [6] does not eliminate all fecal organisms. Pressure cooking is satisfactory. They found chlorine treatment to be useful for utensils and apparatus.

Sterility of Fresh Fish Muscle. Whether fresh fish muscle contains viable microorganisms is still a debated question despite the fact that it has been studied by many investigators. Harrison, Perry, and Smith [7] studied the question for haddock, mackerel, and halibut. Their specimens were carefully caught and handled. Using very careful technic, examination of eight fresh haddock indicated the tissue to be sterile. With these conclusions, those of Gee [8] are in disagreement. Gee removed specimens of muscle from fish under as carefully controlled conditions as possible and was able to culture an aerobic sporeforming organism from fresh muscle. The organism was quite pleomorphic and was believed to have an important share in the breakdown of haddock muscular tissue. Bruns [9] believed that fish muscle was sterile for several days after death if properly preserved on ice. Browne [10] also reported the tissue of fresh fish to be sterile. Ulrich [11] found members of the coliform and Proteus groups in fish. Muller [12] could not find bacteria and, consequently, concluded that fish tissue was sterile. Hunter [13] found the muscular tissue of freshly caught salmon to be sterile.

In view of the fact that Gee reported sporebearing bacteria to be commonly present in fish muscle, and in view of the fact that such bacteria were found to be absent in the slime on market fish, Stewart,[14] also, was prompted to study sterility of fish muscle. Working with eight fish, Stewart was unable to confirm Gee's conclusions. Five of 143 cultures prepared from fish muscle showed growth. These were attributed to contaminated specimens. This seems to be an arbitrary conclusion. Gee [15] published more evidence that muscle tissue of live fish is not necessarily sterile, organisms being obtained from five of 41 fish. On the other hand, Proctor

5. Hunter. 1934. Amer. J. Pub. Health 24, 199-202.
6. Nickerson *et al.* 1939. Idem 29, 619-627.
7. Harrison, Perry, and Smith. 1926. Canad. Fisherman 14, 99.
8. Gee. 1927. J. Infect. Dis., 41, 355-364.
9. Bruns. 1909. Arch. f. Hyg., 67, 209-236.
10. Browne. 1918. Abs. Bact., 26.
11. Ulrich. 1906. Ztschr. f. Hyg. u. Infektionskrank. 53, 176.
12. Muller. 1903. Arch. f. Hyg. 67, 209.
13. Hunter. 1920. J. Bact., 5, 353-361.
14. Stewart. 1930. Gt. Brit. Food Invest. Bd. Rpt., 1930, 137-141.
15. Gee. 1930. Contrib. Canad. Biol. and Fish. 5, 431-439.

and Nickerson [16] could find no microorganisms in muscle of freshly caught haddock. These conclusions were based on examination of 120 excised muscle samples from six haddock.

Discoloration of Halibut. This fish is caught in great numbers on the western coast of the United States and Canada and is shipped in the frozen condition to all parts of North America. A defect of this fish discussed by Harrison and Sadler [3] is the appearance of a yellow or greenish-yellow coloration in the slime about it or on the fish itself. Examination of the slime under the microscope indicated the presence of many bacteria. Inoculation of sound fish with slime from an infected fish reproduced the abnormality indicating that it was due to growth of microorganisms and was an infection. Harrison and Sadler isolated the organism in pure culture and reported it to be a member of the fluorescent group, members of which are widely disseminated in natural waters. Having proven by isolations from over one hundred halibut from many different boats that this organism was the cause of the trouble, Harrison and Sadler then studied the origin of the organism. It was found to be present in ice used for preserving the fish and on the various objects with which the fish came in contact. Very significant was the observation that halibut from sea water did not harbor these organisms. Harrison and Sadler found that chlorination of the water used for making the ice in the amount of three parts per million killed the organisms. They reported that water from which ice is made should be disinfected in some manner. In a longer report on deterioration of halibut Harrison [17] stated that discoloration was most marked in the slime of the dead fish. This is so rich in nitrogen that it is an excellent food for bacteria. Stained films from this slime showed various microorganisms. When discolored slime was streaked on sound whitefish, characteristic discoloration was produced. The causal microorganism proved to be *Pseudomonas fluorescens*. It was isolated from upland surface lake water, neither filtered nor chlorinated, which was used for making ice. The organism was said to penetrate the skin of the fish where it caused putrefaction, *Pseudomonas fluorescens* was not isolated from sea water nor from fish freshly caught until they had been landed aboard the boat. The sole primary source was said to be the ice or ice water from which ice was made. Some 15 other species were identified by Harrison; they were not especially related to fish-spoilage problems. When the skin of halibut was inoculated with certain marine chromogenic bacteria, Bedford [18] found that the flesh became discolored as well as sour in 10 days at 0°C.(32°F.). Later he reported results of investigations of discoloration of stored fresh and frozen fish. Discolorations of special interest to the industry are yellowing and reddening or "rusting" of stored fresh salmon. Some of these defects are bacterial in origin but chemical causes may also be involved. The objectionable bacteria may be killed by disinfection of the fishing boats, thorough cleaning of the fish, and proper handling.

16. Proctor and Nickerson. 1935. J. Bact. 30, 377-382.
17. Harrison. 1929. Canad. J. Res. 1, 214-239.
18. Bedford. 1933. Contrib. Canad. Biol. and Fish. 7, 425; Biol. Bd. of Canada No. 27, 11-14.

Complaints that freshly caught salmon had an earthy taint prompted Thaysen and Pentelow [19] to look into the matter. Actinomyces species were found to be responsible. They were abundant in the water from which the fish came and reached the blood stream of the fish after entering through the gills. The compound which caused the taint could be distilled from cultures.

Microbiology of Fish. Owing to the fact that fish may be caught in unclean waters as well as to the fact that they may undergo rapid decomposition, many investigations have been carried out to learn more about their microbiology. New methods of preservation have had to be evaluated to determine their effect on microorganisms. The subject was reviewed by Griffiths.[20] In an investigation of fish purchased on the open market in Aberdeen, Stewart [21] concluded that the longer the time between catching and marketing, the greater was bacterial contamination. Microscope examination of the slime showed such a heterogeneous flora, that Stewart was prompted to study the relation of this flora to keeping quality and spoilage. The bacteria which were found belonged to the groups found in water, e.g., Achromobacter, Flavobacter, Pseudomonas. Sporebearing bacteria were almost entirely absent. Coliform bacteria were not found, even though some of the fish which were examined came from polluted waters. Anaerobic bacteria were also not found in slime of haddock but were present in small numbers in the intestines. They appeared to belong to the nonspore-forming genus Bacteroides. The anaerobes in the intestines proved to be *Clostridium sporogenes* and *Clostridium putrificum*. Shewan [22] reported isolation of *Clostridium tetani* from the intestines of fish for the first time.

An extensive study of the microbiology of fresh salt-water fish was the subject of a study by Harrison, Perry, and Smith.[7] Their work was more closely concerned with haddock, mackerel, and halibut, but in addition, a few other fish were examined. They first studied the effect of freezing. Fish were kept at 10°C.(50°F., 15°C.(59°F.), and 20°C.(68°F.) for six and 24 hours, and bacteriological examination was made at the end of these times. The results indicated that bacteria increase slowly at 10°C. (50°F.) but somewhat more rapidly at 15°C.(59°F.). After four months' storage, the number never exceeded 600 per gram and in a number of instances was considerably less. Eviscerated fish had a higher bacterial content.

In an investigation of the bacteria causing spoiling of haddock by Gee,[8] isolations were made from fish stored at room temperature for a week or so, after which time the flesh was foul. An organism was isolated which showed considerable pleomorphism. It was believed to be *Bacillus vulgatus*. Its growth seemed to be favored by the presence of 1.5 per cent of salt in the medium. The organism was important in the decay of fish muscle.

19. Thaysen and Pentelow. 1935. Ann. Appl. Biol. 23, 99-104; 105-109.
20. Griffiths. 1937. Food Research 2, 121-134.
21. Stewart. 1931. Gt. Brit. Food Invest. Bd. Ann Rpt. for 1930, 137-141; Rpt. for 1934, p. 93; Rpt. for 1935, p. 82; Rpt. for 1936, p. 99.
22. Shewan. 1938. Gt. Brit. Food Invest. Bd. Ann. Rpt. for 1937, p. 75; also Rpt. for 1938, 79-87.

It has been shown that unopened fish keep better than the opened owing to the fact that evisceration exposes the tissued to attack of bacteria. The intestinal canals of fish are apparently well seeded with many types of bacteria, both aerobic and anaerobic. When the fish is opened these may be released to infect and spoil the meat. Pernansky found both aerobes and anaerobes, many of which exhibited proteolytic tendencies. Wall [23] reported that freshly caught unopened herring kept better than the opened. Anderson [24] reported that the fish with greater amounts of food in the stomach decomposed more rapidly. Such spoilage is discussed again later under ''feedy salmon.''

Fish may, at times, harbor pathogenic bacteria. Johnson [25] has shown that fish may spread *Escherichia coli* and that this organism can multiply in the intestinal contents of fish. It is not difficult to understand how fish might be incriminated in the spread of certain diseases. If the water in which the fish lives, is polluted, objectionable bacteria will certainly get into the intestinal tract. During cleaning, the muscle may be contaminated. Harrison and his colleagues showed that cooking could not be depended upon to sterilize the tissue. Uhlrich [11] attributed a case of paratyphoid fever (type B) to fish. The medical officer of health reported that fish was a common cause of typhoid fever in London. The fish especially involved were plaice which were fried and had been sold ungutted on account of their small size. Cooking cannot be relied upon to destroy objectionable bacteria.

The intestinal contents of fish carry a varied microbiological flora probably determined largely by the food and water from which the fish is taken. Reed and Spence [26] found largely members of the genera Achromobacter, Pseudomonas, Flavobacterium, Bacillus, and members of the Coliform group. Members of the genus Achromobacter were also found in slime and intestinal contents of haddock by Stewart.[27] Micrococci were frequently found in slime but not in intestinal contents. Not many Pseudomonas types were found. Sporeforming bacteria were never found in the slime but were abundant in the intestinal contents. Gibbons [28] reported about the same general variety of microorganisms in the same materials. Special efforts were made by Lucke and Schwartze [29] to relate the bacterial flora of fish to the water from which they came. Fish taken from water with a high bacterial content did not keep well and had an undesirable flavor. The main infection seemed to occur during catching and handling when the fish might be damaged. The surface slime might be disturbed and the intestinal contents voided. Bacteria in sea-water ice and ships' holds are always a source of bacteria in fish. Insufficient refrigeration permit bacteria to develop in large numbers. Many changes were said to be necessary, both on ship and on shore, before some of these difficulties

23. Wall. 1913. Centbl. Bakt., Ref. Pt. I, 56, 701-702.
24. Anderson. 1908. Twenty-sixth Ann. Rpt., Fishery Bd. of Scotland.
25. Johnson. 1904. J. Infect. Dis. 7, 348-354.
26. Reed and Spence. 1929. Contrib. Canad. Biol. and Fish. 4, 259-264.
27. Stewart. 1932. J. Marine Biol. Assoc., United Kingdom 18, 35-50.
28. Gibbons. 1934. Contrib. Canad. Biol. and Fish. 8, 277-280.
29. Lucke and Schwartze. 1937. Arch. f. Mikrobiol. 8, 207-230.

can be eliminated. Further results of investigations quite like those just reported were published by Thjotta and Somme,[30] Snow and Beard,[31] and Levinskaia.[32] Most of the bacteriological work on fresh fish has concerned aerobic bacteria. Anaerobic bacteria are probably as important and perhaps more so in view of their marked ability to bring about decomposition. Shewan [22] did not find anaerobic bacteria in slime but always in the intestinal contents. Those which were identified belonged to the genus Clostridium but were not much related to spoilage.

Spoilage of fresh fish is apparently not caused by members of any one genus. Wood [33] allowed fish to decompose at room temperature and at 40°C.(104°F.) and observed a large number of different bacteria. They came from the slime. Wood believed that the bacteria in the intestinal tract were unimportant in spoilage. His experiments pointed out what so many investigators have found, i.e., that proper handling and clean apparatus will do much to prevent undue spoilage. The bacteria isolated were species commonly found in soil, fresh water, and sea water, the principal genera being Achromobacter, Micrococcus, Flavobacterium, Pseudomonas, Bacillus, Sarcina, and Serratia in the order named. No special flora was present in the intestines, the gut of non-feeding fish being virtually sterile.

Many who have studied these problems have tried to determine the origin of spoilage bacteria and the types which are most prevalent. Bedford [34] reported the number of bacteria in surface water of the sea to be low but to vary within the same locality at different times of year. The lower depths of the sea had fewer bacteria than the surface. Bedford found that fish caught in the vicinity of fresh water are liable to contain more bacteria than those from salt water. However the number of bacteria on the surface of the fish was low and the number in the alimentary tract was not excessive. Some animal intestinal bacteria have been found in the alimentary canal of haddock but not on the surface of the fish. Growth of bacteria may be retarded by properly washing and eviscerating the fish, but under practical fishing and storage growth is rapid. The fishing vessel is a serious source of contamination. Griffiths and Stanby [35] tested eviscerated haddock kept over a period of 21 days and sampled at regular intervals to determine the changes that occurred. Bacterial changes were not suggested as a means of grading fish.

The nature of fish tissue make it susceptible to spoilage. Few foods must be handled more carefully and promptly. Lumley [36] blamed careless handling by trawler crews for spoilage by bacteria. Strict cleanliness and storage in ice is stressed. This advice was in accord with the results of extensive consideration of this problem by Lumley, Paqué, and Reay.[37]

30. Thjotta and Somme. 1938. Acta Path. et Microbiol. Scand. Suppl. 37, 514-526.
31. Snow and Beard. 1939. Food Research 4, 563-585.
32. Levinskaia. 1936. Microbiologia 5, 679-685.
33. Wood. 1940. Oustral. Council Sci. & Indus. Res., Pamphlet 100.
34. Bedford. 1933. Fifth Pacific Sci. Congress Proc., Canada, 5, 3715-3724.
35. Griffiiths and Stanby. 1934. Amer. Fisheries Soc. Trans. 64, 401-406.
36. Lumley. 1933. Gt. Brit. Food Invest. Bd. Leaflet No. 3, London, 1933.
37. Lumley et al. 1929. Gt. Brit. Food Invest. Bd., Rpt. 37.

The bacterial content of decomposed fish would always be high even with slight decomposition. Schönberg [38] found that the most significant bacteria were gram-negative, slender, very motile rods which liquefied gelatin and grew best at room temperature. Gram-negative micrococci, Proteus species, coliform bacteria, and aerobic sporeformers were next in importance.

Tarr's [39] Direct Method for Counting Bacteria in Fish Flesh. The sample of fish is finely minced under conditions which do not permit the access of foreign bacteria. Some of the flesh, selected at random, is added to three times its weight of sterilized distilled water, the weight of fish added being determined indirectly by measuring the volume of water it displaces. Resulting mixture is transferred to a strong glass test tube containing some fine sand. Contents of the tube are stirred very rapidly for about a minute by means of a bent glass stirring rod rotated by a small electric motor. After standing for several minutes in order to permit the sand and coarser flesh particles to settle, the upper layer of rather cloudy liquid can be used for making the direct count and, if desired for purposes of comparison, the viable count as well. Actual count is carried out on a small accurately measured drop (.01 milliliter or about .0006 cubic inch) of liquid, which is placed on clean glass slide and spread over a marked-off definite area of one square centimeter (.155 square inch) with a fine needle. The resulting thin film of liquid is dried in air at about blood temperature. Slide is then placed for one minute in strong (90-95 per cent) grain alcohol, drained, transferred to a solution of blue dye (Loeffler's alkaline methylene blue) for about 30 seconds, rinsed very gently with tap water, and the film then dried in warm air. The bacteria are dyed a very dark blue while the background (consisting chiefly of fish muscle protein) is only a very pale blue. The bacteria seen in a selection of separate regions (''microscope fields'') on this film as viewed under the microscope are counted and from the result it is possible to calculate the number of bacteria in given weight of fish. Result is expressed as the total number of bacteria per gram. Each microscope field represents only a minute fraction (about one seventy-millionth of an ounce) of original fish muscle. Thus if there were exactly 70,000,000 bacteria per ounce of the original muscle and these were absolutely evenly distributed, there would be only one bacterium per field. Experiments have indicated that this method cannot be used directly when there are less than about 3,000,000 bacteria per ounce of fish flesh. Greater numbers are counted with greater degrees of accuracy. The disintegrating apparatus used by Tarr was patterned after that of Haines. [40]

Escherichia coli in Commercial Fish. The position of coliform bacteria in sanitation has prompted investigators to determine whether members of this group have the same significance in fish that they have in other foods. Griffiths and Fellers [41] observed that much of the fresh and frozen fish is sold as fillets or in other ready-to-cook form. This involved much handling. Bacteriological examinations by these investigators revealed that such handling contributed typical *Escherichia coli* to the product. Since these are of fecal origin, it was believed that their presence indicated undesirable conditions in preparation for the market. Fecal *Escherichia coli*, according to Gibbons, [42] are not normal inhabitants of the alimentary tracts of fish except those which are caught near shore. They were said to be seldom present in fish caught at good distances from shore. Perhaps the organism may have the same significance which Hunter [43] suggests it

38. Schönberg. 1930. Berlin. Tierärztl. Wchnschr. 46, 429-435.
39. Tarr. 1941. Pacific Biol. Sta. and Pacific Fish. Expt. Sta. Prog. Rpts., No. 49, 8-10.
40. Haines. 1937. Gt. Brit. Food Invest. Bd., Spec. Rpt. No. 45.
41. Griffiths and Fellers. 1936. Amer. J. Pub. Health 26, 259-264; also Dissertation, Mass. State Col., Amherst, Mass.
42. Gibbons. 1934. Contrib. Canad. Biol. N. S. 8, 291-300.
43. Hunter. 1934. Amer. J. Pub. Health 24, 199-202.

should have in cooked crab meat—that it indicates undesirable conditions of handling. The difficulty of keeping contamination out of a plant where fish are dressed and packed was indicated by Fitzgerald and Conway.[1] *Escherichia coli* was found on backs and gills by these investigators, even after washing them in hypochlorite solutions of strengths up to 100 parts per million. They were inclined to minimize the significance of *Escherichia coli* in fish fillets.

CODFISH

This fish is caught in great numbers off the Grand Banks of Newfoundland. Harrison, Perry, and Smith[7] stated that Cabot in 1498 gave the mainland of North America the Basque name for codfish—"Bacalaos." French, Spaniards, and Portuguese frequented the Grand Banks before 1502, returning to their home ports with great numbers of cod. This was the beginning of an industry now amounting to millions of dollars concerned with the preparation of the fish in different forms.

Preparation of cod, which has been described by Bitting,[44] furnishes good illustration of use of salt for preserving flesh. He reported that 25,000 long tons of salt were used in a year at Gloucester, Mass., alone. As soon as the fish are caught, they are cleaned which consists in removing the head, viscera, and backbone. They are then piled up in the hold and sprinkled with salt. About 1.5 bushels of salt may be used per 100 pounds of fish. Water is drawn from the fish and the brine runs to the bottom of the hold from which it is pumped. Fishermen often attempt to reduce the amount of water taken from fish by using lesser amounts of salt so that the fish will weigh more in port. Souring often results. After the fish are on shore they may be further dried by means of salt. Fresh fish were said to require eight bushels of salt to the hogshead. Bitting stated that fine and coarse salt had about the same ability to extract water from fish over a long period. During the first two days, however, the fine salt accomplished greater dehydration. If the tissue comes in contact with large amounts of fine salt, it becomes "salt burned." The tissue is coagulated while the interior remains soft. The quality of salt was reported by Tressler[45] to have some importance as it has been found to be important in other fields. Calcium and magnesium sulfates are said to retard the penetration of salt. The dry-salt method was found to be superior to the brine-salting method. Very great is the importance of starting with a perfectly fresh fish for salting. Delay in salting allows microorganisms to start to develop and this put a heavier load on salt as a preserving agent.

Reddening of Codfish. Many explanations have been offered for the cause of this defect of salted fish and other foods. Farlow[46] seems to have been one of the first to study the question. He believed that reddening was due to a pigmented, slime-producing organism to which the name *Clathrocystis roseo-persicina* was given. Farlow found the organism about the packing plants and in the salt. Salt was believed to be the source of

44. Bitting. 1911. U. S. Bur. Chem. and Soils, Bull. 133.
45. Tressler. 1920. U. S. Bur. Fisheries, Doc. 884.
46. Farlow. 1878. Rev. Mycol. 6, 197.

the organism on the fish. Later he reported *Sarcina morrhuae* and *Oidium pulvunatum*. Since Farlow's contributions, many others have studied the problem and reported other fungi. Megnin [47] attributed the red color to a fungus, *Coniothecium bertherandi*. Roumeguere [48] believed the trouble was due to *Clathrocystis*. Poulsen [49] isolated an organism which was believed to be *Sarcina morrhuae*. Layet [50] and Edington found coccus forms to which they attributed the trouble. LeDantec [51] distinguished two degrees of redness, apparently caused by different organisms. A sporeforming rod was believed to be of special importance. Results of researches by Le-Dantec [52] attributed it to another organism. This organism was apparently a nonsporeformer and had the ability to grow in strong salt solutions. LeDantec showed that it came from the salt used for salting codfish. He proposed the term "chlorophile" for those organisms which needed salt for growth. Höye [53] believed that there was more than one organism which could form the red pigment; probably a Sarcina and Micrococcus were involved. He also mentioned à red micrococcus described by Johan-Olsen, *Sarcina rosaceae*. Höye believed that the methods of salting might be responsible for the development of the red color. Red bacteria were isolated from specimens of salt. Beckwith [54] isolated a *Diplococcus gadidarum* from reddened fish. The characteristic red color was produced on tubes of shredded codfish. According to Bitting, [44] the organisms which produce this spoilage probably live in sea water, and being salt-tolerant, are able to propagate on the fish. Pierce [55] suggested that the salt be sterilized. Absence of the trouble on the Pacific Coast was attributed by Cobb [56] to the fact that better salt was used. A Spirochaete and a bacillus producing a red color were believed to be the cause of the trouble by Browne.[57] Harrison and Kennedy,[58] Cloake,[59] and others have contributed to the subject, but added little that was new. Practically all of the various bacteria are pleomorphic and salt-tolerant. Harrison and Kennedy's organism grew well in the presence of 15 per cent of salt. The organisms are nonpathogenic as far as can be determined from the contributions which have been made to the subject.

Petrova [60] attributed reddening to *Micrococcus roseus*. The various bacteria which had been isolated and named by others were believed to be one species. *Serratia salinaria* was the name used by Kurochkin.[61] Salt was believed to be the source. A halophilic bacterium requiring as much

47. Megnin. 1884. Rev. Mycol. 12, 197.
48. Roumeguere. 1885. Rev. Mycol. 7.
49. Poulsen. Quoted from other authors.
50. Layet. 1889. U. S. Bur. Fisheries, Vol. 7.
51. LeDantec. 1891. Ann. Inst. Pasteur 5, 565.
52. LeDantec. 1906. Compt. Rend. Soc. Biol. 61, 136-140.
53. Höye. 1901. Bergens Mus. Aarbok. 1901, No. 9; Abs. Canning Tech. 3, 12.
54. Beckwith. 1912. Centbl. Bakt., Pt. 2, 32, 193.
55. Pierce. 1914. The Salton Sea, Wash. 1914.
56. Cobb. 1910. Rpt. of the Commissioner of Fisheries.
57. Browne. 1920. Abs. Bact. 4, 11.
58. Harrison and Kennedy. 1922. Roy. Soc. Canada, Proc. and Trans. 16, 101-152.
59. Cloake. 1923. Gt. Brit. Food Invest. Bd., Spec. Rpt. 18.
60. Petrova. 1932. Microbiologia 1, 192-209; Ann. Inst. Pasteur 55 (1935), 255.
61. Kurochkin *et al*. 1937. Rev. in Biol. Abs. 12, 337.

as 20 per cent of salt, named *Vibrio halobicus desulfuricans* was isolated from salt and canned anchovies by Sontag.[62]

Many of the investigators whose work has been reviewed above have found the organisms in salt. Stuart, Frey, and James[63] and Gibbons[64] confirmed this, the former finding them to be quite common in salt from many places in the world. The species isolated were placed among the higher bacteria. Two organisms were isolated from reddened cod and from salt by Shewan.[65] One was a bacillus and the other a micrococcus. Halophilic bacteria varied greatly in number in various salts—from 0 to 90,000 per gram of undried salt. Shewan believed that bacteria causing this defect could be classed in two main groups, Serratia and Micrococci. At this stage the fish deteriorate rapidly and smell bad.

Another discoloration of dried salt fish caused by a microorganism is "dim" salt fish. It is caused by a halophilic microorganism, *Torula epizoa (Sporendonema epizoum)*, spores of which cause the chocolate-brown spots. Hess[66] found that fish could be contaminated by direct contact with infected fish or by utensils or by salt. Storage of fish below 5°C.(41°F.) prevented growth of the fungus. The fungus does not spoil the fish and may be brushed off. This situation is then comparable to that which obtains with cold-storage beef. Frank and Hess[67] found the organism to be halophilic, requiring a minimum of five per cent of salt, the optimum being between 10 and 15 per cent. Optimal humidity for growth was around 75 per cent. Ultraviolet light had little lethal effect on the organism.

Microbiology of Canned Cod-Fish Cake. Hanzawa and Takeda[68] reported isolation of a strict anaerobic, spore-forming bacterium and two nonsporeformers *(Serratia marcescens* and *Micrococcus acidi lactici)* from a can of swelled codfish cake. The strict anaerobe, believed to be the cause of the spoilage, was a gas former of low heat resistance. It was killed in 60 minutes at 100°C.(212°F.) but not in 30 minutes. Heating under pressure killed it quickly. Although the product may have been understerilized or the cans may not have been sound, such bacteria have been reported in several meat products.

Microbiology of Fresh Salmon. Various interesting problems have been revealed in investigations of this subject. The general flora is influenced by the type of water from which the fish are taken, the methods of handling, and the state of feeding. Hunter[13] found the muscular tissue of freshly caught salmon to be sterile. After 96 hours between 10°C.(50°F.), and 21.1°C.(70°F.), the count increased to as high as 155,000,000 per gram. In a later paper Hunter (1920) reported results of a study to determine what organisms are significant in decomposing salmon. Twenty-one out of 43 cultures were found to be members of the coliform group. In general, Hunter found that the organisms were really water, sewage,

62. Sontag. 1932. Rev. in Chem. Abs. 27, 5367.
63. Stuart *et al.* 1933. U. S. Dept. Agr., Tech. Bull. 383; Food Research 3, 417-420.
64. Gibbons. 1937. J. Biol. Bd. of Canada 3, 70-76.
65. Shewan. 1939. Gt. Brit. Food Invest. Bd., Ann. Rpt. for 1938, p. 113.
66. Hess. 1940. Atlantic Fish. Expt. Sta., Note 68.
67. Frank and Hess. 1941. J. Fish. Res. Bd. Canada 5, 276-285.
68. Hanzawa and Takeda. 1931. Arch. f. Mikrobiol. 2, 333-351.

and soil organisms. It would probably be a difficult matter as Bartlett has pointed out, for the industry to eliminate these organisms in the packing of the fish. Hunter[69] extended his study to samples of decomposing salmon and to sea water in the Alaska region. Members of the coliform group were common. *Aerobacter cloacae* and *Pseudomonas fluorescens* and an unidentified flesh-colored organism were important in decomposition of salmon. Eighty percent of bacteria collected from sea water were also found in decomposing salmon, in the canneries, or in both. Hunter stated that these data confirm the former conclusions that the decomposition of salmon is not due to bacteria acquired in the cannery. Fellers,[70] when in charge of the Pacific Fisheries Investigations for the National Canners Association, also found that the larger number of bacteria in spoiled salmon belonged to the coliform group of bacteria. *Aerobacter cloacae*-like organisms were also common and responsible for considerable spoilage of fish. The anaerobic, sporeforming bacteria were not commonly present in fish. Fellers also studied the penetration of bacteria into the tissue. The greatest contamination came from the gills and through the skin and not from the belly cavity. Salmon, on their way to the spawning grounds, were found to harbor few bacteria in the body cavity. Those that were found were in the stomach and intestines were of the usual water flora.

Fellers' investigations showed that salmon might become heavily contaminated at any of the following places: (a) scows and boats used in transporting salmon; (b) pewing of the fish through the body; (c) on the fish floor where blood, slime, and dead fish may infect good fish; (d) in sliming tanks where, due to insufficient changing, the water becomes badly polluted; (e) cutting machines and fillers; (f) dirty and dusty cans; (g) the water used in canning.

"Feedy" salmon have been found to decompose more rapidly than salmon whose intestinal tracts were empty. Desiring to find out whether decomposition of feedy salmon was entirely due to bacteria, Hunter[69] determined the number of bacteria in the stomach, intestines, and muscle tissues. No correlation was observed between the number of bacteria and the extent of decomposition but evidence was observed to indicate that agencies other than bacteria were concerned with decomposition. This work was extended by Hunter to hatchery salmon. Total counts of bacteria were made from the gills, flesh of the back, flesh of the belly, pyloric ceca, stomach, and intestines. The gill counts varied so greatly that little attention was given it. The highest count from the gills of a salmon which had been out of the water for six days was 3,600,000,000 per gram. The counts from the other organs were not significant since these organs are not eaten. However, they may contribute to foul odors. Hunter studied the anaerobes, but found none pathogenic for guinea pigs by mouth. In general, the organisms involved in spoilage were found to be the same in both the hatchery and migrating salmon. Fellers[71] reported that bacteria

69. Hunter. 1922. J. Bact. 7, 85-110; Amer. J. Hyg. 2, 368-378.
70. Fellers. 1922. The Canner 55, July 29, 1922.
71. Fellers. 1926. J. Bact. 12, 181.

enter the flesh through the mouth, gills, anus, and skin, usually with slime, which is an excellent bacterial medium. The organisms found in decomposing salmon were those of river and sea water and did not constitute a separate group. Salmon flesh remains sterile for 20 to 60 hours after death, depending on such variables as temperature, size of fish, method of handling, and conditions of storage. Of 412 purified cultures obtained from decomposing salmon, 31 per cent were cocci, 4.5 per cent sporulating aerobes, 17.5 per cent aerobic, asporogenous, chromogenic bacilli, 36.5 per cent aerobic asporogenous, achromogenic bacilli, 6.8 per cent yeasts, 2 per cent obligate anaerobes, and 1.7 per cent spirilla. *Escherichia coli* is not a normal inhabitant of the intestines of the salmon. Slime is the greatest single factor in the spread of microorganisms of fish, boats, gear, and canneries. The canning process of 115.6°C.(240°F.) for 90 minutes in one-pound cans renders most of the cans commercially sterile.

Microbiology of Canned Salmon. Much has been written on this subject and probably a good portion of it no longer is applicable to the product as it exists today on the American market. Whereas at one time appreciable insterility existed in canned salmon, the situation is quite the reverse today. This is largely due to refinements in handling the fish after catching and to better methods in the packing plant as well as to better technic in examining the cans in the laboratory. Inspection procedures outlined by Clough and Clark [72] have also had a large part in improving quality. The early literature probably does not reflect the condition of canned salmon today. In the tuna-packing industry, which probably does not differ basically from the salmon-packing industry, Lang [73] reported a general mixed flora in the product up to sterilization. Aerobic rods and cocci were most numerous. Sporeforming organisms were not isolated from unprocessed cans although they were observed at various stages. *Clostridium botulinum* was isolated directly from cuts prior to canning and therefore probably enters the can. Sporeforming bacteria must be uncommon, however, in tuna. Lang was inclined to consider them of importance even in small numbers. He also emphasized that dormant spores might be present in canned tuna.

Those who wish to know the situation which once existed in this industry should consult publications of Bushnell and Utt,[74] Sadler,[75] DeBord,[76] Savage, Hunwicke, and Calder,[77] Weinzirl,[78] and Fellers.[79]

Since the investigations, results of which have just been discussed, were carried out, marked improvement has taken place in the quality of canned salmon. This is due not only to a general improvement throughout the entire food industry in sanitation and knowledge but also in the salmon

72. Clough and Clark. 1934. Amer. J. Pub. Health 24, 1252-1258.
73. Lang. 1935. Univ. of Cal., Pub. in Pub. Health 2, 26.
74. Bushnell and Utt. 1917. Kans. State Bd. Health, Bull. 13, 36-38.
75. Sadler. 1918. Amer. J. Pub. Health 8, 216-220; Roy. Soc. Canada, Proc. and Trans. 3, Sec. V, 135-41.
76. DeBord. 1920. Abs. Bact. 4, 35.
77. Savage, Hunwicke, and Calder. 1922. Gt. Brit. Food Invest. Bd., Spec. Rpt. 11.
78. Weinzirl. 1919. J. Med. Res., 39, 349-413.
79. Fellers. 1927. Univ. Wash., Pubs. Fisheries 1, 157.

industry to introduction of new procedures. Williams and Clark[80] mentioned the use of mechanical vacuum in place of the steam exhaust as an example. They also mentioned the significantly severe processes of 90 minutes at 116.6°C.(242°F.) which are used to soften the bones and make them edible. This is in excess of the cook necessary to protect against spoilage. In spite of the fact that no reports of spoilage owing to understerilization have been made, Williams and Clark made a bacteriological survey of canned salmon with adequate controls to determine the actual bacteriological condition of the product. They found the cans which they examined to be bacteriologically sterile, indicating that packing procedures and processes now in use are adequate. In this paper Williams and Clark discuss the problem of air-borne contaminations on plates made in similar surveys, a subject discussed in this book in Chapter 23. How much contamination may have occurred in former investigations can never be known.

Mild Curing of Salmon. The fish are split down the middle and the backbone cut out. Each half of the fish secured in this manner is then scored eight or nine time with a knife. After being soaked in cold water for an hour or so, the fish is salted in tierces. Little salt is used and consequently the fish must be kept in cold storage until used. This mild-cured salmon is used for smoking. It is quickly freshened by soaking in water and a practically fresh fish is then available for other treatment.

Pickling Salmon. The fish is split and the viscera removed. After washing, it is put into pickling butts with about 15 pounds of salt for each 100 pounds of fish. After a week they are packed into barrels with salt for the market. Dry salting may also be used, in which process the fish are packed into boxes with salt. Smoking is often done after the fish are preserved in a pickle until they can be smoked. They are taken from the pickle and washed free of as much salt as possible. Then they are subjected to smoldering fires for three or four days. Other varieties of fish may be preserved in the same manner.

Growth of and Toxin Formation of Clostridium botulinum in Canned Salmon. *Clostridium botulinum* is able to grow and form toxin in canned salmon. Schoenholz, Esty, and Meyer[81] inoculated cans of salmon with toxin-free spores and after incubation for varying lengths of time secured spoilage. The partially liquefied contents gave off a putrid odor. Six of eight cans of salmon inoculated by Thompson and Tanner[82] spoiled and became toxic. *Clostridium botulinum* is apparently in the cannery, for Lang[73] observed Type A strains in slime and cleaned flesh of salmon before canning. About one per cent of empty cans were also found to harbor this organism.

PRESERVATION OF FISH

Many different procedures are used for preservation of fish. Some of them completely change the appearance and flavor while others maintain the tissue close to the normal and natural condition. All of them repress

80. Williams and Clark. 1942. Food Research 7, 178-185.
81. Schoenholz, Esty, and Meyer. 1923. J. Infect. Dis. 33, 289-327.
82. Thompson and Tanner. 1925. Idem 37, 344-352.

bacterial development or destroy bacteria. Icing has been used to a large extent for holding fish until other methods could be used. Ice may carry many bacteria among which may be species which are definitely objectionable. Watson [83] found some ice being used in fish preservation to contain 25,000 bacteria per milliliter. The predominating organism was *Pseudomonas fluorescens* which caused discoloration of fish muscle. *Bacillus platychoma* and *Bacillus simplex*, which caused decomposition, were also isolated. Watson suggested use of paper to keep fish from coming in contact with the ice.

Various preservatives have been added to fish for many years. According to Tarr and Sunderland,[84] Norwegian experts as early as 1870 prevented deterioration of salted herring shipped to England by adding boric acid to the pickle. The same practice was used in other countries although at times other preservatives were introduced. Stringent food laws, however, have largely prohibited such preservatives although in some countries they are permitted if their presence is indicated on the label. Fish in the past have been immersed into such solutions as sodium hypochlorite, formaldehyde, boric acid, potassium nitrate, and even in strong salt solutions immediately after gutting and just prior to icing. More recently sterilizing ices containing various chemical compounds, such as hypochlorites, benzoic acid, and ozone, have been used. Still more recently the fish have been stored in atmospheres containing large amounts of carbon dioxide. All of these procedures, according to the above-mentioned authors have not been very successful. Experiments in their own laboratories with some ten more or less common preservatives indicated that potassium nitrite in quite low concentrations strongly inhibited the rate of spoilage in fillets. The Canadian Food and Drugs Act of 1938 permits the use of refined sodium nitrite in concentrations of .02 per cent for curing meats and fish. Hydrogen peroxide, hydrochloric acid, and boric acid in the concentrations which were employed were not very effective. Hydrochloric acid and sulfur dioxide resulted in a product with a rather unpleasant appearance. The latter also produced an unpleasant odor and flavor because it apparently acted with the oils in the fish. Chloroform was very active and had the advantage that it later evaporates rather quickly on storage of the fish. Sodium benzoate also showed some activity. Tarr and Sunderland reported that inhibition of bacterial growth varied with each particular preservative and especially with the species of fish. Results of organoleptic examination checked quite well with the results of bacteriological data reported. These authors also reported that the chemical preservatives used were in general more efficient in reducing the number of viable bacteria than was ultraviolet light. Later, Tarr and Sunderland reported that sodium nitrite was as efficient a preservative as was potassium nitrite.

Salt. Large quantities of salt fish are prepared in most countries in the world. The factors involved are probably about the same as those involved

83. Watson. 1934. Canad. Fisherman 21, 25-28.
84. Tarr and Sunderland. 1939. Pacific Biol. Sta. and Pacific Fish. Expt. Sta. Prog. Rpts. 39, 13-16; 40 (1939), 14-17.

in preservation of other foods by salt. A dry cure may be used or the fish may be placed in salt solutions. If the fish carries few bacteria, the load on the curing process is lighter. Bedford [85] observed that immersion of fresh halibut in 20 per cent salt solution for 30 minutes immediately after gutting preserved them well. Criteria were retardation of yellow discoloration of the white skin and the number of bacteria. According to Burova and Nasledysheva [86] pathogenic microorganisms are restrained by salt solutions used in curing fish.

Survival of Pathogenic Bacteria on Salted Fish. Whether salt fish would be significant in spreading any pathogenic bacteria which might be in sea water is questionable even though it is known that *Eberthella typhosa* may exist for some few days. Kenyoun [87] found that this organism could exist in high salt concentrations. Frank and Hess [88] recovered *Eberthella typhosa* from salt fish blocks after 22 days at 5 to 6°C.(41 to 42.8°F.) and from salt media after periods as long as 94 days. *Escherichia coli* was found under the same conditions after 72 days and on salt media after 91 days. *Escherichia coli* is considered a good indicator of pollution when the storage period is known. Its presence indicates previous contaminations and potential danger. Methods of preparation of the fish would probably be one element of safety.

Chlorine Compounds. These compounds are playing a great role in sanitizing food-processing plants. They are also used on the trawlers and in ice used to chill freshly caught fish. Moran and Piqué [89] secured good results when hypochlorites were put into the ice. Results of a comprehensive investigation were reported by Chen and Fellers.[4] Immersion of eulachon before packing in a solution containing .6 per cent of available chlorine for five minutes materially reduced the bacterial content of the fish and enhanced keeping quality. Solutions with less than .2 per cent were not effective. They also reported the beneficial effects of using hypochlorite containing ice. Disinfection with chlorine was also of value when fish was dried. *Torula epizoa* was inhibited (Notevarp and Larsen[90]). Chlorine compounds seem to have been of value in handling of various foods from the sea.

Carbon Dioxide. This gas has been studied as a preservative for many different foods. The results have been quite variable owing to the fact that microorganisms vary in their response to the gas, some being inhibited while others are benefited. Such was the experience of Coyne.[91] Working with various species of Achromobacter that are associated with fresh fish, he observed that moderate or large amounts of carbon dioxide inhibited growth. This was especially marked at 0 to 10°C.(32 to 50° F.) at which temperatures these bacteria could ordinarily grow. In an atmosphere con-

85. Bedford. 1932. Biol. Bd. of Canada, Bull. 29, 3-16.
86. Burova and Nasledysheva. 1929. Hyg. et. Epidemiol. 20-26.
87. Kenyoun. 1925. Pub. Health Rpts. 40, 819-823.
88. Frank and Hess. 1941. J. Fish. Res. Bd., Canada, 5, 249-252.
89. Moran and Piqué. 1924. Gt. Brit. Food Invest. Bd., Ann. Rpt., 1923, 14.
90. Notevarp and Larsen. 1939. Arsberetin. vedkom. Norg. Fiskereir. 1936, 31-37.
91. Coyne. 1932. Chem. and Indus. 51, 119T-121T; Roy. Soc. London, Pros., Ser. B, 113, 196-217.

taining 20 per cent of carbon dioxide, and at a temperature of 0°C.(32°F.) the bacteria were almost completely inhibited. Marked preservative properties of the gas for haddock were also reported by Stansby and Griffith [92] who also commented on improved quality. Coyne believed that the preservative action might be due to an intracellular change in pH owing to permeability of the living cell to carbon dioxide and even to interference with some essential enzyme system.

Nitrites. Sodium nitrite has been shown to exert a preservative action in meat curing. Tarr and Sunderland [93] studied it as a preservative of fish. Dressed halibut, pink salmon, and black cod spoiled less rapidly when dipped into water containing .05 to .2 per cent of sodium nitrite than when packed in ordinary water ice or benzoic acid ice. Its preservative ability was believed to depend on its ability to penetrate the fish tissue. Tarr later reported further confirmation of these observations.

Ultraviolet Light. In view of prohibition of chemical preservatives in fish and fish products Tarr and his colleagues, Young and Sunderland,[94] attempted to use ultraviolet light for keeping fresh fish fillets. They were inclined to interpret their results favorably, for the exposed fish had fewer bacteria and better flavor and odor than the unexposed. The action was admitted to be limited to the surface with no penetration. Five to 10 minutes' exposure was necessary under conditions in their experiments.

Benzoated Brine Dips and Benzoated Ice. Results of an investigation by Fellers and Harvey [95] showed that it was entirely practical to freeze as much as .5 per cent of sodium benzoate in ice. Since its distribution in the ice cake was uneven, they recommended use of this ice in the crushed form. Fish stored in such ice kept several more days than did fish stored in ordinary ice. The benzoates were more effective when acidulated. Good results were also secured by dipping fillets for two minutes into brine containing sodium benzoates. Only slight improvement in keeping quality of dressed halibut and black cod was observed by Tarr and Bailey [96] when the fish were stored in crushed ice containing .1 per cent benzoic acid instead of plain ice. Viable bacterial population and trimethylamine content of the muscle were used as criteria.

Smoked Fish. Smoke is used for curing fish just as it is used for some meats. Hess,[97] in seeking information of the bacteriological aspects of the industry, used artificial media on account of the difficulties of sterilizing fish flesh without changing its character entirely and to obtain a uniform culture material. Three strains of bacteria (a staphylococcus, a nonspore-forming rod [*Proteus vulgaris*] and a sporeformer of the *Subtilis-mesentericus* group) were used in several experiments to determine bacterial action of smoke under various conditions. The arbitrary scale: "Cubic

92. Stansby and Griffith. 1935. Ind. Eng. Chem. 27, 1452-1458.
93. 93. Tarr and Sunderland. 1940. Modern Refrig. 43, 41; Food Research 1 (1936), 145-148; J. Fish. Res. Bd., Canada, 5 (1941), 244-248.
94. Tarr *et al.* 1938. Pacific Biol. Sta. and Pacific Fish. Expt. Sta., Prog. Rpts. No. 38 (1938), 3-4; No. 39 (1939), 16-18.
95. Fellers and Harvey. 1940. Food Research 5, 1-12.
96. Tarr and Bailey. 1939. J. Fish. Res. Bd., Canada, 4, 327-336.
97. Hess. 1927. J. Bact. 15, 7-50.

foot of air admitted to the smoke producer per hour'' gave a fair indication of the smoke concentration. An increase of the amount of air admitted per hour caused uniformly a greater reduction of bacteria, *i.e.*, an increase of the bactericidal power of the smoke, as well as visibly, a higher density or opaqueness of the smoke. Smoke from different sources (sawdust from hardwood, softwood, and mixtures of both) showed practically no difference in bactericidal power after six hours' action upon the test organisms. The rate of reduction of nonsporeformers under experimental conditions was greatest between one-half to two hours of exposure to fairly weak smoke, with an initial weakening of the bacteria during the first half hour and the killing of the more resistant forms during the third hour of exposure. The more concentrated the smoke, the greater was the initial and the total rates of reduction. Bacterial spores were found to be very resistant to smoke, the resistance increasing with increasing age of the spore cultures; 71 per cent of the spores from a seven-months-old spore culture survived exposure to a dense smoke for seven hours, while nonsporing organisms were killed in one to two hours by the same smoke. Penetration of smoke was found to be fairly rapid through peptone-water, slow through a flour paste, and very irregular through slices of fish muscle. The more concentrated the smoke the higher its penetrating power. Smoke constituents which had been absorbed by the smoked media during the exposure, continued to exert a bactericidal action upon the test organisms after the smoking process was finished. Formaldehyde vapors, containing three or more grams of formaldehyde per 100 cubic feet, approximately in the same concentration as they occur in ordinary smoke, have a decided bactericidal action. Formaldehyde is considered one of the chief bactericidal constituents of smoke. The resistance of bacteria against smoke is greatest in media of optimum salt concentration. The influence of the presence of proteins upon the bactericidal action of smoke was determined, using peptone solutions and fish extracts. Both were shown to have a decreasing "quenching" action upon the effect of smoking; this was less conspicuous in case of dense smoke than when less dense smoke was used. The hydrogen-ion concentration of unbuffered media is greatly increased during smoking. The bactericidal action of smoke in buffered media was shown to be greatest in an acid medium and decreasing constantly towards the alkaline side of neutrality. Callow [98] found formaldehyde on various smoked meats, its origin being wood smoke. It has been found in smoked fish as well. Callow stated that the presence of formaldehyde in wood smoke does not prohibit the use of smoke as a preservative in England.

Smoked Haddock and "Finnan Haddies." This type of smoked fish probably had its origin in Findon on the north coast of Scotland. It is now prepared to some extent in the United States and Canada (Patterson [99]). Under some conditions, flavor must be sacrificed for preservation. Fresh haddock are beheaded, split, and eviscerated; an extra cut is also made in the back in order to facilitate curing of the thick back muscles.

98. Callow. 1927. The Analyst 52, 391.
99. Patterson. 1917-1918. Bull. Biol. Sta. Canada.

The fish is then salted in strong brine for 30 minutes. They are then smoked for five to six hours in dense peat or sawdust smoke. The Canadian method, as outlined by Patterson, is a little different. It was found that small fish need not be salted more than 15 minutes. Thirty minutes' salting seemed to be the proper period for the average sized fish—this to be followed by 10 hours' smoking. A longer smoking increased the preservation but detracted from the flavor. Harrison [100] examined the intestinal contents of 12 haddock and reported *Bacillus vulgaris* Hauser to predominate. It was also found on and in the flesh of smoked haddock and haddock which had spoiled. The salting and smoking were found to be insufficient to destroy the organism. This makes it imperative that the fish be carefully handled and the process of treatment started as soon after removal of the fish from the water as possible.

After immersion in strong brine for 20 to 30 minutes, according to Hess,[101] they are removed and placed on iron rods to drain. On these rods, they are hung in the smokehouse where they are, first of all, dried by clear hardwood fires with the smokehouse well ventilated. After drying, the fires are partly smothered with sawdust to produce a dense smoke which is maintained until the desired cure is attained. The total time from the beginning of the cure to the end of smoking is from seven to nine hours. The same process for smoking finnan haddies would require from 13 to 17 hours. If the smoked fillets are to be held for any length of time they are frozen. Hess discussed the preserving value of several of the steps in smoking of fish. Since his discussion is of interest in preservation of different varieties of meat, some of it is presented. The initial pickling in heavy brine causes a decrease in volume but not in weight. The brine draws the water from the tissue but the weight is maintained by salt going into the muscle. Hess stated that this treatment also improved the surface of the meat. The drying just before smoking caused the formation of a pellicle over the surface of the fish. During drying there is sufficient heat to cause slight coagulation of the protein.

FREEZING OF FISH

This method of preservation has the advantage that fish is kept fresh. It is possible to ship frozen fish to inland places and have it fresh and sound. The early history of the industry has been reviewed by Taylor [102] and Stiles.[103] Cobb [104] stated that salmon were frozen as early as 1894. When frozen fish were first marketed they encountered some opposition because the quality was not high. Introduction of efficient freezers and methods for keeping them frozen soon dispelled early prejudice. The frozen fish industry is a large one today.

One of the difficulties in preservation of foods by freezing is loss of considerable water when they are thawed which means loss of flavor and nutrient substances. Investigations revealed that this was not as true

100. Harrison. 1917-1918. Contrib. Canad. Biol. and Fish.
101. Hess. 1929. Food Indus. 1, 208-212.
102. Taylor. 1927. U. S. Bur. Fisheries, Doc. 1016.
103. Stiles. 1922. Gt. Brit. Food Invest. Bd., Spec. Rpt. No. 7.
104. Cobb. 1910. Rpt. Commr. Fisheries.

with quick-frozen as with slow-frozen fish. In the former, the ice crystals are smaller and were believed to cause less rupture of tissue cells, which results in loss of moisture on thawing. While this theory is reasonable it may not explain all of the facts.

Various investigators have shown that the rate of death of bacteria in fresh frozen fish is quite high in the beginning, declines later, and becomes quite constant. Hes [105] followed growth and pigment formation of *Pseudomonas fluorescens* and *Flavobacterium deciduosum* on nutrient agar at zero and just below. They remained active at these temperatures for five weeks. Adaptation to low temperatures was observed. Gibbons [106] made similar observations. Kiser and Beckwith [107] observed a higher death rate of bacteria when frozen. A reduction of 40 to 70 per cent of viable cells was observed when marine bacteria were frozen for eight minutes at —16°C.(3.2°F.) in sea water and 99.9 per cent after 4.5 hours. Freezing at a storage temperature of —28°C.(—18.4°F.) for 10 days caused sharp reduction in the bacterial flora of muscle and intestinal contents of mackerel.

Freezing of Fish in Air. Coolers are used for this purpose, the temperatures of which are kept low enough to freeze the fish. The temperature employed is determined by various factors. It is known that rapid freezing is desired, but the expense involved causes the selection of temperatures as high as are consistent with commercial results.

Freezing in Solutions. According to Taylor,[108] use of brine for freezing fish is not a new idea. Temperatures as low as —12.2°C.(10.4°F.) may be secured with 22.4 per cent of salt and 77.6 percent of water. Taylor stated that the method, introduced a long time ago, was allowed to die out, only to be reviewed again in more recent times.

The fish are put into brine at a temperature below the freezing point of the fish. In brine at a temperature of —17.8°C.(0°F.) fish freeze in from 30 minutes to four hours. Taylor stated that there is some evidence to show that brine-frozen fish are firmer after defrosting than fish which have been frozen in the air. Fish which are frozen in air are said to have large ice crystals in the tissue which cause a breakdown in structure, leaving the fish soft. Experiments were conducted in shipping brine-frozen fish for great distances (2,200 miles in four days) without ice or insulation. They were reported to have arrived in excellent condition. In another case, brine-frozen fish were shipped 1,000 miles by parcel post in a corrugated paper carton without icing. They arrived in fine condition. It seems that brine-frozen fish can be refrozen after being defrosted. It is probable that cold brine has distinct bactericidal action. The advantages of this method of preserving fish for distribution should make it a very useful method in the future. Stiles [103] has reported results of investigations on the freezing of fish in brine. Choice of a cooling solution is limited to one which will not harm the consumer or the tissues of the fish. This practically drives the industry to common salt. Stiles quoted the work Middendorp,

105. Hes. 1934. Canad. Biol. and Fish. 8, 461-472.
106. Gibbons. 1934. Idem 8, 303-310.
107. Kiser and Beckwith. 1942. Food Research 7, 255-259.
108. Taylor. 1921. U. S. Bur. Fisheries, Circ. 53.

who observed that intake of salt varied with time, but that the intake was not the same in various parts of the fish. The wall of the body cavity seems to have the greatest affinity for salt. Almy and Field [109] studied penetration of salt into skin and superficial layers of tissues of weakfish, flounders, and whiting during immersion for different periods of time in cold brines of different temperatures and concentration. Under all conditions salt was found to penetrate under the skin and superficial muscular tissues, but in amounts too small to affect the taste of the cooked fish. The results for salt penetration with varying temperature and concentration of brine were found to be insignificant and inconsistent; fish which had been precooled to about 0°C.(32°F.), before placing in the brine absorbed only 35 to 65 per cent of the salt absorbed when immersed at ordinary temperature. The amount and rate of penetration of salt into tissues varied with the species. With weakfish and flounders, most of the salt was absorbed during the first 30 minutes, while with whiting and herring absorption was more gradual. This was thought to be due to inequalities of fat content of the subcutaneous and body tissues of the fish. Fish frozen in 15 per cent brine were found to gain slightly in weight while those frozen in air at —10°C. (14°F.) lost weight. Subsequent storage of frozen fish in air caused a greater loss. It was found possible to obtain a satisfactory glaze in brine-frozen fish by rinsing in cold water and holding in storage for 12 hours. From the standpoint of bacterial decomposition, there was little choice between the two methods. The subject has been discussed by Birdseye,[110] in reports on results of quick-freezing of animal tissue. Quick-frozen flesh passes through the zone of maximum crystal formation so that the resulting ice crystals are very small and do not rupture or compress the tissue. Birdseye compared "slow-frozen" and "quick-frozen" haddock under the microscope, finding much to favor the quick-frozen product. Birdseye's explanation for the superiority of quick-freezing was doubted by Taylor.[111]

According to Clark [112] and his colleagues, freezing of fish suffices to hold them in their original condition but will not correct any faults owing to careless handling or heat. Only fish of high quality should be frozen. Glazing by surrounding the fish with a coating of ice has distinct advantages. The moisture remains constant and the meat is protected from the action of bacteria and molds. Fish to be stored for three to five months should be reglazed. From —18 to —13°C. (—.4 to 8.6°F.) seem to be the best temperatures. Chemical analyses conducted by Clark could detect no significant changes in fish kept for 27 months or for a longer time than would ordinarily obtain under commercial conditions. Browne [113] studied the bacterial life in fish stored in ice. The fresh fish muscle seemed to be sterile. Drawn fish showed the presence of more bacteria as the storage period lengthened. Undrawn fish stored for two to three weeks in dirty

109. Almy and Field. 1921. J. Ind. Eng. Chem. 13, 927-930; 14 (1922), 203-206; Fishing Gaz., 39 (1922), 20-21.
110. Birdseye. 1929. Ind. Eng. Chem. 21, 573-576; 854-857.
111. Taylor. 1931. Food Indus. 3, 205-206.
112. Clark. 1918. West. Indian. Bull. 17, 56.
113. Browne. 1918. Abs. Bact. 2, 6.

ice showed few bacteria. Browne regards autolysis as a more important factor than bacteria in fish spoilage at low temperatures. While investigations of Clark and Almy,[114] unfortunately, involved no microbiological examination, we may probably establish by inference some of the changes which took place. Both types of fish which were examined were in good condition for 16 and 13 months when glazed with ice. Very little difference was reported between eviscerated and uneviscerated fish when stored in the glazed condition. Unopened fresh herring, examined by Sven,[115] kept well for three weeks to one month, but after this time became poorer and finally molded. Almy, Field, and Hill[116] carried on investigations to determine the relative keeping quality of different kinds of fish in the eviscerated and uneviscerated condition in ice. Sea trout and mullet remained in marketable condition five days longer than Spanish mackerel. Gutting improved the keeping quality of mullet.

Psychrophilic bacteria were found to be commonly present in spoiled ice fillets by Sanborn.[117] The fillets were about 10 months old and had been stored at —5°C.(23°F.). They showed definite signs of spoilage with evidence of bacterial decomposition. The following bacteria were held responsible for the spoilage: *Proteus vulgaris* Hansen, *Chateostylum Fresenii, Eberthella bienstockii* Schröter, *Micrococcus subcitreus* Migula, ad *Micrococcus candidus* Cohn. These organisms are, in the main, putrefactive in character and probably originate in the intestines of the fish. Sanborn believed that better methods of preparation would greatly improve keeping quality.

Very important among the factors influencing spoilage of fish is temperature of storage. Much work has been carried out on the influence of freezing and temperatures just above freezing on the bacterial flora. Nickerson and Proctor[118] followed the changes in frozen fish indicated by chemical examination and tried to relate them to the bacterial flora. The haddock were frozen within an hour of being taken from the sea and kept at —17.8°C.(0°F.) or below until examined. The samples for examination were then incubated at temperatures ranging from 0 to 15°C. 32 to 59°F.) and examined at various periods up to 120 hours. The sterile muscle samples showed a slight development of alkalinity measured as a increased pH; the amino acids showed an increase followed by a definite decrease. The ammonia nitrogen figure tended to show similar results when the fish was kept at 5 to 15°C.(41 to 59°F.). With samples which were naturally bacterially contaminated the changes were rather more pronounced and showed a slight increase in pH, a more definite rise and fall of amino acids, and greater increases in ammonia nitrogen.

Freezing by Glazing with Ice. In order to prevent loss of water from frozen fish and consequent changes caused by dehydration, Bedford[119] glazed frozen fish with a film of ice. This glaze is very brittle and cracks

114. Clark and Almy. 1920. J. Ind. Eng. Chem. 12, 656-663.
115. Sven. 1913. Centbl. Bakt., Pt. 1, Ref. 56, 701-702.
116. Almy, Field, and Hill. 1923. Amer. Food J. 18, 36-38.
117. Sanborn. 1930. J. Bact. 19, 375-382.
118. Nickerson and Proctor. 1935. J. Bact. 30, 383-394.
119. Bedford. 1936. Ice and Refrig. 90, 217-218.

easily when the fish are placed in storage. This is a satisfactory method and effectively controls bacterial development. Most of the published papers on the methods are concerned with methods of treating and storage. Proper packaging and storage of fresh fish products are quite necessary for maintenance of good qualtiy. Birdseye's [110] tests showed that packaging before freezing gives best results as regards thawing resistance, protection from deterioration, adaptability to quick-freezing manipulation, and wrapping cost. A method for testing the relative moisture-vapor-proofness of wrapping materials was devised. Comparative properties of many kinds of wrapping, packaging, and container materials are given.

Frozen fish, particularly oily fish such as salmon, become red sometimes on the cut surfaces, a condition known as "rusting." Bedford [120] believed that the cause was of bacterial origin but he did not isolate any cultures. The red pigment was believed to be a volatile substance from the bacteria which combined with the oil.

CANNED MARINE PRODUCTS

Preservation of certain marine products by canning is a large industry the world over. The problems involved are about the same as those for other canned foods, especially meats. Causes of spoilage, however, are different.

Nongaseous Spoilage. This has been found to be due to aerobic, spore-forming bacteria by Fellers.[121] The group was represented by *Bacillus cereus* and *Bacillus mesentericus*. These bacteria show variable proteolytic properties. The principal changes in the canned fish product are softening of texture, marked turbidity of liquor, slight to marked abnormal odor and taste, and occasional slight discoloration. Fellers reported this type of spoilage to be more marked in cans having low vacuum or none, though the bacteria responsible may grow and produce fewer pronounced changes in cans having good vacuum of eight to ten inches of mercury. Fellers also stressed the fact that distinction must be made between active growth of bacteria in canned foods and mere presence of inactive spores. This situation is much better understood today than when Fellers made the statement. These organisms were also encountered by Lang [73] in underprocessed cans of salmon.

Gaseous Spoilage. This is evidenced by bulged ends of the cans. The microorganisms are usually anaerobic sporeformers among which are *Clostridium welchii* and *Clostridium sporogenes*. Jarvis stated that gas formation of these types is usually accompanied by an extremely foul and offensive odor. Another gas-forming, heat-resistant anaerobe is *Clostridium botulinum*. While this organism has been found in home-canned fish products, it has not been found in factory-canned products since 1925. Lang found no thermophilic, sporeforming gas formers in cans of fish which had been processed.

Thermophilic Spoilage. Jarvis stated that thermophilic spoilage might appear in canned-fish products which are held in warm warehouses. Stor-

120. Bedford. 1934. Cold Storage 37, 66.
121. Fellers. 1927. Univ. Wash., Pub. Fisheries 1, 229-238.

age at temperatures between 4.4°C. (40°F.) to 10°C. (50°F.) will reduce thermophilic spoilage.

Home Canning of Fish and Fish Products. The microbiological problems of home canning of fishery products are the same as those for canning meats in the home. These are discussed at some length in Chapter 23. Jarvis and Griffiths [122] recommended the use of a pressure cooker for sterilization and that no tin container larger than No. 2, nor glass container larger than the wide-mouth pint jar be used. Pressure processes recommended by Jarvis and Griffiths are severe enough to yield a sterile product if strictly followed. They pointed out however, the mere use of a pressure cooker might not be enough. It must be used properly and process times counted only from the time the required temperature and pressure have been reached.

EXAMINATION OF CANNED FISH

The methods used are generally those used with other canned foods, *i.e.*, physical inspection of the containers and physical, chemical, and bacteriological examination of the contents. All of these examinations must be made by those who are competent in each field. Savage *et al.*,[77] Jarvis [123] and Clark, Clough, Fellers, and Shostrom [124] have prepared recommended procedures for examination of canned-fish products. All of them cannot be reproduced here.

Lang's [125] Procedure for Microbiological Examination of Canned-Fish Products. The suggested bacteriological methods concern chiefly the examination of so-called "non-acid," "low-salt" canned fishery products. Such products may be examined for sterility (keeping qualities) or for causes of spoilage owing to inadequate · retort process or mechanical imperfections of the container. Sample cans that are submitted for sterility are in the main normal in appearance. Those cans submitted for determination of spoilage causes are usually abnormal to a degree that characterizes them as "flippers," "springers," "soft swells," or "hard swells." These cans may be further defective in that they have certain mechanical imperfections, such as dents owing to rough handling, faulty cover or side seams, or perforations.

PRELIMINARY INCUBATION

All normal cans submitted for sterility tests and examination for keeping quality should be incubated at 37.5°C. (99°F.) for a period of one month prior to cultural examination. Cans should be laid on their sides in the incubator to prevent drying of the can seams. It is well also to move the container slightly at intervals during the course of incubation. A record should be made of any changes occurring in the condition of the container during incubation.

Although an incubation period of one month is proposed here the time of incubation adopted and reported in the literature by other investigators has been found to vary. Weinzirl [126] used seven days or longer at 37.5°C.; Savage, Hunwicke, and Calder [77] used incubation periods of "several weeks," and Cheyney [127] records one to six weeks, with a two weeks' period as the general average. Cameron,[128] in his report on "Methods for the Examination of Canned Meats," states:

. . . unspoiled samples submitted for examination as to keeping quality should be incubated at 37.5°C. for a period of one month. This time of incubation, necessarily

122. Jarvis and Griffiths. 1936. U. S. Bur. Fisheries, Rpt. No. 2.
123. Jarvis. 1940. Canning Age, July and Sept., 1940.
124. Clark *et al.* 1923. Pacific Fisherman 21, 8 *et seq.*
125. Lang. 1938. J. Assoc. Off. Agr. Chem. 21, 449-452. Reprinted by permission.
126. Weinzirl. 1919. J. Med. Res. 39, 349.
127. Cheyney. 1919. Idem 40, 177.
128. Cameron. 1937. J. Assoc. Off. Agr. Chem. 20, 129.

an arbitrary matter, is considered the longest period that is practicable in the usual case. Anaerobes, which at times may remain dormant for many months, may escape detection, but usually the likelihood of spoilage in the product under ordinary commercial conditions of handling is indicated in this time. It is regarded as unnecessary to incubate at thermophilic temperature, *i.e.*, 55°C., because such spoilage in meat products is extremely rare.

The same conditions cited by Cameron prevail with respect to nonacid canned fishery products, as with meat products, it is unnecessary to test for thermophilic bacteria by incubating at 55°C. according to Lang.[73]

A. Physical Examination and Preparation of the Can.

1. Make a complete set of records concerning the cans submitted (origin of samples, type of product, code marks, label, pertinent information concerning raw material and its pretreatment, and retort processes).

2. Make a record of the condition of the samples, noting mechanical defects, perforations, rust spots, dents, and all other can abnormalites. When spoilage is involved, ascertain the extent and determine whether one or several days' packs are affected.

3. Take all possible precautions to provide aseptic conditions when the cans are opened for cultural or enrichment examination. Have available a clean and disinfected table or desk top constructed of some type of impervious material. (If air-borne contamination is imminent, it is advisable to carry out the cultural or enrichment procedure in a previously disinfected room, or under a hood especially designed for this purpose.) Scrub the container with sand soap, using a brush and warm water. To remove grease, oil, or outside lacquer, wipe the can with some suitable solvent (a solution of equal parts of ethyl alcohol and ethyl ether is recommended).

4. Sterilize the surface of the can at the point to be opened by holding and slowly rotating the can inverted in the flame of a Bunsen burner. (Rotating will serve to secure an even area of sterilization and will prevent scorching the contents.) Heat flat or normal cans in this manner until one of the ends becomes distended, since internal pressure promotes an expelling action ,and helps to avoid contamination when the can is opened. When examining swollen cans do the flaming with caution, and if necessary reduce the internal pressure by refrigeration of the container prior to flaming. When flaming is not practicable, follow the procedure involving treatment with bichloride of mercury (1 + 100) described by Fellers,[129] or that suggested by Cameron,[128] calling for thorough cleansing with 60 per cent alcohol.

B. Removal of Sample.

1. Open the can at the point of sterilization with a suitable and previously sterilized opener. Have the opening as close to the center of the cover as possible and only large enough to permit adequate sampling. (A long handled can opener designed to cut in the circular direction in which the cutting edge travels as the circumference of a circle is best adapted for this purpose. This type of can opener lends itself quite readily to individual wrapping and sterilization, and also has the added advantage of preventing contact of the analyst's hands with the sterilized portion of the can.)

2. Determine the type of instrument to be used for removing the inoculum by the nature of the product under examination. (This operation is discussed by Tanner.[130]) For consistently satisfactory results for canned fishery products use either large aperture pipets or sterile teaspoons, depending upon the product. Sample liquid or semiliquid products with large-bore, untapered, sterile pipets. Sample solid materials wtih teaspoons or other suitable instruments, such as cork borers or brass tubes that have been sterilized.[131] (One advantage in using teaspoons is that a separate spoon may be used for each can, the spoons having been previously sterilized by being placed in a large metal receptacle and subjected to 15 pounds' pressure for 60 minutes.) Remove from the product a representative sample of 10 to 15 grams of material for inoculation into culture media. In making the inoculations carefully observe that the ratio of the volume

129. Fellers. 1936. J. Assoc. Off. Agr. Chem. 19, 430.
130. Tanner. 1936. Idem 19, 432.
131. J. Assoc. Off. Agr. Chem. 20 (1937), 431.

of the sample to that of the medium is not such as to affect the *pH* of the medium. If the can contents are fluid, tube and plate cultures may be made directly. If the material is solid, it may be inoculated directly into medium wide-mouthed flasks, which are cork stoppered and covered with vegetable parchment paper, or if plate cultures are desired, the solid material may be shaken in a sterile bottle with sterile broken glass and sterile saline solution until a proper suspension is secured for use as inoculum.

Place an additional sample in a sterile flask and hold in reserve under refrigeration for possible re-examination or for toxicity tests.

C. Culture Media

Prepare both anaerobic and aerobic cultures from the material secured as a sample. In preparing anaerobic cultures, use an unheated portion of the sample and a portion that has been heated for 30 minutes at 80°C.(176°F.) to destroy vegetative forms in order to test for the presence of anaerobic spores. Prepare an aerobic broth culture. (The preparation of plate cultures is optional and may be desirable under some circumstances.)

The culture media suggested by Cameron,[132] are well adapted to the examination of fishery products. Those prepared from dehydrated media marketed by the Difco Laboratories, Inc., Detroit, Michigan, are especially suitable. Considerable success has been attained with the following media, which are also recommended:

Beef Heart Broth

Distilled water	1000 ml.
Minced fresh fat-free beef heart	500 grams
Difco Neopeptone	10 grams
C. P. NaCl	5 grams

With the exception of the NaCl, mix the ingredients in a steam kettle and boil for approximately 10 minutes. Remove the broth, filter, and adjust to *p*H 7.6 to 7.8 Boil gently for approximately 10 minutes, filter, and add the salt. Bottle or tube, preferably in hard glass containers, and sterilize for 20 minutes at 115°C.(239°F.). The range of the final *p*H should be from 7.0 to 7.4.

Beef Heart Agar

Add two per cent of agar to the above broth; or preferably mix the shredded agar with 500 ml. of the distilled water required, using the other 500 ml. for the preparation of the infusion. Then mix the two portions.

Heart Meat Broth for Anaerobic Enrichment

Place the residue of the ground beef hearts approximately 1 to 1.5 inches deep, into wide-mouthed flasks or tubes. Add the beef heart broth to bring the supernatant liquid 1 to 1.5 inches above the meat, stratify with vaseline, and sterilize in the autoclave at 10 pounds' steam pressure for 20 minutes.

(It is recommended that all culture media be incubated for 24 to 48 hours before use.)

D. Incubation and Culture Study.

Incubate all cultures for at least 48 hours at 37.5°C., and if practicable incubate anaerobic cultures at least 72 hours.

Use the Manual of Methods for Pure Culture Study of Bacteria of the Society of American Bacteriologists as a guide for the further study of microorganisms obtained in the cultural procedure described.

Clark, Clough, Fellers, and Shostrom's [124] Methods for Examination of Canned Salmon. While these procedures were proposed for canned salmon they may probably be used with other canned-fish products. The following instructions have been abstracted from their report:

Description of Parcel. This should be complete as possible, including the species of salmon, the brand and label, the name of the packer, the name of the cannery, the

---

132. Cameron. 1937. J. Assoc. Off. Agr. Chem. 20, 432.

size of the can, the can mark, the case mark, the number of cans or cases, and the exact location of the parcel, with any other data which may be of use in identifying that particular lot of salmon. It is also a good practice to keep copies of the label and to file one with the report. Special attention should be given to the code marks on cans; if different markers were used that fact should be mentioned.

Sampling. Attempt should be made to secure a representative sample by taking one or two cans from a considerable number of cases. Sampling of such products is not easy. If the cans were coded, the problem might not be so difficult. With uncoded packs, some system must be worked out which will permit a representative selection of cans.

When the cases are opened for sampling, they should be examined for swelled, rusty, or leaky cans as well as for the condition of the lacquer and labels. ''Swells,'' ''leakers,'' and badly dented or other obviously abnormal cans should not be included among ordinary samples but percentage of such cans should be determined by careful inspection of all cans in the case. If examination of half of the cans selected from large parcels are found to be of high quality, the remaining half should be retained for a time. These may be used later for checking results of examination and for settling differences of opinion. Not less than 24 to 48 cans should be cut.

Bacteriological and Microscope Examination. A suitable percentage of cans should be examined bacteriologically for presence of living microorganisms. Usually one case of 48 cans is examined if the parcel consists of 1,000 cases or less, but the number tested naturally varies with the quality and character of the salmon, the destination of the shipment, and the information desired. Since the results of careful physical examination of the salmon is of great value in interpreting bacteriological results, the same cans should be used for both tests. If possible it is desirable to incubate 24 or more cans at 30°C.(86°F.) for a week or 10 days to observe whether ''swells'' or ''springers'' appear.

Technic of Taking Cultures. The tops of the cans are carefully cleaned with a disinfectant and sterilized with a gas flame. After cooling, the vacuum is taken and the can immediately pierced with a hot brad-awl about the size of a small lead pencil. Through this opening samples of liquor containing small pieces of flesh are drawn by means of a large pipette and inoculated into suitable nutrient media. The inoculated plates and tubes are usually incubated at 30°C.(86°F.) for 48 to 72 hours before being examined. After that they may be incubated for an additional 48 hours at 55°C. (131°F.) to test for presence of heat-resistant, thermophilic bacteria.

Direct Microscope Examination. Such examination of the liquor is sometimes of value; one may often determine immediately whether active spoilage is present. Results of this method are often of value for confirming results of physical and chemical examinations.

Interpretation of Results. The unusually high processing temperature used in processing salmon precludes the possibility of survival of any but most resistant spore-forming bacteria. When cocci or nonsporeforming rods are present, it is probable that they gained entrance to the can through a leaky gasket or other similar leak. Of course, they may be present owing to gross understerilization. By far the most common organisms found in canned salmon are the harmless, heat-resistant, aerobic, spore-forming bacteria. Anaerobic bacteria which cause intense putrefaction are more rarely found and if present usually form gas and cause swells which are eliminated at the cannery. The bacterium which causes botulism has never been found in commercially canned salmon and it is believed that the usual cook of 115.6°C.(240°F.) for 90 minutes is a safe one to use. Since the bacteria usually found in canned salmon are harmless, unless they cause spoilage within the can, their presence can be of but little significance. Both aerobes and anaerobes, when present, are usually in the form of inactive or dormant spores and do not multiply greatly within the can, owing to the unfavorable environment or unsuitable food substances present. Occasionally incipient bacterial spoilage without the production of swells is found in canned salmon, though it is not at all common.

Molds and yeasts are very seldom found in canned salmon, except in leaky cans. Uncooked salmon is decomposed principally by the active bacteria of the colon aerogenes group, though many cocci and other types may be present. These bacteria usually form gases composed of carbon dioxide and hydrogen, and sometimes other products, such as indol. By bacteriological examination of a large number of empty cans and salt obtained at salmon canneries, it has been found that they contain many spore-forming and other kinds of bacteria, yeasts, and molds usually such as are normally present in soil, dust, and air. It is believed that most of the sporeforming bacteria found in non-sterile cans of salmon are introduced in this way.

SARDINES

The sardine industry is well established in many parts of the world. Packing sardines, according to the practice in Maine, has been carefully studied and discussed by Weber.[133] This fish derives its name from the island of Sardinia about which it was originally found. The name is now applied to various species of small fish which are canned.

Considerable spoilage may occur in the packing of sardines. Much of it is of bacteriological interest. One great source of trouble in the sardine industry is what fishermen call "feedy" fish, *i.e.*, fish which are gorged with food at the time of catching. Such fish go to pieces quickly after removal from water, while those with little food in their stomachs keep much longer. The best method of coping with this difficulty is not to attempt to pack such fish, to eviscerate the fish before packing, or to allow the food to be digested before packing.

The fish packed in Maine as sardines are caught in weirs which are placed in shallow water. From the weirs they are seined and transferred to the fishing boats. The fish are salted in the boat at the rate of 190 to 450 pounds of salt per hogshead (about five barrels) of fish. If the salt is added dry, it draws out the water. When the fishing boat has arrived at the cannery, the fish are taken by means of different devices to the pickling room where they are stored in brine of a strength depending somewhat on that used on the fishing boat. From the pickling solution they are passed to the flaking machine, the fish usually remaining intact. They are evenly distributed on the flakes which are wire screens about three by two feet. On these flakes, they pass through the rest of the steps to the can. The flakes with fish are then steamed for 10 to 15 minutes in a steam chest after which they are taken to a drying room. If the sardines are to be fried in oil, they are not steamed but are dried as usual. From the friers they are taken to the packing room where, after the heads have been removed, they are packed into cans. Oil is then added, either by a special machine, or by a special attachment on the closing machine. Various types of oil are used, cotton seed, olive, etc., depending on the quality of fish which is being packed. After sealing, the cans are processed in boiling water for a varying length of time of from one and three-fourths to even two and one-half hours. Hovden [134] described a different procedure for canning California sardines. The fish are cleaned and thoroughly washed in running salt water. They are not salted. They are thoroughly dried in trays and thoroughly cooked in ovens. All California sardines are pressure processed. Another description of the methods of packing was published

133. Weber. 1921. U. S. Dept. Agr. Bull. 908.
134. Hovden. 1923. The Canner, Jan. 20, 1923.

by Beard.[135] Lang[73] observed progressive increase in the number of bacteria in sardines as they were prepared for the can. In the cutting room where are located both the receiving and brining tanks the fish were usually heavily contaminated. After that the number of bacteria decreased. No true aerobic thermophilic bacteria were observed by Lang. Four main sources of contamination were sea water, air or dust, raw materials, and the empty container. Coliform bacteria were present in sea water. These organisms were believed to originate in the polluted water from which the fish were taken. They were never found in the intestines of the fish.

Processing of Canned Sardines. In his extensive description of the packing of Maine sardines, Weber[133] gave special attention to processing or sterilization. The sealed cans are processed in tanks of boiling water for one and three-fourths to two and one-fourth, sometimes two and one-half hours, according to the individual packer's idea of the time necessary for sterilization. One or two canneries give the cans a pressure cook in retorts of 110°C.(230°F.) for 30 minutes. This does not seem to affect the quality of the fish. Esty[136] reported experimental work carried out to determine the proper pressure cook for sardines packed in oil and mustard. Esty inoculated the cans with an organism which had been isolated from swelled cans of sardines. Cans inoculated with 1,000,000 spores gave 100 per cent swells after process at 100°C.(212°F.) for 210 minutes, 100 per cent swells in cans containing 10,000 spores and processed at 100°C.(212°F.) for 180 minutes. Temperatures of 107.2°C.(225°F.), 110°C.(230°F.), and 115.5°C. (240°F.) gave sterile cans.

Microbiology of Canned Sardines. Not many investigations have been carried out on the presence of viable bacteria in canned sardines. Obst[137] found a bacillus possibly identical with *Bacillus walfishrauschbrand* in pure culture in 287 cans of swelled sardines. Koch's postulates were satisfied. using this organism and sound cans of sardines. The organism was an aerobic, gas-producing, nonsporeforming bacillus. Obst inoculated it into cans which were then processed according to the usual factory methods and temperatures. She was able to fulfill Koch's postulates with the above-mentioned organism and believed that it was identical with Nielsen's[138] organism. It was reported to be quite resistant and to survive boiling for one and one-half hours under the conditions of the experiment.

Weber had an opportunity to study the cause of "swells" in sardines. It soon became evident that the cause of swells in cans and also the so-called "belly breaking" of "feedy" fish was bacteriological. Weber found no aerobic bacteria in swelled cans of sardines, but *Bacillus walfishrauschbrand* Nielsen, a rapid sporeformer, was isolated in pure culture. This organism, according to Weber, was an organism found by Nielsen in whales made sick by being shot with arrows previously inoculated with material from dead whales. Weber also found another organism called Bacillus B. This organism was pathogenic to mice and guinea pigs and produced about

135. Beard. 1926. Canning Age, April, 1927.
136. Esty. 1925. The Canner, March 7, 1925.
137. Obst. 1919. J. Infect. Dis. 24, 158-169.
138. Nielsen. 1880. Centbl. Bakt. 7, 267-271.

the same decomposition as that produced by Nielsen's organism. It did not, however, form spores and was, therefore, much less resistant to heat.

Sadler[139] and his colleagues have published several reports on the spoilage of canned sardines. Most of their organisms seemed to be of the colon-aerogenes type. *Bacillus vulgaris* Hansen was also found. The fish seemed to be infected during packing. Cathcart[140] found bacteria of the coliform type in cans of sardines which gave off gas when they were opened. Sadler, in general, confirmed the conclusions reached by Weber.[133] The National Canners Association at its Eastport, Maine, Laboratory under the direction of Bartlett,[141] carried on some bacteriological studies on sardines. They were able to confirm Obst's conclusions. Bartlett stated that most of the swells of canned sardines were caused by members of the *Escherichia coli* group. These organisms were isolated from fish which were distended with gas as well as from pickle in which "feedy fish" were lying.

A recent survey of sardine canning in Maine by Highlands and Williams[139a] revealed a small number of bacteria in and on the fish and absence of heat resistant types. Anaerobes occurred irregularly and were not numerous. Eight per cent of salt was observed to inhibit bacteria over a commercially practicable holding time. These observations explain why spoilage troubles are infrequent in the Maine sardine canning industry.

Relation of Clostridium botulinum to Fish Canning. This organism is a constant threat to the canning industry, and information as to its presence in raw materials or on articles used in canning is always pertinent. Lang[73] observed it in slime of tuna. Type A toxin was observed in cultures from fish slime and the cleaned fish just before canning. Lang also found *Clostridium botulinum* in washings of empty sardine cans; one per cent of cultures made from washings of 200 sardine cans showed presence of Type A toxin.

Heat-resistance studies on *Clostridium botulinum* by Lang showed considerable variation among the products used. The following results were reported.

Product	Destruction time at 121.1°C. (250°F.) in minutes
Abalone	1.57
Kamaboko	8.97
Mackerel in brine	2.44
Sardines in brine	2.34
Sardines in mustard sauce	6.55
Sardines in oil	8.00
Sardines in tomato sauce	3.66
Shad	1.58
Shad roe	5.61
Squid in ink	0.69
Tempra	6.17
Tuna in oil	6.95

139. Sadler. 1919. Roy. Soc. Canada, Proc. and Trans. 3, Ser. 13, Sect. V. 135-141.
139a. Highlands and Williams. 1943. Food Research.
140. Cathcart. 1906. J. Hyg. 6, 248-250.
141. Bartlett. 1919. The Canner 48, 52.

In oil packs, resistance of *Clostridium botulinum* to heat was much greater. Lang attributed this to differences in the rate of heat penetration into oils over that of moisture alone or a mixture of moisture and oil as well as to the subsequent trapping effect of the oil. Suggested processes for canned-fish products, which will not be presented here, were suggested by Lang.

Sour Pickling or Marinating of Fish. Much fish is pickled in vinegar and a wide field has been opened up. Abst [142] discussed this food, both from the standpoint of flavor as well as keeping quality. The fish is thoroughly washed before salting and addition of vinegar. Better results were secured when the vinegar was boiled and the containers sterilized. Herring is most used in the marinating industry. Abst stated that the first requirement in the preparation of Bismarck herring was to thoroughly cleanse the fresh fish in water and remove the scales. The fish are then drained, the heads cut off, and the entrails removed. The fish are washed in running water again, and carefully drained, then put into a five to six per cent vinegar pickle, containing considerable salt. They remain in this pickle for three to four days, depending on the size. They are then placed in sterilized boxes with the addition of mustard seeds and peppercorns between the layers. They are then covered with a two to three per cent vinegar, containing sugar. The cans are immediately soldered.

Hiedewohl and Henneberg [143] examined swelled cans of marinated herring, finding only acetic acid bacteria with no sporeformers or putrefactive bacteria. In some cases, swells were due to hydrogen, resulting from the action of acid on the metal of the container. Addition of at least two per cent of acetic acid to the liquor was said to be necessary to prevent spoilage by lactic acid bacteria.

SHELLFISH

Since shellfish of various kinds are usually harvested from polluted water they may be public-health problems. The evidence on this point is now accepted. They have been responsible for many outbreaks of typhoid fever and other similar infections. Some of these are discussed in the paragraphs immediately to follow. The significance of this problem is emphasized when it is remembered that the cases of communicable disease caused by them are not confined to the areas where the shellfish are harvested but may extend to great distances inland. Such has been the case with oysters. Stiles [144] reported that cooking would not always destroy objectionable bacteria when they were present. Cooking will not destroy many saprophytic bacteria in fish muscle.

General Sanitation in the Shellfish Industry. For many years practices were permitted in the shellfish industry which did not promote distribution of a sanitary product. In 1932 a committee [145] of the American Public Health Association pointed to the need for improved sanitation of the

142. Abst.
143. Heidewohl and Henneberg. 1930. Deut. Essig. Indus. 34, 177.
144. Stiles. 1911. Amer. J. Pub. Health 1, 623.
145. Hunter (Chairman). 1933. Amer. Pub. Health Assoc. Year Book 1932-1933. 58-61; Fishing Gazette, Nov., 1933.

sea-food industry. They mentioned the necessity for prompt and careful handling of the shellfish and need for proper equipment. Since these early discussions much progress has been made as indicated below under the several types of shellfish.

OYSTERS

On account of the unsanitary conditions of water in which oysters are raised, their control has been a constant problem for health officials. The comprehensive publication by Hunter and Harrison [146] reviews these problems, and Orton [147] has shown how the physiology of the oyster is related to its function in disseminating pathogenic bacteria. Care must be used in generalizing with respect to sanitary quality of oysters from results of water analysis. While the sanitary quality of oysters agrees generally with the quality of water, Fisher and Asker [148] did not observe a strict relationship. Both were better in the winter.

Significance of Oysters in Dissemination of Disease. About 1880 [149] Sir Charles Cameron, health officer of Dublin, discussed relation of oysters to typhoid fever before the British Medical Association. Little attention was given the subject until 1895 when Sir William Broadbent attributed cases of typhoid fever to contaminated oysters. Conn,[150] in a fine epidemiological investigation in the United States, proved to the satisfaction of those interested in public health that an outbreak of typhoid fever among those who had attended a fraternity banquet at Wesleyan University was caused by infected oysters. The chain of evidence was so complete that the relation of insanitary oyster beds to disease was established. Since that time many similar investigations have confirmed Conn's work. Among them were investigatons by Klein,[151] Fuller,[152] Digby and Shenton,[153] Phelps,[154] Gorham,[155] Stiles,[156] Joseph,[157] and many others. In the United States relation of oysters to disease dissemination was not known until Conn did his work. Stiles [156] gave an extended bibliography of contributions to the subject in his publication. Even though it is definitely known that oysters may harbor *Eberthella typhosa*, outbreaks of typhoid fever continue to be traced to them. Banks [158] reported 42 cases of typhoid fever in San Diego, California, from polluted oysters. The etiologic significance of oysters may often be overlooked, especially in inland cities. Brooks [159] reported 50 cases of typhoid fever as due to oysters. Earlier contributions had been made by Pease,[160] Soper,[161] and Stiles.[162]

146. Hunter and Harrison. 1928. U. S. Dept. Agr., Bull. 64.
147. Orton. 1928. Roy. Sanit. Inst. J. 49, 263-274.
148. Fisher and Asker. 1935.
149. Editorial, J. Amer. Med. Assoc., March 28, 1903, 860.
150. Conn. 1894. Weekly Abs. Sanit. Rpts. 9, 1172.
151. Klein. 1903. Brit. Med. J., Feb. 21, 1903.
152. Fuller. 1902. Science 15, 363-364.
153. Digby and Shenton. 1906. Surveyor 30, 653-655.
154. Phelps. 1911. J. Amer. Pub. Health Assoc. 1, 305-308.
155. Gorham. 1912. Amer. J. Pub. Health 2, 24; 77-86.
156. Stiles. 1912. U. S. Dept. Agr., Bur. Chem. Bull. 156.
157. Joseph. 1914. Johns Hopkins Hosp., Bull. 25, 128-131.
158. Banks. 1917. Calif. State Bd. Health, Monthly Bull. 12, 1403.
159. Brooks. 1916. J. Amer. Med. Assoc. 66, 1445.
160. Pease . 1912. Fifteenth Intern.tl. Cong. Hyg. and Demog. Trans.
161. Soper. 1912. Fifteenth Interntl. Cong. Hyg. and Demog. Trans.
162. Stiles. 1912. U. S. Dept. Agr., Bur. Chem. Bull. 156.

The largest and best-known outbreaks of typhoid fever caused by oysters were those in Chicago and New York City in 1925. The great prevalence of typhoid fever in these cities from oysters caused a conference to be called by the Surgeon General of the U. S. Public Health Service in Washington, in February, 1925.[163] Over 150 delegates, consisting of health and food officials and representatives of the oyster industry from 28 different states, convened. The conference arrived at resolutions which, if obeyed by oyster growers and shippers, would make oysters better and safer for use as food.

Bundesen [164] reported a study of an apparently oyster-borne outbreak of typhoid fever in Chicago involving 129 verified cases. The epidemological evidence seemed very convincing that oysters were the cause. Bundesen stated that the New York City outbreak had started about two weeks before. According to Bundesen, blue point oysters were the cause of 65.1 per cent of cases of typhoid fever in Chicago. Part of the epidemic in New York concurrent with the Chicago outbreak was probably due to the same lot of oysters. Harris [165] summarized the characteristics of the New York City oyster-borne typhoid-fever epidemic as did Lumsden, Hasseltine, Leake, and Veldee [163] in Supplement 50 of the Public Health Reports. To prevent further outbreaks of typhoid fever from oysters, Harris advised that greater attention must be given to sources of oysters and the conditions under which they are shipped and handled.

Numerous bacteriological investigations have been reported to convince one of the danger. Fuller [166] carried out observations on oysters in Narragansett Bay. The sewage of the city of Providence, which amounted then to about 14,000,000 gallons per day, was discharged into Narragansett Bay and carried out by the tide, coming into more or less contact with some of the oyster beds. Samples of water and oysters were collected from different localities, and analyses were made of the material while still quite fresh. The results showed that the water, oysters, mussels, and clams for a distance of a quarter of a mile from the sewer opening contained *Escherichia coli* and *Aerobacter aerogenes*. The water and oysters from a bed two miles below the sewer contained the same organism. Thirty per cent of the oysters and about 60 per cent of the water samples from a bed situated in a strong tidal current five miles from the sewer contained *Escherichia coli*. Forty per cent of the oysters and 70 per cent of the water samples from a bed in sluggish water five and one-fourth miles from the sewer contained the bacteria, and oysters from a bed six miles were also infested.

Purification of Oysters. The fact that oysters may often be harvested from polluted waters makes it necessary to subject them to purification procedures several of which yield a satisfactory product. Dodgson-[167] believed that sewage pollution seriously prejudices the oyster industry. Since

163. Lumsden, Hasseltine, Leake, and Veldee. 1925. Pub. Health Rpts., Sup. No. 50.
164. Bundesen. 1925. J. Amer. Med. Assoc. 84, 841-850.
165. Harris. 1925. N. Y. City Dept. Health, Mo. Bull. 15, 18-25.
166. Fuller. 1902. Science 15, 363-364.
167. Dodgson. 1930. Rev. in Biol Abs. 6, 2323.

it is impracticable to eliminate it, the solution seems to lie in purification under government control such as is carried out in England and other countries. Purification is accomplished largely by physiological functioning of the shellfish in sterilized water. They are not exposed to chemical disinfection until purification is completed, when they are immersed for one hour in water containing three p.p.m. of active chlorine. The rationale of purification depends on immobilization of sewage bacteria in the mucoid discharges of the shellfish. The shellfish circulate the water in the tanks many times through their gills during purification, filtering out and immobilizing any bacteria originally free in the water. For this reason sterilization of the water is not essential but is practiced as an added precaution. Dodgson established a standard of purity of not more than five coliform bacteria per milliliter of shellfish substance. Regulations have been enacted in England [168] to protect the public from contaminated oysters. If sanitary inspection of the oyster grounds indicates that the shellfish are polluted, they must be purified by an acceptable method. The American Public Health Association [169] passed a resolution against water storage cleansing, or conditioning of shellfish in certified bodies of water which do not at all times meet the U. S. Treasury Department standards for drinking water. Natural bodies of water which are subject to constant pollution should not be used. In other words, only water of high sanitary quality shall be used.

The splendid work of Dodgson [170] on purification of shellfish has been referred to at various places in this chapter. On several occasions he has described procedures which are employed by the Ministry of Agriculture and Fisheries in Great Britain for control and purification of edible oysters and mussels. Although reference will be made in other places to his work, a general summary of these methods may be given here.

"Oysters and mussels harvested from polluted water areas as a result of extended experimentation are spread on wooden grids in large concrete tanks, hosing them thoroughly at the start, midway, and at the end of the process. They are exposed for two successive periods of 24 hours to water sterilized by chlorine but from which all trace of active chlorine has been removed by sodium hyposulphite, and finally sterilizing the shells by a bath of water containing three p.p.m. of active chlorine. In winter time the oyster baths must be heated artificially to about 54°F., as oysters will not function at the colder water temperatures. The actual purification of the oyster body is, therefore, done by the shellfish themselves flushing out the impurities by means of the sterile water ingested. It was found that chlorine, various hypochlorites, and chloramines interfere with normal functioning and elimination and either prevent or interfere with purification in some degree. Hence the shell sterilization bath is delayed until treatment is complete. This two-day self-purification procedure reduces the lactose-fermenting bacteria from some hundreds or more per ml. to from 0 to 5 per ml. from which the required standard came to be established of not more than five lactose-fractors per ml. Extended bacteriological examinations demonstrate that the above procedure affords a ready method of meeting the standard requirements and had eliminated the transmission of disease through the eating of contaminated shellfish. A considerable discussion of various phases of the bacteriological findings is given, including the natural multiplication of lactose fermenters in polluted sea water and tank water, the advisability of

168. Bull. Hyg. 10 (1935), 137.
169. Amer. Pub. Health Assoc. Year Book, 1937-1938, 36.
170. Dodgson. 1937. Pub. Health 50, 279-284.

conducting the tests at 42°C. or 44°C. instead of at 37°C. and the possibility of multiplication of organisms of the typhoid group in water. The author stresses his view that topographical observations, properly carried out must provide the real criterion of the safety of shellfish growing areas. In other words, the possibility of pollution of the layings is the essential matter and bacteriological examinations are merely ancillary, often unnecessary, and not infrequently misleading.''

Floating. For years oyster growers placed oysters in fresh water in order to remove salt and to cleanse them. The Bureau of Chemistry about 1909 investigated this practice and insisted that such oysters should be labeled ''Floated Oysters.'' In June, 1927, the Bureau of Chemistry prohibited the shipment of floated oysters. (See Food Inspection Decision 110.) Nelson's [171] work seemed to favor the practice of ''floating'' oysters, which was widely prevalent in the North. Oysters are kept on submerged floats in water with less salt than that of the beds; during this time they draw in water as they do in the original beds. This process is called ''floating,'' ''giving the oysters a drink,'' ''freshening,'' and ''fattening.'' The resulting advantages are said to be removal of the mucous, increased volume of the flesh of the oyster, improvement in color and texture, decrease in amount and rapidity of shrinkage, and better retention of water content in transport and storage. In the experiments reported by Nelson, half of the sample from each bed was floated, then compared with the half not so treated. The results of 25 selected experiments were presented. Except in the case of certain ones injured in handling, oysters were found to regulate the amount and quality of the water they ''breathe,'' opening only when the incoming tide brings water containing a certain proportion of salt and refusing to open in fresh water. The process of floating enabled the oysters to rid themselves of the dirt brought from the beds, hence the floated product appeared cleaner. An improvement in color was also noted. When unfloated oysters were shucked in comparison with floated ones, and the two lots were left a few hours in their natural liquor, the former secreted liquor more rapidly, and also considerable slime, in which the coarser part of the dirt becomes entangled. This slime became stringy and the liquor turbid and repulsive, owing to the dirt that was mixed with it. In strong contrast, was the clean and appetizing appearance of the floated lot; here, at first, the liquor was rather small in amount, but as much as in the former cases was finally pressed out through contractions of the tissues. It seemed that the total slime in the two cases was finally approximately equal, though at the start the floated lot seemed to be the more slimy. It was claimed that no deception is involved in the process, since it seems to be impossible to improve the appearance of a poor oyster by it. Water entering the tissues, as it does in the process of floating, is more firmly retained than that held by capillary attraction in the channels of the body, and much more firmly retained than that between the oyster and the shell. This retained water, the author believed, improves the keeping and cooking qualities. No significance was attached to the loss of flavor, as this is said to be due merely to loss of salt which can easily be replaced before serving. It appears to be impossible to have the floats near the beds, or at least it is much more convenient to have them near the storehouses. Nelson concluded that the practice of floating is not injurious if the water in which the oysters are floated is pure, and that the practice is desirable on account of the improvement in the oyster. It was suggested that both floated and unfloated oysters be admitted to the market, since a demand for both kinds exists, and in time the demand for the floated product will be so great as to give it the greater value. Nelson noticed that the experiments were rather limited and that a more prolonged study of the question was desirable. Bodin [172] and Fabre-Domergue [173] floated oysters in tanks through which artificial sea water was pumped. They believed that oysters were purified as quickly in this manner as when floated in natural sea water.

A fairly complete bacteriological study of the process was made by Krumwiede, Park, Cooper, Brund, Tyler, and Rosenstein.[174] Lightly and heavily contaminated oysters

171. Nelson. 1910. New Jersey Agr. Expt. Sta., Ann. Rpt. 209-217.
172. Bodin. 1912. Compt. Rend. Acad. Sci. 154, 446-447.
173. Fabre-Domergue. 1912. Idem 154. 1257-1259.
174. Krumwiede et al. 1928. Amer. J. Pub. Health 18, 48-52.

were used at temperatures high enough to ensure active drinking by oysters. They were placed in natural waters, i.e., ensuring very great changes in the water from tidal flow. Under such conditions oysters native to the water cleared themselves of typhoid bacilli between the 11th and 24th days; oysters obtained from relatively distant waters, between the 9th and 16th days. The original contamination with typhoid bacilli was obtained by causing them to drink in sea water containing feces contaminated with this bacillus. Another experiment with sea water showed that *Eberthella typhosa* may survive in sea water between 19 and 24 days. From their experiments Krumwiede and his colleagues concluded that oysters contaminated with *Eberthella typhosa*, when actively drinking in their natural habitat, become noninfectious in three weeks. Consequently, they believed that an ordinance allowing the transfer of oysters from doubtful waters to clean waters during the closed season, with the provision that no dredging in the latter waters be allowed for a period of four weeks after the transfer, covers observed facts and gives a reasonably generous margin of safety.

An experimental plant for conditioning oysters was built in Norfolk by Messer and Reece.[175] About four gallons of water per bushel of oysters were needed per hour at a water temperature of $10°C.(50°F.)$; at lower temperatures less water was needed. Results of five bacteriological samplings showed reductions of not less than 95 per cent in 30 hours at a temperature range between $9.4°C.(49°F.)$ and $11.7°C.(53°F.)$. Messer and Reece believed that conditioning in tanks was possible with modern equipment and proper methods. Good results were reported by Tohyama and Yasukawa[174] by transfer to uncontaminated water. Even in sea water slightly polluted they reported a reduction of 500 million *Escherichia coli* to 41 in three and one-half days. In naturally infected oysters the *Escherichia coli* score is usually under 500 and rarely beyond 2,000 to 2,300; such oysters will cleanse themselves more rapidly. In clean water Tohyama and Yasukawa thought a stay of 24 to 48 hours was sufficient.

Transplanting. Oysters are frequently transplanted from the beds in which they have been propagated into clean water free from sewage. It has been found that they cleanse themselves in a short time. In polluted water objectionable bacteria may reach the intestinal tract; when the oyster is placed in pure water these are washed out. The rapidity of the cleansing process depends on various conditions. Studies on the rate of purification have been made by Round,[177] Phelps,[178] Bulstrode and Klein,[179] Johnstone,[180] and others.

Gorham [181] pointed out that there is a seasonal variation in the bacterial content of oysters, which should be considered in sanitary work. Oysters collected from one bed in February scored zero, while those collected in May scored 100. From the experimental data presented, Gorham concluded that in warm weather the results of bacterial analyses of oysters "tally very well with the actual conditions as determined by the sanitary survey and, therefore, analyses may be used to determine whether or not certain oysters may be sold for human consumption." But during the cold weather, oysters judged by analyses alone would be pronounced good although they came from within a short distance of a larger sewer outfall. During hibernation, according to Gage and Gorham,[182] oysters tend to purify themselves. Hibernation was defined as a slowing down of biological activity as a result of a reduction of temperature. It has been shown by several different investigators that as the temperature approaches the

175. Messer and Reece. 1937. Pub. Health Rpts., Oct. 15th.
176. Tohyama and Yasukawa. 1935. Jap. J. Expt. Med. 13, 601-618.
177. Round. 1914. Spec. Rpt. to Rhode Island Commr. of Shellfisheries.
178. Phelps. 1911. Fishing Gaz. 28, 705-706.
179. Bulstrode and Klein. 1896. Local Govt. Bd., Ann. Rpt. 24.
180. Johnstone. 1909. J. Hyg. 9, 412-440.
181. Gorham. 1912. Amer. J. Pub. Health 2, 77-86.
182. Gage and Gorham. 1925. Idem 15, 1057-1061.

freezing point the shells of the oyster tend to close and remain closed for the greater part of the time. Gage and Gorham secured further evidence on this phenomenon, and while their data supported the general findings, there were discrepancies which suggested a number of different explanations. One was that oysters might become carriers of *Escherichia coli.* On this question, Wachter [183] stated that oysters from polluted sources might give high scores during the seasons of warmer water and low scores when the water is colder. Consequently, Wachter did not regard low scores during the hibernating periods when the oysters were from polluted water, with the same assurance as low scores for oysters from a non-polluted bed. Wachter also stressed the need for frequent sampling of a bed, since one examination might not indicate its real sanitary condition. Laboratory examinations are liable to be influenced by a number of different factors.

Krumwiede *et al.,*[174] after finding that *Eberthella typhosa* could live for about two weeks in oysters in their natural waters, asked how these data should influence the minimum time that should be required for oysters to remain in clean waters when transported from doubtful sources. They also asked about the effect which the infected oysters would have on oysters in the beds to which they were transported. The Department of Health of New York City allows no dredging of beds to which doubtful oysters have been added for 30 days thereafter. Taking into account a number of facts, it was concluded that three weeks was a sufficiently long time for contaminated oysters to purify themselves. However, it was stated that an ordinance allowing the transfer of oysters from doubtful waters to clean waters during the closed season with the provision that no dredging in the latter waters be allowed for a period of four weeks after the transfer, covers observed facts and gives a reasonably generous excess margin of safety.

Chlorination. The value of chlorine as an agent in the disinfection of water, vegetables, fruits, etc., suggested its use as a sterilizing agent for oysters. Wells [184] has stated that the use of the chemical is now a well-established practice. Some of the pioneer work on the subject was done by Wells. In 1916, he carried out experiments which seemed to indicate that treatment with hypochlorite caused a very satisfactory degree of purification. Exposure for a short time in water containing calcium hypochlorite brought about such purification that the oysters passed the most rigid standard. In 1923, a practical purification plant was described.

This method may be applied under careful regulation to the treatment of many oysters. However, oysters which are heavily polluted before treatment should be so handled that there is a greater safety factor before they are sold to the public. He stated that no oysters scoring higher than 230 or 320 should be purified by this method. With oysters with a higher score, an insufficient margin of safety was allowed. A similar position was assumed also by Krumwiede *et al.,*[185] who reported that chlorine did not rid oysters of all of the contaminating typhoid bacilli, even when amounts of chlorine, times of exposure, and times of drinking or flushing

183. Wachter. 1925. Amer. J. Pub. Health 15, 1066-1068.
184. Wells. 1929. Pub. Health Rpts. 31, 1848-1852; see also Amer. J. Pub. Health 10 (1920), 342-344; 19 (1929), 72-79; Nation's Health 5 (1923), 881-883; Fishing Gaz. 40 (1923), 45-47.
185. Krumwiede *et al.* 1926. Amer. J. Pub. Health 16, 142-152.

were made in excess of those recommended by the New York State Conservation Commission. Krumwiede and his co-workers believed that the best procedure is to grow oysters in uncontaminated water rather than to have to treat contaminated oysters to make them safe. Less satisfactory results were reported by Yasukawa.[186] He found that much of the free chlorine was used by organic matter and was thus not available for destruction of bacteria in the oyster. While *Eberthella typhosa* and *Escherichia coli* mixed with sea water containing as little as one p.p.m. of available chlorine were destroyed in less than five minutes, Yasukawa found it impossible to sterilize oysters immersed for 24 hours in sea water mixed with either of these bacilli even when 500 p.p.m. of chlorine were used. The usual experience was diminution for about 96 hours, after which little change occurred. In more than 50 p.p.m. of chlorine oysters will not respire at all. For these reasons Yasukawa believed that it was better to flood oysters with chlorinated sea water.

Ozonized Water. The little work which seems to have been done on sterilization of shellfish with ozonized sea water indicates considerable success. In investigations by Violle and Rose [187] and Salmon, LeGall, and Salmon [188] the latter found that in a period which is certainly less than four days and probably less than 48 hours shellfish, even if grossly contaminated with pathogenic bacteria, are rendered completely sterile and safe for consumption. No harmful substances were formed and no alteration in flavor was caused by the treatment. Violle's results were equally satisfactory. Infected shellfish were completely sterilized by exposure to ozonized water.

Microorganisms in Market Oysters. The microorganisms present in unpolluted oysters are probably from the water from which the oysters were taken. The first important information to seek and consider is whether oysters from unpolluted areas contain *Escherichia coli*. When an algebraic sum is taken from the available experimental data, one must conclude that this organism is probably not present in unpolluted oysters. Consequently, there is some justification in using it as an indicator of pollution. Phelps [189] concluded from experimental studies that within four days, and possibly within a shorter period of time, a healthy oyster transplanted from polluted to clean waters will rid itself of the evidences of pollution, and argued from this that sewage material which is always associated with *Escherichia coli*, and of which the latter is taken as an index, would also be eliminated. In further tests, such very rapid improvement was shown within two days that there was no reasonable doubt as to the efficacy of very short periods of storage in clean water. Joseph [190] carried out an investigation to determine whether the oysters sold in Baltimore contained organisms derived from the human intestinal tract and whether or not their bacterial content varied with the season of the year. The results of

186. Yasukawa. 1931. Jap. J. Expt. Med. 9, 385-401.
187. Violle and Rose. 1937. Rev. d'Hyg. et de Méd. Prév. 59, 573-575.
188. Salmon *et al.* 1937. Ann. d'Hyg. Pub. Indus. et Sociale 15, 44-50.
189. Phelps. 1911. Fishing Gaz. 28, 705-706.
190. Joseph. 1914. Johns Hopkins Hosp. Bull. 25, 128-131.

the examination indicated the quality of the oysters at the time they were sold and not when collected. The methods of examination were those adopted by the committee of the American Public Health Association on standard methods of shellfish examination. The results indicated that the oysters sold in Baltimore were, as a rule, free from sewage contamination. It was found that in the early fall and in the spring the bacteriological content of oysters was high, while in the cold winter months the bacterial content was low. Results of an investigation by Eliot [191] showed in shucked and shell oysters, kept at laboratory temperature, a marked increase in numbers of *Escherichia coli* in 14 days. The bacteria of the decomposing oyster may be divided into five principal groups: (a) the colon aerogenes group; (b) the streptococci; (c) the "water bacteria," including members of the green fluorescent, the yellow pigmented, the nonpigmented groups, and vibrios; (d) the anaerobes; and (e) the incidental organisms, such as the chromogenic cocci and the aerobic sporeformers.

Since Eliot failed to state the age of the oysters with which he worked, Bacon [192] conducted additional experiments. Bacon collected 400 oysters and held them at 21 to 24°C. (69.8 to 75.2°F.). Scores were determined each day by Standard Methods. An appreciable increase in scores and total counts was observed, thus confirming Eliot's work. Bacon then stated that scores and counts would be misleading, unless they were determined on fresh samples.

A study of the bacterial flora of market oysters was made by Geiger, Ward, and Jacobson [193] during the Chicago epidemic of typhoid fever, caused by oysters, in 1924. No *Eberthella typhosa* were revealed to be present in 784 samples of shucked oysters and 328 samples of shell oysters. Various bacteria were identified, among which were 81 strains closely related to the typhoid group; *Escherichia coli* were, of course, found. Oysters were said to be potential factors in certain infections. Some 11 years later Geiger and Crowley [194] isolated *Staphylococcus aureus* from oysters from the Pacific Northwest. Except for one place no sewage pollution was apparent. By means of intraperitoneal inoculation into kittens, some of the strains were shown to be mildly toxic. Epidemiological findings confirmed the laboratory results.

Escherichia coli is a bacterium used to indicate the sanitary conditions of the grounds from which the oysters are taken. The behavior of this organism in stored oysters is therefore of considerable importance. Tonney and White [195] determined the *Escherichia coli* scores of oysters on successive days during storage at 5 to 8°C. (41 to 46.4°F.). The percentage increase in the score of one lot was 458 in 12 days and of another lot 1,490 in 11 days. Shucked oysters collected in the early part of the season and stored at the above temperatures increased more rapidly in *Escherichia coli* content than oysters gathered in midwinter and stored under similar

191. Eliot. 1926. J. Hyg. 6, 755-776.
192. Bacon. 1927. Pub. Health News 13, 16-23.
193. Geiger *et al.* 1926. J. Infect. Dis. 38, 273-280.
194. Geiger and Crowley. 1937. Amer. J. Pub. Health 27, 991-992.
195. Tonney and White. 1926. Idem 16, 597-602.

conditions. Living shell oysters did not improve in *Escherichia coli* content under dry storage conditions at the above-mentioned temperatures from the 11th to the 83rd day after shipment. After the 28th day a consistent decrease was noted, and after the 60th day the tests for *Escherichia coli* were usually negative. A study of 856 samples of shucked oysters received on the Chicago market showed that 71 per cent would have passed an *Escherichia coli* score of 140; 97 per cent of shell oysters passed a score of 50, while all of 164 samples of clams passed the same score. In view of these results Tonney and White believed that an *Escherichia coli* count of not to exceed 140 for shucked oysters and not over 50 for shell oysters and hard-shelled clams could be recommended. These counts were later adopted as official for Illinois markets. Perry [196] also recognized the possible value of *Escherichia coli* as an indicator of pollution of oysters. He did not believe, however, that pollution tests suitable for drinking waters were equally applicable to shellfish (Perry [197]). Determinations of presence of members of the coliform group could be quite unreliable and may not, under certain circumstances, indicate fecal pollution. Determination of presence of *Escherichia coli* was considered to be a much better index of pollution both in shellfish and the water from which they come. In both of the above-mentioned papers by Perry much discussion is given to tests that might be used. Cellobiose fermentation was looked on with favor as was the Eijkmann Test.

Results of extensive bacteriological examinations are not necessary to show the value of low storage temperatures for oysters. Tanikawa [198] found that at —5°C.(23°F.) the bacterial content of oysters remained approximately constant for 24 days. At 0°C.(32°F.) there was a gradual increase, resulting in a five-fold rise, in the same time. At 5°C.(41°F.) the number of bacteria increased about a thousand times. These experiments were made on minced oysters. Whether this would make a difference is difficult to state.

Reddening of Oysters. Earlier in this chapter the reddening of cod was discussed. A similar trouble exists in the oyster industry, which renders oysters unsightly and unfit for food. Hunter [199] isolated a yeast as the etiologic agent in the spoilage. It was found to be widely distributed in oyster houses and on utensils in and about the houses. The yeast formed a pink pigment. No ascospores were formed.

Bacteria in Decomposing Oysters. Investigations of the microorganisms concerned in spoilage of oysters have been reported by Hunter and Linden.[200] The bacteria were arranged in three groups: (1) types which, upon inoculation into artificially purified oysters or into oyster infusion media, produced foul, putrefactive odors; (2) types which produce acidity or sourness; and (3) types which were inert. In the first group fell bacteria of the genera Serratia, Pseudomonas, Proteus, Clostridium, and Bacillus.

196. Perry. 1929. Amer. J. Hyg. 10, 580-613.
197. Perry. 1939. Food Research 4, 381-395.
198. Tanikawa. 1937. Zentbl. f. Bakt., Pt. 2, 97, 133-147.
199. Hunter. 1920. U. S. Dept. Agr., Bull. 819.
200. Hunter and Linden. 1925. Amer. Food J. 18, 538-540; J. Agr. Res. 30, 971-976.

In the second group, *Aerobacter aerogenes* and *Aerobacter cloacae* were found throughout the culture period of spoilage. *Escherichia coli* and *Escherichia communis* were found during the early stages and streptococci, lactobacilli, and yeasts during the late stages when the hydrogen-ion concentration was between pH 5.0 and 4.6. The organisms of the third group included ordinary bacteria and yeasts. Conclusions reached by Eliot on this subject are quoted above.

Longevity of Eberthella typhosa in Oysters. The recurrence of cases and outbreaks of typhoid fever attributed to oysters has made it important to determine how long *Eberthella typhosa* would live in oysters. While the actual number of days reported by the several investigators is different, the conclusions are not far apart.

Herdman and Boyce [201] floated oysters in water to which typhoid bacilli had been added, and found living bacilli up to 10 days. Field [202] stated that there was no decrease in cells of *Eberthella typhosa* and probably a slight increase after oysters had been removed from an infected tank. Klein [203] found that *Eberthella typhosa* survived in oysters from seven to 11 days. He also reported finding the organism in market oysters. Foot [204] injected shell oysters with one ml. of broth culture of *Eberthella typhosa* and stored them at 50 to 65°C. (122 to 149°F.). Living typhoid bacilli were found for 30 days.

Kinyoun [205] experimented to determine whether oysters contaminated with *Eberthella typhosa* and then stored under usual market conditions would remain potentially dangerous over a sufficient length of time to infect the consumer. The oysters used were large salt-water variety, tonged in Chesapeake Bay and taken to Washington. They were out of the water about eight days before the experiments were started. In the laboratory they were inoculated with two strains of *Eberthella typhosa*. It was found that for 15 days after inoculation *Eberthella typhosa* could be isolated. At this time Kinyoun discontinued his experiments. *Eberthella typhosa* probably does not increase in numbers in the body of the oyster. Herdmann and Boyce were of this opinion. In France, Costa, Hovasse, and Boyer [206] believed that the role of intravalvular sea water in the transmission of typhoid fever was negligible.

Tonney and White [207] infected shucked oysters with *Eberthella typhosa* and stored them at 36.7°C. (98°F.), 21.1°C. (70°F.), and 7.2°C. (45°F.). In the oyster fluid, *Eberthella typhosa* survived in considerable numbers for one, four and 22 days, respectively. Living shell oysters were also infected and stored at 21.1°C. (70°F.) and 7.2°C. (45°F.). At 21.1°C. (70°F.) *Eberthella typhosa* survived in the fluid within the shells for eight days; at 7.2°C. (45°F.), which was said to be the ordinary icing temperature of the trade, the organisms were found to survive for 60

201. Herdman and Boyce. 1899. Roy. Soc., London, Proc. 64, 239-241.
202. Field. 1904. Med. Rec. 65, 900.
203. Klein. 1905. Lancet, Pt. 2, 1113-1114.
204. Foot. 1895. Med. News 66, 320.
205. Kinyoun. 1925. Pub. Health Rpt. 40, 819-823.
206. Costa *et al.* 1925. Compt. Rend. Soc. Biol. 93, 112-114.
207. Tonney and White. 1925. J. Amer. Med. Assoc. 84, 1403-1406.

days. The exterior of the shells of oysters exposed for 48 hours to a four per cent sea salt solution containing large numbers of *Eberthella typhosa*, after storage at 7.2°C.(45°F.), showed the presence of typhoid bacilli on the 23rd day. From these data, Tonney and White concluded that the longevity of *Eberthella typhosa* in oyster juice of both shell and shucked oysters varied with the temperature. In general, that temperature which tended to prolong the life of the oyster was also best for prolonging the viability of the typhoid organisms. The findings of Tonney and White that typhoid bacilli could survive 22 days in shucked oysters and 60 days in shell oysters are in general accord with the data found by others. Data reported by Krumwiede, Park, Cooper, Grund, Tyler, and Rosenstein,[174] in general, confirm those reported by Tonney and White. These latter investigators reported that *Eberthella typhosa* survived in oysters for at least nine to 11 days, but were not found on the 16th and 24th days. These data applied to oysters in their natural waters when the temperature was high enough to insure active drinking.

Similar situations were reported by MacLean,[208] Lancelin,[210] and Gordon and Davey.[211] In these cases shellfish from grossly polluted areas caused illness.

Canned Oysters. Food laws of certain states require that oysters be shipped in sealed containers. Consequently they are packed in tin cans, glass jars, or paraffined paper containers. Griffiths [212] found that vacuum-packing of oysters resulted in a better product and spoilage was delayed.

Frozen Oysters. In an investigation to determine the sanitary condition of market shucked oysters in inland cities Lord [213] examined a series of samples of frozen oysters purchased on the Urbana, Illinois, market. These samples had a decidedly low bacterial content and were in sharp contrast to the liquid shucked oysters. Plating methods yielded very low numbers of bacteria and *Escherichia coli* was found in only two samples. The hydrogen-ion concentration was below 5.4 and the oysters gave no evidence of staleness or decomposition.

Sanitary Quality of Market Oysters. Few comprehensive investigations have been carried out. Lord [213] examined many samples of shucked oysters purchased on the above mentioned market. In general, he observed an unwholesome condition. The numbers of bacteria, as shown by plate counts, were very high and the *Escherichia coli* content was higher than any standard which has ever been suggested. These oysters probably reflect the condition of oysters served generally in inland cities.

BACTERIOLOGICAL EXAMINATION OF SHELLFISH

Active interest in this subject started in 1910 when a committee of the American Public Health Association presented a report on procedures. Since that time many different individuals and groups have proposed

208. MacLean. 1933. New Zealand Rpt. Director-General of Health.
209. Paponnet and Brisou. 1937. Compt. Rend. Soc. Biol. 124, 1228-1230.
210. Lancelin. 1935. Acad. de Med. Bull. 114, 421-425.
211. Gordon and Davey. 1935. Ann. Trop. Med. and Parasitol. 29, 435-437.
212. Griffiths. 1937. Special Memorandum No. 2468-G, U. S. Bur. Fisheries, Wash., D. C.

other procedures. These various methods have been reviewed by Lord.[213] They will not be reviewed in this book. All of them have been proposed to improve methods which existed theretofore and have used *Escherichia coli* as the indicator of pollution of both the shellfish and shellfish waters.

While sampling is a difficult problem in analysis of many foods, it is especially so with shellfish. Some of the variable results may be attributed to difficulty of securing proper samples.

The Food and Drug Manual, giving instructions to officials, analysts, and inspectors of the Bureau of Chemistry relating to procedure for the enforcement of the Food and Drugs Act of June 30, 1906, gave the following instructions for collecting samples of oysters for bacteriological analysis:

69. *Sampling Oysters in the Shell.* Select a sufficient number of oysters of average size, with deep bowls and shells tightly closed, to represent the shipment. Pack in clean cloth bag or other suitable container. Samples kept over 12 hours before reaching the laboratory should be iced in such a manner as to prevent mixing ice water with the oysters. A metal container inside a tub may be used for this purpose.

70. *Sampling Shucked Oysters.* The stock in the container to be sampled must be thoroughly mixed to obtain an even distribution of the meats and the liquor. This may be accomplished either by shaking and inverting several times or by means of a sterilized ladle. Fill a sterilized pint Mason jar by means of a sterilized ladle or dipper. If more than one container is to be sampled every utensil must be washed and sterilized before being used to sample each additional container. Place the samples at once in a carrying case containing cracked ice, so that the sample is cooled to near the freezing point, and deliver to the laboratory as quickly as possible.

In many of the earlier methods of analysis the oyster was merely cut into small pieces which were then manipulated with sand or glass beads to prepare them for analysis. Better preparation of the sample is secured by a disintegrator such as the mixers used at soda fountains. These prepare a smooth, homogeneous mixture for plating and insure presence of *Escherichia coli* in samples removed for plating and culture in fermentation tubes. Sandholzer, Ferguson, and Berry [214] found that macerated oyster meat yielded higher bacterial counts than whole oysters. The count was said to be proportional to the degree of disintegration.

American Public Health Association Method for Bacteriological Examination of Shellfish and Shellfish Waters.[215] This method was proposed by a committee and probably represents the best practice at the time the report was prepared. The term ''shellfish'' was defined as referring to oysters, soft-shelled clams, quahaugs, and mussels. The coliform group was considered to include all organisms which, upon transfer from a positive presumptive test (gas positive in lactose broth), showed fermentation with gas formation in lactose medium containing .00133 per cent of brilliant green and two per cent of bile (brilliant green lactose bile broth).

Escherichia coli was considered to be any member of this group which in pure culture failed to grow in Koser's citrate medium within 24 hours or which showed definite gas formation in modified Eijkman medium incubated at 45.5°C.(113.9°F.).

I. Bacteriological Examination of Shellfish-Growing Waters

Collection and Transportation of Sample—Samples of water from shellfish-growing areas should be collected at various stages of the tide and should also be collected at

213. Lord. 1941. Dissert., Illinois.
214. Sandholzer *et al.* 1941. J. Bact. 41, 98.
215. Amer. Pub. Health Assoc. Year Book, 1941-1942, 158.

different depths if there is any indication of variations in salinity or pollution due to stratification. The samples should be collected in sterile bottles and should be fully protected against contamination both during sampling and after collection. They should be kept at a temperature at or below 10°C.(50°F.) and should be examined as soon as possible after collection. Every sample should preferably be tested within 12 hours from the time of collection and in no case should samples which have been held for more than 30 hours be tested.

Field Record—A record of environmental conditions made at the time of collection of the sample should accompany all water samples collected during the course of a survey to establish the sanitary condition of shellfish-growing waters. This record should include the following essential information:

(a) Date and hour of collection.

(b) Exact location of the sampling station.

Where possible the following supplementary data should be obtained in order to interpret the bacteriological findings:

(a) State of the tide.

(b) Direction and velocity of currents.

(c) Direction and velocity of wind.

(d) Temperature and density of the water.

(e) Depth of the water and depth at which the sample was collected.

(f) Temperature of the air.

(g) Notes on any unusual conditions which may affect the sanitary quality of the water.

(h) Record of rainfall in the immediate past.

A suitable form to be used for reporting this information may be found in the Appendix.[215a]

Procedure—Examinations for bacteria of the coliform group shall be made by primary inoculation into plain lactose broth (see Appendix) with incubation at 37°C. (98.6°F.). After incubation for not more than 48 hours definite gas formation shall be recognized by the presence of visible gas in the upper end of the inverted fermentation tube or by the presence of effervescent gas bubbles visible only when the tube is shaken.

1. Inoculate—

(i) Not less than three tubes with 10 ml. of undiluted water.

(ii) Not less than three tubes with one ml. of undiluted water.

(iii) Not less than three tubes with one ml. of a 1-in-10 dilution of water.

(These dilutions may be altered to suit the degree of contamination of the water.) Incubate tubes for 18 to 24 hours. Observe gas formation in each tube.

(a) *Gas Present*—Any amount of definite gas constitutes presumptive evidence of the presence of coliform bacteria and must be confirmed as described in step 2 below.

(b) Incubate negative tubes an additional 24 hours, making a total of 48 hours' incubation. Observe gas formation.

(i) Gas present in any amount constitutes a doubtful test which must always be confirmed (step 2).

(ii) Absence of any gas after 48 hours of incubation constitutes a final negative test.

CONFIRMATION—A. *Coliform Group*. All positive gas tubes must be confirmed for bacteria of the coliform group.

2. Transfer a loopful (three mm. diameter loop) of culture from the positive primary lactose broth fermentation tube to one of brilliant green bile lactose broth (see Appendix).

(a) Any amount of definite gas formation within 48 hours at 37°C. constitutes a positive test for bacteria of the coliform group.

(b) Absence of gas after 48 hours' incubation constitutes a negative test for bacteria of the coliform group.

215a. This will not be reproduced in this book but is available in the original publication.

B. *Escherichia coli*

Method I.

3. Inoculate E.M.B. plates (see Appendix) from positive lactose broth tubes which have gas present. Incubate at 37°C. for 24 hours.

4. Inoculate tubes of Koser's citrate medium (see Appendix) with a bacteriological needle from several colonies suggestive of *Escherichia coli*. The greatest care should always be exercised to secure apparently pure cultures by using only well-isolated colonies. Only a trace of the colony should be transferred, otherwise too much nutrient material may be provided. Incubate at 37°C.

Absence of growth after 24 hours constitutes a positive test for *Escherichia coli*.

Method II.

5. Inoculate tubes of modified Eijkman lactose medium (see Appendix) with a loopful of culture from primary lactose broth tubes which have gas present. Incubate at 45.5°C.

Any amount of definite gas formation within 48 hours constitutes a positive test for *Escherichia coli*.

Method III.

6. Complete all tests for *Escherichia coli* according to the recommended procedures in the Appendix to *Standard Methods of Water Analysis*.

SHELLFISH

Collection and Transportation of Sample—In general, ten or more oysters, clams, or mussels judged to be representative of the lot and of the average size of the lot under examination, with deep bowls, short unbroken lips and shells tightly closed, shall be selected and prepared for transportation to the laboratory.

Not less than one-half pint of shucked shellfish shall be collected for examination.

Shellfish selected as samples should be placed in a suitable sterilized container (such as a can with watertight lid or canvas bag) which shall be marked for identification. This same mark shall be placed in its proper place on the descriptive form which accompanies the sample. All shellfish for bacteriological examination shall be handled aseptically.

Shellfish samples should be kept at or below 10°C.(50°F.) until examined, but under no condition should they be permitted to come in direct contact with ice.

A sample shall be considered unsatisfactory which has been improperly handled after collection. Samples of shell oysters should preferably be tested within 12 hours from the time of collection and in no case should samples which have been held for more than 20 hours be tested. Samples of shucked oysters should be handled with special care and should, if at all possible, be analyzed within four hours after collection.

Field Record—A record of environmental conditions made at the time of collection of the sample should accompany all shellfish samples taken directly from growing waters. The record should include the following essential information:

(A) Exact location and depth from which they were collected.

(B) Date and hour of collection.

Where possible the following supplementary data should be obtained:

(a) State of tide.

(b) Temperature.

(c) Density of the water.

(d) Whether there has been heavy, moderate, or very little rain during or immediately preceding the period of collection.

(e) Careful notes on any unusual sources of pollution, such as boats, privies, sewers, pasture lands, animals, etc., which might affect bacteriological results.

When samples are collected from packing plants or from the market, records shall be made of:

(a) Date and hour of collection.

(b) Name and address of the place from which the samples were collected.

(c) Exact location of the water in which the shellfish were dug.

(d) Identification of the digger, shipper, and reshipper, and the respective dates on which these transactions took place.

(e) Conditions of storage prior to collection of the sample.

(f) Sanitary conditions in the packing plant.

(g) Temperature at which shellfish were being held.

Forms to be used for submission of these data may be found in the Appendix.[215a]

Procedure—(A) *Preparation of Sample for Examination.*

1. *Unopened Shellfish*—(a) Scrape off excessive growth and loose material from the shellfish and scrub with a stiff brush in running water of known purity until shells are clean and free of all mud, especially in crevices at junction of shells.

The hands of the examiner should be thoroughly washed with soap and water and the brush used for scrubbing the shells should be sterilized by boiling or autoclaving.

(b) Either (1) immerse the scrubbed shellfish for 15 minutes in chlorinated water which will contain not less than 10 p.p.m. free chlorine at the end of treatment as determined by the orthotolidine test and watch the shellfish during treatment and discard any which open and cause bubbling; or (2) rinse in water free of chlorine and of known purity and place on clean paper towels and dry in the air.

(c) Open the shellfish with an oyster knife or other suitable instrument which has been sterilized by flaming or immersion for three minutes in boiling water. The point of the oyster knife can be inserted between the shells after some experience or a small opening can be made with nibbling forceps. Cut the adductor muscle of the upper flat shell if examining oysters and pry the shells apart just wide enough to drain off the shell liquor.

(d) Drain off the shell liquor into a sterile bottle, then lay the oyster on a clean paper towel and pry the shell loose at the hinge. By holding the lower (deep bowl) shell down with the oyster knife and using the knife at the same time as a lever to pry open the upper shell, the anterior edge may be grasped with the left hand and removed with the minimum chance of contamination. The removal of the shell is the most difficult part of the procedure and calls for careful technique to avoid shell liquor running on the handle and contamination of the shellfish.

(e) Cut the body of the shellfish into approximately 10 equal pieces with scissors or oyster knife, previously sterilized by autoclaving, flaming, or immersion in boiling water for three minutes, and empty into the bottle containing the shell liquor. This bottle should be a heavy-walled glass or rubber-stoppered bottle graduated at 200 ml. and 400 ml. Not less than 200 ml. of shellfish with the shell liquor should be tested, but, in no case, should less than six shellfish constitute the sample.

(f) Add about a tablespoonful of a sterile 5-mm. imperforate glass beads to the sample and shake vigorously 50 times, each shake being an up and down excursion of about a foot, time interval not exceeding 30 seconds.

(g) To 200 ml. of this well-mixed sample, add 200 ml. of sterile distilled water. Shake vigorously to mix the sample.

Allow the sample to settle for two minutes.

2. *Shellfish Removed from the Shell*—The examination of shucked shellfish shall be made in an analogous manner to that for shell stock, that is, 200 ml. of the sample (both shellfish and liquor) shall be added to 200 ml. of sterile distilled water after the bodies of the shellfish have been cut up as in step (e) above.

(B) *Examination for Members of the Coliform Group and Escherichia coli*

Examination of shellfish shall be made in a manner similar to that used for the examination of shellfish water samples.

1. *Presumptive Test.*

Using plain lactose broth fermentation tubes, inoculate—

(a) Each 5 tubes with 2 ml. (1 ml. of composite shellfish sample) from sample as prepared under Section A.

(b) Each of 5 tubes with 1 ml. from a 1-in-10 dilution of the composite sample (2 ml. prepared Sample A plus 8 ml. of sterile distilled water); and

(c) Each of 5 tubes with 1 ml. from a 1-in-100 dilution of the composite shellfish sample (1 ml. of 1-in-10 dilution plus 9 ml. of sterile distilled water).

If desired, further decimal dilutions may be carried out. Incubate at 37°C. for a total of 48 hours. Examine after 24 and 48 hours for the presence of gas in the tubes.

The presence of gas in any amount, or the appearance of effervescent gas on shaking a tube, shall constitute a positive presumptive test; the absence of gas, a negative presumptive test.

2. *Confirmation.*

A. *Coliform Group*—All positive tubes may be confirmed for bacteria of the coliform group, as described under Section 2, in the procedure for the examination of shellfish waters, by transfer to brilliant green lactose bile broth.

B. *Escherichia coli*—Confirmation for *Escherichia coli* shall be made by either of the two methods described under Sections 3, 4, and 5 in the procedure for the examination of shellfish waters, that is, either by transfer from the primary lactose broth tubes to E.M.B. plates and further identification in Koser's citrate medium or by transfer to Eijkman lactose medium at 45.5°C.

Any laboratory charged with the responsibility of examining samples of shellfish other than those known to have been freshly taken directly from growing areas would be well advised to complete all tests for *Escherichia coli* according to the procedure recommended in the Appendix to *Standard Methods of Water Analysis.* Such examinations may become the basis of legal action and short cuts are not recommended.

(C) *Colony Counts*—A standard colony count of shellfish samples has been found to be of value as an index of general sanitation and refrigeration.

Colony counts shall be made by inoculating various amounts of sample, as prepared under (A) above, into tryptone-glucose-extract-agar (see Appendix) and incubating plates at 37°C. for 48 hours.

The method of preparing plates and making the counts shall be that recommended by the American Public Health Association as a standard method for the examination of dairy products except that milk shall not be added to the medium (*Standard Methods for the Examination of Dairy Products*, Seventh Edition, 1939).

EXPRESSION OF RESULTS

The number of bacteria of the coliform group shall be expressed as the Most Probable Numbers (M.P.N.) per 100 ml. of sample. The M.P.N. shall be determined by the tables of Hoskins in Public Health Reports **49** (1934), 393-405.

The Eijkmann Test for Coliform Bacteria in Oysters.

This test has received much study in water analysis, the literature of which is reviewed in Chapter 4. Perry and Hajna[216] considered it a valuable procedure when a modified Eijkman medium was used with incubation at 46°C. (114.8°F.). They believed that types other than *Escherichia coli* were eliminated. Payne[217] compared the method with other standard procedures and reported discrepancies. Standard lactose broth was observed to be more sensitive for isolating *Escherichia coli*. Hajna and Perry[218] later reported further evidence for using higher temperatures for isolating *Escherichia coli*. They reported that McConkey's lactose bile was less selective than their medium.

Hunter and Linden[219] attempted to determine whether H-ion concentration could be used to measure the bacterial count and condition of

216. Perry and Hajna. 1935. Amer. J. Pub. Health 25, 720-724.
217. Payne. 1938. Pub. Health Rpts. 53, 2058-2064.
218. Hajna and Perry. 1939. J. Bact. 38. 275-283.
219. Hunter and Linden. 1923. J. Agr. Res. 30, 971-976.

spoiled oysters. A somewhat definite relation existed between the H-ion concentration of the oyster liquor and the odor and general appearance of the oysters. When once tested, the H-ion concentration increased with the progress of spoilage regardless of the temperature or bacterial count. A pH of 5.6 to 6.1 was the critical zone where the oysters were passing from fresh to stale, while from 4.9 to 5.3 the oyster was passing from stale to sour or putrid. Total aerobic counts on oyster liquor did not correlate with physical condition and H-ion concentration of decomposing oysters. Good oysters contained as many as 30,000,000 bacteria per ml., while one often had as few as 12,000 per ml.

Sanitary Condition of Market Oysters. Oysters are indeed perishable products which require adequate refrigeration to prevent deterioration. Most investigations of a bacteriological nature have concerned determination of presence of *Escherichia coli* as an indicator of pollution and not so much the number of bacteria which may be present. The latter does not seem to have justified itself as a matter of importance mainly because the plate count is so high. Especially is this true for bulk oysters shipped to inland communities under indifferent conditions of refrigeration. Lord[213] observed large numbers of *Escherichia coli* in such samples, some of which contained as many as 25,000,000 per 100 grams of oysters. Aerobic plate counts were very high, in one case being 63 below per 100 grams of sour oysters at 20°C.(68°F.).

In sharp contrast were frozen oysters. Examination of 15 samples of frozen shucked oysters revealed an almost sterile product with few *Escherichia coli*, the largest number of the latter organism observed being 80 per 100 grams of oysters. The highest aerobic plate count observed was 28,000 per 100 grams, the average being 710 colonies per 100 grams.

Mussels. These marine mollusks are widely used by people in certain sections of the country. While they may probably cause infections when they come from polluted water, they are better known as the agents for an acute toxemia which they cause at certain times of the year. The California State Department of Health finds it necessary to issue warnings of danger from eating mussels harvested on the coast of that state. Mussels are of interest to food-control officials from the fact that they may harbor pathogenic bacteria, such as *Eberthella typhosa*, and cause "mussel poisoning." Dodgson[220] published a long treatise on mussel purification. On account of the length and importance of this publication, a little more space may be given to it. A survey of causes and extent of pollution of the chief mussel beds of England and of possible preventive measures showed that chlorination of sewage is impracticable owing to lack of treatment and to many sewer outlets. Dodgson said that relief rested in treatment of mussels by cooking, relaying on non-contaminated beds, or purification in tanks. Cooking cannot be controlled and may be insufficient. Experiments, however, showed that when mussels were placed in cold water and heated to boiling for three minutes, they are safe. Relaying in tanks may fail because of lack of suitable areas and lack of co-operation. Dodg-

220. Dodgson. 1928. Gt. Brit. Min. Agr. and Fisheries, Invest., Ser. 2, 10, 1-498.

son believed that purification in tanks was the only safe method; this was also believed to be superior to a bacteriological standard. The latter were believed to be influenced by too many factors to make them reliable.

Purification of Mussels. This is advisable for most mussels. It is accomplished in different ways. Dodgson did not put much faith in relaying in clean water. Suitable areas might not be available and there might be little co-operation. Furthermore, questions might arise with respect to what waters were sufficiently clean. Dodgson reported bleaching powder to be most satisfactory for sterilizing mussels. They failed to open and function in presence of five p.p.m. of available chlorine. A mussel may open its shell and void mucus strings ("Pseudo-feces") without siphoning. These mucus strings were said to contain the bacteria, the water becoming sterile. The anatomical and physiological characteristics concerned in purification discussed by Dodgson will not be reviewed here. In 1936, Dodgson [221] outlined with a little more detail methods used in England for mussel purification. His discussion is especially interesting because it represents British experience. That gross and constantly increasing sewage pollution of oyster beds much be expected, is a foregone conclusion. Dodgson believes that the only solution of the problem is a satisfactory purification system. Unless such a system is workable, molluscan shellfish as a whole will have to be banned. Any system of purification will have to be reliable, relatively simple, and efficient as far as cost is concerned. The Ministry of Agriculture and Fisheries mussel purification system at Conway was described as follows:

Mussel Purification (Conway System)

The installations consist of four reinforced concrete tanks.

No. 1. Storage Tank.—Capacity 90,000 gallons. Estuarine water is pumped into this tank at or about high water and stored until required. (This storage tank is unnecessary in places where sufficient water of the right salinity can be obtained on one side.)

No. 2. Chlorinating Tank.—Capacity similar to No. 1, from which it can be filled in about 20 minutes (by gravity or by pumping).

Nos. 3 and 4. Mussel Purification Tanks.—Capacity, each, 40,000 gallons. The floors are sloping, and divided into parallel channels by concrete ridges which support wooden (pitch pine) grids. By a system of penstocks or sluices the under-grid channels can be flushed out. The mean depth of these tanks is three feet. The capacity of each tank is six tons, or about 150,000 mussels.

A solution of bleaching-powder is added to the polluted water as it enters the chlorinating tank, in quantity sufficient to give a concentration of active chlorine of three parts per million. The water is allowed to stand over one night, when sterilization is complete.

Steps in the Purification Process

I.—The polluted mussels are spread, about two deep, on the grids.

II.—The mussels are hosed with a jet of water (about 130 lb. per square inch pressure) which removes adherent mud, weed, etc., from the shells, and washes it through the grids into the sloping channels which are flushed by water from the penstock sluices.

III.—The tanks are filled with sterile sea water from the chlorinating tank. To the in-coming water is added a solution of sodium thiosulphate (hyposulphite) sufficient

221. Dodgson. 1936. Brit. Med. J., July 25, 1936, 169-174; Pub. Health 50, 279-284.

to neutralize any trace of active chlorine which may remain. In this bath of sterilized chlorine-free water the mussels remain one night. Into it they discharge all foregin matter, including bacteria, from their intestines, mantle cavities, etc., in the form of fine threads or small pellets held together by mucus. These fall to the bottom, the bacteria discharged with them remaining imprisoned in the tenacious and practically insoluble mucus.

IV.—(After 24 hours). The first bath is drained off, and the mussels are again hosed, the matter discharged by the mussels (faeces, etc.) being washed through the grids and flushed away.

V.—Second bath of sterile dechlorinated water, in which the mussels remain another night. The object of this second bath is to get rid, *via* mucoid faeces and pseudo-faeces, of any bacteria discharged free into the water and re-ingested.

VI.—(Second 24 hours). Second bath drained off. Mussels hosed and channels flushed, as in ''II.''

VII.—Mussels covered for one hour with sterile sea water containing three parts per million active chlorine, with a view to-sterilizing the outside of the mussel shells, grids, and tank walls, to which bacteria—some of them released from faeces, etc., during hosing—may be adhering. (There is no danger of such bacteria being splashed inside the shells, because the mussels remain tightly closed. It may be emphasized that this final bath (of one hour's duration) is the only occasion on which the mussels are exposed to active chlorine.

VIII.—Shell-sterilizing bath drained off. The fishermen, after walking through a bath of 1 in 10,000 active chlorine, to sterilize their boots, enter the tanks and pack the mussels in sacks sterilized by 1 in 10,000 chlorine solution. The sacks are sealed with a safety lead bearing the date and the legend ''M.A.F. Conway'' (or ''L.C.C. Lytham'') and are dispatched to market.

The results of purification were checked bacteriologically. A bacteriological standard for purified mussels—not more than five lactose fermenters per ml. minced mussel—was finally adopted. Dodgson [222] did not favor a chemical method of purification because the shellfish refuse to open and act as filters with a consequent failure to purify.

Bacteriological Examination of Mussels. Results of bacteriological examination of shellfish are considered by some as reliable indications of sanitary quality. Few investigators, if any, have given as much attention to this problem as Dodgson.[220, 222] In his first report he questioned the value and interpretation of results. Chance and time interval in sampling was believed to introduce wide divergence in results from the same batch of shellfish. Glucose in the shellfish may also lead to false bacteriological results. Therefore, he did not suggest a bacteriological standard but stated that an acceptable method of purification could be standardized and maintained. In his later report in 1938, Dodgson, in discussing purified mussels, stated that they easily conformed to a standard of not more than five lactose fermenters per ml. of minced shellfish incubated at 37°C.(98.6°F.) for 24 hours, and oysters were capable of a lower standard as they usually show less than two lactose fermenters per ml. Dodgson encountered some occasions when thousands of lactose fermenters were encountered. They were not *Escherichia coli* but belonged to other sections of the coliform group. Since these did not develop at 44°C.(111.2°F.) Dodgson favored adopting that temperature for incubation instead of 37°C.

222. Dodgson. 1938. Roy. Soc. Med. Proc. 31, 925-934.

Bigger's [223] Method for Bacteriological Examination of Mussels. The principal features of this method are rejection of the shell liquor, standardization of the volume of each mussel at 25 ml. by addition of salt solution, and inoculation in duplicate of three dilutions into MacConkey's bile salt lactose broth and reporting the results as positive only when acid and gas are produced in both tubes in 24 hours at 37°C.(98.6°F.). Bigger described his procedure as follows:

METHOD OF EXAMINATION

(1) Ten mussels of average size are selected.

(2) These are washed with running tap water, using a boiled nail brush.

(3) One (A) is grasped wtih a sterile ovum forceps, rinsed under the tap, and then with sterile water.

(4) It is placed on a piece of sterile parchment paper in which it is grasped with the left hand. The shell is held with the flat edge towards the body, the anterior (pointed) end to the left, and the left valve of the shell upwards.

(5) A small portion of the shell at the broad (posterior) end is nibbled away with a sterile nibbling forceps and, through the opening, the blade of a sterile scalpel is inserted. With this the posterior adductor muscle and the other attachments of the mussel to the left valve are cut and, holding them with the paper interposed between them and the hands, the two valves of the shell are separated and the left one removed.

(6) All the fluid in the shell is poured off and, with the help of the scalpel, the body is transferred to a small beaker provided with a graduation at the 25 c.c. level.

(7) The body of the mussel in the beaker is thoroughly minced with a sterile pair of scissors. Sterile saline is added up to the 25 c.c. mark, and mixed thoroughly with the minced body, the scissors being used for this purpose. This is the reconstituted mussel (R.M.).

(8) The whole contents of the beaker are transferred to a larger sterile beaker, and 25 c.c. of sterile saline are added. This is a 1/2 dilution of R.M.

(9) With a sterile 1 c.c. pipetter, 1 c.c. of 1/2 R.M. is added, after mixing with the pipette, to each of two tubes of lactose bile broth (L.B.B.). These are labeled respectively A/.5/1 and A/.5/2.

(10) With the same pipette, 2 c.c. of 1/2 R.M. are added to 8 c.c. of sterile saline in a test-tube, making a 1/10 dilution of R.M.

(11) With a fresh sterile 1 c.c. pipette, 1 c.c. of 1/10 R.M. is added to each of two tubes of L.B.B. These are labeled respectively A/.1/1 and A/.1/2.

(12) With the same pipette 0.2 c.c. of 1/10 R.M. is added to each of two tubes of L.B.B. These are labelled respectively A/.02/1 and A/.02/2.

(13) Operations 3-11 are repeated with the next mussel (B), the cultures being labelled B/.5/1, B/.5/2, B/.1/1, B/.1/2, B/.02/1, and B/.02/2. The same procedure is carried out with the other eight mussels C to J.

(14) The cultures are incubated at 37°F. for 24 hours when the results are read (In the investigation here described an additional reading was made after a further 24 hours' incubation.)

NOTES ON METHOD OF EXAMINATION

(1) In practice it is more convenient to complete steps 3-8 for the ten mussels before steps 9-13 are commenced.

(2) Steps 6-8 may be condensed by transferring the body of the mussel directly from the shell to the large beaker, mincing in it, and making up the volume with sterile saline to 50 c.c.

(3) The instruments are sterilized by boiling in a pie dish over a Bunsen burner. After a few minutes they are transferred with a flamed forceps to another pie dish containing cold sterile water in order to cool them. From this they are removed for use with flamed forceps.

(4) The L.B.B. used is prepared in the usual way, and contains 2 per cent of peptone, 0.5 per cent of sodium taurocholate, 1 per cent of lactose and 1 per cent of Andrade's indicator. So that as much gas as possible may be collected the inner tube

223. Bigger. 1934. J. Hyg. 34; 172-194.

almost fills the bore of the outer. It is kept in position high up in the outer tube by a dimple in the wall of the latter, made by heating a small area of the glass with a blow-pipe flame and pushing in the softened portion with a carbon rod. This device, which was suggested by my laboratory attendant, Mr. W. Kampff, is superior to the usual one of supporting the inner tube on a piece of glass rod.

To avoid the error observed by Dodgson (1928), the production of acid in the medium due to fermentation of glucose derived from the mussel body, a large volume of L.B.B. should be used in each tube. For the tubes containing 0.5 c.c. of R.M., 30 c.c. of medium are used, and 15 c.c. for the tubes containing 0.1 c.c. and 0.02 c.c. of R.M. With these amounts of L.B.B. sufficient acid cannot be produced from the glucose present in the mussel to alter the color of the indicator to red.

(5) One of the innovations requiring mention is the rejection of the shell fluid. This step, which was recommended by the Middleburg Conference, was adopted for two reasons. The first is that this fluid is little more than a sample of the last water in which the mussel opened and is, therefore, little indication of the bacterial content of the mussel body. The second is that its volume is very variable. In freshly examined mussels a large amount may be present. How much of this is included in the sample cultivated depends largely on the operator's skill. It is practically impossible to open a mussel without losing some of the fluid, especially when a fat mussel is present in a shell with a large amount of fluid. The usual procedure of mincing the body in the shell is impossible without allowing some fluid to overflow. In mussels which have been, for some days, out of water little or no shell fluid may be present. Under these circumstances it is impossible to measure a volume of minced body with a graduated pipette unless fluid, such as saline, is added. This is commonly done, but the amount added is not standardized in any way, and such addition introduces a factor of uncertainty. For these reasons it was decided to discard shell fluid, and to replace it by sterile saline.

(6) In the method used by Prof. Eyre (1924) 0.1 c.c. of mussel mince (composed of body plus a variable amount of shell fluid) is the quantity tested. This bears no constant relationship to the volume of the shell contents, and therefore the results obtained cannot be translated into number of *B. coli* per mussel. In the method here described, the reconstituted mussel has a constant volume of 25 c.c., and results obtained by cultivating from various volumes can be reported in terms of bacteria per mussel.

The body volume of an average mussel is about 15 c.c., and 20 c.c. is very rarely attained. The mixture of minced body and saline up to 25 c.c. is generally capable of being manipulated with a pipette. Where the body volume is very large, however, it will be found more convenient to transfer the body to the large beaker, and to make up the volume to 50 c.c. with saline, so giving directly at 1/2 dilution of R.M.

(7) The method of mincing the whole body, in preference to Dodgson's method (1928) of opening the alimentary tract by scraping away part of the body and "stroking" the gills, was adopted, as it was hoped to devise a method which might be used successfully by any bacteriologist called upon to examine shellfish. Dodgson's method requires more knowledge of the anatomy of the mussel than is likely to be possessed by many bacteriologists, and also a considerable amount of skill and experience.

Lobsters. This product was probably packed first at Eastport, Maine, in 1840. A poor product was secured, but arrival of Scotch canners caused improvement. The industry then spread to Canada, where it took on considerable importance. According to Harrison and Hood,[224] from the beginning there was considerable spoilage of a variety known as smut, blackening, or discoloration. Prescott and Underwood [225] seemed to have done some of the pioneer work on spoilage of canned lobster. They established the relation of living bacteria to spoilage. Sound cans were found to be sterile, a conclusion which is probably not in accord with present-day

224. Harrison and Hood. 1923. Roy. Soc. Canada, Proc. and Trans. 17, 145-189.
225. Prescott and Underwood. 1897. Tech. Quart. 10, 183.

ideas about sterility of canned foods. Prescott and Underwood isolated nine species of bacteria which were fully characterized. When the bacteria were put back into sterile cans and the cans processed as in the original manner, spoilage occurred in the majority of cases. Experiments showed, as would be expected, that the bacteria were heat resistant and that they could survive certain processes. Four organisms were isolated by Mac-Phail[226] from canned lobster. They were facultative with respect to oxygen and formed gas. One was a sporeformer.

Harrison and Hood sent out a long questionnaire to all licensed canners. This information, while of indirect bacteriological interest, furnished these workers with the proper background for an intensive study of this problem. The terms smut, blackening, or discoloration were applied to either the container or its contents. Harrison and Hood reported the following changes from the normal:

1. Inky black discoloration of the meat.
2. Inky black discoloration of the can interior.
3. Bluing of the meat.
4. Brown incrustation of the can interior.
5. Brown discoloration of the paper.
6. Black discoloration of the paper.
7. Dull yellowish-white appearance of the meat.
8. Varied, other than blackening or browning; due to bacterial decomposition, manifested in many ways as general decomposition resulting in a greenish yellowish discoloration of parts of the lobster meat and alteration of the pickle producing turbidity without the production of color.

It will be impossible to give a complete review of this valuable paper, but mention may be made of some of the points of bacteriological interest. They brought out two points which were significant from the canning standpoint. "The presence of sulphur and the different pH values for the spring and fall caught lobster, and the chemical cause of discoloration is the liberation of hydrogen sulfide from the meat and the formation of iron sulfide, a black salt." Harrison,[227] with other colleagues in 1921, showed that bacteria were always present in the digestive glands and intestines of freshly caught lobster. Fifty-six cultures were obtained which fell into twenty-one types. Among these was a sporeformer which had characteristics like those of *Bacillus mesentericus*. When these organisms were grown on lobster-peptone-lead-carbonate agar, six of them blackened the medium, seven slightly blackened the surface, while four gave dark and light areas on the medium. Harrison and Hood were unable to conclude from their data, however, that bacteria were the sole cause of blackening of the lobster. Miss Newton, working under the direction of Professor Harrison, isolated a number of sporeforming bacteria from the sea, over 20 of which formed hydrogen sulfide . Thermal death time studies indicated that all of the cultures but one were killed in times much shorter than those used in processing the lobster. The situation has changed greatly since Harrison and Hood's work. An enamel (C-enamel)

226. MacPhail. 1923. Twenty-ninth Ann. Rpt., Dept. of Marine and Fish.
227. Harrison.

developed since then has almost completely conquered black in canned lobster. It is very probable also that bacteria play a less significant role than Harrison and Hood believed.

CRAB MEAT

Although crabs have not had as large a place in the American diet as other shellfish, they are growing in popularity. They are probably subject to the same kind and degree of pollution to which other shellfish are subject. Need for improvement in the sanitary conditions of production, handling, and distribution of fish and shellfish throughout the United States was indicated in a committee report presented to the American Public Health Association in October, 1932.[228] Hunter, who was chairman of this committee, later reviewed in the Fishing Gazette the practices then in use as they related to the sanitary problems. He believed that crab meat was subject to dangerous contamination unless handled properly. The recommendations which he made were such as to indicate that many sources for such contamination existed in machinery and personnel. Jarvis [229] described the Alaska and Japan crab-packing industries but gave little or no information on bacteriological problems.

Purification of Crabs. Since these are harvested in many places from water of questionable sanitary quality, some attention has been given to purification. Nickerson, Fitzgerald, and Messer [230] floated contaminated blue crabs in tanks through sea water containing .5 p.p.m. of chlorine. Such treatment for 24 to 48 hours removed many of the fecal organisms but not all. These investigators, however, considered the procedure to be valuable as it reduced the boiling time for both crabs and lobsters.

Fresh Crab Meat. This has been a product of considerable importance from the viewpoints of sanitation and keeping quality. Owing to the fact that it may become grossly contaminated during pickling, and to the fact that it reviewed no special treatment for coping with the bacteria which it contains, other than storing at low temperatures or freezing, it has generally been regarded with suspicion by food-control officials. Hunter [231] has reviewed these problems which involved cleanliness of plant equipment as well as the more serious matter of personal cleanliness of the employees. The latter problem is more serious because of the fact that the meat must be picked from the crawfish by hand and packed by hand. Numerous samples of fresh, iced crab meat were examined by Tobin and McCleskey [232] for total bacteria count and presence of *Escherichia coli*. Many of the samples were positive for *Escherichia coli*, the most probable numbers exceeding one in 63 per cent of the samples and 10 in 20 per cent. The plate count varies from 87,000 to 16,000,000 per gram. *Escherichia coli* was found to originate largely from hands of workers, ice, and dipping brines. Partial sterilization of crab meat in an autoclave for 15 minutes

228. Amer. Pub. Health Assoc. Year Book, 1932-1933, 58.
229. Jarvis. 1937. The Canner, Sept. 25, 1937; Sept. 28, 1940.
230. Nickerson *et al.* 1939. Amer. J. Pub. Health 29, 619-627.
231. Hunter. 1933. Fishing Gaz., Nov. and Dec. 1933; Jan. 1934; see also Atlantic Fisherman, May 1937.
232. Tobin and McCleskey. 1941. Food Research 6, 157-167.

at 121°C.(249°F.) resulted in a 99.9 per cent reduction of the total bacteria and elimination of *Escherichia coli.* Tobin and McCleskey believed that the use of *Escherichia coli* as an indicator of pollution and undesirable practices was justified.

According to Harris[233] decomposition of fresh crab meat is a progressive proteolysis, accompanied by a rapid and continuous rise in ammonia content and a more or less irregular rise in alkaline reactions; it is not due to sporebearing anaerobes but primarily to the action of the Proteus group, possibly supplemented by some of the Pseudomonas and Flavobacterium groups. Other bacteria isolated belonged to the Escherichia, Zopfius, Alcaligenes, Achromobacter, Micrococcus, Sarcina, and Streptococcus genera. There was no relation (or no close relation) between "age" of decomposition and total aerobic counts or pH. *Escherichia coli* score was high in samples spoiling at room temperature and low in samples spoiling at icebox temperature. Maximum total aerobic count was reached at room temperature the first to fourth days and at icebox temperature the 15th to 20th days; at both temperatures there was a sudden initial rise in bacterial count. The Nessler ammonia test is tentatively proposed for differentiating fresh from spoiled crab meat, before macroscopic signs of spoilage appear.

Canned Crab Meat. This now great industry in the United States has recently been described by Fellers and Harris.[234] It has become an important industry in Japan since 1900 (Oshima[235]). The greatest problem which had to be overcome was blackening caused by formation of ferrous sulfide in the cans. It was revealed that as the difficulty increased the meat approached an alkaline reaction and came almost directly with staleness of material. The trouble was corrected by use of double-lacquered cans and strictly fresh crab meat with buffer solutions to raise the pH. Oshima recommended tartrates, citrates, or a citrate and phosphate mixture to be placed in the can. von Bonde and Marchand[236] also emphasized the necessity for careful methods of packing. The crawfish were kept alive in floater crates until ready for use, graded for size and condition, prepared rapidly for canning, not too tightly packed in lacquered cans or glass jars, thoroughly exhausted, and given a short cook with prompt cooling.

Fellers and Harris[234] described a new method for canning the flesh of the blue crab. The main difficulties have always been serious color and flavor changes in the canned meat resulting from decomposition of unstable proteins. The large amounts of copper have united with ammonia to form blue copper-ammonia compounds which are objectionable. Such reactions have been eliminated by dipping the crab meat into brine containing a trace of aluminum or zinc salts to stabilize the copper.

Fresh crab meat packed in one-pound, snap-lock cans and stored at 1 to 5°C.(33.8 to 41°F.) was examined by Tobin, Alford, and McCleskey[237]

233. Harris. 1932. Amer. J. Hyg. 15, 269-275.
234. Fellers and Harris. 1940. Ind. Eng. Chem. 32, 592.
235. Ishima. 1931. U. S. Bur. Fisheries, Invest. Rpt. 8.
236. von Bonde and Marchand. 1935. Union So. Africa Fish. Marine Biol. Surv. Div., Invest. Rpt. 5, 1-43.
237. Tobin, Alford, and McCleskey. 1941. J. Bact. 41, 96-97; Food Research 7 (1942), 353-359.

at intervals until spoilage occurred. Changes in the total bacterial count, in the predominating species, and in the pH were determined on a large number of samples.

The initial counts varied from about 100,000 to 3,000,000 per gram. When the cans were first put into storage, the flora consisted almost exclusively of cocci, but species of Bacillus, Achromobacter, Flavobacterium, Alcaligenes, Aerobacter, Escherichia, and Pseudomonas were present. The total count increased steadily during storage. After a week, gram-negative rods, chiefly Pseudomonas and Achromobacter, were most numerous. At the time of definite spoilage, after 10 to 15 days of storage, the bacterial population was usually many millions per gram and consisted almost entirely of Pseudomonas and Achromobacter species. These organisms were studied in pure culture and their growth rates at 0°C.(32°F.) and at 4 to 5°C.(39.2 to 41°F.) were determined. The cultures were found to be capable of producing typical spoilage of crab meat at the usual temperature of storage, 1 to 5°C.(33.8 to 41°F.). The pH of the fresh crab meat was usually near 7.2. It increased steadily during storage until, at the time of spoilage, it was 7.8 to 8.2.

CLAMS

Several species of clams are packed along the Atlantic Coast. Since fresh clams have been incriminated in typhoid fever outbreaks it is obvious that they are subject to the same type of contamination to which other shellfish are. In the Annual Report of the Connecticut State Board of Health for 1927, page 128, is an account of such an outbreak caused by eating raw clams. Seven or eight cases appeared in one family. These clams were dug from the Thames River not far from a sewer outlet. Methods of culture, harvesting, and packing were discussed by Reed.[234]

Methods for examining clams are similar to those proposed for oysters. The nature of clams, however, makes some modifications necessary. Clams are more likely to lost water during transportation than oysters. It is, therefore, necessary to take greater precautions to separate different samples of clams from each other. In opening soft clams, it has been found that if two incisions are made through the mantle, the shell water may be poured out without opening the shell. Hard clams are more difficult to open, but if the shell is struck over the dorsal muscle with a small hammer, an opening will be formed permitting the insertion of the knife to cut the muscle.

Sometimes clams and other shellfish contain too little liquor to make all of the tests above described. This is always the case when the shells are very small. Under these conditions, the water from two or more shellfish must be taken together and tested and considered as one.

WINKLES

These are marine mollusks which are harvested in waters along shores and which, consequently, may be polluted.

238. Reed. 1925. Canning Age, Aug. 1925.

Nine cases of typhoid fever were traced in London in 1929 to consumption of winkles purchased from local stall holders. These observations prompted bacteriological examination of winkles by Eyre.[239] Bacteriological examination of a sample of live winkles did not reveal the presence of *Eberthella typhosa* or any similar organism. It did, however, reveal that *Escherichia coli* was present to the number of over 100 per winkle. *Bacillus proteus* and *Streptococcus fecalis* were also present in large numbers. The total number of microorganisms growing at 22°C.(71.6°F.) was 2,140,000 per winkle; at 37°C.(98.6°F.) 850,000 grew. Anaerobic bacteria were also reported to the extent of 10 per winkle. A sample of boiled winkles from the same vendor revealed the presence of *Escherichia coli* to the number of one but not 10 per winkle. Numerous *Bacillus proteus* and *Streptococcus fecalis* cells were also present. The total number of microorganisms capable of growing at 22°C. averaged 4,999 per winkle and at 37°C., 22,000. Apparently the winkles were harvested from beds subject to undesirable and potentially dangerous contamination. Boiling apparently did not render the winkles safe because they were not sterilized by that treatment.

Eyre's [239] Method for Bacteriological Examination of Winkles and Similar Shellfish. The procedure is the result of extended study of winkles to determine their sanitary condition.

1. Take ten (10) winkles at random from the sample.

2. Extract each fish from its shell by means of a strong stilletto and transfer to a sterile mortar.

3. Triturate the bodies of the fish very thoroughly, adding sterile 3 per cent saline solution to a total amount of 10 c.c. to the contents of the mortar during the process.

Allow the emulsion to stand for a few minutes while the debris settles.

Decant the turbid supernatant fluid (O.F.) (original fluid) into a 250 c.c. Erlenmeyer flask (sterile).

It is now assumed that the entire bacterial content from one winkle is contained in each cubic centimeter of the O.F.)

4. Use 0.1 c.c. of the original fluid (equivalent to 1/10 winkle) to inseminate three nutrose agar plates in series.

5. Prepare two surface plate cultures, each with 0.1 c.c. of the O.F. upon Wilson's iron bismuth agar for the detection of members of the typhoid group or Salmonella.

Incubate these five plates at 37°C. for 48 hours.

6. Add 90 c.c. of the sterile hypertonic saline to the winkle bodies in the mortar and mix thoroughly.

7. Transfer the mixture to a sterile conical urine glass. Protect this receptacle by covering it with the half of a petri capsule, and allow it to remain undisturbed for about 10 minutes while the debris settles down. Then decant the supernatant fluid into the flask containing the remainder of the original fluid.

It is now assumed that the bacteria contained in every quanta of 10 c.c. of this "secondary" fluid (S.F.) represent the bacteriological flora of an average winkle.

QUANTITATIVE EXAMINATION

8. Prepare decimal dilutions from 1 c.c. of the secondary fluid, thus:

    (1) 1 c.c. secondary fluid   9 c.c. salt solution A
    (2) 1 c.c. A   9 c.c. salt solution B
    (3) 1 c.c. B   9 c.c. salt solution C
    (4) 1 c.c. C   9 c.c. salt solution D

239. Eyre. 1933. J. Hyg. 23, 1; 33 (1933), 1-9.

9. Prepare a series of agar plates containing, respectively, 1 c.c. of secondary fluid and 1 c.c. from each of the dilutions A, B, C, D. Incubate at 37°C. for 48 hours and then enumerate the resulting colonies.

10. Prepare precisely similar set of gelatine plates. Incubate at 22°C. for 72 hours and then enumerate the resulting colonies. This set of plates also serves for the enumeration of *B. proteus*.

11. A. *B. coli.* Prepare a set of cultures in bile salt lactose broth thus—using double strength medium in large tubes for the first two—and incubate for 24 hours

> (a) 10 c.c. secondary fluid (1 winkle)
> (b) 5 c.c. secondary fluid (½ winkle)
> (c) 2 c.c. secondary fluid (⅕ winkle)
> (d) 1 c.c. secondary fluid (⅒ winkle)
> (e) 1 c.c. fluid from dilution A (see par. 8) 1/100 winkle
> (f) 1 c.c. fluid from dilution B   1/1000 winkle
> (g) 1 c.c. fluid from dilution C   1/10,000 winkle
> (h) 1 c.c. fluid from dilution D   1/100,000 winkle
> (i) 0.1 c.c. fluid from dilution D   1/1,000,000 winkle

12. B. *Streptococci.* Prepare a precisely similar set of cultures using 2 per cent glucose broth instead of bile salt broth.

13. D. *B. proteus.* For the recognition and enumeration of this organism the gelatine plates prepared as per paragraph 10 are again utlized.

14. C. Spores of *B. welchii.* Inoculate into litmus milk

> 10 c.c. secondary fluid
> 5 c.c. secondary fluid
> 2 c.c. secondary fluid
> 1 c.c. secondary fluid

Heat to 80°C. for 10 minutes in water bath and incubate anaerobically for 48 hours.

SHRIMP

Shrimp is a decapod crustacean *(Crago vulgaris)* found especially in waters about the southern states. This product is used fresh when preserved by refrigeration, and large quantities are also canned in tin and glass containers. General features of the industry have been reviewed in various places.[240] Thorough washing at various places in preparation of the meat is necessary to remove foreign matter and spoilage microorganisms.

The shrimp industry is a continual fight with spoilage microorganisms. Most of the improvements which have been introduced into the industry have as a basis better control of them. Cameron and Williams [241] showed the importance of various steps in preparation of shrimp on the basis of its load of microorganisms. One observation is obvious from their work—the extremely large number of bacteria which are always present. This situation makes it necessary to handle the shrimp meat as quickly as possible. Cameron and Williams also mentioned the value of chlorine compounds for cleaning table surfaces and utensils.

Canned Shrimp. Quality of this product depends on prompt icing and careful handling immediately after catching. Shrimp is a very perishable food and since it is taken, as Clarke [242] has stated, from waters where warm weather prevails, special attention must be given to methods which will

240. Canning Age, June 1926.
241. Cameron and Williams. 1934. The Canner, Sept. 1, 1934; Canning Age, Sept. 1934.
242. Clarke. 1937. Amer. J. Pub. Health 27, 655-658.

prevent decomposition. Detection of decomposed fresh shrimp is comparatively easy since it undergoes changes in appearance and odor which are obvious. After canning, however, it is difficult to detect decomposition unless it is extreme. The Food and Drug Administration, by means of experimental packs of shrimp, were able to devise methods for detecting presence of decomposed shrimp in the canned article. Seizure of much canned shrimp caused the packers to impose on themselves an inspection which has brought their product to an acceptable position in the eyes of food-control officials. By 1937 about 95 per cent of shrimp production was under government inspection. Revised regulations governing packing methods to be used by shrimp canners who wish to label their product "Production supervised by the U. S. Food and Drug Administration" became effective July 1, 1937.[243] These included recommendations for construction of the plant, its operation, and processes for the product in both wet and dry packs.

243. The Canner, June 26, 1937.

CHAPTER 21

MEAT AND MEAT PRODUCTS

Meat and meat products are of interest to food bacteriologists for various reasons. Microorganisms have important roles in curing meats, contributing to good color and flavor. They are believed to contribute to flavor of sausage and other specialties. On the other hand, they may spoil meat or even make it deleterious to health. The great meat-preservation industry is based largely on strict control of microorganisms. Every attempt is made to create conditions which will either prevent their development if they are undesirable forms or favor growth if they are desirable forms. In some cases several methods of preservation are applied to the same product.

Both chemical and bacteriological methods have been proposed for determining whether meat has become unsound. Many of them have been found to be of no value. Organoleptic tests, largely used for fresh meats and sea foods, leave much to be desired. Fellers (Chairman)[1] pointed out the difficulties of determining when meats are spoiled. Detection of incipient spoilage is the difficult problem. Those who wish a short review of suggested methods should read the committee report by Fellers. Significance of hydrogen-ion concentration in food spoilage, in general, has prompted some to suggest that changes in fresh meats might mean spoilage. Schmidt[2] stated that a reaction, more alkaline than pH 6.3, indicated incipient putrefaction. When meat was inoculated with pure cultures of bacteria which might be expected in such a product, its reaction was rendered more alkaline. Herzner and Mann[3] stated that a reaction of pH 6.0 to 6.2 indicated incipient spoilage, a value not different from that proposed by Schmidt. It is doubtful whether pH methods can be used for determining the fitness of meat. The pH of meat depends on too many variable factors, such as autolysis, rapidity of chilling, etc. Furthermore, for some people, changes which would alter the pH significantly would be considered desirable. For these reasons, slight changes in pH could not be the only methods for judging the quality of meat. This may not be true for all meat products.

Bacteriological Methods. Even though microorganisms are involved in meat spoilage, ordinary bacteriological methods have not been of much value for determining whether meats are spoiled or not. Conradi[4] suggested an elaborate method which involved isolation of pure cultures. Zwick and Weichel[5] also attempted to use bacteriological methods for detecting undesirable meat. Weaver[6] tried to devise a method based on

1. Fellers. 1929. Amer. J. Pub. Health 19, 389-392.
2. Schmidt. 1928. Arch. f. Hyg. 100, 377-392.
3. Herzner and Mann. 1926. Ztschr. f. Untersuch. der Lebensmtl. 52, 215-242.
4. Conradi. 1909. Zeit. f. Fleisch u. Michyg. 19, 341-345.
5. Zwick and Weichel. 1911. Arb. K. Gsndhtsamt. 38, 327-337.
6. Weaver. 1927. Mich. Agr. Expt. Sta. Tech. Bull. 79, 28.

the appearance of indole-producing bacteria. A hydrogen-sulfide method was also suggested. Schellhorn [7] even proposed a mouse-feeding test. It would be cumbrous for routine work, as Berg [8] stated. Before such methods could be used for detecting unsound meat, much work would have to be done with them on meat from healthy animals. Bacteriological methods probably have distinct limitations in routine meat examination on account of the time consumed and the fact that meat may acquire many bacteria after preparation for the market.

Comparative chemical and bacteriological observations by Wright [9] on fresh and frozen New Zealand lamb, indicated little difference so far as bacterial content was concerned. The surface was infected with bacteria, but the interior remained sterile. It was found by experiment that when kept at a temperature of 15.5 to 25°C. (60 to 77°F.) the surface bacteria could invade the interior of the lamb in five days and the interior of the mutton in seven days, but no bacterial growth or invasion took place at a temperature of —16.7 to —7.2°C. (2 to 19°F.). An extensive report was made by Metzger [10] on the character and extent of bacterial infection in flesh of animals condemned as diseased, but which, under certain restrictions, could be slaughtered and sold in Germany for human food. He believed that by microscope inspection alone, a larger proportion of meat than is necessary may be kept from sale; for this reason it was suggested that more information be sought so that the industry would not suffer. Some have suggested bacteriological examinations with plate cultures which would reveal not only numbers but types as well. Such a practice has not been followed as much in America as on the continent. Pohl, [11] for instance, was able to show presence of *Salmonella enteritidis* in many samples of meat. Haines [12] reviewed the various problems of meat preservation and the microorganisms involved.

Meat Inspection. Attempts to protect the public health by preventing sale of meat from diseased animals have caused federal and state health authorities to establish a comprehensive organization for this purpose. The Bureau of Animal Industry is empowered with these duties for meat and meat products to be sold in interstate traffic in the United States. Meat inspection has been practiced since the earliest times. Moses gave specific instructions. In early days, meat inspection, according to Müller, [13] was related to religious rites and ceremonies, and had nothing to do with preventive medicine. When the science of morbid anatomy became sufficiently developed, meat inspection began to follow the principles laid down by pathologists. According to Wieser, [14] all meat destined for human consumption should be inspected. He collected details of 20 outbreaks of

7. Schellhorn. 1910. Centbl. f. Bakt. I., Orig. 54, 428-450.
8. Berg. 1910. Ztschr. f. Medizinalbeamte, No. 15.
9. Wright. 1912. Soc. Chem. Indus. J. 31, 965-967.
10. Metzger. 1909. Condemned Animals and Bacteria in the Flesh of Animals Slaughtered Under Such Conditions. Diss., Bern. 1909.
11. Pohl. 1938. Ztschr. f. Infektionskrank., Parasitäre Krank u. Hyg. der Haustiere 53, 113-121.
12. Haines. 1937. (Gt. Brit.) Food Invest. Bd., Spec. Rpt. 45.
13. Müller. 1929. Deut. Tierärztl. Wchnschr. 37, 84-87.
14. Wieser. 1930. Ztschr. f. Hyg. u. Infektionskrank 10, 333-355.

food poisoning, traced to ingestion of meat preserved by pickling or smoking. Meat inspection is chiefly concerned with the following diseases: anthrax, actinomycosis, caseous lymphadenitis, foot-and-mouth disease, tuberculosis, and a few of the parasitic diseases *(Cyticercus bovis, C. cellulosis,* and *Trichinella spiralis)* (Grant [15]). Routine inspection not only protects the consumer but also gives valuable information on the distribution of animal diseases. The meat inspection service rendered by the United States Veterinary Corps is, according to Dildine,[16] more extended, for the product is controlled until it is prepared for the table.

Federal Inspection. In the United States, the Department of Agriculture is empowered to inspect meat sold in interstate traffic. The inspection begins even before the live animals are driven to slaughter. If an animal is observed which seems to be ill, it receives a tag marked "U. S. Condemned" or "U. S. Suspect." When the animal is condemned, it cannot be taken into the slaughter room. Suspected animals are slaughtered separately from other animals. This is ante-mortem inspection. Post-mortem inspection involves careful examination of every part of the carcass. According to Mohler,[17] government inspectors, trained veterinarians, start inspection in the case of beef when the animal is skinned. The head is cut off and several lymph glands are opened for signs of abnormality and infection. The tongue is thoroughly examined as are also the cheek muscles to insure freedom from cysts that might produce tapeworms. The viscera are examined with just as much care. These are removed from the carcass and placed before the inspector on a well-lighted table. The carcass is then inspected with equal care. Attention is given to the possibility of nodules on the ribs as signs of tuberculosis. Membranes of the chest and abdomen, the various groups of lymph glands, the kidneys, split backbone, and body generally are carefully examined. If examination of the various portions of the carcass indicates satisfactory condition, the animal is considered to be free from disease and is marked "U. S. Inspected and Passed." Each cut of meat from the carcass may then receive the same stamp of approval—the purple federal meat inspection stamp. The flesh of animals which is condemned by federal inspectors is made into fertilizers and not used for food. Such meat must be destroyed or denatured in the presence of an inspector who has to file a report. Provision is made, however, for use of the flesh of some animals which are infected with tuberculosis. If the lesions are not excessive the meat is sold as "sterilized" after all portions have been heated to 76.7°C.(170°F.) for 30 minutes.

Local Inspection. Not all meat distributed in the United States can be inspected by the Bureau of Animal Industry. Only that which is shipped in interstate traffic can be so inspected. Some meat is inspected by local agencies and much so-called "home-killed" meat is not inspected at all. This is an unfortunate situation. The Bureau of Animal Industry will act in an advisory capacity to cities which wish to institute meat

15. Grant. 1931. Austral. Vet. J. 7, 18-25.
16. Dildine. 1933. Vet. Bull. Sup. Army Med. Bull. 27, 299-312.
17. Mohler. 1926. U. S. Dept. Agr. Misc. Cir. 63.

inspection. They may even stamp inspected meat, using a mark easily distinguishable from the federal stamp. Early in 1926, Chicago made a regulation that no carcass of an animal which had not been inspected by the Bureau of Animal Industry should be shipped into Chicago without the viscera attached.

Microorganisms in Blood and Tissues of Healthy Animals. Whether blood and tissues of animals which appear to be healthy contain viable microorganisms or not, is a controversial matter even though many investigations have been made. The results secured were probably influenced by the technic, media, and methods used. Maurel [18] reported presence of a diplococcus. Conradi,[4] using a special enrichment method, found 72 specimens of tissue, out of 162 pieces taken from 150 animals, to contain bacteria. The liver was most frequently infected, although bacteria were found in 18 out of 59 pieces of muscle. *Salmonella suipestifer* was found on four occasions in the muscle. Bierotti and Machilda [19] also published similar results. Zwick and Weichel [5] reported the liver of animals to be frequently infected. Hoagland *et al.*[20] stated that certain bacteria, chiefly micrococci, might be normally present in tissue of healthy animals slaughtered for beef. These bacteria were said to possess no pathological significance and do not appear to multiply in carcasses during cold storage. Similar conclusions were reached by Wrzosek,[21] Rzegocinski,[22] Horn,[23] Westholz,[24] and many others. This subject is important in the meat-preservation industry, an industry which wages a constant fight with bacteria. Reith's [25] work originated in an attempt to determine the flora of sound and sour hams. Cultures of the muscular tissue of slaughtered hogs showed the presence of bacteria in 77 per cent of 216 specimens; in 37 per cent anaerobes were found. Cultures of the muscular tissues of healthy live hogs, rabbits, and guinea pigs showed the presence of bacteria in 83 per cent of 108 samples; 49 per cent of the samples contained anaerobes. Cultures of the blood of healthy live hogs, rabbits, and guinea pigs showed the presence of bacteria in 84 per cent of 38 samples; 39 per cent contained anaerobes. A brief period of starvation, 36 to 48 hours, had no appreciable effect on the presence of bacteria in the tissues.

Partial identification of bacteria was attempted. Morphological identification of 96 strains gave a grouping as follows:

```
55 (59 per cent) staphylococci
21 (22 per cent) bipolar rods
18 (19 per cent) Gram-positive rods
15 (16 per cent) coccus forms other than staphylococci
 6 ( 6 per cent) Gram-negative rods
```

18. Maurel. 1911. Compt. Rend. Acad. Sci. 70, 241-244.
19. Bierotti and Machilda. 1910. München. Med. Wchnschr. 57, 636.
20. Hoagland, McBryde, and Powick. 1917. U. S. Bur. Anim. Indus., Dept. Bull. 433.
21. Wrzosek. 1903. Bull. Acad. Sci., Cracovie, 759-766.
22. Rzegocinski. 1903. Arch. f. Polonaises des Sci. Biol. et Medicales. 2.
23. Horn. 1910. Ztschr. f. Infektionskrank. Parasitäre Krank. u. Hyg. der Haustiere. 8, 424.
24. Westholz. 1912. (On the Occurrence of Microorganisms in the Mesenteria Glands of Normal Cattle.) Inaug. Diss., Univ. of Bern, Switzerland.
25. Reith. 1926. Amer. Med. Assoc. J. 86, 326; J. Bact. 12 (1929), 367-381.

Reith suggested that the high percentage of cocci and bipolar organisms indicated invasion from the respiratory tract and skin. Very few Gram-negative rods were found. If invasion from the intestinal tract occurred, a high percentage of *Escherichia coli* would be found; only two were reported. The isolation of anaerobic bacteria from the tissues is of importance to the meat industry. Those which were isolated were proteolytic and might produce souring of the meat unless their growth was restricted by refrigeration, pickling solutions, etc. Hoagland, McBryde, and Powick[20] found a small micrococcus in four out of seven carcasses of beef. The organism did not seem to be disseminated throughout the muscular tissue of any one quarter but was encountered only here and there. These authors believed that the organism was present in the tissues at the time of slaughter. It was said to have no significance and did not multiply in the tissues. Possible post-mortem invasion would generally be admitted, although if results by Burn[26] are representative, this would be determined by the species. *Clostridium welchii, Escherichia coli,* and staphylococci were the only species which successfully invaded the bodies of guinea pigs after death. Burn believed that post-mortem invasion could be a factor in accounting for bacteria within organs and body fluids.

Microorganisms on Meat. The significance of microorganisms as agents causing meat spoilage has prompted many investigations of their numbers and types. During transit under cold storage, various microorganisms may develop. Spoilage may be of various types. Achromobacter species of bacteria may cause sliminess and other species may cause rancidity of fat. The bacterial contamination of chilled beef largely determines its life, as Thorpe[27] has stated. He reported that methods of slaughtering and handling have made it possible to hold chilled beef longer. The basic reasons for this were stated by Moran[28] and involves sound hygienic practice of slaughtering, which results in fewer microorganisms to be controlled. Haines,[29] in attempts to learn the extent to which carcasses are contaminated in the slaughterhouse, found few bacteria; they were present in ice brine pipes and in sweepings from floors. He believed that bacterial contamination of carcasses in well-conducted storage warehouses was negligible. Actinomyces species were quite common. He also found that bacteria develop quite slowly on beef at first. During this lag period they are developing on soluble nitrogenous substances already present on the beef. After a lag period of some 40 hours at 37° (98.6°F.), they develop rapidly. Quite wide variations in bacterial count of meats were observed by Brewer.[30] *Escherichia coli* was abundant when counts were high. This was not related to appearance. The samples which Brewer used were cuts which would be purchased in small shops.

Brooks, Haines, Moran, and Pace,[31] in experiments on bacon curing, found many bacteria on sides of fresh pork prepared under laboratory

26. Burn. 1934. J. Infect. Dis. 54, 388-403.
27. Thorpe. 1934. Austral. Vet. J., 10, 219-222.
28. Moran. 1935. Roy. Sanit. Inst. J. 56, 214-216.
29. Haines. 1930. (Gt. Brit.) Food Invest. Bd., Ann Rpt. for 1929, 40.
30. Brewer. 1925. J. Bact. 10, 543.
31. Brooks *et al.* 1940. Food Invest. Bd., Spec. Rept. 49.

conditions. For two batches of pigs, it averaged 2×10^6 and 160,000 per sq. cm. After prechilling operations it was reduced to about 400 per sq. cm.; it was further reduced during chilling to between 100 and 200. Commercial sides of pork gave a mean count after chilling of 28,000, after curing of 60,000, and after maturation of 10^6 or more organisms per square centimeter. Many bacteria were found by Jensen and Hess [222] on the skin of hogs where the jugular vein is stuck. These were significant, for among them many Clostridia were found which could be carried into the blood stream by the sticking knife. Short storage life of chilled beef has been a problem in shipping it from Australia to England. Since microorganisms are responsible for most spoilage, Empey and Scott [32] studied their origin. While various factors are involved in contributing microorganisms to beef, the chief source was the hide and hair of the slaughtered animals. Two different temperatures were used, 20°C.(68°F.) and —1°C.(30.2°F.). The main contamination is bacterial, particularly at 20°C.(68°F.). At —1°C.(30.2°F.) molds and yeasts may constitute 35 per cent of the initial microbial population on beef after slaughter. At —1°C.(30.2°F.) Achromobacter species constituted 90 per cent of the flora. No investigation of types was made at 20°C.(68°F.). Introduction of various sanitary measures caused fewer bacteria to be present. These results were in general confirmed by Ingram.[33] To determine the effect of salt on these organisms, he mixed minced pork with salt in concentrations from 0 to 25 per cent and stored it at 0°C.(32°F.). In concentrations less than four per cent, the meat was covered by a fluid film containing Pseudomonas in practically a pure culture. Putrefaction occurred with a sweet odor at first. In concentrations between four and 10 per cent, the flora was dominated by molds, especially *Thamnidium chaetocladioides*. Species of Cladosporium and Penicillium also occurred. The bacterial flora consisted of yellow Micrococci and Pseudomonas. Above 10 per cent of salt, the flora was restricted to a few yellow micrococci quite like *Micrococcus flavescens* along with an unidentified species of Penicillium. This flora persisted in concentrations of salt up to 25 per cent. Spoilage of meat has been found to be due to various types of microorganisms. An organism of the *Pseudomonas fluorescens* group was found by Haines [34] to produce an unpleasant sour smell. Since it was found to hydrolyze fat in agar media, explanation thus exists for appearance of free acids in fat or stored carcasses. Slime on stored meat was later reported by Haines to be composed of Achromobacter organisms. Other defects of meat were found to be due to other species by Rolle and Pavasar.[35] Similar observations were made by Kolobolotsky.[36] *Escherichia coli* and *Bacillus proteus vulgaris* were found to be active in putrefaction.

Various factors which influence development of bacteria in cultures probably influence their development on meat surfaces. The two most

32. Empey and Scott. 1939. Council Sci. and Indus. Res., Bull. 126.
33. Ingram. 1935. (Gt. Brit.) Food Invest. Bd., Ann. Rpt. for 1934, 77.
34. Haines. 1931. (Gt. Brit.) Food Invest. Bd., Ann. Rpt. for 1930, 45; Soc. Chem. Ind. J., July 3, 1941.
35. Rolle and Pavasar. 1933. Latvigas Biol. Biedribas Raksti 3, 9-16.
36. Kolobolotsky. 1941. Problems of Nutrition. Vol. 2; Rev. in Food Mfr. 17 (1942), 254.

important are temperature and humidity. More is known about effects of temperature than humidity. Ewell [37] observed that growth of bacteria on meat surfaces ceased at relative humidities below 92 per cent and that bacteria grew with great rapidity at the highest attainable humidity of 99 per cent. He also suggested that molds might become acclimated to ozone. However, ozone was said to be useful because it decreased infection. Haines and Smith [38] observed some bacterial growth at a relative humidity of 70 per cent in still air. Growth was, however, in proportion to humidity.

Haines [12] **Methods for Bacteriological Examination of Tissues.** Two methods were devised for enumerating bacteria on tissues, the direct microscope or total count and count of viable organisms by plating on suitable media. The former can be used only when a liquid sample containing one million organisms can be obtained. Suitable dilutions of the fluid are counted in a modified hemacytometer chamber used by Wilson.[39] For the viable count, a series of plates are poured using suitable media. The latter method yields results which are more useful, for pure cultures may be picked and some information gained about the composition of the flora.

Since spoilage of tissues, apart from special cases of anaerobic processes, is due to growth on the surface of the carcass, the best procedure, according to Haines, is to make counts per unit of superficial tissue. His method for this was as follows: A sterile cork borer is pressed vertically into the tissues to a depth of one centimeter or more. By this means a cylinder of tissue is left, and from its top a disc about two millimeters thick is cut with sterile scalpel. The area of this disc may be computed from the diameter of the cork borer. Microorganisms on the surface of the sample may be brought into suspension by shaking vigorously with glass beads and sterile salt solution. When it is believed that bacteria may have penetrated, a thicker disc of meat may be taken and ground, or disintegrated with a mechanical stirrer and sterile sand. Haines' device for this was made with a straight-walled test tube about 15 x 2.5 cm. provided with a bent stirring rod extending through the cork. This is connected at its top to a motor. It is probable that the disintegrators used in the United States in analysis of paper board would be suitable and perhaps superior.

Gas Storage of Meat. This has been introduced in recent years to prolong storage life of meat. Ozone and carbon dioxide are the gases which have had most study. Both have been discussed in Chapter 1.

Ozone. This gas cannot be used in high concentrations because it causes rancidity and bad flavors in the fat. In low concentrations, beneficial effects in controlling microbial life have been claimed for it. Results of experiments by Haines [12] indicated that ozone may react with oxidizable substances to result in a pH of between 4 and 5. This in itself may inhibit growth of bacteria. Haines observed that high concentrations of ozone were required to arrest established growth—of the order of 1,000 p.p.m. by volume. Smaller amounts suffice if admitted with the inoculum. Haines also observed specificity of ozone for certain species while others were not affected. Experiments with lean meat in a saturated atmosphere at 0°C. (32°F.) indicated that 10 p.p.m. had little effect on slime-producing bacteria. For these reasons, ozone was believed to be of little value for inhibiting growth on meat. The amounts required cannot be tolerated by human beings and have deleterious effects on fat.

37. Ewell. 1935. Refrig. Engin. 30, 367-368.
38. Haines and Smith. 1933. (Gt. Brit.) Food Invest. Bd., Spec. Rpt. 43.
39. Wilson. 1922. J. Bact. 7, 405-446.

Carbon Dioxide. This gas has had a checkered reputation in food preservation. Those who favor its use believe that it increases the storage life of meat by inhibiting development of microorganisms. Those who believe to the contrary point to loss of color and flavor and even an accelerated development of certain food-poisoning bacteria. The latter is a factor which cannot be overlooked, for an atmosphere containing appreciable amounts of carbon dioxide favors development of food-poisoning staphylococci. According to Tomkins [40] presence of carbon dioxide increases the latent period of germination and decreases the rate of elongation of germ tubes of fungi on meat. The percentage germination of the species with which he worked was reduced only in concentration noticeably prolonging the latent period. Growth of colonies was retarded by carbon dioxide to a somewhat greater extent than germination. The concentration of carbon dioxide needed to prevent growth depended on temperature, the lower the temperature the smaller the amounts of carbon dioxide needed. Resistance of the different fungi to carbon dioxide varied, *Sporotrichum carnis* needing higher amounts. Tomkins observed that other factors than pH explained inhibitive action of carbon dioxide. About this same time Callow [41] also reported favorable results from storing pork and bacon in carbon dioxide. Small pieces of pork were kept in perfect condition for over two months at 0°C.(32°F.) in desiccators filled with carbon dioxide. Pork stored in air spoiled in 17 days.

Since it was believed that carbon-dioxide storage might aid in transporting chilled beef from Australia to England, Empey and Vickery [42] studied the microbial flora under conditions that would obtain in such shipments. They realized that means must be found for checking proliferation of microorganisms on superficial tissues at temperatures above the freezing point [—1°C.(30.2°F.)], for deterioration is almost wholly due to them. The low temperature bacteria found initially on the beef consisted of at least 95 per cent of types belonging to Achromobacter, the remainder being species of Pseudomonas and Micrococcus. In all tests counts of low-temperature molds obtained immediately after slaughter, and after completion of chilling were extremely low compared with counts of low-temperature bacteria. In one test, after 42 days' storage, no visible mold was present on beef stored in atmospheres of 10 to 12 per cent carbon dioxide, whereas beef stored in air had an average population (per area of two sq. cm.) of 10 to 60 colonies, mostly *Penicillium expansum,* though *Sporotrichum carnis* was also present. Quarters of beef stored in 12 per cent carbon dioxide even for 55 days showed only three or four colonies per quarter, all of *S. carnis.*

To restrict microbial growth on stored chilled beef the temperature should be maintained as near as possible to the freezing point of the muscle tissue, i.e., —1°C. Use of 10 to 12 per cent carbon dioxide in the storage atmosphere increased the storage life of chilled beef from meat plants

40. Tomkins. 1932. Chem. and Indus. 51, 261T-264T.
41. Callow. 1932. Idem 51, 116T-119T.
42. Empey and Vickery. 1933. Austral. Council Sci. & Indus. Res. J. 6, 233-243.

where the initial contamination consists chiefly of Achromobacter by 40 per cent, as compared with storage in air; effectively controlled *P. expansum* and most other meat molds, and moderately restricted the growth of *S. carnis.*

Moran [43] also concurred in the opinion that carbon dioxide was beneficial for storage of chilled beef. He said that in 10 to 20 per cent of carbon dioxide, beef could be kept in first-class condition for 60 to 70 days. This has made it possible for Australia to compete with South America in shipping beef to England. Carbon dioxide does not destroy fungi on beef but merely inhibits them.

Preservation of Meats by Chilling (Cold Storage) and Refrigeration. The value of prompt and adequate chilling of meat is appreciated more today than ever. Quarters or halves are placed in coolers just as soon as possible after slaughter and dressing. Before meat is subjected to other treatment, it is usually thoroughly chilled. The early years of the industry have been reviewed by Stiles.[45] In 1868, Tellier was unsuccessful in carrying meat at slightly above 0°C.(32°F.) from London to South America, but succeeded in 1876 in carrying from Rouen to Buenos Aires, 10 carcasses of beef, 12 of mutton, two calves, one pig, and 50 birds (Stiles). Results of this experimental work was probably the foundation for the great meat industry of South America which finds markets thousands of miles away. Brooks [46] stated that in 1877 the *Paraguay* sailed from Marseilles for Buenos Aires with four frozen quarters of beef and 10 frozen sheep. On the return trip, 80 tons of frozen meat were carried. The trade in frozen meat between England and Australia seems to have had its origin in 1879 when the *Strathleven* sailed from Sydney for London with 40 tons of beef and mutton.

Most meats are ripened or conditioned before distribution. They are held at low temperatures above freezing in order to allow the meat to become tender. The length of the ripening period depends on the type of product desired. Some beef is ripened for as long as six weeks at 1 to 2°C. (33.8 to 35.6°F.). Hoagland, McBryde, and Powick [20] published the results of observations, as did Moran and Smith.[47] Gautier [48] compared fresh meat with that frozen at —3 to —5°C.(26 to 23°F.) for five to six months. He noticed little difference, but stated that a slice of the thawed frozen meat did not keep as well in air at 12 to 18°C.(53.6 to 64.4°F.) as did fresh meat. Richardson and Scherubel [49] studied meat held at above and below freezing [—9°C.(15.8F.)]. Frozen fresh beef was held satisfactorily for 554 days. Observations were published on meat held above zero. As time went on, perceptible changes were apparent, as were reported by Emmett and Grindley [50] and Hoagland, McBryde, and Powick.[20] About the same

43. Moran. 1935. Roy. Sanit. Inst. J. 56, 214-216.
44. Mallmann and Zaikowski. 1940. Natl. Provisioner 103, 16-17.
45. Stiles. 1922. (Gt. Brit.) Food Invest. Bd., Spec. Rpt. No. 7.
46. Brooks. 1924. J. Soc. Chem. Ind. 43, 306T.
47. Moran and Smith. 1929. (Gt. Brit.) Food Invest. Bd., Spec. Rpt. No. 36.
48. Gautier. 1897. Rev. Hyg. et Police Sanit. Ann. 19, 289-303.
49. Richardson and Scherubel. 1909. J. Ind. Eng. Chem. 1, 95-103.
50. Emmett and Grindley. 1909. Idem 1, 413-436.

observations were made by Wright [9] on frozen and fresh New Zealand lamb. Moran and Smith [47] held beef for 17 days at 5°C.(41°F.) with constant improvement. Burrows [51] reported observations on a quarter of beef which was kept frozen for 14 years. No evidences of putrefaction were noticeable. Fibers of the meat appeared to be normal and it was consumed with no ill effects. Even in the frozen condition, slight changes have been reported by Ascoli and Silvestri.[52] Müller [53] stated that microorganisms were almost completely checked in meat and fish stored at 0°C.(32°F.). Richardson [54] believed that any unfrozen juice which existed would be too concentrated to permit bacterial growth.

Temperature of storage is another factor which greatly influences development of microorganisms on meat. According to Lea [55] beef stored at 0°C.(32°F.) for 60 days showed very little bacterial growth. Slight development of mold was observed, however. The odor of the meat was good after this storage period. Little work seems to have been carried out with pathogenic bacteria which might be present. Krüger [56] reported that flesh of slaughtered cattle may sometimes contain Bang's bacillus. He found them in three of 30 cattle. After 14 days' refrigeration the meat was still infectious for small experimental animals. de Saint Moulin [57] found *Clostridium septique* on horse flesh carcasses. Freshly isolated strains were highly pathogenic for guinea pigs.

As a part of their extensive investigations on storage of Australian beef, Scott [58] and Scott and Vickery [59] studied the influence of temperature of storage on microbial content. Such studies are necessary for learning the best conditions for cold storage of beef and its spoilage. Growth was studied on 1.1 mm. thick slices of the *biceps femoris* muscle of the ox. Inoculation of the muscle was accomplished by spraying saline suspensions containing 5×10^6 cells. This method gave fairly uniform distribution of about 1,000 organisms per square centimeter. Slices were stored at temperatures ranging from 1°C. (33.8°F.) to 30°C.(86°F.). The meat was examined after grinding in a mortar to a uniform suspension. Plating was on agar at 20°C.(68°F.). Scott [58] believed that some bacteria are truly psychrophilic and have a low optimum temperature for growth. These would be the species which cause concern to meat packers. Scott and Vickery [59] also resorted to inoculation experiments with Achromobacter on sides of beef. Sharp cooling was found to inhibit development of bacteria. The moisture content of the surface of meat was also found to be a matter of considerable importance. Surface desiccation and rate of cooling of surface tissues determined extent of changes in bacterial population. The greater the rate of cooling the better was the control of bacteria. This very

51. Burrows. 1914. Breeder's Gaz. 68, 484.
52. Ascoli and Silvestri. 1912. Arch. di Farmacol. Sper. e Sci. Aff. 14, 229-244.
53. Müller. 1903. Arch. f. Hyg. 47, 127-193.
54. Richardson. 1908. Premier Cong. Internatl. du Froid et Communications 2, 261-316.
55. Lea. 1931. (Gt. Brit.) Food Invest. Bd., Ann. Rpt. for 1930, 36.
56. Krüger. 1932. Deut. Tierärztl. Wchnschr. 40, 481-484.
57. de Saint Moulin. 1935. Ann. Med. Vet. 80, 207-213.
58. Scott. 1937. Austral. Council Sci. & Indus. Res. J. 10, 338-350.
59. Scott and Vickery. 1939. Austral. Council Sci. & Indus. Res., Bull. 129.

interesting report should be examined by those who are working in this field. Schmidt [60] stated that the belief that meat is a favorable medium for bacteria only above the dew point is erroneous. He stated that development of bacteria varies more nearly exponentially with relative humidity; since bacteria develop well in a relative humidity of 90 to 100 per cent, this degree of humidity should be avoided in refrigerators. A temperature of —5°C.(23°F.) in Haines' [61] experiments was not sufficiently low to inhibit microbial action in frozen meats. His experiments showed that —10°C.(14°F.) was satisfactory. Haines' work involved observations on the rate of growth of microorganisms on a stored carcass of lamb held at —5°C.(23°F.). At first there was a decrease in numbers followed by an increase in numbers, mainly yeasts and molds. Haines' work indicated that microorganisms might also be responsible for changes in fat. Experiments in this field become quite complicated if all of the factors involved are followed. In practical storage of chilled meat some of these factors are temperature, humidity, and rates of air movement. Schwartz and Loeser [62] did not find it possible to inhibit completely either bacterial growth or loss of weight by any combination of these factors. Results of their experiments suggested that the most effective temperature to strive for in meat storage is 0°C.(32°F.) with relative humidity of 90 per cent. Rates of air movement should be such as to ensure fairly uniform composition of air in all parts of the storage chamber.

"Black Spot" on Frozen Meat. As the name indicates, this is made evident by the presence of black spots after cold storage for a time. It presents an unsightly appearance, which may cause difficulties with inspectors. The British food inspectors have had this to contend with in meat imported into England from Argentina, New Zealand, and other countries.

These black spots on frozen beef were studied by Klein,[64] who attributed them to a yeast of the genus Saccharomyces. Animal experiments showed it to be harmless. He stated that it would grow at —2°C.(28.4°F.) but not at —9°C.(15.8°F.). Later, Klein [65] reported *Oidium carnis*, a fungus, as the cause, also found to be nonpathogenic by animal experiments. Klein believed that much beef from Argentina which contained black spots has been needlessly rejected, for the deeper layers of the tissue were satisfactory. The spots did not extend deeper than 1/12 to 1/16 inch.

Müller [66] and Brooks and Kidd [67] attributed black spots to *Cladosporium herbarum*. The latter observed the spoilage on lamb, veal, and rabbit. The spots consisted of mold hyphae which could be easily brushed from the meat. Brooks and Kidd stated that the fungus grew very slowly at —7.8 to —5.6°C.(18 to 22°F.) and produced black spots by inoculation after

60. Schmidt. 1931. Ztschr. f. Gestütk. Kälteindus. Beih. 3, 1-30.
61. Haines. 1931. Chem. and Indus. 50, 223T-227T.
62. Schwartz and Loeser. 1935. Zentbl. f. Bakt., Pt. 2, 91, 395-406.
63. Chodat. 1896-1897. Bull. de l'Herbier Boissier 1896, p. 890.
64. Klein. 1907. Meat Trades' J. 26, 1002; 56, 1003; 62, 1004; 90.
65. Klein. 1909. Meat Trades' J. 30, 234, 260, 261.
66. Müller. 1913. Ztschr. f. Fleisch. u. Milchyg. 24, 97-98.
67. Brooks and Kidd. 1921. Food Invest. Bd., Spec. Rpt. 6.

six months. The fungus seemed to have little effect on the tissues. Mold flora of meat is by no means limited to the species just mentioned. While meat infected with black spot is unsightly, presence of *Cladosporium herbarum* alone does not make it unfit for use. No toxic substances are produced. If the deterioration is accompanied by putrefactive bacteria, it should be condemned.

Monvoisin [68] isolated the following species: *Thamnidium elegans, Mucor mucedo, Rhizopus nigricans,* various Penicillia, and *Cladosporium herbarum.* It was stated again that the molds did not seem to harm meat. Bidault [69] isolated *Cladosporium herbarum,* although it was by no means the most frequent fungus. Bidault, as did Monvoisin, believed that meat became contaminated at time of slaughter. If it is desired to entirely eliminate mold, Bidault and also Wright [70] suggested that care be used at time of slaughter to maintain sanitary conditions and that meat be stored at not higher than —9°C.(15.8°F.). Wright did not consider *Cladosporium herbarum* to be important, because it was the fungus found least frequently. On account of this statement, Brooks [71] was led to repeat some of the experiments reported by Brooks and Kidd [67] and Brooks and Hansford.[72] Mutton was inoculated with spores of *Mucor muceda* and stored at —1°C. (30.2°F.) until growth had started, after which it was stored at —11°C. (12.2°F.) for four and one-half months. After this period, no evidences of black spot appeared, but merely usual growth of *Mucor mucedo.* Similar results were secured with *Penicillium glaucum.* Brooks also stated that the black mycelium of *Cladosporium·herbarum* might be the cause of black spot and that in attempting to isolate this fungus special precautions should be used to secure the fungus since it grows deeper in the tissues than the other molds.

As stated above, growth of fungi on the surface of meat probably does not affect its use as food. Butjagin [73] studied the changes brought about in meat by *Penicillium glaucum* and *Aspergillus niger.* It was found that the growth of these molds caused a loss in dry matter and nitrogen and an increase in the amount of water-soluble nitrogenous bodies. The percentage amount of ether extract in the dry matter diminished, especially during the first month, and the amount of extractives was markedly increased, while the alkalinity of the meat increased slowly, being greater in the case of *Penicillium glaucum* than in the case of *Aspergillus niger.* By growth of these molds a gradually increasing amount of volatile acid was produced. The effect on the production of other bodies is also spoken of, the general conclusion being reached that the Penicillium studied destroys the constituents of meats more quickly than the Aspergillus.

Temperature and humidity are just as important in development of molds on meats as they are for bacteria. This was shown by Kaess.[74] Indif-

68. Monvoisin. 1922. Rec. de Med. Vet. 98, 149-161.
69. Bidault. 1922. Soc. Sci. d'Hyg. Aliment. Bull. 10, 12.
70. Wright. 1923. Soc. Chem. Indus. J. 42, 488-906.
71. Brooks. 1924. Idem 43, 3066.
72. Brooks and Hansford. 1923. (Gt. Brit.) Food Invest. Bd., Spec. Rpt. No. 17.
73. Butjagin. 1905. Arch. f. Hyg. 52, 1-21.
74. Kaess. 1934. Ztschr. f. Gestütk. Kälteindus. Beih. 41, 96-102.

ferent control of temperature may enable common molds to develop on meat, according to Wright.[70] When the temperature is lowered, black spots appear where the molds have grown. He stated that meat stored below —9°C. could be kept for years with no black spots. The whole question of molds in meat and its products was studied by Lewis and Yesair[75] (quoted from Moulton, 1929). They isolated a rather long list of molds from several meat products. Pure cultures were subjected to the action of several disinfectants, among which sodium hypochlorite seemed to be most suitable under plant conditions. It was stated, however, that use of this compound should not supplant ordinary cleaning procedures. It was advised after cleaning as a supplementary procedure.

According to Haines,[76] who followed the development of bacteria on chilled and frozen meat, *Sporotrichum carnis* is able to develop at —5°C. (23°F.) and —7°C.(19.4°F.) on supercooled agar. In no case did the organism grow on frozen agar. Growth of molds on frozen meat in cold-storage lockers was observed by Semenwick and Ball.[77] The species identified were those mentioned throughout the discussion above.

FROZEN MEAT

Much meat is now frozen solid to preserve it. Meat which was frozen by the older slow methods usually yielded much "drip" after it was thawed. The newer methods of quick-freezing have largely corrected this. Microbial development is markedly retarded but not entirely eliminated by freezing. Haines[76] stated that a temperature of —5°C.(23°F.) was not sufficiently low to inhibit growth on frozen meats; —10°C.(14°F.) was satisfactory. Haines'[76] experience with a carcass of frozen mutton held at —5°C.(23°F.) showed a steady drop in numbers of organisms growing best at 37°C.(98.6°F.). On the lean portions of the carcass, after the initial drop, there was marked rise in bacterial numbers of organisms growing on gelatin at 20°C.(68°F.); no such rise was observed on the connective tissue of the carcass. These colonies were largely yeasts and molds. Occasionally a few rods of the fluorescent type were found. In no case was visible growth observed on carcasses stored at —10°C.(14°F.) and below. These organisms, according to Young[78] are contaminating forms which come from soil and which will grow at —1°C.(30.2°F.). He found that 10 to 20 per cent of carbon dioxide in the atmosphere would restrict their growth and not affect the meat.

Pictet and Young[79] exposed a number of common bacteria to a temperature of —70°C. for 108 hours and —130°C. for 20 hours. In general, they were not destroyed, although the virulence of some bacteria was decreased. Koch[80] showed that *Vibrio comma* could resist —10°C.(14°F.) for 10 hours. Macfadyen[81] and Paul and Prall[82] found living cells after exposure to liquid air temperatures (—190°C.), the latter after 100 days. Those which were maintained at room temperature died out rather rapidly.

75. Lewis and Yesair. 1928. Inst. Amer. Meat Packers, Bull.
76. Haines. 1931. Chem. and Indus. 50, 223T-227T; J. Expt. Biol. 8, 379-388.
77. Semenwick and Ball. 1938. Iowa Acad Sci. Proc. 44, 37-43.
78. Young. 1935-37. Brit. Assoc. Refrig. Proc. 33, 121-124.
79. Pictet and Young. 1884. Comp. Rend. Acad. Sci. 98, 747.
80. Koch.
81. Macfadyen. 1900. Proc. Roy. Soc. 66, 180-182.
82. Paul and Prall. Arb. aus dem K. Gsndhtsamt. 26, 73.

Similar conclusions were reached by Sedgwick, Hamilton, and Funk.[83] Ruata[84] found that long exposure to temperatures below freezing was detrimental to bacteria, a conclusion which holds probably only for the organisms and conditions with which he worked. Angkiehong[85] observed marked variations in resistance to freezing among strains of *Shigella dysenteriae*.

The effect of freezing on microorganisms is probably largely determined by some of the conditions which exist. Broadhurst and Gilpin[86] reported that hydrogen-ion concentration was an important factor. While their observations were made on ice cream, it is not unlikely that their conclusions could be extended to other foods. Moran and Smith[47] could not observe a change in the bacterial content of meat stored at 5°C. (41°F.) for 17 days.

Bacteriologists have, in general, stated that bacteria are not destroyed by freezing. This attitude has gradually grown up by faulty reasoning. Suspensions of bacteria have been subjected to low temperatures and, because living cells have been found by subculture, it was believed that freezing did not affect bacteria. Quantitative data indicate, on the other hand, that an appreciably high rate of death occurs. The fact that a small proportion of the cells in a suspension survive does not indicate that freezing has no effect on bacteria. Haines[76] also observed the same results.

The theoretical factors involved in freezing meat have received considerable attention since quick- or sharp-freezing was introduced. One objection to frozen meat is the separation of water as ice on the outside of the muscle fibers. When the meat thaws, this drains away, giving rise to what is called "drip" or "bleeding." The Annual Reports of the Food Investigation Board of Great Britain contain published observations on this phenomenon. Quick-freezing, as stated by Birdseye[87] and the Australian National Research Council, almost completely eliminates "drip." Slow-freezing was said to allow the formation of larger ice crystals which ruptured the meat aggregate more than the small crystals formed in quick-freezing.

Cold-storage meats are frequently covered with molds. They are not destroyed by low temperatures any more than are the bacteria. Consequently, if spores are present on the surface of the meat when it goes into the cooler, they may germinate. Chodat[63] found that spores of *Mucor mucedo* were resistant to cold. Spores of several species of molds were kept frozen in Chodat's laboratory for over three years, at the end of which time viable cells were still present. Some meat which had been in cold storage developed a "musty" odor. This was attributed by Haines[34] to Actinomyces which was found in straw and on other debris taken into the coolers on the feet of employees. Haines reported that the species studied would not grow much below 0°C.(32°F.) and if at all, very slowly. The optimum temperature for growth was 25 to 30°C.(77 to 86°F.). At 33°C.(91.4°F.) the cells of the organism began to be abnormal.

Effect of Freezing on Trichinella spiralis in Meat. Trichinosis is a health hazard in eating uncooked pork. It is due to infestation of fresh pork

83. Sedgwick *et al.* 1917. Abs. Bact. 1, 49.
84. Ruata. 1918. Soc. Chem. Indus. J. 38, 346A.
85. Angkiehong. 1922. Proefschr. Landb. Hoogesch. 1922, 1-70.
86. Broadhurst and Gilpin. 1926. J. Bact. 11, 95-96.
87. Birdseye. 1929. Ind. Eng. Chem. 21, 854.

with a worm, *Trichinella spiralis,* which lives endoparasitically in muscle tissue of swine. In view of the fact that it would be impossible to examine every hog carcass with the microscope, federal officials have enforced adequate refrigeration at below —15°C.(5°F.) for at least 20 days. Ransom [88] had found that this would rid infested pork of the parasite. When meats were preserved by quick-freezing, experiments were carried out to determine how the parasite would be affected. Blair and Lang [89] found the larvae to be killed in a few minutes in ground meat at —17.8°C.(0°F.). The parasite was active in all samples of pork which had been kept at —17.8°C. for 48 hours. Augustine [90] reported that quick-freezing at —1.1°C.(30°F.) followed by one day's storage at zero would destroy the larvae.

Tenderization of Meat. Several different methods for tenderizing meat have been proposed. Tenderization by storage in coolers provided with ultraviolet light has been discussed in Chapter 1. It is based on storage of meat at 12.8 to 18.3°C.(55 to 65°F.). At these temperatures, which are higher than the 2.2°C.(36°F.) ordinarily used in coolers, spoilage will take place. In order to inhibit it, irradiation of the meat with ultraviolet rays has been suggested. Loss of weight by dehydration is controlled by a relative humidity of between 85 to 90 per cent. Ultraviolet light is said to destroy bacteria on the surface of the meat and to maintain a practical degree of sterility on all sides of hanging beef without damage to the carcass or to workmen. The wave length is largely limited to 2537Å. After the desired degree of tenderness has been attained, the meat is chilled to the usual temperature, from .6 to 3.3°C.(33 to 38°F.). This process, then, is based on use of higher temperatures of storage to accelerate enzyme action in the tissues and use of ultraviolet rays to control development of microorganisms on the surface of the meat.

Another method for tenderizing meats involves use of papain prepared from juice of the papaya *(Carica papaya),* as described by Pulley and von Loesecke. [91] Papain is dissolved in slightly acidified water to which other substances, such as alcohol and glycerin, may be added as preservatives. Various commercial tenderizers have been compounded in which this enzyme is the important constituent. Usefulness of these products as meat improvers depends upon their proteolytic activity. Balls and Hoover [92] pointed out that pure papain has at least three kinds of activity: it digests protein, clots milk, and splits ammonium hippurylamid. The first activity is important when it functions as a meat tenderizer, while the second is generally used as a basis of a method for measuring the activity of papain preparations. It is prepared commercially in the tropics by scratching the unripe fruit and collecting the milky exudate in glass or china vessels. The milky liquid, which soon coagulates, must be rapidly dried at low temperatures to prevent spoilage. Balls mentioned the investigation of Hall who

88. Ransom. 1916. J. Agr. Res. 5, 819-854; 17 (1919), 201-221.
89. Blair and Lang. 1934. J. Infect. Dis. 55, 95-104.
90. Augustine. 1933. Amer. J. Hyg. 17, 697-710.
91. Pulley and von Loesecke. 1941. Fruit Prod. J. 21, 37-39.
92. Balls and Hoover. 1937. J. Biol. Chem. 121, 737-745; U. S. Dept. Agr. Cir. 631 (1942).

found that commercial papain may have a high bacterial population, a fact not now generally considered by manufacturers of meat improvers. This fact may also be of great importance from the standpoint of public health if the bacteria added to the meat happen to be undesirable species. The preparation is painted on the meat with a brush and then allowed to stand for a short period. While experiments have been conducted to render hams tender by adding papain to the curing solution when such hams are vein-pumped, the Bureau of Animal Industry of the United States Department of Agriculture does not permit the practice in plants operating under federal inspection. This position seems to be based upon the fact that there would be an excellent opportunity for deception in the use of tenderizers by restaurants as well as the fact that the effect on health of long-continued consumption of meat tenderized with papain is not known. In some instances the use of meat tenderizers has been represented as shortening the time of cooking by a definite percentage, making it possible to cut every portion of the cooked meat with a fork, and finally as an aid to digestion. It has also been shown that papain preparations are not particularly stable but this phase of the problem is a little outside the present interest. Since tenderization of meat is hard to follow quantitatively, Gottschall and Kies [93] devised a simple method for this purpose. Ground meat was found to digest by papain much more rapidly than unground. The enzyme preparation did not penetrate pieces of meat very rapidly.

Another agent used for tenderizing meat is raw pineapple juice which contains the enzyme bromelin. This is an active proteolytic enzyme which will digest some 1,500 times its own weight of proteins. A small amount of the juice or ground fruit pulp may be spread over the meat to be tenderized. Some penetration of the meat may be secured by stabbing it with a fork. Ground meat is attacked much more rapidly.

Tenderized hams are discussed later in this chapter.

Ground Meat (Hamburg Steak). Comminuted meats have wide sale in the United States. They have received considerable bacteriological investigation. Since they may be made from meat scraps and handled carelessly, they are subject to marked bacterial development because grinding thoroughly distributes bacteria, releases juices, and provides a much larger surface for the bacteria. In order to restrict bacterial growth, some dealers have resorted to preservatives. A survey in California indicated the practice to be quite common. Baking soda and sulfur dioxide were used. Stiff fines were levied on those who were guilty.

Possibility of low-grade raw materials being used in the manufacture of Hamburg steak has caused food-control officials to search for methods of examination. Among those studied have been bacteriological procedures. Hoffstadt [94] studied the relation of the bacterial content of meat to the conditions under which it was prepared. Bacterial count of all samples showed great variation in relation to sanitary conditions and organoleptic tests. Hoffstadt believed that enumeration of anaerobic bacteria offered a

93. Gottschall and Kies. 1942. Food Research 7, 373-381.
94. Hoffstadt. 1924. Amer. J. Hyg. 4, 33-42; 43-51.

means by which keeping qualities of ground meats might be measured. According to Weaver,[6] when meat putrefies, a change from coccus to rods occurs. Zeller and Beller [95] stated that until four hours had elapsed, there was little change in bacterial flora of ground meat. The size of pieces influenced the bacterial count. Scraps for preparation of ground meat should be clean and as fresh as possible. Dirt and age mean heavy bacterial contamination which, in turn, means prompt spoilage. Several investigators, including Brewer,[96] have examined such meat for *Escherichia coli*. Its colonies outnumbered those of other microorganisms. It is doubtful whether it could ever be used as an indicator of undesirable conditions. Putrefaction of ground meats seems to be caused by several common bacteria. According to Sirotinina [97] *Bacillus proteus* is quite active in this connection at temperatures above room temperature. *Escherichia coli* also produces decomposition at higher temperatures. Low-temperature storage was believed to inhibit action of these two bacteria.

Bacterial Standards for Control of Ground Meat. Just how valuable bacterial standards are for this purpose is a debated question. Mere plate-count standards of aerobic bacteria are probably of no more value than many such standards for other foods. The ground meat standards which have been suggested have been concerned with aerobic bacteria only. Marxer [98] suggested a bacteriolgical standard of not over 1,000,000 bacteria per gram for judging quality of ground meat. On the other hand, Zweifel [99] did not consider the bacterial count to have any value. He was unable to isolate objectionable organisms and could see little to be gained by merely estimating the number of bacteria present. Weinzirl and Newton [100] believed that Marxer's standard was too low, since practically all ground meats would be condemned. After consideration of various factors they believed that a standard of 10,000,000 per gram was more acceptable. Even with this standard they expected that 50 per cent of the samples might be condemned. They stated that if good sound meat was used, no difficulty would be experienced in keeping well within the 10 million bacteria per gram limit. Weinzirl and Newton later observed that after one year's storage at —10°C.(14°F.) six of 10 samples fell within their proposed standard. LeFevre [101] believed in a bacteriological standard but further believed that the Marxer standard was high enough. Anaerobic and liquefying bacteria were present in all samples. Weinzirl [102] reported further work. The aerobic plate count had no significance so far as putrefaction was concerned. Strains of aerobic bacteria from the meat did not cause putrefaction when reinoculated into meat. On account of difficulties in taking legal action against unsatisfactory ground meat, Elford [103] at-

95. Zeller and Beller. 1920. Ztschr. f. Fleisch. u. Milchyg. 40, 245-252.
96.. Brewer. 1925. J. Bact. 10, 543.
97. Sirotinina. 1937. Rev. in Chem. Abs. 32, 9315.
98. Marxer. 1903. Beiträge zur Frage des Bakteriengehalts und der Haltbarkeit des Fleisches Quoted from Zentbl. f. Le Fevre, 1917.
99. Zweifel. 1911. Zentbl. f. Bakt. I. Orig. 58, 115-125.
100. Weinzirl and Newton. 1914. Amer. J. Pub. Health 4. 413-417; 5 (1915), 833-835.
101. LeFevre. 1917. Amer. Food J. 12, 140-142.
102. Weinzirl. 1924. Abs. Bact. 8, 41.
103. Elford. 1936. Amer. J. Pub. Health 26, 1204-1205.

tempted to determine whether a bacterial standard could be used. He plated proper dilutions on plain nutrient agar and incubated the plates at 37°C.(98.6°F.) for 48 hours. Forty-one samples gave plate counts varying from 100,000 to 20 million colonies per gram. He finally adopted a limiting standard of 10 million. Portland, Oregon, adopted this standard making it an offense to sell any unseasoned ground meat the average bacterial count of which exceeded this standard. Average was defined to mean the "logarithmic average" of the plate counts of all samples taken during a period of not less than four days and including at least four samples taken on separate days. This standard has resulted in considerable improvement since it has been in effect.

Preservatives in Ground Meats. Use of chemical preservatives in ground meat products is as objectionable as it is unnecessary. The Bureau of Animal Industry in Order 211, Regulation 18, prohibited the use of sodium sulfite, a preservative which at one time was quite widely used. Boric acid was also used for this purpose, but is now prohibited in all food products. Stroscher [104] advised against the use of sodium sulfite in meats. Metzger and Fuchs [105] studied sodium benzoate as a meat preservative. After years of attempts to use chemical preservatives, the best practice now consists of the use of sound raw materials and adequate refrigeration. Sound raw materials mean a low bacterial load and a cleaner product. Until 1928, it was permissible to dust preserved meats prepared for export to England with boric acid. Boric acid has, however, been placed among the prohibited chemical preservatives by British medical officers of health.

Prevalence of use of preservatives in ground meat is probably not known. A survey of the practice carried out in California [106] revealed that 80 per cent of 50 establishments openly admitted the use of some type of preservative ranging from common baking soda to sulfur dioxide. Sodium sulfite was commonly used by some vendors.

Development of Clostridium botulinum in Meat Products. Spores of *Clostridium botulinum* are known to be widely distributed in soil. It is not improbable, therefore, that they are present at times on various meat products. Meat is an ideal medium for the development of *Clostriduim botulinum*. Most of the media used in the laboratory consist of ground meat with added water. The several outbreaks of botulism traced to meat products constitute presumptive evidence that meats may carry the spores of *Clostridium botulinum*. Edmondson, Thom, and Giltner [107] inoculated meat balls with toxin-free spores and incubated them at 9°C.(48.2°F.), 20°C.(68°F.), and 30°C.(86°F.). Incubation at 30°C. caused the formation of enough toxin to kill a guinea pig in 18 hours. The sample was slimy and possessed a foul odor. At 9°C. no toxin was formed in three weeks. Thorough cooking would detoxify a product which had become toxic. Meat products have been conspicuously free from botulism when the large amounts which are preserved, are considered.

104. Stroscher. 1901. Arch. f. Hyg. 40, 291-319.
105. Metzger and Fuchs. 1908. Ztschr. f. Untersuch. der Nahr. u. Genussmtl. 15, 715-728.
106. Calif. Dept. Pub. Health, Weekly Bull. 20 (1941), 23.
107. Edmondson et al. 1923. Amer. Food J., March, 1923.

Microbiology of Sausage. Some parts of the carcass are made into sausage. For some types of sausage, the meat is ground and mixed with a binder, usually a starch product. The binder helps to make the sausage stand up. Binders are not now used as much in America as formerly. Spices are added to taste, and the meat is forced into a casing by a sausage stuffer. The casings are slipped over tubes connected with the stuffer. After the casing is filled or the sausage is stiffed, it is linked by giving the casing a twist at definite intervals. If the sausage is to be canned, it is not linked but is hung up to dry. This, in general, is the treatment for fresh sausage. Some sausage is smoked, but such a product is usually made from cured meats and is cooked in water for lengths of time which depend on the type of sausage. The dry sausages are, perhaps, set apart from those which have just been discussed. Their advent in the early days was probably due to lack of adequate refrigeration which drove the makers to drying sausage. Microorganisms may spoil sausage. This may occur during preparation or during storage and may assume different forms, according to Glasser.[108] The entire mass may be impregnated with bacteria which attack the protein and fat, often with gas formation. The sausage may spoil either at the core or at its outermost layers. Sausages which are held too long or at too high temperatures may become rancid if poor fat was used in their manufacture.

Microbiology of sausage is not unlike that of ground meat. The two products may differ, owing to the fact that sausages are often heavily seasoned; some spices have a germicidal effect on bacteria. While most of the work on sausage has been done with the idea of food poisoning in mind, a little has been carried out to determine the types and number of bacteria which are present in normal sausage. Slooten[109] found few bacteria in sausage; some were sterile. Drying, smoking, and plenty of spices tended to lower the microbial content. Sausages are usually stuffed into casings prepared from the gut of domestic animals. These casings are cleaned and pickled in salt. Savage[110] found that salt solutions must be both concentrated and allowed to act for a long time to have much effect on bacteria. Komma[111] found it rather easy to isolate members of the Salmonella group *(Salmonella schottmülleri)* from sausage. Thirty samples contained this organism, while 35 contained *Escherichia coli.* Sacquepee and Loygue,[112] Rommeler,[113] and Brekenfeld[114] also found Salmonella organisms in sausage. Some samples had caused intestinal disturbances. From normal and abnormal sausages aerobic and anaerobic bacteria were isolated. He placed much importance on anaerobic, spore-forming bacteria as causative agents in food poisoning.

Cary[115] made bacteriological examinations of sausages purchased on the market in Chicago. Each market from the which the sausage came

108. Glasser. 1934. Deut. Tierärztl. Wchnschr. 42, 237-239; 269-270.
109. Slooten. 1907. Diss., Bern, Rev. in Koch's Jahresber. 18 (1907), 109.
110. Savage. 1908. Med. Press and Cir. 86, 167.
111. Komma. 1910. Centbl. Bakt. I, Orig. 55, 1-14.
112. Sacquepee and Loygue. 1914. Compt. Rend. Soc. Biol. 76, 820-822.
113. Rommeler. 1909. Deut. Med. Wchnschr. 886-888.
114. Brekenfeld. 1926. Centbl. Bakt., Pt. 1, Orig. 99, 353-385.
115. Cary. 1916. Amer. J. Pub. Health, 6, 124-135.

was scored for general sanitation, refrigeration, and other desirable features. *Escherichia coli* was isolated from 30, *Proteus vulgaris* from 11, Staphylococcus from two, etc. Cary's observations led him to conclude that the casings could not be considered to increase the bacterial count or danger from pathogens. Six samples of pork sausage were cooked in the laboratory in various ways, to determine the hygienic value of home cooking. Four samples cooked in a restaurant were also examined. Ordinary cooking destroyed most of the bacteria, while extra cooking destroyed them all. Guerin's [116] results were similar. Kühl [117] considered the microorganisms on slimy sausage to be of importance. Gauducheau[118] isolated an organism from curing sausage to which he gave the name *Bacillus creatis*. The organism was neither pathogenic nor toxicogenic. It was believed to have some relation to curing and development of proper flavor.

Yeasts also seem to have a role in curing of sausage and formation of slime on the surface. Cesari [119] and Cesari and Guilliermond [120] believed that certain yeasts contributed to the good quality and flavor of these products. Three closely related species were isolated which grew best in media poor in carbohydrates and in the presence of 10 to 15 per cent of salt. An agreeable aroma was formed in protein media. Cesari said that inoculation of the meat during sausage manufacture improved the flavor and prevented putrefaction. All of the species isolated by Cesari and Guilliermond [120] belonged to the genus Debaromyces, with exception of a few species in which spore formation could not be established. Mrak and Bonar [121] found the species from fresh sausage to be Debaromyces. They believed the species to be *Debaromyces Guilliermondii* var. *nova zeelandicus*, Lodder, 1932. Mrak and Bonar did not discuss the significance of these species in sausage. Bacteria as well as yeasts, according to Moser,[122] are related to flavor of sausage.

Some sausages are heavily spiced. While most spices would be too weak to cause inhibition, a few are known to possess germicidal properties. Danielson [123] stated that the amounts of garlic and onions usually used in sausage had no effect on growth of putrefactive or pathogenic bacteria.

Slimy Sausage. This is due to the growth of bacteria on the surface of the sausage. It has been stated now and then that yeasts are the cause of this spoilage. This is probably due to the appearance of the sausage and not to data which have been collected in bacteriological examinations. Sausages are probably inoculated by coming into contact with contaminated objects. Cooking of sausage has been found to reduce, if not completely prevent growth of the offending bacteria. Care must be used after cooking to prevent reinfection. This problem was studied by Roderick and Norton.[124] They stated that a temperature of 73.9°C.(165°F.) maintained for

116. Guerin. 1912. Hyg. Viande et Lait. 6, 197-207.
117. Kühl. 1910. Centbl. Bakt. I, Orig. 54, 5-6.
118. Gauducheau. 1920. Compt. Rend. Soc. Biol. 83, 1277-1278.
119. Cesari. 1919. Compt. Rend. Acad. Sci. 168, 202.
120. Cesari and Guilliermond. 1920. Ann. Inst. Pasteur 34, 229.
121. Mrak and Bonar. 1938. Food Research 3, 615-618.
122. Moser. 1935. Reichsgsndhtsamt. Arb. 10, 905-907.
123. Danielson. 1928. Ztschr. f. Untersuch. der Lebensmtl. 55, 291-294.
124. Roderick and Norton. 1926. Quoted from Moulton's Meat Under the Microscope.

15 or 20 minutes should provide an ample margin of safety above the thermal death point of the cocci. Schroder [125] described ropiness in sausage which he found was due to cocci; they grew best on blood and serum agar and were nonpathogenic for men and white mice. The only change observed in the sausage was ropiness.

Botulism From Sausage. Sausage has caused a few outbreaks of botulism in America and Germany. It has never been an important food in this respect, and the epidemological evidence of some of the outbreaks leave much to be desired. According to Bitter,[126] cooking applied to sausage may be a procedure of some hygienic value. The toxin does not resist high temperatures and would probably be destroyed by cooking in the home. Bitter showed, however, that heat penetration into sausage is not rapid. Large sausages may require cooking for perhaps 30 minutes to detoxify the interior portions.

The spores of *Clostridium botulinum* are in another category. They are so resistant to heat that many types of sausage could not endure a botulinus cook. The danger of insufficient cooking of sausages is illustrated by an outbreak of poisoning among German troops on the Verdun front reported by Baerthlein.[127] In order not to remove the fat, sausages were cooked for but 30 minutes, while it had been shown that 45 minutes were required for satisfactory results. Reports of several outbreaks of botulism attributed to sausage are available in the literature. So-called summer sausages are in a different category, according to Hall,[128] who reported that *Clostridium botulinum* failed to grow and produce toxin in them even when large numbers of viable spores were inoculated in several places and the sausages incubated at 37°C. (98.6°F.) for as long as eight weeks. They spoiled, however, in a few hours when placed in water at 37°C., and strong toxin developed in a few days if they had been inoculated with *Clostridium botulinum.*

Green Rings in Sausage. Green rings occur in sausage about one-eighth of an inch from the casing. According to Lewis and Jensen,[129] the cause is bacterial. They demonstrated that improvements in methods of manufacture which tended to decrease the total number of bacteria in the product at all stages, tended to prevent the development of green rings. The green substance was believed to be methemoglobin. The appearance of the green ring does not indicate that the sausage is unwholesome. Jensen and Urbain [130] have stated that "undercuring" is the explanation given by many practical men in the industry. While some discolorations in meats may be due to undercuring, others are due to chemical changes in which bacterial activity is concerned. Jensen and Urbain found that the microorganisms responsible for formation of green pigments in meats and blood agar are those which oxidize hemoglobin, nitrosohemoglobin, nitrosohemo-

125. Schroder. 1930. Deut. Tierärztl. Wchnschr. 38, 385-388.
126. Bitter. 1911. Hyg. Rundschau 21, 181-189; Deut. Med. Wchnschr. 45, 1300-1302.
127. Baerthlein. 1922. München. Med. Wchnschr. 69, 155-156.
128. Hall. 1932. Food Research 7, 104-110.
129. Lewis and Jensen. 1928. Inst. Amer. Meat Packers Bull.
130. Jensen and Urbain. 1936. Food Research 1, 263-273.

chromogen, and hematin. In addition hydrogen sulfide-forming bacteria cause green discolorations in meat and blood agar. The species of bacteria involved were members of common genera which were found in meat products.

Attempts have been made to use preparations for preserving sausages. Piettre [131] coated them with gelatin, a practice condemned by Bardas.[132]

Brekenfeld [133] introduced a "bacterioscopic" method of sausage examination which revealed presence of both dead and anaerobic bacteria which would not appear in cultures. The results of this procedure applied to meat trimmings from 48 slaughterhouses agreed well with the sanitary conditions which obtained in the houses. The method involves examination with the microscope of stained sections made from various parts of the sausage. The bacteria are revealed in this manner. Moser [134] used the method but did not find it so satisfactory that it could replace older tried methods. Some satisfactory sausages were said to contain bacteria distributed as they are in putrid samples. Furthermore the method could not be used in control work. A histological method of sausage examination was proposed by Thorp and Coburn.[135] Many foreign materials could be detected. The most important pathological condition is the presence of trichinella cysts.

Sour Beef. This is a trade description of spoilage [136] occurring in freshly slaughtered beef which has not been properly cooled. Bunyea [137] studied the question and quoted the following from Ostertag: "Stinking acid fermentation occurs in slaughtered domestic animals when the meat, while still warm, is stored in large pieces and in closed receptacles, or in general, when it is subjected to conditions under which it can not cool. This alteration is characterized by the term 'suffocated'." Bunyea was unable to state whether the spoilage studied by Ostertag was identical with the sour beef which he studied. Bunyea isolated an organism which was thought to be the causal organism. He published a complete description of it.

The organism was said to be an aerobic saprophyte with a wide range of temperature for growth, but with an optimum around 37°C.(98.6°F.). Serological studies identified the organism with *Bacillus megatherium*. Bunyea reported that souring of beef was due to formation of propionic acid. The organism which was isolated was found to be nonpathogenic for guinea pigs, and not to produce toxin in broth or raw beef. Another experiment was also instituted to compare the odor produced by the organism *Bacillus megatherium* and a number of pure cultures of common organisms. None of them were able to reproduce the odor of sour beef. Packers have learned that this type of spoilage can be markedly reduced by rapid chilling of meat. In fact, many defects of meat have been reduced, if not

131. Piettre. 1933. Ann. d'Hyg. Pub., Indus. et Sociale 10, 134-137.
132. Bardas. 1933. Idem 10, 282-285.
133. Brekenfeld. 1931. Arch. f. Hyg. 107, 193-218.
134. Moser. 1935. Ztschr. f. Fleisch. u. Milchyg. 45, 304.
135. Thorp and Coburn. 1937. Amer. Vet. Med. Assoc. J. 90, 506-518.
136. The term "sour" in this spoilage does not mean acid, but rather putrid. Sour beef has all the evidences of putrefaction.
137. Bunyea. 1921. J. Agr. Res. 21, 689-698.

completely eliminated, by prompt and adequate chilling. Haines [29] connected another organism to "sour" beef. The beef upon which he worked became sour a few days after slaughter. An organism which belonged to the fluorescent group was isolated as the cause.

Bone-Taint of Beef. Moran and Smith [47] applied this term to certain putrefactive changes which occur in the neighborhood of the hip joints of otherwise prime carcasses. These changes are accompanied by a bad odor. While the evidence suggests that it is of bacterial origin, some confusion exists in explaining just how infection occurs.[138] One theory, according to Moran and Smith, is that infection proceeds along the iliac arteries into which bacteria gain access during dressing. Other evidence connects its appearance with fatigue of the animal before slaughter. Meat packers have learned the value of handling animals carefully and giving them plenty of water. Rapid cooling of the carcass is now known to be important in preventing this defect, just as it is in other undesirable spoilage. An aerobic, sporeforming rod was isolated from synovial fluid and tissues in and about the hip joint of a beef carcass with "bone-taint" by Haines and Scott.[139] It resembled *Clostridium oedematiens* very closely. Examination of 40 hip joints from normal carcasses indicated that 38 were sterile, one heavily infected with a Streptococcus, possibly of the *fecalis* type, and with a rod, probably a member of the Proteus group.

SMOKING OF MEATS

This is in reality a chemical method of preservation for products of incomplete combustion of wood, corncobs, or other materials are left on the meat. While some of them are permitted in and on meat when they originate in smoke, they are prohibited when added as the pure substance. The Food, Drug, and Cosmetic Act of 1938, interprets that any substance added to food by the process of curing known as smoking, shall not be considered a preservative.

While "liquid smoke" preparations are used by home curers of meat, these preparations are not used by the large packers for two reasons, mainly: they do not give as good results, flavor, and preservative value as does smoke from hardwoods and they are prohibited by the Bureau of Animal Industry for products .prepared under federal inspection and intended for interstate shipment.

Various materials may be used as sources of smoke. Corncobs have been used for some time for smoking meats under domestic conditions. Hickory wood has been much used under commercial conditions. One writer stated that in Germany juniper berries are used for smoking Westphalian hams. When hickory is used, the logs are burned under the hams. Toward the end of the period, hickory sawdust is thrown on to give the hams a brown color. Meats which are smoked have usually been pickled. Smoke is used to improve flavor and to act as a preservative. The length of time required for smoking depends on the size of the piece of meat and results desired.

138. Howarth. 1917. Cold Storage and Ice Assoc. Proc. 14, 33-58.
139. Haines and Scott. 1940. J. Hyg. 40, 154-161.

Smoked meats are subject to attack by molds which grow in moisture on the surface. Consequently, care is used in packing houses in storage of smoked meats. They are smoked and shipped as soon as possible thereafter.

The chemical compounds imparted to meat by smoke have not been extensively studied. Callow [140] found that smoked bacon and ham gave a strong reaction for formaldehyde. Estimates of the amount of formaldehyde content of commercial smoked herring, bloater, kipper, ham, and bacon gave amounts ranging from .5 to 1,000 parts per million. Hess [141] stated that formaldehyde in smoke gives it its bactericidal properties. Vapors, containing three or more grains of formaldehyde per 1,000 cubic feet, approximately the same concentration that is found in smoke, had a definite bactericidal action. While it is quite definitely known that formaldehyde in smoke is germicidal, it is also possible that other constituents may also be germicidal.

Formaldehyde is a prohibited preservative when added to food as such. However, food laws make exception to that which is in smoke. Buchanan and Schryver [142] reported results of actual experiments with dilute solutions of formaldehyde in meat preservation. At that time, much of the meat shipped from South America to England was fumigated on shipboard. Claim was made that the formaldehyde was not absorbed by meat. Buchanan and Schryver's experiment's however, showed that it was present, not only on the surface, but underneath, especially where muscular tissue had not been covered with fat. Meat products with large surface per unit weight must, therefore, absorb considerable amounts.

It is known that smoked meats may contain substances from smoke which cannot be added as such. When wood is distilled in absence of air, methyl alcohol is formed which may be oxidized to formaldehyde. Other substances found to be present are higher aldehydes, ketones, formic, acetic, and higher acids, water, and alcohols. [143] Good smoking practice, according to Jensen, [144] teaches that most cured meats should not be held in the temperature zone of 18.3 to 40.5°C. (65 to 105°F.) for longer than eight hours. He revealed that some bacteria are resistant to smoke while others are killed. Wieser [145] smoked a piece of infected ham until it was completely cured but observed that bacteria were not killed at one centimeter or more beneath the surface.

SALTING OF MEATS

Pettersson [146] showed that the preserving effect of salt in fish and meat was gradual and not sharply defined. Salt was found not to act uniformly on all bacteria but to possess a selective action. Obligate anaerobes were

140. Callow. 1927. Analyst 52, 391-395.

141. Hess. 1928. J. Bact. 15, 33-35.

142. Buchanan and Schryver. 1913. Brit. Food J. 11, 159-160.

143. (Gt. Brit.) Food Invest. Bd., Ann. Rpt. for 1927, 20; Ann. Rpt. for 1937; Analyst 52 (1927), 391.

144. Jensen. 1943. Food Research 8, 377-387.

145. Wieser. 1930. Schweiz. Ztschr. Hyg. 10, 333-335.

146. Pettersson. 1899. Berlin Klin. Wchnschr. No. 42, 915.

found to be inhibited by five per cent concentration; above five per cent, facultative anaerobic and aerobic species developed. Of the cocci and rods which brought about intensive decomposition, the rods were more easily harmed by salt. Most of them were repressed by 10 per cent concentration, although a few developed up to 15 per cent. Most cocci seemed to be able to tolerate 15 per cent. Yeasts appeared in media with greater amounts of salt. DeFreytag [147] studied the question with pathogenic bacteria. Spores of *Bacillus anthracis* were still alive after six months' sojourn in saturated salt solution. The vegetative cells were destroyed in a few hours. The limits for germination of spores in bouillon at 37°C. were between seven and 10 per cent. *Eberthella typhosa* was viable after six months in concentrated salt solution. The organism of hog erysipelas was viable after two months. *Mycobacterium tuberculosis* was not destroyed in three months. Stadler [148] was interested in determining whether meats could be freed from pathogenic bacteria by curing in salt solutions. *Escherichia coli communis* survived seven to eight per cent of salt in solution for six weeks. *Bacillus morbificans bovis* died in a solution of seven to eight per cent of salt in three weeks. *Salmonella enteritidis* in a solution of seven to eight per cent of salt died in four and one-half weeks. *Bacillus proteus vulgaris* did not die in this concentration in three weeks. The limit of salt concentration which inhibited growth of bacteria was 10 per cent. Forster [149] also believed that curing would not necessarily kill pathogenic bacteria in meat. Weichel [150] reported that such bacteria as *Salmonella enteritidis* and *Salmonella schottmülleri* could live for 33 to 95 days, depending on the salt concentration and the temperature. At refrigerator temperatures, there was good development in all concentrations after 71 days. It was also indicated that the number of cells inoculated into the cultures influenced the results. Bacteria inoculated into meat before pickling died so slowly even in strong (19%) brine that pickling could not be said to make infected meat safe. Inoculated meat kept in 12 to 19 per cent of salt showed complete bacterial destruction only after 75 days. In 10 to 13 per cent salt solutions, many living bacteria were present in the interior of the pieces after 80 days. Quite similar conclusions were reached by Karaffa-Korbutt [151] and Serkowski and Tomczak.[152] This review of literature indicates quite clearly that salt in concentrations that could be used in food preservation is not a bactericide but perhaps a preservative for a few species of bacteria.

As an example of an organism which thrives in concentrated brine may be mentioned *Bacteroides halosmophilus*, Baumgartner.[153] Maximum growth occured at salt concentration between 12½ and 15 per cent of salt. The organism is a strict anaerobe, the heat resistance of which is influenced by the salt concentration.

147. DeFreytag. 1889. Arch. f. Hyg. 11, 60.
148. Stadler. 1889. Idem 35, 40.
149. Forster. 1889. München. Med. Wchnschr. No. 29.
150. Weichel. Arb. aus dem K. Gsndhtsamt. 34, 246.
151. Karaffa-Korbutt. 1911. Rev. in Kochis Jahresber. 22, 138.
152. Serkowski and Tomczak. 1911. Ztschr. f. Untersuch. der Nahr. u. Genussmtl. 21, 211-216.
153. Baumgartner. 1937. Food Research 2, 321-329.

Some work has been done to show that salt itself may carry undesirable bacteria. Rappin[154] isolated bacteria from crude and refined salt which caused defects in butter and cheese. Weigmann[155] and Wolff[156] confirmed this work and showed that salt for food preservation should be carefully handled and protected from undue contamination. Yesair[157] found a variable bacterial content in salt. The total counts ranged from 0 to 1,470 per gram in a series of 125 samples. He stated that in the process of refining salt practically all of the bacteria are destroyed. Putrefactive anaerobes, however, were found in mined salt. On account of this Yesair advised against the use of such salt in the meat-preservation industry.

Tanner and Evans[158] observed that strains of microorganisms differ in their resistance to salt. The substrate to which the salt is added has much influence. The amounts of salt which inhibited *Clostridium botulinum* were around 10 per cent. Further data on this question have been reported by Callow.[159] Portions of minced pork were placed in stoppered bottles and various weights of salt added. The bottles were stored at 0°C.(32°F.). After two months the pork with no added salt had putrefied. That with even two per cent of salt had not. Its surface was covered with mold and yeast colonies but no bacterial colonies were visible. Between two and seven per cent, colonies of these organisms became fewer. Above nine per cent, no colonies of any kind could be observed with the naked eye. With the microscope, however, yeast cells and mold spores could be detected in samples containing up to 16 per cent of salt. Then all samples with more than seven per cent of salt were placed at room temperature. In a few days mold growth appeared on the meat containing 11 per cent of added salt but not on meat with 12 per cent or more. Callow confirmed the observation that salt exerts not only a repressive action but a selective action as well. The latter is more pronounced at 0°C. than at room temperature.

DRYING OF MEATS

Exigencies of the world war prompted inquiries into the possibility of drying meats which were to be shipped abroad. Kraybill[159a] mentioned three advantages, conservation of shipping space, conservation of metal containers and to furnish a product which would keep well without refrigeration. He stated that results of experimental work indicated a safe product was secured when prepared according to federal specifications which were quoted for beef. The meat has to be dried so that it contains not more than ten per cent of moisture in any particle when placed in the container.

Another type of product similar to dry or summer sausage, studied by Ritchell, Piret, and Halvarson,[159b] underwent a rapid decrease in viable

154. Rappin. 1920. J. Amer. Med. Assn. 75, 618-619.
155. Weigmann. 1923. Jahresber. Vers. Sta. Molkereiw. Landw.-Kammer Schleswig-Holstein 9-10.
156. Wolff. 1914. Milchw. Zentbl. 43, 545-551.
157. Yesair. 1930. Canning Trade, No. 27, 112-115.
158. Tanner and Evans. 1933. Centbl. f. Bakt. Pt. 2, 88, 48-54.
159. Callow. 1930. (Gt. Brit.) Food Invest. Bd., Ann. Rpt. for 1929, 72.
159a. Kraybill. 1943. Proc. Inst. Food Tech., 90-94.
159b. Ritchell, Piret. and Halvarson. 1943. Ind. and Eng. Chem., 35, 1189-1195.

bacteria during storage in vacuum cans. In forty-nine weeks counts of 21,800,000 in samples containing 28 per cent of water had dropped to 180 bacteria per gram; samples with 25 per cent of water decreased in this time from 24,300,000 to 110 bacteria per gram.

CURING OF MEAT PRODUCTS

Carcasses of hogs are chilled as soon as possible after slaughter and dressing. They are placed in coolers until chilled throughout. When the time comes to cut the carcass, it is brought from the cooler to the cutting floor. Cutting is one of the most important steps in its preparation. The carcass must be cut in such a manner that the packer will receive the greatest return. Certain cuts, which will yield the greatest return, should not be trimmed more than necessary.

Chief among the cuts to which the packers give special attention are the hams. Cutting of hams is the first operation on the cutting floor and one which requires considerable care and skill. Carcasses which are cut at one time have usually been graded for size and weight; consequently, cutters will work for a time on one lot. Cuts are thus kept uniform in weight. Hams are cut from the carcass by sawing at proper angles in order to secure as much of the desirable tissue as possible, as well as to leave as much as possible on certain other cuts. Considerable attention is also given to the shape of the hams. Shoulders are chopped and cut from the carcass and are usually not trimmed to the same extent as are hams.

After the hams have been cut and trimmed, they are ready for the curing cellar. Attention is given to the temperature of the hams when they are ready for the curing pickle. Packers have learned that the temperature should not be above about 2°C.(35.6°F.). This temperature is given as 38°F., by some packers. This matter is carefully watched and if the temperature is too high, the hams are placed again in the cooler in such a manner that the temperature may be lowered to the desired point.

One of the first steps in curing hams is "pumping" or forcing a certain amount of curing pickle into the ham. The solution is placed in a barrel provided with a force pump, each stroke of which delivers a known amount of the curing pickle. The pickle is conducted into the ham by means of a hollow needle or tube fastened to the pump by means of rubber tubing. Pumping the ham in this manner insures entrance of the curing pickle into the ham far more quickly, of course, than it could penetrate from the exterior. It is also necessary to have the cure start throughout the ham as soon as possible. Especially important in this respect is the area in the ham about the bone where undesirable changes may start in a short time. Not all hams are pumped, but this treatment is given hams which go through the usual routine of the meat plant. The curing or pickling solutions are made from salt, sugar, sodium nitrate or sodium nitrite, or both, and water. Another method of pumping is known today as vein-pumping in which the curing solution is forced through the veins for better distribution.

When hams are to be subjected to the effect of the pickling solutions, they are packed tightly into various containers. Tierces, or large casks, may be used. Vats or tanks made of concrete may also be used. Hams must be packed carefully into these containers in order that there shall be a good circulation of the pickle and as even penetration into the meat as possible. The shape of the hams must also be considered. The length of cure is determined to a great extent by the weight of the ham, the concentration of the curing pickle, temperature, etc.

During curing a temperature of 3.3°C.(38°F.) is maintained because if a lower temperature is used, the cure is retarded and a high temperature may cause defects in the curing solution although curing may be accelerated. Some of the results of using various temperatures on behavior of spoilage organisms have been published by Tucker.[160] In general it was found that a temperature of 3.3°C.(38°F.) would suppress spoilage. Tucker also studied the effect of temperatures 1.1°C.(34°F.) and 5.5°C. (42°F.). One organism which he used in his experiments, *Clostridium putrefaciens*, was not hindered much at these temperatures while the other three were. Consequently, possibility of spoilage must be considered even at quite low temperatures. The physical changes which are involved in ham curing are diffusion of salt, nitrate, nitrite, and sugar into the meat and passage of soluble substances from the meat (Greenwood *et al.* [161]).

During the past few years the old methods of curing which required about 90 days' sojourn in curing solutions, have been replaced by some packers with a "quick-cure" requiring only a few days. Hurd [162] stated that this method of curing was here to stay. The use of a stronger curing solution over a shorter time was believed to give a superior product.

Effect of Sodium Nitrate (Saltpeter) on Bacteria. Sodium nitrate has been used so long in meat-curing solutions that its origin is probably unknown. Sausage has been cured with this salt for much over 100 years, and other meat products have probably been cured with it for much longer. When this salt is not used, the meat has a dull, uneven color instead of the bright, red color commonly connected with cured meats. Early students of meat curing generally attributed the value of nitrate to its color effects, but more recent work seems to indicate that it may possess some value as a preservative when used in combination with salt and sugar. When used alone, it may show feeble bactericidal action, as indicated by MacNeal and Kerr.[163]

It is difficult to find results of experiments on the effect of sodium nitrate on bacteria, and many of those which are available are not directly applicable to problems related to meat curing. Statements appear in books to the effect that the nitrate is reduced to nitrite, the latter compound exerting a detrimental effect on bacteria. Crespolani [164] mixed one gram of potassium nitrate with 300 grams of horse flesh and reported that putre-

160. Tucker. 1929. Inst. Amer. Meat Packers, Chicago, Spec. Bull.
161. Greenwood, Griffin, and Lewis. 1939. Amer. Soc. Anim. Prod. Proc. 32, 439-448.
162. Hurd. 1941. Food Indus., June 1941, 67; 114.
163. MacNeal and Kerr. 1929. Studies in Nutrition. Univ. of Illinois. Chapter 9, Vol. 2. 358-389.
164. Crespolani. 1905. Boll. Farm. 44, 697-700.

faction resulted with complete reduction of the nitrate. According to Serafini [165] a five-per cent solution of nitrate exhibited very little antiseptic action. Pettersson [146] reported that meat and fish with from five to 15 per cent of saltpeter putrefied when kept at 25°C.(77°F.). However, it was shown that mixtures of small amounts of saltpeter and salt were active antiseptics. MacNeal and Kerr,[163] as a part of an extensive investigation on the influence of saltpeter on the nutrition and health of man with reference to its occurrence in cured meat, studied the effect of sodium nitrate on bacteria. It is unfortunate that they did not use strains of bacteria which were of greater significance in the meat-preservation industry. They used *Escherichia coli, Clostridium welchii,* and an unidentified Bacillus "Type VIII." They found that potassium nitrate in neutral or alkaline solutions exerted no special restrictive effect on bacterial activity. Under these conditions it was used as food. In acid solutions, however, the results were quite different. A marked bacterial inhibition was noticed. They said that this effect was incomparably greater than that of the corresponding chloride and was best ascribed to the production of small amounts of nitric acid, and of nitrous acid also, in mixtures containing reducing substances. Potassium nitrate was therefore considered to be particularly effective in restricting acid fermentation of organic substances already slightly acid. They further believed that the claim of meat packers, that small amounts of nitrate in meat pickle produced better preservation of the meat, was borne out by their results. It seemed that nitrate was especially valuable in preventing high degrees of acidity or souring of meat. MacNeal and Kerr stated that the effect of saltpeter was probably due to the oxidizing action of the nitrate ion in the presence of hydrogen ion. Stadler [148] gave a formula for a curing mixture which consisted of 250 grams of salt, 10 grams of saltpeter, 30 grams of sugar, and one-half of a glass of red wine. He believed that the sugar and saltpeter functioned only as a color fixative.

In relatively high concentrations, sodium nitrate may have a deleterious effect on bacteria, according to Lewis and Moran [166] who found that 4.4 per cent of this salt was completely effective in checking the proteolytic activity of *Clostridium putrefaciens* in pork-infusion medium. This organism did not reduce nitrate to nitrite so there was no germicidal effect of the latter. A specific effect was exerted on the proteolytic activity of *Clostridium sporogenes* between the concentrations of .5 and 1.0 per cent of sodium nitrate. When salt was present, a combination of five per cent sodium chloride and one per cent of sodium nitrate inhibited proteolysis by this organism. This large amount of nitrate required to inhibit bacterial action would indicate that saltpeter alone could have little significance in meat curing and preservation.

Lehmann [167] and Hoagland [168] found that the nitrate, as such, did not influence the color, but that it had to be reduced to nitric oxide in the

165. Serafini. 1891. Arch. f. Hyg. 13, 173-206.
166. Lewis and Moran. 1928. Inst. Amer. Meat Packers, Bull. 4.
167. Lehmann. 1899. Sitzber. Physiol. Med. Ges. Würzburg 4, 57.
168. Hoagland. 1910. U. S. Dept. Agr., Bur. Anim. Indus., Ann. Rpt. for 1908. 25, 301-314.

meat. The red color was said to be due to nitric oxide hemoglobin which is formed by the action of nitric oxide on hemoglobin. In a later publication, Hoagland [169] reported confirmation of his earlier work. A much later contribution was made by Bernheim and Dixon,[170] who, in attempting to determine the nature of the oxidation-reduction systems in tissues, found that muscular tissue of oxen, sheep, pigs, rabbits, dogs, and chickens would not reduce nitrate to nitrite. The same kind of tissue obtained from rats and guinea pigs possessed this power. Liver tissue was found to be capable of this reduction regardless of the species from which it was taken. This would seem to indicate that some factor other than the meat itself was responsible for the reduction of nitrate to nitrite in cured beef and pork.

Nitrate may apparently be changed into other compounds than nitrite by anaerobic bacteria. Prevot [171] listed many common anaerobes which do not reduce nitrates but cause it to disappear. The only strict anaerobe known to reduce nitrate is a new species, *Eubacterium nitritogenes*, isolated by Prevot. The results of investigations by Riess, Meyer, and Müller [172] on use of sodium nitrate and sodium nitrite in meat preservation in Germany are pertinent. Since 1916, addition of nitrites to meat products has been against the law, but attempts have been made to have the prohibition of its use nullified. It was appreciated that nitrate which is permitted is reduced to nitrite and that, could nitrite as such be added, great saving of time could be accomplished (about one-third). The experiments carried out by Riess, Meyer, and Müller were instituted to answer several questions: (1) Does the addition of sodium nitrite to meat-curing solutions injure the health? (2) Is the saving of time of such significance that nitrites should be used, even though they may be somewhat poisonous? (3) Does the meat pickled with nitrite have the same characteristics as meat pickled with nitrate? They found that the use of nitrite instead of nitrate permitted a much more rapid cure. They also stated that the use of nitrite caused more rapid infiltration of salt. They were unable to detect any appreciable difference in the appearance or keeping qualities. Nitrite content of cured meat was said to be smaller when a nitrite cure was used than when a nitrate cure was used. From 10 to 20 milligrams of nitrite per 100 grams of meat were found in the outer layers, while one-tenth as much was found in the inner layers.

The experiments referred to above, by Riess, Meyer, and Müller, also included study of the bacteria involved. They stated that a review of the literature indicated a confused state of knowledge with regard to the part which bacteria might play in reduction of nitrate. Polenske [173] believed that bacteria were involved in reduction of nitrate in curing solutions. Nothwang [174] took the opposite view. Maassen's [170] experiments indicated a marked action of bacteria on nitrates. Of 109 bacteria, 85 were able to

169. Hoagland. 1914. J. Agr. Res. 3, 211-226
170. Bernheim and Dixon. 1928. Biochem. J. 22, 125.
171. Prevot. 1940. Compt. Rend. Soc. Biol. 134, 350-352; 353-355.
172. Riess, Meyer, and Müller. 1928. Ztschr. f. Untersuch. der Lebensmtl. 55, 325-354.
173. Polenske. 1891. Arb. aus dem. K. Gsndhtsamt. 7, 471-474; 9 (1892), 126-135.
174. Nothwang. 1893. Arch. f. Hyg. 16, 122-150.

reduce nitrates. Riess, Meyer, and Müller conducted experiments to secure information on this question, using, as far as possible, conditions which would obtain in practice. It was noticed by these investigators that better results were secured in wooden barrels than in jars. This situation could not be explained by bacterial contents. Six pure cultures were isolated which were, in turn, used in pure-culture inoculations. Without giving all of the experimental details, it may be stated that large amounts of nitrite were formed only in those flasks which contained meat, showing that some food substances must be present for formation of nitrites. Some bacteria could not form nitrite in the absence of meat, and only a small amount in the presence of it. Temperature was said to have little effect, since the amounts of nitrite formed at both low and high temperatures did not differ materially. Attempts were made by Riess, Meyer, and Müller to follow formation of nitrites from nitrate without presence of bacteria. It was found, however, that bacteria had gotten into these flasks. No conclusions could be reached.

Considerable work has been carried on on the effect of sodium nitrite and nitrate on spoilage bacteria in the meat, as well as on *Clostridium botulinum*. Results of these investigations will be reviewed at greater length.

The Institute of American Meat Packers sponsored an investigation, results of which were reported by Moulton.[176] This work was done with several organisms isolated from spoiled hams: *Clostridium sporogenes*, *Clostridium putrificum*, and *Clostridium putrefaciens*. They were inoculated into media prepared from pork and their action followed by determining the amount of protein cleavage products which were formed. At 37.5°C.(98°F.) five per cent of salt or one per cent of nitrate retarded the action of *Clostridium sporogenes*. Five per cent of salt and one-half to one per cent of nitrate showed still greater inhibition. When two per cent of nitrate was added to five per cent of salt, spoilage was prevented. It was shown that bacteria were not killed; they were merely inhibited and were unable to attack the meat. When sodium nitrite was substituted for the nitrate in a medium containing no salt, .05 per cent prevented spoilage. Nitrite was thus found to be more active in preventing spoilage than nitrate. Experiments were then undertaken to determine the results that would follow the use of less salt. Three to four per cent solution or .9 per cent of nitrate alone showed some inhibition. When nitrite was used in place of nitrate, it was found that one per cent of salt and .15 per cent of nitrite prevented all action.

Similar experiments were also made, using curing cellar temperature, 4.4°C.(40°F.). Pieces of beef were placed in the different curing solutions and allowed to cure for 21 days. At the end of this time, all of the curing solutions, even those with 15 per cent of salt, showed visible growth, while a .25-per cent nitrite curing solution showed no growth. Further experiments all indicated some activity of sodium nitrite in inhibiting bacterial growth.

175. Maassen. 1902. Arb. aus dem K. Gsndhtsamt. 18, 21-77.
176. Moulton. 1929. The Canner, 1930. Conv. Number.

While meat packers once desired a nitrite cure, results of extensive investigations have indicated, at times, that a mixed cure (containing both sodium nitrate and sodium nitrite) is desirable from the standpoint of both spoilage and development of toxin by *Clostridium botulinum.* The preserving effects of such curing solutions have been generally attributed to the nitrites, either those added as such or those secured by reduction of the nitrate; however, some evidence was believed to indicate that nitrate itself may have some value as a preservative. This is a controversial subject.

Much study has been given to the chemical mechanisms by which sodium nitrite imparts the desirable red color to meat. Probably the actual facts are still unknown. Among those who have contributed to the subject are Polenske,[173] Nothwang,[174] Kisskalt,[177] Pettersson,[178] Haldane,[179] Hoagland,[180] and McBryde.[181] The subject is mainly a chemical problem. Haldane stated that red color of cooked meat, preserved with curing solutions containing sodium nitrite, was due to NO-hemochromogen. This compound was said to be produced by the decomposition of NO-hemoglobin by the meat, which caused the red color. NO-hemoglobin was said to be formed in the absence of oxygen and in the presence of reducing agents.

Hoagland [182] believed the action of saltpeter in influencing the color of meat to be due to the formation of oxyhemoglobin. Saltpeter was reduced within the meat to nitrites which, in turn, were changed to nitric oxide. This united with the hemoglobin to give the characteristic red color. Saltpeter, which is used in many pickling solutions, probably exerts little effect on bacteria.

Food-control officials have justly shown concern over the addition of sodium nitrite to meats. As stated above, the Bureau of Animal Industry placed a limit of 200 p.p.m. in the cured product. Much depends on how the determinations are made. If determinations are made on a slice from the surface, the amounts are usually high. If however, the determinations are made on center slices of ham, for instance, the amounts are much lower. It is reasonable to expect more nitrite in the surface of cured meat than in the deeper layers. Samples of cured meats for analysis should be kept cold between the time of sampling and analysis, else there will be a great change in the nitrite situation. Cooking in the home also reduces the quantity of nitrites in meat. This probably justifies a more liberal standard for nitrite content.

Not much work has been done on the effect of curing solutions on pathogenic bacteria, which may be present in the meat. The most direct method, but one susceptible to experimental difficulties would involve the use of meat either naturally or artificially infected. Results of such an experiment with pork from animals artificially infected with swine fever were

177. Kisskalt. 1899. Arch. f. Hyg. 35, 11-18.
178. Pettersson. 1900. Arch. f. Hyg. 37, 171-238.
179. Haldane. 1901. J. Hyg. 1, 115-122.
180. Hoagland. 1910. U. S. Dept. Agr., Bur. Anim. Indus., Ann Rpt., 1908-25, 301-304. J. Agr. Res. 3 (1914), 211-226.
181. McBryde. 1911. U. S. Dept. Agr., Year Book, 383-389.
182. Hoagland. 1908. U. S. Dept. Agr. Bur. Anim. Indus., Ann. Rpt. 301-314.

reported by Zeller and Beller.[183] Pork cured in brine (25%) for 22 to 181 days caused the disease in 12 out of 15 tests (80%). In a second series with the meat of infected pigs preserved in dry salt for periods varying from 22 to 315 days, feeding caused swine fever in 11 out of 13 experiments. When pieces of large intestine were preserved in dry salt for 22 to 164 days, 10 out of 13 sound pigs fed, developed swine fever. Similar experiments with dry salted small intestine set up infection in 10 (one animal recovered) out of 14 tests. The brine solution itself was less infective, for when fed to pigs, only two out of 11 succumbed to swine fever. Seventeen experiments with infected pigs' livers, kept for various periods in a frozen condition, yielded negative results in six cases, infection with death in nine, while two were doubtful. The two experiments, which lasted as long as 196 and 226 days, caused no infection on feeding, suggesting that the virus dies out in time under these condiitons. *Salmonella schottmülleri* and *Salmonella eneridiitis,* in Wieser's [14] experiments were killed in a month or two in 20 to 25 per cent solutions of salt but survived and even multiplied in meat. Henniger [184] reached about the same conclusions.

Brooks *et al.*[185] found that in bacon satisfactory color and flavor is compatible with low nitrite content. The characteristic flavor of bacon is due primarily to action of nitrite on the flesh and satisfactory bacon can be made with salt and nitrite only. Presence of nitrate or microbial action during pickling and maturation is not essential for the development of bacon flavor. These investigators believed that use of nitrite in curing would permit the following changes in commercial practice: (1) greater control of the concentration of nitrite in the curing solution; (2) greater latitude in the composition of tank curing solutions; (3) a reduction in the microbial population on the surface and consequently a better keeping bacon.

Two extensive investigations have been carried out in the author's laboratory. Tanner and Evans [186] used different amounts of sodium nitrate with three different anaerobic bacteria, *Clostridium botulinum,* types A and B, *Clostridium putrificum,* and *Clostridium sporogenes.* Determination of concentrations of sodium nitrate by analysis showed irregular inhibition of seven strains of *Clostridium botulinum.*

Sodium nitrate was not found to be as good a preservative as sodium nitrite by DeBoer and Tanner.[187] Sodium nitrate had no effect on *Clostridium botulinum.* Even amounts as high as three per cent were without effect. When the meat samples were stored at 3.3°C.(38°F.), the temperature used in curing cellars, nitrite formation from nitrates took place slowly in concentrations of nitrate below one per cent. Above this amount sufficient nitrite is formed to materially inhibit bacterial development.

Jensen and Hess [188] studied the effect of sodium nitrate on *Clostridium sporogenes* in a spiced-ham medium. About 50 spores were inoculated into

183. Zeller and Beller. 1929. Centbl. f. Bakt. Pt. 1, Orig., 114, 300-308.
184. Henninger. 1934. Ztschr. f. Fleisch. u. Milchyg. 44, 84.
185. Brooks, Haines, Moran, and Pace. 1940. (Gt. Brit.) Food Invest. Bd.) Spec. Rpt. No. 49
186. Tanner and Evans. 1933. Zentbl. f. Bakt., Pt. 2, 89, 48-54.
187. DeBoer and Tanner. 1944. Illinois Biological Monographs. (In press.)
188. Jensen and Hess. 1941. The Canner, 92, Conv. Number 82-87; Food Mfr. 16, 157-160.

each tube. Growth appeared in 72 hours in the tubes with no nitrate and in the tubes containing .02 per cent. After 76 hours all tubes excepting the ones containing .5 per cent and 1.0 per cent of sodium nitrate showed active growth. No growth appeared in the tubes containing .5 and 1.0 per cent of nitrate after four weeks' incubation. This experiment was carried out with a very small inoculum and no evidence was given as to whether the spores were killed or whether they were merely inhibited.

Effect of Heat on Bacterial Spores in the Presence of Nitrate. It has been suggested that spores of *Clostridium botulinum* might be destroyed by heat in the presence of sodium nitrate. Jensen heated tubes to which 25 spores of *Clostridium botulinum* and various amounts of nitrate had been added at 68.3°C.(155°F.) for five hours. They were not injured nor were the results any different when 1,000 spores were added to the tubes. When the heating was carried out at 80°C.(176°F.) for four hours, some heat injury was apparent. Heating at 93.3°C.(200°F.), a higher temperature than is used in processing chopped ham, showed great injury to spores in presence of one per cent of nitrate. From these results Jensen speculated that in the presence of nitrate, nitrite, and salt spores of *Clostridium botulinum* and *Clostridium sporogenes* might be killed at much lower temperatures than called for in standard canning practice. More convincing results on this question were reported by Yesair and Cameron.[189] Introduction of .1 per cent of sodium nitrate, .005 per cent of sodium nitrite, or two per cent of salt caused greater than 70 per cent reduction in spores.

While admitting that results from laboratory and culture tube experiments are valuable, Jensen and Hess [188] carried out experiments using meat and a strain of *Clostridium sporogenes* which was said to have characteristics of *Clostridium botulinum* with exception of toxin formation. Pork trimmings in batches of 400 pounds were used. These were chopped and divided into two batches of 200 pounds each. One lot was cured with the regular curing ingredients for spiced ham: two per cent sucrose, 3.5 per cent salt, four ounces sodium nitrate, one-half ounce sodium nitrite and one ounce of mixed spice. The other lot of 200 pounds was cured with the same mixture except that sodium nitrate was omitted. To each lot during mixing a suspension of spores of *Clostridium sporogenes* was added so that each six-pound can would contain 10,000 spores. Samples for examination were taken during the experiment. All of the six-pound cans were placed at 37.2°C.(99°F.) for 30 days and then opened for inspection. The meat cured without nitrate but containing nitrite was sound and no can swelled in 30 days. The meat cured with nitrate and nitrite showed gas formation to some extent. Three of the 32 cans swelled, showing that nitrate was conducive to gas formation as Jensen has shown in other publications.

The experiment was repeated using nitrite alone in one batch and nitrate and nitrite in the other. Of 32 cans of meat cured with nitrite alone, 19 became putrid, nine were sound, and four were soft swells with proteolysis and fermentation. Jensen believed that these results showed

189. Yesair and Cameron. 1942. The Canner, 94. Conv. Number, 89-92.

the value of nitrate in inhibiting putrefactive anaerobes. The inhibition was not complete, however. Jensen and Hess reported that nitrate is reduced to hydroxylamine in a nitrate-nitrite-salt-sugar curing mixture. They further believed that this incubated catalase permitted formation of hydrogen peroxide which killed *Clostridium sporogenes*. Using quite different technic DeBoer and Tanner [187] found no effect of sodium nitrate on thermal death time of *Clostridium botulinum* in concentrations of 200 to 400 p.p.m.

Effect of Sodium Nitrite on Bacteria. Nitrites of sodium and potassium have an important role in imparting a desired red color to cured meats. Food-control officials have rightfully regulated composition of curing solutions to prevent addition of unnecessarily large amounts of certain constituents which might injure the health of consumers. Nitrites were added to meat-curing solutions as color fixatives. When nitrates are used, it is assumed that they are reduced to nitrites. During late years, evidence has been accumulating to indicate that nitrites may function to some extent as preservatives.

Use of nitrite in place of nitrate in the curing of meat arose from an observation made by Polenske [173] that nitrite was present in old nitrate curing solution. He believed that reduction of nitrate to nitrite was accomplished by bacterial activity. Nothwang [174] made the same observation, but added that reduction might be due to the meat tissue itself. In light of Bernheim and Dixon's work,[170] Polenske's explanation is more probable. Bernheim and Dixon found that muscular tissue from a considerable number of animals including the ox and the pig was completely without power to reduce nitrate to nitrite. Lehmann [167] and Kisskalt,[177] working separately, found that red color of cured meat was due to nitrite and not to nitrate. Lehmann boiled fresh meat with nitrite in a weak acid solution and secured a product having the red color of cured meat, When treated with sodium nitrate, this red color did not appear. Kisskalt found, in addition, that if meat were allowed to stand several days in contact with nitrate, a red color would result. Haldane [179] proved that the color of meat cured with nitrate and nitrite was due to nitric-oxide- hemoglobin which was formed by the action of nitrous oxide on hemoglobin. He also found that the permanent pink color of boiled cured meat was due to a water insoluble compound which proved to be nitric oxide-hemochromogen. Hoagland [180] repeated Haldane's experiments and obtained the nitric oxide-hemoglobin as the red colored element of cured meat. He concluded that neither nitrates nor nitrites, as such, had any influence in preserving the color of fresh meat. The brown color of meat cured with excessive nitrate was thought to be due to the action of sodium nitrite on hemoglobin. An interesting observation was made by Klut,[190] who noted that some waters would change the color of beef to a lighter or deeper red on boiling. Experiments showed that very small amounts of nitrite were sufficient to cause change in color. Nitrate containing waters might give the color if they were allowed to remain in contact with zinc, for the metal acted as a

190. Klut. 1913. Mitt. Laudesanst. Wasserhyg. 17, 36-39.

reducing agent in this case and the nitrite so produced would cause the change in color.

After it had been shown that the active agent in color fixation was nitrite and not nitrate, efforts were made to use the former in curing solutions. Among the first to recommend it was Glage[191] who proposed the use of partially reduced nitrate prepared by heating dry saltpeter in a kettle. This procedure, of course, led to a product of unknown nitrate-nitrite composition which, when used in the curing of meat, gave somewhat irregular results. From this time on, however, commercial preserving salts containing nitrite appeared on the market. Auerback and Riess[192] found that meat cured with nitrite contained more of this salt than meat cured with nitrate. They found that meat exposed to action of an ordinary curing solution containing five per cent potassium nitrate for several weeks contained, at the most, a few milligrams of nitrite per 100 grams of meat. Amounts exceeding 10 milligrams per 100 grams were found only in the surface portions. Curing solutions which contained a large amount of sodium nitrite caused it to penetrate uniformly into the meat. Ten to 40 milligrams per 100 grams were found in surface samples. Auerback and Riess believed that amounts of sodium nitrite exceeding 15 milligrams per 100 grams indicated that a nitrite cure had been used. Pollak[193] found that a nitrite cure was practical. The amount of nitrite in the finished product was even smaller than usually found in meat cured with nitrate. Careful control was required in order to obtain good results. Experimental work on a commercial scale by Lewis, Vose, and Lowery[194] demonstrated that a nitrite cure, when properly carried out, yielded a product equal, or superior, to that resulting from a nitrate cure. The amount of sodium nitrite found to be most satisfactory was one-tenth the amount of sodium nitrate usually used. The resulting product contained no more, and often less, nitrite than when the customary amount of saltpeter was used. These conclusions were, in general, concurred in by Kerr, Marsh, Schroeder, and Boyer.[195]

The results of this investigation were confirmed by Riess, Meyer, and Müller[172] who compared the effects of curing solutions containing nitrite with those containing nitrate. They found that meat cured with nitrite never contained more than 10 mg. of sodium nitrite per 100 grams and frequently only a fraction of a milligram was found. They also pointed out that meat cured with two per cent saltpeter[196] contained, in addition to the traces of sodium nitrite, 100 to 150 mg. of saltpeter. The possibility exists that this saltpeter may be transformed suddenly under uncontrolled conditions into nitrite. They recommended, as a result of their experiments, a salt mixture containing not more than .6 per cent sodium nitrite with sodium chloride. When this mixture was stored in dry rooms, very little

191. Glage. 1909. Diss. Berlin.
192. Auerbach and Riess. 1919. Reichsgsndhtsamt. Arb. 51, 532-544.
193. Pollak. 1922. Ztschr. f. Angew. Chem. 35, 229-232.
194. Lewis et al. 1925. Ind. Eng. Chem. 17, 1243-1245.
195. Kerr et al. 1926. J. Agr. Res. 33, 541-551.
196. Saltpeter, according to Reiss, Meyer, and Müller, refers to a mixture of sodium and potassium nitrates.

destruction of nitrite occurred, but when it was placed in wet rooms, appreciable loss took place in a short time. Riess, Meyer, and Müller found that the advantages of use of .6 per cent sodium nitrite curing mixtures were as follows: (1) a curing time of one-half to one-third that usually necessary with saltpeter; (2) thorough reddening of meat and thorough salt penetration proceeded faster when this cure was used; (3) nitrite content of the finished product was no larger and was frequently smaller than that receiving a nitrate cure; (4) appearance, odor, flavor, and keeping quality of such products were equal to, or superior to, those cured with saltpeter.

The equivalence of sodium nitrate to sodium nitrite in meat curing has been stated to be 10 to 1 by Lewis and Moran [166]; others have stated it to be 5 to 1 and lower. An exact equivalence which will hold under all conditions is probably not possible since the conditions which obtain in each separate experiment will greatly affect the results. Assuming that nitrites are somewhat germicidal, the number of nitrate-reducing bacteria influence the results. If nitrate reduction is slow, there will be less effective nitrite. At the Iowa Agricultural Experiment Station,[197] nitrites proved effective in a concentration of 1/10 to 1/20 that of nitrates generally used. A desirable color was not produced until the concentration of salt was at least 10 per cent. It is quite well established that constant equivalence values do not exist, for the amount of nitrite resulting from bacterial reduction of nitrate would depend upon many different factors: type, numbers and activities of microorganisms, physical conditions which obtain in the curing solution, time of curing, etc.

Another factor of importance is that constant relationships do not seem to exist between the amount of ingredients in curing solutions and their incidence in cured meats. This seems to be borne out by data in publications of Kerr, Marsh, Schroeder, and Boyer [195] and others. This would seem to indicate, therefore, that it might be better to control amounts of nitrate and nitrite in the finished product than in the curing solution.

Saltpeter (sodium nitrate) has had the longest use in meat-curing solutions. Since nitrates must be reduced to nitrites, packers desired to use nitrites as such to avoid the dangers which might result from inadequate conversion of nitrates to nitrites. Losses from uneven or inadequate fixation of color were not uncommon. Since many bacteria exist which may reduce nitrites, it is necessary either to add sufficient to fix color before it is used up or to have a constant source supply (nitrates). The nitrate cure permitted this but the nitrite cure introduced the hazard of nitrite disappearance. Consequently, there may be much merit in the mixed cure in which both nitrates and nitrites are added. The nitrates may act as a reservoir for replacement of lost nitrite.

Regulation of the amounts of these salts used in meat-curing solutions rests in the United States with the Bureau of Animal Industry and the bureau has rightfully been diligent to prohibit the use of unnecessarily

197. Iowa Agr. Expt. Sta., Ann. Rpt. 1926, 28-29.

large amounts. Too little is known, however, about the toxicity of nitrites in cured meat products.

The conditions caused by the first World War made it necessary for the Secretary of the United States Department of Agriculture [198] to revise regulations to permit the immediate use of sodium nitrate (Chile saltpeter) in place of potassium nitrate for curing of meat in establishments where federal inspection is maintained. This salt has been used since then in spite of the fact that many packers claim that better results are secured with potassium nitrate. In 1922 the United States Department of Agriculture [199] amended the rules to permit, among other things, saltpeter and nitrate of soda.

Amendment 4 to B.A.I. Order 211, revised, issued October 19, 1925 [200] permitted the use of saltpeter, nitrate of soda, and nitrite of soda. This was indeed a mixed cure and a distinct departure from former practice. The bureau stated that meats could be successfully cured with quantities of sodium nitrite that would not result in the presence of more than 200 parts per million in the finished meats. It was stated that, in general, the correct quantity of nitrite is approximately one-tenth that of nitrate. The substitution of one pound of nitrite for each 10 pounds of nitrate was recommended. The basis for this ratio (10 to 1) is hard to determine.

After use of excessive amounts of sodium nitrate in pumping pickle was observed by the Bureau of Animal Industry in 1926,[201] a warning was issued that amounts of saltpeter or sodium nitrate over one per cent would be held excessive in pumping pickle.

Immediately after release of these rulings, the bureau began to record itself in favor of a nitrite cure as the approved cure for comminuted meats and sausage. It was suggested that the use of nitrate be eliminated when as much as one-quarter ounce of sodium nitrite is used per 100 pounds of meat. This opinion was based on the observations that satisfactory cured meat could be made with such a cure.

Although many meat packers favored the nitrite cure, others believed that a mixed cure containing both nitrate and nitrite, was more satisfactory. It was suggested that, although nitrites made cured meats red, a little residual nitrate would be desirable to act as a constant source of nitrites. Accordingly, in the fall of 1931, the chief of the Bureau of Animal Industry issued a statement permitting one-quarter ounce of nitrite, and two and three-quarter ounces of nitrate per 100 pounds of meat in curing solutions. The arguments in favor of such mixed cures were several. The most important was that satisfactory cured meats had been prepared for years with a mixed cure and to change abruptly to the nitrite-cure would change the properties of the final products from those packing plants which had worked out a satisfactory procedure. Furthermore, it would be unnecessary to rely absolutely on the activities of nitrate reducing bacteria.

198. U. S. Dept. Agr. Bur. Anim. Indus., Service and Regulatory Announcements, January, 1925.
199. Idem Reg. 18, Sec. 6, Par. 2, B.A.I. Order 211 (1922).
200. Idem, October, 1925.
201. Idem January, 1926.

The amount of nitrite in cured meats naturally varies with the product and the method used for curing it. Moulton [202] has summarized the knowledge on this question. Lewis and Vose [203] reported from 42 to 53 parts per million of nitrite in a ham which had received a regular nitrate cure. Jones [204] reported 72 to 960 parts per million of nitrite in American ham. In his published article the methods of sampling, analysis, and manipulation of the samples were not given. The amounts which would be secured would depend largely on type of sample and its treatment after collection.

The ruling of the B.A.I. that the finished product contain less than 200 parts per million is in many respects meaningless. Nothing was said as to how or when the samples were to be taken. It is apparent that a surface sample of a ham recently removed from a curing solution with 600 or 700 p.p.m. of nitrite would show nitrite content considerably in excess of 200 p.p.m. On the other hand, a sample from a deeply seated area in the ham would show a nitrite content well within the limits of 200 p.p.m. Unless the method of sampling is specified, a ruling such as the one under discussion can but lead to confusion. A standard such as that just mentioned is meaningless unless standard procedures or methods are used in its enforcement.

Another very serious element for error is the technic used for preparation and handling of the sample. If the samples are not properly prepared and analyzed immediately, nitrate and nitrite data will be inaccurate. Bacteria may reduce nitrates and yield very high nitrite results, or, on the other hand, they may decompose the nitrites giving lower data than should be expected. Samples for the determination of nitrates must be analyzed promptly or stored under adequate refrigeration only for very short periods of time.

In some products such as spiced luncheon loaf in tin cans, the nitrite content decreases rapidly during storage, the rate of disappearance depending on the temperature of storage and probably the numbers and activity of the bacteria present. Ruyle and Tanner,[205] in an examination of commercial canned meats, did not find curing salts in sufficiently high concentration to prevent development of common anaerobes. After storage for several months the nitrite content in many cans is zero and almost so in the majority. Cooking, as carried out in the home, also destroys nitrite in cured meats. Results of experiments have shown that boiling and frying frequently destroys all of the nitrites, not even a trace showing on analysis even with products which have received a commercial nitrite or nitrate cure.

Nitrates are readily reduced to nitrites by many different chemical substances and microorganisms. In the preservation of meats with curing solutions containing nitrate only, it is well known that it must be reduced to nitrite before the color may be fixed.

202. Moulton, C. R., 1929. Meat Through the Microscope. Univ. of Chicago Press, Chicago, Ill.
203. Lewis and Vose. 1929. Dept. Sci. Res., Inst. Amer. Meat Packers, Chicago.
204. Jones. 1933. Analyst 58, 140-143.
205. Ruyle and Tanner. 1935. Centbl. f. Bakt., Pt. 2, 92, 436-449.

Bacteria are known to be active in reducing nitrates and probably play the most important role in this respect in meat-curing solutions containing nitrates. The subject has been studied mainly from the standpoint of agriculture and methods for determining the reduction with pure cultures. Maassen [175] studied the process with over 100 species of microorganisms in peptone broth containing five per cent of potassium nitrate. Eighty-five of these species formed large amounts of nitrites. Maassen stated that the amount of potassium nitrate used hindered the growth of some of the bacteria. He also stated that some of them were hindered by the nitrite formed showing that it has a detrimental effect on bacteria. Results of investigations by many others have shown the importance of bacteria as nitrate-reducers.

It is possible that the meat itself may also reduce nitrates. Abelous and Gerard [206] reported results of an investigation which seemed to indicate the presence of an enzyme in horse flesh which reduced nitrates. Their conclusions have been criticized, however, on the basis that they did not work with sterile extracts and the reduction they attributed to the enzyme may have been brought about by microorganisms. Bernheim and Dixon [170] obtained just the opposite results. Horovitz-Vlasova [207] reported *Bacillus halobicus,* an obligate halophilic organism which reduces nitrates to nitrites and then to free nitrogen. Zobell [208] showed that many bacteria could reduce nitrates to nitrites. The latter, in turn, were also reducible. Stickland [209] reported nitrate reduction by *Escherichia coli.*

Nitrites may also be decomposed by bacteria and some of the loss in nitrite must be attributed to microorganisms.

Inhibition of growth of bacteria by sodium nitrite is dependent upon the pH of the substrate, according to Tarr.[210] At pH 6, he found .02 per cent of sodium nitrite to entirely inhibit or strongly retard growth, while at pH 7 little or no inhibition was observed. A marked variation in susceptibility of different bacteria to nitrite was observed. Bittenbender, Degering, Tetrault, Feasley, and Gwynn,[211] using *Staphylococcus aureus* and *Escherichia coli,* found no destruction of these organisms by 30.8 per cent solutions in 10 minutes at pH 3 to 8. In view of such results as these, Tarr believed that sodium nitrite may be a bacteriostat rather than a bactericide.

DeBoer and Tanner [187] also found sodium nitrite to possess marked inhibitory action on microorganisms in meat held at 3.3°C.(38°F.). Amounts as low as .2 per cent not only preserved meat but actually reduced the number of bacteria. The bacterial flora in meat with nitrite became simpler, finally consisting mainly of small rods without spores. Tanner and Evans [212] several years before had also found sodium nitrite to be bac-

206. Abelous and Gerard. 1899. Compt. Rend. Acad. Sci. 129.
207. Horovitz-Vlasova. 1931. Izv. Tzentral. Nauch.-Issledovated Inst. Pischevoi Vkusovoi Prom. 6-35; Chem. Abs. 28 (1931), 1416.
208. Zobell. 1932. J. Bact. 24, 273-281.
209. Stickland. 1931. Biochem. J., 25, 1543-1544.
210. Tarr. 1941. Nature 147, 417-418; J. Fish. Res. Bd., Canada 5 (1941), 265-275.
211. Bittenbender *et al.* 1940. Ind. Eng. Chem. 32, 996-998.
212. Tanner and Evans. 1934. Centbl. f. Bakt., Pt. 2, 91-1-14.

tericidal. Acidity is an important factor. Variations in pH may explain different results secured by investigators under various conditions. Tarr [213] made similar observations. Whether sodium nitrite will inhibit *Clostridium botulinum* seems to depend on several factors among which the number of cells appears to be most important. With heavy inoculations, probably much heavier than those which would be encountered in actual practice, the amounts of sodium nitrite permitted would probably not be of any value. With light inoculations with few spores of *Clostridium botulinum*, the results are different.

PHARMACOLOGY OF NITRITES

The chemical properties of sodium and potassium nitrite made the pharmacology of these salts of importance in meat preservation. Most of the evidence in literature, however, involves ingestion of far larger amounts of nitrite than are used in meat curing and certainly larger amounts than would be found in cooked cured meats as they would be prepared for the table. There seems to be no evidence to indicate that the amounts of nitrite ordinarily found in cured meats are harmful.

Since sodium nitrite and nitrate have been added to meat curing solutions, many investigators have suggested that these salts might have a detrimental effect on the health of human beings. Important among the reports which have been published are those by Grindley and MacNeal.[214] Physiologically nitrites are very active, and they reached the conclusion that their poisonous action in large doses was due to two factors. The first was the effect on the blood. They found that animals poisoned with nitrite had had a large part of the blood oxyhemoglobin changed to methemoglobin. The second factor was the direct effect on the tissues. The nature of this action was not definitely known, but Grindley and MacNeal believed that it was direct tissue asphyxia. Nitrites have been found to be toxic for all animals examined, both hemoglobin containing and non-hemoglobin containing. This includes insects, arachnidae, protozoa, infusoria and mammals. Many plants were also injured by nitrites.

Riess, Meyer, and Müller [172] gave, as an introduction to their paper, a brief history of the use of nitrite in meat curing in Germany. Since 1916 it had been forbidden in the industrial preparation of meat products. The dangerous properties of the salt were demonstrated by the dosages regarded as permissible in medical practice. The German pharmacopoeia gave, as the largest single dose for an adult man, .3 gram and as the largest daily dose one gram. The Swiss pharmacopoeia gave as the corresponding doses .1 and .3 gram. Doses of .2 to .3 gram can produce humming in the ears, vertigo, sensitivity to light, nausea, cyanosis, and irregularity in heart action. The literature was found to contain records of severe illness caused by .3 to .6 gram. It was considered in Germany that any material that affected the health of men in amounts of less than one gram should be used with greatest care. However, they found by experiment that a carefully

213. Tarr. 1942. J. Fish. Res. Bd., Canada 6.
214. Grindley and MacNeal. 1917. Studies in Nutrition, Univ. of Ill., 1917.

controlled curing process made possible the use of nitrite in the preparation of cured meats without the resulting product containing this substance in quantities sufficient to be detrimental to health. Riess, Meyer, and Müller's experimental work seemed to be complete. They found that substitution of nitrate with nitrite decreased the curing time by one-third. Addition of .6 per cent of nitrite to common salt was sufficient when using 80 grams of salt for 1,000 grams of meat.

There are few data on the reaction of the salts of nitrous acid on bacteria, but one would suspect that a substance affecting so many other types of living things might have some influence on such small organisms as bacteria. Lewis and Moran [166] found this to be the case. Their experiment included determinations of the effect of nitrite alone and also the effect of combinations of nitrite with sodium chloride. They found that .2 per cent of sodium nitrite, the lowest concentration used in their work, completely inhibited proteolysis in cultures of *Clostridium putrefaciens*. In another experiment using concentrations of .01 to .05 per cent, they observed no inhibition at any concentration below .05 per cent. Apparently, the effective concentration lies between .05 and .2 per cent sodium nitrite. An experiment was also conducted with beef round covered with a solution containing nitrite, nitrate, or chloride. The nitrite solutions contained .03, .06, .09, .12, and 18 per cent of sodium nitrite. After nine days, growth and putrefaction were present in all the vessels containing nitrate and salt of concentrations 10 times that of the nitrite. The nitrite-beef combinations showed no evidence of spoilage even after 21 days. This would seem to indicate that nitrite is very effective in inhibiting bacterial growth even in very low concentrations. The actual amount of effective nitrite must have been lower than the percentage concentrations appearing in the tables, for the amount of meat added was not considered in the calculations. The effect of nitrite, according to these data, must be different for *Clostridium putrefaciens* than for the ordinary meat flora. Whether inhibition of bacteria would be noticeable in the curing cellar is another matter.

The experiment on the effect of combinations of sodium nitrite and sodium chloride was performed with *Clostridium sporogenes* as the test organism. Proteolysis for the 48-hour period was inhibited at .05 per cent sodium nitrite in all the salt concentrations from one to five per cent. However, for the seven- to 14-day period, proteolysis was observed in all nitrite concentrations from zero to .2 per cent (the highest sodium nitrite concentration used) in all the tubes containing zero to two per cent salt. In other words, after two weeks' incubation, growth had appeared over the entire range in the tubes containing nitrite only. Proteolysis was checked in nitrite concentrations at and above .05 per cent in salt concentrations of three to five per cent. In another similar experiment, these authors found that concentrations of .05 per cent and above prevented proteolysis in the absence of salt for the same incubation period. The difference between the effective concentration for these two experiments is the difference between .05 per cent and .2 per cent or .15 per cent.

Some attention has been given to the formation of nitrites from nitrates in the intestines and the possible evil effects of the former. Barth,[215] in 1879, studied the effect of Chile saltpeter on animals which had accidentally ingested it. Symptoms of illness resulted including weakness, unconsciousness, muscle twitchings, etc. Barth attributed the symptoms to nitrites formed from the nitrates, an opinion which was not generally accepted by toxicologists. Binz and Gerlinger [216] confirmed Barth's work and believed that nitrite poisoning occurred. The experiments just reported leave the situation in an unsatisfactory state. Clear-cut conclusions cannot be reached on the toxicity of nitrites in foods. It is evident, also, that the amounts of nitrite used in the above experiments were considerably greater than would be found in cured meats.

A comprehensive investigation of the effect of saltpeter in the diet was carried out at the University of Illinois in 1907 and 1908.[214] Twenty-four subjects were used in these experiments. The results of this investigation indicated that potassium nitrate as used in meat-curing solutions showed no effect on the subjects. Mathews,[214] who studied the pharmacology of nitrates and nitrites in this investigation, stated that the potassium in the potassium nitrate could be disregarded when the nitrate was taken in such small doses as those given in the experiments. The nitrate ion, in itself, was said to possess about the same physiological power as the chlorine ion. Sodium nitrate as such was said to have the same action on metabolism and nearly all tissues of the body as sodium chloride.

The situation for sodium nitrite is apparently different. Mathews quoted a number of cases of illness following ingestion of nitrites but the amounts were usually greatly in excess of those used in curing solutions. Data from injection experiments are not pertinent to this discussion.

Tarr [213] observed that addition of sodium nitrite to the diet of cats on the basis of an average-size man consuming one pound of fish containing .2 per cent of this salt daily for six days did not affect growth or development of internal organs.

Effect of Heat on Nitrite Content of Cured Meats. Heat used in cooking destroys nitrite in meat. Cooking should probably not be relied on to destroy large quantities of nitrite. Brooks and his colleagues [185] observed that other factors than concentration of nitrite in cured meat influenced nitrite destruction during heating. Roughly the time required for 50 per cent destruction increased with the initial concentration, ranging from 13 to 120 minutes for values of 30 to 589 grams of sodium nitrite per 10^6 grams of tissue. From these results, the authors claimed that reduction from a high to a low content of nitrite could not be expected. With amounts of nitrite not over 200 p.p.m. reduction was probably significant. DeBoer and Tanner also observed destruction of sodium nitrites in meat by heating.

Effect of Mixed Curing Solutions on Bacteria. Meat-curing solutions contain salt, saltpeter, sodium nitrite, and sugar and, in addition, various

215. Barth. 1879. Inaug. Dissert., Bonn.
216. Binz and Gerlinger. 1901. Arch. f. Internatl. Pharmacodyn. et Thér. 9, 441-450.

substances which are extracted from the meat. While much work has been done on the effect of the single ingredients on microorganisms, it is a question how far the conclusions may be used for inferring what the effect would be in combination with the other ingredients. Mixed curing solutions probably developed from salt solutions and vary greatly in composition. Evans and Tanner [217] stated that commercial curing solutions were effective in preventing growth and toxin formation when the proportions of curing mixture used in their experiments were such that the critical concentrations of sodium chloride were approximated.

Administrative Regulations Concerning Use of Sodium Nitrate and Sodium Nitrite in Meat Products (De Boer and Tanner [187]). In the United States, regulation of the amounts of nitrates and nitrites used in meat curing originates from the Bureau of Animal Industry of the United States Department of Agriculture. In January, 1925, a ruling was issued that sodium nitrite could be used in curing solutions but that the cured product must not contain more than 200 p.p.m. of nitrite, since meat given a nitrite cure has been found to be higher in nitrites than when cured with nitrates alone. In 1931, the Bureau of Animal Industry ruled that "mixed curing solutions" containing both nitrate and nitrite, shall contain not more than one-quarter ounce of nitrite or two and three-quarter ounces of nitrate per 100 pounds of meat. A prior ruling had fixed the amount of nitrate in straight nitrate curing solutions as three ounces per 100 pounds.

The Canadian Government (1941) regulation in regard to the use of nitrates and nitrites in meat curing are similar to those of the United States. Both nitrates and nitrites may be used and no limits are placed on the amounts to be used in curing, but the finished product shall not contain more than 200 p.p.m. of nitrites. The supervision rests with the Veterinary Director General in the Department of Agriculture.

In Great Britain the use of saltpeter in conjunction with common salt is permitted. However, a provisional regulation dated October 20, 1939, (1940) made by the Minister of Health, makes the addition of sodium or potassium nitrite to bacon and hams now permissible. On April 30, 1940, this provisional regulation was amended as follows: "No person shall manufacture for sale or sell any cooked cured meat intended for human consumption other than bacon or ham, which contains sodium or potassium nitrite in proportions exceeding 200 parts per million calculated as sodium nitrite."

German regulations (1936) permit the use of salt-sodium nitrite pickling compound for certain meats, containing between .5 and .6 per cent of sodium nitrite. Use of saltpeter simultaneously with a nitrite and sodium chloride mixture is prohibited. However, for large cuts of meat saltpeter may be used together with a mixture of nitrite and sodium chloride provided not more than one kilogram of it is present for every 100 kilograms of the nitrite-sodium chloride mixture. Recently, suggestions have been made for the establishment of a legal maximum amount of

217. Evans and Tanner. 1934. Zentbl. f. Bakt., Pt. 2, 91, 135-147.

nitrates in order to keep the maximum amount of nitrites formed within the limits set by the Act of 1934.

France permits the use of saltpeter in meat curing but regulations specify that nitrites cannot be used (1936).

Swiss regulations (1936) are similar to those of Germany. A salt-nitrite mixture colored by spices, such as mace and paprika, is specified. This mixture shall not contain more than .6 per cent of the weight of the salt as sodium nitrite and cannot be sold in quantities less than 25 kilograms and then only by official establishment (1932).

Italian regulations specify that saltpeter may be present together with sodium chloride for curing purposes to the extent of .25 grams per 1,000 grams of salt (NaCl) (1932).

Spain does not permit the use of saltpeter or the nitrites of sodium and potassium in meat-curing solutions (1932).

Sweden and Norway have no state regulations governing the use of curing salts. Any authority exercised regarding food handling rests with local authorities. However, most of them permit the use of saltpeter in meat curing (1932).

Danish regulations specify that in meat and meat products produced for export only sodium chloride, sodium or potassium nitrate mixtures, and sugar are to be used (1932).

In the Netherlands saltpeter may be used but nitrites are not permitted in meat curing (1932).

Belgium permits the use of sodium and potassium nitrate in amounts sufficient to form the red color in cured meat (1932).

Austria does not permit the use of saltpeter and nitrites of sodium and potassium in meat. Only sodium chloride can be used (1932).

In Czechoslovakia no specific regulations exist regarding the use of saltpeter in meat curing; however, the use of any preservative harmful or injurious to health is prohibited (1932).

Romania permits the use of salt and saltpeter in the preservation and curing of meat (1932).

Bulgaria also permits saltpeter and salt in meat curing (1932).

In Poland saltpeter can be used alone and in combination with sodium chloride to the extent of 300 milligrams of saltpeter for 100 grams of meat or meat products (1932).

In Hungary 2,000 milligrams of nitrate are permitted to be used per kilogram of meat. The amount of nitrate in sausage shall not exceed 250 milligrams per kilogram (1932).

In Argentina (1941) the use of both nitrates and nitrites is subject to governmental regulation. *Nitrate:* The brine that is used to prepare meats, hams, etc., cannot contain more than one-hundredth part of sodium or potassium nitrate in relation to the percentage of sodium chloride used. *Nitrite:* It is permissible to add sodium nitrite to meats or preserved meats in quantities which do not exceed 150 to one million parts, or a proportion equivalent to fifteen-thousandths per cent (.015 per cent), provided that it does not contain impurities which could alter the product.

As mentioned elsewhere in this chapter, such regulations are difficult to interpret since they do not stipulate how the samples shall be taken. Definite methods of sampling ought to be stated. The amount of nitrite used should be only that required for production of good-quality cured meat. Excessive amounts in the curing solution would increase the cost of meat curing.

Microbiology of Curing Solutions. Results of comprehensive investigations on this subject have not been published. Not much is known about the numbers of bacteria which may be present or the species which result from the selective action of the curing agents. The latter are mainly species which can endure salt or need it. Sturges[218] and Heideman[218] believed that, for this work, the situation would be clearer if they grouped the organisms according to salt relations, disregarding for the time being their morphological characteristics. With this in mind, the following scheme was proposed:

HALOPHILIC ORGANISMS

Organisms which grow on media containing 12 per cent NaCl.

GROUP I. SALT OBLIGATE

Organisms requiring for growth salt in concentrations greater than one per cent.

GROUP II. SALT PREFERENTIAL

Organisms which grow more luxuriantly in media containing more than one per cent salt than on standard media and usually exhibiting extreme irregularities on the latter.

GROUP III. SALT FACULTATIVE

Organisms which grow with equal luxuriance on standard and on 12 per cent NaCl media.

GROUP IV. SALT TOLERANT

Organisms which grow on 12 per cent media (often exhibiting irregular forms) but grow more luxuriantly on standard media.

The brines or curing solutions used by Heideman usually contained about 15 per cent of salt, a few per cent of sugar and a little nitrate. Five organisms were studied. He found that sugars were necessary for the formation of "rope," as well as a proper hydrogen-ion concentration. Sturges has shown that old brine in which hams are being cured contains many bacteria of varied property and function. He isolated 100 cultures which showed very diverse characteristics.

The medium used has great influence on the results which are secured in plating curing solutions. Haines[219] secured the greatest number of colonies on salt-pork agar. He found that salt was also necessary in all diluting fluids else from 50 to 90 per cent of the flora did not develop. Twenty per cent of salt in these solutions was most suitable. Wide diversity of types was reported. Horowitz[220] also found the salt concentration in the curing solution to be important. He isolated bacteria which could reduce nitrates to nitrites but this ability became less and less as concentration of

218. Sturges. 1923. Abs. Bact. 8, 14; Heideman. Idem 8, 14.
219. Haines. 1939. .(Gt. Brit.) Food Invest. Bd., Ann. Rpt. for 1938, p. 75.
220. Horowitz. 1931. Ztschr. f. Untersuch. der Nahr. u. Genussmtl. 62, 596.

salt increased. From old curing solutions an organism was finally isolated which reduced nitrates to nitrites with formation of gas. Without presence of salt it would not develop at all. Besides this organism two other types were found. One produced acetyl-methyl-carbinol while the other was lipolytic. The former were aerobic, sporeforming bacteria of *Bacillus subtilis* type. In curing solutions acetyl-methyl-carbinol is formed from sugar in the curing solution and also from glycogen in meat muscle. The lipolytic type was a coccus named *Micrococcus lipolyticus*. This organism caused spoilage in bacon and other fat-containing meat products. Its activity was stopped by keeping the temperature below 5°C.(41°F.). Another nitrate-reducing organism, or the same one described above, was named *Bacillus halobicus* by Horovitz-Vlasova.[207] It formed gas in curing solutions and was described as an obligate halophilic organism which reduced nitrates to nitrites and nitrogen.

Brooks *et al.*,[185] on bacteriological analysis of curing solutions from tanks in which bacon was being cured, reported the "total" or direct microscope count of bacterial cells to be very high, of the order of 10^7 to 10^8 per ml. The proportion of this flora viable on laboratory media was greatly influenced by the technic adopted. When media containing salt are used, more viable bacteria are revealed. It was difficult for Brooks and his colleagues to present their results. Commercial curing solutions were said to contain a viable flora, 10 per cent of which is viable on "ordinary" media and 90 per cent is viable as special flora on "special" media.

"Ropy" Curing Solutions. This abnormality of curing solutions is caused by encapsulated bacteria which also cause "rope" in other foods. Heideman[218] isolated five organisms which produced ropiness in curing solutions. They grew best at pH 8 and very little below pH 6. Another bacterium causing this defect was named *Micrococcus lipolyticus* by Horovitz-Vlasova[207]; it resembled *Micrococcus albus* and *Micrococcus flavus-liquefaciens*.

Gas Formation in Canned Cured Meat Products. Canned cured meats, ham, spiced ham, and a few other comminuted products, are subject to deterioration accompanied by gas formation. Jensen, Wood, and Jansen[221] and Jensen and Hess[222] have traced this spoilage to members of the genus Bacillus although these organisms are considered to be nongas-formers from carbohydrates. Consequently, formation of large amounts of carbon dioxide in sugar-cured meat products at temperatures from 23.9 to 48.9°C. (75 to 120°F.) presented a problem of scientific and economic importance. Jensen and Hess prepared a special medium of finely ground spiced ham from a sound can filled into culture tubes half full. This was then wetted down with a .4-per cent solution of sodium nitrate and two per cent of cane sugar. After sterilization the medium was inoculated with Pasteur pipettes from the bottom to the surface. Gas production was indicated by numerous trapped bubbles. Sodium nitrate is essential for gas production.

221. Jensen *et al.* 1934. Ind. Eng. Chem. 26, 1118-1120.
222. Jensen and Hess. 1941. Food Research 6, 75-83; 273-326.

In no case was gas produced when nitrate was absent. It was shown that nitrates, sugars, and cured meat must be present together. When nitrate is absent, anaerobic fermentation may take place.

HAM SOURING, "BONE STINK," OR BONE TAINT

These are terms which have grown up in the industry for a type of spoilage which causes considerable loss. The term "sour" is used to indicate a condition of putrefaction and not formation of acidity, as might be expected. To detect the spoilage an instrument known as a "trier" is used. It is stuck into the ham at various places and withdrawn. If a putrid odor is noted on the trier after it has been withdrawn, the presence of an area of putrefaction within the ham is indicated. Various types of sour hams have been described by McBryde [223] and Jensen and Hess.[222] The latter prepared a comprehensive discussion of the problem in which results of their own investigations are reported. The six types which Jensen and Hess described are related mainly to the area in the ham which is affected:

(a) "Shank sour" or sour tibial marrows.

(b) "Body sour" or sour meat, not marrows. (Also called "loin sour.")

(c) "Aitchbone sour" or souring of os pubis remaining in the ham.

(d) "Stifle-joint sour" or souring of area around articulation of femur and tibia-fibula.

(e) "Body-bone sour" or sour femur marrow.

(f) "Butt sour" or sours in butt between the aitchbone and muscle.

(g) "Puffers" or a gaseous condition, no longer encountered.

Microorganisms Involved in Ham Souring. Many different species have been reported as the specific cause. Klein [224] studied so-called miscured hams. From them, he isolated an organism to which the name *Bacillus foedans* was given. His description of "miscured" hams leaves little doubt but that he had what is called today "sour" hams. The organism was anaerobic but spores were not reported. Jensen and Hess [222] equated this organism with *Bacillus putidus* of Weinberg. McBryde,[223] after a careful study of ham-souring, reported that the anaerobic, sporebearing organism *Clostridium putrefaciens* was the etiologic agent.

Inoculation experiments into soured hams reproduced "bone stink." The organism spread rapidly in hams which were artificially soured. The organism concerned was an anaerobic sporeformer and thus naturally fitted to develop in the interior of the ham. McBryde advised more thorough pumping of the ham with the pickle so that the entire interior would become saturated. The partly pumped or milk-cure hams gave most spoilage.

Clostridium putrefaciens seemed to be sufficiently different from described species to justify a new name. McBryde presented the evidence to show that it differed from Klein's *Bacillus foedans* but did not discuss its relation to *Clostridium putrificum*. A complete description of *Clostridium putrefaciens* may be found in McBryde's bulletin. A few of the salient characters of interest to food bacteriologists will be given. The opti-

223. McBryde. 1911. U. S. Dept. Agr., Bur. Anim. Indus. Bull. 132.
224. Klein. 1908. Lancet I, No. 26, 1832-1834.

mum temperature for growth was 20 to 25°C.(68 to 77°F.). No growth was secured at 37°C.(98.6°F.). At 8 to 10°C.(46.4 to 50°F.) it developed slowly. Furthermore, it was said to develop at 1 to 2°C.(33.8 to 35.6°F.), the temperatures of curing cellars. The vegetative form of the organism was killed in 10 minutes at 55°C.(131°F.). The spores survived a temperature of 80°C.(176°F.) for 20 minutes but were said to have been killed at 100°C.(212°F.) in 10 minutes. McBryde stated that three per cent of sodium chloride or three per cent of potassium nitrate in glucose pork broth inhibited the organism. It was able to live for 30 days in a solution containing 23 per cent of sodium chloride and six per cent of potassium nitrate.

McBryde believed that the organism was introduced into the ham by various instruments, such as thermometers, etc. Boyer and others, as discussed below, reported that it was disseminated throughout the carcass from the moment of slaughter. and might be present in the tissues of the living animal. Lewis and Moran [166] attributed sour hams to *Clostridium sporogenes*. They found proteolytic bacteria in fresh hams, a finding in agreement with Boyer. Moran was able to reproduce ham souring in 21 out of 25 inoculations of the specific organism into normal hams. He was able to find no evidence that would relate McBryde's *Clostridium putrefaciens* with his organism isolated from sour hams and believed to be *Clostridium sporogenes*.

It would be logical in such spoilage as sour hams to expect to find *Clostridium putrificum*, as reported by Tucker.[160] Jensen and Hess,[222] however, never encountered it as the cause of sour hams.

Boyer [225] carried out some bacteriological studies on fresh chilled hams as a starting point for a study of the spoilage of sour hams. Twenty-nine hams which had gone through the routine of inspection were examined. The collection period extended over six months. Cultures were taken with the customary precautions. Boyer found that not only the meat but the joint fluid and bone marrow of such hams were hardly ever sterile. Both aerobic and anaerobic bacteria were found. These bacteria are probably the cause of spoilage. Consequently, the development of these forms must be controlled.

Hams from dressed hog carcasses taken from the killing floor 45 minutes after slaughter were found to harbor microorganisms in the interior musculature, synovial fluid, and bone marrow. According to Boyer, the following bacteria were isolated from such hams: *Clostridium putrificum*, *Clostridium histolyticum*, *Clostridium sporogenes*, *Clostridium tertium*, and an unidentified organism resembling *Clostridium oedematiens*. Numerous other organisms also were found.

Jensen and Hess [222] believed that the various types of sours are not caused by the same organism which probably helps to explain some of the differences of opinion which obtains as to the etiologic agent. They isolated quite a variety of bacteria which varied according to the type of sour ham examined. They said:

225. Boyer. 1923. Amer. Food J. 18, 197-200; J. Agr. Res. 33 (1926), 761-768.

"The old-style, 60-day cure presented problems in ham souring which were obviated by the quick vein-pump cure of hams. The psychrophiles causing sours in quick-cured hams must grow rapidly at low temperatures.

"The bacteria which can grow at 0 to 3.3°C.(32 to 38°F.) in marrows and the bacteria which are salt tolerant can cause any kind of sour. These bacteria are *Achromobacter*, genus *Bacillus*, *Pseudomonas*, Proteus group, *Serratia*, *Clostridia*, micrococci, streptobacilli, and a miscellaneous group.

"Sours in the quick-cured hams are prevented by bleeding hogs properly, adequate refrigeration of carcasses and subsequently the ham, sawing for sealed-shank marrows, prompt handling, bacteriologically controlled pickle, and strict general sanitation in the pork block."

Origin of Ham-Souring Microorganisms. While some of the earlier investigators made general statements about this subject, we are indebted to Jensen and Hess for a critical discussion. Boyer [225] found no evidence that the organisms found gained entrance through killing floor operations. Boyer concluded that the organisms responsible for ham souring were disseminated through the carcass from the moment of slaughter and are possibly present in the blood and tissues of the living animal. Alteration in killing floor operations was not considered to be of help in preventing development of the causative organism. Prompt handling and adequate chilling were believed to be important. This was confirmed by a low incidence of spoilage where these factors were watched. Jensen and Hess' results indicated that contaminated salt might have a role in ham souring but that curing sugar was without significance. Large nonpermissible amounts of sodium nitrate (exceeding 100 pounds per 1,000 gallons of curing solution permitted by the Bureau of Animal Industry) suppressed bone-souring bacteria. They found that the skin of the neck was heavily seeded with bacteria among which were many anaerobes. These, it was shown, could get into the blood stream when the hog was stuck.

While Jensen and Hess found that normal, prime hogs might harbor bacteria in their blood, organs, and muscle, none of these were of the ham-souring type. They found the blood to be infected by the sticking knife and the sticking operation to introduce ham-souring bacteria into the circulation, bones, and tissues.

Tenderized Hams. These are really precooked hams. The cooking is accomplished by heating, during smoking, at temperatures which destroy connective tissues and make the meat more tender. These hams may also be given a mild cure which has made them popular with the public. Such hams are distinctly perishable products and must be handled as such. Failure to do this has resulted in numerous outbreaks of food poisoning. Slocum and Linden [226] mentioned occurrence of 20 such outbreaks, apparently due to staphylococci, all attributed to ingestion of "ready-to-eat" hams or tongues. They believed that relation of these meats to food poisoning was as great as that of pastry products. Quite a similar situation was reported by the New York State Department of Health [227] where epidemological evidence again pointed to tenderized hams. One outbreak consisted of five cases in two households. The ham which caused them was steamed

226. Slocum and Linden. 1939. Amer. J. Pub. Health 29, 1326-1330.
227. Health News, N. Y. State Dept. Health 8, (1941), 10-11.

for three hours shortly after purchase and baked for one hour the following day. It was then stored without refrigeration and thus obviously mishandled. The weather at the time was unreasonably warm. Laboratory examination revealed the presence of many *Staphylococcus aureus* and another organism quite like *Escherichia coli*. Moulton [228] classed these hams with custard-filled pastry products. Tendered hams are apparently a good medium for staphylococci.

One outbreak of food poisoning presumably caused by tenderized ham, reported by Bole,[229] may have been due to a member of the genus Proteus. Enterotoxin-producing organisms of the genera Staphylococci or Salmonella were not isolated. Bole suggested that the enterotoxin-producing abilities of Proteus species be investigated.

Just where the trouble lies remains to be seen. A good part of it is probably faulty handling after the hams have left the packer. These "ready-to-eat" hams are in quite a different category than the old-type hams which are given a heavier cure and are not precooked. The homemaker may consider tenderized hams to be like the old hams and fail to consider them as perishable products. Tenderized hams must be handled under conditions which will preclude contamination by objectionable microorganisms. The Bureau of Animal Industry in a letter to the New York State Department of Public Health discussed these hams as follows:

"During the last six or eight years there have been three changes taking place in the meat trade: first, a gradual reduction in the salt ingredient in some curing procedures; second, the injection of curing solutions throughout the ham or shoulder either through the circulatory system or by many punctures with hollow needles; and third, the long heating of the cured meat at the time of smoking at relatively low cooking temperatures and for a period of time sufficient to reduce the tenacity of the connective tissues of the meat to render it more tender than meat not so treated would be. In the main, the change in flavor and texture of the meat brought about by the mild cures and "tendering" treatment has gained acceptance in the trade. A good many meat packers are distributing smoked hams that have been in cure a matter of days instead of weeks, as formerly. These new-process hams resemble in outward appearance the old-style hams, but they may be labeled to show that they are ready to eat, as they are, in fact, cooked hams, having been cooked at low temperature, but for many hours so that the heat has reached the inner portions and rendered all portions of the ham acceptable for eating without further cooking, if desired.

"These developments or changes in the meat-curing business, in some cases at least, bring the cured meat into a condition that makes it a favorable medium for the development of organisms if proper care is not taken all along the line from the establishment to the consumer's table.

"In the federally inspected establishments we are taking pains to see that clean practices are followed to avoid in every practicable way the possible contamination of the meat. In most cases of food poisoning which we have looked into, we have found that the trouble comes to the partakers after the meat has been in the keeping of the retailer or the consumer a few days."

BACON

Bacon is a meat specialty prepared by curing, drying, and smoking sides and backs of hogs. Its manufacture is a large industry in America and Canada from which countries large amounts are exported. Methods

228. Moulton. 1940. Natl. Provisioner 103, 13 and 34.
229. Bole. 1940. J. Bact. 39, 343.

for curing bacon are not essentially different from those used in curing of ham. Quality of bacon depends on many factors involving both chemical and bacteriological changes.

Microbiology of Bacon Curing. Microorganisms reduce nitrates in the curing solution to nitrites which in turn impart a red color to the product and probably contribute to the flavor. While these facts are known, not much is known about the species which are involved and the factors which influence their activities. Lochhead [230] tried to count the number of bacteria in a curing solution used in preparation of Wiltshire bacon; he found that usual media and technic were inadequate. A suitable incubation temperature was important as was presence of salt in culture media. The standard procedures with incubation temperature of 37°C.(98.6°F.) showed little more than one per cent of the bacteria revealed when a 10-per cent salt-agar medium was used. Lochhead also found that exposure to tap water for even 45 seconds may kill or inhibit as many as 90 per cent of the countable microorganisms. Contamination of meat to be made into bacon places a larger load on the curing process; furthermore, definitely objectionable species might be introduced which would interfere with the proper changes. Garrard and Lochhead [231] isolated 40 microbial types in which Micrococci predominated, which are representative of precuring contamination. Organisms were also found which resembled those in bacon slime. Varying degrees of salt tolerance were noted, micrococci showing the greatest ability to grow at higher concentrations. With 25 per cent of sodium chloride only two species grew. Increasing salt concentrations interfered with nitrate reduction by the bacteria which were able to grow. This suggested that nitrate reduction in curing solutions is a function of the halophilic bacteria rather than of the precuring contaminants. Five groups of microorganisms were made according to their salt resistance or ability to survive. Much greater resistance to salt was shown in curing solutions than in salt broths of similar salt content. Some of the precuring contaminants were able to survive the curing solutions and were suggested as the cause of storage defects. Importance of proper culture media was also shown by results of experiments by Gibbons [232] with representative curing solutions. Highest numbers of bacteria were secured in 10 per cent salt-agar medium incubated at 20°C.(68°F.). The lowest number was secured on nutrient agar incubated at 37°C.(98.6°F.). Counts on media with no salt, four per cent, and 10 per cent of salt incubated at 20°C. gave intermediate values. The number of bacteria in spent curing solutions was higher than in cover solutions. Pumping solutions showed a surprisingly large number of bacteria. Analytical errors owing to sampling, diluting, and counting were relatively small when compared with the other sources of variance. Some of the variations in counts were suggested to be due to presence of different types and species. Gibbons finally concluded that 10 per cent salt agar incubated at 20°C. gave most consistent results.

230. Lochhead. 1938. Prog. Rpts. to Dominion Agr. Bacteriologist for 1934. 1935, 1936. Ottawa, 1938, p. 31.
231.Garrard and Lochhead. 1938. Canad. J. Res. 17, D, 45-58.
232. Gibbons. 1940. Idem 18, 191-201; 202-210; 19 (1941), 61-74.

Results of later investigations by Gibbons and White [233] indicated little change owing to time or depth in the bacterial content of Wiltshire tank pickle during cure. A decided decrease occurred in the number of bacteria on the surface of the sides. Settling of bacteria from the pickle was not responsible for this increase. Of the normal commercial practices of salting the sides prior to cure and washing and wiping after cure, wiping was the most important in reducing the bacterial population on the surface of the meat. Wiltshire sides, according to Gibbons,[232] are matured for a week or 10 days after removal from the curing tank. During this time microorganisms may develop on them. Whether they are involved in flavor production is not known; however, Gibbons said development may lead to "slime formation" or taint. Visible growth or slime formation became evident when the logarithm of the number of organisms per square centimeter exceeded 7.2. This was not always the case, for some sides did not become slimy at much lower counts while some required many more. This seemed to be related to the species of microorganisms present. The number of bacteria on the sides was found to be correlated with the age of the sides from cure or from packing. The growth rate is slow during the first eight to 10 days from packing, after which it decreases. Sides having an initial load of 100,000 organisms per square centimeter at packing may be expected, according to Gibbons, to remain free from slime for 20 to 25 days if stored at $1.1°C.(34°F.)$. Gibbons did not observe any correlation between the number of bacteria in the product and the number in the curing solution.

Bone Taint in Bacon. This is a deterioration around the rib bones observed in certain Australian bacon by Smith.[234] The causal agent was found to be an obligate, halophilic bacterium to which the name *Vibrio costicolus* was given. Smith was able to reproduce the defect by inoculation and under controlled conditions of cure. Another halophilic organism, *Vibrio halonitrificans*, was very active in forming nitrite from nitrate. This organism was a strict aerobe and was not believed to possess importance in the regular cure given Australian bacon. Proper conditions for appearance of this bone taint of bacon are favorable temperature and concentration of salt. To prevent development of *Vibrio costicolus* a higher saline level in the curing process at or above the saline death point for the species must be maintained. The organism, it was suggested, might also be controlled by using a dry temperature for the flitch of bacon at or near the death temperature of the organism.

Molds are troublesome microorganisms on smoked meats. Various methods have been proposed for preventing their growth. Many of the procedures have inhibited them but have not entirely prevented development. Francioni [235] found this to be the case with 55 per cent alcohol and dipping in hot water. Rubbing with borax-pepper-molasses mixture also aided in controlling molds. Mold growth was effectively prevented by storing the meat in cottonseed oil. Storing in an atmosphere of carbon

233. Gibbons and White. 1941. Idem 19, 61-74.
234. Smith. 1938. Roy. Soc. Queensland, Proc. 49, 50-51.
235. Francioni. 1933. Rev. in Chem. Abs. 30 (1936), 2653.

dioxide also restricted mold growth. The value of some of these procedures probably rests on the fact that air supply is cut off. Molds are apparently inhibited by strong currents of air. A forced air stream of five to 12 centimeters per second at temperatures of 3°C.(37.4°F.) to 6°C.(42.8°F.) and with a relative humidity of 90 per cent, according to Kaess,[236] retarded surface growth of *Penicillium flavoglaucum* and *Mucor racemosus*. Retardation was proportional to the velocity of the air current. Carbon dioxide has been found to retard mold development by Moran, Smith, and Tomkins [237]; 10 per cent of this gas in air reduced mold growth by one-half. Twenty per cent almost completely inhibited mold development. Similar amounts of nitrogen had no effect.

MEAT PASTES

These products made from various kinds of meat and fish are more popular in England than in America. Their microbiology has been discussed by Crossley.[238] They may be made from any kind of meat or fish which is cooked and then mixed by machinery. Crossley stated that such pastes are then placed in glass jars and sealed with a cover and rubber gasket. These jars are then given a pressure cook for sterilization. Spoilage may be caused by either faulty closure or underprocessing. Bacterial spoilage has been found to be due to *Clostridium sporogenes* and *Clostridium putrificum*. Ten minutes' heating at 115.6°C.(240°F.) was said to be sufficient for destruction of the spores of these organisms as well as the spores of *Clostridium botulinum*. American strains of the latter microorganism are much more resistant. Crossley believed that the final product should be proven by bacteriological methods to be satisfactory before it is shipped. Faulty sterilization was reported by Clarenburg [239] as the cause of spoilage of liver paste.

BACTERIOLOGICAL EXAMINATION OF MEAT

Bacteriological examination is one of several methods used for judging quality of meat. The value of results secured in this manner is still doubtful. Bacteriological methods are valuable, of course, for demonstration of presence of pathogenic bacteria. Whether bacterial standards, such as are used with other foods, can be applied to fresh meat products is still undetermined.

Bickert's [240] Method for Bacteriological Examination of Meat and Sausage Products. Appreciating that the usual methods used for bacteriological examination of meat are quite tedious, Bickert undertook investigations to determine their accuracy as well as to search for better methods. He believed that biochemical methods should be used where possible for judging the quality of meat and that bacteriological examination of meat and meat products was feasible only under special circumstances such as research. Routine bacteriological examination of meat is too tedious and there would be considerable uncertainty in interpreting the results.

When bacteriological examinations of meat are to be made, it is essential that the sample be adequate and that it be sufficiently disintegrated. Bickert excluded such

236. Kaess. 1934. Ztschr. f. Gestütk. Kälteindus. Beih. 31. 153-156; 96-102.
237. Moran, Smith, and Tomkins. 1932. Soc. Chem. Indus. J. 51, 114-116T.
238. Crossley. 1938. J. Hyg. 38, 205-216.
239. Clarenburg. 1931. Tijdschr. u. Diergencesk. 58, 1331-1333.
240. Bickert. 1930. Ztschr. f. Untersuch. der Lebensmtl. 59, 345-364.

implements as mortars for disintegrating the meat on account of the possibility of contamination. He suggested the use of a ball mill with quartz sand and a little physiological sodium chloride solution to give fluidity. Twenty grams of meat were ground with 20 grams of sterile quartz sand and 80 ml. of sterile physiological salt solution for one hour at 120 rotations per minute. This is then brought to 200 ml. with sterile salt solution and carefully mixed for 15 minutes. This material is then sampled for enumeration of microorganisms. Gelatin and agar were used as the plating medium. Bickert rightly placed very little confidence in results secured by plating. He compared a number of available methods for enumerating bacteria and reached the conclusion that a new one was needed. The method which was finally developed seems to be a modification of that proposed by Fries.[241] Bickert, however, substituted for the yeast cells, spores of saprophytic bacteria or Staphylococci since there was then less difference in size. The spores were treated with cold silver-nitrate solution and a reducing agent in order to make them more suitable for the method. A cold saturated solution of silver nitrate was carefully flowed onto an agar slant culture of the spore forms to be used. After three to five minutes it was removed and the slant washed several times with distilled water in order to remove all of the silver nitrate. This was followed by a reducing agent (two to four grams of pyrogallic acid and five ml. of formalin in 100 ml. of water). The reducing agent causes the silver nitrate treated spores to assume a black color. Excess of reducing fluid should be removed by repeated washing.

The bacterial content of the material to be tested is determined by mixing it (nine parts) with the standard fluid (one part). A drop of carbol fuchsin is then added. The spores remain black while the bacteria are stained red. A drop of this well-mixed fluid is transferred to a slide by means of a pipette and a cover glass dropped over it. This is carefully pressed down and sealed with vaseline or wax. The slide is counted, the calculation being made as follows:

$$X = \frac{\text{Vol. of Test Fluid}}{\text{Vol. of Bacterial Fluid}} \times \frac{\text{Sum of Counted Bacteria}}{\text{Sum of Counted Test Bacteria}} \times K$$

X = Count of unknown.

K = Count of the test fluid or suspension.

The standard suspension should be diluted if necessary. The mixture should be such that there are from five to eight bacteria in each field.

The standard suspension should be counted by a hemacytometer counting chamber.

Hoagland, McBryde, and Powick's [242] Method of Meat Examination. The following technic was used by these investigators in a study of the changes in fresh beef during storage. The method will be given as the authors reported it.

In examining the quarters bacteriologically the following procedure was adopted: A slice or section from three to four inches thick was cut from the upper portion of the round. From this slice a rectangular block extending from the outer surface to the bone was cut. (An illustration is given in the original paper.) This block, which measured about four and one-half to eight inches and weighed from six to eight pounds, was first immersed in actively boiling water for three minutes, next in bichloride solution (.5 per cent) for five minutes, and was then wrapped in sterile gauze which had been wrung out in the bichloride solution. This was done in order to sterilize the surface of the meat and to prevent the growth and possible penetration of bacteria from the outside, pending the taking of cultures. It was not always possible to make cultures immediately, but they were always made within two hours; and during this time the block of meat was kept wrapped in the bichloride gauze and at cold-storage temperature 1.1 to 2.2°C. (34 to 36°F.).

The short immersion in the boiling water served to coagulate the muscle protein to the depth of three to five mm., but did not cause sufficient elevation of the inside temperature to have any injurious effect on the bacteria present. A test was made by

241. Fries. 1921. Centbl. f. Bakt. 86, 90-96.
242. Hoagland, McBryde, and Powick. 1917. U. S. Dept. Agr., Bur. Anim. Indus. Bull. 433, Feb. 15, 1917.

introducing a thermometer into a block of meat of the size described above so that the bulb rested at the center of the great mass, and there was no appreciable rise in temperature during the three-minute interval in the hot water. The outer zone of coagulated protein served to prevent the penetration of the bichloride solution into the meat.

Beginning about one inch from the outer surface a series of cultures were taken at intervals of an inch, proceeding from the outside toward the bone, and these cultures were numbered as indicated in a diagram. In taking the cultures a series of sterile scalpels were used, one being used to cut through the outer or surface portion, and others to make deeper cuts in order not to carry in any of the bichloride solution adhering to the surface of the meat. Plugs of meat about a centimeter square were used in making the cultures. Cultures were made in neutral beef broth and in glucose agar from which the air had been expelled by boiling. When clouding occurred in the bouillon cultures, agar plates were poured and the organisms present were plated out.

Garrard and Lochhead's [231] **Method for Determining Bacteria on Surface of Meat.** These authors used what they termed a filter paper impression method using Whatman No. 3 filter paper cut into squares of four sq. cm. and sterilized in Petri dishes in hot air at 120°C.(248°F.). Samples were taken by pressing a square of filter paper firmly against the meat tissue for 20 seconds with sterile forceps; the square was then dropped into a 750-ml. Erlenmeyer flask containing 500 ml. of physiological salt solution and 75 grams of broken glass. The flasks were shaken until the filter paper was disintegrated. The contents of the flask were then plated with nutrient agar in the usual manner. Garrard and Lochhead combined the contents of flasks in order to pool the samples when they desired to do so. The observations of Wilson [243] are pertinent.

Bacteriological examination of cured meats and curing solutions require special media, as shown by Garrard and Lochhead,[231] Landerkin,[244] and Cook, Gibbons, Wingler, and White.[245] In general these investigators reported that the rate of colony development and the total number of colonies varied with the salt concentration of the medium. Landerkin also found that incubation of plates at 20°C.(68°F.) resulted in higher counts than at 37°C.(98.6°F.). Bacterial counts on 5-, 10-, and 15-per cent salt agars showed a definite relation to each other on over 200 samples taken over five years. Such results indicate the importance of using the right media.

Crossley's [228] **Method for Examination of Meat and Meat Products.** Crossley proposed a new method for examination of meat and meat products using milk as a basic medium in place of meat and egg preparations. He summarized the method as follows:

Medium: Skimmed milk containing one per cent of peptone and .01 per cent of brom-cresol-purple is tubed in 10-ml. quantities and heated in the Arnold steam sterilizer for 20 minutes on four successive days. Control tubes should be incubated. The peptone is not essential but shortens the reaction time.

Inoculation: One and one-half to two grams of paste taken from the center of a jar with a sterile instrument (spatula or section lifter) are inoculated into a tube of medium. This heavy inoculation of paste is an essential part of the procedure.

Incubation: The tubes are incubated from three to four days at 37°C.(98.6°F.). The tubes do not need to be made anaerobic either with paraffin or reduced iron.

Types of Reaction: These are essentially those secured with the Ayer's milk tube described in the chapter on milk.

CANNED MEATS AND MEAT PRODUCTS

Canned meats and meat products are now a regular part of the diet of man. While considered in former times to be the cause of much illness,

243. Wilson. 1922. J. Bact. 7, 405-446.
244. Landerkin. 1940. Food Research 5, 205-222.
245. Cook *et al.* 1940. Canad. J. Res., Sect. D, 18, 123-134.

public confidence has been regained. Many of the early statements about the danger of canned meats were based on assumptions with little or no satisfactory evidence to support them. Canned meats are satisfactory products today, and add variety to the diet. In early times, sailors and others who were away from supplies of fresh meat had to use salt meat entirely. Appert's [246] statement regarding the benefits of his method of preservation were certainly not overstressed. Emergency food rations made up largely of meat and meat products are of great importance in wars and explorations.

Procedures Used in Canning Meats. The general procedures of canning meats are not unlike those discussed in Chapter 23 for vegetables.

Containers. These may be either of glass or tin. The tin containers are probably most commonly used on account of the ease with which they can be handled. They may be processed with greater ease, also. The tin can has been discussed fully in Chapter 23.

With some meat products zinc compounds, such as zinc oxide, may be incorporated in the enamel to prevent sulfide discoloration. Enamel containing the zinc ion, according to Hallman,[247] is known as ''C'' enamel.

Precooking. Practically all meat is cooked to a greater or lesser extent before being placed in the can. This treatment tends to reduce the bulk.

Canning. This is done either by hand or machinery. Meats packed in glass containers are usually packed by hand. Such meat products as potted meat, hash, etc., may be placed in the cans by an automatic filling machine. After the cans are filled, they are sealed on the closing machine.

Exhausting. Vacuum is just as desirable in canned meats as in vegetables. It has been discussed in Chapter 23. It has the same function in canned meats that it has in canned vegetables, i.e., to relieve the stress on the closed container during processing, to prevent discoloration of the product, provide concave ends by which the consumer may determine that the product has not spoiled, to prevent ''flippers'' at high altitudes, etc. Vacuum-packed foods are known to be superior to those which are not.

Weiner [248] reviewed the various methods for securing vacuum in meat cans. While the vacuum-closing machine may be the best way of securing vacuum in some products, it is not so satisfactory for others.

Processing. As soon after filling as possible, the cans should be processed. A long delay between filling and processing allows development of bacteria which in turn places a heavier load on the process. A discussion of processing as applied to various foods, has been given in Chapter 23. Many of the principles discussed there are applicable to meats. However, it is probably true that much less is known about the facts involved in processing meats than is known with respect to many other foods. The time and temperature of the process is determined by factors, such as the size of the can, the character of the product—whether it is solidly packed with no free liquor or whether there is free liquor to aid in carrying the heat into the can—and a number of other factors. Kossowicz [249] recommended that meat packed in 250-ml. tins should receive a cook of at least 120 to 125°C.(248 to 257°F.) for 45 minutes. With this process, he secured very little spoilage. Muntsch [250] believed that in processing canned meats the center of the can must reach 120°C.

Sterilization of canned meat products is a more difficult problem than sterilization of certain canned vegetables and fruits. Canned meat products are more compact and have much less water. The center of the can must reach retort temperature in order to secure a product which will keep. Clarenburg and Zwart [251] claimed that the bacterial

246. Appert, N. See Chapter 23 for reference.
247. Hallman. 1936. Canning Age 17, 196-199.
248. Weiner. 1936.
249. Kossowicz. 1917. Chem. Ztg. 41, 673-674.
250. Muntsch. 1931. Ztschr. f. Hyg. u. Infektionskrank. 112, 395-412.
251. Clarenberg and Zwart. 1937. Tijdschr. u. Diergeneesk. 64, 383-397

load in the meat product was the factor which really determined the process which had to be used. A culture of *Clostridium botulinum* containing 35,000 spores required 50 minutes' heating at 115°C.(239°F.) to destroy it, while only 10 minutes were required when 13 spores were present. Data on the time factor indicated that the strain used by Clarenburg and Zwart was less resistant than most American strains. Attempts to learn more about heat resistance of bacterial spores in canned meats led Gutschmidt [252] to heat spores treated in different ways. He found that spores coated with a layer of coagulated serum or fat were much more resistant to heat than untreated spores. The former required 20 minutes at 120°C.(248°F.) for destruction, while the latter required only six minutes. Five minutes at 134°C.(273.2°F.) was the optimum time required to kill unprotected spores. With the cans which Gutschmidt used 60 minutes were required for the center of the can to reach this temperature. This higher temperature of sterilization resulted in a better product than a lower temperature.

A distinction is made between "absolute" and "commercial" sterility of canned meats as is done with other canned foods. Commercial sterility is that condition in which viable bacteria are present but they do not develop to cause spoilage.

Heat Penetration Into Canned Meats. In general canned meats permit somewhat slower penetration of heat than many other foods. They are solidly packed and heat must enter by conduction and not by convection.

Cooling of Canned Meats. This process is just as necessary with canned meats as it is with other foods. The quality of the product may be harmed if cooling is not promptly and adequately done. Hallman [253] said that the temperature of the can after cooling should not exceed 40.6°C.(105°F.). This is in order to prevent spoilage by thermophilic bacteria which grow in a temperature range of 43.3 and 71.1°C.(110 and 160°F.). Cooling may be accomplished in different ways. The cans may be cooled in the retort with cold water or placed in it after removal from the retort. They may also be cooled in the retort under pressure. Hallman stated that spray cooling was becoming quite popular among meat canners.

BACTERIA IN CANNED MEATS

Viable bacteria were once believed to be present in most cans of meat or meat products. While this may have been the case in the early days of the canning industry, it is probably no longer true. The advances in plant sanitation and processing have yielded a product which is quite free from viable bacteria. Results reported in the earlier literature probably no longer hold for the modern product. In some cases these results were based on contaminated plates, for it is not easy to open cans without introducing foreign bacteria.

Those bacteria which have been reported, in general, have been anaerobic sporeformers. *Clostridium welchii* was observed to be the cause of swells in canned beef by McClung and Wheaton.[254] It was present in the raw beef and was not destroyed during parboiling at a temperature of approximately 100 to 110°C.(212 to 230°F.). Delays in the canning procedure allowed gas to be formed; this caused swelling of the cans. The organism was killed during processing so no health hazard was involved.

Thermophilic Bacteria in Canned Meats. These bacteria which have been so important in canned vegetables have not been important in canned

252. Gutschmidt. 1934. Veröffentl. aus dem Gebiete des Heeres Sanitatswesen. 90, 61-80.
253. Hallman. 1938. The Canner, Conv. Number.
254. McClung and Wheaton. 1936. Food Research 1, 307-318.

meats, at least those to which no cereals are added. Recently, Jensen and Hess [255] pointed out that thermophilic sporeforming bacteria have become significant in meat products to which soya flour, grits, or meal have been added. However, if specific conditions of treatment are observed, these bacteria are restrained in their action as long as 50 days, according to results of one experiment. Thermophilic spoilage was said to be inhibited by curing with three and one-half pounds of sodium chloride, two and one-third ounces of sodium nitrate, and one-eighth ounce of sodium nitrite per 100 pounds of meat if the six-pound can and contents are retorted at 112.7°C.(235°F.) for three hours, 20 minutes after evacuating and sealing.

BACTERIAL EXAMINATION OF CANNED MEATS

The gross technic does not differ much from that used with other canned foods. Special attention is usually given to the media used. Canned meats are submitted to the laboratory for one of the following reasons (Cameron [256]):

1. Unspoiled samples—for examination for sterility.
2. Unspoiled samples—for examination for keeping quality.
3. Spoiled samples—for examination for causes of spoilage.

Frei and Krupski,[257] who discussed this subject, stated that leaking cans will usually show a flora made up of bacteria, yeasts, and molds. He observed that cans with flat or concave ends might contain viable bacteria. Seeberger [258] relied much on the sound of cans when shaken. This, at best, would be a questionable method for cans which were just beginning to spoil. Where the contents had undergone marked spoilage, this test might be of some value.

Considerable study was given this subject by Savage,[259] in England. Observations were first made on canned foods at five ports of entry. Savage stated that considerable trouble was experienced with leaking cans.

Savage [260] studied the methods for the examination of canned meats at various places in England and outlined the following procedure for the ports of entry in England:

A. *Extent to which the tins are examined.* The actual number of tins in any one consignment is usually so large, often running into tens of thousands, that it is impracticable, and experience shows it to be unnecessary, to examine each tin separately and a working compromise is adopted which varies slightly in the different ports studied.

In all the ports there is an examination by the trade for their own purposes which primarily has nothing to do with the question of suitability or unsuitability for food. It is obviously of importance for commercial purposes for the trade to know the proportion of rejects. The plan generally adopted is for the canned meat to be examined at the wharf by the wharfingers, and usually 10 per cent of these cans are examined. The allowance for rejects is based upon this 10-per cent examination.

This trade examination is utilized by the Food Inspectors who are always about these wharfs. If only a small portion of this 10 per cent is rejected by the trade then

255. Jensen and Hess. 1943. Food Indus. 15, 66-67.
256. Cameron. 1937. Assoc. Off. Agr. Chem. J., Aug. 1937, 429-432; also Aug. 1936, 433-438.
257. Frei and Krupski. 1919. Schweiz. Arch. f. Tierheilk 60, 445-470.
258. Seeberger. 1919. Schweiz. Arch. f. Tierheilk 61, 367-377.
259. Savage. 1920. (Gt. Brit.) Food Invest. Bd., Spec. Rpt. No. 3.
260. Savage. 1922. (Gt. Brit.) Food Invest. Bd., Spec. Rpt. No. 10.

this is generally accepted and the whole consignment is passed If the percentage rejected is considerable, the consignment is stopped pending an examination of the whole parcel. This again is usually done by the wharfinger's men, constantly controlled by the Food Inspector.

The same percentage is not adopted throughout, nor it is clear that any very hard and fast figure is used. At Bermondsey (London) the Port Authority's inspectors go through the whole consignment if more than two and one-half per cent of the 10 per cent examined is rejected. In Stepney (London), Bristol, and Manchester no definite figure is adopted, but in practice it is about this amount. At Liverpool, if less than two per cent is rejected, the consignment is passed.

Some such procedure is the only one practicable under the circumstances and seems to work well in practice. The wharfinger men are impartial, and there is no inducement for them to be otherwise. From the trade point of view it is important not to pass any consignment with a high proportion of rejects, since the larger retailers to whom the cases are sent are well acquainted with the signs of defective tins and will certainly throw them out, erring, if anything, on the side of an undue stringency, since the local retailer will not accept any tin with the slightest sign of defect.

Indeed, while on the one hand there is but little likelihood of the trade examiners passing unsound tins, there is a decided tendency for them to reject tins which may be perfectly good, but which, not coming up to the standard of the ultimate retailer, would be rejected by him and charged back upon the wholesale importer. This point is of great importance to the importer and large retailer and will be referred to again below.

It is evident that the value of the procedure set out above must turn essentially upon the capability of the warfinger examiners, but this point is more conveniently discussed after the actual methods employed have been considered.

B. *The criteria relied upon to detect unfit cans.* With some modifications as to interpretation, the methods employed in the different ports are throughout the same. A full examination of the unopened tin comprises inspection, palpation, percussion, and sometimes shaking, a form of auscultation. To a doctor, therefore, the methods employed strikingly resemble those employed by him for the physical examination of the human chest.

Inspection. Well-defined holes, marked indentations, and other signs of gross ill-usage are at once detected by inspection.

Signs of extensive rust may not indicate anything against the contents, but they lessen the commercial value of the parcel and, when extensive, have on this ground to be dealt with by the trade. Also, if there is much rust, it is extremely likely that a proportion of the tins will have rusted through in places and so give rise to a high proportion of leaky tins, which will have increased by the time the tins reach the consumer.

Consignments with many rusty tins are therefore subjected to special scrutiny and are frequently all looked over and treated by repainting. A parcel treated at Liverpool warehouse may be given as an illustration. In this case the cause of the rust was the common one of the labels being put on and pasted all over the tin with paste too wet. The excess water caused rusting, indicated by the labels being marked extensively with a number of brown stains. With many of the tins, the process had gone so far as to cause definite perforations. The whole consignment was treated by having the labels scraped off and the rust marks examined. If the tins were sound they were repainted and relabelled, the fresh labels being wrapped round and pasted only along a narrow strip instead of all over.

The most important defect detected by inspection is the presence of any swelling or ''blowing.'' In general, this is accepted as a sign of gaseous decomposition of the meat, and is shown by the ordinary flat or slightly concave surface being bulged, owing to the presence of the gases of decomposition within. Although easy of detection and deduction, common sense has to be employed if mistakes are to be avoided.

As explained above, the presence of a vacuum insures the meat being in contact with the tin all over. If, therefore, the tin is subjected to ill-usage and dents are caused, it is obvious that this will cause the tin to bulge slightly elsewhere to find room for the meat. The presence of a bulge in such specimens should not give rise to difficulty as the cause is so manifest.

Theoretically, some light bulge might be due to overfilling with meat, but this does not often occur with tins as imported, as overfilled cans are detected at the cannery and returned to be better filled.

Definite bulging of the tin, if meat is the food packed, is, in general, reliable evidence of the presence of gas within the tin, and such gases with this kind of food are invariably due to bacteria, and therefore justify rejection.

Inspection will also show the number of vent holes, but this is not of much practical assistance. It is sometimes assumed that the presence of a second vent hole indicates that the tins have been vented to let out gases caused by bacterial decomposition, and then resealed. In reality, such procedure would be of no practical use in the case of meat products. Meat infected with bacteria sufficient to produce gases in amount to cause definite blowing would almost certainly be of bad odor. Apart from any question of commercial honesty, it would not pay commercially to try to sell such meat, as the loss of reputation would be too serious. It is not merely a question of venting and resealing; the meat in the tin would have to be heated to a high temperature both to kill contained bacteria and to ensure a vacuum when it cooled. On the other hand, during the canning of meat several contingencies may occur which makes it a perfectly legitimate procedure to make a second solder hole, and this without casting the slightest aspersion upon the character of the meat.

In one factory in Chicago, tinned mutton was being put up in cans, the central hole of the tops being closed when cold, i.e., without any vacuum. The cans were then heated in the kettles and vented when taken out by the central hole being touched with a hot iron to melt the solder. They were resealed immediately after the escape of the air and steam. In this way a good vacuum was obtained. The venting might equally well have been done through a fresh hole, and then there would have been two vent holes without any reflection upon the quality of the meat.

No adverse significance can be attached to the presence of more than one solder hole in otherwise sound tins of meat.

Palpation. The Inspector picks up the can to examine it, and so in this way at once notices any change from the normal feel. When the vacuum is lost the tin ceases to be closely adherent to the meat, in one or more places or even extensively, and there is a springy feel which is quite distinctive. This loss of vacuum can only be due to access of air or production of gas, and is therefore always associated with a definite note when percussed.

Percussion. In practice apart from obviously blown or otherwise obtrusively unsound tins, reliance is placed mainly upon percussion, i.e., the character of the sound yielded by tapping the surface of the tin. This is usually done by a piece of wood, but some inspectors prefer their fingers.

As already explained, the cans are so sealed as to ensure that there is considerable vacuum inside when they cool. The pressure of the outside atmosphere insures that the meat is in contact with the tin all over. In consequence, when such a sound tin is struck anywhere (except often immediately under the cap) it emits a dull note. If not in contact there is air or other form of gas and the note is tympanitic.

In practice, it is commonest to find the note defective in parts only and not all over, but in bad cases it may be defective over every part of the tin.

The procedure generally followed is to reject tins which fail to give the normal dull note everywhere, but some differences in practice were met.

In certain of the areas investigated all such tins were thrown out, but in other districts rather more latitude was allowed. Thus, in both Liverpool and Manchester it was recognized that a defective note at either end only might be due to insufficient filling, and the tins would be passed. At Manchester, they employ the common sense practice of opening one or two such tins of any consignment actually to see their condition, and then if these are found good the whole consignment is passed.

Shaking. Only if the meat is in an advanced stage of decomposition and partially liquid are any results of value likely to be obtained. The ordinary canned meat tin is solid throughout and yields no sound on shaking.

When fresh meat, i.e., not salted or corned, is canned, a little water is usually added to prevent the final product being too dry, and it is possible through careless manipulation for this to be excessive. Such tins, when shaken, shake loose with a characteristic sound, and although they may be perfectly good are liable to be rejected by the retail trade.

The following is an example of such a consignment. A parcel of several thousand one-pound tins of a well-known brand came to the port of Bristol and were passed as sound by the Food Inspector at Avonmouth. They then came into Bristol by road, and the purchasers had the usual 10-per cent examination made. A considerable proportion of the tins were found to be what the trade call ''sloppy,'' i.e., the contents shook about and evidently liquid was present. The purchasers in consequence refused to accept the consignment unless the Health Department would certify the tins as good, although they had already been passed. The percentage of blown tins was small and not above the average. Six of the ''sloppy'' tins were examined in the laboratory and all were found sterile and the meat in good condition, apart from a little excess of liquid of no importance from the standpoint of health.

A very large number of tins have to be examined, and while the above methods are all employed if necessary, in practice the examination is very rapid. The Inspector has each case emptied out on a table. He then picks up each tin in turn. A very superficial scrutiny is sufficient while almost subconsciously the feel of it in his fingers will detect any springy areas. He then taps each tin in a number of places. If satisfied as to the sound note and the impression conveyed through his fingers the Inspector passes the tin, while those not satisfactory in any particular are subjected to a more careful examination along the same lines.

In this way, many hundreds of tins can be easily examined within an hour without much risk of anything abnormal being overlooked.

In order to prove the merit of the above procedure Savage visited the wharves and received the tins for laboratory studies after they had been passed by the inspectors. He found that many satisfactory tins of meat were being rejected with an unnecessary consequent economic loss. This made it apparent that some improvements should be made in several directions.

1. Utilization of the above tests but with different standards on the part of inspectors.

2. Preparation of additional physical tests.

3. Opening the cans for examination.

National Canners Association [246] **Suggested Procedures for Examination of Canned Meat Products.** The Technical Meat Committee of this association has found the following procedures to be satisfactory. In these procedures more attention is given to the media to be used to favor development of spoilage bacteria.

(a) Before being cultured, unspoiled samples submitted for examination as to keeping quality should be incubated at $37.5°C.$ for a period of one month. This time of incubation, necessarily an arbitrary matter, is considered the longest period that is practicable in the usual case. Anaerobes, which at times may remain dormant for many months, may escape detection, but usually the likelihood of spoilage in the product under ordinary commercial conditions of handling is indicated in this time. It is regarded as unnecessary to incubate at thermophilic temperature, i.e., $55°C.$, because such spoilage in meat products is extremely rare.

(b) Samples submitted for examination for cause of spoilage should be given direct microscopical examination in order to obtain general information regarding the bacterial flora. Ordinary laboratory stains, such as carbol fuchsin or gentian violet, are suitable in preparing mounts. The gram stain is not recommended. A gram-negative result would be of little significance because of lack of knowledge regarding the age of the bacteria in the spoiled material.

The various steps in culturing technic are described in order as follows:

A. *Physical examination and preparation of the can:*

1. Note and record all marks of identification, either embossed on the can or appearing on the label.

2. Remove labels. Record any physical defects, such as rustiness, pinholing, dents, improper closure, or defective side seams. Plainly mark for inspection questionable points if the can is to be pumped or given any other physical examination after it is opened.

3. Clean the container with soap and water; if it is greasy, it may be found helpful, especially at the site of opening, to apply a suitable solvent, such as petroleum ether, alcohol, or naphtha.

4. For sterilization at the site of opening, preferably grasp the container in the hand and hold the previously cleaned top in the flame of a Bunsen burner, distributing the heat with a circular motion. Do not play the burner down upon the top of the can because this will result in a concentration of heat at the top, causing scorching of the material, and it might lead to spurting of the contents when the opening is made. Such sterilization also causes a release of vacuum in the can, which will prevent any contamination that might result from an inrush of air when the opening is made. When containers are badly swollen, it may be unwise to flame in the manner described. In such instances apply the treatment described by Fellers,[261] who suggests sterilization with bichloride of mercury (1 + 1000). As an alternative it is suggested that the cans be thoroughly cleaned with 60 per cent alcohol. Whichever later treatment is used, first thoroughly cleanse the cans with soap and water, as it is possible that neither the bichloride nor the alcohol treatment would insure complete destruction of spore contaminants in the time that elapses between the sterilization treatment and the opening of the container. Thus mechanical removal of contamination should be regarded as an essential partial treatment.

B. *Removal of sample:*

1. *Opening of container.* After flaming, or otherwise sterilizing the point of opening, make an aperture with an appropriate type of opener, which has also previously been sterilized by flaming. (Openers of the spiral or circular type, which cut a circular disk around a central puncture made by the instrument, are preferred, because those that make the cut at the can seam offer greater opportunity for the contamination that arises from excessive manipulation and greater surface exposure.) With liquid products, puncture an opening with a sharpened instrument of appropriate diameter. This subject has been discussed in detail by Tanner.[262]

2. *Inoculum.* As suggested by Tanner (*ibid.*), determine the type of instrument used for the removal of the inoculum by the character of the food under examination. Sample liquid or semiliquid food products with sterile untapered pipets or inverted 10-ml. pipets. Sample solid material with sterile cork borers or brass sampling tubes after they have been wrapped in paper and sterilized for 30 minutes at 15 pounds in the autoclave. Stopper the samples with cotton plugs, and force the solid material into culture tubes by means of a sterile glass rod or some similar device. As also suggested by Tanner, the sample should consist of at least 15 grams of food material, which may be cultured directly into one culture tube or flask, but preferably into at least three culture vessels. If the material is solid, mix it with sterile water as a preliminary step to inoculation.

3. *Sampling of product fractions.* If it seems to be desirable to obtain inocula from component parts (fat-liquid-meat) of unspoiled canned meats, use special procedures based upon pre-incubation at a relatively high temperature. This has been done with

261. Fellers. 1936. Assoc. Off. Agr. Chem. J. 19, 430.
262. Tanner. 1936. Idem 19, 432.

roast beef in 24-ounce cans, corned beef in six-pound soldered cans, and Vienna sausage in one-half-pound cans.

Descriptive procedures are as follows:

Roast beef:

Separate roast beef into its component parts by pre-incubation at 50°C. for 24 hours. Draw off the liquid portion into a sterile, glass-stoppered, wide-mouthed bottle, and place in the incubator to permit the fat to separate from the liquid portion. Pipet off 10 ml. of the separated fat layer and add to 25-30 ml. of a dispersing agent (two per cent gum tragacanth and one per cent gum arabic in water). Agitate the fat and dispersing agent well in a mechanical agitator and make inoculations. Pipet samples of the liquid portion from underneath the fat layer and culture directly. After freeing the meat from all liquid, remove with a sterile cork borer and culture.

Corned beef:

Separate the fat by incubating at 50°C. for two days and then chilling immediately. (This results in the separation of a large amount of fat.) After chilling, open the cans at two points: (a) at the top, at which point a fat sample can be obtained, and (b) on the side or about the center, removing the sample of meat by a sterile cork borer. Add the fat to the dispersing agent and culture, but culture the meat directly.

Vienna sausage:

Prior to opening, incubate the cans 24 hours at 37°C. Remove liquid samples by means of sterile pipets inserted through an opening in the top of the can. After removing all liquid, mash the sausages in the same can and remove samples for culture.

In a meat product that is processed under pressure, understerilization usually results in the survival of sporeforming anaerobes—principally those of the putrefactive group. Thus anaerobic media are of special importance in the examination of canned meats. In addition, as a preliminary to plating and pure culture study, enrichment media are necessary to propagate nonsporing bacteria and aerobic or facultative anaerobic sporeformers. The following media are recommended for the purposes indicated. Special media for thermophilic bacteria are not necessary.

(1) *Veal infusion broth.* This medium is satisfactory both as an enrichment medium and as a propagator of anaerobes. It is prepared as a standardized, dehydrated product and is marketed under the name of "Bacto-veal Infusion Medium" by the Difco Laboratories, Inc., Detroit, Michigan. Because of its standardization, its use in this form is recommended.

(2) *Bacto-nutrient broth.* Recommended as an alternative enrichment medium. This product is also manufactured in dehydrated form by the Difco Laboratories, Inc.

(3) *Liver broth and beef heart peptic digest.* Recommended as an alternative anaerobic media. These products were described in a previous report.[263]

As to culture methods for further study of the organisms isolated by enrichment, it is recommended that The Manual of Methods for Pure Culture Study of Bacteria of the Society of American Bacteriologists serve as a guide.

D. Routine examination:

It is recommended that original cultures be incubated at 37.5°C. for 48-72 hours.

Jellied Meat Products. These products are subject to spoilage by bacteria from various sources. Allen[264] found the empty cans to be heavily ladened with bacteria and molds, many of which were removed by steaming. The gelatin used for filling the space between the meat also carried many bacteria. When these products spoiled, it started on the surface. Aerobic and anaerobic cultures showed the presence of *Bacillus subtilis*, *Bacillus proteus*, and *Bacillus mesentericus*. *Clostridium welchii* was

263. Cameron. 1936. Idem 19, 436.
264. Allen. 1919. Amer. Vet. Med. Assoc. J. 14, 394-397.

found in several specimens. No members of the Salmonella group were found.

Allen reported the results of several attempts to sterilize gelatin and jellied meat products. It was the general feeling among packers that sterilization in the final package at a temperature sufficiently high to destroy the bacteria, might harm the jellying powers of the gelatin. Allen found, however, that a jelly of good consistency could be held in an autoclave at a temperature of 115.6°C.(240°F.) for as long as 35 minutes without affecting the product. A poor jelly, however, could not be so treated. Several experimental packs were put up, the results of which showed that sterilization in the final package under pressure was possible.

Mincemeat. This is a meat product which has much favor in America. It is a heavily spiced mixture of chopped meat, apples, and raisins. The preservation of mincemeat is probably due to its content of spices and acids. Bachmann [267] has shown from experiments carried out in the laboratory that *Clostridium botulinum* would grow in mincemeat with indications of spoilage after a week. Bachmann stated that mincemeat should be completely sterilized or else heated to the boiling point before tasting. Sterilization of mincemeat in tin or glass containers is not difficult because heat does not cause deterioration. It is processed in the hot-water bath with success.

Meat products have caused a little botulism. While Bidault [265] and Curfman [266] have shown this possibility, meats have been remarkably free when the vast amount which has been used is considered.

Home-Canned Meats. The basic principles are the same as those discussed elsewhere for factory-canned meats. Both glass jars and tin cans are used by the home canner. Nelson and Berrigan [268] and Nelson and Knowles [268] studied rates of heat penetration into meats packed in tin cans and in glass jars. They used a 12-quart pressure cooker the cover of which was provided with a thermometer which extended into the center of the can. This technic was not the best for it has been found that thermocouples avoid some of the errors introduced by thermometers. They also inoculated the meat with test organisms: *Clostridium botulinum*, *Escherichia coli*, a heat-resistant strain of *Streptococcus fecalis*, and *Bacillus mesentericus*. In solid meat packs 10 pounds of steam, 115.5°C.(240°F.), were insufficient to destroy the bacteria used as test organisms. Sterilization of No. 2 cans was obtained with 15 pounds pressure at 121° C. (249.8° F) for 65 minutes.

Home-canned meats should be processed only under steam pressure at temperatures and times which have been found to be adequate. Boiling water processes are inadequate to prevent spoilage and may be dangerous.

Serological Identification of Meats. These procedures are used to detect substitution of one type of meat for another, usually, though not always, a cheaper meat for a more expensive. The best-known serological method

265. Bidault. 1924. Compt. Rend. Soc. Biol. 90, 1002-1003.
266. Curfman. 1916. Amer. Med. Assoc. J. 67, 1040.
267. Bachmann. 1923. J. Infect. Dis. 33, 236-239.
268. Nelson and Berrigan. 1939. J. Agr. Res. 59, 465-474; with Knowles 61 (1940), 753-759.

for this purpose is the precipitin test. It is based on the fact that *precipitins* appear in the blood serum of animals which receive intraperitoneal injections of a foreign protein, such as blood serum of another animal or an extract of the tissues of another animal. When the blood serum of this first animal is mixed with the antigen (extract of tissue, blood serum, etc.) a cloudy precipitate forms. The precipitate appears only when the prepared rabbit-blood serum is mixed with the substance with which the rabbit was injected. In this manner, it is possible to inject a number of rabbits with various substances which it may be desired to test for and have them on hand ready for use. The technic is a precise one and must be carefully carried out.

This method has not been widely used in America for there is not the need for it as in some foreign countries where flesh of certain animals, such as the horse, is used for food. Countries in which large amounts of sausage are eaten have used the precipitin test for detecting presence of certain proteins. It is desirable in some cases to know whether ingredients contain pork or horseflesh. Roza and Mazzaracchio [269] and Piegai [270] used the precipitin test for these purposes. They found the test to be useful in sausage analysis if due precautions were taken for avoiding error and for proteins which had not been completely coagulated or denatured by heat. For sausages which had been cooked so long that the protein had been completely denatured, some success was achieved by pancreatic digestion before making the test. Piegai found that he could detect the presence of mutton in beef sausage or vice versa even in amounts of five per cent or less. It had been believed generally that the precipitin test could not be used with closely related zoological species. He was also able to use the test in identifying pork and horseflesh in sausage when the state of putrefaction might cause a negative result to be expected.

Identification of Meat With Precipitin Test. The precipitin test seems to have been of greatest use, for detecting horse meat in sausage or proving that deer had been slain out of season. The test may be applied to salted and to cooked meats. When these are being tested the antisera must be prepared with such meats and not with fresh meat.

Preparation of Antigen. The antigen to be used depends on the type of meat that is suspected. If horse meat is suspected in sausage the antigen for preparing the antiserum will have to be horse meat. If there is some doubt about the type of meat, a number of antisera for various possible meats must be prepared. The rabbit is most commonly used for preparing precipitating sera. The antigen is injected either intraperitoneally, intravenously, or subcutaneously. It may be either the serum from the animal whose meat is suspected or a decoction of the meat itself. The latter is probably more specific. Dumitrescu and Manulescu,[271] in detecting horseflesh in preserved sausage, injected rabbits every five days with increasing amounts of horse serum starting with five ml. and using progressively 10, 20, 40, 60, and 80 ml. of horse serum. After the third injection, the serum was titrated. The injections were continued until a minimum strength of precipitin of one to 10,000 was secured. This preliminary titration is important since no two rabbits react in the same manner. Consequently it is advisable to determine the titer of the blood and to use more than one rabbit for each antiserum. The blood serum of the animals whose meat is suspected may not be readily obtain-

269. Roza and Mazzaracchio. 1938. Rend. Inst. Sanita Publica 1, 269-300.
270. Piegai. 1939. Indus. Ital. delle Conserve Aliment. 14, 135-137.
271. Dumitrescu and Manulescu. 1915. Rev. in Chem. Zentbl. 1915, II, 761-762.

able and consequently a decoction of the flesh may have to be used. About 30 grams of the meat under examination should be covered with 100 ml. of sterile physiological salt solution. This is then allowed to stand overnight in a refrigerator, after which it should be filtered clear by any of the usual methods. Some technicians advise that this should be adjusted to a neutral reaction and diluted wtih sterile water until only a slight even turbidity is formed by the addition of concentrated nitric acid. The less the amount of fat in the above protein solution, the easier will it filter. Before injection, the protein solutions should be sterilized by passage through a stone filter. The sterilization of this water extract before injection is very important since the mortality among the rabbits is high anyway owing to anaphylaxis and infection.

Preparation of Antisera. The details for this need not be given here since they are so well stated in books on pathological technic.[272] Certain it is, however, that this, like all serum reactions requires careful clean work. After the antisera have been prepared they may be preserved by .1 to .4 per cent of tricresol. The antisera should be active in high dilutions and each serum must be specific for its proteins.

The strength of the precipitin serum should be followed as it is being formed in the rabbit. Hektoen[273] proposed the following combination: Small, perfectly clean, and perfectly clear glass tubes are best, the lumen being about .5 cm. in diameter. In each of a series of such tubes in a rack, is placed .5 ml. of antigen dilution, the first tube receiving the lowest dilution, the next the next higher, etc. (for example 1:500, 1:1000, 1:1500, 1:2000, etc.); there is now introduced by means of a capillary pipette .1 ml. of antiserum at the bottom of each tube, special care being taken to get a precise line of contact between the two fluids. The antiserum also can be run in slowly at the side of the tube; being heavier than the diluted antigen it will go to the bottom of the tube, but the line of contact will not be quite so sharp as when it is introduced at the bottom with a pipette. The tubes which are kept at room temperature are now watched for the formation of a grayish-white precipitate at the plane of contact between the fluids. If a precipitate forms at once in the antigens dilution of 1:1000, the antiserum is strong enough to be used for forensic purposes. An antiserum that forms a precipitate almost at once in thousandfold dilution of antigen usually gives reactions in much higher dilutions—1-20,000, or higher, after a longer time, say twenty minutes.''

While the rabbit has been most commonly used, Sutherland[274] in India used the fowl. He found that fowl was more reliable than the rabbit. Hektoen, however, advised the rabbit precipitin production since it is abundant in this country. When an antiserum must be prepared against rabbit protein, the fowl may be used. The guinea pig does not yield a strong precipitating serum.

Nötel[275] stated that a highly active antiserum was necessary and that from 10 to 12 injections of the antigen should be made. The animals should not be bled until after six days. Fiehe[276] gave rabbits four injections of 15 ml. of horse blood every five days. He also stated that powerful antisera were necessary.

Procedure for the Test. This should be carried out only after the antisera have been shown to be potent and specific. In the final test the combinations are so arranged that the procedures and the components are well checked up. Schneider[277] suggested the following:

Tube 1, 2 ml. unknown extract (1-300) + .1 ml. anti-horse serum.
Tube 2, 2 ml. unknown extract (1-300) + .1 ml. normal rabbit serum.
Tube 3, 2 ml. horse-flesh extract (1-300) + .1 ml. of anti-horse serum.
Tube 4, 2 ml. pork extract (1-300) + .1 ml. of anti-horse serum.
Tube 5, 2 ml. beef extract (1-300) + .1 ml. of anti-horse serum.
Tube 6, 2 ml. saline solution + .1 ml. of anti-horse serum.

272. Methods for taking blood from experimental animals have been discussed in various books in the fields of pathogenic bacteriology and pathology.
373. Hektoen. 1918. Amer. Med. Assoc. J. 70, 1273-1278.
274. Sutherland. 1918.
275. Nötel. 1902. Ztschr. f. Hyg. u. Infektionskrank. 39, 373-378.
276. Fiehe. 1907. Ztschr. f. Untersuch. der Nahr. u. Genussmtl. 13, 744-751.
277. Schneider. 1915. Microbiology of Foods. P. Blakiston's Son & Co.

Schneider advises stratifying the immune sera in the tube. They should be kept at room temperature. If "tubes 1 and 3 show a clouding within five minutes and if a definite precipitate forms within thirty minutes, the other tubes remaining perfectly clear, the extract is probably one of horseflesh or the flesh of some other single-toed animal."

According to Dumitrescu and Manulescu [271] the skin and from one to two mm. of the outer layer are removed from about 20 grams of sausage and the remainder freed as much as possible from fat. This is then ground fine and mixed with nine per cent physiological salt solution to a thick paste and allowed to stand in a refrigerator for 50 hours with frequent shaking. The liquid is then pressed out, centrifuged, and the layer of fat removed. To each 2.5- and 5.0-ml. portions of this decoction are added 25 ml. physiological salt solution, the mixtures being centrifuged until perfectly clear. To four uniform 12-cm. test tubes are added the following solutions:

No. 1. About one ml. of undiluted physiological salt extract of sausage containing horseflesh.

No. 2. Same as No. 1.

No. 3. One drop of horse serum and one ml. of physiological salt extract of the suspected sausage.

No. 4. One ml. of serum from a sausage free of horseflesh.

To each of tubes 1, 3, and 4 is added .1 ml. of seroprotein and to tube 2, .1 ml. of the serum of an untreated rabbit. In tubes 1 and 3, after agitation, a cloudiness appears which slowly increases in 30 minutes to a precipitate. Tubes 2 and 4 should remain clear. This test detects two per cent of horseflesh with an antiserum active in a dilution of 1:18,000. A serum which is active only in a dilution of 1:1000 gives practically no reaction.

The precipitin test is applicable only to sausages which have not been cooked. Cooking, of course, coagulates the protein.

Stokes and Stoner [278] in applying the precipitin test to blood used the following technic which may be followed in its application to the detection of foreign proteins:

No. 1. The test proper: Two ml. of unknown solution plus .1 ml. immune serum.

No. 2. Control: Two ml. of unknown solution plus .1 ml. immune serum.

No. 3. Control: Two ml. of diluted blood of that species of animal whose blood is suspected to be present in the unknown solution plus .1 ml. immune serum.

No. 4. Control: Two ml. of unknown solution alone.

No. 4. Control: Two ml. of diluted blood serum of a different species of animal from that suspected to be present in the unknown solution plus .1 ml. immune serum.

These combinations, while devised for blood, may be used for foods, especially proteins, by substituting the physiological salt solution extracts of the meats for the blood serum.

Just as there is a group agglutination between certain bacteria, as with members of the colon-typhoid group, for instance, we also have a "group precipitation" by proteins which come from closely related animals. It is impossible to differentiate between *Escherichia coli* and *Eberthella typhosa* when low dilutions of antisera are used. In the same way, it is impossible to distinguish between proteins and blood from man and the primates. Schneider stated that the proteins from horses and donkeys cannot be differentiated by this test.

Some limitations exist in application of the precipitin test in the food industries. Proteins from animals which are closely related cannot be separated. It may not be needed in the United States, for other methods are available in some cases. It has been useful in Europe where it has helped to detect presence of horseflesh in meat preparations. Dumitrescu and Manulescu,[271] Nötel,[275] Fiehe,[276] Uhlenhuth, Weidanz, and Weder-

278. Stokes and Stoner. 1917. Boston Med. and Surg. J. 3, 65-72.

man,[279] Windmuller,[280] Weidanz,[281] Goujoux,[282] Schmidt,[283] Uhlenhuth and Weidanz,[284] Blanc,[285] Saint-Fernin,[286] Behre,[287] and Baier and Reuchlin [288] have discussed the technic in many cases and the results secured with the method. Yoshinaga [289] used the test in Japan for detecting frog and other meat in turtle products.

According to Baier and Reuchlin [288] drying, pickling, smoking, or preserving of meat does not mask or prevent use of precipitin test. They also used putrid and moldy meat. Bolin [290] stated that rabbits immunized to cooked meat had specific precipitins for the uncooked specific protein and at the same time had nonspecific precipitins for cooked meats of different species. Meats held at 15 pounds' pressure for 10 minutes were unsuitable as antigens. He also stated that immature animals were not suitable for precipitin production.

Ferguson, Racicot, and Rane's [291] Precipitin Test for Determination of Soybean Flour in Sausages. This method was proposed for establishing presence of soybean flour in sausages as well as to show the approximate quantity.

Preparation of Antisoy Serum. Rabbits were immunized according to the method proposed by Glynn. An antigen was prepared by extracting 10 grams of a commercial soybean flour with 100 ml. of five per cent sodium chloride for 12 to 15 hours with intermittent shaking. The extract was filtered through paper and diluted with an equal volume of distilled water. The freshly prepared extract thus diluted was used for the injections. The antigen contained an average of 55.4 mg. of soy protein nitrogen per 100 ml.

Six rabbits were given three courses of intraperitoneal injections of increasing amounts of the antigen. Each course consisted of five injections of 2, 4, 6, 8, and 10 ml., respectively, the injections being given five days apart. A three weeks' rest period followed the fifth injection of the first two courses.[292] Nine days after the last injection of the third course the animals were bled from the heart under sterile conditions, 50 ml. being drawn from each, and the blood was pooled. After clotting, the clear serum was removed and filtered through a Berkefeld filter. Before use, it was concentrated to one-half its volume in a cellophane bag in front of an electric fan, since it had been found that this procedure produced a quicker acting serum in the testing of unknown samples.

The rabbits were then placed on a definite injection-bleeding schedule. Five days after the bleeding an injection of 10 ml. of the antigen was given, and on the 9th day following the injection 50 ml. of blood were taken. This procedure of alternate injec-

279. Uhlenhuth, Weidanz, and Wederman. 1908. Arb. aus dem K. Gsndhtsamt. 28, 449-476.
280. Windmuller. 1912. Diss. Berlin.
281. Weidanz. 1907. Ztschr. f. Fleisch. u. Milchyg. 18, 73-78.
282. Goujoux. 1912. Hyg. Viande et Lait 4, 65-78.
283. Schmidt. 1909. Biochem. Ztschr. 14, 294-348.
284. Uhlenhuth and Weidanz. 1912. Schweiz. Med. Wchnschr. 48, 724.
285. Blanc. 1921. Ann. des Falsif. 4, 49-57.
286. Saint-Fernin. 1912. Idem 4, 334-338.
287. Behre. 1908. Ztschr. f. Untersuch. der Nahr. u. Genussmtl. 15, 521-524.
288. Baier and Reuchlin. 1908. Idem 15, 513-520.
289. Yoshinaga. 1909. München. Med. Wchnschr. 56, 2526.
290. Bolin. 1931. Amer. Vet. Med. Assoc. J. 31, 163-170.
291. Ferguson *et al.* 1942. Assoc. Off. Agr. Chem. J. 25, 533-537.
292. An antigen prepared with two per cent urea solution as the solvent in place of the five per cent NaCl was used during the third course on three of the rabbits showing the lowest titer at the end of the second course. It was noted that two per cent urea has approximately the same solvent power for soy protein as has five per cent NaCl, and that it can be injected full strength without irritation. By this means, approximately double the amount of soy protein was injected into these low-titered rabbits during the third course in an effort to determine whether or not a more potent serum could be obtained. The results show that such an antigen produced a serum equal in potency to that of the other rabbits. Further study of the antigen prepared with urea solution is anticipated.

tions and bleedings was continued over a period of several months, and it resulted in the accumulation of a large quantity of serum of more or less constant titer.

The strength or titer of the serum in terms of soybean flour protein is based on the method proposed by Glynn,[293] with variations as to the time and temperature of incubation. The actual method of titration is as follows:

Extract 1 gram of soybean flour with 100 ml. of 5% NaCl for 1 hour, with intermittent shaking, and filter through paper. Set 10 Wasserman-size test tubes in a rack and place 1 ml. of the original undiluted extract in the first tube and 1 ml. of a dilution of the extract made with .5% NaCl in each of the remaining tubes so that each succeeding tube has one-half the concentration of extract.

Add .2 ml. of serum to each tube, shake to mix, and incubate in a 56°-60°C. water bath. Examine every 10 minutes for the presence of a distinct flocculating precipitate. (The tube farthest to the left showing the characteristic precipitate is the so-called "indicator" tube. The tubes to the left of the "indicator" tube will remain uniformly cloudy, whereas several of those nearest to it on the right will show the precipitate in decreasing amounts, with those on the extreme right remaining cloudy. The serum with the highest titer is that in which the "indicator" tube is farthest to the right, or in other words, in which a given amount of serum will form a precipitate with the least amount of soy protein.)

In the actual use of the serum for the determination of soybean flour in sausages, it was found that the best results were obtained when the serum had been standardized against sausage of a known soybean flour content. It was noted that an "indicator" tube, in the case of an extract containing both soybean flour and sausage, is a different tube from that observed in the case of an extract prepared from an equal quantity of the flour alone, in the same dilution. It is believed that the presence of the meat proteins, added salt, milk powder, curing agents, etc., may tend to shift the zone of optimal precipitation as has been shown for other serological procedures. The method followed in this standardization is identical with the method for testing an unknown sample.

Procedure for the Test. Pass sample of sausage of the frankfort type known to contain no soybean flour through a sausage grinder three times. Place 25 grams of the ground material to which is added .25 gram of soybean flour and 100 ml. of 5% NaCl solution in a bottle, stopper, shake in a machine for 1 hour, and filter through paper. (The sausage, based on the moisture determinations on a number of samples, is assumed to contain 50% of moisture; 25 grams of sausage would therefore, provide ca. 12.5 ml. of water, which when added to the original 100 ml. gives a total volume of 112.5 ml. Since .25 gram of soybean flour is therefore extracted by 112.5 ml. of solution, the dilution of the extract is 1:450. The dilutions and amounts of extract and serum used are shown in the set-up of a typical test illustrated in the following table. Incubate

TUBE	1	2	3	4	5	6	7	8	9	10
Dilution	1-450	675	900	1350	1800	2700	3600	5400	7200	10,800
Antigen (ml.)	0.8	0.8	0.8	0.8	0.8	0.8	0.8	0.8	0.8	0.8
Serum (ml.)	0.2	0.2	0.2	0.2	0.2	0.2	0.2	0.2	0.2	0.2
1st Reading	Cl	Cl	Cl	Cl	+	+	+	±	Cl	Cl

Tube 5 is the "indicator" tube. Its dilution is 1:1800
$$1800 \div 900 = 2\% \text{ soybean flour.}$$

2nd Reading	+	+	+	±	±	Cl	Cl	Cl	Cl	Cl

Tube 1 is positive. This tube or a tube representing a lower dilution than 1-450 is the "indicator." The per cent of soybean flour cannot be greater than
$$450 \div 900 = 0.5\%.$$

3rd Reading	Cl	Cl	Cl	Cl	Cl	Cl	+	+	+	+

Tube 7 is the "indicator" tube. Its dilution is 1:3600
$$3600 \div 900 = 4\% \text{ soybean flour.}$$

293. Glynn.

for 1½ hours and read.[294] (The tube farthest to the left showing a distinct precipitate or flocculation at the end of 1½ hours is the ''indicator'' tube. Assuming that this is Tube No. 3, for example, this would mean that the lowest dilution at which a sausage containing 1% of soybean flour gives a precipitate under the conditions of the test is 1-900 with the serum that is being standardized.) In testing sausages of unknown composition, the dilutions are made up as if the sausage contained 1 per cent of soybean flour. (It will actually contain no soybean flour or else a multiple of 1 per cent.) For convenience the tubes may be labeled left to right with the same dilution numbers as if the sausage contained 1 per cent; i.e., 1-450, 675, 900, 1350, 1800, 2700, 3600, 5400, 7200, and 10,800.

Suppose that in the testing of an unknown sample, the ''indicator'' tube is No. 3. This means that this tube contains the same quantity of soy protein as did Tube No. 3 in the standardization test. The sample used in standardization contained one per cent of soybean flour. Therefore, since the dilutions of corresponding tubes in the two tests are the same, the unknown sample must also contain one per cent. But suppose that Tube No. 5, in the unknown sample, had been the indicator instead of Tube No. 3. Since Tube No. 5 contains double the dilution of Tube No. 3, or one-half the amount of soy protein, it follows that the original sausage must have contained two per cent of soybean flour. If Tube No. 8 had been the indicator, then the original sample contained six per cent, since there is only one-sixth the amount of soy protein in Tube No. 8 as in Tube No. 3.

POULTRY

The nature of the flesh of fowls and the necessity of shipping it long distances have made it imperative to understand changes which it may undergo. Cold storage above freezing has been much used for preserving fowls, although recently freezing solid has been introduced. Pennington[295] stated that changes which take place in a fowl in three weeks in the chill room are about equal to those which take place in a house refrigerator in from five to seven days. When fowls were stored below freezing, loss of flavor was reported after nine months. McBryde and Powick[296] reported that bacteria and molds were of no consequence during storage because they did not penetrate the tissues. Wiley[297] and his colleagues stated that the tissue of cold-storage fowls contained many bacteria as against none in the flesh of fresh fowls. Pennington had found bacteria, but they were fewer as storage temperatures approached 0°C.(32°F.).

Poultry has been shipped either drawn or undrawn. Comparative observations on the quality of both types were made by Pennington[298] and Brown.[299] Pennington's work was carried out under commercial conditions and indicated that in the process of cleaning the flesh becomes heavily seeded with bacteria. Undrawn fowls are not so heavily seeded with bacteria. Brown gave more attention to the activity of bacteria on cold-stored fowls. Poultry stored at a temperature of —15 to —25.6°C.(5 to —14°F.) undergo no bacterial spoilage. These temperatures destroyed many bacteria, but not the more resistant species. When the fowls were allowed to

294. Because of the inherent differences in the rate at which rabbit serum will flocculate, it was found that this incubation time permitted a complete reaction.

295. Pennington. 1917. J. Biol. Chem. 29, 31-32.

296. McBryde and Powick. 1917. U. S. Dept. Agr. Bull. 433, 100.

297. Wiley. 1908. U. S. Dept. of Agr., Bur. Chem. Bull. 115.

298. Pennington. 1911. U. S. Dept. Agr., Bur. Anim. Indus. Cir. 70.

299. Brown. 1907. Mass. Dept. Pub. Health Ann. Rpt. 39, 285-366.

thaw, the surfaces became moist and bacteria were thus able to grow. Drawn chickens placed in cold storage showed many more bacteria than undrawn.

Results quite similar to these were also reported by Boos.[300] When drawn and undrawn fowls were taken from cold storage and exposed to a temperature of 20°C.(68°F.), the undrawn birds showed better keeping qualities. An improved method of drawing was said to yield fowls showing "perfect keeping qualities," while the undrawn fowls underwent rapid decomposition.

Bissell[301] stated that turkeys and presumably other domestic fowls or game, were not detrimental to health if held for a year in cold storage. He believed, however, that they should be carefully prepared.

Studies on deterioration of chilled, dressed poultry were made several years by the Department of Agriculture of the Dominion of Canada. While it is generally believed that bacteria cannot grow below —10°C.(14°F.), various species of cold-tolerant organisms are known to develop well below freezing. This problem was studied with 144 birds which were precooled to —1.1°C.(30°F.) and then packed regularly in a box. These birds were examined when freshly packed and after two, four, six, and eight weeks. Bacterial counts were made of the skin and breast tissue of each bird. A notable increase in the average bacterial numbers on the skin surface at temperatures of —1.1 and 0°C.(30 and 32°F.), more pronounced at the former, was noticed. It was observed that the birds acquired a surface odor before there was any decomposition of, or significant increase of bacteria in, the muscle tissue examined. Lochhead and Landerkin[302] believed that the deterioration of dressed poultry at 30 and 32°F., to the point where the birds acquired a noticeable odor, is essentially a surface spoilage owing to bacterial growth. With the birds held at 0°C.(32°F.), this initial sign of spoilage was first observed after four weeks, being apparent with those stored at —1.1°C.(30°F.) after six weeks. Even a difference of two degrees in storage increased the keeping ability of the birds. Compared with the skin, the bacterial content of the breast muscle was very low. During the period of the test these changes were insignificant.

The predominant bacteria on the skin were representative of the genera Micrococcus, Flavobacterium, and Achromobacter. Comparison was also made with birds held at —2.2°C.(28°F.). Bacterial development was noted at this temperature even though the birds were frozen at this temperature.

The susceptibility of cold-stored poultry to decomposition after removal from refrigerated storage, as compared with the freshly killed product, was also studied. Bacterial decomposition appeared to be most rapid in frozen poultry while that of chilled poultry meat was intermediate between the frozen and freshly killed product. The relative decomposition of chilled

300. Boos. 1907. Mass. Dept. Pub. Health Ann. Rpt. 39, 263-283.

301. Bissell. 1909. Buffalo Dept. Health.

302. Lochhead and Landerkin. 1935. Sci. Agr. 15, 765-770; Prog. Rpt. to Dominion Agr. Bacteriologist for 1934-36. Ottawa, p. 27.

and frozen meat may be expected to vary with the time and temperature of storage and the manner of freezing and defrosting.

Mallmann [303] found that formation of slime on squab ducklings was caused by aerobic, nonsporeforming bacteria resembling *Bacillus mesentericus*. The carcasses were found to be infected by utensils and dressing rooms of the packing plant. Pure cultures of the organism isolated reproduced the spoilage. Slime formation was delayed by addition of sodium hypochlorite to the storage tanks and by dipping the dressed ducklings in saturated salt brine.

REFERENCE BOOKS

EDELMANN, R. (Revised by Mohler, J. R., and Eichhorn, A.). 1939. Textbook of Meat Hygiene, With Special Consideration of Ante-mortem and Post-mortem Inspection of Food Producing Animals. Lea and Febiger, Philadelphia, Pa.

JENSEN, L. B. 1942. Microbiology of Meats. Garrard Press, Champaign, Ill.

MOULTON, C. R., AND LEWIS, W. L. 1940. Meat Through the Microscope. Ind. Edit. Inst. of Meat Packing, University of Chicago.

OSTERTAG, ROBERT VON. 1934. Textbook of Meat Inspection. Bailliere and Cox, London, England.

303. Mallmann. 1932. J. Agr. Res. 44, 913.

CHAPTER 22

MICROBIOLOGY OF EGGS AND EGG PRODUCTS

Eggs and egg products are important articles in the diet. They are perishable and must be handled carefully lest they assume characteristics which render them undesirable. The problem is quite difficult since a large part of the lay occurs in the spring. This makes it necessary to hold the abundance of these months against the need of others. Furthermore, the mass of production must take place in rural areas, making it necessary to ship eggs for long distances to urban centers. In view of the problems which are connected with shipment and storage, it is desirable to know as much as possible about the chemistry and bacteriology of eggs. Moran and Piqué [1] discussed with considerable completeness the storage of eggs. Microbiological problems have been presented in a report of the Food Investigation Board of Great Britain by Haines. [2] Another discussion of the egg problem, by Perard, [3] is a special thesis on prompt handling of clean, fresh eggs. Circular 583 (1941) of the U. S. Department of Agriculture is also very good.

The oviduct of the hen is located in the rear part of the body cavity. The yolk is the first part to develop and this takes place in the ovary which may contain a large number of minute yolks. Each is contained in a sac, or follicle, through which it secures its nourishment while developing. After development, the yolk, enclosed in its vitellin membrane, escapes from the yolk sac and descends through the oviduct. If fertilization occurs, it occurs soon after the egg has entered the oviduct and before any albumen is deposited about it. About 40 per cent of the albumen is said to be laid down as the yolk passes through the upper half of the oviduct. After passage through this albumen-forming region, it reaches the isthmus where the shell membranes are added with about 10 to 20 per cent more albumen. The uterus is then reached, where the remainder of the shell is added. During passage through the vagina, just before its expulsion from the cloaca, it probably receives the outer gelatinous coating on the shell. (See Benjamin. [4])

Schneiter [5] classified eggs and egg products into the following groups:

1. Shell eggs

2. Broken eggs
   (a) Whole eggs
   (b) Egg whites
   (c) Egg yolks

3. Dried eggs
   (a) Albumen or whites
   (b) Yolk
   (c) Whole or mixed eggs

4. Frozen eggs
   (a) Albumen or whites
   (b) Plain yolk
   (c) Sugar yolk
   (d) Salt yolk
   (e) Glycerine yolk
   (f) Whole or mixed eggs

1. Moran and Piqué. 1926. (Gt. Brit.) Food Invest. Bd. Spec. Rpt. No. 26.
2. Haines. 1939. Microbiology in the Preservation of the Hen's Egg. Idem No. 47.
3. Perard. 1933. Fifth World's Poultry Cong. 3, 371.
4. Benjamin. 1915. N. Y. Agr. Expt. Sta. (Cornell Univ.) Bull. 353.
5. Schneiter. 1939. Assoc. Off. Agr. Chem. J. 22, 625-628.

Grading of Eggs. This is essentially a commercial problem in which bacteriology has not had a role. In commerce, eggs are usually graded by candling, a process which is to the egg industry what sanitary inspection is to milk and water. Frazier,[6] Stiles and Bates,[7] Moran and Piqué,[1] and the California State Board of Health[8] have devised systems for grading eggs. In the United States the Federal Government[109] puts eggs into four grades: U. S. Special (retail Grade AA), U. S. Extra (retail Grade A), U. S. Standard (Grade B), and U. S. Trade (Grade C). Eggs with dirty shells are graded U. S. Extra Dirty, U. S. Standard Dirty, and U. S. Trade Dirty, according to their quality. Complete descriptions of these grades have been published by the U. S. Department of Agriculture in Circular 583, published in 1941. Moran and Piqué[1] reported the grades in use in England. Since none of these grading systems use bacteriological criteria, they will not be reproduced here.

"Leakers" and "dirties" are problems in the egg industry. Leakers permit their contents to run out, wherein bacteria develop in great numbers. The heavily seeded material may then act as an inoculum when it reaches the shells of sound eggs. Furthermore, the types of organisms will be those which are able to develop in the egg.

Dirties appear during wet weather and sometimes during hot weather when moisture from the hen's body allows more dirt to adhere to the shell. Many of these are used for local consumption or for drying since they do not keep well. In examination of eggs with dirty shells, Pennington[9] secured widely divergent results. The minimum number of bacteria was 400 and the maximum number 1,500,000 per gram at 20°C.(68°F.). The number of *Escherichia coli* varied from 10 to 10,000 in six samples. It has been reported by many investigators that dirty eggs do not keep well. Often these eggs are washed but this process lowers the keeping quality since it removes the delicate membrane or film of mucous on the surface of the shell.

Since bacteria develop in eggs in different ways, different kinds of rot are known. The fertile egg is much more liable to rot than is the sterile egg. Benjamin[4] described the following rots: *White rots* are common and often called water rots, sour, or addled eggs. They represent the first stages in bacterial decomposition. Such eggs have an enlarged air cell before the candle and a mixed interior. When opened, they are usually a light yellow in color and watery. *Mixed rots* represent a more advanced stage of decomposition and are characterized by thin interiors; in the open conditions, they give off an odor of hydrogen sulfide and sourness. The yolk is rarely intact. *Black rots* are eggs in which the contents are very dark and may be easily shaken about in the shell. When opened the odor is much like that of hydrogen sulfide. In appearance, the contents are mixed and very watery.

6. Frazier. 1917. Amer. Food J. 12, 39.
7. Stiles and Bates. 1912. U. S. Dept. Agr., Bur. Chem. Bull. 158.
8. Calif. State Dept. Pub. Health Weekly Bull. 10 (1931), 129-130.
9. Pennington *et al.* 1914 . U. S. Dept. Agr., Bur. Chem. Bull. 51.

Black rot of eggs was reported by Bohart [10] to result from reduction of sulfur compounds with consequent formation of hydrogen sulfide. She inoculated sterile egg white in culture tubes with anaerobic and facultative anaerobic bacteria from black rot eggs. No blackening resulted even after incubation for 60 days. However, *Clostridium sporogenes* and *Clostridium putrificum* were isolated from eggs which underwent black-rot spoilage after inoculation under aseptic conditions with facultative anaerobic proteolytic bacteria. Continued study seemed to indicate that practically all anaerobic proteolytic bacteria will produce black-rot spoilage if given the right conditions. Bennetts [11] observed an organism of the genus Serratia as the cause of putrefaction of eggs.

Kuhl,[12] from the examination of large numbers of eggs, concluded that for trade purposes the following would be a good classification of commercial eggs: fresh eggs, those up to eight or 10 days old; eggs not over four weeks old; cooking eggs, any offered for sale which are not spoiled. Such a classification would be difficult to apply by food-control officials. Furthermore, it would not always accomplish the results that systems of grading insure. The conditions which obtain during the storage of any food product must also be considered. Age alone is of little value as a criterion of quality.

Fresh eggs are usually desired. This need not indicate that eggs which are not newly laid are undesirable. It is difficult to secure a satisfactory definition of the term "fresh," as applied to eggs. It is equally difficult to find methods for determining whether an egg conforms to the definition after one has been adopted. Schweizer [13] proposed a method based on determination of the hydrogen-ion concentration. A hole was made in the egg, one ml. egg white pipetted off and mixed with one ml. indicator and five ml. isotonic sodium chloride solution for colorimetric pH determination. Phenolphthalein and m-nitrophenol were used as indicators. Eggs held at 8°C.(46.4°F.), 20°C.(68°F.), and 28°C.(82.4°F.) showed an increase of pH from 7.7 to 9.5 in 10 days, because of loss of carbon dioxide. Eggs treated with water glass or lime water did not appreciably increase in pH. Eggs stored in air showing a pH of 9.4 or over must be judged as over eight days old. Another method was proposed by Zach,[14] who believed that the luminescence of eggs increased with age. However, it was stated that the storage temperature of the egg had to be known, for luminescence became greater at higher storage temperatures. Such a method would probably not be adaptable to routine work.

Molds in Eggs. Eggs which are not stored under proper conditions frequently develop molds. The hyphae usually extend toward the air cell and produce sufficient growth to give what is known as a mold spot. To prevent this deterioration, eggs must be stored under good conditions.

10. Bohart. 1930. Amer. J. Hyg. 11, 168-173.
11. Bennetts. 1931. Austral. Vet. J. 7, 27-31.
12. Kuhl. 1914. Hyg. Rundschau. 24, 253-259.
13. Schweizer. 1929. Mitt. aus dem Geb. der Lebensmtl. Untersuch. u. Hyg. 20, 203-209.
14. Zach. 1929. Mitt. aus dem Geb. der Lebensmtl. Untersuch. u. Hyg. 20, 209-215.

Smith [15] confirmed this by storing a few eggs at relative humidities of 90, 95, 98, and 100 per cent and at temperatures of 0, 5, and 10°C. (32, 41, and 50°F.). Mold development, as would be expected, was found to be greatly influenced by these factors. At a temperature of 10°C. (50°F.) and a relative humidity of 100, mold growth appeared in five days. Lower humidities and lower temperatures delayed development of the molds which were naturally present in the eggs. Besides the molds which may be present within the egg, there may be others on the shell. These may be numerous and may cause trouble if the eggs are not stored in clean, dry places. Tomkins,[16] by means of a washing process, found between 200 and 500 spores per egg. When eggs are held in a humid environment these spores develop and cover the egg shell with dense growth. At lower humidities less mold growth occurs but the eggs may assume a musty odor. While most molds on the exterior of the egg develop only on the shell, a few have been known to penetrate the shell membrane.

In 1864, Mosler [17] stated that sound eggs could be infected by *Penicillium glaucum* and *Mucor mucedo*. Zimmerman [18] reported the isolation of *Melrosporium verruculosum, Torula ovicola, Penicillium glaucum*, and séveral other microorganisms from decayed eggs. Zopf [19] frequently isolated *Hormodendron cladosporioides* from eggs. Gueguen [20] isolated *Cladosporium herbarum*. Resistance to molds, according to Brtnik,[21] might be exhibited for three months. Consequently, he believed that there was need for a careful inspection of establishments handling eggs. Kossowicz [22] found that old eggs are more susceptible to mold invasion than are fresh eggs; this is probably to be expected. Postolka [23] confirmed this opinion. Marked growth of molds took place after either natural or artificial infections in the testacea but rarely in the yolk. Natural infection was caused by *Penicillium glaucum* and *Cladosporium herbarum*. Under experimental conditions, almost any mold will attack and penetrate the egg. Postolka stated that with even great infection with molds, no putrefaction takes place. Considerable study was given to this question by Moran and Piqué,[1] who examined eggs encountered in stores. Too many data were reported to reproduce here. However, molds belonging to the genera Sporotrichum, Penicillium, Cladosporium, Alternaria, and others were reported. In a study of a new type of mold spoilage of shell eggs, James and Swenson [24] isolated two molds, Penicillium and Cladosporium. Inoculation experiments showed that eggs shipped in seasoned wooden cases developed the spots to a negligible extent. Eggs shipped in cases of unseasoned wood from California to New York showed the development of mold to a marked degree.

15. Smith. 1931. (Gt. Brit.) Food Invest Bd., Ann. Rpt. for 1930, p. 97.
16. Tomkins. 1937. Idem for 1936, p. 53.
17. Mosler. 1864. Lafars Technical Mycology, English Trans. by Calter. Vol. 2, 378.
18. Zimmermann. 1878. Ber. der Natur. Gesell. Chemnitz., p. 3, Landw. Jahrb., 755.
19. Zopf. 1890. Breslau.
20. Gueguen. 1898. Soc. Mycol. de France, Bull. Trimest 14, 88.
21. Brtnik. 1916. Centbl. Bakt., Pt. 2, 46, 427-444.
22. Kossowicz. 1916. Centbl. Bakt., Pt. 2, 46, 330.
23. Postolka. 1916. Wien. Tierärztl. Monatsschr. 3, 3-11.
24. James and Swenson. 1930. J. Bact. 19, 55.

Cladosporium herbarum is apparently one of the most troublesome fungi causing mold spoilage of eggs. Experiments by Weston and Dillon [25] revealed that it developed rapidly on eggs and in less than 14 days penetrated the shell membranes. They compared the size of pores in the shell with the diameter of hyphae and found that the latter could easily find their way into the egg. Several hyphae entered a pore together and penetrated directly through the air spaces. While the albumen in affected eggs was not contaminated after one month, the membranes were severely attacked. Baeza [26] also isolated several different fungi from eggs. Species of the genera Hormodendron and Alternaria were most common. Infection from contaminated material was believed to take place after laying.

The importance of humidity in mold growth on eggs was again shown by Sharp and Stewart.[27] A dark mold developed on eggs stored at 1.1°C. (34°F.) for three months or more at relative humidities between 96 and 100 per cent. Slight development occurred under the same storage conditions with a relative humidity of 90 per cent. The hypothesis was proposed that under this last set of conditions, failure of the mold to develop luxuriantly might be due to a restriction of the food supply as controlled by moisture. White growth of mold on the shell increases mold infection of the interior of eggs if they are held for a sufficiently long time. While a few species of fungi have been most commonly isolated from moldy eggs, Mallmann and Michael [28] recognized that different species might be the cause. Molds were said to originate from handling and packing after the eggs had reached the storage plant. Mallmann and Michael repeatedly isolated representatives of 10 genera from eggs and packing material; the majority belonged to the genus Penicillium but no one species predominated. Not all of the molds penetrated into the egg interior during cold storage. Only two genera were isolated from the interior of eggs, most of which belonged to Penicillium; four strains of Hormodendron were isolated.

These investigators also made a few experiments to determine whether a mycostat could be used for preventing mold development. After considerable study they recommended sodium pentachlorphenate in .4-per cent solutions to be incorporated in the fillers, flats, and cases. They could detect no difference in quality of eggs which were stored in strawboard containing this compound. Importance of egg containers as sources of molds was indicated by results of investigations by Toop.[29] After storage for some eight months at —6°C.(31°F.) and at a relative humidity of 87 per cent, six per cent of the cases were found to be affected with mold. Various factors, such as the type of wood and age of the case, greatly influence appearance of mold.

Enzymes in Eggs. Rullmann [30] found catalase in eggs which were bacteria free. The amount had no relation to the age and was about equal in

25. Weston and Dillon. 1927. Poultry Sci. 6, 251-258.
26. Baeza. 1934. Ann. Parasitol. Humaine et Connparée 12, 543-550.
27. Sharp and Stewart. 1936. N. Y. Agr. Expt. Sta. (Cornell Univ.) Mem., 191.
28. Mallmann and Michael. 1940. Mich. Agr. Expt. Sta., Tech. Bull. 174.
29. Toop. 1939. U. S. Egg and Poultry Mag. 45, 397-399.
30. Rullmann. 1916. Centbl. Bakt., Pt. 2, 45, 219-230.

the yolks and whites. In putrid eggs the amount was so large that the sample had to be diluted. Pennington and Robertson [31] studied this question, using eggs of known history. They experimented to determine the presence of pepsin, trypsin, lipase, catalase, and reductase. Lipase content increases from a little in a fresh egg to a large amount in a stale egg. The catalase content of a fresh egg was found to be variable.

Factors Influencing Bacterial Content of Eggs. A study of this question involves two points, the first being the entrance of bacteria before the shell is put down, and the second, the contamination after laying, owing to improper handling, etc. While the first point has been studied, the data are not convincing. Mauer,[32] in quoting the work of Pernot,[33] stated that infection of the yolks, even in the normal ovary is possible. Zimmerman,[18] Abel and Draer,[34] Cao,[35] McClintock,[36] Poppe,[37] and others maintained that the oviduct is not sterile. Contradictory to this are the data of Horowitz [38] and Rettger.[39] Obviously, under abnormal conditions the oviduct may be infected. This has been found to be true with *Salmonella pullorum (Bacillus pullorum)* and the white diarrhoea of chicks. Bushnell and Mauer [40] pointed out that there are factors which lower the vitality of the hen and render her unable to resist invading bacteria. Hadley and Caldwell [41] thought that the preponderance of yolk infections indicated that bacteria are present in the ovaries of the hen. Lamson [42] reported bacteriological studies with reference to the cause of decomposition and sources of infection of eggs, the part played by temperature, and precautions to be observed in preserving eggs. Dissections of hens were made by Lamson for examination of the ovary and oviduct. Bacteria were present in the oviduct of the hen, even in the upper portions, so that an egg may be infected in the earlier stage of its formation, particularly at the time when the white or albumen is secreted. A diseased condition of the ovary of the hen may cause infection of the eggs. Eggs may be infected after they have been laid, as it is possible for the bacteria to pass through the pores of the shell. Moisture plays a part in such infections; while the fresh egg is covered with a normal mucilaginous coating, it it difficult to infect if kept in a dry place. Infection is not difficult, however, when the egg is moist. Many egg shells are defective, caused by not feeding the hens a sufficient amount of shell-forming food. Eggs are liable to be infected soon after they are laid. Nine species of bacteria were found in one nest, hence Lamson thought that nesting material was a great source of infection; if it has been allowed to remain unchanged for a long time it becomes foul and teems with bacteria.

31. Pennington and Robertson. 1912. U. S. Dept. Agr., Bur. Chem. Circ. 104.
32. Mauer. 1911. Kansas Agr. Expt. Sta. Bull. 180.
33. Pernot. 1909. Oregon Agr. Expt. Sta. Bull. 703.
34. Abel and Draer. 1895. Ztschr. f. Hyg. u. Infektionskrank. 19, 61.
35. Cao. 1908. Rev. in Bull. Inst. Pasteur. 6, 472.
36. McClintock. 1894. Modern Med. and Bact. Rev. 3, 144.
37. Poppe. 1910. Arb. aus dem K. Gsndhtsamt. 34, 186.
38. Horowitz. 1902. Baumgarten's Jahresber. 19, 984.
39. Rettger. 1913. Conn. Agr. Expt. Sta. Bull. 75; Centbl. Bakt. Pt. 2, 39, 611.
40. Bushnell and Mauer. 1914. Kansas Agr. Expt. Sta. Bull. 201.
41. Hadley and Caldwell. 1916. Rhode Island Agr. Expt. Sta. Bull. 164.
42. Lamson. 1908. Conn. Agr. Expt. Sta. Bull. 55.

Whatever the means of infection, larger percentages of the July, August, and early September eggs were infected or contained a greater number of bacteria (at a time when they were called fresh) than the eggs of the other months of the year, particularly when compared with eggs laid during the months of April, May, and June. This corroborated the opinion of egg packers, who invariably prefer April, May, and June eggs to those produced during the other months of the year. The fact that an egg contains bacteria does not mean that it is worthless. The question is mainly whether or not they are present in large numbers, and if present in small numbers, whether or not they are likely to multiply. Bacteria which are commonly found in eggs do not multiply at low temperatures. An egg that is kept at $1.1°C.(34°F.)$ is safe from decomposition. Repeated experiments have shown that the rapid growth of bacteria does not occur until the temperature is raised over $13°C.(55°F.)$. While there is some growth at temperatures lower than $13°C.(55°F.)$, it is very slow. At the temperature of $37°C.(98.6°F.)$ the bacteria in eggs multiply rapidly. In order to demonstrate the rapid multiplication of bacteria resulting in decomposition a dozen (January) eggs were taken, in six of them small holes were made, and into each egg bacteria from a rotten egg were introduced on a platinum loop. These holes were sealed with wax and the eggs thus infected, together with the six untreated eggs, were placed in an incubator running at a temperature of $43.3°C.(110°F.)$. In 48 hours, the six eggs which had been infected were so badly decomposed that they were very offensive, and the remaining six showed no changes in them. Tice [43] reported results of a chemical and bacteriological examination of some eggs of known history which seemed to indicate that eggs laid under clean conditions and stored in cases in a warehouse, in such manner as to be protected from dirt and excessive moisture, could be kept for as long as 10 months, without showing appreciable evidence of putrefactive decomposition. Mauer [32] published a lengthy study of various factors which affected the bacterial content of eggs. Eggs were examined for the presence of *Escherichia coli*, the work being undertaken as a part of a study of the economic aspects of the egg industry, and particularly with reference to the deterioration of frozen and desiccated eggs. Sixty fresh, clean eggs from 30 different hens collected twice a day from trap nests, 50 eggs obtained from local farms, and 25 dirty eggs obtained from a packing house were used. The dirty eggs were at least three weeks old and were fairly covered with droppings. The colon bacilli were absent from the contents of all the eggs studied, from the shells of about 77 per cent of the clean eggs, and from 82 per cent of the farm eggs but were found on the shells of all the dirty eggs.

Experiments were made under a variety of conditions, including low temperature, with eggs smeared with feces and egg, and with a suspension of *Serratia marcescens*. In general, the results indicated that the microorganisms under consideration did not penetrate the unbroken shells of the eggs. These data were contrary to those published by others.

43. Tice. 1911. New Jersey Bd. Health, 35th Ann. Rpt., p. 275.

Experiments also showed that concentrated egg albumen did not exercise bactericidal action upon *Escherichia coli,* a conclusion in harmony with that of other investigators. Indeed, the presence of large numbers of colon bacilli in frozen and desiccated eggs would be impossible if the egg possessed bactericidal properties for this organism. It seemed, therefore, that the only explanation for the absence of *Escherichia coli* from fresh eggs and from the oviduct was the lymphoid structure of the mucosa of the oviduct. This probably causes the removal, by leucocytic activity, of colon bacilli which have reached the oviduct, together with other intestinal organisms.

Mauer concluded that fecal matter is the source of many of the colon bacilli often present in egg preparations. The bacterial content of canned eggs may be greatly reduced by separating only clean eggs. All soiled eggs which either directly or indirectly might give rise to fecal contamination of the egg meat, should be utilized without separating the white from the yolk.

Results of investigations since the above reports were published have not changed the situation. Andresen [44] and Zagaevskii and Liutikova[45] observed microorganisms in eggs, the degree of infection being determined largely by conditions under which the eggs were handled. The latter investigators found eggs to be more sterile than other workers have found.

Chinese Eggs (Pidan). Such eggs appear regularly in the dietary of the Chinese. They are prepared by placing fresh eggs in a mixture of ashes, lye, earth, rice hulls, and lime. They are left for about a year. Bacteriological investigations by Dold and Meiling [46] showed the presence of *Bacillus subtilis* and other members of this group. The flora seemed to be quite extensive in that many different kinds of bacteria and other lower fungi were found. Different names are given these products, such as pidan, houeidan, and dsaoudan. Pidan is made by packing the eggs in a mixture of salt and ashes. The other products are made in a similar, though not identical, manner. Hanzawa [47] isolated a number of bacteria but unfortunately did not study them at great length. Tso [48] stated that Chinese preserved eggs, or "pidan," are produced on a commercial scale from fresh ducks' eggs and are, perhaps, as much relished by the Chinese people as cheese is in Western countries. In preserving, each egg is coated with a layer about seven millimeters thick of a mixture containing pure soda five parts, burned straw ash 25 parts, table salt four parts, slaked lime 40 parts, and boiling water 26 parts. This again is covered with rice husks to prevent sticking. The eggs are laid in earthenware jars and sealed with wet clay for a month. By that time both the white and the yolk are coagulated. The white has turned dark brown and the yolk is greenish gray with concentric rings of different shades of gray. These eggs are marketed with their coverings on, and are usually consumed within six

44. Andresen. 1932. Diss., Tierärztliche Hochschule, Berlin, 41 pp.
45. Zagaevskii and Liutikova. 1937. Voprosy Pitaniya, 84-88.
46. Dold and Meiling. 1916. Arch. f. Hyg. 95, 300; Centbl. Bakt., Pt. 2, 47 (1916), 538.
47. Hanzawa. 1913. Centbl. Bakt., Pt. 2, 418-419.
48. Tso. 1925. Soc. Expt. Biol. and Med. Proc. 23, 263.

months of production. The taste of these eggs can only be very imperfectly described as somewhat caustic and piquant, and the odor is largely ammoniacal. In eggs produced in this manner there was, according to Blunt and Wang,[49] a marked increase in the ash content and the alkalinity of the ash. There was a partial decomposition of the proteins and the phospholipoids, resulting in excessive production of free ammonia and in a diminution of the yolk fat. It was believed that these characteristic changes were brought about by the combined action of bacteria and enzymes, as well as by the alkali preservative.

While the data from Zörkendorfer's [50] experiments may not be directly pertinent to the subject discussed in this paragraph, they are of indirect interest. He examined a large number of spoiled eggs in order to determine the number of bacteria present and their connection to spoilage. Many types were found, some of which, when grown in pure culture and inoculated into fresh eggs, caused them to spoil in a very short time. These bacteria were arranged in two groups: (1) those which formed hydrogen sulfide, and (2) those which caused the appearance of a greenish-blue color.

Rot of Eggs. Such eggs, of course, are not used for human consumption but are either discarded or sold for industrial purposes. Various microorganisms have been isolated. *Bacillus fluorescens liquefaciens, Micrococcus roseus,* and *Staphylococcus aureus* were isolated as causes by Pavarino.[51] Anaerobic bacteria were believed to be the main cause of rot by Bohart.[10] Nearly all of the anaerobes which she tried would produce the decomposition if given long enough time and the right conditions of temperature and humidity.

Another fungus, *Proteus melanovogenes,* was reported by Miles and Halnan [52] to be the specific cause of black rot in eggs which had been imported into England. This organism produced black rot experimentally when introduced into normal eggs. It apparently penetrates normal egg shells. The organism was found in soil and manure in England. According to Haines,[53] the shell of an egg may be heavily infected with a heterogeneous flora, including members of the genera Proteus and Pseudomonas which are capable of rotting eggs. Haines grouped the different rots into black rot, red rot, green rot, and a miscellaneous group. Black rots were believed to be almost entirely due to strains of Proteus, but some stains of Pseudomonas cause blackening. Red and green rots are caused by particular stains of Pseudomonas. Atypical strains of coliform bacteria produced a fish odor.

Green rot of eggs, observed by Platt and Anderson,[54] was found to be due to a species of Pseudomonas and a proteolytic enzyme which causes a liquefaction of the egg contents. On candling the entire egg interior appeared green, the yolk being a little darker than the white.

49. Blunt and Wang. 1916. J. Biol. Chem. 28, 125-134.
50. Zörkendorfer. 1893. Arch. f. Hyg. 16, 367-401.
51. Pavarino. 1930. Ann. Sper. Agrar. 3, 117.
52. Miles and Halnan. 1937. J. Hyg. 37, 79-97.
53. Haines. 1938. Idem 38, 338-355.
54. Platt and Anderson. 1939. J. Dept. Agr. Sci., Australia 42, 1040.

Permeability of the Shell. The shell about the egg may be regarded as a semipermeable membrane and, therefore, not resistant to bacteria. Wittich reported the infection of eggs by molds. Wilm [55] succeeded in infecting eggs with *Vibrio comma*. When the eggs were covered with a broth culture, the organisms passed through the shell in from 15 to 16 hours. Golokow,[56] Piorowski,[57] Lange,[58] and Poppe [37] demonstrated the same thing with other bacteria, both pathogenic and nonpathogenic. Opposed to this work is that of Mauer,[32] Hoppert,[59] Sachs-Müke,[60] Zörkendorfer.[50] Kossowicz [61] showed that *Bacillus proteus* penetrated the shell very easily. Such data given above suggest the ability of bacteria to penetrate the shells of eggs and thus emphasize the necessity of storing eggs under sanitary conditions. Kossowicz reported that contamination of the egg by microorganisms may occur while in the ovarian duct, but not after it is laid until age causes loss of resistance. No organisms had entered eggs four weeks old; only *Cladosporium herbarum* had entered after eight weeks, *Phytophthora infestans* after 12 weeks, and *Rhizopus nigricans* after five months. The germicidal power of the albumen decreased rapidly with age. In addition to his own work, Kossowicz summarized data from a large number of experiments of others. In his own experiments he reported that a large number of fresh eggs were held from two to three days at temperatures of 20 to 30°C.(68 to 86°F.), and their contents were inoculated into various culture media. With very few exceptions these eggs were found to be sterile. Experiments in which eggs were exposed to various kinds of bacteria under conditions corresponding closely to those under which eggs are often stored in the home, in transportation, and in the trade showed that bacteria could easily penetrate the unbroken shell of the egg and cause decay. This was especially true of the very common putrescible organism, *Bacillus vulgaris*. It was also shown by similar experiments that molds could penetrate the shell under conditions in which moisture and temperature played an important part. At high temperature *Cladosporium herbarus*, and at low temperature *Penicillium glaucum*, are the most active organisms which cause molding of eggs. The shells of old eggs were said to be more easily and quickly penetrated by the molds than those of fresh eggs. Some yeasts were also found to penetrate. Eggs, the shells of which were soiled by the contents of either fresh or decayed eggs, were found to be more susceptible to the invasion of microorganisms. An extended discussion was given of the various methods employed for preservation, from which the author drew the conclusion that the most suitable method is cold storage in rooms which have been filled with carbon dioxide or else packing the eggs in milk of lime or in water glass. Kossowicz[62] later reaffirmed his contention that bacteria could penetrate the egg shell in refutation of the

55. Wilm. 1895. Arch. f. Hyg. 23, 145.
56. Golokow. 1896. Baumgarten's Jahresber. 12, 583.
57. Piorowski. 1895. Arch. f. Hyg. 25, 145.
58. Lange. 1907. Arch. f. Hyg. 62, 201.
59. Hoppert. 1912. Thesis, Univ. of Wis.
60. Sachs-Müke. 1907. Arch. f. Hyg. 62, 229.
61. Kossowicz. 1913. Die Zersetzung und Haltbarmachung der Eier. Wiesbaden. J. F. Bergman.
62. Kossowicz. 1916. Centbl. Bakt., Pt. 2, 46, 330.

claims of Rullmann,[30] who did not admit it. The latter claimed never to have observed the penetration of bacteria into eggs the shells of which were intact.

Pennington [63] reported a comprehensive investigation of the bacterial content of eggs, the number found and listed being 36 varieties per 100 eggs. In the 57 experiments, 18 had a decidedly greater number of bacteria in the yolk; 11 had the majority in the white and 21 had an almost even distribution; seven were sterile. Both Plymouth Rock and Leghorn eggs were used, and spring and autumn, fertilized and unfertilized, eggs were compared. According to Pennington, the differences in bacterial content which were observed depend upon breed and the conditions under which the eggs were laid as well as the season. In general, the autumn eggs contained a greater number of bacteria than the early spring eggs. That perfectly fresh eggs from healthy hens may contain bacteria is a generally recognized fact. That they are sometimes sterile is also admitted. Whether the organisms enter the egg during its passage down the oviduct or whether they penetrate the shell either at the time of laying or afterward are questions on which opinions are contrary. The fact that certain pathogenic organisms characteristic of fowls, as vibrios of chicken cholera, have been found in the egg argues for infection in the oviduct, as does the presence of foreign bodies, such as small insects; while the trade experience indicates that organisms can enter through the shell.

As to the manner in which bacteria get into eggs, the experiments of Zörkendorfer [50] indicate that neither the outer shell nor the membrane next the shell are impervious to bacteria. Fresh eggs were inoculated with different forms of bacteria by placing them on the outside of the shell. After a few days colonies of these bacteria were found growing on the inside of the shell. Fresh eggs were also laid in bouillon cultures, and after a few days the bacteria contained in the bouillon were recognized in the egg. In other trials eggs were blown, the shells filled with nutritive gelatin, and the ends sealed up with paper. These artificial eggs were then sterilized in a steam bath, after which they were placed on a mass of egg which had become putrid. When, after a few days, the shells were removed without disturbing the gelatin, a number of colonies of bacteria were found on the side next to the spoiled egg. These colonies were separated from one another, indicating, as in former trials, that the bacteria enter the shell at particular places. Such experiments are open to criticism. They would have to be made with the greatest of care.

Some practical observations were made bearing on the keeping of eggs. It was found that a moist atmosphere was favorable to spoiling, probably because moist air was more favorable to the growth of bacteria on the outside of the shell. A low temperature was unfavorable but was not proof against spoiling, since nearly all of the bacteria found grew in a refrigerator, although slowly. The majority of the bacteria found were killed by a temperature of about 50°C.(122°F.). In view of this it was suggested that heating eggs one or two days at that temperature and then storing

63. Pennington. 1909. J. Biol. Chem. 7, 109-132.

them in a dry place would probably be effectual in most cases, although this does not entirely preclude the action of bacteria which might get on the outside of the shell. The most effectual precaution suggested was that of·excluding the supply of oxygen which the bacteria require for growth. This is often done by placing the eggs in lime water, but with unsatisfactory results, as it imparts an unpleasant taste to the eggs. The author proposed to exclude oxygen by coating the shell with a solution of some kind which closes the pores of the shell airtight. Practical trial of this method gave very encouraging results. A large number of eggs were inoculated with bacteria and then some of the eggs were coated. Those not coated spoiled within a week, but the coated eggs kept perfectly for two months without change in color, flavor, or odor. The exact nature of the coating was not given.

In bacteriological tests made by Rettger [39] of more than 10,000 eggs of different ages, under various degrees of incubation, yolks from fresh eggs showed a positive test for bacteria other than *Salmonella pullorum* of 9.15 per cent. The yolks of artificially incubated eggs showed 2.75 per cent positive tests during the first week of incubation, 1.3 per cent the second, and 3.6 per cent the third week. The small percentage of positive results for eggs which had been incubated from one to three weeks was considered a noteworthy fact. A more exact method was employed in testing the yolks of fresh eggs, and in this case the test was reduced to 3.86 per cent. It was believed that these results were, in all probability, considerably above the actual figures, could accidental invasion of bacteria in the tests be entirely prevented. Experiments with eggs incubated one to two weeks indicated that fertilized eggs did not become more subject to bacterial invasion of the yolk than the infertile eggs. Examination of the whites of 582 eggs indicated that 1.2 per cent contained bacteria, although many of the tests were made during the summer months. No *Salmonella pullorum*, the organism of white diarrhea, was detected in the white, although it was recovered from the yolk. Undoubtedly, there was some contamination in these tests, and it was believed safe to say that the whites of fresh normal eggs are, as a rule, sterile. Fermentation tests made of the whites of 105 eggs for *Escherichia coli* were negative. In noting the kinds of organisms found in the yolks of fresh and incubated eggs, it was observed that a large percentage in both cases were staphylococci, usually *Staphylococcus albus* or *Staphylococcus aureus*, indicating that there was considerable contamination in the examination. Also the occurrence of a large number of members of the subtilis group would suggest the same thing.

Rettger reviewed the results obtained by earlier investigators which are not in harmony with those which he obtained. He suggested that the methods employed in making previous tests may have been at fault and it was highly improbable that normal fresh eggs contain bacteria and molds in such large proportions as various investigators have indicated. It was stated that the developing ova in the ovary of a laying hen were, as a rule, sterile unless the ovary was infected with the organism of bacillary white diarrhea. In 200 bacteriological examinations, Rettger was unable to detect bacteria, molds, or other microorganisms except *Salmonella pullorum*. The blood was ruled out as a source of infection and examinations of the oviducts showed them as a rule to be sterile except at or near the cloaca. The views of Horowitz [38] substantiated those of Rettger. It was believed that autosterilization of the oviduct is due to the following: (1) phagocytosis, (2) mechanical action of the walls of the oviduct, and (3) bactericidal action of the secretions. Success in preserving eggs with sodium silicate was cited as an indication that sound fresh eggs are as a rule sterile. The fact that many market eggs are decomposed was accounted for by storage under unfavorable circumstances, i.e., filthy conditions and warm temperature and the fact that bacteria are given an opportunity to enter when the gelatinous coating is removed from eggs during washing and handling.

Decomposition of eggs, according to Haines and Moran,[64] was occasioned mainly by bacteria which entered the egg after laying. They showed that the shell is porous and permits bacteria to enter. Relative temperatures of the egg and its environment were found to be important. If the temperature of the egg was higher than a fluid containing bacteria in which it was immersed, bacteria were readily drawn into the egg by suction as the egg cooled. About the same conclusions were reached by Rievel [65] from results secured with a different technic.

Bacteria in Egg White. Available data on this subject are conflicting. Many of those who have found no bacteria in egg white have assumed that this component of the egg possessed a bactericidal action. Wurtz,[66] Rettger Sperry,[67] Scholl,[68] Horowitz,[38] Turro,[69] Laschtschenko,[70] and Riezicka[71] reached the same conclusions. Sperry [72] showed that cold-storage eggs exhibited the same action. Bainbridge,[73] Poppe,[37] Hoppert,[59] Mauer,[32] and Laschtschenko [70] found no germicidal action. Mauer was especially interested in *Escherichia coli*. Rettger and Sperry employed *Clostridium putrificum* and *Bacillus edematis maligni* as the test organisms. Egg white in test tubes was heavily inoculated with the test organisms and incubated under conditions favorable to their development. In the yolk, which was treated in the same manner, evident putrefaction set in, while in egg white, bacteria were destroyed since examination with the microscope failed to demonstrate presence of cells. Haines [53] observed that 98 per cent of whites of eggs which he examined were sterile.

Hadley and Caldwell,[41] in their extensive investigation of eggs, reported data which confirm that of Rettger and Sperry. Fleming and

64. Haines and Moran. 1940. J. Hyg. 40, 453-461.
65. Rievel. 1939. Ztschr. f. Hyg. u. Infektionskrank. 122, 41-53.
66. Wurtz. 1890. Centbl. Bakt. 7, 352.
67. Rettger and Sperry. 1912. J. Med. Res. 26, 55.
68. Scholl. 1893. Arch. f. Hyg. 17, 535.
69. Turro. 1902. Centbl. Bakt., Pt. 1. Orig., 32, 107.
70. Laschtschenko. 1909. Ztschr. f. Hyg. u. Infektionskrank. 64, 419.
71. Riezicka. 1912. Arch. f. Hyg. 77, 369.
72. Sperry. 1913. Science 38, 413.
73. Bainbridge. 1911. J. Hyg. 11, 341.

Allison [74] have shown that egg white contains a bacteriolytic, bactericidal, and bacterio-inhibitory substance which they named *lysozyme*. On a susceptible bacterium, the lytic power was still manifest when the egg white was diluted 50,000,000 times. The bacteriolytic power of egg white from different species of birds varied considerably when tested on the same organism. The egg yolk had a very slight antibacterial action on a susceptible organism, but when tested on a less susceptible organism, it apparently had no antibacterial power and to some extent inhibited the bactericidal action of the egg white. Egg white inhibited the growth of most of the pathogenic bacteria tested, and had a definite lethal or lytic effect on many of these bacteria, e.g., Staphylococcus, Streptococcus, Menigococcus, *Eberthella typhosa, Bacillus anthracis*, etc. The lysozyme of egg white resisted peptic and tryptic digestion, and following the ingestion of raw egg white by mouth the number of streptococci in the feces was temporarily much reduced. Egg white added to blood *in vitro* maintained its antibacterial action, and when injected intravenously into an animal it conferred on the blood serum of the animal marked antibacterial powers which were evident after several hours.

May's [75] work on the germicidal action of egg white on *Salmonella pullorum* may be mentioned here. He went over some earlier work in which dilutions of egg white one to 20 were used and which seemed to indicate an indifferent action of the egg white towards the bacteria used with the exception of *Bacillus proteus zenkeri* which was killed off quickly in high dilutions. In the repeated experiments, eggs from one to five days old were used. They had been kept in an ice chest until used. In general, May was unable to demonstrate definite germicidal or inhibitory effect in one to 20 or higher dilution of egg albumen. He did observe, however, inhibition by undiluted egg white or by very low dilution.

Sharp and Whitaker [76] found that the germicidal power of egg white was markedly influenced by hydrogen-ion concentration, which decreases rapidly during the first few days' storage of untreated eggs in a ventilated room. These investigators explained the conflicting results of previous workers on the basis that they did not take into account the age of the eggs and, consequently, the hydrogen-ion concentration, when testing the germicidal action of the white. For vegetative cells of *Bacillus subtilis* egg white was very germicidal at all hydrogen-ion concentrations, while the spores were more resistant. The toxic substance which killed the vegetative cells was separated from the egg white by dialysis, the diffusate becoming nongermicidal on standing. The hydrogen-ion concentration corresponding to that at the time the egg was laid, permitted growth, while the hydrogen-ion concentration corresponding to that of whites which have been stored a few days in air, was germicidal to a number of common organisms. In another paper, Sharp [77] placed hydrogen-ion concentration first among the factors involved in the preservation of eggs.

74. Fleming and Allison. 1924. Lancet, 1924, Pt. 1, 1903.
75. May. 1924. Rhode Island Agr. Expt. Sta. Bull. 197.
76. Sharp and Whitaker. 1927. J. Bact. 14, 17-46.
77. Sharp. 1929. Science 69, 278-280.

Bacteria in the Egg Yolk. Practically all investigators are agreed that yolk contains the greater number of bacteria. Hadley and Caldwell [41] found 8.7 per cent of 2,520 eggs infected in the yolks. Mauer [32] is said to have found 18.1 per cent of the yolks to be infected. Bushnell and Mauer [40] found 23.7 per cent. Rettger's data were corrected to show a yolk infection of 9.9 per cent, covering examinations over a period of three years. Qualitative studies of the bacteria in eggs have been reported by several investigators. Rettger [39] gave the following bacteria:

Fresh eggs	Number of times found
Staphylococcus, usually *aureus* or *albus*	74
Subtilis, usually *B. mesentericus* or *B. ramosus*	60
Escherichia coli and closely related organisms	43
Proteus group	30
Streptococcus	14
Micrococcus (tetragenus, etc.)	9
Streptothrix	6
Diphtheroid bacillus	5
Putrefactive anaerobes	5
Pseudomonas fluorescens	2
Mold	4
Bacillus mucosus	3
Mixed	2

Hadley and Caldwell studied 40 different strains isolated from eggs. Among them were found 11 cocci, 28 rods, and one spirillum. No streptococci were reported. They observed no member of the hemorrhagic, septicemia, intestinal, proteus, colon, enteritidis, typhoid dysentery or diphtheria groups. *Salmonella pullorum* was not observed in 2,520 eggs. No anaerobic bacteria were sought. Hadley and Caldwell noticed more different types of bacteria on control plates than on egg plates. The percentage of infected eggs found by different investigators is given below:

Name	Examined	Per cent infected
Rettger	3,510	9.5
Rettger (10 ml. samples)	647	3.86
Bushnell and Mauer	2,759	23.70
Hadley and Caldwell	2,520	8.70
Mauer	600	18.10

Hadley and Caldwell's work may be summarized as follows:

Of 2,510 fresh eggs from 65 hens examined by the indirect method, 8.8 per cent showed infection of the yolk. None of 111 whites examined showed the presence of bacteria while the yolks of the same eggs gave a percentage of 4.5 per cent, less than the average of 8.8 for the series. The percentages of infection obtained for individual hens per year varied between 2.8 and 15. No hen laid sterile eggs during the whole year. No correlation was observed between the percentage of infection for any individual hen and the degree of fecundity. Approximately the same amount of infection was found among fertile eggs (6.9 per cent of 422 eggs examined) as among infertile eggs (8.9 per cent infected out of 315 eggs). Infection of eggs seemed to have no relation to hatchability. No definite seasonal variation of infection was observed, nor did the eggs from pullets and hens vary greatly as to bacterial content.

Wagner [78] described *Bacillus mycoides* var. *ovoaethylicus* as capable of producing alcoholic fermentation in eggs without evidence of putrefaction. Infected eggs cannot be distinguished from sound eggs by superficial examination. Wagner stated that the membranes remained intact and the only visible evidence of infection was a number of lens-shaped colonies about one millimeter in diameter distributed through the outer yolk. A great number of eggs were examined by Wagener,[79] especially for *Pseudomonas aeruginosa*. This organism was found in only a few specimens.

Liquid Egg. Few food products are more perishable than eggs when they have been removed from their shells. Spoilage is greatly inhibited, however, by using high-quality eggs and breaking them under strictly sanitary conditions. In view of the fact that spoilage is due largely to activities of microorganisms, studies of the microbial population become important. Eggs have been found to contain pathogenic bacteria, which suggests a possible health hazard, though slight, of liquid eggs. This product cannot be pasteurized as can other products to make them safe. Mallmann and Churchill [80] have stressed the significance of low numbers of bacteria. The keeping quality of egg contents was said to be determined by the number of putrefactive bacteria which are in the product when prepared. This number, in turn, is influenced by methods used in processing.

Liquid eggs are liable to be heavily seeded with bacteria. Their chemical constitution makes them quite susceptible to microbial attack if they are not handled under the most satisfactory condition. This has been shown by Thomas [81] and by the Bristol Health Committee.[82] The former found extensive bacterial contamination in imported frozen eggs, while the latter authority found coliform bacteria to be frequently present in liquid eggs imported into England from China. Other microorganisms, such as aerobic sporeformers, Staphylococci, and a few Streptococci, were also found. Since liquid-egg products are usually used for making pastries, they were examined also for these bacteria. Coliform bacteria seemed to be destroyed by baking but the other species appeared able to survive. This was not considered to be a menace to health but was believed to interfere with the keeping quality of the products.

Mallmann and Churchill's [80] **Procedure for Detecting Bacteria in Liquid-Egg Meats During Processing.** This is a direct microscope method which the authors believed could easily be applied to plant control. Samples may be collected and taken to the laboratory or films may be made in the field and mailed to the laboratory. The procedure, as given by Mallmann and Churchill, follows:

78. Wagner. 1916. Ztschr. f. Untersuch. der Nahr. u. Genussmtl. 31, 233-237.
79. Wagener. 1929. Rev. in Bull. Inst. Pasteur 27, 938.
80. Mallmann and Churchill. 1942. Ice and Refrig., May 1942.
81. Thomas. 1935. Pub. Health 48, 320-322.
82. Brit. Med. J., 1936, p. 365.

Collection of the Sample. For plant control, samples of the product can be collected at any point after the egg meats have been churned to give an even distribution of the bacteria in the entire mass.

Samples may also be taken as scrapings from equipment to detect sources of contamination or samples may be taken of individual eggs if desired.

The sample is collected by dipping the tip of a sterile wooden applicator into the egg meats to be examined.

Preparation of the Film Slide. A drop of the egg meat is discharged on a clean microscope slide placed beneath a standard-thickness oiled paper cut so that an area one centimeter wide the length of the slide is exposed. The egg meat is deposited at the end of the slide. Using another clean slide the egg meat is spread evenly over the exposed area by drawing the end of the second slide over the egg meat and drawing the excess ahead of the slide and leaving behind a continuous film of constant thickness. The spreader slide should be held lightly in the fingers at an angle of 45° to the slide to be smeared. The waxed paper margins on the slide serve to hold the egg meat within a straight channel and act as a guide to give a constant depth to the film. A clean spreader slide must be used for each sample.

After the egg meats have been spread the slide is removed and the waxed paper guide is discarded. The smeared slide is dried in a horizontal position. A warm table may be used to facilitate drying.

Staining the Film. After the film is thoroughly dried it is immersed in the following staining bath:

1 gm. methylene blue (certified for bact. use)
500 ml. 95 per cent ethyl alcohol
5 ml. conc. hydrochloric acid.

The slide should remain in the staining bath from three to five minutes.

The slide is removed from the staining bath and dipped into tap water. The slide should remain in the water just long enough to remove the excess stain from the film without decolorizing the bacteria. Care should be taken not to leave the slide too long in the water, because the film will take up water and wash off the slide.

The film should be dried in a horizontal position using a warm table if examination is to be made immediately.

Examination of the Stained Film. The film is examined by means of the microscope using a 1.8 to 2 mm. oil immersion objective and 10X eyepiece. Artificial light passed through a red Wratten filter No. 24 or its equivalent should be used. White or blue lights fail to give sufficient contrast to show the faintly stained blue organisms. The bacteria appear bluish-black in color with a red background due to the filter. Only the bacteria retain the stain. A very slight amount of color is retained in the background of egg meats to aid in focusing the microscope.

The area of the microscope field should be determined and the reported count should be the number of bacteria per square centimeter of film. One hundred microscopic fields should be counted to obtain an accurate count.

If the diameter of the microscope field is .17 mm. with a 10X eyepiece, there will be 4,424 fields per square centimeter of film area.

It will be observed that in this procedure no attempt has been made to report the results of the direct microscope method by the customary bacteria per gram. The number of organisms per gram is not important provided the evaluating system gives the number of bacteria on a comparable basis so that the number in one sample can be compared with another. This is accomplished in this test by maintaining a film of constant thickness so that the number of bacteria per square centimeter of film represents a constant volume. Standards for this procedure can be set by an analysis of a large number of counts based on eggs from various sources with diverse bacteria contents.

A comparison with the plate count can be made roughly, but it must be remembered that the microscope procedure shows all the stainable bacteria, and that not all these bacteria will necessarily grow on nutrient agar medium used at present for measuring the bacteria counts of egg meats. In one sample of egg meats examined the bacteria count by the plating method at 20°C.(68°F.) for 72 hours was relatively low, whereas the direct microscope count was high. When the agar plates were incubated for seven days many colonies appeared that were invisible in 72 hours. At this time the direct microscope count and the plate counts were comparable.

An approximation of the relative relationship of the direct microscope count and the plate count follows:

RELATIONSHIP OF DIRECT MICROSCOPE COUNT AND PLATE COUNT

Direct microscope count number per 1 sq. cm. film	Plate count bacteria per gm. egg meat
4,500	750,000
450	75,000
45	7,500

The writers stated that these figures were approximations and were based on too few samples to be dependable comparisons even if comparisons were permissible.

Frozen Eggs. This has become a large industry in America. Numerous reports have been made concerning the microorganisms involved. The marked susceptibility of eggs to bacterial decomposition, as well as the fact that unfit eggs may be used, presents some interesting bacteriological problems. Stiles and Bates [7] prepared frozen eggs in the laboratory from second-grade eggs. Such a product generally had a bacterial content of 1,000,000 per gram. Frozen eggs prepared from spots, rots, and blood rings gave a bacterial content of 4,000,000 to 1,000,000,000 per gram with a relatively high content of *Escherichia coli* and streptococcus. Pennington *et al.*[83] pointed out the difficulties of proper sanitary control of the industry. Keith [84] suggested that the addition of sucrose to the broken eggs before freezing would improve their quality. In France, where during hot weather many cases of food poisoning have been traced to cakes and pastries with so-called cream fillings, bacteriological examinations of canned frozen eggs revealed a mixed flora of molds and bacteria. French food-control officials advised careful control of the industry. Bordas [85] believed that frozen eggs could be a menace to health unless they were of good quality before freezing and kept frozen until consumed.

Mauer,[32] Pennington,[86] and Stiles and Bates [17] pointed out the evil consequences that might result from the use of unsound eggs. Mauer believed that when a bad egg was encountered, the hands and utensils with which it came in contact should be washed in clean water or treated with live steam. Similar observations were made by Pennington and Robertson.[81] Stiles and Bates reported that frozen-egg products prepared in the laboratory in Washington from second-grade eggs comprising "undersized," "dirties," and "weak eggs" generally showed a total bacterial content of less than 1,000,000 organisms per gram, while dried eggs prepared from the same grades usually contained a total bacterial content of less than 4,000,000 organisms per gram, both kinds containing but a very small number of *Escherichia coli*; from a bacteriological standpoint they were

83. Pennington *et al.* 1916. U. S. Dept. Agr. Bull. 224.
84. Keith. 1910. Rev. in Chem. Abs. 5 (1911), 3103.
85. Bordas. 1922. Rev. d'Hyg. 44, 613.
86. Pennington *et al.* 1914. U. S. Dept. Agr. Bur. Chem. Bull. 51.

considered to be an edible product. Frozen products made from "light spots," "heavy spots," "blood rings," and "rots" showed bacterial counts generally ranging from about 1,000,000 to 1,000,000,000, while dried eggs made from the same grade contained from 4,000,000 to more than 1,000,000,000 organisms per gram with a relatively high proportion of *Escherichia coli* and Streptococci in both the frozen and dried material, indicating an unwholesome article, unfit for food, and only useful for technical purposes. While the principal of preserving food by the abstraction of moisture and refrigeration was recognized as a perfectly legitimate business when applied to wholesome products, no amount of freezing and desiccation will rejuvenate eggs already decomposed in whole or in part. The experiments reported on frozen- and dried-egg products kept at low temperatures indicated during the early part of storage a general rise in the bacterial content with a subsequent decline in numbers. This decline was more marked in the case of dried eggs containing 10 per cent added sugar than in similar products to which no sugar was added, indicating that the sugar had acted as an antiseptic, as might be expected; such an addition might, therefore, be employed to conceal inferiority. The egg industry in this country constitutes so valuable a source of food that it is essential that undesirable practices attending any branch of it be remedied. Increased care in the production and handling of this highly perishable article on the part of the producer and the buyer will, to a large extent, bring about desired conditions.

Samples of imported Chinese frozen eggs, analyzed by Verge and Grasset,[87] gave counts on gelatin of 85,000 per gram of yolks, 5,000 for the whites and 30,000 for the whole eggs. After standing for 48 hours at laboratory temperature, these counts had increased to 3,600,000, 360,000, and 4,000,000, respectively. On account of the large number of bacteria in frozen eggs, Cartier [88] believed that this method of preservation should be used only when other methods could not be employed. He reported counts as high as 104 million per gram in mixed whites and yolks.

Quick-freezing according to Swenson and James [89] yielded a better product than slow-freezing. They also observed some improvement in quality from carbonation just before freezing. Combination of use of one per cent of salt and quick-freezing was also a good practice. Nielsen and Garnatz [90] later stated that from 10 to 14 per cent of salt added to egg products retarded bacterial growth during mixing and freezing and, combined with the action of $-18°C.(-.4°F.)$ storage temperature, reduced the number of viable bacteria to less than 10 per cent of the original count in the first month of storage.

Frozen eggs, in some cases, may be shipped long distances. Those from China are best known. The Ministry of Health of Great Britain [91] found frozen eggs packed in China suitable for consumption when properly

87. Verge and Grasset. 1928. Rec. de Méd. Vét. 114, 657-672.
88. Cartier. 1928. Rev. de Path. Compar. 28, 706-708.
89. Swenson and James. 1933. U. S. Egg and Poultry Mag. 41, 16-19.
90. Nielsen and Garnatz. 1940. First Food Conf., Inst. Food Technol., Proc. 289-294.
91. Gt. Brit. Min. of Health, Chief Med. Off. Ann. Rpt. for 1934, p. 120.

packed and handled. Bacterial counts were low and no communicable disease had been traced to such a product.

Schneiter's [92] **Procedures for Microbiological Examination of Frozen Eggs.** The bacteriological examination of egg products involves different factors for each different class, but only methods for the microbiological examination of frozen egg products are to be considered at this time.

The major portion of the output of the frozen egg industry is utilized in the preparation of food products that receive little or no heat processing during their manufacture. It is, therefore, essential that the frozen egg products used be free from large numbers and types of viable microorganisms, which may induce rapid spoilage or be of potential danger to health when incorporated in foods.

Microbiological methods for the examination of frozen egg products should include procedures for the determination of (1) the total numbers of microorganisms and (2) the incidence of types of microorganisms that may be dangerous to health or conducive to food spoilage.

While the presence of large numbers of viable microorganims in frozen egg products is indicative of the use of poor quality shelf stock, unsatisfactory manufacturing procedures, or insanitary plant conditions, a high incidence of coliform organisms and hemolytic types of bacteria may be, in addition, indicative of potential danger to health.

The following microbiological methods are proposed:

I. SAMPLING

EQUIPMENT

(1) Electric drill with auger (12″ x 1″), (2) alcohol burner, (3) alcohol (95% C_2H_5OH), (4) absorbent cotton, (5) two tablespoons, (6) sample containers (sterile 1 qt. or 1 pt. Mason jars), (7) hammer and steel strip (12″ x 2″ x 0.25″) or other tool for opening cans, (8) water pail, (9) towels, and (10) record book, pencils, etc.

PROCEDURE

Select a representative number of cans from lot (square root of total). Note and record all marks of identification, for example: firm name and location, brand, type product, code or lot numbers, etc. Sterilize auger and tablespoons by sponging off with alcohol-soaked cotton and heating in flame of alcohol burner. Wash drill and spoons in pail of water and re-sterilize after each container sampled. Open the containers aseptically. Drill three cores equidistant between side and center of can and one-third of periphery apart. Transfer drillings from can to sample container with sterile tablespoon. Examine product organoleptically by smelling at opening of drill-hole after sample is removed. (Heat produced by electric drill intensifies odor of egg material, thus facilitating the organoleptic examination.) Record odors as normal, putrid, sour, or musty.

Refrigerate samples with dry ice if analysis is to be delayed or sampling point is at some distance from laboratory. Carry out sampling procedure under as nearly aseptic conditions as possible.

II. ANALYTICAL PROCEDURE

PREPARATION OF SAMPLE

Thaw frozen egg material as rapidly as possible in order to prevent an increase in the numbers of microorganisms present and at temperatures sufficiently low to prevent destruction of microorganisms (20°-30°C.). (Frequent shaking aids in thawing the frozen material. Thawing temperatures may be maintained by the use of a water bath.)

Thoroughly mix each thawed sample with spoon or electric stirrer before analysis. Prepare a 1-10 dilution by aseptically weighing 5.0 grams of egg material into a wide-mouthed glass-stoppered bottle containing 45 grams of sterile physiological salt

92. Schneiter. 1939. Assoc. Off. Agr. Chem. J. 22, 625-628; also 25 (1941), 740-745.

solution (0.85% NaCl per 1,000 ml. distilled water) and 1 tablespoonful of glass shot. Agitate the 1-10 dilution thoroughly to insure complete solution or distribution of the egg material in the diluent. Prepare serial dilutions from 1-100 to 1-100,000,000 for inoculation into various culture media. Inoculate all media within 15 minutes after the sample is prepared.

PLATE COUNTS

Inoculate duplicate plates with 1 ml. portions of all dilutions from 1-1,000 to 1-1,000,000. (Nutrient agar or dextrose agar may be employed as plating media.) Incubate one set of plates at 20°-30°C. for 3 days and the second set of plates at 37°C. for 3 days. Express final results as numbers of viable microorganisms per gram of egg material. (Uniformly higher counts are always obtained on plates incubated at 20°-30°C.)

INCIDENCE OF COLIFORM GROUP

Inoculate 1.0 ml. portions from suitable dilutions (1-10 to 1-100,000,000) of egg material into fermentation tubes of lactose broth. Incubate at 37°C. for 24-48 hours.

Streak Levine's eosin methylene blue agar plates from all lactose broth cultures showing gas production. Incubate plates at 37°C. for 24-48 hours. Examine E.M.B. agar plates for colonies of microorganisms of the coliform group.

Inoculate from colonies of the coliform types of bacteria appearing on E.M.B. agar plates to nutrient agar slants. Incubate at 37°C. for 24 hours. Purify cultures for further study.

Obtain biochemical reactions of purified cultures by Kovac's test, indol production; methyl red (M.R.) and Voges Proskauer (V.P.) tests; and Koser's sodium citrate test, utilization of sodium citrate as the sole source of carbon.

NOTE: Follow procedure recommended in *Standard Methods of Water Analysis*, 8th Ed., 1936, of The American Public Health Association for Biochemical Reactions.

HEMOLYTIC TYPES OF MICROORGANISMS

Inoculate petri plates with 1 ml. portions of all dilutions from 1-100 to 1-1,000,000. Pour plates with veal-infusion agar containing 6% of defibrinated horse, sheep, or rabbit blood (0.6 ml. of blood per 10 ml. of media). Cool agar to 40°C. and add blood just prior to pouring plates. (Incubate plates for 24 hours at 37°C.) Express final results as numbers per gram.

ANAEROBIC TYPES OF MICROORGANISMS

Inoculate tubes containing chopped meat media with 1 ml. portions of all dilutions from 1-10 to 1-100,000. Incubate for 3 days at 37°C.

DIRECT MICROSCOPE COUNTS

Place 0.01 ml. of the 1-10 or 1-100 dilutions of egg material on a clean microscope slide and spread over an area of 1.0 sq. cm. Permit the smear preparation to dry on a level surface at 30°-40°C. Proceed as directed in *Standard Methods of Milk Analysis* of the American Public Health Association (latest edition). Multiply total count by 10 or 100, since the original smear preparation was made from a 1-10 at 1-100 dilution in order to obtain the numbers of bacteria per gram of egg material.

III. CULTURE MEDIA

STANDARD METHODS MEDIA

Prepare as recommended in *Standard Methods of Water Analysis*, 8th Ed., 1936, of The American Public Health Association.

Nutrient agar, lactose broth, Levine's eosin methylene blue agar, tryptophane broth, methyl red-Voges Proskauer peptone medium, and Koser's sodium citrate medium.

Other media include (a) *Dextrose agar.*—Standard nutrient agar plus 1.0% dextrose. (b) *Veal infusion agar.*—Ground lean veal, 500.0 grams, and distilled water, 1000.0 ml. Infuse overnight in refrigerator and strain through cheesecloth without pressure. Make up to original volume and skim off any fat. Steam in Arnold 30 minutes and filter through paper. Add:

	per cent		grams
Peptone (Difco)	1.0	or	10.0
NaCl	0.5	or	5.0
Agar	1.5	or	15.0

Steam in Arnold to dissolve. Adjust reaction to pH 7.6 and steam in Arnold 15 minutes. Filter through Buchner funnel with paper pulp mat, by the aid of suction. Use egg albumen for clarification when necessary. Distribute 10 ml. quantities into test tubes or 80 ml. quantities into bottles. Sterilize at 15 lbs. pressure for 20 minutes. Final pH 7.4. (For hemolytic tests agar should be cooled to 40°C. and 6% of defibrinated horse, sheep, or rabbit blood added prior to pouring plates (0.6 ml. of blood per 10 ml. of media.)

(c) *Holman's cooked meat medium (alkaline).*—Distilled water, 1000 ml., ground fresh lean beef, 500 grams, bacto-peptone, 5 grams, and C. P. NaCl, 5 grams. Infuse the beef-water mixture overnight in refrigerator. Strain through several layers of cheesecloth and press out broth, retaining the meat press cake. Add distilled water to the infusion to make 1 liter. Add the peptone and heat in the Arnold or boil 10 minutes. Filter, and add salt. Add normal NaOH until alkaline to phenolphthalein. Heat in Arnold 15 minutes to clear and filter. Distribute the pressed-out beef remaining from the infusion into medium sized tubes (150 x 20 mm.), approximately 2 grams into each tube, and add 10 ml. of the cleared alkaline broth. Sterilize in the autoclave at 15 lbs. pressure for 15 minutes. Final reaction should be pH 7.2-7.4. Store in refrigerator. Prior to using, boil the tubed medium for at least 10 minutes to expel adsorbed oxygen and cool promptly in a water bath.

The Manual Methods for Pure Culture Study of Bacteria of the Society of American Bacteriologists should be used as a guide for the further study of microorganisms obtained in the cultural procedures described.

In order to determine whether these procedures were satisfactory, Schneiter [92] submitted identical samples to several collaborators who used the recommended methods in examining them. Most of the plate counts reported by all collaborators were in agreement with respect to grading the samples as of good or bad bacteriological quality. Several exceptions were observed but were believed to be within the possibility of experimental error. Results reported for the incidence of coliform bacteria were in close agreement for all samples but three. Wider discrepancies were observed in the results of microscope counts made by two collaborators.

Organoleptic tests [93] have been applied to frozen eggs by federal food-control officials. These involve the organs of touch, taste, and smell. Results of this method are determined largely by the experience of those who make the tests and are not always confirmed. This was shown in an alleged adulteration of frozen eggs in 1941.

DRIED EGGS

Production of dried eggs has become a great industry during recent years. One reason for this is the amount required for export. Production capacity for 1941 was anticipated to exceed 150 million pounds.[94] The chemical nature of eggs makes it necessary to use every precaution possible

93. Notices of Judgment Under the Federal Food, Drug and Cosmetic Act, Federal Security Agency, March 1943, No. 3508.
94. Stateler. 1941. Indus. 13, 40 *et seq.*

in securing a high-grade raw product and to handle it carefully in clean apparatus during drying. While bacteria are generally credited with much of the deterioration in egg products, it is known that enzymes may be involved as well as metals. Traces of the latter may lead to rancidity. The microbial content of dried eggs has been found to be high. Haines [95] mentioned three reasons for this: the desire to store the highest grade eggs in the shell and the use of lower grade eggs for drying, introduction of many microorganisms on the shell into the egg during breaking, and multiplication of bacteria in the stored egg powder.

Some of the early work on dried eggs was carried out by Stiles and Bates [7] with eggs which were dried under laboratory conditions and on samples which were imported. Bacteriological examination of 75 samples of dried imported egg whites showed that nine out of 75 samples, or 12 per cent, contained 1,000,000 organisms or less per gram while 46 samples, or 61.3 per cent, showed 10 million or more per gram. Fifty-two per cent of samples of commercially dried eggs showed 100 million or more bacteria per gram. Whether these heavy bacterial loads were due to low-grade eggs or to faulty handling during and after drying could not be stated. The bacterial numbers just quoted were apparently only those species which grew on aerobic plates. Pennington [83] reviewed the methods of manufacture of dried eggs and reported results of bacteriological examinations of many samples, histories of which were known. For breaking purposes reputable firms use all under-sized or over-sized, dirty, cracked, or shrunken eggs. Such eggs should be candled, broken, and dried under chilled conditions. The lowest count on flaky dried eggs was 65,000 per gram and the highest count was 20,000,000 per gram. The average count for 48 samples was 3,600,000. The number of *Escherichia coli* varied from 0 to 1,000,000. About three times as many bacteria were found in the dried product as in the liquid egg. Ross [96] examined 248 samples of dried eggs which had been stored at different temperatures, finding that the desiccated egg loses a large percentage of the bacteria originally present if stored for a relatively short period. A more rapid diminution of bacteria results if the storage takes place at higher temperatures. He stated that a product even from spots and worse, might satisfy the ordinary bacterial tests if stored for a period of a few months.

Sartory and Flament [97] examined some desiccated commercial egg powders and found a strict aerobic flora. *Staphylococcus citreus, Escherichia coli, Bacillus subtilis*, etc., were isolated. Ten thousand aerobic bacteria per gram in dried eggs were reported by Marcardier and Goiyon.[98] *Penicillium glaucum* was always present. Since dried eggs are not sterile, they are subject to bacterial decomposition. These authors stated that each package of egg powder should bear the date of manufacture and should not be shipped far. Wyant [99] reported the bacteriological examination of two

95. Haines. 1939. (Gt. Brit.) Food Invest. Bd., Spec. Rpt. No. 47.
96. Ross. 1914. Iowa Acad. Sci. Proc. 21, 33-49.
97. Sartory and Flament. 1920. Acad. de Med. Bull. 83, 46-47.
98. Marcardier and Goiyon. 1920. Ann. des Falsif. 13, 96-97.
99. Wyant. 1922. Mich. Agr. Expt. Sta. Ann. Rpt., 1920.

samples of dried eggs. One sample contained 40,000,000 per gram and the other 60,000,000. Two specimens of dried eggs analyzed at the Michigan Agricultural Experiment Station [100] contained 40,000,000 and 66,000,000 bacteria per gram. Lactose fermenting bacteria were absent. In a study of the bacteriology of dried eggs, DeBord [101] found a variable content of bacteria. In general, there was agreement between the quality of the raw product and the method of dehydration. The counts in whole eggs dehydrated by the spray process varied from 350 in the good egg to 1,160,000 in the "spots." In the product prepared by the vacuum drum process from whole egg the counts varied from 45,000 in the good egg to 2,400,000 in the "rots." The yolk, in general, showed more bacteria than the white. The count in stored dehydrated egg depends on several factors, such as initial count, length of time in storage, and temperature in storage. An initial count of 350 in a good egg decreased to 300 in 10 months when held at 37°C.(98.6°F.) and at 20°C.(68°F.), while a count of rotten eggs decreased to 1,350 when held at 37°C. In another sample of rotten eggs the count increased from 235,000 to 430,000 in three months.

Bacteriological Examination of Dried Eggs. Stiles and Bates [7] stated that solid egg products should be examined on the gram basis. Weigh five grams into a sterile glass-stoppered bottle and add enough water to make a one to 10 dilution. Addition of sterile glass beads to the bottle before agitation facilitates disintegration of the sample. After thorough shaking the sample should be plated in dilution of one to 10,000 and higher to about one to 10 million. Incubate the plates from three to five days at both 37°C.(98.6°F.) and room temperature.

Presence of coliform bacteria may be determined by inoculating fermentation tubes containing various media, such as brilliant green bile, formate ricinoleate broth, or other similar media. Presence of Streptococci may be determined by staining films prepared from the fermentation tubes.

Bacterial Standards for Dried Eggs. Questionable sanitary quality of eggs and conditions under which they were dried, prompted food control officials to seek methods which might be used in the industry. These have included examination of the eggs, inspection of establishments in which they are dried and finally examination of the final product. Among the latter are "plate counts" which have been used for examination of other foods. Plate count standards for dried eggs have been difficult to determine. Consequently there is no agreement with respect to what they should be. This prompts one to wonder why those which are used were adopted and on what grounds. Goresline [101a] recently said that high bacterial counts indicate laxity of supervision and faulty equipment in the egg drying plant. He failed, however, to tell what a high count is in dried eggs.

Circular 583, Eggs and Egg Products of the U. S. Department of Agriculture, gives no bacterial standards. Von Loesecke in his *Drying and Dehydration of Foods* stated that dried whole eggs should not contain

100. Mich. State Bd. Agr., 59th Ann Rpt., 1920.
101. DeBord. 1925. J. Agr. Res. 31, 155
101a. Goresline. 1943. Proc. Inst. Food Tech., 70-76.

more than 300,000 viable organisms per gram. More detailed standards have been issued by the Quartermaster Corps of the U. S. Army, as follows:

"Standard Bacterial Plate Count—

"a. Shall not exceed one hundred fifty thousand (150,000) per gram. The plating medium shall be Standard Nutrient Agar and the plates shall be incubated at 37°C. for 48 hours.

"b. Coliform organisms shall not exceed one hundred (100) per gram when examined under methods prescribed in the Standard Methods for Examination of Dairy Products, American Public Health Association, 1941.

"c. Yeast and mold count shall not exceed one hundred (100) cells per gram respectively when incubated on Potato Dextrose Agar at 32°C., for 48 hours."

Those who use plate counts frequently ascribe to them an accuracy which they do not possess. Plate counts are subject to many errors. They have been discussed in several other places in this book and for milk especially on page 320. The quotation from Wilson's, *The Bacteriological Grading of Milk* applies as much to dried eggs as it does to milk.

In the dairy industry the results secured from the agar plate are now said to be merely an "estimate." This word has a general meaning, to calculate approximately, roughly appraise or to form an opinion without the use of precision apparatus or technic. Breed (1927) who suggested use of the term *estimate*, said that as far as milk was concerned, no one had ever actually counted the number of bacteria in a cubic centimeter of milk in the same way that the number of people in a room have been counted. If this is true for milk how much more it would hold for a product like dried eggs.

Another objection is that "plate counts" do not consider the type of organism which is involved. This is more important than numbers. A "count" of microorganisms in egg powder of 100 per gm. might be much more significant than a count of 200,000 per gm. The former might be harmful pathogenic bacteria while the latter might be harmless saprophytes no more significant in dried eggs than in any other food. "Plate counts" have been largely used as whips in the past over the heads of manufacturers and others who did not understand them and who were led to believe that they were significant. Bacteriologists should be the first to wake up to the false implications which are involved.

Fermentation of Egg Whites. Egg whites contain sugar which tends to cause darkening during storage. In order to prevent this trouble, egg whites are fermented to remove the sugar content. Resulting also from the fermentation is an increase in acidity and thinning of the thick portions which allows the mucin to be removed. According to Conquest [102] the best temperature for this is 26.7 to 29.4°C. (80 to 85°F.) and the time two days. During fermentation, foam forms and the product is improved by removal of various types of foreign matter. Success of fermentation is measureable by the odor of the finished product. At one time, high acidities resulting from fermentation were neutralized but the practice has been discontinued. Conquest stated that the Chinese once used ammonium hydroxide, depending on subsequent treatment, to get rid of the excess.

102. Conquest. 1941. Food Indus. 13, 95.

Aerobacter aerogenes and *Escherichia freundii* were reported by Stuart and Goresline [103] to be the predominating bacteria in normal fermentations of egg white. In abnormal fermentations members of the genera Proteus, Pseudomonas, and Serratia predominated. In these fermentations proteolysis occurred and a longer time was required for the egg white to reach a pH of 6.1 which had been correlated with reduction in free sugar. Egg white from fresh eggs with a low initial number of bacteria fermented slowly and irregularly. When many bacteria were present, fermentation was rapid and regular. Egg white separated from storage eggs with a large number of bacteria, which originated in the egg and not from shell contamination, fermented slowly. No members of the genera Aerobacter and Escherichia were found in these whites. A much better product was secured when they were present than when the fermentation was carried on by other species.

PRESERVATION AND STORAGE OF EGGS

Eggs are produced mainly during a few months of the year. Consequently, it is necessary to resort to methods of preservation. The nature of the egg and its chemical constitution make it very susceptible to attack by microorganisms. Jones and DuBois [104] classified the various methods of preservation as follows: (1) low temperatures; (2) airtight packing; (3) sealing with various agents, and (4) immersing in preserving solutions. They believed that the bacteria which were contributed to the egg by careless methods of handling were more important than the congenital forms. Sharp [105] reviewed much literature on this subject. He believed that oil coating of the shell was the cheapest and most successful method of preserving eggs. This prevents loss of moisture and carbon dioxide. Swenson [106] also described a vacuum-oil process which delayed deteriorative changes in eggs.

Gas Storage of Eggs. Continued storage of eggs presents many problems which have to be considered. A balance must be maintained between factors each of which alone has distinct disadvantages. Moran [107] stated that the relative humidity should not exceed 85 per cent during storage at —.6°C.(31°F.) else mold development ultimately penetrates the shell. At this humidity, however, evaporation is appreciable (.12 per cent per week). This results in a larger air cell with loss of quality in the egg. In view of this fact, the ideal situation is to store eggs in a saturated atmosphere, or nearly so, and use some method of inhibiting molds. "Gas storage" in atmospheres of carbon dioxide which inhibits molds was believed to offer some hope. Some 60 per cent of carbon dioxide was required to completely inhibit mold development over nine months on eggs stored at 0°C.(32°F.). Lower amounts, such as 2½ per cent, have but slight inhibitory value.

103. Stuart and Goresline. 1942. J. Bact. 43, 47; 44 (1942), 541-549.
104. Jones and DuBois. 1920. J. Ind. Eng. Chem. 12, 751-757.
105. Sharp. 1937. Food Research 2, 477-498.
106. Swenson. 1938. Idem 3, 599-608.
107. Moran. 1937. (Gt. Brit.) Food Invest. Bd., Ann. Rpt. for 1936, p. 53.

Ozone has been suggested as a preservative for eggs. The amount used in the atmosphere must be small and well controlled. Ten per cent of ozone in the air, according to Haines,[108] produced eggs which were "off" in flavor. Eggs treated with air with but three per cent of ozone did not have an unpleasant taste after 12 weeks' storage. Furthermore mold growth was inhibited on the eggs.

Candling of Eggs. The control of the commercial egg industry by chemical or bacterial analyses is very impracticable. Pennington [63] has pointed out that each egg is a package by itself and an analysis of it would in no way indicate the condition of the lot. This has made it necessary for those engaged in food control to look for other methods for determining the fitness of eggs for consumption. Candling has developed to satisfy this need. It consists in ascertaining the character of an egg by allowing light to penetrate the contents.[109] Different contrivances are used to do this. An electric light yields the most satisfactory results, since it is constant in intensity and quality. Many cheap types of candling devices are used. Benjamin [109] has described two common ones. The accurate use of the candling apparatus demands some experience before reliable results may be obtained. Pennington *et al.*[109] have published instructions for candling eggs. Those wishing a complete classified description of eggs before the candle and outside of the shell will be rewarded by reading this bulletin.

Jenkins and Hendrickson [110] have reported an investigation on the accuracy of commercial grading of opened eggs. This was made by means of a bacteriological study of 2,052 individuals breaking stock eggs. These investigators found that despite careful candling a small number of these eggs (13.5 per cent) were found to contain more than 100 bacteria per ml. The remaining 86.5 per cent contained less than 100 per ml. They stated that "there was a progressive rise in the percentage of bacterial contamination through the following series: clean whole eggs, dirty whole eggs, clean cracked eggs, dirty cracked eggs, clean leaking eggs, and dirty leaking eggs." Eggs with weak yolks showed more bacteria than eggs with firm yolks. It was also determined, as by others, that some eggs contain bacteria which cannot be determined by appearance or odor. The composite samples of breaking stock eggs might contain from a few to many bacteria. Another candling device was described by Moran and Piqué.[1]

Collection of Samples of Eggs for Bacteriological Examination. The difficulties of sampling food products for analysis are clearly brought out in analysis of eggs. Each egg is a separate package, the chemical and bacteriological condition of which does not necessarily indicate the situation for other eggs. About all the analyst can do is to select a sufficient number to allow him to generalize more readily than if but one egg were examined.

108. Haines. 1935. (Gt. Brit.) Food Invest. Bd. Ann. Rept. for 1934, p. 47.
109. Those who are interested in candling eggs will find the following publications of special interest:
    Benjamin. 1914. The interior quality of market eggs. N. Y. Agr. Expt. Sta. (Cornell Univ.) Bull. 353.
    Pennington, Jenkins, and Betts. 1918. How to candle eggs. U. S. Dept. Agr. Bull. 565.
110. Jenkins and Hendrickson. 1918. U. S. Dept. Agr. Bull. 391.

The Food and Drug Manual, giving instructions to officials, analysts, and inspectors of the Bureau of Chemistry relating to procedure for the enforcement of the Food and Drugs Act of June 30, 1906, made the following statements concerning the collection of samples of egg products for bacteriological examination:

EGG PRODUCTS

Frozen Eggs. Before beginning operations, provide as many clean sterilized containers, preferably quart Mason jars, as there are samples to be drawn, also a two-inch ship auger, chisel, metal spoons, supply of alcohol, towels, and receptacles for hot water used in the frequent recleansing of the utensils. A few extra sterilized containers are desirable to provide for breakage or accident.

Before drawing the sample, all instruments used must be sterilized immediately before using. They must again be cleansed thoroughly and sterilized before being used on each subsequent subdivision of the sample collected. In drawing samples, cores sufficient to pack a quart jar should be taken midway between the center and circumference at equidistant points from each other. The cores can best be drawn by boring with a sterilized ship auger from the top to the bottom of the container after first removing, with a sterilized chisel, the surface layer of the frozen material. The cores from each container should constitute a separate subdivision of the sample.

The turnings or chips of the sample cores should be introduced into the sterilized container without permitting the material to come in contact with the fingers or any other contaminating object. When necessary, a sterilized spoon may be used to remove the material attached to the auger and pack it in jars. Such portions of the spoon as are touched by the fingers or any other contaminating object must not be permitted to touch the product. Nothing should be permitted to touch the inside of the container covers, which should never be inverted. The containers should not be opened, nor the interior exposed to the air longer than is absolutely necessary to admit the sample. After receiving its portion of the sample each container should be identified, sealed, and immediately placed on ice or in a sharp freezer.

The inspector should note carefully the condition of the product at the time of sampling, and record the appearance and odor. Samples which are satisfactory for bacteriological examination will also suffice for chemical analysis. In cases where deemed advisable, however, one or more original packages of the product may also be submitted.

All samples must be delivered to the laboratory in their original frozen condition. If delivery can be made in a short time, pack in sufficient ice to hold during transit. If the laboratory is at a distance, the subdivisions should remain in a sharp freezer until solidly frozen, after which they may be iced for shipment. It has been found that the samples may be shipped in good condition by wrapping the jars with waxed paper, then packing them tightly in a container with sawdust to prevent breakage. This container is then braced in the center of another container, such as a box or barrel, and is surrounded by sawdust over which sufficient water is poured while in the sharp freezer, allowing the sawdust and water to freeze into a solid cake. The water should be added slowly to prevent any possibility of water entering the sample containers. This method of packing will keep the sample in good condition for two or three days. Mark the shipping package "Perishable," "Rush." This notation should also appear on the shipping receipt.

Liquid egg products should be thoroughly mixed. Samples must be taken with sterilized instruments and placed in sterilized containers, preferably quart Mason jars. The precautions outlined for sampling frozen egg products must be observed. If it is impossible to deliver the samples to the laboratory on the day collected, they should be frozen and forwarded as previously indicated.

Shell eggs, wherever located, may be examined by candling. When decomposition is indicated, but not clearly evident under the candle, the eggs should be broken to determine their actual condition. The results of the examination should be reported to the station under an official I. S. number on the field egg candling report form (C. 471).

In commercial practice the following amounts are considered representative samples for candling:

In lots of 100 cases or less, candle one-half case from each of five different cases.

In lots of 100 to 300 cases, candle one-half case from each of eight different cases.

In lots of over 300 cases, candle one-half case from each of 10 different cases.

Where cases run uneven, or the lot consists of current receipts, candle a larger number of cases, and with small shipments of this class, candle from 20 to 50 per cent of the lot. In consignments made up of separate lots or grades, as indicated by different marks or branding, each lot and grade should be examined and reported separately. (See U. S. Dept. Agr. Bul. 565, "How to Candle Eggs.")

Bacterial Examination of Eggs. Much discussion has passed back and forth over the methods of egg analysis. The early methods were probably faulty, as Hadley has said, and data from the earlier work must be accepted with some reservation. Hadley has discussed the methods of analysis and any one interested in that subject should consult his work.

Poppe's [37] Method. The egg should be thoroughly cleansed with a brush and soap and placed for about one-quarter of an hour into 1-100 mercuric chloride. Then it is rinsed in sterile water and dried after treatment with alcohol and ether. Both ends are then punctured by means of a sterile needle and the egg placed in the neck of a sterile flask into which the white may run; a second sterile flask may be used to receive the yolk.

Kossowicz's [61] Method. Wash the egg in 65 per cent alcohol and then flame the end which is to be opened. Rupture the shell with a sterile instrument and remove the contents with the aid of a sterile platinum needle, to suitable media. Kossowicz used a pair of sterile tongs for holding the egg.

Stiles and Bates' [7] Method. The eggs should be washed in a solution of bichloride of mercury (1/1000) or 5 per cent phenol for a few minutes after which they should be dried with sterile cotton and placed with the large end uppermost in a small beaker. The air space is then scorched with a gas flame for a few seconds. An opening should be made immediately into the cavity with sterile forceps, a sufficient amount of the shell being removed without rupturing the membrane below. When this is accomplished the latter should be broken with a hot platinum spatula and with a sterile pipette .5 ml. of the white of the egg quickly removed and placed in the necessary Petri dishes for cultures. The remaining egg white is then decanted, leaving the unbroken yolk in the shell. With another sterile pipette, the yolk sac is ruptured and suitable portions of its contents removed for study. While this procedure guards against contamination, the breaking up of the respective layers of the egg when out of this shell is difficult, and sometimes the inability to do so interferes seriously with the obtaining of quantitative results. With the eggs which have been in cold storage for considerable periods a separation of the whites and the yolks is not possible.

Bushnell and Mauer's [40] Method. The egg should be cleaned with brush and soap and immersed for 10 minutes in a one to 500 solution of mercuric chloride. It is transferred with sterile crucible forceps to a small conical graduate, acute pole uppermost. The corrosive sublimate is removed and the egg dried by washing it first with alcohol and then with ether. The acute pole is scorched to kill spores, etc., that might remain. The egg is then immediately removed from the graduate by the operator holding it by the blunt pole, turning the acute pole down. The hands of the operator should have been thoroughly greased with vaseline to avoid contamination of the flasks by bacteria which might drop off the hands while handling the eggs. With sharp, stout forceps, which have been sterilized in the flame, a hole about one-half cm. in diameter is made into the acute pole. Holding the egg with the acute end down, and making the stab from below prevents contamination from above. The shell around the hole is flamed briskly and the egg is put with the acute pole upon the neck of a tall 300-ml. Erlenmeyer flask containing 100 ml. of sterile bouillon. The blunt end of the egg is heated with a Bunsen flame, while a close watch is kept on the hole. The heating expands the air in the air space and this expels the contents of the egg. As soon as about one-half of the albumen has run into the flask the heating is interrupted. The cotton plug is quickly removed from a sterile flask, the neck of the flask is flamed and the egg is transferred from the first to the second flask. Sometimes it is necessary to invert the egg, as soon as the heating is discontinued, to prevent all of the albumen from running into the first flask. In this case it often happens that a little of the egg content runs down the outside of the shell, where it may become contaminated. To prevent such material from getting into the next flask, it is cemented to the shell by being heated in the flame. The expulsion of the albumen into the second flask should be done slowly and watched closely. As soon as the yolk appears in the hole the heating is interrupted and the egg is tilted from one side to the other to allow the rest of the albumen to run out. In the same manner the yolk is expelled in two portions. The success of this method depends largely on the size of the hole. If this is too small, it is hard to separate the white from the yolk; if it is too large, it is difficult to expel the yolk in two separate portions. Sometimes the yolk obstructs the hole before all of the albumen is obtained. If the yolk does not retract after cooling, the egg is inverted for a moment. Often the vitelline membrane will not rupture, and the yolk will come out in one piece. This can be prevented by puncturing the membrane with a sterile platinum needle. In this manner four flasks are obtained from each egg, two of them containing albumen and two of them containing yolk. The flasks are repeatedly shaken to mix the contents well. It is of advantage to have tall flasks because the contents can be mixed more easily without wetting the cotton plug. Two flasks, one with albumen and one with yolk, are incubated at 38°C.(100.4°F.) for 48 hours, and the other flasks are incubated at 20°C.(68°F.) for five days. After this period of development subcultures on agar slants are made to determine if growth has taken place.

Rettger's[39] **Method for the Bacterial Examination of Eggs.** The egg to be examined is placed small end up, in an egg cup or holder. The upper half of the egg is flamed with a Bunsen burner, the cup being turned constantly so that every part of the upper half of the shell is brought into brief contact with the flame. While the egg is held in the hand the upper end of the shell is removed with sterile scissors, leaving an opening about one inch in diameter. The white is poured out, care being taken to prevent it from running down the side of the shell. At this point the edge of the opening is flamed after which the entire yolk is poured out into a wide-mouthed flask, or better still, a large tube especially designed for this work by Rettger. Previous to introducing the yolk, definite amounts of nutrient bouillon are placed in the flasks (25-50 ml.) or tubes (25 ml.) which are plugged with cotton and sterilized. The yolk and bouillon should be thoroughly mixed. In case the test tube is used this process is greatly facilitated by the presence of a small glass rod about one and one-half inch in length. The tubes should then be placed in the 37°C.(98.6°F.) incubator and after 72 hours' incubation agar streaks made from them. These should be incubated for 24 to 48 hours.

Hadley and Caldwell's[41] **Method.** The egg shell should be thoroughly disinfected before any opening is made. This may be accomplished by first washing the egg, if soiled, with soap and water and a wad of cotton, then immersing for 10 minutes in 1:5,000 mercuric chloride solution, containing either citric acid or ammonium chloride to increase the penetrating power. The egg may then be plunged into 95 per cent alcohol, removed, drained, and ignited to dry the surface. These operations can be carried on in a suitably constructed wire rack in which the eggs can await examination, being meanwhile protected from air contamination.

Next, as a final precaution, the egg should be well flamed at the end opposite the air space until a very thin layer (1-2 mm.) of the albumen lying close to the shell is coagulated. The amount of heating required can be ascertained by experience. After this, by means of sterile forceps, a hole about two cm. in diameter is made at the flamed end and the white poured into a tube or flask containing 25 ml. of the desired medium. Next, the opening in the shell is enlarged to about three cm. The yolk is allowed to run gently out of the shell onto a circle of sterile filter paper (kept in a small pile under the bell jar). The paper is then so inclined that the yolk rolls about until the white is entirely removed by the paper, after which the yolk is rolled off the edge of the paper into a tube or flask containing at least 25 ml. of culture medium, an amount somewhat greater than the volume of the average yolk. Great care must, of course, be taken not to rupture the yolk membrane before the yolk is poured into the tube. The yolk may then be broken by means of a sterile glass rod and mixed with the broth.

The preparation is now ready for incubation which may be carried on for 48 hours at 37°C.(98.6°F.), followed by 48 hours at 20°C.(68°F.). The white may be mixed with the broth and grown in the same manner. At the end of the period of incubation the tubes should be again mixed by rotation to insure distribution of the bacteria, and a small amount on a straight needle transferred from each to ordinary tubes containing broth. The broth tubes are incubated at 37 and 20°C., as were the original tubes, and examined for growth at the end of four days. In case growth appears plate cultures are made.

It should be borne in mind that the recommendations made above are suitable only for fresh eggs in which it is desired to examine the yolk and white separately. In old market eggs, or preserved eggs in which the yolk is weakened, and in decomposed eggs in which the yolk and white have become mixed, different methods would be required; and here, as in the bacteriological examination of other egg products, the technique must be evolved in accordance with the particular aim of the investigation.

Schneiter's suggestions on procedures for bacteriological examination of frozen eggs are given earlier in this chapter. They may also be applied to examination of other egg products.

Mustiness in Eggs. This characteristic of food products has usually been connected with molds, although the statements have not always been founded on laboratory data. Musty eggs have a very strong characteristic odor which is masked with difficulty by cooks and bakers. Turner [111] studied musty eggs and was able to isolate specific bacteria which caused the trouble. The yolks of such eggs appeared to be normal, but the white showed a definite opalescence suggestive of bacterial contamination. Direct microscopic examination made on the egg white showed numerous small gram-negative, somewhat bipolar cocco-bacilli. The microorganism was apparently present in pure culture. Turner believed it to be a new species and named it *Achromobacter perolens*. Turner was able to reproduce the spoilage using fresh normal eggs. His results seemed to indicate that the organism could easily penetrate the shell of eggs, especially those which had been washed. The same defect was encountered in the state of Iowa by Levine and Anderson.[112] Two new species and one variety of bacteria were described under the names: *Pseudomonas gaveolens*, *Pseudomonas mucidolens*, and *Pseudomonas mucidolens* var. *tarda*. Each of these organisms produced a strong must odor when inoculated into eggs. *Achromobacter perolens* was found to be the cause of an outbreak of musty eggs by Spanswick.[113]

Another odor defect of eggs, designated as a hay odor, was attributed by Hieronymi and Rodenkirchen [114] to *Aerobacter cloacae*. Cultures of this organism infected eggs in five to six days; its growth limits were between 3°C.(37.4°F.) and 45°C.(113°F.) with the optimum at 30°C.(86°F.).

111. Turner. 1927. Austral. J. Expt. Biol. and Med. Sci. 4, 57-60.
112. Levine and Anderson. 1932. J. Bact. 23, 357.
113. Spanswick. 1930. Amer. J. Pub. Health 20, 73-74.
114. Hieronymi and Rodenkirchen. 1939. Tierärztl. Rundschau. 483-486.

PATHOGENIC BACTERIA IN EGGS

Although eggs are not important causes of communicable diseases, they are known to occasionally harbor pathogenic bacteria. These reach the interior of eggs either by infection in the oviduct of the hen or by contamination of the shell after laying. It has been shown above that various microorganisms may penetrate the shell and that penetration is more rapid at high temperatures and humidities. A pathogenic, hemolytic Streptococcus was isolated from eggs by Trossarelli and Massano.[115] Although Braga [116] recognized the possibility of pathogenic bacteria in eggs, he was unable to isolate any member of the more well-known genera. Members of the genera Escherichia and Salmonella were isolated.

Mycobacterium Tuberculosis in Eggs. Since fowls are susceptible to tuberculosis, the question arises whether eggs from infected hens might be harmful. The organism which causes avian tuberculosis has never been considered to be of much significance for human beings. Fowls are not especially susceptible to human and bovine tuberculosis, although data are appearing that they may be more susceptible to the bovine type than formerly supposed. While the danger from eating eggs from infected hens may be remote. there is little reason for continuing the use of eggs from hens which are known to be infected. Fitch, Lubbehusen, and Dikmans [117] have been studying this question from the standpoint of control of avian tuberculosis. Their results indicated that *Mycobacterium tuberculosis* was not transmitted through the egg. Poppe [37] had reported similar conclusions. None of the bacteria which he isolated from eggs were pathogenic. A different situation is indicated by results of experiments by Lichtenstein.[118] She found *Mycobacterium tuberculosis* a sufficient number of times in market eggs to conclude that the danger of obtaining infected eggs on the market should not be underestimated. Lichtenstein also artificially infected eggs with *Mycobacterium tuberculosis* (avium). *Mycobacterium tuberculosis* (avium) was isolated from these eggs up to 167 days after infection and was demonstrable with the microscope up to the 198th day. Artificial inoculation experiments with the avian type of *Mycobacterium tuberculosis* of hens were made by Bonnet and Leblois.[119] Eggs from these hens were examined for *Mycobacterium tuberculosis* for nine months. In view of the fact that no microorganisms were found, Bonnet and Leblois concluded that danger of avian tuberculosis in many was unlikely from eating eggs from infected hens.

Liverani [120] reported that *Mycobacterium tuberculosis* (avis) frequently passes into the reproductive organs and egg of the naturally or artificially infected fowls. Virulent bacilli of the mammalian types, both human and bovine, when intravenously injected into the fowl in large doses may be detected many days later in the same organs and the eggs. When 30 inocu-

115. Trossarelli and Massano. 1938. Gior. di Batteriol. e Immunol. 20, 1059-1071.
116. Braga. 1938. Bol. Inst. Vital Brazil 21, 5-109.
117. Fitch, Lubbehusen, and Dikmans. 1924. Amer. Vet. Med. Assoc. J. 1928, 72. 636-649.
118. Lichtenstein. 1932. Ztschr. f. Tuberk. 64, 256.
119. Bonnet and Leblois. 1939.
120. Liverani. 1934. Compt. Rend. Soc. Biol. 115, 133-134.

lations of egg yolk had been made into culture media, eight, or 26 per cent, gave growth. All of the cultures inoculated with egg white were negative. Three yolks of six eggs from hens which died of avian tuberculosis gave pure cultures of *Mycobacterium tuberculosis* (avis). It is obvious that eggs may carry viable tubercle bacilli, the type determined largely by the contacts which the hen may have had.

Salmonella pullorum in Eggs. Pullorum disease is a Salmonella infection of fowls in which the eggs may harbor *Salmonella pullorum*. Other Salmonella diseases of fowls also result in the specific etiologic agent in eggs. This situation has caused some concern among health officers. Tittsler, Heywang, and Charles [121] showed that practically every hen having ovarian *Salmonella pullorum* infection will eventually produce infected eggs. The actual percentage of such eggs is low but varies with the individual. Eggs artificially inoculated with *Salmonella pullorum* were to be completely sterilized only after five minutes' boiling. Somewhat similar results had been reported earlier by Rettger, Hull, and Sturgess.[122] They gave some study to the presence of *Salmonella pullorum* in eggs from infected hens. They showed that eggs which were infected with *Salmonella pullorum* may produce abnormal conditions in young chicks and also when fed to young rabbits, guinea pigs, and kittens. In young kittens the symptoms were those of severe food poisoning owing to members of the paratyphoid group. Further interesting data were secured by these investigators in regard to the effect of cooking on the organism in eggs, though this may not always be the case. Their experiments showed that boiling or frying did not always sterilize the egg as far as *Salmonella pullorum* was concerned. Soft boiling, coddling, or frying on one side did not always render the egg yolk free of viable bacteria. These data show that eggs which have been put through some sort of cooking processes may not be safe for consumption and may be the cause of digestive disturbances. Andresen [123] believed that flocks could be kept from pullorum disease with care to sanitary conditions and infected birds.

Duck eggs, in the past few years, have been incriminated in food poisoning. Scott,[124] Charles,[125] Beller,[126] Clarenburg and Dornick,[127] Meissner and Kofer,[128] and others have published results of investigations. Scott reviewed some of the earlier literature and also reported results of his own experiments. Some of the outbreaks of food poisoning resulted from infections of custards with Salmonella species in the eggs. Meissner and Kofer described an outbreak of food poisoning affecting 50 guests at a wedding party. Fromme [129] reported numerous outbreaks which were caused by duck eggs which had been used in preparation of potato salad.

121. Tittsler, Heywang, and Charles. 1928. Penn. Agr. Expt. Sta. Bull. 235; Poultry Sci. 9 (1930), 107-110.
122. Rettger, Hull, and Sturgess. 1915-1916. J. Expt. Med. 23, 475-489.
123. Andresen. 1932. Diss. Tierärztliche Hochschule, Berlin, 42.
124. Scott. 1930. Brit. Med. J., July 12, 1930, 56-57.
125. Carles. 1914. Repert. pharm. 26, 385.
126. Beller. 1935. Reichs-Gesundheitsblatt. 10, 940-942.
127. Clarenburg and Dornick. 1932. Nederl. Tijdschr. v. Geneesk. 76, 1579-1592.
128. Meissner and Kofer. 1934. Deut. Tierärztl. Woch. 42, 717-720.
129. Fromme. 1933. Deut. Med. Wchnschr. 59, 655-656; 60, 1969-1970.

Salmonella enteriditis and the Breslau bacillus were isolated. Numerous other outbreaks have been reported which have to be left for review in the author's book, "Food-Borne Infections and Intoxications." In Germany laws have been passed which compel prominent labeling of duck eggs when offered for sale.

Lichtenstein's [118] Method for Determining the Presence of Mycobacterium tuberculosis in Eggs. The egg is well washed with soap and hot water and then rinsed with sterile water and absolute alcohol. It is then punctured at both ends with a sterile glass rod, one end placed over the mouth of a glass measuring cylinder, and the contents allowed to flow into the cylinder. Four or five eggs are used in each preparation and the volume of egg mass measured. The egg mass is next mixed with a three-per cent solution of antiformin either in a mortar with glass beads or otherwise. Six parts of antiformin are used to one of egg. The mixture is then placed on a mechanical shaker so that a homogeneous mixture is secured. The material is then centrifuged at 3,500 to 5,000 r.p.m. for about 30 minutes. The sediments from the tubes are then centrifuged again in physiological sodium chloride solution, washed, and re-centrifuged three times. The supernatant liquid is poured off and the sediment used for examination. Films may be stained and cultures made in suitable culture media. Lichtenstein used Petragnani's medium which he had found to be the best. Undoubtedly other modern media would be just as satisfactory.

REFERENCE BOOKS

Eggs and Egg Products. U. S. Dept. Agr., 1941. Circular 583.

TANNER, F. W., 1933. Food-Borne Infections and Intoxications. Garrard Press, Champaign, Illinois

CHAPTER 23

MICROBIOLOGY OF CANNED FOODS

Preservation of foods in sealed containers, commonly called canning, is a great industry in the United States. While canning is generally practiced in factories located as near the source of raw products as possible, it is also done in the homes of America. The great problem is to preserve foods in such a manner that they are as near like the fresh products as possible, to preserve their nutritive qualities, and to rid them of microorganisms which spoil them or make them deleterious to health.

The history of the preservation of foods by canning is rather extensive and goes back to a remote experimental period in the development of microbiology. Indeed, some of the early investigations in fermentation were really attempts to preserve foods in hermetically sealed containers. Probably the first experimental work which had bearing on the subject was conducted by Needham, who attempted to preserve various organic materials by heating them in closed containers; since they did not keep, he assumed that life had developed spontaneously. It remained for Pasteur to discredit this explanation.

In 1795, the French government did much to stimulate the preservation of foods by offering a prize of 12,000 francs for the most satisfactory procedures. In 1810, the French Minister of the Interior awarded the prize to Nicholas Appert, a man who, as a pickler, fermentologist, and confectioner, had gained much experience in the care and preparation of foods. His book, *The Art of Preserving Animal and Vegetable Substances*,[1] ran through four editions the first of which appeared in 1811. The real significance of Appert's inventions was not realized until after his death. Appert's son was then made a Chevalier in the Legion of Honor to atone, in part, for the lack of recognition accorded his father. This early work was carried out in France and we may regard the canning industry as having originated in that country. The utensils which Appert used were crude when compared with our present-day equipment.

Appert did not explain the fundamentals upon which his methods rested, although elimination of air and application of heat were believed to be important factors. So many different theories were proposed that the French government appointed Gay-Lussac to investigate the matter. This scientist stated that decomposition was caused by the presence of air, and that if air were driven out, no oxidation could take place. The discovery of microorganisms, however, rendered this theory untenable. Pasteur, in 1860, proved that decomposition was caused by microorganisms and that, to control food spoilage, other things than presence of air must be considered.

1. Appert's manual, "The Book for All Households, of the Art of Preserving Animal and Vegetable Substances for Many Years," has been translated from the French by K. G. Bitting. Glass Container Association of America, Chicago, 1920.

Appert's first problem was to find a container in which materials could be preserved after they had been sterilized. He finally chose one made of glass.

In 1810, an English tin plate worker by the name of Peter Durand was granted a patent by the English government. While he was probably not the originator of the process, his work did much to stimulate interest. About the same time, a Mr. Saddington read a paper before an English society on "A Method for Preserving Fruits Without Sugar for House or Sea Stores." The method proposed by Saddington resembled very closely the modern cold-pack process. Pierre Antoine Angilbert, a Frenchman, probably made the first real advance in the perfection and use of tin cans for food preservation. After the fruit had been placed in a can, a piece of tin with a small hole in it was soldered on the can. After the process the hole was tipped with solder.

In America, Thomas Kensett was the first to use the tin can in food preservation. He packed various sea foods, such as salmon and oysters. At this time cans were hand made and a great amount of time was consumed in their manufacture. In 1839, Winslow attempted to pack corn in Maine. He applied to the United States government for a patent which was granted in 1862. The Civil War did much to hasten the day of canned foods. Winslow was a whaler and saw the suffering from scurvy to which sailors and others on an inadequate diet were susceptible. Canned fruits and vegetables were desired to supplement the monotonous diet supposed to cause scurvy. The history of canning is covered in a number of publications, notably those of Judge [2] and Bitting.[3]

How Long Will Canned Foods Keep? If all microorganisms in a can of food are destroyed and the ingress of others prevented, canned foods should keep indefinitely, so far as microorganisms are concerned. Slow chemical changes, however, may render the food inedible. One case is on record where tinned food remained edible for 90 years. Corned beef and pea soup were brought back from an arctic depot where they had lain for 86 years. In another case, canned peas which had been mislaid for 24 years were edible. In the *Canner* for April, 1927, are recorded the results of the examination of a can of beef which was 81 years old. A similar report in the same journal for October 5, 1929, records observations on canned meat and milk over 35 years old.

Canned foods of historic interest have been examined in a thorough manner by several groups of investigators.[4] They examined the foods from all angles. Only the investigation by Wilson and Shipp, which was bacteriological in nature, need by reviewed here.

A can of Parry's "Roast Veal," canned in 1824, yielded on very careful examination, three strains of sporeforming anaerobes which had remained viable for over 100 years. Similar examination of a can of Libby's

2. Judge. 1914. A History of the Canning Industry. Nat Canners Assoc., Ann. Conv. 7, 162.
3. Bitting. 1925. A series of articles on "The History of Canning" starting in the August, 1925, issue of *Canning Age*.
4. Drummond and Lewis. 1938. Chem. and Indus. 57, 808-814; Macara, 1938, Idem 57, 827-828; Wilson and Shipp, 1938, Idem 834-836; Lewis, 1938, Idem 914-917.

canned tripe, packed in 1880, and a can of carrots packed in 1885, yielded completely negative results.

General Sanitation of Canning Plants. The food packer, by using clean materials and handling them in a cleanly manner, will greatly reduce the load on the sterilizing process which he is using. The practical phases of the question were discussed by McMeans.[5] Cleanliness and general sanitation have a real monetary value to the canner. As is stated elsewhere in this chapter, the procedures used in canning each food are founded on conditions which obtain in the average canning factory. They include both raw materials in the average state of freshness and average apparatus. If, by using careless unsanitary procedures, the average process times and temperatures are overloaded, many of the cans will not be sterilized and the contents will later spoil. Aspects of the problem from the viewpoint of the Food and Drugs Act are reviewed by Linton.[6] The main object of high sanitary standards is a high-quality canned food. White[7] discussed the general examination which could be given the can itself. Savage[8] believed that canned foods were definitely less liable than ordinary foods to be a source of food poisoning.

GENERAL PROCEDURES IN CANNING

No one set of procedures can be used with all foods. Some foods require more washing or special preliminary treatment. In the following paragraphs a few of the basic procedures which are used with many foods are discussed.

Raw Materials. If the finished product in the can is to be high grade in every respect, the raw materials must be the best that can be secured. For this reason and not alone on account of expense, canning factories are located near the source of raw materials. Many vegetables lose their fresh appearance and taste soon after harvesting. Beans become tough and stringy. Fruits become soft and the skins broken, making them susceptible to the attack of microorganisms.

Preparation. The procedure followed depends entirely on the product. It is obvious that a different method must be used for peas than for strawberries. Lima beans must be threshed from the vines and graded. Corn is usually cut from the cob after careful inspection. String beans must be snipped, and some fruits must be pitted.

Grading. Some foods packed in tin cans are not graded, while with others the practice is carried to extremes. There are, for example, some 25 or more grades of peas and many grades for other foods.

Washing. Most foods to be preserved by canning are thoroughly washed. The methods which are used depend on the type of food as well as the type of soil on which it is grown. Some vegetables grown in sandy soil require less washing than those grown on clay soils. This is not always the case,

5. McMeans. 1920. The Canner, July 24, 1920.
6. Linton. 1922. U. S. Dept. Agr. Bull. 1084.
7. White. 1936. J. State Med. 44, 530-540.
8. Savage. 1939. Lancet, Nov. 4, 991-996.

however. Washing probably removes many bacteria which would otherwise have to be destroyed later by the process.

Scalding or Blanching. Many fresh foods are scalded or blanched early in the canning procedure. Magoon [9] tabulated the following reasons:

1. Removal of substances which give undesirable flavors to the canned product.
2. Improving the color of the cut-out material by bringing the color to the surface where it is "set" or "coagulated" by the subsequent treatment.
3. Removal of mucilaginous substances from the raw materials.
4. Shrinking and softening of tissues facilitating a full container.
5. Production of clearer liquor in the can.
6. Destruction of bacteria thus lightening the load on the process.

Considerable attention has been given to the effect that blanching might have on the bacteria. Probably most of the nonsporeforming bacteria would be greatly reduced in numbers while the sporeformers might not be greatly harmed. Magoon stated that the water of the scalding bath might, at times, contaminate the food, provided it was used over and over again. This is especially true for the thermophilic bacteria, as shown by Cameron [10] in his experiments to find the origin of spoilage organisms.

Bushnell [11] reported that blanching was of no value in reducing the time necessary for processing canned foods. The results of Bushnell's experiments should probably not be applied to foods packed under commercial conditions. The same question was studied by Bruett,[12] who stated that spores of bacteria were not made more sensitive to heat by sudden chilling. In the "cold-pack" process, blanching was found to have no bacteriological justification on the grounds of increased susceptibility of the bacteria to heat because of cold shocks. Blanching was said, however, to have a cleaning action. Undoubtedly, many nonsporeforming bacteria are killed, but blanching as such does not possess great advantages as far as the process is concerned. Burke [13] also found that blanching had no effect on the spores of resistant sporeformers.

Exhausting for Vacuum. The object of the exhaust in canning practice is to force air or gas out of the can by having the contents of the can as hot as possible before closing. If the can is sealed while it is hot, a vacuum will result when it cools. With some foods which permit very slow penetration of heat, it is often necessary to tip the can under vacuum. The gas in a can of food comes from entrained air in the food and air in the head space. It is the oxygen in this gas which causes considerable trouble with some food products. Clark, Clough, and Shostrom [14] of the National Canners Association have presented the theoretical and practical significance of vacuum. Other discussions of the same subject have been prepared by Daughters [15] and Gray.[16]

9. Magoon. 1925. Canning Age, Jan., 1925, 22-29.
10. Cameron. 1930. The Canner, Conv. Number, 139.
11. Bushnell. 1918. J. Ind. Eng. Chem. 6, 432-436.
12. Bruett. 1919. J. Ind. Eng. Chem. 11, 37-39.
13. Burke. 1919. Amer. Med. Assoc. J. 72, 88-93.
14. Clark, Clough, and Shostrom. 1923. Pacific Fisherman, June and July, 1923.
15. Daughters. 1926. The Canner, Aug. 7, 1926.
16. Gray. 1928. The Canner, April 14, 1928.

Exhausting was apparently practiced quite early since it was believed that a vacuum was necessary to make foods keep. Appert believed that oxygen should be removed. It is now known that vacuum in itself has little relation to bacterial spoilage. It may influence, to a certain extent, the types of bacteria which may develop in that a poor exhaust will leave more oxygen in the can, but the direct effects of vacuum are not significant. However, it does play a role in chemical spoilage to which the canned foods are susceptible.

Adam and Stamworth [17] have stated that the vacuum which occurs on cooling a can below its closing temperature is primarily caused by changes in vapor pressure and partial air pressure. The effect in both cases increases with the closing temperature and that due to partial air pressure is kept at its highest value by the prevention of cooling of the head space between exhaust and closing. This may be best achieved and controlled by clinching the cans before exhausting. The causes of change in the vacuum on storage are discussed and new methods of vacuum measurement and their limitations were described.

Some of the foods preserved by canning contain large amounts of air. Data were published on this subject by Culpepper and Moon,[18] as well as by Baker [19] and Clark.[20] Exhausting serves to remove some of this air. If the exhaust time is not right, gases entrained in the foods themselves are not removed, vacuum in the can may be lowered, and more trouble from corrosion and perforation may result. Insufficient exhausting will also cause flippers since the vacuum will not be great enough to hold the ends of the can in.

Various methods are used in practice for obtaining an exhaust in canned foods. Some are more applicable to certain foods than to others.

Exhausting by Heat. This is the oldest and under many conditions the best method for getting the air out of the can. The period of exhaust and the time required depend on the food. Certain foods, such as sweet potatoes and meats allow such slow heat penetration that it is necessary to place them in the cans while quite hot. It is almost impossible to secure sufficient heat at the center of the can. Bigelow and his colleagues at the Research Laboratories of the National Canners Association found slower heat penetration with these foods that with any foods studied. The absence of convection currents probably explains it.

Exhausting by Mechanical Means. By this method the cans are closed in a chamber in which a high vacuum is maintained. This method has been used for many products packed in glass and more recently has been applied to vegetables and fruits in tin containers.

Clark, Clough, and Shostrom [14] gave the following reasons for obtaining a vacuum in canned salmon. These probably hold equally well for other foods in tin containers.

1. To keep the ends of the can flat or collapsed. This is important since one important criterion of a satisfactory can of food is the condition of the ends. Cans with flat conclave ends are usually satisfactory although some types of spoilage are not

17. Adam and Stamworth. 1932-1933. Univ. of Bristol, Fruit and Vegetable Preserv. Res. Sta. Ann. Rpts., Campden, 61-70.
18. Culpepper and Moon. 1929. The Canner, Feb. 16 and April 20, 1929.
19. Baker. 1912. Eighth Internatl. Cong. Appl. Chem. 18, 45-49.
20. Clarke. 1923. The Canner, Pt. 2, March 3, 1923, 148-152.

accompanied by gas formation. Bulged ends may be due to lack of vacuum or generation of hydrogen.

2. To reduce the strain on the cans during processing. When the sealed can is processed in the retort considerable pressure is developed. Cans which enter the retort with a good vacuum will have the lowest pressure produced during cooking in the retort.

3. To restrict or prevent growth of certain species of bacteria. The removal of oxygen prevents the growth of aerobic bacteria—those which grow best in the presence of free oxygen.

4. To prevent undesirable changes, such as destruction of accessory substances, and to reduce the chemical reactions between the container and its contents.

Factors Which Influence the Vacuum in Canned Foods. The vacuum which a can will have depends on a number of factors. These have been discussed numerous times in the literature. Clark, Clough, and Shostrom [14] later summarized them as follows:

1. *Time and temperature of exhaust.* The vacuum attained in a can will depend certainly on the temperature. This is in turn dependent on the time that the can is heated. The higher the temperature to which the can is heated, the more vapor is formed to condense in the sealed can.

2. *Fill of the can and head space.* The head space is made up of air, the oxygen in which, will be slowly used up producing a vacuum.

3. *Exhaust with cans open or with lightly clinched covers.* In the salmon industry, according to Clark *et al.,*[14] better vacua are secured with the covers loosely clinched. There is better retention of heat. This may also be due to steam getting into the can to replace the air.

4. *Delay between exhaust box and closing machine.* Any delay here will cause a loss of heat and will thus negate the exhaust.

5. *Loose or tight seams.* In order to hold a good vacuum the seams of the can must be tight. Loose seams may allow air to escape in the retort and the seams may close after the can has left the retort. Some cans of vacuum packed food show a vacuum of 24 inches.

6. *Fresh or stale foods.* Clark, Clough, and Shostrom found that stale salmon caused more carbon dioxide in cans than fresh salmon. In the retort most of this carbon dioxide is driven into the head space.

7. *Use of heavy tin plate having several expansion rings.* Cans with heavy plate in the ends will not be pushed out easily. This factor, strictly speaking, does not influence the vacuum but the can will possess flat ends. Such a can will also resist changes in appearance owing to gas formation by bacteria or to atmospheric conditions.

8. *Altitude.* Springers may result from altitude even though the contents of the cans are satisfactory. Low vacuum cans usually become springers at high altitudes.

Vacuum itself probably has very little effect on microorganisms. The few reports which have been made on this subject indicate that bacteria may live for long times in vacuum. Some of the species with which Brown [21] worked were alive after five years in vacuum. Lowering of the temperature, along with vacuum, apparently increases the longevity of bacteria. Bitting [22] reported that vacuum of 25 inches did not check the development of yeast or *Oidium lactis* but did check that of Aspergillus species. While vacuum does not have much influence on the microorganisms, it has become a very important factor in canning. Gas-forming bacteria tend to reduce vacuum in a tight container in which they are able to grow.

Maclinn and Feller's [23] **Method for Determining the Vacuum in Glass Jars.** Two methods were proposed for determining vacuum in all-glass jars used in the preservation of foods.

21. Brown. 1932. J. Bact. 23, 34; Absts. Bact. 9 (1925), 8.
22. Bitting. 1925. The Canning Age, April, 1925, 413.
23. Maclinn and Fellers. 1936. Food Research 1, 41-44.

Vacuum-Desiccator Method. A large vacuum desiccator is connected with pressure rubber tubing to a vacuum pump. The connections should be tight so that a vacuum of 27 to 29 inches can be attained. An ordinary Chapman water pump attached to the water faucet will usually answer the purpose. The jar of food, vacuum in which is to be determined, with clamps removed is immersed in an open glass container with enough water to cover the jar. This container with the immersed glass jar is then placed in the vacuum desiccator. The lid is replaced and the stop cock opened. A vacuum gauge should be placed in the line to indicate the vacuum. The air is slowly exhausted. When the vacuum inside of the desiccator exceeds that in the jar, the glass cover will lift and bubbles escape. The vacuum gauge should be read at this instant. Some difficulties may be encountered if the jars have been packed a long time on account of the rubber rings sticking to the glass.

Water-Displacement Method. This method depends on displacement by water of a certain volume of the head space, depending on the vacuum (partial pressure) present in the jar. The jar is weighed after processing; this weight includes the complete container and contents. The jar is then immersed in water in an inverted position and the seal broken, which permits the head space to fill with water in proportion to the vacuum in the head space. Still holding the jar inverted, the water levels inside and outside the jar are made the same, the cap is replaced, the clamps tightened, and then the jar is removed from the water, wiped off, and weighed. The difference in weight between the second and first weighings gives the amount of water sucked in. The lid is then removed and the jar completely filled with water, including the volume under the glass cover. This weight minus the first weighing gives the volume of the head space, and from the weight of the water sucked in, the vacuum can be calculated. The technic is very simple. An example is given:

(a) Weight of the jar and contents after processing... 980 gm.
(b) Weight after opening under water...1,030 gm.
(c) Gain in weight (b—a)...   50 gm.
(d) Weight of jar and contents completely full................................1,050 gm.
(e) Original head-space volume (d—a)...   70 gm.
(f) Vacuum $\dfrac{(b-a)}{(d-a)} \times 30$..21.4 inches.

HEAT PENETRATION IN PROCESSING CANNED FOODS

Few of the earlier workers in the field gave attention to the rate of heat penetration into various food products preserved by canning. Prescott and Underwood,[24] who attempted to follow the temperature changes in cans of corn by sealing registering thermometers in the cans, observed that, regardless of the retort temperature, the temperature of the can reached it in the same time. This has been observed by others since then. Belser,[25] working on a number of common fruits and vegetables, observed considerable variation in the time required to come to retort temperature. Studies by the National Canners Association (Bigelow, Bohart, Richardson, and Ball[26]) culminated in an extensive report dealing with most of the common fruits and vegetables packed in tin cans and glass. The older methods of working, involving the use of thermometers, were replaced by those in which thermocouples were used. The use of this apparatus has made it possible to follow the temperature change at the center of a can which is being processed under ordinary conditions. Magoon and Culpepper[27]

24. Prescott and Underwood. 1897. Tech. Quart. 10, 183-199; 11 (1898), 6-30.
25. Belser. 1905. Arch. f. Hyg. 54, 107-148.
26. Bigelow *et al.* 1920. Natl. Canners Assoc. Bull. 16-L.
27. Magoon and Culpepper. 1921. U. S. Dept. Agr. Bulls. 956, 1022, and 1265.

also published the results of studies of the rate of heat penetration into various canned foods.

Factors Influencing Rate of Heat Penetration Into Canned Foods. Several factors, as would be expected, influence the rate of penetration of heat into canned foods. The investigators in the Research Laboratories of the National Canners Association have stated some of them as follows:

1. *Shape and size of the container.* It is apparent that a large can of food would require longer to come to retort temperature than a small one. This is due to the fact that heat has further to travel from the outside to the center of the container. Larger cans also have less surface in proportion to the volume than smaller ones.

2. *Consistency of the food product.* A food product with considerable free liquor would allow more rapid penetration of heat than one which is solid or viscous. This is well indicated by curves which have been published by the National Canners Association as well as by Magoon and Culpepper.[27] The latter investigators started their studies on heat penetration by using distilled water in No. 2, No. 3, and No. 10 cans. In No. 2 cans the temperature of the bath was reached in about nine minutes, the No. 3 can being only slightly slower than the No. 2. The No. 10 can required 10 minutes. Studies were also made with brine and sugar solutions to see whether the addition of these materials had any effect. Salt had little effect as did dilute sugar solutions. Concentrated sugar solutions, however, had considerable effect in retarding penetration of heat. One, two, three, four, and five per cent starch solutions were also studied. The curves which graphically showed the results indicate a progressive inhibition to heat as the concentration of starch is increased. The differences between one, two, and three per cent solutions were not great, however, but they did exist.

3. *Reaction of the food.* This is offered as one of the factors influencing heat penetration. It is probably of less importance than other factors.

4. *Location of the can in the retort.* Bigelow and his colleagues, Bohart, Richardson, and Ball,[26] observed that with corn, cans at the center of the crate heated as rapidly as cans at the outside. Furthermore, no difference could be found between cans which were thrown into the crates promiscuously and those which were stacked solid. The situation was different with milk. The cooker must contain steam only under pressure. If mixtures of air and steam obtain in the cooker, the pressure on the gauge will not indicate the actual temperature. In order to avoid air pockets in cookers, canners allow a little steam to escape during the cooker process, a procedure known as "bleeding." It keeps the steam moving in the retort.

5. *Agitation.* Cooking in agitating cookers permits more rapid penetration of heat with some foods. The cans may be rotated on their axis or they may receive irregular agitation.

6. *Initial temperature.* The can should be as hot as possible when it enters the retort. Many investigators have stated that cans at lower temperatures will heat faster in a retort than cans at higher temperatures. The important factor, however, is the time that the can is at retort temperature, for it is this temperature which causes the greatest reduction in the number of viable cells. It has been shown that cans heated to different temperatures and placed in a retort and processed together will reach retort temperature in the same time.

7. *Temperature of the retort.* It is obvious that this factor will have a bearing on the rate of heat penetration into cans.

Discussion of methods for determining heat penetration is outside the scope of this book. The subject is covered by Magoon and Culpepper,[27] Ball,[28] Bigelow et al.,[26] and others.

Slope of the Heat-Penetration Curve. Heat-penetration curves are plotted from results of observations on temperature changes at that area in the can of food which is heated most slowly. Such results are usually

28. Ball. 1923. Natl. Res. Council. Bull. 7.

secured with thermocouples. Even though the efficiency of the process is largely determined by the rate of penetration of heat into the can, accurate information on the subject came rather late in the development of canning technology. Those who desire to read into the subject should consult the papers by Bigelow, Bohart, Richardson, and Ball [26] and Ball.[29] In these publications many curves for the rate of heat penetration into many different foods may be consulted. The ideal situation would be to have a curve for every food in the various sized containers under all of the various methods of packing. The great amount of work which would be involved prevents this. Consequently, canning technologists have been driven to calculation of heat-penetration curves for some foods. The procedures may be secured from the bulletins mentioned above, but especially from a publication by Ball.[29]

STERILIZING PROCESSES

This is the step in which attempt is made to destroy microorganisms which may later spoil canned foods. It has been defined by the National Canners Association [30] as the heat treatment expressed in terms of temperature and time given the product after the container is permanently sealed.

Ball [28] stated that the object in processing canned foods is the attainment of sterility with respect to the most resistant microorganism present which would cause spoilage. Some have distinguished between the terms processing and sterilizing. Sterility is the ideal toward which canners strive, but which is not easy to attain with some foods without harming the quality. Some processed foods may contain heat-resistant spores, such as those of thermophilic bacteria. Some such spores have been shown to resist over 20 hours' boiling and to withstand the maximum process times and temperatures regarded as satisfactory. To absolutely destroy such resistant spores might render the food unsuitable for sale.

Consequently, some canning technologists have modified the term "sterilization" to indicate the bacteriological condition attained in some foods by processing. Since the term "sterilization" implies the absolute destruction of all living organisms, and since this condition may not be attained in some processed foods, the term "commercial sterilization" has been introduced. The term indicates the condition of some processed canned foods in which viable spores exist. The contents of the can remain commercially sound as long as the cans are properly handled. In this manner, the results of sterilization procedures (complete sterility) are distinguished from the results of processing (commercial sterility). Closely connected to this discussion are the methods of determining sterility. Though it would be possible to destroy any number of resistant spores in a can of food, the food might be so changed that it would be unfit for sale. Ball [31] prepared a fine review, mostly along historical lines, which should be read by those who are trying to secure a complete picture of sterilization methods for

29. Ball. 1927. The Canner, Jan. 22, 1927; Univ. of California, Pub. in Public Health 1, 15, 245 (1928).

30. Processes for Non-Acid Canned Foods in Metal Containers. Natl. Canners Assoc. Bull. 26-L, Fifth Ed, 1942.

31. Ball. 1938. Food Research 3, 13-55.

canned foods. The object of processing, then, is not so much the complete sterilization of the food as it is to make it keep and be wholesome.

Several methods are used for processing canned foods. Two general methods are most commonly used—dry steam and hot water. Since there was considerable difference in opinion among canners over the efficiency of these methods, the National Canners Association made numerous tests with several kinds of products cooked by both methods. The results, reported by Bigelow et al.,[26] showed no difference in rate of heat penetration whether processing was done in steam or hot water (under steam pressure).

Continuous cookers have been introduced in recent years and found to be satisfactory with some foods. In these cookers the cans are rotated, a factor which, with many foods, speeds up heat penetration. Such cookers are used in the processing of canned milk. The introduction of the continuous cooker is the result of effort to introduce rapid mechanical features into the process procedure. These cookers are cylindrical shells placed in horizontal position (Flannery[32]). Inside the cooker is a helical runway for the cans of food. On this runway the cans progress from the intake end to the outlet end. The cans enter and leave the cooker through valves so constructed that the can is introduced and released from the cooker without altering greatly the conditions within the cooker. These cookers are operated at such speeds that every can receives the same heat treatment. The cans are passed to a mechanical cooler when they leave the cooker.

Principles Involved in Processing. The process may be considered to be disinfection by moist heat and probably subject to the laws of disinfection. Since the rate of disinfection is an orderly time process and dependent upon the number of living cells present, it is obvious that the canner should keep the microbial load in his product as low as possible. The fewer the bacterial spores the easier is processing. Process times and temperatures are based on average contamination. Duckwall,[33] in the early days when attempt was being initiated to apply scientific principles to what had been generally the art of canning, recognized the value of reducing contamination to the minimum. Actual laboratory investigations by Esty and Meyer[34] showed beyond dispute the effect of increasing numbers of spores on the amount of heat required to destroy them. Larger numbers required more heat for destruction. Hallman and Stevenson[35] stated the following as being involved in determination of a process for any canned food:

1. Determination of the thermal death time of heat-resistant spores of the spoilage organism with which the food might become contaminated under commercial conditions.

2. Determination of the rate of penetration of heat into the can of food under consideration.

3. Calculation of the theoretical process from the thermal death time and heat-penetration data.

4. Checking the theoretical process by processing inoculated cans and incubating to determine whether the inoculated microorganism has been destroyed.

32. Flannery. 1929. Food Indus. 1, 651 and 694.
33. Duckwall. 1905. Canning and Preserving of Food Products.
34. Esty and Meyer. 1922. J. Inf. Dis. 31, 650-663.
35. Hallman and Stevenson. 1932. Ind. Eng. Chem. 24, 659.

It is necessary to know the maximum resistance to heat of spores of spoilage bacteria as well as of those which might render the food hazardous to health. In the latter category falls *Clostridium botulinum*. Many investigations have been carried out to learn more about heat resistance of *Clostridium botulinum* under conditions simulating those in canned foods. The well-known publication of Esty and Meyer [36] gave maximum resistance of spores of *Clostridium botulinum* in standard phosphate solution at different temperatures.

One of the more recent attempts along these lines is that by Townsend, Esty, and Baselt [37] who worked with a sporeforming anaerobe which produced spores having a high heat resistance (No. 3679 isolated by Cameron [38]) and several strains of *Clostridium botulinum*. The details of their experiments need not be reproduced here. They concluded that heat resistance of *Clostridium botulinum* is different in canned foods than in neutral phosphate solution. Heat-resistance characteristics of anaerobe No. 3679 were found to be unlike those of *Clostridium botulinum* in food media but were similar in neutral phosphate solution.

Factors Influencing Processing. Processing is influenced by many factors. It should not be looked upon as the mere application of heat to a food in a closed container. If this were all that is involved, less bacterial spoilage would occur and the canner could easily sterilize the food by using a sufficiently long process time. However, the quality of the food has to be considered. Probably the two factors which rule more than others in the selection of process times and temperatures are quality of food and understerilization. Under the latter term is included, of course, the effect of heat on spores of *Clostridium botulinum*. Canners have to face the question of having safe cooks or processes.

Among the various factors which may affect the sterilizing value of the process, Bigelow [39] listed the following:

1. The initial temperature may be too low.
2. The contents may be too closely packed.
3. The accuracy of the retort thermometer.
4. The amount of care exercised in holding the retort thermometer at the desired temperature.
5. The ''coming up'' time of the retort.
6. The influence of the temperature control apparatus on the ''coming up'' time and initial temperature of the retort.
7. The size and shape of thermometer pockets.
8. The amount of venting and the position of the vents.
9. The construction of the retort, especially the distributing system on steam pipe.
10. The amount of water in the retort during processing.
11. The manner in which very small cans are stacked in the retort.
12. The manner of cooling the product and the promptness with which it is cooled after processing.

The hydrogen-ion concentration of the food product has much to do with the efficiency of the process. Bigelow and Cathcart [40] discussed its

36. Esty and Meyer. 1922. J. Infect. Dis., 31, 650.
37. Townsend, Esty, and Baselt. 1938. Food Research 3, 323-346.
38. Cameron. 1927. The Canner 64, No. 10, Pt. 2, 146.
39. Bigelow. 1922. The Canner, Feb. 18, 1922.
40. Bigelow and Cathcart. 1921. Natl. Canners Assoc. Bull. 17-L.

significance in processing canned foods. From their work, it is evident that fruits have an acidity greater than that represented by pH 4. In general the process required decreases as the food products are more acid. The few exceptions, however, were suggested to be due to heat penetration. Some foods with a hydrogen-ion concentration which suggests a high process may require a short one. Peas, for instance, might appear to need a longer process than other foods of the same hydrogen-ion concentration. Heat penetration, then, seems to be more important than hydrogen-ion concentration in processing. Processing itself tends to raise the hydrogen-ion concentration of certain foods.

Another factor of importance is presence of sugar or heavy sirups. At various places in this book, the slowing effect of these on destruction of bacteria by heat has been discussed. Here an instance in the canning industry will be mentioned. It was conceived that when sugar needed to be added to a product about to be canned that it could be added as such to the can before the food was put in and that it would distribute itself throughout the can during the process. Braun, Hays, and Benjamin [41] found that this was not the case. Dry sugar was found not to dissolve but to form strata of sugar sirups in the container. These retarded heat transfer to the interior of the can. Consequently foods sweetened with dry sugar, may require more drastic heat treatment than foods sweetened with sirups.

Vacuum Processing of Canned Foods. A few years ago a method of packing and processing foods was introduced without water or brine. It was spoken of as "waterless processing" or "vacuum packing." The vegetables are filled into the can, the air is removed by a vacuum pump or replaced with steam before sealing or processing. Many foods canned in this manner are superior both as to appearance and flavor as well as keeping quality. Vacua of from 20 to 27 inches are attained immediately after closing. Such foods seem to be more easily sterilized. Tanner and Mc-Crae [12] found that spores of *Clostridium botulinum* were more easily destroyed when heated in tubes in which the vacuum had been reduced to 17 mm. before closing. Konrich [43] carried out experiments on the effect of vacuum on the temperatures required for processing meat in cans. In no instance was he able to show that exhausted cans were more easily processed. His conclusions are probably applicable only to the conditions under which he worked.

Control of Processing. More is involved in processing than merely making canned foods keep. They must be safe. Soundness of a can of food does not necessarily require that the product be sterile in the surgical sense. It is not a question, according to Esty [44] whether viable bacteria are present but whether the food is wholesome.

41. Braun, Hays, and Benjamin. 1941. Food Indus. 13, 47-49; 64-65; Canning Age 22, 172, 180-182.

42. Tanner and McCrae. 1923. J. Bact. 8, 269-276.

43. Konrich. 1931. Ztschr. f. Hyg. u. Infegtionskrank. 112, 62.

44. Esty. 1935. Amer. J. Pub. Health 25, 165-170.

Processing is, in general, not under active control by official groups. Relation of certain canned foods to botulism prompted the California State Department of Public Health to attempt to give this important step in canning official supervision. Canning inspection started in 1920 under jurisdiction of the Bureau of Pure Food and Drugs. After 1920, more and more supervision was given this work until finally, in 1925, an act was passed and approved by the governor creating a Division of Cannery Inspection to regulate canning. Important in this effort to pack and market wholesome canned foods is coding of cans. This makes it possible to identify any lot of questionable quality and segregate it if necessary. In addition to the type of control mentioned above is that involving laboratory analysis of the contents of the can. Esty reviewed the problems involved. He emphasized the complexity of determination of causes of spoilage.

Experimental Determination of Processes for Canned Foods. In the earlier days when canning was more of an art, processes were arrived at by experience. Each canner used times and temperatures which he thought were satisfactory and used them as long as little spoilage resulted. It was a trial-and-error method and was based on natural contamination which at the time may have been low. When his product was more heavily contaminated, the spoilage which resulted prompted him to make adjustments usually increasing the process. Only rarely could a packer make some of the determinations which are regarded as necessary. Williams [45] mentioned them as measurement of heat penetration, inoculation with a selected test spoilage organism, calculation of a final process, and checking it with experimental packs. Processes are calculated by a formula of Ball[29] involving heat-resistance data on test bacteria and heat-penetration data on the food in the can. This is the theoretical process.

Good results in processing depend on adequate penetration of heat to that part of the can which heats most slowly as well as the heat resistance of spoilage bacteria most likely to spoil the food in question. If the food happens to be one in which food-poisoning bacteria may develop, they must also be considered, especially the arch enemy of the canning industry *Clostridium botulinum*.

Cameron [46] has described a series of experimental packs involving corned beef hash and potted meats. Those who desire specific details of Cameron's work may consult the original report. Only the general features of the experimental pack need be given here. In such work it is necessary to have very resistant typical bacteria with which to inoculate the food. If corn is being packed it may be inoculated with the spores of a resistant thermophile, such as No. 1518 described by Cameron and Esty.[47] The heat resistance of this organism can be easily determined. In the experimental packs with meat products, Cameron finally secured a putrefactive anaerobe which had a heat resistance of 12 hours at $100°C.(212°F.)$. This organism was added to the corned beef hash and potted meat. After the organism has

45. Williams. 1940. Inst. Food Technol. Proc. 2, 323-327.
46. Cameron. 1930. The Canner, Conv. No., p. 195, Feb. 21, 1931.
47. Cameron and Esty. 1926. J. Infect. Dis. 39, 89-105.

been added to the food product, it is canned and processed at the calculated times and temperatures. The cans are then stored under conditions which will cause spoilage. In this manner, it is possible to check the theoretical process with the actual results obtained when it is used. Before the days of research laboratories, each canner had to make his own experiments. He usually used those process times and temperatures which gave the least spoilage. Now the processes are based upon carefully carried out experiments and are no longer secured by trial and error.

Much discussion has occurred on the method that shall be used for incorporating the test bacteria in the food and the type of inoculum that shall be used. The object is to secure spores of representative resistance and place them in that part of the can which will probably receive the lowest heat treatment. That, of course, may be the center. Little information of value would be secured by filling the can and placing the organism on the top just under the cover. The only satisfactory method is to mix the spores with the food before it is filled into the cans. This is not difficult with such foods as peas and corn but requires special attention in the case of meats, fish, and sweet potatoes. In the case of meats which are in fine pieces or ground, the spores may be incorporated while the meat is being stirred in a mixer. The spores should be thoroughly incorporated in a small amount of the food and this inoculated portion added in small portions to the entire batch. In this manner, the spores will be distributed as nearly as possible as they are in natural infection. It is more difficult to incorporate the test organisms in such materials as ham, fish, and sweet potatoes. In this case, the organisms may be carried on pieces of thread which may be placed in the can where the bacteria are desired. The practice of putting the bacteria into one place in a can by means of a pipette is to be questioned. Such a procedure may place too many bacteria at one place.

Another question which has to be settled is the type of inoculum. Shall it be dry soil or an aqueous suspension of spores? In Chapter 2, the methods for preparing spore suspensions used in recognized procedures for determining thermal death times are given. These are, in general, pure-culture suspensions. Since these methods were devised, some have suggested that the test bacteria could be carried in soil which has not been sterilized. These suggestions originated in the desire to secure an inoculum as near a natural one as possible. Since opinions are not yet in agreement on these problems, the various methods of inoculation will not be discussed further.

It is also necessary in experimental packs to select the proper test organism with which to inoculate the food. This selection is usually made from studies on causes of spoilage of the product under consideration. It is necessary to know the nature and type of spoilage likely to occur when the food is underprocessed. Williams [45] reviewed this problem. As a result of extensive heat-resistance studies and types of spoilage caused by them, the following test organisms have become important and have been used in many experimental packs.

1. *Clostridium sporogenes*, strain No. 3679, with a heat resistance in excess of the maximum recorded for *Clostridium botulinum*. This is used

for nonacid products and in some cases for semi-acid products. This organism is a *putrefactive anaerobe*. Cultures are best incubated at 30°C.

The best known member of the group is No. 3679, much used in heat resistance studies in inoculated packs of certain foods. Merrill and Reed [45a] observed that it grew better, i.e., gave higher counts when grown in pork agar medium in deep "shake" tubes. The same experience held for *Clostridium botulinum*. Definitely higher counts were also secured when both putrefactive anaerobe No. 3679 and *Clostridium botulinum* (strain 62-A) were incubated at 27°C. instead of 37°C. The incubation time which Merrill and Reed used was 21 days. They also reported higher heat resistance of strain 3679 when the pork agar medium was used.

It was also reported [45a] that this organism is somewhat inhibited by salt in concentrations of 2.5 per cent and completely so by 7.5 per cent.

2. *Clostridium thermosaccharolyticum*, strain No. 3814. This is a thermophilic anaerobe which is used for semi-acid products where approximate end point of survival is to be indicated by spoilage.

3. *Bacillus stearothermophilus,* strain No. 1518. This is a flat-sour-producing organism and is used in foods in which flat-sour spoilage is the problem. Spores of this organism are much more resistant to heat than spores of the putrefactive anaerobic types. Thus where the maximum resistance of *Cl. botulinum* in phosphate buffer solution at 115°C.(239°F.) is 10 minutes, and of No. 3679 is in the range of 15 to 16 minutes, the resistance of the thermophilic anaerobe No. 3814 is in the range of 60 to 70 minutes and of flat sour No. 1518 is 130 to 140 minutes.

Williams said that the choice of which organism to use in a product is governed by the nature of the product and, to some extent, by the objective of the work. If a process protective against spoilage owing to thermophilic bacteria is desired, the flat-sour type is the organism of choice for low-acid products. With products in which thermophilic spoilage is not a problem, or where a process protective of health but not necessarily protective against thermophilic spoilage is desired the putrefactive anaerobe is the organism of choice. This latter type gives irregular growth in semi-acid products, but this fact does not speak against its use. With such products all inoculated cans are subcultured, and the determination of the end point is based upon the cultural results rather than upon the spoilage results.

An equally difficult question is the number of spores which shall be used. The National Canners Association believed that this should not be fixed but should be graded to obtain definite resistance values. In work of this kind one never knows what natural contamination would be.

The process range should start with one which will result in 100-per cent spoilage on one extreme and include, on the other, one which will result in no spoilage. Possible processes between these points will have to be evaluated on their merits, if that which gives complete sterilization cannot be used.

45a. Merrill and Reed. 1940. Nat. Canners Assoc., Ann. Rpt. to Res. Committee. p. 16.

Fractionation of Spore Suspensions. When using inoculated packs to secure information on process times and temperatures it becomes necessary to obtain spore suspensions of heat resistant bacteria with which to inoculate the food under study. If the object is to destroy *Clostridium botulinum,* it is desirable to have an organism with a resistance in phosphate buffer solution pH 7.0 of from 10 to 15 minutes at 115.5°C.(240°F.); if on the other hand, the object is to guard against spoilage, a more resistant organism must be used which will resist heating for 35 minutes at 240°F. Owing to the fact that wide variations may exist in the resistance of spore suspensions prepared from the same strain of a bacterium, Yesair and Cameron[45b] sought a method of bringing some order into spore inoculation work. They did it by "fractionating" spore suspensions into fractions with different heat resistances by use of a supercentrifuge. The medium in which the spores (putrefactive anaerobe) had been propogated was centrifuged. The effluent was recentrifuged and this was repeated several times. Thus three spore suspensions were secured which had the following heat resistances:

　　　1st Fraction: survived 20 min. at 240°F., destroyed in 25 min.
　　　2nd Fraction: survived 10 min. at 240°F., destroyed in 15 min.
　　　3rd Fraction: survived 5 min. at 240°F., destroyed in 10 min.

This makes it possible to obtain spores of any desired resistance up to the maximum resistance of the spore suspension. If a spore suspension with a resistance of 30 minutes at 240°F. is desired, it is only necessary to obtain a spore crop with higher resistance and apply the centrifuge method to obtain spores of lower resistance.

Calculation of the Theoretical Process. Ball[29] briefed this procedure as follows:

1. Determination, by the glass-tube method, of the thermal destruction times at different temperatures of the organism which is known or assumed to be present in the food. In these tests, the organisms are suspended in a medium as nearly like that provided by the food itself in the can as it is possible to use. The data are plotted in a curve known as a thermal death-time curve, the two coordinates of which express time and temperature, respectively.

2. The rate of heat penetration to and the rate of cooling at the centers of the cans of food, identical with those for which the process is to be determined, are found by making tests with instruments specially designed to measure temperature at the center of a can. A thermocouple and potentiometer indicator are generally used for this work. These data are plotted in time-temperature curves known as heating and cooling curves.

3. The data represented by the heating, the cooling, and the thermal death-time curves are treated mathematically by the methods described in N.R.C. Bulletin No. 37.[28] The result gives the time theoretically necessary to process the cans at the given temperature to give complete sterilization with respect to the organisms studied in heat-resistance tests.

The best method of checking the validity of calculated processes is to run heat-resistance tests by the can method. This method consists of actually processing cans of food that have been inoculated with the organism on which the glass-tube heat-resistance tests had been made. Checks made in this manner have demonstrated that the

---

45b. Yesair and Cameron. 1936. Nat. Canners Assoc. Ann. Rpt. to Res. Committee for 1935, p. 11; also for 1936, p. 11; J. Bact. 31 (1936), 2-3.

degree of dependence that may be placed in calculated processes is directly proportional to the degree of accuracy with which the conditions can be controlled.

The National Canners Association [30] has published recommended processes for nonacid foods. Processing such foods in boiling water was not recommended.

Commercial Sterility of Canned Foods. The ideal process would probably be one which would destroy all forms of life in the can of food. This would be a condition of "absolute sterility" such as is thought of in surgery. While this would be possible to attain in canned foods by using sufficiently high temperatures for sufficiently long times, the food would probably be ruined as a commercial article. Consequently, canning technologists and others have come to recognize a condition of relative sterility for canned foods known as "commercial sterility." A "commercially sterile" canned food is one which has been processed by heat in such a manner that it will not spoil under ordinary market conditions, even though it may not have been completely sterilized. The few organisms which survive are usually sporeforming bacteria of no sanitary significance or hazard to human health. These are often thermophilic bacteria in the spore stage which cannot germinate if the food is held at temperatures below 43.3°C.(110°F.). Occasionally spores of anaerobic mesophilic bacteria may survive.

The only organism which worries the canner is *Clostridium botulinum.* Attempt is made, when processes are being determined, to destroy the most resistant spores of this organism.

Acidification of Canned Foods. As discussed more completely elsewhere in this chapter, canned foods are roughly grouped into two classes, **acid** foods and nonacid foods. The former are generally satisfactorily processed at 100°C. while the latter must be given a steam-pressure cook at temperatures above boiling. Among foods in the latter group are a number (brussels sprouts, artichokes, broccoli, and mushrooms) which are ruined for the market by such heavy processing. In order to be able to give them lighter processes, they are acidified to lower the pH below 4.5, which is recognized as critical for development of *Clostridium botulinum.* It should be clearly recognized that the spores of this organism may not be destroyed but are merely prevented from developing. Consequently, it is most important to insure that the pH is below 4.5. Cruess, Fong, and Lin [48] published the results of a study of this question. The importance of pH in processing was also brought out by Bigelow and Esty,[49] Bigelow [50] and Ball.[28] Bigelow showed the logarithmic nature of thermal death-time curves.

Food-Phosphate Factors. These were introduced to provide a means of expressing heat resistance of an organism when both neutral phosphate and the food under consideration are taken into account.

48. Cruess, Fong, and Lin. 1925. Hilgardia (Calif. Agr. Expt. Sta.) 1, 507-508.

49. Bigelow and Esty. 1920. J. Infect. Dis. 27, 602-612.

50. Bigelow. 1921. Idem 29, 528.

They are arrived at as follows:

$$\frac{\text{thermal death time in food juice}}{\text{thermal death time in phosphate (pH 6.98)}} \times 360.$$

The decimal thus secured is known as the "food factor." The two tests are made simultaneously. The value 360 in this equation is the thermal death time of 212°F. of the most resistant strain of *Clostridium botulinum* which has been isolated. The food factor is, therefore, a ratio of the resistance of the organism under study to its resistance in neutral phosphate solution.

Criticisms of "food factors" are the same as those for thermal death-time determination. Furthermore, the actual food itself is not used and the conditions under which it is canned are not maintained. Penetration of heat into a food juice would probably take place at a quite different rate than in the food itself. Other possibilities for variation, if not error, may be mentioned.

COOLING OF CANNED FOODS

After processing, the canner must lower the temperature of the can as rapidly as possible and as low as possible. The heat must be removed in order to stop the cook. Unless this is done promptly, the canner may suffer losses owing to alteration of the color and other undesirable changes in the food.

The technical phases of cooling will not be discussed here. They are just about as complicated as are those involved in heating the can. This phase of the subject may be studied in the publications of Ball.[28, 29] An article in the *Canning Age*, June 1924, stated that among the dangers to be avoided by proper cooling the following are important:

Thermophilic Spoilage. This may occur in pork and beans and in corn in which the process has not been quite sufficient to kill all the spores of thermophilic bacteria. If the cans remain hot at a temperature above 43.3°C.(110°F.) for a long period, spoilage is almost certain to result sooner or later.

Loss of Quality. The product which otherwise may have possessed good quality may suffer loss of quality owing to improper cooling, such as:

(a) Stack burn, resulting in a darkened product occurring in corn, pork and beans, catsup, etc.

(b) Cloudy liquor, occurring in peas.

(c) Pink discoloration, occurring in the light-colored fruits such as apples, pears, etc.

(d) Soft, mushy products, where the raw product is very tender and must be handled with care. In this group may be mentioned as examples, tomatoes, cherries, berries, dill pickles, etc.

The thermophilic bacteria which have been shown by various investigators to be widespread in nature, are especially significant in connection with cooling. They possess a high optimum temperature and therefore have a high maximum temperature. The spores of some strains are able to withstand the processes given some foods. When they do survive, the food which contains them must be adequately and promptly cooled and stored at a sufficiently low temperature to prevent germination. When the canned foods are adequately cooled and are stored in cool warehouses, they will remain satisfactory for a long time. Should the temperature rise, owing either to warm weather or other factors, the spores germinate and spoilage results.

The canner may use one of a number of methods to get the heat out of the can. The following methods are used for water cooling:

1. The cans are dumped on a belt and sprayed.
2. The cans are dumped on a belt and dragged through a tank of cold water.
3. The cans may be passed through a tank of water in the crates used in the cooker.
4. The cans may be sprayed in the crates which are kept stationary.
5. The cans may be cooled under pressure.

Early canning practice involved only air cooling. This, at best, could only be a slow and perhaps inefficient method. The water cooling methods where the can is agitated a little probably get the heat out of the can most quickly.

Especially interesting are the mechanical coolers used frequently in connection with mechanical cookers. These are usually pressure coolers. The cooler is kept from one-half to two-thirds full of water and pressure is maintained with air to prevent distortion of the cans. The cans are delivered automatically to the cooler on runways from the cooker.

While, generally speaking, it is good practice to cool canned foods immediately after processing before they are stored in the warehouse, some canners secure good results by storing them away hot, without cooling. Cooking then goes on for an indeterminate time. Canners who do this make allowance in selecting process times for the cooking which may go on in the warehouse. Cans which are stored before they are cool may take a long time to come down to room temperature and may, therefore, remain for a long time at temperatures which are optimum for organisms which have survived the process.

Cooling water must be kept bacteriologically clean. It must not contain large numbers of bacteria which spoil canned foods. The vacuum of cans which are being cooled is increasing; if there are cans which are not tightly closed, some of these organisms may be drawn in and spoil the food during storage. Examination of the cooling water is one important part of studies on canning factory sanitation.

Attempts have been made in recent years to sterilize water in the cooling tank with chlorine. This practice rests on results of experiments which have shown its value. Scott,[51] Cameron,[52] Woerz,[53] and Merrill[54] have reported their observations which clearly demonstrated reduction of spoilage bacteria. About two p.p.m. has been found to be sufficient to keep the water free from living bacteria. Scott reported that some of the cans were rusted but Woerz never encountered them.

The Container (Tin Can). While glass jars are used to some extent for preservation of foods in hermetically sealed containers, tin cans are much more widely used. The number of sizes and shapes is very confusing. According to Bitting, many factors have been responsible for present sizes.

51. Scott. 1937. Canning Age, April, 190-191.
52. Cameron. 1939. The Canner 88, No. 12, Pt. 2, 68.
53. Woerz. 1940. Canning Age, June, 304-305.
54. Merrill. 1938. The Canner 86, No. 12, Pt. 2, 67. .

First, cans were made to utilize a standard sheet of metal; later, they were made to hold a definite amount of food, either by volume or weight. Finally, cans were made to hold a quantity of a product to retail at a certain price. Cans are made from tin plate, which is sheet steel rolled very thin and coated with tin.

Manufacturers of tin plate have carried out much research to perfect their product. Some of these investigations, especially those [55] to determine how various tin plates behave when used for making cans in which various products will be preserved, have cost large sums of money. The layman is prone to lay many of the supposed defects and difficulties in preserving canned foods to tin plate with a thin layer of tin. He fails to realize that, at best, plate is not completely covered with tin. The weight of tin on the plate may be said to have little significance in food preservation.

When canning started in this country as a method of food preservation, the cans were put together with solder. These handmade cans were soon followed by those made with machines, and solder was still used. Later still the "hole and cap" can was developed and widely used until it was replaced by the modern "open-top" or sanitary can. The "hole and cap" can had a hole in the cover through which the food was introduced. A solder-hemmed cap was then placed over this hole and heat applied to close the can. Objections on the part of the consumers and practical disadvantages made a place for the 'open-top" can of today. It is easier to clean and more easily filled. It does not necessitate reducing foods to a pulp. The only solder used on a "sanitary" can is at the side seam and this is so small in amount that it cannot possibly affect the contents if one is prone to consider its use objectionable. The double seam must be carefully and accurately executed, else the can will not be sealed tightly. The components of the double seam are shaped like the letter "U." The leg of one letter (the top) is placed between the legs of the other (the can). When these are firmly pressed together, a joint is secured which is called a double seam. The parts of the closing machine which fasten the cover to the can are very important and are given constant attention throughout the canning season. These are spoken of as the chuck, first operation seaming roll, and second operation seaming roll. (See Fig. 4.) These are very carefully machined. The chuck, as is well indicated in the illustration, fits into the countersink of the can covers. This acts as a wall against which the seaming rolls act to make the double seam. The first seaming roll folds the flanges on both the can cover and the side of the can together. Both pieces of metal are given the "U" shape. The second operation seaming roll then presses these "U"-shaped pieces of metal together, which, with the gasket between, should make a tight joint. The operation of the rolls in perfecting a double seam is influenced by the can lift which lifts the can up to the rolls. If the can is not lifted high enough the flange on the

55. "Relative Value of Different Weights of Tin Coating on Canned Food Containers." Report of an investigation by a technical committee representing the National Canners Association, the American Sheet and Tin Plate Company, and the American Can Company, National Canners Assoc., Wash., 1917. Also "Canned Food Containers," Bull. 22-L., National Canners Assoc., Washington, D. C., 1923.

sides of the can is too short or it may be made too long by lifting it too high. The double seams are usually made according to certain dimensions which need not be mentioned in a book of this nature. Detailed information, however, may be found in papers by Miller,[56] Foss,[57] and Stevens.[58]

Some cans are enameled on the interior and are known as enamel-lined cans. The enamel may be applied either before the tin plate is cut, or it may be sprayed into the can after it has been made, or both. It is not used so much to prevent corrosion, although it may function in this way with one or two foods, but to cause the container and its contents to retain their natural color.[59] With products subject to perforations, enameled cans usually pin-hole faster than plain cans; for example, this is true with

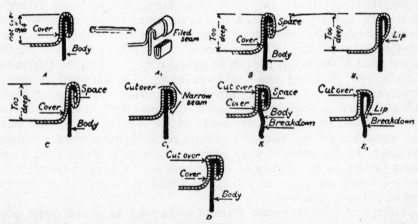

Fig. 4. Showing construction of double seams on sanitary cans. (After Esty and Stevenson, 1925.) A and A₁, correct completed seams; B nad B₁, incorrect seams due to incorrect setting of seaming rolls on closing machine; C and C₁, incorrect seams due to incorrect setting of machine; D, incorrect seam resulting from worn seaming roll; E and E₁ incorrect seam due to too much base pressure.

apples and cider. Perforations are troublesome to canners of acid fruits. Elimination of air in such fruits has been found to reduce perforations to a minimum. In this manner the exhaust becomes a very important factor in canning procedure. The presence of air gently increases perforation.

Considerable investigational work has been done on the theory and chemical mechanism by which air is related to perforation. This will not be reviewed in this book. Those who desire to study this phase of the question may secure a start in the literature by consulting the publications of Kohman.

Corrosion of Tin Cans. This subject is not microbiological in nature and, consequently, must be but briefly treated here. Mantell and Lincoln[60]

56. Miller. 1926. Canning Age, Aug., 1926.
57. Foss. 1923. Canning Age, April, 1923.
58. Stevens. 1927. Canning Age, Sept., 1927; July, 1928, p. 609.
59. This point is borne out by the use of plain cans for Royal-Ann cherries. Plain cans are used in this case to reduce the color in the red spots. The trade desires such cherries without color.
60. Mantell and Lincoln. 1926. Canning Age, Oct., 1926.

distinguished three types of corrosive effects: discoloration, perforation, and etching. Great emphasis has been placed on the relation of air to this problem. Huenink [61] found it very important in canned apples, but not so much so in pumpkin. Clark [62] continued Huenink's work by analyzing the gas. It was too rich in carbon dioxide and too poor in oxygen to be air. The subject has been developed much further by Kohman,[63] Culpepper and Magoon,[64] and many others.

Cleaning and Sterilization of Tin Cans. It is obvious that thorough washing of the tin can in which foods are to be preserved may be an important step in canning. Bitting [65] reported that sterilization of the container insured greater freedom from spoilage. Kremer and Klueter [66] of the Wisconsin Dairy and Food Commission, who made an extensive study of the sanitary condition of cans at the filling machines, believed that adequate washing was necessary. Fellers [67] examined 387 unused cans and jars for microorganisms. The counts ranged from a few hundred to 162,000 bacteria and 22,000 molds per can in one cannery. Cans received from the manufacturer contained fewer microorganisms. The principal groups of organisms found were cocci 28.1 per cent; aerobic, sporeforming bacilli 14.8 per cent; nonsporeforming bacilli 10.4 per cent; anaerobes 21 per cent; Actinomyces 6.7 per cent; molds 24 per cent; yeasts 5.6 per cent; and undetermined 8.3 per cent. Thermophliic bacteria were relatively abundant. In his extensive work on canned marine products Lang [68] also found the can to be a source of microorganisms. Among these was *Clostridium botulinum* Type A, which was found to be present in one per cent of 200 cans examined.

Storage of Canned Foods. Canned foods must be stored under good conditions. Temperature is very important from the microbiological as well as the chemical viewpoint. Chemical reactions between the container and its contents are materially retarded at low temperatures, and thermophilic bacteria are inhibited. Kohman and Sanborn [69] studied these problems. Sweating, leading to rusting and deterioration, may also occur if the cans are held at warehouse temperatures higher than the temperature of the cans themselves. Proper storage of canned foods may conserve quality as Joslyn [70] and Norris [71] advised. Both advised holding at 0°C. (32°F.) in order to reduce chemical changes which lead to deterioration.

HOME-CANNED FOODS

Just how our modern methods of home canning originated is not known. They could not have been derived from the type of experiments which are known to be necessary today. The science of bacteriology had not yet come

61. Huenink. 1921. The Canner, March, 1921.
62. Clark. 1923. The Canner, March 3, 1923, Pt. 2, 148-152.
63. Kohman. 1925. Canning Age, Conv. Digest, 1925, 191-196.
64. Culpepper and Magoon. 1929. The Canner, Feb. 16; Canning Age, July, 1928.
65. Bitting. 1925. Canning Age, April, 1925.
66. Kremer and Klueter. 1924. Idem 5, 937.
67. Fellers. 1928. Amer. J. Pub. Health 18, 763-770.
68. Lang. 1935. Calif. Univ. Pub. in Public Health 2, 50.
69. Kohman and Sanborn. 1927. Ind. Eng. Chem. 19, 514.
70. Joslyn. 1936. Ice and Cold Storage 39, 90.
71. Norris. 1936. Idem, p. 181.

into its own as an aid to canning technology. Among the first publications to desseminate instructions for home canning was Farmers' Bulletin 359 [72] issued in 1909 by the United States Department of Agriculture. In this a five-hour process in boiling water or intermittent sterilization was recommended even for nonacid foods.

In 1918 Benson [73] gave the next statement for the United States Department of Agriculture on home-canning technic. In this bulletin attention was called to the fact that hitherto the canning of vegetables and meats had been generally considered to be too complicated for the home, but that by the method adopted by the Department it was found to be relatively simple to can practically any food product in the home with ordinary kitchen equipment. This method of canning, described by Benson, was intended primarily for use in northern and western states. Why it could not apply equally well to foods packed in other sections of the country was not stated. Three general methods of processing were recommended: hot water-bath (212°F.), water-seal process (214°F.), and the steam-pressure cooker. Apparently, the boiling-water process at 212°F. was not giving satisfactory results. The instructions which were given for operating these outfits concerned mainly the mechanical features of the procedures. Practically no discussion of basic bacteriological problems was presented. A time table was included for processing all sorts of foods according to the several methods mentioned above.

Farmers' Bulletin 853 by Creswell and Powell [74] also appeared in 1918, recommending procedures for home canning of fruits and vegetables to canning club members of southern states. Considerable attention was given to sterilization and processing of home-canned foods and causes of spoilage. The homemaker was thus given the reasons for processing. A distinction was made between sterilization and processing. The former was applied to methods wherein all living microorganisms were killed and processing to a heat treatment which made the foods keep under proper conditions of storage even though viable spores might still be present. The new departure in this bulletin in methods of processing was introduction of "fractional" or intermittent sterilization in hot water and the pressure cooker. The intermittent method of processing was suggested because of the fact that spores of some species of bacteria resisted five hours' boiling. It was hoped that spores which survived the first heating period would germinate into vegetative cells and be destroyed during the second or third sterilization period. The authors stated that processing for one to one and one-half hours in boiling water on three successive days would ordinarily sterilize beans, peas, and corn in quart jars. During warm weather an interval of 18 hours between process periods was advised.

Farmers' Bulletin 1211, published in October 1921,[75] contained a much more complete discussion of processing, especially as far as different methods were concerned. Both the "one-period" or "continuous" process and

72. Breazeale. 1909. U. S. Dept. Agr., Farmers' Bull. 359.
73. Benson. 1918. U. S. Dept. Agr., Farmers' Bull. 839.
74. Creswell and Powell. 1918. U. S. Dept. Agr., Farmers' Bull. 853.
75. U. S. Dept. Agr., Farmers' Bull. 1211 (1921).

the "fractional" or "intermittent" process in boiling water were described. The time tables included suggested processes for boiling water and in the steam-pressure cooker.

Farmers' Bulletin 1471, by Stanley [76] appeared in May 1926. The suggested procedures in this bulletin show a distinct departure from those in the above-mentioned bulletins, and, for the first time, results of bacteriological research seem to have been considered. The process methods were arranged for acid and nonacid foods. Since it had been shown that *Clostridium botulinum* might survive six hours' boiling, the recommendations read that nonacid vegetables and meats should be processed under steam pressure. Boiling-water processes were permitted for fruits, tomatoes, pickled beets, and pimientos. The 1931 and 1932 revisions of Bulletin 1471 contained few modifications. An entirely new edition of this publication appeared as Farmers' Bulletin 1762, by Stanley, Steinbarger, and Shank in September 1936, followed by several revisions. It repeats instructions concerning canning given in Bulletin 1471 and recommends that nonacid foods should not be canned in the home if a pressure cooker is not available for sterilization.

The above discussion might suggest that the Bureau of Home Economics was the only bureau in the United States Department of Agriculture which has been concerned with canning technology. Such was not the case, for Magoon and Culpepper [27] of the Bureau of Plant Industry for some time prior to 1926 had been studying and publishing the results of experimental work on canning technology. While their work was not directly concerned with home-canning problems, their data showed convincingly the inadequacies of many procedures recommended. Thus there was involved the interesting situation of the Department's issuing through one of its agencies recommendations which were bacteriologically unsound, while from another bulletins were being published which gave bases for safe recommendations.

Practically all states have issued bulletins giving instructions for home canning. Examination of these publications indicates that the recommended procedures vary greatly. Some of them are acceptable from the point of view of good canning technology but most of them are not. Many such authorities are not following the recommendations of the United States Department of Agriculture as recorded in Bulletin 1762. They still recommend processing of nonacid foods in boiling water, thus making it possible for the foods to spoil or lead to intoxications.

Other sources of information for home canners are publications distributed by manufacturers of apparatus and supplies for home canners and by magazine and newspaper food bureaus. Many statements in these publications are both misleading and scientifically unsound. Moreover, their recommendations often show inconsistencies similar to those noted in some of the extension bulletins. Popular cookbooks are also inclined to

76. Stanley. 1926. U. S. Dept. Agr., Farmers' Bull. 1471.
77. In addition to these federal bulletins are many from state experiment stations, some are reliable but most of them are not.

fall into such errors and inconsistencies, and even home economics text-books might well be examined on these points before their recommendations are accepted without qualification.

Methods of Processing Home-Canned Foods. The common methods of home canning are briefly discussed from the bacteriological point of view in the following paragraphs.

The Cold-Pack. This method involves packing raw materials into jars cold, followed by brining or siruping, closing, and heating usually in a water bath. It has been responsible for much spoilage and many outbreaks of botulism since its introduction about 1917. When used for preserving vegetables and meats, it is a dangerous method. When used on fruits it may give many jars which are not sterile; considerable spoilage will result unless they are stored under ideal conditions not always available in the ordinary home. This method permits practically the entire load of micro-organisms on the raw materials to go into the jar, since blanching may not destroy many of them. The process to which the jars are subjected must then be relied upon to destroy spores. Results of many experiments have shown that hot-water-bath processing of cold-packed vegetables and meats does not sterilize them. The Bureau of Home Economics has characterized this method of processing as wasteful and dangerous.

The origin of the process times recommended for the boiling-water method is difficult to determine. They could not have been based on results of bacteriological examination of jars so canned nor an adequate examination, after incubation, of experimental packs. Had such data as well as those from heat-penetration studies been considered, the times indicated would have been far too long to command the attention of the home canner.

The Hot-Pack. The foods are precooked for a period of time before they are packed into the jar. The jars are processed immediately. Such treatment probably yields a safer food than the cold-pack method although there is no certainty that bacteria are destroyed in the kettle. However, if precooking in the kettle is sufficiently long and is done at sufficiently high temperatures, viable bacteria are probably materially reduced in numbers, thus leaving fewer to be destroyed when the jar is cooked.

Oven Processing. This method is recommended by stove manufacturers and some manufacturers of canning equipment to be used in the home. It is an expensive and unsafe method to use. Oven-processed foods in glass jars are unsealed during the processing, and therefore the temperature may not go above 212°F. Consequently, the temperature at the center of the jar of food never reaches oven temperature (250 to 275°F.). Heat penetration is slower with this method of processing than with any other. Studies at the Indiana Agricultural Experiment Station [78] have shown this. When processing a quart jar of water with an initial temperature of 68°F. (20°C.) in a preheated oven with heat regulator set for 275°F.(135°C.), from 95 to 110 minutes were required for the contents of the jar to reach boiling temperature; whereas for a similar jar at the same initial tempera-

78. Indiana Agr. Expt. Sta., Rpt. of Director for 1930, 51-52.

ture processed in a water bath of vigorously boiling water, only 20 to 25 minutes were required for the contents to reach the boiling point. With higher initial temperatures, the difference in time in the two methods of processing was not so great. When the initial temperature of the contents of the quart jar was 158°F.(70°C.), it required from 50 to 55 minutes for the temperature at the center of the jar to reach the boiling point when the processing was done in a preheated oven set for 275°F. and 15 to 18 minutes when the processing was done in the water bath.

Further information on this subject was published by Stienbarger.[79] In her experiments the oven temperatures, 250 and 275°F., generally recommended for oven canning were used. Quart glass jars were used in all tests. Temperatures were registered by thermometers from the centers of the jars. In the following temperatures, corrections have been made for the heat of the oven, which in these instances was 275°F. Cubed squash, with an initial temperature of 108°, reached 175°F. in 70 minutes and 212°F. in two hours. Crushed squash with a higher initial temperature, 147°F., required 95 minutes to reach 175°F., and two hours to reach the boiling temperature. Sliced carrots with initial temperatures of 140 to 147°F. reached 212°F. in 65 to 75 minutes. Green beans cut into one-inch lengths with initial temperatures of 180 to 183°F. reached 212°F. in 30 minutes and others with initial temperatures of 167 to 169°F. required 60 to 75 minutes to reach 212°F. Spinach, with an initial temperature of 171°F. reached 212°F. in 78 minutes, whereas another jar with an initial temperature of 165°F. reached 212°F. in 95 minutes. Plums with an initial temperature of 163°F. reached 213°F. in 55 minutes, but a similar jar with an initial temperature of 133°F. required 86 minutes to reach 213°F. Applesauce, with an initial temperature of 156°F., reached boiling in 60 minutes, while with an initial temperature of 86°F. another jar required 95 minutes to reach the boiling point.

In order to secure actual information on the behavior of *Clostridium botulinum* in oven-processed foods, experiments were carried out during the winter and spring of 1931 in the author's laboratory. The vegetables were packed in glass jars in the usual manner. After inoculation the jars were then placed in an oven regulated to 135°C.(275°F.), when the timing was begun, and processed for five hours. A jar was removed from the oven every 15 minutes after the first hour and a half. As soon as the jar has been removed from the oven, the seal was completed at once and the jar air-cooled by an electric fan. The jars were inverted, allowed to stand overnight, and examined the next morning for imperfect seals, after which they were incubated at 37°C. for from one to five days. When the jars were removed from the incubator they were dipped into lysol solution and dried before opening. Samples were removed with sterile glass tubing. A sample was removed for feeding directly to guinea pigs and another for culture. There is little need for discussing the results in great detail. They showed that even a five-hour process in an oven at 135°C.(275°F.) did not destroy spores of *Clostridium botulinum* in the foods used.

79. Stienbarger. 1931. U. S. Dept. Agr., Yearbook, 418-419.

The temperature in the jar located in a hot-air oven should not rise perceptibly above 212°F., as the container is only loosely closed, and loss of the product will occur if heated above 212°F. The curves indicate that jars placed in an oven really heat more slowly, and do not obtain a temperature during the process above that reached in the boiling-water bath.

The pressure process suggested for products such as peas should produce adequate sterilization; however, the boiling-water processes of 180 minutes or oven processes of 180 to 240 minutes suggested by some of the prominent home-canning books will obtain only from 10 to 16 per cent of the sterilizing value of suitable pressure processes.

Hot Water-Bath Processing. This method of processing was probably introduced into home canning from the bacteriological laboratory where it was used for sterilizing materials which were believed to be decomposed by steam-pressure sterilization. Such materials usually have a light load of bacteria and if properly handled may be sterilized by heating at 100°C. (212°F.) for varying lengths of time. The situation is quite different for vegetables in glass jars. Here the bacterial load is usually quite heavy and, in turn, may include decidedly heat-resistant species.

The sterilizing value of this, as of any process, depends largely on the penetration of heat into the container. Less work has been reported on heat-penetration rates into jars used in home canning than into tin containers used in the factory. Those who desire information on the rate of heat penetration into foods in glass jars may consult the publications of Magoon and Culpepper.[27] One of the first to give attention to this subject for home-canned foods was Denton.[80] She reported that it required 45 minutes for the temperature at the center of a jar of sliced carrots to reach 98°C., where it remained during the rest of the processing period. This meant that the internal temperature was at its maximum (98°C.) for 75 minutes. Castle [81] also used a thermometer fitted into a hole in the tops of Mason jars which were processed in boiling water. The important finding from her paper for this discussion is the long time required for the interior of the jars to come to 100°C. In most cases this greatly exceeded the process times recommended in bulletins on home canning. In the last conclusion drawn from her paper Castle warned that vegetables preserved in this manner should always be heated before use to avoid danger of botulism. Heat-penetration studies in an extensive investigation on home canning at Iowa State College by Redfield, Nelson, and Sunderlin [82] also showed slow penetration of heat into glass jars.

Glass jars are usually left only partially sealed when processed in boiling water. In Massachusetts recommendations were that the jars should be fully sealed. In order to ascertain whether this method was safe and satisfactory, Fellers, Levine, and Maclinn [83] observed some 16,500 jars of many different products packed in western Massachusetts. Partially sealed jars developed only negligible pressures while those which were fully sealed

80. Denton. 1918. J. Home Econ. 10, 548-552.
81. Castle. 1919. J. Home Econ. 11, 246-251.
82. Redfield, Nelson, and Sunderlin. 1928. Iowa State College. J. of Sci. 3, 7-28.
83. Fellers, Levine, and Maclinn. 1937. Mass. Agr. Expt. Sta., Bull. 341.

developed from two to six pounds' pressure which was withstood without bursting. This was believed to be practical in every way.

The Steam-Pressure Cooker. This is by far the safest method of processing, but the recommendations in many bulletins are somewhat indefinite. Steam pressure of only 10 pounds is recommended by one large jar manufacturer for all goods. Another with essentially the same process times recommends steam pressure of from 10 to 15 pounds. Significance of the relation of temperature to pressure is subordinated. Practically all "authorities" on home canning advise the homemaker to follow the directions which come with the cooker.

The steam-pressure process has been recommended by the Bureau of Home Economics of the United States Department of Agriculture. Containers of nonacid vegetables processed according to the recommendations of the Bureau gave only two per cent of spoilage. If a pressure cooker is not available, some method of preservation other than canning should be used for vegetables. Botulism outbreaks argue against the boiling-water process.

The success of any method of processing canned foods is determined largely by the rapidity of heat penetration into the container and the thermal destruction time of spoilage microorganisms at the pressure and temperature. This is easily understood when thermal resistance of *Clostridium botulinum* at 212 and 240°F. is compared. The resistance of this organism at 212°F. is 330 minutes while at 240°F. it is only 10 minutes in neutral phosphate solution. Unless sufficient heat penetrates to the center of the jar to destroy microorganisms the product may spoil. Much sound information is available from careful studies long since reported by Ball,[29] Magoon and Culpepper,[27] and Bigelow, Bohart, Richardson, and Ball.[26] These publications cover the subject quite completely and present sufficient data for those advising home canners, if they will only use them. Magoon and Culpepper studied the glass jar with various foods.

As the relation of inadequate processing to botulism and the relatively greater difficulty of processing nonacid foods was established, acidification of nonacid foods with lemon juice or vinegar was suggested. Having established that a pH of 4.5 had protective action by inhibiting development of *Clostridium botulinum*, it was believed that this could be attained by addition of acid. Nonacid foods are highly buffered; consequently such large amounts of acid would have to be added that flavor would be affected. Sunderlin, Nelson, and Levine,[84] for instance, found that acidification of asparagus and sweet corn with phosphoric or citric acid made a two-hour process satisfactory, whereas without acid even a process time of twice as long was not sufficient.

No outbreak of botulism has been caused by foods canned in American factories since 1924.* This fortunate situation results from careful studies about *Clostridium botulinum*, heat penetration into canned foods, and

---

84. Sunderlin, Nelson, and Levine. 1928. Iowa State Col. J. Sci. 2, 189-212.

* One outbreak was attributed to a mushroom sauce which may be considered to be a specialty product and not an ordinary canned vegetable packed in great amounts.

other factors important in canning. The situation for canning in the home is not so satisfactory. Each year sees its toll of human lives which, to a great extent, may be credited to some extension services, editors of cookbooks, and manufacturers of supplies for the home canner. How long such a situation will be allowed to continue remains to be seen. In some states serious outbreaks of poisoning had to occur before any real advance could be made in changing unsound recommendations. Recent summaries of outbreaks and cases of botulism in California [85] by the California Department of Public Health for the years 1899-1939 indicated 130 outbreaks, 300 cases, and 184 deaths. Meyer and his associates in the same state gathered statistics of 367 outbreaks in the United States over the same period. Only 83 were caused by commercially canned foods. The other 284 outbreaks were caused by home-canned foods. Total cases in the 43 years numbered 1,052 with 687 deaths, a fatality rate of 65 per cent. How many unrecognized cases occurred will never be known.

If graduates of schools of home economics and others who consider themselves capable of recommending procedures for the homemaker do not recognize all bacteriological knowledge, they should be forced to do so by those whose duty it is to conserve the public health. (This has been done by the Food and Drug Administration.[86] Interstate shipments of foods processed in boiling water were seized and destroyed.) It would be unfortunate to have to resort to legal procedures to indicate that those who distribute unsound literature have some responsibility to the public. Furthermore, those who interpret scientific data for those who are less informed, must leave nothing unsaid. Improperly processed home-canned foods are hazardous.

Canned-food technologists are agreed that nonacid foods must be processed only under steam pressure. Steam-pressure cookers have been devised for this purpose, but the mere use of such a cooker is not sufficient, for it must be correctly used and the non-technical homemaker must be taught to appreciate the necessity of following instructions which come with the cooker. Some of these instruction books should be more carefully written.

Practically all pressure cookers depend on a pressure gauge alone for controlling temperature. This is probably satisfactory if the gauge is of high quality and all air is removed from the cooker. The pressure gauges furnished with some cookers are probably untrustworthy. However, good canning practice should provide for a reliable thermometer with which the actual temperature may be determined. This is necessary not only because the atmosphere in the cooker may contain considerable air, but because the gauges may become faulty by use year after year without inspection and adjustment.

Bacteriological Condition of Home-Canned Foods. Two main problems are involved in home canning of perishables, spoilage and food poisoning. They are closely interlinked, for some of the organisms which cause intoxi-

85. Calif. State Dept. Pub. Health, 36th Biennial Rpt. for 1938-1940, 24-26; Amer. Med. Assoc. J. 121 (1943), 1286.
86. U. S. Food and Drug Administration, Rpt. of Chief for the Year Ending June 30, 1931, 10-11.

cations are also spoilage organisms. They may bring about gross evidences of spoilage and in addition form a metabolic product which is poisonous. Spoilage in home-canned foods has received too little emphasis because most homemakers keep no records. Any pack of home-canned foods in which considerable spoilage occurs is potentially dangerous. The argument that poisonings have never resulted in the area or state does not have much weight since it is known that *Clostridium botulinum* is widespread in nature.

Some who are serving in an advisory capacity to home canners take comfort from the fact that foods in which *Clostridium botulinum* has developed usually show visual evidences of spoilage and would, therefore, be excluded from the diet. This may be true for certain foods, but it may not be true for all home-canned foods. Schoenholz, Esty, and Meyer [87] showed quite clearly that evidence of spoilage and toxin formation were quite irregular. Foods in which there were no evidences of spoilage have caused serious outbreaks of poisoning.

Results of the few investigations which have been carried out are in good agreement. They show that home-canned foods frequently contain viable organisms and show high incidence of understerilization. Lang [88] found a heterogeneous flora. The most frequent cause of spoilage was an organism, said to have been a butyric-acid organism, isolated from 185 jars, spores of which resisted 100°C.(212°F.) for six hours, as well as intermittent processing at 100°C. for one hour at intervals of 18 and 24 hours. The frequency of occurrence of bacterial spores in jars of good quality varied from 20 per cent for tomatoes to 80 per cent for spinach. Spores of the subtilis-mesentericus group were able to withstand 100°C. for from five and one-half to 10 hours. Biester *et al.*[89] reported 50 per cent spoilage in foods processed in boiling water. The jars were incubated at 37°C. (98.6°F.) before examination.

Bacteriological examination of a large number of cans of asparagus packed in 1918 by the division of home economics at the University of Kansas [90] revealed many jars with viable organisms, most of which were heat resistant. A later report in 1920 indicated that *Bacillus subtilis* and *Bacillus mesentericus* predominated in jars to which salt had been added. Presence of acid to the extent of .1 per cent caused rapid destruction of bacteria.

The Bureau of Home Economics of the U. S. Department of Agriculture observed spoilage in home-canned foods of packs for two years (Stienbarger[91]). Results were just about the same as reported by other investigators. Of 3,434 jars of various kinds of food, 48 per cent showed spoilage after processing in the open water bath. The foods in which greatest spoilage occurred were meats, fish, corn, lima beans, and peas. Hot packing gave less spoilage than cold packing. The conclusion to be

87. Schoenholz, Esty, and Meyer. 1923. J. Infect. Dis. 33, 289-327.
88. Lang. 1921. J. Home Econ. 13, 448-449.
89. Biester *et al.* 1921. Idem 13, 494-495.
90. Kansas Agr. Expt. Sta., Ann. Rpt. for 1919, 76; for 1920, 40-41.
91. Stienbarger. 1933. U. S. Dept. Agr., Mimeographed Report.

drawn from this report is that high temperatures are needed for preservation of nonacid foods. These are attained only with steam pressure.

Perhaps the most extensive investigation of home-canning methods was carried out at Iowa State College by Sunderlin, Nelson, and Levine,[84] who made observations on 2,732 jars of vegetables and meats processed in boiling water. The data which were published do not speak well for home-canning procedures. With corn, for instance, 15 per cent spoilage was secured with a four-hour process, the longest which was used. Similar data were secured with several other foods. The authors stated that the possibility of food poisoning was not investigated. The large percentage of spoilage and the still larger percentage of unsterile cans would indicate to anyone familiar with botulism that practically all of the cans prepared in these experiments were potentially dangerous. Such data give further proof of the danger of using hot-water processes for nonacid foods. Under the conditions of their experiments, two and one-half hours in boiling water were found to be satisfactory for beans and chard and three hours for beef and pork.

Modification of the recommendations from the United States Department of Agriculture for home-canning technic was markedly affected by the botulism situation in the United States soon after 1916. Dickson[92] tested the efficiency of the then recommended procedures using peas, beans, and corn. Each jar was inoculated with spores of *Clostridium botulinum*. The jars were placed in boiling water and processed according to instructions. After three weeks all showed evidences of fermentation with gas formation and a strong butyric acid odor when opened. Administration of filtered juice to guinea pigs caused death. These results caused Dickson to state that the cold-pack method of canning vegetables was neither safe nor efficient if the raw materials happened to carry spores of *Clostridium botulinum*. The United States Department of Agriculture through bacteriologists in its Bureau of Chemistry and States Relation Service[93] denied Dickson's statements. In spite of the fact that outbreaks of botulism were being caused by home-canned foods, they stated that there was no danger that botulism would result from eating fruits and vegetables which had been canned by any of the recommended methods provided the methods had been carefully followed. They further argued (on the basis of statements in textbooks) that the spores of *Clostridium botulinum* were destroyed by heating for one hour at $79.4°C.(175°F.)$. Evidence indicating a much greater heat resistance had already been published. Burke[94] showed that spores of *Clostridium botulinum* were very resistant to heat. She reported that the spores of some strains would resist boiling for three hours or more and that methods of canning by boiling the fruit or vegetables in an open kettle and sealing in clean jars by the cold-pack (one-period) method, or by fractional sterilization on three successive days, could not be relied upon to destroy the spores of *Clostridium botulinum*.

92. Dickson. 1917. Amer. Med. Assoc. J. 69, 966-968.
93. U. S. Dept. Agr. 1917. Weekly News Letter 5, 6.
94. Burke. 1919. Amer. Med. Assoc. J. 72, 88-92.

She stated that pressure canning with a sufficiently long sterilization period was the only safe method.

Dickson [95] in another statement emphasized again that prevention of botulism depended not on curtailing the use of either home-canned or commercially canned foods but upon education of the public to possible danger of botulism from improperly canned foods. Commercial canners faced this situation squarely and spent hundreds of thousands of dollars to learn proper methods of processing. The result is that commercially canned foods in America have been free from botulism hazards for about two decades.

Home-canning experts in many states take confidence from the fact that no botulism has been caused by products packed in their states. There is false security in such a position, for if the results of bacteriological research are to be believed, spores of *Clostridium botulinum* are widely disseminated in soil, and home canners constantly face the possibility of the presence of spores of this organism in home-canned foods. However slight the the possibility may be, any illness with 60 per cent mortality is serious and naturally strikes terror to a community. When it is remembered that it can be prevented by proper methods of processing, carelessness becomes doubly inexcusable. Those who hold positions from which they may speak with authority on canning methods, must consider all phases of the problem and data which are being published every day. There is little reason for them to suggest dangerous procedures.

A few bacteriologists as well as a few teachers of home economics apparently believe that the possible relation of improperly home-canned foods to botulism is a much-flouted problem of little real significance. As has been pointed out, since 1924 there has not been a single outbreak of botulism from ordinary factory-canned foods; one outbreak has been attributed to a specialty, mushroom sauce. Bacteriologists, physicians, and health officers may have a part in correcting the present unfortunate situation. The time has come for a thorough appraisal of the procedures which are recommended to the homemaker for canning fruits, vegetables, and meats. Until recommendations such as are now distributed by the United States Department of Agriculture in Farmers' Bulletin 1762 are adopted generally, intoxication from and gross spoilage in packs of home-canned foods will continue. The yearly toll of deaths from botulism caused by home-canned vegetables and vegetable mixtures should stimulate health authorities to exert pressure which will lead to safe and adequate recommendations. Until these recommendations can be corrected spoilage and poisonings will continue. A warning has been issued by the California Department of Public Health. [96] Fellers [97] made an emphatic statement on this question and advised that something be done to curb the publication and distribution of dangerous literature. He called attention to the fact that the United States Depart ment of Agriculture gives sound advise.

95. Dickson. 1921. Calif. State Bd. Health, Bull. 16, 36-38.
96. Calif. State Dept. Pub. Health, Weekly Bull., Feb. 4, 1933.
97. Fellers. 1927. Amer. J. Pub. Health 17, 470-475.

Schoenholz, Esty, and Meyer [98] as long ago as 1923 warned that foods canned in the home by some methods were unsafe. They stated that facilities for maintaining temperatures above the boiling point were not always available in the home. Furthermore, glass jars were usually used in which it would be more difficult to determine evidences of spoilage. Despite these warnings, every year since 1923 has had its outbreaks of botulism caused by home-canned foods. In addition to the above warnings are those of the American Public Health Association [99] and the American Medical Association.[100] Tanner [101] reviewed the whole situation, pointing out that the responsibility of those who give instructions in home-canning methods is to give only methods which will insure a safe product that will keep.

Canning Compounds. To prevent spoilage and food poisoning resulting from faulty processing some home canners have resorted to use of chemical preservatives, such as salicylic acid, boric acid, and similar compounds. So-called "canning compounds" have been marketed. Levine [102] examined one which contained 95 per cent of boric acid and five per cent of sodium chloride. The manufacturers recommended 15 to 20 minutes' boiling with seven grams of the compound per quart for the preservation of fruits and vegetables. In this concentration, Levine and Weldin observed a selective action on bacteria. Some varieties of *Escherichia coli* and several of the aerobic sporeformers failed to grow in media containing the compound. *Clostridium botulinum* grew in twice the concentration recommended. The compound seemed to have little effect on the bacteria usually present on vegetables. The same compound was studied by Edmondson, Thom, and Giltner [103] who arrived at similar conclusions. Boric acid at best is a feeble antiseptic. As a chemical preservative its use in foods is prohibited by the Food and Drug Administration.

MICROORGANISMS IN CANNED FOODS

While canned foods may not be completely sterile, they are in much better condition bacteriologically than in former years. Since some canned foods may contain viable microorganisms which do not develop as long as cans are held under certain conditions, they are characterized by canned food technologists as "commercially sterile." Investigational work in this field must be carried on under rigorous laboratory conditions to prevent contamination of plates and cultures. Air-borne contamination has been shown to occur. When testing sterility of a product such contamination becomes very significant. It would probably not be significant in such bacteriological work as water or milk analysis because a few more colonies would not materially affect the results. Williams and Clark [104] discussed

98. Schoenholz, Esty, and Meyer. 1923. J. Infect. Dis. 33, 289-327.
99. Amer. Pub. Health Assoc. Year Book, 1934-1935, 56.
100. Amer. Med. Assoc. J. 105 (1935), 205; 109 (1937), 1046; 121 (1943), 1286; 122 (1943), 144.
101. Tanner. 1934. J. Home Econ. 26, 365-376; Amer. J. Pub. Health 25 (1935), 301-313; Amer. Dietet. Assoc. J. 11 (1935), 18-27.
102. Levine. 1923. J. Home Econ. 15, 64-70.
103. Edmondson, Thom, and Giltner. 1922. U. S. Dept. Agr. Cir. 237.
104. Williams and Clark. 1942. Food Research 7, 178-185.

this problem for canned salmon. Their statements are probably applicable to other foods. Improvement in bacteriological condition of canned foods is also due to rigorous processes which have been introduced as well as to better technology in general.

A few of the earlier contributions are reviewed below because of their significance in the historical background of an industry which has been placed on a firm basis by science and technology.

Russell [105] isolated two different species of bacteria from canned peas which caused a gaseous fermentation. The organisms were probably facultative thermophiles, although it was not definitely established. The trouble was checked by raising the process. Poincarré and Macé [106] reported the isolation of living bacteria from several different kinds of canned foods.

About this same time canned sea foods began to receive the attention of bacteriologists. MacPhail,[107] in a study of blackening of lobster, isolated three bacteria and a micrococcus which were believed to be the causes of the trouble. The same year, Prescott and Underwood [24] isolated and described seven bacilli and two micrococci from canned clams and canned lobster. The next year, Prescott and Underwood spent the summer in Maine on a study of sweet-corn spoilage. Eleven bacilli and one micrococcus were isolated from spoiled cans. They were not cognizant, at this early day, of the importance of thermophilic bacteria but did report that there were two kinds of souring, one with gas formation and the other without. It is quite possible that the bacteria which were isolated were facultative thermophiles and grew on plates incubated at 37°C.(98.6°F.) or lower. They fulfilled Koch's postulates. Large losses were also being experienced in canning of peas. Harding and Nicholson [108] had an opportunity to study a serious outbreak of spoilage in central New York. The peas had a disagreeable odor resembling hydrogen sulfide. Whether this was the sulfide spoilage of peas of the present day probably cannot be known. Microscope examination of the liquor from a spoiled can revealed the presence of a rod-shaped, sporeforming organism. Experiments were conducted which showed that heating a two-pound can of peas for 30 minutes at 115.4°C.(240°F.) destroyed the organism. When this process was used in the factory, the spoilage ceased. Harding and Nicholson thus worked with a spoilage of peas which has more recently been found to be caused by thermophilic bacteria.

As early as 1904, von Wahl [109] discussed differences in the resistance of spores. He noted the fact that heat resistance is closely bound with the medium in which the spores are heated and that repeated cooking may so alter the menstruum that the heat resistance is changed. Other contribu-

105. Russell. 1895. Wis. Agr. Expt. Sta., 12th Ann. Rpt. 227-231.

106. Poincarré and Macé. 1899. Chem. News 60, 132.

107. MacPhail. 1897. Suppl. No. 2 to the 29th Ann. Rpt., Dept. of Marine and Fisheries, Canada, 29, 1-33.

108. Harding and Nicholson. 1904. N. Y. State Agr. Expt. Sta. Bull. 249.

109. von Wahl. 1904. Rev. in Koch's Jahresber. 15, 169.

tions were made by Belser,[25] Cathcart, [110] Pfuhl,[111] McBryde,[112] Burgess,[113] and Zavella.[114]

One of the most significant contributions to knowledge of spoilage of peas, corn, and many other canned foods was made by Barlow.[115] He showed for the first time that thermophilic bacteria caused spoilage of canned foods. In order to determine the organisms which were causing the spoilage, he first worked with underprocessed corn. He also noticed that cans at the center of the stack in the warehouse showed greater spoilage.

Examinations of canned foods up to this time had been made largely on small numbers of cans and on cans which were spoiled. No large-scale examination of cans purchased on the market had been made. Consequently, publications of Weinzirl [116] and Cheyney[117] are especially interesting. They purchased cans of food on the open market which were apparently in satisfactory condition. While it is wrong to reach conclusions by summarizing data from fruit, vegetable, and meat products, Weinzirl reported that 19.2 per cent of sound cans of food contained viable spores. Many of the organisms isolated showed very low heat resistance which would seem to indicate that the cans from which they were isolated may not have possessed tight closure. Among the various microorganisms which were isolated were four thermophilic bacteria to which new names were given: *Bacillus aerothermophilus*, *Bacillus thermoindifferens*, *Bacillus stearophilus*, and *Bacillus thermoalimentophilus*. Cheyney found that only eight per cent of 725 cans contained viable organisms. In a private communication he reported that examination of 2,200 cans showed the same results. Savage [118] also examined canned foods selected from importations into England. He examined 178 cans, excluding canned condensed milk which is known to contain viable bacteria, 38.8 per cent of which were not sterile. The percentage not sterile varied from 100 for crab, 83 for lobster, 64 for meat (kind not stated) to 22 for fruit (kind not stated). Savage considered the types of bacteria present to be more important than the sterility. Proteolytic and fermentative properties were the most important characteristics causing unsoundness. Savage punctured 17 sound cans of fish products to allow the ingress of sterile air. They were incubated for from five to 16 days and then sealed and incubated. Twelve of them spoiled. Savage thus showed that many cans of food contain viable aerobic and anaerobic bacteria which are stimulated to grow by the presence of air. The same thing was shown for yeasts in condensed milk. Viable yeast cells could be present in cans of condensed milk and cause no fermentative changes as long as air was kept out. Savage isolated a new

110. Cathcart. 1906. J. Hyg. 6, 248-250; Centbl. Bakt. 18, 356.
111. Pfuhl. 1908. Ztschr. f. Hyg. u. Infektionskrank. 61, 209-212.
112. McBryde. 1907. U. S. Dept. Agr., Bur. Anim. Indus. Rpt., 279-296.
113. Burgess. 1912. The Canner and Dried Fruit Packer.
114. Zavella. 1916. The Canning of Fruits and Vegetables. John Wiley & Sons, Inc., New York, N. Y.
115. Barlow. 1912. Univ. of Illinois, Thesis.
116. Weinzirl. 1919. J. Med. Res. 39, 349-413.
117. Cheyney. 1919. J. Med. Res. 40, 177-197.
118. Savage. 1923. Lancet. I, 527-529.

organism, *Bacillus pleofructi*, which was able to decompose canned fruit. Thus air ingress is regarded as of great importance, since it may allow the development of bacteria which are already in the can of food.

Twenty-four per cent of 900 cans of commercially sound canned corn was found by Michael and Tanner [119] to have viable organisms. While these cans showed evidences of spoilage after they had been incubated, it is probable that they would have remained normal on the market. Imported canned shallots (onions) were found by Prickett [120] to harbor viable thermophilic bacteria. Anaerobic thermophilic bacteria were not found.

McClung and Wheaton [121] found *Clostridium welchii* the cause of gas formation in boiled beef. The spoilage was peculiar because the cans were "swells" when they came from the retort, quite an unusual situation. The gas which caused the swelled condition was largely hydrogen. Failure to isolate viable bacteria from the cans greatly complicated the problem. Bacteriological surveys of the packing plant and raw products gave cultures in which a wide variety of bacteria were present. The specific organism involved was found to be *Clostridium welchii*. It seemed to the authors that the meat was contaminated with the organisms when received at the canning plant. During parboiling, the temperature was not raised sufficiently to destroy them. They quickly developed in the can of meat which was closed under vacuum. At this time the temperature of the meat in the cans was about 100 to 110°C. (212 to 230°F.) Delays in processing would give organisms sufficient time to develop. The presence of this organism was not believed to have any public-health significance.

SPOILAGE OF CANNED FOODS

Canned foods are subject to various kinds of spoilage. They may be attacked by microorganisms which have survived processing or gained access to the can through imperfections in the container or may undergo chemical spoilage by reacting with the metal of the container. The discussions in this book will consider especially spoilage caused by microorganisms. This is a broad, intricate subject in itself on account of the various types of food involved and the various types of microorganisms concerned in spoilage thereof.

Bacteria which spoil canned foods may be classified according to the changes which they produce or their own characteristics. These groups seem to be quite well demarked and are generally used for convenience, as pointed out by Cameron and Esty [122] and Cameron, Williams, and Thompson. [123] Three groups are made up of thermophilic bacteria.

1. *"Flat-Sour"-Producing Thermophilic Bacteria.* These bacteria produce acid in cans without gas formation. Consequently the ends of the cans remain flat. Two types are involved depending on whether nonacid or acid foods are involved.

119. Michael and Tanner. 1936. Food Research 1, 99-112.
120. Prickett. 1931. J. Infect. Dis. 49, 271-280.
121. McClung and Wheaton. 1936. Food Research 1, 307-318.
122. Cameron and Esty. 1940. Food Research 5, 549-557.
123. Cameron, Williams, and Thompson. 1928. Natl. Canners Assoc. Bull. 25-L.

Nonacid Foods: *Bacillus stearothermophilus* is a member of this group of bacteria causing "flat-sour" spoilage of vegetables. These bacteria are facultative with respect to oxygen, which makes it possible for them to grow under widely divergent conditions. Spores with quite high heat resistance are formed.

Acid Foods: There is a newer type of spoilage that affects products which are relatively acid in character, particularly tomatoes and some tomato products. *Bacillus thermoacidurans* is the typical species of spoilage organism. It is an aerobic, acid-tolerant bacterium, spores of which are not as heat resistant as are the spores of other spoilage bacteria. It is discussed on page 667.

2. *Thermophilic Anaerobic Bacteria.* These bacteria grow only in the absence of air. They form very heat-resistant spores. Growth is accompanied with both gas and acid production so that the container swells. *Clostridium thermosaccharolyticum* is the name given to these organisms.

3. *"Sulfide Spoilage" Thermophilic Bacteria.* The name "sulfur stinker" was given to these bacteria when they were first isolated. *Clostridium nigrificans* in the type species.[138] It produces large amounts of hydrogen sulfide which turns the contents of cans of food in which it has developed, quite dark. Economically this group is not important for it causes few outbreaks. When it does strike, however, its effects are spectacular and costly.

The above groups are composed of thermophilic bacteria. Several other groups of bacteria exist which are not thermophilic but which cause much loss.

4. *Putrefactive, Anaerobic Bacteria.* These are the truly putrefactive anaerobic bacteria, growth of which is indicated by gas formation and digestion. The anaerobic, sporeforming species are in this group.

Yeasts as Spoilage Organisms of Canned Foods. Yeasts have not been significant organisms in spoilage of canned foods. They may cause spoilage in some fruits in sirup which have not been processed at sufficiently high temperatures or for a sufficiently long time. At best the spoilage caused by yeasts is relatively insignificant. Townsend and Powers[124] found the most-resistant spoilage organism in orange juice was a heat-resistant yeast which survived up to one minute at 76.7°C.(170°F.).

Molds as Spoilage Organisms of Canned Foods. Molds have not caused much trouble for the canner. On one or two occasions they have been found to have survived the process and caused spoilage. The best-known and most-typical cases are those reported by Olliver and Smith[125] and Williams, Cameron, and Williams.[126] The former isolated *Byssochlamys fulva* from processed fruits in England. Its ascospores resisted 86 to 88°C. (186.8 to 190.4°F.) for 30 minutes. Williams, Cameron, and Williams[126] isolated a mold from canned blueberries. Sartory and Meyer[127] also reported a mold from canned foods. *Byssochlamys fulva* has been studied

124. Townsend and Powers. 1939. Natl. Canners Assoc., Ann. Rpt. to Res. Committee, 1938; p. 29.
125. Olliver and Smith. 1933. J. Bot. 72, 196; Chem. and Indus. 53 (1934), 166T-172T.
126. Williams, Cameron, and Williams. 1941. Food Research 6, 69-73.
127. Sartory and Meyer. 1940. Acad. de Med. (Paris) Bull. 123, 98-101.

especially by investigators in England. Hirst and McMaster [128] reported that spoilage of canned fruits by this mold took the form of a complete breakdown in texture so that on slight shaking it disintegrated completely. In some cases the mold could be detected by the naked eye, while in others the microscope was required to detect it. The can may be swelled, but in most cases the cans examined had a good vacuum. The spores of this fungus were found on a few samples of fruit on which it was carried into the factory. Heat-resistance studies of the spores in various canned fruits indicated appreciable resistance. Hirst and McMaster used fruits as the substratum, which might account for shorter survival periods than were reported by Olliver. Further experiments by Hull [129] revealed that longer survival times were observed when the spores were heated in sucrose. Actual survival times depended on the conditions under which the experiments were carried out. A temperature of 87.8 to 93.3°C.(190 to 200°F.) was necessary at the center of the can under experimental inoculation; natural infection was destroyed at an internal temperature of 82.2°C. (180°F.). Hull believed that in order to destroy resistant spores 90.5°C. (195°F.) at the center of the can would be necessary. Gillespy's [130] results seemed to confirm this.

Some of the conditions which influence heat resistance of ascospores of *Byssochlamys fulva* in fruits are concentration of sucrose and presence of a little sulfur dioxide. Gillespy observed what has been observed with bacteria and yeasts that the more sugar present the harder it is to destroy the ascospores. Small concentrations of sulfur dioxide at pH values below 3.7 increased the lethal effects of heat on these ascospores.

Classification of Types of Spoilage of Canned Foods on the Basis of Acidity. Canned foods are divided into two, and perhaps three, classes as regards processing. Bigelow and Cameron [131] and Cameron and Esty [132] have referred to these as *nonacid, semiacid,* and *acid* foods. Cameron and Esty suggested the following classification which they termed, "Acidity Classification of Spoilage Types":

> Group 1. Low acid, pH 5 and higher.
> Group 2. Medium acid, pH 5 to 4.5.
> Group 3. Acid, pH 4.5 to 3.7.
> Group 4. High acid, pH 3.7 and below.

Group 1. Low Acid, pH 5 and Higher. Cameron and Esty placed meat and marine products, milk and certain of the common vegetables in this group. The common thermophilic bacteria may spoil all of these foods although they do not ordinarily attack meat and marine products. Mesophilic putrefactive anaerobes are important agents of spoilage in this group.

Since Barlow [115] revealed that thermophilic bacteria were important in certain types of canned-food spoilage, numerous others have reported the

128. Hirst and McMaster. 1932-1933. Bristol Univ. Fruit and Vegetable Preserv. Res. Sta. Ann. Rpt., Campden Glos, 53-60.
129. Hull. 1933-1934. Idem. 64-73; 1934-1935, 65-73.
130. Gillespy. 1938. Idem 68-77; 1940, 54-61.
131. Bigelow and Cameron. 1932. Ind. Eng. Chem. 24, 655-658.
132. Cameron and Esty. 1940. Assoc. Off. Agr. Chem. J., Aug., 1940; see also foot note 118.

isolation of such organisms. Donk [133] isolated a species to which he gave the name *Bacillus stearothermophilus* from corn. Shaw [134] isolated 23 strains of thermophilic bacteria from fruits and vegetables. She proposed the name *Bacillus pepo* for one strain from pumpkin.

Stevenson [135] gave two explanations for "black beets"; one was that the discoloration was enzymic in nature and the other was that it was a bacterial spoilage. Cameron, Esty, and Williams [136] had an opportunity to study an outbreak of spoilage of this nature in sliced beets. The spoilage was said to be due to understerilization but in order for the bacteria to produce their characteristic effect, it is necessary that an abnormally large amount of iron be present in the beet liquor. The causal organism was described and named *Bacillus betanigrificans*. The iron was said to accelerate the growth of the organism. The organism did not grow at 55°C. (131°F.).

Malodorous or "sulfide spoilage" of peas and corn is not a significant one as far as the number of outbreaks is concerned; it is serious, however, for the packer when it does occur. Cameron [137] stated that the research laboratory of the National Canners Association had a record of only four outbreaks in corn and one in peas. Hydrogen sulfide gas is produced, to which the bad odor is due. The can remains flat, owing to the fact that the gas formed dissolves in the liquor. The sulfur compounds react with the iron which gives the liquor a black color. Cameron investigated the source of these thermophilic bacteria in canned peas by investigating the water, salt, sugar, and tanks in which the brines were made. He discovered the organism which Werkman and Weaver [135] named *Clostridium nigrificans*. This organism caused a very pronounced spoilage in peas, evidenced by the blackening of the liquors. Cameron's work seemed to indicate that the canned peas were seeded with the spores of this organism by the brine which was prepared in wooden tanks. Shavings from the staves of the wooden hot-water tank were found to be badly infected with the spores of the hydrogen sulfide-producing, thermophilic organism. Cameron, Williams, and Thompson [123] have made a longer report on this spoilage.

Group 2. Medium Acid, pH 5 to 4.5. In this group, which Cameron and Esty said was really a subdivision of Group 1, are principally meat and vegetable mixtures and "specialties," such as spaghetti, soups, and sauces. Bacteria involved in this group are essentially those mentioned above for Group 1; in some of these foods putrefactive anaerobes may develop, resulting in nongaseous changes in the food.

Group 3. Acid, pH 4.5 to 3.7. In this group are tomatoes, pears, figs, pineapples, and nectarines. These products are subject to spoilage by nonsporeforming, aciduric bacteria and sporeforming anaerobes allied to *Clostridium pasteurianum*. Some of the organisms which fall in this group

133. Donk. 1919. Abs. Bact. 3, 4-5; J. Bact. 5 (1920), 373-374.
134. Shaw. 1928. J. Infect. Dis. 43, 461-474.
135. Stevenson. 1925. The Canner, Conv. No. 106.
136. Cameron, Esty, and Williams. 1936. Food Research 1, 73-82.
137. Cameron. 1928. Canning Age, 217.
138. Werkman and Weaver. 1927. Iowa State Col. J. Sci. 2, 57-61; Iowa Agr. Expt. Sta., Bull. 117.

have been studied by Townsend.[139] They were isolated from swelled cans of tomatoes, pears, pineapple, pimientoes, and chilies. Some of the strains were sufficiently acid-tolerant to grow in almost any canned food if the medium was otherwise suitable. Spoilage caused by nonsporeforming, coccoid bacilli indicated to Townsend understerilization or defective can seams. Cooks of certain acid foods which give a temperature of only 98.8°C.(210°F.) at the center of the can are not high enough for sterilization if any considerable number of spores are present.

The strains which Townsend used, isolated from the foods mentioned above, were arranged in four groups as follows:

Group I. Facultative anaerobes. Small, gram-positive, coccoid bacilli, producing gas in certain food juices but not in artificial media. They do not produce spores and are nonmotile. They are saccharolytic and some strains are remarkably tolerant to acids. The resistance to heat is very low.

Group II. Facultative anaerobes. Small, gram-positive, nonsporeforming, motile, coccoid bacilli. They are very saccharolytic and produce a great deal of gas. The heat resistance is very low.

Group III. The flat-sour organisms. Facultative anaerobes. Short, gram-positive, motile rods, forming central spores. They are very saccharolytic but do not produce gas. A resistance to heat of 16 minutes at 100°C.(212°F.) using 800 spores, has been obtained.

Group IV. Obligate anaerobes. Form clostridia at sporulation. Small to long, gram-positive rods with oval, subterminal spores. They are very saccharolytic, with the production of much gas. The resistance to heat of one strain is 13 minutes at 100°C. (212°F.), using 1,000 spores.

All of the organisms studied were mesophiles, since optimum temperature for growth was 37°C.(98.6°F.). The characteristics of the organisms were given in considerable detail by Townsend, although in several instances only general statements could be made. This grouping was quite similar to one published previously by Esty.[140]

Heat-resistance studies were carried out by Townsend [141] with cultures from each group using generally accepted methods. Spore crops were secured by growing the organism in liver broth at 30°C.(86°F.) for 16 to 20 days. After concentration by centrifuging, the spores were stored at about 5°C.(41°F.) in a portion of the medium in which they had been grown.

"Heat resistance was determined by the method of Bigelow and Esty [142] using two-ml. amounts of suspension in six-mm., inside-diameter Pyrex tubes, sealed after filling. Three tubes of each suspension were removed from the water bath at each time interval and immediately cooled. The thermal death-time tubes were then subcultured into tubes of liver broth from which the air had been exhausted by boiling, stratified with vaseline to provide anaerobic conditions, and incubated at 30°C. Gas production was the criterion for growth. A one-minute lag was allowed from the time the tubes were put in the water bath until the start of the heating test was recorded. Three temperatures were used, 90, 95, and 100°C.(194, 203, and 212°F.). Foods tested were tomatoes, pears, and apricots of different pH values."

The spore suspensions were standardized by dilution in liver-broth tubes after heating in boiling water for two minutes and cooling. Obser-

139. Townsend. 1929. Centbl. Bakt., Pt. 2, 78, 161-172.
140. Esty. 1929. The Canner, Conv. Number, Feb. 23, 1929, p. 191.
141. Townsend. 1939. Food Research 4, 231-237.
142. This is given in detail in Chapter 2.

vations were made at 90, 95, and 100°C.(194, 203, and 212°F.) in phosphate buffer solution at pH 7.0 and in juices of tomato, canned pears, and canned apricot. Townsend [141] published results in a large table.

Acid-tolerant, butyric acid-producing, sporeforming anaerobes which had caused a number of outbreaks of spoilage in canned fruits and tomatoes in widely separated districts were isolated and studied by Townsend. One strain was thoroughly studied for its heat-resistant characteristics. Townsend reported its characteristics and especially its heat resistance in some 10 different acid food products.

According to Townsend, these bacteria are widely distributed in the soil. Owing to their ability to endure higher sugar concentrations and acid, they have become of importance in the canning industry. Control is difficult, for their presence in canned food does not result from factory contamination but rather from presence in raw materials as brought into the factory. About the only alternative, according to Townsend, is acidification since marked reductions in pH greatly affect the resistance of the spores to heat. Townsend's results indicated that to destroy spores of these organisms in tomato juice at 100°C. twice as long at pH 4.5 as at pH 4.1 is required and nearly five times as long as at pH 3.8.

These organisms were also isolated from bursting swelled cans of pineapple by Spiegelberg,[143] who recognized two culture types. In general they were similar to *Clostridium pasteurianum* as described by Winogradsky [144] and others. Spiegelberg also found pH to be important in controlling these bacteria. He concluded that a final pH of 4.4 or below and processing to a given temperature in the can of 87.8°C.(190°F.) would prevent spoilage in canned pineapple by *Clostridium pasteurianum, Lactobacillus plantarum,* and *Leuconostoc mesenteroides.* The percentage of butyric swells in this work was proportional to the number of spores added to the cans before processing.

A special group of organisms studied by Mickle and Breed,[145] Pederson,[146] and Pederson and Breed [147] has been especially troublesome in tomato products. Gaseous spoilage of these products was traced to an organism to which the name *Lactobacillus lycopersici* was given by Mickle. Two hundred and sixty-six strains of tomato-products spoilage organisms were studied by Pederson. All were members of the genus Lactobacillus and were unable to withstand the temperatures used in bottling catsup or in canning other products.

Investigation of serious outbreaks of spoilage in canned tomatoes resulted in isolation of a thermophilic, sporeforming anaerobe by Woerz and Lenane.[150] Spoilage reached 10 per cent in some daily packs. Good growth with gas formation occurred in less than 24 hours at 51.6°C.(125°F.). The

143. Spiegelberg. 1940. Idem 5, 115-130; 439-455.
144. Winogradsky. 1894. Arch. Sci. Biol. 3, 297-352.
145. Mickle and Breed. 1925. N. Y. State Agr. Expt. Sta., Tech. Bull. 110.
146. Pederson. 1929. Idem Tech. Bull. 150.
147. Pederson and Breed. 1929. Idem Bull. 570.
148. Berry. 1933. J. Bact. 25, 72-73.
149. Stern, Hegarty, and Williams. 1942. Food Research 7, 186-191.
150. Woerz and Lenane. 1943. The Canner, Feb. 6, 11-12. 24.

anaerobe formed spores none too readily and exhibited considerable resistance to heat. It withstood boiling for at least 15 minutes in tomato juice
having a pH of 4.2. It was definitely thermophilic, growing only at a
temperature of 43.3°C.(110°F.) or higher. Discovery of such an organism
as this as the cause of gaseous spoilage of tomatoes indicates that accepted
methods of processing might not always be adequate. Application of sufficient heat to destroy spores of this organism might result in an inedible
product. Consequently, Woerz and Lenane believed that the answer to
this problem is more than increasing processing time.

The foods in this group have been generally considered to be free from
any botulism hazard. Occasionally, however, some canned food in the group
has caused this intoxication. Slocum, Welch, and Hunter [151] listed nine
outbreaks of botulism from eating acid food products. This tabulation was
included in a report of an outbreak caused by home-canned tomatoes. The
pH of a quart jar which seemed to be normal in appearance and odor was
4, well within the critical value of 4.5 which is considered to separate potentially dangerous foods from those which are not. It is well to point out,
however, that this value was secured with *Clostridium botulinum* in pure
culture in acid foods. All but one of the above nine outbreaks were caused
by home-canned foods which were not well sterilized. In several it was
shown that other bacteria were present which may have destroyed some
of the acid and permitted *Clostridium botulinum* to grow. Slocum *et al.*
found in addition to *Clostridium botulinum* a sporeforming bacillus and
a coccus.

Group 4. High Acid, pH 3.7 and Below. This group, according to
Cameron and Esty,[132] includes foods which are relatively free from spoilage
caused by sporeforming bacteria, such as kraut, pickles, berries, grapefruit, citrus fruit juices, and rhubarb.

METHODS FOR EXAMINATION OF CANNED FOODS

Bacteriologists examining canned foods should know as much as possible about the conditions under which the food is canned. They should
also give attention to the can from which the food was taken. The presence
of perforations would greatly influence the conclusions which are drawn
from the bacteriological data. Below are given methods for both bacteriological and physical examination of the containers.

TYPES OF SPOILAGE

A number of characteristic names have been slowly developed for indicating abnormal conditions of canned foods. Few of them may be regarded as absolute terms;
however, they indicate in a general way the type and, in some cases, the degree of
abnormality. They have become convenient terms and have wide usage.

Flat Sours. A flat sour is a flat can (one with concave ends) which shows the presence of greater acidity than the normal. There is no characteristic production of gas,
the decomposition having stopped in the acid stage. The absence of gas leaves the
ends of the cans flat and not bulged. These two characteristics, flat ends and an acid
reaction, indicate the origin of the term. Since no gas is characteristically formed, this
type of spoilage cannot be readily detected from the exterior. The causes of flat sours

151. Slocum, Welch, and Hunter. 1941. Food Research 6, 179-187.

are probably not complicated. They are due almost entirely to understerilization or leaky cans. Thermophilic bacteria are especially significant in the production of flat sours.

Swells. These are cans with bulged ends. They result from a number of causes one of which is bacterial growth. Gas formed in cans forces the ends of the cans out and gives them a bulged, distorted appearance. The several causes of swells may be tabulated:

1. Biological swells—resulting from the development of gas-forming bacteria.
2. Chemical swells—resulting from the action of the contents of the can on the container with formation of hydrogen.
3. A third type due to chemical decomposition of the material in the can—"Schaumgärung."
4. A fourth type may be due to overfilling at low temperatures..
5. A fifth type may be due to altitude where the cans would be under reduced pressure.

Serger [152] classified the causes of swells as follows:
1. Gas formation from bacterial growth—true of biological swells.
2. Gas formation from chemical processes—chemical swells.
3. Absorbed gas—pseudo swells.
4. Pressure generation by freezing—cold swells.
5. Pressure formation by cellular dilations.

He divided the swells under the first subdivision into two parts, (a) those which are infected after sterilization and (b) those which are understerilized. Serger has shown that the pressure may reach 3.5 atmospheres.

The conditions favoring the formation of hydrogen swells and perforations were stated to be as follows by Morris and Bryan:[153]
1. Low acidity (syrup in the neighborhood of pH 4).
2. Lacquer on the inside of the can.
3. The presence of substances, such as sulfides, which accelerate corrosion with products of high acidity.
4. Storage of the canned foods at high temperatures, and inefficient cooling of the cans after processing.
5. The presence of solids and other substances which absorb tin salts and so encourage de-tinning and consequent exposure of the iron.
6. Inefficient exhausting which leaves oxygen in the can after sealing and encourages de-tinning.
7. Insufficient head space in the can so that any hydrogen which may be produced will cause the can to swell rapidly.

The microbiology of biological swells is discussed at various places in this book. Swells which occur in nonacid or vegetable foods are due mostly to growth of bacteria, while those in acid foods are due to chemical reactions between the metal and the acids. Esty [154] reported that of 338 swelled cans of fruit tested, 231 were due to hydrogen formation and 107 to biological fermentation; of a total of 600 cans of swelled tomatoes all were found to be unsterile.

Lueck [155] called the attention of canners to the possibility of "frothy fermentation" or "Schaumgärung." The name was applied to a type of spoilage erroneously attributed to understerilization. This type of spoilage, as the name indicates, is characterized by the appearance of considerable amounts of carbon dioxide which give to the product a frothy or foamy

152. Serger. 1921. Ztschr. f. Untersuch. der Nahr. u. Genussmtl. 41, 49-68.
153. Morris and Bryan. 1931. Food Invest. Bd., Spec. Rpt. No. 40.
154. Esty. 1926. Canning Age, June, 1926.
155. Lueck. 1925. Canning Age, Dec., 1925.

appearance. It occurs mostly in sirup products, such as table sirups, malt extract, prunes in sirup, etc., and may cause the bacteriologist some concern. About all of the evidences of bacterial spoilage will be present, yet no viable microorganisms can be isolated.

Sturgess, Drake, and Parsons' [156] **Method for Determining the Swelling Rate of Canned Foods.** The inadequacies of the older unscientific methods for determining the swelling rate of canned foods caused Sturgess, Drake, and Parsons to apply the familiar principle of determining density by weighing under water. It is obvious that the change in density of a given sealed container will be a measure of the increase or decrease in volume of the container. This can occur in canned foods only because of evolution or absorption of gases. A large rough balance of an accuracy of .1 gram is arranged so that a fine piano wire can be attached to the bottom of one pan and passed through holes of suitable size drilled through the base of the balance and table top. The wire terminates in a small hook which engages a small copper loop previously soldered to the cans to be tested. The wire, immersed in water to the operating level, is carefully weighed and a tare made and added permanently to the weights in the other pan. The container is of a suitable size to accommodate the type of can to be tested. It is equipped with an electric heating element of 100-200 watts, a thermometer, and an air stirrer. The authors believed that thermostatic control of the temperatures was unnecessary. Manual control to within .5°C. was sufficient.

When the bath has been adjusted to the temperature at which incubation has been carried out, the can is quickly immersed in the water, care being taken to avoid entrapment of air under and along the flanges of the can. The weight is determined by adding suitable weights. If the wire is sufficiently fine, no special care need be taken to have the water level exactly constant since the error involved is only the weight of a section of wire corresponding to the difference in level.

For all practical purposes it is sufficient to assume that the density of water is unity at the operating temperatures. To determine swell, it is necessary only to measure the weight of a given can under water at various intervals, the decrements in weight in grams being equivalent to the swell in milliliters. If it is desired to calculate the percentage swell of a given can, it is necessary to know the approximate initial volume of the can. This, of course, involves simply weighing the can in air.

Following the simple relations involved:

W_{air} = weight of can in grams in air
W_{water} = initial weight of can in grams in water
V = initial volume of can
D = average density

$$V = W_{air} - W_{water}$$

$$D = \frac{W_{air}}{W_{air} - W_{water}}$$

If W = the decrement in weight in water, the percentages swell S is

$$S_2 = \frac{W \times 100}{V}$$

Sturgess, Drake, and Parsons found that variations of two ml. in volume on cans of 3,000 to 4,000 ml. could be detected. The variation in weight may be shown by plotting the ''percentage swell'' against the time in days.

Composition of Gases in Canned Foods. Baker [157] found no oxygen in gas from sound cans of food. He attributed this to oxidation of tin and

156. Sturgess, Drake, and Parsons, Food Indus. 3, 105.
157. Baker. 1912. Eighth Internatl. Cong. Appl. Chem. 18, 45-49.

iron salts, and combination was nascent hydrogen. The following analyses were reported for hydrogen swells:

	Red raspberries 18 mo. old	Strawberries 18 mo. old
Carbon dioxide	8.40	12.60
Oxygen	.00	.00
Hydrogen	65.50	72.40
Nitrogen	26.10	15.00

These results agree well with those of Tonney and Gooken [158] and Serger.[152]

Breathers. A breather is a can which is probably bacteriologically tight but not "airtight." Consequently air passes back and forth into the can through the gasket depending on the temperature of storage. Breathers are cans with low vacuum. From the standpoint of spoilage and food decomposition, breathers may not be of much significance since the gasket may act as a filter keeping microorganisms out of the can.

Springers. A springer is a can which is slightly bulged at one or both ends. Springers may be potential bacterial or chemical swells. Springers may also result from improper exhausting, packing cold, etc. They become slightly bulged when stored under warm conditions owing to expansion of the gases in the can. Loss of vacuum on account of imperfect closure may also cause springers.

The problem of springers in canned meats has been extensively reviewed by Hallman.[159] While only one factor may be involved in causing them, several may be involved. Generally speaking, springers may be reduced in incidence by employing methods of canning which insure good vacuum in the can. This requires proper exhausting and filling, leaving a little head space, and not overfilling.

Flippers. A flipper is a can the ends of which may be driven out by striking against a hard object. Flippers are one step removed from springers. They are generally due to insufficient exhaust or loss of vacuum. The lines demarking springers, flippers, and swells are not definite. Under different temperature conditions a flipper may be made to become a springer and a springer, a swell. This, of course, is without reference to the condition of the contents. These terms cannot be given strict scientific definition but the trade seems to have accepted the term "swell" for spoiled cans and the terms "flipper" and "springer" for cans which are not necessarily spoiled.

Buckled Can. A buckled can is one which has been handled in a rough manner which has caused the end panel to be permanently bent out of shape. This usually occurs near the seam. Buckled cans may also be caused by insufficient exhaust, or overfilling. With large-diameter cans, such as the No. 10s', buckles can scarcely be avoided with heavy process unless the cans are cooled under pressure.

Understerilization. This term does not need definition. If the container is tight so that no bacteria may enter, the presence of viable spores would be due to understerilization. Bacteriologists are often asked why processes which have apparently given satisfactory results for years, suddenly become inadequate with great spoilage resulting. Process times and temperatures have been adopted for what may be termed average conditions, i.e., average bacterial load or contamination, average resistance of these bacteria, etc. If, for instance, the number of spoilage bacteria to be killed is excessive, all of them will not be killed and understerilization will result. The sudden appearance of heat-resistant spoilage bacteria has upset many processes. Before the presence of viable bacteria in cans of food may be attributed to underprocessing, the condition of the container must be ascertained by an experienced technologist.

158. Tonney and Gooken. 1908. Amer. Food J., 3.
159. Hallman. 1941. Food Indus. 13, 67-68.

Botulism and Canned Foods. Commercially canned foods have been remarkably free from botulism since 1924. Since then only one outbreak has been reportedly due to a commercially preserved product, and that was a specialty product, mushroom sauce. This situation results from a carefully planned attack on the botulism problem by canners. It is reviewed in *Food-Borne Infections and Intoxications* by the author of this book.

Origin of Spoilage Bacteria in Canned Foods. Spoilage bacteria have been found to come from various sources. The relative importance of each depends to a large extent on the food.

Spoilage Organisms in Raw Foods. Such organisms can rarely be eliminated. They may be reduced somewhat in numbers by such operations as peeling and washing. Cameron [160] did not consider soil contamination of raw foods as important unless there was direct mechanical transfer. Similar conclusions had been reached 10 years earlier by Cameron, Williams, and Thompson.[123] These are probably general conclusions for all foods and surveys which they made. Townsend [161] showed that certain areas are heavily seeded with thermophilic bacteria which cause spoilage in canned asparagus. Soil was taken from certain badly infected fields and inoculated into cans of asparagus. Spoilage varied from 100 per cent for the top 12 inches to none at 36 to 42 inches in depth.

Various species of bacteria were isolated by Highlands [162] from freshly cut, whole-grain corn. Those which were reported were of no significance to the canner. No thermophilic bacteria were found.

Spoilage Organisms on Canning-Plant Equipment. Bacteriologically unclean canning-factory equipment may contribute significant numbers of spoilage bacteria to food to be canned. This knowledge has become the basis for efforts in factory sanitation. This involves more than mere dressing up of the factory. In addition, washing with steam and hot water and scraping are resorted to. Cameron, Williams, and Thompson's [123] bacteriological field studies in canning revealed that when undue spoilage occurs from understerilization, much of it results from accumulation of spores of spoilage bacteria in various units of factory equipment. In canning of peas and corn, such development is possible where heat is used. Blanching and filling equipment and wooden brine tanks were potential sources of contamination. Cameron[163] made the same observations for pumpkin.

In 1926 and 1927, Cameron and his colleagues found that the use of wooden brine tanks, on account of their construction, might contribute significant numbers of microorganisms to corn. When metal-lined tanks were used, fewer bacteria were contributed to the brine. Cameron[46] reported more results to confirm this opinion secured from experimental packs during the season of 1929 before the annual meeting of the National Canners Association in Chicago. Marked resistance to heat on the part of anaerobic thermophilic bacteria was observed by Paine.[164]

160. Cameron. 1938. Food Research 3, 91-99.
161. Townsend. 1932. J. Infect. Dis. 51, 129-136.
162. Highlands. 1938. J. Bact. 36, 315.
163. Cameron. 1937. Canning Age 18, 146-148.
164. Paine. 1931. Centbl. Bakt., Pt. 2, 85, 122-129.

Another important source of spoilage organisms may be the canning factory itself if it is not properly cleaned. Outbreaks of spoilage have been traced to development of spoilage bacteria at some place in the factory. The foodstuff was, in this way, contaminated by large numbers of those bacteria which the canner strives to avoid. Thorough cleaning-up stopped these outbreaks. Cameron's work showing that the wooden brine tank produced contamination has just been mentioned. That blanchers, silkers, cutters, etc., may also infect the foodstuff has also been well proven. When these are made bacteriologically clean, the contribution of spoilage bacteria is greatly reduced. Every effort must be made to remove every particle of food when the day's run is ended, else bacteria will have an opportunity to develop. This is best accomplished with a steam hose and brushes.

Whether a canning factory is free from excessive numbers of undesirable bacteria is best proved by bacteriological tests. These should be made on the salt, sugar as outlined in Chapter 19, soil, and the various pieces of machinery in the canning factory.

Spoilage Organisms in Ingredients Added to Canned Foods. Canned-food technologists, as a part of the entire program of restricting contamination of canned foods, had to give attention to certain ingredients, such as sugar and starch. In some instances much of the good which had resulted from prompter handling of raw foods and better factory sanitation had been negated by spoilage microorganisms in the ingredients. These were frequently prepared under ideal conditions for fostering development of these microorganisms.

The first ingredient to be actively investigated was sugar. Since this work is discussed in Chapter 19 of this book, it will not be treated here. In addition to sugar other ingredients, such as dry milk, sirups, malt extract, various sweetening agents, and flour, may harbor spoilage bacteria.

This problem for the canner has been partially solved by preparation of materials by the manufacturer which are relatively free from the undesirable bacteria. As mentioned elsewhere in this book, standards have been established for sugar and standard methods prepared for use with them.

That spoilage bacteria in ingredients just mentioned may be significant to the canner has now been definitely proven. Cameron, Williams, and Thompson, in their plant surveys, found sugar in use which contained 25 and 40 flat-sour-producing bacteria per gram. Corn brine containing a maximum amount of 225 pounds of sugar in 200 gallons of water would yield cans of corn containing 450 and 750 spores per can, respectively. The actual significance of thermophilic canned food spoilage bacteria in sugar has been shown in Chapter 19. Results of investigations with sugars having different numbers of thermophilic bacteria have definitely related canned food spoilage to contaminated sugar.

Spoilage Organisms on Machinery in the Factory. Bacteriologically clean equipment in the canning factory is necessary to keep the load on the process as light as possible. The importance of this was shown by Cameron, Williams, and Thompson.[123] They observed thermophilic contamination of peas and corn to increase by plant shutdown. It was greatest in the morning after overnight shutdown. When the plant operated steadily, thermophilic contamination steadily decreased.

An important source of spoilage organisms in some plants were the wooden brine tanks which became soft and porous. Bacteria became imbedded in the wood and were contributed to the brine. While not all wooden brine tanks are in this category, they are potentially hazardous and should be examined bacteriologically if there is reason to suspect them. Metal or metal-lined tanks are best.

Another source of spoilage bacteria may be the fillers and blanchers. Contamination in the latter, according to Cameron, Williams, and Thompson,[123] is built up during a shutdown. Under steady operation such contamination was washed out and became less and less. They advised, therefore, running the blancher with a full flow of water for 30 minutes or so before actual canning operations begin.

Investigation of Outbreaks of Spoilage in Canned Foods. These must be complete and adequate in every respect. They should be carried out by, or under the direction of, experienced technologists, for the proper interpretation of results requires considerable knowledge of canning procedure and microorganisms which have been proven to cause spoilage. The following are basic. The whole subject was completely presented by Cameron, Williams, and Thompson.[123]

Selection of Spoiled Cans. In many outbreaks of spoilage this is not difficult. If the cans are "hard swells," such cans, of course, are the ones to examine. On the other hand, if the spoilage is due to development of flat-sour producing bacteria, the problem is not so easy. In this case the spoiled cans may give no visual evidence that they are unsound and the analyst must use his ingenuity.

In the latter case the first thing he may do is to incubate the cans in order to develop the organism which is causing the trouble. Townsend [165] recommended 36.7°C.(98°F.) for 14 days and 57.2°C.(135°F.) for 12 days for low-acid products and 29.4°C.(85°F.) for fruits. While these recommendations were for determining sterility, they are satisfactory for any other purpose.

Gross Observations on the Cans. In addition to those recommended by Esty and Stevenson [166] and quoted on page 1000, Townsend recommended determination of vacuum, net and drained weights, head space, and pH because some of this information indicates how the product was packed. Vacuum and pH determinations will indicate microbial growth and formation of acids by flat-sour-producing bacteria. Loss of vacuum may be due to gas formation by microorganisms. If the contents of such cans are to be used for bacteriological examination, the above observation must be made very carefully so as not to contaminate the samples. An important part of this so-called physical examination is observation of all code marks on the can and a record of labels.

165. Townsend. 1939. Western Canner and Packer. June, July, and August, 1939.
166. Esty and Stevenson. 1925. J. Infect. Dis. 36, 486-500.

After all the above, the can itself must be carefully "taken down" by an experienced can technologist to determine whether the seams were properly made to prevent ingress of microorganisms.

Microscope and Bacteriological Examination of Contents of Can. Such observations must be made on samples which have been collected very carefully and not subjected to possibilities of contamination. Only experienced canned-food bacteriologists appreciate the care which must be taken.

Direct microscope examination may be made of a film of the food spread on a glass slide and stained. Such observations will indicate the general type of microorganism present.

Bacteriological examination must be made with the best technic and culture media known to support development of spoilage bacteria. These special directions are given a few pages farther on in this chapter.

Plant Survey—Collection of Samples in the Canning Factory. This work is necessary to determine whether any practice in the factory is seeding the food with undue numbers of spoilage bacteria. Samples must, therefore, be taken of the raw, unwashed food, at the washer, blancher, brine tank, and from cans about to be closed for the retort. When wooden equipment is used, small pieces should be examined to determine whether the wood is seeded with spores. Samples of water and brine should also be examined. Townsend pointed out the value of data collected during the packing period. Undue amounts of spoilage in the product packed after shutdowns would indicate development of spoilage bacteria on bacteriologically unclean machine surfaces and lines. Owing to dilution such contamination would decrease during the packing period.

The cooling water should not be overlooked for this may be heavily contaminated. The cans enter the cooling tanks hot. During cooling, bacteria in the cooling water might be drawn into the can through microscopic leaks. Cooling water with few bacteria would be of little importance but water heavily seeded might contribute many bacteria to the can. Under some conditions cooling water should be chlorinated and observations regularly made to insure maintenance of sufficient residual chlorine.

Interpretation of Results. After having collected all possible data, the problem is to decide on the real cause and to institute procedures for correcting the difficulty.

Incubation Tests on Canned Foods. The subject of incubation was discussed above in connection with the laboratory examination of canned foods. Incubation tests are also of great value in another connection, as discussed by Thompson and Cameron.[167] They are used in the canning factory to determine "commercial sterility" during the days that the factory is in operation. Thompson and Cameron stated that contamination was heavier during the first few minutes after the factory is in operation, and since this contamination will decrease as the factory is operated, they advised taking cans from the first crate from each line in the morning and again in the afternoon. This would give cans with the greatest and prob-

167. Thompson and Cameron. 1928. The Canner, June 9, 1928.

ably the fewest bacteria and would therefore represent the best and the worst cans for the day. It was advised that two cases be taken from each line at each sampling period for incubation. One case should be incubated at 37°C.(98.6°F.) and the other at 55°C.(131°F.). This type of incubation gives the canner evidence of danger within a few days after operation of the factory has started. The cans should be carefully marked in such a manner that a complete record may be kept.

Incubation at 55°C.(131°F.). Incubation at this temperature should show the presence of thermophilic bacteria of both the "flat-sour" and "swell-forming" groups as well as growth of the obligate and facultative thermophiles. The true or obligate thermophiles will grow only at 55°C. The presence of the flat-sour thermophiles can only be determined after the cans have been opened by testing the contents with an indicator such as brom-cresol-purple. The changes in color from purple to yellow show the presence of acid and should be taken as a danger signal.

Another serious spoilage which can be determined only after the cans have been opened is "sulfide spoilage." The food, usually corn and peas, shows a dark discoloration. This type of spoilage should develop in three or four days at 55°C. and in about 10 days at 37°C.(98.6°F.). When this type of spoilage appears, there may be an immediate increase in the process since this is one of the most serious types of spoilage with which to deal, or measures may be taken to decrease contamination of the food product. The appearance of swells after incubation at 55°C. should cause the canner to provide better cooling.

Incubation at 37°C.(98.6°F.). Incubation at this temperature should show the presence of facultative thermophilic and mesophilic bacteria. These organisms will grow at the usual temperatures of storage, and foods containing them are quite liable to spoil.

Swells which appear on incubation may be due to thermophilic, gas-forming bacteria or to non-thermophilic, anaerobic sporeformers.

Criteria of Spoilage. The analyst must use every possible observation to reach the proper diagnosis of spoilage. In most cases there is some reason prompting the request for examintion of the cans. They may have been regarded as the causal agent in illness or have been prepared from unsound raw materials. The examination may be prompted by the desire of a food official to determine the character of the product. Finally, the packer may desire to know the organisms involved in an undue amount of spoilage.

The most evident criterion of spoilage is the absence of flat ends. If the ends are bulged, it means that the can has been overfilled, improperly exhausted, understerilized, insufficiently cooled, or subjected to some other defect in the process of manufacture. The bacteriologist must determine whether the can has received sufficient heat treatment to destroy all forms of life in its contents. The absence of bacteria does not necessarily indicate that they were not present at an earlier time. They may have been destroyed by their own products of catabolism. Bacteriological results, of course, are most valuable in determining whether the contents of the can are sterile.

Another criterion of spoilage is the evidence that is available after the can is open. In some cases, no bacteriological tests are necessary to prove this. They may be valuable, however, in determining the characters of the bacteria causing the spoilage. However, the detection of spoilage by judging the appearance of the canned product is not always a safe method. The analyst must be familiar with the normal product and thus be able to use it as the standard with which to compare the suspected food.

Sampling and Data Accompanying the Sample. This is very important and a procedure to which the packer or person desiring the examination often gives too little attention. The analyst is better fitted if he has knowledge with regard to the various steps used in canning the food under examination. These should include, of course, the times and temperatures of the process and other steps in the preparation of the food.

The number of cans which should be used by the analyst is determined only by the purpose of the examination. It is obvious that the examination of a single can would yield results which would not be conclusive. It is better to examine even five or six or more, when they are available, especially if the results are to be used in the control of the packing process. Along with the cans which are under suspicion should be sent a few cans which are thought to be normal. The analyst may wish to examine the latter, or even to inoculate them with microorganisms isolated from the spoiled cans. Bigelow, of the Research Laboratories of the National Canners Association, suggested that at least a case of the food to be examined be sent to the laboratory. The best plan is for the analyst to go to the canning factory and collect the samples himself. At least a case of the smaller size cans should be available at the laboratory. Under certain conditions cans should be taken from the lines during the day in order to get a distribution which would include the product packed under different conditions. Esty and Stevenson,[166] and Cameron [168] have published methods for examination of canned foods. Excerpts from these publications are quoted below:

TECHNIC AND SYSTEM OF CULTURES

Condition of Container. After incubation and cooling to room temperature, the external condition of the can is classified as flat, flipper, springer, soft or hard swell. The condition of the seams is recorded, and a search for 'pin holes'' made if acid products are under observation. Any other points are noted which may have a bearing on the final diagnosis, among which are code, make of can, and any regular marks or dents on the cover or on the side seam, as they may indicate the year of packing.

Incubation of the Can. Cans which are flippers, hard swells, or springers may not need incubation previous to examination, provided this condition is due to bacterial growth. Cans which are normal in appearance, however, should be incubated where the the question is one of sterility. On account of the possible presence of thermophiles, some of the cans should be incubated at high temperature, 55°C.(131°F.). Where there are sufficient cans, six or eight should be incubated at 37°C.(98.6°F.) and 55°C.(131°F.), and as fast as abnormalities appear they should be removed from the incubator and

168. Cameron. 1938. Assoc. Off. Agr. Chem. J. 21, 452-454; see also Idem, August, 1937.

subjected to examination. Pfuhl [169] advised keeping the can in the incubator for eight to 14 days to give opportunity for the anaerobic and facultative anaerobic bacteria to develop. After opening, the hole should be plugged and the can replaced in the incubator. This will allow the aerobic bacteria to develop. Another set of cultures should then be made. Weinzirl,[116] in his study of the bacteria in canned foods, incubated them for seven days at 37°C.(98.6°F.).

Cleansing and Opening the Container. Good practice is first to thoroughly scrub the can with soap and water. A good precaution is to follow this by wiping with alcohol. The final preparation for opening consists in flaming the end to be opened. Here it is highly desirable to hold the end to be flamed above the flame as convection currents are set up including distribution of the heat. If the can end is flamed from above, most of the heat is retained in the upper head space, and charring of the product occurs which may obscure the normal odor and taste. Flat cans are flamed until flipping occurs, as internal positive pressure is a desirable safeguard against laboratory contamination.

There is some hazard attached to the flaming of swelled cans. This is obviated to some extent by cooling in an icebox, then thoroughly wiping with alcohol and igniting.

The unopened container should be examined in order to determine whether the ends are flat, and the condition of the seams should be noted. The surface of the can should be carefully examined for evidences of rust. If the ends are concave, as they should be, the presence of vacuum is probably indicated and likewise the absence of bacterial spoilage.

Examination for Perforations. The presence of an undue amount of rust on the can indicates that pin holes and similar perforations may be present. While this condition may be determined with certainty after the can has been emptied, cleaned, and dried, some information may be secured before it is opened by going over it with a stiff, sharp-pointed needle.

Testing for Vacuum. If the container has bulged ends, there will, of course, be no need for testing for vacuum. If, however, the ends are concave, some information can be secured by determining the vacuum. The ordinary vacuum gauge is provided with a rubber cork, which thoroughly seals the can when the tip of the gauge is forced into the cover of the can. The vacuum gauge used in the author's [170] laboratory is provided with a side arm carrying a small stopcock into which cotton is forced. After the vacuum reading has been made, the stopcock may be turned to relieve the vacuum. The air that is sucked into the can is filtered through the sterile cotton, thus preventing access of extraneous bacteria.

OPENING THE PREPARED CONTAINER

Location of Aperture. Specimens of food products from the surface layers of the can are undesirable, at least for some products, because these areas receiving the greatest heat treatment are less liable to show viable bacteria. Therefore, the aperture through which specimens of food are removed should be so placed that a generous sample may be secured from the center of the can. Heat has penetrated more slowly to this area, and it is here that any possible viable bacteria may be found.

Instruments for Opening Containers. Among the various types of instruments used for opening the container are screw drivers, can openers, and a number of other blunt-edged tools. Most of them are objectionable because they may contaminate the product by forcing a piece of metal into the food, and thereby introduce bacteria and disturb the contents of the can. If the can is slack filled, this is not a serious problem, but in some products there is enough free liquor to cause it to flow out over the cover, especially if the can has been heated to sterilize the ends. A disk of metal should be cut from the sterilized cover with a sterile instrument made for the purpose, and the sample should be removed through this aperture. Then a larger portion of the metal may be cut out with the can opener, but the analyst should be very careful to make the opening at least one-half inch from the double seam on the can. The contents of the can may then be carefully removed and the can thoroughly washed and dried to enable further

169. Pfuhl. 1904. Ztschr. f. Hyg. u. Infektionskrank. 48, 121.
170. Tanner. 1936. Assoc. Off. Agr. Chem. J., August, 1936.

examination of the seams, if that is desired. Various devices made by the author for this purpose are shown in Fig. 5.

Protection of Container After Opening. After opening the can, the analyst may protect the top from contamination by placing a sterile cover of a Petri dish over it. The can proper then functions as the lower half of the Petri dish.

REMOVAL OF SAMPLE

Sample. The sample should consist of at least 15 grams of food material. If desirable, a second sample may be stored in a sterile container until the examinations have been completed, and a third sample may be used for enrichment.

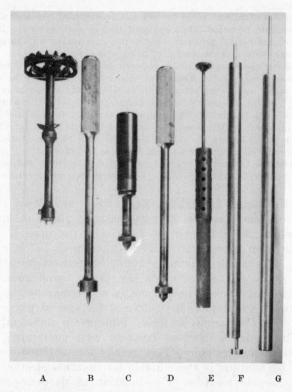

A   B   C   D   E   F   G

FIG. 5. Showing various instruments used for removing samples for bacteriological examination form canned foods. A and B, devices for cutting a hole in a can; note the sharp cutting edges. C and D, devices for punching holes in cans. E, F, and G, hollow tubes of metal for removing speciments of solid food. These instruments are provided with plungers by which the sample is pushed from the tube.

Instruments Used. The type of instrument used is determined by the sort of food under examination. Liquid food products, such as thin soups or tomato juice, may be sampled with a sterile pipette made from ordinary glass tubing about 14 inches long and having fire-polished ends. With solid portions of food glass tubing is less liable to clog than is the ordinary pipette. Solid food materials, such as sweet potatoes and roast beef, may be sampled by forcing an instrument made like a cork borer through a one-inch opening in the top of the can and pushing it to the bottom of the can in order to secure as large a sample as possible. In the writer's laboratory special instruments provided with plungers force the sample out quickly into a sterile container, which has been previously prepared to receive it. These instruments are 10 inches long and three-quarters of an inch in diameter. Several types devised by the author are shown in Fig. 5.

Enrichment of Contents of Can. There may be times when the conditions in the can are not entirely suitable for bacterial development. In cases where negative results have been secured in the bacterial examination, enrichment methods may be used for determining the presence of bacteria. These consist of creating a favorable environment by adding some culture medium to the can and subsequently incubating it. The addition of dextrose broth by means of a sterile syringe through a very small opening is a very satisfactory procedure since it contains the food products necessary for the development of most bacteria.

Organoleptic Examination. When the can has been opened, the odor and appearance of the contents should be noted. It is apparent that no statements can be made unless the analyst knows the normal product. That is the main reason why normal cans of the food should be sent with those suspected of being unsound.

Culturing. After the sample has been removed, as outlined above, it must be homogenized or otherwise prepared for inoculation into media. This may be done for solid foods, such as meats and sweet potatoes, in an electrically driven mixer, such as the Stevens Mixer[171] or the Eskimo Whiz-Mix Disintegrator, both of which are the type of mixers used at soda fountains. Extra cups for each may be sterilized in advance.

In case of little information about the types of bacteria which may be present, the analyst should probably err on the side of too much data than too little. Therefore, a search for nonspecific microorganisms should be made as follows:

Inoculate dextrose tryptone broth for incubation aerobically and anaerobically at 37°C.(98.6°F.) and at 55°C.(131°F.). Do the same in dextrose tryptone agar in Petri dishes.

Nonacid Products—Vegetables, Meat, Fish, and Milk.

Problems of canned-food technology require that emphasis be placed on spoilage types concerning which it is desired to know (1) the general morphology, (2) ability to form spores, (3) relation to oxygen, (4) relation to temperature, (5) general gas and acid-producing properties in the presence and absence of oxygen, each of which has special significance.

In addition to the more common media which may be used, if desired, are special media which have been devised for special purposes.

For Flat-Sour-Producing Bacteria. Platings in sufficiently high dilution should be made in dextrose tryptone agar containing brom cresol purple to give isolated colonies. This usually means that several dilutions are plated. This medium is also suitable for isolation of other aerobic and facultative anaerobic bacteria. For isolation of flat-sour-producing bacteria, incubators should be at 55°C.(131°F.). Cameron, Williams, and Thompson[123] described the changes which take place in this medium as follows:

"Flat-sour colonies are characteristic. The surface colony is usually round, measures from two to five millimeters in diameter, and contains a typical opaque central 'spot.' By reason of acid production in the presence of the indicator, the colony is set off by a halo of yellow in a field of purple. . . . Subsurface colonies are small and are not consistent as regards form. A more complete description of these bacteria is given in an earlier publication."

For Thermophilic Anaerobic Bacteria. For thermophilic bacteria not producing hydrogen sulfide, liver broth should be used. The cultures are

---

171. The former is made by the Stevens Electric Company of Racine, Wis., and the latter by the Bersted Manufacturing Company of Fostoria, Ohio.

stratified with plain yeast water agar after inoculation. Cameron, Williams, and Thompson [123] described the changes which indicate presence of thermophilic bacteria as follows:

"Thermophilic anaerobes are manifest by the splitting of agar (that used for overlaying the liquid liver broth) and the presence of acid after incubation at 55°C. (131°F.) in liver broth stratified with agar or in deep dextrose yeast wafer agar tubes. Usually a 'cheesy' odor is apparent. In sulfite agar there may be a general blackening of the medium as a result of the production of hydrogen by the organism and consequent reduction of the Na_2SO_3 incorporated in the medium."

Inoculations may also be made into corn meal-liver medium. The medium need not be steamed and requires no seal or other method of securing anaerobiosis. Thermophilic anaerobic bacteria free gas in this medium and may digest the medium.

For Thermophilic Anaerobic Bacteria Causing Sulfide Spoilage. Inoculate into Cameron's sulfite agar medium in a culture tube to which a nail or clean iron slip has been added at the time of tubing.* Incubate at 55°C. Changes in this medium which indicate the presence of sulfide spoilage bacteria were described by Cameron, Williams, and Thompson,[123] as follows:

"In sulfite agar after anaerobic incubation at 55°C.(131°F.) the sulfide spoilage bacteria (or *Cl. nigrificans*) are detected through the formation of characteristic, distinct, blackened, spherical areas. There is no production of acid which is discernible through the use of indicator media. Owing to the solubility of H_2S and its fixation by the iron of the $FeCl_3$ incorporated in the sulfite medium, no splitting of the agar occurs. See also the report of Werkman and Weaver."[138]

For Putrefactive Spoilage Bacteria. Inoculate into beef heart-peptic digest broth, egg-meat mixture, or pork infusion. Evidences of growth will be those usually related to development of putrefactive bacteria: vigorous gas formation, darkening of the medium, and foul odors.

Acid Products—Tomatoes and Fruits. Spoilage types of microorganisms peculiar to these products are limited to yeasts and nonsporeforming, mesophilic, facultative anaerobic, acid-loving bacteria. Special media having tomato juice as a base have been useful for separating spoilage types from organisms unable to grow in acid substrate. A liquid medium, tomato-dextrose broth, consists of tomato juice and nutrient broth in equal parts with addition of one per cent of dextrose, sterilized with or without pressure. The solid medium is made by adding three per cent agar to the tomato-dextrose broth. This medium may be sterilized in flowing steam or prepared by adding the sterile agar solution to the sterile tomato-broth medium.

The procedure for these acid food products, therefore, resolves itself into the inoculation of aerobic tubes of tomato-dextrose broth, with the parallel inoculation of nutrient sugar broths, to be incubated at 35°C. (95°F.) to 37°C.(98.6°F.). After enrichment for plating and purification of tomato spoilage types, the tomato agar is desirable.

For detection of flat-sour-producing bacteria of the *Bacillus thermoacidurans type*, in tomato juice, the original juice or enrichment cultures

* The National Canners Association has since developed a medium containing ferric citrate instead of the nail or iron strip. This medium is described in Chapter 27.

The Examination of Spoiled Canned Foods: A Summary of Significant Features and Their Relation to the Cause of Spoilage.
(After Esty and Stevenson, 1925.)

Significant Features	NONACID PRODUCTS			ACID PRODUCTS	
	SPOILAGE FROM UNDERSTERILIZATION		Spoilage from Leakage of Can	Spoilage from Understerilization	Spoilage from Leakage of Can
	"Flat Sours"	"Swells"			
Condition of container	Flat	Swelled	Swelled	Swelled	Swelled
Microscopic examination of direct smears from can	Rods, with or without apparent spore formation, usually apparently pure cultures.	Rods, with or without apparent spore formation, usually apparently pure cultures.	Evident impure cultures usually containing coccus forms.	coccoid bacilli to very long rod forms.* Yeast? bacilli to very long rod forms.* Yeast?	Apparently impure cultures ranging from coccoid bacilli to very long rod forms. Yeast.
Physical examination of contents	Usually sloppy in appearance; normal or sour odor.	Fermented appearance; sour or putrid odor.	Fermented appearance; sour or putrid odor; sometimes variations in appearance and color in different cans of the same sample.	Fermented appearance; sour, cheesy or alcoholic odor.	Fermented appearance; sour, cheesy or alcoholic odor.
Cultures	Aerobic and anaerobic growth at 37°C. and 55°C. or 55°C. alone; usually evidence of spore formation in agar; microscopic examination should check direct smears.	Growth anaerobically with gas at 37°C. or 55°C., or both 37°C. and 55°C.; if aerobic growth occurs without gas formation at 37°C. and 55°C. alone the presence of a flat sour type is also suggested; microscopic examination should check direct smears.	Usually gas anaerobically and aerobically at 37°C. with or without growth at 55°C.; microscopic examination should show mixed culture and show presence of non-heat-resistant types.	Growth in special acid mediums at 37°C. with or without gas production; if no gas is produced reinoculate in sound cans to determine ability to produce swell; microscopically pleomorphic forms with possible presence of yeast.	Growth in special acid mediums at 37°C. with or without gas production; if no gas is produced reinoculate in sound cans to determine ability to produce swell; microscopically pleomorphic forms with possible presence of yeast.
Seam examination	No leaks on pressure testing; seams and general condition of container good.	With "hard swells" leaks on pressure testing may be due to straining; seams should give indication of original sound condition.	Leaks on pressure testing; seams or general condition of can faulty.	No leaks on pressure testing; seams and general condition of container good.	Leaks on pressure testing; seams or general condition of can faulty.

* This apparent impurity of culture is usually found to be due to the extreme pleomorphism evidenced by the group of organisms most significant in the spoilage of acid products.

should be plated in proteose-peptone-acid agar of Stern, Hegarty, and Williams.[149]

Microscope Examination of Contents. Smears made direct from the canned product often give valuable information in the final correlation of results. Here, the ordinary carbolfuchsin or gentian violet stains usually give the results desired. Record is made of the apparent condition of the flora, whether pure or mixed, the presence of non-heat-resistant forms, of which the cocci are typical, and the presence of spores.

Examination of Cultures. Cultural observations are made on both aerobic and anaerobic tubes at 37°C.(98.6°F.) and 55°C.(131°F.), special note being made as to the presence of gas and acid and the temperature at which they are found. A microscope examination of positive cultures gives evidence as to the general morphology of types present, and the degree of purity of the original food contaminant.

When bacteriologic evidence indicates understerilization, cultures are purified by any of the common methods. After assurance as to the ability of the purified culture to form spores (in nonacid products), it is set aside for immediate or later classification.

In the event of an exhaustive study, the heat resistance of the spore is determined by the method of Esty and Williams. Finally, an attempt is made to reproduce spoilage by inoculation into sterile samples of the particular food from which it was isolated. With acid foods, since thermophiles and sporeforming bacteria do not appear to enter as causative spoilage agents, observations are confined to the single temperature and the heat resistance tests apply only to vegetative forms.

Savage[172] and Clark, Clough, Fellers, and Shostrom[173] have also outlined procedures for the examination of canned fish products. The former had to do with canned foods received at ports of entry in England, while the latter was concerned with canned salmon.

Autosterilization. Bacteriologists frequently encounter outbreaks of spoilage which have all of the earmarks of bacterial spoilage but from which no viable bacteria can be made to grow. If proper technic has been used and if several attempts have been made to demonstrate growth without success, it may be concluded that the bacteria which caused the spoilage died out—a phenomenon spoken of as *autosterilization*. The death of the bacteria may be considered to have been caused by an accumulation of products of metabolism, organic acids for instance. Frequently microscope examination will show the presence of many bacterial cells.

Cameron's Method for Sampling the Contents of Cans of Food Before Incubation. It is frequently desirable to make preliminary observations on the contents of cans of food before they are incubated. The problem is one of sealing the can after a small portion of the contents has been removed. Cameron, by correspondence, kindly gave the author the following method used in the laboratories of the National Canners Association. Besides the usual materials and apparatus, some Goodyear Repair Gum for patching inner tubes and Goodyear Cold Patching Cement should be available. The repair gum should be cut into squares from one to one and a quarter inches on a side. These should be sterilized after wrapping in paper or being placed in some sort of container at 15 pounds' pressure for 30 minutes. The can should be prepared for opening in the usual manner. A hole is made in the can through which a portion of the contents is withdrawn. Then a fairly heavy film of patching cement is applied about the hole and ignited. When it has burned itself out a square of repair gum is removed from the sterile package, the cloth torn off, and the fresh surface applied to the opening of the can. When the can top has cooled, another application of patching cement may be applied about the gum. The can may then be incubated. Gas production during incubation will be indicated by bulging of the gum.

Crossley's[174] Method for Detecting Certain Sporeforming Bacteria in Canned Foods. This is a simple, inexpensive method developed for routine examination of canned foods for anaerobic, sporeforming bacteria causing spoilage. The medium finally adopted was

172. Savage. 1920. Gt. Brit. Food Invest. Bd., Spec. Rpts. 3 and 10.
173. Clark, Clough, Fellers, and Shostrom. 1923. Pacific Fisherman, Sept. and Oct.
174. Crossley. 1941. Soc. Chem. Indus. J. 60, 131-136.

sterile skim milk containing one per cent of peptone and .01 per cent brom cresol purple. It was heavily inoculated with the sample (from 1.5 to 2 grams) and incubated for three to four days at 37°C.(98.6°F.). Striking reactions, such as color change of the indicator, curd formation, and digestion or gas formation, permit detection and rough classification of anaerobic, sporeforming bacteria in food.

Another problem which has not been faced in the past by bacteriologists involves testing packs of canned foods. It probably enters all bacteriological work. In much laboratory work it may probably be ignored but not in work which involves determination of sterility, as may be the case with canned foods. It is the problem of contaminated plates and cultures. It is a problem which deserves more attention than bacteriologists have been willing to give it. This situation was emphasized to the author a few years ago when, in a cooperative investigation in which numerous control plates were made, many of them were contaminated with Micrococci. This work was done by mature bacteriologists and not by individuals who failed to realize the need for good technic. No problem is involved when a selective medium for some special organism is being used or where a plate count is being made, for appearance of a few extra colonies would make little difference since they would be only few in number. However, Williams and Clark [104] pointed out that in testing for sterility in any material, and especially where cultures are made on ordinary nutrient media and incubated at mesophilic temperatures, air-borne contamination may be very confusing to the bacteriologist and unjust to the packer. Examination of cans of food in the laboratory for sterility has always introduced the problem of what to do with plates made from the food which show but one colony. When such colonies are bacteria which are nonsporeformers with very low heat resistance, and are forms which are not indigenous to the product, they should be ignored. Bacteriologists should be careful before stating that a food product is not sterile. Multiple control plates and tubes should be made and not just a single one. A single control plate might remain sterile while several of the test plates receive contamination from the air. Such a situation would give misleading results.

General Examination of the Container. The container from which samples with organisms came should be examined. It must be shown to be sound and tight, else the value of the result of bacteriological examination may be seriously questioned. This should usually be done by an expert who is familiar with the structure of a can and is able to recognize serious defects. A few of the methods by which "leakers" may be detected will be mentioned with brief discussion. Bitting and Bitting summarized them as follows:

1. Tapping the can with a metal bar. Normal cans will sound dead. Savage [172] used this method for judging the fitness of canned meats. He called it a "percussion" test.

2. Drop the can into boiling water. A stream of bubbles will come from the can if it leaks.

3. Immerse the can in water in a heavy closed jar and apply vacuum.

4. The Young vacuum tester will indicate the vacuum. Cans with no vacuum may inferentially be considered to be leakers.

5. The can may be closed with solder and tin and air forced into it. An apparatus is available with which cans may be "pumped."

Examination of Seams. In order to determine whether the double seam is tight, it may be examined after filing and taking apart. While only an expert should pass judgment on the quality of a seam, the technic is shown in Fig. 6.

Significance of Results of Bacteriological Examination of Canned Foods. The laboratory examination of canned foods, no matter how complete,

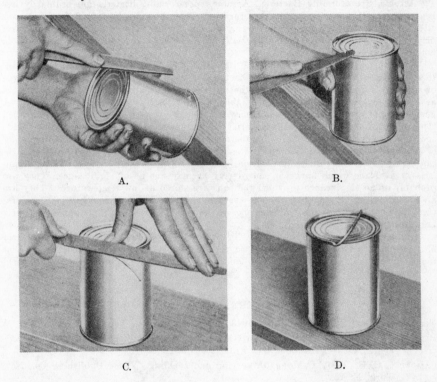

A. B.

C. D.

Fig. 6. Showing the technic for inspection of double seams on tin cans. *(Courtesy of the American Can Company.)*

A. Hold the can firmly and file a notch through the seam to the body of the can, using a sharp three-cornered file.

B. Starting at the notch, file through one thickness of tin around the entire seam.

C. Use the edge of the file to force down the cover hook.

D. Bend up the cover hook for observation and measuring the can hook. If the seam is loose, wrinkles will appear on the cover hook; the can hook should not be less than 1/16 inch lng.

would be worth very little without an accurate interpretation to the packer or layman who knows very little about the significance of such data. It goes without saying that microorganisms are undesirable in canned foods. The very object of the process is to seal the food in a container which would preclude exposure to bacterial action.

Nonsporeforming Bacteria. The presence of vegetative, nonsporulating bacteria in canned foods indicates that the cans were not processed properly or that the containers leaked. It is difficult to think of a vegetative bacterium which could withstand the cooks given to common canned foods. Having satisfied oneself that the cans were processed, the other explanation for the presence of these bacteria is leaky cans. This indicates the importance of a careful examination of the can for defects in manufacture. This should include complete stripping of the can. The nonsporeforming bacteria are usually forms of low heat resistance. Such bacteria might be drawn into the can if the seams were faulty when the can is in the cooling tank.

Aerobic, Sporeforming Bacteria. Aerobic, sporeforming bacteria are ordinarily less heat resistant than the anaerobic sporeformers. Their presence in canned food indicates either insufficient processing or leaky cans. In some cases, the presence of these bacteria may be due to underprocessing. Especially might this be true for foods processed in boiling water.

Anaerobic, Sporeforming Bacteria. Bacteriologists rather frequently find that non-thermophilic, anaerobic, sporeforming bacteria cause swells in canned foods. This type of spoilage is about as important as other types and is usually due to understerilization as well as leaky cans. Appearance of this spoilage justifies inspection of the can. A good example of the spoilage which may be caused by these bacteria is the so-called "putrefactive spoilage" of canned corn. This spoilage is distinguished from "sulfide spoilage" in that the latter is due to thermophilic bacteria.

Obligate Thermophilic Bacteria. The presence of obligate thermophilic bacteria in canned foods indicates understerilization, lack of proper cooling, or both. These organisms in flat cans which have not soured may or may not be of significance. They are probably of no significance provided the cans are stored at low temperatures. They are always potentially dangerous, for the can may be stored at sufficiently high temperatures to permit germination of the spores. Growth of obligate thermophilic bacteria indicates inadequate cooling.

Faculative Thermophilic Bacteria. The presence of facultative thermophilic bacteria also indicates inadequate cooling. Since facultative thermophiles are able to grow at room temperature, cans of food which contain them are quite liable to spoil when held for a long time.

REFERENCE BOOKS

The Canned Food Reference Manual, 1943. American Can Co., New York, N. Y.

BITTING, A. W., 1937. Appertizing; or the Art of Canning. Its History and Development. Trade Pressroom, San Francisco, Calif.

CAMPBELL, C. H., 1937. Canning, Preserving and Pickling. Vance Publishing Co., New York, N. Y.

JONES, O., AND JONES, T. W., 1937. Canning Practice and Control. Chapman & Hall, London, England.

TANNER, F. W., 1933. Food-Borne Infections and Intoxications. Garrard Press, Champaign, Ill.

CHAPTER 24

MICROBIOLOGY OF MISCELLANEOUS FOOD PRODUCTS

The difficulties of arranging a book of this nature has made it seem advisable to discuss the microbiology of several food products in a separate chapter.

Microbiology of Olive Oil. Freshly prepared olive oil, according to Chiappella,[1] may contain as many as 1,000 bacteria per ml. Six months after pressing, this number falls to between 350 and 800 per ml. in the sediment and from 10 to 40 in the supernatant layers. Mechanical purification by sedimentation was believed to explain reduction in numbers of bacteria, although it is not inconceivable that some species would die out in such an unfavorable medium. Acid oils were reported by Chiappella to be germicidal. Good olive oil should be neutral and, therefore, exert less action on microorganisms. Acid oils may result from bacterial fermentation of some constituents of the oil.

Chiappella observed survival of pathogenic bacteria in olive oil of good quality. Staphylococci, Streptococci, *Pseudomonas aeruginosa, Escherichia coli*, and *Eberthella typhosa* did not live longer than 40 to 50 days; *Vibrio comma* succumbed in 15 days. *Bacillus anthracis* lived for a few months. It was thought probable that all of the sporulating bacteria could live for months. From the above data, Chiappella advised that care be used in handling olives during and before pressing. Kurpjuweit[2] inoculated cultures of *Escherichia coli*, Staphylococcus, *Corynebacterium diphtheriae, Pseudomonas aeruginosa, Micrococcus ureae*, and *Eberthella typhosa* into olive oil. They lived, on the average, for about 10 days, and the period of existence of each organism seemed to be related to its ability to endure anaerobic conditions.

According to Pigulewski and Charik,[3] olive oil is quite susceptible to attack by bacteria. They used strains of bacteria isolated from rancid butter. One strain caused deposition of a solid substance, which was considered to be ketostearic acid, formed from oleic acid. Rancidity of oil may, therefore, be due to bacterial decompositions. Guargena[4] carried out experiments to determine longevity of bacteria in oils. Cottonseed, linseed, olive, sesame, almond, castor, and cod-liver oils, and butter and lard were used. *Pseudomonas aeruginosa* survived for 30 days in lanolin, almond oil, and cottonseed oil; in sesame and olive oils and butter, *Serratia marcescens* lost is vitality between the 10th and the 30th day. Similar results were secured with *Oidium albicans* and *Saccharomyces niger*. *Stahpylococcus citreus* died out in castor oil after the 20th day. Feeding

1. Chiappella. 1903. Ann. d'Ig. Sper. 13. 118-144.
2. Kurpjuweit. 1903. Centbl. Bakt., Pt. 1, Orig. 33, 157-160.
3. Pigulewski and Charik. 1928. Biochem. Ztschr. 200, 201-210.
4. Guargena. 1905. Riv. d'Ig. e San. Pub. 16, 71-87.

of fat to guinea pigs reduced the intestinal flora, indicating, perhaps, an action on bacteria.

It is a difficult matter to rid oils of bacteria. They seem to be protected from the action of heat and survive amounts of it which are lethal in much shorter periods when organisms are suspended in another menstruum. This may be due to absence of water in the oil.

Bactericidal Properties of Oils. Just how significant this property of oils is, is difficult to determine. Mazzetti[5] noticed that certain vegetable oils (olive, linseed, almond, soy, and castor) acquired definite, though weak, bactericidal powers when brought to high temperatures and cooled. Especially was this true of linseed oil. Tung oil and sardine oil were reported to be germicidal by Hirabayashi.[6] Görtzen[7] tested the following oils for their effect on bacterial behavior: cod-liver oil, olive oil, peanut oil, turpentine, yellow vaseline, lanoline, and eucerin. Most of them contained few bacteria which would indicate that bacteria could not grow readily in them. None of them except turpentine showed any inhibitive action on growth of bacteria. Arachis oil has been shown to be germicidal.

Microbiology of Peanut Butter. This is an important food, microbiology of which has not been studied to any extent. Questionable sanitary conditions of manufacture of peanut butter prompted Hall and Van Meter[8] to investigate its microorganism content to determine whether it could be correlated with manufacturing procedures. They observed some bad conditions which in no way probably reflect the situation today. Since the days when Hall and Van Meter did their work, great improvements have occurred in the food-processing industry, some of which have occurred in the making of peanut butter. Hall and Van Meter examined 29 samples in none of which could coliform bacteria be demonstrated. In view of the fact that some of the samples were prepared under questionable sanitary conditions, it was assumed that peanut butter exerted a germicidal action on microorganisms or that they died out because foods were not available. Hall and Van Meter showed that germicidal action was possessed by arachis oil, the oil of the peanut, toward *Escherichia coli* and a few pathogens (*Eberthella typhosa, Salmonella schottmülleri,* and *Salmonella paratyphi*). Plate counts of peanut butter were not high, the larger proportion of samples showing less than 100 colonies per gram, only two samples showing over 5,000. Addition of water to peanut butter was claimed to invite spoilage.

Microbiology of Salad Dressings and Similar Products. Salad dressings are composed of materials which are subject to microbial spoilage. In addition to spoilage of this type there are others evidenced by separation, loss of consistency, rancidity, and discoloration. Gray[9] called attention to the possibilities for introducing great numbers of microorganisms and to the several constituents which may be used by bacteria. He found

5. Mazzetti. 1929. Rev. in Biol. Abs. 7, 1149.
6. Hirabayashi. 1935. Soc. Trop. Agr. J. 7, 110-113.
7. Görtzen. 1935. Zentbl. Bakt., Pt. I, Orig., 134, 169-181.
8. Hall and Van Meter. 1918. Amer. Food J. 13, 463.
9. Gray. 1927. The Canner, Aug. 26, 1927, 31-34.

bacterial spoilage to be greater in mayonnaise which contained chopped pickles, pimientos, and similar materials than in plain mayonnaise. In the latter the principal inhibitor for bacteria is acid. Molds, however, may develop in presence of considerable acid. They do not cause much trouble in plain mayonnaise but are more likely to develop when starch and pectin have been added. Gray emphasized the fact that many microorganisms may reach the salad dressing from ingredients. An old egg or egg product might contribute so many bacteria that the preservative agents might not be able to keep them in control. In view of this possibility, it is wise to use only ingredients with a low microbial content. Increasing the acid content has been known to prevent development of large numbers of potentially active spoilage bacteria.

A common spoilage of mayonnaise is caused by fermentation of sugars by microorganisms. Its prevention is based on either elimination of these bacteria in ingredients or preventing their development.

Acidity has been mentioned by various investigators as the important factor in keeping mayonnaise. *Escherichia coli* was found to disappear from it in 24 hours at room temperature by Vladimirov and Nefedieva.[10] When added in large numbers, however, it lived for six to seven days at room temperature and longer at 2 to 3°C.(35.6 to 37.4°F.). Other bacteria were also inhibited and destroyed by acid.

Bachmann [11] examined 15 brands of mayonnaise, 12 of other salad dressings, six of olive mayonnaise, and six of olive relish. With the exception of a few samples of homemade mayonnaise, only commercial products were studied, and the condition of all of the samples was good when the cans were opened. Of the entire number of cans, only four were found to contain anaerobes and these were nontoxic. The number of aerobic organisms varied from 0 to 17,400 per ml. The largest percentage of sterile cans was found among the salad dressings other than mayonnaise. These contained a starch paste, and it was thought that the heat used in preparing the paste and the acidity of the product were the chief factors contributing to sterility. The most probable source of contamination was considered to be the egg yolks. From 12 cans, sporeforming rods with morphological and cultural characteristics similar to *Bacillus subtilis* and *B. mesentericus* were isolated. *Escherichia coli,* when introduced into the various preparations, disappeared rapidly. *Bacillus subtilis* remained viable for a longer period of time. These products are susceptible to several types of spoilage. Anaerobic sporeforming bacteria cause, at times, a gaseous fermentation. It is necessary to use good vinegar to prevent much of the trouble. Iszard [12] described an organism which caused spoilage in a number of samples of mayonnaise. It was said to agree in all respects with *Bacillus petasites.* Inoculation experiments showed that this organism could spoil mayonnaise. Attempts were made then to determine the origin of the organism. These showed that it was present in the foundation paste; 10,000 colonies per

10. Vladimirov and Nefedieva. 1937. Rev. in Chem. Abs. 32, 7955.
11. Bachmann. 1916. J. Ind. Eng. Chem. 8, 620-623; 10 (1918), 121-123.
12. Iszard. 1927. Canning Age, April.

gram were counted. This product could not be sterilized by heat, and attempts were then made to determine whether the organism could be repressed by the addition of some special substance. It was found that lactic acid in a concentration of 1.75 per cent was sufficient to arrest bacterial development. An outbreak of spoilage in Thousand Island dressing was found by Pederson [13] to be due to activities of *Bacillus vulgatus*. This organism came from the pepper and paprika. Pederson suggested two methods of protecting salad dressing from such bacteria: first, maintenance of such acidity that the organism cannot grow and second, sterilization of the ingredient which contains the offending bacteria. *Bacillus lekitosis* [14] is another bacterium said to cause mayonnaise decomposition. Charlton, Nelson, and Werkman [15] isolated *Lactobacillus fructivorans* from spoiled salad dressing. Such spoilage as just mentioned was attributed by Vladimirov and Nefedieva [10] to improper preparation. They considered properly prepared mayonnaise to be hardly a favorable medium for development of microorganisms, especially on account of low pH (4.1 to 4.5). Vegetative forms cannot live in it but spores may live for a long time. *Escherichia coli* disappeared in 24 hours at room temperature. At lower temperatures, longevity would be much longer. This was the experience also with other bacteria and molds.

Microbiology and Preservation of French Mustard. Prepared mustard is subject to microbial spoilage if not properly handled. Much of the work on this subject has been done by Kossowicz.[16] His results showed that freshly ground mustard may contain bacteria and spores of the Subtilis-Mesentericus group as it leaves the mill. Decomposition of mustard was said to be brought about by bacteria which were not active gas formers, although gas-forming bacteria are frequently present. Sterilization seemed to be an unsuitable method for making mustard keep. Kossowicz suggested that it was advisable to add some white mustard seed to the mash and to have higher acetic acid content, using garlic vinegar where possible. Kossowicz reported the presence of Torulae in mustard which had undergone spoilage. This mustard contained many gas bubbles and considerable alcohol. A number of species of bacteria belonging to the aerobic sporeforming group of bacteria were present. Campbell [17] reported considerable fermentation in prepared mustard from bacterial contamination. Examination of jars revealed the presence of gas with a distinct hydrogen sulfide odor. The same organism which caused this spoilage was found in samples from empty barrels in which mustard had been stored. Campbell found the organism to be of the aerobic sporeforming type, probably quite like those described by Kossowicz. He believed the trouble to be due to contamination of the prepared mustard with some Chinese seed. Low acidity permitted the bacteria to develop. Prevention of this type of spoilage involves use of low-count raw materials, proper acidity, and heat treat-

13. Pederson. 1930. J. Bact. 20, 99-106.
14. Annual Rpt. Dept. Agr. and Markets, Legislative Doc., No. 37 (1932), 107.
15. Charlton *et al.* 1934. Iowa State Col. J. Sci. 9, 1-11.
16. Kossowicz. 1910. Ztschr. der Landw. Versuchsw. Österr. 13, 95; 14 (1911), 20 and 59.
17. Campbell. 1938. Canning Age, April.

ment after the product is in the jars. Bartarelli and Marchelli [18] observed spoilage of mustard owing to growth of a member of the Proteus group. The spoilage was characterized by a peculiar odor and the appearance of gas bubbles. The organisms could be demonstrated by direct microscope examination. Bertarelli and Marchelli believed that the mustard had been infected by anchovies used in its preparation.

Copra. This is the dried meat of the coconut which has become an important commercial article in sections of the world where the coconut palm grows. Unless carefully prepared it is subject to mold deterioration. Moisture content of copra has been considered to be one of the important factors influencing deterioration. Fishlock [19] stated that well-dried copra containing six per cent of moisture could be safely stored for long periods. Any superficial gray-green mold which appears on it may be considered to be harmless. The undesirable dark-colored molds cannot develop because of low moisture content. Fishlock's observations were made over a period of 62 weeks. Ward [20] agreed with Fishlock that copra with less than six per cent of moisture would keep. When moisture exceeds this amount it is liable to microbial deterioration. Action is most rapid at 12 to 15 per cent, when it is due both to bacteria (two species causing pitting and slime described) and to fungi (especially *Aspergillus flavus*, *Aspergillus niger*, and *Aspergillus tamarii*). At moisture contents approaching seven per cent growth is confined to the *Aspergillus glaucus* section and Penicillium spp. Brill, Parker, and Yates [22] have greatly amplified our knowledge of this subject. They showed that bacteria played a minor role in the deterioration of copra, since usually there is too little moisture present to permit bacterial growth. When they do grow, it is usually on fresh copra which has a sufficiently high moisture content. Brill and his colleagues stated that copra which has less than 20 per cent of water is practically free from bacterial action; above this water content, the changes brought about by fungi are more important. Brill, Parker, and Yates found four molds on copra and coconut meat undergoing spoilage. The conidial masses differed in color, which permitted rapid separation of these species. In regard to the moisture required for their development, they arranged themselves in the following order: Rhizopus sp. (white mold), a mold occurring only on fresh meat and forming loose masses of white mycelium with many black sporangia; *Aspergillus niger*, a species occurring on copra with a relatively high water content; and, *Aspergillus flavus*, found most commonly on moldy copra; and *Penicillium glaucum*, usually found on copra with a low water content. These species were quite fully described, but the descriptions will not be reproduced here.

Microbial Spoilage of Coconut Oil. Few data have been published on this subject; there seems to be a general belief that microorganisms are of very little significance in this connection. Walker [21] reported, however,

18. Bertarelli and Marchelli. 1908. Ztschr. f. Untersuch. der Nähr. u. Genussmtl. 16, 353-539.
19. Fishlock. 1930. Gold Coast Dept. Agr. Bull. 22, 233-238.
20. Ward. 1937. Fed. Malay States Dept. Agr., Sci. Ser. No. 20, 95-108.
21. Walker. 1906. Philippine J. Sci. 1, 117-142.
22. Brill, Parker, and Yates. 1917. Idem. 12, 55-86.

that they might have great significance in affecting the quality of coconut oil. Walker's work showed that bacteria and other fungi may cause much spoilage. According to Stokoe [23] rancidity of coconut oil by Penicillium sp. is due to formation of methyl-amyl, methyl-heptyl, and methyl-nonyl ketones. The biochemistry of the deterioration will not be discussed here.

Microbial Spoilage of Cocoa Butter. This spoilage has become of economic importance in relation to the use of vegetable oils and fats in the manufacture of butter substitutes.

According to Batten and Bywaters,[24] cocoa butter is resistant to development of microorganisms and production of rancidity. They reported development of a mold in a large block of cocoa butter, weighing 28 pounds. When the block was broken a number of dull black spots were seen. These spots were studied and found to consist of hyphae of a mold. Cultural studies indicated the presence of *Penicilium glaucum*, a pink yeast, and a species of Aspergillus, believed to be *Aspergillus oryzae*. Small pockets of water were seen throughout the block, and it was believed that spores of the fungi had been introduced in this manner. The importance of water was proven by experiment; it was stated that little fear of molding need be entertained if cocoa butter is kept free from water. Discussion of this paper by several investigators showed that molding of fat was not an uncommon phenomenon.

CARBONATED BEVERAGES

Various factors in manufacture and use of carbonated beverages give these products considerable interest to the food bacteriologist and sanitarian. They were made at times in places of questionable cleanliness and were subject to microbial spoilage. The conditions under which these products are now made are probably satisfactory. These drinks consist of flavoring extract, sugar, water, and often some substance to produce a foam. That they are susceptible to the development of bacteria is indicated by the fact that they frequently become cloudy and ropy. Ropiness is caused by capsulated organisms which find these products favorable for their development. It is a difficult matter to disinfect a bottling plant after it has been infected with such organisms. All appliances must be kept absolutely clean and sterilized where possible. The author examined one bottle of root beer which was cloudy and ropy. The usual capsulated sporebearing organism was isolated. When inoculated into a sound bottle of root beer, the disease was reproduced. A committee of the American Public Health Association [25] deemed it advisable to study methods for controlling the microbiological condition of such beverages and the bactericidal value of certain procedures in their preparation.

Investigations were undertaken by Young and Sherwood [26] to determine whether or not pathogenic organisms could withstand the unfavorable environment in bottled carbonated beverages a sufficient length of time to reach the consumer. It was found that the number of organisms in the

23. Stokoe. 1928. Biochem. J. 22, 80-93.
24. Batten and Bywaters. 1918. Soc. Chem. Indus. J. 37, 242-243.
25. Amer. Pub. Health Assoc. Yearbook, 1940-1941, p. 96.
26. Young and Sherwood. 1911. J. Ind. Eng. Chem. 3, 495.

beverages examined was extremely small, except for those which had been introduced experimentally. There was a decided reduction in number of such organisms after standing 244 hours uncarbonated. There was a very marked reduction in numbers of all three organisms introduced, and especially of *Eberthella typhosa*, owing to conditions existing in the carbonated bottles. The organisms were not completely killed during the time of the entire experiment. *Serratia marcescens* and *Escherichia coli* seemed to be somewhat more hardy than *Eberthella typhosa*. Undoubtedly the longevity of *Eberthella typhosa* depends to a great extent upon the virulence of the organism; as the results above show that some of the organisms will live longer than the beverage is normally on the market, the manufacturer should not depend upon the sterilizing effect of the carbon dioxide and other substances used. From the observation that the hardy individuals can resist these adverse conditions for a considerable length of time, it is apparent that a satisfactory water should be used and every attempt made to maintain cleanliness and prevent contamination during manufacture and storage. Allen *et al.*[27] presented the results of a sanitary survey of the soft-drink industry of the state of Kentucky. The methods employed in the survey were similar to those developed in milk inspection. Sanitary inspections were made of the plants where these products were prepared, including an investigation of the equipment used. Especial attention was given to the methods employed in washing bottles. The necessity for thorough sterilization of the bottles or other containers was emphasized. It was recommended that they be kept in live steam from 30 to 40 minutes and any subsequent contamination guarded against. Chemical and bacteriological examinations of the water used in the manufacture of soft drinks showed that many of the plants were using water which needed purification by filtration or sterilization. The results of the bacteriological examination of the soft drinks are presented in detail; some of the conclusions drawn were that the bacteriological count of the finished product is not a correct index of the sanitary conditions existing during manufacture, and that although carbon dioxide gas is somewhat germicidal, it cannot be relied upon as a sanitary safeguard since it does not inhibit or kill all microorganisms.

Members of *Bacillus subtilis* group were commonly found by Gaucher and Geors.[28] When *Escherichia coli* and *Eberthella typhosa* were inoculated into lemonade, they increased rapidly for 15 days and then fell off in numbers. Koser and Skinner[29] inoculated carbonated beverages with several pure cultures. *Eberthella typhosa* and *Salmonella schottmülleri* were killed more quickly than *Escherichia coli*. Sporeforming bacteria, as evidenced from data secured with *Bacillus, mesentericus* and *Bacillus sporogenes*, were quite resistant. Similar experiments were carried out by Yynovskii[30] wherein unpasteurized, nonalcoholic drinks were inoculated with *Eberthella typhosa, Shigella dysenteriae,* and *Salmonella schottmül-*

27. Allen *et al.* 1915. Kentucky Agr. Expt. Sta. Bull. 192.
28. Gaucher and Geors. 1915. Ann. des Falsif. 8, 94-98.
29. Koser and Skinner. 1922. J. Bact. 7, 111-121.
30. Yynovskii. 1937. Rev. in Chem. Abs. 32, 8.

leri, several strains each. The organisms survived for times not longer than three to four days, most of them dying out before.

In an investigation of the effect of carbon dioxide on bacteria, results not unlike those quoted from publications of others, were reached by Donald, Jones, and MacLean.[31] They stated that one of the reasons for adding carbon dioxide to beverages was its definite germicidal power. Beverages produced under very unsanitary conditions never contained *Escherichia coli*. This indicated that some factor was operating which was detrimental to bacteria. To determine this factor they bottled ginger ale in the following ways:

1. Plain without gas.
2. Under high pressure of nitrogen.
3. Under moderate pressure of carbon dioxide.
4. Under high pressure of carbon dioxide.

The authors stated that reductions in bacterial population were due to carbon dioxide and not to the pressure. Experiments were then carried out with ginger ale inoculated with *Eberthella typhosa* with different amounts of carbon dioxide. Uncarbonated beverage was found to allow a rapid growth of bacteria. Donald, Jones, and MacLean pointed out that a beverage carbonated and prepared under proper conditions, improved with age. That the germicidal effect of carbon dioxide is not due to pressure, since pressure in itself seems to have little influence on the organisms, except over a longer period of time and in a degree greater than that employed in commercial practice, is claimed by Levine.[32]

Stokes[33] found a variable number of bacteria in these beverages. The variable number was attributed to dirty bottles. He called attention to the fact that small portions of the contents were usually left in the bottle. In these, large numbers of bacteria grew to have significance when the bottles were filled. Extensive studies have been carried out at Iowa State College by Levine.[32] Of 69 samples, 12 per cent contained over 100,000 bacteria per ml. These organisms were said to have originated in the water used, the sirup, and unclean apparatus. General sanitation and sterilization were offered as remedies. Similar data have been reported by Kilcourse.[34] In a study of the sanitary features of the dispensing of 'soft'' carbonated drinks, he determined the bacterial content and the presence of *Escherichia coli*. The counts ran from two to 500 colonies per ml. with one having a count of 100,000. Five out of 25 specimens gave positive presumptive evidence of the presence of *Escherichia coli*. Forman[35] found few bacteria in 60 samples of soda water.

The importance of the carbonated-beverage industry in Chicago caused the Health Department through its Bureau of Food Inspection to study the various phases of the industry. Kilcourse[34] reported the efforts of the Health Department to improve conditions. The first problem was to

31. Donald, Jones, and MacLean. 1924. Amer. J. Pub. Health 14, 122-128.
32. Levine. 1923. Amer. Bottler, April, 1923.
33. Stokes. 1920. Amer. J. Pub. Health 10, 308-311.
34. Kilcourse. 1923. Amer. J. Pub. Health 15.
35. Forman. 1925. N. J. Dept. Health, Pub. Health News 10, 228-230.

secure a sterile bottle. After study through a special committee appointed for the purpose, the following approved methods of bottle sterilization were adopted:

1. *Machine Alkali.* (a) Minimum proportion of caustic alkali to soda ash, 2 to 1; (b) use minimum charge (1.5 pounds per cubic foot water); (c) make solution 12 hours before use, to allow mixing; (d) minimum alkali reckoned as NaOH (sodium hydrate) always to equal, or exceed, 1 per cent (10 grams per liter); (e) clean machine out thoroughly at least once each week.

2. *Wash and Rinse Water.* (a) Water supply must be safe; (b) water must have sufficient pressure to effect complete rinsing, no alkali left in bottles; (c) spiral rinsing stream suggested as more effective than direct stream.

3. *Machine.* (a) Minimum temperature of caustic solution always to be at least 48.9°C.(120°F.)—automatic thermoregulator suggested; (b) maximum speed to expose bottles *within* the caustic solution at least 10 minutes; (c) examine each brush daily; keep brushes overnight, or when not in use, in moderately strong soda solution; (d) be certain that the caustic solution is not diluted by leakage or seepage.

A score card was devised for use in sanitary inspections of bottling plants. The data which are of interest at present are those secured from bacteriological examination of so-called soft drinks. In order to determine the general bacteriological condition of these products, 25 samples were collected at random for analysis. It was found that the bacterial count varied between two and 500 colonies per ml., with one sample showing a plate count of 100,000 per ml. Eliminating this specimen, the average count of the other 24 was 100 bacteria per ml. Five of the samples showed *Escherichia coli.* These data are interesting in relation to Knapp and Buchanan's [36] statement that a satisfactory nonalcoholic beverage could be made which would have not more than 100 bacteria per ml. and be free from the members of the coli group.

Discussion of the microbiology of such products as carbonated beverages might well end with a brief review of the effect of carbon dioxide as such on bacteria. D'Arsonval and Charrin [37] reported that a pressure of 50 atmospheres of carbon dioxide sterilized cultures of *Pseudomonas aeruginosa* in six to 24 hours (Koser and Skinner). Similar results were published by Larson *et al.*[38] Prucha and Brannon,[39] in a study of carbonated ice cream, reported that carbon dioxide under the conditions under which they worked, did not kill pure cultures of bacteria. The investigations of Bruschettini,[40] Frankel,[41] Altana,[42] Grossman and Mayerhauser,[43] Pasteur and Joubert,[44] Buchner,[45] Liborius [46] and others quoted by Allen seem to show that carbon dioxide exerts a selective action on bacteria. Some are completely killed off, while others are not harmed and will even increase in numbers in its presence. Whether carbonated beverages con-

36. Knapp and Buchanan. 1925. Amer. J. Pub. Health 15, 1053-1056.
37. D'Arsonval and Charrin. 1893. Compt. Rend. Soc. Biol., 1893, 532.
38. Larson *et al.* 1918. J. Infect. Dis. 22, 271-279.
39. Prucha and Brannon. 1922. Ill. Agr. Expt. Sta. Cir. 256.
40. Bruschettini. 1907. Riv. d'Ig. e San. Pub., June 16, 1907, 356-366.
41. Frankel. 1889. Ztschr. f. Hyg. u. Infektionskrank. 5, 332-362.
42. Altana. 1907. Riv. d'Ig. e San. Pub., 293-309.
43. Grossman and Mayerhauser. 1877. Quoted by Allen *et al.* 1915. Ky. Agr. Expt. Sta. Bull. 192.
44. Pasteur and Joubert. 1862. Compt. Rend. Acad. Sci.
45. Buchner. 1885. Arch. f. Hyg. 3, 361-442.
46. Liborius. Quoted by Allen *et al.*, 1915. Ky. Agr. Expt. Sta. Bull. 192.

tain many or few microorganisms, then, depends on the initial contamination. Corper [47] reported that three per cent of carbon dioxide had inhibitory effects, while 15 per cent had bactericidal powers. These data are of special significance in the dairy industry where the problem has been studied by Rettger [48] and others.

Deterioration of Carbonated Beverages by Yeasts. The saccharine nature of carbonated beverages, the fact that the closed bottles are not pasteurized, and the lack of marked germicidal properties by the constituents make them susceptible to the attack of microorganisms.

McKelvey [49] found yeasts to be very frequent causes of spoilage of carbonated beverages. Of over 1,500 samples examined during a period of two years, about 85 per cent had spoiled as a result of yeast growth. Of 132 samples of sugar obtained from 125 bottling plants in 28 states, 62 were found to contain yeasts (47 per cent). Carrot sugar, saturated with calcium sulfate, was found to be suitable for the development of yeast spores and the production of large quantities for experimental work. Yeast spores obtained from carrot calcium sulfate agar were tested as to their resistance to heat in sirups of various concentrations of cane sugar. In general, the higher the concentration of sugar the longer was the time required to kill the yeasts under examination.

Bacterial Spoilage of Carbonated Beverages. As stated above, carbonated beverages usually contain bacteria. Most of them seem to be dormant, but occasionally they may grow and cause spoilage. A rather common defect, owing to growth of bacteria, is development of rope. This deterioration is quite similar to that which occurs in bread and milk. The organism which causes it is a capsulated, aerobic sporeformer. Prevention of this spoilage depends on thorough cleaning of the bottling plant and a destruction of spores of spoilage bacteria.

Microbiological Analysis of Carbonated Beverages. A committee of the American Public Health Association [50] proposed the following procedure: At least two representative bottles of any particular flavor shall be taken per three-hour period of plant operation or of stock at point of sale. Each bottle shall be opened aseptically and the top given a light flaming. Remove a sample with a 10-ml. pipette with one-ml. markings; plate one-ml. portions and .1-ml. portions in nutrient agar, wort agar, or Sabourard's agar. Incubate three days at 28 to 30°C.(82.4 to 86°F.). Report microorganisms as mesophilic bacteria, yeasts, and molds per milliliter of beverage.

NUT MEATS

These have become a sanitary problem owing largely to the fact that they have been shelled and handled under very unsatisfactory conditions. They are not only eaten as such but are added to other foods, such as frozen desserts, the bacteriological quality of which is guarded carefully. Should they harbor *Escherichia coli*, the coliform test could not be used

47. Corper. 1921. Amer. Rev. Tuberc. 5, 562.
48. Rettger. 1922. Natl. Assoc. Ice Cream Mfr.
49. McKelvey. 1926. J. Bact. 11, 98.
50. Amer. Pub. Health Assoc. Year Book, 1941-1942, 99.

for determining the sanitary quality of a food to which they are added. For these reasons much bacteriological work has been done on nut meats during the last few years. Weinzirl [51] examined 600 samples of nut meats for presence of *Escherichia coli*. He reported presence of this organism on .5 to two per cent of the samples tested. He concluded that nut meats were not an important source of *Escherichia coli* found in candies. In an attempt to learn more about the bacteriological quality of ingredients of ice cream Newman and Reynolds [52] found a low bacterial content on the samples which they examined. A similar desire on the part of Prucha [53] prompted examination of nut meats. Six of 20 samples were free from microorganisms; five others had bacterial counts greater than 30,000 per gram; two showed very high numbers. Mold spores were found to be present in a few samples. *Escherichia coli* was present in four samples. This organism was believed to come from the hands of those who shelled the nuts. DePew [54] suggested greater care in handling shelled nuts and wearing of rubber gloves by the shellers. Since nut meats often show evidence of contamination by human beings, Tracy and Brown [55] studied methods for improving their sanitary quality. The best treatment studied was to dip the nuts into hot (180°F.) sucrose solution for 30 to 60 seconds, then dry for 2.5 minutes in a 250°F. oven. The nuts should then be kept in cold storage, preferably in glassine bags, until used. Nuts treated in this way contained less than 100 bacteria per gram and were free from *Escherichia coli*. Different methods of soaking nut meats raised their moisture content and injured their texture. Iverson [56] believed that roasting the nuts in butter improved their flavor. Such a practice would also lower their microbial content considerably.

Clark and Booth [57] observed quite a wide variation in bacteria content among different samples and different kinds of nut meats. Exposure of meats during sale tended to raise their bacterial content. Those which were sold in cellophane bags were generally better than those sold in bulk. Pecans gave the most variable results, the highest counts being obtained from a few samples. Mixed nuts gave consistently higher average counts. Aerobic sporeforming rods were the most common type of organism encountered. Seven, or 3.12 per cent, of 224 samples gave cultures of *Escherichia coli*. Staphylococci were present in 54, or 24 per cent, of 224 samples examined. Tests were run to determine characteristics of these organisms. While the results of the tests were not conclusive, they do indicate that some of the staphylococci isolated may be of sanitary significance. Artificially contaminated nut meats stored at room temperature contained viable cells of *Eberthella typhosa* for three to four weeks, *Escherichia coli* for five weeks, and *Staphylococcus aureus* for nine to 10 weeks.

51. Weinzirl. 1929. Amer. J. Hyg. 10, 265-268.
52. Newman and Reynolds. 1930. Calif. Agr. Expt. Sta. Mo. Bull.
53. Prucha. 1936. Proc. 36th Ann. Conv. Internatl. Assoc. Ice Cream Mfrs. 2, 40-46; J. Milk Technol. 2 (1939), 127.
54. DePew. 1936. Idem 2, 46-52.
55. Tracy and Brown. 1936. Idem 32.
56. Iverson. 1938. Proc. 38th Ann. Conv. Internatl. Ice Cream Mfrs. 2, 7.
57. Clark and Booth. 1940. Inst. Food Technol. Proc.

More comprehensive investigations have been carried out by Wenzel and Black [58] who examined black walnuts, English walnuts, pecans, almonds, pistachio nuts, cashew nuts, and peanuts from six ice cream plants and one retail store, using dextrose agar incubated at 37°C.(98.6°F.) for six samples, and dextrose agar and tryptone agar incubated at 37 and 32°C.(98.6 and 89.6°F.) for 14 samples. Incubation at 32°C. increased the total number of bacteria and predominating species more than modification of the medium; glucose tryptone agar at 32°C. consistently yielded the highest counts. Aerobic bacterial counts varied with different nut meats; anaerobic and thermophilic counts were negligible. Gas was obtained in lactose or brilliant green bile broth with five samples, but *Escherichia coli* was not present. Yeast and mold counts increased with poor storage conditions. Nut meats treated by canning in sugar syrup or roasting in butter and salt gave lower counts, and those exposed in poor containers to air, dust, and room temperature gave higher counts. Bacillus, Actinomyces, Streptococcus, Sarcina, Micrococcus, Flavobacterium, Lactobacillus, and Leuconostoc species were isolated; none were pathogens. Twenty of 30 species of predominating organisms identified were Bacilli, *Bacillus subtilis* being present in 50 per cent of the samples.

No coliform bacteria were found by Ostrolenk and Hunter [59] on any of 34 samples of nuts in the shell, the samples having been shelled aseptically. *Escherichia coli* was present in all but two of 11 varieties in from four to 68 per cent of 548 samples representing 200 retail market samples, 234 domestic shelling-plant samples, and 114 imported samples from eight countries in Europe and the Orient and from Mexico. Artificially contaminated nut meats stored at room temperature contained viable *Escherichia coli* for approximately 68 days. Examination of 102 samples of nut meats for biochemical Colon-Aerogenes types indicated that when large numbers of *Escherichia coli* are present correspondingly large numbers of *Aerobacter aerogenes* and intermediates are found.

To evaluate the sanitary significance of coliform bacteria on nut meats, Ostrolenk and Welch [60] attempted to ascertain the origin of these bacteria on pecan meats. They found shell stock to harbor coliform bacteria. Tempering water was also highly polluted, *Escherichia coli* being demonstrated in some cases in .0000001 ml. Ostrolenk and Welch showed that chlorination markedly reduced the coliform bacteria. This along with general sanitary procedures were considered to be desirable.

Ostrolenk and Welch's [60] Method for Bacterial Examination of Pecan Meats. Fifty-gram samples of pecans were washed in 50-gram amounts of sterile water and the washings inoculated in decimal dilutions into standard lactose broth. Cultures showing gas formation after 24 hours incubation at 37°C.(98.6°F.) were streaked on eosin methylene blue agar plates.

Association of Official Agricultural Chemists [91] Method for Microbiological Examination of Nut Meats and Nut Products. This method was adopted in 1942 as tentative until it could be subjected to critical examination.

58. Wenzel and Black. 1939. Food Research 4, 191-201.
59. Ostrolenk and Hunter. 1939. Idem 4, 453-460.
60. Ostrolenk and Welch. 1941. Idem 6, 117-125.
61. Assoc. Off. Agr. Chem. J. 25 (1942), 109-110.

Place in sterile 125-ml. bottle, fitted with a ground-glass stopper, 50 grams of nut meats, comprising particles selected at random from sample or subsample. Use strict aseptic precautions in opening the package, carton, jar, or other receptacle holding the sample, and in transferring meats to sterile bottle use a metal spoon sterilized by immersion in alcohol followed by heating by direct flame.

Add to nut meats 50 ml. (or 50 grams) of sterile water. Shake vigorously three minutes or longer, if necessary, to effect a thorough washing of the nut meats. Following this agitation, allow specimen to stand about five minutes, again shake vigorously, and withdraw quantities of the suspension for direct inoculation of culture media and for the preparation of serial dilutions.

CULTURE TECHNIC

Transfer to series of fermentation tubes of lactose broth two-ml. portions of original washings and of 1:10 and 1:100 dilutions of the washings. (In view of dilution originally effected by washing 50 grams of nut meats in 50 ml. of water, a two-ml. inoculum is required in each case to permit interpretation of results in terms of washings of 1, .1, and .01 gram of nut meats.) Incubate lactose broth cultures 24 hours at 37°C. (98.6°F.) and examine for gas production.

Inoculate a series of plates with two-ml. portions of 1:100 and 1:1000 dilutions of the washings. Pour plates with nutrient agar and incubate for 48 hours at 37°C. Determine total aerobic counts and express as numbers per gram of nut meats.

From the lactose broth cultures showing gas, streak plates poured with Levine's eosin-methylene-blue or Endo agar. Incubate plates 24 hours at 37°C. Examine the eosin-methylene-blue or Endo agar plates for colonies of organisms of the coliform group. Select representative colonies for transfer to nutrient agar slants. Incubate the slant cultures for 24 hours at 37°C. Purify cultures for further study. Ascertain the biochemical reactions of the purified cultures by the following tests: Kovac's test: indol production; methyl red (M.R.); and Voges-Proskauer (V.P.) tests; Koser's sodium citrate test: utilization of sodium citrate as sole source of carbon.

Follow the procedures recommended in Standard Methods of Water Analysis, eighth edition (1936), of the American Public Health Association, under Appendix 1, Section · XVII (Differentiation—Coli-Aerogenes Group Organisms).

The biochemical types encountered usually fall within the following six classes:

Indol	M.R.	V.P.	Citrate	Type
+	+	—	—	*Escherichia coli*
—	+	—	—	*Escherichia coli* (atypical)
+	+	—	+	*Escherichia freundii* (coli intermediate)
—	+	—	+	*Escherichia freundii* (atypical coli intermediate)
—	—	+	+	*Aerobacter aerogenes*
+	—	+	+	*Aerobacter aerogenes* (atypical)

Coliform organisms giving other sets of reactions may occasionally be encountered.

In a later report in the same journal, Ostrolenk [62] stressed study of the presence of *Escherichia coli* on nut meats since this organism is commonly used as an indicator of pollution of fecal origin. The presence of this organism on such products might indicate that they are contaminated and might be potential sources of disease. He compared the results of washings from whole nut meats with the washings from thoroughly ground-up specimens and the washings of 10-gram subsamples with the washings of 50-gram subsamples. Results of these investigations were not published.

Germicidal Action of Vegetable Juice.
Certain vegetable juices have been shown to be bactericidal. Whether this action is due to a single substance or to a composite has not been demonstrated.

62. Ostrolenk. 1942. J. Assoc. Off. Agr. Chem. 25, 736.

Onion Juice. The chief volatile constituent of onion juice is generally believed to be allyl sulfide. Walker, however, quotes results of experiments by others to show that this is in error and that a disulfide is involved. Walker, Lindegren, and Bachmann [63] reported the presence of fungicidal substances in onion juice. One of these substances is neither removed nor broken down by heat and another, which is volatile, passes off from extracted juice within a few hours at room temperature. While Walker, Lindegren and Bachmann's work was done mainly with higher fungi, others, as indicated below, have extended it to common bacteria.

Lovell [64] observed a bactericidal effect of onion vapors. The action was not as strong as that of garlic vapors and is more easily exhausted. Temperature seemed to have influence because bactericidal emissions from one gram of onion increased from 10°C.(50°F.) to 37°C.(98.6°F.). He worked with *Mycobacterium smegmatis, Bacillus subtilis, Bacillus mycoides,* and *Serratia marcescens.* Results of a more comprehensive investigation on onion juice were published by Fuller and Higgins.[65] Two varieties of onions were employed in which the influence of different concentrations of onion juice on bacterial growth was studied. The bacteria tested belonged to the following groups or genera: *Bacillus subtilis,* coliform, Pseudomonas, Salmonella, Proteus, and Staphylococcus. The *Bacillus subtilis* group was the most susceptible to the inhibitory power of the juice. Species in the genera Proteus, Staphylococcus and Salmonella were alike in their tolerance, and were slightly more resistant than those in the *Bacillus subtilus* group. Coliforms and those belonging to the genus Pseudomonas were the most resistant.

Age, variety, and storage of the onions had no apparent effect on the potency of the juice expressed from them later. Filtration through a Seitz filter produced a potent juice. Intermittent sterilization by steam weakened the toxic property, and sterilization by steam under pressure destroyed most of it. The pH of the juice did not appear to influence its toxicity.

Escherichia coli produced acid but no gas in the juice. *Aerobacter aerogenes* produced acid and an abundance of gas. The behavior of "intermediates" depended upon whether they approached *Escherichia coli* or *Aerobacter aerogenes* the more closely in their general reactions.

Garlic Juice. Early general observations indicated that garlic juice might be harmful to bacteria as were a few other vegetable juices. Walton, Herbold, and Lindegren [66] reported that garlic vapors have a bactericidal effect. *Mycobacterium butyricum* and *Mycobacterium smegmatis* were more susceptible to the bactericidal effect of garlic vapors than *Escherichia coli, Serratia marcescens,* or *Bacillus subtilis.* Boiled and autoclaved garlic were not germicidal. Matsumosuke and Shin-ichi [67] also showed the antiseptic value of constituents of garlic. Their exact chemical nature does not seem

63. Walker, Lindegren, and Bachmann. 1923. J. Agr. Res. 24, 1019-1040; 30 (1925), 175-187.
64. Lovell. 1937. Food Research 2, 435-438.
65. Fuller and Higgins. 1939. J. Bact. 39, 101; Food Research 5 (1940), 503-507.
66. Walton *et al.* 1936. Food Research 1, 163-169.
67. Matsumosuke and Shin-ichi. 1937. Rev. in Chem. Abs. 31, 8537.

tò be known. Vollrath, Walton, and Lindegren [68] provisionally identified the bactericidal substance of crushed garlic and onions as acrolein or crotonaldehyde. To confirm this Ingersoll, Vollrath, Scott, and Lindegren [69] tested the bactericidal properties of crotonaldehyde. Vapors from about one-per cent solutions of either acrolein or crotonaldehyde will poison the surface of agar plates.

Horse-radish. This root has also been found to contain bactericidal substances. Foter and Golick [70] found that the bactericidal effect of the vapors of horse-radish were most pronounced at 37.5°C.(99.5°F.), decreasing with lowering of the temperature. Horse-radish vapors were much more bactericidal than those of onion or garlic but were more quickly exhausted than those of garlic. The bacteria used were ordinary species. Foter later reported that the active principle in crushed horse-radish is allyl isothiocyanate. This compound, together with methyl isothiocyanate and ethyl isothiocyanate, exhibits bactericidal effects on a variety of microorganisms when tested by several methods. The bactericidal efficiency of the oils can be more accurately determined by dilution in agar or by the preparation of aqueous suspensions than by exposure of agar plates to the vapors from similar dilutions. Allyl isothiocyanate is a pungent volatile oil which irritates the eyes and burns the skin.

SPICES

Spices are of interest to microbiologists for two reasons. Some of them are appreciably germicidal and destroy or repress bacteria; others may harbor many microorganisms among which may be just the species that food technologists attempt to keep out of foods. The former aspect of spice microbiology has been discussed in Chapter 1 and will not be considered here. The latter problem was not appreciated until Jensen, Wood, and Janson [71] showed the significance in food-preservation industries of contaminated spices. High total and spore counts at 37°C.(98.6°F.) and 48°C.(118.4°F.) were observed in all of four samples of black pepper (coarse and fine), white pepper, and coriander. The black pepper showed the highest contamination with a total count of 47,000,000 and a spore count of nearly 2,000,000 per gram at 37°C.(98.6°F.). At 48°C.(118.4°F.) the counts were 44,000,000 and 400,000, respectively. The white pepper contained a lower number of bacteria and the coriander the smallest number. Having shown that spices are highly contaminated, the next problem was to study methods for sterilizing them. Two methods were attempted, ultraviolet light and steam pressure. Results with the former method were not encouraging because of the fact that this type of energy does not penetrate. Sterilization under steam pressure gave promising results. Cameron [72] reported wide variation in the bacterial content of spices even of the same kind.

68. Vollrath, Walton, and Lindegren. 1937. Soc. Expt. Biol. and Med. Proc. 36, 55.
69. Ingersoll *et al.* 1938. Food Research 3, 389-392.
70. Foter and Golick. 1938. Food Research 3, 609-613. Foter. 1940. 5, 147-152.
71. Jensen, Wood, and Janson. 1934. Ind. Eng. Chem. 26, 1118.
72. Cameron. 1937. The Canner 84, No. 12, Pt. 2, 96.

These observations stimulated much work in the laboratories of the National Canners Association by Yesair and Cameron.[73] A personal visit to a spice-manufacturing plant and observations on methods of handling indicated that the problem is mainly one of removal of the contaminating bacteria, particularly those which may cause deterioration in foods to which they are added. No evidence exists that any health hazard is involved. Bacteriological examination of 127 samples of spices from several sources showed marked variations in bacteria content of similar spices. Black pepper was the most heavily contaminated spice, the counts of seven samples ranging from 1,200,000 to 16,300,000 per gram. The numbers of molds, acid-tolerant bacteria, and aerobic mesophilic bacteria were also high, but thermophilic aerobes were few. Putrefactive anaerobic bacteria were not found in 116 samples. Cloves contained few microorganisms. Many of these bacteria could be eliminated by screening methods. Two large tables were published by Yesair and Williams[74] in which counts of many spices were given.

Fabian, Krehl, and Little[75] observe counts of bacteria in market samples of spices which ranged from 0 to 67,000,000 per gram. Peptonizing bacteria were present in over 10 per cent of the total number. Samples of oils of spices, 50-per cent emulsions of spices and spices in sugar-soluble base were found to be sterile.

Bactericidal action of spices has been discussed on page 44.

Sterilization of Spices. This, apparently, is the only satisfactory method of meeting the problem. Little progress seems to be probable from efforts to control contamination at the source. Consequently, those who have had to meet the problem have resorted to special treatment of the spices. Various substances have been used under various conditions. Yesair and Williams[74] observed that moist heat was an effective means of sterilizing black pepper, which was used in their experiments because of its high contamination. Even though they observed a loss of some 10 per cent of potency of the spice by heating at 15 pounds' pressure for 15 minutes, this was more than compensated by spoilage reduction.

A method of sterilizing spice by ethylene-oxide *in vacuo* at an elevated temperature was patented by Griffith and Hall[76] and described by Hall.[77] When studied by Yesair and Williams[74] with black paper, the method gave practical sterility. A few other methods were studied by these investigators but the results were not significant. Ultraviolet light was unsatisfactory. Griffith and Hall's method subjects the material to high vacuum and then exposes it to undiluted ethylene-oxide in a concentration of not less than three quarters of a pound per 35 cubic feet at a temperature not less than 21.1°C.(70°F.) to 26.6°C.(80°F.) for at least two and one-half hours.

73. Yesair and Cameron. 1938. The Canner 86, No. 12, Pt. 2, 108-110.
74. Yesair and Williams. 1942. Food Research 7, 118-126.
75. Fabian, Krehl, and Little. 1939. Idem 4, 269-286.
76. Griffith and Hall. 1938. U. S. Patent 2,107,697; reissued March 9, 1943, No. 22,284.
77. Hall. 1938. Food Indus. 10, 424-425, 464-467.

Microbiological Examination of Spices. Presence of not only large numbers of microorganisms in spices but especially types which have been shown to cause spoilage makes it desirable to analyze them. The methods for this are quite like those used for other foods. The culture media should be known to favor the organisms being determined. The Committee on Microbiological Examination of Foods of the American Public Health Association has published recommended procedures [52a] based largely on well-known procedures for determining presence of certain types of organisms in canned foods, sugar, and starch.

Samples. Take a 50 gm. sample from each of three containers and pack into glass jars for transmission to the laboratory.

Preparation of Samples. Weigh the spice after thorough mixing on a sterile paper or directly into a flask. Owing to differences in bacterial content the committee recommended the following amounts:

Whole spices	10 gm.
Bulky spices	2 gm.
Ground spices	1 gm.

Add sterile water to the spice sample up to the 100-ml. mark if a dilution flask is used or bring the weight of the sample and flask up to 100 gms. Shake vigorously for five minutes and allow to settle before specimens for plating are removed.

Bacteriological Examination. Numbers of various types of microorganisms should be expressed per gram of spice.

Total Bacterial Count. Plate in the usual manner 1 ml. or more of the suspension prepared above, using any of the ordinary agar media. The committee recommended Brom-Cresol Purple Tryptone Agar medium or nutrient agar with incubation for 48 hours at 37°C. or 55°.

Acid-Tolerant Microorganisms. Plate with wort agar and incubate at 25°C. for five days.

Detection of Spores. Vegetative cells are killed by boiling the suspension for five minutes. Plate 1-ml. portions on Brom-Cresol Purple Tryptone Agar medium and incubate for two days at 37°C. and 55°C.

Putrefactive Anaerobes. Use liver broth medium and inoculate as directed in Chapter 23 where these organisms are sought for in canned foods.

Thermophilic Anaerobes. In food microbiology two types are of interest, those producing hydrogen sulfide and those producing none of this gas. Procedures are given for determining presence of these species in canned foods in Chapter 23, and in starch and sugar in Chapter 19.

Flavoring Extracts. Some of these have been found to contain many bacteria. Prucha [53] found *Escherichia coli* in some color solutions but not in flavoring extracts. DePew [54] recommended pasteurization to rid them of bacteria. Tracy and Brown [55] attempted to heat color solutions and flavoring extracts before use.

52a. Microbiological Examination of Spices. Amer. J. Pub. Health 33 (1943) 725-728.

CHAPTER 25

MICROBIOLOGICAL METHODS OF ASSAYING FOODS FOR VITAMINS

BY FRED W. TANNER, JR., PHD.

Use of microorganisms for determining nutritional properties of foods has opened new methods of research. Bacteria and yeast nutrition studies have led to solution of many vitamin problems and have aided in their discovery and isolation. During the last few years they have become another tool for nutritionists because of their ability to replace animals in biological assay of certain foods for vitamins of the B-complex.[1]

Animal and vegetable extracts have long been incorporated in bacteriological media either to insure growth or to maintain maximum rates of multiplication and fermentation. Requirements of bacteria for certain accessory substances led Wildier in 1901 to suggest the existence of a substance indispensable for development of yeasts which he called "bios." A few years later Funk introduced the term "vitamine" to designate factors required by animals for proper growth and development. After animal experiments had shown "vitamines" to consist of several substances capable of curing or preventing certain pathological conditions, much effort was expended on their isolation and chemistry and on whether other forms of life needed them. Parallel investigations on bacterial "growth factors" were being conducted. For reviews of this phase, the reader is referred to Tanner,[2] Miller,[3] Peskett,[4] Koser and Saunders,[5] Williams,[6] Fulmer,[7] Barker,[8] and Robbins and Kavanagh.[9] Relation of growth factors to vitamins has been discussed by Peterson.[10]

Yeast metabolism seemed to have something in common with animal metabolism when Meyerhoff in 1918 found the coenzyme of yeast in animal tissue. Bacterial dehydrogenases also received much attention, and a relationship between dehydrogenases and coenzymes became apparent. Respiratory enzymes were under active investigation; in 1932 Warburg and Christian found a combination of the yellow enzyme, a second enzyme prepared from yeast, and a coenzyme prepared from red corpuscles of horse blood which could oxidize hexose-monophosphate. This yellow enzyme contained riboflavin as a prosthetic group. Kuhn and co-workers demonstrated that pure riboflavin stimulated growth of rats maintained on diets low in vitamin B_2. Other riboflavin-containing enzymes have been

1. Williams. 1941. Science 93, 412-414.
2. Tanner. 1925. Chem. Rev. 1, 397-472.
3. Miller. 1930. J. Chem. Ed. 7, 257-267.
4. Peskett. 1933. Biol. Rev. 8, 1-45.
5. Koser and Saunders. 1938. Bact. Rev. 2, 99-160.
6. Williams. 1941. Biol. Rev. 16, 49-80; 1941, Enzymologia 9, 387-394.
7. Fulmer. 1939. Ann. Rev. Biochem. 8, 611-626.
8. Barker. 1941. Ann. Rev. Biochem. 10, 553-586.
9. Robbins and Kavanagh. 1942. Bot. Rev. 7, 411-471.
10. Peterson. 1942. Biol. Symposia 5, 31-43.

isolated, such as d-amino oxidase, xanthine oxidase, and cytochrome reductase. Jansen and Donath[11] isolated crystalline thiamine from rice bran. In 1932, Windaus [12] and his colleagues isolated this vitamin from yeast and established its empirical formula. Williams [13] and co-workers characterized and synthesized thiamine, and the following year Lohmann and Schuster[14] showed that carboxylase from yeast contained a phosphate ester of thiamine, Lwoff and Lwoff [15] observed that the growth factor for *Hemophilus influenzae* and *parainfluenzae* could be replaced by cozymase or Warburg's coenzyme. Niacin (nicotinic acid) was shown to function as a growth factor for *Staphylococcus aureus* by Knight [16] and by Mueller [17] for diphtheria organisms. The anti-black tongue activity of niacin was demonstrated the same year. Existence of pantothenic acid was first suspected by Williams in 1931 in nutritional studies with yeast. Its chemical structure was determined [18] in 1940. The vitamin activity of the substance was clearly established in 1939 by Jukes [19] and Woolley, Waisman, and Elvehjem,[20] who showed that it prevented a chick dermatitis which had been recognized since 1930. Biotin was also shown to be identical with vitamin H, which prevented a specific dermatitis caused by continuous ingestion of raw egg white, and the "coenzyme R" of Allison, Hoover, and Burke,[21] which greatly stimulated growth of *Rhizobium trifolii*. Inositol was isolated from a "bios" concentrate in 1928 by Eastcott,[22] but its vitamin activity was not recognized until 1940 when Woolley [23] showed it to cure alopecia in rats. With the advent of the sulfur drugs the anti-sulfanilamide action of p-aminobenzoic acid was revealed and it was soon proved to be an essential metabolite for bacteria and animals. Recently a substance called "folic acid," apparently identical with the "norite eluate factor" for *Lactobacillus casei*, has been isolated but its chemical identity and action in animals has not been reported though it occurs in bacteria, vegetable, and animal tissues. Pfiffner *et al.*[24] have suggested that folic acid may be identical with a factor reported by Hogan and Parrott[25] called " vitamine B_c" capable of curing severe anemia in chicks. Other growth-stimulating factors have been described, but these have not as yet been identified.

11. Jansen and Donath. 1926. Dienst der Volksgezondh. Nederland. Indië. Meded. Pt. K. 186; Konikl. Akad. Wetenschappen Amsterdam. Wisk. Naturk. Afd. 35, 923.

12. Windaus *et al.* 1932. J. Physiol. Chem. 294, 123; Nachr. Ges. Wiss. Göttingen., Math. Physik. Klasse 207, 324.

13. Williams. 1936. Amer. Chem. Soc. J. 58, 1063-1064; 1504-1505.

14. Lohmann and Schuster. 1937. Naturwissenschaften 25, 36; Angew. Chem. 50, 221.

15. Lwoff and Lwoff. 1936. Compt. Rend. Acad. Sci. 203, 520-522; Roy. Soc., London, Proc. 122, 352.

16. Knight. 1937. Biochem. J., 31, 731-737.

17. Mueller. 1936. J. Bact. 34, 429-441; J. Biol. Chem. 120, 219-224.

18. Williams and Major. 1940. Science 91, 246; Amer. Chem. Soc. J. 61, 454-457; 62, 1776-1779; 1779-1784; 1784-1785; 1785-1790.

19. Jukes. 1939. Amer. Chem. Soc. J. 61, 975-976; J. Biol. Chem., 129, 225-231.

20. Woolley *et al.* 1939. Amer. Chem. Soc. J. 61, 977-978; J. Biol. Chem. 129, 673-679.

21. Allison, Hoover, and Burke. 1933. Science 78, 217-218.

22. Eastcott. 1928. J. Phys. Chem. 28, 1094-1111.

23. Woolley. 1940. Science 92, 384-385.

24. Pfiffner *et al.* 1943. Science 97, 404-405.

25. Hogan and Parrott. 1940. J. Biol. Chem. 132, 507.

The chemistry of vitamins and their physiological action has been reviewed by Rosenberg [26] and Evans *et al.*[27] Many other reviews of this subject have been prepared from time to time, notably those appearing in the *Annual Reviews of Biochemistry*.

One of the most important advantages of microbiological assays is the relatively shorter time required for them than for other methods. None of the bacterial methods described in this chapter require more than a three-day incubation period; some yeast methods require only a few hours. Also, the materials and equipment required are relatively inexpensive; generally the usual bacteriological equipment is all that is required. On the other hand, animal experiments require long periods of feeding on a regulated diet free of the vitamin under assay prior to feeding of the assay materials. Chemical methods for members of the B-complex are limited to thiamine, riboflavin, and niacin; for other members, microbiological methods are distinctly advantageous where only small quantities of material are available, for instance, in plant- and animal-tissue experiments.

Microbiological methods share with chemical methods the difficulty involved in preparation of samples prior to assay. Complete extraction of vitamins from their protein complexes without destruction must be accomplished. Animal assays may be performed on unaltered materials, though larger amounts of materials must be stored during the period of assay when vitamin contents may undergo change. Animal experiments must be used to prove biological requirements for a particular compound. Like animal assays, microbiological assays require a basal medium supplying all growth-stimulating agents except the one under assay. In microbiological methods hydrolyzed casein, supplemented by amino acids and along with known vitamins, is often used to supply the nitrogen requirements. These preparations undoubtedly contain many as yet unidentified substances; it is important that these constituents be present in such concentration that only the one missing compound under assay will produce stimulation in growth of the test organism. Microbiological assays of certain natural materials have shown that ordinary methods of preparation of samples prior to assay may not always remove other stimulatory and inhibitory agents; *Lactobacillus casei* may be inhibited or stimulated by small amounts of fatty acids or urea. Hydrolysis of cereal products by strong acids or alkalies produces a compound biologically active for *Lactobacillus arabinosus* and also possessing characteristic reactions of nicotinic acid when determined colorimetrically. Whether this substance is biologically active in animals has not been established.

Specificity of microorganisms for derivatives of vitamins often is in proportion to their activity in animals, though some exceptions to this statement already exist. More information is needed to determine whether these derivatives are present in nature, and if they are, whether the assay organisms used at the present time are capable of being stimulated prop-

26. Rosenberg. 1942. Chem. and Physiol. of the Vitamins. Interscience Publishers, New York, N. Y.
27. Evans *et al.* 1942. The Biological Actions of the Vitamins. Univ. of Chicago Press, Chicago, Ill.

erly by them. Otherwise, vitamin potencies determined by microorganisms may not reveal the true biological potency of the material as determined by the higher animals.

A rapidly developing field of study has recently been revealed in the antivitamins. Avidin and the sulfa drugs have been shown to interfere with biotin and p-aminobenzoic acid metabolism respectively. Snell [28] reported a sulfonic acid structurally so similar to pantothenic acid that it interferes with pantothenic acid metabolism by organisms requiring the preformed vitamin. Others have been described by Barnett and Robinson.[29] It has been suggested that these compounds may result in another class of chemotherapeutic agents similar to the sulfa drugs.

A new application of microbiology in the general field of biochemistry is developing in microbiological determinations of amino acids. While such a discussion is outside the realm of this chapter, it is well to include some of the literature to date. Pollack[30a] employed a modification of Snell, Eakin, and Williams [128] yeast growth method for the determination of thiamine for the determinations of β-alanine. More recently Kuiken, Norman, Lyman, and Hale [30b] have modified the Snell and Wright *Lactobacillus arabinosus* method for the assay of nicotinic acid by supplementing the medium with p-aminobenzoic acid and a tomato concentrate preparation and replacing the casein hydrolyzate with a mixture of amino acids (glutamic acid, tryptophane, threonine, valine, leucine, isoleucine, cystine, lysine, and phenylalanine). The method is particularly suitable for the determination of valine, leucine, and isoleucine. Shankman [30c] has reported other amino acids necessary for this organism and Shankman, Dunn, and Rubin [30d] have proposed the assay of eight amino acids including methionine. Horowitz and Beadle [30e] reported that an X-ray induced mutant of *Neurospora crassa* had lost its ability to synthesize choline, and have reported a microbiological assay based on this observation. Bonner, Tatum, and Beadle [30f] have announced that another mutant requires supplements of isoleucine and valine. Schenck [30g] has proposed a microbiological assay for β-alanine employing the diphtheria bacillus.

THIAMINE

This vitamin is known under various names both in the United States and abroad, the most common names being thiamine, aneurin, and vitamin B_1. The pertinent facts about it have been summarized by Waisman.[31]

Thiamine* (vitamin B_1, antiberiberi, antineuritic, antipolyneuritic, $C_{12}H_{17}N_4OSCl \cdot HCl$, a pyrimidine, thiazolium derivative).

*No uniformity exists in spelling names of vitamins. Some authorities use an e as the last letter while others do not. Consequently both spellings will be found in the literature.

28. Snell. 1941. J. Biol. Chem. 141, 121-128.
29. Barnett and Robinson. 1942. Biochem. J. 36, 357-363; 364-367.
30a. Pollack. 1943. J. Am. Chem. Soc. 65, 484-485.
30b. Kuiken, Norman, Lyman, and Hale. 1943. Science 98, 226; J. Biol. Chem. 151, 615-626.
30c. Shankman. 1943. J. Biol. Chem. 150, 305-310.
30d. Shankman, Dunn, and Rubin. 1943. J. Biol. Chem. 150, 477-478; Idem 151, 511-514.
30e. Horowitz and Beadle. 1943. J. Biol. Chem. 150, 325-333.
30f. Bonner, Tatum, and Beadle. 1943. Arch. Biochem. 3, 71-91.
30g. Schenck. 1943. J. Biol. Chem. 149, 111-115.
31. Waisman. 1942. Amer. Dietet. Assoc. J. 18, 363-365.

Properties: Water-soluble. Destroyed by sustained elevated temperatures. Sensitive to alkali. Destroyed by sulfite. Not readily destroyed by oxidation.

Function: Essential for utilization of carbohydrates as a part of coenzyme, cocarboxylase. Maintains and stimulates appetite and normal intestinal functions. Necessary for normal nerve action. Specific for the deficiency disease, beriberi.

Symptoms Associated With Deficiency: Poor appetite. Digestive disturbances. Irritability. Nervousness. Weakness. Slow heart rate. Cardiovascular upsets. Loss in weight. Multiple neuritis. Edema and muscular atrophy. High blood pyruvic acid.

Daily Requirement: Man, 1.5 to 2.3 mg. Woman, 1.2 to 1.8 mg. Children (1-12 years), 0.4 to 1.2 mg.; (12-20 years), 1.2 to 2.0 mg.

Occurrence in Natural Foodstuffs: Chiefly pork muscle, rolled oats, whole wheat, rye (whole grain), walnuts, green peas, Lima beans, peanuts, milk, corn, beef liver, egg, lean beef, potatoes.

Chemically it is composed of two main parts, commonly called pyrimidine and thiazol, the complete formula being

4-methyl-5-β-hydroxy-ethyl-N-[(2-methyl-4-amino-pyrimidyl-5)]-methyl-thiazolium-chloride-hydrochloride.

Thiamine occurs in all plant and animal tissues, the latter, particularly liver, being excellent sources. Vegetables contain relatively small amounts. Williams and Spies [32] discussed the chemistry and physiology of thiamine while Jolliffe [33] considered the clinical aspects of thiamine deficiencies.

Schopfer and Jung's [34] Method for Microbiological Assay for Thiamine. This method is based on growth of *Phycomyces blakesleeanus* in an asparagine-mineral salt solution. The basal medium proposed by Schopfer and Jung had the following composition:

Potassium dihydrogen phosphate (KH_2PO_4)	0.5 gm.
Magnesium sulfate ($MgSO_4 \cdot 7H_2O$)	1.5 gm.
Asparagine	4.0 gm.
Dextrose	100.0 gm.
Distilled water	1,000.0 ml.

Bonner and Erickson [35] reported that commercial asparagine contained traces of thiamine, removable by recrystallization from water. Cultures are made with 25 ml. of the basal medium in 100-ml. Erlenmeyer flasks. Bonner and Erickson, and Meiklejohn, [36] and Sinclair [37] modified the procedure by using 10 ml. of medium in 50-ml. Erlenmeyer flasks. Bonner and Erickson added their assay material to the above medium, whereas Meiklejohn and Sinclair used such concentrations of the basal medium and assay material that dilution with water to a total volume of 10 ml. gave a final medium of the above composition. The flasks are sterilized at 15 pounds pressure for 15 minutes, cooled, and inoculated with a spore suspension of *Phycomyces blakesleeanus* prepared from malt agar slants. The number of spores used as an inoculum had no significant effect, over a thousandfold range either in blanks, standards, or assay material. [35] Flasks are incubated for 10 days at 20 to 25°C.(68 to 77°F.). At the end of this period the mycelium mat is removed by filtration on previously weighed filter paper or, as preferred by some workers, by a suitable stirring rod. The mycelium mat is dried and weighed. By interpolation from a standard curve, prepared from growth data from a series of standards prepared with each assay series, thiamine contents of the assay material may be computed. Standards are prepared containing 0, 0.05, 0.10, 0.15, 0.20, 0.30, and 0.40 μg. of thiamine. Bonner and Erickson have shown the standard

32. Williams and Spies. 1938. Vitamin B₁ (Thiamine) and Its Use in Medicine. The MacMillan Co., New York, N. Y.

33. Jolliffe. 1942. (See footnote 27.)

34. Schopfer and Jung. 1937. Compt. Rend. V. Cong. Internatl. Tech. et Chem. des Industries Agricoles. Scheveningue. 1, 22-34.

35. Bonner and Erickson. 1938. Amer. J. Bot. 25, 685-691.

36. Meiklejohn. 1937. Biochem. J. 31, 1441-1451.

37. Sinclair. 1938. Idem 32, 2185-2199.

curve to be practically linear up to 0.40 μg. of thiamine per flask. The linearity may be increased somewhat by employing a larger amount of asparagine.[35]

Leonian and Lilly [38] emphasized that major and minor elements should be included in the medium to secure maximum growth of the test organism and eliminate a non-specific stimulation of the organism in the flasks containing assay material. The quantity of glucose and ratio of glucose to amino acids on one hand and thiamine on the other exert marked influence upon growth. Glycine was recommended as a nitrogen source instead of asparagine. Schopfer [39] employed glycine while Burkholder and McVeigh [40] recommended asparagine. The effect of various factors on growth of *Phycomyces blakesleeanus* has been reported by these authors using the following medium:

Glucose	40.0 gm.	Fe	0.05 mg.
Asparagine	4.0 gm.	Zn	0.10 mg.
KH$_2$PO$_4$	1.5 gm.	Cu	0.02 mg.
MgSO$_4$·7H$_2$O	0.5 gm.	Mn	0.01 mg.
		B	0.01 mg.
Distilled water to 1 liter		Mo	0.016 mg.

Boron was supplied as boric acid, molybdenum as molybdate, and the other metals as sulfates. Increasing asparagine from four to eight grams per liter produced only slight increase in dry weight of Phycomyces mycelium. As already reported by Schopfer [39] little or no growth occurred in the medium having an initial pH below 3 or above 7. Within the range of pH 3.5 to 4.6 the amount of growth was essentially the same. Presence of citrates also enhanced growth, not because of its buffer effect, but probably because it served as an auxiliary carbon source since a phosphate buffer had no effect.

Temperature of incubation plays an even more important role. Maximum mycelium yields occur at 15°C.(59°F.) but fall off rapidly below and above this temperature, more so at lower thiamine levels. Decrease in yields is less marked at high thiamine levels. The lower yields recorded above 15°C. were not due to autolysis; only 10 per cent loss in weight of mycelium occurred in 19 days at 25°C.

The amount of surface area also influenced yields of mycelium; nearly maximum yields were obtained where the surface area of the medium was 100 to 150 sq. cm. Thus, any considerable difference in size of culture vessels in comparable experiments will introduce an important variable. Burkholder and McVeigh [40] used the *Phycomyces blakesleeanus* method in studies of thiamine contents of green plants, using 25 ml. of medium in 125-ml. Erlenmeyer flasks incubated 10 days at 20°C.(68°F.) after which the fungus mats were dried and weighed. With maize-leaf tissue, thiamine values per gram of material were practically constant through the range of 0.1 to 0.4 gram per flask but were considerably higher outside this range. With a number of different plants, samples of about 100 mg. gave minimum values. It may be necessary to determine these points by preliminary experiments. The possibility exists that inhibiting or stimulating agents may be added with the assay material, though Bonner and Greene [41] have reported satisfactory agreement between direct Phycomyces assays and thiamine determinations by a thiachrome method. The "Z factor" of Robbins and Hamner [42] may be involved.

Henry, Riker, and Duggar [24a] have demonstrated that glucose concentrations of five and ten per cent produced essentially the same assay values. Glycine, aspartic acid and asparagine were each demonstrated to be suitable nitrogen sources. Employing glycine and asparagine as nitrogen sources, thiamine values were almost identical; aspartic acid gave an average value slightly higher. Glycine was preferred because of its purity and relatively low cost. It was used in a concentration of 2.27 grams per

38. Leonian and Lilly. 1940. Amer. J. Bot. 27, 18-26.
39. Schopfer. 1937. Protoplasma 28, 381-434.
40. Burkholder and McVeigh. 1940. Amer. J. Bot. 27, 634-640; 853-856.
41. Bonner and Greene. 1938. Bot. Gaz. 100; 226-237.
42. Robbins and Hamner. 1940. Idem 101, 912-927.
42a. Henry, Riker, and Duggar. 1943. J. Agr. Res. 67, 89-110.

liter. Incubation periods of seven days were preferred. Considerable increase in mycelium weights were noted between the fifth and sixth days; the difference between assay results determined at seven and eight days were negligible. The medium employed by Henry *et al.* was prepared double strength with magnesium sulfate, 0.5 gm.; potassium dihydrogen phosphate, 1.5 gm.; zinc, 0.2 p.p.m.; iron, 0.2 p.p.m.; manganese, 0.02 p.p.m.; glucose, 100 gm.; glycine, 4.54 gr., and distilled water to make 500 ml. The pH was adjusted to 5.5 with sodium hydroxide. To 50 ml. of this medium was added thiamine solution or tissue extract and the volume then brought to 100 ml. with distilled water. Twenty-five-milliliter portions of this solution were added to each of four 250-ml. Erlenmeyer flasks, giving a quadruplicate series for each concentration. The check series included concentrations of crystalline thiamine from 0 to 0.3 micrograms per 25 ml. of medium.

Hamner *et al.*[42b] have discussed the *Phycomyces* assay as adapted to the routine assay for thiamine in a large number of materials. Good results were obtained in comparing the results with those obtained by the rat-curative and thiochrome methods, when applied to vegetable materials. It gives consistent results on wheat. On meats, the fungus method gave consistently higher results.

Phycomyces blakesleeanus, besides utilizing the thiamine molecule, will grow equally well in a mixture of the thiazole and pyrimidine which were the two fractions used by Williams and Kline [43] in synthesizing the molecule. Robbins and Kavanagh [44] showed that in mixtures of thiazole and pyrimidine these two components of the vitamin molecule are utilized in equimolecular amounts. Bonner and Erickson showed that the growth resulting is equivalent to that of equimolar thiamine. Thiochrome is inactive. However, the organism will not grow in the presence of either fraction of the molecule alone. This fact makes it possible to directly assay either the pyrimidine or thiazole content of biological materials. Rats are unable to utilize mixtures of the two fractions in place of the vitamin molecule.

The effect of several anologues of pyrimidine, thiazole, and thiamine were studied by Robbins and Kavanagh.[45] Much variation existed as to the thiamine requirements of fungi and their ability to utilize either or both of the fraction of the thiamine molecule. Such a grouping was first proposed by Robbins [46] and has been expanded by Robbins and Kavanagh.[9] This suggests another method of assaying for thiamine or its components.

The *Phycomyces blakesleeanus* assay of thiamine in blood was applied by Meikeljohn.[47] His method was criticized by Sinclair [48] on the basis that the nitrogen sources as well as other factors in blood were affecting the

42b. Hamner, Stewart, Matrone. 1943. Food Res. 9. 444-451.
43. Williams and Kline. 1936. Amer. Chem. Soc. J. 58, 1504-1505.
44. Robbins and Kavanagh. 1937. Proc. Nat. Acad. Sci. 23, 499-502
45. Robbins and Kavanagh. 1942. Bot. Rev. 8, 411-471.
46. Robbins. 1938. Natl. Acad. Sci. Proc. 24, 53-56.
47. Meikeljohn. 1937. Biochem. J. 31, 1441-1451.
48. Sinclair. 1938. Idem 32, 2185-2199.

apparent thiamine values. Lehmann and Nielson [49] reported the medium should be maintained between pH 5.7 and 6.8 and that asparagine concentration could be varied between 0.2 and 0.4 per cent without affecting the growth so long as the quantity of thiamine did not exceed 0.4 μg.

Increase in rate of alcoholic fermentation, as measured by carbon dioxide evolution, by *Saccharomyces cerevisiae* on the addition of thiamine chloride was first recognized by Schultz, Atkin, and Frey [50] as a method for quantitative determination of this vitamin. Theirs was one of the first microbiological assay methods to be successfully employed. The complete method as first used was published in 1937. The yeast fermentation method for thiamine assay has been modified slightly by Josephson and Harris [51] so that microdeterminations of this vitamin may be made in Summerson-Warburg equipment.[52] The only interfering substance of any significance thus far found is 2-methyl-5-ethoxymethyl-6-amino pyrimidine.[50] The corresponding 5-hydroxymethyl compound is a hydrolysis product of thiamine and also is an active stimulant. Except for its possible existence in urine, it has not been found to any great extent in nature.

The method as first described employed no correction for stimulation by substances other than thiamine. Nicotinic acid was soon found to interfere with the assays of certain substances and this compound was then added to the basal medium.[53] Adenylic acid was inactive. When the direct-assay method was applied to urine numerous interfering compounds, notably the pyrimidine portion of the thiamine molecule, were encountered. Consequently an indirect assay was employed in which thiamine was assayed by difference between the total stimulation recorded and that given by an equivalent amount of urine freed of thiamine. Thiochrome, an oxidation product of thiamine is biologically inactive. Alkaline ferricyanide under controlled conditions may be used to oxidize thiamine to thiochrome and this procedure was adopted.[54] This procedure was not very satisfactory because the efficiency of the oxidation varied from time to time. More recently, Schultz, Atkin, Frey, and Williams [55] have shown that sodium sulfite may be used to destroy thiamine by cleavage of the molecule forming 2-methyl-6-aminopyrimidine-5-methyl sulfonic acid and 4-methyl-5-(β-hydroxy)-ethyl thiazole, both of which are inactive toward yeast. Cocarboxylase, (diphosphothiamine) is also inactive, while the above-mentioned interfering pyrimidine is unaffected. Thus, as the method has been more recently revised [56] "the thiamine content of an unknown substance is equivalent to that portion of the fermentation activity of the substance which can be destroyed by treatment with sulfite." The method described here is that reported in 1942 and employes one-half

49. Lehmann and Nielsen. 1941. Acta Med. Scand., Suppl., 123, 374-389; Chem. Abs. 36 (1942), 1986.
50. Schultz, Atkin, and Frey. 1937. Amer. Chem. Soc. J. 59, 948-949; 2457-2460.
51. Josephson and Harris. 1942. Ind. Eng. Chem., Anal. Ed. 14, 755-756.
52. Summerson. 1939. J. Biol. Chem. 131, 579.
53. Schultz, Atkin, and Frey. 1938. Amer. Chem. Soc. J. 60, 1514-1515.
54. Schultz, Atkin, and Frey. 1938. Amer. Chem. Soc. J. 60, 3084-3085; J. Biol. Chem. 136 (1940), 713-717.
55. Schultz, Atkin, Frey, and Williams. 1941. Amer. Chem. Soc. J. 63, 632-633.
56. Schultz, Atkin, and Frey. 1942. Ind. Eng. Chem., Anal. Ed. 14, 35-39.

the quantities of reagents and assay materials employed in the original method. Also, a new type fermentometer is described.

Schultz, Atkin, and Frey's [56] Fermentation Method for Assaying for Thiamine With Saccharomyces cerevisiae. Two preparations are made of each substance to be analyzed—one treated with sulfite and one untreated—then fermentation activities are determined with the aid of a fermentometer. The difference, expressed in terms of pure thiamine chloride, is taken as a measure of the thiamine content of the unknown.

Preparation of Samples: A water-soluble substance is dissolved in a convenient volume of water (depending upon the potency of the sample). Insoluble materials must be finely divided either in the dry state by grinding or in the wet state by means of the Waring Blendor or its equivalent. The latter procedure has been found particularly useful in the preparation of bread and tissue samples. The suspension should be dispersed well enough to permit the measurement of an accurate aliquot by means of a pipette. The solution or suspension is made acid to Congo red paper with sulfuric acid and heated to 100°C.(212°F.) for 20 minutes. This is conveniently done in an Arnold steam sterilizer. When cool the solution is made to volume and a portion is taken for sulfite treatment (described below). The remainder is neutralized to neutral litmus paper by means of sodium hydroxide and is then used for the determination of total fermentation activity—i.e., before sulfite tretament.

Treatment With Sulfite: In a 50-ml. Pyrex Erlenmeyer flask is placed an aliquot (not exceeding 20 ml. in volume) of the samples prepared as above, and 0.7 ml. of N sulfuric acid and 5 ml. of a freshly prepared solution of sodium sulfite, containing 0.2 gram of the salt per 5 ml., are added. The reaction is adjusted to pH 5.2 to 5.6 with dilute sulfuric acid or sodium hydroxide solutions using bromcresol purple as an outside indicator to set the pH. The flask is capped with a 30-ml. beaker, heated to 100°C. for 30 minutes, and then cooled. Excess sulfite is destroyed by the addition of the exact quantity of a three-per cent solution of hydrogen peroxide. The end point of the reaction is determined with the aid of an outside indicator made by mixing one drop of five-per cent potassium iodide, one drop of one-per cent soluble starch indicator, and one drop of 50-per cent sulfuric acid. This mixture develops a pink tinge which gets darker with time. If a drop of a sulfite-containing solution is transferred to this indicator by means of a glass rod, the pink color is discharged. As the end point of the titration is approached the pink color fails to disappear, and when an excess of peroxide is present a deep violet color appears.

When the excess sulfite has been destroyed the solution is neutralized to neutral litmus with sodium hydroxide and made to volume, and an aliquot portion is used for the determination of residual fermentation activity.

REAGENTS FOR THE FERMENTATION ACTIVITY

All chemicals used should be the best grade commercially available.

Solution A: One liter contains 180 grams of ammonium dihydrogen phosphate, 72 grams of diammonium hydrogen phosphate, and 0.2 gram of nicotinic acid. This solution should be sterilized by heating at 100°C. (Arnold sterilizer) for 30 minutes. If desired, the sterile buffer solution may be transferred to a sterile automatic buret and thereafter kept at room temperature. If such a buret is not available the solution may be handled in the same manner as Solution B.

Solution B: One liter contains 200 grams of glucose (anhydrous), 7 grams.of magnesium sulfate ($MGSO_4 \cdot 7H_2O$), 2.2 grams of potassium dihydrogen phosphate, 1.7 grams of potassium chloride, 0.5 gram of calcium chloride ($CaCl_2 \cdot 2H_2O$), 0.01 gram of ferric chloride ($FeCl_3 \cdot 6H_2O$), and 0.01 gram of manganese sulfate ($MnSO_4 \cdot 4H_2O$). Solution B should be distributed in 500-ml. Erlenmeyer flasks, cotton-plugged, and sterilized at 100°C. on three successive days. Thereafter the flasks should be capped with foil or paper and then may be stored at room temperature. After a flask has been opened (for use) it is kept in a refrigerator at 4°C. until empty.

Thiamine Standard Solution: A quantity of crystalline thiamine chloride is dried over phosphorous pentoxide for 24 hours. A weighed amount is dissolved in distilled water to make a solution containing 0.1 mg. of thiamine chloride per milliliter. A sub-dilution is made to contain 1 μg. per milliliter. This solution is distributed in 200-ml. Erlenmeyer flasks (cotton-plugged), sterilized at 100°C. for 20 minutes on two successive days, and then treated like Solution B.

Yeast Suspension: Fleischmann bakers' yeast (10 grams) or its equivalent is weighed into a deep weighing scoop or a small beaker. The small foil-wrapped cakes of yeast or the high-vitamin B_1 bakers' yeast should not be used. Distilled water is added to the yeast, slowly at first, until a smooth, heavy cream has been produced, and then enough is added to make the volume of the suspension to 200 ml. This suspension is made just prior to each run.

Fermentometer: The fermentameter consists of a water thermostat maintained at 30 ± 0.2°C., a shaking device, and a series of gasometers. The new fermentometer described by Schultz, Atkin, and Frey [56] is based on a parallelogram. Two racks, each holding six reaction bottles in clips of spring-tempered bronze, are placed along the long side of the parallelogram. The inside corners of these racks are joined by hinges to two small plates which are supported by hinges in such a manner that they may pivot. By proper adjustment of the hinges all bottles may receive a uniform shaking motion. An excentric drive is applied at a rate of about 96 r.p.m.

The reaction bottles are connected by rubber tubing to gasometers, six on each side mounted on detachable boards. The gasometers consist of 260-ml. graduated cylinders (graduations at each two ml.) which are drawn together sufficiently at each end to attach rubber tubing. The upper end is connected to the reaction bottle and the lower end to a leveling bulb. Each contains 10 per cent calcium chloride colored blue with cupric chloride.

In conducting the assay, 2.5 ml. of Solution A and 7.5 ml. of Solution B are dispensed into each reaction bottle, followed by addition of the thiamine-containing solution under assay. In reaction bottles No. 1 and No. 2 are placed one microgram and two micrograms, respectively, of thiamine solution. In reaction bottle No. 3 is placed an aliquot of the test sample, containing between one and two micrograms of thiamine. In reaction bottle No.4 is placed an aliquot of the same sample of the sulfite treatment. If the fermentation activity of a large aliquot of the unknown or the sulfite-treated unknown is still below one microgram, one may add one microgram of thiamine to the unknown and thus bring it into the proper range. Distilled water is then added to each reaction bottle to make the volume to 40 ml. Noting the time, 10 ml. of the yeast suspension containing 0.5 gram of moist compressed yeast is added to each bottle as rapidly as possible. A free flowing pipette is desirable for this operation.

With a minimum of wasted time all the reaction bottles are placed in the fermentometer and connected to the gasometers. Shaking is started and after two to three minutes the initial reading of the gas volumes is made. At the end of three hours from the time of adding the yeast suspension, the final reading of the gas volume is made. The difference represents the gas evolved.

The fermentation activities of the treated and untreated samples are calculated in terms of micrograms of thiamine per gram of sample, and the difference between these values represents the true thiamine content.

The apparatus and technic may be considered satisfactory when duplicate fermentation measurements, made simultaneously, differ by less than two per cent. Uniform temperature, uniform shaking, freedom from leaks, and accurately calibrated gasometers are necessary if this criterion is to be met. When making these preliminary tests it is also desirable to check the rate of shaking, making certain that the rate is not so slow that the yeast settles out of suspension, thereby causing a supersaturation of carbon dioxide and consequent irregular gas evolution. On the other hand, the shaking rate should not be so fast that the reaction mixture is violently thrown against the stopper.

The difference in the three-hour gas total between one and two μg. of thiamine should not be less than 20 ml. and preferably closer to 30 ml. If the increase in fermentation rate is satisfactory, the apparatus and solutions are ready for use. The fermentation activity of an unknown is established on the basis of linearity of response between the stimulation produced by one and two μg. of thiamine. If the fermentation activity of a large aliquot of the unknown is still below one μg., as frequently happens after sulfite treatment, one may add one μg. of thiamine to the unknown and thus bring it into the proper range.

Where routine thiamine assays are made on the same material prepared according to an unchanging process and formula, Laemmle and Barlow [57] have shown that a calculated sulfite blank may be used. Comparison of assays made by the thiochrome method and the fermentation method with sulfite blank and calculated blank was applied to enriched bread. Closer agreement between the two methods was obtained when the calculated blank was applied.

Knott, Kleigler, and Torres-Bracamonte [58] applied the fermentation technic to the determination of pyrimidine and thiamine in milk, as have Gorham, Abels, Robins, and Rhoades [59] to the determination of these two substances in blood cells and urine. Bunzell [60] has adapted the yeast fermentation method to micro-determinations of thiamine through the use of enzyme reaction vessels to which a manometer is attached, graduated so that each division is equivalent to 100 μg. carbon dioxide. A simpler vessel of similar design was described earlier.

Williams, McMahan, and Eakin's [61] Method for Assaying for Thiamine With Saccharomyces cerevisiae. Williams, McMahan, and Eakin developed a satisfactory thiamine assay based on growth response of *Saccharomyces cerevisiae*. The two strains used were American Type Culture Collection No. 578 and the "Old Process" strain of the Fleischmann Company. The basal medium consists of the following reagents:

Sucrose	20.0 gm.
KH_2PO_4	2.0 gm.
$(NH_4)_2SO_4$	3.0 gm.
l-asparagine	0.75 gm.
$CaCl_2$	0.25 gm.
$MgSO_4 \cdot 7H_2O$	0.25 gm.
H_3BO_3, $ZnSO_4$, $MnCl_2$, $TlCl_3$	1.0 mg. each
$FeCl_3$	0.5 mg.
$CuSO_4 \cdot 5H_2O$	0.1 mg.
KI	0.1 mg.
Inositol	5.0 mg.
Biotin	0.2 μg.
Calcium pantothenate	300.0 μg.
Pyridoxine hydrochloride	20.0 μg.
Folic acid	0.5 μg.
Vitamin-free hydrolyzed casein	0.4 gm.*
Distilled water to make 1 liter	

* This amount of hydrolyzed casein is double the amount recommended in the original description of this method. (Univ. of Texas Pub. 4237, p. 11 (1942).

The pH of the basal medium is approximately 4.7. If it is more acid than pH 4.3 the yeast fails to grow satisfactorily.

Buffer Solution for Thiamine Assay:

Acetic acid, glacial	3.75 gm.
Sodium acetate, anhydrous	5.00 gm.
Distilled water to make 1 liter	

57. Laemmle and Barlow. 1942. Cereal Chem. 19, 540-546.
58. Knott, Kleigler, and Torres-Bracamonte. 1943. J. Nutr. 25, 49-58.
59. Gorham *et al.* 1942. J. Clin. Invest. 21, 161.
60. Bunzell. 1917. J. Biol. Chem. 17, 409-411; Ind. Eng. Chem., Anal. Ed. 14, 279-280;
61. Williams, McMahan, and Eakin. 1941. Univ. of Texas, Pub. 4137, 34-35.

In this buffer solution (pH 4.7) all thiamine solutions may be heated without danger of destruction. This is approximately the pH of the basal medium and permits good growth of the yeast.

Buffer Solution Containing Thiamine-Free Liver and Yeast Extract:

Thiamine-free liver extract (25 mg./ml.)................................. 5 ml.
Thiamine-free yeast extract (25 mg./ml.)................................ 5 ml.
Buffer solution to make..50 ml.

Thiamine-Free Liver and Yeast Extracts: Five grams of liver paste (Wilson's Laboratories 1-20) are added to 195 ml. of water, autoclaved for 15 minutes, and cooled to room temperature. The pH is adjusted to approximately 3. Ten grams of Fuller's earth are added, the mixture is shaken for 30 minutes, filtered, and the pH is adjusted to approximately 1. After autoclaving again for 15 minutes and cooling, a second 10-gram portion of Fuller's earth is added and the mixture is shaken for at least two days. At the end of this time it is filtered, the pH is adjusted to 4.5 to 4.8, and filtered again. The filtrate is divided into five-ml. portions, placed in plugged test tubes, autoclaved 15 minutes, and stored in the refrigerator until ready for use.

The same procedure is followed for Difco yeast extract.

Method of Assay: Assays are carried out in ordinary bacteriological test tubes, supported in a convenient rack which may be autoclaved.

A set of standard thiamine levels is set up with each assay series, corresponding to 0, 0.0002, 0.0004, 0.0006, 0.0008, 0.0012, and 0.0020 μg. of thiamine. Owing to the instability of thiamine, all standard solutions are prepared in the buffer solution described above.

Various amounts of tissue extracts to be assayed are diluted with buffer by preliminary experiment or estimate so as to contain from 0.0001 to 0.0012 μg. of thiamine. Volumes up to .1 ml. may be used. All samples are pipetted by the use of syringe-type micropipettes, after which 0.4 ml. of buffer solution containing thiamine-free liver extract and thiamine-free yeast extract are added to each tube.

Enough basal medium to supply two ml. per tube for all the tubes in the test is put into one flask, and another 10 to 15 ml. portion of medium is put into a smaller flask to be used in seeding. The medium, racks of tubes, a 10-ml. and a one-ml. graduated pipet are steamed for 10 minutes and then cooled to room temperature. The small flask of medium is inoculated from an agar slant of the organism. The yeast is suspended uniformly and the number of milligrams of moist yeast cells per milliliter of solution is determined by use of a suitable photoelectric colorimeter and the appropriate calibration curve. By calculation, enough of this suspension is taken to inoculate the large amount of medium with 0.08 mg. of moist yeast per 100 ml. of medium. After introduction of the yeast suspension and thorough shaking, two ml. of the medium are added to each tube in the test. The tubes are shaken thoroughly and placed in a 30°C. (86°F.) water bath for a growth period of approximately 15 hours.

The turbidity produced in the various tubes after 15 hours' incubation may be quantitatively determined in a photoelectric colorimeter or thermoelectric turbidimeter. When the tubes are removed from the incubator, they are placed in the refrigerator for 10 minutes to retard the rate of growth of the organism. They are then diluted with five ml. of a saturated solution of chlorothymol. The tubes are then shaken vigorously, allowed to stand for a few moments to discharge air bubbles, suspended again by less vigorous shaking, and then read in the turbidimeter.

Extensive direct comparisons of thiamine values in identical extracts by this and other methods were not reported. However, recovery of thiamine added to various animal tissues showed satisfactory recovery. Autolysis for 24 hours was relied upon to convert the cocarboxylase of the tissue into a form assimilable by the yeast.

The thiazole and pyrimidine fractions of the thiamine molecule are both active under the conditions used in this test. Comparative assays with thiamine show that on an equimolecular basis the pyrimidine portion has approximately 30 per cent and the thiazole portion approximately 70 per cent of the activity of pure thiamine chloride.

Treatment of thiamine with sodium sulfite under the conditions described by Schultz, Atkin, Frey, and Williams [55] results in destruction of approximately 70 per cent of the activity of the vitamin. Cocarboxylase, the phosphoric acid ester of thiamine, is practically inactive as a growth stimulant in this test. It may be converted to thiamine by enzyme action, thus it may be possible to differentiate between the amounts of cocarboxylase and free thiamine in tissue.

Silverman and Werkman's [62] Fermentation Method for Assaying for Thiamine With Proprionibacterium pentosaceum. They showed that the addition of thiamine to cells of *Proprionibacterium pentosaceum* in a medium free of the vitamin resulted in an almost immediate increase in their anaerobic pyruvate metabolism as judged by the evolution of carbon dioxide. The assay is based on the above observation.

The stock culture of *Proprionibacterium pentosaceum* was grown on a medium consisting of 1 per cent glucose, 0.3 per cent yeast extract (Bacto), and 0.2 per cent peptone (Bacto). It was transferred daily, four drops of inoculum being transferred to 25 ml. of the above medium, and incubated at 30°C.(86°F.).

The basal medium employed in the assay consisted of the following:

Glucose	1.0	per cent
Sodium acetate	0.6	per cent
Ammonium sulfate	0.3	per cent
Cystine	0.005	per cent
Hydrolyzed casein	0.075	per cent

Ether extract of three grams yeast extract per 100 ml. Speakman's salts in half concentration

Three hundred ml. of the above medium were placed in 500-ml. flasks and also in 25-ml. and five-ml. portions.

In preparation for a thiamine assay the actively growing cells of *Proprionibacterium pentosaceum* from 25 ml. of the yeast extract-peptone medium were aseptically recovered by centrifugation, washed twice with two 10-ml. portions of sterile distilled water, and resuspended in five ml. of sterile water. One drop of this suspension was used to inoculate a five-ml. portion of the basal medium. This culture was incubated 24 hours at 30°C., centrifuged, the cells washed with 10 ml. of sterile water, resuspended in five ml., and the entire contents used to inoculate a 25-ml. portion of the basal medium. This in turn was incubated for 24 hours at 30°C. and, after washing in 10 ml. of sterile water, was employed as an inoculum for 300 ml. of the basal medium. The contents of the flask were incubated for 72 hours at 30°C., the cells obtained were washed twice in distilled water, and then employed as test organisms for a manometric assay for thiamine. The second washing was carried out in a 12-ml. graduated centrifuge cup and the volume of cell paste was recorded after 20 minutes centrifuging at about 1,900 r.p.m.

The cell paste obtained from a single flask of medium was made up to 12 ml. with M/15 phosphate (pH 5.6) and one ml. of this suspension was placed in the main vessel of each Warburg cup. Nine mg. of pyruvic acid as sodium pyruvate were employed as a substrate and placed in the side arm. Varying amounts of thiamine contained in a volume of 0.1 ml. of water were added to the cells in the main vessel. After shaking in the water bath at 30°C. for 30 minutes, the contents of the side cup were tipped into the main vessel and readings taken. The atmosphere was nitrogen from which all oxygen had been removed by passage over hot copper. Total volume contained in the cups was in all cases 2.3 ml. Simple Warburg manometers are employed and details of manometric technic are described by Dixon.[63]

Carbon dioxide measurements are made at the end of 2.5 hours and are corrected for endogenous carbon dioxide production. The method may be used to assay for thia-

62. Silverman and Werkman. 1938. Soc. Expt. Biol. and Med. Proc. 38, 823-827; J. Bact. 38 (1939), 25-32.
63. Dixon. 1934. Manometric Methods, Cambridge Univ. Press.

mine in concentrations of 0.002 to 0.25 µg. Fairly accurate approximations of thiamine may be obtained if extracts are tested in several dilutions with their vitamin contents within the range of the test described.

The manometric determination is not affected by the presence of the pyrimidine or thiazole fraction of thiamine nor by nicotinic acid in the amounts tested (up to 10 µg.).

Silverman and Werkman reported satisfactory assays on 0.025 to 0.05 gram of dried bacterial cells but on no other materials.

One difficulty with this method lies in the fact that *Proprionibacterium pentosaceum* is able to become adapted to the synthesis of thiamine on serial transfer in a medium free from the vitamin.

Niven and Smiley's Method for Assaying for Thiamine With Streptococcus salivarius as the Test Organism. Stock cultures are maintained as stab cultures in a meat infusion agar plus one per cent tryptone, 0.1 per cent glucose, 0.2 per cent K_2HPO_4, 1.5 per cent agar and an excess of $CaCO_3$. The thiamine-free basal medium, as finally diluted, contains the following:

Casein hydrolyzate	0.5 gm.
Thiamine-free yeast extract	0.3 gm.
Glucose	1.0 gm.
Phosphate buffer (0.4 M, pH 7.4)	10.0 ml.
Salt solution	1.0 ml.
Sodium thioglycolate	10.0 mg.
Uracil	0.5 mg.
Nicotinic acid	50.0 µg.
Riboflavin	50.0 µg.
Calcium pantothenate	50.0 µg.
Biotin (methyl ester)	0.1 µg.
Distilled water to	100.0 ml.

Hydrolyzed Casein: A 10 per cent acid-hydrolyzed vitamin-free casein solution is prepared in the usual manner with the use of sulfuric acid and subsequent removal of the acid with barium hydroxide. Traces of thiamine, if present, are removed with norite (20 gm. per 100 gm. casein) at pH 3.0. Since the test organism is able to synthesize tryptophane, it is unnecessary to replenish the hydrolyzate with this amino acid.

Thiamine-Free Yeast Extract: Six grams of Difco yeast extract are dissolved in 200 ml. of water and autoclaved for 15 minutes. The pH is adjusted to 3, 10 gm. of Fuller's earth are added, the mixture is shaken for 30 minutes. After filtering, the filtrate is adjusted to pH 1 and autoclaved another 15 minutes. On cooling, a second 10-gm. portion of Fuller's earth is added and the mixture is shaken mechanically overnight. After filtering, 1.5 gm. of K_2HPO_4 are added to the filtrate, which is then adjusted to pH 7.4 and autoclaved another 15 minutes. The resulting precipitate is filtered out and the volume adjusted to 200 ml. and the preparation sterilized in convenient amounts. The added phosphate serves a twofold purpose of destroying the remaining traces of thiamine and removing substances which would precipitate in the complete medium.

Other Medium Constituents: A stock solution of phosphate buffer is made by mixing equal volumes of 0.4 M K_2HPO_4 and KH_2PO_4 and adjusting to pH 7.4.

Stock solution of salts consists of 10 gm. of NaCl, 0.8 gm. of $MgSO_4$, 40 mg. of ferrous sulfate ($FeSO_4 \cdot 7H_2O$) and 12 mg. of manganese chloride in 100 ml. of distilled water.

The assay is conducted in standard bacteriological test tubes which have been selected to be free from scratches and are of constant diameter. The above medium is prepared double strength, and five-ml. aliquots dispensed in each tube. Distilled water is added in such quantities that the final volume will be 10 ml. after addition of the test solution. Thiamine is destroyed on autoclaving in neutral or alkaline solutions,

63a. Niven and Smiley. 1943. J. Biol. Chem. 150, 1-9.

so it must be added aseptically after sterilization of the basal medium. Volumes of the test solution up to five ml., estimated to contain between 0.1 and 0.6 millimicrogram of thiamine, may be used.

Inocula are prepared in the above medium containing 10 millimicrograms of thiamine per 10 ml.; 0.5 ml. of this culture is mixed with 10 ml. of sterile saline solution and one drop of this suspension is employed as inoculum for the assay tubes. Inocula may be subsequently prepared by repeated subculture on the basal medium supplemented with thiamine.

A standard curve is constructed from turbidity measurements of tubes of the basal medium supplemented with thiamine, in the range of 0.1 to 2.0 millimicrograms of thiamine per 10 ml. of medium.

The test organism does not respond to the thiazole or pyrimidine fractions of the vitamin, either alone or in combination. Sulfite cleavage of pure thiamine solutions indicated complete destruction of the vitamin. Cocarboxylase is approximately 40 per cent more active than thiamine on an equimolecular basis. Takadiastase treatment of cocarboxylase solutions lowered the activity of the solution to the normal value.

Gaines and Stahly [64] have suggested that *Leuconostoc mesenteroides* may be used for assaying for thiamine, nicotinic acid, pyridoxin, pantothenic acid, and biotin in a medium consisting of acid-hydrolyzed casein, cystine, tryptophane, glucose, and inorganic salts. This method would have distinct advantages over the yeast methods in that growth responses could be determined by turbidity measurements or by titration of the acid produced during growth, thus making the method similar to many of the bacterial methods for other members of the vitamin-B complex.

RIBOFLAVIN

The known functions of riboflavin lie in the flavin-containing enzymes associated with carbohydrate and purine metabolism. In this group of enzymes the prosthetic groups may be either of two forms, riboflavin mononucleotide or dinucleotide. The biologically active flavin is a derivative of isoalloxazine with two methyl groups and a pentose sugar, d-ribose. Prior to isolation of the pentose sugar it was called "lactoflavin," "ovoflavin," or "heptaflavin." The properties of the vitamin have been summarized by Waisman.[31]

Riboflavin (vitamin G, lactoflavin, ovoflavin, $C_{17}H_{20}N_4O_6$, ribose alloxazine derivative).

Properties: Water-soluble, greenish fluorescent pigment. Stable to heat. Deteriorates on exposure to light. Rapid destruction in alkali and exposure to light.

Function: Component of flavoproteins which act as important enzymes in tissue respiration. Prevents abnormal eye changes which result in dimming of vision. Necessary for maintenance of normal nerve structure. Necessary for normal growth.

Symptoms Associated With Deficiency: Impaired growth. Lack of vigor. Impairment of tissue respiration. Weakness. Loss of body weight. Glossitis. Cheilosis (fissures at corner of mouth). Neuritis. Vascularizing keratitis. Cataract.

Daily Requirement: Man, 2.2 to 3.3 mg. Woman, 1.8 to 2.7 mg. Children (1-12 years), 0.6 to 1.8 mg.; (12-20 years), 1.8 to 3.0 mg.

Occurrence in Natural Foodstuffs: Chiefly beef liver, milk, eggs, lean beef, pork muscle, whole wheat, oats.

In animals riboflavin deficiency is manifest by retardation and later by complete cessation of growth. In rats the skin and eyes are involved, and in advanced cases the eyelids are often stuck together with serous, reddish fluid. Unless treated, death usually follows. General lack of vigor

64. Gaines and Stahley. 1943. J. Bact. 45, 441-449.

and pediculosis are associated with chronic deficiencies. In chicks, riboflavin deficiencies produce a so-called "curled-toe paralysis." Egg production and hatchability are influenced. Sudden fatal collapse is a syndrome in dogs and pigs. The role of riboflavin in nutrition has been discussed by György.[65]

Snell and Strong's [66] Method for Assaying for Riboflavin. This widely used assay method for riboflavin is based on the proportional response of *Lactobacillus casei* ε (Amer. Type Culture Collection, No. 7469) to varying amounts of riboflavin. Kemmerer [67] recommended tentative adoption of the method by the Association of Official Agricultural Chemists for determination of riboflavin in yeast, dried skim milk, alfalfa meal, whole-wheat and white flour. A similar procedure, using the same organism, has been developed by Landy and Dicken.[68] It is given later in this chapter. The organism used by Snell and Strong is believed to be identical with *Bacillus casei* ε of Freundenreich and Thoni.[69] Its actual identity may be doubtful. Some have called it *Lactobacillus helveticus*. Tittsler, Rogosa, and Whittier,[70] however, have shown that the particular strain used in the assays is more closely related to *Lactobacillus casei* than to *Lactobacillus helveticus* from its growth conditions and the fact that it forms d-lactic acid. Also it may be pointed out that true strains of *Lactobacillus casei* give maximum growth in the basal medium in the absence of riboflavin, whereas members of the *Lactobacillus helveticus-bulgaricus-acidophilus-lactic* group fail to grow in the medium regardless of the presence of riboflavin.

Specificity of the Test Organism: Ability of certain synthetic flavins to supplant riboflavin was investigated by Snell and Strong.[71] The 13 flavins studied were classified as follows:

I. Those supporting growth as the sole source of flavin on repeated subcultures:
6,7-dimethyl-9-(d,1'-ribityl)-isoalloxazine (riboflavin)
6-methyl-9-(d,1'-ribityl)-isoalloxazine
7-methyl-9-(d,1'-ribityl)-isoalloxazine
6-ethyl-7-methyl-9-(d,1'-ribityl)-isoalloxazine

II. Those possessing detectable activity only in the presence of suboptimal amounts of riboflavin:
6,7-dimethyl-9-(d,1'-arabityl)-isoalloxazine
6,7-dimethyl-9-(l,1'-arabityl)-isoalloxazine
5-ethyl-7-methyl-9-(l,1'-arabityl)-isoalloxazine
5,6-benzo-9-(d,1'ribityl)-isoalloxazine

III. Those possessing no detectable activity under any of the test conditions tried:
6,7-dimethyl-9-(l,1'-sorbityl)-isoalloxazine
9-(l,1'-arabityl)-isoalloxazine
6,7,9-trimethyl-isoalloxazine (lumiflavin)
6,7-dimethyl-alloxazine (lumichrome)
riboflavin tetraacetate

Of the flavins listed in Group I, only the last approached the activity of riboflavin. A comparison of the biological activity of the above flavins in rats showed a very close correlation with the activity for *Lactobacillus casei* ε. The test organism is also able to grow well where the basal medium is supplemented with certain combined forms of riboflavin. Feeney and Strong [72] obtained sucessful assays of Warburg's flavin-adenine-dinucleotide and two samples of milk flavo-protein. However, addition of relatively

65. György. 1942. (See footnote 27.)
66. Snell and Strong. 1939. Ind. Eng. Chem., Anal. Ed. 11, 346-350.
67. Kemmerer. 1941. Assoc. Off. Agr. Chem. J. 24, 413-423; 25 (1942), 459-464.
68. Landy and Dicken. 1942. J. Lab. and Clin. Med. 27, 1086-1092.
69. Freundenreich and Thoni. 1904. Landw. Jahrb. der Schweiz. 18, 526
70. Tittsler, Rogosa, and Whittier. 1942. J. Bact. 43, 56-57.
71. Snell and Strong. 1939. Enzymologia 6, 196-199.
72. Feeney and Strong. 1940. J. Biol. Chem. 133, xxxi.

large amounts of pyridoxine, pantothenic acid, nicotinic acid, factor W, biotin, cocarboxylase, cozymase, and adenylic acid to the basal medium had no significant effect on the assay of pure riboflavin. Amino acid requirements of this organism have been discussed by Hutchings and Peterson.[73]

The basal medium, the concentration of which is twice the desired final concentration, is composed of the following constituents:

Photolyzed sodium hydroxide treated peptone......................	10 gm.
(plus sodium acetate)	
Cystine hydrochloride...	200 mg.
Yeast supplement..	2 gm.
Glucose...	20 gm.
Inorganic salts—Solutions A and B...	5 ml. each
Distilled water to one liter; pH adjusted to 6.6-6.8.	

The constituents of the medium are prepared as follows:

Photolyzed Sodium Hydroxide-Treated Peptone: A mixture of 40 grams of peptone (Difco) in 250 ml. of water and 20 grams of sodium hydroxide in 250 ml. of water is exposed in a 25-cm. crystallizing dish to light from a 100-watt bulb with reflector at a distance of approximately 20 cm. for six to 10 hours, and is then allowed to stand at room temperature for an additional 18 to 14 hours (24 hours in all). The sodium hydroxide is neutralized with glacial acetic acid (27.9 ml.), seven grams of anhydrous sodium acetate are added, and the mixture is diluted to 800 ml. This solution contains an equivalent of five per cent of peptone and six per cent of sodium acetate, which is ten times the concentration of these materials in the final medium. It is preserved under toluene. The above treatment destroys other substances[74] which are essential for growth. These are supplied in the yeast supplement.

Riboflavin in the above solution may be removed completely if the alkaline solution is placed in a large Erlenmeyer flask and is allowed to stand in direct sunlight for 24 hours. The Texas investigators recommend incubation at 37°C., for 24 hours.

Yeast Supplement: To a solution of 100 grams of Bacto yeast extract in 500 ml. of water, 150 grams of basic lead acetate (Horne's sugar reagent) suspended in 500 ml. of water are added, and the precipitate is filtered off. Ammonium hydroxide is added to a pH of about 10, and the precipitate formed is again filtered off. The filtrate is just acidified with glacial acetic acid, the excess lead precipitated with hydrogen sulfide, and the lead sulfide filtered off. All the riboflavin is removed by this treatment. The filtrate is made to a volume of 1,000 ml. and stored under toluene in a refrigerator. One ml. of this preparation is equivalent to 100 mg. of the original yeast extract.

Strong and Carpenter[75] have produced a satisfactory yeast supplement by omitting the first filtration after addition of the basic lead acetate. Instead, the mixture was made alkaline with ammonia and was then filtered. This procedure is much less laborious.

Entirely satisfactory yeast supplements were also prepared from whole autolyzed yeast (Difco) rather than from yeast extract as originally recommended. These supplements have been used at a level equivalent to 20 mg. of the whole autolyzed yeast per tube.

Cystine: A solution of cystine hydrochloride containing one mg. per liter is prepared by suspending in water and adding the least possible amount of hydrochloric acid required to effect solution and then diluting to the required volume. It is stored under toluene.

Inorganic Salts: Solution A consists of 25 grams each of the mono- and di-potassium hydrogen phosphate dissolved in 250 ml. of water.

Solution B consists of 10 grams of $MgSO_4 \cdot 7H_2O$, 0.5 gram NaCl, 0.5 gram $FeSO_4 \cdot 7H_2O$, and 0.5 gram $MnSO_4 \cdot 4H_2O$ dissolved in 250 ml. of water.

73. Hutchings and Peterson. 1943. Soc. Expt. Biol. and Med Proc. 52, 36-38.
74. Snell, Strong, and Peterson. 1938. Amer. Chem. Soc. J. 60, 2825.
75. Strong and Carpenter. 1942. Ind. Eng. Chem., Anal. Ed. 14, 909-913.

Standard Riboflavin Solutions: For a stock solution, pure crystalline riboflavin is accurately weighed and dissolved in warm 0.02 N acetic acid (12 grams glacial acetic acid per liter of water). A convenient concentration is 100 μg. per ml. For use from day to day a more dilute (10 μg. per liter) solution is prepared from the stock solution by diluting with water. These solutions must be carefully protected against sunlight which rapidly destroys riboflavin.

The assays are carried out in ordinary bacteriological test tubes (20 x 150 mm. is a convenient size). A metal wire rack which holds each tube separately and upright is very convenient but not necessary if the tubes are properly marked. Into each test tube dispense five ml. of the basal medium and a suitable aliquot of the riboflavin-containing extract. The contents of each tube are then diluted, when necessary, to give a total volume of 10 ml. Thus as much as five ml. of the extract to be assayed may be added. The volumes indicated should be measured with an accuracy of ±0.1 ml. The tubes are plugged with cotton, sterilized in an autoclave at 15 pounds pressure for 15 minutes, and allowed to cool. They are then ready for inoculation.

Stock cultures of the organism may be carried as stabs in yeast extract agar containing one per cent glucose. For inoculum, a transfer is made to a sterile tube of the basal medium to which has been added 0.5 to 1.0 μg. of riboflavin per 10 ml., previous to sterilization. The culture is incubated 24 hours at 37°C.(98.6°F.); the cells are centrifuged aseptically and resuspended in an equal volume of 0.9 per cent sodium chloride solution. Resuspension in twice their original volume of saline is also satisfactory. One drop (about 0.05 ml.) of this suspension is used to inoculate each assay tube. The inoculated assay tubes are incubated at 37°C. for one to three days.

With each set of assays there is set up a series of tubes (at least in duplicate) containing per 10 ml. of diluted medium, 0, 0.05, 0.10, 0.15, 0.20, 0.30, and 0.50 μg. of riboflavin. These are inoculated and incubated along with the assay tubes. By measuring the response of *Lactobacillus casei* ϵ in these tubes, a standard curve may be constructed from which the riboflavin contents of the assay material may be computed.

Several methods may be used to determine the bacterial response to supplemental riboflavin. Snell and Strong [66] employed measurement of turbidity produced by the growth of the organism, using an Evelyn [76] photoelectric colorimeter with a 540 mμ. filter, though other photoelectric colorimeters are suitable. The assay tubes must be well shaken to suspend all bacterial cells uniformly; medium and cells are transferred to the colorimeter tube or cuvette and the percentage of incident light transmitted is read directly from the galvanometer. However, it is pointed out that this method cannot be used when turbid or highly colored extracts are assayed. Corrections for the turbidity of extracts are not generally valid, since turbidity is frequently altered by the acid produced during the growth of the test organism.

A second method, which is probably more accurate and is generally applicable, is the titration of lactic acid produced during growth. Contents of the tubes may be transferred to 125-ml. Erlenmeyer flasks, the tubes rinsed thoroughly with water, and the combined solutions titrated with 0.1 N sodium hydroxide. Bromthymol blue is a satisfactory indicator, using two drops of a one-per cent alcoholic solution. Electrometric titrations, employing a glass electrode are very satisfactory. Silber and Mushett [77] have suggested that pH measurements after incubation may be used as an index of growth. A spread of about two pH units occurs over the range of the standard curve, 0.05 to 0.5 μg. of riboflavin. These

76. Evelyn. 1936. J. Biol. Chem. 115, 63-75.
77. Silber and Mushett. 1942. J. Biol. Chem. 146, 271-272.

measurements were considered satisfactory after 24 hours' incubation and checked well with determinations made after 72 hours' incubation, both by pH measurement and direct titration.

Snell and Strong reported that maximum turbidity develops in the medium in approximately 24 hours, remaining constant for about 48 hours then slowly decreasing. Turbidity measurements are therefore best made at the end of 24 hours' incubation. Acid production increases steadily until about the third day, so titrations generally are made after 72 hours. Emmett, Bird, Brown, Peacock, and Vandenbelt[78] reported precision results obtained by turbidity measurements at 24 hours and acidimetric determinations at 72 hours, irrespective of type of degree of potency of the sample.

The evaluation of the response of the organism in terms of riboflavin is most conveniently done by plotting the titration values (or photoelectric colorimeter readings) of the standards against micrograms of riboflavin per tube. From this standard curve, calculations are easily made for the riboflavin in the material under assay. Variations in the standard curve are relatively small from day to day.

To yield valid results the riboflavin content of the assay cultures must fall on the straight-line portion of the curve above 0.05 μg. riboflavin per tube, i.e., between 0.05 and 0.25 μg. per tube. Assays should be carried out at different levels, at least three. Only those assays giving concordant results at the different levels should be used. The values obtained at the different levels should be averaged for the final results.

PREPARATION OF BIOLOGICAL MATERIALS FOR ASSAY

Where possible, finely divided materials should be used. Extraction of riboflavin may be accomplished in several ways. For most materials autoclaving at 15 pounds pressure for 15 minutes in a large volume of water is recommended. Extractions may also be effected by boiling in 0.1 N hydrochloric acid or autoclaving with the acid, with subsequent neutralization, provided not more than 50 mg. of sodium chloride are added to the assay tubes with the aliquot to be assayed.

With some substances, especially those high in riboflavin and not containing interfering substances, suspensions of the materials after autoclaving may be added to the assay tubes without adversely affecting the results. For materials low in riboflavin and Fuller's earth adsorbates, Arnold, Lipsius, and Greene[79] followed the procedure of Supplee, Sender, and Jensen[80] using 80-per cent aqueous acetone as the extracting agent. The acetone was removed before dilution to volume.

Scott, Randall, and Hessel[81] found poor agreement between the microbiological method and the Hodson and Norris[82] fluorometric method in the case of wheat flour and flour enriched with riboflavin. In some cases

78. Emmett *et al.* 1941. Ind. Eng. Chem., Anal. Ed. 13, 219-221.
79. Arnold *et al.* 1941. Food Research 6, 39-43.
80. Supplee *et al.* 1939. Ind. Eng. Chem., Anal. Ed. 11, 495-499.
81. Scott, Randall, Hessel. 1941. J. Biol. Chem. 141, 325-326.
82. Hodson and Norris. 1939. Idem 131, 621-630.

the values for recovery of added riboflavin by the former method amounted to 200 to 300 per cent recovery. They reported takadiastase treatment after autoclaving in 0.1 N hydrochloric acid would remove the stimulatory factor. Barton-Wright [83] found ptyalin gave more satisfactory results. Barton-Wright and Booth [84] have supplemented the medium with asparagine, xylose, nicotinic acid, and pantothenic acid. Xylose was reported to produce more concordant results between replicate tubes as well as a greater spread between concentration levels.

Andrews, Boyd, and Terry [85] noted appreciably lower values when the weight of the assay sample (cereals) increased. Centrifuging aqueous extractions decreased but did not eliminate this tendency; takadiastase treatment prior to removal of suspended solids resulted in lower values, but riboflavin recoveries remained high. If it is assumed that added riboflavin is quantitatively recovered, the values representing the difference between total flavin found and that added may be a measure of the growth factors or "apparent flavin." Thus the difference between the flavin values from assay of centrifuged aqueous extractions treated with takadiastase and the value obtained for "growth factors" gives a riboflavin value in close agreement with those found by fluorometric determinations on samples before and after takadiastase treatment. Gluten, a major constituent of flour, was inactive as a stimulating agent, Bauernfeind, Sotier, and Boruff [86] found aqueous or 0.1 N hydrochloric acid extracts of riboflavin from meat scraps, fish meal, distillers' dried solubles, and liver meals contained stimulatory agents. The stimulating agents could be removed from the extraction residues or from the assay material previous to riboflavin extraction by lipoid solvents, such as acetone, methyl alcohol, and methyl ether. Addition of these latter extracts to the basal medium in the presence of riboflavin resulted in abnormally high recoveries of the vitamin. Fatty acids containing 16-carbon atoms or more were markedly stimulatory as were their esters and calcium salts. A 12-carbon alcohol, 12-, 15-, and 16-carbon aldehydes, an 11-carbon lactone, lecithin, and fusel oil residues also produce appreciable stimulation. Many of these same extracts and compounds produced the same effect in the microbiological pantothenic acid assay. Bauernfeind et al. pointed out that agreement of results at different levels of assay is not always a good index of the absence of stimulatory agents; the amount of such agents is a contributing factor. If the stimulation occurs at different levels along the linear portion of the curve, agreement of results at different levels may occur. These authors recommended elimination of stimulatory agents through one of the following procedures: (1) the use of clarified extracts, (2) preliminary extraction of the dried samples with a lipoid solvent after which an autoclaved aqueous suspension of the product may be used for assay, (3) inclusion of photolyzed extracts of the product in the riboflavin basal medium or the inclusion of an alkaline- or acid-treated extract of the product in the

83. Barton-Wright. 1942. Nature 149, 696-697.
84. Barton-Wright and Booth. 1943. Biochem. J. 37, 25-30.
85. Andrews, Boyd, and Terry. 1942. Ind. Eng. Chem., Anal. Ed. 14, 271-274.
86. Bauernfeind, Sotier, and Boruff. 1942. Idem 666-671.

pantothenic acid medium, as was previously suggested by Eckhard, György, and Johnson [87] who found such a procedure satisfactory when assaying blood for riboflavin. However, Wegner, Kemmerer, and Fraps [88] reported addition of alkaline-photolyzed extracts of rice bran, wheat bran, and whole-wheat flour was not feasible owing to the inability to standardize the response when the extracts are in the medium. Alkaline-photolyzed extracts of whole-wheat flour produced more exaggerated acid production by *Lactobacillus casei* in the presence of lower levels of riboflavin. Materials removed by ether extraction stimulated acid production but the enhancing value of the photolyzed solution was reduced only slightly. These factors suggested that photolysis at pH 11 produced a substance which stimulated acid production by the test organism. Wheat-flour extracts which had been passed through florisil at pH 6.7 to remove riboflavin did not contain the substance activated by photolysis but did contain a factor capable of exerting some stimulation. Concentrated extracts of rice bran, wheat bran, or whole-wheat flour passed through florisil to remove riboflavin and then added to assay tubes containing one μg. of riboflavin caused production up to 20.6 ml. of 0.1 N acid, which is well beyond the 9 to 10 ml. previously considered the maximum. Addition of a similar amount of the concentrate to the 0.05-μg. level of riboflavin produced 6.9 ml. of 0.1 N acid. Addition of pyridine to the assay tubes also caused stimulation of acid production.

Since numerous methods have been proposed for overcoming the presence of stimulatory and inhibitory substances in certain materials, notably cereals, Strong and Carpenter [75] compared some of the proposed methods with others of their own initiation. Direct assay of whole-wheat flour after hydrolysis with 0.1 N hydrochloric acid by autoclaving showed a wide drift in riboflavin values depending on the amount of assay material present, with a tendency toward decreasing values in the presence of increasing amounts of the assay material. Similar, but more striking, are the results obtained by assaying cornstarch (which contains less than 0.20 μg. of riboflavin per gram) to which had been added five μg. per gram of riboflavin. Direct assay after hydrolysis in 0.1 N acid by autoclaving gave values ranging from 9.5 to 1.4 μg. per gram (1 ml. and 4 ml. of suspension per tube, respectively). The method of Scott *et al.*,[81] involving takadiastase treatment previous to autoclaving, was unsatisfactory in removing the stimulatory agent. The method of Andrews, Boyd, and Terry [85] and those suggested by Strong and Carpenter gave results which checked well at all levels of assay material. Assay for riboflavin in the presence of ether-soluble extracts of cornstarch resulted in high and variable values decreasing as the amount of the extract increased. The following two procedures were found satisfactory in removing the stimulating agents.

Procedure 1: A weighed sample containing approximately 10 μg. of riboflavin was suspended in 50 ml. of 0.1 N HCl and the suspension autoclaved for 15 minutes at 15 pounds pressure. After cooling the autoclaved suspension was adjusted to pH 4.5 (or until a heavy precipitate appeared) with 2.5 N sodium acetate solution, and the volume

87. Eckhard *et al.* 1941. Soc. Expt. Biol. and Med. Proc. 46, 405-409.
88. Wegner *et al.* 1942. J. Biol. Chem. 144, 731-745.

made to 100 ml. The mixture was filtered by pouring repeatedly through a fluted, No. 40 Whatman filter paper until a clear filtrate resulted. A 50-ml. aliquot of the filtrate was adjusted to pH 6.6 to 6.8 and diluted to 100 ml. before assay. In the case of a few samples it was advantageous to filter a second time after the pH had been adjusted to 6.6 to 6.8.

Procedure 2: This was the same as above, except that the 50-ml. aliquot of the first filtrate was shaken out three times with 30-ml. portions of ether. Without removing dissolved ether the aqueous phase was adjusted to pH 6.6 to 6.8 and diluted to 100 ml., and the aliquots were added directly to the assay tubes.

Strong and Carpenter [75] also confirmed Bauernfeind *et al.*[86] with regard to the stimulating activity exhibited by various fatty acids. The effect was found to depend on the absolute amounts of riboflavin and fatty acid present in the tube and also on the ratio between the two. Very marked effects were noted at ratios of 1:500 and 1:1,000. In general the greatest effects were noted at the lowest levels of riboflavin. Oleic and stearic acid markedly stimulated the bacterial response while palmitic acid and particularly linoleic acid acted as potent inhibitors. Bauernfeind *et al.* found linoleic acid to inhibit and stimulate growth, depending on its concentration. Mixtures of fatty acids also gave high results. On the other hand, neutral fats have little disturbing influence on the riboflavin assay. Lecithin gave considerable stimulation when the ratio of riboflavin to lecithin was high. Synthetic wetting agents, sodium salts of various alkyl sulfosuccinic acid esters, which lower surface tension of neutral solutions, proved to be inert at the concentrations tested. Wegner, Kemmerer, and Fraps [89] observed the precipitation at pH 4.5 following acid hydrolysis resulted in more reliable riboflavin assays on wheat products. Results of comparative investigations of microbiological and fluorometric methods for riboflavin in patent flour, enriched flour, and dried yeast were reported by Kemmerer [90] and Andrews.[91] Microbiological methods were found to be satisfactory.

Association of Official Agricultural Chemists' Method for Assaying Foods for Riboflavin.[92] The following procedure is a tentative one for determination of riboflavin in yeast and dried skim milk, modified for wheat flours or other materials containing less than 10 parts per million of riboflavin.

To 10 grams of whole-wheat or white flour add about 140 ml. of 0.1 N HCl. Mix well and autoclave 15 minutes at 15 pounds pressure. Cool to room temperature. By means of a pH apparatus adjust the pH to 4.5 with 1 N NaOH. Filter the sample carefully, pouring the first few milliliters that come through back onto the filter paper. Wash the precipitate two times with 10-ml. portions of distilled water buffered with one ml. of phosphate solution (J.A.O.A.C. 1941, 24, 413) and adjust to pH 4.5 with 0.1 N HCl. Adjust the pH of the filtrate to 6.6 to 6.8 and dilute to 200 ml. Assay the solutions at two or more levels, such as two and three ml. for whole-wheat flour and three and four ml. for white flour, using four tubes on each level. Set up standard tubes (four on each level) on 0.0, 0.05, 0.10, 0.15, and 0.20 microgram levels of riboflavin.

McIntire, Schweigert, Henderson, and Elvehjem [93] applied the following riboflavin extraction procedure to meats. Two grams of meat were homogenized in N/10 sulfuric acid. Then 0.2 gram clarase and 0.2 gram papain were added in five ml. of 2.5 M sodium acetate, followed by 24 hours' incubation at 37°C.(98.6°F.). The samples were

89. Wegner *et al.* 1942. J. Biol. Chem. 547-551.
90. Kemmerer. 1943. Assoc. Off. Agr. Chem. J. 26, 81-87.
91. Andrews. 1943. Cereal Chem. 20, 3-23.
92. Kemmerer. 1942. Assoc. Off. Agr. Chem. J. 25, 459-464.
93. McIntire *et al.* 1943. J. Nutr. 25, 143-152.

autoclaved, neutralized, and filtered. The filtrates were extracted with ether according to the method of Strong and Carpenter; the aqueous layer was transferred to 100-ml. volumetric flasks and made to volume. Suitable aliquots were then taken for assay. Papain preparations contain negligible amounts of riboflavin but clarase preparations contained about 0.45 μg. per gram, so corrections are necessary in calculating the riboflavin content of the samples.

Thus it seems that variations in riboflavin calculated from different assay levels with certain products can be attributed to free fatty acids present in the substance being tested. Inhibition and stimulation may be produced by the same substances; substances which stimulate an organism at one concentration may have the reverse activity at a higher concentration. Strong and Carpenter pointed out that oleic acid has been reported stimulatory for the diphtheria bacillus (Cohen, Snyder, and Mueller [94]) in concentrations in the same order as for *Lactobacillus casei* by themselves and Bauernfeind, Sotier, and Boruff.[86]

Results of investigations by Bauernfeind *et al.* and Strong and Carpenter showed that preparation of cereals and certain other samples for microbiological riboflavin assays should consist of two main steps—(1) hydrolysis, and (2) a procedure designed to remove fat-soluble interfering substances. It was pointed out that hydrolysis should be sufficiently drastic to decompose various combined forms of riboflavin and thus reduce the problem to determination of a single compound, though the method has been shown to measure some combined forms of the vitamin.[72] Others may exist which are not measured. Also riboflavin itself is less likely to be lost in subsequent precipitations than certain combined forms, such as riboflavin phosphate which has been shown to have a greater affinity for at least one protein than does riboflavin.[95] The removal of interfering substances from the hydrolysate can be accomplished successfully in most cases by careful filtration. Ether extraction is equally effective but is complicated by emulsion formation, if much solid matter is present, and is time consuming (for routine assays). Such extractions are desirable in the case of high-fat materials, such as cheese, fish meal, etc. Obviously extraction must follow the hydrolysis to remove fatty acids thereby liberated. Similar treatment of samples has been satisfactory in removing stimulatory factors affecting the microbiological assay method for pantothenic acid, which also uses *Lactobacillus casei* as the test organism. The assay for nicotinic acid, employing *Lactobacillus arabinosus*, is but little disturbed by fatty acids.

Feeney and Strong [96] have reported stimulation of the assay organism by l-asparagine in a medium free of yeast supplement. A mixture of adenine, guanine, and the "norite eluate factor" also exerted some activity and, when combined with asparagine, maximum stimulation was observed. Thus this latter mixture could, under certain conditions, replace the norited yeast supplement. In much higher concentrations, glutamine was also active. Glutamine and asparagine together produced maximum stimu-

94. Cohen, Snyder, and Mueller. 1941. J. Bact. 41, 581-591.
95. Kuhn and Rudy. 1936. Ber. Deut. Chem. Gesell. 69, 2557-2567.
96. Feeney and Strong. 1942. Amer. Chem. Soc. J. 64, 881-884.

lation, but glutamic acid was strongly inhibitory and at a level of 18 mg. per tube completely inhibited growth. Aspartic acid also nullified the stimulatory effect of asparagine but not that of glutamine or glutamic acid. Glutamine would even counteract inhibition caused by aspartic acid.

In the assay for riboflavin 100 μg. of adenine and guanine were inhibitory, 2.5 mg. of asparagine per tube produced a definite decrease in bacterial response, and aspartic acid was inert at a level of 4.4 mg. per tube. Inhibition was sufficient to cause an error of 20 per cent in riboflavin assays. However, Feeney and Strong point out that the effects of these inhibitory and stimulatory compounds are obtained at such high concentrations that they are of no practical importance in the riboflavin assay. Bauernfeind et al.[36] detected no action by asparagine at levels of five mg. per tube.

Fraser, Topping, and Isbell [97] applied the microbiological method to the assay of riboflavin in urine and tissue of riboflavin-depleted dogs and rats. Assays of urines of certain dogs showed considerable "drifting" which was later shown to be due to the presence of urea.[98] Blood was successfully assayed by Strong, Feeney, Moore, and Parsons [99] by direct assay after a five to tenfold dilution. In assay tubes containing more than 0.2 ml. of blood, large amounts of red-brown, fibrous, solid material were present interfering with the titration and apparently inhibiting normal growth of the organism, perhaps owing to fatty acids, as noted by Strong and Carpenter.[75] Quantitative extractions of riboflavin from blood were also obtained by the following procedure:

A mixture of 15 ml. of human blood, 100 ml. of water, and one ml. of 10-per cent hydrochloric acid was centrifuged one hour, and the supernatant liquid decanted from the small gummy precipitate. The supernatant liquid was stirred for one-half hour with two grams of Lloyd's reagent (hydrous aluminum silicate), centrifuged, and the adsorbent combined with the above precipitate. The filtrate which still contained the bulk of the blood solids contained no riboflavin, and when known amounts of riboflavin were added to it, quantitative recoveries were obtained. The combined adsorbent and precipitate were found to contain riboflavin equivalent to 0.64 μg. per ml. of the original blood. Direct assay of the blood gave 0.54 μg. per ml. No difficulties were encountered in the assay of urine directly. Over 98 per cent of the riboflavin could be removed by adsorbing on Lloyd's reagent; the riboflavin thus adsorbed could be successfully assayed by adding the adsorbate directly to the assay tubes. Andrews, Boyd, and Terry [85] obtained quantitative recoveries of pure riboflavin after adsorption on Fuller's earth, when assayed as the solid.

PANTOTHENIC ACID

The function of this vitamin is unknown, though presumably it is associated with some enzyme system. Chicks on pantothenic acid-free diets suffer from a specific dermatitis. Incrustations occur about the eyes, corn-

97. Fraser, Topping, and Isbell. 1940. Pub. Health Rpts. 55, 280-289.
98. Isbell, Wooley, and Fraser 1941. Idem 56, 282-285.
99. Strong et al. 1941. J. Biol. Chem. 137, 363-372.

ers of the mouth, and areas between the toes. Feathering is retarded. Hatchability of eggs is influenced by pantothenic acid though egg production is apparently not decreased by a deficiency. Retardation of growth in rats, mice, pigs, and chicks results from a deficiency. Depigmentation of fur of animals has been attributed to pantothenic-acid deficiencies though other factors apparently are involved also. Typical skin lesions may appear. Nervous and endocrine systems may be involved. The role in human physiology is uncertain, but its present status is reviewed by Gordon.[100] Some of the pertinent information has been summarized by Waisman [31] as follows:

Pantothenic Acid (chick antidermatitis factor, filtrate factor, etc. $C_9H_{17}O_5N$, N-(α,γ,dihydroxy-β,β,dimethylbutyryl)-β-amino-propionic acid).

Properties: Water-soluble, stable to heat, destroyed by strong acids or alkalis, occurs in natural materials in combined form.

Function: Role in normal metabolism is unknown.

Symptoms Associated With Deficiency: Precise role in human physiology not established.

Requirement: Unknown, but animal experiments indicate it to be somewhere between thiamin and nicotinic acid figures.

Occurrence in Natural Foodstuffs: Chiefly brewers' yeast (dry), liver, egg yolk, and peanuts.

The chemistry and biochemistry of pantothenic acid has been reviewed by Williams.[101]

In the concentration of pantothenic acid, Williams and Saunders [102] employed a yeast-growth method for assaying for the vitamin. Snell, Pennington, and Williams [103] have shown that the Lactobacillus method gives reasonably good agreement with the yeast method. Pennington, Snell, Mitchell, McMahan, and Williams [103a] more recently stated that the yeast method, when applied to the assay for pantothenic acid in crude tissue extracts, was not as specific as the bacteria method. Atkin, Schultz, Williams, and Frey [104] suggested a simpler method using yeast which is described in detail in the discussion of pyridoxine later in this chapter. The bacteria methods have been widely adopted because of simplicity. Snell and Wright [105] have stated that their nicotinic acid assay method, using *Lactobacillus arabinosus* 17-5, may be slightly modified to permit its use in assaying for pantothenic acid. Landy and Dicken [68] proposed a method using *Lactobacillus casei* ε similar to those proposed by Pennington *et al.* and Strong *et al.* Silber and Unna's [106] pantothenic acid medium was essentially the medium of Snell and Strong for riboflavin assay except that the yeast-extract supplement was replaced with thiamine, 10 μg.; pyridoxine, 10 μg.; nicotinic acid, 10 μg.; and riboflavin, 1 μg. Assays with this medium agreed within experimental error with similar assays in which the yeast-extract supplement was used. Assays for riboflavin were performed

100. Gordon. 1942. (See footnote 27.)
101. Williams. 1943. Adv. Enzymology 3, 253-287.
102. Williams and Saunders. 1934. Biochem. J. 28, 1887-1893.
103. Snell *et al.* 1940. J. Biol. Chem. 133, 559-565.
103a. Pennington *et al.* 1941. Univ. of Texas Pub. 4137, 14-17.
104. Atkin *et al.* 1943. Ind. Eng. Chem., Anal. Ed. 15, 141-144; 16 (1944), 67-71.
105. Snell and Wright. 1941. J. Biol. Chem. 139, 675-686.
106. Silber and Unna. 1942. Idem 142, 623-628.

exactly as those for pantothenic acid except that riboflavin supplement of one microgram per tube was replaced with one microgram of pantothenic acid.

Pelczar and Porter's [107] Method for Microbiological Assay for Pantothenic Acid. This is based on the requirement of *Proteus morganii* for pantothenic acid. In presence of pantothenic acid the organism can grow well in an inorganic salt medium. More luxuriant growth is obtained on glucose-meat infusion medium. The authors were unable to secure as good growth on the inorganic salts medium by the addition of other known factors, so the medium was supplemented with alkali-treated proteose peptone.

The basal medium is prepared as follows: A solution of 4.5 grams of K_2HPO_4, 0.5 gram $(NH_4)_2SO_4$, and 0.5 gram NH_4Cl is adjusted to pH 7.4, the volume is adjusted to a liter with distilled water, and is autoclaved.

To 950 ml. of this medium are added aseptically:

$Fe(SO_4)(NH_4)_2SO_4 \cdot 6H_2O$............(0.002 M in 0.002 M HCl) 20 ml.
$MgSO_4 \cdot 7H_2O$..(0.4 per cent in water) 10 ml.
Glucose..(50 per cent in water) 10 ml.
Nicotinic acid............ ....(0.001 M in water) 10 ml.
Cystine..(0.15 M in 0.1 M HCl) 10 ml.
Alkali-treated proteose peptone... 10 ml.

Alkali-Treated Proteose Peptone: The alkali-treated proteose peptone is prepared by dissolving Bacto-proteose-peptone to a concentration of 10 per cent in N sodium hydroxide and autoclaving at 15 pounds for one hour to effect complete inactivation of the pantothenic acid. Neutralize with glacial acetic acid, filter to remove the precipitate, and finally autoclave for 10 minutes at 15 pounds. This serves as the stock solution.

The basal medium is dispensed in 10-ml. amounts in sterile cotton-plugged test tubes.

With each group of assays run, it is necessary to establish a standard curve by plotting growth of the test organism as measured by the turbidity produced against the amounts of calcium pantothenate in the respective tubes, ranging from 0.0001 to 0.001 μg. per ml. of basal medium.

In applying the method to biological material, finely ground specimens (the method of Potter and Elvehjem [108] is convenient) are autoclaved at 15 pounds pressure for 30 minutes at neutrality with a large volume of water, after which any voluminous precipitate is removed by filtration through paper. The filtrates are then autoclaved again for 10 minutes to sterilize, and serve as the stock material for assay. Suitable volumes of extracts to be assayed are added to the basal medium (the authors used up to 0.8 ml.); the tubes are inoculated and incubated.

In most instances no interference was reported by opacity or color of the extracts since dilution serves to reduce this error. However, when opacity or color is imparted to the assay medium it is necessary to clarify by an absorbing agent such as kieselguhr.

The inoculum is prepared by transferring *Proteus morganii* from a 24-hour agar slant to 10 ml. of the basal medium containing 0.0005 μg. calcium pantothenate per ml. After 24 hours' incubation one drop of this culture is transferred to 10 ml. of similar medium. One drop of this second subculture is used to inoculate the assay tubes. After 24 hours' incubation the response to pantothenic acid contained in the assay material is determined by a suitable photoelectric turbidimeter, and the pantothenic acid concentration is computed from the standard curve.

Proteus morganii requires the intact pantothenic acid molecule. No growth occurs when its components, β-alanine and α-hydroxy, β-dimethyl-α-butyrolactone, are substituted. Dorfman, Berkman, and Koser [109] have recently shown that in the metabolism of

107. Pelczar and Porter. 1941. J. Biol. Chem. 139, 111-119; Soc. Expt. Biol. and Med. Proc 43, 151-154.
108. Potter and Elvehjem. 1936. J. Biol. Chem. 114, 495-504.
109. Dorfman, Berkman, and Koser. 1942. J. Biol. Chem. 144, 393-400.

the test organism, the vitamin is involved in the pyruvic acid metabolism, presumably to acetic acid, though the possibility that it acts on some other metabolic step involving pyruvic acid or some intermediate derived from pyruvic acid has not been eliminated.

Pennington, Snell, and Williams' [110] **Microbiological Assay for Pantothenic Acid.** This method employs *Lactobacillus casei* ε (American Type Culture Collection No. 7469). The general technic is much the same as that in the Snell and Strong method for riboflavin assays.

The basal medium is composed of the following constituents, the concentration of which refers to the final dilution. For assay purposes, it should be made up in **double** this concentration.

Alkali-treated peptone	0.5	per cent
Glucose	1.0	per cent
Sodium acetate	0.6	per cent
Alkali-treated yeast extract, equivalent to yeast extract	0.1	per cent
Acid hydrolyzed casein, equivalent to casein	0.2	per cent
Cystine	0.01	per cent
Riboflavin	0.01	mg. per cent
Inorganic salts, Solutions A and B	5.0	ml. each
Adjust pH to 6.6-6.8		
Distilled water to make 1 liter		

The constituents of the medium are prepared as follows:

Alkali-Treated Peptone: Forty grams of Bacto-peptone in 250 ml. of water are treated with 20 grams of sodium hydroxide dissolved in 250 ml. of water. The mixture (1 N in NaOH) is allowed to stand at room temperature for 24 hours. The sodium hydroxide is neutralized with glacial acetic acid (27.9 ml.), seven grams of anhydrous sodium acetate (11.6 grams of the hydrate) are added, and the mixture is diluted to 800 ml. The solution may be preserved under toluene.

(Note: This is the same alkali-treated peptone used in the Snell and Strong riboflavin assay method.)

Acid-Hydrolyzed Casein: Fifty grams of casein are mixed with 250 ml. of 25-per cent sulfuric acid. The mixture is autoclaved for 10 hours at 15 pounds pressure. The sulfuric acid is removed with barium hydroxide (341 grams of $Ba(OH)_2 \cdot 8H_2O$). Any excess barium ion is carefully removed with sulfuric acid, and the pH adjusted to 7 with sodium hydroxide. The solution is made to a volume of 450 ml., autoclaved for 10 minutes, and filtered. It is preserved under toluene.

The removal of large amounts of barium sulfate from the above solution is often tedious. An alternative procedure for preparing hydrolyzed casein has been shown satisfactory by the Texas workers and is generally preferred because of its simplicity. Fifty grams of commercial vitamin-free casein is mixed with 500 ml. of approximately constant boiling hydrochloric acid (prepared by mixing equal parts of concentrated hydrochloric acid and distilled water). The mixture is boiled under reflux for eight to 10 hours and the acid removed by vacuum distillations to a sirup. The process is repeated after dilution with water. The sirup is dissolved in water, neutralized with sodium hydroxide, and diluted to 500 ml.

Alkali-Treated Yeast Extract: A solution of 20 grams of Difco yeast extract in 200 ml. of 0.05 N sodium hydroxide is autoclaved at 15 pounds pressure for 30 minutes. The solution is neutralized with glacial acetic acid, autoclaved an additional 10 minutes to coagulate precipitated proteins, and filtered. The volume is adjusted to 200 ml. (100 mg. per ml.) and the solution preserved under toluene.

Inorganic Salts: Solution A consists of 25 grams of potassium monohydrogen phosphate and 25 grams of potassium dihydrogen phosphate dissolved in 250 ml. of water.

110. Pennington *et al.* 1940. J. Biol. Chem. 135, 213-222.

Solution B consists of 10 grams of magnesium sulfate heptahydrate, 0.5 gram of sodium chloride, 0.5 gram of ferrous sulfate heptahydrate, and 0.5 gram of manganese sulfate tetrahydrate dissolved in 250 ml. of water. Salts precipitate from Solution B when it stands in air; it need be renewed only when a uniform suspension can no longer be secured by shaking. It has been stated that a few drops of concentrated hydrochloric acid added to Solution B will prevent precipitation.[111]

Procedure: The procedure is much the same as employed in the microbiological assay for riboflavin of Snell and Strong. Test tubes are supported in a wire or metal rack, which may be autoclaved. Five ml. of the basal medium (twice the concentration in the above table) are dispensed into each tube along with suitable aliquots of the samples under analysis (not exceeding five ml.). All tubes are made to a volume of 10 ml. with distilled water. The tubes are plugged with cotton and sterilized at 15 pounds pressure for 15 minutes. After cooling to room temperature, they are ready for inoculation.

With each set of assay tubes a series of tubes containing known amounts of d-calcium pantothenate are set up. The following levels are satisfactory to establish the standard curve: 0, 0.01, 0.02, 0.05, 0.10, and 0.20 μg. pantothenate per tube. The volume is then adjusted to 10 ml. These tubes are sterilized at 15 pounds and inoculated at the same time as the assay tubes.

The inoculum is prepared by centrifuging the cells from a 24-hour culture grown in the basal medium containing 0.20 μg. calcium pantothenate, and resuspending in double the original volume of 0.9 per cent saline solution. A drop of this suspension is used as the inoculum. All tubes after inoculation are incubated at 37°C.(98.6°F.) for 24 to 72 hours, depending on the method employed for measuring the response.

The response to pantothenic acid may be measured by turbidimetric measurements after 24 hours' incubation using a photoelectric colorimeter. Caution must be exercised to suspend all cells before measurements are taken; or, after 72 hours' incubation, the lactic acid produced by the test organism may be titrated. Pennington, Snell, and Williams recommended using a glass electrode because of the color of the medium and its buffer capacity, or diluting the medium and titrating, using brom thymol blue as the indicator. More recently Silber and Mushett [112] have employed direct pH measurements at either 24 or 72 hours with good results.

The following microtechnic has been employed when only minute amounts of material are available for assay.[103a]

Cultures are grown in the depressions of white porcelain spot plates. The depressions are moistened with 10-per cent benzene solution of paraffin which facilitates handling of the solution to be added later. The spot plates, each with a plate glass cover to fit, are then supported in a basket covered with cloth towel and autoclaved. The medium, etc. are measured with the aid of a 0.1-ml. graduated pipette drawn to a needle-like point and controlled by a hypodermic syringe attached by a length of rubber tubing to the opposite end. The standard pantothenic acid solutions and a solution for analysis are added to the depressions in the spot plates. Standard depressions containing 0, 0.0002, 0.0004, 0.001, 0.002, and 0.004 μg. of calcium pantothenate are satisfactory to establish the standard curve.

Various amounts of tissue extract must be selected to contain approximately 0.0002 to 0.001 μg. of pantothenic acid. Volumes up to 0.1 ml. may be used. The contents of each depression are then diluted if necessary to 0.1 ml.

The cells from a 24-hour culture of inoculum grown as in the above method are centrifuged out aseptically and washed by centrifuging twice in 0.9 per cent saline solution. With the aid of a sterile pipette the resuspended organisms are transferred to the previously sterilized basal medium (one drop per five ml.). After thorough shaking, 0.1 ml. of this medium thus inoculated with *Lactobacillus casei* ϵ is added to each depression in the spot plates. The sterile cover plates are then sealed with Scotch tape. The spot plates are then placed in a 37°C. incubator for an incubation period of 48 hours.

111. Lewis. 1942. J. Biol. Chem. 146, 441-450.
112. Silber and Mushett. 1942. Idem 146, 271-272.

Titration of lactic acid produced during growth is employed as a measure of the response to pantothenic acid. A Kirk[113] microburette is employed containing 0.1 N alkali. The end point is determined electrometrically using a special micro saturated calomel half cell and a platinum electrode. Quinhydrone is added to the solution before titration and the progress of the titration is followed with a galvanometer sensitive to 0.15 micro-amperes per mm. division.

A standard curve is obtained with each set of assays. The samples for assay are dosed at increasing levels of concentration and the pantothenic acid content of each unknown is read from the standard curve. Usually three concordant results at different levels are averaged to obtain a final figure. These results usually agree with each other at least within ±10 per cent.

Morgareidge, Flower, and Edel[114] have noted some variations in the ability of the basal medium to support growth of *Lactobacillus casei*, which was attributed to the acid-hydrolyzed casein and autoclaved or charcoal-treated yeast extract. Rice-bran concentrate was found to be an efficient substitute containing other unknown growth factors for this organism and to be easily freed of pantothenic acid. Such a medium gave consistent results over a fifteenfold range of assay levels.

Strong, Feeney, and Earle's Method[115] for Microbiological Assay for Pantothenic Acid. Strong, Feeney, and Earle also proposed a microbiological assay method for pantothenic acid using *Lactobacillus casei* є as the test organism. It is very similar to the method of Pennington *et al.*, but differs slightly with respect to the basal medium. The basal medium contains the following ingredients:

Sodium hydroxide-treated peptone	0.5	per cent
Sodium acetate	0.6	per cent
Glucose	1.0	per cent
Cystine	0.01	per cent
Asparagine	0.025	per cent
Riboflavin	100.0	μg.
Inorganic salts, Solutions A and B	5.0	ml. each
Yeast supplement, equivalent to autolyzed yeast	5.0	grams
pH adjusted to 6.6-6.8		
Distilled water to make 1 liter		

This is the composition of the final diluted medium. For assay purposes it is prepared double strength, five ml. are dispensed in test tubes, and aliquots of the sample to be assayed (not more than five ml.) are added. The contents of each tube are then diluted to a volume of 10 ml. The tubes are then plugged with cotton and sterilized at 15 pounds pressure for 15 minutes. With each set of assays, standards are prepared containing the following amounts of d-calcium pantothenate per tube: 0, 0.025, 0.05, 0.075, 0.100, 0.125, and 0.150 μg.

CONSTITUENTS OF THE MEDIUM

Yeast Supplement: A solution of 25 grams of whole autolyzed bakers' yeast, obtained from Difco Laboratories, Inc., Detroit, Michigan, in 500 ml. of water is adjusted to pH 1.5 with concentrated hydrochloric acid and 25 grams of activated charcoal (Norite A) are added. The mixture is stirred for 20 minutes at room temperature and the charcoal removed by either centrifuging or filtering with suction. In the latter case a 0.5-cm. layer of moistened Filter-Cel (Johns-Manville, standard) is used on the paper. In either case the Norite is not washed, and a small amount of

113. Sisco, Cunningham, and Kirk. 1941. J. Biol. Chem. 139, 1-10.
114. Morgareidge, Flower, and Edel. 1943. Abs. of papers read before Amer. Chem. Soc.. April 12-15, 1943.
115. Strong, Feeney, and Earle. 1941. Ind. Eng. Chem., Anal. Ed. 13, 566-570.

charcoal coming into the filtrate on centrifuging is disregarded. The pH of the liquid is readjusted to 1.5 and the adsorption is repeated as before. The solution is then brought to neutrality with sodium hydroxide, filtered to remove any charcoal present, and diluted to 1,000 ml. One milliliter of the final solution is thus equivalent to 25 mg. of autolyzed yeast. It is desirable that the preparation of the yeast supplement be carried through as rapidly as convenient, so that the solution is not kept strongly acid for longer than one to two hours. This preparation is stored under toluene in the refrigerator.

Asparagine: A one-per cent aqueous solution of l-asparagine monohydrate is prepared, and stored under toluene.

Sodium Hydroxide-Treated Peptone: This is the same preparation used in the Snell and Strong procedure for riboflavin and by Pennington *et al.* in their pantothenic acid assay.

Salt Solutions: These also are the same as used in the above-mentioned assays.

Calcium Pantothenate Standard Solutions: Standard solutions of d-calcium pantothenate are prepared in 0.05 M phosphate buffer (pH 6.8 to 7.0). One is diluted to a concentration of 50 μg. per ml. from which a second is prepared containing 0.5 μg. per ml. The former is used to replenish the latter, which in turn is used from day to day in setting up assays. Aliquots are diluted accurately with water for setting up the standard curve. Solutions are preserved under toluene in a refrigerator.

More recently Neal and Strong [122] have reported that the best response to pantothenic acid is obtained when the inoculum is grown directly from the stab culture. Also, weekly instead of monthly transfers of the stab culture are recommended.

A slight modification [122] of the medium of Strong, Feeney, and Earle is recommended to produce greater growth response to pantothenic acid and to reduce the tendency for "drifts" in results of assays of certain substances, notably brans, which contain water-solubles [88,123,124] capable of stimulating the bacterial response. The sodium acetate concentration was increased two per cent, the yeast extract concentration doubled, glutamic acid added in a concentration of 0.25 per cent and Vitab supplement equivalent to .0075 per cent Vitab is added. These concentrations refer to the final diluted medium.

Yeast Supplement: This was prepared as before [115] except that Darco G-60 was used for the adsorption, and the adsorption was carried out in a volume of 240 ml. After the second charcoal treatment the filtrate was neutralized with solid sodium hydroxide and diluted to 250 ml. The supplement was thus four times as concentrated as previously described, since each milliliter was equivalent to 100 mg. of whole autolyzed yeast.

Vitab Supplement: Seventy-five grams of Vitab (National Oil Products Co.) were dissolved in 500 ml. of water, the pH was adjusted to 1.2 to 1.5 with concentrated hydrochloric acid, and the mixture was stirred with 50 grams of activated charcoal (Darco G-60) for 20 minutes at room temperature. The charcoal was filtered off, the pH readjusted to 1.2 to 1.5 and the adsorption repeated. The filtrate was neutralized to pH 6.8 with concentrated sodium hydroxide, filtered again and diluted to 1,000 ml. with distilled water. One milliliter of the final solution therefore contained the equivalent of 75 mg. of Vitab.

Preparation of Samples for Assay: These methods apply to both Lactobacillus methods for assaying for the vitamin. Extracts of natural materials may be prepared by autoclaving for 30 minutes at 15 pounds pressure finely ground or homogenized samples (Potter and Elvehjem [108]) at neutrality with a large volume of water. Acid or alkali inactivates pantothenic acid by cleavage.[115a] Pennington, Snell, and Williams [110] found

115a. Weinstock, Mitchell, Pratt, and Williams. 1939. Am. Chem. Soc. J. 61, 1421-1425.

certain materials did not give results agreeing satisfactorily when calculated at different assay levels. Among these were urine, oysters, and mushrooms. The variations could be overcome by adding to the basal medium a pantothenic acid-free supplement, prepared by acid treatment, of the sample in question. In the case of urine this supplement was prepared by making the urine 0.5 N with sulfuric acid, and autoclaving at 15 pounds pressure for 15 minutes. Excess sulfate was removed with barium hydroxide. With oysters and mushrooms the supplements were prepared by a similar treatment of aqueous extracts equivalent to 100 mg. per ml. of the fresh tissue. The supplements were added to the basal medium in approximately ten times the highest concentration used for the assay sample.

Blood was assayed by Strong, Feeney, and Earle [115] by diluting fivefold and assaying directly without autoclaving. These workers also assayed directly other liquid materials, such as milk and urine which are easily and completely soluble in water, by diluting a convenient volume and neutralizing if necessary. No inhibition was noted with urine.

Certain materials, such as yeast and animal tissues, contain a "combined form" of pantothenic acid which is not available for *Lactobacillus casei* . Some chick assays on such materials have been much higher than reported by microbiological methods (Strong, Feeney, and Earle [115]). In order to determine the total pantothenic acid content of animal tissues and yeast samples it is necessary first to subject them to autolysis or to an enzyme digestion. Wright *et al.*,[116] following the suggestion of Pennington, Snell, and Williams, allowed animal tissue to autolyze for 24 hours under benzene, after homogenization according to the method of Potter and Elvehjem, or using a Waring blendor. Strong, Feeney, and Earle employed 48-hour incubation at 37°C. of a slightly acid (pH 5) aqueous suspension of one part of the sample and two parts of clarase powder. Fruits, vegetables, cereals, eggs, and dairy products did not show any significant increase in apparent pantothenic acid content when subjected to this treatment. Waisman, Henderson, McIntire, and Elvehjem [117] have shown hot water extraction (autoclaving) of animal tissues gave erratic pantothenic acid values. Homogenization, followed by autoclaving at the natural pH, gave more consistent results. Pepsin digestion of both fresh and dried samples of the same tissues following homogenization gave higher values than untreated fresh or dried tissues. Autolysis gave practically equal values on fresh tissues. Equal weights of animal tissue and clarase and twice as much clarase gave higher values than pepsin treatment. Pancreatin (Merck) appeared to give even better extraction because it gave more complete liquefaction. None of these enzyme preparations had any effect on the amide linkage of the vitamin and each furnished only insignificant amounts of pantothenic acid. Pancreatin digests were made in buffered solutions (pH 7.0 to 7.5) so no pantothenic

    116. Wright, McMahan, Cheldelin, Taylor, Snell, and Williams. 1941. Univ. of Texas Pub. 4137, 38-60.
    117. Waisman *et al.* 1941. J. Nutr. 23, 239-248.

acid was destroyed either by acid or alkali. With some tissues clarase gave just as good liberation. Cheldelin, Eppright, Snell, and Guirard [118] have also used enzymic liberation of pantothenic acid, comparing autoclaving, autolysis at natural pH, and the following enzyme preparations at their optimum pH: takadiastase, malt diastase, pancreatin (24 hours at 37°C.), and three hours digestion with takadiastase followed by five hours with papain at 45 to 57°C. (113 to 116.6°F.) In general, values for pantothenic acid are highest after digestion of the samples with takadiastase. Autolysis or hot water extraction (autoclaving) were substantially less effective, although considerable amounts are released by these methods. In the case of beef liver and spinach, autolytic enzymes appeared able to free essentially all of the vitamin. For assay purposes, these workers suggest employing the combined action of takadiastase and papain. They suggest that the ease with which these "combined forms" are broken down by the carbohydrate splitting preparations (some of which also possess high phosphatase activity) suggests the possible presence in tissue of certain pantothenic acid ester, amide, or glucose type linkages. Willerton and Cromwell [119] found digestion of yeast and liver preparations with takadiastase released much pantothenic acid and brought the values obtained from these materials by microbiological methods to levels approximating those obtained by chick assays. Perhaps variable efficiency of different enzyme preparations for liberating pantothenic acid noted by different workers can be attributed to variations in the activities of the preparations. Mylase P [120] liberated more pantothenic acid than did clarase, according to Busirk and Delor. [121] They used a sodium acetate buffer (pH 4.2) and incubation periods of two hours at 50 or 37°C. overnight.

It must be remembered that most commercial enzyme preparations are crude and may therefore contain significant amounts of the vitamin in question. Each lot should be standardized. Busirk and Delor noted that 75 per cent of the pantothenic acid in Mylase P could be removed by dialysis at 5°C. (41°F.) for 12 hours without impairing the enzyme activity.

The stimulatory action of a large number of compounds on *Lactobacillus casei* ε in the riboflavin assay of Snell and Strong were also found to give similar action when the organism was used in the pantothenic acid assay of Pennington *et al.* and of Strong, Feeney, and Earle. [75, 86, 122]

In the medium of Strong, Feeney, and Earle, Feeney and Strong [96] reported five mg. of glutamic acid, 2.5 grams of asparagine, or 100 μg. of glutamine were as effective in supplementing the basal medium as a quantity of norited yeast extract equivalent to 25 mg. of yeast extract. Adenine and guanine, when added to the complete medium, produced a definite inhibition at a level of 100 μg. per tube; whereas glutamic acid, uracil, and thymine were without effect. The effects of these compounds were noted at such high concentrations the authors believed they had little

118. Cheldelin *et al.* 1942. Univ. of Texas Pub. 4237, 15-36.
119. Willerton and Cromwell. 1942. Ind. Eng. Chem., Anal. Ed. 14, 603-604.
120. Wallerstein Laboratories, 180 Madison Ave., New York, N. Y.
121. Busirk and Delor. 1942. J. Biol. Chem. 145, 707-708.
122. Neal and Strong. 1943. Ind. Eng. Chem., Anal. Ed. 15, 654-657.

practical significance insofar as their interference in the riboflavin and pantothenic acid assays are concerned. Bauernfeind et al.,[86] employing the assay medium of Pennington, Snell, and Williams, were unable to observe stimulation by asparagine at levels of five mg. per tube. Pennington et al.[61] have reported identical assay values in parallel assays using their method and that of Strong, Feeney, and Earle.

Clarke, Lechycka, and Light [123] have noted a substance in wheat flour producing increased acid production. The elimination of certain substances has been discussed by Bauernfeind et al, and Strong and Carpenter.[75]

Until recently, it has been thought that approximately 10 ml. of 0.1 N acid was the maximum capacity of most organisms of the lactic acid group. However, Wegner, Kemmerer, and Fraps [88] have shown that addition of wheat-bran concentrates to the riboflavin assay medium of Snell and Strong will allow production of twice as much acid, if the carbohydrate portion of the medium is increased sufficiently so as not to be a limiting factor. A similar observation has been reported by Clarke, Lechycka, and Light,[123] using rice-polishings concentrate. Addition of 400 mg. or more of rice-polishings concentrate per tube resulted in production of 20 to 23 ml. of 0.1 N acid. The ability to support this additional acid production was not affected by one treatment with Fuller's earth at pH 4. Autoclaving with sodium hydroxide at pH 12 for 30 minutes at 15 pounds destroyed the factor. About half of the activity was destroyed by takadiastase treatment at 50°C. overnight. From these observations Light and Clarke [124] studied the pantothenic acid medium of Pennington, Snell, and Williams [110] in the hope of improving the medium with respect to its ability to support greater acid production. With increased dosage of rice-polishings concentrate, they noted a plateau of 10 ml. of 0.1 N acid was reached, but that addition of more rice concentrate resulted in a rapid increase in acidity up to 22 ml. of 0.1 N acid. This could not be explained on the basis of buffer capacity of the rice concentrate. Glucose addition to the basal medium resulted in a higher and shorter plateau level. With pure calcium pantothenate, 200 mg. of glucose per tube in the basal medium allowed a maximum of 13 ml. of 0.1 N acid in contrast to 10 ml. on the original basal medium containing 100 mg. glucose per tube, yet the rice concentrate supported 22 ml. acid production. If the basal medium was supplemented with thiamine hydrochloride, 100 μg.; pyridoxine hydrochloride, 100 μg.; nicotinic acid, 100 μg.; choline chloride, 12,000 μg.; inositol, 12,000 μg.; biotin 2 and added riboflavin, 100 μg. (all per tube); the maximum acid production on addition of pure calcium pantothenate was raised to 16 to 17 ml. The medium of Landy and Dicken [68] was able to support a maximum acid production of 18 ml. with additional glucose, while the plateau in the middle-dose range of rice concentrate was eliminated by the addition of asparagine. Omission of asparagine reduced the maximum acid value from 20 to 15 ml.

A medium containing casein hydrolysate and a peptone preparation supported more acid production than the medium containing casein alone,

123. Clark et al. 1942. J. Biol. Chem. 142, 957-958.

yet the casein fraction may be eliminated if the peptone concentration is doubled. These media show a plateau at 20 ml. of 0.1 N acid, but acid production may be raised to 35 to 40 ml. if large quantities of yeast concentrate or of liver extract are tested with sufficient substrate. Pantothenic acid alone is not the stimulating factor, nor are folic acid and biotin and glutamic acid. With these latter media, satisfactory dose-response curves are obtained for pantothenic acid between 0.04 and 2.56 μg. with acid production of 4.5 to 22.5 ml.

When the photolyzed peptone preparation of Snell and Strong is substituted for the casein in the medium and riboflavin as replaced by calcium pantothenate, preliminary studies have indicated that the medium thus modified is satisfactory for the assay for riboflavin.

The medium proposed by Light and Clarke [124] is as follows:

Peptone preparation of Pennington, Snell, and Williams	40 ml.
Glucose, anhydrous	8 gm.
l-asparagine	50 mg.
l-tryptophane	20 mg.
l-cystine	20 mg.
Salt solution A	1 ml.
Salt solution B	1 ml.
Guanine hydrochloride	1 mg.
Adenine sulfate	1 mg.
Xanthine	1 mg.
Uracil	1 mg.
Thiamin hydrochloride	2 mg.
Riboflavin	2 mg.
Pyridoxine hydrochloride	2 mg.
Nicotinic acid	9 mg.
Choline chloride	20 mg.
Inositol	20 mg.
Distilled water to 100 ml.	
pH adjusted to 6.8	

Neal and Strong [122] expressed doubt as to the advisability of extending the titration range above 10 or 11 ml., since the large amount of acid may unfavorably influence the growth and vigor of the test organism, and the growth response is not a linear function of pantothenic acid concentrations.

BIOTIN

Biotin is one of the most powerful physiological agents known. It was discovered and later isolated in the form of the methyl ester in 1935 by Kögl.[125] Kögl and Tönnis [126] were successful in isolating 1.1 mg. of crystalline material from 250 kg. of Chinese egg yolk, representing a yield, after 16 steps, of 1.4 per cent. Thus the original material contained only 80 mg. of biotin. These workers followed the concentration of the substance with the aid of a yeast-growth assay method, relying on a five-hour incubation period after a heavy inoculation of one mg. of yeast cells per

124. Light and Clarke. 1943. J. Biol. Chem. 147, 739-747.
125. Kögl. 1935. Ber. Deut. Chem. Gesell. 68, 16.
126. Kögl and Tonnis. 1936. Ztschr. f. Physiol. Chem. 242, 43-73.

ml. of medium. In this case, Williams [127] has pointed out that other requirements of the test organism are supplied by the inoculum, for he and his co-workers [128] have shown that in the absence of pyridoxine, biotin is inactive.

A few years earlier Allison, Hoover, and Burk [129] reported a factor necessary for the growth of Rhizobium which they named "coenzyme R." A third group of investigators were attempting to isolate the factor marked for its ability in inhibiting the deleterious effects produced by feeding raw egg white. This factor was called "protective factor X" by Boas, "the protective factor against egg-white injury" by Parsons, and "vitamin H" by György. Then a remarkable merging of these independent lines of study occurred. Nilsson *et al.*[130] showed the biotin methyl ester of Kögl could replace "coenzyme R" in the metabolism of Rhizobium. West and Wilson,[131] independently using crude preparations, suggested that biotin and coenzyme R were identical. Finally du Vigneaud and co-workers [132] showed biotin could prevent the raw egg-white injury, thus indicating the identity of the three agents. Biotin and the raw egg-white factor, now called avidin, combine in such a way that biotin is inactive in the animal and microorganism. That different forms of biotin exist in nature has been demonstrated by Oppel [133] and Burke and Winzler.[134] Oppel reported 20 to 50 per cent of the yeast-growth biotin activity in urine was unaffected by addition of avidin or egg white. Burke and Winzler have found even higher amounts in urine of dog, horse, rat, cow, mouse, and sheep. In fact it was found in most all tissues and foodstuffs. The yeast activity of this avidin-uncombinable fraction, unlike biotin, is greatly reduced by boiling or autoclaving at natural pH values. This fraction is also inactive for Rhizobium and is designated by these writers as "miotin." A residual, comparatively heat-stable, avidin-uncombinable fraction produced by autoclaving miotin, is designated as "tiotin." A third unidentified biotin vitamer, "rhiotin," active for Rhizobium but not for yeast, is avidin-combinable and stable to acid and neutral autoclaving. It may be detected in human or rat urine after addition of excess avidin and precipitation of the avidin-biotin complex with acetone. Both rhiotin and miotin were inactive in the mouse, at least in doses equivalent to curative doses of biotin. *Escherichia coli* excretes large amounts of avidin-uncombinable biotin vitamers.

These vitamers are believed to be chemically closely related to biotin. Yeast growing in the presence of submaximum amounts of avidin-uncombinable biotin is able to completely convert them to a combinable form. Also, free biotin may be converted to an avidin-uncombinable form, presumably miotin. The diaminocarboxylic acid derived from biotin by

127. Williams. 1941. Biol. Rev. 16, 49-80.
128. Snell, Eakin, and Williams. 1940. Amer. Chem. Soc. J. 62, 175-178.
129. Allison *et al.* 1933. Science 78, 217-218; J. Bact. 27 (1934), 561-581.
130. Nilsson *et al.* 1939. Naturwissenschaften 27, 389.
131. West and Wilson. 1940. Enzymologia 8, 152-162.
132. du Vigneaud *et al.* 1940. Science 92, 62-63; 243-245.
133. Oppel. 1943. Amer. J. Med. Sci. (in press); quoted from Burke and Winzler.
134. Burke and Winzler. 1943. Science 97, 57-60.

du Vigneaud *et al.*[135] also was converted to an avidin-combinable form.

Melville *et al.*[135a] have recently described the preparation of desthiobiotin methyl ester from biotin methyl ester. The former compound is structurally the same as biotin except that the sulfur atom has been removed and the thioether linkage thereby replaced by hydrogen atoms. This compound exhibits full biotin activity (on a weight basis; on a molarity basis it is slightly lower because of the lower molecular weight) for *Saccharomyces cerevisiae*. Yeast growth activity can be inhibited by avidin, indicating the urea grouping is necessary for the biotin-avidin combination. Desthiobiotin is inactive for *Lactobacillus casei*.

Biotin has been shown to be a nutrilite requirement of certain anaerobes, *Clostridium butylicum*[136] as well as *Clostridium sporogenes*.[137] It is also a growth requirement for many filamentous fungi, reviewed by Robbins and Kavanagh.[45]

Lampen, Bahler, and Peterson's[138] **Microbiological Method for Assaying for Biotin.** These investigators described a biotin assay method employing *Clostridium butylicum*. The method was devised by Peterson, McDaniel, and McCoy[137] and also used by Lampen, Kline, and Peterson.[139] This organism on a basal medium of two per cent glucose, one per cent asparagine, and 0.11 per cent salts (K_2HPO_4, 10 gm.; KH_2PO_4, 10 gm.; $MgSO_4 \cdot 7H_2O$ 4 gm.; NaCl, 0.2 gm.; $MnSO_4 \cdot 4H_2O$, 0.2 gm.; $FeSO_4 \cdot 7H_2O$, 0.2 gm. per liter) requires only the addition of biotin for maximum growth.[136, 137] The measure of growth is the turbidity as read in a photoelectric colorimeter. The organism requires anaerobic conditions for growth.

The stock culture is carried on sterile soil and a loopful is inoculated into a test tube of the basal medium containing 0.25 per cent peptone. After 18 to 20 hours' incubation, 10 ml. of this solution is centrifuged and resuspended in 10 ml. of sterile, freshly boiled water. Three drops of this washed culture are added to each tube.

Culture tubes (25 x 200 mm.) are graduated at 36 ml. for the determination. A small amount of reduced iron is placed in each tube to aid in maintaining anaerobic conditions. The biotin solution for the standard curve or an extract of the material to be assayed, dissolved in 10 ml. or less, is placed in the tube and the volume brought to 11 ml. with water.

The basal medium is prepared in such concentrations that additions of 25 ml. of it to each tube, i.e., to the 36-ml. mark, will give the desired concentration. The pH of this basal medium should be 6.5 to 6.7 before addition. The tubes are plugged and autoclaved for 30 minutes at 15 pounds pressure. They are cooled quickly and inoculated immediately. An oat-jar is prepared by filling a suitable container one-fourth full with oats and adding just enough water to cover the oats. The assay tubes are placed in the jar and a glass top sealed on with plasticine. The respiration of the oats removes the oxygen and establishes a partial pressure of carbon dioxide. The jar is then placed in the incubator for three days at 37°C. (98.6°F.).

After incubation the tubes are removed, shaken well, and their turbidity read against the uninoculated basal medium set at 100. With excess biotin a reading of 15 to 20 is obtained. One-half of the difference between the inoculated control and the maximum reading, arbitrarily taken as 20, is taken as half-maximum growth. A unit is defined as the quantity of material per milliliter of medium which is required to give half-maximum growth. This unit is 0.01 millimicrogram for pure biotin, and by comparison to the unit weight, the biotin content of crude materials may readily be calculated.

135. du Vigneaud *et al.* 1942. Soc. Expt. Biol. and Med. Proc. 50, 374-375.
135a. Melville, Brown, and du Vigneaud. 1943. Science 98, 497-498.
136. Snell and Williams. 1939. Amer. Chem. Soc. J. 61, 3594.
137. Peterson, McDaniel, and McCoy. 1940. J. Biol. Chem. 133, lxxvi.
138. Lampen, Bahler, and Peterson. 1942. J. Nutr. 23, 11-21.
139. Lampen, Kline, and Peterson. 1941. J. Biol. Chem. 140, lxxiv.

The authors noted that considerable variation exists between duplicate tubes, even on pure biotin, and place the accuracy of the method at ±20 per cent.

If the pH of the medium is brought to 6.3 before autoclaving, a flocculent precipitate appears during autoclaving and incubation. Consequently, the medium must be adjusted to pH 6.6 to 6.7. Though use of the oat jar for maintaining anaerobic conditions is cumbersome, reduced iron, sodium thioglycolate, gave unsatisfactory results in that many tubes failed to initiate growth. Addition of agar, cystine or sodium hydrosulfite, was also unsatisfactory. Lampen, Kline, and Peterson have noted that irregularities may occur owing to variations in reagents, vigor of culture, anaerobic conditions, and perhaps other factors.

Snell, Eakin, and Williams' [140] **Yeast Method for Assaying for Biotin.** They reported a yeast-growth method for assaying for biotin. The test organism is a certain strain of *Saccharomyces cerevisiae*, designated by them as the ''F.B.'' strain, which they isolated from Fleischmann's compressed yeast. This strain has been deposited with the American Type Culture Collection. The basal medium contains:

Sucrose	20.0 gm.
Ammonium sulfate	3.0 gm.
Potassium dihydrogen phosphate	2.0 gm.
Magnesium sulfate heptahydrate	0.25 gm.
Calcium chloride dihydrate	0.25 gm.
Boric acid	1.0 mg.
Zinc sulfate	1.0 mg.
Manganese chloride	1.0 mg.
Thallium chloride	1.0 mg.
Ferric chloride	0.5 mg.
Cupric sulfate pentahydrate	0.1 mg.
Potassium iodide	0.1 mg.
l-Aspartic acid	0.1 gm.
Inositol	5.0 mg.
β-alanine	0.5 mg.
Thiamine	20.0 μg.
Pyridoxine	20.0 μg.

Distilled water to 1 liter

Addenda to the basal medium are dissolved in two ml. of water in 50-ml. Erlenmeyer flasks and sterilized by steaming for five minutes. After cooling, 10 ml. of the previously sterilized basal medium containing 0.02 mg. of suspended yeast are pipetted into each flask which is set unstoppered and without agitation in an incubator at 30°C. (86°F.) for the growth period of approximately 16 hours. Very clean glassware is essential for proper results. The authors have noted the method is sensitive to the presence of toxic substances in tissue extracts or on the glassware itself.

At the end of the growth period the yeast suspension is diluted with 10 ml. of saturated aqueous thymol and shaken mechanically for three to five minutes. The amount of yeast present is determined by use of a photoelectric colorimeter. The same instrument is used to gauge the seeding in the basal medium at the start, the concentration being determined indirectly from a heavy suspension from which the proper dilution is taken.

Blank cultures (no addenda) and cultures containing known amounts of biotin (0.000025 to 0.00025 μg.) are run simultaneously with the unknowns, and the amounts of biotin in the unknown samples are read off the standard curve, in which the galvanometer readings are plotted against the known amounts of biotin added.

The above procedure has been slightly modified so that assays are carried out in bacteriological test tubes which are conveniently supported by a wire or metal rack which may be autoclaved. The standard biotin solutions and solutions for analysis are added to the tubes. Standard tubes containing 0, 10, 20, 30, 50, 70, and 100 mμg. of

140. Snell, Eakin, and Williams. 1940. Amer. Chem. Soc. J. 62, 175-178; Univ. of Texas, Pub. 4137, 18-21.

biotin are satisfactory to establish the standard curve. Various amounts of practically clear tissue extracts may be selected by preliminary experiments or estimates to contain approximately 10 to 80 mμg. of biotin. Volumes up to one ml. may be used. The contents of all tubes are then diluted, if necessary, to one ml. with water. Then five ml. of previously sterilized basal medium, containing 0.2 mg. per 100 ml. of the test organism, are added to each tube. The open tubes are then placed in the 30°C. incubator for a growth period of approximately 16 hours.

For establishing the standard curve, either free biotin or biotin methyl ester may be used, since the yeast is able to utilize either with equal efficiency.

Du Vigneaud *et al.*[141] have employed the Snell, Eakin, and Williams' yeast method, with certain modifications, for following the concentration and determination of activities of certain derivatives of biotin. The Fleischmann strain 139 *Saccharomyces cerevisiae* was used and turbidity measurements were made with a Klett-Summerson photoelectric colorimeter with a blue filter (Klett No. 42). This instrument is equipped with a logarithmic scale so that turbidity readings observed are a linear function of yeast growth. By plotting the turbidity readings against the logarithms of the concentrations of assay material, an S-shaped curve is outlined.

Snell *et al.* used several methods for preparing samples for assay. Clear aqueous extracts were obtained by autoclaving the finely ground material for 10 minutes at 15 pounds pressure in a large volume of water. If necessary, the extract was clarified by filtering with filter-cel. Casein samples were hydrolyzed with sulfuric acid and the sulfate ion removed with barium hydroxide. Liver tissue was allowed to autolyze before assay. A more complete discussion is given below.

Hertz's [142] **Modification of the Snell, Eakin, and Williams' Microbiological Method for Assaying Biotin.** A modification of the Snell, Eakin, and Williams [140] yeast-growth method for assaying for biotin has been proposed by Hertz through the addition of a biotin-free casein hydrolysate. Elimination of nonspecific stimulation of yeast growth is claimed, particularly as encountered in human and canine urine samples. The technic of the assay is somewhat different from that employed by Snell *et al.*

The medium requires the following ingredients of highest purity:

Sucrose	34.0 gm.
Ammonium sulfate (anhydrous)	5.0 gm.
KH$_2$PO$_4$	4.0 gm.
d-l-aspartic acid	170.0 mg.
MgSO$_4$	450.0 mg.
CaCl$_2$	450.0 mg.
Mineral salts (cf. Snell *et al.*)	0.18 mg. equivalent
Inositol	9.0 mg.
10% biotin-free casein hydrolysate	1.0 gm. equivalent (pH 3.0)
Thiamin	1.0 mg.
Pyridoxin	1.0 mg.
Calcium pantothenate	0.5 mg.
Distilled water to 1 liter	

The pH of this preparation without adjustment is usually between 3.8 and 4. These materials are added successively. Gentle warming may be required to dissolve completely. The medium may be stored in the refrigerator for at least three weeks without deterioration.

141. Du Vigneaud, Hofmann, Melville, and György. 1941. J. Biol. Chem. 140, 643-651.
142. Hertz. 1943. Soc. Expt. Biol. and Med. Proc. 52, 15-17.

The test is carried out in previously calibrated photometric tubes measuring 180 x 20 mm. In each culture tube five ml. of the above medium are added to variable proportions of the test materials and the final volume in all tubes is adjusted to 10 ml. with distilled water.

A stock culture of *Saccharomyces cerevisiae* (No. 139, obtained from the Fleischmann Company) is carried at room temperature on Sabouraud's agar, transfers being made at least every three days. The test inoculum is prepared from a 24-hour culture grown at 37°C. in test medium to which has been added an effective quantity of biotin. This culture is washed twice with normal saline and its final concentration is adjusted turbidimetrically so that the 0.5 ml. used for each test culture contains approximately 0.05 mg. of suspended cells.

The test cultures are incubated without plugs for 18 to 22 hours at 37°C. in a forced-draft incubator.

Assay values are determined turbidimetrically in relation to a standard curve obtained for each run in duplicate with crystalline biotin dilutions ranging in content from 1×10^{-4} to 5×10^{-4} μg. per culture.

Samples may be prepared either by hot water or acid extraction, depending on the nature of the material to be tested. Only water-clear preparations may be employed.

The following compounds were found to have no effect on the assay results: pimelic acid, nicotinic acid, riboflavin, adenine, guanine, uracil, choline, and ethanolamine.

Considerable care must be taken to keep the age and preparation of the inoculum quite constant. Variations in this regard will alter the results from day to day.

Another yeast-growth method has been reported by Atkin, Schultz, Williams, and Frey.[104] This method is discussed in detail in the section on pyridoxin below. West and Woglam[143] used *Rhizobium trifolii* based on the medium used by West and Wilson.[144] Robbins and Schmidt[145] have suggested a biotin assay based on the weight of mycelium of *Ashbya gossypii* produced in 15 to 20 days' growth on a basal medium of inorganic salts, sucrose, inositol, and thiamine.

Biotin is a growth factor for *Lactobacillus casei* ε, and assay methods using this organism have been proposed. One by Landy and Dicken[68] will be discussed in detail in a subsequent section of this chapter.

Shull, Hutchings, and Peterson's[146] Method for Assaying for Biotin. The first method employing *Lactobacillus casei* ε for the assay of biotin was that of Shull, Hutchings, and Peterson. Its advantages over the yeast methods lies in the fact that lactic acid production may be used to gauge the response of the assay organism and thus overcomes the difficulties of colored and turbid solutions encountered when turbidimetric determinations of yeast growth are used.

Stock cultures of *Lactobacillus casei* ε are carried as stabs in yeast extract-glucose agar in a refrigerator until used. The inoculum for the assay is started two days before the assay is to be set up. A transfer is made from a stab culture to a tube of liquid medium (10 ml.) containing 0.5 per cent Difco yeast extract, 0.6 per cent sodium acetate, 0.5 per cent glucose, and 0.05 ml. of mineral salts Solutions A and B per tube. The culture is incubated at 37°C. for 24 hours and then transferred to the sterile biotin-free basal medium described below. A two-per cent inoculum is used for the transfer, i.e., 0.2 ml. per 10 ml. of the biotin-free basal medium. This inoculum supplies sufficient biotin for a good growth of the organism. This culture is incubated for 15 to 20 hours at 37°C. One drop (0.05 ml.) of this suspension is used to inoculate each tube in the assay series.

143. West and Woglam. 1941. Science 93, 525.
144. West and Wilson. 1940. Enzymologia 8, 152.
145. Robbins and Schmidt. 1939. Torrey Bot. Club Bull. 66, 139-150.
146. Shull, Hutchings, and Peterson. 1942. J. Biol. Chem. 142, 913-920.

Shull and Peterson [146a] found the above inoculum was satisfactory when the drop size was constant. An increased titer always resulted when more than one drop of the heavy inoculum was added per tube. Another procedure has been devised which gives more consistent results and is independent of the size of inoculum (one to three drops). Transfer the stock culture to 10 ml. of yeast extract medium, described above, 24 hours before the assay is set up. After 20 to 30 hours' incubation at 37°C., the cells are centrifuged and resuspended in 10 ml. distilled water. One drop (.05 ml.) of the resuspended cells is transferred to 10 ml. sterile water, and one drop of this dilute suspension is used in each assay tube for inoculum.

The final composition of the basal medium is as follows:

Peroxide-treated hydrolyzed casein	0.50 per cent
Peroxide-treated norited yeast filtrate	0.15 per cent
Tryptophane	0.0075 per cent
Cystine	0.01 per cent
Asparagine	0.02 per cent
Glucose	1.0 per cent
Sodium acetate	1.0 per cent
Pyridoxine	0.02 mg. per cent
Pantothenic acid	0.02 mg. per cent
Riboflavin	0.01 mg. per cent
Nicotinic acid	0.10 mg. per cent
p-Aminobenzoic acid	0.01 mg. per cent
Adenine	1.00 mg. per cent
Guanine	1.00 mg. per cent
Mineral salts, 0.5 ml. each, Solutions A and B in 100 ml. of medium.	

For assay purposes the medium is prepared in twice this concentration for dispensing into the assay tubes.

CONSTITUENTS OF THE MEDIUM

Peroxide-Treated Hydrolyzed Casein: One hundred grams of vitamin-free casein with 375 ml. of water and 125 ml. of concentrated sulfuric acid are hydrolyzed for 15 hours at 120°C.(248°F.) in an autoclave. The 15-hour treatment hydrolyzes the casein sufficiently for the organism to utilize the hydrolyzate, but it is not long enough to destroy completely the "eluate factor" required by *Lactobacillus casei* ε.[147] Six hundred and forty grams of $Ba(OH)_2 \cdot 8H_2O$ suspended in 400 ml. of boiling water are added to the hydrolyzate and the precipitated barium sulfate is filtered off with filter-cel. The filter cake is removed and thoroughly broken up in 500 ml. of hot water. The washings from the filter cake are added to the main filtrate. The pH of the filtrate is adjusted to 3 with sodium hydroxide. The solution is then diluted to 1,500 ml. with water and 15 ml. of Superoxol[148] are added. The solution is thoroughly stirred and allowed to stand for 24 hours at room temperature, 25 to 32°C.(77 to 89.6°F.). The pH is then adjusted to 7 with sodium hydroxide and one per cent of powdered manganese dioxide is added. The solution is mechanically stirred until no more oxygen is evolved (about 15 minutes) and filtered with suction. The filtrate is then diluted to 2,000 ml. with water.

Peroxide-Treated Norite Yeast Filtrate: Twenty grams of Bacto-yeast extract are dissolved in one liter of distilled water and the pH is adjusted to 2 with concentrated

146a. Shull and Peterson. 1943. J. Biol. Chem. 151, 201-202.

147. Snell and Peterson. 1940. J. Bact. 39, 273; Hutchings *et al.* 1941. J. Biol. Chem. 141, 521-528.

148. Superoxol, 30 per cent hydrogen peroxide. Merck & Co., Inc., Rahway, N. J.

sulfuric acid. Four grams of norite A are added, the adsorption is carried out at 56 to 60°C. (132.8 to 140°F.) with mechanical stirring for half an hour. The norite is removed by filtration with the aid of filter-cel. The pH of the filtrate is adjusted to 3 with 10 N sodium hydroxide and the volume is made up to 3,000 ml. with water. Thirteen ml. of Superoxol are added, and the solution is allowed to stand at room temperature for 24 hours. The pH is then adjusted to 7 with 10 N NaOH, and 13 grams of powdered manganese dioxide are added. The solution is mechanically stirred until the evolution of oxygen ceases. The manganese dioxide is removed by vacuum filtration. The final volume should be about 1,325 ml.

Shull and Peterson [146a] have noted at times poor growth in the above medium even in the presence of excess biotin. This was attributed to a low level of folic acid ("eluate factor") supplied by the yeast extract preparation. By the above procedure the removal of biotin often brings the folic acid to a critical level. A new procedure for its preparation has given satisfactory assays:

Twenty grams of Bacto yeast-extract are dissolved in a liter of distilled water and adjusted to pH 2 with sulfuric acid. Four grams Norite A are added, the absorption carried out at 55 to 60°C. with mechanical stirring for 30 minutes. The norite is filtered off and the filtrate is saved for later use. The norite is eluted with 200 ml. 50-per cent ethanol at room temperature for 15 minutes. This eluate, containing a part of the biotin of the original material is discarded and the norite eluted a second time with 200 ml. solution containing 10 parts ammonium hydroxide (28 per cent), 50 parts 95 per cent ethanol and 40 parts distilled water at 55 to 60°C. The extracted norite is discarded and the eluate is distilled *in vacuo* to remove the ethanol and ammonia. The eluate is then diluted to 200 ml. and adjusted to pH 3. Ten grams Super Filtrol are added and the mixture is stirred for 15 minutes at room temperature. The Super Filtrol adsorbs the eluate factor but leaves most of the biotin in the filtrate. After filtration, the Super Filtrol is eluted with 200 ml. of the ammoniacal ethanol solution, described above, for 15 minutes at room temperature. This eluate is distilled *in vacuo* until the ethanol and ammonia are removed. It is then added to the norite-yeast filtrate from the first operation and the combined solution is made to 1,300 ml. The solution is adjusted to pH 3 and 13 ml. superoxol (30 per cent hydrogen peroxide) are added to oxidize the small amount of biotin contained in the solution. The solution is allowed to stand for 24 hours at room temperature, after which the pH is adjusted to 7 and 15 mg. of MnO_2 are added with stirring. When evolution of oxygen has ceased the solution is filtered and is ready for use in the assay.

Vitamin Solution: Two hundred ml. of stock solution containing 100 μg. of pyridoxine, 100 μg. of calcium pantothenate, 50 μg. of riboflavin, 500 μg. of nicotinic acid, and 50 μg. of p-aminobenzoic acid per ml. is prepared. This solution is stored with added toluene in a refrigerator.

Adenine-Guanine-Cystine Solution: One liter of a stock solution containing 500 μg. per ml. of adenine, 500 μg. per ml. of guanine, and one mg. per ml. of cystine is prepared by dissolving these compounds in water with the addition of the least amount of sulfuric acid to effect solution.

Mineral Salt Solutions: Solutions A and B are the same as employed in the Snell and Strong riboflavin procedures, and the two pantothenic acid procedures described previously in this chapter.

The basal medium is prepared double strength, and after adjusting the pH to 5.6, five ml. are dispensed into test tubes. Solutions to be assayed are added to one set of tubes. Biotin for the standard curve is added to the other set. The final volume in each tube is made up to 10 ml. with distilled water. The tubes are plugged, with cotton and autoclaved for 15 minutes at 120°C. After cooling, the tubes are inoculated with one drop of inoculum as described above. The tubes are then incubated for three days at 37°C. After incubation the contents of each tube are titrated with 0.1 N NaOH. Brom thymol blue may be used as an indicator though phenol red gives a better end point.

Lactobacillus casei ε is unable to utilize the methyl ester of biotin, consequently the biotin to be used for this assay should be in the form of the free acid. By hydrolyzing the methyl ester as described by du Vigneaud *et al.*[149] the full activity of the biotin may be restored. The range of biotin used for calibration of the standard curve is from 40 to 1,000 mμg. (.04 to 1.0 μg.) per tube. The curve is then constructed by plotting the milliliters of 0.1 N alkali used in the titration against the amounts of biotin per tube. The extremities of the curve do not give valid results, so samples should be dilute so that their titers do not come at these portions off the curve.

It has been shown by Nielsen, Shull, and Peterson[150] that biotin inactivated by hydrogen peroxide treatment, as in the *Lactobacillus casei* assay of Shull, Hutchings, and Peterson,[146] while inactive for *Lactobacillus casei* and the rat, still has marked potency for yeast apparently owing to resynthesis of the vitamin. In the assay of biological materials for biotin oxidizing conditions should be avoided in the preparation of the sample. Intestinal synthesis of biotin in rats varies with different rations, and becomes very low when sulfaguanidine is incorporated in the diet. Stokes and Gunness[150a] reported *Lactobacillus casei* to be capable of utilizing biotin methyl ester, though at a somewhat slower rate than the free acid.

It has been shown repeatedly that the biotin contents of certain products as determined by microbiological methods depends on the method of preparation of the samples. Snell, Eakin, and Williams[140] showed the existence of "bound" biotin in liver tissue, a form of biotin unavailable for the test organism, which may be liberated by autolysis. Assays of egg-yolk extracts were not increased by autolysis. Peterson and co-workers[137] noted that strong acid hydrolysis would release bound biotin, though prolonged acid hydrolysis may destroy some biotin in certain tissues. Biotin in fruit and grasses appears to occur free, that of grains, nuts, and vegetables is partially bound, and that of yeast and animal tissues is mainly in the bound form. Landy and Dicken[151] preferred acid hydrolysis because of the danger of bacterial production of biotin during autolysis. Lampen, Bahler, and Peterson[152] have compared various biotin extraction procedures. Liver was extracted with 4 N and 7 N sulfuric acid by autoclaving for one hour, with no destruction noted after four hours. With yeast one hour with 4 N sulfuric acid gave maximum values, but after two to three hours some destruction was noted. Autolysis liberated biotin more readily from yeast than from liver. Autolysis for 24 hours, either with toluene or toluene-chloroform, released 80 to 90 per cent of the biotin of yeast, with maximum liberation in six days. No destruction occurred during three weeks of autolysis. No inhibition by chloroform of the liberation of biotin during autolysis, as experienced by György,[153] was noted. Lampen *et al.*[152] found biotin liberation from liver by autolysis was slow and incomplete, never more than 30 per cent becoming available. Treatment with pepsin for seven days at 50°C.(122°F.) was incomplete. Hydrolysis with trypsin for three hours at 50°C. completely liberated biotin. Boiling the liver to destroy enzyme activity lowered the yield of biotin as

149. du Vigneaud *et al.* 1941. J. Biol. Chem. 140, 763-766.
150. Nielsen, Shull, and Peterson. 1943. J. Nutr. 24, 523-533.
150a. Stokes and Gunness. 1943. Soc. Expt. Biol. and Med. Proc. 54, 28-31.
151. Landy and Dicken. 1941. Soc. Expt. Biol. and Med. Proc. 46, 449-452.
152. Lampen, Bahler, and Peterson. 1942. J. Nutr. 23, 11-21.
153. György. 1939. J. Biol. Chem. 131, 733-744.

did using lower temperatures. For routine assays of materials known to contain the bound forms of biotin, Lampen *et al.* homogenized samples and hydrolyzed them in 2 N sulfuric acid for two hours, followed by removal of the sulfate with barium hydroxide. Hydrolysis in milk for one hour with 1 N sulfuric acid gave maximum values. A simpler method, giving equal values, involved diluting five ml. of milk to 50 ml. with an acetate buffer of pH 4.6, filtering off the casein, and assaying the filtrate.

Biotin in green plants and vegetables exists in a free, water-soluble form available for the test organism. Some destruction was noted with tomatoes. Biotin in fruits is also water soluble. Soybeans, navy beans, and rye appeared to contain bound biotin, whereas corn and barley did not. The values for wheat were contradictory. The biotin in nuts is firmly bound, requiring 2 N or 4 N sulfuric acid for its liberation, though in some instances destruction was noted when the stronger acid was used.

That large amounts of biotin are released by autolysis of tissue was first reported by György[153] and confirmed by Snell, Eakin, and Williams.[140] Thompson, Eakin, and Williams[154] noted that neither enzyme hydrolyses, autolysis, or a mixture of clarase and caroid were as efficient in liberating bound biotin as acid hydrolysis. Two or more hours of autoclaving in 6 N sulfuric acid yielded maximum values, though 6 N hydrochloric acid was somewhat more effective. Some destruction of biotin was noted after prolonged hydrolysis with strong acids. Cheldelin[155] used enzyme liberation as a routine procedure. Papain was most effective with other proteolytic enzymes being more effective than carbohydrases. The effectiveness of autolysis varied greatly with different tissues. The only protein-biotin complex so far discovered is that with avidin which is not attacked by enzymes of the digestive tract. Manure samples showed increased biotin assay after acid hydrolysis.[156]

AVIDIN

Feeding of a nutritionally adequate diet containing raw egg white causes a type of injury in rats and chicks commonly called "raw egg white injury." Replacement of the raw egg white with cooked egg white reverses or prevents the injury. Tissues of chicks maintained on the former diet were found to be deficient in biotin.[157] It was concluded that the injury was not due to any direct toxin, but rather was produced indirectly by making the biotin of the diet unavailable to the animal. Eakin, Snell, and Williams[158] successfully demonstrated *in vitro* inactivation of biotin and showed that a protein constituent of unheated egg white formed a stable complex with biotin which could not be recovered by dialysis, and that the combination occurs stoichiometrically. Yeast, Rhizobium, and other microorganisms are also unable to utilize biotin in such a complex. The protein responsible for the complex is called "avidin." It is not a

154. Thompson, Eakin, and Williams. 1941. Science 94, 589-590.
155. Cheldelin, Eppright, Snell, and Guirard. 1942. Univ. of Texas Pub. 4237, 15-36.
156. Lampen, Bahler, and Peterson. 1942. J. Nutr. 23, 11-21.
157. Eakin, McKinley, and Williams. 1940. Science 92, 224.
158. Eakin, Snell, and Williams. 1940. J. Biol. Chem. 136, 801-802; 140 (1941), 535-543.

vitamin; perhaps the term "anti-vitamin" is appropriate. Eakin and colleagues concentrated the protein and Pennington, Snell, and Eakin [159] later crystallized it. After concentration it was soluble in half-saturated ammonium sulfate. When saturated ammonium sulfate was added to incipient precipitation, the precipitate removed by centrifugation, and the clear supernatant solution chilled in a refrigerator, needle-like crystals formed in an hour. Slow crystallization resulted in large plate-like crystals. Both forms retained high activity on repeated crystallizations, though some potency was lost during the processes. Crystals in presence of the mother liquor for three weeks in a refrigerator lost 75 per cent of their activity, though dry crystals at room temperature retained full potency after three months. The crystalline material gave a positive Molisch test, indicating the substance may be a protein with a large carbohydrate moiety.

Eakin, Snell, and Williams' [158] **Avidin Assay Method.** A modification of the yeast-growth method for assaying biotin [140] has been used in the assay of avidin.[159] The test is set up in duplicate and the assay of one set is carried out without heat sterilization. The duplicate set is sterilized in the customary manner by steaming for 15 minutes at 100°C.(212°F.), thus permanently denaturing the avidin and releasing biotin from the complex. The difference in biotin content between the heated and unheated aliquots gives a direct measure of the amount of biotin-inactivating protein present.

Cultures containing known amounts of biotin are run with each test to give the values for the points of the standard curve. A solution containing the active protein is diluted to such a volume that it contains 0.002 to 0.006 units per ml. A 0.1-ml. aliquot of the standard biotin solution is added to 0.1 mg. of each protein sample; these samples are incubated for 30 minutes at room temperature and then diluted to 10 ml. Aliquots of 0.2, 0.4, and 0.8 ml., diluted to one ml. with water, are used for both the heated and unheated assays. One of the duplicate sets of standard and sample tubes is sterilized by steaming for 15 minutes at 100°C.

The medium and yeast used are those described in the biotin assay method of Snell, Eakin, and Williams.[140] The medium is sterilized, cooled, and seeded with an aliquot of yeast suspension to contain approximately 0.002 mg. of moist yeast per ml. of medium. After the yeast is thoroughly suspended, five ml. of the inoculated medium are added to each tube, and the cultures are incubated without agitation at 30°C.(86°F.) for 16 to 18 hours. The yeast growth is then determined turbidimetrically. The amounts of biotin in the aliquots tested are read from the curves obtained by plotting the readings given by the biotin standards. The difference in biotin values (in micrograms of biotin) found for a heated and unheated aliquot of a sample gives the units of avidin in that aliquot.

A unit of avidin is the amount of concentrate of sample capable of inactivating one μg. of biotin. Raw egg white usually varies from 0.4 to 0.6 units per ml.

That there are different types of biotin-avidin complexes has recently been shown by Burke and Winzler.[160]

INOSITOL

Meso-inositol was the first pure substance to be isolated from "bios"[161] and shown to be part of the yeast-growth stimulatory activity. It has been shown to serve as a yeast-growth factor by numerous workers. Janssen [162] showed it to be indispensable for Wildier's yeast, and Williams,

159. Pennington, Snell, and Eakin. 1942. Amer. Chem. Soc. J. 64. 469.
160. Burke and Winzler. 1943. Science 97, 57-60.
161. Eastcott. 1928. J. Phys. Chem. 32, 1094-1111.
162. Janssen. 1935. Arch. Internatl. de Physiol. 40, 975.

Eakin, and Snell [163] reported it to be required by other strains of *Saccharomyces cerevisiae.*

Demonstration of vitamin activity of meso-inositol was the result of work of Woolley [164] who showed it to cure alopecia in rats which had been fed on a diet devoid of this factor.

The salient characteristics of inositol were given by Waisman [31] as follows:

Inositol ($C_6H_{12}O_6$, an H—OH group on every carbon link of the hydrogenated benzene ring).

Properties: Sugarlike compound, very soluble in water.

Function: Unknown. Importance in nutrition has been shown through rat and mice experiments. Some evidence for lipotropic action.

Distribution: Exists in all grains, heart muscle, and yeast.

Lack of information concerning the activity of this compound may be partially accounted for by the lack of specific satisfactory methods for its determination. Eastcott employed a yeast-growth method but its application was limited. Kögl and Hasselt [165] also used the same principle. Winter [166] and Young [167] summarized various procedures. These relied wholly or in part on isolation of the compound. Such procedures require large samples and are laborious and time-consuming. Woolley [164] showed that for liver extracts, at least, these methods are not quantitative. As more yeast-growth factors have been isolated and identified, specific inositol methods based on yeast growth have been developed. One of the first satisfactory methods was proposed by Williams, Stout, Mitchell, and McMahon. [168]

Williams, Stout, Mitchell, and McMahon's [168] Method for Microbiological Assay for Inositol. This method employed the Gebrüder Mayer strain of *Saccharomyces cerevisiae* (Amer. Type Culture Collection). The inositol-free medium is as follows:

Sucrose	20.0	gm.
Potassium dihydrogen phosphate	2.0	gm.
Ammonium sulfate	3.0	gm.
l-Asparagine	3.0	gm.
Calcium chloride	0.25	gm.
Magnesium sulfate	0.25	gm.
Boric acid, zinc sulfate, thallium chloride, manganese sulfate	1.0	mg. each
Ferric chloride	0.5	mg.
Copper sulfate	0.1	mg.
Potassium iodide	0.1	mg.
Vitamin-free hydrolyzed casein	0.2	gm.
Biotin	0.2	μg.
Calcium pantothenate	300.0	μg.
Folic acid	0.5	μg.
Thiamine hydrochloride	20.0	μg.
Pyridoxine hydrochloride	20.0	μg.
Distilled water to 1 liter		

163. Williams, Eakin, and Snell. 1940. Amer. Chem. Soc. J. 62, 1204-1207.
164. Woolley. 1940. Science 92, 384; J. Biol. Chem. 139 (1941), 29-34.
165. Kögl and Hasselt. 1936. Ztschr. f. Physiol. Chem. 242, 74-80.
166. Winter. 1934. Biochem. J. 28, 6-10.
167. Young. 1934. Idem 28, 1428-1443.
168. Williams *et al.* 1941. Univ. of Texas Pub. 4137, 27-30.

Calf's Liver Supplement for Method A of Inositol Test: This supplement is made up by preparing an extract of calf's liver in the same way as indicated for the preparation of autolysates, except that the concentration is equivalent to 75 mg. of tissue per ml. instead of 25 mg. per ml. The extract is put in plugged tubes, autoclaved 15 minutes at 15 pounds pressure, and stored in a cool place. This extract should be assayed, and if it contains much over 500 micrograms of inositol per gram of liver it should not be used.

Tissue autolysates are prepared by homogenizing, according to the method of Potter and Elvehjem,[108] and allowing the sample to autolyze under benzene for 24 hours at 37°C. The autolyzed tissue is then washed into 0.1 N acetic acid and steamed in an autoclave for 30 minutes to insure removal of the benzene and cessation of enzyme action.

Method A: Assays are carried out in bacteriological test tubes. These are conveniently supported in a wire or metal rack which may be steamed. Standard tubes contain 0, 0.16, 0.32, 0.48, 0.64, and 0.80 µg. of inositol in a volume of from 0 to 0.1 ml. Tissue extracts are diluted so that volumes of 0.01 ml. to 0.1 ml. contain from 0.1 to 0.8 µg. of inositol. The standard and sample dilutions are pipetted with a syringe-type micro-pipette.

Enough basal medium to supply two ml. per tube for all the tubes in the test is placed in one flask, and about 10 to 15 ml. of medium is put in a small flask to be used for seeding. One ml. of a calf's liver autolysate (equivalent to 75 mg. of calf's liver) is added to each 100 ml. of basal medium. This supplement provides certain yeast-growth substances which are as yet unknown but does not contain enough inositol to interfere with the test. The medium, racks of tubes, a 10-ml. graduated pipette, and a one-ml. graduated pipette are steamed in the autoclave at 100°C. for 10 minutes and then cooled to room temperature. The small flask of medium is seeded from an agar slant. The yeast is suspended uniformly and the number of milligrams of moist yeast cells per milliliter of solution is determined by use of a photoelectric colorimeter and the appropriate calibration curve. By calculation, enough of this suspension is taken to seed the larger amount of medium with 0.15 mg. of moist yeast cells per 100 ml. of solution. After introduction of the yeast suspension and thorough shaking, two ml. of the medium are added to each tube in the test. The tubes are placed in a 30°C. water bath for growth periods of 15 hours.

The turbidity produced in the various tubes after 15 hours incubation is quantitatively determined in a photoelectric colorimeter. When the tubes are removed from the incubator they are placed in the refrigerator for 10 minutes to slow down the rate of growth of the test organism. They are then removed and diluted with five ml. of saturated chlorothymol solution. If the test consists of only a few tubes, only the dilution with chlorothymol is necessary. Before reading in the colorimeter the tubes are shaken vigorously, then allowed to stand a few moments to allow the air bubbles to rise and break, suspended again by less vigorous shaking, and read.

A standard curve (response to pure inositol) is obtained with each set of assays. The samples for assay are dosed at increasing levels of concentration and the inositol content of each tube is read from the standard curve. Usually three or more concordant results at different dosage levels are averaged to obtain the final curve. At random, selection of assay values obtained from single cultures showed a percentage deviation from the mean of 3.3 per cent.

Method B: Autolysates from some tissues seem to contain an especially high concentration of inhibitory or stimulatory materials that cause varying assay values or poor recoveries of added inositol. In these cases Method B is employed. The procedure is the same as for Method A except that instead of adding the liver-extract supplement, an autolysate of the tissue being tested is added. The amount of tissue autolysate added depends on the inositol content of the tissues. For tissues containing about 500 µg. of inositol per gram of moist tissue, an amount of autolysate equivalent to one mg. of moist tissue is added for each milliliter of basal medium used in the test. If the amount of inositol in the tissue is greater than 500 µg. per gram, a proportionately smaller amount of autolysate is added (and vice versa).

Woolley's[169] **Yeast Method for Assaying for Inositol.** Vitamin-free casein was hydrolyzed by heating in an autoclave at 15 pounds pressure for 16 hours with 7 N sulfuric acid and the acid was removed from the hydrolysate with barium hydroxide. The filtrate from the barium sulfate was adjusted to pH 6 with sodium hydroxide. An aliquot of this hydrolysate equivalent to 2.5 grams of casein was mixed with 100 grams of glucose, 8.3 grams of ammonium nitrate, 4.2 grams of potassium dihydrogen phosphate, 2.1 grams of magnesium sulfate, 0.7 gram of calcium chloride, and approximately 300 ml. of water and heated in an autoclave (15 pounds for 15 minutes). The precipitate which formed was removed and to the filtrate was added the nondialyzable portion of 10 grams of rice-bran extract (Vitab, National Oil Products Company). This latter preparation was made by dissolving rice-bran extract in water and dialyzing against running water for 48 hours. The mixture of growth factors described below was added, followed by the concentrate of Bios II, described by Lucas,[170] equivalent to 10 grams of malt sprouts. The volume was then adjusted to 500 ml. and the solution was preserved with toluene. The growth-factor mixture was composed of 0.5 mg. of thiamine, 0.5 mg. of riboflavin, 0.5 mg. of pyridoxine, 1 mg. of nicotinic acid, 2.5 mg. of choline chloride, 1 mg. of pimelic acid, 5 mg. of asparagine, 0.05 mg. of biotin, 0.5 mg. of sodium pantothenate, 2.5 mg. of uracil, and 2.5 mg. of adenine. Biotin was supplied as a concentrate which contained one per cent biotin, prepared according to the method of Woolley, McDaniel, and Peterson.[171] Crystalline biotin was substituted without affecting the results.

Preparation of Bios II Concentrate According to Lucas.[170] Nine hundred seventy-five ml. of water are brought to boiling and 150 grams of dried rootlets of sprouted malt (combings) are added with stirring. The temperature is held between 80 and 85°C.(176 and 185°F.) for 10 to 15 minutes, during which time the roots become swollen. The whole is then transferred to a press and squeezed as dry as possible, yielding 650 to 700 ml. of a light brown infusion. This is concentrated by boiling *in vacuo* at a temperature of 35 to 50°C.(95 to 122°F.) to one-quarter of its volume. To the concentrate is added twice its volume of 95-per cent alcohol, stirring meanwhile. A voluminous, stringy precipitate is removed by filtration, leaving a clear, reddish filtrate which contains the whole bios but only 60 per cent of the solids of the original infusion.

The alcoholic filtrate is concentrated *in vacuo* (35 to 50°C.) to one-tenth the volume of the original infusion. To this ''alcoholic concentrate'' is added a hot, saturated, aqueous solution of barium hydroxide in quantity determined as explained below. A slimy precipitate is formed which is not removed and a strong smell of ammonia or amines is given eff. Barium hydroxide is added until the clear supernatant liquid no longer gives an immediate precipitate when a few drops of concentrated baryta water are added. Between 30 and 60 grams of $Ba(OH)_2 \cdot 7H_2O$ per liter of infusion are required. The precipitate, after it has been filtered off, is washed with dilute alcohol (two volumes of 95-per cent to one volume of water), and the filtrate and washings are combined for extraction of Bios II. This ''Bios II liquor'' is saturated with carbon dioxide to remove the barium ions, the carbon dioxide being removed by boiling *in vacuo* and the precipitate filtered off. Any excess barium must be removed with sulfuric acid. The filtrate is evaporated *in vacuo* at as low temperature as possible until large bubbles are formed which completely fill the vessel; this occurs when the volume has been reduced to one-tenth to one-fifteenth that of the original infusion. Acetone is added until no further precipitation occurs; at first it is a milky precipitate disappearing on shaking; on further addition of acetone a heavy, red, oily liquid separates and later a yellowish gum (''acetone precipitate'') forms which adheres to the walls of the vessel. From 0.8 to 1.5 volumes of acetone are required. The precipitate is removed, washed with acetone, and the washings added to the filtrate which is concentrated *in vacuo* until the reddish-yellow residue is almost the consistency of a gum. This is washed with warm acetone to dissolve Bios II (acetone equal to about

169. Woolley. 1941. J. Biol. Chem. 140, 453-459.
170. Lucas. 1924. J. Phys. Chem. 28, 1180-1200.
171. Woolley *et al.* 1939. J. Biol. Chem. 131, 381-385.

half the original volume of solution is used). The acetone is evaporated *in vacuo* leaving a thick, reddish liquid, which is diluted with water to the original volume of the infusion. It contains 80 to 90 per cent of the Bios II of the original extract.

Woolley employed the Hansen No. 1 strain of Toronto yeast *(Saccharomyces cerevisiae)* which was maintained on slants of the basal medium plus an aqueous extract of malt sprouts (extract of 10 grams of malt sprouts per 100 ml. of medium). The organisms were transferred to liquid medium of the same composition and grown for 24 hours at 30°C.(86°F.). The cells were then collected by centrifugation and washed three times with sterile phosphate buffer. They were then suspended in a volume of buffer 20 times that of the original culture. One drop (0.05 ml.) of this suspension was used for inoculation of each flask. This inoculum introduced about 70,000 cells whose dry weight was approximately seven μg.

Preparation of Samples for Assay: A quantity of material expected to contain approximately 20 μg. of inositol was refluxed in 18 per cent hydrochloric acid for six hours. Many times it was convenient to use larger samples and to conduct the final estimation with aliquots. With moist samples or solutions enough concentrated hydrochloric acid was used to produce a concentration of 18 per cent acid in the mixture. After the hydrolysis was completed, the solution was concentrated under reduced pressure to dryness, and adjusted to a volume such that one ml. contained approximately two μg. of inositol.

Assay Procedure: Five-ml. portions of the basal medium were placed in 50-ml. Erlenmeyer flasks. Aliquots of the sample prepared as above are added to various flasks in order to cover the range of one to 0.1 μg. of inositol per ml., in the final solution. At the same time a series of flasks was prepared which contained 10 to 0.05 μg. of inositol per ml. Enough water was added to each flask to produce a final volume of 11 ml. The flasks were sterilized in an autoclave (15 pounds for 15 minutes), inoculated, and placed in a water bath at 30°C. for 16 hours. The contents of each flask were then examined quantitatively for turbidity in a photoelectric colorimeter. A standard curve was drawn relating colorimeter readings (turbidity) to micrograms of inositol.

It was found essential to maintain constant temperatures in all flasks. Variations of 1°C. vitiated the results. For this reason, a water bath was used in preference to the usual type of incubator in which variations in temperature frequently are observed in different parts of the cabinet.

Woolley [172] reported on the biological specificity of inositol for rats and yeast. Of the compounds tested only meso-inositol, mytilitol, soy bean cephalin, and inositol hexacetate were active in the rat; of these, only meso-inositol was 100 per cent active for the yeast. Mytilitol had about 10 per cent activity for yeast, which Woolley believed might have been due to contamination with inositol. Inositol monophosphate and tetraphosphate had about five per cent and two per cent of the activity of meso-inositol. Inosose, an oxidation product of inositol, was inactive, thus making it appear doubtful that this compound acts as an intermediate in the metabolism of the vitamin.

The yeast-growth method of Alkin, Schultz, Williams, and Frey,[104] given in the pyridoxin discussion, is easily adopted to the assay for inositol. It has certain advantages over the methods described above.

PYRIDOXIN

Following the isolation of thiamine (vitamin B_1) from the vitamin B complex, it was soon apparent that the "vitamin B_2," under which designation all remaining B vitamins other than thiamine were grouped, was

172. Woolley. 1941. J. Biol. Chem. 140, 461-466.

of a multiple nature. Goldberger and Lillie [173] and Chick and Roscoe [174] reported a dermatitis produced in rats fed a diet deficient in this "vitamin B_2" complex, having "pellagra-like" characteristics. György and co-workers separated this complex into two fractions, one the real vitamin B_2 (riboflavin) and the second containing the factor preventing rat pellagra which he named vitamin B_6. This was subsequently differentiated from the human pellagra factor (now recognized as nicotinic acid) and likewise the dog anti-blacktongue factor which Elvehjem, Madden, Strong, and Woolley [175] recognized as nicotinic acid. The "rat pellagra" was termed acrodynia. In 1938 the isolation of crystalline vitamin B_6 was announced independently by five groups of workers—Lepkovsky,[176] Keresztesy and Stevens,[177] György,[178] Kuhn and Wendt,[179] and Ichiba and Michi.[180] Keresztesy and Stevens [177] reported their crystalline compound had a formula $C_8H_{11}NO_3$. Stiller, Keresztesy, and Stevens [181] the following year reported vitamin B_6 to be 2-methyl-3-hydroxy-4,5-(hydroxymethyl)pyridine, further proof of which was supplied by Harris, Stiller, and Folkers.[182] The synthesis of the vitamin was accomplished by Harris and Folkers [163] and simultaneously by Kuhn, Westphal, Wendt, and Westphal.[184]

The function of this vitamin is unknown beyond the fact that it prevents or cures acrodynia in rats. Deficiencies may be manifest by convulsions in pigs, dogs, rats, and chicks. Certain types of anemia have been attributed to deficiencies of the vitamin. Waisman [31] characterized pyridoxin as follows:

Pyridoxine (vitamin B_6, rat-antidermatitis vitamin, $C_8H_{11}NO_3 \cdot HCl$, a hydroxymethyl pyridine derivative).

Properties: Water-soluble. Less soluble in ether, alcohol, chloroform, and fat. Destroyed on exposure to light.

Function: Not definitely established. May be involved in fatty acid metabolism or synthesis of fat from protein.

Symptoms Associated With Deficiency: Indefinite. May be involved in certain muscular derangements. Possible role in prevention of certain anemias.

Requirement: Animal experiments indicate requirement is approximately that of thiamine.

Occurrence in Natural Foodstuffs: Chiefly whole wheat, soy bean, milk, beef liver, yellow corn, beef kidney, brewers' yeast, pork muscle, cabbage.

Pyridoxin stimulates yeast growth. It is required in nutrition of Streptococcus hemolyticus and certain other hemolytic streptococci as well

173. Goldberger and Lillie. 1926. Pub. Health Rpts. 41, 1025-1029.
174. Chick and Roscoe. 1927. Biochem. J. 21, 689-711.
175. Elvehjem et al. 1937. Amer. Chem. Soc. J. 59, 1767; J. Biol. Chem. 123 (1938), 137.
176. Lepkovsky. 1938. Science 87, 169-170.
177. Keresztesy and Stevens. 1938. Soc. Expt. Biol. and Med. Proc. 38, 64-65; Amer. Chem. Soc. J. 60. 1267-1268; 61 (1939), 1237-1242.
178. György. 1938. Amer. Chem. Soc. J. 60, 983-984.
179. Kuhn and Wendt. 1938. Ber. Deut. Chem. Gesell. 71, 780-782; 1118.
180. Ichiba and Michi. 1938. Inst. Phys. and Chem. Res., Tokyo, Sci. Papers 34, 623-626.
181. Stiller, Keresztesy, and Stevens. 1939. Amer. Chem. Soc. J. 61, 1237-1242.
182. Harris, Stiller, and Folkers. 1939. Amer. Chem. Soc. J. 61, 1242-1244.
183. Harris and Folkers. 1939. Science 89, 347; Amer. Chem. Soc. J. 61, 1245-1247.
184. Kuhn et al. 1939. Naturwissenschaften 27, 469-470.

as lactic acid bacteria, such as *Streptobacterium plantarum*. Möller, Zima, Jung, and Moll [185] have shown that 2,4-dimethyl-3-hydroxy-5-hydroxymethyl pyridine had slight pyridoxin activity and that 2,4,5-trimethyl-3-hydroxy pyridine had no activity when determined with a strain of *Streptobacterium plantarum*. Bohonos, Hutchings, and Peterson [186] reported the vitamin to be required by *Lactobacillus casei* ε, *Lactobacillus arabinosus* 17-5, and a strain of *Lactobacillus delbruckii* but not by the strains tested of *Lactobacillus pentosus*, *Lactobacillus lactis*, and *Leuconostoc mesenteroides*. Those strains not requiring external sources of the vitamin were found capable of synthesis. *Lactobacillus casei* ε was able to store an amount of the vitamin above its physiological requirements when grown in a pyridoxine-containing medium. Consequently its reaction to increasing. increments of pyridoxin added to an otherwise pyridoxin-free medium were quantitatively variable. The amount of pyridoxin necessary for maximum growth and acid production depended upon the size of inoculum. Also pyridoxin requirements increased as the oxygen tension of the medium was reduced. No derivatives of pyridoxin were as active as the vitamin, though the diacetyl derivative had about 80 per cent of the activity of the vitamin whereas the triacetyl derivative was inactive. In the rat these compounds were equally potent and of the same activity as the vitamin.[187] Substitution of bromine for the hydroxyl of the hydroxymethyl group resulted in still lower activity. Other derivatives had about 30 per cent of the activity of the vitamin.

Landy and Dicken [68] employed *Lactobacillus casei* ε in an assay for pyridoxin, described later in this chapter. The objections offered by Bohonos *et al.* probably will be encountered in this procedure.

Using a colorimetric method for determination of pyridoxin, Scudi,[188] following studies of urinary elimination, has shown that a small amount of the vitamin is altered at the 4-hydroxymethyl group. A larger fraction is conjugated, presumably through the 3-hydroxyl group by man and the dog but not by the rat. Scudi [188] has shown that water-soluble extracts of rice bran also contain free and conjugated forms of pyridoxin. Whether these combined forms are similar to those found by Snell, Guirard, and Williams,[189] discussed below, is not known.

Williams, Eakin, and McMahon's [168] Method for Assaying for Pyridoxin. One of the first microbiological methods for the assay of this vitamin was that of Williams, Eakin, and McMahan [168] based on the growth response of the Gebrüder Mayer strain of *Saccharomyces cerevisiae*. The method is similar to the yeast-growth method of Williams *et al.* for the assay of thiamine.

185. Möller *et al.* 1939. Naturwissenschaften 27, 228-229.
186. Bohonos, Hutchings, and Peterson. 1942. J. Bact. 44, 479-485.
187. Unna. 1940. Soc. Expt. Biol. and Med. Proc. 43, 122-124.
188. Scudi. 1941. J. Biol. Chem. 139, 707-720.
   Scudi, Koones, and Keresztesy. 1940. Soc. Expt. Biol. Med. Proc. 43, 118.
   Scudi, Unna, and Antopol. 1940. J. Biol. Chem. 135, 371-372.
   Scudi, Buhs, and Hood. 1942. Idem 142, 323-328.
   Scudi, Bastedo, and Webb. 1940. Idem 136, 399-406.
189. Snell, Guirard, and Williams. 1942. J. Biol. Chem. 143, 519-530.
189a. Williams, Eakin, and McMahan. 1941. Univ. of Texas Pub. 4137, 24-26.

The basal medium contains the following components:

Sucrose	20.0 gm.
Potassium dihydrogen phosphate	2.0 gm.
Ammonium sulfate	3.0 gm.
l-Asparagine	3.0 gm.
Calcium chloride	0.25 gm.
Magnesium sulfate	0.25 gm.
Boric acid, zinc sulfate, thallium chloride, manganese chloride	1.0 mg. each
Ferric chloride	0.5 mg.
Copper sulfate	0.1 mg.
Potassium iodide	0.1 mg.
Vitamin-free hydrolyzed casein	0.2 gm.
Biotin	0.2 μg.
Calcium pantothenate	300.0 μg.
Folic acid	0.5 μg.
Inositol	5.0 mg.
Thiamine hydrochloride	20.0 μg.

Distilled water to make 1 liter

Assays are carried out in bacteriological test tubes. These are conveniently supported by a wire or metal rack which may be steamed. The standard pyridoxin solution and solutions for analysis are added to the tubes. Standard tubes in triplicate contain 0, 0.05, and 0.1 ml. of a standard solution containing 0.004 μg. of pyridoxin per ml., or 0, 0.0002, and 0.0004 μg., respectively. Various amounts of tissue extracts from 0.01 to 0.1 ml. are pipetted with a syringe-type micropipette.

Enough basal medium is placed in a separate flask to supply two ml. per tube for all tubes under test and to this are added two ml. of pyridoxin-free liver extract and two ml. of pyridoxin-free yeast extract per 100 ml. of basal medium. Another 10 to 15 ml. of medium is put into a small flask to be used in seeding. The medium, racks of tubes, a 10-ml. graduated pipette, and a one-ml. graduated pipette are steamed in the autoclave at 100°C. (212°F.) for 10 minutes and then cooled to room temperature. The small flask of medium is seeded from an agar slant. The yeast is suspended uniformly and the number of milligrams of moist yeast cells per milliliter of solution is determined by the use of a photoelectric colorimeter and the appropriate calibration curve. By calculation, enough of this suspension is taken to seed the larger flask with 0.05 mg. of moist yeast suspension per 100 ml. of solution. After introduction of the yeast suspension and thorough shaking, two ml. of the medium are added to each tube in the test. The tubes are placed in a 30°C. water bath for a growth period of 15 hours.

The turbidity produced in the various tubes after 15 hours' incubation is quantitatively determined in a photoelectric colorimeter. When the tubes are removed from the incubator, they are placed in the refrigerator for 10 minutes to arrest the rate of growth of the test organism. They are then removed and diluted with five ml. of saturated chlorothymol solution. If the test consists of only a few tubes, only the dilution with chlorothymol is necessary. Before reading in the turbidimeter, the tubes are shaken vigorously, then allowed to stand for a few moments to allow the air bubbles to rise and break, suspended again by less vigorous shaking, and read.

Pyridoxin-Free Liver Extract: Five grams of liver paste (Wilson Laboratories 1-20) are mixed with 195 ml. of water and autoclaved 15 minutes at 15 pounds pressure, cooled to room temperature, and adjusted to pH 1 with HCl. Ten grams of Fuller's earth are added and the mixture is shaken intermittently several times a day for four days. The supernatant liquid is then decanted, adjusted to pH 4.5 to 5 and pipetted into test tubes (five-ml. portions) which are plugged and autoclaved at 15 pounds for 15 minutes. Three days later the tubes are again autoclaved as before.

Pyridoxin-Free Yeast Extract: Five grams of Difco Bacto yeast extract are treated in the same manner as the liver paste.

A standard curve (response to pure pyridoxin) is obtained with each set of assays. The samples for assay are dosed at increasing levels of concentration and the pyridoxin content of each tube is read from the standard curve. Usually three or more concordant results at different dosage levels are averaged to obtain a final figure. A random selection of assay values obtained from single cultures showed a percentage deviation from the mean of 4.7 per cent.

Few data are available regarding the pyridoxin content of tissues and no direct comparison of this method with others was made. It appears, however, that values obtained by this method are considerably lower than the "vitamin B_6" values obtained by animal and chemical assays. Since the method as outlined seems to give consistent assays and recoveries for free pyridoxin, the authors were of the opinion that there may be other chemical substances present in tissue extracts which function as "vitamin B_6" in animal tests. Rat assays by the method of Conger and Elvehjem [190] give considerably higher values.

Siegel, Melnick, and Oser [190a] encountered difficulty in completely removing pyridoxine from the yeast and liver preparations. The use of Lloyd's reagent was more effective. "To the acidified (pH 1.0) liver and yeast extract solutions, described by the original authors,[168] are added 2 gm. of Lloyd's reagent and the suspension is shaken occasionally during the next 24 hours. After filtration the solution is treated again with the same quantity of the adsorbent. The mixture is then centrifuged, and the clear supernatant removed, adjusted to pH 4.5 to 5.0, bottled, and sterilized in the autoclave for 15 minutes at 15 pounds pressure." Other growth factors were also removed, necessitating their replacement. Biotin content of the medium was increased to 0.1 μg. and the casein hydrolysate to 2.5 ml. per 100 ml. of basal medium. Tryptophane was added in concentrations of 0.2 mg. per 100 ml. of medium.

The method of Williams et al. did not allow for complete extraction of bound pyridoxine. Siegel et al. recommended autoclaving test suspensions of solutions for 30 minutes at 15 pounds pressure in 2 N sulfuric acid to render bound forms of the vitamin available for the yeast. The results agree with those obtained by chemical and biological assays.

Atkin, Schultz, Williams, and Frey's Method for Pyridoxin Assay. Since the discovery of the growth-promoting effects of pyridoxin for yeasts,[191] yeast-assay methods for this vitamin have been investigated. The method devised by Atkin, Schultz, Williams, and Frey [192] is claimed to have distinct advantages over the previously proposed methods in that the technic has been simplified and the medium improved, principally because of the choice of yeast for its specific response to pyridoxin. The technic of the assay is fully described by Atkin, Schultz, and Frey.[193]

The assays are carried out in matched pyrex test tubes, 18 x 150 mm., with lips. Culture tubes without lips were not found suitable. Test tubes having an outside diameter of 17.8 to 18 mm. inclusive, when measured at the point of path of the light beam of the photoelectric colorimeter, were considered adequate. The tubes were matched, after cleaning, by filling with distilled water, and transmission tests made in a suitable

190. Conger and Elvehjem. 1941. J. Biol. Chem. 138, 555.
190a. Siegel, Melnick, and Oser. 1943. J. Biol. Chem. 149, 361-367.
191. Eakin and Williams. 1939. Amer. Chem. Soc. J. 61, 1932.
    Schultz, Atkin, and Frey. 1939. Idem 61, 1931.
192. Atkin et al. 1943. Ind. Eng. Chem., Anal. Ed. 15, 141-144; 16 (1944) 67-71.
193. Atkin, Schultz, and Frey. 1943. Arch. Biochem. 1, 9-16.

photoelectric colorimeter, such as the Lumetron 400.[194] Tubes showing less than one per cent deviation from the reference tube are satisfactory.

Previous to running an assay a calibration curve, showing the relationship between yeast concentration and per cent absorption, is prepared, using commercial compressed yeast. In all measurements the test tubes contain 10 ml. of suspension. This curve is convenient when standardizing the concentration of the inoculum used in the assay.

Because the method used in the determination of pyridoxin may also be employed for the determination of other vitamins, such as pantothenic acid, biotin, and inositol, it is convenient to prepare individual solutions of the various components of the basal medium and to combine them in the different ways required by the several methods. The basal pyridoxin-free medium contains the following ingredients for each five ml.: sugar and salts solution, 2.5 ml.; potassium citrate buffer, 0.5 ml.; casein hydrolysate, 0.5 ml.; thiamine solution, 0.25 ml.; inositol solution, 0.25 ml.; biotin solution, 0.10 ml.; calcium pantothenate, 0.125 ml. For a set of 40 tubes, for example, forty times the above amounts are measured into a mixing cylinder and diluted to 200-ml. volume.

The ingredients of the basal medium are prepared as follows:

Sugar and Salts Solution: One liter contains 200 grams of C. P. glucose (anhydrous), 2.2 grams of monopotassium phosphate, 1.7 grams of potassium chloride, 0.5 gram of calcium chloride ($CaCl_2 \cdot 2H_2O$), 0.5 gram of magnesium sulfate, 0.01 gram of ferric chloride, and 0.01 gram of magnesium sulfate.

Potassium Citrate Buffer: One liter contains 100 grams of potassium citrate ($K_2C_6H_5O_7 \cdot H_2O$) and 20 grams of citric acid ($14H_2C_6H_5O_7 \cdot H_2O$).

· *Casein Hydrolyzate Solution:* Eighty ml. of S.M.A. Corporation "vitamin free" casein hydrolyzate (10 per cent solution) neutralized to pH 4 to 6 (alkacid paper) and diluted to 100-ml. volume.

Thiamine Solution: Ten micrograms per ml.

Inositol Solution: One mg. per ml.

Biotin Solution: S.M.A. Corporation [195] biotin concentrate diluted so that it contains approximately 0.8 μg. per ml.

Calcium Pantothenate Solution: Two hundred μg. per ml.

A strain of *Saccharomyces carlsbergensis*, No. 4228, is carried on Difco malt slants. A slant is incubated for 24 hours at 30°C. and is then stored in the refrigerator for not more than two weeks. To prepare an inoculum for the assay, a fresh slant is prepared 24 hours earlier and incubated at 30°C. A quantity of fresh growth is removed by a sterile wire loop and suspended in 10 ml. of sterile 0.9-per cent saline solution in a colorimeter tube. The concentration of the yeast is estimated with the photoelectric colorimeter and is adjusted to a concentration of one mg. of moist yeast per ml. with addition of sterile saline.

For the assay, five ml. of the basal pyridoxin-free medium are placed in each test tube, plus a solution of the unknown extract or of pure pyridoxin hydrochloride together with water to make a total volume in each tube of nine ml. The tubes are plugged and steamed 10 minutes, cooled, and inoculated with one ml. each of the yeast suspension. The tubes are then shaken at 30°C. for 16 to 18 hours and the yeast growth is estimated in the photoelectric colorimeter. A reference curve which consists of a series of tubes containing 0, 5, 10, 15, 20, 30, and 40 millimicrograms of pyridoxin, is included in each assay run.

It is desirable to make turbidity readings at both 16 and 18 hours and to average all results to obtain the estimated value. All values are reported on the basis of pyridoxin hydrochloride employed as a reference standard.

It has been found that more reproducible results are obtained if the tubes are shaken throughout the growth period. A shaking machine, such as those devised for the Kahn test, and fitted with a suitable test tube holder, is placed in a water or air thermostat maintained at 30°C.

194. Manufactured by the Photovolt Corp., New York, N. Y.
195. S.M.A. Corp., Chagrin Falls, Ohio.

Although pyridoxin is relatively soluble, it is extracted from most plant and animal tissues with difficulty. Williams et al.[189a] found that autolysis increases the pyridoxin contents of animal-tissue extracts. Atkin et al. have not found this method applicable to foods and tissues. The efficiency of extraction was found to depend upon the volume of extraction medium as well as the presence of acid. For most substances extraction with 180 ml. of 0.055 N sulfuric acid yielded maximal values. Insoluble materials should be powdered, if dry, or macerated with water in a Waring Blendor or its equivalent. A portion containing between two and four micrograms of pyridoxin is suspended in 180 ml. of 0.055 N sulfuric acid (one ml. of 10 N sulfuric acid and 179 ml. of water). The suspension or solution is heated in an autoclave at 20 pounds pressure for one hour, then cooled, neutralized to pH 5.2, and diluted to 200 milliliters. If the solution is turbid it is centrifuged and the clear supernatant liquid is used for the assay. In exceptional cases, such as white flour, the turbidity remains but can be removed if the extract is treated with a knife point of clarase at 37°C. for 30 minutes, followed by centrifugation. Wheat and wheat products require more acid to give maximal pyridoxin values; 180 ml. of .44 N sulfuric acid (eight ml. of 10 N sulfuric acid and 172 ml. of water) yielded nearly maximal values.

Enzymic hydrolysis may be used also, though digestion with clarase did not always yield values as high as those from acid hydrolysis. Some soluble vitamin concentrates were found to contain a bound form of pyridoxin which was not active in the test until acid autoclaved or enzymically digested. The enzymic digestion is conducted as follows:

A portion of the sample containing between two and four μg. of pyridoxin is suspended in a small quantity of water in a graduated test tube, 0.5 ml. of potassium citrate buffer (pH 5.2) is added, and the volume is made to 10 ml. The tube is steamed for 30 minutes, cooled, and a quantity of clarase equal to the weight of the sample, but not less than 100 mg., is added. A few drops of benzene are added, and the tube is tightly corked and incubated for three days at 37°C. or two days at 45°C. At the end of the incubation the tube is steamed for 20 minutes and the contents are diluted to 200 ml.

Another strain of yeast is apparently satisfactory for assaying pyridoxin. Burkholder[196] used Saccharomyces oviformis, No. 782 (Northern Regional Research Laboratory, U.S.D.A.) and the basal medium proposed by Williams for his strain of Saccharomyces cerevisiae.

In a detailed study of the nutrition of Streptococcus lactis R Snell, Guirard, and Williams[197] observed that natural products contained a substance which could be derived from pyridoxin by metabolic processes, which far surpassed pyridoxin in its physiological activity for this organism. This substance was tentatively called "pseudopyridoxin." Later Snell[198] showed that if heat sterilization was avoided, pyridoxin had little growth-promoting activity for this organism. Activity was restored on autoclaving with the basal culture medium; the degree of activity increasing with the period of heating. The effect was traced to interaction

196. Burkholder. 1943. Amer. J. Bot. 30, 206-211.
197. Snell, Guirard, and Williams. 1942. J. Biol. Chem. 143, 519-530.
198. Snell. 1942. Soc. Expt. Biol. and Med. Proc. 51, 356.

during autoclaving between pyridoxin and the amino acids of the medium; presumably "pseudopyridoxin" or a substance of similar high activity for the organism was formed in small amounts. Snell and Guirard [199] noted that alanine in large amounts could completely replace pyridoxin as a growth factor for *Streptococcus lactis* R, while glycine inhibited growth. Glycine inhibition could be reversed by addition of pyridoxin or dl-alanine. β-alanine, dl-serine, and dl-threonine also showed inhibitory activity but to a lesser degree. Alanine, glycine, serine, and threonine are among the amino acids essential for this organism. Pyridoxin is also required by *Lactobacillus casei* ε but alanine is incapable of replacing the vitamin for this organism. The fact that alanine is capable of replacing pyridoxin in the nutrition of *Streptococcus lactis* R suggests that the vitamin may be synthesized by the organism from alanine.

Snell, Guirard, and Williams' [197] **Method for Assay of "Pseudopyridoxin."** For the assay of the pyridoxin-like substance which has great activity for *Streptococcus lactis* R a sample microbiological method was used, though at the present writing the significance of this material is not known. The assay procedure does not give true values for this substance, but rather, it is determined in terms of pyridoxin.

For assay purposes the following medium was used:

			Amounts per 250 ml. basal medium
Solution 1			250 ml.
Hydrolyzed casein	5.0	gm.	
Sodium acetate	6.0	gm.	
Tryptophane	0.05	gm.	
Cystine hydrochloride	0.1	gm.	
Water to make	500.0	ml.	
Solution 2			5 ml.
Adenine sulfate	100.0	mg.	
Guanine hydrochloride	100.0	mg.	
Uracil	100.0	mg.	
Water to make	100.0	ml.	
Glucose			5.0 gm.
Solution 3			1.0 ml.
Thiamine hydrochloride	1.0	mg.	
Calcium pantothenate	1.0	mg.	
Riboflavin	1.0	mg.	
Nicotinic acid	1.0	mg.	
Folic acid concentrate*	0.001	mg.	
Biotin	0.004	mg	
Water to make	20.0	ml.	
Inorganic salts**			
Solution A			2.5 ml.
Solution B			2.5 ml.

* Folic acid concentrates are prepared according to the method of Mitchell, Snell, and Williams, 1941. J. Am. Chem. Soc. 63, 2284.
** These are the same salt solutions employed in the Lactobacillus assay methods, i.e., Snell and Strong, 1939, Ind. Eng. Chem., Anal. Ed. 11, 346.

199. Snell and Guirard. 1943. Natl. Acad. Sci. Proc. 29, 66-73.

The assay organism is *Streptococcus lactis* R (American Type Culture Collection No. 8043).

Acid-hydrolyzed casein is prepared by refluxing 50 grams of Labco vitamin-free casein with 500 ml. of constantly boiling hydrochloric acid for eight to 10 hours. Excess hydrochloric acid is removed by repeated concentrations *in vacuo*. The resulting sirup is dissolved in water, adjusted to pH 3, and shaken for 10 minutes with one part of activated charcoal (Darco G-60) to 10 parts of solids and then filtered.

Assays are carried out in test tubes. For the standard curve, tubes containing from 0 to three μg. of pyridoxin are prepared. Various amounts of tissue extract are selected by experiments which are approximately equivalent in growth effect to these amounts of pyridoxin. All tubes are diluted to five ml. with water and five ml. of the basal medium is added. Tubes are plugged with cotton and then sterilized at 15 pounds pressure for 10 minutes. After cooling to room temperature, they are ready for inoculation. Cells for inoculum are prepared by transferring from a stab culture of the test organism to a tube containing 10 ml. of basal medium supplemented with three μg. of pyridoxin. This culture is incubated at 30°C. for 16 to 30 hours before use. The cells are centrifuged out aseptically, then resuspended in 10 ml. of 0.9-per cent saline solution, and an aliquot of this suspension is diluted to barely visible turbidity. One drop of the diluted suspension is used to inoculate each assay tube. The tubes are then incubated at 30°C. for a growth period of 16 hours. Turbidities of the resulting cultures are determined with a photoelectric colorimeter. Results are expressed in terms of pyridoxin, i.e., the number of micrograms of pyridoxin which produces the same growth effect as the sample in question. The actual amount of the growth-promoting material present is unknown.

In rat tissues, Snell, Guirard, and Williams noted that the amount of pseudopyridoxin paralleled that of the pyridoxin in the ration and not the pseudopyridoxin content. Rats maintained on low-pyridoxin diets excreted very little pyridoxin or pseudopyridoxin, while those maintained on high-pyridoxin diets excreted large amounts of both substances. Animal passage apparently converts part of the ingested pyridoxin to the more highly active (for *Streptococcus lactis* R) pseudopyridoxin.

Streptococcus lactis R does not utilize the pyridoxin molecule as such but converts traces of it to the more highly active "pseudopyridoxin" which is utilized. No detectable decrease in the amount of pyridoxin in a medium following maximum growth of the organism was noted. According to this view the pseudopyridoxin rather than the pyridoxin molecule is necessary for utilization. More information on this interesting observation is needed before one may fully understand the role of this factor.

By X-ray treatment Beadle and Tatum [200] secured mutants of *Neurospore* species which had lost their ability to synthesize certain of the B vitamins. An assay method for pyridoxin has been reported by Thompson, Isbell, and Mitchell,[201] employing a mutant of *Neurospora crassa*. Stokes, Foster, and Woodward,[202] employing a mutant of *Neurospora sitophila* which Beadle and Tatum had reported to be unable to synthesize pyridoxin, found that this mutant could produce the vitamin under certain conditions, namely, in pyridoxin-free media supplied with ammonium-nitrogen and maintained at a pH between 6 and 7. The parent strain was able to synthesize the vitamin at all pH levels up to 7.8 (at which no growth occurred) and from varied nitrogen sources.

200. Beadle and Tatum. 1941. Natl. Acad. Sci. Proc. 27, 499-506.
201. Thompson *et al*. 1943. J. Biol. Chem. 148, 281-287.
202. Stokes *et al*. 1943. Arch. Biochem. 2, 235-245.

Stokes, Larsen, Woodward, and Foster's Neurospora Assay for Pyridoxin. Even though cultural conditions of the organism influence its requirements for pyridoxin, Stokes et al.[202a] reported successful microbiological assay for pyridoxin employing a "pyridoxinless" mutant of *Neurospora sitophila*. The assay is based on dry weight of mold mycelium produced, and consequently is not influenced by highly colored or turbid solutions. The organism is apparently not influenced by "pseudopyridoxin." The results agree closely with those of animal assays on the same or similar biological materials.

Stock cultures of the organism are carried on Sabouraud's agar slants (maltose, 38 gm.; Bacto-peptone, 8 gm.; Bacto-malt extract, 2 gm.; agar, 20 gm.; 1 liter of water). Pink or orange colored spores usually are abundant at the upper portion of slant in four to five days. After sporulation, the cultures are stored in the refrigerator until used. Fresh cultures are prepared every three weeks.

Basal Medium. The basal medium, in twice the desired final concentration is as follows:

Sucrose	30.0 gm.
Ammonium tartrate	10.0 gm.
Monopotassium phosphate	5.0 gm.
Magnesium phosphate	1.0 gm.
Sodium chloride	0.2 gm.
Calcium chloride	0.2 gm.
Ferric chloride	10.0 mg.
Zinc sulfate	2.0 mg.
Biotin	8.0 μg.
Distilled water	1.0 liter

The medium may be opalescent but this does not interfere with the assay. The zinc represses sporulation, which facilitates harvesting of the mold. The potassium dihydrogen phosphate buffers the medium initially at approximately pH 5, which is essential since growth without pyridoxin will occur if the pH rises above 5.8 to 6.0. Ammonium tartrate also aids in keeping the pH below the critical values, for as the ammonium ion is utilized by the organism, tartaric acid accumulates in the medium.

Assay Procedure. Five ml. aliquots of the basal medium are placed in 50 ml. Erlenmeyer flasks. A set of reference flasks is prepared containing 0.1 to 1.0 μg. of pyridoxin (free base, not the hydrochloride). Blanks containing no pyridoxin are included. For unknown solutions, aliquots of 0.5 to 2.0 ml. are added to the basal medium. The flasks are plugged and sterilized at 15 pounds pressure for 15 minutes. After cooling, the flasks are inoculated with a spore suspension of *Neurospora sitophila*. The inoculum is prepared by removing with a platinum loop a small portion of growth, consisting primarily of spores, from an agar slant and making a uniform suspension in 10 ml. of sterile water. Each flask receives one drop of this suspension. Small variations in the number of spores inoculated do not affect the assay, though a very light inoculum may prevent the standard curve from rising to its normal maximum growth level of 40 to 45 mg. of mycelium. This may occur also if the culture is too old. A heavy inoculum may increase the growth in the blanks above the customary 1 mg. of mycelium.

The inoculated flasks are incubated at 30° for five days, during which time a pellicle or mycelium mat develops on the surface of the medium. After incubation, the cultures are steamed at 100°C. for five minutes and the mycelium harvested with a stiff wire needle. The mycelium mat is pressed dry between two paper towels, rolled into a small pellet, and dried at 100°C. for two hours. Glazed porcelain spot plates are convenient for handling the mycelium during drying and weighing. The dry mycelium is weighed to the nearest mg. on an analytical balance.

Preparation of Samples. Insoluble materials are ground or homogenized prior to extraction. An appropriate sample, generally 1 to 5 grams, is mixed with 40 ml. of 1 N HCl in a 250 ml. Erlenmeyer flask and autoclaved at 15 pounds pressure for one hour. If the sample is completely in solution, it is cooled and diluted to 50 ml.. If an

202a. Stokes, Larsen, Woodward, and Foster. 1943. J. Biol. Chem. 150, 17-24.

appreciable amount of insoluble material remains, the sample is filtered through paper, the filtrate washed twice with water, and the filtrate diluted to 50 ml.

Destruction of Thiamine. Thiamine in the sample must be destroyed since it stimulates growth of the test organism in the presence of suboptimum amounts of pyridoxin. A modification of the sulfite cleavage method of Schultz, Atkin, and Frey is used. Ten ml. of the extract are pipetted into a 50 ml. Erlenmeyer flask and 0.7 ml. of 10 N NaOH added, followed by 5 ml. of a freshly prepared one per cent solution of anhydrous sodium sulfite. The pH of the mixture is adjusted to 8 with 1 N NaOH, cresol red being used as an outside indicator. The cleavage of thiamine is carried out at pH 8 instead of pH 5 as recommended, because it was found that considerable destruction of pyridoxin occurs when solution of pyridoxin plus thiamine are treated with sulfite at pH levels of less than 8. Also the amount of sulfite is one-half that suggested by Schultz, Atkin, and Frey[191] to avoid toxic effects encountered with larger amounts. However, it is sufficient to destroy 100 μg. of thiamine. After adjustment to pH 8, the mixture is steamed at 100°C. for 30 minutes, cooled, and treated with an exact quantity of fresh two per cent hydrogen peroxide solution to destroy the excess sulfite. Usually five to 10 drops are required to reach the end point (p. 1030). The volume is made to 20 ml. with water and the sample is assayed for pyridoxin as described above.

It has been noted that with certain samples, such as peptone or malt extract, there is a tendency at higher aliquot levels for the pH of the medium to rise above the critical pH of 5.8. When this occurs, maximum growth of the organism is produced irrespective of the amount of pyridoxin present. This can be controlled by doubling the potassium dihydrogen phosphate concentration.

Though thiamine can partially replace pyridoxin in the nutrition of *Neurospora sitophila,* other growth factors such as nicotinic acid, pantothenic acid, p-aminobenzoic acid, riboflavin, inositol, folic acid, uracil, adenine, guanine, and xanthine do not stimulate the organism in presence of sub-optimum levels of pyridoxin.

FOLIC ACID

One of the as yet unidentified members of the B-complex has been named "folic acid" by Mitchell, Snell, and Williams[203] because of its abundant occurrence among leaves and greases. Hutchings, Bohonos, and Peterson[204] objected to this name because it does not suggest the material, yeast, from which it was first obtained nor its many abundant sources, such as liver, kidneys, milk, peptone, mushrooms, etc. They recommend to defer naming until its chemical identity is established.

This substance is probably identical with the "norite eluate factor" of Snell and Peterson[147] which serves as a growth factor for *Lactobacillus casei* ε. It was originally discovered in yeast extract by Snell and Peterson which was separated into two fractions. One is adsorbed on Norite A charcoal, the "norite eluate factor," and the second is the filtrate fraction which can be replaced by biotin. From the properties of a concentrate prepared from a water-soluble liver fraction, Snell and Peterson reported the eluate factor to be predominately a basic substance, though having some acidic properties. Some precipitation tests indicated the factor might be a purine or closely related compound. More information has been supplied by Hutchings, Bohonos, and Peterson,[204] including a method of preparation. Heating a concentrate at 125°C.(257°F.) for 15 minutes with 1 N sulfuric acid resulted in 75-per cent loss in potency while 25-per cent potency was lost when heated with 1 N sodium hydroxide. Since the mate-

203. Mitchell, Snell, and Williams. 1941. Amer. Chem. Soc. J., 63, 2284.
204. Hutchings, Bohonos, and Peterson. 1941. J. Biol. Chem. 141, 521-528.

rial is acidic, it was suggested that inactivation by acid might be due to lactone formation, though unsuccessful regeneration experiments with alkali seemed to exclude this possibility. The factor is completely precipitated by mercury, zinc, and copper and to a lesser extent by silver, cadmium, barium, calcium, and nickel. Zinc offers some selectivity useful in further purification. It has fewer basic properties than previously thought. It is strongly adsorbed under acid conditions and is quantitatively adsorbed on norite, Fuller's earth, superfiltrol, and, to a lesser degree, on aluminum hydroxide Cγ, aluminum oxide, and anthranilic acid, though elution from these latter substances is incomplete. It is insoluble in common organic solvents, with the exception of glacial acetic acid, formamide, and dioxane (only slightly soluble). The factor is not destroyed by pepsin, trypsin, ficin, yeast peptidase, or commercial phosphatase preparations. It is present in Labco vitamin-free casein and is not destroyed until the casein is completely hydrolyzed. Hutchings *et al.* suggest the factor is an integral part of the protein and does not become subject to attack until the protein is destroyed. The activity was destroyed by esterification with ethyl alcohol-hydrochloric acid at room temperature, and 50 per cent of the activity was regenerated by sodium carbonate hydrolysis. At least part of its acidity is attributed to a carboxyl group. Activity is destroyed by nitrous acid indicating the presence of a free amino group. In the presence of pyridine, the activity is destroyed by acetic anhydride or benzoyl chloride, also suggestive of an amino group.

Stokstad prepared a substance from solubilized liver believed to have properties of nucleotide in that it contained nitrogen and phosphorus and gave a positive Bial test for pentose. However Mitchell, Snell, and Williams [203] reported their material to be free of phosphorus and to be 100 times more active than Stokstad's factor, suggesting that the latter's factor contained impurity. The nucleotide theory is also refuted by Hutchings *et al.* on the basis that organic phosphorus is not necessary for activity; and destruction and phosphorus liberation were not parallel. Mueller and Miller [206] reported the "norite eluate factor" of Snell and Peterson was required by *Clostridium tetani* and that Stokstad's "nucleotide" was equally effective. Attempts to replace this latter factor with thymine and guanine were generally unsuccessful though indications from occasional experiments pointed toward a partial effect by thymine. Stokstad [205] later agreed that his preparation was free of phosphorus. He reported preparations made from liver and yeast. The compound from liver gave a methyl ester which could be precipitated repeatedly from ethyl alcohol in a yellow gelatinous form without change in biological activity. Bladed crystals of the ester were obtained by slow evaporation of methyl alcohol solutions. From yeast a crystalline compound was obtained. The free acid of this had the same absorption spectrum in 0.1 N NaOH, pH 7, as the material isolated from liver. The methyl esters prepared from liver and yeast were hydrolyzed to yield preparations having

206. Mueller and Miller. 1941. J. Biol. Chem. 140, 933-934.
205. Stokstad. 1941. J. Biol. Chem. 139, 475-476; 149, 573-574, 1943.

equal potency for *Lactobacillus casei* ε. When assayed by the method of Mitchell and Snell [215] the preparation from yeast was only half as active as that from liver. This suggests the substances isolated from liver and yeast are different. Stokstad suggested the compound prepared from liver was identical with that obtained by Pfiffner *et al.*[211] Half-maximum growth of *Lactobacillus casei* ε was obtained by both investigators with 0.00005 μg. per ml. of their respective preparations. Elementary analyses agreed well with data presented by Pfiffner *et al.*

That this substance may be of importance in several fields of biology has been indicated. Hutchings *et al.* have found that growth of *Lactobacillus helveticus, Lactobacillus delbruckii, Proprionibacterium pentosaceum,* and *Streptococcus lactis* were stimulated by addition of this factor. Growth of *Bacillus lactis acidi, Lactobacillus arabinosus, Lactobacillus pentosus, Bacillus brasicae, Leuconostoc mesenteroides,* and *Lactobacillus gayonii* were not stimulated, but in every case these organisms had synthesized significant amounts of the factor. In rats, Mitchell, Snell, and Williams [203] reported slight growth increases, though Hutchings *et al.*[207] have been unable to secure significant increases, which was suggested to be due to bacterial synthesis, as also suggested by Mitchell *et al.* Some evidence is at hand that this factor is required by the chick.[207]

Under certain dietary conditions, Hogan and Parrott [208] have shown that chicks failed to grow and developed severe anemia curable by liver extracts. The existence of a specific factor was recognized and called "vitamin B_c" for which Hogan and O'Dell [209] developed a chick assay. Mills, Briggs, Elvehjem, and Hart [210] reported a concentrate representing Peterson's "eluate factor" to prevent anemia in chicks. Pfiffner, Brinkley, Bloom, Brown, Bird, Emmett, Hogan, and O'Dell [211] isolated Hogan's "vitamin B_c" as orange-colored spherulites which exhibited typical crossed extinction when crystallized from water. After repeated recrystallizations it separates into clusters of thin, yellow, sphere-shaped platelets. It did not melt at 360°C. (680°F.), but darkened and charred from about 250°C. (482°F.). An ash-free sample showed the following analysis: carbon 50.50, hydrogen 4.78, and nitrogen 19.91. The crystalline methyl ester shows no melting point, has only five per cent of the activity of the original acid, and can be converted to the acid. The acid form is highly active for *Lactobacillus casei* ε, half-maximum growth being produced by .00005 μg. per ml. of culture medium. Pfiffner and his colleagues suggested that the "eluate factor," "folic acid," and Hogan's "vitamin B_c" are identical and proposed retention of the latter name until its chemical identity is established. Nielsen and Elvehjem [212] and Martin [213] have demonstrated that folic acid is capable of counteracting growth inhibition of rats owing to succinylsulfathiozole and sulfaguanidine, indicating synthesis of the vitamin by

207. Hutchings, Bohonos, Hegsted, Elvehjem, and Peterson. 1941. J. Biol. Chem. 140, 681-682.
208. Hogan and Parrott. 1940. J. Biol. Chem. 132, 507.
209. Hogand and O'Dell. 1943. (In press.)
210. Mills *et al.* 1942. Soc. Expt. Biol. and Med. Proc. 49, 186.
211. Pfiffner *et al.* 1943. Science 97, 404-405.
212. Nielsen and Elvehjem. 1942. J. Biol. Chem. 145, 713.
213. Martin. 1942. Soc. Exptl. Biol. and Med. Proc. 51, 353.

intestinal bacteria. Synthesis by the intestinal flora has also been suggested by Mitchell and Isbell.[214] The preparation of vitamin B_c from beef liver has been described by O'Dell and Hogan.[214a]

Mitchell and Snell's [215] Assay Method for Folic Acid. For the assay of folic acid, Mitchell and Snell have employed *Streptococcus lactis* R as the test organism. More recently, Landy and Dicken [68] have employed *Lactobacillus casei* ε in the assay. This procedure will be discussed in a subsequent part of this chapter, since by their medium other members of the vitamin B complex may also be assayed. The medium of Mitchell and Snell contains the following components:

Vitamin-free hydrolyzed casein	10 gm.
(Charcoal treated, Darco G-60)	
Sodium acetate	12 gm.
Glucose	20 gm.
Tryptophane	100 mg.
Adenine sulfate	20 mg.
Cystine hydrochloride	200 mg.
Guanine hydrochloride	20 mg.
Xanthine	20 mg.
Uracil	20 mg.
Thiamine chloride	200 μg.
Pyridoxine hydrochloride	200 μg.
Calcium pantothenate	200 μg.
Riboflavin	400 μg.
Nicotinic acid	200 μg.
Biotin	0.4 μg.
Inorganic salts, Solutions A and B	5 ml. each
Distilled water to 1 liter	
pH adjusted to 6.6 to 6.8	

This medium is a modification of that used by Snell and Peterson [216] for *Lactobacillus casei* ε in obtaining the "norite eluate factor." Adenine, guanine, uracil, and xanthine have been added since these compounds stimulate the growth of the test organism.[217]

For preparation of the inoculum the above medium is diluted with an equal portion of distilled water and one mg. of liver extract (Wilson and Company, fraction B) is added per 10 ml. of medium. About 10 ml. of medium are used in each tube. *Streptococcus lactis* R is transferred from stock culture to the above medium, incubated for 14 to 30 hours at 30°C., centrifuged, and resuspended in sterile saline solution.

Assays are carried out in bacteriological test tubes. Each tube contains five ml. of the basal medium to which is added the prepared assay material. The final contents of each tube is then diluted to 10 ml. The tubes are plugged with cotton and sterilized at 15 pounds pressure for 15 minutes.

Standard tubes containing 0, 20, 40, 60, 100, and 200 mg. of liver extract B (potency = 1) are satisfactory for establishing the standard curve. Results are expressed empirically, assuming pure folic acid to have a potency of 40,000. Thus the potency is based upon the liver extract fraction B (Wilson and Company) which is assumed to have a potency of one.

It has been pointed out that too much charcoal treatment of acid-hydrolyzed casein results in a medium that supports growth of the test organism poorly, even in the presence of "folic acid." Perhaps this is the result of removal of p-aminobenzoic acid, since Isbell [218] has reported similar experience, alleviated by addition of the vitamin, in preparing the basal medium of Snell and Wright for nicotinic acid assay.

214. Mitchell and Isbell. 1942. Univ. of Texas Pub. 4237, 125.
214a. O'Dell and Hogan. 1943. J. Biol. Chem. 149, 323-337.
215. Mitchell and Snell. 1941. Idem Pub. 4137, 36-37.
216. Snell and Peterson. 1940. J. Bact. 39, 273-285.
217. Snell and Mitchell. 1941. Natl. Acad. Sci. Proc. 27. 1-7.
218. Isbell. 1942. J. Biol. Chem. 144, 567-568.

Growth responses by the test organism are measured tubidimetrically, using a photoelectric colorimeter.

NIACIN (NICOTINIC ACID)

Nicotinic acid is a vitamin. Its functions were given by Waisman [31] as follows:

Nicotinic Acid (niacin, P-P vitamin, anti-blacktongue factor. $C_6H_5NO_2$, 3 pyridine carboxylic acid).

Properties: Most stable of water-soluble vitamins. Not affected by acids, alkali, heat.

Function: Component of two important coenzymes, coenzyme I (cozymase) and coenzyme II, both concerned in glycolysis and tissue respiration.

Symptoms Associated With Deficiency: Erythematous skin lesions. Inflammation of all mucous membranes. Anorexia. Loss in weight. Nervous disturbances. Dementia. Diarrhea. Frank pellagra with accompanying glossitis, dermatitis, etc.

Daily Requirement: Man, 15 to 23 mg. Woman, 12 to 18 mg. Children (1-12 years), 4 to 12 mg.; (12-20 years), 14 to 20 mg.

Occurrence in Natural Foodstuffs: Chiefly beef liver, peanut butter, beef kidney, chicken, pork loin, salmon, yeast (dry), ham, brown rice, whole wheat.

The vitamin activity of this compound in curing disease was first reported by Elvehjem, Madden, Strong, and Woolley.[219] It was reported later as a curative agent for deficiency diseases in other animals. Its function in nutrition of certain microorganisms has also been established. Knight [220] showed that it stimulated development of *Staphylococcus aureus*; Koser, Darfman, and Saunders,[221] the dysentery bacilli; Mueller,[222] *Corynebacterium diphtheriae*; Hornibrook,[223] *Hemophilus pertussis*; and Rane and Subbarow,[224] the pneumococcus.

Numerous methods have been proposed for assaying for nicotinic acid and its compounds. Many of them are not sufficiently specific. Frazer, Topping, and Sebrell [225] assayed urine for nicotinic acid using *Shigella paradysenteriae*, Sonne, as the test organism. Later, Isbell, Wooley, Butler, and Sebrell [226] reported quantitative assay for nicotinamide and related substances in blood, urine, and spinal fluid. Querido, Lwoff, and Lotosto [227] used Proteus sp. for determining nicotinamide and related compounds in the same materials. Dorfman, Harwitt, Koser, and Saunders [228] assayed milk, blood, urine, and saliva.

According to results of investigations of Lwoff and Lwoff [229] the V-factor in blood which satisfies growth requirements of *Hemophilus influenzae* and *Hemophilus parainfluenzae* may be replaced by coenzyme I or II, which have been shown to be diphosphopyridine and triphosphopyridine

219. Elvehjem *et al.* 1937. Amer. Chem. Soc. J. 59, 1767; J. Biol. Chem. 123 (1938), 137.
220. Knight. 1937. Biochem. J. 31, 731.
221. Koser *et al.* 1938. Soc. Expt. Biol. and Med. Proc. 38, 311.
222. Mueller. 1937. J. Bact. 34, 439.
223. Hornibrook. 1940. Soc. Expt. Biol. and Med. Proc. 45, 598-599.
224. Rane and Subbarow. 1940. J. Biol. Chem. 134, 455-456.
225. Frazer *et al.* 1938. Pub. Health Rpts. 53, 1836.
226. Isbell *et al.* 1941. J. Biol. Chem. 139, 499-510.
227. Querido *et al.* 1939. Compt. Rend. Soc. Biol. 130, 1580; 131, 182; Bull. Soc. Med. Exotique 32, 784.
228. Dorfman *et al.* 1939. J. Biol. Chem. 128, XX; Soc. Expt. Biol. and Med. Proc. 43, 434.
229. Lwoff and Lwoff. 1937. Roy. Soc. London, Proc. 122B, 352, 360.

nucleotide, respectively, by Warburg. It cannot be replaced by adenylic acid, nicotinic acid, nicotinamide, diethylamide, o-dihydropropylnicotinamide, or the product formed when either coenzyme is kept at 100°C. and pH 8.5 for 20 minutes. Assays based on response of this organism when aliquots of blood, urine, and tissue were added to a basal medium free of the V-factor were made by Kohn,[230] Pittman and Frazer,[231] and Kohn, Klein, and Dann.[232]

Since the V-factor is known to be comprised of coenzymes I and II and perhaps other related compounds, the assays for the V-factor are calculated with reference to the response of the test organism to coenzyme I. Schlenck and Gingrich [233] have recently shown that nicotinamide nucleoside, a compound of coenzyme, can also function as the V-factor.

Hoagland and Ward's [235] Method for Microbiological Assay for the V-Factor. In the methods mentioned above in which Hemophilus sp. have been used as test organisms, growth responses have been determined turbidimetrically, using photoelectric colorimeters. Since this technic may be completely unreliable in those instances in which insoluble or pigmented material containing V-factor are added to the basal medium, Hoagland, Ward, Gilder, and Shank [234] observed that nitrate reduction can be used as a quantitative expression of its metabolic activity and that nitrite production in a standard medium may be used as a reliable measure of the V-factor content of materials. The complete assay procedure has been given by Hoagland and Ward.[235] Sensitivity of nitrite determination permits use of such small aliquots of test material that color and turbidity do not interfere. The method of Shinn [236] has been used for determining nitrites.

Preparation of Medium: The medium which has been found most satisfactory for quantitative determination of the V-factor is composed of two per cent of Difco proteose-peptone, .6 per cent of sodium chloride, and 0.2 per cent of sodium or potassium nitrate as the source of nitrite. After sterilization in the autoclave at 116°C.(240.8°F.) for 20 minutes, rabbit, sheep, or human blood was added.

Preparation of Inoculum: Standard inocula were prepared in five ml. of a stock broth composed of two per cent proteose-peptone, 0.6 per cent sodium chloride, 0.1 mg. of autoclaved hemin, and 0.06 μg. of purified coenzyme as the V-factor. Nitrate was omitted in order to prevent transfer of nitrite with the inoculum. Organisms carried on heated blood agar by weekly transfers were inoculated into a tube of stock broth and incubated overnight at 37°C. After three transfers in stock broth the organisms were ready to use. When 0.1 ml. of such a culture was inoculated into 10 ml. of medium no multiplication or reduction of nitrate occurred unless the medium contained V-factor.

A number of strains of *Hemophilus influenzae* have been used in the development of this technic. Although strains were found to differ markedly in the rate and total amount of nitrite produced in a given medium, when the same strain was used for the production of a standard curve and the determination of the V-factor content of a given test material, results were obtained which checked closely with determinations of the V-factor with other strains.

230. Kohn. 1938. Biochem. J. 32, 2075-2083.
231. Pittman and Frazer. 1940. Pub. Health Rpts. 55, 915-925.
232. Kohn *et al*. 1939. Biochem. J. 33, 1432-1444.
233. Schlenck and Gingrich. 1942. J. Biol. Chem. 143, 295.
234. Hoagland *et al*. 1942. J. Expt. Med. 76, 241.
235. Hoagland and Ward. 1942. J. Biol. Chem. 146, 115-120.
236. Shinn. 1941. Ind. Eng. Chem., Anal. Ed. 13, 33.

Preparation of Coenzyme Standard: Coenzyme I, suitable for establishing V-factor curves, was prepared from yeast by the method of Williamson and Green.[237] A solution containing 1.5 mg. per ml. of a preparation of coenzyme previously dried to constant weight was passed through a Berkefeld filter. An aliquot of the sterile filtrate was compared with another sample of coenzyme I of which the purity had been established by analysis for phosphorus and by measurement of extinction coefficient at 3400 Å following reduction of dithionite. The filtrate was then diluted to contain 15μg. of coenzyme per ml. delivered aseptically in 0.5-ml. quantities into sterile tubes, frozen and dried *in vacuo,* and stored in a desiccator over calcium chloride at 0°C.(32°F.). Frequent assays demonstrated that coenzyme preparations treated and stored in this manner are stable for many months. Klein[238] described another procedure for the preparation of the pyridine nucleotides and their separation.

Determination of Nitrite Produced by Hemophilus influenzae: For the determination of nitrite the technic of Shinn[236] has been found very satisfactory. In this method the color produced by the diazotization of sulfanilamide and subsequent coupling of the diasotized compound to N(1-naphthyl) ethylenediamine is a measure of the nitrite in the reaction mixture. From a 1-ml. pipette 0.1 ml. of the culture was delivered into a colorimeter tube containing 8.5 ml. of water. The interior of the pipette was then washed two or three times with a small quantity of the material in the tube to insure complete delivery. This was followed successively by 1 ml. of .2-per cent sulfanilamide, 0.2 ml. of 0.1-per cent N(1-naphthyl)ethylenediamine dihydrochloride, and 0.2 ml. of 6 N hydrochloric acid. The deep red color which developed upon coupling of diazosulfanilamide with N(1-naphthyl)ethylenediamine was maximum within 15 to 20 minutes and was stable for at least 24 hours. The color intensity was read in a photoelectric colorimeter with Filter 520 (maximum transmission).

Coenzyme Standard Curve: Six concentrations of sterile coenzyme, 0, 0.0075, 0.01, 0.025, 0.03, and 0.0375 μg., respectively, were added in triplicate to nine ml. of media described above in 50-ml. Erlenmeyer flasks, and sufficient sterile water added to bring the volume to 10 ml. The flasks were then inoculated with 0.1 ml. of the standard culture of *Hemophilus influenzae* previously described and incubated for 48 hours at 37°C.; 0.1 ml. of the 48-hour culture was then added to 8.5 ml. of water and the nitrite determined as described above.

The range of nitrite concentration which can be determined by diazotization and production of color by coupling is a narrow one. This technical limitation is further increased by the fact that the amount of nitrite produced by *Hemophilus influenzae* is relatively great for small increments of coenzyme. For these reasons it has been found best, in most instances, to limit the amount of culture taken for nitrite analysis to 0.1 ml. However, with certain strains of *Hemophilus influenzae* which reduce nitrates less effectively 0.2 to 0.5 ml. of the culture media may be required for an accurate determination. When one ml. or less of the medium is taken for analysis, even great turbidity of the culture medium owing to added test material does not interfere significantly with the photoelectric determination of color intensity.

Although standard curves of nitrite production with a given strain of *Hemophilus influenzae* are fairly constant from day to day, enough variation occurs to make it necessary to set up a new series of standards for each set of coenzyme test materials. Since *Hemophilus influenzae* responds indifferently to coenzyme I and coenzyme II,[221] determinations of the total V-factor have been expressed in terms of coenzyme I.

Preparation of Blood for V-Factor Determination: Blood was drawn under sterile precautions into sterile test tubes containing ammonium and potassium oxalates in the proportions suggested by Wintrob.[239] The solution of oxalates was filtered to insure sterility and dried in the tubes at 65°C.(149°F.) before use. Preliminary dilution and laking of freshly drawn blood were performed with a volumetric 0.5 ml. pipette carefully wiped free of blood on the outer surface with sterile gauze and rinsed into 4.5 ml. of sterile water. From this 1:10 dilution further dilutions were made. Amounts of

237. Williamson and Green. 1940. J. Biol. Chem. 135, 345.
238. Klein. 1940. Idem 134, 43-57.
239. Winetrob. 1929. J. Lab. and Clin. Med. 15, 287.

diluted blood representing usually 0.005 to 0.001 ml. of whole blood were added to nine ml. of media in duplicate flasks, and as a rule a second series of similar dilutions was prepared and set up in the same manner. The volume of media and test material was brought to 10 ml. with sterile water and the flasks were inoculated with 0.1 ml. of the standard inoculum and incubated for 48 hours. At the end of the incubation period 0.1 ml. of each culture was mixed with 8.5 ml. of distilled water, according to the manner described for the preparation of the standard coenzyme curve, and the nitrite determined colorimetrically. The V-factor content of the blood dilution was read directly from the standard curve and expressed finally as micrograms of coenzyme per ml. of erythrocytes. The erythrocyte volume was determined on an aliquot of one ml. of blood in a Winetrob hematocrit tube.[239] Previous methods for the microbiological determination of coenzyme have called for the heating of laked blood before it is added to the medium. In this study the results of a number of experiments have shown that heating the blood to 85°C. caused no change in the growth response of *Hemophilus nifluenzae*, hence was considered unnecessary.

Axelrod and Elvehjem's [240] Method for Microbiological Assay for Coenzyme I. A yeast method, specific for the assay for coenzyme I has been employed by Axelrod and Elvehjem, adapted from similar methods by von Euler [241] and Myrbäch,[242] who noted that the addition of varying amounts of coenzyme I to a washed yeast preparation produced rates of fermentation which were proportional, within certain limits, to the amount of coenzyme I added.

The rate of carbon dioxide evolution is measured in a respirometer. Since no oxygen uptake is demonstrated, uncorrected readings are taken for carbon dioxide evolution. A significant amount of carbon dioxide is not absorbed by the liquid medium at the low partial pressure of carbon dioxide developed. The fermentation is carried out with air in the gas space. The flasks are shaken at 100 to 120 oscillations per minute in a water bath maintained at 30°C.(86°F.). After an equilibrium period of five minutes, the fermentation is allowed to proceed for one hour with readings taken every 10 minutes. The taps are opened momentarily when necessary. After an induction period of 10 to 20 minutes the rate of carbon dioxide evolution reaches a maximum which is maintained for 20 to 30 minutes. The rate then begins to decrease. Maximum rate of carbon dioxide evolution is proportional to the amount of coenzyme I present. Since the apozymase always contains traces of coenzyme I it is necessary to determine the rate of carbon dioxide evolution in the absence of any added coenzyme I and to subtract this basal value from all subsequent readings.

Apozymase: This term is used by von Euler and Myrbäch to designate a washed yeast preparation which contains all of the enzymes necessary for the yeast fermentation except coenzyme I. It is prepared from brewers' yeast. Filtered yeast is spread out in shallow pans and dried for three hours at room temperature with the aid of a fan. This dry yeast is stable for six months when stored in a refrigerator. Twenty grams of dry yeast are washed with 800 ml. of distilled water at room temperature for 30 minutes, the yeast centrifuged, and the procedure repeated twice. Washed yeast is then spread on glass plates and dried rapidly with a fan. The apozymase is ground finely and stored in a desiccator. The yield is approximately 10 grams. This is stable for about two weeks, but it is best to prepare the apozymase weekly.

The rate of fermentation is a function of the concentration of apozymase. Axelrod and Elvehjem found the saturation point to be about 300 mg. per Barcroft vessel, but 200 mg. per vessel gave satisfactory results.

Glucose: Eighty mg. glucose in 0.2 ml. buffer were placed in each flask.

Magnesium and Manganese Ions: One hundred mg. of each ion is added to each vessel as the chloride. These ions are necessary to establish maximum rate of fermentation. Manganese ions have the greater effect, but magnesium ions give a slight additional stimulation.

240. Axelrod and Elvehjem. 1939. J. Biol. Chem. 131, 77-84.
241. von Euler. 1936. Ergeb. der Physiol. 38, 1.
242. Myrbäch. 1936. In Nord and Weidenhagen's Ergeb. der Enzymefarschung, Leipsig 2, 139.

Hexose Diphosphate: The sodium salt is prepared from the calcium salt by treating with the calculated amount of sodium oxalate. The solution is brought to pH 6.2 and made to a concentration of 10 mg. of organic phosphorus per milliliter. Only traces of inorganic phosphorus are present. The rate of fermentation is a function of the amount of hexose diphosphate, and maximum rate is obtained in the presence of four mg. of organic phosphorus (equal to 22 mg. of sodium hexosediphosphate). Four tenths of a milligram of hexosediphosphate solution is added to each flask. This solution is stored in the frozen state.

Buffer—0.1 M Sodium and Potassium Phosphate, pH 6.2: A total of 0.8 mg. of buffer is added to each flask, making the final buffer concentration 0.04 M. This is optimum for the yeast used, but small variations in molarity cause significant decreases in the rate of fermentation. Yeasts vary with respect to the optimum phosphate molarity, so each yeast used for assay purposes must be tested.

Tissue extracts do not contain enough phosphate to alter the fermentation rate significantly. The optimum pH range for dry yeast fermentation is pH 6.2 to 6.6, and the pH must not vary from this range.

Coenzyme I: Coenzyme I is made up in a concentration of 50 μg. per ml. with distilled water and is stored in the frozen state. Its activity remains constant for two months. A typical fermentation set-up is represented as follows:

Mg. and Mn. solution	0.1 ml.
Buffer solution	0.6 ml.
Glucose	0.2 ml.
Hexosediphosphate	0.4 ml.
Coenzyme I	
Tissue extract	0.7 ml.
Water	
Apozymase	200.0 mg.

A two-ml. volume is always used and two ml. of water are placed in the left-hand flask.

Addition of thiamine, cocarboxylase, riboflavin, yeast and muscle adenylic acid, and nicotinic acid had no effect upon the fermentation, therefore are not limiting factors in the assay. Coenzyme I is the only limiting factor. Coenzyme II is not determined by this method.

Coenzyme I is rapidly inactivated after death of the animal. Enzymatic destruction is rapid when normal structure is disrupted. This necessitates the rapid inactivation of enzymes to preserve coenzyme I. However, coenzyme I is heat-labile under certain conditions.

Extraction of Coenzyme I From Blood: Blood is obtained from guinea pigs and rats by heart puncture, from chickens by bleeding from external carotid artery, and from humans and dogs by venipuncture. Oxalate is used as an anticoagulant. Little loss of coenzyme I is encountered as long as the blood cells are intact; it is all confined in the corpuscles. Blood may be held overnight in a refrigerator without loss of potency.

Red cells are washed with isotonic saline and centrifuged long enough to insure maximum packing effect. Then two ml. are pipetted with five ml. of water at 80°C. (176°F.), stirred, immediately placed in a water bath at 80°C. for five minutes, and cooled. Cells are then homogenized by the method of Potter and Elvehjem.[108] Four-tenths to 0.8 ml. of supernatant liquid are suitable for carbon dioxide evolution measurements.

Extraction of Coenzyme I From Animal Tissue: Animals are sacrificed in the absence of any anesthesia; the tissue is rapidly removed and cut into thin slices and placed on slabs of solid carbon dioxide. The rate of inactivation of coenzyme I is greatly decreased as long as the tissue remains in the frozen state. Rat liver is stable for two weeks, though rat kidney and brains decrease in potency after one week.

Frozen tissues are ground to a fine powder in a mortar. Samples are weighed on a cold watch glass (0.5 to one gm.), washed into 25 ml. of boiling water with five ml. of warm water, boiled for two minutes, immediately cooled, made to volume and aliquots removed for assay. In the final concentration, 20 to 30 mg. of tissue are usually chosen, corresponding to 0.4 to 0.8 ml. extracts.

Snell and Wright's[205] **Method for Microbiological Assay for Nicotinic Acid.** The microbiological assay for nicotinic acid proposed by Snell and Wright has certain advantages over other methods. It has a sensitivity 20 to 100 times that possible with existing chemical methods. The test organism is nonpathogenic, and acid production may be used as an index of growth response to nicotinic acid, thus removing the limitations introduced when turbidity measurements are required in turbid or colored solutions.

The test organism is *Lactobacillus arabinosus* 17-5 (American Type Culture Collection No. 8014). Stab cultures are carried in yeast extract-glucose agar and are transferred monthly. After transfer, cultures are incubated at 30°C.(86°F.) for 24 to 48 hours, then held in a refrigerator. Inoculum for assay tubes is prepared by transferring from the stock culture to a sterile solution of the basal medium to which 0.1 μg. per ml. of nicotinic acid has been added. This culture is incubated at 30°C. for 18 to 36 hours, centrifuged, and resuspended in sterile saline solution.

The constituents of the basal medium are prepared as follows:

Acid-Hydrolyzed Casein: Fifty grams of "vitamin-free" casein are hydrolyzed with 250 ml. of 25-per cent sulfuric acid. Ordinary technical casein (and some "vitamin-free" caseins) contain considerable amounts of nicotinic acid. The mixture is autoclaved for 10 hours at 15 pounds pressure. The sulfuric acid is removed with barium hydroxide. Any excess of barium ion is carefully removed with a minimum amount of sulfuric acid and the solution is adjusted by dilution or evaporation to contain 100 mg. of dry matter per milliliter. It is preserved under toluene. Traces of nicotinic acid (and other vitamins) can be more completely removed from the hydrolysate by stirring the above solution at pH 3 with 10 mg. per ml. of active charcoal and filtering, but this is not recommended as a general procedure.

A simpler method of hydrolyzing casein is by use of constant boiling hydrochloric acid. Fifty grams of casein are dissolved in constantly boiling hydrochloric acid (equal volumes of concentrated HCl and water) and refluxing from eight to 10 hours. The acid is removed by repeated vacuum distillations, the sirup neutralized, and the volume adjusted with distilled water.

Treatment of acid hydrolysate of casein with activated charcoal for the removal of traces of nicotinic acid may result in a medium which does not permit maximum acid production. Isbell[274] has shown that the addition of one μg. of p-aminobenzoic acid to 10 ml. of medium will restore the full activity to the medium. Pimelic acid, inositol, choline hydrochloride, thymus nucleic acid, adenosine, xanthin, and some organic preparations were also effective although purity of these compounds was in doubt. Thus, p-aminobenzoic acid is shown to be a growth factor for *Lactobacillus arabinosus* 17-5, and on this basis Lewis[111] developed an assay.

Cystine: A solution of cystine hydrochloride containing one mg. of cystine per ml. is prepared by suspending cystine in water and adding the least possible amount of hydrochloric acid to effect solution and then diluting to the required volume with water. It is kept under toluene.

Adenine, Guanine, and Uracil: A solution is prepared containing one mg. per ml. of each of these constituents. Solution is effected by prolonged heating in the presence of a few drops of hydrochloric acid. It is stored in the refrigerator and is renewed at frequent intervals.

Thiamine, Calcium Pantothenate, and Pyridoxine: Stock solutions are prepared containing 100 μg. per ml. dissolved in distilled water. They are stored in the refrigerator and renewed at frequent intervals.

Riboflavin: A solution of riboflavin containing 100 μg. per ml. is prepared in 0.02 N acetic acid and kept in the refrigerator. Unnecessary exposure to light should be avoided and a fresh solution prepared at frequent intervals.

Biotin: Any concentrate which is free from significant amounts of nicotinic acid may be used. Suitable concentrates can be obtained by following the Kögl and Tönnis procedure.[126] A convenient procedure has been outlined by Snell and Wright. Crystalline preparations of biotin and its methyl ester, recommended for use whenever possible, are now available commercially. The free acid should be used, since this organism, unlike yeast, is unable to utilize the methyl ester. A suitable hydrolysis procedure for preparing free biotin from the methyl ester has been described by du Vigneaud *et al.*[149]

Inorganic Salts: Solutions A and B are prepared according to directions given in the instructions for the riboflavin assay.

BASAL MEDIUM *

Acid-hydrolyzed casein	0.5	per cent
Tryptophane	0.01	per cent
Cystine	0.01	per cent
Glucose	1.0	per cent
Sodium acetate	0.6	per cent
Adenine	10.0	p.p.m.
Guanine	10.0	p.p.m.
Uracil	10.0	p.p.m.
Thiamine	0.1	p.p.m.
Calcium pantothenate	0.1	p.p.m.
Pyrodoxine	0.1	p.p.m.
Riboflavin	0.2	p.p.m.
Biotin	0.4	p.p.billion pure biotin

Inorganic salts, Solutions A and B, 10 ml. each per liter
pH adjusted to 6.6 to 6.8

*These concentrations are based on the final composition of the medium when the tubes are ready to sterilize. It should be made up in twice this concentration for dispensing in the tubes.

Some investigators have experienced difficulty in obtaining low blanks when using Snell and Wright's method. Tepley, Strong, and Elvehjem [243] observed some of the constituents of the medium, such as casein, biotin concentrates, and cystine preparations might be sources of contamination. Vitamin-free casein or acid-washed casein, prepared according to the method of Arnold and Elvehjem,[244] gave satisfactory blanks. Extraction of the casein with alcohol reduced the blank titration to about 0.5 ml. of N/10 alkali. High blank values may be overcome by preparing the casein hydrolysate by hydrochloric acid hydrolysis of previously purified casein, and subsequently treating the hydrolyzate with active charcoal.[252]

Nicotinic acid and its amides have equal activities for the organism. Cozymase when assayed was found to contain 17 per cent of nicotinamide (theoretically, 18 per cent). Trigonelline is inactive. Nicotinuric acid shows the same activity as its theoretical equivalent of nicotinic acid.

Preparation of Samples for Analysis: The treatment of the sample for assay will vary somewhat with the material to be tested. Animal tissues should be finely ground and extracted with a large volume of water at 15 pounds pressure for 30 minutes followed by filtration. Color or slight turbidity in the test sample does not influence the results. Preliminary autolysis of the tissue sample does not increase the extracted nicotinic acid, as is reported in the case of biotin[128] and pantothenic acid.[110] Extraction with alkali does not increase the assay values. Milk powder and animal tissue show essentially the same apparent nicotinic acid content after treatment by enzyme digestion or hot extraction with sulfuric acid or sodium hydroxide.[245]

Enzymatic liberation of vitamins from animal tissue has been reported satisfactory for routine assays.[245, 246] It has been used for extraction of

243. Tepley *et al.* 1942. J. Nutr. 23, 417-423.
244. Arnold and Elvehjem. 1938. Idem 15, 429.
245. Cheldelin and Williams. 1942. Ind. Eng. Chem., Anal. Ed. 14, 671-675.
246. Williams *et al.* 1941. Univ. of Texas Pub. 4137 and 4237.

vitamins from plant tissue, though some doubt exists as to the proper pretreatment for liberating nicotinic acid.

Cheldelin and Williams [245] showed autoclaving in a large volume of water for 30 minutes and enzymatic liberation gave essentially the same nicotinic acid values for green peas. On the other hand, they reported a 35 to 40 per cent greater recovery of nicotinic acid from lima beans and black-eyed peas when hydrolyzed by 30 minutes autoclaving in 1 N sulfuric acid. Cereal products have been more extensively studied. Snell and Wright relied upon water to extract the nicotinic acid without removing substances reported by Kodicek [247] to interfere with chemical determinations of the vitamins. These substances are extracted by alkali treatment. When grain is sufficiently finely ground, water extracted nearly as much nicotinic acid as did eight per cent sodium hydroxide. However, Cheldelin, and Williams,[245] Melnick,[248] and Andrews, Boyd, and Gortner [249] have reported aqueous extraction gives variable results, depending on the severity of treatment. Repeated aqueous extraction by autoclaving gives results approaching those obtained after alkaline hydrolysis. Oser, Melnick, and Siegel,[250] using a chemical method, reported alkaline extraction to give higher nicotinic acid values than water extraction, since treatment of aqueous extracts with alkali raises the apparent nicotinic acid content to that found by direct extraction with sodium hydroxide.

Andrews, Boyd, and Gortner,[249] using the Snell and Wright method, have also noted wide difference in nicotinic acid values depending on pretreatment of sample prior to assay. Aqueous and 0.1 N sulfuric acid extraction gave the same value, whereas 1.5 per cent sodium hydroxide, 3 N hydrochloric acid extraction, and alkaline hydrolysis of aqueous extracts gave nearly 100 per cent greater value. Regardless of the type of extraction procedure used, recovery experiments of added nicotinic acid were quantitative. Both alcohol-soluble and alcohol-insoluble fractions of whole-wheat flour exhibited nicotinic acid activity which could be enhanced by alkali treatment. Adsorption of nicotinic acid and the unknown factor occurred simultaneously on Lloyd's reagent. Of milled wheat-products only wheat germ was found to behave similar to animal tissues and yeast in giving practically the same nicotinic acid values with aqueous and alkaline extraction. This fact suggested to Andrews et al.[249] that two forms of nicotinic acid are involved, one being present in "living" or potentially living tissue and being more readily available than that requiring alkali to liberate it and another found in "storage tissue," such as bran and flour which are present in wheat primarily to protect the germ and supply it with food during germination.

Tepley, Strong, and Elvehjem [243] have used strong acid or alkali to give complete liberation of nicotinic acid from cereal. For most products

247. Kodicek. 1940. Biochem. J. 34, 712.

248. Melnick. 1942. Cereal Chem. 19, 553-567.

249. Andrews, Boyd, and Gortner. 1942. Ind. Eng. Chem., Anal. Ed. 14, 663-666.

250. Oser, Melnick, and Siegel. 1941. Paper presented before Amer. Chem. Soc. Atlantic City, N. J.

they found water satisfactory, though they relied on alkaline hydrolysis to insure complete extraction from fruits and vegetables.

Krehl, Strong, and Elvehjem [252] have suggested the following extraction procedure. Sodium hydroxide proved undesirable for general use on account of soap formation with high-fat samples.

Dry materials are finely ground and fresh materials are mechanically homogenized in water with a Waring Blendor or a Potter-Elvehjem homogenizer. One gram of material is suspended in 50 ml. N hydrochloric or sulfuric acid and the suspension is autoclaved for 20 minutes at 15 pounds pressure. The cooled mixture is adjusted to pH 6.6 to 6.8 with N sodium hydroxide, and diluted to such a volume that each milliliter contains approximately 0.05 microgram of nicotinic acid. Filtration is unnecessary but does no harm. Water-soluble materials are dissolved in the acid, autoclaved, neutralized, and diluted as above.

Results of investigations comparing microbiological and chemical methods for assaying for nicotinic acid in cereals have been reported by Melnick [248] and Cheldelin and Williams.[245] Significant increases were noticed in apparent nicotinic acid content of cereals after acid or alkaline hydrolysis in comparison with aqueous or enzyme hydrolysis. Clear extracts obtained by enzymatic hydrolysis of bread or flour showed increased nicotinic acid content after hydrolysis with acid or alkali. Green, Black, and Howland [251] reported substantial agreement of results of the chemical and microbiological assay method of Snell and Wright when applied to commercial B-complex products, such as yeast, yeast extract, liver extract, and rice-bran concentrate. Hydrolysis of sample with strong acid often gave slightly higher values than aqueous extracts particularly in products of cereal origin and their concentrates. Trigonelline, the betaine of nicotinic acid, has been suggested as the unknown substance. Andrews et al.[249] observed that when trigonelline was subjected to aqueous or alkaline extraction, no nicotinic acid was recovered. In presence of urine, trigonelline has been shown to be partially converted to a substance giving the color reactions of nicotinic acid. Strong alkali will give greater conversion. Cheldelin and Williams observed no conversion after autoclaving 30 minutes in presence of 2 N sodium hydroxide. Certain substances, such as asparagine, accelerated the reaction. Ammonium sulfate, urea, glutamine, β-alanine, acetamide, and urotropin can also replace asparagine under conditions of alkaline hydrolysis. Cheldelin and Williams believed that under these conditions, the high conversions obtained in presence of asparagine or β-alanine may be due to slow production of ammonia (or —NH_2 groups) in the reaction mixture. On the other hand, the apparent increase in nicotinic acid in cereal products produced by acid hydrolysis cannot be explained by conversion of trigonelline. Large amounts of trigonelline failed to affect the apparent nicotinic acid content of whole-wheat bread. Addition of reducing agents also failed to produce significant increases. Melnick expressed doubt that trigonelline was involved. Dried cowpeas relatively rich in trigonelline did not show the great increase in apparent nicotinic acid after acid or alkaline hydrolysis. Results

251. Green, Black, and Howland. 1943. Ind. Eng. Chem., Anal. Ed. 15, 77-78.
252. Krehl, Strong, and Elvehjem. 1943. Ind. Eng. Chem., Anal. Ed. 15, 471-475.

of the methods of Melnick, Oser, and Siegel,[253] Dann and Handler,[254] and Melnick and Field [255] agree substantially with those of Snell and Wright's method when comparable methods of sample preparation were used. Also the microbiological methods of Darfman, Koser, Horwitt, Beckman, and Saunders [228] gave good results when compared with Snell and Wright's procedure. The Bina, Thomas, and Brown [256] procedure was unsatisfactory. Using the Dann and Handler chemical method, Cheldelin and Williams observed substantial agreement in results with the microbiological assay procedure when parallel methods of extraction of nicotinic acid were used. With dry yeast, however, the chemical method gave satisfactory results only after sulfuric acid hydrolysis.

Thus in summary for cereal products at least, mild aqueous extraction gives the lowest nicotinic acid values. Predigestion of the sample with enzymes gives only slightly higher figures. Maximum values, more than twice those resulting from aqueous extraction, were obtained on acid or alkaline extracts. These values are approximated in the assays of exhaustive aqueous extracts. Melnick has stated: "It is impossible to state at the present time exactly how much of the total nicotinic acid in cereal products is the unknown nicotinic acid derivative. Because of the ready hydrolysis of the compound, it is conceivable that some conversion to nicotinic acid occurs even in mild aqueous extracts during the subsequent sterilization (autoclaving) of the test solutions prior to inoculation with microorganisms."

A statement as to the proper treatment for assay, whether by chemical or microbiological procedures, must await the determination of the biological activity of the unknown substance in animals. A little evidence thus far accumulated suggests that it is biologically active. Morgareidge [257] reported that a dog black-tongue curative assay conducted on a rice-bran concentrate gave a value of 1.65 mg. of nicotinic acid per gram (Waisman, Mickelson, McKibben, and Elvehjem [258]), while microbiological assay values were 0.83 mg. prior to and 1.65 mg. after alkaline hydrolysis.

Brown, Thomas, and Bina [259] have reported much lower nicotinic acid values on certain wheat fractions after oxidation with hydrogen peroxide than have been reported by others. Certain chromogens encountered in chemical assays were also eliminated. These workers claimed the lower values were more nearly representative of the anti-pellagra activity of these substances. Krehl, Strong, and Elvehjem [252] repeated the work on whole wheat and were unable to corroborate their findings.

Krehl, Strong, and Elvehjem's Modification of the Snell and Wright Microbiological Assay for Nicotinic Acid and Nicotinamide. Certain difficulties have been encountered in the Snell and Wright method, namely, relatively high blanks resulting from inefficient removal of nicotinic acid from the acid-hydrolyzed casein, and variations in the

253. Melnick, Oser, and Siegel. 1941. Ind. Eng. Chem., Anal. Ed. 13, 879-883.
254. Dann and Handler. 1941. J. Biol. Chem. 140, 201-213.
255. Melnick and Field. 1940. Idem 134, 1-16.
256. Bina, Thomas, and Brown. 1941. Cereal Chem. 18, 661-666.
257. Morgareidge. 1942. (Quoted from Melnick, Footnote 249.)
258. Waisman, Mickelson, McKibben, and Elvehjem. 1940. J. Nutr. 19, 483-492.
259. Brown, Thomas, and Bina. 1943. Cereal Chem. 20, 201-211.

standard curve implying a lack of specificity of the assay. An improved medium has been proposed by Krehl, Strong, and Elvehjem [252] which supports a greater acid production by *Lactobacillus arabinosus* 17-5 and gives greater reliability and reproducibility of assay results. The glucose and sodium acetate concentrations were increased to two per cent, resulting in a definite improvement in the bacterial response to nicotinic acid. Two per cent glucose alone had no effect. Cystine concentration was doubled as certain workers had reported a linear standard curve over a wider range and higher acid production. Since activated-charcoal treatment of acid-hydrolyzed casein sometimes creates a deficiency in p-aminobenzoic acid, this vitamin has been incorporated in the basal medium. Biotin concentration has been reduced from 0.4 to 0.2 part per billion. The new medium in its final concentration is shown here. For dispensing into culture tubes, it is prepared in double this concentration.

Acid-hydrolyzed casein	0.5	per cent
Tryptophane	0.01	per cent
Cystine	0.02	per cent
Glucose	2.0	per cent
Sodium acetate	2.0	per cent
Calcium pantothenate	0.1	p.p.m.
Thiamine chloride	0.1	p.p.m.
Pyridoxin	0.1	p.p.m.
Riboflavin	0.2	p.p.m.
Biotin	0.2	p.p.billion
p-aminobenzoic acid	0.1	p.p.m.
Adenine	10.0	p.p.m.
Guanine	10.0	p.p.m.
Uracil	10.0	p.p.m.

Inorganic salts, Solutions A and B, 10 ml. each per liter of basal medium

Unless otherwise specified, the preparation of the various constituents of the basal medium is the same as given by Snell and Wright.

Acid-Hydrolyzed Casein: One hundred grams of "vitamin-free" casein are twice extracted by stirring 15 minutes at room temperature with two to three volumes of 95-per cent ethyl alcohol and filtered. The casein is then gently refluxed with 300 ml. of concentrated hydrochloric acid for 16 to 20 hours. The casein hydrolyzate is concentrated to a paste *in vacuo* on a 70 to 80°C.(158 to 176°F.) water bath, 200 ml. of water are added, and the concentration repeated. The residue is dissolved in about 700 ml. of water, adjusted to pH 4 (yellow-green to bromocresol green, outside indicator) with saturated sodium hydroxide solution, 20 grams of an activated charcoal (Norite A or Darco G-60) are added, and the mixture is stirred for one hour at room temperature. The charcoal is removed by gravity filtration, the pH adjusted to 6.6 to 6.8, and the filtrate diluted with distilled water to 1,000 ml. Each milliliter is equivalent to 100 mg. of the original casein. The final solution should be no darker than a pale straw color. Any sediment occurring in the casein hydrolyzate on standing may in general be eliminated by autoclaving for one hour at 15 pounds pressure.

Biotin: The contents of an ampoule containing 25 micrograms of biotin as the free acid are diluted to 250 ml. so that each milliliter contains 0.1 microgram. One ml. of inorganic salt Solution A is added as the solution is being diluted to volume.

When biotin methyl ester is used, the contents of a 25-microgram ampoule are added to 50 ml. of 0.1 N hydrochloric acid and autoclaved for one hour at 15 pounds pressure. One ml. of inorganic salts Solution A is added, the pH is adjusted to 6.6 to 6.8, and the volume is made to 236 ml. Each milliliter, therefore, contains 0.1 microgram of biotin, since 25 micrograms of biotin methyl ester theoretically yields 23.6 micrograms of the free acid on hydrolysis. The use of 0.1 N hydrochloric acid is specified because autoclaving of neutral solutions of biotin methyl ester did not bring about complete hydrolysis.

Since certain fatty acids have been shown to interfere with microbiological determinations of riboflavin and pantothenic acid where *Lactobacillus casei* ε is used as the test organism, Krehl, Strong, and Elvehjem [252] have reported the effects of certain fatty acids on the nicotinic acid assays employing *Lactobacillus arabinosus* 17-5 as the test organism. Oleic, stearic, and palmitic acids were without effect, while linoleic tended to give slightly high assay values.

Atkin, Schultz, Williams, and Frey's Method for Differentiating Nicotinic Acid and Nicotinamide by Microbiological Assay. Nicotinic acid and its amide have equal vitamin potencies in animals and microorganisms, consequently the method of Snell and Wright determines the combined effect of both compounds. With the advent of commercial preparation designed for therapeutic uses, the assay of either of these compounds may be of interest. Atkin, Schultz, Williams, and Frey [260] have reported a method based on the Hofmann reaction, [261] e.g., the action of bromine and potassium hydroxide upon amines. When applied to nicotinamide, β-aminopyridine is formed, [262] which is apparently inactive microbiologically.

To one ml. of a solution containing one mg. of nicotinamide add five ml. of water and one one ml. of saturated bromine water, followed by three ml. of 30-per cent potassium hydroxide. Allow the solution to stand at room temperature for 20 minutes and then steam for 20 minutes. Cool, add an excess of 10 N sulfuric acid (blue to Congo red), then remove any excess of bromine by use of a four-per cent solution of sodium bisulfite. Use an outside starch iodine indicator to determine the end point. The final solution after neutralizing is assayed by the Snell and Wright procedure. Thus, only nicotinic acid is determined after treatment and nicotinamide may be determined by estimating the vitamin activity before and after the treatment.

Another microbiological procedure for assaying for nicotinic acid employing *Lactobacillus casei* ε has been proposed by Landy and Dicken. [68] It is given later in this chapter.

p-AMINOBENZOIC ACID

The vitamin activity of p-aminobenzoic was discovered by Ansbacher. [263] It is a growth-promoting factor for chicks and a chromotrichia factor for rats. Siene [264] reported nutritional achromotrichia in man to be favorably influenced by the compound. Woods and Fildes [265] had previously observed in *in vitro* experiments an antisulfanilamide action by p-aminobenzoic acid. Woods [266] showed similar activity by a factor in yeast extracts and suggested this compound. Rubbo and Gillespie [267] isolated it from yeast. Fildes [268] suggested that p-aminobenzoic acid is a metabolite for bacteria.

A semi-quantitative method for assaying for p-aminobenzoic acid, using *Clostridium acetobutylicum* as the test organism, has been employed by Rubbo and his colleagues. [269] This vitamin is synthesized by various microorganisms. Landy, Larkum, and Oswald, [270] using *Acetobacter suboxydans*, believed that was an "essential metabolite" synthesized by many bacteria.

260. Atkin, Schultz, Williams, and Frey. 1943. Am. Chem. Soc. J. 65, 992.
261. Hofmann. 1885. Berichte 18, 2734.
262. Pictet and Crepieux. 1895. Berichte 28, 1904.
263. Ansbacher. 1941. Science 93, 164.
264. Siene. 1941. Science 94, 257.
265. Woods and Fildes. 1940. Soc. Chem. Indus. J. 59, 133.
266. Woods. 1940. Brit. J. Exptl. Path. 21, 74.
267. Rubbo and Gillespie. 1940. Nature 146, 838.
268. Fildes. 1940. Lanset 238, 955.
269. Rubbo, Maxwell, Fairbridge, and Gillespie. 1941. Austral. J. Expt. Biol. and Med. Sci. 19, 185.
270. Landy, Larkum, and Oswald. 1943. Soc. Expt. Biol. and Med. Proc. 52, 338-341.

Landy and Dicken's Method for Assaying for p-Aminobenzoic Acid. This vitamin was shown to be a growth factor for *Acetobacter suboxydans* by Lampen, Underkofler, and Peterson.[271] From these facts, Landy and Dicken[272] reported a microbiological assay procedure using *Acetobacter suboxydans* (American Type Culture Collection, No. 621) as the test organism.

The test organism is carried on yeast-extract glycerol agar (0.5 per cent Bacto yeast extract, five per cent glycerol, pH 6). Stock cultures are transferred at monthly intervals and are refrigerated in the interim. Inoculum for assays is prepared by transfer from the stock culture to a flask of basal medium to which has been added 0.5 μg. of p-aminobenzoic acid. The inoculum culture is incubated at 30°C.(86°F.) for 24 hours prior to use and is transferred daily from the preceding liquid culture, being returned to a stock culture at weekly intervals.

The composition of the basal medium, in twice the desired final concentration, is as follows:

Casein hydrolyzate*..	0.6 gm.
Glycerol..	10.0 gm.
Tryptophane..	20.0 mg.
Cystine..	15.0 mg.
Potassium hydrogen phosphate, K_2HPO_4............................	100.0 mg.
Potassium hydrogen phosphate, KH_2PO_4............................	100.0 mg.
Magnesium sulfate, $MgSO_4 \cdot 7H_2O$....................................	40.0 mg.
Sodium chloride, NaCl..	2.0 mg.
Ferrous sulfate, $FeSO_4 \cdot 7H_2O$..	2.0 mg.
Manganese sulfate, $MnSO_4 \cdot 2H_2O$....................................	2.0 mg.
Calcium pantothenate..	200.0 μg.
Nicotinic acid...	200.0 μg.

Distilled water to 100 ml.

pH adjusted to 6.0

* This purified casein hydrolyzate may be obtained from the Res. Labs. of S.M.A. Corp., Chagrin Falls, Ohio. Other purified casein hydrolyzates are equally effective.

Landy and Streightoff[273] observed that when the casein hydrolyzate employed in the basal medium is treated with Darco G-60 charcoal (10 per cent by weight) at pH 2.5 for 30 minutes, growth response to lower concentrations of p-aminobenzoic acid is variable and generally subnormal. Adenine, guanine, and xanthine, 50 μg. each per 10 ml. culture, were found effective in overcoming this variability, and sensitivity of the test organism to the vitamin was increased. This is particularly true below 0.03 μg. of p-aminobenzoic acid per tube. Adenine, in quantities of 150 μg. per culture, can replace the combination of the three purine bases, though more uniform results were obtained in the presence of the three purines. Uracil was inactive.

Assay Procedure: Five ml. of the basal medium and dilutions of material under test made up to five ml. with distilled water are placed in 50-ml. Erlenmeyer flasks. *Acetobacter suboxydans* is an obligate aerobe. Small Erlenmeyer flasks permit heavier growth of 10-ml. cultures than do the usual bacteriological culture tubes. Similarly, a set of reference flasks is prepared containing from 0.01 to 0.10 μg. of p-aminobenzoic acid. Blanks containing no p-aminobenzoic acid are included. The flasks are plugged with cotton and autoclaved at 15 pounds pressure for 15 minutes. After cooling they are inoculated with a suspension of *Acetobacter suboxydans*. A 24-hour culture, grown as described above, is centrifuged and washed; cells are resuspended in 15 ml. of saline solution, a drop of which serves as inoculum for each flask. Flasks are incubated at 30°C. for 48 hours. Following incubation, 10 ml. of distilled water are added to each flask to dilute the culture suitably for measurement of turbidity and the contents are thoroughly mixed by shaking. Growth response to increments of p-aminobenzoic acid

271. Lampen, Underkofler, and Peterson. 1942. J. Biol. Chem. 146, 277-278; J. Bact. 1943. (In press.)
272. Landy and Dicken. 1942. J. Biol. Chem. 146, 109-114.
273. Landy and Streightoff. 1943. Soc. Expt. Biol. and Med. Proc. 52, 127-128.

is determined by measurements of turbidity with a photoelectric colorimeter. From a standard curve so prepared, the p-aminobenzoic acid test sample may be calculated. Results from at least three assay levels should be averaged for the final results.

Preparation of Sample for Assay: Materials which are soluble in water are assayed without further treatment. Insoluble materials, such as food stuffs, grains, and animal tissues, are finely divided, extracted with 10 to 20 volumes of water at 15 pounds pressure for 30 minutes, and centrifuged or filtered. Such treatment has yielded maximum assay values. Body fluids require special handling, since many have been found to inhibit growth of the test organism. The inhibitory action of blood, spinal fluid, ascitic fluid, and urine is readily overcome by autoclaving. Blood is prepared for assay as follows: The sample is laked with an equal volume of distilled water and autoclaved. Three volumes of water are added to the autoclaved blood while hot, and the sample is shaken for several minutes to dispense and extract the protein precipitate. The suspension is centrifuged and the supernatant filtered to give a clear extract suitable for assay. Other body fluids may be prepared for assay by the above procedure. They do not show inhibition and give values in good agreement at various levels.

Landy and Dicken have shown the growth test is specific for p-aminobenzoic acid. Substitution, whether in the amino or carboxy group, sharply reduces or completely removes biological activity.

Lewis Method for Microbiological Assay for p-Aminobenzoic Acid. This method uses *Lactobacillus arabinosus* 17-5 (American Type Culture Collection, No. 8014). Isbell[274] reported submaximum growth of the organism in the nicotinic acid assay medium of Snell and Wright unless supplements of this compound are added. From this information Lewis[111] has proposed the following assay method.

The following basal medium is used, the composition of which is indicated in its final dilution. For assay purposes it is prepared in double this concentration.

Glucose	1.0 per cent
Norite-treated, acid-hydrolyzed casein	0.5 per cent
l-cystine	0.01 per cent
l-tryptophane	0.01 per cent
Sodium acetate	0.6 per cent
$K_2HPO_4 \cdot 3H_2O$	0.05 per cent
KH_2PO_4	0.05 per cent
$MgSO_4 \cdot 7H_2O$	0.02 per cent
NaCl	0.001 per cent
$FeSO_4 \cdot 7H_2O$	0.001 per cent
$MnSO_4 \cdot 4H_2O$	0.001 per cent
Adenine	10.0 p.p.m.
Guanine	10.0 p.p.m.
Uracil	10.0 p.p.m.
Thiamine	0.1 p.p.m.
Riboflavin	0.2 p.p.m.
Pantothenic acid	0.1 p.p.m.
Nicotinic acid	0.4 p.p.m.
Pyridoxine	0.1 p.p.m.
Biotin	0.0004 p.p.m.

The components are prepared as follows:

Norite-Treated, Acid Hydrolyzed Casein: One hundred grams of vitamin-free casein are hydrolyzed under a reflux for nine hours with 1,000 ml. of 6 N hydrochloric acid. To remove most of the hydrochloric acid the mixture is then concentrated *in vacuo* to a thick sirup, dissolved in water, and reconcentrated. The sirup is diluted to 900 ml., adjusted to pH 3 with concentrated sodium hydroxide, and stirred for 30

274. Isbell. 1942. J. Biol. Chem. 144, 567-568.

minutes with nine grams of norite A (Pfanstiehl). The activated carbon is removed by filtration through a Whatman No. 3 filter paper, and the norite treatment and filtration repeated. The filtrate is adjusted to pH 6.8 with concentrated sodium hydroxide, and is diluted to 1,000 ml. The hydrolyzed casein is stored in the refrigerator. On standing, precipitation of tyrosine occurs. No difference in results has been noticed whether this precipitate is discarded or whether it is included in the basal medium.

Adenine, Guanine, and Uracil: A solution containing one mg. per ml. of each of these chemicals is convenient. One hundred mg. of uracil, 124 mg. of guanine hydrochloride, and 174 mg. of adenine sulfate are suspended in a small volume of water, two ml. of hydrochloric acid are added, and the mixture is heated to solution and then diluted to 100 ml.

Vitamin Supplement: A solution containing one mg. of thiamine, two mg. of riboflavin, one mg. of pantothenic acid, four mg. of nicotinic acid, one mg. of pyridoxine, and four μg. of biotin per 100 ml. is prepared. Pure, synthetic vitamins are used in all cases except that of biotin. Here crystalline biotin is used. The solution is stored in the refrigerator and is renewed monthly. This is conveniently done by diluting more concentrated solutions of the individual vitamins, which are stable for longer periods. Exposure of riboflavin to light should be minimized.

For a liter of medium, use 20 gm. glucose, 12 gm. sodium acetate, 200 mg. l-tryptophane, 200 ml. l-cystine solution, 100 ml. hydrolyzed casein, 20 ml. of adenine-guanine-uracil mixture, 20 ml. of vitamin supplement, 10 ml. each Solutions A and B, inorganic salts (Snell and Strong[66]), and adjusted to pH 6.8.

The assay is carried out according to the methods used in the other assay procedures employing Lactobacillus cultures. Five-ml. aliquots of the basal medium are dispersed into culture tubes, appropriate aliquots of p-aminobenzoic acid solution for the standard curve and solutions or suspensions to be assayed are added, and the total volume made to 10 ml. with distilled water. The tubes are plugged with cotton and autoclaved at 15 pounds pressure for 10 to 15 minutes. The tubes are cooled, inoculated, and incubated at 30°C.(86°F.).

The stock culture of *Lactobacillus arabinosus* 17-5 is carried in yeast extract-glucose agar stab culture. Transfers are made monthly, incubated at 30°C. for 24 hours, then stored in the refrigerator. For subculturing, the basal medium is diluted with an equal volume of water to which one millimicrogram of p-aminobenzoic acid per 10 ml. has been added. The organism is incubated in this medium for 24 hours at 30°C., the cells are centrifuged and resuspended in the original volume of 0.9 per cent sodium chloride solution. The assay tubes are inoculated from this suspension.

The assay range is approximately 0.15 to 0.5 micrograms of p-aminobenzoic acid per tube. A standard solution containing 10 μg. per ml. of p-aminobenzoic acid is diluted to contain 0.10 millimicrograms per ml. This standard is dispensed in 0, 1, 1.5, 2, 2.5, 3, 3.5, 4, 4.5, and 5 ml. aliquots. Two or more replicates are used at each level. A standard curve is prepared, plotting the titratable acidity produced by the test organism against the level of the vitamin.

Preparation of Samples for Assay: Lewis made only preliminary studies of methods for liberating p-aminobenzoic acid from biological materials. The method has been applied only to water-soluble materials, water-soluble extracts from natural products, and yeast suspensions. In some cases samples were autoclaved in 1 N sodium hydroxide for 30 minutes at 13.5 pounds pressure, after which they were neutralized and assayed. In many of these cases increased p-aminobenzoic acid assays were found. Autoclaving solutions of the vitamin in water or 0.1 N sodium hydroxide at 10 pounds pressure for 10 minutes resulted in no destruction, whereas under the same conditions solutions in 1 N sodium hydroxide gave 10 per cent inactivation while solutions in 10 N sodium hydroxide gave 50 per cent inactivation. Sulfuric acid in concentrations from 0.1 to 10 N gave approximately 30 per cent inactivation, as did similar solutions in hydrochloric acid. Repeated autoclaving was relatively more detrimental under acidic than under alkaline conditions.

Specificity of the Method: Samples of o- and m-aminobenzoic acid had only slight activity which perhaps could be attributed to impurities of p-aminobenzoic acid. Rubbo et al.[299] found the sodium salt, ethyl ester, and p-aminobenzaldehyde to possess activity for *Clostridium acetobutylicum* approximately equal to that of p-aminobenzoic acid. They also found the benzoyl derivative, the diethylaminomethyl ester, and p-nitrobenzoic acid to have approximately 10 per cent of the activity of the vitamin. p-Aminophenylacetic acid had about 10 times the activity of the vitamin for *Clostridium acetabutylicum.*

By means of x-ray or ultraviolet light treatment, Beadle, Tatum, Horowitz, and Bonner [275] induced genetic changes in *Neurospora crassa* which, in some cases, have been concerned with vitamin synthesis. One mutant lost the ability to synthesize the thiazole fraction of the thiamine molecule. Another cannot combine the thiazole and pyrimidine moieties. Other mutants have not been able to synthesize pyridoxin, nicotinic acid, p-aminobenzoic acid, pantothenic acid, and choline. Each of these mutants responds quantitatively to the addition to the culture medium of the vitamin which cannot be synthesized. The response can be measured either as dry weight attained under standard conditions or as rate of advance of a mycelial front along a special growth tube containing an agar medium.

Thompson, Isbell, and Mitchell's Method for the Microbiological Assay for p-Aminobenzoic Acid. Using a strain designated by Beadle and Tatum as *Neurosporo crassa* p-aminobenzoicless No. 1633, Thompson, Isbell, and Mitchell [201] have developed an assay technic for this vitamin. The basal medium consists of the following components:

Ammonium tartrate	5.0 gm.
Potassium dehydrogen phosphate	1.0 gm.
Ferric chloride	5.0 mg.
Ammonium nitrate	1.0 gm.
Magnesium sulfate heptahydrate	0.5 gm.
Sodium chloride	0.1 gm.
Calcium chloride	0.1 gm.
Sucrose	15.0 gm.
Biotin	4.0 µg.
Washed agar	20.0 gm.
Acid-hydrolyzed vitamin-free casein	1.0 gm.
Enzyme digested beef liver extract	0.5 gm.
Enzyme digested beef muscle extract	0.1 gm.
Charcoal-treated yeast extract	0.1 gm.
Distilled water	1.000 ml.

Acid-Hydrolyzed Vitamin-Free Casein: Fifty grams of vitamin-free casein are hydrolyzed by boiling under reflux for 10 hours in 500 ml. 6 N hydrochloric acid. The acid is removed by repeated vacuum distillation. After adjusting the pH to 3 and the volume to 500 ml., five grams of activated charcoal (Darco G-60) are added, the suspension shaken for 15 minutes, and filtered to remove the charcoal. The pH is then adjusted to 7 and the solution is preserved under toluene.

Enzyme-Hydrolyzed Beef Liver and Muscle: Ten grams of fresh beef liver or muscle, finely ground, are suspended in 50 ml. of acetate buffer solution, pH 4.5, containing 0.1 gram clarase and caroid. After 24 hours' autolysis under benzene, the benzene is removed by steaming, and the extract filtered.

Charcoal-Treated Yeast Extract: Ten grams of Difco yeast extract are dissolved in 100 ml. distilled water and adjusted to pH 3. Two grams of Darco G-60 are added and the suspension shaken for 15 minutes, filtered, and adjusted to pH 7.

275. Beadle, Tatum, Horowitz, and Bonner. 1943. Abstracts, American Chemical Society Meeting, April 12-15.

Washed Agar: Commercial agar preparations often contain considerable quantities of vitamins, including p-aminobenzoic acid, which is removed by washing 15 to 20 times with distilled water in a 24- to 48-hour period.

The stock culture of the *Neurospora crassa* mutant is carried on the basal medium containing 0.05 μg. of p-aminobenzoic acid per 10 ml.

The inoculum is prepared by thoroughly dispersing a loopful of spores in one to two ml. of sterile liquid agar medium identical in composition with the assay medium except for addition of five mμg. p-aminobenzoic acid. This is poured into sterile Petri dishes, incubated 16 hours at 30°C., and then stored in a refrigerator until used. During this time the spores will have germinated and incipient mycelium, uniformly distributed, will be just visible to the naked eye.

The Assay: Standard p-aminobenzoic acid solutions and solutions for assay are pipetted into a test tube and diluted to one ml. To this are added 15 ml. of the agar basal medium, the tube is autoclaved for 15 minutes and the contents immediately transferred to sterile Petri dishes. When the plates are cool they are inoculated by placing blocks of agar cut from the inoculum culture plates, with sterile eight-mm. cork borers fitted with a plunger for extruding the agar block. The agar block should be placed in the center of the plate and care should be exercised that the inoculum block be nearly round, for its slope affects the slope of the colony formed. Each plate is incubated at 30°C. for 20 hours, after which the diameter of the mold colony is measured with calipers. The size of the colony is in proportion to the amount of p-aminobenzoic acid present.

For establishing the standard curve, similar plates are prepared containing four to 45 mμg. of the vitamin and incubated with the assay plates..

Preparation of Samples for Assay: Data secured by Mitchell, Isbell, and Thompson's [276] method suggest that aqueous extraction of the vitamin, as employed by Landy and Dicken, yields only a fraction of the total contained. Enzymatic hydrolysis, according to the method of Cheldelin *et al.*[277] or autolysis (Blanchard [278]) are not reliable in liberating all of the vitamin. Alkaline hydrolysis (0.1 to 5 N NaOH) destroys about 15 per cent of the vitamin in pure solution and presumably about the same extent in tissue. Yet 6 N sulfuric acid gives maximum extraction despite about 15 per cent destruction, and Thompson *et al.* relied on this procedure, carried out as follows:

One to five grams of sample, finely ground, to which are added five ml. of 6 N sulfuric acid per gram, are autoclaved at 15 pounds pressure for one hour. The acid is neutralized with barium carbonate; the resulting barium sulfate and other undissolved material are filtered off. The pH is then adjusted to neutrality. Neutralizing the sulfuric acid with sodium hydroxide or ammonium hydroxide is not permissible as excessive amounts of salts are toxic to the test organism.

Many substances were found to contain bound p-aminobenzoic acid liberated only by acid hydrolysis. Notable among these were animal tissue, urine, wheat, egg, spinach, carrots, and potatoes; yeast and sweet potatoes have 10 per cent or less of the "bound" form.

The organism is apparently specific in its requirements for p-aminobenzoic acid. Beadle and Tatum [200] tested a large number of compounds none of which were active over a fraction of one per cent of the activity of the vitamin. Thompson *et al.*[201] noticed that the amide had 0.03 per cent of the activity of the p-aminobenzoic acid.

Landy and Dicken's [68] Method for Assaying for Presence of Certain Members of the Vitamin-B Complex. This method, which involves use of *Lactobacillus casei* ε, may be used for assaying for riboflavin, pantothenic acid, biotin, folic acid, pyridoxin, and nicotinic acid. In the assay procedure the particular vitamin under assay is omitted from the basal medium. Proper amounts are used for preparation of the respective standard curves.

276. Mitchell, Isbell, and Thompson. 1943. J. Biol. Chem. 147, 485-486; 148, 281-287.

277. Cheldelin, Eppright, Snell, and Guirard. 1942. Univ. of Texas Pub. 4237.

178. Blanchard. 1941. J. Biol. Chem. 140, 919.

COMPLETE MEDIUM FOR LACTOBACILLUS CASEI*

Casein hydrolyzate	0.5 gm. (dry weight)
Sodium acetate trihydrate	0.6 gm.
Glucose	1.0 gm.
Asparagine	25.0 mg.
Tryptophane	10.0 mg.
Cystine	10.0 mg.
Salt solution A	0.5 ml.
Salt solution B	0.5 ml.
Guanine hydrochloride	500.0 μg.
Adenine sulfate	500.0 μg.
Xanthine	500.0 μg.
Uracil	500.0 μg.
Thiamine hydrochloride	10.0 μg.
Biotin (free acid)	0.5 μg.
Folic acid concentrate (50% folic acid)	1.0 μg.
Riboflavin	20.0 μg.
Calcium pantothenate	20.0 μg.
Nicotinic acid	20.0 μg.
Pyridoxine	40.0 μg.
Distilled water to	100.0 ml.

pH adjusted to 6.8

Salt Solution A		Salt Solution B	
K_2HPO_4	5.0 gm.	$MgSO_4 \cdot 7H_2O$	10.0 gm.
KH_2PO_4	5.0 gm.	NaCl	0.5 gm.
Water	50.0 ml.	$FeSO_4 \cdot 1H_2O$	0.5 gm.
		$MnSO_4 \cdot 2H_2O$	0.337 gm.
		Water	250.0 ml.

* For assay purposes the medium is prepared in double concentration. The above represents the concentration of the various components in the final dilution.

Medium: The composition of the complete medium is given in the above table. It is essential that all constituents be of the highest purity. Best results are obtained if the medium is prepared just before use. Stock solutions of tryptophane, cystine hydrochloride, salt solutions A and B, and purine bases may be kept on hand, using toluene as a preservative where necessary. Since the purine and pyrimidine bases are not readily soluble in water, it has been found convenient to dissolve them in the casein hydrolyzate. After the addition of riboflavin to the medium, exposure to light should be avoided.

It is necessary that great care be taken in the preparation of the casein hydrolyzate, since this is the only constituent whose composition is not chemically defined; it is, therefore, the only source of variation. Purified or "vitamin-free" casein should be reprecipitated several times in order to remove traces of interfering vitamins, particularly nicotinic acid and pyridoxine. Reprecipitation is followed by the usual acid hydrolysis, and the resulting hydrolyzate is treated with activated carbon, primarily for the removal of any biotin present. Culture medium containing casein hydrolyzate prepared in this fashion supports maximum growth of the test organism and yields satisfactory blanks for all the six vitamin assays.

Purification of Casein: To one liter of distilled water at 50°C. (122°F.) 100 grams of casein are added gradually with stirring. This mixture is stirred for 30 minutes, three grams of sodium bicarbonate (dissolved in a convenient volume of water) are added, and the stirring is continued until the casein is dissolved. It may be necessary to add more water. When solution is complete, the pH is adjusted to 4.6 with 10-per cent hydrochloric acid. The casein precipitate is allowed to settle and is removed by filtration. The reprecipitation procedure is repeated several times, depending upon the purity of the original casein. As a rule, several reprecipitations are necessary before satisfactory blanks can be obtained in culture medium prepared with the resulting hydrolyzate.

Preparation of Casein Hydrolyzate: One hundred grams (dry weight) of the reprecipitated casein are hydrolyzed with 500 ml. of 25-per cent sulfuric acid for 10 hours at 15 pounds pressure. The sulfuric acid is neutralized with barium hydroxide and the barium sulfate is removed by filtration.

Treatment of Casein Hydrolyzate With Activated Carbon: Casein hydrolyzate solution in a concentration of 10 per cent (total solids) is acidified to pH 3 and treated with Nuchar (one gram of Nuchar to 10 grams of casein). The mixture is stirred for one hour and filtered through filter-cel. The resulting hydrolyzate may be preserved under toluene or sterilized by autoclaving. Following incubation the amount of growth is determined by titration of the acid produced, using 0.1 N sodium hydroxide. Titration may be colorimetric with bromthymol blue as the indicator, or electrometric, using either glass or quinhydrone electrode. Values obtained from the dilutions of the vitamin standard are used to construct a standard curve from which the vitamin content of any dilution of sample may be calculated. Typical standard curves for all six vitamins required by *Lactobacillus casei* were presented.

Preparation of Inoculum: Stock cultures of *Lactobacillus casei* are carried in yeast-dextrose-agar stabs and are transferred as recommended by Snell and Strong. A 24-hour culture of *Lactobacillus .casei* in 10 ml. of yeast dextrose broth is centrifuged, and the bacteria are washed in 10 ml. of 0.85 per cent sodium chloride solution. The washed sediment is resuspended in four ml. of saline, and one ml. of the resulting suspension is added to 85 ml. of saline. One-tenth milliliter of this dilute suspension per tube serves as the inoculum.

Assay Procedure: For assay for any of the six vitamins, basal medium of twice the concentration given above is prepared with omission of the vitamin under test. Dilutions of the sample to be assayed are distributed into culture tubes, five ml. of basal medium added, and the final volume adjusted to 10 ml. with water. Similarly, tubes containing the basal medium with different levels of the vitamin are prepared, from which a standard curve may be established. The following are the concentrations per tube supporting maximum growth: riboflavin, 0.5 μg.; pantothenic acid, 0.4 μg.; pyridoxin, 0.8 μg.; nicotinic acid, 0.8 μg.; folic acid, 0.025 μg.; and biotin, 0.005 μg. Several levels of the vitamin, all less than the amount required for maximum growth of the test organism, should be used in the standards. A blank containing no vitamin supplement should be included.

All tubes are sterilized for 15 minutes at 121°C.(250°F.) and cooled to room temperature. They are inoculated with a saline suspension of *Lactobacillus casei* ϵ centrifuged from a 24-hour culture grown in 10 ml. of yeast extract glucose broth, washed with 10 ml. of saline solution, and resuspended in 350 ml. of saline. One-tenth ml. of this dilution serves as the inoculum. The tubes are incubated at 37°C.(98.6°F.) for 72 hours and the growth response determined by the usual titration procedure.

CHAPTER 26

MEDIA AND THEIR PREPARATION

Bacteria are such small organisms that their environment is very important. When grown in the laboratory, they must have, among other things, the right foods.

Standard Methods and Media. All media should be prepared according to accepted formulas. In the United States, the American Public Health Association has published *Standard Methods of Water Analysis* and *Standard Methods for the Examination of Dairy Products*, in both of which methods for preparation of culture media have always been recommended.[1] The Society of American Bacteriologists also sponsors a *Manual of Methods for the Pure Culture Study of Bacteria* which includes a section on preparation of culture media. Numerous bacteriologists have shown the importance of uniform media. They have been found necessary in disinfection work, in the fermentation industries, and in examination of foods for spoilage. In some cases progress has been delayed because proper culture media were not used.

CONSTITUENTS OF MEDIA

While there are many different substances which may be used for culturing bacteria, a certain few have given such good results that they are used in many of our common media. These substances furnish as near optimum conditions as possible for the common bacteria. For those which do not grow well on ordinary media, certain pathogenic forms for instance, special media which embody the essential food substance must be prepared. Some of the pathogenic bacteria grow better if a little blood serum or hemoglobin are added. That the composition of the medium has great influence on the results obtained in bacteriology is well shown by Dawson[2] and others. He was able to vary such properties as the formation of enzymes, the agglutinating power, etc., by changing the composition of the medium. In some instances, it seemed as if a new strain of organism had been formed. Various factors which enter into making a good media have been studied. It should be borne in mind that the several ingredients used for making media may not be sterile.

Water Content of Constituents Used in Culture Media. The various ingredients which are used in culture media absorb water, and if comparable media are to be prepared, dry materials must be used. Agar and gelatin are especially prone to take up considerable amounts of water. Browne[3] reported that agar stored in an atmosphere of 60 per cent humidity took up 20 per cent of water in nine days and 42 per cent in 25 days. Other ingredients of culture media absorbed much water in this period. Such

1. Other discussions of media and their preparation may be found in Pure Culture Study of Bacteria, Biotech Publications, Geneva, N. Y., Leaflet II, and in the National Formulary, American Pharmaceutical Assoc., Washington, D. C.
2. Dawson. 1919. J. Bact. 4, 133.
3. Browne. 1922. J. Ind. Eng. Chem. 14, 712-714.

results indicate that materials must be stored in tight containers else considerable error may be introduced into media making. The Digestive Ferments Company reported that unless shredded agar is kept in a tight container, it may contain 38 per cent of water by weight. Unless agar is kept dry, allowance must be made for water absorption.

Since colony structure and shape depend so much on the medium, Nungester[4] devised a method for determining the hardness of agar which consisted of noticing the time required for a brass plunger .5 mm. in diameter to sink into the agar .1 mm. under a given weight. Differences in hardness of the agar were found to affect colony form of the R-S type of *Bacillus anthracis.* Such results convince one that the medium is a very important agent in the culture of bacteria.

Peptone. Commercial peptones are added to common media to supply organic nitrogen. It has been quite satisfactorily demonstrated that bacteria cannot utilize nitrogen in proteins until they have been hydrolzed to simpler compounds. Consequently, bacteriologists have resorted to mixtures of the cleavage products which are distributed under the name of peptones. Important among these are the amino acids, which are hydrolyzed from protein molecules.

Many analyses of peptones are available in the literature, but as Banzhaf and Hirschleifer[5] have pointed out, they may mean very little because in many cases the methods of analysis are not known.

Witte's peptone was formerly specified for all bacteriological media. Berry[6] and Conn[7] reported that equally good results are secured with the domestic peptones as with those of foreign manufacture.

Berry's conclusions were based on results secured by comparing colonies of *Eberthella typhosa, Escherichia coli,* and a streptococcus on agar containing two per cent of different peptones. In an extensive comparative investigation on methods of milk analysis in New York City, Conn found practically no difference in results secured with media made from three different peptone preparations. Conn considered one to be as good as another.

Chemical analyses of various peptones have been reported by a number of investigators. Myers[8] found a variation among peptones in abiltiy to give a test for hydrogen sulfide. Witte's brand gave better results than some domestic brands. Yaoi,[9] in general, confirmed Myers' results. He reported that Witte's brand contained the largest amount of cystine. The buffering action of various peptones, according to Bronfenbrenner,[10] may be quite different. These variations are probably of little importance in routine work. They may become very important in specialized work. Calvert,[11] Gage and Adams,[12] Sedgwick and Prescott,[13] Wright,[14] Tilley,[15] and Wilcox[16] all reported variation in results with different peptones. Treece[17] stated that gas-producing substances may be present in various amounts and thus give different gas ratios. The source of the gas did not seem to be in the carbohydrate radicals. Results of analyses by McAlpine and

4. Nungester. 1929. Soc. Expt. Biol. and Med. Proc. 26, 457-458.
5. Banzhaf and Hirschleifer. 1914. N. Y. City Dept. Health, Collected Studies Bur. Labs., 8, 223-225.
6. Berry. 1914-1915. *Ibid.*, p. 288.
7. Conn. 1915. U. S. Pub. Health Rpts. 30, 3-48.
8. Myers. 1920. J. Bact. 5, 231.
9. Yaoi. 1926. Japan Med. World 6, 114-116.
10. Bronfenbrenner. 1921. Soc. Expt. Biol. and Med. Proc. 19, 16-17.
11. Calvert. 1924. Amer. Water Wks. Assn. J. 12, 307-310.
12. Gage and Adams. 1904. J. Infect. Dis. 1, 358.
13. Sedgwick and Prescott. 1895. Amer. Pub. Health Assoc. 20, 450.
14. Wright. 1917. J. Bact. 2, 315-346.
15. Tilley. 1923. J. Bact. 8, 287-295.
16. Wilcox. 1922. Abs. Bact. 6, 89.
17. Treece. 1928. J. Infect. Dis. 42, 495-500.

Brigham [18] of several common American peptones did not show significant differences as far as bacterial nutrition was concerned. Reddish and Burlingame,[19] however, observed that resistance of *Staphylococcus aureus* being used in disinfection work was maintained more consistently in media made with one brand of peptone. When other brands were used, resistance was reduced.

A troublesome situation in some peptones was discovered by Wright.[20] Peptones from which media were made were found to contain an enormous number of rod-shaped organisms which had the shape of *Bacillus mycoides*. The contamination was so heavy in the peptone under study that these cells appeared in the finished broth. Although the cells were dead they caused trouble by appearing in the films. O'Meara and Macsween [21] have called attention to the possibility of copper in peptones interfering with bacterial development. Many bacteria failed to grow in media containing peptone and traces of copper.

Tryptone and Tryptoses. Tryptone is a peptone, devised by the Digestive Ferments Company as especially suitable for indol formation by bacteria. Since its introduction for this purpose, its usefulness has been extended to other fields. Tryptone was adopted for the standard plating medium by *Standard Methods for the Examination of Dairy Products*, 1939 edition. Tryptose is another special peptone devised for meeting growth requirements of members of the genus Brucella. Its use, also, has been extended to other fields. Chemical and bacteriological examination of different animal and vegetable peptones by Hook and Fabian [21a] showed some variation in composition. Whether they are significant would be difficult to determine.

Meat Extract. This is an important constituent of laboratory media. Several brands are available in the American market. Its manufacture has been described by Bigelow and Cook.[22] Formerly, Liebig's Meat Extract was specified for media. Also the extractives from the meat were prepared by soaking ground lean beef in water for 24 hours. Five hundred grams of ground lean beef were soaked in 500 ml. of distilled water in the refrigerator. At the end of this time it was filtered through cheesecloth or flannel and brought back to the original volume by adding distilled water. This meat infusion was used as the base to which the other constituents were added. Its chemical composition is not far different from that of the commercial meat extract. Gage and Adams,[12] however, have shown that the chemical composition is variable. The reaction and the organic solids are variable. This is probably due to the different grades of meat used. High amounts of fat and connective tissue will tend to give a product weaker in strength. The kind of beef might help to explain the variation in chemical content.

Gelatin. This was first used in culture media by Koch. Since that time, it has become firmly established in the bacteriological laboratory. The manufacture of gelatin has been described by Thiele,[23] who stated that all varieties, whether used for bacteriological, photographic, or food purposes,

18. McAlpine and Brigham. 1928. J. Bact. 16, 251-256.
19. Reddish and Burlingame. 1938. Amer. Pharm. Assoc. J. 27, 231-234.
20. Wright. 1926. J. Path. and Bact. 29, 221.
21. O'Meara and Macsween. 1937. Idem 44, 225-234.
21a. Hook and Fabian. 1943. Mich. Agr. Expt. Sta. Tech. Bull. 185.
22. Bigelow and Cook. 1908. U. S. Bur. Chem. Bull. 114.
23. Thiele. 1912. J. Ind. Eng. Chem. 4, 446-451.

are prepared in about the same manner. The amino acids in gelatin were studied at some length by Dakin.[24] Gershenfeld and Tice,[25] after a study of various gelatins on the market, recommended pork-skin gelatin as best for bacteriological work.

Agar-Agar. This substance has played a great role in bacteriology. Hitchens and Leiking[26] stated that Frau Hesse, in Saxony, introduced the substance during the late 1880's. Koch later recognized its value and adopted it in his own laboratory. This substance, according to Whittaker,[27] is derived from many plants but principally from those of the genus Gelidium, which grow on rocks along the sea coast. It is carefully cleaned by heating and washing and finally dissolved and filtered, after which it is dried in various shapes. Fellers[28] found a remarkable uniformity upon analysis of 16 agars from various sources.

Chemically agar is a carbohydrate, a hexosan of the cellulose group of the polysaccharides. It is not utilized by many bacteria, differing in this manner from gelatin.

Commercial shredded agar should be thoroughly washed before it is used in bacteriological culture media. Ayers[29] reported that large amounts of calcium and magnesium inhibited bacteria. These salts should, therefore, be removed from the agar.

It is known that the agar medium has some influence on the colonies of microorganisms which develop on it. One may wonder to what extent the work on microbic dissociation and similar topics has been influenced by the media used. According to Thomson and Thomson,[30] various agars have different strength and toughness. They might, therefore, give media with significantly different properties.

In recent years, dehydrated synthetic culture media have appeared on the market in large quantities. Levine[31] reported that it was uneconomical to prepare small batches of agar media from their constituents when dehydrated products were available. Dehydrated products make it easier to prepare media of uniform composition

At the base of agar slants, a fluid is often seen which was formerly considered to be water by many bacteriologists. However, Pijper[32] maintained that this was a dilute solution of agar medium and stated that it would be more accurate to call it agar serum, and that it is merely the product of secretion caused by syneresis. When microorganisms are planted on the surface of an agar slant, they are bathed with this agar serum and thereby secure their food. Agar media, therefore, are not solid or liquefiable solid media. Hitchins[33] has suggested the use of media containing small amounts of agar. The use of such media is said to favor

24. Dakin. 1920. J. Biol. Chem. 44, 499-529.
25. Gershenfeld and Tice. 1941. J. Bact. 41, 645-652.
26. Hitchins and Leiking. 1938. Idem 35, 21.
27. Whittaker. 1911. Amer. J. Pub. Health 1, 632-639.
28. Fellers. 1916. J. Ind. Eng. Chem. 8, 1128-1133.
29. Ayers. 1920. J. Bact. 5, 89-98.
30. Thomson and Thomson. 1924-1925. Annals Pickett-Thomson Res. Lab. 1, 217-228.
31. Levine. 1927. Iowa Acad. Sci. Proc. 34, 91.
32. Pijper. 1920. So. African Med. Rec. 17, 372.
33. Hitchins. 1921. J. Infect. Dis. 29, 390; Abs. Bact. 6 (1922). 36.

the growth of some bacteria which are otherwise studied with difficulty. Hitchins pointed out the usefulness of such media in the culturing of anaerobic bacteria. In media containing .1 per cent of agar there are varying oxygen tensions possible. At the top of the medium aerobic conditions are available, since the low amount of agar cannot fill completely the volume of liquid. Below this, anaerobic conditions which prevent the ingress of oxygen are created by the agar. Healy [34] also reported that the liquid often found at the bottom of agar slants is not water but an exudate from the agar gel. This contains food substances and, in some cases, produces better growth of the bacteria than the agar surface itself. Besides the food substances which it contains, it probably exerts a physical influence in delaying evaporation during incubation.

REACTION OF MEDIA

Most bacteria have optimum acidities at which they develop. Consequently, it is necessary to adjust media to certain acidities when they are being studied. The desired pH is indicated for each special medium when it is quite removed from the neutral point. Methods for determining pH are many and are treated in many different books. Bacteriologists who wish information in considerable detail may consult *Pure Culture Study of Bacteria*, Leaflet IX, Biotech. Publications, Geneva, N. Y.

Colorimetric Estimation of Hydrogen-Ion Concentration. A person usually has some idea of the range of hydrogen-ion concentration of the substance which he is studying. If he is adjusting the reaction of a bacteriological culture medium, prepared according to standard methods, he will know that it will probably be about pH 6.6 to 6.8. If he desire to adjust the reaction to pH 7.0 he knows brom-thymol-blue will have to be used since its pH range is 6.0 to 7.6. Very often, however, he will not know the reaction and must, therefore, make a rough test to get the range.

Rough Test. The directions prepared by Dr. Taylor of the Lamotte Chemical Company may be followed. To make the test, fill a graduated test tube to the mark (10 ml.) with the solution to be tested and add .5 ml. of brom-thymol-blue solution. The range of this indicator is pH 6.0 to 7.6, and covers the neutral point pH 7.0. The use of the indicator will tell whether the solution is neutral, acid, or alkaline. Brom-thymol-blue is yellow at 6.0 and a deep blue at 7.6. If a color is secured which lies between yellow and deep blue the reaction is between 6.0 and 7.6. If the latter, no further rough tests are necessary. If, however, a yellow color had been obtained on addition of brom-thymol-blue, the pH would have been 6.0 or lower. Then another tube should be filled to the mark (10 ml.) with the unknown solution and .5 ml. of brom-cresol-green added since this indicator has a range of pH 4.0 to 5.6. This indicator is yellow at pH 4.0 and a deep blue at pH 5.6. If the color is between yellow and deep blue the pH is between 4.0 and 5.6. It will be noticed that in the illustrations just taken the range from 5.6 to 6.0 was not covered. For this range we have chlor-phenol-red with a range of 5.2 to 6.8. The above technic may be repeated with any of the indicators. As soon as the proper indicator is found, more delicate and accurate observations may be made.

Accurate Measurements. Having used the rough test for securing the range, let us assume that brom-thymol-blue indicator was found to be the proper one and that we now wish to know just where the reaction of the unknown substance falls between 6.0 and 7.6. For this purpose a set of color standards and a comparator are required. A set of such standards consists of nine standard tubes and one tube of distilled water. These tubes will have definite pH values of 6.0, 6.2, 6.4, and so on up to 7.6, to each of which .5 ml. of brom-thymol-blue has been added. These tubes are made in exactly

34. Healy. 1926. J. Bact. 12, 179.

the same manner as are those with the unknown solution except that the pH of each tube is known. Having these standards the analyst must now simply match the tube with the unknown material with the standards. Attention must be called to the fact that an error may be introduced by matching against the color standards at either end of a given set. For instance, a test sample may match the brom-thymol-blue pH 7.6 tube and yet have a much higher pH value, owing to the fact that pH 7.6 is the end of the range for this indicator.

Adjustment of Reaction of Culture Media. Place eight ml. of distilled water in a graduated test tube (10 ml.) and add two ml. of the agar or broth to be tested. Add .5 ml. of brom-thymol-blue. The desired color is green with a yellowish tint. It may be compared, however, with the standard tube with a pH of 6.6. If it is not at this pH, dilute NaOH should be added from a burette until the desired color is secured. Multiply the number of milliliters of dilute NaOH required to bring the two ml. of medium to the proper reaction by 500 to find out how much should be added to adjust one liter of medium.

Sterilization of Culture Media. Culture media are generally sterilized in the autoclave. The high temperature and pressure have been said to induce changes in some of the constituents which cause anamalous results. Hasseltine,[35] for instance, compared standard lactose broth compounded before sterilization with the same basic medium to which lactose was added after tubing and sterilization. Greater amounts of gas were formed in the standard medium. Hasseltine believed this was due to hydrolysis of lactose during sterilization. Mudge[36] reached opposite conclusions with lactose and maltose. He stated that heating these sugars in free-flowing steam for three consecutive days caused more hydrolysis than heating in the autoclave at 15 pounds for 15 minutes. However, he advised sterilization of sugar solutions by filtration. Wolff[37] did not believe that the alterations in the media were significant. However, he was cautious enough to state that organisms more delicate than those he used might give different results. McAlpine[38] confirmed Mudge's results.

The factors involved in sterilization of culture media are quite like those involved in all methods of high-pressure steam sterilization. Canners, for instance, have learned much about such things as loading the retort and rate of heat penetration into containers. Little work on the latter has been done by bacteriologists. The canners have learned that success in processings cans of food depends on careful consideration of factors which may cause difficulty in sterilization. Benton and Leighton[39] determined the actual temperatures which were attained by media during autoclave sterilization. Large flasks of media took 15 minutes to reach autoclave temperature, 120°C.(248°F.). Culture tubes of media at the center of tightly packed baskets took 10 minutes longer to reach autoclave temperature than those at the outside of the basket. Barkworth[40] came to similar conclusions.

35. Hasseltine. 1917. U. S. Pub. Health Rpts. 32, 1878-1887.
36. Mudge. 1917. J. Bact. 2, 403-416.
37. Wolff. 1921. Brit. J. Expt. Path. 2, 266-275.
38. McAlpine. 1923. Abs. Bact. 7, 11.
39. Benton and Leighton. 1925. J. Infect. Dis. 37, 353-358.
40. Barkworth. 1931. Centbl. Bakt., Pt. 2, 84, 353-357.

Standard Methods of Water Analysis, Eighth Edition, prescribes sterilization of all culture media in the autoclave at 15 pounds (120°C.) for 15 minutes after the pressure has reached 15 pounds. All air is to be forced from the autoclave by allowing live steam to stream through it for a few minutes before the pressure is allowed to rise. *Standard Methods for the Examination of Dairy Products* prescribes 20 minutes at the above temperatures. In addition the autoclave is to be equipped with both a thermometer and pressure gage. Whether these recommendations are adequate would be determined by the methods of packing the media in the autoclave.

Great care must be used in sterilization of media in laboratories in which *Clostridium botulinum* and thermophilic bacteria are being studied. These bacteria form very heat-resistant spores which easily survive ordinary methods of sterilization.

Effect of Sterilization on Reaction of Culture Media. Bacteriologists usually adjust the reaction of culture media before sterilization and assume that it has not been changed. It is known that changes occur in the autoclave which may not be significant in routine work but which should not be overlooked in more careful research. An alkaline medium containing glucose or lactose is rarely the same after sterilization. The best way to avoid these changes is to sterilize sugar solutions separately and add them aseptically to the sterile peptone base when the medium is needed.

Sterile sugar solutions will keep for a long time. Henry and Marshall [41] stored 20-per cent solutions of several sugars at 5°C.(41°F.) for 20 months successfully. Grace and Highberger [42] reported that the reaction of culture media could change during storage, a fact that should not be overlooked. Evidence on this subject is both good and sufficient. Hesse [43] noted an increase in titratable acidity after sterilization. Deeleman,[44] in order to make up for the changes in the reaction caused by sterilization, corrected the reaction by adding sterile acid or alkali after sterilization. Dernby [45] found that sterilization of bouillon caused the pH to be raised. He explained this on the basis that carbon dioxide was driven off from bicarbonates, thus increasing the concentration of carbonates and making the media more alkaline.

According to Mudge, the acidity produced during sterilization is due to a reaction between sugar and amino groups. Clark [46] explained the changes as due to oxidation of sugar as well as to greater solution of glass at higher temperatures. That the sugars are altered by sterilization was suggested by Dernby and Allander.[47] They found that when sugar was present in bouillon, acid was formed during sterilization. When no sugar was present, the hydrogen-ion concentration was slightly higher after autoclaving but later returned to its original value. Similar observations

41. Henry and Marshall. 1927. J. Lab. and Clin. Med. 12, 474-477.
42. Grace and Highberger. 1920. J. Infect. Dis. 26, 457-462.
43. Hesse. 1904. Ztschr. f. Hyg. u. Infektionskrank. 14, 1-22.
44. Deeleman. 1897. Arb. K. Gsndhtsamt. 13, 374-402.
45. Dernby. 1921. Ann. Inst. Pasteur. 35, 277-290.
46. Clark. 1915. J. Infect. Dis., 17, 109.
47. Dernby and Allander. 1921. Biochem. Ztschr. 123, 245-271.

were recorded by Foster and Randall.[48] Smith[49] reported hydrolysis of maltose by heating in the autoclave. Autoclaving sugar solutions for 30 minutes at 120°C.(248°F.) was much more destructive than "momentary heating," according to Davis and Rogers[50]; it was found to be only slightly more restructive than the usual intermittent method. They did not consider heating the sugar apart from the medium to be necessary. Differences in results of fermentation tests carried out with both types of media were not significant. Momentary autoclaving of all sugar broths at pH 6.6 was recommended. Another effect of autoclaving sugar media, observed by Baumgartner,[51] is formation of substances which increase the rate of destruction by heat of microorganisms.

Sterilization by autoclaving at 112°C.(233.6°F.) for 15 minutes or steaming for 30 minutes on three successive days, of reducing sugars dissolved in McIlvaine's buffer or nutrient broth results in the formation of material which increases the rate of thermal destruction when *Escherichia coli*, suspended in such solutions, is heated at 54°C.(129.2°F.). In autoclaved glucose-broth at 37°C.(98.6°F.) growth of *Escherichia coli* was slightly inferior to that in filtered sterilized media. These effects appear to be due to the direct toxic action of material formed during heat sterilization. Production of toxic material is increased by increasing the heat treatment of the solutions; it is formed concurrently with caramel. For its production in distilled water solution, the heat treatment must be sufficient to cause caramelization. The toxic material is not produced when reducing sugar solutions are sterilized by filtration. Filter-sterilized glucose, galactose, lactose, maltose, sucrose, mannitol, and glycerol in .5 M concentrations in buffer or broth were all found to decrease the rate of thermal destruction of *Escherichia coli*. A preliminary chemical investigation failed to reveal the nature of the toxic material. Advantages of media which have not been heated have been mentioned frequently. Schweizer[52] described apparatus and procedures for accomplishing cold sterilization.

When working with heat-resistant bacteria it is necessary to give special attention to sterilization of apparatus and media. *Clostridium botulinum* and some of the thermophilic bacteria causing spoilage of canned foods are in this category.

Sugar-Free Media. Sugar-free media are necessary in careful fermentation work. Smith[53] observed that muscle sugar might reach as high as .3 per cent. Such sugar must be eliminated.

The commonest and perhaps most useful method for accomplishing this is to inoculate the medium with a pure culture of *Escherichia coli* and incubate overnight. Randall and Hall[54] advised the use of *Clostridium welchii*. It seemed to give more complete decomposition of sugar, since gas

48. Foster and Randall. 1921. J. Bact. 6, 143-160.
49. Smith. 1932. Biochem. J. 26, 1467-1472.
50. Davis and Rogers. 1938.
51. Baumgartner. 1938. J. Bact. 36, 369-382.
52. Schweizer. 1936. Arch. f. Mikrobiol. 7, 297-314.
53. Smith. 1895. Centbl. Bakt. 18, 2-9.
54. Randall and Hall. 1921. J. Infect. Dis. 29, 344-358.

formation went on after the commonly used organisms, such as *Escherichia coli,* had ceased growing.

BOUILLON MEDIA

Such media form the base from which many others are made. Cook and LeFevre [54] studied bacteriological bouillons to determine how much variation occurred when they were prepared according to standard procedures. They found that beef bouillons were fairly constant in composition, but contained more creatin and creatinin than the meat extract or liver bouillons. The liver bouillons showed greatest variation. Comparisons of "infusion" media and "meat extract" media showed more nutrient material in the "infusion" media. From their results it seems advisable to add peptone to the coagulated meat juice, and not before this coagulation.

Nutrient broths or plain bouillons are usually made from water, peptone, and meat extractives. The extractives are secured either in commercial meat extract or by soaking fresh meat in water.

Nutrient Broth (Standard Methods for the Examination of Water and Sewage).

1. Add three grams of meat extract and five grams of peptone to a liter of distilled water.
2. Heat slowly on the steam bath to at least 65°C.(149°F.).
3. Adjust reaction so that the pH after sterilization will be between 6.4 and 7.0.
4. Bring to a boil, cool to 25°C.(77°F.), and filter through paper until clear.
5. Distribute in test tubes, about 10 ml. in each tube.
6. Sterilize in the autoclave at 15 lb. pressure (120°C. or 248°F.) for 15 minutes after the pressure reaches 15 lb.

A concentrated nutrient bouillon was suggested by Moon.[56] The ingredients for 10 liters were added to one liter of water and stored after autoclaving. Moon stated that an exceedingly clear medium was secured and that considerable titrating and filtering were eliminated. By this procedure one would not avoid changes in reaction owing to reheating for sterilization.

Standard Nutrient Broth, Standard Methods for the Examination of Dairy Products, 1941 Edition. The medium is compounded as follows:

Tryptone, Bacto	1,000 ml.
Beef extract	5 gm.
Distilled water	3 gm.

Coconut-Milk Medium. Blauvelt [57] recommended use of unsterilized coconut milk as a culture medium. The fluid is drawn aseptically from ripe coconuts with a sterile syringe and added to either plain broth or plain agar in concentrations of 10 to 25 per cent. Growth of microorganisms was said to be about doubled on this medium.

Brewer's [58] Thioglycollate Medium for Cultivating Anaerobic Bacteria. This medium was devised to provide a clear culture medium for anaerobic bacteria. Glucose infusion broth containing .05 per cent of agar is the base. To this is added .1 per cent of thioglycollate to provide proper oxidation-reduction potential. The practical value of this medium rests mainly in the fact that no effort need be made to make the medium anaerobic. An E_h indicator may be employed to give color to any portion of the medium when it becomes aerated. Although other media have been used successfully for the "aerobic" cultivation of anaerobes, this is the first clear liquid medium which will remain anaerobic for a long time without the aid of a seal or of special apparatus. For example, tubes of this medium which were stored for a month at room temperature

55. Cook and LeFevre. 1918. Amer. J. Pub. Health 8, 587-589.
56. Moon. 1927. Idem 17, 640.
57. Blauvelt. 1939. J. Lab. and Clin. Med. 24, 420-423.
58. Brewer. 1940. Amer. Med. Assoc. J. 115, 598-600; J. Bact. 39 (1940), 10.

and then inoculated (test-organisms: *Clostridium novyi, Clostridium tetani, Clostridium septicum, Clostridium botulinum, Clostridium histolyticum, Clostridium welchii, Clostridium sporogenes,* and several strains of anaerobic streptococci) gave growth equivalent to that obtainable in control cultures in "anaerobe" jars. A comparative study of this medium with other media employed for the cultivation of anaerobes was made.

A sugar-free base medium for fermentation reactions, a modification of the above medium, was proposed by Reed and Orr.[59] It contained:

Bactopeptone or proteose peptone......................................	20.0 gm.
Sodium chloride...	5.0 gm.
Sodium thioglycollate..	1.0 gm.
Agar..	1.0 gm.
Water..	1,000.0 ml.

Sugars in amounts of one per cent are added to the base before tubing and sterilization.

Mickle and Breed's[60] Tomato-Juice Broth. This medium was found to be useful for isolation and growth of tomato products spoilage bacteria.

Nutrient broth..	900 ml.
Tomato juice or tomato pulp.....................................	100 ml.
Reaction pH 6.8 to 7.2	

Place the material in Durham fermentation tubes. Sterilize under 10 lb. pressure for 15 minutes, or fractionally in an Arnold sterilizer for 30 minutes on three successive days. Incubate between 20 and 41°C.(68 and 105.8°F.). (Room temperature is satisfactory.)

A solid tomato-juice agar was made by adding 10 per cent of tomato juice to ordinary nutrient agar just before sterilization.

Pederson's[61] Yeast-Water Tomato Juice. This medium was used for determining the types of spoilage bacteria in tomato products. A clear yellow tomato juice was prepared by boiling, macerating, and filtering tomatoes through cheesecloth. The medium had the following composition:

Yeast water..	900 ml.
Filtered tomato juice..	100 ml.
Reaction pH 6.6 to 6.8	

Autoclave at 15 lb. pressure for five hours a 10-per cent suspension of starch-free yeast. Allow to settle in the refrigerator several days. When clear, decant the supernatant liquid.

Place in Durham fermentation tubes and sterilize in the autoclave at 10 lb. pressure for 15 minutes, or fractionally in an Arnold sterilizer. For a plating medium dissolve 1.5 per cent agar in the yeast water and add the tomato juice just before sterilization.

Liver-Broth Medium for Detection of Thermophilic Bacteria Not Producing Hydrogen Sulfide in Canned Foods.[62] This medium is used for detecting presence of *Clostridium thermosaccharolyticum* and other putrefactive and mesophilic anaerobic bacteria. Mix chopped beef liver with water in proportion of 500 gm. to 1,000 ml. Boil the mixture slowly for one hour, adjust to about pH 7.0, and boil for an additional 10 minutes. Then press the boiled material through cheese cloth and make liquid to 1,000 ml. Add 10 gm. of peptone and one gm. of dipotassium phosphate to the broth. In tubing introduce from one-half to one inch of previously boiled ground beef liver into the tube.

Before using, unless it is freshly prepared, exhaust the medium by subjecting to streaming steam for at least 20 minutes, and after inoculation, stratify it with a

59. Reed and Orr. 1941. War Med. 1, 493-510.
60. Mickle and Breed. 1925. N. Y. Agr. Expt. Sta. Tech. Bull. 110.
61. Pederson. 1929. N. Y. Agr. Expt. Sta. Tech. Bull. 150.
62. Official and Tentative Methods of Analysis, Assoc. Off. Agr. Chem., fifth edition, p. 642.

two to two and one-half inch layer of plain nutrient agar which has been cooled to 50°C.(122°F.).

Linden's [63] Medium for Yeasts and Molds. While this medium has been especially recommended for yeasts in tomato products, it is probably satisfactory for examination of other foods for these fungi.

Tryptic milk digest	100 ml.
Bacto yeast extract	2 gm.
Tomato juice	100 ml.
Dextrose	10 gm.
Distilled water to make	1,000 ml.

Prepare the tryptic milk as follows: To a liter of skim milk, add sufficient anhydrous sodium carbonate to adjust the reaction to pH 8. Add a paste consisting of two grams of Fairchild's trypsin, or two ml. of freshly prepared enzyme. Add 25 ml. of chloroform and incubate at 30°C.(86°F.) for 24 to 48 hours. Agitate at intervals and maintain the optimum pH. After digestion neutralize with 10 per cent hydrochloric acid, and heat in a double boiler or on a water bath to remove the chloroform. Sterilize 100-ml. aliquots in the autoclave for 15 minutes at 15 lb. pressure.

Place in fermentation tubes, or medium-sized test tubes, and sterilize in the autoclave for 15 minutes at 15 lb. pressure or fractionally. Before using, heat the tubed medium in boiling water 10 minutes, cool, and inoculate. When fermentation tubes are not available, overlay the tubed broth with vaspar seal. For a plating medium, add 15 grams of agar and dissolve by boiling, or heating, in an Arnold sterilizer, adding the tomato juice before sterilization.

Carbohydrate Broths. These are usually made by adding one per cent of the carbohydrate to plain broth. With media prepared from meat infusion to be used in research work, or where very accurate results are desired, it may be necessary to remove the muscle sugar. With ordinary media made with meat extract this is probably not necessary. Careful attention, however, must be given to the carbohydrates. Masucci and Ewe [64] have stated that sugars for bacteriological media should be carefully selected and stored in tight containers, since they are quite hygroscopic.

Nutrose Medium (Purwin and McNutt [65]). Nutrose in one-per cent solution was substituted for sugar-free broth and peptone in the preparation of carbohydrate media. This gave good results with 172 strains of 20 different organisms. The medium had the following composition:

Nutrose	1.0 part
Water	90.0 parts
Sodium chloride	0.5 parts

Mix and allow to stand overnight. Adjust reaction to pH 7.7. The mixture should be steamed in the Arnold for two hours and filtered through cotton. Add one per cent of Andrade's indicator.

Stickel and Meyer's [66] Peptic Digest Media. Stickel and Meyer devised a number of inexpensive media for bacteriological work. These media were later used by Meyer in his work on botulism.

I. PREPARATION OF PEPTIC DIGEST BROTH OF LIVER, BEEF OR
HUMAN PLACENTA

Preparation of Stock Digest Broth. 1. Wash clean, and mince finely five or more large pigs' stomachs. Mince an equal amount of clean pig or beef liver, cheap fat-free beef, placenta, or blood clots.

63. Linden. 1936. Assoc. Off. Agr. Chem. J. 19, 445; 21 (1938), 454-457.
64. Masucci and Ewe. 1920. J. Lab. and Clin. Med. 5, 609-612.
65. Purwin and McNutt. 1924. Abs. Bact. 8, 1695.
66. Stickel and Meyer. 1918. J. Infect. Dis. 23, 68-81.

2. Mix in the following proportions:

Minced stomachs... 400 gm.
Minced liver, beef, or placenta.. 400 gm.
Hydrochloric acid (Baker Chemical Co.)............................ 40 gm.
Tap water at 50°C.(122°F.)...4,000 gm.

Keep the mixture at 50°C.(122°F.) for 18 to 24 hours.[1]

3. Make a biuret and also a tryptophane test.[2] When both reactions are positive, the digest has a yellowish-greenish color and contains very little undigested debris.

4. Transfer to large bottles[3] and steam for 10 minutes at 100°C.(212°F.) to stop digestion. Strain the digest through cotton, or preferably store overnight in the refrigerator and decant after 24 hours.

5. Warm the filtrate or decanted digest to 70°C.(158°F.) and neutralize with sodium carbonate (twice normal solution) to litmus at this temperature.

6. Sterilize[4] (if not to be used at once) in the autoclave at 10 lb. pressure for 15 minutes, or for 30 minutes at 100°C.(212°F.) on two successive days and store away.

This stock digest is used for the various media as follows:

(a) *Plain Digest-Broth.* 1. Filter the desired amount into a flask.

2. Add .2 per cent dibasic potassium phosphate (K_2HPO_4).

3. Set the desired reaction by using litmus, or, preferably, to a definite H-ion concentration (pH 7.0 to 7.5) by one of the reliable methods recommended for the determination of the H-ion concentration. (Hurwitz, Meyer, Ostenberg, Clark, and Lubs or Cole and Onslow.)

4. Heat the broth in the steamer at 100°C.(212°F.) for 15 minutes.

5. Correct the reaction and filter through paper.

6. Distribute in the receptacles used for cultures and sterilize at 100°C.(212°F.) according to the usual routine method.

(b) *Sugar-Free Digest-Broth.* 1. Inoculate the sterile ''stock'' digest in a flask or bottle with one per cent of a 24-hour-old broth culture of *Bacillus saccharolyte* or *Escherichia coli* and incubate for 12 to 18 hours at 37°C.(98.6°F.).

2. Steam for 20 minutes.

3. Adjust the reaction and add .2 to .4 per cent dibasic potassium phosphate and two per cent purified talcum. Filter through paper, distribute for use, sterilize; or use the turbid, killed saccharolyte culture (without previous cleaning) for the preparation of agar. Note method given under ''c.''

(c) *Stock Digest Agar.* 1. Take a measured quantity (8 to 10 liters) of stock digest; add .2 per cent dibasic potassium phosphate (K_2HPO_4), and two per cent of agar[5] fiber.

2. Autoclave at 10 lb. pressure for three-quarters of an hour or heat in a double-boiler to 100°C. and keep the mixture at this temperature until the agar is dissolved.

3. Restore the volume lost by evaporation.

4. Set the reaction very lightly alkaline to litmus or to pH 7.3 by using twice normal NaOH or KOH. Special attention should be given to the adjustment of the reaction, because some commercial agar fiber hydrolyzes readily in the presence of acid.

---

[1] It is advisable to digest the mixture in glass or porcelain receptacles. They have been accustomed to placing museum jars with the digest in a large, electrically regulated water-bath. Very good results. however, have also been obtained by using a large enameled pot equipped with a ''Therm-Elect'' thermo-regulator and heating unit installed by the Electric Sales Service Company of San Francisco.

[2] To five ml. of filtered digest add .1 ml. of five per cent solution of copper sulphate; mix and then add five ml. normal sodium hydroxide. Pink color indicates complete peptonization.

To 10 ml. of neutralized and filtered digest add, slowly, bromine water until the maximum purple coloration is reached.

[3] The bottles in which the Baker Chemical Company supplies hydrochloric or sulfuric acid are excellent for this purpose.

[4] Overheating by long continued sterilization should be avoided, the medium becoming dark brown and losing considerable of its nutritive value.

[5] The inexpensive agar fiber of the present market varies considerably in quality and contains from 10 to 15 per cent water. Some lots of agar will be improved by previous treatment with glacial acetic acid (.2 to .3 per cent) and subsequent thorough washing.

5. Cool to 60°C.(140°F.) and add the white of an egg, beaten with the crushed shells (or, for the sake of economy, ordinary beef or sheep serum in the quantity of 25 to 50 ml. per liter).

6. Autoclave for one hour at 115°C.(239°F.).

7. Filter through cotton and distribute in bottles of 200 to 500 ml. quantities.

8. Sterilize in the customary manner.

(d) *Trypsinized Digest Broth.* 1. Peptic digest prepared up to Stage 4 of the general outlines is not strained or placed in the refrigerator, but is cooled at 80°C. (176°F.) and made faintly alkaline to litmus with twice normal KOH or twice normal sodium carbonate.

2. Cool to 37°C.(98.6°F.) and add one per cent pancreatic extract (prepared according to the methods given in Plimmer's Practical Organic and Biochemistry, London, 1915, p. 405, or in the paper of Cole and Onslow, *Lancet*, 1916, 2, p. 10) or "Bacto" trypsin (marketed in sterile ampoules by the Digestive Ferments Company, Detroit).

3. Keep the mixture at 37°C.(98.6°F.) for three to 10 hours depending on the action of the trypsin and the digestion desired. Control the process by repeated tests for tryptophane.

4. When trypsinizing is sufficiently advanced, render slightly acid with glacial acetic acid and bring slowly to boiling point for 10 minutes.

5. Filter through paper, or keep in cool place overnight and decant the clear liquid in the morning.

6. Add .2 per cent dibasic phosphate, adjust the reaction to faintly alkaline or to the desired H-ion concentration, and treat in the manner outlined in Section "a," or use for the preparation of agar.

(e) *Sugar-Free Trypsinized Digest Broth.* This can be prepared by the following modification of the method given in Section "d."

1. At Stage 2 of the process, add simultaneously with the pancreatic extract or trypsin solution .2 per cent of dibasic potassium phosphate, one per cent calcium carbonate, and one per cent of a 24-hour-old broth culture of *Bacillus saccharolyte.*

2. Incubate at 37°C.(98.6°F.) for 12 to 18 hours and control the digestion by tryptophane tests and removal of carbohydrates by the gas formation in fermentation tubes.

3. When the digest is sugar-free, steam for 15 minutes and use for the preparation of agar; or

4. Set to the desired reaction and steam for another 15 minutes.

5. Filter through paper; the calcium carbonate present will assist materially in obtaining a perfectly clear filtrate.

6. Distribute and sterilize in the usual manner.

II. Preparation of Tryptic Digest Broth of Human Placenta or Beef Heart

1. Prepare some fresh beef hearts by removing the fat and vessels, mince finely, and weigh. Fresh, human placentas are rinsed in water * and also passed through a meat chopper.

2. To 500 gm. of the minced beef hearts or human placentas, add 1,000 gm. of tap water. Make faintly alkaline to litmus with normal KOH or Na₂CO₃, and heat slowly to 70 to 80°C. for 5 to 10 minutes.

3. Cool to 37°C. and add one per cent pancreatic extract or "Bacto" trypsin (details are given under Heading 1, Section "d"), and keep at 37°C.(98.6°F.) for two to five hours. Control the progress of digestion by repeated biuret and tryptophane tests. In case the digestion is extended over a period of six hours, it is necessary to add chloroform or toluene.

4. When the process is sufficiently advanced, render slightly acid with glacial acetic acid and boil slowly for 15 minutes.

5. Either filter or decant the clear fluid which results on placing the digest overnight in a cool place.

6. Adjust the reaction, add .2 per cent dibasic potassium phosphate, and, if necessary, add the minerals (chloride of magnesium, sodium, etc.), in which the broth is deficient for reasons.*

7. Heat for 15 to 30 minutes in the steamer at 100°C.(212°F.) and filter again, if necessary.

8. Sterilize at 100°C.(212°F.) on three consecutive days, if not to be used at once.

III. Peptic and Tryptic Digests of Whole Blood or Blood Clots

(a) *Peptic Digests.* 1. Obtain from the abattoirs in clean containers 10 liters of fresh beef blood. Decant and store the serum which has separated on standing in a refrigerator from 12 to 18 hours).

2. Weigh the blood clots and mix each 100 gm. with one liter of tap water.

3. Place the mixture in an enameled pot, bring slowly to a boil, and under constant stirring keep it at this temperature for five minutes.

4. Cool to 50°C., add to each liter of the mixture 100 gm. of mixed pigs' stomach (for preparation, see the instructions given in the appendix under Method 1), transfer to glass or porcelain receptacle, and finally add one per cent hydrochloric acid.

5. Digest at 50°C.(122°F.) for 18 to 24 hours and treat the resulting digest as outlined in Method 1. (Steps 3 to 6, and Section ''a,'' Steps 1 to 3.)

6. Clear the neutralized broth or agar by adding five to 10 per cent of the decanted beef serum, steam for 45 to 60 minutes.

7. Remove the flasks or bottles from the steamer and allow the clot to form a compact mass; decant or, better, centrifuge the medium to remove it.

8. Sterilize at 100°C.(212°F.) as customary.

(b) *Tryptic Digests.* 1. The preparation of the blood substratum for digestion is practically identical, as given under Section ''a,'' Stages 1 to 4. Use, however, 500 gm. of blood clot to one liter of tap water.

2. Strain the fluid portion of the mixture through cheesecloth and pass the residue through a fruit press. Cool to 37°C.(98.6°F.).

3. Make the thick, brownish fluid slightly alkaline to litmus, add one per cent pancreatic extract and keep at 37°C. for five to 24 to 48 hours.

4. The further treatment of the digest is the same as given under Heading II, Stages 4 to 8.

5. The neutralized broth or agar can be cleared with decanted serum, the resulting medium is excellent for primary isolation of highly parasitic organisms.

Dubovsky and Meyer's [67] Beef Heart-Peptic Digest Broth. This medium was said to be especially suitable for formation of toxin by *Clostridium botulinum.* The authors outlined its preparation as follows:

(1) Slowly heat to boiling finely ground, fat-free heart, 1,000 gm., and tap water, 1,000 ml.; adjust to a reaction of pH 8.0 to 8.2. Then cool and carefully skim off the layer of fat which floats on the cold medium. To each liter of beef-heart mash, add two liters of peptic digest broth, see (2). Adjust the reaction to pH 7.2 to 7.4.

(2) Wash clean and mince finely five or more large pigs' stomachs. Mix in the following proportions: minced pig stomachs, 400 gm.; minced liver, 400 gm.; hydrochloric acid (Baker Chemical Co.), 40 gm.; and tap water at 50°C., 4,000 gm.

Keep the mixture in glass or porcelain receptacles for 18 to 24 hours. Make biuret and also tryptophane tests. When both reactions are positive, the digest is green-yellowish and contains little undigested debris. Transfer to large bottles and steam for 10 minutes at 100°C. to stop digestion. Strain the digest through cotton or preferably store overnight in the refrigerator and decant after 24 hours. Warm the decanted digest to 70°C. and neutralize with sodium carbonate (twice normal solution) to litmus at this temperature. Filter the desired amount, add .2 per cent of dipotassium phos-

---

* In case distilled water is used or the tap water is poor in calcium and other minerals, calcium, sodium, and magnesium chloride, as well as phosphate, have to be added. The following amounts have proven satisfactory: sodium chloride .5 per cent; calcium chloride .01 per cent; magnesium sulphate .02 per cent, and dibasic calcium phosphate .2 per cent.

67. Dubovsky and Meyer. 1922. J. Infect. Dis. 31, 501-540.

phate; adjust to pH 7.4, and mix with beef-heart mash. Adjust the final reaction and sterilize for one hour at 18 lb. of pressure. Incubate for five days and repeat the same sterilization for one hour at 18 lb. of pressure.

Before inoculation, ''exhaust'' in the manner suggested for the liver-broth medium. After inoculation, stratify with sterile vaseline.

For general use, this medium carries the obvious disadvantage that it is difficult to prepare. Where any intensive study of putrefactive spoilage is made, however, it is regarded as a valuable medium.

Darby and Mallmann's [68] **Medium for Coliform Bacteria.** The following medium was developed as an enrichment medium for coliform bacteria in sanitary work. Bacto-tryptose was found to be superior to Bacto-peptone in the base medium.

Bacto-tryptose	2.0 per cent
Lactose	0.5 per cent
K₂HPO₄	0.4 per cent
KH₂PO₄	0.15 per cent
NaCl	0.5 per cent
Water	1.0 liter

This medium was especially devised for water analysis.

Tryptone Broth—Standard Methods of Water Analysis, A. P. H. Assoc., Eighth Edition, Test for Indol. Add 10 grams of Bacto-tryptone to 1,000 ml. of distilled water and heat with stirring to obtain complete solution.

MacConkey's Broth (Single Strength). This medium has had an important place in sanitary work in Great Britain. Its preparation is described on page 372 of this book.

Bailey's [69] **Modified "Hormone" Gelatin Broth.** Select a good gelatin, weigh out 10 gm. and dissolve it in a liter of distilled water, then proceed exactly as in the method described for preparation of the agar medium as described below. Bailey [69] claimed that this medium was especially valuable for preserving cultures of organisms like the penumococcus which die out quite rapidly on laboratory media.

Jackson and Muer's [70] **Liver Broth:**

Beef liver	500 gm.
Peptone (Witte's)	10 gm.
Dextrose	10 gm.
Potassium phosphate	1 gm.
Water	1,000 gm.

1. Chop 500 gm. of beef liver into small pieces and add 1,000 ml. of distilled water. Weigh the infusion and container.

2. Boil slowly for two hours in a double boiler, starting cold, and stirring it occasionally.

3. Make up the loss in weight by evaporation and strain through a wire strainer.

4. To filtrate add 10 gm. of peptone, 10 gm. of dextrose, and one gm. of potassium phosphate. Weigh the infusion and container.

5. After warming this mixture in a double boiler and stirring it for a few minutes to dissolve the ingredients, titrate with N/20 sodium hydroxide, using phenolphthalein as an indicator, and neutralize with normal sodium hydroxide.

6. Boil vigorously for 30 minutes in a double boiler, and five minutes over a free flame with constant stirring to prevent the caramelization of the dextrose.

7. Make up any loss in weight by evaporation, and filter through cotton flannel and filter paper.

8. Tube and sterilize in an autoclave for 15 minutes at 120°C. (248°F.).

Cameron, Williams, and Thompson's [71] **Liver Broth Medium.** While this medium was devised especially for the detection of thermophilic anaerobes in canned foods and sugar, it has wider uses. Cameron described its preparation as follows:

68. Darby and Mallmann. 1939. Amer. Water Wks. Assoc. J. 31, 689-706.
69. Bailey. 1925. J. Infect. Dis. 36, 340-342.
70. Jackson and Muer. 1911. J. Infect. Dis. 8, 289-294.
71. Cameron, Williams, and Thompson. 1928. Natl. Canners Assoc. Bull. 25-L.

Five hundred grams of chopped beef liver are mixed with 1,000 ml. of water and boiled slowly for one hour, after which the boiled material is pressed through cheese-cloth and the liquid is made to 1,000 ml. To the broth are added 10 grams peptone and one gram K_2HPO_4. The reaction is adjusted to pH 7.0. In tubing one-half inch to one inch of the previously boiled ground beef liver is introduced into the tube.

Eyre's [72] Oyster Media. The following media were used by Eyre in the examination of oysters.

Oyster Broth. Mince the bodies of oysters to the weight of 500 grams. Extract at 37°C.(98.6°F.) for 30 minutes in 1,000 ml. of sterilized sea water. When sea water is not available use three per cent of sodium chloride. Filter, tube, and sterilize. Reaction need not be adjusted.

Oyster Agar. To oyster broth described above, add two per cent of powdered agar.

Oyster Gelatin. Add 10 per cent of gelatin to oyster broth described above.

Nitrate Broth. This is a special broth containing nitrite-free nitrate. It may be prepared in different ways. *Standard Methods for the Examination of Water and Sewage, 1912,* recommended a medium of the following composition:

Tap water...1,000 ml.
Witte's peptone..   1 gm.
Potassium nitrate (nitrite free).. 0.2 gm.

Another formula is as follows:

Distilled water..1,000 ml.
Leibig's meat extract..   3 gm.
Potassium nitrate c.p. ....   10 gm.

Breed [73] has shown that by increasing the peptone content of nitrate broth to five grams per liter more uniform results were obtained when 50 cultures of *Escherichia coli* were tested for nitrate reduction. With soil bacteria one per cent peptone seemed to allow more constant results. He concluded that nitrate destruction must be tested for in media which allow vigorous growth of the organisms. Suitable nitrate broths may have to be devised to fit each group.

Trypsin Broth (Gordon et al.[74]). Take some fresh beef heart free from fat and vessels, mince the meat very finely, and weigh. To each one-half kilo add one liter of water and make faintly alkaline to litmus with 20 per cent KOH solution. Heat this slowly to 75°C.(167°F.) to 80°C.(176°F.) for five minutes. Cool to 37°C.(98.6°F.) and add one per cent of liquor trypsine compositum, and keep it at 37°C. for two and one-half to three hours. When trypsinizing is finished, test for peptone with copper sulfate and KOH, then render slightly acid with glacial acetic acid, and bring slowly to boil for one-quarter hour. Leave overnight in a cool place, and siphon off the clear liquid in the morning. Make faintly alkaline to litmus, and sterilize in an autoclave at 118°C. (244.4°F.) for one hour on each of two days (if not to be used at once).

Trypsin has been employed in the preparation of a number of culture media to hydrolyze some of the complex nitrogenous bodies and make them more available to the bacteria. While such media have been most generally used with pathogens, they are being used now for some non-pathogens, such as the anaerobic sporeformers.

Dextrose Potassium Phosphate Broth:

Witte's peptone.. 5 gm.
Dextrose.. 5 gm.
Di-potassium hydrogen phosphate.. 5 gm.

Heat with occasional stirring over steam for 20 minutes. Filter and cool to 20°C. (68°F.). Dilute to 1,000 ml. with distilled water. Tube and sterilize. (*Standard Methods of Water Analysis,* 1917, p. 210.)

72. Eyre. 1923. Roy. Micros. Soc. J., 385-394.
73. Breed. 1915. Science 41, 661.
74. Gordon, Hine, and Flack. 1916. Brit. Med. J., p. 678.

Tryptone Broth. To 1,000 ml. distilled water add five gm. di-potassium phosphate, .3 gm. tryptophane, and one gm. peptone. Heat until the ingredients are thoroughly dissolved, tube, and sterilize at 15 lb. for 15 minutes. Some American peptones are standardized to contain tryptophane. If such peptone is used, the tryptophane in the above formula may be omitted and the peptone increased to five gm.

Peptone Solution (Dunham):

Witte's peptone	10 gm.
Distilled water	1,000 ml.

Reaction not adjusted.

Herring Broth (Sadler [75]). In his investigations on the bacteriology of swelled canned sardines, Sadler used the following broth: Fresh herrings were washed and ground up, no part being discarded. This ground mass was mixed with the sea water to the rate of one part of herring to one-half part of sea water and heated for several hours in an autoclave or Arnold. After cooling, the fat was skimmed off and the mixture heated again. It is then strained through cheesecloth, the filtrate serving as a standard herring extract, used in the preparation of other media. Good results were obtained by Sadler with the following mixture:

Standard broth	1,000 ml.
Sea water	500 ml.
Peptone	15 gm.

These ingredients were heated together in an Arnold, the reaction adjusted to 1+ with phenolphthalein.

Endo's Broth or Bouillon. This medium is prepared like Endo's agar, except that agar is not added. It has been used for detecting *Escherichia coli.* According to McAuliffe and Farrell [76] addition of one ml. of milk to fuchsin lactose broth causes such amounts of the dye to be absorbed that the medium may lose some of its selectivity in detecting coliform bacteria.

Crystal Violet Broth (Salle [77]). This medium was proposed by Salle for the presumptive test for *Escherichia coli;* the author described its preparation as follows:

Place one gram of crystal violet in a glass stoppered bottle of 150-ml. capacity and add 50 ml. of 95 per cent alcohol. Shake thoroughly and then add 50 ml. of distilled water. Shake well again, until all of the dye is dissolved. Pipette 20 ml. of this one per cent solution into a liter volumetric flask. Add sufficient water to make 1,000 ml. This gives a 1:5,000 solution of crystal violet.

The medium for the presumptive test is now prepared as follows:

Peptone, Difco	15.0 gm.
K_2HPO_4	15.0 gm.
KH_2PO_4	3.0 gm.
Lactose	15.0 gm.
Crystal violet (1:5,000)	21.5 ml.
Distilled water to make the quantity = 2,000 ml.	

Mix ingredients and stir until solution is effected. Distribute the medium into test tubes, 20 ml. to each tube. Sterilize in an Arnold sterilizer or in the streaming steam of an autoclave for 10 minutes. Only one heating is necessary to sterilize. Autoclaving under pressure will decompose some of the dye, making the medium unfit for use. It is not necessary to adjust the reaction of the medium as this is controlled by the buffer salts.

The composition of this medium was determined for a sample of 10 ml. of water in 30 ml. of medium. If smaller samples are desired, an adjustment must be made in order not to alter the proportions of various constituents.

75. Sadler. 1918. Canadian Biol., pp. 181-215.
76. McAuliffe and Farrell. 1938. Amer. J. Pub. Health 28, 1217-1221.
77. Salle. 1930. J. Infect. Dis. 41, 1-8.

Brilliant Green Lactose Bile (Muer and Harris[78]). The following medium was found to possess a distinct selective action on *Escherichia coli* in the presumptive test in water analysis. Its preparation was given as follows:

1. Heat one liter of distilled water in a double boiler until water in the outer vessel boils.
2. Add 50 grams of dried ox gall and 10 grams of peptone, stirring until all ingredients are dissolved.
3. Continue boiling for one hour.
4. Remove from the flame and add 10 grams of powdered lactose.
5. Filter through cotton flannel until clear.
6. To each liter of the filtrate add 10 ml. of a one-per cent solution of brilliant green.
7. Tube and sterilize in autoclave for 15 minutes at 15 pounds pressure.

McAuliffe and Farrell[76] pointed out that when milk is added to such a medium as brilliant green lactose bile, so much of the dye may be absorbed that the medium will lose some of its selectivity. Kline[79] found that some lots of brilliant green were bacteriostatic and might not be satisfactory in culture media. Other materials in the medium were shown by Stark and Curtis[80] to be active in reducing the toxicity of .00133 per cent of brilliant green. This amount of brilliant green in one per cent peptone and one per cent lactose completely inhibited growth of all members of the coliform group. When two per cent of ox gall was added, growth of the Escherichia strains was accelerated but Aerobacter strains were slightly inhibited. Stark and Curtis believed that media containing an inhibitory substance are subject to error unless the affects of other substances (proteins) are understood. Further consideration of this question is given later in this chapter.

AGAR MEDIA

Agar media are frequently like liquid media except that agar is added to give a medium which is solid at room temperature. Plain agar is a basic medium to which many other materials may be added to give special media. Thomson and Thomson[30] stated that nutrient agar should not be overheated. Prolonged heating changes the color from a faint straw-colored tint to a deep yellow or brown. This change is apparently due to either acid or alkali hydrolysis. Prolonged heating causes a loss of jellying power. Furthermore, the deep brown substance formed by heating in the presence of alkali may be detrimental to the growth of some bacteria.

Preparation of Nutrient Agar (Standard Methods of Milk Analysis). Old Formula. The final medium is not unlike that secured by other methods. The following ingredients are used:

Agar (market, not oven dried)....................................	1.5 per cent
Beef extract...	0.3 per cent
Peptone...	0.5 per cent
Distilled water...	1,000.0 ml.

Procedure No. 1. Mix all of the ingredients together, cold. Heat in an autoclave at 15 lb. pressure for 40 to 90 minutes according to the quantity of medium being made in each batch. Allow the autoclave to cool very slowly so as not to disturb the sediment. Decant through a cotton filter, taking care not to pour the sediment on the cotton until the bulk of the liquid has passed through.

This simple procedure with certain brands of peptone and grades of agar gives excellent results.

Procedure No. 2. Where large quantities of agar are to be prepared the following procedure has been found useful. Prepare two separate solutions:

78. Muer and Harris. 1920. Amer. J. Pub. Health 10, 874-875.
79. Kline. 1935. Idem 25, 314-318.
80. Stark and Curtis. 1936. J. Bact 32, 375.

MIXTURE A.

Beef extract, .3 per cent of total quantity of medium to be made.

Peptone, .5 per cent of total quantity of medium to be made.

Distilled water, 40 per cent of total quantity of medium to be made.

Place in a kettle. Weigh kettle with contents. Heat on stove to boiling, and boil five minutes. If absolutely necessary to adjust reaction (see Reaction), do so at this point and boil again. Make up with hot distilled water that lost by evaporation. Do this by weight. Filter through paper or paper pulp in a Buchner funnel. (See below.)

MIXTURE B.

Agar, oven dried, 1.2 per cent (market 1.5 per cent) of total quantity of medium to be made. Soak and wash under tap in sieve. Weigh before and after soaking to determine quantity of water absorbed. Add distilled water, 60 per cent of total quantity of medium to be made, minus that absorbed by the agar during the washing.

Mix A and B (agar not yet melted). Heat mixture over stove, stirring at frequent intervals until agar is entirely melted. Then boil and stir constantly for 20 minutes. Make up weight lost by evaporation, by adding hot distilled water. Keep kettle of agar in chamber of flowing steam while preparing funnel for filtering.

Filter through cotton until clear. For 10-liter amounts it is suggested that either a Sharpless or a nine-inch Buchner funnel with a suction pump be used. The ordinary filtration pump attached to a water faucet producing about 11 inches of vacuum gives good results.

Prepare paper pulp by soaking scraps of ordinary filter paper for 36 to 48 hours in a large wide-mouthed bottle. The paper and water should be in the ratio of six sheets of soft absorbent filter paper (20 by 20 inches) to two and one-half liters of hot water. Moisten the paper and tear it into fragments about one-quarter to one-half inch square. Shake vigorously at intervals to make the suspension fine and uniform. When ready to prepare the nine-inch funnel, take 400 to 500 ml. of the paper pulp and dilute it with about three liters of very hot water. Cut a piece of surgeon's lint (or cotton flannel) to fit the bottom of the funnel exactly. Rinse the funnel with hot water. Place in it the lint with the fleecy side uppermost. Pour in the hot paper pulp suspension carefully so as to cover the lint with an even layer about one-eighth to one-quarter inch thick. Over this lay a disk of filter paper. Place a four-liter suction flask under the funnel and apply the suction to draw the water into the filtration flask until the pulp is firm, yet somewhat moist. The agar will not go through too dry a filter.

The funnel and the paper pulp must be hot when the agar is poured in, carefully and slowly, striking the disk of filter paper which prevents the breaking of the surface of the paper pulp. Discard the first 100 ml. of agar which come through as they contain some of the water from the pulp.

Even in the first filtration the agar should come through very clear. Keep the remainder of the unfiltered agar hot in flowing steam while the first part is running through the filter.

Ordinarily the temperature of the agar in the funnel is 80°C.(176°F.) to 85°C. (185°F.), but the last portions will come through well as low as 50°C.(122°F.) to 55°C. (131°F.).

Keep the filtered agar hot in flowing steam, while preparing a second funnel in the same way as the first. Then filter as before.

Preparation of Nutrient Agar (Standard Methods of Water Analysis). This is the official medium adopted by the American Public Health Association.

Add three grams of beef extract, five grams of peptone, and 15 grams of agar (undried market product as stored in the ordinary laboratory cupboard) to 1,000 ml. of distilled water. Boil until all the agar is dissolved. Cool to 45°C.(113°F.) in a cold water bath, then warm to 65°C.(149°F.) in the same bath, without stirring.

Make up the lost weight with hot distilled water and adjust reaction so that the pH value, after the final sterilization, will be between 6.2 and 7.0.

Bring to a boiling temperature, stirring frequently; restore the lost weight with hot distilled water and clarify. Distribute in the desired containers.

Tryptone-Glucose Extract-Milk Agar (Standard Nutrient Agar) of Standard Methods for Examination of Dairy Products, Eighth Edition. This medium has been adopted as the standard nutrient agar for counting bacteria in milk by the American Public Health Association. It is compounded as follows:

Agar		15 gm.
Beef extract	0.3 per cent;	3 gm.
Tryptone	0.5 per cent;	3 gm.
Glucose	0.1 per cent;	1 gm.
Distilled water		1,000 ml.

One per cent of skim milk is to be added just before final sterilization in all cases where dilutions greater than one to 10 are made. This medium was proposed by Bowers and Hucker [81] because it permitted higher counts and larger colonies. It has been generally accepted by bacteriologists.

American Association Medical Milk Commissions, Inc.,[82] Agar Medium. The medium required for determining the bacterial count of certified milk is composed as follows: agar, 1.5 per cent; beef extract, .3 per cent; peptone, one per cent; sodium chloride, .5 per cent; dextrose, .1 per cent; all in distilled water. The final reaction after sterilization shall be pH 6.8 to 7.2. The beef extract and the peptone used shall be such as to give the highest count and the largest colonies. Wilson Nutri-Peptone or a mixture of equal parts of Difco Proteose Peptone and Tryptone were found to be satisfactory. The colonies shall be counted after 48 hours' incubation at 37°C.(98.6°F.). This medium gives considerably higher counts than ordinary agar.

Simmons'[83] Citrate Agar Medium. This medium was prepared by adding agar to Koser's citrate medium as follows:

Agar	20.0 gm.
Sodium chloride	5.0 gm.
Magnesium sulfate	0.2 gm.
Ammonium hydrogen phosphate $(NH_4)H_2PO_4$	1.0 gm.
Potassium hydrogen phosphate K_2HPO_4	1.0 gm.
Sodium citrate, 2.77 gm. sodium citrate, 5½ H_2O	2.0 ml.
Distilled water	1,000.0 ml.
Brom-thymol blue (1.5 per cent alcoholic)	10.0 ml.

After dissolving the various salts in sterile distilled water, add 20 grams of clean, washed agar and sterilize the mixture at 15 pounds for 15 minutes in an autoclave. After adjusting the reaction to pH 6.8, add the indicator.

Veal Infusion Agar.[84] This medium has many uses in practical bacteriology. The formula given here is used as the base for blood agar for detecting presence of streptococci and staphylococci in frozen-egg products. For preparation of blood agar .6 ml. of blood is added per 10 ml. of base medium.

Mix 500 grams of ground lean veal and 1,000 ml. of water. Infuse overnight in refrigerator and strain through cheesecloth without pressure. Make up to original volume with water and skim off any fat. Steam in Arnold 30 minutes and filter through paper. Add peptone (Difco), one per cent or 10 gm.; NaCl, .5 per cent or five gm.; and agar, 1.5 per cent or 15 gm.

Steam in Arnold to dissolve ingredients. Adjust reaction to pH 7.6 and steam in Arnold 15 minutes. Filter through Büchner funnel with paper pulp mat, by aid of

81. Bowers and Hucker. 1935. N. Y. Agr. Expt. Sta. Tech. Bull. 228. Standard Methods for the Examination of Dairy Products, eighth edition, p. 22.
82. Methods and Standards for the Production of Certified Milk. Amer. Assoc. Med. Milk Comns., New York, N. Y., 1939, p. 18.
83. Simmons. 1926. J. Infect. Dis. 39, 209-214.
84. Official and Tentative Methods of Analysis, Assoc. Off. Agr. Chem., fifth edition, p. 641.

suction. Use egg albumen for clarification when necessary. Add fresh white of one egg previously beaten with 50 ml. of the medium or its equivalent in desiccated egg white (1.5 gm.) to each liter of the medium before adjustment of reaction and after cooling to 50°C.(122°F.). Shake thoroughly to insure solution of egg white. Allow to stand 20 minutes. Heat in Arnold for 15 minutes to coagulate egg white. Shake vigorously and reheat. Filter. Adjust reaction to pH 7.6. Steam in Arnold 15 minutes. Filter. Distribute 10-ml. quantities into test tubes or 80-ml. quantities into bottles. Sterilize at 15 lb. pressure (121°C.) for 20 minutes. Final pH is 7.4. For hemolytic tests, cool melted agar to 40°C.(104°F.) and add six per cent of defibrinated horse, sheep, or rabbit blood prior to pouring plates (.6 ml. of blood per 10 ml. of media).

Pork Extract-Agar Culture Medium.[85] This was developed in the laboratory of the National Canners Association for making anaerobic spore counts of putrefactive anaerobic bacteria and *Clostridium botulinum.*

Fresh pork shoulder or loin is trimmed of fat and ground; this is then mixed with water, one pound of pork to a liter of water, and boiled for one hour. Sodium hydroxide is used to adjust the reaction to about pH 7.4. When the pork extract is cool, place in a refrigerator so that the fat may be readily removed by hand. After this make up the extract to one liter and add the following ingredients to one liter of extract:

Difco peptone	5.0 gm.
Difco tryptone	1.5 gm.
Dextrose	1.0 gm.
Potassium hydrogen phosphate (K_2HPO_4)	1.5 gm.
Agar	15.0 gm.

Dissolve the ingredients and adjust the reaction to pH 7.4. Place the culture medium in several flasks and sterilize. After sterilization place the medium at 55°C.(131°F.) in a tilted position for several hours, or overnight, during which time a sediment forms in the bottom of the flask. The clear medium may then be decanted from the sediment and tubed and sterilized at 15 pounds pressure for 30 minutes.

Carbohydrate Agar Media. These media are usually made by adding one per cent of the carbohydrate to the agar. As shown by the work of Mudge,[36] Hasseltine,[35] McAlpine,[38] and others, the carbohydrates should probably be sterilized separately. Kleinberger[86] stated that in making agar shake cultures for determining sugar fermentation, the tubes must be shaken vigorously to distribute bubbles of oxygen, as an abundant supply is very essential except for anaerobes. The time of beginning gas formation and the amount of gas produced depend partly on the number of bacteria in the inoculum, which is opposite for the findings in liquid media. Fermentation activity can be brought to a maximum by passages through the appropriate carbohydrate medium. Bouillon for the preparation of the agar must be made sugar-free by fermentation with *Escherichia coli.* Most carbohydrates should be sterilized separately in 25-per cent solutions and added to the agar just prior to use. The hydrogen-ion concentration which is optimum for a given species must be used and is very important.

Levine[87] and Burling and Levine[88] have stated that .5 per cent lactose broth should be used in the presumptive test for coli bacteria in water analysis. With the higher carbohydrate content of the broth, the limiting hydrogen-ion concentration is reached more quickly.

85. Personal Communication from National Canners Assoc.
86. Kleinberger. 1925. Centbl. Bakt., Pt. 1, 96, 181-213.
87. Levine. 1918. Amer. Water Wks. Assoc. J. 5, 168-171; Engin. Contr. 49 (1918), 34.
88. Burling and Levine. 1918. Amer. J. Pub. Health 8, 306-307.

Litmus Lactose Agar (Bendick[89]). Bendick has devised the following for litmus agar:

Agar	15 gm.	Lactose	1,000 ml.
Beef extract	5 gm.	Calcium carbonate	20 gm.
Salt	10 gm.	Litmus	4 gm.
Peptone	10 gm.	Distilled water	100 gm.

The agar, beef extract, salt, and peptone are dissolved in 1,000 ml. of water. This is cleared with egg and filtered. No adjusting of the reactions is necessary. This is put into flasks (250 ml. in a 44 ml. flask). One gram of $CaCO_3$ is added and the whole sterilized. Finally to each flask are added 25 ml. of Kahlbaum's aqueous litmus and five grams of lactose. Tube by pouring direct to the tubes from the flasks and keeping the contents well mixed.

Litmus Lactose Agar. Meyer[90] has shown that a litmus lactose agar prepared from three per cent agar gives plates which are free from many of the objections incident to plates made from a lesser per cent of agar. The results obtained were approximately equivalent to Endo's medium agar.

Herring Agar. To 500 ml. of the standard herring extract, which is described in another place, were added 500 ml. or 1,000 ml. of sea water, peptone at the rate of one per cent, and agar at the rate of 1.2 per cent. This mixture after heating was prepared for use in the usual manner.

Harde and Hauser's[91] Fish Media. Two media were prepared from flesh of the whiting.

First Medium. The flesh of the whiting is cut into one-milliliter pieces; one such piece is placed in each culture tube and eight ml. of distilled water are added and the medium sterilized at 120°C.(248°F.) for 20 minutes.

Second Medium. Five hundred grams of flesh of the whiting are boiled in 1,000 ml. of water for 30 minutes. This is then filtered through paper and sterilized for 20 minutes at 120°C.(248°F.). This base, after the reaction has been adjusted, may be used for the preparation of agar or gelatin without the addition of other ingredients.

Kulp's[92] Agar Medium for Lactobacillus acidophilus. When studying the effect of tomato juice on the growth of various bacteria, Kulp found that much larger colonies were secured when it was added to a medium having the following composition:

Agar	10 gm.
Difco peptone	10 gm.
Tomato juice	300 ml.
Water	700 ml.
Reaction	pH 7

The tomato juice is secured by filtering the liquid portion of canned tomatoes through filter paper. The above mixture should be autoclaved to dissolve the agar and finally sterilized at 15 pounds for 15 minutes. Kulp stated that this medium would have a final reaction of about pH 6.5.

Kulp and White's[63] Tomato Juice Agar. This medium has been used for examination of acid foods for aciduric spoilage bacteria.

Tomato juice (400 ml.)	20 gm.
Bacto peptone	10 gm.
Bacto peptonized milk	10 gm.
Bacto agar	12-15 gm.
Distilled water to make 1,000 ml.	

Pour plates fairly thick to provide for subsurface growth.

89. Bendick. 1913. Fifteenth Internatl. Cong. Hyg. and Demog. Trans. 2, 40.
90. Meyer. 1917. J. Bact. 2, 237-240.
91. Harde and Hauser. 1919. Compt. Rend. Soc. Biol. 82, 1304.
92. Kulp. 1927. Science 66, 512-513.

Milk Powder Agar (Ayers and Mudge[93]). These investigators have proposed three media prepared from milk powder which they claim have advantages over the ordinary standard agar.

Medium A. Ingredients for one liter.

      (a)

    5 grams of skimmed milk powder

250 ml. distilled water

    1 gram sodium dibasic phosphate (Sorensen's phosphate[94])

      $(Na_2HPO_4 + H_2O)$

      (b)

    5 grams of peptone

250 ml. distilled water

    3 grams meat extract

To make the milk powder solution "a" a good grade of skimmed milk powder should be used. The ingredients of this part of the medium are prepared by placing the five grams of milk powder into 20 ml. of cold distilled water and stirring until dispersed. The phosphate should be dissolved in distilled water and added to the milk powder solution after which the mixture should be heated on a steam bath for about 10 minutes until a grayish precipitate appears. More distilled water should be added and the heating continued; too long heating must be avoided since it will cause a darkening of the medium. Filter and make up to 250 ml. with distilled water.

The extract solution "b" should be prepared and filtered, after which it should be made up to 250 ml. with distilled water. This will give a total volume of 500 ml. to which three per cent of washed agar should be added. No adjustment of the reaction is necessary.

Medium B. The authors have proposed this medium since *Medium A* is slightly cloudy: To make this medium simply substitute in the formula for *Medium A* the following: two grams of peptone and one gram of meat extract instead of five grams of peptone and three grams of meat extract. The medium in other respects is made exactly the same. No adjustment of the reaction is necessary as it will be about pH 7.0 to pH 7.1, brown or slightly brown-red with phenol red.

Medium C. This medium is prepared from washed agar, skimmed milk powder, and yeast extract, as follows:

Ingredients for One Liter of Medium

      (a)

    5 grams of skimmed milk powder

    1 gram of sodium dibasic phosphate

250 ml. distilled water

      (b)

    10 grams of pure dry yeast

250 ml. distilled water

Mix "a" and "b" and add 500 ml. of double strength (three per cent) washed agar solution.

The yeast extract should be made from fresh dry yeast which contains no added fillers. To facilitate filtering the yeast should be heated at a temperature of 105°C. (221°F.) to 110°C.(230°F.) for five hours. The extract is made by steaming 10 grams of yeast in 100 ml. distilled water for 45 minutes in an Arnold, then filtering until the filtrate is clear and brilliant. Make up to 250 ml. with distilled water.

The milk powder solution and yeast extract are then mixed and 500 ml. of double strength washed agar (three per cent) are added.

93. Ayers and Mudge. 1920. J. Bact. 5, 565.

94. Sorensen's phosphate is sodium dibasic phosphate with 12 molecules of water of crystallization $(Na_2HPO_4 + 12H_2O)$ which has been *air dried* so that instead of 12 molecules of water it contains but two molecules.

Milk Powder Agar (Zoller [95]). One hundred and twenty grams of Bacto-Nutrient agar are stirred into four liters of distilled water. Two grams of pure sodium citrate are added and the whole heated in streaming steam for five minutes.

Twenty-five grams of skimmed milk powder are stirred into 100 ml. of distilled water. A thick mixture should be made with the powder and a small amount of water. After all lumps are gone, the remainder of the water may be added.

Stir six grams (1.2 gm. per liter) of disodium phosphate ($Na_2HPO_2 + 2 H_2O$) into 30 ml. of water and heat to boiling. Add the phosphate solution to the milk powder solution, stir and set in the autoclave and steam for five minutes, while the agar is being melted.

Remove the agar and stir it. Also remove the milk-phosphate solution and add another 50 ml. of distilled water. Replace both the agar and the milk phosphate solution in the autoclave and heat for five minutes at five pounds pressure. Filter the milk phosphate solution through absorbent cotton. Add five grams of lactose to the filtered milk liquid and make up to one liter with distilled water. Mix this milk powder solution with the hot melted agar and place the hot medium in the flasks or bottles destined to receive it. Sterilize at 15 pounds for 15 minutes.

Ayers and Johnson's [96] Medium for Determination of Coliform Bacilli in Ice Cream. These investigators studied 53 different combinations of ingredients, finally finding that the following was most satisfactory:

Agar	1.5 per cent
Asparagine	0.3 per cent
Sodium phosphate (dibasic)	0.1 per cent
Lactose	1.0 per cent
Saturated litmus solution	2.0 per cent

Muer and Jackson's [70] Liver Agar:

Beef liver	500.0 gm.
Peptone (Witte's)	10.0 gm.
Dextrose	10.0 gm.
Potassium phosphate (K_2HPO_4)	1.0 gm.
Water	1,000.0 gm.

1. Chop 500 gm. of beef liver into small pieces, add 500 ml. of distilled water, and boil slowly for two hours, stirring occasionally.

2. Add five gm. of agar (dried at 105°C.[221°F.] for 30 minutes) to 500 ml. of distilled water and digest for 30 minutes in an autoclave at 120°C.(248°F.) (15 lb.).

3. After making up the loss by evaporation, strain the liver infusion through a wire strainer, add 500 ml. of the filtrate to the agar solution.

4. To the filtrate add 10 gm. of peptone, 10 gm. of dextrose, and one gram of potassium phosphate. Weigh the infusion and container.

5. After warming this mixture in a double boiler and stirring it for a few minutes, to dissolve the ingredients, titrate with N/20 sodium hydrate, using phenolphthalein as an indicator, and neutralize with normal sodium hydrate.

6. Boil vigorously for 30 minutes in a double boiler and five minutes over a free flame with constant stirring to prevent the caramelization of the dextrose.

7. Make up any loss in weight by evaporation, and filter through cotton flannel and filter paper.

8. Tube and sterilize in an autoclave for 15 minutes at 120°C.(248°F.) (15 lb.).

Hasley and Schalter's [97] Liver Media. One pound of fresh beef liver is ground, and 1,000 ml. of water, 10 gm. of peptone, five gm. of sodium chloride, 25 gm. of agar, and one egg are added; with constant stirring the mixture is heated over a free flame to 70°C.(158°F.); nine ml. of normal sodium chloride solution are added and the container

95. Zoller. 1923. Amer. J. Pub. Health 13, 384.
96. Ayers and Johnson. 1914. Science 39, 802-803.
97. Hasley and Schalter. 1939. J. Lab. and Clin. Med. 24, 523-525.

is placed in an Arnold sterilizer and heated in flowing steam for 60 to 80 minutes; it is then removed, the coagulum loosened from the sides of the container, and allowed to remain at room temperature for five to 10 minutes. If the clot is firm and the liquid is poured slowly, a clear fluid will be obtained without the necessity of filtering, but the authors' routine procedure is to pour the medium through a small amount of glass wool loosely placed in a funnel, to remove the larger particles which may have separated from the coagulum. For liver broth, the ingredients are the same except that no agar is used. Nine ml. of normal sodium hydroxide per liter gives a final pH of 6.6 to 6.8.

Casein Medium (Norris[98]). The use of a dry nutritive powder prepared from caseinogen was proposed. A substrate of 10 per cent caseinogen in an .8-per cent solution washing soda was digested with .5 per cent of pancreatic extract at 37°C.(98.6°F.) for 24 hours. After filtering through muslin, the mixture was concentrated to a thick paste which kept for six months. When it was used in media neither peptone nor meat extract had to be added.

Watson's Sucrose Milk Agar Medium. Watson[99] used this medium for the study of the intestinal flora. The broth was prepared as follows: Meat extract 1,000 ml., peptone 10 grams, and sodium chloride five grams were mixed and evaporated down to one-fifth of the original bulk and made up to volume with whole milk. Two per cent of sucrose was added after the medium had been neutralized.

Brom-Cresol-Purple Milk of Clark and Lubs.[100] Clark and Lubs proposed substituting brom-cresol-purple for litmus in milk. They found that no change could be observed with litmus which could not be followed equally well with brom-cresol-purple. In some instances, litmus was rendered useless by destruction whereas the brom-cresol-purple continued to function as a good indicator.

The milk was prepared as follows: Add 10 ml. of a .5-per cent solution of brom-cresol-purple to one liter of milk. The concentration of dye should be about .005 per cent. The dye was prepared as follows: .5 gm. was ground to a fine powder and 14 ml. of N/10 NaOH added. Dilute the mixture with 90 ml. of distilled water and then make up to 1,000 ml.

Raw Sugar Cane Juice Agar (Owen[101]). Fresh raw cane juice should be heated, filtered through cotton, and solidified with two per cent agar.

Raw Sugar Agar (Owen[101]). This medium was used by Owen in his investigations on the microorganisms in sugar:

Second sugar (80°C.[10%])	100 gm.
Tap water	1,000 ml.
Agar	2 per cent

Raw Sugar Peptone Agar (Owen[101]):

Second sugar	100 gm.
Peptone	10 gm.
Agar, two per cent	20 gm.
Tap water	1,000 ml.

Sucrose Agar of Greig-Smith (Quoted by Owen[101]). This medium was devised for enumerating the microorganisms in cane sugar products:

Cane sugar	10.0 per cent
Potassium chloride	0.5 per cent
Sodium phosphate	0.2 per cent
Peptone	0.1 per cent
Agar	2.0 per cent
Reaction + 0.5 Fuller's Scale.	

98. Norris. 1920. Indian J. Med. Res. 7, 704-710.
99. Watson. 1922. Lancet. 127.
100. Clark and Lubs. 1917. J. Agr. Res. 10, 105-111.
101. Owen. 1914. Louisiana Agr. Expt. Sta. Bull. 146 (Baton Rouge).

Haberman's [102] **Molasses Agar Medium for Isolation of Yeasts.** The medium consisted of meat extract agar containing eight per cent of sorghum molasses for isolation and two per cent for cultivation and adjusted to pH 5.5 with HCl. Monilia, Trichophyton, or Epidermophyton was recovered from eight of 14 cases of suspected dermomycosis. Soil cultures gave a greater number and variety of fungi than those on malt agar or Wassman's agar. Pure cultures of Rhizopus, Absidia, Penicillium, Aspergillus, Mucor, Alternaria, and Cunninghamella and *Saccharomyces cerevisiae* grew more rapidly, and reproductive structures in most cases appeared earlier than on other media.

Raw Juice Peptone Agar (Owen [102]**):**

Fresh filtered raw cane juice	1,000 ml.
Peptone, 1 per cent	10 gm.
Agar	20 gm.

Molasses Peptone Agar (Owen [102]**):**

Final molasses	160 gm.
Peptone	10 gm.
Agar	20 gm.
Tap water	1,000 ml.

Cameron, Williams, and Thompson's [71] **Sulfite Agar Medium for Detecting Presence of Sulfide Spoilage Bacteria.** Its preparation was described as follows:

Sulfite agar is prepared by adding .1 per cent sodium sulfite and three per cent sucrose to plain yeast water agar. At the time of tubing, a clean iron strip or nail is placed in the tube. The medium should be used within a week after preparation. Yeast water is prepared by autoclaving at 15 pounds pressure for five hours a 10-per cent suspension of starch-free yeast. This is allowed to settle for several days. When clear, the supernatant liquid is decanted and made into a medium containing 1.5 per cent agar.

A modified sulfite agar medium, developed later,[84] is prepared as follows: Tryptone 10 gm., sodium sulfite (Na_2SO_3) one gm., agar 20 gm., and water 1,000 ml. At time of tubing, place a clean iron strip or nail in the tube. No adjustment in reaction is necessary. The medium should be fresh as should the sodium sulfite solution also. Sulfide spoilage bacteria form characteristic blackened spherical areas. Owing to solubility of hydrogen sulfide and its fixation by the iron, gas is not noted.

A new medium has been developed in the laboratories of the National Canners Association. In place of the iron strip or mail 10 ml. of a five per cent solution of iron citrate is substituted in the regular sulfite medium formula. It is necessary to heat the citrate solution in order to completely dissolve the citrate. The formula is as follows:

Tryptone	10 gm.
Agar	20 gm.
Sodium sulfite	1 gm.
Water	1,000 ml.
Iron citrate*—10 ml. of a five per cent solution.	

* Iron Citrate Merck (Ferric Citrate) U. S. P. III. Pearls.

Dextrose Tryptone Agar for Detecting Presence of Flat-Sour Spoilage Bacteria. This medium resulted from several years' study for a medium which was easily prepared.[103] Its greatest use has been in examination of canned foods, sugar, and starch for thermophilic bacteria of the *Bacillus stearothermophilus* type. When used for this purpose it must be incubated at 55°C.(131°F.). It has the following composition:

Tryptone	10 gm.
Agar	15 gm.
Dextrose	5 gm.
Water	1,000 ml.

102. Haberman. 1938. Amer. J. Clin. Path., Tech. Suppl. 2, 20-22.
103. Williams. 1936. Food Research 1, 217-221.

The reaction should be adjusted to pH 7. It may be bottled in 100-ml. quantities and sterilized at 121°C. (15 lb.) for 30 minutes. Brom-cresol-purple (.004 per cent) should be added before plates are poured. This will give a medium with a purple background in which flat sour-producing bacteria will appear as yellow colonies.

Tryptone-Glucose-Yeast Extract-Agar Medium.[104] This medium has been used for examining fermented foods. Its preparation is as follows:

Agar	1.5 per cent
Yeast extract	0.3 per cent
Tryptone	0.5 per cent
Glucose	0.1 per cent
Water, distilled	

The reaction should be adjusted to pH 6.6 to 7.0. The medium is sterilized in the usual manner and distributed into tubes or flasks.

Corn Agar (After Barlow[105]). This medium was used by Barlow in his pioneer work on flat sour corn caused by thermophilic bacteria.

Corn	1,000 gm.
Sucrose	80 gm.
Agar	60 gm.
Litmus	100 gm.
Water	4,000 gm.

Stir the corn into the boiling water, add to other materials, boil five minutes, heat in an autoclave and cool slowly; the heavy matter settles off. The clear supernatant agar may be drawn off and tubed.

Potato Decoction Agar (Jensen[106]). Two average-sized potatoes are washed, pared, and sliced thin. To these are added about two times their volume of water. This is then heated for two hours but never allowed to boil. Filter through cotton and then add 30 grams of agar and five grams of glucose. Cook in the autoclave at 17 to 18 pounds pressure. Distribute into culture tubes, plug, and sterilize in the autoclave at 17 to 18 pounds.

Mickle and Breed[60] made tomato juice agar medium by adding 10 per cent of tomato juice to ordinary nutrient agar.

Potato-Dextrose-Agar Medium. This medium is used for determination of yeasts and molds in dairy products. It is recommended in *Standard Methods for the Examination of Dairy Products*, eighth edition, page 112. It has the following composition:

Agar	1.5 per cent
Glucose	2.0 per cent
Infusion from 200 gm. potato	1,000.0 ml.

The reaction is adjusted to pH 3.5 ± 0.1 at time of pouring.

The potato infusion is prepared by boiling 200 gm. of sliced potato in 1,000 ml. of water for one hour; then strain through double thickness of clean toweling and restore to original volume. Add glucose and agar and dissolve in the autoclave at 115°C. (239°F.), filter, and distribute in flasks.

Tittsler and Sandholzer's[107] Peptone-Iron-Agar Medium. This medium was devised for detection of hydrogen-sulfide formation. The usual method of testing for hydrogen sulfide has been by a lead acetate-agar medium, in which a brownish discoloration is produced along the line of growth. Numerous workers have expressed dissatisfaction with this method. Tittsler and Sandholzer recommend its replacement by peptone iron agar (Difco). In this medium the production of hydrogen sulfide gives rise to an intense blackening, which becomes visible more rapidly than the brownish discoloration in lead acetate agar. In an examination of 376 strains of different groups of bacteria,

104. Amer. J. Pub. Health 33 (1943), 727.
105. Barlow. 1912. Univ. of Illinois, Thesis.
106. Jensen. 1912. N. Y. Agr. Expt. Sta. (Cornell Univ.) Bull. 110.
107. Tittsler and Sandholzer. 1937. Amer. J. Pub. Health 27, 1240-1242.

it was found that the two media gave almost identical results, but that the reaction in the iron medium was very much easier to interpret than that in the lead medium. Its formula is as follows:

Proteose peptone (Difco)	20.0 gm.
K₂HPO₄ (anhydrous)	1.0 gm.
Bacto agar	15.0 gm.
Ferric citrate	0.5 gm.
Distilled water	1,000.0 ml.

Dissolve by boiling, put up in deep tubes, and sterilize at 15 pounds for 15 minutes. Inoculate in one or two places between the agar and the glass, carrying the wire to the bottom of the tube.

Brom-Cresol-Purple Agar (Torrey's Modification [108]). Five hundred grams of chopped beef heart (other meat material may be used) are boiled in one liter of water for 15 minutes over a free flame. It is then strained through canton flannel or cotton as usual. Make up the loss by adding water and then add 10 grams of peptone and 15 grams of flaked agar. Heat in the Arnold steam sterilizer until dissolved. Adjust the reaction to pH 7.4 and place in the Arnold sterilizer for 30 minutes. Readjust the reaction if necessary. Filter through absorbent cotton and add to the filtrate 10 grams of lactose and sufficient saturated alcoholic solution of brom-cresol-purple (generally about .75 ml.) to give the desired depth of color for a poured plate. Put into flasks in 200-ml. amounts (sufficient for six plates) and autoclave at 15 pounds for 10 minutes.

Hitchin's Agar Medium.[33] To sugar-free broth, add .1 per cent of washed or purified agar; fill into ordinary culture tubes and sterilize. Carbohydrates may be added before sterilization or after separate sterilization in order to avoid hydrolysis. Before inoculation the tubes should be heated in a water bath until a control tube containing one ml. of one per cent methylene blue shows considerable reduction. The tubes may then be cooled to 45°C.(112°F.) and held at that temperature until inoculated. For inoculation, the material should be carried to the bottom of the tube. Indicators such as Andrade's or phenol red may be used.

Enslow's [109] Modification of Hitchins' Agar Medium. This medium was developed in order to adapt Hitchins' medium to fermentation studies. It had the following composition:

Tap water	1,800 ml.
Witte's peptone	10 gm.
Potassium phosphate (K₂HPO₄)	17 gm.
Agar	2 gm.

For rough indication of fermentation, the mere addition to this medium of the fermentable substance and of a suitable indicator suffices, but for accurate determinations a sugar-free base is necessary. The above materials are heated together in the Arnold for 30 minutes, filtered through paper, and diluted with hot distilled water to 2,000 ml. The hydrogen-ion concentration is then determined and adjustment made with sodium hydroxide. The fermentable substances are added in .5-per cent concentrations. The indicator is brom-thymol-blue and the final pH between 7.2 and 7.6. The medium is tubed in 10-ml. amounts and sterilized by the fractional method.

Another application of semisolid agar was mentioned by Falk, Bucca, and Simmons[110] for testing biological products for contamination. When such contaminants as diphtheroids, staphylococci, *Pseudomonas pyocyanea*, and hay bacilli were present in bacterial vaccines, antibacterial serums, antitoxic globulins, and the broth control, media containing .06 to 25 per cent agar were the most dependable for detection of bacterial growth. In addition to the usual .03 per cent glucose biologic products broth, media containing .1 per cent agar was chosen for the routine testing of biologic products for sterility. These experiments confirmed and extended the studies of Hitchins (1921)

108. Torrey. 1926. J. Infect. Dis. 39, 351-369.
109. Enslow. 1923. U. S. Pub. Health Rpts. 38, 2129-2132.
110. Falk, Bucca, and Simmons. 1939. J. Bact. 37, 121-131.

and Spray (1936). Applications to other materials and procedures involving bacterial growth are also indicated.

Spray's Semisolid Media for Cultivation of Anaerobic Bacteria. Spray [111] used semisolid media for cultivating anaerobic bacteria. Such media contained sufficient agar to check convection currents. It was possible to cultivate the anaerobes without a seal or use of an anaerobic container. Under such conditions cultivation of anaerobes was no more difficult than cultivation of aerobes. The following media were used by Spray.

Anaerobic Plating Medium. Make liver infusion; boil 50 gm. of Bacto liver powder in 1,000 ml. of distilled water. Filter through cotton and make up to 1,000 ml. by pouring hot water through the filter. Adjust the reaction to pH 7.3 to 7.4. To prepare 1,000 ml. of agar medium, take 1,000 ml. liver infusion (above), 77 gm. Difco North gelatin agar, 37 gm. Difco Brain-Heart Infusion powder, and two gm. sodium nitrate. Boil to dissolve and add water to make one liter. Retitrate and adjust to pH 7.3 to 7.4. Autoclave in a flask and cool to solidify and fix precipitates. When solidified, remelt and add water to make one liter. Tube about eight cm. deep, preferably in 200 x 15 mm. tubes. Autoclave 15 to 20 minutes at 15 pounds pressure.

Spray's [111] Special Media for Anaerobic Bacteria. The following media were developed by Spray for use in identifying anaerobic bacteria as described in his article in 1936.

Iron-Gelatin Medium for Liquefaction Determination. The medium is composed as follows:

Difco Nutrient gelatin	128 gm.
Dextrose	1 gm.
Distilled water	1,000 ml.

Dissolve in a double boiler to avoid scorching. Adjust the reaction to pH 7.3 to 7.4 and add water to make one liter. Tube about eight cm. deep in 200 x 15 mm., or in 200 x 13 mm. tubes. Add to each tube one strip of iron (as in Iron-Milk) and autoclave as usual. All cultures are incubated at 37°C. (98.6°F.) and are tested daily in ice water—if negative for at least 30 days.

Iron-Milk Medium. Spray recognized five different reactions of anaerobes in this milk medium. It was compounded as follows: Mix fresh whole milk well and tube about eight cm. deep in 200 x 15 mm., or in 200 x 13 mm. tubes. Add to each tube one strip of No. 26 gauge black stove-pipe iron, cut about 50 x 7 mm. Autoclave as usual, but reduce the pressure slowly when completed to avoid wetting or blowing of plugs.

Nitrate Semisolid Agar for Nitrate Reduction. The medium is compounded as follows:

Peptone	5.0 gm.
Difco neopeptone	5.0 gm.
Agar flakes	2.5 gm.
Distilled water	1,000.0 ml.

Boil to dissolve and add water to make a liter. Adjust the reaction to pH 7.3 or 7.4; then add:

Potassium nitrate	1.0 gm.
Glucose	0.5 gm.

Dissolve and mix well. Tube about eight cm. deep in 200 x 15 mm. or 13 mm. tubes and autoclave. The test is performed after 72 hours' incubation, using .6 per cent dimethyl-alpha- naphthylamine with sulfanilic acid, both in dilute acetic acid.

Sugar-Free Fermentation Base Medium.

Neopeptone	10.0 gm.
Tryptone, Difco	10.0 gm.
Agar flakes	2.5 gm.
Distilled water	1,000.0 ml.

111. Spray. 1936. J. Bact. 32, 135-155.

Boil to dissolve and add water to make one liter. Adjust the reaction to pH 7.3 to 7.4. Andrade or other indicators may be added or omitted. They are usually reduced, although many organisms show typical fermentative reactions. Divide into lots, and add one per cent of the desired sugars. Reserve one lot to be tubed without sugar as a control. Tube about eight cm. deep in 200 x 15 mm., or better 200 x 13 tubes, and autoclave.

Semisolid Stock Culture Medium:

Brain-heart infusion powder, Difco	37.0 gm.
Tryptone, Bacto	10.0 gm.
Sodium chloride	5.0 gm.
Agar flakes	2.5 gm.
Distilled water	1,000.0 gm.

Boil to dissolve and add water to make one liter. Retitrate and adjust to pH 7.3 to 7.4. Filter twice through cotton with slight suction, and tube about six cm. deep, preferably in 150 x 13 mm. tubes. Autoclave as usual.

Lead Acetate Semisolid Agar Medium. To make one liter, take 36 grams Difco Lead Acetate Agar (two per cent agar). Infuse this for 30 minutes, shaking frequently in one liter of warm (37°C.) distilled water to dissolve all ingredients except the agar. Filter through cotton, with slight suction, to remove the agar. Make the volume to one liter by pouring warm water through the cotton filter. Add to this 2.5 grams agar flakes, and boil to dissolve the agar. Make the volume to one liter and adjust the reaction to pH 7.3 to 7.4. Tube about eight cm. deep, and autoclave as usual.

NOTE: Prepared by this method the medium displays quantitatively distinct reactions with the various anaerobes. Spray was unable to reproduce these distinctions by other formulas or other modes of preparation (1936).

Agar Gelatin Medium (North [112]):

Lean chopped beef or veal	500 gm.
Agar	10 gm.
Gelatin	20 gm.
Peptone	20 gm.
Sodium chloride	5 gm.
Distilled water	1,000 ml.

Adjust neutral to phenolphthalein. North stated that this medium is excellent for streptococci, pneumococci, and diphtheria bacilli because it is soft and moist and can be used at 37°C.(98.6°F.). It is claimed to be of special value in keeping stock cultures.

Russell's Medium. [113] This medium was devised for studying the colon-typhoid group. It is prepared by adding enough five per cent aqueous solution of litmus to plain agar (two or three per cent) to give it a distinct purple-violet color. Next, one per cent of lactose and one-tenth of one per cent of glucose dissolved in a little water are added and the medium tubed for slants.

On this double sugar tube, *Eberthella typhosa* gives, after an incubation period of from eight to 18 hours, an extremely characteristic appearance; the surface growth is filiform and colorless, the upper part of the tube is unchanged in color, but the lower part is a brilliant uniform red. The entire point of the medium rests upon the difference in the changes produced by the growth of *Eberthella typhosa* under aerobic and under the imperfect anaerobic conditions found in the butt of the tube, where the bacillus obtains its oxygen by breaking down the glucose with the liberation of considerable acid; on the surface, however, in the presence of free oxygen, no acid is formed.

Escherichia coli, which is often slow in producing acid on the Endo plate, shows abundant gas and acid formation on this medium. The tube is reddened throughout, both above and below, and since the abundant lactose is attacked equally with the glucose, there is exuberant gas formation.

The *Bacillus fecalis alkaligenes* and other alkali formers leave the medium unchanged or slightly bluer. The staphylococcus reddens the tube above but leaves it blue below;

112. North. 1909. J. Med. Res. 20, 359-363.
113. Russell. 1911. J. Med. Res. 25, 217.

the *streptococcus intestinalis*, when it grows well, gives a beaded growth and reddens the tube slightly throughout. *B. subtilis*, which is commonly found in feces, usually leaves the medium unchanged but may redden it below without producing gas, yet the heavy, rough surface growth suffices for its differentiation. *B. pyocyaneus* gives a greenish-blue surface growth and leaves the color of the medium unchanged. *B. proteus* produces small gas bubbles in the depth and reddens and then decolorizes the butt very early, while the upper part of the tube is unchanged except for the spreading surface growth.

All dysentery bacilli alter the medium in the same manner as typhoid, yet the quantity of acid produced is small and the reddening is usually confined to the line of inoculation. This reaction is so characteristic that this medium is used in isolating dysentery bacilli; in fact, the same media and technic are used for both typhoid and dysentery.

The paratyphoids leave the upper part of the medium unchanged. The surface growth is like typhoid but in the butt of the tube, in addition to the reddening, are found a few small gas bubbles. The only organisms which may simulate the paratyphoids are slow colons, and these must be thrown out by agglutination tests and further observation of the sugar tube.

Kligler [114] stated that by adding .5 per cent of basic lead carbonate to Russell's medium, a good differentiation between *Salmonella paratyphi* and *Salmonella schottmülleri* may be secured. Krumwiede and Kohn, [115] by adding one per cent of sucrose to Russell's medium, found that a large percentage of "intermediates" giving a typical paratyphoid reaction could be excluded.

Kligler suggested the substitution of mannite for lactose in Russell's medium for the differentiation of the Shiga and Flexner types of *Shigella dysenteriae (Bacterium dysenteriae)*. The color changes in Russell's medium for several of the members of the colon-typhoid group are given in Chapter 4. The Digestive Ferments Company prepare a dehydrated Russell's medium which is very satisfactory.

Nichols, [116] in the course of some work on the nature of changes in the Russell double sugar culture caused by *Eberthella typhosa*, made the observation that this organism formed carbon dioxide in appreciable amounts. Nichols believed that the characteristic color changes in the Russell medium were due not to direct oxygen requirements but to the retention of carbon dioxide in the butt of the tube and its escape from the slant also to alkaline reversion of other acids. Further work reported by Nichols and Wood [117] indicated that carbon dioxide was both respiratory as well as fermentative in origin. Phenol red was said to be the best indicator for this medium since it showed both the acid change in the butt and the alkaline change on the slant when *Eberthella typhosa* was being cultured.

Another attempt to explain the color changes on the Russell double sugar tube was made by Wheeler. [118] He mentioned the original explanation of Russell, which involved the oxygen supply, and claimed that it was partly correct. He found that *Eberthella typhosa* fermented all of the dextrose in a Russell sugar tube within 21 hours, regardless of the oxygen supply. This was contrary to Russell's conception of the way in which oxygen produced its effect. Volatile acid production had no direct bearing on the appearance of the Russell double sugar tube. Wheeler stated that the characteristic changes were due to the influence of oxygen on alkali production. In the slant, where oxygen is plentiful, sufficient alkali is produced within 18 to 24 hours to neutralize all of the acid formed by the fermentation of .1 per cent of dextrose, and the slant is alkaline. In the butt, where oxygen is scanty, the amount of alkali produced in 24 hours is not sufficient to neutralize all of the acid formed by the fermentation of .1 per cent of dextrose, and the butt is acid. The alkaline reaction seen in the butt after five to eight days, is due to slow, continued alkali production within the butt, not to a diffusion downward of alkaline substances produced in the butt.

114. Kligler. 1917. Amer. J. Pub. Health 7, 1042-1044.
115. Krumwiede and Kohn. 1917. J. Med. Res. 37, 225-227.
116. Nichols. 1921. J. Infect. Dis. 29, 82-85.
117. Nichols and Wood. 1922. J. Infect. Dis. 30, 321-322.
118. Wheeler. 1924. J. Infect. Dis. 34, 13-38.

Cummings [119] recommended undecolorized acid fuchsin for use in Russell's triple sugar-agar medium. He believed that it permitted more clear-cut reactions and exerted no inhibitory effect on bacteria.

Kligler's [120] Iron Agar for Coliform and Typhoid Organisms. This medium combines the principles of the Russell double sugar agar and Kligler's lead acetate agar into one medium. The Bacto dehydrated medium has the following composition:

Bacto-tryptone	20 gm.
Bacto-lactose	10 gm.
Bacto-dextrose	1 gm.
Ferric ammonium citrate	0.5 gm.
Sodium chloride	5 gm.
Sodium thiosulfate	0.5 gm.
Bacto-phenol red	0.025 gm.
Bacto-agar	15 gm.

The reactions on this medium are not unlike those on Russell's double sugar agar.

REACTIONS OF VARIOUS MICROORGANISMS IN KLIGLER'S IRON AGAR
(After Digestive Ferments Co.)

Organism	Fermentation reaction		Hydrogen sulfide
	Slant	Butt	
Escherichia coli	Y	Y G	—
Aerobacter aerogenes	Y	Y G	—
Eberthella typhosa	N C	Y	+ *
Salmonella paratyphi (Paratyphoid A)	N C	Y G	—
Salmonella schottmüelleri (Paratyphoid B)	N C	Y G	+
Salmonella enteritidis (Gaertner)	N C	Y G	+
Salmonella typhimurium (Aertrycke)	N C	Y G	+
Proteus vulgaris	N C	Y G	+
Shigella dysenteriae (Shiga)	N C	Y	—
Shigella ambigua (Schmitz)	N C	Y	—
Shigella alkalescens	N C	Y	—
Shigella sp. (Newcastle type)	N C	Y or Y G	—
Shigella paradysenteriae (Flexner, Hiss, Strong)	N C	Y	—

NC=no change—or increase in alkalinity—red. Y=acid—yellow. G=gas bubbles in medium. + = no blackening. — = no blackening.

* *Eberthella typhosa* usually produces a black ring at the base of the slant, but may be extended.

MacConkey's [121] Agar Medium. This medium has been used for many years in Great Britain in sanitary work. The following formula is taken from *The Bacteriological Examination of Water Supplies* of the Ministry of Health of London.

Commercial sodium taurocholate	5 gm.
Peptone	20 gm.
Sodium chloride	5 gm.
Washed shredded agar	20 gm.
Distilled water	1,000 ml.

Steam until the solids are dissolved. Cool to 50°C.(122°F.) and adjust the reaction at 50°C. to pH 7.6 or 7.8. Add egg white, using the albumen from one egg for every three liters of medium. Autoclave at 10 pounds pressure for 15 minutes and filter hot through Chardin paper. Adjust the reaction of the filtrate at 50°C. to pH 7.3 or at room tem-

119. Cummings. 1930. J. Infect. Dis. 47, 359-366.
120. Kligler. 1918. J. Expt. Med. 28, 319.
121. MacConkey. 1905. J. Hyg. 5; 333.

perature to pH 7.5. Add 10 grams of lactose and about 10 ml. of a one-per cent neutral red solution. Mix thoroughly, distribute into flasks, and sterilize.

Violet Red Bile Agar. This medium was developed by the Digestive Ferments Company for counting coliform bacteria in water, milk, dairy, and food products directly. The Bacto-product has the following composition:

Peptone	10 gm.
Lactose	10 gm.
Bile salts	1 gm.
Yeast extracts	5 gm.
Agar	15 gm.
Neutral red	0.05 gm.
Crystal-violet (DC-1)	0.004 gm.

This medium has been favorably reported on by several investigators.[122]

Nichols and Wood's[117] **Modification of Russell's Double Sugar Medium.** Make a three-per cent extract agar; clear; add one per cent of lactose, .1 per cent of glucose, and five per cent of a .2-per cent water solution of phenol red. Correct the reaction to pH 7.2 to 7.4 while the medium is hot. Tube, sterilize, and slant in such a manner that there is a deep butt with a long slant.

Krumwiede and Kohn's[115] **Modification of Russell's Double Sugar Medium.** This modification of the Russell medium consisted in adding one per cent of sucrose. The medium had the following composition:

Peptone	10 gm.
Agar	15 gm.
Lactose	10 gm.
Sucrose	10 gm.
Dextrose	1 gm.
Sodium chloride	5 gm.
Andrade's indicator	.025 gm.

Adjust to neutrality.

Kendall and Ryan's[123] **Double Sugar Agar.** A double sugar agar containing sucrose and mannitol for use along with Russell's medium was proposed. It was used in the identification of intestinal bacteria. The medium is prepared as follows: One per cent of sucrose and .1 per cent of mannitol are added to 2.5 per cent of nutrient agar and the reaction adjusted so that Andrade indicator is faintly pink when hot. One per cent of Andrade indicator is added to the medium and the medium sterilized either in the autoclave or Arnold steam sterilizer. The tubes should be slanted, leaving a butt at the point where the slanted surface begins, of about one cm. in depth. This medium will distinguish between the bacteria that act on sucrose and mannitol.

Jordan and Harmon's[124] **Medium for Differentiating Paratyphoid Group.** This medium was proposed to obviate some of the disadvantages of Brown, Duncan and Henry's medium. Jordan and Harmon's medium will give a perfectly definite differentiation between *Salmonella aertrycke* and *Salmonella schottmülleri*. Its preparation was described by Jordan and Harmon as follows:

Agar	20 gm.
Difco peptone	10 gm.
Sodium potassium tartrate (Rochelle salts)	10 gm.
Sodium chloride	5 gm.
Distilled water	1,000 ml.
Alcoholic solution of phenol red (0.2%)	12 ml.

The medium should be adjusted to a pH of 7.6 to 7.8 and is best used in tubes unslanted, a stab inoculation being made. Observations should be made at 24- and

122. Bartram and Black. 1936. Food Research 1, 551; Babel and Parfitt. 1936. J. Dairy Sci. 19, 497; Miller and Prickett. 1938. Idem 21, 559.
123. Kendall and Ryan. 1919. J. Infect. Dis. 24, 400-404.
124. Jordan and Harmon. 1928. J. Infect. Dis. 42, 238-241.

48-hour intervals, although the reaction in tubes is generally stable, for at least seven days. The paratyphoid strains that impart an acid reaction to the medium give a distinct yellow color in the lower portion of the tube, with a surface zone of from four to seven mm. which remains red, while those strains that produce an alkaline reaction give a diffuse homogeneous reddish coloration.

Huntoon's [125] **Hormone Agar.** This medium containing chopped beef heart or steak is supposed to contain certain agents which favor the growth of bacteria. They are probably erroneously called "hormones." The method of preparation was described as follows:

Chopped beef heart or steak (must be comparatively fresh)	500 gm.
Water	1,000 gm.
Peptone (Bacto peptone)	10 gm.
Agar (Bacto Agar)	16 gm.
Salt	5 gm.
Whole egg	1 gm.

All of the ingredients are placed in an ordinary enamelware vessel, preferably a large coffee pot, and heated over an open flame with constant stirring until the red color of the meat infusion changes to brown, at a temperature of about 68°C.(154.4°F.). Care should be taken not to run the temperature much above this point as the medium then begins to clot, which is undesirable at this time.

The medium is now titrated with normal sodium hydroxide until it is slightly alkaline to litmus paper and then one ml. per liter is added in addition.

The vessel is covered and placed in the Arnold sterilizer or in a water bath at a temperature of 100°C.(212°F.) for one hour, removed, and the firm clot which has formed is separated from the sides with a rod and the vessel returned to the sterilizer or water bath at 100°C.(212°F.) for one and one-half hours.

It is removed and allowed to stand at room temperature for about 10 minutes in a slightly inclined position; during this time the fluid portion separates and may be removed by pipetting or, in case of the coffee pot, by simply pouring it off carefully. If it is poured through a fine wire sieve, many small particles of meat clot may be caught.

The product is allowed to stand in tall cylinders for 15 to 20 minutes, until the fat present has risen to the surface where it can be removed. The medium is tubed and sterilized by the intermittent method. Autoclaving is to be avoided.

If the medium, although usually clear enough for practical purposes, seems too turbid, further clearing may take place by filtration through glass wool, asbestos wool, sedimentation, or centrifugalization.

Huntoon's Semisolid Agar Medium. This medium is prepared like the medium just described with the exception that five grams instead of 16 grams of agar are used. This medium is tubed in 10-ml. amounts and employed for stab inoculations. Huntoon stated that it was especially suited for preservation of stock cultures.

Bailey's [86] **"Hormone" Agar.** A medium rich in accessory substances was described as a "hormone" medium. It was prepared as follows:

1. Dissolve in one liter of distilled water 15 gm. of agar shreds which have previously been washed thoroughly in running water and allow to cool between 50°C. (122°F.) and 60°C.(140°F.). This step we believe to be important, because it reduces the amount of heating necessary after the addition of the meat and brings the agar suspension into contact with all of the meat particles before any coagulation has occurred.

2. Add 500 gm. of lean beef or beef heart (chopped to moderate fineness), bring to a boil, and cook slowly for 15 or 20 minutes.

3. Filter through an ordinary round flour sieve (colander type) about 16 mesh to the inch. Allow the agar and meat mixture retained on the sieve to become more or less evenly spread out, so that it acts as a filter, and again pour the filtrate through it. Filtration carried on in this way occurs with sufficient rapidity to allow several filtra-

125. Huntoon. 1918. J. Infect. Dis. 23, 169-172.

tions before cooling, if such are necessary to make the medium entirely clear. Egg need not be used.

4. Add peptone, 10 gm., and sodium chloride, five gm. Boil for about five minutes.

5. Correct to the desired reaction (pH 7.5).

The sodium hydroxide used to correct the reaction is likely to cause a brownish discoloration of the medium if it is added before the meat is removed by filtration. This does not occur when it is added after the meat has been filtered out.

6. Allow to stand in a warm place for a few minutes until the precipitate produced by the hydroxide settles out, and then decant the supernatant fluid.

With this procedure little precipitate is formed and little waste occurs.

7. Tube and sterilize by the fractional method or autoclave for about 20 minutes at five pounds of pressure.

It has been found that the medium is not damaged by autoclaving at low pressure, and a practice may be made of autoclaving tubed medium once and the medium in flasks twice.

Crystal Violet Agar (Salle[77]). Salle proposed this medium for differentiating *Escherichia coli* and *Aerobacter aerogenes*. The results were said to be equivalent to a confirmed and partially confirmed test as provided for in *Standard Methods for the Examination of Water and Sewage*. Salle described it preparation as follows:

Peptone, Difco	5.0 gm.
K₂HPO₄	5.0 gm.
KH₂PO₄	1.0 gm.
Agar	20.0 gm.
Distilled water	1,000.0 ml.

No adjustment of the reaction is required. This is controlled by the buffer substances. The ingredients are mixed and boiled until the agar is dissolved. The loss of water owing to evaporation is restored. The agar is not filtered, but distributed directly into 250 ml. Erlenmeyer flasks, 100 ml. to each flask. When ready to use, .5 gram lactose is added to each flask, and the agar melted in an Arnold sterilizer or in boiling water. After the agar is melted the following dyes are added to the contents of each flask: erythrosin (two per cent aqueous), two ml.; methylene blue (one per cent aqueous), one ml.; and brom-cresol-purple (one per cent aqueous), two ml. The agar is rotated in the flask to obtain a uniform mixture and then poured into sterile petri dishes.

Salle gave instructions for the preparations of the dye solutions. While the composition of different lots and brands may vary, this matters little for methylene blue and brom-cresol-purple. The erythrosin, however, caused considerable trouble. Instructions were given by Salle in his original report for preparing these solutions.

The growth of coliform bacilli on Salle's medium, which contains erythrosin, was found to be very irregular by Liebert and Kaper.[126] When no growth at all occurred, the medium was observed to be slightly discolored. Investigations showed that this was due to the effect of light. The strongly fluorescent erythrosin apparently converted the shorter light waves (not necessarily ultra-violet) into longer waves with the accompanying production of hydrogen peroxide. Other dyes, such as eosin and fluorescein, had a similar effect. If the medium is exposed to light before inoculation, sufficient hydrogen peroxide may be formed to inhibit growth entirely. Bacilli exposed to light in the presence of these dyes may be killed by the intracellular production of hydrogen peroxide from the dye which the organisms have absorbed.

Salle's phosphate buffered broth, containing one part crystal violet to 700,000 parts water, was tested by Stark and England[127] on seven laboratory stock strains of the Escherichia- Aerobacter group, and on 164 Escherichia-type organisms recently isolated from human feces. Forty-three per cent of these fecal cultures gave negative results

126. Liebert and Kaper. 1937. Antonie van Leeuwenhoek Nederland. Tijdschr. v. Hyg. Microbiol. et Serol. 4, 164.

127. Stark and England. 1933. J. Bact. 25, 439-445.

after 48 hours' incubation at 37°C.; all gave positive results in standard lactose broth. Cultures producing negative results in 48 hours eventually produced gas, some requiring as long as five days for 10-per cent gas to be produced; the organisms were not killed, but growth was delayed. Results tend definitely toward the conclusion that Salle's crystal-violet broth should not be adopted as a standard test medium in water analysis. To maintain the proper margin of safety, no medium should be used, which sometimes gives negative results in presence of fecal pollution.

Chapman and Berens [128] observed that staphylococcus strains plated on proteose-lactose agar containing a final concentration of 1-300,000 crystal violet (National Aniline and Chemical Company) gave rise to white colonies, violet colonies, or orange colonies having usually a violet fringe. As a rule the strains giving rise to either of the latter two types of colony were hemolytic, produced coagulase, and were toxic to rabbits on intravenous inoculation; while strains giving rise to white colonies were negative in all these respects. The agreement was not perfect, but was sufficiently good to justify the authors in their conclusion that the colonial appearance on crystal violet agar should be of considerable help in differentiating pathogenic from non-pathogenic strains of staphylococci.

Tonney and Noble's [129] Improved Ferrocyanide-Citrate Agar for Direct Enumeration of Colon-Aerogenes Organisms. This medium was first proposed in 1928. The modified medium was reported in 1931 as follows:

I. PREPARATION OF STOCK MEDIUM AND "COVER" AGAR.

Many laboratories will find it more convenient and economical to prepare the stock medium in 10-liter, or larger, quantities. On this basis, the following formula, one and one-half times the required strength, is given:

Distilled water	20 liters
Agar, shredded	300 gm.
Sodium ammonium phosphate, C. P.	30 gm.
Acid potassium phosphate (KH_2PO_4) C. P.	15 gm.

Procedure

1. Three hundred grams of shredded agar are placed in a cheesecloth bag of four thicknesses.

2. The bag of agar is then placed in a container of approximately six gallons capacity and 20 liters of distilled water added. After 24 hours, discard the free water and press the water from the agar by twisting and squeezing it. Replace bag in container and add 20 liters more of distilled water. This process is repeated until the end of the fourth 24-hour period. After the batch has been drained as usual, rinse the container and empty the agar from the bag into the container. Then add more distilled water to make a three-per cent agar for stock or the two-per cent agar and water "cover" as needed.

3. If the autoclave is not large enough to receive the large container, transfer the batch to two smaller containers with covers and mark the water level for the purpose of replacing loss by evaporation. Melt the agar in the autoclave.

4. Replace loss by evaporation. Add 30 grams of sodium ammonium phosphate, C. P. and 15 grams of acid potassium phosphate, C. P. to the batch and mix thoroughly. The salts readily dissolve. If two containers are used, add salts as above and pour the contents of containers back and forth to assure the same concentration throughout.

5. Adjust the reaction to pH 7 with brom thymol blue.

6. Filter the agar through a sterile filter and deliver measured quantities by sterile graduate into presterilized plugged bottles. Any convenient quantity may be measured. We have found it convenient to put 140 ml. in a bottle. This quantity fits in well with convenient amounts of solutions A and B. Bottles are then paper capped for protection and steamed in the Arnold for 15 minutes only.

128. Chapman and Berens. 1935. Jour. Bact. 29. 437-448.

129. Tonney and Noble. 1928. Amer. Water Wks. Assoc. J. 23. 1202-1208.

7. The two-per cent agar in distilled water is merely melted, filtered, distributed into presterilized plugged containers, and autoclaved.

II. PREPARATION OF STOCK SOLUTIONS A AND B.

Solution A. (One liter.)*

Anhydrous sodium sulfite. Na_2SO_3 C. P.	3.8 gm.
Acid potassium phosphate. KH_2PO_4 C. P.	7.5 gm.
Sodium ammonium phosphate. $NaNH_4HPO_4·4H_2O$ C. P.	45.4 gm.
Distilled water, sterile	817.0 ml.
20% lactose, sterile	140.0 ml.
4% alcohol (95%) basic fuchsin	18.0 ml.
9% potassium ferrocyanide. $K_4Fe(CN)_6·3H_2O.$ C. P.	
steamed in streaming steam 15 minutes	25.0 ml.

Procedure

1. Add 4.6 grams of anhydrous sodium sulfite, C. P. to a two-liter flask.

2. Add 167 ml. of sterile distilled water and bring to a boil avoiding unnecessary loss of moisture by evaporation. (Boiling also may be accomplished in smaller containers of glass, porcelain, or granite ware and then transferred to the stock flask.)

3. Cool and add 421 ml. of sterile 20-per cent lactose solution, C. P. If the latter has been stored at low temperature, it will assist in cooling the heated sulfite solution.

4. Add 8.8 ml. of a saturated alcoholic (95%) solution of basic fuchsin.

5. Add 401 ml. of sterile 20 per cent potassium ferrocyanide solution C. P.

Stock solution B consists of 2.5 per cent ferric citrate; 400 ml. will be required for use in conjunction with one liter of solution A.

The concentration of ingredients in Solutions A and B is one and one-half times the required strength for use in planting 10 ml. portions of an equal ratio with three per cent stock agar, resulting, of course, in two per cent agar having ingredients of single strength.

III. ADDITION OF SOLUTIONS A AND B TO STOCK AGAR AND POURING OF PLANTED PLATES.

1. On the basis of using 20 ml. of stock medium and 10 ml. of "cover" agar per plate, determine the number of bottles of medium and cover needed and melt in the Arnold or in a container of water over a free flame.

2. Set up and label the necessary number of petri plates. To those plates which are to receive one ml. or less of inoculant, add 10 ml. of sterile distilled water.

3. To each bottle of melted stock agar add (a) 12.5 ml. of Solution A and agitate thoroughly; (b) five ml. of Solution B and agitate thoroughly. Hold the bottles of cyanide citrate medium in a container of water or water bath between 47 and 60°C. (116.6 and 140°F.). Keep the "cover" agar warm enough to pour when ready.

4. Plant the plates. This is done while the medium is cooling down or being held at a given temperature.

5. With the cyanide citrate agar at low enough temperature to be harmless to the organisms and high enough to avoid too rapid solidification while mixing with the cool or cold inoculant (probably 46 to 47°C. will be about right), add 20 ml. water to the plate and mix thoroughly. This is easily accomplished by slightly lifting one side of the cover.

6. When plates have hardened, add 10 ml. of "cover" agar. This may be pipetted or poured, provided fair judgment of amount is used. A little more or less is of little consequence, except that when too thin some colonies may come through and spread, thus hiding a deeper one which may thus be lost in the count. When the "cover" has hardened, invert the plates in a 37°C. incubator for 42 to 48 hours.

* This formula from a private communication. November, 1931.

130. Tonney and Noble. 1931. J. Infect. Dis. 48, 413-417.

7. Count the plates by means of a standard hand lens and counting frame having a white background affording transmitted light by illumination from the sides.

According to Tonney and Noble [130] some of the practical advantages of the direct plating method in cyanide-citrate agar are as follows: It has greater simplicity than fermentation methods (consists only of planting the plates and counting them after incubation); it yields results in a shorter time (completed observations in 42 to 48 hours, presumptive indications in 36 hours); it gives separate *Escherichia coli* and *Aerobacter aerogenes* counts and their numerical relation to each other, as well as the total count; it gives a more accurate index than is obtainable by use of liquid media. Direct counts are not obscured by overgrowths and are not interfered with by other common lactose-fermenting organisms, such as *Clostridium welchii* or *Bacillus aerosporus*. The ''pour plate'' process is an excellent method of isolating pure cultures of *Escherichia coli* and *Aerobacter aerogenes*. Deep colonies fished from a poured plate are apt to yield pure strains.

Sodium Desoxycholate Agar Medium. The American Association of Medical Milk Commissions [82] recommends preparation of this medium as follows:

Distilled water..1,000 ml.
Peptone.. 10 gm.

Boil for a short time and filter through paper. Neutralize if necessary. Add the following:

Agar (granular, U. S. P.).. 17 gm.
Sodium hydroxide (N/1).. 2 ml.

Heat in the Arnold steamer or the autoclave until the agar is dissolved. If the autoclave is used, restore the volume of the medium with distilled water. Add the following substances in the order given:

Sodium desoxycholate.. 1 gm.
Sodium chloride... 5 gm.
Dipotassium phosphate.. 2 gm.
Lactose.. 10 gm.
Ferric ammonium citrate, ferric sodium citrate,
    or ferric potassium citrate.. 2 gm.

Adjust the reaction to pH 7.5 and add
Neutral red (certified; 1% aqueous sol.).................................3.3 gm.

Tube and sterilize for 15 minutes in the Arnold steamer, longer if distributed in flasks. Autoclaving is not necessary because Gram-positive sporeforming bacteria do not grow in the medium. The medium should be heated as little as possible and only sufficiently to kill vegetative cells. Store in the dark because neutral red is decolorized by light. The following peptones have been found satisfactory: Proteose (Difco), Wilson, Nutri, Fairchild, Witte, and Armour; the following were less satisfactory, Bacto (Difco), Neo (Difco).

American Association of Medical Milk Commissions, [82] **Blood Agar Medium.** The blood agar medium shall be prepared as follows:

Finely ground lean pork, veal, or beef................................ 500 gm.
Distilled water..1,000 ml.
Peptone... 10 gm.
Sodium chloride... 5 gm.
Granulated agar, U. S. P.. 15 gm.

Mix the meat with the water, infuse for one hour, and then boil for five minutes. Strain through wire or cotton gauze and filter through paper. Restore the volume to 1,000 ml. Add the peptone and the salt. Adjust reaction to pH 7.8. Boil for 15 to 20

82. Methods and Standards for Production of Certified Milk, Amer. Assoc. Med. Milk Comm. 1939. p. 18; see also Leifson. 1935. J. Path. and Bact. 40, 581.

*Growth and Appearance of the Colonies of Various Types of Bacteria on
Desoxycholate and Desoxycholate-Citrate Agars* [131]

Bacteria	Desoxycholate agar	Desoxycholate-citrate agar
Coli	Large colonies with even red color	Considerably inhibited. Colonies like those on desoxycholate agar
Aerobacter	Large mucoid colonies having pink centers and colorless peripheries	Considerably inhibited. Colonies like those on desoxycholate agar
Proteus	Large, non-spreading, smooth colonies, with touch of brown in center	Many strains inhibited. Colonies develop brown centers
Alkaligenes	Large, smooth, colorless colonies	Usually no growth
Pyocyaneus	Large olive-colored colonies with raised centers and diffuse edges	Large, olive-colored, slightly granular, opaque colonies
Typhoid	Large colorless colonies (where isolated) with raised center and irregular thin edges	Fairly large, translucent, bluish-looking colonies, with slightly granular structure
Paratyphoid "A"	Large, smooth, colorless colonies	Large translucent colonies, somewhat more smooth and more regular edges than typhoid
Salmonella in general	Large colorless colonies, usually with touch of brown in center	Large, colorless, opaque colonies, usually with touch of brown in center
Dysentery— Flexner	Large, smooth, white and opaque colonies with smooth, even edges	Large, colorless, milky opaque, smooth colonies with even edges
Dysentery— Sonne	Same as Flexner type	No growth (?)
Dysentery— Shiga	Same as Flexner type but smaller	No growth (?)
Gram-positive bacteria	No growth	No growth

minutes. Filter through paper and restore volume or weight. Add the agar and heat to boiling with constant stirring. Add five ml. of N/1 NaOH. Autoclave for 15 minutes. Restore the weight with boiling water and stir well. Place a sterile lid over the vessel and allow the medium to sediment at room temperature overnight. Next morning spoon off the clear agar from the surface or remove the solidified agar from the vessel and cut off and discard the sediment. Melt, distribute into tubes or flasks, and sterilize in the autoclave. The final reaction should be pH 7.2 to 7.6. (It is recommended that several liters of agar be prepared at one time.)

Hall and Lothrop's [132] **Honey Agar.** Aggregates of flocculated materials, normal to honey agar, were eliminated by preheating honey with a suspension of coloidal clay— bentonite. The nutritive values of honey agars made from clarified honey of three floral types (tupelo, fruit bloom, and clover) were compared with those of honey agars made from the same honeys without clarification. Five cultures of sugar-tolerant yeasts were selected for plate and slant studies. The diameters (in mm.) and total numbers of colonies developing on plates poured with clarified *versus* unclarified honey agars were equal, within the limits of accuracy for dilution-plate methods. The amount of yeast growth on honey-agar slants made with clarified honey approximated that on slants made with unclarified honey. Cultural and physiological characteristics of yeast propagated on clarified honey agar remained unaltered.

131. From publication of Baltimore Biological Laboratory.
132. Hall and Lothrop. 1934. J. Bact. 27, 349-355.

Eisenberg's[133] **Nile Blue Culture Medium for Lipolytic Microorganisms.** This medium makes use of Nile blue sulfate as an indicator for detecting changes in neutral fats. Its preparation and use were described as follows:

PREPARATION OF THE MEDIUM

(a) Dissolve 20 gm. agar (Bacto) in 1,000 ml. of beef infusion broth prepared according to the directions of Zinsser and Bayne-Jones (1935). Filter through absorbent cotton and adjust the reaction to pH 7.4. Distribute in 100-ml. amounts in flasks and sterilize in the autoclave at 15 pounds pressure for 20 minutes.

(b) *Dye-Fat Emulsion:* Dissolve four gm. ossein gelatin (200 Bloom, isoelectric point at pH 5.6) in 100 ml. of distilled water at 60°C.(140°F.). Add sufficient N/10 NaOH solution to raise the pH to 7.2. The gelatin solution, while still warm, is shaken vigorously in a large stoppered bottle with 100 ml. of cottonseed oil (U.S.P.) to which has been added .1 gm. Nile blue sulfate (C. I. No. 913, dye content 90 per cent, solubility .15 gm. in 100 ml. water). The mixture is then put through a hand homogenizer until the oil globules are about 10 microns in diameter. This emulsion has a light blue color and after sterilization in the autoclave at 15 pounds pressure for 20 minutes turns deep pink. At room temperature the emulsion solidifies, but by placing it in the incubator at 37°C.(98.6°F.) a day before it is to be used no difficulty in pipetting is experienced.

(c) *Preparation of Plates:* When plates are to be poured 100 ml. of the sterile infusion agar base are liquefied, and while still hot, 10 ml. of the sterile dye-fat emulsion are added aseptically. The whole is well mixed and allowed to cool at 45°C. (113°F.) before being poured into plates. Before inoculation the medium has a rich salmon-pink color.

The medium is equally efficient both with pour and streak plates, the former being desirable for quantitative work. Colonies of organisms which decompose fats appear as light blue colonies surrounded by a narrow zone of decolorized, transparent medium when incubated for three to four days at room temperature. Non-lipolytic colonies appear white or pink.

Starr's[134] **Spirit Blue Agar for Detection of Lipolytic Microorganisms.** Starr suggested a sensitive differential medium which is easy to prepare, is not toxic to bacteria, and permits ''indisputable detection of fat-splitting microorganisms.'' The preparation is as follows: Dissolve 30 gm. agar, 10 gm. tryptone, and five gm. yeast extract in approximately 900 ml. distilled water, by autoclaving; to this add 25 ml. of a 20-per cent cottonseed oil emulsion (10 gm. powdered gum arabic ground thoroughly in 100 ml. Wesson oil and 400 ml. warm distilled water) and 50 ml. of .3-per cent freshly filltered alcoholic spirit blue (National Aniline); bring up to 1,000 ml. with distilled water, and autoclave 15 minutes at 15 pounds (121°C.). The medium must be stored in a refrigerator until used. Plates made from it appear pale lavender; lipolysis is indicated by a permanent deep blue beneath and around the colony.

Turner's[135] **Differential Plating Medium for Lipase-Producing Bacteria.** This medium causes the lipase-producing colony to show a dark-blue zone about it. It is composed as follows: Sugar-free meat digest fluid, 1,000 ml.; dibasic sodium phosphate, five gm.; agar, 30 gm.; melt clear and adjust to pH 7.6. Autoclave. Add 1.25 gm. of Nile blue sulfate in 100 ml. of 25-per cent ethyl alcohol. Tube in six- to seven-ml. amounts in previously sterilized tubes. Heat in the Arnold sterilizer for 15 minutes. When used the agar is melted and cooled to 45 to 50°C.(113 to 122°F.). A sterile emulsion of fat is added to about 10 per cent volume; .7 ml. for seven-ml. tube. Cream of cottonseed oil made according to the directions of the U. S. Pharmacopeia for codliver oil, except 25 per cent more water is used than prescribed, may be used. The inoculum and emulsion are thoroughly mixed with agar, poured into a Petri dish, and allowed to harden. The plates should be incubated under anaerobic conditions. The typical colony is apparent after 24 hours. Streak plates are not satisfactory.

133. Eisenberg. 1939. Stain Technol. 14, 63-67.
134. Starr. 1941. Science 93, 333-334.
135. Turner. 1928. Soc. Expt. Biol. and Med. Proc. 25, 318-320.

Jensen and Grettie's [136] modification of emulsion medium, which may be incubated either at 20°C.(68°F.) or 37°C.(98.6°F.), was made as follows:

Agar stock

Nutrient agar 100 ml.
$$Na_2HPO_4 \frac{.5 \text{ gm.}}{pH\ 7.4}$$

Oil emulsion

100 ml. refined coconut oil (or palm oil), two gm. gum tragacanth added to hot distilled water, 200 ml. Shake until the globules are about 10μ in diameter. Autoclave at 15 pounds for 15 minutes.

Jensen and Grettie then added .75 ml. of the oil emulsion and .75 ml. of .1 per cent Nile blue sulfate aqueous solution to each five and one-half ml. of melted agar. Portions of the well-mixed medium are then cooled to 42°C.(107.6°F.), the inocula in dilutions added, and plates poured in thin layers. The lipase-forming colonies are, at first, deep blue in color.

Reed and Orr's [50] Plating Medium for Anaerobes. They added .1 per cent of dextrose and two per cent of agar to the sugar-free broth of Breiner, described above.

A second formula was proposed as follows:

Proteose peptone	20.0 gm.
Sodium phosphate	2.0 gm.
Dextrose	1.0 gm.
Sodium thioglycollate	1.0 gm.
Agar	20.0 gm.
Water	1,000.0 ml.
Adjust to pH 7.6.	

The plates were incubated upright in a Fildes jar.

Greenberg's [137] Semisolid Agar Medium for Isolating Anaerobic Bacteria. This medium was proposed as especially useful for this purpose.

Proteose peptone	10 gm.
Tryptone	10 gm.
Sodium thioglycollate	1 gm.
Agar	3 gm.
Distilled water	1,000 ml.

Adjust the reaction to pH 7.4, dispense in tubes in 10-ml. amounts, and autoclave at 15 pounds for 20 minutes.

Proteose Peptone Acid Medium of Stern, Hegarty, and Williams. [138] This medium was devised for isolation of *Bacillus thermoacidurans* from canned tomato juice. The following composition proved to be most satisfactory:

Proteose peptone (Difco)	5 gm.
Yeast extract (Difco)	5 gm.
Glucose	5 gm.
K₂HPO₄	4 gm.
Distilled water	500 ml.

(K_2HPO_4)

The ingredients are dissolved in the water, and the pH adjusted to five with dilute HCl. In a separate flask 20 grams of agar are dissolved in 500 ml. of water, and then both solutions are sterilized for 30 minutes at 15 pounds pressure. When the medium is ready to be used, the melted agar is mixed with the sterilized nutrients at 45 to 55°C. (113 to 131°F.).

136. Jensen and Grettie. 1937. Food Research 2, 97-120.
137. Greenberg. 1941. Canad. Pub. Health J. 32, 84-85.
138. Stern, Hegarty, and Williams. 1942. Food Research 7, 186-191.

ENDO'S MEDIUM

This medium was reported by Endo [139] as especially suitable for differentiation of *Eberthella typhosa* from *Escherichia coli*. Since the original medium was proposed, there have been many modifications. Young and Marshall [140] have stated that many of them are not as satisfactory as the original formula.

Endo's Medium (after Kendall [141]):

I. PREPARATION OF AGAR
   (a) Prepare plain, sugar-free agar, using 15 gm. agar per liter.
   (b) Adjust to a point just alkaline to litmus.
   (c) Place in flasks in 100-ml. quantities and sterilize.

II. PREPARATION OF THE INDICATOR
   (a) Prepare a 10-per cent basic fuchsin solution in 96-per cent alcohol. This solution is fairly stable if kept away from the light.
   (b) Prepare a 10-percent solution of chemically pure anhydrous sodium sulfite. (One gm. in 10 ml. water.) This solution does not keep.
   (c) Add one ml. of II (a) to 10 ml. of II (b) and heat in the Arnold sterilizer for 20 minutes. The color of the solution should be nearly discharged. This solution must be prepared each day. It does not keep.

III. PREPARATION OF MEDIUM
   (a) Add one gm. of lactose to 100 ml. of the agar and place in the autoclave until melted and lactose is dissolved.
   (b) Add enough of II (c) to impart a pink color (about one ml.).
   (c) Pour into sterile Petri dishes and allow to harden. In the above medium Kendall has reduced the agar content to 1.5 per cent. The original formula of Endo called for a three-per cent solution which was supposed to prevent diffusion of the acid.

Endo's Medium (Hygienic Laboratory Method). Hasseltine [142] has described the preparation of this medium as follows: It consists of a three-per cent agar which is titrated and corrected to $+.5$ to phenolphthalein, to which is added 3.7 ml. of a 10-per cent solution of anhydrous sodium carbonate. For convenience it is flasked, sterilized, and stored in 200-ml. quantities. When ready to use the following ingredients are added to 200 ml. of agar as follows:

(a) Dissolve two gm. chemically pure lactose in 25 to 30 ml. of distilled water, with the aid of gentle heat.

(b) Dissolve .5 gm. of anhydrous sodium sulfite in 10 to 15 ml. of distilled water.

(c) To the sulfite solution add one ml. of saturated solution of basic fuchsin in 95 per cent alcohol.

Add the fuchsin sulfite solution to the lactose solution and then add the whole to the agar. Pour plates at once, and after hardening dry for 15 minutes in the incubator.

Teague [143] has shown that a 10-per cent solution of sodium sulfite may be heated for 20 minutes at 15 pounds with practically no change. If this is then kept covered with a layer of petroleum, it may be kept for three weeks at room temperature.

Endo's Medium (After Levine [144]). Levine states the method of preparation as follows:

Distilled water	1,000 ml.
Peptone (Difco)	10 gm.
Dipotassium phosphate	2-5 gm.
Agar	15-30 gm.

139. Endo. 1904. Centbl. Bakt., Pt. 1, Orig., 35, 109.
140. Young and Marshall. 1925. J. Lab. and Clin. Med. 10, 532-535.
141. Kendall. 1911. J. Med. Res. 25, 95-99.
142. Hasseltine. 1918. U. S. Pub. Health Rpts. 32, 1878-1887.
143. Teague. 1918. J. Amer. Med. Assoc. 70, 454.
144. Levine. 1918. J. Infect. Dis. 23, 43-47.

These ingredients should be boiled until dissolved and the loss by evaporation made up with distilled water. No adjustment of the reaction is necessary; neither is filtration necessary if the medium is to be used for streaked cultures. Store in quantities of 100 ml. in Erlenmeyer flasks and when used add the following materials:

20 per cent lactose solution..1 gm. or 5.0 ml.
10 per cent alcoholic solution of basic fuchsin........................ 0.5 ml.
Freshly prepared sodium sulfite solution.................................. 2.5 ml.

The theory of the reaction in Endo's medium has been explained in different ways. DeBord [145] quoted the investigations of Harding and Ostenberg,[146] who stated that the red color was due to the formation of aldehyde, and of Robinson and Rettger,[147] who believed that the reaction was due to acid and not aldehyde. DeBord attempted to clear up the question by comparing these reactions with those obtained when true Schiff's fuchsin aldehyde reagent [148] was used. DeBord concluded that Schiff's reagent would detect aldehyde formation in glucose and lactose media. Further, he found that the color change was produced with aldehydes only in the presence of acids. He considered the red color formed in Endo's medium by *Escherichia coli* to be due to the formation of both acid and aldehyde. Kahn [149] believed that the metallic sheen of typical *Escherichia coli* colonies on this medium is due to the evaporation of volatile substances produced in the metabolism of these bacteria.

Muller [150] concluded that the color change in Endo's agar medium was due to the formation of both acid and aldehyde. Barnewitz and Flecke [151] showed that *Eberthella typhosa* produced small amounts of acid in both carbohydrate and carbohydrate-free media. The red color of Endo's agar they believed to be due to the formation of amino salts. They found that hydrochloric acid would not restore the color to basic fuchsin which had been decolorized with sodium sulfite but that lactic acid would.

Harris [152] reported that the reaction of Endo's agar should be between pH 7.4 and 7.8. The use of Witte's peptone gave a less satisfactory medium than when three brands of American peptone were used. Harris found that the kind of dye also had influence on the quality of the medium. Basic fuchsin which contained a mixture of rosaniline and pararosaniline gave more consistent results than basic fuchsin containing chiefly rosaniline. Genung [153] also believed that the quality of peptone was partly responsible for varying results in the use of Endo's agar. One trouble in the use of this medium has been the diffusion of color or the substances causing the color change. It is interesting to note that she found that Witte's peptone gave less diffusion. One difficulty in the preparation of Endo's agar is that it

145. DeBord. 1918. J. Bact. 2, 309-314.
146. Harding and Ostenberg. 1912. J. Infect. Dis. 11, 109.
147. Robinson and Rettger. 1916. J. Med. Res. 29, 363.
148. According to DeBord, on authority of Mulliken, Schiff's fuchsin-aldehyde reagent is prepared by dissolving .2 gram basic fuchsin in 10 ml. freshly saturated solution of sulfur dioxide. After standing for some time, the solution should be a straw color. This is, then, made up to 200 ml. with distilled water and kept in a dark place.
149. Kahn. 1918. J. Bact. 3, 547-554.
150. Muller. 1924. Compt. Rend. Soc. Biol. 90, 653-655.
151. Barnewitz and Flecke. 1924. Centbl. Bakt., Pt. 1, 92, 359-362.
152. Harris. 1925. Mil. Surg. 57, 280-285.
153. Genung. 1925. Abs. Bact. 9, 3.

should not be prepared and stored in large amounts. It is far better to be able to prepare the amount that is needed. This is possible with the availability of dehydrated Endo's agar as prepared by the Digestive Ferments Company.

Margolena and Hensen [154] confirmed Neuberg and Nord's theory that Endo's medium acts as a trapping agent for the intermediate product, acetaldehyde, which causes the Endo reaction. *Escherichia coli* was grown in a medium of a composition similar to Endo's medium with the exception that the sulfite fuchsin and agar were left out. When the fuchsin-sulfite mixture was added after 24, 36, and 48 hours, or after three and 10 days of incubation at 37°C., no reaction appeared. The substance that causes the reaction is formed only when the bacteria are grown in the presence of sulfite. When picric acid and ether are added to the red compound produced by the coliform organism in Endo's medium and the mixture is shaken, the color remains in the watery layer and thus the dye color that appears in the medium is not restored fuchsin, but a new substance. The work confirms LaGrange [155] who worked on this problem.

Brilliant Green Lactose Bile (Muer and Harris [78]). The following medium was found to be especially valuable in preventing the development of anaerobic bacteria in the presumptive test in water analysis.

Distilled water	1,000.0 gm.
Ox gall (dried)	50.0 gm.
Peptone	10.0 gm.
Lactose	10.0 gm.
Brilliant green	0.1 gm.

Distilled water is heated in a double boiler until the water in the outer container boils. Fifty grams of dried ox gall are added, with 10 grams of peptone, and dissolved. Boiling should be continued for one hour. After removing from the flame 10 grams of lactose are added. Filter and add 10 ml. of a one-per cent solution of brilliant green. Sterilize in tubes at 15 pounds for 15 minutes.

Dunham and Schoenlein [156] studied the medium proposed by Muer and Harris and reported that it did not show appreciable inhibition of *Escherichia coli*. They showed further that a medium containing two per cent of bile, one per cent of peptone, one per cent of lactose, and 1-75,000 brilliant green permitted more rapid development of *Escherichia coli* at pH 6.9 that did the original brilliant green bile at its optimum pH. It is well to point out that some of the diverse conclusions which have been reached with brilliant green media may be due to the brand of dye used. Different brands and lots of dye vary greatly in efficiency. Rakieten and Rettger [157] and Berry and Daniels [158] made observations to this effect. A selective action of brilliant green has been discussed earlier in this chapter under liquid media (Stark and Curtis [80]). Hook and Hitchner [159] also made such observations.

All cultures exhibited a greater dye tolerance when larger inocula were used. Aerobacter strains grew at a much higher dye concentration than

154. Margolena and Hansen. 1933. Stain Technol. 8, October.
155. LaGrange. 1932. Compt. Rend. Soc. Biol. 110, 419-421.
156. Dunham and Schoenlein. 1926. Stain Technol. 1, 129.
157. Rakieten and Rettger. 1927. J. Infect. Dis. 41, 93-110.
158. Berry and Daniels. 1928. Amer. J. Pub. Health 18, 883-892.
159. Hook and Hitchner. 1937. J. Bact. 33, 88.

the Escherichia strains. Within the genus the various cultures of both Escherichia and Aerobacter exhibited marked differences in dye tolerance, being more marked in representatives of the Escherichia group. Upon prolonged incubation many cultures produced visible growth at a dye concentration inhibitory during a shorter incubation period. A preliminary study with a few representative strains of *Escherichia coli* and *Aerobacter aerogenes* showed that when a 1:10 dilution of a 24-hour-old culture of the various strains was streaked on nutrient agar containing a 1:200,000 concentration of the dye, all *Escherichia* cultures showed no visible growth after 48 hours, while all Aerobacter strains grew rapidly. Further tests with 103 cultures, comprising 19 Aerobacter strains, 61 Escherichia strains, and 23 intermediates, differentiated by the M.R.-V.P., indol, citrate, and cellobiose tests, confirmed the results from the preliminary study with Escherichia and Aerobacter strains. The authors suggest the above procedure as a further means of differentiating the latter.

Lead Acetate Agar. Add .1 per cent of lead acetate to plain agar, tube, and sterilize. This medium has been useful for separating some of the paratyphoid bacteria. *Salmonella paratyphi* does not blacken this medium while *Salmonella schottmülleri* does. This medium is inoculated on the surface as well as by stabbing into the butt of the tube.

Kligler's [160] Lead Acetate Agar. Kligler proposed the following medium for differentiating members of the colon-typhoid group:

(1) Meat infusion agar containing three-fourths per cent or one per cent agar (depending on the moisture content of the agar).

(2) .1 per cent glucose.

(3) .05 per cent of lead acetate.

The optimum reaction should be pH 7.2 to 7.6. The agar is prepared in the usual way except that three-fourths to one per cent of agar is used instead of the usual 1.5 per cent. This gives a semisolid medium which has several advantages. Gas production is readily observed by the diffusion of bubbles and breaking up of the medium.

The sugar and lead acetate are dissolved in water separately, sterilized, and added to the agar under aseptic conditions. It is necessary to cool the agar to about 60°C. (140°F.) before adding the lead acetate and to rotate the tube to insure uniform distribution. Kligler reported the following changes for the organisms indicated:

Eberthella typhosa—Browning along the line of growth.
Salmonella paratyphi—No browning, but gas formation.
Salmonella schottmülleri—Browning and gas formation.
Eberthella dysenteriae—Neither browning nor gas.

This has been confirmed by Jordan and Victorson,[161] who used a medium containing 1.5 per cent of agar. Morishima [162] also described a similar method. The differentiation is secured in about the same way as with Kligler's method.

Bailey and Lacy's [163] Modification of Kligler's Lead Acetate Medium. These investigators found phenol red to be a better indicator than Andrade's in Kligler's lead acetate medium. Their medium was prepared as follows:

Bacto beef extract	5 gm.
Peptone	10 gm.
Sodium chloride	5 gm.
Agar shreds	15 gm.
Tap water	1,000 ml.

160. Kligler. 1917. Amer. J. Pub. Health 7, 1042-1044.
161. Jordan and Victorson. 1917. J. Infect. Dis. 21, 544.
162. Morishima. 1918. J. Bact. 3, 19-22.
163. Bailey and Lacy. 1927. J. Bact. 13, 182-189.

The agar should be washed in running water and then heated in the required amount of water until dissolved. The other ingredients should then be added. Adjust the reaction to pH 7.4 and boil for a few minutes, adjust the reaction again, and allow to settle. The clear supernatant agar should then be decanted into another container and accurately divided into 100-ml. quantities. Sterilize at 10 pounds pressure for 20 minutes.

To each 100 ml. of medium add one gram of lactose, .1 gram of glucose, and .05 gram lead acetate after the medium has been melted and cooled to 50°C.(122°F.). Then add five ml. of a .02-per cent phenol red solution, tube, and sterilize at 15 pounds for 15 minutes.

Morishima's [162] **Medium for Differentiating Members of the Colon-Typhoid Group.** Prepare meat infusion agar in the usual manner (Morishima cleared his medium with egg) and titrate to —.2 and —.4 with phenolphthalein as the indicator. Prepare a two-per cent solution of neutral lead acetate and heat for 30 minutes at 100°C.(212°F.) in a water bath. Five ml. of this solution should be added to 100 ml. of the melted agar and cooled to 60°C.(140°F.). Transfer this lead acetate agar to test tubes to a depth of about 1.5 ml. If the lead acetate is tubed while hot, the lead acetate settles to the bottom of the tube. This may be prevented by cooling the medium to 60 to 70°C.(140 to 158°F.) before tubing.

To 10 ml. of China blue (one per cent solution) add .4 ml. of normal sodium hydroxide and heat on the water bath for 10 minutes at 100°C.(212°F.). The color changes from blue to brown during the heating. One and one-fifth ml. of this decolorized China blue are added to 100 ml. of nutrient agar of reaction —.2 to —.4. One per cent of lactose and .1 per cent of glucose are added and the mixture is heated 10 minutes in the water bath at 100°C.(212°F.). This medium should be cooled to about 60°C.(140°F.) and should then be placed to about the same depth on the lead acetate. Incubate the tubes overnight and remove any contaminated ones in the morning.

Culture	Gas production	Bottom layer	Top layer
Eberthella typhosa	—	Black	Pale blue
Salmonella paratyphi	+	No change	Pale blue
Salmonella schottmülleri	+	Black	Colorless
Salmonella enteriditis	+	Black	Colorless
Escherichia coli	++	Black or no change	Deep blue

Methyl-Red-Voges-Proskauer Medium. *Standard Methods for the Examination of Water and Sewage* prescribed the following media:

(a) *Peptone Medium.* 1. To 800 ml. of distilled water add five gm. of Proteose-Peptone, Difco, or Witte's Peptone (other peptones should not be substituted), five gm. C. P. dextrose, and five gm. dipotassium hydrogen phosphate (K_2HPO_4). A dilute solution of the K_2HPO_4 should give a distinct pink with phenolphthalein.

2. Heat over steam, with occasional stirring, for 20 minutes.

3. Filter through folded filter paper, cool to 20°C.(68°F.), and dilute to 1,000 ml. with distilled water.

4. Distribute 10-ml. portions in sterilized test tubes.

5. Sterilize by the intermittent method for 20 minutes on three successive days.

(b) *Synthetic Medium.* 1. Dissolve seven gm. anhydrous disodium phosphate (Na_2HPO_4) or 8.8 gm. crystallized disodium phosphate ($Na_2HPO_4 \cdot 2H_2O$), two gm. potassium acid phthalate, one gm. aspartic acid, and four gm. dextrose in 800 ml. of warm distilled water.

2. Cool and dilute to one liter at room temperature.

3. Sterilize in autoclave for 15 minutes after the pressure has reached 15 pounds, provided the total time of exposure to heat is not more than one-half hour.

Bacto M.R.-V.P. medium, dehydrated, may be used if desired.

Hucker and Wall's [164] Medium for Nitrate Reduction and Ammonia Formation. The following medium for determining ammonia formation from organic sources was reported:

Peptone	4.0 per cent
Dextrose	0.2 per cent
Potassium phosphate (K_2HPO_4)	0.5 per cent
Agar	15.0 gm.
Water	1,000.0 ml.

Add one ml. of a 10-per cent solution of phenol and one per cent (available chlorine) sodium hypochlorite solution to the surface of this medium. A blue color formed in one-half hour indicates ammonia formation.

Ammonia formation from inorganic sources may be determined with the following medium:

Water	1,000.0 ml.
Agar	15.0 gm.
Dextrose	10.0 gm.
Potassium nitrate	1.0 gm.
Calcium chloride	0.5 gm.
Potassium phosphate (K_2HPO_4)	0.5 gm.

Other sources of nitrogen than potassium nitrate may be used if desired. To determine ammonia formation add two ml. of neutral formaldehyde or the test given with the medium mentioned above.

Eosin Brilliant-Green Agar (Teague and Clurman [165]). This medium was devised for the rapid isolation of *Eberthella typhosa* from stools and was prepared in the following manner: 500 gm. of chopped beef are placed in one liter of distilled water and kept in the refrigerator overnight. The infusion is squeezed through cheesecloth, heated in the Arnold sterilizer and passed through filter paper. Witte's peptone (one per cent), chemically pure sodium chloride (.5 per cent) and agar (1.5 per cent) are added to the warm infusion, the peptone being rubbed into a paste in a little warm water. Then heat the flask of medium in the autoclave for 30 minutes at 120°C.(248°F.). Adjust the reaction to 1+ by adding 2N sodium hydroxide, cool to 55°C.(131°F.), clear and filter through cotton. Put into flasks in 100-ml. quantities and sterilize at 120°C.(248°F.) for 20 minutes.

When ready to use, melt the agar and add one per cent each of sucrose and lactose. To every 50 ml. of agar add one ml. of a three-per cent solution of yellowish eosin. From the stock solution of brilliant green in 50 per cent alcohol, a one-sixth-per cent solution is prepared in distilled water and one ml. of this is added to each 50 ml. of the agar. After the dyes are well distributed, pour into plates.

Eosin Methylene Blue Agar. The disadvantages in the use of Endo's Agar caused Holt-Harris and Teague [166] to study a new medium. They investigated the combinations of certain dyes with eosin. Eosin methylene blue agar was found to be a useful medium for differentiating *Escherichia coli* colonies from colonies of *Eberthella typhosa*. This differentiation was possible since the medium between the colonies was not colored by diffusion of acid from the colonies of *Escherichia coli*. The authors claimed the following advantages of eosin methylene blue over Endo's agar:

1. Earlier differentiation of *Escherichia coli* from other forms.
2. A greater percentage of colorless forms turn out to be *Eberthella typhosa*.
3. Complete inhibition of certain organisms which form small colonies on Endo's medium.
4. No change of color of plate on exposure to light.
5. Slight variations in reaction of medium do not affect it severely.

164. Hucker and Wall. 1922. J. Bact. 7, 515-518.
165. Teague and Clurman. 1916. J. Infect. Dis. 18, 647-652.
166. Holt-Harris and Teague. 1916. J. Infect. Dis. 18, 596-600.

Eosin-Methylene Blue Agar (Levine [144]). This is a modification of Holt-Harris and Teague's medium and was found by Levine to allow a close separation between *Escherichia coli* and *Aerobacter aerogenes*. Levine described its preparation as follows:

Distilled water	1,000 ml.
Peptone (Difco)	10 gm.
Dipotassium phosphate	2 gm.
Agar	15 gm.

Boil ingredients until dissolved and make up any loss by evaporation. Place measured quantities in flasks and sterilize at 15 pounds for 15 minutes. Just prior to use, add to each 100 ml. of the melted agar, prepared as above, the following constituents:

Sterile (20 per cent lactose)	1 gm. or 5 ml.
Aqueous (2 per cent) eosin (yellowish) solution	2 ml.
Aqueous (2 per cent) methylene blue solution	2 ml.

Pour the medium into dishes, allow them to harden in the incubator, and inoculate in the usual way. There should be no adjustment of the reaction, and filtration of the medium is not necessary.

Levine [167] has also studied the medium in the differentiation of certain bacteriological indicators in water analysis and has shown the usefulness of this medium in sanitary work. The medium was also used in France and found to fulfill in many ways the ideal medium which will accurately differentiate between *Aerobacter aerogenes* and *Escherichia coli*.

Gilbert and Coleman [168] compared some of the more common differential media for isolating members of the colon typhoid group. Eosin brilliant green agar and brilliant green agar cannot be used alone, since they both inhibit *Shigella dysenteriae*. Eosin methylene blue agar was quite satisfactory. Kendall's modification of Endo's medium was not as satisfactory as the original formula or Robinson and Rettger's modification. Chesney [169] found that phenol red and brom-cresol-purple were good indicators in lactose agar for the isolation of members of the typhoid dysentery group from stools. Brom-cresol-purple, however, gave better differentiation. There is no reason why these indicators could not be used for isolation.

Eosin Methylene Blue Agar—Standard Methods for the Examination of Water and Sewage. Add 10 grams of Difco peptone, two grams of potassium phosphate (K_2HPO_4), and 15 grams of undried agar to 1,000 ml. of distilled water. Boil until all of the ingredients are dissolved and make up the loss by evaporation with distilled water. The reaction need not be adjusted.

Place measured quantities of the above medium (100 or 200 ml.) in flasks or bottles, plug, and sterilize in the autoclave. Use 15 pounds pressure for 15 minutes. Just before using, melt the stock agar and add the following ingredients to each 100 ml.:

Fve ml. sterile 20-per cent lactose solution.

Two ml. two-per cent solution of yellowish eosin.

Two ml. .5-per cent solution of methylene blue.

Mix the medium thoroughly and pour into Petri dishes; allow to harden. Inoculate this medium by streaking on the surface. If desired, all of the ingredients may be added to the medium before sterilization. The color may disappear during sterilization but will return when the medium has cooled.

Skinner and Murray [170] stated that the addition of crystal violet in a concentration of 1 to 1,000,000 to the above-mentioned "Standard Methods" eosin methylene blue medium inhibited the development of spreading colonies. It was also stated that a

167. Levine. 1921. Iowa Eng. Expt. Sta. Bull. 62.
168. Gilbert and Coleman. 1922. Abs. Bact. 6, 35.
169. Chesney. 1922. J. Expt. Med. 35, 181-186.
170. Skinner and Murray. 1924. J. Infect. Dis. 34, 585-591.

sharper differentiation between *Escherichia coli* and *Aerobacter aerogenes* could be made. Panganiban and Schoble [171] reported that eosin-methylene-blue agar gave a higher percentage of positive results than other media when examining stools for *Shigella dysenteriae*.

Differentiation of Aerobacter aerogenes and Escherichia coli on Eosin-Methylene Blue Agar (From Bull. 72, Digestive Ferments Company)

	Escherichia coli [1]	*Aerobacter aerogenes* [2]
Size	Well-isolated colonies are 2-3 mm. in diameter.	Well-isolated colonies are larger than coli; usually 4-6 mm. in diameter or more.
Confluence	Neighboring colonies show little tendency to run together.	Neighboring colonies [2] run together quickly.
Elevation	Colonies slightly raised; surface flat or slightly concave, rarely convex.	Colonies considerably raised and markedly convex; occasionally the center drops precipitately.
Appearance by transmitted light	Dark, almost black, centers which extend more than ¾ across the diameter of the colony; internal structure of central dark portion difficult to discern.	Centers deep brown; not as dark as *Escherichia coli* and smaller in proportion to the rest of the colony. Striated internal structure often observed in young colonies.
Appearance by reflected light	Colonies dark, button-like, often concentrically ringed with a greenish metallic sheen.	Much lighter than *Escherichia coli*, metallic sheen not observed except occasionally in depressed center when such is present.

[1] Two other types have been occasionally encountered: One resembles the type described, except that there is no metallic sheen, the colonies being wine colored. The other type of colony is somewhat larger (4 mm.), grows effusely, and has a marked crenated or irregular edge, the central portion showing a very distinct metallic sheen. These two varieties constitute about two or three per cent of the colonies observed.

[2] A small type of aerogenes colony, about the size of the colon colonies, which shows no tendency to coalesce, has been occasionally encountered.

Brom-Cresol Purple Lactose Agar (Torrey [108]**).** This medium was devised by Torrey as a useful one for the study of the fecal flora. It was prepared as follows:

Five hundred grams of chopped beef heart (other meat material may be used) are boiled in one liter of water for 15 minutes over the free flame. Strain through cotton flannel and absorbent cotton as usual. Make up loss in filtrate with water and add 10 grams peptone and 15 grams flaked agar. Heat in Arnold until in solution. Adjust reaction to pH 7.4, and place in Arnold for 30 minutes. Readjust reaction, if necessary. Filter through absorbent cotton and add to filtrate 10 grams lactose and sufficient saturated alcoholic solution of brom-cresol-purple (generally about .75 ml.) to give the desired depth of color for a poured plate. Put in flask in 200-ml. amounts (sufficient for six plates) and autoclave at 15 pounds for 10 minutes.

Torrey stated that the Difco dehydrated medium could be used but the medium prepared from fresh meat gave a greater variety of bacterial types and had better differential value.

GELATIN MEDIA

Nutrient Gelatin. 1. Add three gm. of beef extract and five gm. of peptone to 1,000 ml. of distilled water, and add 100 gm. of gelatin dried for one-half hour at 105°C. (221°F.) before weighing.

2. Heat slowly on a steam bath to 60°C.(140°F.) until the gelatin is dissolved.

3. Make up lost weight, titrate, and if the reaction is not already between +.5 and +1, adjust to +1.

171. Panganiban and Schoble. 1919. Philippine J. Sci. 14, 235-237.

4. Filter through cloth and cotton until clear.

5. Distribute in test tubes, 10 ml. to each tube, or in larger containers if desired.

6. Sterilize in the autoclave at 15 pounds (120°C.[248°F.]) for 15 minutes after the pressure reaches 15 pounds.

Whey Gelatin. Add 10 per cent of gelatin to clarified whey. This medium is of value in studying certain members of the lactic acid bacteria group.

Thornton's Agar Medium. This medium was proposed by Thornton [172] as especially used for preventing spreading colonies. It has the following composition:

Potassium phosphate (K_2HPO_4)	10.0	gm.
Magnesium sulfate ($MgSO_4 + 7H_2O$)	0.2	gm.
Calcium chloride ($CaCl_2$)	0.1	gm.
Sodium chloride (NaCl)	0.1	gm.
Ferric chloride ($FeCl_3$)	0.002	gm.
Potassium nitrate (KNO_3)	0.5	gm.
Asparagine	0.5	gm.
Mannitol	1.0	gm.
Agar	15.0	gm.
Water to	1,000.0	ml.

The phosphate, nitrate, and asparagine should be dissolved in distilled water and the magnesium sulfate, calcium chloride, sodium chloride, and ferric chloride added from the standard solutions in the order named. The agar is then added and dissolved at 100°C.(212°F.). The medium should then be filtered at 100°C.(212°F.) by being passed through a 1.2-inch layer of absorbent cotton—twice if necessary. Cool to 60°C.(140°F.) and adjust the reaction to pH 7.4 with brom-thymol-blue as the indicator. Tube and sterilize.

Litmus Gelatin. This may be prepared from lactose gelatin, the reaction of which must be neutral. Deposit one ml. of sterile litmus solution in the sterile Petri dish with the sample and pour in the melted gelatin. Shake the dish until the litmus is evenly distributed throughout. Incubate at 20°C.(68°F.). This medium is of much value in studying the bacteria in milk.

Raisin Gelatin (Besson [173]). Make a decoction of raisins by grinding and stewing 50 to 100 grams of raisins in 1,000 grams of water for one hour. Filter and add 100 grams of gelatin and a pinch of sodium phosphate. Boil for two or three minutes. Neutralize and finish as usual.

Wort Gelatin. 1. Measure 900 ml. of beer wort in a sterile flask.

2. Weigh 100 grams gelatin (10 per cent) and add it to the wort in the flask.

3. Bubble live steam through for 10 minutes to dissolve the gelatin.

4. Cool to 60°C.(140°F.), clarify with egg.

5. Filter and tube.

Gelatin Agar (Besson). By mixing agar and gelatin a medium is obtained with a melting-point between that of either plain agar or plain gelatin.

Peptone broth	1,000 gm.
Gelatin	80 gm.
Agar	5 gm.

Or

Gelatin	50 gm.
Agar	8 gm.

Dissolve the gelatin in the broth, neutralize, and then add the agar. Sterilization must not be accomplished above 115°C.(239°F.). (See North's Agar Gelatin Medium.)

172. Thornton. 1922. Ann. Appl. Biol. 9, 241-274.

173. Besson. 1913. Practical Bacteriology, Microbiology and Serum Therapy, Longmans, Green & Co., New York, N. Y.

Jackson and Muer's[70] **Liver Gelatin:**

Beef liver	500 gm.
Peptone (Witte's)	10 gm.
Dextrose	10 gm.
Potassium phosphate (K_2HPO_4)	1 gm.
Water	1,000 ml.

1. Chop 500 grams of beef liver into small pieces and add 1,000 ml. of distilled water. Weigh the infusion and container.

2. Boil slowly for two hours in a double boiler, starting cold, and stirring it occasionally.

3. Make up the loss in weight by evaporation and strain through a wire strainer.

4. Cool the filtrate to 50°C.(122°F.). Add 10 per cent of sheet gelatin and stir a few minutes until dissolved.

5. Add one per cent of peptone, one per cent of dextrose, and one-tenth (.1) per cent of potassium phosphate.

6. Stir until the ingredients are dissolved, keeping the temperature below 50°C. (122°F.).

7. After warming this mixture in a double boiler and stirring it for a few minutes to dissolve the ingredients, titrate with N/20 sodium hydroxide, using phenolphthalein as an indicator, and neutralize with normal sodium hydroxide.

8. Boil vigorously for 30 minutes in a double boiler and for five minutes over a free flame, with constant stirring to prevent the caramelization of the dextrose.

9. Make up any loss in weight by evaporation and filter through cotton flannel and filter paper.

10. Tube and sterilize in an autoclave for 15 minutes at 120°C.(248°F.).

Worth's[174] **Medium for Stock Cultures.** The maintenance of stock cultures in as vigorous and unchanged condition as possible, is a very important matter in laboratories where many pure cultures have to be maintained. Worth worked out a medium which would do this for many bacteria. This medium is described by the author as follows:

Nutrient Gelatin:

Chopped beef	500 gm.
Water	1,000 ml.

Heated in a water bath 50 to 55°C. for one hour.
Strained through bag cloth, volume restored.

Peptone	10 gm.
Sodium chloride	5 gm.
Gelatin	100 gm.

Dissolved, filtered, adjusted to one per cent acid.
Sterilize for 20 minutes at 110°C.(230°F.).

Supplee's Medium for Streptococci. This medium was devised by Supplee for the preservation of cultures of streptococci. It was reported in a paper by Ayers and Johnson.[175]

Meat infusion: (any desired amount)

Gelatin	2 per cent
Agar	2 per cent
Peptone	1 per cent

Nutrose (.5 per cent, or one per cent glucose)
Reaction adjusted to neutral with phenolphthalein.

174. Worth. 1919. J. Bact. 4, 603-608.
175. Ayers and Johnson. 1924. J. Bact. 9, 111-114.

Ayer and Johnson's [175] **Medium for Stock Cultures.** The following medium was proposed by Ayers and Johnson for the preservation of stock cultures of streptococci as well as other bacteria. The medium has the following composition:

Meat infusion:

Peptone (Parke, Davis and Co.)... 1.0 per cent
Gelatin (Difco)... 1.0 per cent
Casein (pure, Hammarsten)... 0.5 per cent
Glucose.. 0.05 per cent
$Na_2HPO_4+2H_2O$ (Sorenson's phosphate)..................... 0.4 per cent
Sodium citrate.. 0.3 per cent
Agar.. 0.75 per cent

Ayers and Johnson suggested the following methods for the preparation of this medium:

Preparation of One Liter

A

Meat infusion broth.. 500 ml.
Peptone (Parke, Davis and Co.)................................ 10 gm.
$Na_2HPO_4+2H_2O$ (Sorenson's phosphate)............ 2 gm.

Heat until dissolved and then adjust to pH 7.8.

B

Distilled water... 150 ml.
Casein (pure, Hammarsten's)..................................... 5 gm.
$Na_2HPO_4+2H_2O$ (Sorenson's phosphate)............ 2 gm.

Heat until dissolved, add to A, and to the resulting mixture of A and B add 10 grams of gelatin (Difco).

C

Heat the mixture, A plus B, after adding the gelatin in the autoclave at 15 pounds for 10 minutes.
Add .5 gram of glucose.
The reaction should be pH 7.6.
Filter through paper.

D

Prepare 250 ml. of three-per cent agar. Filter through cotton and dissolve three grams of sodium citrate in the melted agar.

E

Mix agar and filtered solution from (C) and make up to 1,000 ml. by adding distilled water.

F

Tube and sterilize for 20 minutes at 15 pounds in the autoclave. After sterilizing allow tubes to cool slowly. If a slight precipitate has formed, it will settle or be absorbed in a short time; in either case the medium is not affected. The final pH is 7.5.

Reed and Orr's [59] **Medium for Gelatin Liquefaction by Anaerobes.** This medium was used by these authors for characterizing gas-gangrene anaerobes.

Gelatin... 50 gm.
Bactopeptone... 10 gm.
Sodium phosphate (Na_2HPO_4)............................... 2 gm.
Dextrose... 1 gm.
Sodium thioglycollate.. 1 gm.
Water.. 1,000 ml.

Browne's [176] **Raw Cane Sugar Medium.** This medium was used for studying the fungi which spoiled sugar. A 30-per cent solution of raw cane sugar of the ordinary 96°

176. Browne. 1918. J. Ind. Eng. Chem. 10, 178.

type is boiled with a little salt-free alumina cream, filtered, and diluted when cold to a concentration of 20° Brix. This stock solution may be sterilized and preserved. A solid medium is prepared by adding 15 grams of agar to 1,000 ml. of the medium.

Honey Agar (Fabian and Quinet[177]**).** This medium was found to be necessary for isolation of spoilage organisms from fermented honey. Honey agar is made by mixing one part of honey and two parts of three-per cent nutrient agar. Adjust to pH 6.8 to 7.0; tube and sterilize.

Gee's Fish Media. Gee[178] used the following media in a study of bacteria which spoiled haddock. A fresh haddock was received from the fishing boats and the fresh muscle ground in a food grinder. To 500 grams of ground flesh, add 1,000 ml. of tap water and stir cold for one hour. Then heat the mixture so as to reach boiling in 20 minutes. After five minutes' boiling, pour the mixture through coarse filter paper. This gives a clear, faintly yellowish-green broth which should be autoclaved for 20 minutes at 15 pounds pressure in order to precipitate all of the remaining coagulable protein. After another filtration, the medium may be tubed and sterilized in the autoclave for 15 minutes at 15 pounds. This gives a clear culture fluid.

For solid media, such as fish agar, 1.5 per cent of agar is dissolved in the fish broth and filtered. The reaction of such media was found to be pH 6.6 to 6.8.

Spronck's[179] **Peptone-Yeast Extract.** To five liters of water add 1,000 gm. commercial yeast, not brewers' yeast. Boil for 20 minutes with stirring, pour into cylindrical vessels, and leave for 24 hours. Decant the cloudy liquid and add five gm. of sodium chloride and 10 gm. of peptone per liter. Neutralize exactly and then make alkaline to seven per cent with sodium hydroxide. Filter through Chardin paper and pour into flasks. Sterilize at 115°C.(239°F.).

Wine. Before sterilizing make neutral in the ordinary way.

Prune Decoction. Macerate 50 gm. of prunes in one liter of distilled water and allow to stand in the refrigerator until the next morning. Filter and tube for sterilization.

Pea-Flour Extract (Gordon et al.[74]**).** Take 100 gm. of pea flour and add one liter of distilled water with 100 gm. of salt. Mix and steam for one-half hour, stirring constantly. Allow to settle and filter, then sterilize and label "saline pea extract." This pea-flour extract should preferably be freshly made for each batch of agar. This medium was especially designed to replace Witt's peptone.

Capaldi's Egg Medium. A few loopfuls of egg yolk are added to a tube of liquefied agar, previously cooled to 45 to 47°C.(113 to 116.6°F.).

Dorset's Egg Medium. Eggs are broken into a flask and the yolks broken with a needle or glass rod. The flask is shaken until the yolks and whites are thoroughly mixed. Foam formation should be avoided. Distribute in culture tubes and sterilize in a Koch inspissator or autoclave in the same manner as blood serum.

Egg-Meat Mixture (Rettger[180]**).** *A.* One-half pound of lean chopped beef is stirred up in 250 ml. of water and, after neutralizing the meat acids with sodium carbonate, the mixture is heated in an Arnold sterilizer for 30 minutes, with occasional stirring. It is then set away in a cold place for several hours after which the fatty scum is removed.

B. The whites of three eggs are mixed with 250 ml. of water, and after neutralizing, the albumen is coagulated, with occasional stirring, by heating in the Arnold sterilizer for 30 minutes.

A and *B* are then mixed and introduced into a liter flask, along with 2.5 gm. (.5 per cent) of powdered calcium carbonate. The flask is plugged with cotton and sterilized for 30 minutes, at 110 to 112°C.(230 to 233.6°F.) (autoclave).

Holman's[181] **Cooked-Meat Medium.** This medium was devised by Holman for studying anaerobic bacteria. It is prepared from fresh beef, freed from fat and other gross fibers. It is finely minced, ground in a mortar, and mixed with an equal part of water.

177. Fabian and Quinet. 1927. Mich. Agr. Expt. Sta. Tech. Bull. 92.
178. Gee. 1927. Studies Biol. Sta. of Canada 3, 349-363.
179. Spronck. 1898. Ann. Inst. Pasteur 12, 701-704.
180. Rettger. 1906. J. Biol. Chem. 2, 71-86.
181. Holman. 1919. J. Bact. 4, 149-155.

Then it is slowly heated to boiling, with constant stirring, to allow the soluble albumins to coagulate about the meat particles. This coagulated albumin serves in itself as a favorable medium for the anaerobes, as Tarozzi has shown. The emulsion of meat medium is then neutralized, or made slightly alkaline, using hot titration with phenolphthalein, tubed at least two inches high and autoclaved at 115°C. for at least an hour. Just before use the tubes are put in flowing steam and suddenly cooled. The seeding is done by pipette or needle.

Linden's [182] Modification of Holman's Cooked-Meat Medium. According to Linden addition of 10 per cent tomato juice to Holman's cooked-meat medium gave satisfactory results for the isolation of the aciduric bacterial flora of acid canned foods undergoing decomposition. It is desirable to note also that a partial atmosphere of carbon dioxide in many instances appears to enhance the growth of the lactobacilli on solid culture media. While some of the culture media given above may serve to detect the presence of yeasts, the special media commonly used are acid in reaction and contain suitable carbohydrates.

Linden's [182] Acid-Meat Medium for Aciduric Spoilage Bacteria. This medium was devised for detecting the presence of spoilage bacteria in acid foods, such as tomato products. The medium has the following composition:

Distilled water	1,000 ml.
Ground fresh lean beef	500 gm.
Proteose peptone	5 gm.
Sodium chloride, C. P.	5 gm.
Dextrose, C. P.	10 gm.

Infuse the beef in the water overnight in a refrigerator. Then heat in flowing steam or boil for 30 minutes. Strain through several layers of cheesecloth and squeeze out the liquid. Bring the infusion back to one liter. Add the peptone and heat in flowing steam or boil for 10 minutes. Filter and add the salt. Acidify with C. P. lactic acid to pH 4.7, add the dextrose, and filter.

Distribute the pressed-out beef into medium-size test tubes (150 x 20 mm.) about two grams in each tube, and add 10 ml. of the broth. Sterilize in the autoclave. The final reaction should be pH 4.8. Prior to using, boil the tubed medium for 10 minutes to expel oxygen, and cool.

Linden modified this medium by adding to each 1,000 ml. of broth as prepared above, 11 gm. of acetic acid and 12 gm. potassium citrate. This gives a final pH of 4.5.

Cooked-Meat Medium (Torrey's [108] Modification of Robertson's Medium). Torrey described its preparation as follows:

Beef heart (fresh and finely minced)	500 gm.
Peptone	10 gm.
Water	1 liter

This mixture, with the meat particles evenly suspended, is cooked in a double boiler with just enough heat to cause a slight simmering for about 10 minutes and the reaction adjusted to pH 7.2. The cooking is then continued for about one and one-half hours and the reaction readjusted, if necessary. The broth is decanted and the meat is then placed in test tubes, 16 to 17 mm. inside diameter, so that there is a column about five cm. high. After autoclaving these tubes and the broth in the flask at 15 pounds for 15 minutes, the latter is added to the meat tubes in five ml. amounts. The tubes are then placed in the Arnold on two successive days for 20 minutes. This method prevents the fluid being forced up into the cotton plug as is apt to occur if fluid and meat are placed together in tubes and then autoclaved.

Bengtson's [183] Coagulated Egg-White Medium. This consisted of beef infusion broth adjusted to a reaction of pH 7.6 with a piece of coagulated egg white in the bottom of the tube. This medium was used for studying the *Clostridium botulinum* group. Bengtson stated that the coagulated egg, if attacked, became smaller and the edges became rounded off.

182. Linden. 1936. Assoc. Off. Agr. Chem. J. 19, 440; 21 (1938), 454-457.
183. Bengtson. 1924. U. S. Public Health Service, Hyg. Lab. Bull. 139.

Ayers and Rupp's [184] Medium for the Colon-Aerogenes Group. In this medium lactose is the only source of carbon, and sodium ammonium phosphate the only source of nitrogen. The medium consists of two solutions:

1. Sodium ammonium phosphate .4 per cent, acid potassium phosphate .2 per cent, and lactose one per cent, dissolved in distilled water.

2. A filtered three-per cent solution of agar in distilled water.

Mix Solutions 1 and 2 in equal proportions while hot and put up in definite amounts of 100 ml. or more in flasks or bottles and then sterilize. The three-per cent agar solution is made up separately and kept in stock merely for convenience. Agar can be added directly to Solution 1 at the time of preparation if desired, using 1.5 per cent. A slight precipitate may appear upon sterilization but this does not interfere with the count and may not appear on the plate.

Jenkins [185] Tomato-Extract-Culture Medium. Cut the fruit into small pieces and steam for two hours, in water sufficient to cover the fruit. Filter and add 1.6 per cent of agar and heat for 30 minutes at 120°C.(248°F.). Adjust the reaction to —5 Eyre's scale with 40 per cent sodium hydroxide. Filter to remove the precipitate and again adjust the reaction. Tube while hot.

Ox-Bile Medium. Dissolve one per cent lactose and one per cent peptone in fresh ox bile, filter, and place in fermentation tubes. Sterilize in an Arnold on three successive days.

Decoction of Dried Fruits. 1. Macerate 50 to 100 gm. of dried fruit in a liter of water for several hours, then stew them in the water.

2. Pass through a coarse sieve.

3. Boil. Filter.

4. Tube and sterilize at 115°C.(239°F.).

The liquid is slightly acid and is useful for cultivating molds. Otherwise make neutral.

Barsiekow's Medium. Prepare and sterilize separately the two following solutions:

A.	Sodium chloride	0.5 gm.
	Nutrose	1.0 gm.
	Water	75.0 gm.
B.	Water	25.0 gm.
	Litmus	To give blue color
	Sugar (the one desired)	1.0 gm.

Add sufficient litmus to give an amethyst color. After cooling mix and distribute in tubes.

Bread. Soak some slices of white bread in distilled water and sterilize at 115°C. (239°F).

Crumble some bread and allow to dry. Grind when dry and put in Petri dishes or Erlenmeyer flask and add water to moisten (about 2½ parts of water to one part of bread by weight).

Sterilize at 115°C.(239°F.) for 20 minutes.

Medium for Acetic-Acid Bacteria. The following medium was reported by Janke [186] as especially suitable for vinegar bacteria:

Potassium diphosphate	0.4 gm.
Ammonium diphosphate	1.0 gm.
Magnesium sulfate	0.4 gm.
Glycerol	5.0 ml.
Succinic acid	1.0 gm.
Alcohol	3.0 pct. by vol.
Water	1,000.0 ml.

184. Ayers and Rupp. 1918. J. Bact. 3, 433-436.
185. Jenkins. 1923. J. Path. and Bact. 26, 116-118.
186. Janke. 1921. Centbl. Bakt., Pt. 2, 53, 81.

Fowler and Subramaniam's [187] **Medium for Acetic-Acid Bacteria.** Alcohol, four per cent by volume; acetic acid, two per cent (vinegar containing acetic acid to this amount); phosphates of calcium, magnesium, and potassium, .05 per cent; yeast water, 10 ml., prepared by boiling seven per cent by weight of dry yeast with water, and filtering until quite bright; the whole being made up with sterile water to 100 ml.

Medium for Acetic-Acid Bacteria. Prepare beer wort or malt medium with four per cent of alcohol and about .3 per cent of acetic acid or sterile vinegar. Incubate at about 25.6°C.(78°F.).

POTATO AND STARCH MEDIA

Potato Gelatin (Goadby). Add 100 gm. of gelatin to one liter of glycerol potato broth. Boil, adjust the reaction, filter, and sterilize.

Glycerol Potato Broth. Wash, peel, and grind 1,000 gm. of potato. Soak this in a liter of water for 24 hours. After filtering add three to five per cent of glycerol and tube for sterilization.

Potato Agar (McBeth [188]**).** Pare, steam, and mash a quantity of potatoes. To 100 gm. of mashed potato add 800 ml. of tap water and steam for one-half hour, filter through cotton.

> Potato solution... 500 ml.
> Agar.. 15 gm.
> Nutrient solution (same as for cellulose agar)...................... 500 ml.

Starch Agar. Make one liter of ordinary peptone agar. Add to this a two-per cent paste of potato starch. This should be added at as low a temperature as possible to the neutral agar.

To use, pour plates with the sterile tubed starch agar and streak with the culture. After incubation for five days, pour over weak solution of Lugol's iodine.

Starch Agar ((Vedder [189]**).** Prepare a liter of beef infusion in the usual way. Meat extract does not give as good results. To this add 1.5 per cent of agar. No peptone or salt should be added. Cook and clarify the medium and add 10 grams of cornstarch to each liter. The starch is best rubbed up in a mortar in a little agar. One per cent of starch gives the best results. Tube and sterilize in the usual manner. This medium is especially valuable in the growth of gonococci.

Elsner's Potato Medium. 1. Peel and grate 500 grams of potato.

2. Grind up and soak in distilled water for 12 hours.

3. Strain and allow to stand. Filter to clear.

4. Make up to one liter and dissolve 15 per cent of gelatin.

5. Adjust reaction to acid and sterilize.

Potato Infusion. Wash and grind up a few potatoes. To each 30 gm. of potato, add a liter of distilled water and allow to stand in the refrigerator overnight. In the morning, filter and boil the filtrate. Filter again if necessary and tube for sterilization. If the infusion is too acid, adjust the reaction as usual.

Potato Mash. Clean and cut a large potato into slices. Boil until soft and grate or press through a ricer. Distribute this in layers in Petri dishes and sterilize at 120°C. (248°F.) for 20 minutes. The slices may be placed in the Petri dishes without mashing if desired.

Starch Jelly (Smith [190]**).** To 10 ml. of Uschinsky's solution add one gm. of clean aseptic starch. Rub this up in the slanted fluid. Plug the tubes tightly and place in an inspissator or Arnold in the slanted condition. Heat for two hours on five successive days at 85 to 93°C.(185 to 199.4°F.). If water is lost, this must be made up by the addition of distilled water.

Potato Agar (Thomas). The potatoes are carefully washed, pared, sliced, then slowly heated for two hours in approximately two volumes of water. At the close of the heating the water is allowed to boil. The whole is then filtered through cloth, water

187. Fowler and Subramaniam. 1923. Indian Inst. Sci. J. 6, 147-172.
188. McBeth. 1913. U. S. Dept. Agr., Bur. Anim. Indus. Bull. 266.
189. Vedder. 1915. J. Infect. Dis. 16, 385-388.
190. Smith. 1898. Centbl. Bakt., Pt. 2, 5, 102.

being added to make up the loss of any evaporation. After filtering, one per cent shredded agar is added to this filtrate. It may then be heated in an autoclave for 30 minutes at 15 pounds, after which it may be tubed or filtered, if desired, before tubing.

Starch Agar (McBeth[188]). To 800 ml. of boiling water add 10 gm. of potato starch suspended in a little cold water. Concentrate by boiling to 500 ml. This breaks up the starch grains and should give a nearly transparent starch solution.

Starch solution	500 ml.
Agar	10 gm.
Nutrient solution (same as for cellulose)	500 ml.

SYNTHETIC MEDIA

Such media are usually prepared from pure chemical compounds. Uschinsky's synthetic medium is a good example and has been widely used. Hulton-Fraenkel[191] proposed several such media.

Koser's[192] Citrate Solution. Koser reported further work on his citrate solution for differentiating *Escherichia coli* of intestinal origin from non-fecal *Aerobacter aerogenes*. The former were found to be unable to utilize the carbon in the citrate molecule and thus does not grow while the latter organism, *Aerobacter aerogenes*, grows well. Koser reported two possible media as follows:

Medium 1

Distilled water	1,000.0 ml.
Sodium chloride (NaCl)	5.0 gm.
Magnesium sulfate (MgSO₄)	0.2 gm.
Ammonium phosphate (NH₄) H₂PO₄	1.0 gm.
Potassium phosphate (K₂HPO₄)	1.0 gm.
(Sodium citrate: 5½ H₂O ....2.77 gm.)	2.0 gm.

Medium 2

Distilled water	1,000.0 ml.
Sodium ammonium phosphate (microcosmic salt Na[NH₄]HPO₄+4H₂O)	1.5 gm.
Potassium phosphate (KH₂PO₄)	1.0 gm.
Magnesium sulfate (MgSO₄)	0.2 gm.

Sodium or potassium citrate as given in *Medium 1* above.

After dissolving the various salts in sterile distilled water, add 20 grams of clean, dry agar and sterilize the medium at 15 pounds for 15 minutes. After adjusting the reaction to pH 6.8, add the indicator and distribute into tubes. Simmons[83] prepared a solid medium by adding agar to Koser's citrate solution. Its preparation has been described above.

Doloff's[193] Synthetic Medium. This simplified medium was devised for propagating *Escherichia coli*.

Ammonium tartrate, recrystallized	5 gm.
Lactose	5 gm.
Ammonium phosphate (NH₄)₂HPO₄	.01-.02 gm.
Water	1,000 ml.

The reaction of this medium after sterilization is between pH 5.0 to 5.2.

BLOOD AND BLOOD SERUM MEDIA

Blood Serum. Beef blood should be collected at the abattoir in clean containers and placed in the refrigerator until a clot has formed. The clear serum should then be decanted, or better, siphoned off into a sterile flask. For the preparation of Loeffler's

191. Hulton-Fraenkel. 1919. J. Infect. Dis. 24, 9-16; 19-21.
192. Koser. 1924. J. Bact. 9, 59-77.
193. Doloff. 1926. Science 64, 254.

blood serum, one part of glucose broth is mixed with three parts of the serum. This is then distributed into test tubes (or other containers) and placed in the inspissator in a slanted position. Small tin ointment boxes make good containers when the blood serum is to be used for routine diphtheria examinations. After coagulation has been accomplished, the boiled serum should be sterilized in the autoclave at a temperature of about 112°C.(233.6°F.). If desired, intermittent heating in the Arnold may be used.

Blood Agar for Streptococci (Becker [194]**).** Standard agar used in water analysis is placed in quantities of 40 to 100 ml. in flasks. These are heated until the agar is melted, and then cooled to 45 or 50°C.(113 or 122°F.). One milliliter of defibrinated human blood is added for each six ml. of the agar base and the whole is thoroughly shaken. Approximately seven ml. are used for each plate. Surface streaks are made and observations made after 24 hours at 27°C.(80.6°F.). Isolated colonies only should be studied.

MILK MEDIA

Sterile milk is a good medium for the propagation of most bacteria. It has been modified in different ways to give many different media.

Kulp's [195] **Casein-Digest Medium.** This medium was prepared in 1923 by Kulp for the study of *Lactobacillus acidophilus* and *Lactobacillus bulgaricus*. Kulp described the method of preparation as follows: One hundred grams of casein are dissolved in one liter of one-per cent sodium carbonate; one and one-half grams of Fairchild's trypsin (powder) are added with a little chloroform for a preservative. This mixture is then incubated for 24 to 48 hours at 37 to 40°C.(98.6 to 104°F.); it should then be heated in a double boiler to drive off the chloroform and made slightly acid with 15 per cent hydrochloric acid. Finally it is boiled for a few minutes and filtered. One hundred ml. of the digest representing 10 grams of the original casein, plus three grams of commercial meat extract are used as the base for each liter of medium desired. A digest of "Klim" was also prepared and gave good results. A casein digest broth was also found to be a good medium for indole formation.

Safford and Stark's [196] **Skim-Milk Agar.** The composition was as follows:

Fresh raw skim milk	2.0 per cent
Bacto peptone	0.5 per cent
Bacto beef extract	0.1 per cent
Glucose	0.1 per cent
Agar	1.5 per cent

Fresh skimmed milk was used, for it was believed a better medium was secured with it than if powdered milk were used. The raw skimmed milk was added to the medium just prior to sterilization.

Hydrolyzed Casein Medium (Cannon [197]**).** Zipfel proposed the addition of tryptophane to a synthetic medium for the determination of indol formation. Cannon realized the high cost of tryptophane and suggested the use of a hydrolyzed casein which is prepared as follows: Ten grams of casein are hydrolyzed by 200 ml. of 10-per cent sulfuric acid. The mixture is kept on the water bath for 24 hours after which it is neutralized by saturated barium hydroxide. This will precipitate the sulfate. Evaporate the resulting solution until the amino acids crystallize. Half of the preparation is then dissolved in 500 ml. of Zipfel's synthetic medium, which has the following composition:

Asparagin	5.0 gm.
Ammonium lactate	5.0 gm.
Potassium acid phosphate	2.0 gm.
Magnesium sulfate	0.2 gm.
Distilled water	1,000.0 gm.

194. Becker. 1916. J. Infect. Dis. 19. 754-759.
195. Kulp. 1923. Abs. Bact. 7.
196. Safford and Stark. 1935. J. Dairy Sci. 18. 539.
197. Cannon. 1916. J. Bact. 1. 535-536.

Sherman and Albus'[108] **Medium for Cultivating Lactobacilli.** The medium proposed had the following composition:

Fermentable carbohydrate... 1.0 per cent
Peptone.. 1.0 per cent
Dried yeast.. 1.0 per cent
Butter fat.. 1.0 per cent
Agar.. 0.2 per cent
Reaction.. pH 6.5-7.0

The agar is not absolutely essential but favors the growth of some cultures.

Casein Agar (Ayers[199]**).** Preparation of one liter.
Casein solution:
  300 ml. distilled water.
  10 grams casein (Eimer & Amend C. P. casein prepared according to
    Hammarsten).
  7 ml. normal sodium hydroxide.
Agar solution:
  500 ml. distilled water.
  10 grams agar.
After dissolving casein, make up to 500 milliliters.
To 300 ml. of water (distilled) add:
  10 grams casein (Eimer & Amend C. P. casein prepared according to
    Hammarsten).
  7 ml. normal sodium hydroxide.

Dissolve casein by heating to boiling. It is desirable to let this solution stand for several hours to get a perfect solution. This is not necessary, however. Make up volume to 500 ml. and bring the reaction of the solution to between +0.1 and +.02 Fuller's scale. Do not allow solution to become alkaline to phenolphthalein or over +0.2. If the casein is weighed accurately and the normal solution is accurate, the reaction will be about +0.2.

The agar solution is prepared by dissolving 10 grams agar in 500 ml. of water. Both casein and agar solutions should be filtered, then mixed. Tube and sterilize in autoclave under pressure for 20 minutes; then cool the tubes quickly in cold water or ice water. The final reaction of the medium will be about +0.1 Fuller's scale. If the medium is alkaline the bacterial growth will be restricted. If the medium is more than +0.1 some of the casein may be precipitated during sterilization. The casein agar should be clear and almost colorless when poured in a Petri dish. Sometimes the casein will be slightly precipitated during sterilization or the cooling, but it is of no consequence since on pouring into plates the precipitate, on account of its finely divided condition, becomes invisible.

Whey Agar. Add a few drops of acetic acid to boiling milk until the casein is precipitated. Neutralize, or bring to one per cent +. Dissolve one per cent peptone, two per cent dextrose, and 1.5 per cent agar. Filter, tube, and sterilize.

Plain Milk. This may be made from fresh skimmed milk or from skimmed milk powder.

Desiccated milk.. 100 gm.
Distilled water.. 1,000 gm.

The milk powder should be added to about 200 ml. of the distilled water and thoroughly mixed. Beating with an egg beater often serves this purpose. It should then be made up to a liter. Sterilize in an Arnold.

Litmus Milk. Add sterile litmus or azolitmin to plain skimmed milk until the color is a distinct lavender. Tube in any of the laboratory apparatus and sterilize.

198. Sherman and Albus. 1922. Abs. Bact. 6, 17.
199. Ayers. 1913. U. S. Dept. Agr., Bur. Anim. Indus., Ann. Rpt. 1913, 225-235.
200. Hamilton. 1921. J. Bact. 6, 43-44.

Litmus Milk Powder. Hamilton [197] prepared litmus milk powder as follows: Litmus cubes were extracted with boiling distilled water and evaporated to a thin paste after decantation. This was then treated with an access of acetic acid, evaporated to dryness, treated with 95 per cent alcohol, filtered, dissolved in water, and evaporated. One part of this indicator was added to 52.7 parts of dried skimmed milk powder. One part of the litmus milk powder was dissolved in 9.5 parts of water to make litmus milk.

Clark and Lubs' [201] **Brom-Cresol-Purple Milk.** They suggested brom-cresol-purple instead of litmus in milk cultures. They compared the two indicators and found that brom-cresol-purple was just as delicate as litmus and had the same adaptability. In some tests and culture media litmus is decolorized and does not function as an indicator while brom-cresol-purple acted as a true indicator of hydrogen-ion concentration. During sterilization litmus undergoes a temporary decolorization while brom-cresol-purple does not. The indicator may be added to the milk to give the depth of color desired. Baker [202] substituted brom-thymol-blue for litmus in culture media.

Bronfenbrenner, Davis, and Morishima's [202] **Milk Media.** These investigators used fresh milk and milk whey for culture fluids.

Milk Medium. Heat fresh milk in the Arnold sterilizer for 15 minutes and then place on ice for eight to 12 hours; separate the cream. Dilute one part of milk with three parts of water. Add an indicator (mixture of China blue and rosolic acid) at the rate of 2.5 ml. per 100 ml. of diluted milk; boil for five minutes; if too acid, adjust the reaction until a pale gray color is secured. Distribute in sterile tubes with inverted vials and autoclave at 15 pounds for 10 minutes.

Milk-Whey Medium. Siphon the milk from under the cream and bring it to a boil; then add 2.5 ml. of a 10-per cent manganese chloride solution to each 100 ml. of medium. Cool as soon as the clot forms and filter through a single layer of cloth. Adjust to neutrality and dilute the filtrate with double its volume of distilled water. Add one ml. of cresol-red indicator for each 100 ml. of medium. Place in sterile culture tubes having inverted vials and autoclave for 10 minutes at 15 pounds.

Transparent milk has been proposed by Brown and Howe [204] as a useful culture medium. They prepared it by diluting one part of skimmed milk with two parts of distilled water and then adding .4 per cent of sodium citrate. It may be filtered after an hour or so, although this is said to be unnecessary if the milk is allowed to stand long enough. To avoid caramelization of the sugar the reaction should be adjusted to pH 6.8. Oxalated milk was also prepared in the same manner.

Litmus Milk From Skimmed-Milk Powder (Vierling [205]**).** Dissolve 30 gm. of skimmed milk in 200 ml. distilled water over a warm water bath; add four ml. of an 18-per cent solution of potassium chloride and heat for 40 minutes on a steam bath for precipitation of casein. Remove excess potassium chloride by adding two ml. normal sodium hydroxide and heat for 25 minutes. Filter and make up to 500 ml. by addition of 150 ml. of distilled water and 150 ml. physiological salt solution, then add .02 to .03 gm. of peptone. After 30 minutes' sterilization add 20 to 30 ml. of sterile litmus solution. Standardize by N/10 sodium hydroxide or lactic acid.

Hunter's [206] **Medium for Lactobacillus acidophilus.** Hunter found the following medium to be very useful for propagation of microorganisms of the aciduric group:

Casein	15.0 gm.
Peptone	15.0 gm.
Beef extract	3.0 gm.
Trypsin	1.5 gm.
Water	1,000.0 ml.

This mixture was made slightly alkaline; chloroform was added to preserve it during incubation at 37°C.(98.6°F.) for 48 hours. After removal from the incubator the

201. Clark and Lubs. 1917. J. Agr. Res. 10, 105-111.
202. Baker. 1922. J. Bact. 7, 301-305.
203. Bronfenbrenner, Davis, and Morishima. 1919. J. Med. Res. 39, 345.
204. Brown and Howe. 1922. J. Bact. 7, 511-514.
205. Vierling. 1922. Centbl. Bakt., Pt. 1, Orig. 88, 93-94.
206. Hunter. 1924. Abs. Bact. 8, 8.

medium was boiled to drive off the chloroform. The reaction was adjusted to pH 7.0, and 15 grams of lactose and 50 ml. of a two-per cent solution of sodium oleate were added.

Litmus Whey (Petruschky). Fresh milk is slightly warmed and treated with dilute hydrochloric acid to precipitate the casein. This is filtered off and dilute sodium carbonate added to the filtrate to neutrality. This is then steamed for two hours to precipitate any casein which is changed to acid albumin by the dilute hydrochloric acid. After filtration a clear neutral solution should be the result. This is colored with litmus, tubed, and sterilized. After growth the amount of acid may be determined by standard reagents.

Rice Milk (Besson [173]):

Milk	150 gm.
Peptone broth	50 gm.
Powdered rice	100 gm.

Distribute the mixture in Petri dishes one to two cm. deep. Heat to 115°C.(239°F.) for 20 minutes. The mixture solidifies and forms an opaque layer.

Dialyzed Milk. Dialyzed milk may be prepared by the addition of 10 ml. of hydrogen peroxide to 500 ml. of milk. Two hours later hydrogen peroxide should be added again, and after four to five hours the whole is dialyzed. The sugar content is reduced 50 per cent and the normal quantities of fat and proteins are preserved. The milk is diluted one-fifth.

Milk Agar (Hastings [207]). This medium is prepared by adding to ordinary nutrient agar, which has been melted and cooled to 50°C.(122°F.), 10 per cent sterile skimmed milk. If the milk is added to the agar while hot, the casein will be precipitated in coarse flocculent masses. The medium is poured into sterile Petri dishes and after hardening is streaked with the cultures. After incubation, if proteolytic action is present, there will be a clear zone about the streak which will not change when treated with dilute acids. This distinguishes the acid formers from the proteolytic bacteria.

Casein-Digest Medium. This medium was reported by Townsend [208] as having been adapted by Sommer for the production of spores of *Clostridium botulinum*.

Make a one per cent sodium carbonate solution equal in volume to the amount of medium desired. To this add 10 per cent casein and heat in a water bath or double boiler until the casein is well in suspension. Cool to about 40°C.(104°F.), and add two-thirds gm. of pancreatin (or trypsin) per liter. Distribute in flasks for digestion, using chloroform or toluene as preservative. Incubate overnight (approximately 18 hours). Boil off the preservative and acidify strongly with 5N hydrochloric acid (down to pH 5.6 to 5.2). Filter. Neutralize with 5N sodium hydroxide, and add .5 per cent Liebig's beef extract and .5 per cent dibasic sodium phosphate. Make up to volume and check the reaction to pH 7.2 to 7.6. Sterilize at 15 pounds pressure for 45 minutes. Five-tenths per cent glucose is added before sterilization for some organisms.

Whittaker's [209] Synthetic-Milk Medium. Whittaker reported the following method for making artificial milk:

"Fifteen grams of pure caseinogen are dissolved in 100 ml. of a one-per cent solution of sodium hydroxide in distilled water. Eighteen to 24 hours may be required for a complete solution. After the caseinogen is dissolved the solution is diluted to about 900 ml. with distilled water. Ten grams of lactose and .1 gram of calcium chloride are added and the solution made up to 1,000 ml. with distilled water. It is then neutralized and made +.3 with N/1 hydrochloric acid, using phenolphthalein as an indicator. This medium is sterilized in an autoclave at 107°C.(224.6°F.) for 20 minutes. The finished product should be a clear, transparent solution. When the medium has a reaction of +.3 about 24 hours are usually required for coagulation with an active strain of *Escherichia coli*. When the reaction is neutral a somewhat longer time may be required

207. Hastings. 1904. Centbl. Bakt., Pt. 2, 12, 590-592.
208. Townsend. 1929. Idem 78, 161-172.
209. Whittaker. 1912. Amer. J. Pub. Health 2, 162.

to produce similar results. This medium has been thoroughly tested on the routine test for *Escherichia coli* and apparently meets all requirements.''

YEAST MEDIA

Fred, Peterson, and Davenport's[210] **Yeast-Water Medium.** This medium was prepared in 1920 as follows:

Four hundred and fifty grams of pressed yeast were steamed three to four hours with 4.5 ml. of tap water with occasional stirring. This infusion was allowed to stand undisturbed until a heavy deposit of yeast cells and other suspended matter had settled to the bottom of the vessel. The portion above this deposit was poured off and neutralized in liter flasks. The flasks were allowed to stand one to two weeks, when the supernatant liquid was siphoned off and used without clearing or filtering.

Dienert and Guillerd's[211] **Autolyzed Yeast Medium.** This medium, devised for use in place of more expensive peptone media, is prepared as follows:

Five hundred grams of pressed yeast are heated to 50°C. (122°F.), which temperature is favorable for the action of the endotryptase but not for the action of bacteria. The liquefaction is complete in less than 24 hours, yielding about 400 ml. of the autolyzed fluid. This is diluted to 2,000 ml. with water and heated to 100°C. (212°F.) for 30 minutes. It is then neutralized, filtered, and finally made up to 7,500 ml.

Eberson's[212] **Yeast Media.** This medium was prepared for culturing delicate organisms which grew scantily on the usual media. The meningococcus is a good example of such a bacterium. Eberson prepared this medium as follows:

Thoroughly macerate 10 grams of baker's or brewer's yeast in 100 ml. of water for 20 minutes and then steam for two hours, not exceeding a temperature of 100°C. (212°F.). Filter twice through filter paper. A clearer medium may be secured by clarifying with liquor ferri oxychlorati before filtering. By the use of glass wool, chemical clarification may be dispensed with and the absorption by filter paper of "accessory food products" may be prevented. Prepare a 2.5-per cent agar having a pH of 7.4 with or without peptone or salt. To each 60 ml. of the agar add 40 ml. of the yeast decoction. Sterilize in the autoclave for 20 to 30 minutes and slant. A semisolid yeast agar (.5 per cent) is prepared similarly and the culture tubes inoculated with a series of stabs. Indications are that this culture medium will prolong the viability far beyond the periods observed for the solid media.

Burky[213] found this medium a very suitable one for maintaining cultures of bacteria which are usually grown with difficulty.

Johanson and Broadhurst's[214] **Yeast Medium.** This medium was proposed as a substitute for meat-extract media. It contained the following ingredients:

Water	1,000 ml.
Peptone	10 gm.
Salt	5 gm.
Yeast (Fleischmann's)	2 cakes

It should be pointed out that the addition of the cakes of yeasts introduced considerable starch also.

Kligler's Yeast Medium. Kligler[215] prepared a medium which may be used in place of the commoner meat media. He has described its preparation as follows:

''Two hundred grams of drained or centrifuged brewer's yeast are suspended in a liter of water, two grams of NaH_2PO_4 are added as buffer, and the reaction adjusted by the addition of N/NaOH to pH 6.1. Then five ml. of chloroform are added and the mixture is thoroughly shaken and incubated at 37°C. for two days. It is necessary to shake the flask occasionally during the incubation to maintain sterility. At the end of the incubation period, the reaction is brought to pH 7.4 and the autolysate heated in a

210. Fred, Peterson, and Davenport. 1920. J. Biol. Chem. 42, 175-189.
211. Dienert and Guillerd. 1919. Compt. Rend. Acad. Sci. 168, 256-257.
212. Eberson. 1919. Abs. Bact. 3, 10.
213. Burky. 1924. Amer. Med. Assoc. J.
214. Johanson and Broadhurst. 1926. J. Bact. 11, 87.
215. Kligler. 1919. J. Bact. 4, 183-188.

water bath or in the Arnold for 30 minutes. It is then filtered through paper, tubed, and autoclaved. Agar is prepared by adding 15 grams of agar directly to one liter of the unfiltered autolysate and stirring thoroughly to immerse or soften the agar shreds or powder. This mixture is then heated over the free flame or in the autoclave until the agar is completely dissolved. The reaction is then adjusted to pH 7.4, the mixture is heated on a water bath or in an Arnold for half an hour, and the partially clear supernatant fluid is decanted to an Erlenmeyer flask or other vessel. The agar is then cooled and whole egg added to clear. The medium is finally steamed in the Arnold for one-half to three-quarters of an hour, filtered, tubed, and autoclaved.''

Neill, Sugg, Richardson, and Fleming's[216] **Yeast-Culture Media.** Neill and his colleagues found the yeast media, preparation of which is described below, satisfactory in all routine bacteriological procedures for which meat infusion peptone media are used. They described the preparation of the medium as follows:

I. Preparation of ''5% Yeast'' Broth

The medium, found satisfactory as a routine substitute for meat-infusion-peptone broth, was prepared by the following steps. For convenience, the amounts of material are expressed in terms of 10-liter lots of medium.

1. Infusion of the dried yeast. Warm 10 liters distilled water to 40°C., add 500 grams Fleischmann's dried yeast to the water and infuse at 40°C. for 30 minutes; raise temperature to 50°C. and continue the infusion for 90 minutes.

2. Preliminary adjustment of pH of the infusion before boiling. Add eight per cent (2.0N) sodium hydroxide to the infusion until phenol red gives a faint pink when added to samples of the turbid yeast suspension (about 40 ml. 2.0N NaOH are usually required). Add 30 grams $Na_2HPO_4 \cdot 12H_2O$ previously dissolved in 100 to 200 ml. of warm water.

3. Boiling and preliminary filtration of yeast infusion. Raise temperature to boiling; stirring is necessary when the temperature approaches the boiling point. Boil for one to three minutes. Filter through paper.

4. Adjustment of volume. Add water to compensate for loss due to evaporation and filtration, until volume is 9.5 liters.

5. Final adjustment of pH. The broth is perfectly clear after filtration in Step 3, and colorimetric tests always show the pH to have dropped below 7.0. Adjust by addition of sodium hydroxide until pH is from 7.2 to 7.4. Add 150 grams $Na_2HPO_4 \cdot 12H_2O$ previously dissolved in 500 ml. warm water. The addition of this phosphate usually raises the pH to about 8.0 with media prepared from most lots of the dried yeast. If a final pH of 7.8 is desired, the broth should be readjusted by addition of alkali, or acid, if it is not pH 8.0 after addition of the phosphate at this stage. (We prefer to adjust the pH with NaOH added in the order described to a point sufficient to enable the last addition of phosphate to raise the pH to 8.0. This point [usually pH 7.2 to 7.4] varies to some extent with different lots of yeast, but is fairly constant in different batches prepared from the same lot of dried yeast.)

6. Precipitation at 120°C.(248°F.) before final filtration. Distribute the adjusted broth into large flasks and autoclave five minutes at 120°C.(248°F.). This causes precipitation of material that would otherwise be precipitated during the final sterilization. The precipitate is well separated from the clear supernatant liquid and the medium filters as rapidly as ordinary broth. This heating usually causes a drop in pH from 8.0 to 7.9.

7. Final sterilization. Distribute the filtered broth in the desired containers and sterilize 12 to 15 minutes at 120°C.(248°F.). This usually causes the pH to drop to 7.8.

II. Preparation of Agar Medium With ''5% Yeast'' Broth as Base

1. Preliminary softening of agar. Add 250 grams agar to about two liters water and let it soak until time for its addition to the medium.

2. Preparation of yeast broth base. Proceed as in Steps 1, 2, and 3 described under I. (Use 10 liters water as the decrease in volume will compensate for the water added to the agar.)

216. Neill, Sugg. Richardson, and Fleming. 1929. J. Bact. 17, 329-337.

3. Adjust volume of broth, if decrease in volume after filtration has reduced it lower than 7.5 liters.

4. Adjustment of pH. Raise pH to about 7.4 to 7.5. Add 150 grams phosphate dissolved in about 500 ml. water as in Step 5 in I. This should bring reaction to at least pH 8.1, and if final pH of 7.8 is desired, the reaction should be readjusted if it is now below pH 8.0.

5. Addition of agar. Add agar softened by previous soaking in Step 1.

6. Solution of agar and precipitation before final sterilization. Autoclave for 15 minutes at 120°C.(248°F.) instead of the five minutes employed in Step 6 of I, in order to dissolve the agar. Filter through cotton and test pH which should now be pH 7.8 to 7.9.

7. Final sterilization. As in analogous step in I.

III. PREPARATION OF "12% YEAST" BROTH

This medium is prepared by essentially the same procedure as described in I for "5% yeast" broth with the exception that the amount of dried yeast is increased to 120 grams per liter. The additional amount of yeast makes the preparation of this medium much more time consuming, for filtration which is rapid with the "5%" medium is slow with the "12%" medium.

IV. PREPARATION OF AGAR MEDIUM WITH "12% YEAST" BROTH AS BASE

Agar medium may be prepared by the addition of 2.5 per cent agar to the "12% yeast" broth.

Savage and Hunwicke's [217] **Yeast-Water Medium.** One hundred gm. of ordinary brewers' yeast and one liter of distilled water are well mixed and autoclaved in a flask at 120°C.(248°F.) for 10 minutes. After being filtered twice through chardin filter paper, the yeast water is usually sufficiently clear for use. One per cent of sucrose is then dissolved in it, and litmus solution added. The medium is tubed in double tubes in amounts of about 10 ml.. The tubes are autoclaved to sterilize, as any partial alteration of the sucrose would not matter. Yeasts grow well in this medium.

Friedmann's [218] **Nutrient Medium From Yeasts.** Ten grams of dried yeast and five grams of sodium chloride are allowed to stand with one liter of water for three-quarters of an hour at room temperature and then boiled for one hour in a steam chamber. To the hot, turbid liquid are added five ml. of colloidal iron solution (liquor ferri oxychlorati) with stirring, the whole is heated again for 20 minutes and filtered through a double pleated filter, the filtrate being returned to the filter until it runs through clear. The liquor is then sterilized by heating, and serves as well as meat extract for the preparation of nutrient agar, fuchsin agar, litmus milk agar, or Löffler's blood serum.

Reiter's [219] **Nutrient Medium From Yeast.** Washed brewers' yeast is converted, by careful drying, into a light powder which can be kept indefinitely. On account of its hydroscopic character it is best preserved in closed glass vessels. For the preparation of nutrient broth, one part of this dried yeast is mixed with 100 parts of water, allowed to stand for an hour and then heated for another hour in an autoclave. The liquid is then filtered, fast through cotton wool and afterwards through filter paper. The extract thus obtained constitutes an excellent substitute for meat broth and can be used for the preparation of agar media. The use of a larger proportion of dried yeast is not advisable, since the growth of colonies is not improved thereby, and their characteristic features become less conspicuous. Addition of peptone to yeast extract is unnecessary.

Hall and Lothrop's [132] **Clarified Malt-Extract Medium for Yeasts and Molds.** This is a clear medium compounded as follows:

Dry malt extract (Difco)...100 gm.
Distilled water...1,000 ml.

Dissolve powdered malt extract in the water by heating in an Arnold sterilizer, or on the water bath. Adjust to pH 4.7 and cool to 50°C. Add slowly 100 ml. of a five per

217. Savage and Hunwicke. 1923. Gt. Brit. Food Invest. Bd., Spec. Rpt. No. 13.
218. Friedmann. 1918. München. Med. Wchnschr. 65, 76.
219. Reiter. 1918. Deut. Med. Wchnschr. 43, 1201-1202.

cent suspension of Bentonite (colloidal clay) and mix vigorously. Hold at 50 to 75°C. (122 to 167°F.) for 30 minutes, then filter through a fluted paper filter until clear. Heat the filtrate in the autoclave 10 minutes at 15 pounds pressure, and filter through paper to remove any precipitate formed. Distribute into tubes and flasks. For a plating medium, dissolve by heating two per cent agar-agar in the clarified broth and filter if necessary through cotton and cheesecloth. To avoid further precipitation sterilize at 10 pounds pressure for 15 minutes and cool promptly. (Bacto Malt Extract Broth can now be obtained in convenient dehydrated form and may be substituted for the above medium.)

Devereux's[220] **Yeast-Extract Media for Bacterial Examination of Milk.** The following media supported luxuriant growth of *Lactobacillus acidophilus* and *Lactobacillus bulgaricus*. The medium had the following composition:

Yeast extract (Difco)	5 gm.
Peptonized milk (Difco)	10 gm.
Salt	5 gm.
Dextrose	10 gm.
Water	1,000 ml.

Adjust the pH to 7.0 and autoclave for 15 minutes at 15 pounds. For a solid medium add 15 grams of washed agar to each liter of the above medium.

MEDIA FOR CULTIVATION OF YEASTS

These must be more acid than media for bacteria. In addition to those mentioned below, a few others are described in Chapter 8.

Sabouraud's[221] **Agar Medium for Yeasts.** This medium has the following composition:

Agar	20 gm.
Peptone	20 gm.
Glucose	40 gm.
Water	1,000 ml.

The ingredients should be mixed in the usual manner. The reaction should be adjusted to about pH 4.0 or lower. Care must be used in sterilization else it may not solidify.

Beer Wort (Eyre[222]**).** 1. Weigh out 250 gm. malt and put into a flask.

2. Add 1,000 ml. distilled water heated to 70°C.(158°F.) and close flask with rubber stopper.

3. Place the mixture in a water bath at 60°C.(140°F.) and allow the mixture to stand for one hour.

4. Stain through cheesecloth into clean flask and heat in an Arnold for 30 minutes.

5. Filter through paper.

6. Tube in 10-ml. quantities and sterilize in an Arnold.

Reddish[223] has proposed the following substitute for brewery wort:

"One hundred grams of dry extract of malt are dissolved in 900 ml. of distilled water. This is then made up to 8° Kaiser (saccharometer) by adding about 100 ml. of distilled water. The reaction is then adjusted to 1.5 per cent acid. After cooking in the autoclave for 15 minutes at 15 pounds pressure, the medium is filtered through filter paper and sterilized. It should not be sterilized at the same temperature and pressure at which it was cooked for a precipitate will come down. Agar may be added to this solution to give a solid medium."

"Near Beer Agar Medium for Yeasts. Secure a bottle of any of the so-called "near beers" and pour the contents into a beaker; boil for several minutes in order to rid the fluid of carbon dioxide. Dilute 400 ml. of the "near beer" with 600 ml. of distilled water. Add 1.5 per cent of agar, dissolve, tube, and sterilize in the usual

220. Devereux. 1932. Amer. J. Pub. Health 22, 1291-1294; 23 (1933), 149-51.
221. Sabouraud. 1892-1893. Ann. Dermatol. Syphilol.
222. Eyre. 1903. Elements of Bacteriological Technic. W. B. Saunders & Co., Philadelphia, Pa.
223. Reddish. 1919. Abs. Bact. 3, 6.

manner. In order to prepare a liquid culture medium, proceed as directed in the paragraph above but do not add the agar.

Lactic Acid-Dextrose Agar for Yeasts. Prepare dextrose agar in the usual manner and pour into Erlenmeyer flasks in quantities of 100 ml. or 50 ml. Plug and sterilize. When ready to use the medium, melt a flask of the dextrose agar containing 100 ml. and, with a sterile pipette, add four ml. of the sterilized five per cent solution of lactic acid. Shake, to thoroughly mix, and distribute into plugged tubes, plates, flasks, etc.

Savage and Hunwicke's [217] Sucrose-Mineral Medium for Yeasts. While this medium was devised for isolating yeasts from cans of condensed milk, it would probably be useful in other fields.

Ammonium sulfate	4.7 gm.
Dihydrogen potassium sulfate	0.75 gm.
Magnesium sulfate	0.10 gm.
Sucrose	50.00 gm.
Water	1,000.00 ml.

Sterilize in double tubes.

Weldin's [223] Medium for Yeasts. Weldin used the following medium for yeasts: Malt extract (Difco) 15 gm., K_2HPO_4 one gm., NH_4Cl one gm., distilled water 1,000 ml. The medium is adjusted with citric acid to pH 5.4 to 5.6. A solid medium on which yeasts grow vigorously is malt extract (Difco) 15 gm., K_2HPO_4 three gm., NH_4Cl one gm., agar 20 gm. (amount of agar, however, optional). The medium is adjusted with citric acid to pH 5.4 to 5.6.

Gorodkowa's [225] Medium for Determining the Presence of Ascospores in Yeasts. This medium was proposed for showing the presence of ascospores in yeasts. It has the following composition:

Distilled water	100.0 gm.
Agar	1.0 gm.
Meat extract	1.0 gm.
Sodium chloride	0.5 gm.
Glucose	0.25 gm.

This medium may be used as slants in test tubes or poured into Petri dishes. It was said to stimulate the formation of ascospores in three or four days.

Maneval's [226] Modification of Gorodkowa's Medium:

Distilled water	100.0 ml.
Liebig's meat extract	0.3 gm.
Sodium chloride	0.5 gm.
Dextrose	0.25 gm.
Agar	1.5 to 2.0 gm.

Sterilize at 15 pounds pressure.

Mrak, Phaff, and Douglas' [227] Medium for Ascopore Formation in Yeasts and Other Fungi. Grind equal amounts of washed, but unpeeled, carrots, beets, cucumbers, and potatoes and add an equal weight of water. Autoclave the mixture at 10 pounds pressure for 10 minutes after which the solid portion should be strained off with cheesecloth and pressure. The pH of the extract is usually about 5.7 and the Balling degree about 4. Two per cent of agar is added to the extract, which is dissolved by heating. Distribute as slants and sterilize at 15 pounds pressure for 15 minutes. Mrak and his colleagues obtained good sporulation on this medium within seven days.

224. Weldin. 1927. Iowa Acad. Sci. Proc. 34, 89-80.

225. Gorodkowa. 1909. Centbl. Bakt., Pt. 2, 24, 318-319.

226. Maneval. 1924. Bot. Gaz. 78, 122-123.

227. Mrak, Phaff, and Douglas. 1942. Science 96, 432.

Shutt's [228] **Malt Extract-Agar Medium for Yeast and Mold Analysis of Butter.** Shutt used the following medium for yeast and mold analysis of butter:

Malt extract (Panomalt)	45 gm.
Agar, market	15 gm.
Water, tap	1,000 ml.

Dissolve, filter, and dispense into 250 ml. lots and sterilize. Before pouring plates, acidify the melted medium by adding 10 ml. of a sterile five-per cent solution of lactic acid to 250 ml. of medium. The final reaction should be approximately pH 3.5.

Hertz and Levine's [229] **Fungistatic Medium for Enumeration of Yeasts.** This medium consists of malt extract agar into which is incorporated 100 parts per million of diphenyl after the melted basal medium has been cooled to between 50°C. (122°F.) and 60°C. (140°F.). The basal medium consists of:

Malt extract (Difco)	20 gm.
Peptone (Difco)	1 gm.
Ammonium chloride	1 gm.
K_2HPO_4	1 gm.
Agar	20 gm.
Water	1,000 ml.

Lactic acid to bring reaction to pH 4.5 to 4.7.
(7.0 ml. N/1 lactic acid solution for control medium.)

Dissolve the ingredients in the water and dispense in 100-ml. portions in bottles and sterilize. This medium without fungistatic substances may be used as control medium.

Linden's [182] **Clarified Malt-Extract Medium for Yeasts and Molds.** The medium most extensively used in the Beer Wort, or Malt Extract Medium, suggested by Eyre.[222] Various modifications exhibit the same difficulty as this medium, that is, formation of precipitates during sterilization. Recently, Hall and Lothrop [182] devised a satisfactory yeast medium, utilizing the clarifying principle of a five-per cent suspension of Bentonite on honey. This clarification technic has been applied to malt extract media with favorable results. The directions follow:

Dry malt extract (Difco)	100 gm.
Distilled water	1,000 ml.

Dissolve the powdered malt extract in the water by heating in an Arnold sterilizer, or on the water bath. Adjust to pH 4.7 and cool to 50°C. Add slowly 100 ml. of a five-per cent suspension of Bentonite (colloidal clay) and mix vigorously. Hold at 50 to 75°C. (122 to 167°F.) for 30 minutes, then filter through a fluted paper filter until clear. Heat the filtrate in the autoclave 10 minutes at 15 pounds pressure, and filter through paper to remove any precipitate formed. Distribute into tubes or flasks. For a plating medium, dissolve by heating, two per cent agar-agar in the clarified broth, and filter if necessary through cotton and cheesecloth. To avoid further precipitation sterilize at 10 pounds pressure for 15 minutes and cool promptly.

REFERENCE BOOKS

LEVINE, M., AND SCHOELEIN, H. W., 1930. A Compilation of Culture Media for the Cultivation of Microorganisms. The Williams and Wilkins Co., Baltimore, Md.

Pure Culture Study of Bacteria. Biotech. Pub., Geneva, N. Y. (Use latest edition.)

Materials and Preparations for Diagnostic Use. The National Formulary, sixth edition, 1939. American Pharmaceutical Assoc., Washington, D. C. (Also as a preprint.)

Manual of Dehydrated Culture Media and Reagents. Difco Laboratories, Detroit, Mich. Sixth edition, revised 1939.

228. Shutt. 1924. J. Dairy Sci. 7, 357-360.
229. Hertz and Levine. 1942. Food Research 7, 430-441.

INDEX

A

Abnormal flavor of concentrated milk, 560

of milk, 297

Abnormal milk, detection by microscope, 346

Acetic acid bacteria, culture medium for, 1156

Acetic acid fermentation, 724

Acetyl-methyl-carbinol, 194

in butter, 462

Achromobacter aromafaciens in cream ripening, 459

Acid-coagulating bacteria in cream, 449

Acid foods, spoilage of, 981

Acid-fast stain, 66

Acid formation from sugars, 70

in milk, 254

Acid fruits, spoilage, 639

Acid meat medium for aciduric bacteria, 690

Acidity of milk, 250

Acidification of canned foods, 961

Acidity of canned foods and spoilage, 982

Acidophilus milk, preparation, 578

storage, 581

unfermented, 578

Acidophilus tablets, 582

Acidophilus therapy, 578

Actinomyces, 124

Action of bile on bacteria, 616

Adhesion culture, Lindner's, 142

Adjustment of reaction of media, 476

Adulteration of foods, 50, 52

Adulteration of pressed yeast, 149

Advantages of milk pasteurization, 394

Aerobacter aerogenes, longevity in nature, 218

methylene blue differentiation, 200

Aerobic sporeforming bacteria, 92

in condensed milk, 554

Agar count in water analysis, 162

culture media, 1119

culture medium, Amer. Assoc. Med. Milk Comm., 1121

dehydrated culture media, 1105

for culture media, 1105

gelatin culture medium, 1131

medium for milk analysis, Brit. Min. of Health, 338

medium of MacConkey, 1133

plates, pin-point colonies, 287

serum in agar slants, 1105

slants, agar serum in, 1105

slice and disc methods for surface examination, 487

Aging of ice cream mix, 530

meat in ultraviolet light, 41

Air, bact. in stable air, 256

dissolved in media, 182

Alkali-forming bacteria in milk, 273

Alkyl sulfates in presumptive test, 208

Alternaria, 123

Alternate freezing and thawing, 27

Amer. Pub. Health Assoc., Differentiation of coliform bacteria, 192

dirt test for milk, 311

method for yeasts in butter, 486

plate count of milk, 335

proc. for colon count in water exam., 163

presumptive test procedure in water exam., 178

reductase test, 382

Ammonia production, 75

medium for, 1148

Amylase test, 427

Animals, pathogenicity of microorg. for 77

Amylo-process, 110

Anaerobic bacteria, 100

as indicators of water pollution, 170

in candies, 778

in condensed milk, 555

Spray's arrangement, 103

Spray's semi-solid media, 1130

spurious presumptive tests, 180

thioglycollate culture medium for, 1110.

Anaerobic spore test, Savage, 290

Weinzirl, 290

Analysis of vinegar, 729

Anthomyces, 154

Antibodies in milk, 302

Appearance, abnormal of milk, 297

Appert, 945

Apple juice, clarification, 641

disease from, 641

filtration, 642

freezing, 644

pasteurization, 643

preservation, 643

ropy, 645

"Approved milk," New York City, 319

Aroma of butter, 461

Aromatic odor in milk, 300

1169